Safety Symbols

These symbols appear in laboratory activities. They alert you to possible dangers and remind you to work carefully.

General Safety Awareness Read all directions for an experiment several times. Follow the directions exactly as they are written. If you are in doubt, ask your teacher for assistance.

Physical Safety If the lab includes physical activity, use caution to avoid injuring yourself or others. Tell your teacher if there is a reason that you should not participate.

Safety Goggles Always wear safety goggles to protect your eyes in any activity involving chemicals, heating, or the possibility of broken glassware.

Lab Apron Wear a laboratory apron to protect your skin and clothing from harmful chemicals or hot materials.

Plastic Gloves Wear disposable plastic gloves to protect yourself from contact with chemicals that can be harmful. Keep your hands away from your face. Dispose of gloves according to your teacher's instructions.

Heating Use a clamp or tongs to hold hot objects. Test an object by first holding the back of your hand near it. If you feel heat, the object may be too hot to handle.

Heat-Resistant Gloves Hot plates, hot water, and hot glassware can cause burns. Never touch hot objects with your bare hands. Use an oven mitt or other hand protection.

Flames Tie back long hair and loose clothing, and put on safety goggles before using a burner. Follow instructions from your teacher for lighting and extinguishing burners.

No Flames If flammable materials are present, make sure there are no flames, sparks, or exposed sources of heat.

Electric Shock To avoid an electric shock, never use electrical equipment near water, or when the equipment or your hands are wet. Use only sockets that accept a three-prong plug. Be sure cords are untangled and cannot trip anyone. Disconnect equipment that is not in use.

Fragile Glassware Handle fragile glassware, such as thermometers, test tubes, and beakers, with care. Do not touch broken glass. Notify your teacher if glassware breaks. Never use chipped or cracked glassware.

Corrosive Chemical Avoid getting corrosive chemicals on your skin or clothing, or in your eyes. Do not inhale the vapors. Wash your hands after completing the activity.

Poison Do not let any poisonous chemical get on your skin, and do not inhale its vapor. Wash your hands after completing the activity.

Fumes When working with poisonous or irritating vapors, work in a well-ventilated area. Never test for an odor unless instructed to do so by your teacher. Avoid inhaling a vapor directly. Use a wafting motion to direct vapor toward your nose.

Sharp Object Use sharp instruments only as directed. Scissors, scalpels, pins, and knives are sharp and can cut or puncture your skin. Always direct sharp edges and points away from yourself and others.

Disposal All chemicals and other materials used in the laboratory must be disposed of safely. Follow your teacher's instructions.

Hand Washing Before leaving the lab, wash your hands thoroughly with soap or detergent, and warm water. Lather both sides of your hands and between your fingers. Rinse well.

Correlation to National Science Education Standards	
Content Standard	**Chapter/Section/Page**
Content Standard G • History and Nature of Science	
G-1 Science as a Human Endeavor	Ch. 1: p. 2, p. 22, p. 25; Ch. 2: p. 40; Ch. 3: p. 70, pp. 78–79; Ch. 4: pp. 100–105, pp. 108–110, pp. 113–115; Ch. 5: Sec. 5.1; Ch. 6: p. 163, p. 170, pp. 178–179; Ch. 7: p. 218; Ch. 8: pp. 252–253; Ch. 9: p. 262, p. 266, p. 276; Ch. 10: pp. 292–293, pp. 303–304, p. 309, pp. 312–313; Ch. 11: p. 338; Ch. 12: p. 357, pp. 363–365, p. 372, pp. 374–375, p. 382; Ch. 13: p. 391, pp. 395–396, p. 401; Ch. 14: p. 414, p. 416, pp. 422–423; Ch. 15: p. 456, p. 459; Ch. 16: p. 474, p. 482, p. 486; Ch. 17: p. 516, pp. 518–519; Ch. 18: p. 534, pp. 536–537, p. 539, p. 551; Ch. 19: pp. 581–583; Ch. 20: p. 601; Ch. 21: p. 635, p. 643; Ch. 22: 661, pp. 676–681; Ch. 24: p. 748, p. 762; Ch. 25: pp. 790–794, p. 797, pp. 806–807, p. 810; Ch. 26: pp. 828–829, p. 838, p. 847, p. 852, pp. 854–855
G-2 Nature of Scientific Knowledge	Ch. 1: p. 3, p. 5, p. 6, pp. 9–10, p. 16; Ch. 2: p. 40; Ch. 3: p. 70, pp. 78–79; Ch. 4: pp. 100–101, pp. 103–105, pp. 108–110, pp. 113–116; Ch. 5: Sec. 5.1; Ch. 6: pp. 170–176, pp. 178–179; Ch. 8: pp. 252–253; Ch. 9: p. 262, p. 266; Ch. 10: p. 292, p. 303, p. 309, pp. 312–313; Ch. 12: pp. 363–365, p. 372, pp. 374–375, p. 382; Ch. 13: p. 391, pp. 395–396, p. 401; Ch. 14: p. 414, p. 416, pp. 422–423; Ch. 15: p. 459; Ch. 16: p. 474, p. 482, p. 486; Ch. 17: pp. 518–519; Ch. 18: p. 534, pp. 536–537, p. 539, p. 551; Ch. 19: pp. 581–583; Ch. 21: p. 635, p. 643; Ch. 22: p. 661, pp. 676–681; Ch. 24: p. 762; Ch. 25: pp. 791–794, pp. 806–807, p. 810; Ch. 26: pp. 828–830, pp. 834–835, pp. 837–838, p. 840, p. 847, pp. 849–852, p. 854
G-3 Historical Perspectives	Ch. 1: p. 5; Ch. 2: p. 40; Ch. 3: p. 70, pp. 78–79; Ch. 4: pp. 100–101, pp. 104–105, pp. 108–109, pp. 113–115; Ch. 5: Sec. 5.1; Ch. 6: pp. 178–179; Ch. 7: p. 219; Ch. 8: pp. 252–253; Ch. 9: pp. 262–263, p. 266, p. 276; Ch. 10: pp. 292–293, p. 303, p. 309, pp. 312–313; Ch. 11: 338–339; Ch. 12: pp. 363–365, p. 372, pp. 374–375, p. 382; Ch. 13: p. 391, pp. 395–396, p. 398, p. 401; Ch. 14: p. 414, p. 416, pp. 422–423; Ch. 15: p. 456, p. 459; Ch. 16: p. 474, p. 482, p. 486; Ch. 17: pp. 518–519; Ch. 18: p. 534, pp. 536–537, p. 539, p. 551; Ch. 19: pp. 581–583; Ch. 20: p. 601, pp. 614–615, pp. 620–622; Ch. 21: p. 635, p. 643; Ch. 22: p. 661, pp. 676–678, pp. 680–681; Ch. 24: p. 762; Ch. 25: pp. 790–794, pp. 806–807, p. 810; Ch. 26: p. 829, p. 838, pp. 845–849, p. 852, p. 854

AAAS Benchmarks

Correlation to AAAS Benchmarks	
Content Standard	**Chapters**
1 • The Nature of Science	
1A The Scientific World View	1, 2, 3, 4, 7, 9, 10, 13, 15, 16, 17, 18, 20, 21, 22, 25, 26; Appendix A
1B Scientific Inquiry	1, 2, 4, 5, 16, 22, 25, 26; Data Analysis: Ch. 9, 22; Concepts in Action: Ch. 1; all Inquiry Activities, Quick Labs, Exploration Labs, Consumer Labs, Forensics Labs, Application Labs, and Design Your Own Labs in Ch. 1–26; Appendices A–G
1C The Scientific Enterprise	1, 4, 6, 10, 12, 13, 15, 18, 19, 21, 22, 25, 26; How It Works: Ch. 12, 13; Concepts in Action: Ch. 11, 17, 18; Issues in Science: Ch. 9, 23; Math Skills; Appendix B
2 • The Nature of Mathematics	
2A Patterns and Relationships	1, 4, 5, 6, 8, 9, 11, 12, 13, 14, 16, 17, 19, 20, 21, 22, 23, 24, 25, 26; Math Skills: Ch. 3; Inquiry Activity: Ch. 5, 21; How It Works: Ch. 24; Concepts in Action: Ch. 24, 25, 26; Quick Lab: Ch. 18, 22; Exploration Lab: Ch. 12, 17, 25, 26; Application Lab: Ch. 15; all Data Analysis features; Math Skills; Appendices A–C
2B Mathematics, Science, and Technology	1, 3, 4, 5, 6, 7, 8, 10, 11, 12, 13, 14, 15, 16, 18, 20, 22, 24, 25, 26; Concepts in Action: Ch. 4, 26; Math Skills: Ch. 6, 10, 11, 12, 14, 15, 16, 17, 18, 20; How It Works: Ch. 1, 6; all Data Analysis features; Math Skills; Appendices A–C, I
2C Mathematical Inquiry	1, 3, 4, 5, 6, 7, 11, 13, 18, 26; Problem Solving Activity: Ch. 4; Quick Lab: Ch. 12 (2), 26; Application Lab: Ch. 21, Math Skills; Appendices A–K, I
3 • The Nature of Technology	
3A Technology and Science	1, 2, 3, 6, 8, 10, 12, 18, 20, 24, 25, 26; Concepts in Action: Ch. 4, 6, 7, 9, 11, 14, 15, 16, 17, 18, 19, 20, 21, 23; How It Works: 3, 5, 7, 12, 14, 16, 18, 19, 22, 25; Using Technology; Appendices A–B
3B Design and Systems	1, 6, 7, 8, 13, 14, 16, 17, 18, 20; Concepts in Action: Ch. 2, 3, 4, 6, 11, 13, 14, 15, 16, 19, 20; How It Works: Ch. 14, 16, 17, 21, 25; Problem Solving Activity: Ch. 21; Forensics Lab: Ch. 20
3C Issues in Technology	8, 9, 10, 15, 23, 24, 25; Issues in Science: Ch. 2, 9, 17, 20; Data Analysis: Ch. 3; Concepts in Action: Ch. 9; How It Works: Ch. 12, 16
4 • The Physical Setting	
4A The Universe	1, 3, 10, 12, 18, 19, 25, 26; How It Works: Ch. 26; Concepts in Action: Ch. 25, 26; Issues in Science: Ch. 25; Data Analysis: Ch. 13; Appendix H
4B The Earth	10, 12, 15, 22, 23, 24, 25; How It Works: Ch. 24; Concepts in Action: Ch. 24; Appendices D–E
4C Processes that Shape the Earth	5, 6, 9, 15, 16, 17, 22, 23, 24, 25; Concepts in Action: Ch. 22, 23; How It Works: Ch. 23; Inquiry Activity: Ch. 23; Exploration Lab: Ch. 22; Appendices F–G
4D Structure of Matter	1, 2, 3, 4, 5, 6, 7, 8, 9, 10, 12, 15, 20, 21, 22; How It Works: Ch. 2, 5, 6, 7, 8, 10; Concepts in Action: Ch. 10; Inquiry Activity: Ch. 7, 10; Consumer Lab: Ch. 6; Appendix D

TEACHER'S EDITION

Prentice Hall
Physical Science
Concepts in Action
with Earth and Space Science
Discovery Channel School
Wysession • Frank • Yancopoulos

PEARSON
Prentice Hall

IN ASSOCIATION WITH DK Publishing

Needham, Massachusetts
Upper Saddle River, New Jersey

About the Authors

Michael Wysession

Michael Wysession received his Ph.D. in geophysics from Northwestern University in 1991. He is an Associate Professor in Earth and Planetary Sciences at Washington University in St. Louis, Missouri. His area of specialization is using seismic waves to explore Earth's interior. Dr. Wysession is an author on more than 50 scientific publications. For his research, he was awarded a Packard Foundation Fellowship, and in 1996 was awarded a Presidential Faculty Fellowship at the White House. He also has created educational simulations to accurately show how seismic waves propagate.

David Frank

David Frank completed his Ph.D. at Purdue University. For the last ten years he has been the head of the Physical Sciences Department at Ferris State University in Big Rapids, Michigan. He has taught general chemistry courses for science majors and for allied health students. With the assistance of his colleagues, he helped develop a new B.A. program in biochemistry. He has taught students in the university's Math/Science/Technology program, which enrolls gifted high school students. Recently he has worked with Michigan's "Connecting With the Learner" group, which produced a toolkit to help elementary and secondary teachers address diversity issues in the classroom.

Sophia Yancopoulos

Sophia Yancopoulos received her Ph.D. in physics from Columbia University. She has done postdoctoral research in astronomy at Yale University and in biophysics at the Mount Sinai School of Medicine. She considers teaching to be a vital and exciting part of her experience, having taught at Barnard College, Vassar College, the Stevens Institute of Technology, and Columbia University, as well as at Bronx High School of Science. She has worked on a neutrino oscillations experiment at Fermi National Laboratory, conducted experiments on acoustic modeling, and analyzed data on the extreme astrophysics of neutron stars. She currently teaches in the physics department at Manhattan College and in their graduate program in biotechnology.

PEARSON
Prentice Hall

ISBN 0-13-166316-X

1 2 3 4 5 6 7 8 9 10   09 08 07 06 05

Physical Science: Concepts in Action

Support Resources

Prentice Hall
Physical Science
Concepts in Action
Prentice Hall
Physical Science
Concepts in Action
Earth and Space Science
Frank • Wysession • Yancopoulos
Easy Planner
Prentice Hall
Physical Science
Concepts in Action
Laboratory Manual
Prentice Hall
Physical Science
Concepts in Action
Guided Reading and Study Workbook
with Math Support
Prentice Hall
Physical Science
Concepts in Action
Computer Test Bank
with ExamView® CD-ROM
Prentice Hall
Physical Science
Concepts in Action
Chapter and Unit Tests
Prentice Hall
Physical Science
Concepts in Action

- **Student Edition**
- **Student Edition with Earth and Space Science**
- **Interactive Textbook**—online and on CD-ROM
- **Teacher's Edition**
- **Teacher's Edition with Earth and Space Science**
- **Easy Planner with Earth and Space Science**
- **Laboratory Manual**
- **Reading and Study Workbook with Math Support**—English and Spanish
- **Math Skills and Problem Solving Workbook**
- **Computer Test Bank with ExamView® CD-ROM**
- **Chapter and Unit Tests**—English and Spanish
- **Test Preparation Blackline Masters**
- **Test Prep Workbook**
- **Test Taking Tips with Transparencies**
- **Transparencies Plus**
  - Presentation Pro CD-ROM
  - Teaching Transparencies
- **Probeware Laboratory Manual with CD-ROM**
- **Discovery Channel Video and DVD Field Trips**
- **Teacher Express CD-ROM**
- **PHSchool.com Web site**

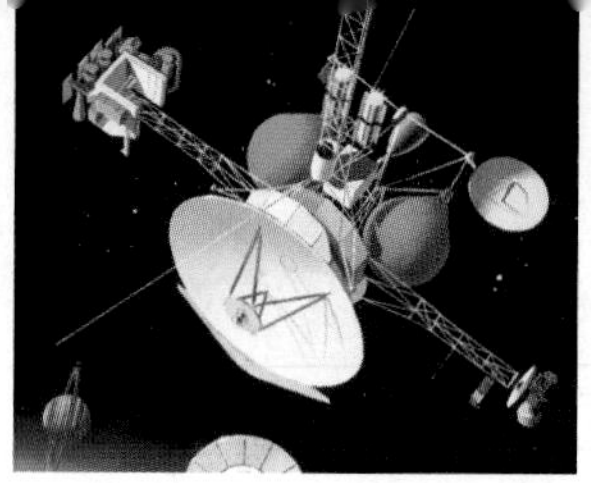

Contents in Brief

Teacher's Edition

Student Edition

Discovery Channel School
Prentice Hall
Physical Science
Concepts in Action
Wysession • Frank •

More Relevant Than Ever

CONCEPTS in Action

Terminal Speed

Imagine you are a sky diver about to step out of a plane and fall through the air. What forces will you experience during your fall? How can you use these forces to combine an exhilarating experience with a safe landing?

Sky diving relies on two principles of physics. First, if there is nothing to support you, the force of gravity will cause you to accelerate downwards. Second all fluids—including air—produce a drag force that opposes the motion of an object moving through the fluid. The speed of a falling object increases until the drag force equals the force of gravity. At this point, the net force is zero and the sky diver falls at a constant, terminal speed.

The actual terminal speed depends on several factors. For example, an object with greater mass has a greater gravitational force on it, increasing its terminal speed. Thinner air, such as air at very high altitudes, increases velocity by decreasing the drag force. A sky diver can also partially control the drag force, and terminal speed, by changing shape. Opening the parachute dramatically increases the drag force and lowers the terminal speed to about 4.5 meters per second—a speed suitable for landing.

Upward drag force
Helmet for protection
Alimeter showing altitude
Harness
Downward force of gravity
Sky diver lands standing up
4 Landing The sky diver pulls down on the control lines to achieve a safe and steady low-speed landing.

370 Chapter 12

Wysession
Frank
Yancopoulos

Give students the skills to succeed with strong reading support

■ Reading Focus

Introduce students to the Key Concepts, Vocabulary, and Reading Strategy in the lesson. A graphic organizer helps visual learners understand difficult-to-understand concepts.

■ Key Concepts

Clearly identified **before, during,** and **after** every section, Key Concepts encourage students to focus on the big ideas of science.

■ Reading Checkpoints

Reinforce students' understanding of the material just covered.

■ Section Assessments

Evaluate students' comprehension of material at the end of each section.

14.1 Work and Power

Reading Focus

Key Concepts
- Under what conditions will a force do work?
- How are work and power related?

Vocabulary
- work
- joule
- power
- watt
- horsepower

Reading Strategy
Using Visuals Before you read, preview Figures 1 to 3. Copy and complete the table below based on the work described in the caption for each figure.

WORK → divided by time ☐ ; is less than *Fd* when ☐ ; is zero when ☐

Planning a trip is hard work. First you need to make arrangements for where to stay during your visit. Next you need to buy your ticket and decide what to pack. Then you need to get to the airport or bus station. All this may seem like a lot of work. But scientists use the word work with a different meaning.

What Is Work?

Recall that a force can move an object or change the motion of an object ... already moving. **Work** is done on an object when a force moves the object. **For a force to do work on an object, the object must move and at least part of the force must act along the direction of motion.** Lifting a barbell, picking up a book from the floor, and tossing a newspaper onto a front porch are examples of work.

Work Requires Motion A force can do work by starting an object in motion or by changing the speed of a moving object. For example, when you lift a barbell as shown in Figure 1, you do work on the barbell to start it moving. Suppose the barbell is moving upwards ... in the same direction. Then the force you exert ... rk on the barbell to make it move even faster. ... o work by keeping an object in motion despite ... riction or gravity. On your trip, you might ride ... e airport. For the most part, you move at con... e upward force the elevator floor exerts on you ... e of gravity. Even though the force the elevator ... not changing your motion, it does work because ... me direction as your motion.

What Is Power?

Have you ever heard the expression "Time is money?" Often people are not just concerned about getting work done; they want it done fast! And that requires power. The word power is used in many ways. People describe a storm, a country, or a concert as powerful. In baseball, power hitters hit a lot of home runs and power pitchers throw the ball at tremendous speed. But power, like work, has a very precise meaning in science.

Power is the rate of doing work. key It takes more power to do work at a faster rate. You can increase power by increasing the work done in a given time or by doing a given a mount of work in less time. Suppose you visit relatives on your trip and decide to help out by mowing their lawn. Figure 3 shows a neighbor mowing a lawn of the same size, but with a mower that cuts a wider path through the grass. Both lawn mowers will do the same total amount of work to cut the grass, assuming they exert the same force to cut each blade of grass. But the wider mower can cut the grass in less time, so it does the same amount of work at a faster rate. The wider lawn mower is more powerful.

Reading Checkpoint *How do you calculate the work done on an ...*

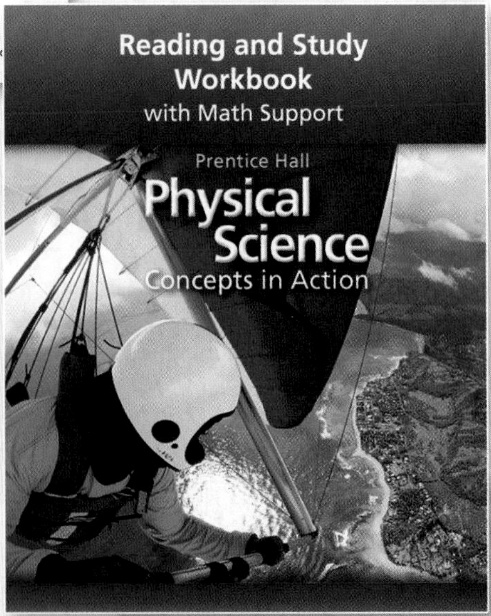

Reading and Study Workbook
with Math Support
Prentice Hall
Physical Science
Concepts in Action

Section 8.4 Assessment

Reviewing Concepts
1. How is pH related to the strength of an acid?
2. What determines the degree to which an acid or base is weak or strong?
3. Are strong acids and bases good electrolytes? Explain why or why not.
4. Why is pure water neutral?
5. What does pH measure?

Critical Thinking
6. **Relating Cause and Effect** If you add another liter of water to 1 liter of a 1-molar solution of hydrochloric acid, what happens to the number of hydronium ions in solution? What happens to the concentration?
7. **Interpreting Diagrams** In the formulas on page 248, what does the symbol with the two arrows facing in opposite directions mean?
8. **Comparing and Contrasting** Would you expect oranges to work as well as lemons in making a battery? Explain your answer.

Writing in Science

Explain a Concept Write an analogy that will explain how a reaction reaches equilibrium at different points. (*Hint:* Think about various activities in your life where the balance changes.)

Solutions, Acids, and Bases 249

and with strong math support.

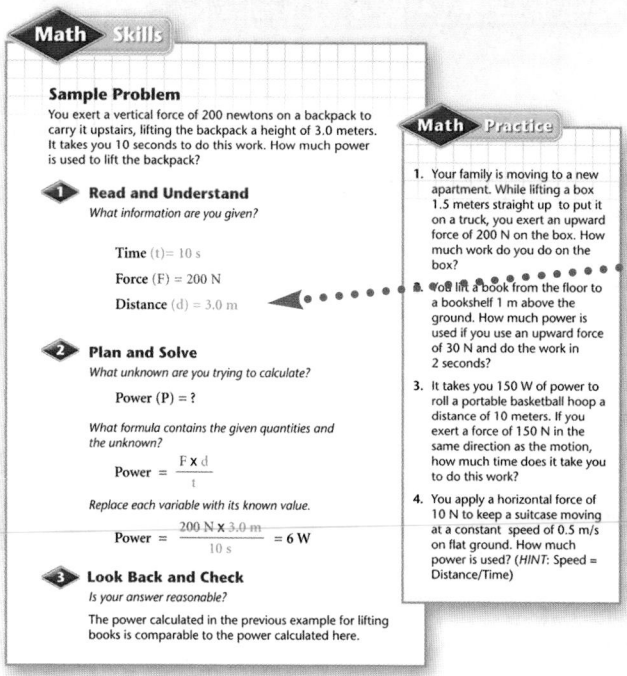

Math Skills

Sample Problem

You exert a vertical force of 200 newtons on a backpack to carry it upstairs, lifting the backpack a height of 3.0 meters. It takes you 10 seconds to do this work. How much power is used to lift the backpack?

1 Read and Understand

What information are you given?

Time (t) = 10 s

Force (F) = 200 N

Distance (d) = 3.0 m

2 Plan and Solve

What unknown are you trying to calculate?

Power (P) = ?

What formula contains the given quantities and the unknown?

$$\text{Power} = \frac{F \times d}{t}$$

Replace each variable with its known value.

$$\text{Power} = \frac{200\text{ N} \times 3.0\text{ m}}{10\text{ s}} = 6\text{ W}$$

3 Look Back and Check

Is your answer reasonable?

The power calculated in the previous example for lifting books is comparable to the power calculated here.

Math Practice

1. Your family is moving to a new apartment. While lifting a box 1.5 meters straight up to put it on a truck, you exert an upward force of 200 N on the box. How much work do you do on the box?
2. You lift a book from the floor to a bookshelf 1 m above the ground. How much power is used if you use an upward force of 30 N and do the work in 2 seconds?
3. It takes you 150 W of power to roll a portable basketball hoop a distance of 10 meters. If you exert a force of 150 N in the same direction as the motion, how much time does it take you to do the work?
4. You apply a horizontal force of 10 N to keep a suitcase moving at a constant speed of 0.5 m/s on flat ground. How much power is used? (*HINT*: Speed = Distance/Time)

Math Skills/Math Practice

A three-step problem-solving method, with numerous opportunities for practice at point of use, encourages students to Read and Understand, Plan and Solve, and Look Back and Check.

■ Color-coded variables

Aid student navigation and help reinforce math comprehension.

Key Formulas and Equations

Set off in boxes, Key Formulas and Equations help students easily locate and remember the skills.

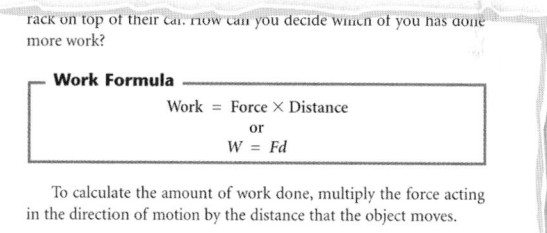

rack on top of their car. How can you decide which of you has done more work?

Work Formula

Work = Force × Distance

or

$W = Fd$

To calculate the amount of work done, multiply the force acting in the direction of motion by the distance that the object moves.

Data Analysis

Students analyze real-world experimental data with graphs and draw conclusions from the information. Excellent practice for state and national tests.

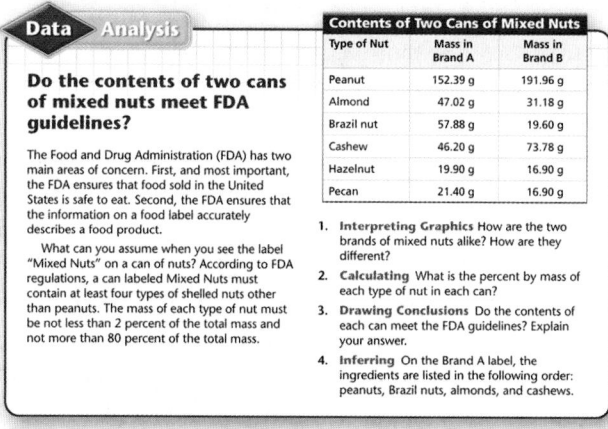

Data Analysis

Do the contents of two cans of mixed nuts meet FDA guidelines?

The Food and Drug Administration (FDA) has two main areas of concern. First, and most important, the FDA ensures that food sold in the United States is safe to eat. Second, the FDA ensures that the information on a food label accurately describes a food product.

What can you assume when you see the label "Mixed Nuts" on a can of nuts? According to FDA regulations, a can labeled Mixed Nuts must contain at least four types of shelled nuts other than peanuts. The mass of each type of nut must be not less than 2 percent of the total mass and not more than 80 percent of the total mass.

Contents of Two Cans of Mixed Nuts

Type of Nut	Mass in Brand A	Mass in Brand B
Peanut	152.39 g	191.96 g
Almond	47.02 g	31.18 g
Brazil nut	57.88 g	19.60 g
Cashew	46.20 g	73.78 g
Hazelnut	19.90 g	16.90 g
Pecan	21.40 g	16.90 g

1. **Interpreting Graphics** How are the two brands of mixed nuts alike? How are they different?
2. **Calculating** What is the percent by mass of each type of nut in each can?
3. **Drawing Conclusions** Do the contents of each can meet the FDA guidelines? Explain your answer.
4. **Inferring** On the Brand A label, the ingredients are listed in the following order: peanuts, Brazil nuts, almonds, and cashews.

Math Skills and Problem Solving Workbook
Prentice Hall
Physical Science
Concepts in Action

Math Skills and Problem Solving Workbook

Section-based math instruction and math practice for mastering problem solving and key content.

Reading and Study Workbook with Math Support

Worksheets and summaries, organized around every section of the *Student Edition*, support students in mastering reading and math skills.

Reach all students with real-world examples...

We've proudly partnered with Dorling Kindersley to bring you Concepts in Action for the most vivid visual information available!

CONCEPTS In Action

Terminal Speed

Imagine you are a sky diver about to step out of a plane and fall through the air. What forces will you experience during your fall? How can you use these forces to combine an exhilarating experience with a safe landing?

Sky diving relies on two principles of physics. First, if there is nothing to support you, the force of gravity will cause you to accelerate downwards. Second all fluids—including air—produce a drag force that opposes the motion of an object moving through the fluid. The speed of a falling object increases until the drag force equals the force of gravity. At this point, the net force is zero and the sky diver falls at a constant, terminal speed.

The actual terminal speed depends on several factors. For example, an object with greater mass has a greater gravitational force on it, increasing its terminal speed. Thinner air, such as air at very high altitudes, increases velocity by decreasing the drag force. A sky diver can also partially control the drag force, and terminal speed, by changing shape. Opening the parachute dramatically increases the drag force and lowers the terminal speed to about 4.5 meters per second—a speed suitable for landing.

Upward drag force
Helmet for protection
Harness
Downward force of gravity
Alimeter showing altitude
Parachute
Sky diver lands standing up

The Sky Diving Sequence

No matter what the starting altitude, any sky dive consists of the same basic stages, starting with the jump from the plane.

1 Jumping out Upon jumping, the sky diver begins accelerating at a rate of 9.8 meters per second per second in free fall. Within a few seconds she will reach maximum speed.

2 Falling freely Sky divers usually jump from a height of about 3000 meters and fall freely for about 45 seconds before opening the parachute. The top speed reached, known as terminal speed, is about 52 meters per second. Falling from very high altitudes where the air is thinner and the drag force is less, can produce higher terminal speeds.

3 Slowing the fall Usually the parachute is fully open by the time the sky diver is 300 meters above the ground. The parachute causes rapid deceleration and allows the sky diver to make a steady descent, using the control lines to steer.

4 Landing The sky diver pulls down on the control lines to achieve a safe and steady low-speed landing.

Going Further

- Research the development and use of the parachute and prepare a poster presentation of your findings. Be sure to include a development time line listing names and dates of significant contributions and advancements.
- Take a Discovery Channel Video Field Trip by watching "Air Forces".

370 Chapter 12 … Forces and Motion 371

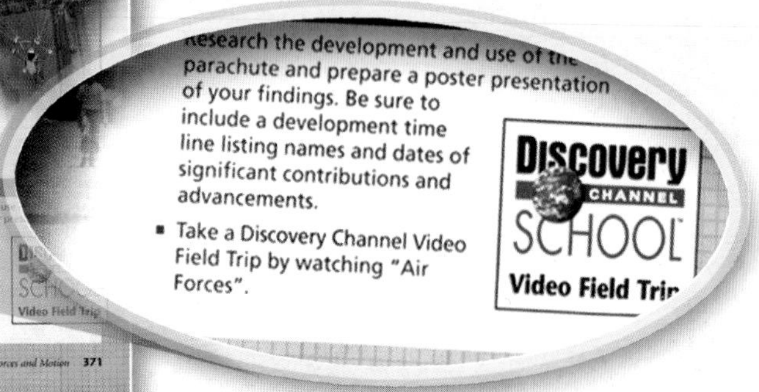
Research the development and use of the parachute and prepare a poster presentation of your findings. Be sure to include a development time line listing names and dates of significant contributions and advancements.

- Take a Discovery Channel Video Field Trip by watching "Air Forces".

Discovery Channel School
Video Field Trip

Concepts In Action

These features integrate vivid photographic illustrations with incisive text to support students in their exploration of science. The concepts can be reinforced with *Discovery Channel Video Field Trips* that correlate with the topics.

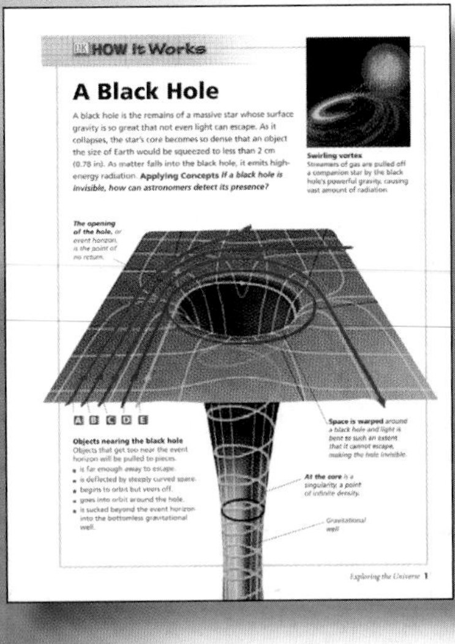
HOW It Works

A Black Hole

A black hole is the remains of a massive star whose surface gravity is so great that not even light can escape. As it collapses, the star's core becomes so dense that an object the size of Earth would be squeezed to less than 2 cm (0.78 in). As matter falls into the black hole, it emits high-energy radiation. **Applying Concepts** ***If a black hole is invisible, how can astronomers detect its presence?***

Swirling vortex Streamers of gas are pulled off a companion star by the black hole's powerful gravity, causing vast amount of radiation.

The opening of the hole, or event horizon, is the point of no return.
A B C D E
Objects nearing the black hole
Objects that get too near the event horizon will be pulled to pieces.
is far enough away to escape.
is deflected by steeply curved space.
begins to orbit but veers off.
goes into orbit around the hole.
is sucked beyond the event horizon into the bottomless gravitational well.
Space is warped around a black hole and light is bent to such an extent that it cannot escape, making the hole invisible.
At the core is a singularity, a point of infinite density.
Gravitational well

Exploring the Universe 1

How It Works

From Dorling Kindersley, in-depth schematic illustrations of familiar objects—such as space suits, thermometers, and airbags—help students connect the science they learn with the science that surrounds them.

Discovery Channel Video Field Trips

26 exciting segments support Concepts in Action topics with dramatic impact. Students will explore air pollution, solar cars, fiber optics, and more.

9 types of inquiry activities!

1. Inquiry Activity
2. Quick Lab
3. Exploration Lab
4. Design and Experiment Lab
5. Consumer Lab
6. Forensic Lab
7. Application Lab
8. Problem-Solving Activity
9. Data Analysis

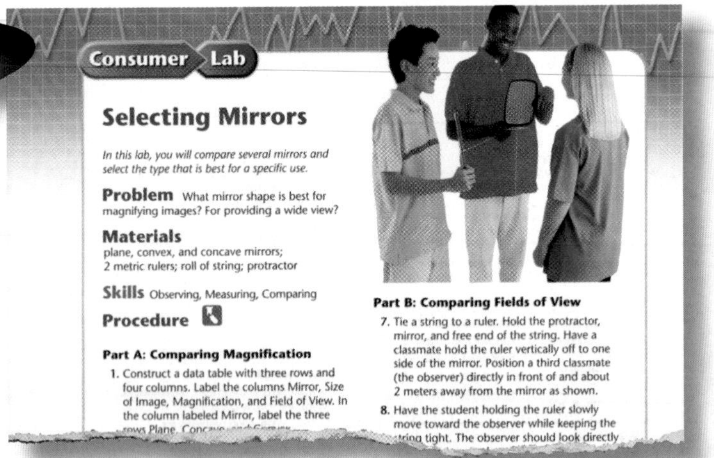
Consumer Lab

Selecting Mirrors

In this lab, you will compare several mirrors and select the type that is best for a specific use.

Problem What mirror shape is best for magnifying images? For providing a wide view?

Materials plane, convex, and concave mirrors; 2 metric rulers; roll of string; protractor

Skills Observing, Measuring, Comparing

Procedure

Part A: Comparing Magnification

1. Construct a data table with three rows and four columns. Label the columns Mirror, Size of Image, Magnification, and Field of View. In the column labeled Mirror, label the three rows Plane, Concave, and Convex.

Part B: Comparing Fields of View

7. Tie a string to a ruler. Hold the protractor, mirror, and free end of the string. Have a classmate hold the ruler vertically off to one side of the mirror. Position a third classmate (the observer) directly in front of and about 2 meters away from the mirror as shown.
8. Have the student holding the ruler slowly move toward the observer while keeping the string tight. The observer should look directly

Labs and Activities

Address all learning abilities. These easy-to-manage labs reinforce process skills and offer hands-on exploration of relevant and motivating topics

and with point-of-use assessment.

Chapter Assessment and Standardized Test Prep

Check student assessment every step of the way—vital practice for test-taking success.

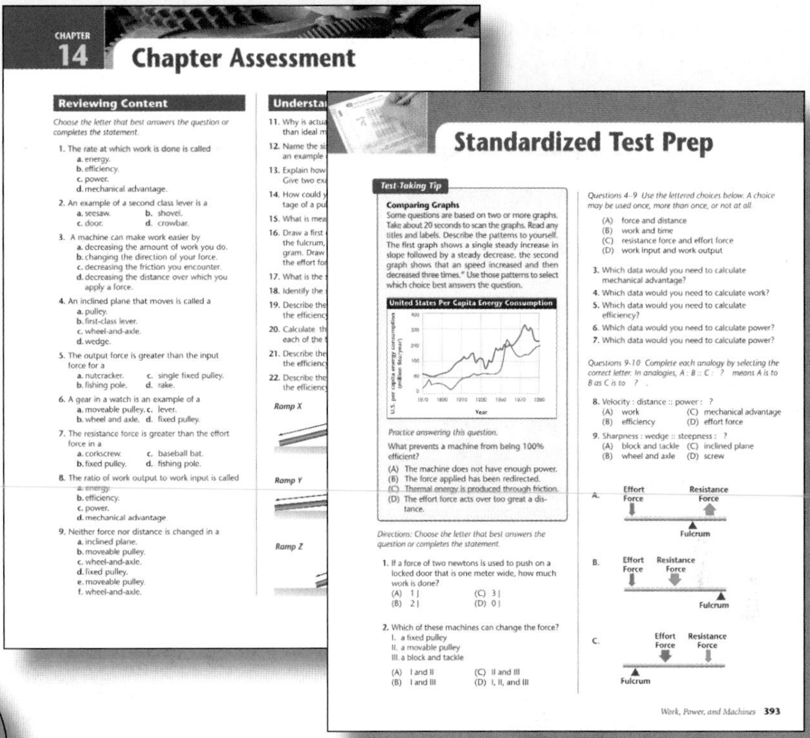
CHAPTER 14
Chapter Assessment
Reviewing Content
Standardized Test Prep
Test-Taking Tip
Comparing Graphs
United States Per Capita Energy Consumption
Work, Power, and Machines 393

Test Preparation Blackline Masters
Prentice Hall Physical Science Concepts in Action
Computer Test Bank with ExamView® CD-ROM
Prentice Hall Physical Science Concepts in Action
Chapter and Unit Tests
Prentice Hall Physical Science Concepts in Action
Test Prep Workbook
Prentice Hall Physical Science Concepts in Action

Program Assessment Resources

- *Computer Test Bank Book with ExamView® CD-ROM*
  - —Create and print tests in minutes from a bank of over 2000 questions.
  - —Over 200 dynamic questions that allow you to generate new values in a question with a click of the mouse.
- *Chapter and Unit Tests—English and Spanish*
  - —Two tests for each chapter:
    Test A for average students
    Test B for basic students
  - —Two Unit Tests for each unit
- *Test Preparation Blackline Masters*
  Help you evaluate student knowledge and provide test-taking practice.
- *Test Preparation Workbook*
  Students practice taking tests to improve their scores on standardized tests.

On the Web and CD-ROM

Interactive Textbook
CHAPTER 14
Chapter Assessment continued
Critical Thinking
Concepts in Action
Math Skills
Interactive Textbook

The ***Interactive Textbook*** provides online homework and interactive assessment opportunities tied to the *Student Edition*. Students monitor their progress at point of use with ongoing assessment, helpful hints,and instant feedback. They'll know immediately if they're on track!

Available online at **PHSchool.com.**

Tools that make teaching easier

Online Solutions

Access to a world of resources under one roof!

- **PHSchool.com** goes hand-in-hand with the Student Edition for additional support—student activities, chapter assessment, teacher support, and many more resources—with every chapter.

Go Online PHSchool.com

- **sciLINKS,** at point of use in the text, provides Web links chosen and updated by the National Science Teacher's Association—with downloadable worksheets that address internet literacy.

NSTA sciLINKS www.SciLinks.org

- **Science News**® provides current published articles, linked by topic.

Stay current with SCIENCE NEWS® www.phschool.com

- **Planet Diary** features weekly reports on environmental news and natural phenomena such as earthquakes, tornadoes, and hurricanes.

PLANETDIARY

Teacher's Edition

NSTA sciLINKS www.SciLinks.org

The Teacher's Edition:

- Provides the support and flexibility you need, with activities labeled by level of difficulty.
- Includes built-in content support with authors' suggestions for teaching the big ideas.
- Provides teaching methods straight from the National Science Teacher's Association.
- Includes detailed descriptions on how to implement reading stategies to help teachers improve reading literacy.

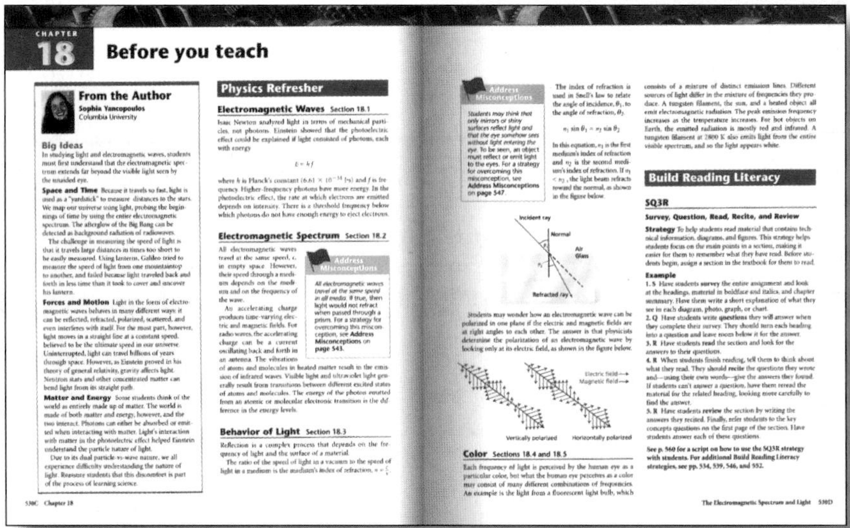
CHAPTER 18
Before you teach
From the Author
Physics Refresher
Electromagnetic Waves
Electromagnetic Spectrum
Behavior of Light
Address Misconceptions
Build Reading Literacy
Color

Planning and Presentation Resources

Transparencies Plus

- **Presentation Pro® CD-ROM**
  Electronic access to all of the program's transparencies allows you to create exciting custom slide show presentations at the click of a mouse.
- **Transparencies**
  450 dynamic transparencies include Interest Grabbers, Section Outlines, Graphic Organizers, Chapter Pretests, and Illustrations from the text—all organized by chapter and referenced in the *Teacher's Edition*.

Program Resources
Easy Planner
Prentice Hall
Physical Science
Concepts in Action
Easily organized lessons in one convenient resource!

TRANSPARENCIES PLUS
Transparencies With Prentice Hall Presentation Pro CD-ROM
Prentice Hall
Physical Science
Concepts in Action
12 Section 14–1 Interest Grabber
What Is a Machine?
A machine is a device with which you can do work in a way that is easier or more effective. Keep in mind that machines do not have to be complex gadgets that run on electricity or fuel.
1. Make a list of the five examples of
your classroom.
explain why
20 Figure 2–2 Isotopes of Carbon
Nonradioactive carbon-12
Nonradioactive carbon-13
Radioactive carbon-14
6 electrons
6 protons
6 neutrons
6 electrons
6 protons
7 neutrons
6 electrons
6 protons
8 neutrons
PRENTICE HALL
PRESENTATION PRO
Prentice Hall
Physical Science
Concepts in Action

Easy Planner

in Spiral-Bound Format

Everything you need for daily planning is in one place.

This all-in-one resource includes:

- Lesson Plans for each lesson.
- A Planning Guide for each chapter to address different ability levels.
- Reduced pages of all core teaching ancillaries.

PRENTICE HALL
Teacher EXPRESS
Plan • Teach • Test

Teacher Express CD-ROM

Teacher Express is a new suite of instructional tools to help teachers plan, teach, and test. Powerful lesson planning, resource management, testing, and an interactive Teacher's Edition are available on one convenient CD-ROM to make class preparation quick and easy!

Reading Comprehension: What Research Suggests

Dr. Nancy Romance • Florida Atlantic University

Q&A

Q: Why are science texts often difficult for students to read and comprehend?

A: In general, science texts present complex literacy and knowledge demands on learners. They have a more technical vocabulary and a more demanding syntax, and place a greater emphasis on inferential reasoning. When considering these attributes in conjunction with recent findings about students' lack of prior content knowledge and literacy skills, it becomes increasingly important for science teachers to adopt new ways of helping students interact with science text.

Q: What does research say about how comprehension is facilitated?

A: Modern understanding of comprehension emphasizes the importance of in-depth prior knowledge and how that knowledge is organized. Studies comparing novices and experts show that the conceptual organization of experts' knowledge is very different from that of novices. For example, experts emphasize core concepts when organizing knowledge while novices focus on superficial details. To facilitate comprehension, effective teaching strategies should support and scaffold students as they build an understanding of the key concepts and concept relationships within a text unit.

Q: What strategies can teachers use to facilitate comprehension?

A: Three complementary strategies are very important in facilitating student comprehension of science texts. First, guide student interaction with the text using the built-in strategies. Second, organize the curriculum in terms of core concepts (e.g., Key Concepts in each section). Third, develop visual representations of the relationships among the key concepts and vocabulary that can be referred to during instruction. Teachers can also guide students' own construction of concept maps using these steps:

1. Select a portion of text that is the current focus of instruction.
2. Ensure students are able to read the passage fluently—present difficult vocabulary words before reading the passage.
3. Highlight text features that guide students' thinking about the concepts presented.

Dr. Nancy Romance

Dr. Nancy Romance has been a Professor of Science Education for 13 years at Florida Atlantic University. She was formerly Science Curriculum Supervisor for Broward County. She was a science classroom teacher for 12 years.

4. Guide development of a visual representation of the concept relationships.
   a. Have students identify core concepts emphasized in the passage. Write each concept on a sticky note and attach these randomly on chart paper or the board.
   b. Guide students to organize the sticky notes in a hierarchical structure, linking concepts to indicate relationships. Label the links.
5. Re-read the text passage, referring to the draft concept map. Revise the map as needed.
6. Display the map for later review or expansion and have students keep a copy for study and review outside class.
7. Assign additional reading materials related to the passage and have students revise their concept map as they read.

More teaching strategies to Build Reading Literacy can be found throughout the *Teachers Edition* in the Before You Teach pages before each chapter and in the teaching suggestions for each section. These detailed examples give science teachers reading expertise.

Q: How does *Physical Science: Concepts in Action* facilitate comprehension?

A: The concept of "considerate" text—one that provides instructional support for comprehension—has been built into the *Student Edition* through the careful design of text features.

- **Real-world applications:** An emphasis on real-world applications of the key concepts activates prior knowledge and gives students a framework for understanding new information.
- **Overall text organization:** Text structured in an outline format and key concepts highlighted in boldface type enable students to see the relationships between the big ideas and supporting details.
- **Consistent section structure:** Each section identifies Key Concepts, Critical Vocabulary, and a Reading Skill with a sample graphic organizer to help students create visual representations.
- **Frequent self-assessment:** Relevant photos and carefully constructed graphics include questions to help students recognize the thinking processes being used in learning. The Reading Checkpoints and Section Assessments let students track their comprehension.

Each of these instructional features provides a strong literacy framework for science teachers as they guide student interaction with the text. Each, in turn, also serves as a scaffold for students as they become more independent learners.

Internet Resources: Valuable Tools for High Schools

Cathy Dickerson • Humbolt County Office of Education

Connecting to the Information Super Highway

The challenge presented to education in the 1990s was to connect all classrooms to the "Information Super Highway" by the new millennium. By 2001 nearly 90% of all middle and high school classrooms in the U.S. had computers connected to the Internet, and over 50% of students reported accessing Internet resources primarily from school. Today those percentages approach 100%, as more than 1.5 million pages are added, daily, to the World Wide Web. Our new challenge is to focus on using these vast information resources to enhance educational experiences for our students.

Over the past 5 years, real-time access to data collections from current scientific research has grown, free and low-cost virtual science explorations have been posted online for direct observation of scientific phenomena, and access to scientists for descriptions or clarifications of conceptual understandings has increased. Teachers who make wise use of Web resources can extend the breadth and depth of classroom learning and prepare students for academic and technical futures.

Using Web Resources

While there is a wealth of information on the Internet, scaffolding Web experiences for students can reduce the chances for misdirection and wasted time and increase the educational value of the activity. Successful scaffolding strategies used by teachers include:

- Pointing students to educational Web sites or portals rather than general search engines as starting points.
- Providing links to pre-selected Web resources for assignments or embedding.
  pre-selected links in student assignments.
- Selecting or designing projects and research questions that require synthesis and analysis of gathered information.

Cathy Dickerson

Cathy Dickerson is currently a curriculum specialist for technology with the Humboldt County Office of Education. Cathy has been in education for 20 years, most of that time teaching science in elementary and secondary classrooms. A native of Arcata, California, she directed the SCORE Science Website project for the California Department of Education, was recognized with a Humboldt County "Excellence in Teaching" award, served as County program manager for math and science professional development, and has presented at conferences for technology, science and mathematics. Cathy received a master's degree in Computing and Technology for Education from Humboldt State University in 2001, a Multiple Subjects Teaching Credential from Humboldt State University in 1982 and a Bachelor's of Arts degree at Stanford University in 1980.

Central to use of Internet resources in standards-based education is the need for critical evaluation of information sources. Because the Web is an open-publishing, unmoderated medium, students often find misleading and sometimes blatantly false information. Both teachers and students must be able to critically evaluate sources of information so that learners focus on materials that develop conceptual understanding rather than misleading material. To this end learners must be able to discriminate between valid, reputable sources, and those that are not.

Go Online PHSchool.com

Go Online with *Physical Science: Concepts in Action*

According to research, the most significant variable in determining the educational impact of technology-based resources is the teacher. Go Online features, in every chapter of *Physical Science: Concepts in Action*, take the guesswork and planning time out of developing meaningful Internet experiences.

NSTA SCILINKS www.SciLinks.org

Through SciLinks, the National Science Teacher's Association's topic-based Web resource service, students can access web resources that have been reviewed by science teachers for their grade-level appropriateness and relationship to the topic under study. In addition, students can download a blackline master that guides them through a process of reviewing the web resources, and identifying the source of the information. Teachers can download background information about the specific web resources available to use in assessing student responses.

1-800-848-9500 PHSchool.com

Other online activities at PHSchool.com include chapter labs in which students can share their data with others around the country and utilize a national data pool for making inferences and drawing conclusions. Also, students can visit *Science News*® to access current information on science topics and Planet Diary for news of the latest events affecting the global environment. And, students can research careers as they begin to prepare for the workplace. All this in addition to self-grading assessments to help students stay on track with content standards.

Go Online activities help students develop their ability to evaluate Web resources, access the latest information, and interact with students across the country. Take advantage of all the Internet has to offer—a multitude of opportunities for students to research, experience, contribute, and learn!

Pacing Guide

The Pacing Guide below suggests one way to schedule your instructional time for Basic (students who need additional help), Average (all students), and Enriched (students who need to be challenged) students.

	CHAPTERS/SECTIONS		
Week	**Basic Students**	**Average Students**	**Enriched Students**
1	1.1, 1.2	1	1
2	1.3, 1.4	2	2
3	2	3	3
4	3.1, 3.2	4	4
5	3.3, 4.1	5	5
6	4.2, 4.3	6.1, 6.2, 6.3	6
7	5.1, 5.2	6.4, 7.1	7.1, 7.2, 7.3
8	5.3, 6.1	7.2, 7.3	7.4, 7.5
9	6.2, 6.3, 6.4	7.4, 7.5	8
10	7.2, 7.3, 7.4	8	9
11	8.1, 8.3	9	10.1, 10.2
12	9.1, 9.2, 9.3	10.1, 10.2	10.3, 10.4
13	10.1, 10.2	10.3, 10.4	11
14	10.3, 11.1	11	12
15	11.2, 11.3	12.1, 12.2	13
16	12.1, 12.4	12.3, 12.4	14
17	13	13	15
18	14.1, 14.2	14	16
19	14.3, 14.4	15	17.1, 17.2
20	15	16	17.3, 17.4
21	16	17.1, 17.2	18.1, 18.2, 18.3
22	17.1, 17.2	17.3, 17.4	18.4, 18.5
23	17.3, 17.4	18.1, 18.2, 18.3	19
24	18.1, 18.2, 18.5	18.4, 18.5	20.1, 20.2
25	19.1, 19.2	19.1, 19.2, 19.3	20.3, 20.4
26	20.1, 20.3	20.1, 20.2, 20.3	21
27	21	21	22.1, 22.2, 22.3
28	22.1, 22.3	22.1, 22.2, 22.3	22.4, 22.5, 22.6
29	22.4, 22.5	22.5, 22.6, 23.1	23.1, 23.2, 23.3
30	23.2, 23.4	23.2, 23.3, 23.4	23.4, 23.5, 23.6
31	23.6, 24.1, 24.2	23.5, 24.1	24.1, 24.2, 24.3
32	24.5, 24.7	24.2, 24.3, 24.4	24.4, 24.5, 24.6, 24.7
33	25.1, 25.2	24.5, 24.6, 24.7	25.1, 25.2, 25.3
34	25.3, 25.4	25.1, 25.3, 25.4	25.4, 25.5, 25.6
35	26.1, 26.2	25.5, 26.1, 26.2	26.1, 26.2
36	26.3, 26.5	26.3, 26.4, 26.5	26.3, 26.4, 26.5
Total	**36 Weeks**	**36 Weeks**	**36 Weeks**

1 Week = 2 1/2 blocks or 5 periods

National Science Education Standards

Correlation to National Science Education Standards	
Content Standard	**Chapter/Section/Page**
Content Standard A • Science as Inquiry	
A-1 Abilities necessary to do scientific inquiry	Ch. 1: pp. 8–11, pp. 16–21, Sec. 1.4; Ch. 2: p. 58; Ch. 4: p. 111; Ch. 11: p. 335, p. 345; Inquiry Activities, Quick Labs, Exploration Labs, Consumer Labs, Forensics Labs, Application Labs, Design Your Own Labs, Problem Solving Activities, Math Skills, Data Analysis: Chapters 1–26; Appendices A–G
A-2 Understandings about scientific inquiry	Ch. 1: pp. 7–10, pp. 12–14, pp. 16–21, Sec. 1.4; Ch. 2: p. 48; Ch. 4: p. 102; Ch. 11: pp. 345–348; Ch. 14: pp. 413–415, p. 424; Ch. 22: p. 688; Inquiry Activities, Quick Labs, Exploration Labs, Consumer Labs, Forensics Labs, Application Labs, Design Your Own Labs, Problem Solving Activities, Math Skills, Data Analysis: Chapters 1–26; Appendices A–G
Content Standard B • Physical Science	
B-1 Structure of Atoms	Ch. 1: p. 5; Ch. 4: p. 101, p. 103, p. 105, Sec. 4.2, pp. 114–118; Ch. 5: p. 134, p. 139; Ch. 6: p. 158, p. 160; Ch. 7: p. 204; Ch. 10: pp. 292–294, Sec. 10.2, p. 303, p. 305, pp. 308–311, pp. 314–315; Ch. 12: pp. 379–380; Ch. 13: pp. 390–392; Ch. 15: p. 452; Ch. 21: p. 632; Ch. 23: p. 734; Ch. 26: p. 829; Appendix C
B-2 Structure and Properties of Matter	Ch. 1: p. 5; Ch. 2: Sec. 2.1, pp. 42–44, pp. 45–47, pp. 49–52, pp. 52–53; Ch. 3: pp. 68–70, pp. 72–74, p. 77, p. 80, p. 85, pp. 87–88, p. 91; Ch. 4: pp. 101–103, pp. 111–113; Ch. 5: pp. 127–129, Sec. 5.2, Sec. 5.3, p. 147; Ch. 6: Sec. 6.1, Sec. 6.2, pp. 171–175, Sec. 6.4, pp. 182–183; Ch. 7: pp. 196–197, p. 200, p. 202, pp. 204–207, p. 217; Ch. 8: pp. 228–231, p. 234, p. 240, p. 242, pp. 244–245, Sec. 8.4; Ch. 9: pp. 262–267, Sec. 9.2, pp. 275–277; Ch. 16: p. 476, p. 479; Ch. 22: Sec. 22.2, Sec. 22.3, pp. 691–692, p. 695; Appendices C–D
B-3 Chemical Reactions	Ch. 2: pp. 54–57; Ch. 5: pp. 140–141, pp. 143–144; Ch. 7: pp. 192–194, p. 197, p. 199, p. 201, pp. 202–204, Sec. 7.3, Sec. 7.4, Sec. 7.5, pp. 220–221; Ch. 8: pp. 230–231, p. 233, Sec. 8.3, Sec. 8.4, p. 251, p. 254; Ch. 9: p. 268, p. 270, p. 274, p. 282; Ch. 10: p. 299; Ch. 15: p. 451; Ch. 16: p. 487; Ch. 22: p. 674; Ch. 23: pp. 710–711; Appendix A, Appendix C
B-4 Motions and Forces	Ch. 1: p. 5; Ch. 3: p. 75; Ch. 11: Sec. 11.1, Sec. 11.2, pp. 332, 336, 337; Ch. 12: Sec. 12.1, Sec. 12.2, pp. 370–371, Sec. 12.3, Sec. 12.4; Ch. 13: Sec. 13.2, pp. 398–399, Sec. 13.3; Ch. 14: pp. 412–415, Sec. 14.2, pp. 421–423, pp. 425–426, Sec. 14.4, p. 436, p. 439; Ch. 15: p. 449; Ch. 20: Sec. 20.1, Sec. 20.2, Sec. 20.3, pp. 618–619, pp. 621–622; Ch. 21: Sec. 21.1, Sec. 21.2, pp. 640–645, pp. 648–649; Ch. 24: p. 770; Ch. 26: p. 837
B-5 Conservation of Energy and the Increase in Disorder	Ch. 1: p. 6; Ch. 3: p. 71, p. 73, p. 76, p. 78, pp. 82–83, p. 86, pp. 88–89; Ch. 4: p. 102; Ch. 7: pp. 208–209; Ch. 11: Sec. 11.3; Ch. 15: pp. 447–448, p. 450, p. 452, Sec. 15.2, pp. 460–461, p. 463, p. 465, p. 467; Ch. 16: Sec. 16.1, pp. 479–480, pp. 482–485, pp. 489–490; Ch. 18: p. 533, p. 543, pp. 547–549, p. 551, p. 558, pp. 560–562; Ch. 20: p. 605; Ch. 24: pp. 755–756; Ch. 26: pp. 830–831, p. 836

Correlation to National Science Education Standards	
Content Standard	**Chapter/Section/Page**
Content Standard B • Physical Science (continued)	
B-6 Interactions of Energy and Matter	Ch. 6: pp. 182–183; Ch. 8: p. 232; Ch. 10: p. 294, p. 307; Ch. 15: p. 452; Ch. 16: p. 481; Ch. 17: Sec. 17.1, p. 504, p. 507, Sec. 17.3, p. 514, p. 518, p. 520; Ch. 18: pp. 532–533, pp. 535–536, p. 538, pp. 540–545, Sec. 18.3, Sec. 18.4, p. 554, pp. 556–557, p. 559; Ch. 19: Sec. 19.1, pp. 572–573, Sec. 19.2, pp. 581–584, pp. 589–590, p. 592; Ch. 20: p. 602, p. 607, pp. 619–622; Ch. 21: pp. 640–641; Ch. 22: p. 660, p. 684, pp. 686–687, p. 689; Ch. 26: p. 830, pp. 836–837, pp. 844–845, p. 852
Content Standard C • Life Science	
C-1 The Cell	Ch. 5: pp. 146–147; Ch. 7: p. 212, p. 218; Ch. 8: pp. 250–253; Ch. 9: pp. 278–280, pp. 282–284; Ch. 24: p. 747
C-2 The Molecular Basis of Heredity	Ch. 9: pp. 279–280
C-3 Biological Evolution	Ch. 23: pp. 735–736, p. 738
C-4 The Interdependence of Organisms	Ch. 17: p. 513
C-5 Matter, Energy, and Organization in Living Systems	Ch. 5: p. 143, pp. 146–147, p. 149; Ch. 9: p. 264, p. 275, p. 278, p. 280, pp. 282–283; Ch. 24: p. 747
C-6 The Behavior of Organisms	Ch. 17: p. 515, p. 517; Ch. 19: p. 580, Sec. 19.4
Content Standard D • Earth and Space Science	
D-1 Energy in the Earth System	Ch. 10: p. 296; Ch. 11: p. 343; Ch. 12: p. 381; Ch. 15: p. 464; Ch. 16: p. 481; Ch. 22: p. 662, p. 676, pp. 679–683, pp. 685–686, p. 693, p. 695; Ch. 23: p. 705, pp. 725–726; Ch. 24: p. 747, p. 753, pp. 755–758, pp. 765–769, pp. 778–781; Ch. 25: pp. 797–798, p. 801, pp. 805–806; Ch. 26: pp. 828–829, pp. 831–833
D-2 Geochemical Cycles	Ch. 9: pp. 267–268; Ch. 22: pp. 674–675, p. 691, pp. 695–696; Ch. 23: p. 705, Sec. 23.1, pp. 710–712, p. 717, p. 719, p. 725; Ch. 24: pp. 760–761, p. 764; Appendices C–D
D-3 The Origin and Evolution of the Earth System	Ch. 22: pp. 660–661, p. 663, pp. 672–674, pp. 677–679, p. 681, pp. 683–684, pp. 687–690, p. 692, p. 694; Ch. 23: pp. 709–710, Sec. 23.3, Sec. 23.4, pp. 728–730, Sec. 23.6; Ch. 25: p. 792, p. 796, pp. 798–801, pp. 803–805, pp. 807–808, pp. 811–817, Sec. 25.5; Ch. 26: p. 829, p. 850, p. 854
D-4 The Origin and Evolution of the Universe	Ch. 1: p. 5; Ch. 25: pp. 804–805, pp. 807–809, pp. 811–815, p. 817; Ch. 26: p. 837, p. 839, Sec. 26.3, p. 845, pp. 847–851, Sec. 26.5; Appendix H

National Science Education Standards (continued)

Correlation to National Science Education Standards	
Content Standard	**Chapter/Section/Page**
Content Standard E • Science and Technology	
E-1 Abilities of Technological Design	Ch. 4: pp. 106–107, p. 109; Ch. 7: p. 218; Ch. 8: p. 238; Ch. 18: p. 542; Ch. 21: p. 646
E-2 Understandings About Science and Technology	Ch. 1: pp. 3–4, pp. 12–13, p. 25; Ch. 2: p. 48; Ch. 4: p. 111; Ch. 6: pp. 182–183; Ch. 10: pp. 305–307, p. 309; Ch. 11: pp. 340–341; Ch. 12: p. 382; Ch. 13: pp. 402–403; Ch. 14: p. 434; Ch. 17: p. 516, pp. 522–523; Ch. 18: p. 540, p. 542, pp. 544–545, pp. 554–556, p. 560; Ch. 19: p. 581, pp. 586–587, p. 591; Ch. 20: pp. 614–617, p. 619; Ch. 21: pp. 640–641; Ch. 23: p. 731; Ch. 24: Sec. 24.6; Ch. 25: pp. 792–795; Ch. 26: p. 835, pp. 848–849
Content Standard F • Science in Personal and Social Perspective	
F-1 Personal and Community Health	Ch. 1: p. 11; Ch. 2: pp. 52–53; Ch. 5: p. 144, p. 146, pp. 148–149; Ch. 7: p. 201, pp. 210–211; Ch. 8: p. 228, p. 233, p. 240, pp. 252–253; Ch. 9: p. 269, pp. 270–272, p. 284; Ch. 10: p. 297, pp. 306–307, p. 312; Ch. 11: p. 338; Ch. 12: p. 366; Ch. 15: p. 461; Ch. 17: pp. 522–523; Ch. 18: pp. 543–545, p. 560; Ch. 19: p. 587, pp. 590–592; Ch. 20: pp. 612–613, p. 623; Ch. 21: pp. 640–641, p. 644; Ch. 23: p. 731; Ch. 24: p. 750, p. 782; Ch. 25: p. 795
F-2 Population Growth	Ch. 9: p. 281; Ch. 10: p. 312; Ch. 15: p. 462; Ch. 17: p. 513; Ch. 24: p. 782; Appendix E
F-3 Natural Resources	Ch. 5: pp. 141–145; Ch. 9: p. 268, pp. 270–271, p. 273; Ch. 15: Sec. 15.3; Ch. 21: p. 646
F-4 Environmental Quality	Ch. 9: pp. 270–272; Ch. 10: p. 312; Ch. 15: p. 463, p. 466; Ch. 16: p. 488; Ch. 17: p. 513; Ch. 24: p. 782
F-5 Natural and Human-Induced Hazards	Ch. 3: p. 71; Ch. 5: p. 143; Ch. 7: pp. 210–211; Ch. 9: p. 269, pp. 270–272; Ch. 10: p. 296, p. 306, pp. 311–313; Ch. 17: pp. 522–523; Ch. 18: p. 544; Ch. 22: p. 685, p. 688, p. 690, p. 692; Ch. 23: p. 712; Ch. 24: p. 750, pp. 770–773, p. 782
F-6 Science and Technology in Local, National, and Global Challenges	Ch. 2: p. 59; Ch. 9: p. 281; Ch. 10: p. 302; Ch. 17: p. 513; Ch. 19: p. 579; Ch. 20: p. 608; Ch. 23: p. 718; Ch. 25: p. 802

Correlation to AAAS Benchmarks	
Content Standard	**Chapters**
4 • The Physical Setting (continued)	
4E Energy Transformation	1, 3, 4, 6, 7, 8, 9, 10, 15, 16, 18, 20, 21, 22, 26; How It Works: Ch. 8, 15, 16; Inquiry Activity: Ch. 15; Concepts in Action: Ch. 15, 16
4F Motion	1, 4, 11, 14, 15, 17, 18, 19, 21, 22, 24, 26; Concepts in Action: Ch. 11, 12, 13, 18; How It Works: Ch. 13, 18
4G Forces of Nature	4, 5, 6, 8, 10, 11, 12, 13, 15, 18, 20, 21, 25; Concepts in Action: Ch. 6, 12, 16, 21; How It Works: Ch. 13, 26; Exploration Lab: Ch. 13
5 • The Living Environment	
5A Diversity of Life	9
5B Heredity	11; Concepts in Action: Ch. 8
5C Cells	5, 9; Problem Solving Activity: Ch. 7; Concepts in Action: Ch. 5, 8
5D Interdependence of Life	15, 23, 24; Issues in Science: Ch. 17, 23; Concepts in Action: Ch. 7
5E Flow of Matter and Energy	5, 9, 10, 15, 23
5F Evolution of Life	23; Issues in Science: Ch. 17, 23
6 • The Human Organism	
6A Human Identity	9; Concepts in Action: Ch. 1
6B Human Development	
6C Basic Functions	3, 17, 18, 19; Concepts in Action: Ch. 8, 17, 18, 24
6D Learning	1, 4, 5
6E Physical Health	5, 8, 9, 10, 18, 20; Concepts in Action: Ch. 2, 5, 8, 10, 15, 17, 21; How It Works: Ch. 8, 19; Issues in Science: Ch. 2
6F Mental Health	
7 • Human Society	
7A Cultural Effects on Behavior	
7B Group Behavior	
7C Social Change	1, 9; Issues in Science: 2, 9, 19, 20, 23, 25
7D Social Trade-Offs	15, 25; Issues in Science: Ch. 2, 9, 10, 17, 19, 20, 23
7E Political and Economic Systems	2; Data Analysis: Ch. 16; Issues in Science: Ch. 2, 19, 20, 25
7F Social Conflict Issues in Science:	Ch. 2, 9, 17, 19, 23
7G Global Interdependence	15, 25; Data Analysis: Ch. 15; Issues in Science: Ch. 9, 17, 25

AAAS Benchmarks (continued)

Correlation to AAAS Benchmarks	
Content Standard	**Chapters**
8 • The Designed World (continued)	
8A Agriculture	3, 8, 15, 18; Concepts in Action: Ch. 5; Issues in Science: Ch. 2
8B Materials and Manufacturing	2, 5, 6, 8, 9; Concepts in Action: Ch. 9; How It Works: Ch. 2, 7, 8, 9; Data Analysis: Ch. 3
8C Energy Sources and Use	8, 9, 10, 15, 16, 18, 21, 24; Concepts in Action: Ch. 9; How It Works: Ch. 10, 16; Data Analysis: Ch. 15; Issues in Science: Ch. 9, 20
8D Communication	1, 12, 17, 18, 20, 24; Data Analysis: Ch. 1, 18; How It Works: Ch. 21; Concepts in Action: Ch. 11, 17, 19, 20; Issues in Science: Ch. 19
8E Information Processing	20, 24; Concepts in Action: Ch. 4, 6, 17, 20; How It Works: Ch. 4, 11, 20; all Data Analysis features; all Labs
8F Health Technology	17, 18; Concepts in Action: Ch. 4, 10, 19, 21
9 • The Mathematical World	
9A Numbers	1, 3, 8, 11, 13, 26; Quick Lab: Ch. 1, 18; all Data Analysis features; Concepts in Action: Ch. 26; all Labs; Math Skills; Appendices A–C, I
9B Symbolic Relationships	1, 3, 5, 7, 10, 11, 12, 13, 14, 15, 20, 22, 26; Data Analysis: Ch. 1, 2, 6, 9, 12, 14, 16, 19, 21, 24, 26; How It Works: Ch. 6, 14; Math Skills: 6, 7, 10, 11, 12, 14, 15, 16, 17, 18
9C Shapes	13, 19, 22, 23, 24, 26; Concepts in Action: Ch. 14, 23, 26; How It Works: Ch. 23; Problem Solving Activity: Ch. 8
9D Uncertainty	1, 2, 3, 4, 6, 8, 10, 26; Data Analysis: Ch. 2, 9, 13, 14, 15, 24, 26; Problem Solving Activity: Ch. 7; Application Lab: Ch. 1, 21; Forensics Lab: Ch. 2, 4, 20; Exploration Lab: Ch. 3, 5, 8, 11, 12, 13, 18, 22, 24, 26; Consumer Lab: Ch. 6, 9, 14; Design Your Own Lab: Ch. 7, 16; Math Skills
9E Reasoning 4; Issues in Science:	Ch. 9, 10, 17, 19, 20, 23, 25; all Data Analysis features; Math Skills; Appendix I
10 • Historical Perspectives	
10A Displacing the Earth from the Center of the Universe	25, 26
10B Uniting the Heavens and Earth	12, 25; Concepts in Action: Ch. 13
10C Relating Matter & Energy and Time & Space	10, 15; How It Works: Ch. 26
10D Extending Time	22, 23, 26
10E Moving the Continents	22
10F Understanding Fire	2, 4, 5, 7, 9; Concepts in Action: Ch. 7; Forensics Lab: Ch. 4
10G Splitting the Atom	4, 7, 10, 18, 22, 23, 25; Concepts in Action: Ch. 10; How It Works: Ch. 10

Correlation to AAAS Benchmarks

Content Standard	Chapters
10 • Historical Perspectives (continued)	
10H Explaining the Diversity of Life Issues in Science	Ch. 17
10J Harnessing Power	6, 16, 17; How It Works: Ch. 4, 6; Concepts in Action: Ch. 6, 20
11 • Common Themes	
11A Systems	16, 20, Concepts in Action: Ch. 15, 16; Problem Solving Activity: Ch. 21
11B Models	3, 4, 5, 6, 7, 9, 12, 14, 16, 17, 18, 19, 21, 22, 23, 24, 25, 26; Concepts in Action: Ch. 4, 6, 8, 9, 11, 13, 15, 16, 19, 20, 21, 22, 23, 24, 25; How It Works: Ch. 2, 7, 9, 10, 12, 14, 16, 17, 18, 19, 20, 21, 24, 25, 26; Problem Solving Activity: Ch. 4, 23; Quick Lab: Ch. 6, 8, 9, 10, 16, 18, 19, 20, 21, 22, 23, 24, 25; Exploration Lab: Ch. 10, 23, 25; Appendix A
11C Constancy and Change	1, 3, 7, 8, 11, 14, 16, 17, 20, 26; Data Analysis: Ch. 1, 9, 12, 14, 15, 16, 18, 26; Problem Solving Activity: Ch. 7; Concepts in Action: Ch. 8; Quick Lab: Ch. 15; Application Lab: Ch. 21; Exploration Lab: Ch. 22, 26; Design Your Own Lab: Ch. 7, 16
11D Scale	1, 18, 19; Concepts in Action: Ch. 4, 26; Problem Solving Activity: Ch. 4; Appendices A–B
12 • Habits of the Mind	
12A Values and Attitudes	1; Concepts in Action: Ch. 18; all Inquiry Activities
12B Computation and Estimation	1, 14, 15, 16, 21; Inquiry Activity: Ch. 7; Math Skills: Ch. 1, 3, 6, 7, 10, 11, 12, 14, 15, 16, 17, 18, 20; Quick Lab: Ch. 1, 2, 5, 7, 11, 14, 15, 17, 26; Application Lab: Ch. 1; Problem Solving Activity: Ch. 4, 6, 8; Data Analysis: 2, 3, 12, 13, 14, 16, 18, 19; Concepts in Action: Ch. 11, 14; Exploration Lab: Ch. 3, 13, 25; Consumer Lab: Ch. 14; all Design an Experiment Labs; Appendix I
12C Manipulation and Observation	all Labs; Inquiry Activity: Ch. 2, 4, 6; Appendices A, B, I
12D Communication Skills	Application Lab: Ch. 1, 15; Issues in Science: Ch. 2?; Data Analysis: Ch. 1; Problem Solving Activity: Ch. 4, 7, 21; Concepts in Action: Ch. 6, 20; Quick Lab: Ch. 10; Consumer Lab: Ch. 9; Exploration Lab: Ch. 11, 22, 25; How It Works: Ch. 1, 3, 4, 5, 6, 13, 15, 22
12E Critical-Response Skills	Issues in Science: Ch. 2, 9, 10, 17, 19, 20, 23, 25; Appendix I

Inquiry Skills

Science Process Skills

The Prentice Hall ***High School Physical Science*** program provides comprehensive practice and assessment of science skills, with an emphasis on the process skills necessary for inquiry. The chart lists the skills covered in the program and cites page numbers where each skill is covered.

	Labs and Activities	Caption and Assessment Questions
Observing	37, 60, 90, 117, 119, 125, 150, 157, 167, 184, 203, 214, 220, 227, 232, 248, 254, 285, 291, 316, 330, 349, 355, 360, 389, 405, 450, 476, 481, 499, 524, 525, 531, 563, 569, 585, 593, 606, 612, 629, 637, 648, 668, 687, 703, 714, 739, 789, 819, 827	56, 70, 74, 101, 130, 138, 159, 224, 278, 420, 451, 538, 552, 742, 824, 835
Inferring	18, 24, 42, 56, 60, 67, 71, 79, 90, 99, 102, 160, 191, 214, 227, 232, 233, 243, 317, 330, 349, 401, 433, 445, 476, 481, 493, 524, 525, 531, 542, 569, 599, 629, 632, 649, 697, 703, 714, 722, 734, 739, 749, 775, 789, 853, 855, 857	8, 17, 44, 51, 58, 64, 96, 103, 117, 122, 129, 143, 154, 168, 169, 196, 207, 209, 219, 224, 239, 241, 244, 258, 272, 274, 276, 280, 284, 296, 297, 301, 304, 305, 315, 320, 331, 336, 348, 361, 377, 382, 386, 391, 393, 397, 404, 417, 420, 421, 455, 459, 466, 470, 475, 490, 496, 505, 516, 528, 534, 544, 566, 573, 575, 580, 585, 592, 596, 603, 626, 636, 639, 652, 668, 678, 683, 700, 711, 738, 742, 754, 777, 782, 786, 796, 813, 815, 820, 824, 837, 849, 852, 860
Predicting	60, 61, 99, 119, 128, 157, 167, 185, 221, 248, 255, 265, 278, 327, 365, 380, 392, 411, 424, 463, 481, 542, 544, 599, 623, 632, 648, 649, 671, 697, 703, 705, 714, 749, 775, 783, 827, 853, 856	44, 57, 81, 102, 122, 129, 140, 154, 164, 181, 188, 205, 224, 234, 263, 288, 297, 301, 305, 352, 362, 368, 382, 397, 408, 416, 419, 449, 470, 478, 480, 492, 496, 507, 536, 545, 549, 553, 566, 589, 596, 603, 630, 633, 639, 643, 646, 652, 675, 683, 691, 696, 708, 712, 714, 720, 729, 742, 751, 771, 786, 820, 829, 844, 860
Measuring	26, 27, 92, 150, 254, 285, 349, 405, 438, 439, 467, 593, 856	
Calculating	26, 42, 71, 150, 151, 196, 221, 317, 349, 377, 392, 405, 424, 429, 433, 438, 439, 454, 491, 493, 505, 542, 575, 623, 739, 775, 793, 821, 832, 853	18, 20, 30, 96, 109, 122, 175, 188, 198, 209, 224, 235, 239, 258, 299, 301, 320, 352, 357, 369, 376, 386, 408, 435, 442, 470, 478, 496, 528, 566, 626, 647, 652, 700, 742, 792, 809, 824, 833, 860
Classifying	128, 135, 151, 203, 232, 243, 278, 445, 467, 668	3, 6, 11, 58, 68, 96, 122, 154, 171, 177, 188, 205, 224, 237, 265, 269, 274, 280, 288, 320, 442, 487, 545, 672, 685, 700, 710, 742, 754, 764, 778, 786, 849
Using Tables and Graphs	24, 26, 27, 71, 92, 93, 119, 150, 160, 273, 285, 300, 349, 377, 429, 433, 454, 463, 467, 491, 623, 648, 649, 667, 697, 775, 783, 853, 857	23, 25, 30, 64, 85, 96, 112, 127, 134, 172, 173, 208, 215, 258, 288, 334, 352, 386, 392, 470, 496, 543, 575, 700, 704, 742, 747, 786, 804, 811, 824, 860

Science Process Skills (continued)		
	Labs and Activities	**Caption and Assessment Questions**
Using Models	173, 265, 291, 300, 304, 316, 317, 544, 606, 612, 671, 687, 705, 714, 739, 766, 793, 819, 821, 856	11, 30, 96, 166, 169, 188, 193, 219, 224, 231, 308, 382, 408, 442, 528, 538, 596, 860
Posing Questions	1, 629, 668	64, 118, 496
Designing Experiments	1, 99, 167, 220, 221, 493	7, 11, 30, 51, 64, 154, 224, 258, 288, 337, 352, 386, 408, 470, 507, 596, 626, 633, 667, 669, 742, 786
Formulating Hypotheses	79, 90, 117, 119, 157, 167, 220, 261, 273, 327, 355, 360, 389, 411, 499, 502, 667, 745, 783	30, 122, 138, 284, 478, 496, 528, 549, 558, 562, 603, 643, 669, 692, 700, 729, 742, 786, 805, 812, 814
Forming Operational Definitions	135, 405, 659	288, 528
Controlling Variables	27, 473, 524, 525	78, 122, 496
Analyzing Data	18, 61, 90, 93, 196, 221, 254, 285, 300, 317, 383, 405, 429, 439, 463, 525, 563, 571, 632, 649, 671, 697, 734, 739, 745, 783, 793, 821, 857	39, 47, 64, 143, 154, 288, 352, 470, 476, 515, 613
Drawing Conclusions	42, 61, 71, 79, 93, 102, 117, 119, 125, 151, 184, 185, 221, 227, 243, 255, 278, 285, 317, 360, 380, 401, 405, 424, 439, 445, 450, 454, 467, 493, 505, 524, 531, 542, 559, 563, 571, 593, 623, 637, 667, 697, 734, 749, 783, 789, 821, 827, 855, 857	55, 64, 81, 91, 96, 105, 154, 164, 181, 224, 284, 288, 392, 601, 622, 647, 700, 738, 742, 824
Communicating Results	1	386
Evaluating and Revising	46, 56, 61, 99, 285, 317, 330, 360, 389, 491, 493, 649	6, 215, 320

Inquiry Skills (continued)

Critical Thinking Skills		
	Labs and Activities	**Caption and Assessment Questions**
Comparing and Contrasting	18, 27, 37, 42, 46, 67, 93, 119, 128, 135, 151, 160, 173, 185, 214, 255, 411, 424, 473, 493, 502, 544, 559, 599, 659	6, 25, 43, 58, 64, 69, 81, 96, 105, 112, 116, 118, 122, 129, 131, 138, 145, 188, 203, 224, 234, 241, 247, 249, 258, 288, 293, 310, 348, 352, 362, 373, 386, 390, 396, 408, 414, 416, 418, 442, 464, 466, 496, 501, 503, 512, 521, 545, 562, 566, 577, 578, 584, 592, 596, 622, 626, 639, 647, 652, 663, 674, 675, 689, 696, 700, 715, 717, 724, 742, 751, 754, 757, 761, 786, 791, 794, 800, 801, 804, 809, 815, 824, 839, 844, 847, 855, 860
Applying Concepts	46, 90, 185, 191, 203, 227, 304, 317, 365, 377, 383, 401, 433, 439, 450, 563, 575, 593, 623, 634, 749, 766, 827, 857	14, 20, 50, 51, 64, 74, 81, 86, 89, 91, 96, 110, 112, 122, 138, 144, 154, 169, 175, 181, 188, 194, 198, 213, 215, 224, 245, 258, 269, 274, 288, 320, 328, 337, 344, 348, 352, 362, 369, 377, 379, 386, 393, 397, 404, 408, 412, 416, 420, 426, 430, 435, 442, 447, 452, 454, 456, 457, 459, 463, 466, 470, 478, 483, 492, 496, 503, 507, 512, 521, 528, 538, 548, 549, 553, 562, 566, 573, 578, 585, 592, 596, 605, 607, 613, 619, 621, 622, 626, 637, 639, 647, 652, 663, 675, 683, 700, 708, 717, 748, 759, 764, 768, 771, 777, 780, 782, 786, 794, 818, 820, 824, 833, 836, 839, 860
Interpreting Diagrams/ Photographs	21, 49, 87, 111, 137, 163, 201, 277, 314, 335, 366, 402, 434, 465, 488, 520, 560, 591, 620, 688, 756, 795, 845	4, 11, 41, 44, 77, 85, 122, 161, 169, 200, 204, 217, 258, 268, 294, 311, 358, 432, 491, 492, 503, 512, 528, 533, 540, 553, 566, 571, 572, 596, 604, 610, 631, 647, 662, 669, 682, 705, 706, 707, 719, 727, 733, 734, 736, 750, 753, 754, 758, 766, 776, 779, 799, 829, 830, 832, 838, 842
Making Judgments		6, 30, 118, 258, 288, 320, 331, 369, 386, 470, 496, 592, 626, 742, 824
Problem Solving		30, 154, 239, 331, 352, 566, 607, 613, 652
Using Analogies	125	73, 74, 105, 122, 154, 162, 197, 245, 275, 280, 331, 496, 622, 661, 824, 855
Relating Cause and Effect	71, 160, 273, 473, 585	64, 72, 96, 105, 122, 154, 188, 249, 288, 386, 397, 431, 442, 483, 489, 509, 528, 548, 566, 603, 626, 633, 639, 647, 663, 679, 689, 693, 696, 712, 717, 724, 728, 759, 860
Making Generalizations	128, 160, 261, 499, 775	48, 96, 145, 154, 164, 188, 224, 264, 320, 426, 435, 442, 503, 511, 514, 528, 786, 824, 860

Graphic Organizers

	Pages
Concept Maps and Web Diagrams	2, 7, 38, 62, 75, 94, 152, 158, 176, 186, 199, 212, 222, 256, 275, 286, 298, 318, 342, 350, 372, 384, 406, 427, 440, 446, 494, 500, 514, 526, 564, 580, 594, 624, 630, 650, 709, 713, 778, 796, 834
Compare-and-Contrast Tables	22, 378, 468, 532, 570, 670, 755, 790, 822, 846, 858
Venn Diagrams	68, 206, 228, 246, 308, 550
Flowcharts	84, 113, 453, 546, 558, 642, 690, 719, 760, 840
Cycle Diagrams	486
Outlines	216, 588, 664, 765
Tables	14, 22, 28, 45, 54, 100, 108 (KWL), 120, 126, 130, 139, 165, 170, 192, 235, 240, 262, 272, 282, 292, 303, 328, 332, 356, 363, 390, 394, 400, 412, 417, 421, 462, 474, 479, 504, 508, 539, 574, 600, 604, 609, 618, 635, 660, 676, 684, 704, 725, 732, 746, 752, 774, 803, 810, 818, 822, 828, 852

Reading Strategies

Using Prior Knowledge	7, 240, 390, 514, 580, 630, 834
Previewing	2, 14, 130, 199, 235, 262, 292, 474, 500, 676, 732, 852
Predicting	170, 328, 394, 604
Building Vocabulary	45, 212, 363, 421, 446, 479, 504, 574, 660, 684, 704, 752, 778, 796, 828
Identifying the Main Idea	126, 275, 462, 508, 600, 635, 774, 818
Identifying Cause and Effect	75, 176, 453, 725
Comparing and Contrasting	22, 68, 206, 228, 246, 308, 378, 532, 570, 670, 755, 790, 846
Sequencing	113, 158, 486, 558, 642, 690, 719, 760, 840
Relating Text and Figures	54, 165, 356, 412, 609, 746
Summarizing	38, 84, 100, 282, 342, 372, 400, 417, 427, 539, 618, 803, 810
Outlining	216, 588, 664, 765
Monitoring Your Understanding	108, 139, 192, 272, 303, 332, 546

Materials List

Item	Quantity	Chapter
Alcohol, isopropyl (95%)	5 mL	8.1 QL, 9 IA
Alligator clips	5	20 Lab
Alum	20 grams	6 IA
Aluminum foil	1 sheet	1 Lab, 19.3 QL
Aluminum foil strips	1	20.3 QL
Aluminum strip	1	5.2 QL, 20.2 QL
Antacid tablet	1	7 IA
Apples, ripe	1	9.3 QL
Ascorbic acid solution	50 mL	7 Lab
Bags, paper	2	4 IA
Bag, plastic	1	22 IA
Bags, plastic freezer	5	23 IA
Bags, plastic (resealable)	1	5.1 QL, 7 IA
Bag, large plastic	1	10.2 QL
Baking powder	1 g	2 Lab, 8.3 QL
Baking soda	25 g	2 Lab
Balance	1	1 Lab, 5 Lab, 7 IA, 7.1 QL, 16 Lab
Ball	1	25.1 QL
Ball, blue plastic-foam	1	6 Lab
Ball, black plastic-foam	1	6 Lab
Balloons, long	4	12 Lab
Balloon, small, round	1	8 IA, 12.4 QL, 16.1 QL, 17 Lab
Basketball	1	15.1 QL
Basalt sample	1	22 IA
Battery, 6-volt	1	20.3 QL, 21.2 QL
Battery, 9-volt	1	20 Lab
Battery clip	1	20 Lab
Beads, green	5 32	10 IA 10.3 QL
Beads, purple	7 32	10 IA 10.3 QL
Beaker, 25-mL	2	8 Lab
Beaker, 100-mL	1	8 Lab, 16.2 QL, 24 IA
Beaker, 150-mL	1	7 Lab
Beaker, 250-mL	1	1.3 QL, 6.2 QL, 7.2 QL, 23.1 QL
Beaker, 500-mL	1	3 Lab
Beverage can, empty	1	3.2 QL
Beverage, carbonated (in plastic bottle with cap)	1	8 IA
Bicycle, multispeed	1 per class	14 Lab
Bingo chips	5	4 IA
Biotite sample	1	22 IA
Blocks	1	23 Lab

Item	Quantity	Chapter
Blueberries, frozen	$\frac{1}{4}$ cup	8.3 QL
Board, 1 meter long	1	11 IA, 14 IA, 14.3 QL
Board with 2 nails	1	14 Lab
Board, short	1	14 IA
Bolt	1	7.1 QL
Books	6 2	14 IA, 14.3 QL 21.1 QL
Boric acid solution	5 mL	4 Lab
Bottle, plastic 2 L	1	16.1 QL
Bottle, plastic with cap	1	13.3 QL
Bread	1 slice	9.3 QL
Bubble solution	1 bottle	12.4 QL
Bubble wand	1	12.4 QL
Bucket of hot water	1	8 IA
Bulb, fluorescent	1	18.5 QL
Bulb, clear incandescent	1	18.5
Bunsen burner	1	4 Lab
Calcite sample	1	22 IA
Calcium chloride solution	5 mL	2.3 QL, 4 Lab
Calculator, solar	1	15 IA, 25 Lab, 26.1 QL
Can	1	13 Lab
Cardboard box	1	15.2 QL
Cardboard box divider	1	24.5 QL
Cardboard sheet, large (30 cm x 100 cm)	1	23 Lab
Cardboard sheet, small	1	18 IA
Cardboard tube	2 1	17 Lab 19.3 QL, 21 Lab
Carbon sample	1	2 IA
Cash register paper tape	1	22.5 QL
Chairs with backs	2	12 Lab
Chlorine bleach solution	1–10 drops	7 Lab
Clamp	1	15 Lab, 16 Lab
Clay, modeling	1 piece	13 IA, 15.2 QL, 23 Lab
Clay sample	1 teaspoon	23.3 QL
Coin	1	12.2 QL
Compass, magnetic	1	25 IA
Conglomerate sample	1	22 IA
Container, clear plastic	2	19 IA
Copper sample	1	2 IA
Copper strips	2 1	8.4 QL 20.2 QL
Copper(II) chloride solution	5 drops	7.4 QL
Copper(II) sulfate solution	5 mL 20 mL	2.3 QL, 4 Lab 7.2 QL
Cornstarch, solid	25 grams	2 Lab

Item	Quantity	Chapter
Cornstarch, liquid	15 mL	9.3 QL
Cotton, balls	1	9 IA
Crime scene sample	1	2 Lab
Cups, paper	1	23 Lab
Cups, plastic	1 4	24.1 QL 8.3 QL
Cups, plastic foam	2 1	2.3 QL, 8.3 QL 16 IA, 16 Lab
Cups, plastic foam with lid	1	16 Lab
Dish, small	1	23.3 QL
Dominoes	20	10 Lab
Dropper pipet	2 3 1	8.3 QL 8 Lab 9 Lab, 11 Lab, 13.3 QL, 16.2 QL, 17 IA
Dry ice	small piece	3.3 QL
Dropper bottles	3	2 Lab
Dye bath, methyl orange	1	6 Lab
Electrical socket, portable	1	26.1 QL
Epsom salt	20 grams	6 IA
Eraser	2	12.1 QL
Evaporating dish	1	8 Lab, 23.1 QL
Feldspar, sample	1	22 IA, 22.2 QL
Filter paper, square	1	9 IA
Flashlight	1	15 IA, 17 Lab, 20 IA
Flashlight, one brighter than the other	2	26 IA
Flask, Erlenmeyer 250-mL	1	3.3 QL
Fluorite sample	1	22 IA
Food coloring	1	16.2 QL, 17.1 QL
Food coloring, different colors	2	9 IA
Forceps	1	5 Lab, 11 Lab
Galena sample	1	22 IA, 22.2 QL
Glass slide	1	20.2 QL
Gloves, leather (thick)	1 pair	14 Lab
Graduated cylinder, 10-mL	3 1	2.3 QL 5.2 QL, 8.1 QL, 8 Lab, 11 Lab
Graduated cylinder, 25-mL	1	7.4 QL, 9 Lab
Graduated cylinder, 50-mL	1	5 Lab, 7 Lab
Graduated cylinder, 100-mL	1 2	1.3 QL, 3.3 QL, 7 IA, 11 Lab, 16 IA
Graduated cylinder, 250-mL	1	13 Lab
Graduated cylinder, 500-mL	1	16 Lab
Granite sample	1	22 IA

Item	Quantity	Chapter
Graphite sample	1	22.2 QL
Gravel sample	1 teaspoon	23.3 QL
Grip exerciser, spring loaded	1	15 Lab
Gum drops, white	7	6 Lab
Halite sample	1	22 IA, 22.2 QL
Hammer	1	22 IA
Hand lens	1	22 IA, 23.3 QL
Hornblende sample	1	22.2 QL
Hot plate	1	3.2 QL, 3 Lab, 3.2 QL, 6 Lab, 8 Lab, 16 Lab, 22.3 QL, 23.1 QL
Hydrochloric acid solution	3 mL	8 Lab
Hydrochloric acid solution, dilute	5 mL	4 Lab, 5.2 QL
Ice, crushed	250 mL	3 Lab, 24 IA
Ice cubes	12	16.1 QL, 22.2 QL, 23.1 QL
Ice water	200 mL	16 Lab
Index card	1	12.2 QL, 24.1 QL, 26 Lab
Iodine solution	1–2 drops	2 Lab
Iodine-starch solution	50 mL	7 Lab
Iodine solution in dropper bottle	1	9.3 QL
Iron filings, small container	1	21.1 QL
Iron nail	1	20.2 QL, 21.2 QL, 22.2 QL
Jar, tall, narrow with cover	1	23.3 QL
Juice, apple	10 mL	9 Lab
Juice, lemon	10 mL	8.3 QL
Juice, orange	10 mL	9 Lab
Juice, pineapple	10 mL	9 Lab
Knife, plastic	1	8.4 QL
Labels	2	8 Lab
Laboratory cart	1	14 IA
Lauric acid, in test tube with thermometer	1	3 Lab
Light filters, blue, green, and red	1 each color	18 IA
Light sources, blue, green, and red	1 each	18 Lab
Lead shot	1	5 Lab
Lemon, fresh-large	1	8.4 QL
Limestone sample	1	9 IA, 22 IA
Newspaper	1	10.1 QL, 19.1 QL, 22 IA
Nuts, threaded	2	12 Lab

Materials List (continued)

Item	Quantity	Chapter
Magnesium	1 strip	5.2 QL
Magnet, bar	2 1	21 IA, 21.1 QL 21 Lab
Manganese dioxide	0.1 g	7.4 QL
Marbles	1 2 3	11 IA 11 Lab 4 IA
Marble sample	1	9 IA
Marker	1	26 Lab
Marker, fluorescent (neon)	2	4.3 QL
Markers, felt-tip (water-based ink)	1	6.2 QL, 18 IA
Marker, waterproof	1	23 IA
Marshmallows	30	9 IA
Mass, standard 100g	1	13 Lab
Mass, standard 500 g	1	14.4 QL
Mass, standard 1 kg	1	14.3 QL
Meter stick	1	12 Lab, 14.4 QL, 14 Lab, 15.1 QL, 15.2 QL, 17 IA, 17.1 QL, 17 Lab, 19.1 QL, 25.1 QL, 25 Lab, 26.1 QL, 26.5 QL, 26 Lab
Metal rod	1	2.2 QL
Methylene blue indicator	1	9 Lab
Mirror, small	1	17 Lab, 19.1 QL
Mirror, plane	1	19 Lab
Mirror, concave	1	19 Lab
Mirror, convex	1	19 Lab
Model, sun and planets (to scale)	1	25 Lab
Multimeter	1	8.4 QL, 20 Lab, 21 Lab
Newspaper	1	19.1 QL, 22 IA, 23 Lab
Nichrome wire loop	1	4.1 QL
Nuts	2	7.1 QL
Oil, vegetable	50 mL	18 IA
Olivine sample	1	22.2 QL
Paint pigment	1	9 IA
Paint chip strips (red, green, and blue)	3	5.1 QL
Pan	1	3.2 QL
Paper clips, Small, metal	5 20	4 IA 21.2 QL
Paper, graph	1 sheet	1 Lab, 3 Lab, 5 Lab, 9.2 QL, 11 IA, 11 Lab, 15.2 QL, 15 Lab, 21 Lab, 22 Lab, 26 Lab

Item	Quantity	Chapter
Paper, construction-black	1 sheet	6 IA, 18.2 QL, 19.3 QL
Paper, loose leaf	1	25 IA, 25.5 QL
Paper, stapled stack	6 sheets	5 IA, 7.2 QL
Paper strip	1	20.2 QL
Paper strips, 2 cm x 20 cm	2	25.5 QL
Paper towels	1 sheet 3–5 sheets	6 Lab, 13 Lab, 16.2 QL, 23 Lab, 24 IA
Paper, test (chromatography)	1 strip	6.2 QL
Paper, white unlined	1 sheet 2 sheets 3 sheets	5 Lab, 7 IA, 21.1 QL 10.3 QL 18 IA, 26 Lab
Paper, white unlined	1 large sheet	18 Lab, 25 Lab
Pebbles	5	4 IA
Pen, felt tipped	1	22.5 QL
Pencils, colored	1 set	18.5 QL
Pencil, glass marking	1	2.3 QL, 7.4 QL
Pencil	1	14.4 QL, 22.5 QL, 23 Lab, 25 IA, 25.5 QL, 26 Lab
Pennies	4 5 1	4 IA 12 IA 22.2 QL
Periodic table	1	5 Lab, 10.3 QL
Petri dish	1	6.2 QL, 22.3 QL
Petri dishes, plastic	2	18.2 QL
pH paper	1 strip	8 Lab
Phenolphthalein indicator solution	2–5 drops	8 Lab
Pin, straight	1	19.3 QL
Plastic bottle with cap (large)	1	1.3 QL
Plastic bottle with cap (medium)	1	1.3 QL
Plastic bottle with cap (small)	1	1.3 QL
Plastic bucket	1	16.1 QL
Plastic container, large	1	3 IA
Plastic container, clear and large	1	17 IA, 17.1 QL
Plastic foam balls	1	9 IA
Paper plates, small	6	9.3 QL
Plastic plate	1	9.3 QL, 20.2 QL
Plastic tub	1	13 Lab
Platinum wire	1	7.4 QL
Potassium chloride	1 g	8.1 QL
Potassium chloride solution	5 mL	4 Lab

Item	Quantity	Chapter
Potato, raw	0.1 g 1 slice	7.4 QL 9.3 QL
Protractor	1	19 Lab
Pumice stone	5	23 IA
Pyrite sample	1	22.2 QL
Raisins	70	9 IA
Resistor, 100 ohms	1	20 Lab
Resistor, 1000 ohms	1	20 Lab
Resistor, 1 ohm	2	20 Lab
Resistor, 10 ohms	2	20 Lab
Ring stand	1	16 Lab
Rocks, small	5–10	23 Lab
Rope, 3-m	1	17.2 QL
Rubber band	1 4	14 Lab, 17 Lab 19.3 QL
Rubber sample	1	2 IA
Ruler, metric (30 cm)	1 2	1 IA, 1 Lab, 2.2 QL, 4.1 QL, 5 Lab, 6.2, 3.2 QL, 7 IA, 10 Lab, 11.1 QL, 11 Lab, 12.1 QL, 15 Lab, 23 Lab 19 Lab
Salol (phenyl salicylate)	2 grams	22.3 QL
Sand	1 teaspoon	23.3 QL
Sandstone sample	1	22 IA
Salt, non-iodized	1 teaspoon 20 grams	4 IA 6 IA
Sodium chloride solution	5 mL	4 Lab
Scalpel	1	17 Lab
Scissors	1	1 IA, 1 Lab, 2.2 QL, 5 Lab, 6 Lab, 7 IA, 12.1 QL, 17 Lab, 23 Lab, 25.1 QL
Shampoo, clear	100 mL	11 Lab
Shoes, 3 different kinds	3	14.3 QL
Silicon piece	1	5.2 QL, 5 Lab
Slate sample	1	22 IA
Sling psychrometer	1	24 Lab
Soap	1 bar	6 Lab
Sodium chloride solution	5 mL	2.3 QL
Sodium hydroxide solution	3 mL	8 Lab
Soil, potting	1 bag per class	23 Lab
Spatula	5 4	2 Lab 6 IA
Spectroscope	1	18.5 QL
Sponge	1	13 Lab
Spoon, long handled	1	24 IA

Item	Quantity	Chapter
Spoon, tea	1	8.3 QL, 22.3 QL, 23.3 QL
Spot plate	2 1	2 Lab 7 Lab
Spring scale	1	13 Lab, 14 IA, 14.3 QL, 14.4 QL
Spring scale, high capacity	1	15 Lab
Stain, methylene blue	5 mL	9 IA
Stapler	1	6.2 QL, 6 Lab
Steel bolts	10	16 Lab
Steel file	1	22.2 QL
Steel sample	1	2 IA
Sticky note	1	12.1 QL
Stirring rod	1 3	1 IA, 3 Lab, 8.1 QL, 8 Lab, 9 Lab, 16 IA
Stirring rod, glass-extra long	1	11 Lab
Straw, drinking	1	12 Lab, 23 Lab
String	3 meters 20 cm 50 cm 1 roll	12 Lab 13 Lab 16 Lab, 25.1 QL 19 Lab
Sugar	15 mL	6 IA, 9 IA
Sugar solution, cold	1 Liter	24.5 QL
Sugar solution, warm and colored	1 Liter	24.5 QL
Sulfur piece	1	5.2 QL
Sunscreen	1 bottle per class	18.2 QL
Suspect's shoe sample	1	2 Lab
Switch	1	21.2 QL
Syringe and plunger	1	3 IA
Table, relative humidity	1	24 Lab
Tank, clear shallow (3–4 Liter)	1	24.5 QL
Tape, masking	2, 10-cm strips	3.2 QL, 11 Lab, 12 Lab, 14.4 QL, 14 Lab, 18 Lab, 19.1 QL, 21.1 QL
Tape, measuring	1	16.1 QL, 17.2 QL
Tape, transparent	2 10-cm strips	4.1 QL, 17 Lab, 25.5 QL
Tape, transparent	4 strips	25 IA, 26 Lab
Tennis ball	1	15.1 QL
Test circuit (9-V battery & 6-V bulb)	1	20.2 QL
Test strips, fabric	2	6 Lab
Test tube (10-mL)	2	8 Lab

Materials List (continued)

Item	Quantity	Chapter
Test tubes	3 4 5	2.3 QL 5.2 QL, 9 Lab 7.4 QL
Test tube, large	2	8.1 QL
Test-tube rack	1	2.3 QL, 5.2 QL, 7.4 QL, 8 Lab, 9 Lab
Thermometer	1 2	3.3 QL, 3 Lab, 8.1 QL, 8.1 QL, 16 IA, 24 IA 16 Lab
Thermometer (liquid crystal)	1	2.2 QL
Threaded spools, 3 with different diameters	4	14 Lab
Thumbtacks, unpainted	2	20.3 QL
Tin strip	1	5 Lab
Tongs	1	3.2 QL, 6 Lab, 7.2 QL, 22.3 QL
Toothpick	1 box per class 30	6 Lab, 13 IA 9 IA
Toy, glow-in-dark	1	4.3 QL
Toy, wind-up	1	15 IA
Tub, plastic	1	24.1 QL
Tubing, glass	2	19 IA
Twine, heavy	20 cm	15 Lab
Ultraviolet lamp	1	4.3 QL
Vinegar, white	10 mL	2 Lab, 8.3 QL
Wallpaper, 1-cm squares	100	10.2 QL
Washers	2	7.1 QL

Item	Quantity	Chapter
Wash bottle of water (distilled)	1	2 Lab, 4 Lab
Watch, or clock with a second hand	1	2.2 QL, 3 Lab, 3.2 QL, 6 Lab, 10 Lab, 11 IA, 11 Lab, 12 Lab, 17.2 QL, 22.3 QL, 23.3 QL, 24 Lab
Watch glass, large	1	8 Lab
Watch glass (borosilicate)	2	22.3 QL
Water bath, boiling water	1 per class	16 Lab
Water, hot	50 mL	2.2 QL
Water, distilled	25 mL	8.1 QL, 8 Lab
Water, hot	50 mL	2.2 QL
Wax paper, 10-cm squares	2	17 Lab, 19.3 QL
Weight, fishing	1	13 Lab
Window cleaner	1–10 drops	8.3 QL
Wires with stripped ends	2	20.3 QL
Wire, insulated with stripped ends, 20-cm long	1	21.2 QL
Wire, insulated with stripped ends, 1-m long	1	21.2 QL
Wood block	1	13 Lab, 20.3 QL
Wood sample	1	2 IA
Wood splints	4 1	6 IA 7.4 QL, 20.2 QL
Zinc, solid piece	1	7.2 QL
Zinc strip	1	8.4 QL

Prentice Hall
Physical Science
Concepts in Action
Discovery Channel School
with Earth and Space Science
Wysession • Frank • Yancopoulos

PEARSON
Prentice Hall

Needham, Massachusetts
Upper Saddle River, New Jersey

DK

Prentice Hall
Physical Science
Concepts in Action
with Earth and Space Science

Prentice Hall

Physical Science

Concepts in Action

With Earth and Space Science

The cover photograph of a hang glider shows chemistry, physics, and Earth science concepts in action.

Print Components
Student Edition
Student Edition With Earth and Space Science
Teacher's Edition
Teacher's Edition With Earth and Space Science
Easy Planner With Earth and Space Science
Laboratory Manual
Laboratory Manual, Teacher's Edition
Reading and Study Workbook
  With Math Support
Reading and Study Workbook
  With Math Support, Teacher's Edition
Chapter and Unit Tests
Test-Taking Tips With Transparencies
Test Preparation Blackline Masters
Standardized Test Preparation Workbook

Technology
Interactive Textbook Online and CD-ROM
Transparencies Plus
  Teaching Transparencies
  Presentation Pro CD-ROM
Probeware Lab Manual With CD-ROM
Discovery Channel Field Trips Videotapes
Discovery Channel Video Field Trips DVD
Computer Test Bank With CD-ROM
Teacher Express CD-ROM
Web site at PHSchool.com

Spanish Resources
Spanish Reading and Study Workbook
Spanish Chapter and Unit Tests
Spanish Section Summaries on Audio CD

Acknowledgments appear on page 954, which constitutes an extension of this copyright page.

PEARSON
Prentice Hall

ISBN 0-13-166308-9

1 2 3 4 5 6 7 8 9 10   08 07 06 05 04

About the Authors

Michael Wysession

Michael Wysession received his Ph.D. in geophysics from Northwestern University in 1991. He is an Associate Professor in Earth and Planetary Sciences at Washington University in St. Louis, Missouri. His area of specialization is using seismic waves to explore Earth's interior. Dr. Wysession is an author on more than 50 scientific publications. For his research, he was awarded a Packard Foundation Fellowship, and in 1996 was awarded a Presidential Faculty Fellowship at the White House. He also has created educational simulations to accurately show how seismic waves propagate.

David Frank

David Frank completed his Ph.D. at Purdue University. For the last ten years he has been the head of the Physical Sciences Department at Ferris State University in Big Rapids, Michigan. He has taught general chemistry courses for science majors and for allied health students. With the assistance of his colleagues, he helped develop a new B.A. program in biochemistry. He has taught students in the university's Math/Science/Technology program, which enrolls gifted high school students. Recently he has worked with Michigan's "Connecting With the Learner" group, which produced a toolkit to help elementary and secondary teachers address diversity issues in the classroom.

Sophia Yancopoulos

Sophia Yancopoulos received her Ph.D. in physics from Columbia University. She has done postdoctoral research in astronomy at Yale University and in biophysics at the Mount Sinai School of Medicine. She considers teaching to be a vital and exciting part of her experience, having taught at Barnard College, Vassar College, the Stevens Institute of Technology, and Columbia University, as well as at Bronx High School of Science. She has worked on a neutrino oscillations experiment at Fermi National Laboratory, conducted experiments on acoustic modeling, and analyzed data on the extreme astrophysics of neutron stars. She currently teaches in the physics department at Manhattan College and in their graduate program in biotechnology.

Contributing Writers

Steve Miller
Science Writer
State College, Pennsylvania

Polly Weissman
Science Writer
New York, New York

Dr. Carolyn Sumners
Houston Museum of Natural Science
Houston, Texas

T. Griffith Jones
P.K. Yonge Developmental Research School
College of Education—University of Florida
Gainesville, Florida

Contributing Writers for DK

Robert Dinwiddie M.A. M.Sc.
Science Writer
London, England

Susan Watt M.A. M.Sc.
Science Writer
London, England

Reading Consultant

Bonnie Armbruster, Ph.D.
Department of Curriculum and Instruction
University of Illinois
Champaign, Illinois

Laboratory Activity Writers

Robert W. Arts
Associate Professor of Physics
Pikeville College
Pikeville, Kentucky

Hasan Fakhrudin
Physics Instructor
Indiana Academy for Science, Mathematics, and Humanities
Muncie, Indiana

Yvonne Favaro
Science Teacher (retired)
Englewood Cliffs, New Jersey

JoAnne Mowczko, Ed.D.
Science Writer
Gaithersburg, Maryland

Brian Rohrig
Science Teacher
Columbus Public Schools
Columbus, Ohio

Safety Consultant

Dr. Kenneth R. Roy
Director, Science and Safety
Glastonbury Public Schools
Glastonbury, Connecticut

Content Reviewers

Albert Altman, Ph.D.
Department of Physics and Applied Physics
University of Massachusetts–Lowell
Lowell, Massachusetts

Paul D. Beale, Ph.D.
Department of Physics
University of Colorado
Boulder, Colorado

Howard Brooks, Ph.D.
Department of Physics and Astronomy
DePauw University
Greencastle, Indiana

Jeffrey C. Callister
Teacher of Earth Science (retired)
Newburgh Free Academy
Newburgh, New York

Paul C. Canfield, Ph.D.
Department of Physics
Iowa State University
Ames, Iowa

Brant J. Chapman, Ph.D.
Department of Chemistry and Biochemistry
Montclair State University
Upper Montclair, New Jersey

David Cinabro, Ph.D.
Department of Physics and Astronomy
Wayne State University
Detroit, Michigan

Dennis P. Clougherty, Ph.D.
Department of Physics
University of Vermont
Burlington, Vermont

Frank Colby, Ph.D.
Professor of Meteorology
University of Massachusetts–Lowell
Lowell, Massachusetts

David R. Curott, Ph.D.
Professor Emeritus
University of North Alabama
Florence, Alabama

Charles C. Curtis, Ph.D.
Department of Physics
The University of Arizona
Tucson, Arizona

Donald Elliott, Ph.D.
Department of Physics
Carroll College
Waukesha, Wisconsin

Deborah Freile, Ph.D.
Department of Physics, Astronomy, and Geology
Berry College
Mt. Berry, Georgia

Joel Goldberg, Ph.D.
Department of Chemistry
University of Vermont
Burlington, Vermont

Michael W. Hamburger, Ph.D.
Department of Geological Sciences
Indiana University
Bloomington, Indiana

Alice K. Hankla, Ph.D.
The Galloway School
Atlanta, Georgia

David O. Harris, Ph.D.
Department of Chemistry and Biochemistry
University of California
Santa Barbara, California

Xiaochun He, Ph.D.
Department of Physics and Astronomy
Georgia State University
Atlanta, Georgia

Gary L. Hickernell, Ph.D.
Professor of Chemistry
Keuka College
Ossining, New York

David Kanis, Ph.D.
Department of Chemistry
Chicago State University
Chicago, Illinois

Glenn C. Kroeger, Ph.D.
Department of Geosciences
Trinity University
San Antonio, Texas

David Markowitz, Ph.D.
Professor of Physics, Emeritus
University of Connecticut
Storrs, Connecticut

Robert J. Mellors, Ph.D.
Department of Geological Sciences
San Diego State University
San Diego, California

David J. Morrissey, Ph.D.
Department of Chemistry
Michigan State University
East Lansing, Michigan

George S. Mumford, Ph.D.
Professor of Astronomy, Emeritus
Tufts University
Medford, Massachusetts

Thomas W. Nalli, Ph.D.
Chemistry Department
Winona State University
Winona, Minnesota

Lesley Putman, Ph.D.
Department of Chemistry
Northern Michigan University
Marquette, Michigan

Stanley Raucher, Ph.D.
Department of Chemistry
University of Washington
Seattle, Washington

John C. Ridge, Ph.D.
Department of Geology
Tufts University
Medford, Massachusetts

Scott M. Rochette, Ph.D.
Department of the Earth Sciences
State University of New York at Brockport
Brockport, New York

Jeffrey C. Rogers, Ph.D.
Department of Geography
Ohio State University
Columbus, Ohio

Larry Rosenhein, Ph.D.
Department of Chemistry
Indiana State University
Terre Haute, Indiana

Mark Rosenthal
Meteorologist
Newton, Massachusetts

Gerald Royce, Ph.D.
United States Naval Academy
Annapolis, Maryland

George Schatz, Ph.D.
Department of Chemistry
Northwestern University
Evanston, Illinois

Sara Seager, Ph.D.
Carnegie Institution of Washington
Washington, D.C.

Surajit Sen, Ph.D.
Department of Physics
State University of New York at Buffalo
Buffalo, New York

Jerry Shi, Ph.D.
Natural Sciences Division
Pasadena City College
Pasadena, California

Steven L. Shropshire, Ph.D.
Department of Physics
Idaho State University
Pocatello, Idaho

Paul B. Steinbach, Ph.D.
Department of Chemistry
Stephen F. Austin State University
Nacogdoches, Texas

Paul R. Stoddard, Ph.D.
Department of Geology and Environmental Geosciences
Northern Illinois University
DeKalb, Illinois

Chuck Stone, Ph.D.
Department of Physics
North Carolina Agricultural and Technical State University
Greensboro, North Carolina

Douglass F. Taber, Ph.D.
Department of Chemistry and Biochemistry
University of Delaware
Newark, Delaware

Jason R. Telford, Ph.D.
Department of Chemistry
University of Iowa
Iowa City, Iowa

John R. Villarreal, Ph.D.
College of Science and Engineering
The University of Texas–Pan American
Edinburg, Texas

Nanette Wachter, Ph.D.
Department of Chemistry
Hofstra University
Hempstead, New York

Jerry D. Wilson, Ph.D.
Lander University–Professor Emeritus
Greenwood, South Carolina

Teacher Reviewers

Ann C. Andrex
James H. Blake High School
Silver Spring, Maryland

Javier Artinano
Austin Preparatory School
Reading, Massachusetts

Frederick C. Bantz
Reservoir High School
Fulton, Maryland

Dr. Louise Baxter
Bainbridge High School
Bainbridge Island, Washington

Dale Beames
Coral Springs High School
Coral Springs, Florida

Alice C. Best
T. C. Roberson High School
Asheville, North Carolina

David R. Blakely
Arlington High School
Arlington, Massachusetts

Mark W. Breerwood
Cypress Springs High School
Cypress, Texas

Bernadine Hladik Cook
Johnstown High School
Johnstown, New York

Melissa Lynn Cook
Oakland Mills High School
Columbia, Maryland

Chris Cunningham
Capital High School
Olympia, Washington

Maryellen Duffy
Andover High School
Andover, Massachusetts

Brad Gammon
Coral Springs High School
Coral Springs, Florida

Roger Gaspar
Bishop Connolly High School
Fall River, Massachusetts

Paul A. Girard
Haverhill High School
Haverhill, Massachusetts

Eileen Gratkins
George N. Smith Junior High School
Mesa, Arizona

Roy G. Hammit
Mesa High School
Mesa, Arizona

Charles W. Kellogg, Ph.D.
Masconomet Regional School District
Topsfield, Massachusetts

David Kelso
Manchester High School Central
Manchester, New Hampshire

Jerome Leonard Kraut
Francis Lewis High School
Fresh Meadows, New York

Michelle S. Krug
Coral Springs High School
Coral Springs, Florida

Horace (Rog) Lucido
Roosevelt High School
Fresno, California

Deborah A. Maner
School for the Talented and Gifted
Dallas, Texas

Angie L. Matamoros, Ph.D.
ALM Consulting
Weston, Florida

Mark McCandless
The Galloway School
Atlanta, Georgia

Bruce A. Mellin
Brooks School
North Andover, Massachusetts

Daniel R. Mullaney
Walpole High School
Walpole, Massachusetts

Noreen Paeth
Curie Metropolitan High School
Chicago, Illinois

Joel Palmer
Mesquite Independent School District
Mesquite, Texas

Joyce A. Reamy
Calvert Hall College High School
Baltimore, Maryland

Pam Rhoda
Owen High School
Black Mountain, North Carolina

Mark Servis
DeWitt High School
DeWitt, Michigan

F. Lee Slick
Morgan Park High School
Chicago, Illinois

Deanna M. Swartzfager
Blake High School
Silver Spring, Maryland

Stephen Mark Tuccelli
Somerville Public Schools
Somerville, Massachusetts

Thomas Vaughn
Arlington High School
Arlington, Massachusetts

Renee Zimmerman
St. John's Preparatory School
Danvers, Massachusetts

Activity and Laboratory Field Testers

Nicholas Bernice
Northern Highlands Regional High School
Allendale, New Jersey

John Bingamon
Thurston High School
Redford, Michigan

Eva Brooksetta Davidson
Vance High School
Charlotte, North Carolina

Ashley P. Day
R S Central High School
Rutherfordton, North Carolina

Richelle Dull
ZB Vance High School
Charlotte, North Carolina

Carolyn C. Elliott
South Iredell High School
Statesville, North Carolina

Lisa Endicott
LaFollette High School
Madison, Wisconsin

Katherine M. Ewing
Sanderson High School
Raleigh, North Carolina

Lisa Freeman
Seymour High School
Seymour, Indiana

Mary Louise Freitas
Peoria High School
Peoria, Arizona

Susan J. Grabowski
Schurz High School
Chicago, Illinois

Herbert H. Gottlieb
Martin Van Buren High School (retired)
Queens Village, New York

Margaret A. Holzer
Chatham High School
Chatham, New Jersey

Brad Laatsch
Vance High School
Charlotte, North Carolina

Beth Meade Leavitt
Wade Hampton High School
Greenville, South Carolina

Ellen Loehman
Manzano High School
Albuquerque, New Mexico

Susan McCullen
Big Rapids High School
Big Rapids, Michigan

Amy McLaughlin
Pasadena High School
Pasadena, California

Al Pangburn
Pioneer School District
Yorkshire, New York

Richard Payne
Cobleskill–Richmondville Central School
Richmondville, New York

A. Marie Pool
Clinton High School
Clinton, Oklahoma

Alan Seidman
Margaretville Central School
Margaretville, New York

Tom Skaar
Ben L. Smith High School
Greensboro, North Carolina

Thomas L. Tokarski
Westchester Magnet Academy
Purchase, New York

James R. White
Southside High School
Chocowinity, North Carolina

John P. Wilbur
Caledonia-Mumford Schools
Caledonia, New York

Contents

Physics 322

KOREA

Earth and Space Science 654

Warm wishes from the tropics!

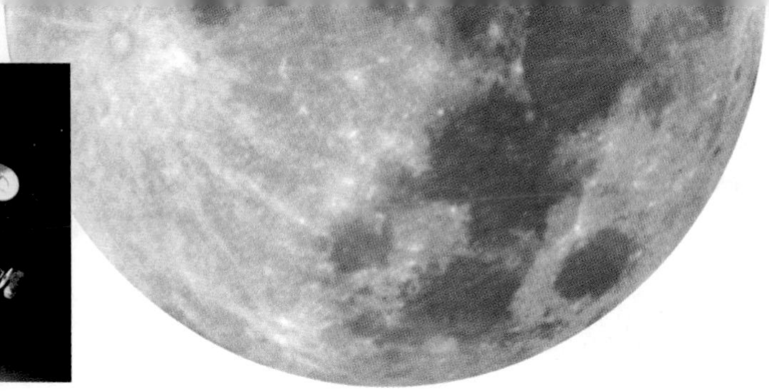

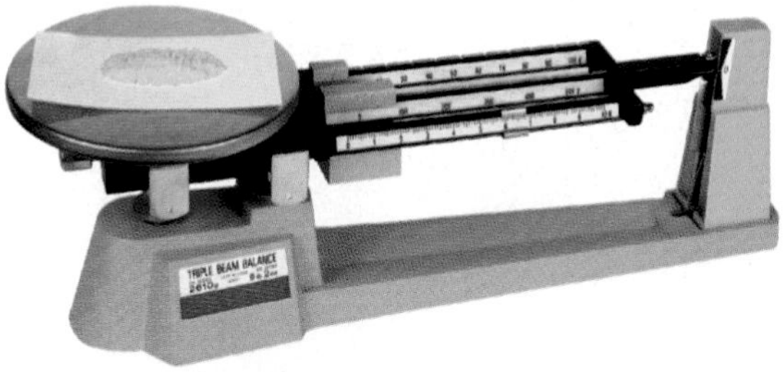

Labs and Activities

Inquiry Activity

Begin each chapter with an activity that sets a purpose for reading.

Quick Lab

Introduce and reinforce key lesson content using simple materials.

Exploration Lab

Practice and develop science methods.

Consumer Lab

Make science concepts relevant by testing consumer products.

Forensics Lab

Develop investigation skills in an engaging context.

Application Lab

Apply concepts in a real-world context.

Design Your Own Lab

Design and carry out open-ended experiments.

Probe or sensor versions are available in the Probeware Lab Manual.

Go Online PHSchool.com Share data with students from across the country at phschool.com

Problem-Solving Activity

Apply science content in a new situation.

Math Skills

Develop math skills with sample problems and practice problems.

Data Analysis

Organize and analyze data to draw conclusions.

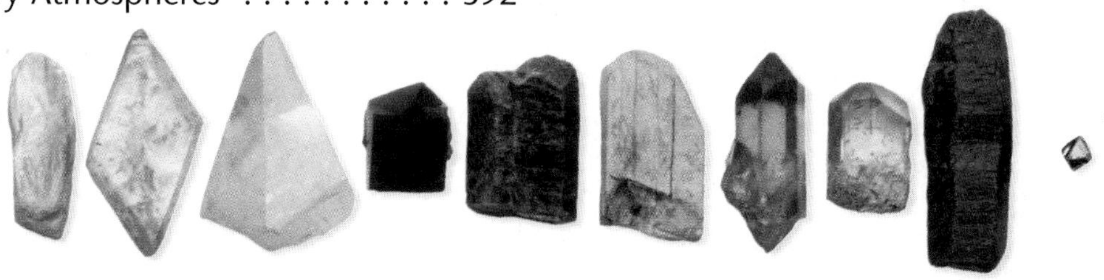

Features

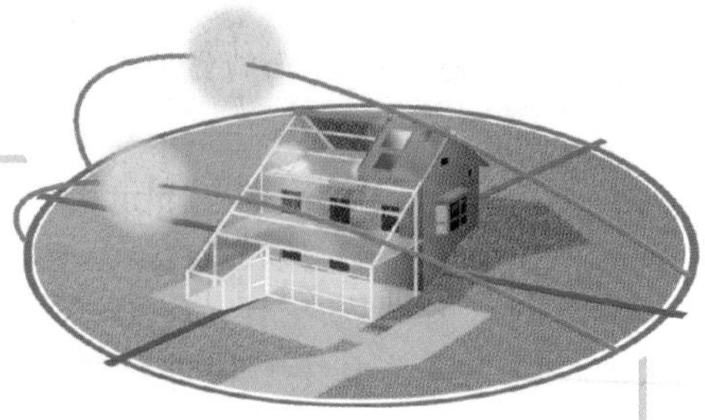

CONCEPTS in Action

Discovery Channel School

Explore science in depth with supporting Discovery Channel videos.

HOW It Works

Understand technology with exciting visual essays.

SCIENCE and History

Explore key developments in the history of science and technology.

issues in SCIENCE

Evaluate opposing viewpoints on current issues in science.

Careers in Science

Consider a variety of occupations that apply science.

CHAPTER 1

Planning Guide

Use these planning tools
Easy Planner
Teacher Express

SECTION OBJECTIVES	STANDARDS NATIONAL (See p. T18.)	STANDARDS STATE	ACTIVITIES and LABS
1.1 What Is Science? pp. 2–6 1 block or 2 periods **1.1.1** **Explain** how science and technology are related. **1.1.2** **List** the major branches of natural science and **describe** how they overlap. **1.1.3** **Describe** the main ideas of physical science.	A-1, A-2, B-1, B-2, B-4, B-5, D-4, E-2, G-1, G-2, G-3		**SE** Inquiry Activity: How Do Scientists Use Their Observations? p. 1 L2 **TE** Teacher Demo: The Compass, p. 3 L2
1.2 Using a Scientific Approach, pp. 7–11 1 block or 2 periods **1.2.1** **Describe** the steps in a scientific method. **1.2.2** **Compare** and **contrast** facts, scientific theories, and scientific laws. **1.2.3** **Explain** the importance of models in science. **1.2.4** **Explain** the importance of safety in science.	A-1, A-2, E-2, F-1, G-2		**TE** Build Science Skills: Observing, p. 8 L2 **TE** Teacher Demo: Flaps on an Airplane, p. 10 L2
1.3 Measurement, pp. 14–20 1 block or 2 periods **1.3.1** **Perform** calculations involving scientific notation and conversion factors. **1.3.2** **Identify** the metric and SI units used in science and **convert** between common metric prefixes. **1.3.3** **Compare** and **contrast** accuracy and precision. **1.3.4** **Relate** the Celsius, Kelvin, and Fahrenheit temperature scales.	A-1, A-2, G-2		**SE** Quick Lab: Comparing Precision, p. 18 L2 **SE** Application Lab: Determining the Thickness of Aluminum Foil, pp. 26–27 L2 **TE** Teacher Demo: Conversion Factor, p. 18 L2 **LM** Investigation 1A: Evaluating Precision L2 **LM** Investigation 1B: Measuring Volume and Temperature L1
1.4 Presenting Scientific Data, pp. 22–25 1 block or 2 periods **1.4.1** **Organize** and **analyze** data using tables and graphs. **1.4.2** **Identify** the relationship between a manipulated variable and a responding variable. **1.4.3** **Explain** the importance of communicating data. **1.4.4** **Discuss** the process of peer review.	A-1, A-2, E-2, G-1		

Ability Levels	
L1	For students who need additional help
L2	For all students
L3	For students who need to be challenged

Components							
SE	Student Edition	RSW	Reading & Study Workbook	CUT	Chapter & Unit Tests	T	Transparencies
TE	Teacher's Edition			CTB	Computer Test Bank	iT	Interactive Textbook
LM	Laboratory Manual	MSPS	Math Skills & Problem Solving Workbook	TP	Test Prep Resources	P	Presentation Pro CD-ROM
PLM	Probeware Lab Manual			DC	Discovery Channel Videotapes & DVDs	GO	Internet Resources

RESOURCES PRINT and TECHNOLOGY		SECTION ASSESSMENT
RSW Section 1.1	L1	SE Section 1.1 Assessment, p. 6
T Chapter 1 Pretest	L2	iT Section 1.1
Section 1.1	L2	
P Chapter 1 Pretest	L2	
Section 1.1	L2	
SCILINKS GO Motion	L2	
RSW Section 1.2	L1	SE Section 1.2 Assessment, p. 11
DC Cracking the Case	L2	iT Section 1.2
T Section 1.2	L2	
P Section 1.2	L2	
SCIENCE NEWS GO Nature of science	L2	
RSW Section 1.3	L1	SE Section 1.3 Assessment, p. 20
RSW Math Skill	L2	iT Section 1.3
MSPS Section 1.3	L2	
T Section 1.3	L2	
P Section 1.3	L2	
PLANETDIARY GO Universal measurements	L2	
PHSchool.com GO Data sharing	L2	
RSW Section 1.4	L1	SE Section 1.4 Assessment, p. 25
MSPS Section 1.4	L2	iT Section 1.4
T Section 1.4	L2	
P Section 1.4	L2	
SCILINKS GO Graphing	L2	

Go Online

Go online for these Internet resources.

PHSchool.com
Web Code: ccd-0010
Web Code: cca-0015

SCIENCE NEWS
Web Code: cce-0011

NSTA SCILINKS
Web Code: ccn-0011
Web Code: ccn-0014

PLANETDIARY
Web Code: ccc-0013

Materials for Activities and Labs

Quantities for each group

STUDENT EDITION

Inquiry Activity, p. 1
25 mL of copper(II) chloride solution in a 50-mL beaker, scissors, metric ruler, aluminum foil, glass stirring rod

Quick Lab, p. 18
3 plastic bottles of different sizes, beaker, graduated cylinder

Application Lab, p. 26
metric ruler, aluminum foil, scissors, balance, graph paper

TEACHER'S EDITION

Teacher Demo, p. 3
compass, magnet, chalk

Build Science Skills, p. 8
low-wattage incandescent bulb, power source for the bulb

Teacher Demo, p. 10
sheet of paper

Build Science Skills, p. 12
modeling clay, at least 5 different toy cars with similar-sized tires that have different tread, cooking oil, magnifying glass

Teacher Demo, p. 18
1-lb object, 0.25-lb object, balance

Chapter Assessment

CHAPTER ASSESSMENT

SE Chapter Assessment, pp. 29–30
CUT Chapter 1 Test A, B
CTB Chapter 1
iT Chapter 1
PHSchool.com GO
Web Code: cca-0015

STANDARDIZED TEST PREP

SE Chapter 1, p. 31
TP Diagnose and Prescribe

Interactive Textbook

Interactive Textbook with assessment at PHSchool.com

CHAPTER 1

Before you teach

From the Author

Michael Wysession
Washington University

Big Ideas

The universe has rules. Science discovers these rules. Science is both a body of knowledge and a set of many different processes for revealing this knowledge. Science works by developing models of reality. Old models must continuously be unlearned to make way for new models. All students may eventually play a part in this exciting endeavor.

Space and Time The natural universe is big and old. Our universe is about 40 billion light-years in diameter (and most of it is not observable!), and is more than 13 billion years old. Our solar system (including Earth) is about 4.5 billion years old. So much is already known about our universe that its study is divided into many different branches of science. These divisions are artificial, however, as nature doesn't know physics from chemistry or biology. Much of science is interdisciplinary.

Forces and Motion Much of science involves the study of the application of forces to objects and the motions that result. Science uses standard techniques and units of measurement to study these forces and motions. Scientific observations always have limits to their accuracy and precision. Much of mathematics has been developed in order to interpret these observations.

Matter and Energy The energy of the universe was created in the initial moments of the big bang. Since then, energy has continuously converted between many different forms. Matter formed from energy during the early cooling of the universe, soon after the big bang. Common matter as we know it consists of less than 4% of the observable universe, but people are interested in it because people are made of matter.
In the current physical model, matter is made of discrete particles like quarks (and many other particles). Quarks combine to form protons and neutrons, which in turn combine with electrons to form atoms, which bond together to form the molecules of the matter of our world. This model may change, as it has many times in the past.

Science Refresher

What Is Science? 1.1

Science is a system of knowledge and methods for finding that knowledge. Technology is the application of scientific knowledge to solve a problem. A mutually beneficial relationship exists between science and technology: Technology may be developed to answer a scientific question, and science may be used to solve a technological problem.

Natural science is organized into three main branches (physical, chemistry, Earth science) that are subdivided into many overlapping areas. Approaching problems or questions from more than one direction can make them easier to understand or lead to new discoveries. It may also help scientists modify or invalidate theories. Scientific knowledge changes very rapidly, and scientists must keep up with the latest research because it can affect their own research.

Using a Scientific Approach 1.2

A scientific method is a plan for gathering information in order to solve a problem or better understand an event. Such methods allow scientists to document their procedures, observations, and findings and then share them with other scientists. As scientists share data and continue research, the body of scientific knowledge increases. Scientific theories are developed to explain observations. Scientists can also consolidate observations into scientific laws. Models can help scientists understand phenomena that are too difficult to observe directly. Models may be small-scale models or complex mathematical representations running on powerful supercomputers.

Measurement 1.3

Much of the data scientists collect can be distilled or aggregated into measurements—quantitative data. Scientific notation simplifies communication of and calculations with very large and small numbers. A standard system of measurements facilitates communication and replication of experimental results. A revised version of the metric system, the International System of Units (SI) is the standard used

Address Misconceptions

Students may think that the metric system is more accurate than the English system of units. However, accuracy and precision are related to measuring tools and methods, not the system of units. For a strategy to overcome this misconception, see **Address Misconceptions** on **page 16.**

Go Online PD LINKS NSTA
For: Teaching methods for science skills
Visit: www.SciLinks.org/PDLinks
Web Code: ccn-0199

to make scientific measurements. SI is based on seven standard units of measure, which may be modified with prefixes (to make the units appropriate for the data collected) or combined to form derived units.

SI Base Units

Quantity	Unit	Symbol
Length	meter	m
Mass	kilogram	kg
Temperature	kelvin	K
Time	second	s
Amount of substance	mole	mol
Electric current	ampere	A
Luminous intensity	candela	cd

Accuracy is how close a measurement is to the actual value of what is being measured. Precision is how exact a measurement is. The number of significant figures in a measurement indicates its precision.

Presenting Scientific Data 1.4

Address Misconceptions

Students may think that graphs validate data. This is false because a graph is merely a method for reporting data. (One way to validate data is to make multiple measurements, often by repeating an experiment.) For a strategy to overcome this misconception, see **Address Misconceptions** on **page 24.**

Scientific information is most useful when it is shared. Preferred formats for presenting data are clear and easy to understand. The simplest way to present data is to use data tables. The use of graphs and other visual aids can help scientists spot relationships and trends in the data.

Scientists report their experimental procedures and results (to both the scientific community and the general public) through a variety of media, literature, and events. The process of peer review allows scientists to share and debate ideas, and is crucial to the progress of science.

Build Reading Literacy

Use Prior Knowledge

Linking New Learning to Familiar Concepts

Strategy Help students construct meaning by linking new information to familiar concepts. Some references indicate that activating prior knowledge is the most important of all reading strategies. Choose a section from Chapter 1, such as pp. 2–6, to use in modeling this strategy. You may also wish to use questions such as those on p. xviii to activate prior knowledge.

Example

1. Have students turn to the pre-selected section, read the opening paragraph, and survey the headings and visuals. Ask students to recount experiences they have had with the topic, and what they already know or believe they know about each subheading. Write student responses on the board. If noticeable misconceptions arise during this discussion, begin to address them immediately.
2. Have students generate and write several questions or predictions about the topic, based on their prior knowledge.
3. Ask students to read the section with the purpose of answering their questions or confirming or refuting their predictions. Divide the section into several parts, and have students pause after each part to evaluate or revise predictions.
4. After reading, discuss with students the information learned. Discuss any new understandings that refute prior misconceptions.
5. Repeat the process for the chapter's remaining sections.

See p. 19 for a script on how to use the use prior knowledge strategy with students. For additional Build Reading Literacy strategies, see pp. 5, 7, and 22.

ASSESS PRIOR KNOWLEDGE

Use the Chapter Pretest below to assess students' prior knowledge. As needed, review these Science Concepts and Math Skills with students.

Review Science Concepts

Section 1.1 Ask students if they have encountered the terms *science* and *technology* before. Have students briefly discuss what they know about science and technology and how each is part of daily life.

Section 1.2 Have students recall situations in which steps must be done in a specific order (playing a game) and situations in which the order may be flexible (cleaning a room). Ask students how these two approaches might relate to science.

Section 1.3 Ask students if they are familiar with English and metric units of measurement. Have students list the type of quantity that each unit is used to measure.

Section 1.4 Have students recall ways in which they have organized and communicated information, for example when preparing a school report or invitations to a party.

Review Math Skills

Conversion Factors; Scientific Notation; Bar, Circle, and Line Graphs Students need to divide and multiply numbers in scientific notation, convert between measuring units, and interpret data in graphs.

Direct students to the **Math Skills** in the **Skills and Reference Handbook** at the end of the student text.

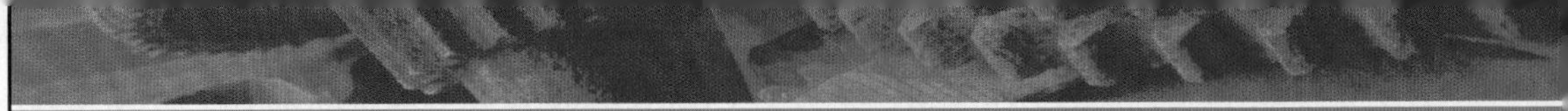

CHAPTER

1 Science Skills

CONCEPTS in Action

How do science concepts apply to your world? Here are some questions you'll be able to answer after you read this chapter.

- How do scientists plan to study Mars in the future? *(Section 1.1)*
- Which keeps you drier in the rain, walking or running? *(Section 1.2)*
- How many stars are there in the Milky Way galaxy? *(Section 1.3)*
- What is Earth's crust made of? *(Section 1.4)*

Discovery Channel School

Video Field Trip

Cracking the Case

- How do police investigators use scientific methods to solve a crime? *(page 12)*

A technician tends a reactor that contains bacteria. The bacteria produce proteins that will be used in medicines. ▶

xviii *Chapter 1*

Chapter Pretest

1. True or False: Science and technology are not related. *(False)*

2. Which of the following are areas of science? *(d)*
   - **a.** Biology and chemistry
   - **b.** Astronomy and geology
   - **c.** Zoology and botany
   - **d.** All of the above

3. Why do scientists document their observations and experiments? *(Sample answer: to remember them correctly or analyze them at a later time)*

4. Which number is largest? *(a)*
   - **a.** 1.13×10^9
   - **b.** 3.51×10^3
   - **c.** 5.88×10^5
   - **d.** 7.92×10^2

5. Which unit can be used to measure volume? *(c)*
   a. m **b.** m^2 **c.** m^3

6. Which of these units is the longest? *(c)*
   a. Meter **b.** Centimeter
   c. Kilometer **d.** Millimeter

7. What is the slope of a line? *(The ratio of a vertical change to the corresponding horizontal change)*

8. What types of graphs have you seen before? *(Sample answers: line, bar, and circle graphs; pictograph. Some students may also be familiar with histograms.)*

Chapter Preview

Inquiry Activity

How Do Shaking and Heating Affect a Carbonated Beverage?

Procedure

1. Remove the cap from a plastic bottle of carbonated beverage (a solution of carbon dioxide in water). Observe what happens.
2. Fit a balloon tightly over the top of the bottle. Holding the bottle over a sink, shake it several times from side to side. Observe any changes in the balloon and the liquid.
3. Place the bottle in a bucket of hot water. Observe any further changes in the balloon.

Think About It

1. **Observing** What happened when you removed the cap from the bottle?
2. **Inferring** What caused the balloon to expand?
3. **Drawing Conclusions** How did shaking affect the rate of the change in the beverage?
4. **Applying Concepts** How would storing a carbonated beverage in a refrigerator affect what happens when the cap is removed?

Discovery Channel School **Video Field Trip**
Suspended in Blood

Encourage students to view the Video Field Trip "Suspended in Blood."

ENGAGE/EXPLORE

Inquiry Activity

How Do Shaking and Heating Affect a Carbonated Beverage? L2

Purpose In this activity, students begin to describe the effects of temperature and agitation on the solubility of a gas in a liquid.

Address Misconceptions

Students may think that solutes can be only liquids or solids. Challenge this misconception by asking students to explain their observations in this activity.

Skills Focus **Observing, Inferring**

Prep Time 5 minutes

Materials plastic bottle of carbonated beverage, small balloon, bucket, hot water

Class Time 15 minutes

Safety Have students wipe up any liquid spilled on the floor.

Expected Outcome Prior to opening the bottle, students will not see any bubbles. Once the bottle is opened, bubbles will begin to appear in the liquid. A little foam may appear depending on whether the bottle was shaken prior to opening. After the balloon is placed on the bottle and the bottle is shaken, the balloon will inflate somewhat due to carbon dioxide being released. If the beverage is at room temperature, there will be more bubbles than if the beverage was chilled.

Think About It

1. After the cap is removed, many bubbles appear in the liquid.
2. Acceptable answers include suggesting that a gas was dissolved in the liquid and that shaking the bottle allowed the gas to escape.
3. Shaking the beverage caused bubbles to form more rapidly (thus inflating the balloon).
4. Storing the beverage in a refrigerator would reduce the formation of bubbles.
Visual

Section 8.1

8.1 Formation of Solutions

1 FOCUS

Objectives

8.1.1 **Describe** how a substance can dissolve in water by dissociation, dispersion, or ionization.

8.1.2 **Describe** how the physical properties of a solution can differ from those of its solute and solvent.

8.1.3 **Identify** energy changes that occur during the formation of a solution.

8.1.4 **Describe** factors affecting the rate at which a solute dissolves in a solvent.

Reading Focus

Key Concepts

- What are three processes that can occur when substances dissolve?
- What are some properties of a solution that differ from those of its solvent and solutes?
- What happens to energy when a solution forms?
- What factors affect the rate of dissolving?

Vocabulary

- solute
- solvent
- dissociation
- dispersion
- ionization

Reading Strategy

Comparing and Contrasting Copy the Venn diagram below. Contrast dissociation and ionization by listing the ways they differ.

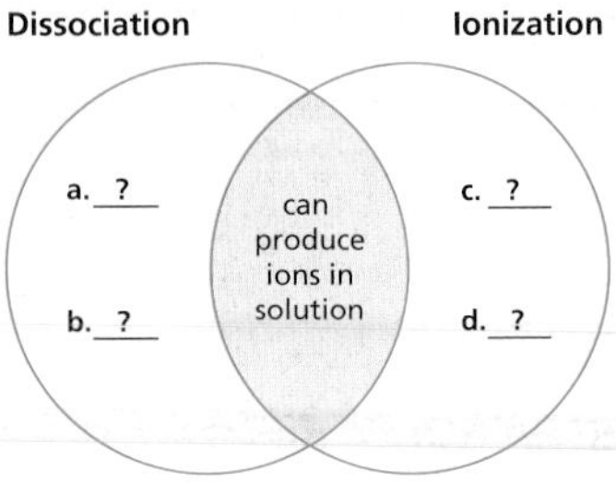
Dissociation
Ionization
a. ?
b. ?
can produce ions in solution
c. ?
d. ?

Figure 1 If divers surface too quickly from great depths, the nitrogen that has dissolved in their blood and other tissues bubbles out of solution. These bubbles can become trapped in joints and cause great pain, a condition called "the bends."

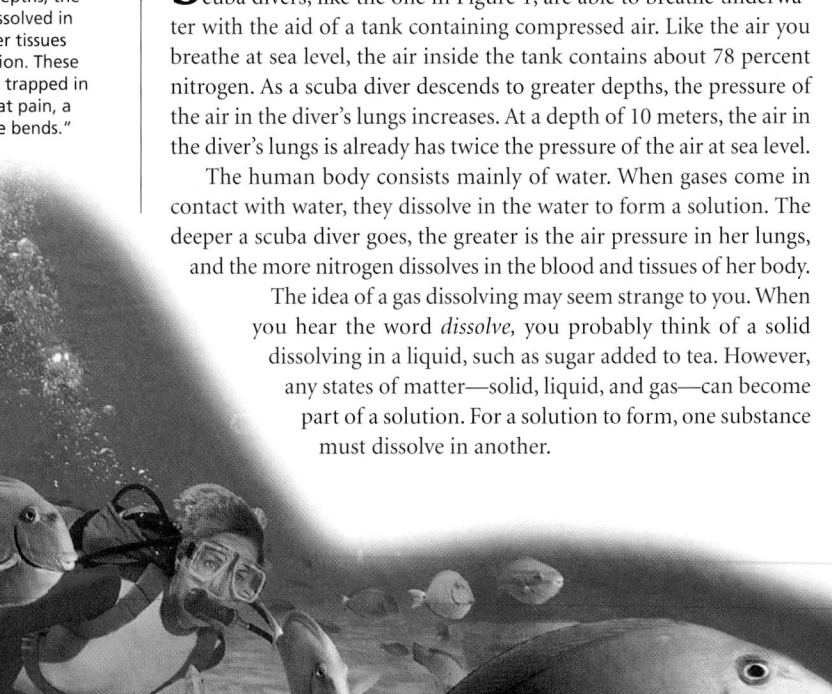

Scuba divers, like the one in Figure 1, are able to breathe underwater with the aid of a tank containing compressed air. Like the air you breathe at sea level, the air inside the tank contains about 78 percent nitrogen. As a scuba diver descends to greater depths, the pressure of the air in the diver's lungs increases. At a depth of 10 meters, the air in the diver's lungs is already has twice the pressure of the air at sea level.

The human body consists mainly of water. When gases come in contact with water, they dissolve in the water to form a solution. The deeper a scuba diver goes, the greater is the air pressure in her lungs, and the more nitrogen dissolves in the blood and tissues of her body.

The idea of a gas dissolving may seem strange to you. When you hear the word *dissolve,* you probably think of a solid dissolving in a liquid, such as sugar added to tea. However, any states of matter—solid, liquid, and gas—can become part of a solution. For a solution to form, one substance must dissolve in another.

Reading Focus

Build Vocabulary L2

Word Forms Ask students to name the verb forms for the three types of dissolving: *dissociation, dispersion,* and *ionization. (Dissociate, disperse, and ionize)* Give a definition of each term and have students discuss how these words give clues as to what type of particle is involved in each type of dissolving.

Reading Strategy L2

a. Physical change
b. Ions are present before and after.
c. Chemical change
d. Ions are present after, but not before.

2 INSTRUCT

Integrate Biology L2

To avoid decompression sickness, or "the bends," scuba divers make "decompression stops" as they return to the surface. They rise from deeper waters very slowly and pause periodically to allow the dissolved gases to come out of solution. Scuba divers are at risk for the bends even in water as shallow as 10 m. However, the bends is not a problem for diving animals or people who dive without scuba tanks. Ask, **Why do you think decompression sickness is not a risk when diving without scuba tanks?** *(People who dive without scuba tanks take one breath at the surface and hold it while diving underwater. They have the same amount of gas in their body at the surface as they have throughout the dive, so they do not get a dangerous level of dissolved gases in their blood and tissues.)* **Logical**

Section Resources

Print
- ***Reading and Study Workbook With Math Support,*** Section 8.1
- ***Transparencies,*** Chapter Pretest and Section 8.1

Technology
- ***Interactive Textbook,*** Section 8.1
- ***Presentation Pro CD-ROM,*** Chapter Pretest and Section 8.1
- ***Go Online,*** NSTA SciLinks, Solutions

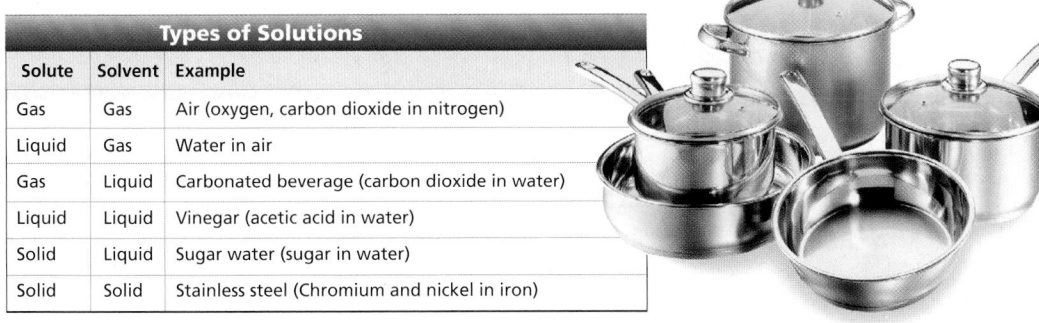

Types of Solutions		
Solute	**Solvent**	**Example**
Gas	Gas	Air (oxygen, carbon dioxide in nitrogen)
Liquid	Gas	Water in air
Gas	Liquid	Carbonated beverage (carbon dioxide in water)
Liquid	Liquid	Vinegar (acetic acid in water)
Solid	Liquid	Sugar water (sugar in water)
Solid	Solid	Stainless steel (Chromium and nickel in iron)

Figure 2 A stainless steel pot or pan is a solution of chromium and nickel in iron. In a solution, the solvent is the substance in the greatest quantity.

Dissolving

Recall that a solution is a homogeneous mixture of two or more substances. Every solution has two types of components. A **solute** is a substance whose particles are dissolved in a solution. The substance in which the solute dissolves is called the **solvent.** For example, seawater is a solution in which salt is the solute and water is the solvent.

Solutes and solvents can take the form of a solid, liquid, or gas. The solution takes the state of the solvent. Figure 2 lists some common solutions and the states of their respective solutes and solvents. Air, for instance, is a solution of several gases dissolved in another gas. Nitrogen, making up about 78 percent of air, is the solvent. Oxygen, carbon dioxide, argon, and other gases are solutes.

You are probably most familiar with solutions in which water is the solvent. Carbonated drinks, hot tea, and seawater are just a few examples of the many water-based solutions you might have encountered. **Substances can dissolve in water in three ways—by dissociation, dispersion, and ionization.**

Dissociation of Ionic Compounds For a solute to dissolve in water, the solute and solvent particles must attract one another. However, the particles within the solute are attracted to one another, and the particles within the solvent are attracted to one another. So before a solution can form, the attractions that hold the solute together and the solvent together must be overcome.

Figure 3 illustrates how a sodium chloride crystal dissolves in water. Sodium chloride is an ionic compound. Water is a polar molecule, and is attracted to the ions in the solute. The crystal dissolves as the sodium and chlorine ions are pulled into solution, one by one, by the surrounding water molecules. The process in which an ionic compound separates into ions as it dissolves is called **dissociation.**

Reading Checkpoint *How does sodium chloride dissolve in water?*

Figure 3 When an ionic compound dissolves in water, the charged ends of water molecules surround the oppositely charged ions.

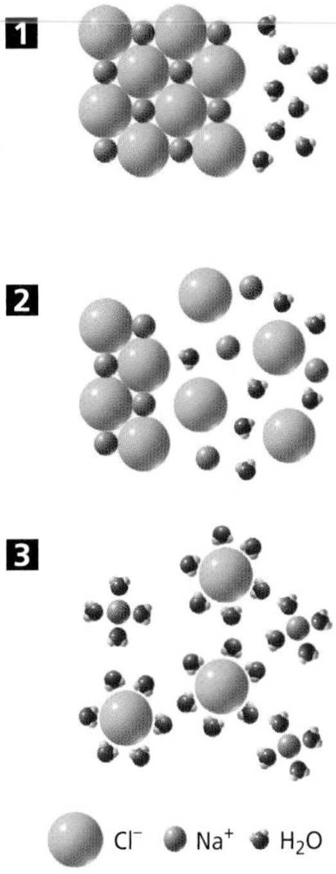
1
2
3
Cl^- Na^+ H_2O

Dissolving

Build Reading Literacy L1

Relate Text and Visuals Refer to page **190D** in **Chapter 7**, which provides the guidelines for relating text and visuals.

Have students read the text on pp. 229–230 describing different ways in which a substance can dissolve in water. Then, have students form groups of three. Each student will choose a type of dissolving. Encourage students to use Figure 3, Figure 4, or the diagram in the passage to explain to their group what happens on the particle level when substances dissolve by dissociation, dispersion, or ionization.
Visual, Logical

Address Misconceptions L2

Many students do not differentiate between solvent and solute particles when learning about solutions. Challenge this misconception by having students examine the keys at the bottom of Figure 3 and Figure 4. Have them note the different colors and sizes used to differentiate between solvent and solute particles. Point out that these figures show models of particles in order to represent the movement and relationship of solvent and solute particles. The figures do not show what the atoms, molecules, and ions actually look like. For example, the colors, shapes, and relative sizes of the particles are symbolic and do not represent the actual characteristics of the particles.
Visual

Customize for Inclusion Students

Hearing Impaired
If you have students with hearing impairments, have students draw what happens to solvent and solute particles during dissociation, dispersion, and ionization. Encourage them to label their illustrations and provide brief written descriptions.

Answer to . . .

Reading Checkpoint *Sodium chloride dissolves by dissociating into ions.*

Use Visuals L1

Figure 4 Have students examine Figure 4. Ask, **What symbol is used to represent water molecules?** *(A larger red sphere with two smaller blue spheres attached)* **How are the sugar molecules arranged in the beginning?** *(The sugar molecules are arranged in a packed crystal.)* **What symbol is used to represent sugar molecules?** *(A purple, two-ringed structure, with the rings joined at one point)* **How are the sugar molecules arranged in the end?** *(The sugar molecules are spread out and mixed in uniformly with the water molecules.)*
Visual

Build Science Skills L2

Predicting Have students look at the figure in the text on ionization of molecular compounds. Ask, **What ions would be produced as molecules of hydrogen bromide, HBr, dissolved in water?** *(Hydronium ions [H_3O^+] and bromide ions [Br^-])*
Logical, Visual

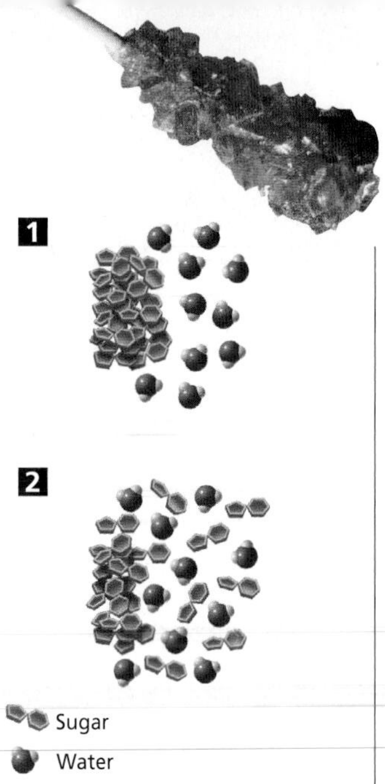
1
2
Sugar
Water

Figure 4 Saliva dissolves the sugar in hard candy by dispersion. As water molecules collide with sugar crystals, attractions develop between the water molecules and sugar molecules at the surface of the solid.

Dispersion of Molecular Compounds When you place a piece of hard candy on your tongue, the sweet taste spreads, or disperses, throughout your mouth. The water in your saliva dissolves the sugar and flavoring in the candy. Sugar dissolves in water by **dispersion,** or breaking into small pieces that spread throughout the water.

Both sugar and water are polar molecules, so they attract one another. Because the water molecules are constantly moving, they collide frequently with the surface of the sugar crystals, as shown in Figure 4. Attractions form between the water molecules and the exposed sugar molecules. When enough water molecules have surrounded a sugar molecule, the attractions between them are great enough to overcome the attractions holding the sugar molecule to the surface of the crystal. The sugar molecule breaks free, and is pulled into solution by the water molecules.

As more sugar molecules break free of the crystal, another layer of sugar molecules is exposed to the water, and the process repeats. The solute particles become evenly spread throughout the solvent.

Reading Checkpoint *How does sugar dissolve in water?*

Ionization of Molecular Compounds Hydrogen chloride, HCl, is a molecular compound in which a hydrogen atom and a chlorine atom share a pair of electrons. Recall that a hydrogen atom has only one proton and one electron. When HCl gas dissolves in water, the hydrogen proton from each HCl molecule is transferred to a water molecule. For each HCl molecule that reacts, a hydronium ion, H_3O^+, and a chloride ion, Cl^-, are produced.

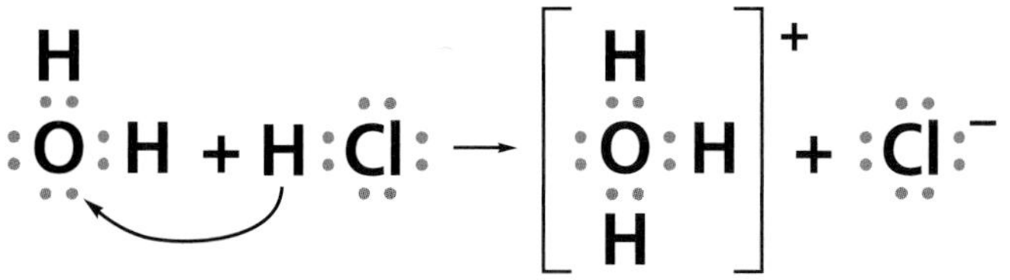

Notice that when hydrogen chloride and water form a solution, two molecular compounds react to form two ions. The process in which neutral molecules gain or lose electrons is known as **ionization.** Unlike dissociation and dispersion, which are physical changes, dissolving by ionization is a chemical change. The solution that results contains new substances. When a solute dissolves by dissociation, the ions pulled into solution are the same ions present in the solute. When a solute dissolves by ionization, the ions in solution are formed by the reaction of solute and solvent particles.

Chapter Preview

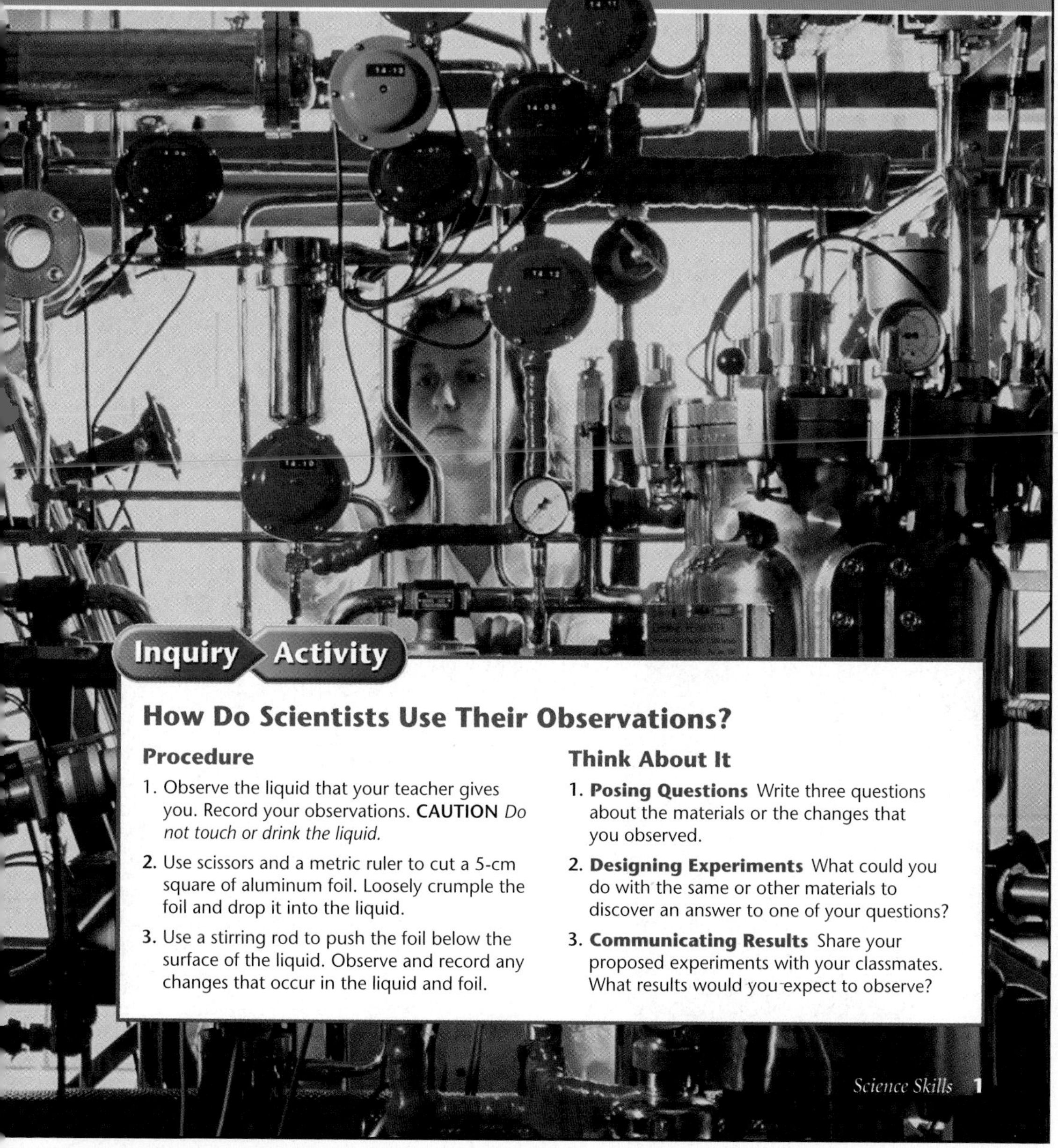

Inquiry Activity

How Do Scientists Use Their Observations?

Procedure

1. Observe the liquid that your teacher gives you. Record your observations. **CAUTION** *Do not touch or drink the liquid.*
2. Use scissors and a metric ruler to cut a 5-cm square of aluminum foil. Loosely crumple the foil and drop it into the liquid.
3. Use a stirring rod to push the foil below the surface of the liquid. Observe and record any changes that occur in the liquid and foil.

Think About It

1. **Posing Questions** Write three questions about the materials or the changes that you observed.
2. **Designing Experiments** What could you do with the same or other materials to discover an answer to one of your questions?
3. **Communicating Results** Share your proposed experiments with your classmates. What results would you expect to observe?

Discovery Channel School **Video Field Trip**

Cracking the Case

Encourage students to view the Video Field Trip "Cracking the Case."

ENGAGE/EXPLORE

Inquiry Activity

How Do Scientists Use Their Observations? L2

Purpose In this activity, students begin to ask specific questions that can lead to testable hypotheses.

Address Misconceptions

This activity can help students overcome the misconception that science consists of an unchanging body of known facts. Students observe that experiments can test hypotheses and produce new information even when the materials involved are not well-understood.

Skills Focus **Observing**

Prep Time 5 minutes

Materials 25 mL of copper(II) chloride solution in a 50-mL beaker, scissors, metric ruler, aluminum foil, glass stirring rod.

Advance Prep Prepare copper(II) chloride solution in advance. Use 50 g solid copper(II) chloride ($CuCl_2$) per 100 mL water.

Class Time 15 minutes

Safety Students should wear safety goggles, a lab apron, and plastic gloves. Students should wash their hands with warm water and soap or detergent and dispose of the used materials in a chemical waste container.

Teaching Tips

- You may need to demonstrate the use of a metric ruler.

Expected Outcome The solution will bubble and lose some of its blue color. The foil will darken, acquire rust-colored patches, and partly dissolve.

Think About It

1. Possible answers: What is the blue liquid? What other materials would make the blue liquid bubble? What made the foil change color and break up?
2. Students should describe a plan for making additional observations that would help answer one of their questions. Students may suggest repeating the activity with other materials, such as paper, rubber, or steel, instead of the aluminum foil.
3. Students should cite specific expected results such as bubbling, dissolving of the foil, or no change. **Visual**

Section 1.1

1 FOCUS

Objectives

1.1.1 **Explain** how science and technology are related.

1.1.2 **List** the major branches of natural science and **describe** how they overlap.

1.1.3 **Describe** the main ideas of physical science.

Reading Focus

Build Vocabulary L2

Word-Part Analysis Tell students that many words in science consist of roots to which prefixes and/or suffixes are added. Explain that the root is the key to a word's meaning. Ask students to identify the roots in the vocabulary words and to name other words with the same root. Students may suggest *sci-, conscience; tech-, technique; phys-, physical; geo-, geography; astro-, astronaut;* and *bio-, biography.*

Reading Strategy L2

a. Earth and space **b.** Life
c. The study of nonliving things
d. The study of Earth and the universe beyond Earth

2 INSTRUCT

Science From Curiosity

Build Science Skills L2

Predicting Tell students that it can be difficult to prove the existence of something invisible. Place a large candle in a jar and light it. Ask, **What do you predict will happen if the jar is covered? Explain your prediction.** *(The candle will go out once the oxygen in the jar is used up.)* Cover the jar with aluminum foil so students can check their prediction. Ask, **What invisible substances did you assume in your explanation?** *(Oxygen, carbon dioxide)*
Visual, Group

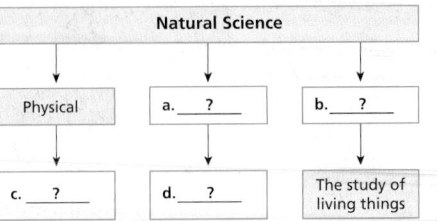

1.1 What Is Science?

Reading Focus

Key Concepts

- How does the process of science start and end?
- What is the relationship between science and technology?
- What are the branches of natural science?

Vocabulary

- science
- technology
- chemistry
- physics
- geology
- astronomy
- biology

Reading Strategy

Previewing Skim the section to find out what the main branches of natural science are. Copy the concept map below. As you read, complete the concept map based on what you have learned.

Natural Science
- Physical → c. ___?___
- a. ___?___ → d. ___?___
- b. ___?___ → The study of living things

Suppose you could send a robot to another planet. What kinds of experiments would you program the robot to carry out? Before you programmed the robot, you would need to figure out what information you wanted it to gather. Scientists are currently developing robots, like the one in Figure 1, that they plan to send to Mars. These robots are being designed to examine the atmosphere, rocks, gravity, and magnetic fields of the planet.

Science involves asking questions about nature and then finding ways to answer them. This process doesn't happen by itself—it is driven by the curiosity of scientists.

Figure 1 In July 1997, the six-wheeled Sojourner rover became the first robot to explore planet Mars. The next generation of Mars rovers will help scientists further study the planet's geology, geography, and climate.

Science From Curiosity

Throughout history, human beings have had a strong sense of curiosity. Human curiosity led to the use of fire, the building of tools, and the development of languages. Have you ever checked what was living at the bottom of a pond? Taken off the cover of a baseball to see what was inside? Tried putting more chocolate or less in your milk to find out how much would give the best flavor? These are all examples of curiosity, and curiosity is the basis of science.

Section Resources

Print
- ***Reading and Study Workbook With Math Support,*** Section 1.1
- ***Transparencies,*** Chapter Pretest and Section 1.1

Technology
- ***Interactive Textbook,*** Section 1.1
- ***Presentation Pro CD-ROM,*** Section 1.1
- ***Go Online,*** NSTA SciLinks, Motion

Science is a system of knowledge and the methods you use to find that knowledge. Part of the excitement of science is that you never know what you will find. For instance, when you flip over a rock, will you see crawling insects, a snake, or nothing at all? You won't know until you look. **Science begins with curiosity and often ends with discovery.**

Curiosity provides questions but is seldom enough to achieve scientific results. Methods such as observing and measuring provide ways to find the answers. In some experiments, observations are qualitative, or descriptive. In others, they are quantitative, or numerical. Some experiments are impossible to do, such as observing what happened at the start of the universe. Scientists cannot go back in time to observe the creation of the universe. However, they can use the evidence of the universe around them to envision how this event occurred.

Reading Checkpoint *What is science?*

Science and Technology

As scientific knowledge is discovered, it can be applied in ways that improve the lives of people. **Technology** is the use of knowledge to solve practical problems. While the goal of science is to expand knowledge, the goal of technology is to apply that knowledge. Imagine living in the late 1700s, when there were no televisions, cars, antibiotics, or electricity. In a relatively small amount of time, people's lives changed dramatically. Perhaps your grandparents were born at a time when there were no televisions, and your parents were born at a time when there were no personal computers. Technology will have also changed your world dramatically by the time the generation following yours comes along.

Figure 2 illustrates the rapid evolution of the telephone, a technology invented in 1876. Within two years, the first telephone operators were connecting calls by hand. The first coin-operated phones appeared in 1889. By 1927, it was possible to make a phone call from New York to London. World War II saw the development of the first mobile telephones, which paved the way for modern cellular phones. Today, you can communicate by telephone between almost any two places in the world.

Science and technology are interdependent. Advances in one lead to advances in the other. For example, advances in the study of physics led to the invention of the transistor. The use of transistors, in turn, led to advances in various other scientific fields, such as computer science and space science.

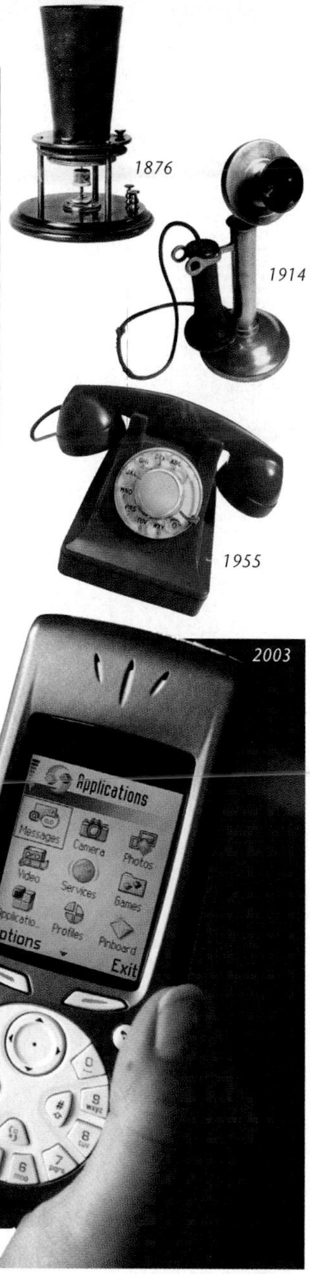

1876
1914
1955
2003
Applications
Messages
Camera
Photos
Video
Services
Games
Profiles
Pinboard
Options
Exit

Figure 2 Telephones have quickly evolved from cumbersome, expensive machines to practical, cheap tools for communicating. **Classifying** ***How is a telephone an example of both science and technology?***

Teacher Demo

The Compass **L2**

Purpose Students observe that a compass needle does not always point north.

Materials compass, magnet, chalk

Procedure Tell students that a compass is an instrument that is used to locate north. Show students where north is on the compass. Move around the room and show students that the compass needle continues to point toward north. Place the chalk near the east edge of the compass and ask students what happens. Replace the chalk with the magnet and show students that the needle has been deflected toward the east or west. Move the compass around the magnet to show that the compass needle continues to point toward or away from the magnet.

Expected Outcome The chalk has no effect on the compass, but the magnet deflects the compass needle toward the magnet. **Visual, Logical**

Science and Technology

Use Visuals **L1**

Figure 2 Ask students to look at the different phones. Ask, **Do you regularly use a phone with a rotary dial or push buttons?** *(Most students will use a push-button phone.)* **How do you think phones have changed between 1955 and 2003?** *(Push buttons replaced dials, phones became cordless, and cellular phones were invented.)* **What is the difference between cellular and cordless phones?** *(Cordless phones must be close to a base unit. Cellular phones work over a larger area.)* **How have cellular phones increased the area in which phone service is available?** *(Wires are not needed to carry the phone signals, so phone service is available in more places.)* **Visual**

Customize for Inclusion Students

Learning Disabled
Reinforce the idea that technology plays an important role in the students' daily lives. Ask students to list several things they experience every day that depend on modern technology. Have students share their lists. Discuss each item and technology's role in it. Next, have students describe how modern technology affects them in the classroom. For example, students may mention that calculators and computers help them find and learn new information. Some students may point to the write-on boards that have replaced chalkboards, and other students may point out insulated glass, durable carpeting, an intercom system, or other parts of the classroom building as examples of technology at school. Students may also note that ballpoint pens and other writing instruments make writing much easier and much less messy than the quill pens used before the American Revolution.

Answer to . . .

Figure 2 *Technology: It is an application of knowledge to solve the problem of long-distance communication. Science: It can be used to demonstrate various areas of study, including the physics of sound and of electricity, and the properties of materials.*

Reading Checkpoint *Science is a system of knowledge and the methods used to find that knowledge.*

Branches of Science

Integrate Biology **L2**

The area of science that deals with the connections between biology and physics is biophysics. It is a very broad area that includes biomolecular systems, neural networks, immunology, evolution, and population biology. Each of these components of biophysics, as well as many others, studies how a biological response (from an organism or an ecosystem, for example) is determined by the laws of physics. Encourage students to learn about one of the areas of study within biophysics. Have students make a poster that shows how physics and biology contribute to understanding in that specialty.
Visual, Portfolio

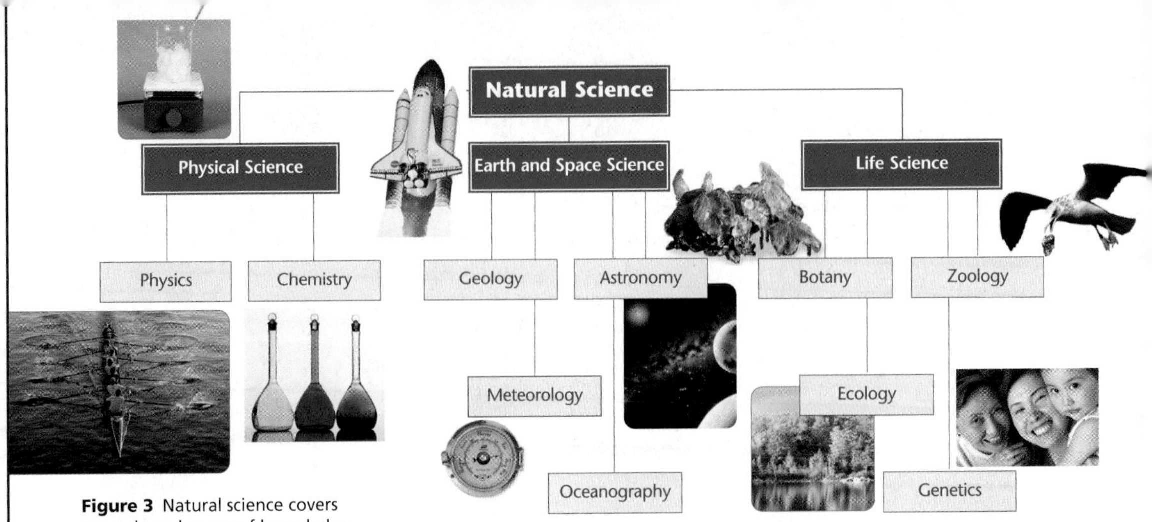
Natural Science
Physical Science
Earth and Space Science
Life Science
Physics
Chemistry
Geology
Astronomy
Botany
Zoology
Meteorology
Oceanography
Ecology
Genetics

Figure 3 Natural science covers a very broad range of knowledge. **Interpreting Diagrams** ***How could you change this diagram to show how the branches of science can overlap?***

Branches of Science

The study of science is divided into social science and natural science. **Natural science is generally divided into three branches: physical science, Earth and space science, and life science.** Each of these branches can be further divided, as shown in Figure 3.

Physical science covers a broad range of study that focuses on nonliving things. The two main areas of physical science are chemistry and physics. **Chemistry** is the study of the composition, structure, properties, and reactions of matter. **Physics** is the study of matter and energy and the interactions between the two through forces and motion.

The application of physics and chemistry to the study of Earth is called Earth science. The foundation of Earth science is **geology,** the study of the origin, history, and structure of Earth. Geology has traditionally focused on the study of Earth's rocks. However, modern Earth science also involves the study of systems that may include living organisms. The foundation of space science is **astronomy,** the study of the universe beyond Earth, including the sun, moon, planets, and stars.

The study of living things is known as **biology,** or life science. Biology is not only the physics and chemistry of living things, but the study of the origin and behavior of living things. Biologists study the different ways that organisms grow, survive, and reproduce.

The problem with subdividing science into different areas is that there is often overlap between them. The boundary around each area of science is not always clear. For instance, much of biology is also chemistry, while much of chemistry is also physics. And a rapidly growing area of physics is biophysics, the application of physics to biology.

Reading Checkpoint *What is physical science?*

Facts and Figures

Technological Advances During the twentieth century, rapid technological changes have occurred in areas other than communications. For example, advances in transportation, especially air travel, dramatically changed society. At the beginning of the century, the Wright brothers flew a propeller-powered airplane 120 feet in 12 seconds. On October 4, 1957, the Soviet Union launched a basketball-sized satellite called *Sputnik I* into Earth's orbit, making it the first satellite. Another milestone occurred on July 29, 1969, when Neil Armstrong and his crew flew to the moon. Armstrong was the first person to walk on the moon.

The Big Ideas of Physical Science

What are the basic rules of nature? You can read this book to find out. As a sneak preview, some of these rules are summarized here. You can think of them as the big ideas of physical science. Keep in mind that there are also unknown rules of nature that are waiting to be discovered. In fact, you can take part in the search for these unknown laws if you become a scientist. Even though scientists have already discovered a great deal about the universe, there is still much to learn.

Space and Time The universe is both very old and very big. The age of the universe is about 13,700,000,000 (13.7 billion) years. The observable universe is about 700,000,000,000,000,000,000,000,000 (700 million billion billion) meters in diameter. The diameter of Earth is "only" 12,700,000 meters. To get an idea of how big this distance is, the diameter of a giant beach ball is about 1 meter.

Matter and Change A very small amount of the universe is matter. Matter has volume and mass, and on Earth usually takes the form of a solid, liquid, or gas. All matter that you are familiar with, from plants to stars to animals to humans, is made up of building blocks called atoms. Atoms consist of even smaller building blocks called electrons, protons, and neutrons.

Forces and Motion If you push on something that is sitting still, it starts to move. If you push on something that is already moving, you will change its motion. Forces cause changes in motion. As Figure 4 shows, your world is filled with motion and forces. Calculating these forces can sometimes be very challenging. For example, on a NASA mission to Mars, the Mars Exploration Rover must blast off from Earth with enough speed to escape Earth's gravity. The rocket must then travel a great distance through space and land delicately on a planet that is moving very rapidly around the Sun. The laws of physics allow these movements to be calculated exactly so that the NASA robots get to where scientists want them to go.

Go Online NSTA SCI LINKS

For: Links on motion
Visit: www.SciLinks.org
Web Code: ccn-0011

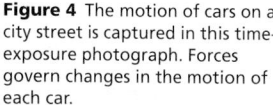

Figure 4 The motion of cars on a city street is captured in this time-exposure photograph. Forces govern changes in the motion of each car.

The Big Ideas of Physical Science

Build Reading Literacy L1

Outline Refer to page **156D** in **Chapter 6**, which provides the guidelines for an outline.

This part of the section provides students with an excellent opportunity to practice outlining skills. The paragraphs are parallel in construction and each one has a subhead. Tell students to write the subheads, leaving room between each one. As students read, they can list details under each subhead.

Visual, Logical

Go Online NSTA SCI LINKS

Download a worksheet on motion for students to complete, and find additional teacher support from NSTA SciLinks.

Answer to . . .

Figure 3 *By drawing dotted lines to connect related areas of science, you could show how the branches of science overlap. Another way to illustrate these overlapping relationships would be to reconfigure the branched diagram as a Venn diagram.*

Reading Checkpoint *Physical science is a branch of natural science that focuses on nonliving things. The two main areas of physical science are physics and chemistry.*

Section 1.1 (continued)

Science and Your Perspective

Use Community Resources L2

Ask a local scientist to talk to your class about how rapidly science changes, including changes so far during the students' lifetimes. **Interpersonal**

Address Misconceptions L2

Some students may incorrectly think that all the major discoveries in science have been made, and that current scientific work is only filling in details. Point out that science still has many unknowns, including how to cure the common cold and predict the weather with certainty. **Logical, Verbal**

3 ASSESS

Evaluate Understanding L2

Call on students to name and describe a branch of science. They may describe a main branch or an area shown in Figure 3, or another area.

Reteach L1

Use Figure 2 to review the relationship between science and technology. Emphasize that over time advances in technology can lead to the use of new materials and the addition of new features to machines like the telephone.

Writing in Science

Possible answers: Students might describe how areas of life science overlap with physical science.

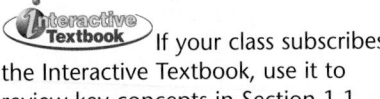

Interactive Textbook If your class subscribes to the Interactive Textbook, use it to review key concepts in Section 1.1.

Figure 5 Panels on a solar car convert energy from the sun into the mechanical energy of its moving parts.

Energy Energy exists in many forms. Moving objects have a kind of energy called kinetic energy. Objects moved against a force have another kind of energy called potential energy. Energy also exists in matter itself. When one form of matter changes into another form, energy is either absorbed or released. Matter itself can also be changed into energy.

Energy can be transferred from one form or object to another, but it can never be destroyed. If you push on a door and it swings open, you transfer energy from yourself to the door. Your cells are using the chemical energy stored in the food you have eaten to supply energy to your muscles, which then transfer energy to the door.

Science and Your Perspective

As you read this book, remember that science is both a process and a body of knowledge. The information in this book represents the best up-to-date models of how the universe works. However, like all models, some of these models will be rejected and replaced in the future. For instance, more moons revolving around Jupiter and Saturn will most likely be discovered as telescopes get better. It is therefore possible that by the time you read this book Saturn will be known to have more than the 30 moons currently identified. Be skeptical. Ask questions. Be aware that the scientific facts of today might change tomorrow. However, believe in the scientific process that has discovered them. And believe that you may be the one who makes the discoveries that will change scientific facts in the future.

Section 1.1 Assessment

Reviewing Concepts

1. How does the scientific process start and end?
2. How are science and technology related?
3. What are the branches of natural science?
4. Explain the advantages and disadvantages of subdividing science into many different areas.
5. Why do scientists seek to discover new laws of the universe?

Critical Thinking

6. **Evaluating** Why does the progress of science require both curiosity and methodology? Explain the role of each in scientific investigations.
7. **Making Judgments** Advances in science do not always immediately lead to advances in technology. Why are such scientific advances still valuable?
8. **Classifying** Is the study of the muscle movements in the human body an example of biology or of physics? Explain.

Writing in Science

Compare and Contrast Paragraph Write a paragraph comparing two branches of science. (*Hint:* Use an example that shows how these branches can overlap.)

Section 1.1 Assessment

1. The scientific process begins with curiosity and often ends with discovery.
2. Science and technology are interdependent. Advances in one lead to advances in the other.
3. Natural science is divided into physical science, Earth and space science, and life science.
4. Dividing science into branches makes it easier to understand such a broad subject. However, dividing science into "strict" branches neglects the fact that different areas of science frequently overlap.
5. Scientists seek to discover new laws of the universe because they are curious and wish to understand how the natural world is governed.
6. Scientific investigations are often initiated by curiosity. For example, an observed event might prompt you to ask a question. To answer that question, however, you need to use a systematic method that can provide evidence such as experimental or observational data.
7. Even if a scientific discovery does not immediately lead to advances in technology, that discovery is still useful because it adds to the overall body of scientific knowledge.
8. Both. Because muscle movements involve motion and forces, they fall under the study of physics. However, because muscle movements are specific to living things, they also fall under the study of biology.

1.2 Using a Scientific Approach

Reading Focus

Key Concepts

- What is the goal of a scientific method?
- How does a scientific law differ from a scientific theory?
- Why are scientific models useful?

Vocabulary

- scientific method
- observation
- hypothesis
- manipulated variable
- responding variable
- controlled experiment
- scientific theory
- scientific law
- model

Reading Strategy

Using Prior Knowledge Before you read, copy the web diagram below. Add to the web diagram what you already know about scientific methods. After you read this section, revise the diagram based on what you have learned.

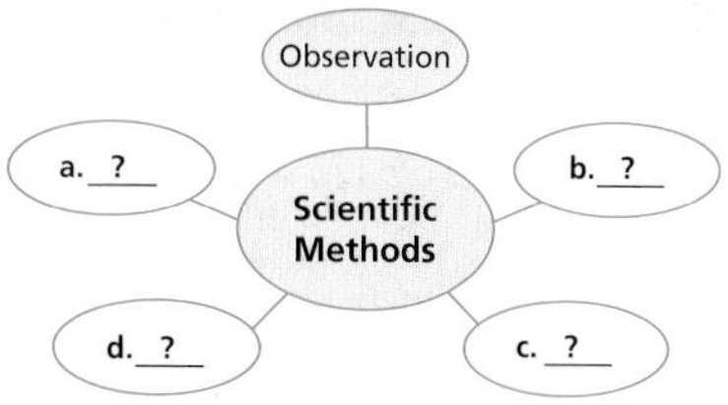

Observation
a. ?
b. ?
Scientific Methods
d. ?
c. ?

If you've ever been caught in the rain without an umbrella, your first instinct was probably to start running. After all, the less time you spend in the rain, the less water there is falling down on you. So you might think that running in the rain keeps you drier than walking in the rain over a given distance. However, by running in the rain you run into more raindrops than by walking, thereby wetting more of your face, chest, and legs. Have your instincts been getting you wetter instead of keeping you drier?

You now have a question that you can try to answer with a scientific approach. Which keeps you drier in the rain—walking or running?

Scientific Methods

In order to answer questions about the world around them, scientists need to get information. An organized plan for gathering, organizing, and communicating information is called a **scientific method.** Despite the name, a scientific method can be used by anyone, including yourself. All you need is a reason to use it. **The goal of any scientific method is to solve a problem or to better understand an observed event.**

Figure 6 This cricket player is running in the rain. **Designing Experiments** *How can you test if running in the rain keeps you drier than walking in the rain over the same distance?*

Section Resources

Print

- ***Reading and Study Workbook With Math Support,*** Section 1.2
- ***Transparencies,*** Section 1.2

Technology

- ***Interactive Textbook,*** Section 1.2
- ***Presentation Pro CD-ROM,*** Section 1.2
- ***GoOnline,*** *Science News,* Nature of science

Section 1.2

1 FOCUS

Objectives

1.2.1 **Describe** the steps in a scientific method.

1.2.2 **Compare** and **contrast** facts, scientific theories, and scientific laws.

1.2.3 **Explain** the importance of models in science.

1.2.4 **Explain** the importance of safety in science.

Reading Focus

Build Vocabulary L2

Paraphrase Tell students to write the vocabulary terms on a sheet of paper and leave enough space to write the definitions. As students read, they should write the definition in their own words.

Reading Strategy L2

a. Forming a hypothesis
b. Testing a hypothesis
c. Drawing conclusions
d. Developing a theory

2 INSTRUCT

Scientific Methods

Build Reading Literacy L1

Sequence Refer to page **290D** in **Chapter 10,** which provides the guidelines for a sequence.

Figure 7 is a flowchart that shows the steps of a scientific method. Remind students to refer to this figure when reading about a particular step to help themselves understand how that step fits into the sequence of steps in a scientific method.
Visual

Answer to . . .

Figure 6 *Possible answer: Take two identical pieces of absorbent cloth and measure the mass of each. Give the cloths to two people to hold at arm's length during a rain storm. One person should walk a fixed distance, and the other should run the same distance. Compare the masses of the wet pieces of cloth.*

Section 1.2 (continued)

Build Science Skills L2

Observing ACTIVITY

Purpose Students observe that as the distance from a light source increases, the brightness decreases.

Materials low-wattage incandescent bulb, power source for the bulb

Class Time 10 minutes

Procedure Darken the room and turn on the bulb. Tell students that its light can be considered to be coming from a single point (a point source). Ask two or three volunteers to walk around the room and observe whether the light from the bulb is visible in all parts of the room. Be sure that volunteers observe the light's brightness at various distances from the bulb.

Expected Outcome Students will see that the bulb radiates light in all directions and that as distance from the bulb increases, the bulb's brightness decreases.
Kinesthetic, Visual, Group

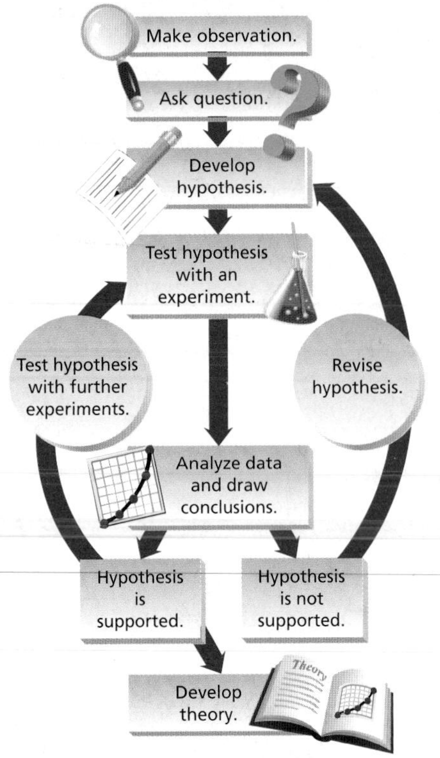

Make observation.
Ask question.
Develop hypothesis.
Test hypothesis with an experiment.
Test hypothesis with further experiments.
Revise hypothesis.
Analyze data and draw conclusions.
Hypothesis is supported.
Hypothesis is not supported.
Develop theory.
Theory

Figure 7 A scientific method provides a useful strategy for solving problems.
Inferring *Is an observation required in order for you to arrive at a question? What does this tell you about the strictness of the scientific method?*

Figure 7 outlines an example of a scientific method. Each step in the method shown involves specific skills, some of which you will be learning as you read this book. It is important to note that scientific methods can vary from case to case. For example, one scientist might follow the steps shown in Figure 7 in a different order, or another might choose to skip one or more steps.

Making Observations Scientific investigations often begin with observations. An **observation** is information that you obtain through your senses. Repeatable observations are known as facts. For example, when you walk or run in the rain, you get wet. Standing in the rain leaves you much wetter than walking or running in the rain. You might combine these observations into a question: How does your speed affect how wet you get when you are caught in the rain?

Forming a Hypothesis A **hypothesis** is a proposed answer to a question. To answer the question raised by your observations about traveling in the rain, you might guess that the faster your speed, the drier you will stay in the rain. What can you do with your hypothesis? For a hypothesis to be useful, it must be testable.

Reading Checkpoint *What is a hypothesis?*

Testing a Hypothesis Scientists perform experiments to test their hypotheses. In an experiment, any factor that can change is called a variable. Suppose you do an experiment to test if speed affects how wet you get in the rain. The variables will include your speed, your size, the rate of rainfall, and the amount of water that hits you.

Your hypothesis states that one variable, speed, causes a change in another variable, the amount of water that hits you. The speed with which you walk or run is the **manipulated variable,** or the variable that causes a change in another. The amount of water that you accumulate is the **responding variable,** or the variable that changes in response to the manipulated variable. To examine the relationship between a manipulated variable and a responding variable, scientists use controlled experiments. A **controlled experiment** is an experiment in which only one variable, the manipulated variable, is deliberately changed at a time. While the responding variable is observed for changes, all other variables are kept constant, or controlled.

Customize for English Language Learners

Increase Word Exposure
Ask students who are learning English to make flashcards for each step of the scientific method shown in Figure 7. Tell students to write the English words describing the steps on an index card. They should also write a brief definition in their first language on the back of each card. Students can make the flashcards as they read the section. Then, have students shuffle their cards and place the steps of the scientific method in the correct order. Students may refer to the definition on the back of the card if they need help. Reinforce that the scientific method shown in Figure 7 is only one of many possible methods.

In 1997, two meteorologists conducted a controlled experiment to determine if moving faster keeps you drier in the rain. In the experiment, both scientists traveled 100 yards by foot in the rain. One of them walked; the other ran. By measuring the mass of their clothes before and after traveling in the rain, the scientists were able to measure how much water each had accumulated. One of the controlled variables was size—the two scientists were about the same height and build. Another was the rate of rainfall—the scientists began traveling at the same time during the same rainstorm on the same path. A third was the ability to absorb water—the scientists wore identical sets of clothes.

Drawing Conclusions The scientists' rainy-day experiment produced some convincing data. The clothes of the walking scientist accumulated 217 grams of water, while the clothes of the running scientists accumulated 130 grams of water. Based on their data, the scientists concluded that running in the rain keeps you drier than walking—about 40 percent drier, in fact. Now you have scientific evidence to support the hypothesis stated earlier.

What happens if the data do not support the hypothesis? In such a case, a scientist can revise the hypothesis or propose a new one, based on the data from the experiment. A new experiment must then be designed to test the revised or new hypothesis.

Developing a Theory Once a hypothesis has been supported in repeated experiments, scientists can begin to develop a theory. A **scientific theory** is a well-tested explanation for a set of observations or experimental results. For example, according to the kinetic theory of matter, all particles of matter are in constant motion. Kinetic theory explains a wide range of observations, such as ice melting or the pressure of a gas.

Theories are never proved. Instead, they become stronger if the facts continue to support them. However, if an existing theory fails to explain new facts and discoveries, the theory may be revised or a new theory may replace it.

Scientific Laws

After repeated observations or experiments, scientists may arrive at a scientific law. A **scientific law** is a statement that summarizes a pattern found in nature. For example, Newton's law of gravity describes how two objects attract each other by means of a gravitational force. This law has been verified over and over. However, scientists have yet to agree on a theory that explains how gravity works. **A scientific law describes an observed pattern in nature without attempting to explain it. The explanation of such a pattern is provided by a scientific theory.**

Go Online SCIENCE NEWS

For: Articles on the nature of science

Visit: PHSchool.com

Web Code: cce-0011

Figure 8 An environmental scientist collects a sample for a water pollution study. After analyzing the sample, the scientist can draw conclusions about how the water became polluted.

Scientific Laws

Build Science Skills L2

Inferring Reinforce the difference between a scientific theory and a scientific law. Ask, **How are scientific laws affected by new scientific theories?** *(Scientific laws aren't affected because new theories are new explanations of the observations. Scientific laws are descriptions of patterns in nature; they do not explain. Theories are explanations of patterns observed in nature.)* **If a scientific law were developed in one country, would it apply in a different country? Explain your answer.** *(Scientific laws apply everywhere. Scientific laws are different from legal and political laws, which apply only in specific countries.)* **Logical**

Address Misconceptions L2

Some students may incorrectly think that every hypothesis becomes a theory and then a law. Help students understand the basic definitions of these three terms. For example, tell students that a hypothesis is a reasonable idea, or reasonable guess, that is often much narrower in scope than a theory. Explain that some ideas or guesses are incorrect, incomplete, or only partially correct. Tell students that a theory is an explanation, and help them realize that some explanations are incorrect. When students thoroughly understand the definitions of these three terms, they will realize that these are not always part of a progression. **Verbal**

Go Online SCIENCE NEWS

Science News provides students with current information on articles on the nature of science.

Answer to . . .

Figure 7 *No, an observation is not required in order for you to be able to pose a question. This tells you that the scientific method should not be thought of as a strict sequence of steps, but rather a flexible set of guidelines for investigating a problem. The flexibility of the scientific method allows for scientists to be creative in their problem solving.*

Reading Checkpoint *A proposed answer to a question*

Scientific Models

Teacher Demo

Flaps on an Airplane L2

Purpose Students observe how models can be used.

Material sheet of paper

Procedure Tell students that the flaps on airplane wings help control how the plane flies. Point out that because you do not have an airplane in the class, you will use a model to observe how wing flaps can affect an airplane's flight. Fold the sheet of paper into a paper airplane. Throw the plane so the class sees how the plane flies without flaps. On the trailing edge of each wing, cut a flap. Bend the flaps into different positions such as both up, both down, or one up and one down. Throw the plane with different flap positions and observe how the plane flies. Ask students if they think the wing flaps on a real airplane would have the same effect.

Expected Outcome Students should see that using the paper airplane as a model for a real airplane is appropriate. With both flaps down, the plane descends; with both up, it ascends. With one flap up and the other down, the plane turns in the direction of the flap that is up.
Visual, Logical

Figure 9 Two engineers discuss a computer-aided design, or CAD, of an aircraft component.

Scientific Models

If you have ever been lost in a city, you know that a street map can help you find your location. A street map is a type of **model,** or representation, of an object or event. **Scientific models make it easier to understand things that might be too difficult to observe directly.** For example, to understand how Earth rotates on its axis, you could look at a globe, which is a small-scale model of Earth. The computer model in Figure 9 represents the interior of an airplane. Other models help you visualize things that are too small to see, such as atoms. As long as a model lets you mentally picture what is supposed to be represented, then the model has done its job.

An example of a mental, rather than physical, model might be that comets are like giant snowballs, primarily made of ice. Scientists would test this model through observations, experiments, and calculations. Possibly they would even send a space probe—a visit to a comet really is planned! If all of these tests support the idea that comets are made of ice, then the model of icy comets will continue to be believed.

However, if the data show that this model is wrong, then it must either be changed or be replaced by a new model. If scientists never challenged old models, then nothing new would be learned, and we would still believe what we believed hundreds of years ago. Science works by making mistakes. The fact that newer models are continually replacing old models is a sign that new discoveries are continually occurring. As the knowledge that makes up science keeps changing, scientists develop a better and better understanding of the universe.

Reading Checkpoint *What is a model?*

Working Safely in Science

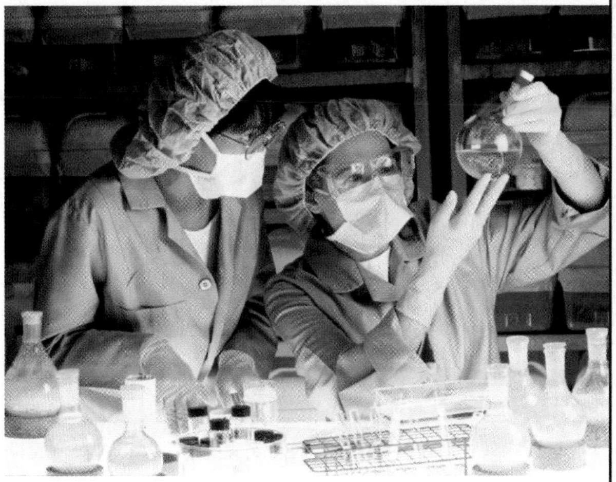

Scientists working in the field, or in a laboratory, like those in Figure 10, are trained to use safe procedures when carrying out investigations. Laboratory work may involve flames or hot plates, electricity, chemicals, hot liquids, sharp instruments, and breakable glassware.

Whenever you work in your science laboratory, it's important for you to follow safety precautions at all times. Before performing any activity in this course, study the rules in the Science Safety section of the Skills Handbook. Before you start any activity, read all the steps. Make sure that you understand the entire procedure, especially any safety precautions that must be followed.

The single most important rule for your safety is simple: Always follow your teacher's instructions and the textbook directions exactly. If you are in doubt about any step in an activity, always ask your teacher for an explanation. Because you may be in contact with chemicals you cannot see, it is essential that you wash your hands thoroughly after every scientific activity. Remember, you share responsibility for your own safety and that of your teacher and classmates.

Figure 10 Safety plays an important role in science. **Interpreting Photos** ***What safety measures are these scientists taking in their laboratory work?***

Section 1.2 Assessment

Reviewing Concepts

1. What is the goal of scientific methods?
2. How does a scientific law differ from a scientific theory?
3. Why are scientific models useful?
4. What are three types of variables in a controlled experiment?
5. Does every scientific method begin with an observation? Explain.

Critical Thinking

6. **Classifying** The scientists who tested the hypothesis on running in the rain performed only one controlled experiment that supported their hypothesis. Can their supported hypothesis be called a theory? Explain.
7. **Designing Experiments** Suppose you wanted to find out how running affects your pulse rate. What would your hypothesis be? Explain how you could test your hypothesis.
8. **Using Models** A scientific model can take the form of a physical object or a concept. List one example of each type of model. How does each one resemble what it is supposed to model?

Writing in Science

Descriptive Paragraph Write a paragraph describing the steps of a scientific method. (*Hint:* Before you write, use a flowchart to arrange your steps in a particular order.)

Working Safely in Science

Use Visuals **L1**

Figure 10 Emphasize that students must study the safety rules before they do lab activities. Ask, **Why are these scientists wearing goggles?** *(Because when a liquid is poured or heated, it could splash into their eyes.)* **Visual**

3 ASSESS

Evaluate Understanding **L2**

Ask students to name scientific laws. If they name a theory instead of a law, help them understand why what they chose is a theory and not a law.

Reteach **L1**

Use Figure 7 to review the scientific method. Point out that when scientists learn new information, they may go back to an earlier step in the method.

Writing in Science

A scientific method can begin with an observation that leads to a question and a hypothesized answer. Next, the hypothesis is tested either by making further observations or by performing an experiment. Conclusions are then drawn from the data.

Interactive Textbook If your class subscribes to the Interactive Textbook, use it to review key concepts in Section 1.2.

Answer to . . .

Figure 10 *They are wearing goggles, gloves, lab coats, and hair nets.*

Reading Checkpoint *A representation of an object or event*

Section 1.2 Assessment

1. The goal of scientific methods is to solve a problem or to better understand an observed event.
2. A scientific law describes an observed pattern in nature without attempting to explain it. The explanation of such a pattern is provided by a scientific theory.
3. Scientific models make it easier to understand things that might be too difficult to observe directly.
4. Three types of variables in a controlled experiment are manipulated variables, responding variables, and controlled variables.
5. No. The order of the steps within a scientific method can vary from case to case.
6. Although the data from the meteorologists' experiment supported their hypothesis, the scope of their investigation is too narrow to be considered a theory. A scientific theory explains a broad set of observations and/or supported hypotheses—not just a single hypothesis.
7. Students will likely hypothesize that running increases one's pulse rate. Students can test their hypotheses by performing a controlled experiment in which the manipulated variable is speed (e.g., running, walking, or standing still) and the responding variable is pulse rate.
8. Possible answer: A globe, a physical model of Earth, has the same shape as Earth. The quantum mechanical model of the atom describes the behavior of electrons around the nucleus.

Forensic Science L2

Background

Forensic science is any aspect of science that relates to law. It includes methods for identifying, collecting, and analyzing evidence that may be related to a crime. At a crime scene, data is often identified and collected. Data collection may include taking fingerprints; collecting hair, blood, or tissue samples; or making plaster casts of tire prints or footprints. Depending on the nature of the crime and the crime scene, investigators may also collect samples of soil, pollen, fibers from clothing, or other materials at the crime scene. In the laboratory, technicians study and analyze the samples so that they can provide investigators with accurate information. Data analysis can shed light on what happened, where it happened, and even who might have committed the crime.

Build Science Skills L2

Analyzing Data ACTIVITY

Purpose Students compare tire tracks to determine which ones were made by the same toy car.

Materials modeling clay, at least 5 different toy cars with similar-sized tires that have different tread, cooking oil, magnifying glass

Class Time 30 minutes

Preparation Flatten a piece of clay for each group of students. Lightly oil the tread of all the tires on the toy cars. Choose a car and roll the tire across each piece of clay to make an impression.

Safety Students who are allergic to corn or olives should wear plastic gloves and dispose of them carefully.

Procedure Tell students that they are forensic scientists and they must find out which car was at the scene of a crime based on a tire track from the scene. Give students a piece of clay with a tire track and another piece of unmarked clay. Have students use the clay to test each car's tires and, as needed, use the magnifying glass to find a match. Ask each group to write a short paragraph stating what they did and why they think they have identified the car that made the tracks.

Expected Outcome Students should correctly identify the car by the similar tire patterns. **Logical, Visual, Group**

Forensic Science

The first job of police officers at a crime scene is to seal off the area so that potential evidence is not disturbed. Such evidence will be sent to a forensic science laboratory for examination.

Forensic science is the use of scientific methods, such as fingerprint matching or the analysis of clothing fibers, to solve crimes. As techniques in analytical chemistry have become more advanced, the amount of information that can be gleaned from tiny crime-scene samples has grown. Forensic science is becoming ever more powerful as a crime-solving tool.

Criminal investigators need to use several scientific techniques. They include making observations, establishing the problem to be solved, collecting evidence and gathering information, forming hypotheses, analyzing evidence, testing hypotheses, and drawing conclusions.

Collecting evidence and forming a hypothesis
Forensic scientists take photographs and collect materials from the crime scene. Investigators use all of the information gathered to formulate hypotheses about how and why the crime took place.

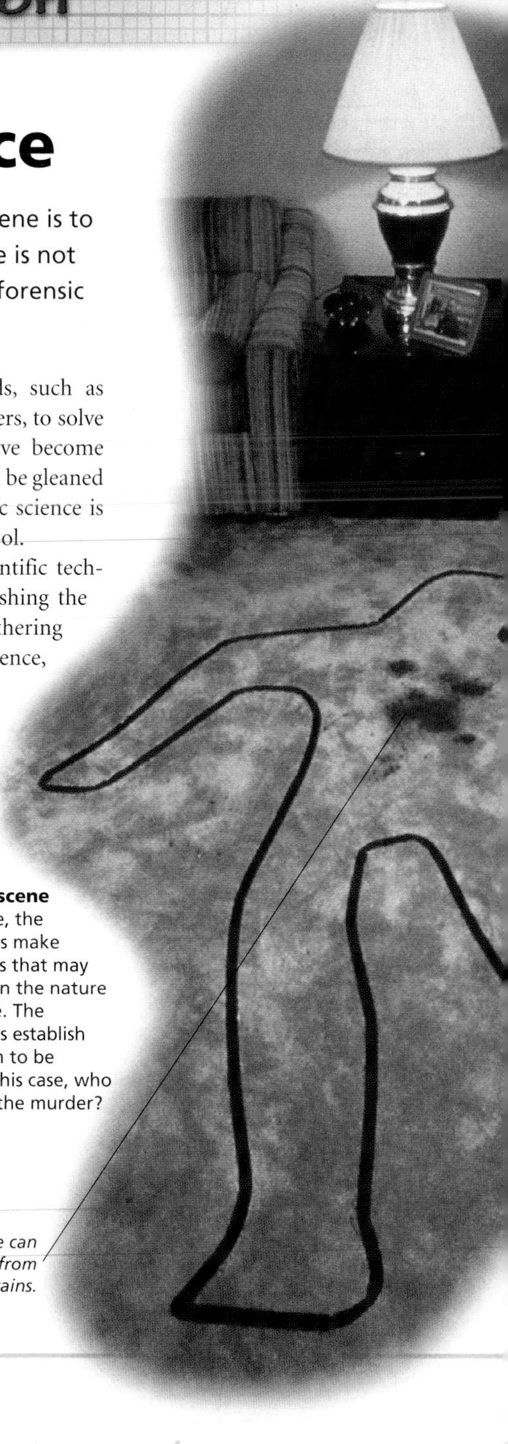

The crime scene
At the scene, the investigators make observations that may shed light on the nature of the crime. The investigators establish the problem to be solved—in this case, who committed the murder?

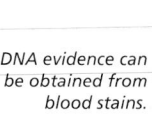

DNA evidence can be obtained from blood stains.

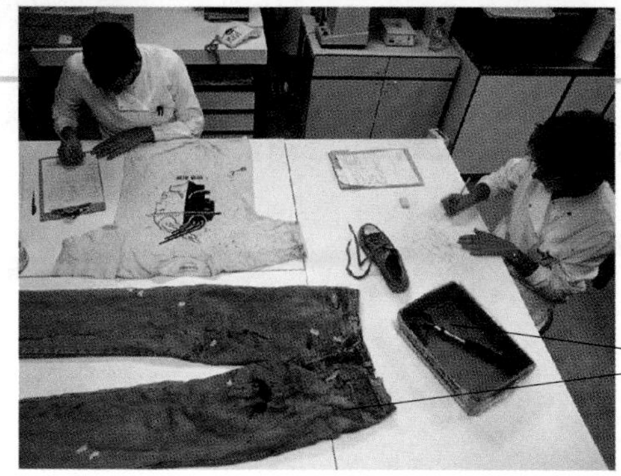

Analyzing the evidence
Much of the physical evidence must be analyzed in a laboratory. With a blood sample, for example, DNA is extracted and analyzed and the blood type is established.

Forensic blood sampling *Articles from a crime scene, such as the blood-stained clothing and the hatchet shown here, may match DNA to a suspect.*

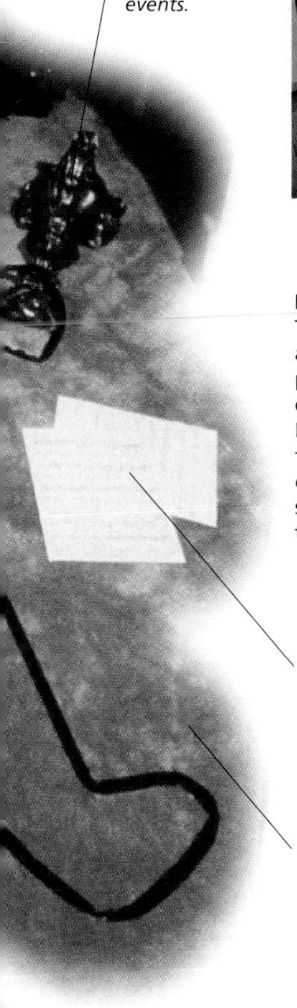

Displaced objects can help determine a sequence of events.

Testing hypotheses against the evidence
Investigators now test hypotheses on who committed the crime—looking for matches in DNA, fingerprints, or clothing fibers, for example. In some cases, this testing excludes a suspect. In other cases it strengthens the case against a particular person.

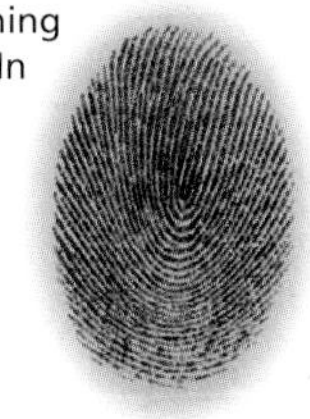

Drawing conclusions
To build a convincing case against a suspect, various pieces and types of evidence may be needed. Evidence might include a fingerprint match, a piece of clothing left at the crime scene, or a connection to the murder weapon.

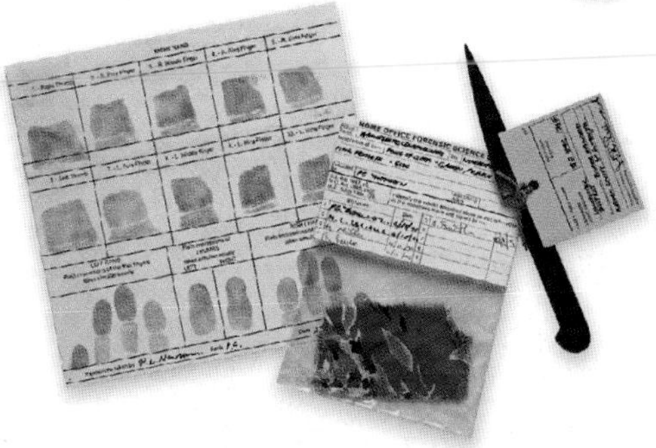

Documents may provide evidence for a motive.

Fibers can link a suspect to a crime scene.

Going Further

- Describe how criminal investigators use scientific methods to solve their cases. (*Hint:* start by creating a flowchart of a scientific method. Then identify how criminal investigators carry out each step.)
- Take a Discovery Channel Video Field Trip by watching "Cracking the Case."

Discovery Channel School **Video Field Trip**

Going Further

A scientific method can include the following steps: observing, posing questions, formulating a hypothesis, testing the hypothesis, and drawing conclusions. When criminal investigators arrive at a crime scene, they make observations and collect evidence. The questions they pose might include, "Who committed the crime?" or "How was the crime committed?" Investigators may then form hypotheses concerning possible suspects and the methods used to commit the crime. By analyzing the evidence obtained (e.g., fingerprint or DNA analysis), they can test their hypotheses. The results of these analyses may allow investigators to draw conclusions about the criminal's identity and methodology.
Logical

Video Field Trip

Cracking the Case

After students have viewed the Video Field Trip, ask them the following questions: **What is the main goal of forensic science?** *(To analyze clues to reconstruct past events)* **What discovery led to the use of fingerprinting in forensic science?** *(The discovery that no two people had the same fingerprints)* **What do forensic scientists look for in the pattern of a fingerprint so that they can identify who the fingerprint belongs to?** *(The tiny imperfections such as ridges that end abruptly, ridges that split, and ridges that form little dots; also where these are located with respect to one another)* **How do detectives find fingerprints on an object?** *(The old method involved spreading powder on the area. The powder adhered to traces of sweat left behind by contact with the fingers. The powder was then lifted off with transparent tape, showing the pattern. Newer methods use fluorescent powder and high intensity lasers to find prints that could otherwise be missed.)* **Name two things police detectives and forensic scientists might do to track down the identity of a car that left a suspicious tire track at a crime scene.** *(Student answers may include measure and photograph the area, make a mold of the tire track, and look for irregularities in the mold of the tire tread that are unique to that tire.)*

Section 1.3

1 FOCUS

Objectives

1.3.1 **Perform** calculations involving scientific notation and conversion factors.

1.3.2 **Identify** the metric and SI units used in science and **convert** between common metric prefixes.

1.3.3 **Compare** and **contrast** accuracy and precision.

1.3.4 **Relate** the Celsius, Kelvin, and Fahrenheit temperature scales.

Reading Focus

Build Vocabulary L2

LINCS Use LINCS to help students learn and review section vocabulary, including *scientific notation*: **L**ist parts that they know (*Scientific* means "related to science," and *notation* means "a system of symbols."); **I**magine a picture (Students might visualize a series of symbols written in a table.); **N**ote a sound-alike word (*Notation* is similar to *note*.); **C**onnect the terms in a sentence *(The scientist used scientific notation to communicate her results.)*; **S**elf-test (quiz themselves).

Reading Strategy L2

Possible answers may include:
a. What is SI? SI is a set of metric measuring units used by scientists.
b. What are base units? Base units are the fundamental units of SI. There are seven SI base units, including the meter, the kilogram, the kelvin, and the second.

2 INSTRUCT

Using Scientific Notation

Use Visuals L1

Figure 11 Ask, **Would it be easy to count the number of stars shown in the photo?** *(No)* **Why might using scientific notation be appropriate when counting the number of stars?** *(The number of stars could be very large.)* **Visual, Logical**

1.3 Measurement

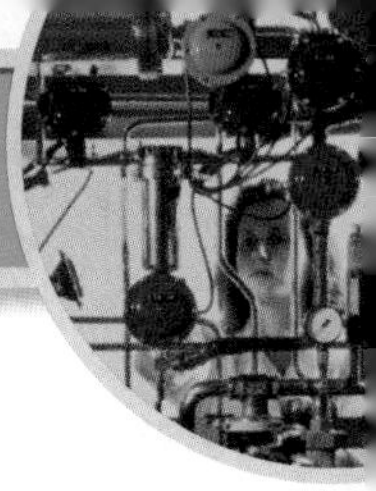

Reading Focus

Key Concepts

- Why is scientific notation useful?
- What units do scientists use for their measurements?
- How does the precision of measurements affect the precision of scientific calculations?

Vocabulary

- scientific notation
- length
- mass
- volume
- density
- conversion factor
- precision
- significant figures
- accuracy
- thermometer

Reading Strategy

Previewing Make a table like the one below. Before you read the section, rewrite the green and blue topic headings as questions. As you read, write answers to the questions.

Measurement
Why is scientific notation useful?
a. ______ ? ______
b. ______ ? ______

How old are you? How tall are you? The answers to these questions are measurements. Measurements are important in both science and everyday life. Hardly a day passes without the need for you to measure amounts of money or the passage of time. It would be difficult to imagine doing science without any measurements.

Figure 11 Scientists estimate that there are more than 200 billion stars in the Milky Way galaxy. **Applying Concepts** ***What is this number in scientific notation?***

Using Scientific Notation

How many stars do you see in Figure 11? There are too many to count. Scientists often work with very large or very small numbers. For example, the speed of light is about 300,000,000 meters per second. On the other hand, an average snail has been clocked at a speed of only 0.00086 meter per second.

Instead of having to write out all the zeroes in these numbers, you can use a shortcut called scientific notation. **Scientific notation** is a way of expressing a value as the product of a number between 1 and 10 and a power of 10. For example, the number 300,000,000 written in scientific notation is 3.0×10^8. The exponent, 8, tells you that the decimal point is really 8 places to the right of the 3.

For numbers less than 1 that are written in scientific notation, the exponent is negative. For example, the number 0.00086 written in scientific notation is 8.6×10^{-4}. The negative exponent tells you how many decimals places there are to the *left* of the 8.6. **Scientific notation makes very large or very small numbers easier to work with.**

Section Resources

Print
- ***Laboratory Manual,*** Investigations 1A and 1B
- ***Reading and Study Workbook With Math Support,*** Section 1.3 and **Math Skill:** Using Scientific Notation
- ***Math Skills and Problem Solving Workbook,*** Section 1.3
- ***Transparencies,*** Section 1.3

Technology
- ***Interactive Textbook,*** Section 1.3
- ***Presentation Pro CD-ROM,*** Section 1.3
- ***Go Online,*** *Planet Diary,* Universal measurements; PHSchool.com, Data sharing

When multiplying numbers written in scientific notation, you multiply the numbers that appear before the multiplication signs and *add* the exponents. For example, to calculate how far light travels in 500 seconds, you multiply the speed of light by the number of seconds.

$$(3.0 \times 10^8 \text{ m/s}) \times (5.0 \times 10^2 \text{ s}) = 15 \times 10^{10} \text{ m} = 1.5 \times 10^{11} \text{ m}$$

This distance is about how far the sun is from Earth.

When dividing numbers written in scientific notation, you divide the numbers that appear before the exponential terms and *subtract* the exponents. For example, to calculate how long it takes for light from the sun to reach Earth, you would perform a division.

$$\frac{1.5 \times 10^{11} \text{ m}}{3.0 \times 10^8 \text{ m/s}} = \frac{1.5}{3.0} \times 10^{11-8} \text{ s} = 0.50 \times 10^3 \text{ s} = 5.0 \times 10^2 \text{ s}$$

Go Online PLANETDIARY

For: Links on universal measurements
Visit: PHSchool.com
Web Code: ccc-0013

Math Skills

Using Scientific Notation

A rectangular parking lot has a length of 1.1×10^3 meters and a width of 2.4×10^3 meters. What is the area of the parking lot?

1 Read and Understand

What information are you given?

Length $(l) = 1.1 \times 10^3$ m

Width $(w) = 2.4 \times 10^3$ m

2 Plan and Solve

What unknown are you trying to calculate?

Area $(A) = ?$

What formula contains the given quantities and the unknown?

$A = l \times w$

Replace each variable with its known value.

$$A = l \times w = (1.1 \times 10^3 \text{ m})(2.4 \times 10^3 \text{ m})$$
$$= (1.1 \times 2.4)(10^{3+3})(\text{m} \times \text{m})$$
$$= 2.6 \times 10^6 \text{ m}^2$$

3 Look Back and Check

Is your answer reasonable?

Yes, the number calculated is the product of the numbers given, and the units (m^2) indicate area.

Math Practice

1. Perform the following calculations. Express your answers in scientific notation.
   a. $(7.6 \times 10^{-4} \text{ m}) \times (1.5 \times 10^7 \text{ m})$
   b. $0.00053 \div 29$
2. Calculate how far light travels in 8.64×10^4 seconds. (*Hint:* The speed of light is about 3.0×10^8 m/s.)

Math Practice

Solutions **L2**

1. a. $(7.6 \times 10^{-4} \text{ m})(1.5 \times 10^7 \text{ m}) = (7.6 \times 1.5)(10^{-4+7})(\text{m} \times \text{m}) = 11 \times 10^3 \text{ m}^2 = 1.1 \times 10^4 \text{ m}^2$

1. b. $0.00053/29 = (5.3 \times 10^{-4})/(2.9 \times 10^1) = (5.3/2.9) \times 10^{(-4-1)} = 1.8 \times 10^{-5}$

2. $(3.0 \times 10^8 \text{ m/s})(8.64 \times 10^4 \text{ s}) = (3.0 \times 8.64)(10^{8+4}) \text{ m} = 26 \times 10^{12} = 2.6 \times 10^{13} \text{ m}$

(Note: This is how far light travels in one day.)

Logical

For Extra Help **L1**

Reinforce the concepts of adding exponents when numbers in scientific notation are multiplied and subtracting exponents when numbers in scientific notation are divided.
Logical

Direct students to the **Math Skills** in the **Skills and Reference Handbook** at the end of the student text for additional help.

Additional Problems **L1**

1. Perform the following calculations:
a. $1.5 \times 10^3 \text{ m} \times 1.0 \times 10^5 \text{ m}$
($1.5 \times 10^8 \text{ m}^2$)
b. $4.5 \times 10^3/0.9$ *(5.0×10^3)*
Logical, Portfolio

Go Online PLANETDIARY

Find links to additional activities and have students monitor phenomena that affect Earth and its residents.

Customize for Inclusion Students

Visually Impaired
To help visually impaired students understand the concepts of length, mass, and volume, give students common objects. Ask students to describe the objects in regard to their lengths, masses, and volumes. Help students to understand the definitions of these terms during the exercise.

Answer to . . .

Figure 11 *2×10^{11}*

SI Units of Measurement

Address Misconceptions **L2**

Some students may incorrectly think that scientists use the metric system because it is more accurate than other measurement systems. Point out to students that the units of the measurement system have little to do with accuracy. Help students overcome this misconception by measuring one object with several different centimeter- and inch-rulers. Have students record the measurements. List the metric measurements in one column on the board and the English measurements in another column. Point out that all the measurements in the metric column are similar to one another and that the measurements in the English column are also similar to one another.
Visual

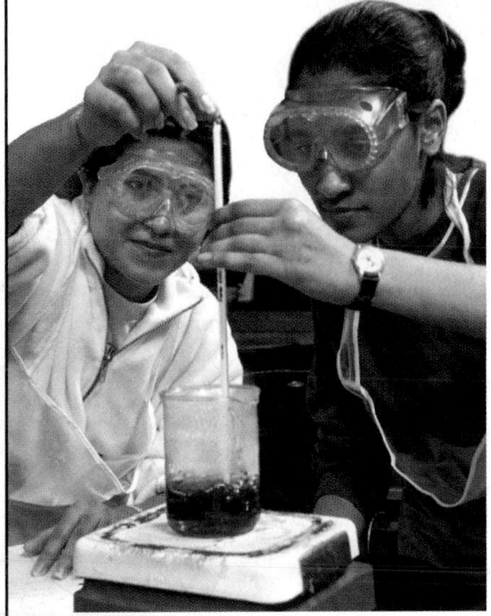

Figure 12 A measurement consists of a number and a unit. One of the units used to measure temperature is the degree Celsius.

SI Units of Measurement

For a measurement to make sense, it requires both a number and a unit. For example, if you told one of your friends that you had finished a homework assignment "in five," what would your friend think? Would it be five minutes or five hours? Maybe it was a long assignment, and you actually meant five days. Or maybe you meant that you wrote five pages. You should always express measurements in numbers and units so that their meaning is clear. In Figure 12, students are measuring temperature in degrees Celsius.

Many of the units you are familiar with, such as inches, feet, and degrees Fahrenheit, are not units that are used in science. **Scientists use a set of measuring units called SI, or the International System of Units.** The abbreviation stands for the French name *Système International d'Unités.* SI is a revised version of the metric system, which was originally developed in France in 1791. By adhering to one system of units, scientists can readily interpret one another's measurements.

Base Units and Derived Units SI is built upon seven metric units, known as base units, which are listed in Figure 13. In SI, the base unit for **length,** or the straight-line distance between two points, is the meter (m). The base unit for **mass,** or the quantity of matter in an object or sample, is the kilogram (kg).

Additional SI units, called derived units, are made from combinations of base units. Figure 14 lists some common derived units. For example, **volume** is the amount of space taken up by an object. The volume of a rectangular box equals its length times its width times its height. Each of these dimensions can be measured in meters, so you can derive the SI unit for volume by multiplying meters by meters by meters, which gives you cubic meters (m^3).

SI Base Units

Quantity	Unit	Symbol
Length	meter	m
Mass	kilogram	kg
Temperature	kelvin	K
Time	second	s
Amount of substance	mole	mol
Electric current	ampere	A
Luminous intensity	candela	cd

Figure 13 Seven metric base units make up the foundation of SI.

Derived Units

Quantity	Unit	Symbol
Area	square meter	m^2
Volume	cubic meter	m^3
Density	kilograms per cubic meter	kg/m^3
Pressure	pascal ($kg/m{\cdot}s^2$)	Pa
Energy	joule ($kg{\cdot}m^2/s^2$)	J
Frequency	hertz (1/s)	Hz
Electric charge	coulomb ($A{\cdot}s$)	C

Figure 14 Specific combinations of SI base units yield derived units.

Facts and Figures

The Meter The meter was originally defined by the French Academy of Science in 1791. At that time, a meter was intended to be one ten-millionth part of the quadrant of Earth. This length was transferred to a platinum bar with polished ends. The bar could be measured at a specific temperature to define the length of a meter. Later measurements of Earth showed that the length of the bar was not one ten-millionth of the quadrant. However, the meter's length was not changed. It was redefined to be the length on the bar. In 1960, the length of a meter was more precisely defined by the number of wavelengths of light, of a very precise color, emitted by krypton-86. This method was difficult to perform and was quickly replaced with the current method. Currently, a meter is defined as the distance light travels in a vacuum in $\frac{1}{299{,}792{,}458}$ second.

SI Prefixes			
Prefix	Symbol	Meaning	Multiply Unit by
giga-	G	billion (10^9)	1,000,000,000
mega-	M	million (10^6)	1,000,000
kilo-	k	thousand (10^3)	1000
deci-	d	tenth (10^{-1})	0.1
centi-	c	hundredth (10^{-2})	0.01
milli-	m	thousandth (10^{-3})	0.001
micro-	μ	millionth (10^{-6})	0.000001
nano-	n	billionth (10^{-9})	0.000000001

Figure 15 Metric prefixes allow for more convenient ways to express SI base and derived units.

Another quantity that requires a derived unit is density. **Density** is the ratio of an object's mass to its volume.

$$\text{Density} = \frac{\text{Mass}}{\text{Volume}}$$

To derive the SI unit for density, you can divide the base unit for mass by the derived unit for volume. Dividing kilograms by cubic meters yields the SI unit for density, kilograms per cubic meter (kg/m^3).

Reading Checkpoint *What is the SI derived unit for density?*

Metric Prefixes The metric unit for a given quantity is not always a convenient one to use. For example, the time it takes for a computer hard drive to read or write data—also known as the seek time—is in the range of thousandths of a second. A typical seek time might be 0.009 second. This can be written in a more compact way by using a metric prefix. A metric prefix indicates how many times a unit should be multiplied or divided by 10. Figure 15 shows some common metric prefixes. Using the prefix *milli-* (m), you can write 0.009 second as 9 milliseconds, or 9 ms.

$$9 \text{ ms} = \frac{9}{1000} \text{ s} = 0.009 \text{ s}$$

Note that dividing by 1000 is the same as multiplying by 0.001.

Metric prefixes can also make a unit larger. For example, a distance of 12,000 meters can also be written as 12 kilometers.

$$12 \text{ km} = 12 \times 1000 \text{ m} = 12{,}000 \text{ m}$$

Metric prefixes turn up in non-metric units as well. If you work with computers, you probably know that a gigabyte of data refers to 1,000,000,000 bytes. A megapixel is 1,000,000 pixels.

Figure 16 A bar of gold has more mass per unit volume than a feather. **Inferring** ***Which takes up more space—one kilogram of gold or one kilogram of feathers?***

Build Science Skills L2

Inferring Have students look at Figure 15. Ask, **What factor are the metric prefixes based on?** *(10)* **How does that make it convenient for converting between units?** *(The numbers stay the same but the decimal point moves.)*
Logical, Visual

Build Math Skills L1

Conversion Factors Give students the conversion factors 1 in = 2.54 cm and 1 ft = 30.48 cm. Divide students into pairs, and have each pair measure the lengths of at least three different objects of various sizes, such as a pencil, a desktop, and the floor of a room. Direct the pairs to calculate the measurements of each object in inches, feet, centimeters, meters, and kilometers. *(Answers will vary depending upon the objects measured.)* Ask students which conversion factors they used to make their calculations.
Kinesthetic, Logical

Direct students to the **Math Skills** in the **Skills and Reference Handbook** at the end of the student text for additional help.

Answer to . . .

Figure 16 *Because feathers are less dense than gold, one kilogram of feathers takes up more space than one kilogram of gold.*

Reading Checkpoint *The SI derived unit for density is the kilogram per cubic meter (kg/m^3).*

Teacher Demo

Conversion Factor L2

Purpose Students observe how conversion factors work.

Materials 12-in. object, 3-in. object, metric ruler

Procedure Give students the conversion factor 1 in. = 2.54 in. Measure the 12-in. object and report its length in centimeters. Tell the students the length in inches of the 3-in. object. Ask them to use the conversion factor to calculate its length in centimeters. *(7.6 cm)* Measure the object and report the length in centimeters.

Expected Outcome Students see how conversion factors convert between units of different measure. **Visual, Logical**

Quick Lab

Comparing Precision L2

Objective
After completing this lab, students will be able to
- describe and distinguish accuracy and precision.
- compare the precision of measuring devices.

Skills Focus **Measuring, Comparing**

Prep Time 10 minutes

Class Time 15 minutes

Safety Caution students to handle glassware carefully.

Teaching Tips
- Provide 3 different plastic bottles with labels removed, and a beaker and graduated cylinder large enough to contain the volume of each bottle.
- If necessary, use paper cups instead of plastic bottles.

Expected Outcome The graduated cylinder will provide a more precise measurement than the beaker.

Nutrition Facts
Serving Size 1 oz (28g/about 18 chips)
Servings Per Container 7
Amount Per Serving
Calories 150 Calories from Fat 80
% Daily Value*
Total Fat 9g 14%
Saturated Fat 1g 5%
Polyunsaturated Fat 1g
Monounsaturated Fat 7g
Cholesterol 0mg 0%
Sodium 160mg 7%

Figure 17 Nutrition labels often have some measurements listed in grams and milligrams. **Calculating** *How many grams are in 160 milligrams?*

The easiest way to convert from one unit of measurement to another is to use conversion factors. A **conversion factor** is a ratio of equivalent measurements that is used to convert a quantity expressed in one unit to another unit. Suppose you want to convert the height of Mount Everest, 8848 meters, into kilometers. Based on the prefix *kilo-*, you know that 1 kilometer is 1000 meters. This ratio gives you two possible conversion factors.

$$\frac{1 \text{ km}}{1000 \text{ m}} \qquad \frac{1000 \text{ m}}{1 \text{ km}}$$

Since you are converting from meters to kilometers, the number should get smaller. Multiplying by the conversion factor on the left yields a smaller number.

$$8848 \cancel{\text{m}} \times \frac{1 \text{ km}}{1000 \cancel{\text{m}}} = 8.848 \text{ km}$$

Notice that the meter units cancel, leaving you with kilometers (the larger unit).

To convert 8.848 kilometers back into meters, multiply by the conversion factor on the right. Since you are converting from kilometers to meters, the number should get larger.

$$8.848 \cancel{\text{km}} \times \frac{1000 \text{ m}}{1 \cancel{\text{km}}} = 8848 \text{ m}$$

In this case, the kilometer units cancel, leaving you with meters.

Quick Lab

Comparing Precision

Materials

3 plastic bottles of different sizes, beaker, graduated cylinder

Procedure

1. Draw a data table with three rows and three columns. Label the columns Estimate, Beaker, and Graduated Cylinder.
2. Record your estimate of the volume of a plastic bottle in your data table. Then, fill the bottle with water and pour the water into the beaker. Read and record the volume of the water.
3. Pour the water from the beaker into the graduated cylinder. Read and record the volume of water.
4. Repeat Steps 2 and 3 with two other plastic bottles.

Analyze and Conclude

1. **Analyzing Data** Review your volume measurements for one of the bottles. How many significant figures does the volume measured with the beaker have? How many significant figures does the volume measured with the graduated cylinder have?
2. **Comparing and Contrasting** Which provided a more precise measurement—the beaker or the graduated cylinder?
3. **Inferring** How could you determine the accuracy of your measurements?

Analyze and Conclude
1. Answers will vary, depending on the size of the beaker and graduated cylinder. Typically, the graduated cylinder measurement will have more significant figures than the beaker measurement.
2. The graduated cylinder
3. By comparing them to measurements made with a container known to be accurate **Visual, Logical**

Limits of Measurement

Suppose you wanted to measure how much time it takes for you to eat your breakfast. Figure 18 shows two clocks you could use—an analog clock and a digital clock. The analog clock displays time to the nearest minute. The digital clock displays time to the nearest second (or one sixtieth of a minute). Which clock would you choose?

Precision The digital clock offers more precision. **Precision** is a gauge of how exact a measurement is. According to the analog clock, it might take you 5 minutes to eat your breakfast. Using the digital clock, however, you might measure 5 minutes and 15 seconds, or 5.25 minutes. The second measurement has more significant figures. **Significant figures** are all the digits that are known in a measurement, plus the last digit that is estimated. The time recorded as 5.25 minutes has three significant figures. The time recorded as 5 minutes has one significant figure. The fewer the significant figures, the less precise the measurement is.

When you make calculations with measurements, the uncertainty of the separate measurements must be correctly reflected in the final result. **The precision of a calculated answer is limited by the least precise measurement used in the calculation.** So if the least precise measurement in your calculation has two significant figures, then your calculated answer can have at most two significant figures.

Suppose you measure the mass of a piece of iron to be 34.73 grams on an electronic balance. You then measure the volume to be 4.42 cubic centimeters. What is the density of the iron?

$$\text{Density} = \frac{34.73\ \text{g}}{4.42\ \text{cm}^3} = 7.857466\ \text{g/cm}^3$$

Your answer should have only three significant figures because the least precise measurement, the volume, has three significant figures. Rounding your answer to three significant figures gives you a density of 7.86 grams per cubic centimeter.

Accuracy Another important quality in a measurement is its accuracy. **Accuracy** is the closeness of a measurement to the actual value of what is being measured. For example, suppose the digital clock in Figure 18 is running 15 minutes slow. Although the clock would remain precise to the nearest second, the time displayed would not be accurate.

Reading Checkpoint *What is accuracy?*

SNOOZE/LIGHT
3:00 00
12 25 MON 10:38

Figure 18 A more precise time can be read from the digital clock than can be read from the analog clock. The digital clock is precise to the nearest second, while the analog clock is precise to the nearest minute.

Limits of Measurement

Build Reading Literacy L1

Use Prior Knowledge Refer to page **2D** in this chapter, which provides the guidelines for using prior knowledge.

Have students make a three-column chart with columns headed Term, Prior Knowledge, and New Knowledge. Tell students to write *accuracy* and *precision* in the first column and then fill in the Prior Knowledge column. Discuss students' responses and determine whether they have misconceptions about these terms. If so, begin to address those misconceptions directly in discussion. After students finish reading, have them complete the third column, correcting or revising their prior knowledge as needed.
Verbal

Use Visuals L1

Figure 18 Have students look at the figure and read the caption. Ask, **How precisely does this digital clock measure time?** *(It measures time to the second.)* Ask, **How precisely does the analog clock measure time?** *(It is divided into five-minute intervals, so time to the nearest minute can be estimated.)* **What would make the analog clock more precise?** *(The clock would be more precise if it had tick marks for minutes, and a second hand.)*
Visual

Facts and Figures

Measuring Time Precisely As scientific knowledge increases, so does the accuracy and precision of time measurements. In the seventeenth century, Robert Hooke developed a mechanically powered clock. It was based on Galileo's 1583 observation that each swing of a pendulum takes the same amount of time. Early pendulum clocks were much more accurate and precise than hourglasses, which may have been precise to within an hour or two.

Quartz clocks, developed in 1929, are more precise. They generally lose only one five-hundredths of a second per year. Atomic clocks measure time using the frequencies at which atoms absorb or emit light. They are the most precise clocks today. Today's cesium atomic clocks are projected to neither lose nor gain a second in 1,000,000 years. Even more precise time measurements are based on pulsars, radio pulsations from collapsed stars.

Answer to . . .

Figure 17 *The measurement 160 milligrams is equivalent to 0.160 gram.*

Reading Checkpoint *Accuracy is the closeness of a measurement to the actual value of what is being measured.*

Measuring Temperature

Use Visuals L1

Figure 19 Have students look at the figure. Ask, **Is any one of the three scales more accurate than the others?** *(No, they all can be used to measure temperature accurately.)* **Why do you think scientists use degrees Celsius for measuring temperature?** *(Some students may note that the range between the freezing and boiling points is 100 degrees and that like other SI units of measure, it can easily be divided into hundredths. Other students may say that it is just an agreed-upon standard.)*
Visual, Logical

3 ASSESS

Evaluate Understanding L2

Ask students to write three conversion problems (with solutions) based on the prefixes used in the metric system. Have students take turns analyzing and solving the problems in class. Note that even incorrectly worded problems are useful, as students can be asked to identify and correct the errors.

Reteach L1

Use Figure 15 to help students understand how prefixes modify units of measurement. Give students examples such as kilogram, milliliter, and microsecond and ask students to name units that are larger and smaller.

Math Practice

Solutions

7. a. 3.72×10^{-11} g;
$3.72 \times 10^{-11}\ \text{g} \times (\frac{1\ \text{kg}}{1000\text{g}}) =$
3.72×10^{-14} kg
b. 4.5×10^{10} km;
$4.5 \times 10^{10}\ \text{km} \times (\frac{1000\ \text{m}}{1\ \text{km}}) =$
4.5×10^{13} m
8. $V = (\pi r^2 \times l) =$
$(3.14)\ (6.5 \times 10^{-3}\ \text{cm})^2\ (1.1\ \text{cm}) =$
$(3.14)\ (6.5 \times 6.5)\ (10^{-3\ -3})\ (1.1)$
$(\text{cm} \times \text{cm} \times \text{cm}) = 145.9 \times 10^{-6}\ \text{cm}^3 =$
$1.5 \times 10^{-4}\ \text{cm}^3$

Interactive Textbook If your class subscribes to the Interactive Textbook, use it to review key concepts in Section 1.3.

Common Temperatures	Fahrenheit (°F)	Celsius (°C)	Kelvin (K)
Water boils	212	100	373
Human body	98.6	37	310
Average room	68	20	293
Water freezes	32	0	273

Figure 19 Temperature can be expressed in degrees Fahrenheit, degrees Celsius, or kelvins.

Measuring Temperature

A **thermometer** is an instrument that measures temperature, or how hot an object is. The How It Works box on page 21 describes how a bulb thermometer measures temperature.

The two temperature scales that you are probably most familiar with are the Fahrenheit scale and the Celsius scale. On the Fahrenheit scale, water freezes at 32°F and boils at 212°F at sea level. On the Celsius (or centigrade) scale, water freezes at 0°C and boils at 100°C. A degree Celsius is almost twice as large as a degree Fahrenheit. There is also a difference of 32 degrees between the zero point of the Celsius scale and the zero point of the Fahrenheit scale. You can convert from one scale to the other by using one of the following formulas.

$$°C = \frac{5}{9}(°F - 32.0°) \qquad °F = \frac{9}{5}(°C) + 32.0°$$

The SI base unit for temperature is the kelvin (K). A temperature of 0 K, or 0 kelvin, refers to the lowest possible temperature that can be reached. In degrees Celsius, this temperature is −273.15°C. To convert between kelvins and degrees Celsius, use the following formula.

$$K = °C + 273$$

Figure 19 compares some common temperatures expressed in degrees Celsius, degrees Fahrenheit, and kelvins.

Section 1.3 Assessment

Reviewing Concepts

1. Why do scientists use scientific notation?
2. What system of units do scientists use for measurements?
3. How does the precision of measurements affect the precision of scientific calculations?
4. List the SI units for mass, length, and temperature.

Critical Thinking

5. **Applying Concepts** A bulb thermometer gives an indoor temperature reading of 21°C. A digital thermometer in the same room gives a reading of 20.7°C. Which device is more precise? Explain.
6. **Calculating** Convert −11°F into degrees Celsius, and then into kelvins.

Math Practice

7. Write the following measurements in scientific notation. Then convert each measurement into SI base units.
   a. 0.0000000000372 g
   b. 45,000,000,000 km
8. The liquid in a bulb thermometer falls 1.1 cm. Calculate the liquid's change in volume if the inner radius of the tube is 6.5×10^{-3} cm.

Section 1.3 Assessment

1. Scientific notation is useful because it makes very large or very small numbers easier to work with.
2. Scientists use a set of measuring units called SI.
3. The precision of a calculated answer is limited by the least precise measurement used in the calculation.
4. Kilogram (kg), meter (m), kelvin (K)
5. The digital thermometer (which yields a measurement with three significant figures) is more precise than the bulb thermometer (which yields a measurement of only two significant figures).
6. −11°F = −24°C = 249 K

Thermometer

A bulb thermometer consists of a sealed, narrow glass tube, called a capillary tube. It has a glass bulb at one end and is filled with colored alcohol or mercury. The thermometer works on the principle that the volume of a liquid changes when the temperature changes. When warmed, the liquid in the bulb takes up more space and moves up the capillary tube.

Interpreting Diagrams ***Why is a thermometer with a narrow tube easier to read than a thermometer with a wide tube?***

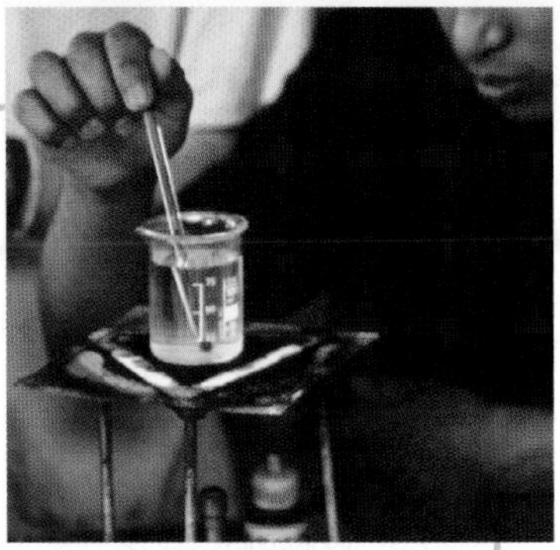

Measuring temperature Thermometers are useful scientific instruments. They can be used to measure the static temperature of a material, or to record the change in temperature of a substance being heated, as shown above.

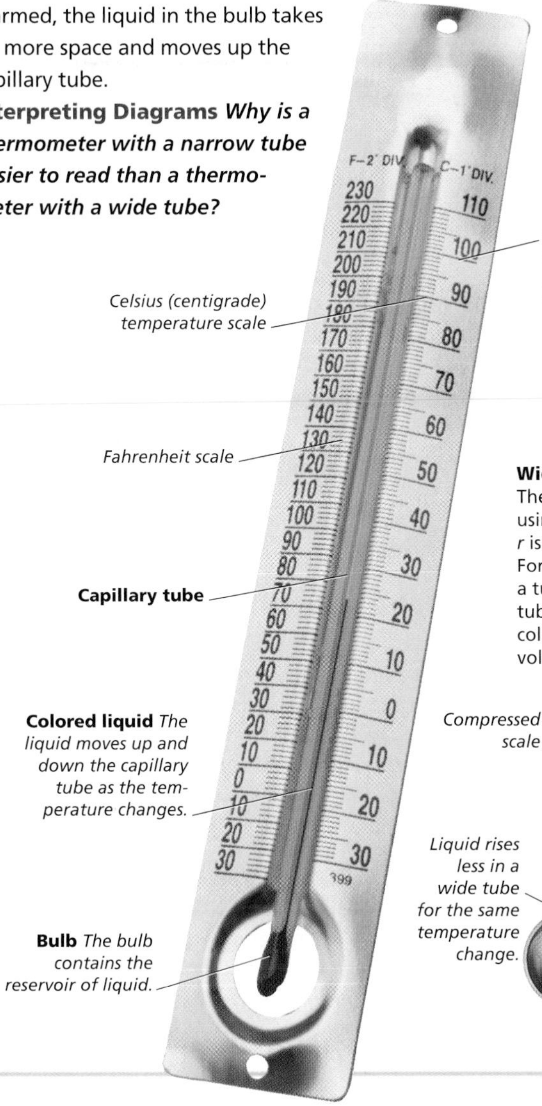
F–2° DIV.
C–1° DIV.
Celsius (centigrade) temperature scale
Fahrenheit scale
Capillary tube
Colored liquid The liquid moves up and down the capillary tube as the temperature changes.
Bulb The bulb contains the reservoir of liquid.

Scale *The scale indicates the temperature according to how far up or down the capillary tube the liquid has moved.*

Wide or narrow?
The volume of a tube is calculated using the formula $V = \pi r^2 l$, where r is the radius and l is the length. For a given volume, if the radius of a tube is decreased (as in a capillary tube), the length of the liquid column increases. Any change in volume is then easier to see.

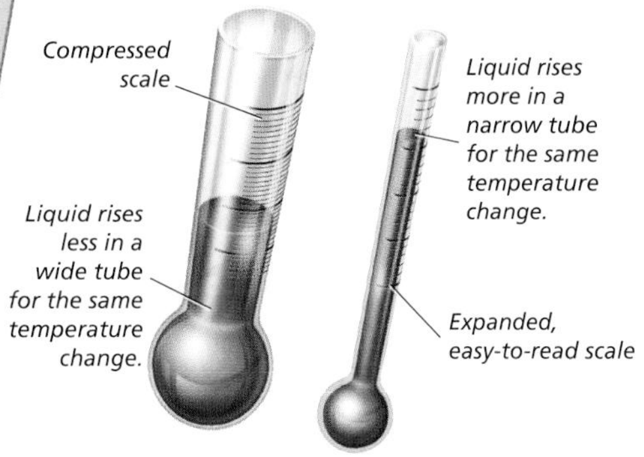
Compressed scale
Liquid rises less in a wide tube for the same temperature change.
Liquid rises more in a narrow tube for the same temperature change.
Expanded, easy-to-read scale

HOW It Works

Thermometer **L2**

Liquid thermometers work because the liquid expands and contracts. Point out to students that all liquids do not expand at the same rate. Students may also be familiar with spiral metal thermometers found in outdoor thermometers, cooking thermometers, and thermostats. The spirals are strips made of two different metals. As the temperature changes, the two metals expand or contract differently. This expansion or contraction moves a pointer needle that points at the temperature.

Interpreting Diagrams The scale markings on a narrow-tube thermometer are further apart (and hence easier to read) than the corresponding markings on a wide-tube thermometer. It is also easier to record a temperature change on a thermometer with a narrow tube because for a given change in the thermometer liquid's volume, the narrow thermometer will show a greater change in the height of the liquid.
Logical

For Enrichment **L3**

Tell students that in the early 1600s, Galileo created a thermometer based on density. Interested students can find out more about Galileo's thermometer and create a brief report and illustration.
Portfolio

1 FOCUS

Objectives

1.4.1 **Organize** and **analyze** data using tables and graphs.
1.4.2 **Identify** the relationship between a manipulated variable and a responding variable.
1.4.3 **Explain** the importance of communicating data.
1.4.4 **Discuss** the process of peer review.

Reading Focus

Build Vocabulary L2

Paraphrase Tell students to write the vocabulary terms on a sheet of paper, leaving enough space beside each to write a definition and a mathematical formula. As students read the section, they should look for these terms. When they encounter one, they should write their own definition and a formula that illustrates the term.

Reading Strategy L2

a. A line represents variable *y* plotted vs. variable *x*. **b.** Showing how one variable responds to changes in another **c.** Scaled bars are used to represent various measurements. **d.** Comparing two sets of similar data **e.** A divided circle, with each "slice" representing a proportional fraction **f.** Showing how a part relates to the whole

2 INSTRUCT

Organizing Data

Build Reading Literacy L1

Preview Refer to page **36D** in **Chapter 2**, which provides the guidelines for a preview.

Ask students to skim Organizing Data. Tell them to pay particular attention to the figures. Ask, **Where else have you seen graphs?** *(Newspapers, television news, magazines, books, and so on)* Ask, **Why is data presented in graphs instead of in text?** *(Graphs make the data easier to read and understand.)*
Visual, Logical

1.4 Presenting Scientific Data

Reading Focus

Key Concepts

- How do scientists organize data?
- How can scientists communicate experimental data?

Vocabulary

- slope
- direct proportion
- inverse proportion

Reading Strategy

Comparing and Contrasting After you read this section, compare types of graphs by completing the table below.

Type of Graph	Description	Used For
Line	a. ?	b. ?
Bar	c. ?	d. ?
Circle	e. ?	f. ?

Much of the information you get every day comes from the news media. Newspapers, television, radio, and the Internet let you access a wealth of information about events going on in the world. But in order for news to be useful, it must be communicated. If a news reporter witnesses an event but doesn't report it, then he might as well not have seen it. If the event is reported, then it must be described in a clear, organized manner for it to be understood and appreciated. Like the news, scientific data become meaningful only when they are organized and communicated.

Organizing Data

Scientists accumulate vast amounts of data by observing events and making measurements. Interpreting these data can be a difficult task if they are not organized. **Scientists can organize their data by using data tables and graphs.** These tools make it easier to spot patterns or trends in the data that can support or disprove a hypothesis.

Data Tables The simplest way to organize data is to present them in a table. Figure 20 is a data table that shows the average annual precipitation for seven U.S. cities. The table relates two variables—a manipulated variable (location) and a responding variable (average annual precipitation).

Average Annual Precipitation for Selected U.S. Cities

City	Average Annual Precipitation (cm)
Buffalo, N.Y.	98.0
Chicago, Ill.	91.0
Colorado Springs, Colo.	41.2
Houston, Tex.	117.0
San Diego, Calif.	25.1
Tallahassee, Fla.	166.9
Tucson, Ariz.	30.5

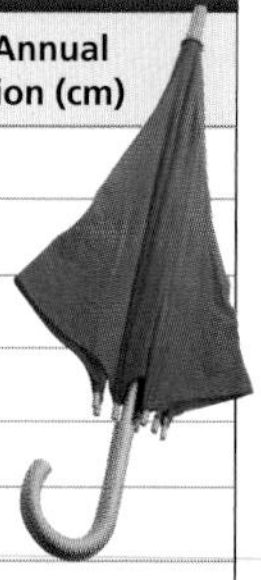

Figure 20 Using a table is a simple way to present data visually.

Section Resources

Print
- ***Reading and Study Workbook With Math Support,*** Section 1.4
- ***Math Skills and Problem Solving Workbook,*** Section 1.4
- ***Transparencies,*** Section 1.4

Technology
- ***Interactive Textbook,*** Section 1.4
- ***Presentation Pro CD-ROM,*** Section 1.4
- ***Go Online,*** NSTA SciLinks, Graphing

22 Chapter 1

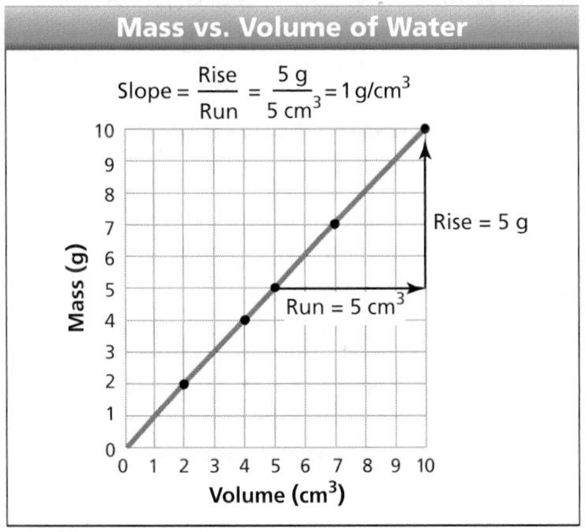

Mass vs. Volume of Water
Slope = Rise/Run = 5 g/5 cm3 = 1 g/cm3
Rise = 5 g
Run = 5 cm3
Mass (g)
Volume (cm3)
0 1 2 3 4 5 6 7 8 9 10

Figure 21 Plotting the mass of water against the volume of water yields a straight line.
Using Graphs ***What does the slope represent?***

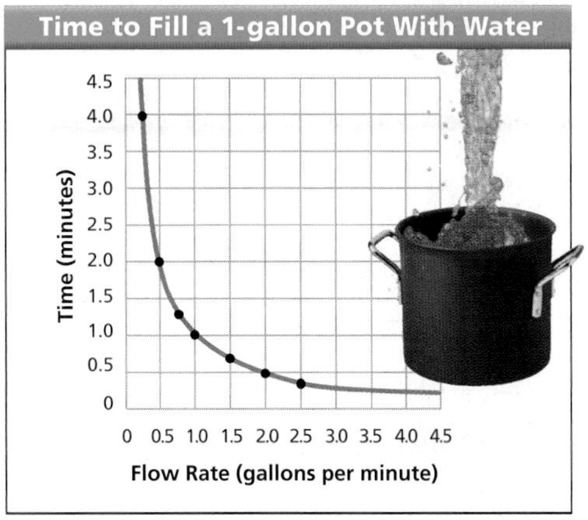

Time to Fill a 1-gallon Pot With Water
Time (minutes)
0 0.5 1.0 1.5 2.0 2.5 3.0 3.5 4.0 4.5
Flow Rate (gallons per minute)

Figure 22 In an inverse proportion, the product of two variables remains constant. Each point on the graph above represents the same volume of water: 1 gallon.

Line Graphs A line graph is useful for showing changes that occur in related variables. In a line graph, the manipulated variable is generally plotted on the horizontal axis, or *x*-axis. The responding variable is plotted on the vertical axis, or *y*-axis, of the graph.

Figure 21 is a line graph that shows how the mass of water increases with volume. The data points yield a straight line. The steepness, or **slope,** of this line is the ratio of a vertical change to the corresponding horizontal change. The formula for the slope of a line is

$$\text{Slope} = \frac{\text{Rise}}{\text{Run}}$$

"Rise" represents the change in the *y*-variable. "Run" represents the corresponding change in the *x*-variable. Note that in Figure 21, because mass per unit volume is density, the slope represents the density of water.

The relationship between the mass and volume of water is an example of a direct proportion. A **direct proportion** is a relationship in which the ratio of two variables is constant. For example, suppose you have a 3-cubic-centimeter sample of water that has a mass of 3 grams. Doubling the volume of the sample to 6 cubic centimeters results in doubling the mass of the sample to 6 grams. Tripling the volume to 9 cubic centimeters results in tripling the mass to 9 grams.

Figure 22 shows how the flow rate of a water faucet affects the time required to fill a 1-gallon pot. Figure 22 illustrates an **inverse proportion,** a relationship in which the product of two variables is a constant. If you start with a flow rate of 0.5 gallon per minute, you will fill the pot in 2 minutes. If you double the flow rate to 1.0 gallon per minute, you reduce the time required to fill the pot to 1 minute, or one half of the original time.

Go Online NSTA SCILINKS

For: Links on graphing
Visit: www.SciLinks.org
Web Code: ccn-0014

Build Science Skills L2

Using Graphs and Tables Use Figure 21 to help students review how to read line graphs. Point out the labels on the horizontal and vertical axes. Ask, **What is the volume of 3 g of water?** *(3 cm^3)* **What is the mass of 9 cm^3 of water?** *(9 g)* **What do you think the mass of 15 cm^3 of water would be? Explain your answer.** *(15 g. The mass of water is directly proportional to the volume.)*
Logical, Visual

Use Visuals L1

Figure 22 Point out that there are seven points on the line graph for which there is known data. Ask, **At a flow rate of 3.5 gallons per minute, how long would it take to fill a 1-gallon pot with water?** *(About 0.25 min)* **Why is a line graph more useful than a data table for making inferences or estimates like this?** *(With a line graph, you can choose a value on one axis, such as 3.5 gallons per minute, and use the line to read the corresponding value, such as 0.25 min, on the other axis. With a data table, you are limited to values in the table.)*
Visual

Go Online NSTA SCILINKS

Download a worksheet on graphing for students to complete, and find additional teacher support from NSTA SciLinks.

Customize for English Language Learners

Build a Science Glossary
Encourage English language learners to make a science glossary as they read the section. Suggest that they start with the vocabulary terms and then add any other new words they encounter. Encourage students to write brief definitions of each term or draw an illustration that helps them understand the term.

Answer to . . .

Figure 21 *The slope of the graph shown represents density, or mass per unit volume.*

Data Analysis

Faster Than Speeding Data **L2**

Answers

1. The greater the modem speed is, the shorter the upload time.

Data Transfer Rate vs. Modem Speed

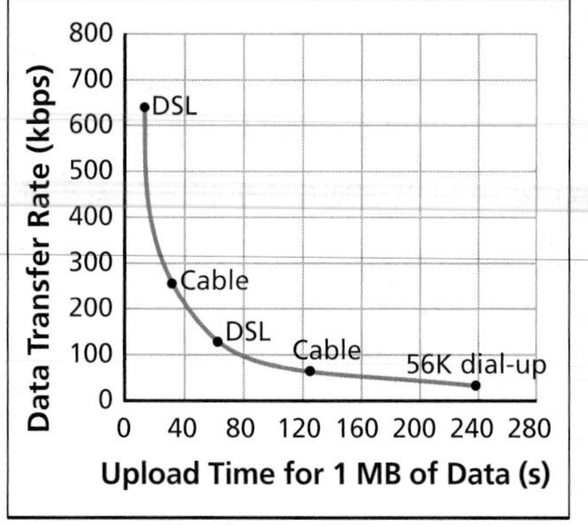
Data Transfer Rate (kbps)
800
700
600
500
400
300
200
100
0
DSL
Cable
DSL
Cable
56K dial-up
0 40 80 120 160 200 240 280
Upload Time for 1 MB of Data (s)

2. Doubling the data transfer rate would halve the upload time.

For Extra Help **L1**

Explain that modem speeds are similar to speed measurements for vehicles. For example, a car moving at 50 km/h will travel 50 km in one hour. The speed of the modems is measured in kilobits per second. If students need help constructing a line graph, refer them to the **Math Skills** in the **Skills and Reference Handbook** at the end of the student text. **Logical**

Address Misconceptions **L2**

Some students may mistakenly think that graphs validate data. Point out to students that graphs are merely a method of presenting data. If necessary, work with students to graph a set of inaccurate data. For example, estimate the average daily temperatures for the past week, double them, and graph the results. Tell students that this graph is inaccurate because it is based on flawed data. Tell students that one way to validate data is to make multiple measurements. **Logical**

Use Visuals **L1**

Figure 23 Ask, **On the bar graph, which pairs of cities have similar annual precipitation?** *(Buffalo and Chicago; San Diego and Tucson)* **Visual**

Data Analysis

Faster Than Speeding Data

A modem is a device used to send and receive data. For example, if you upload an image to a Web site, the modem in your computer converts the data of the image into a different format. The converted data are then sent through a telephone line or cable TV line. The smallest unit of data that can be read by a computer is a binary digit, or "bit." A bit is either a 0 or a 1. Computers process bits in larger units called bytes. A byte is a group of eight bits.

The table shows the data transfer rates for modems used in home computers. Data transfer rates are often measured in kilobits per second, or kbps. The time required to upload a 1-megabyte (MB) file is given for each rate listed.

Modem Speeds

Type of Modem	Data Transfer Rate (kbps)	Upload Time for 1 MB (s)
56K dial-up	33.6	238
Cable	64	125
DSL	128	63
Cable	256	31
DSL	640	13

1. **Using Graphs** Use the data in the table to create a line graph. Describe the relationship between data transfer rate and upload time.
2. **Inferring** How would doubling the data transfer rate affect the upload time?

Bar Graphs A bar graph is often used to compare a set of measurements, amounts, or changes. Figure 23 is a bar graph of the data from Figure 20. The bar graph makes it easy to see how the data for one city compare with the data for another.

Circle Graphs If you think of a pie cut into pieces, you have a mental model of a circle graph. A circle graph is a divided circle that shows how a part or share of something relates to the whole. Figure 24 is a circle graph that describes the composition of Earth's crust. The entire circle represents the mass of Earth's crust. Each "slice" of the circle represents a percentage of that mass corresponding to a specific substance.

Average Annual Precipitation for Selected U.S. Cities

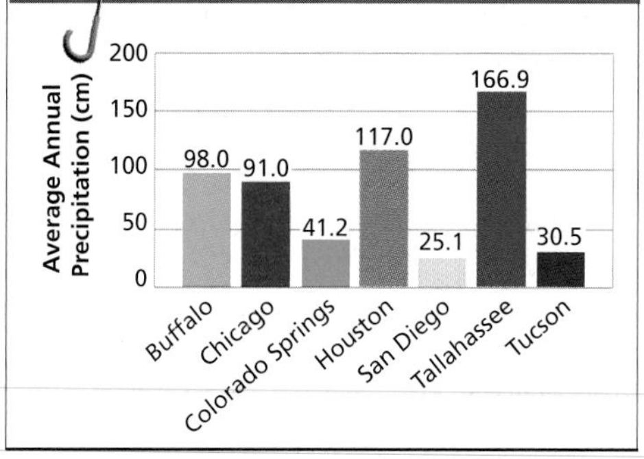
Average Annual Precipitation (cm)
200
150
100
50
0
98.0
91.0
41.2
117.0
25.1
166.9
30.5
Buffalo
Chicago
Colorado Springs
Houston
San Diego
Tallahassee
Tucson

Figure 23 A bar graph is useful for comparing several measurements.

Composition of Earth's Crust

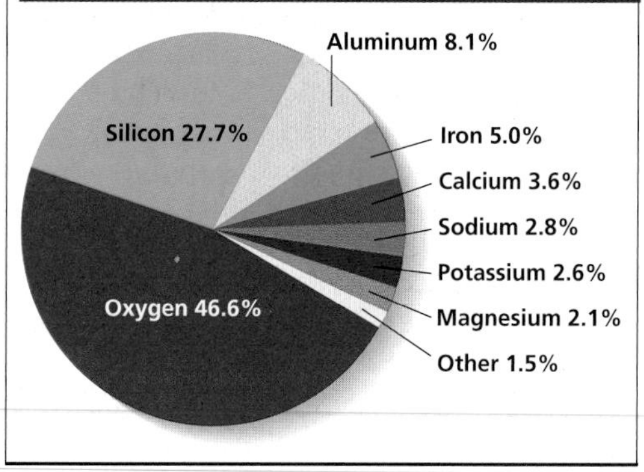
Aluminum 8.1%
Silicon 27.7%
Iron 5.0%
Calcium 3.6%
Sodium 2.8%
Potassium 2.6%
Oxygen 46.6%
Magnesium 2.1%
Other 1.5%

Figure 24 A circle graph is useful for showing how a part of something relates to the whole.

Facts and Figures

Scientific Journals Thousands of scientific journals are published around the world. Some of them include articles on a broad range of topics, while others are narrowly focused. The decision that scientists make about where to publish their research depends on the nature of their results. Publishing in a well-known journal makes the research available to scientists in many different areas. Publishing in a narrowly focused journal means that the information will reach a smaller group of scientists. However, this small group includes scientists who are likely to need the information for their own research. Because it is not possible for scientists to read all the journals—or even all the journals in a single field—they must carefully choose the journals they read and the journals in which they publish their research.

CITRONELLA:

Figure 25 At a science fair, students communicate what knowledge they have gained by using scientific methods.

Communicating Data

A crucial part of any scientific investigation is reporting the results. **Scientists can communicate results by writing in scientific journals or speaking at conferences.** Scientists also exchange information through conversations, e-mails, and Web sites. Young scientists often present their research at science fairs like the one in Figure 25.

Different scientists may interpret the same data differently. This important notion is the basis for peer review, a process in which scientists examine other scientists' work. Not only do scientists share research with their peers, but they also invite feedback from those peers. Peer review encourages comments, suggestions, questions, and criticism from other scientists. Peer review can also help determine if data were reported accurately and honestly. Based on their peers' responses, the scientists who submitted their work for review can then reevaluate how to best interpret their data.

Section 1.4 Assessment

Reviewing Concepts

1. How do scientists organize data?
2. How can scientists communicate experimental results?
3. What does a given point represent on a line graph?
4. The density of copper is 8.92 g/cm^3. If you plotted the mass of copper in grams versus the volume in cubic centimeters, what would the slope of the line be?

Critical Thinking

5. **Comparing and Contrasting** When would you choose a line graph to present data? When would you choose a bar graph?
6. **Using Tables and Graphs** Count the number of students in your class with blue eyes, brown eyes, and green eyes. Display these data in a table and bar graph.

Connecting Concepts

Scientific Methods Reread the description of scientific methods in Section 1.2. Then write a paragraph explaining which steps in a scientific method might require data to be organized. (*Hint:* You might use information diagrammed in Figure 7.)

Communicating Data

Integrate Language Arts L2

Communicating ideas and results is an important part of science. From published papers to an e-mail exchange between scientists, scientific writing must be clear and concise. Ask students to write one paragraph about the importance of written communication in science. Tell them to revise and rewrite their paragraph as needed.
Verbal, Portfolio

3 ASSESS

Evaluate Understanding L2

Show students a graph or chart from a newspaper or similar source. Ask students to create a data table that represents the data on the graph or chart.

Reteach L1

Use Figures 21 and 22 to compare the meanings of *direct proportion* and *inverse proportion.*

Connecting Concepts

Possible answer: Scientific methods often require data to be organized and presented. For example, when making observations, you might want to organize them into a table. When testing a hypothesis, you might conduct an experiment that produces numerical data; such data must be recorded and organized in order to be useful. By presenting experimental data in a graph, you can analyze your measurements for trends that may help in evaluating your hypothesis.

Interactive Textbook If your class subscribes to the Interactive Textbook, use it to review key concepts in Section 1.4.

Section 1.4 Assessment

1. Scientists can organize their data by using tables and graphs.
2. Scientists can communicate results by writing in scientific journals and speaking at conferences.
3. A given point on a line graph generally represents two measurements corresponding to two related variables, one plotted on the horizontal axis and the other plotted on the vertical axis.
4. The slope would be 1.
5. A line graph is useful for showing how one variable changes with respect to another (for example, how one's distance changes with respect to time). A bar graph is useful for comparing a set of measurements (for example, how the average temperatures of various U.S. cities compare).
6. Students' graphs should show three bars representing three different groups of classmates (blue-eyed, brown-eyed, and green-eyed).

Consumer Lab

Determining the Thickness of Aluminum Foil **L2**

Objective
After completing this activity, students will be able to
- perform conversions and calculations with metric units.
- compare the precision of measurements.

Skills Focus **Measuring, Using Graphs, Calculating**

Prep Time 10 minutes

Class Time 30 minutes

Safety Caution students to be careful with sharp instruments.

Teaching Tips
- Refer to Appendix B to show students how to use a balance.
- Aluminum foil is usually made of 8111 alloy aluminum, which is 98.5% aluminum, with small amounts of iron and silicon. Pure aluminum has a density of 2.70 g/cm^3.
- In Step 5, remind students that there are 10 mm per cm. Therefore, there are 1000 mm^3 per cm^3. As a result, the density of aluminum is 0.00271 g/mm^3.

Expected Outcome Precision increases with increased size of the foil square, but the estimate of thickness does not tend to increase or decrease consistently as a result.

Sample Data The average thickness of standard aluminum foil is 0.01625 mm. Manufacturers tolerate 10% variation in this thickness.

Length (mm)	Area (mm^2)	Mass (g)	Volume (mm^3)	Thickness (mm)
50.0	2500	0.10	36.9	0.015
100.0	10,000	0.40	148	0.015
200.0	40,000	1.60	590	0.0148

Consumer Lab

Determining the Thickness of Aluminum Foil

Many products such as aluminum foil are too thin to measure easily. However, it is important for manufacturers to know how thick they are. They wouldn't be useful if they were made too thick or too thin. In this lab, you will use the same method that manufacturers use to determine the thickness of aluminum foil.

Problem
How can you determine the thickness of aluminum foil?

Materials
- metric ruler
- aluminum foil
- scissors
- balance
- graph paper

Skills
Measuring, Calculating, Using Graphs

Data Table

Length (mm)	Area (mm^2)	Mass (g)	Volume (mm^3)	Thickness (mm)

Density of Alumnium = ________ g/mm^3

Procedure

1. On a separate sheet of paper, make a copy of the data table shown. Include the information below the data table.
2. Cut out three squares of aluminum foil with sides of the following lengths: 50 mm, 100 mm, and 200 mm.
3. To determine the area of the 50-mm foil square, measure the length of one of its sides and then square it. Record the length and area in your data table.

4. Place the foil square on the balance to determine its mass. Record the mass of the foil square in your data table.
5. You will need the density of aluminum foil to calculate the volume of the foil square from its mass. The density of aluminum foil is 2.71 g/cm^3. Convert cm^3 to mm^3 and record the density of aluminum foil (in g/mm^3) on the line provided below your data table.
6. To determine the volume of the foil square, divide its mass by its density in g/mm^3. Record the volume in your data table.
7. To determine the thickness of the foil square, divide its volume by its area. Record this thickness in your data table.
8. Repeat Steps 3 through 7 using the 100-mm foil square.
9. Repeat Steps 3 through 7 using the 200-mm foil square.
10. Construct a graph of your data. Plot length on the horizontal axis and thickness on the vertical axis. Draw a straight line connecting all three points.

Analyze and Conclude

1. **Measuring** How many significant figures were there in your measurement of the length of each square of aluminum foil?
2. **Using Graphs** What effect, if any, did the length of the square have on your estimate of the thickness of the foil?
3. **Comparing** Which estimate of thickness was most precise? Explain your answer.
4. **Controlling Variables** What factors limited the precision of your measurements?

Go Further Aluminum is composed of small particles. Each particle has a diameter of 2.86×10^{-10} m. Calculate how many particles make up the thickness of the foil. Then, calculate the number of particles in the 50-mm square. Finally, determine the mass of one particle.

Go Online PHSchool.com

For: Data sharing
Visit: PHSchool.com
Web Code: ccd-0010

Analyze and Conclude

1. There were three significant figures for the 50-mm square and four for the 100- and 200-mm squares.
2. The length of the square had no effect on the estimated thickness of the foil.
3. The thickness calculated for the 200-mm square is the most precise because it has the most significant figures (three). The precision of a calculated answer is limited by the least precise measurement used in the calculation. For the 200-mm square, the least precise measurement (mass) has three significant figures. For the 50- and 100-mm squares, the least precise measurement (mass) has only two significant figures.
4. Precision was limited by the spacing of the smallest markings on the ruler, and the balance.
Logical

Go Further

Assuming that the particles (atoms) are spheres packed closely together so they are touching and arranged in orderly rows, the thickness of the foil can be expressed as a number of particles by converting the calculated thickness from units of mm to m and dividing by the diameter of a particle. This method leads to an estimated thickness of approximately 56,800 atoms for standard aluminum foil. The number of atoms in the foil can be found by dividing the volume of the foil by the volume of an atom. The mass of an aluminum atom (4.48×10^{-23} g) is calculated by dividing the mass of the foil by the number of atoms in the foil.
Logical

Go Online PHSchool.com

Students should see that increasing the size of the foil sample increases the precision, but not the value of the thickness measurement. Students' results will depend on their own data and the data on the site.

Chapter 1

Study Guide

Study Tip

Gather Materials
Tell students to gather the materials they will need before they begin to study. Explain that students should also have available a few sheets of blank paper. As students study, they can write or sketch key ideas. Tell students that putting key ideas on paper can help them understand and remember the ideas later.

Thinking Visually

a. A fundamental unit of measurement
b. Meter
c. A unit of measurement that is formed by combining base units
d. Cubic meter (m^3)

Assessment

Interactive Textbook If your class subscribes to the Interactive Textbook, your students can go online to access an interactive version of the Student Edition and a self-test.

Reviewing Content

1. c **2.** d **3.** b
4. b **5.** c **6.** b
7. c **8.** b **9.** c
10. c

Understanding Concepts

11. Example: The study of Mars falls under the branch of space science. However, studying Mars might also involve analyzing the chemistry of substances found on Mars, which falls under physical science. If scientists search for evidence of life on Mars, then their studies might also fall under life science.
12. The goal of any scientific method is to solve a problem or to better understand an observed event.
13. Controlled experiments are useful in that they can show how one variable (the responding variable) changes with respect to another variable (the manipulated variable), while the remaining variables are controlled.
14. You might modify your hypothesis or formulate a new hypothesis based on your experimental results.

CHAPTER 1

Study Guide

1.1 What is Science?

Key Concepts
- Science begins with curiosity and often ends with discovery.
- Science and technology are interdependent. Advances in one lead to advances in the other.
- Natural science is generally divided into three branches: physical science, Earth and space science, and life science.

Vocabulary
science, *p. 3*
technology, *p. 3*
chemistry, *p. 4*
physics, *p. 4*
geology, *p. 4*
astronomy, *p. 4*
biology, *p. 4*

1.2 Using a Scientific Approach

Key Concepts
- The goal of a scientific method is to solve a problem or to better understand an observed event.
- A scientific law describes an observed pattern in nature without attempting to explain it. The explanation of such a pattern is provided by a scientific theory.
- Scientific models make it easier to understand things that might be too difficult to observe directly.

Vocabulary
scientific method, *p. 7*
observation, *p. 8*
hypothesis, *p. 8*
manipulated variable, *p. 8*
responding variable, *p. 8*
controlled experiment, *p. 8*
scientific theory, *p. 9*
scientific law, *p. 9*
model, *p. 10*

1.3 Measurement

Key Concepts
- Scientific notation makes very large or very small numbers easier to work with.
- Scientists use a set of measuring units called SI.
- The precision of a calculation is limited by the least precise measurement used in the calculation.

Vocabulary
scientific notation, *p. 14*
length, *p. 16*
mass, *p. 16*
volume, *p. 16*
density, *p. 17*
conversion factor, *p. 18*
precision, *p. 19*
significant figures, *p. 19*
accuracy, *p. 19*
thermometer, *p. 20*

1.4 Presenting Scientific Data

Key Concepts
- Scientists can organize their data by using data tables and graphs.
- Scientists can communicate results by writing in journals or speaking at conferences.

Vocabulary
slope, *p. 23*
direct proportion, *p. 23*
inverse proportion, *p. 23*

Thinking Visually

Using Tables Use information from the chapter to complete the table below.

Type of Unit	Description	Example
Base	a. ___?___	b. ___?___
Derived	c. ___?___	d. ___?___

Chapter Resources

Print
- ***Chapter and Unit Tests,*** Chapter 1 Test A and Test B
- ***Test Prep Resources,*** Chapter 1

Technology
- ***Computer Test Bank,*** Chapter Test 1
- ***Interactive Textbook,*** Chapter 1
- ***Go Online,*** PHSchool.com, Chapter 1

CHAPTER 1

Assessment

Interactive textbook with assessment at PHSchool.com iText

Reviewing Content

Choose the letter that best answers the question or completes the statement.

1. The application of knowledge to solve practical problems is known as
   a. science. b. curiosity.
   c. technology. d. experimentation.

2. Which is not a branch of natural science?
   a. physical science b. life science
   c. Earth science d. social science

3. What is the purpose of an experiment?
   a. to communicate data
   b. to test a hypothesis
   c. to prove a scientific law
   d. none of the above

4. A representation of an object or event is called
   a. a scientific law. b. a model.
   c. a hypothesis. d. a variable.

5. Which value is equivalent to 5×10^6?
   a. five thousand b. fifty thousand
   c. five million d. fifty million

6. What is the SI base unit of mass?
   a. gram b. kilogram
   c. milligram d. pound

7. An electric generator produces 10 megawatts. This amount is equivalent to
   a. 10,000 watts. b. 1,000,000 watts.
   c. 10,000,000 watts. d. 0.010 watt.

8. Which of the following is a ratio of equivalent measurements that is used to convert a quantity expressed in one unit to another unit?
   a. slope b. conversion factor
   c. derived unit d. density

9. When the ratio of two variables is constant, their relationship can be described as
   a. inversely proportional.
   b. interdependent.
   c. directly proportional.
   d. parallel.

10. Which of the following would best suit data that describe how a part relates to the whole?
    a. line graph b. bar graph
    c. circle graph d. scientific notation

Understanding Concepts

11. Give an example of a case where the branches of natural science appear to overlap.

12. What is the goal of a scientific method?

13. How are controlled experiments useful?

14. Suppose you perform an experiment, and the resulting data do not support your hypothesis. What is the next step you might take?

15. What are some safety precautions that you should follow when working in the laboratory?

16. What is scientific notation?

17. What are the SI base units for length and temperature?

18. How do derived units differ from base units?

19. How is the precision of a calculated result related to the precision of the measurements used in the calculation?

20. How can you convert a temperature expressed in degrees Celsius to kelvins?

21. Which of the following graphs describes a direct proportion?

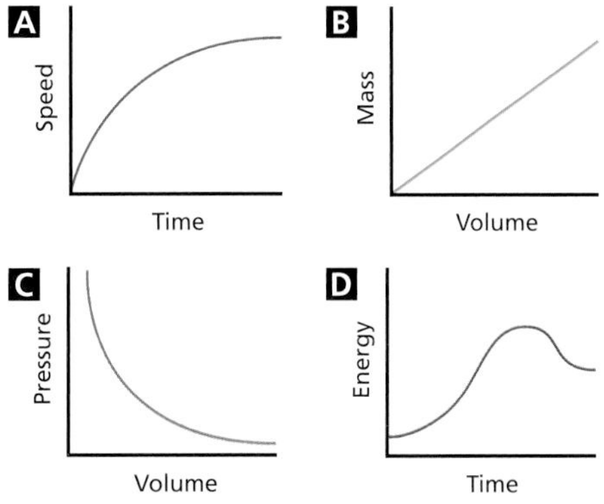

A
Speed
Time
B
Mass
Volume
C
Pressure
Volume
D
Energy
Time

22. Why is it important for scientists to communicate their results?

Assessment (continued)

15. Some safety precautions you should follow when working in the laboratory include reading through all the steps of any activity, making sure you understand the entire procedure, following directions exactly, and asking your teacher if you're not sure about how to proceed.
16. Scientific notation is a way of expressing a value as the product of a number between 1 and 10 and a power of 10.
17. The SI base unit for length is the meter. The SI base unit for temperature is the kelvin.
18. Derived units are combinations of base units. A base unit is a fundamental unit of measurement.
19. The precision of a calculated answer is limited by the precision of the measurements used in the calculation. For example, if the least precise measurement in a calculation has three significant figures, then the calculated answer can have at most three significant figures.
20. To convert from degrees Celsius to kelvins, you can use the following formula: K = °C + 273
21. B
22. It is important for scientists to communicate their results so that they can share the knowledge they have gained with others, and also get feedback from other scientists.

Homework Guide

Section	Questions
1.1	1–2, 11, 33
1.2	3–4, 12–15, 23–24, 26, 31–32
1.3	5–7, 16–19, 25, 28, 30
1.4	8–10, 20–22, 27, 29

Critical Thinking

23. Some students may hypothesize that objects of greater mass fall to the ground faster than objects of lesser mass. Others may hypothesize that mass does not affect the rate at which objects fall.
24. In designing their experiments, students might suggest dropping a heavy object and a light object from the same height and measuring how long each takes to fall to the ground. (A more qualitative design might suggest releasing both objects simultaneously and observing if one reaches the ground before the other, without taking any measurements.) Height is controlled. The manipulated variable is the mass of the object. The responding variable is time.
25. 13.5 km
26. Everything drawn on a map represents a thing or place that is scaled down. For example, solid lines on the map might represent streets and highways; a green polygon on the map might represent a park; a gray square on the map might represent a building.
If you plan a trip to an unfamiliar place, a map can help you by showing you how the streets are oriented. If a road forks on the map, you will see it fork as you travel on the road. If you navigate two rights and then a left on the map, you should be able to match that route to the environment you travel in.
27. Average speed = 80 km/h

Driving Distance vs. Time

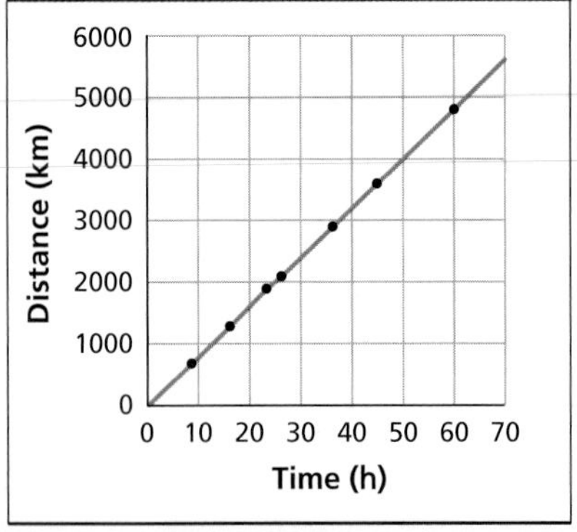

6000
5000
4000
3000
2000
1000
0
Distance (km)
0 10 20 30 40 50 60 70
Time (h)

Math Skills

28. 16°C; 289 K
29. The mass of the pennies is directly proportional to the number of pennies. Measuring the mass of one penny yields a ratio (i.e., grams per penny) that is constant. You can then measure the mass of all the pennies. Dividing the total mass by the mass of one penny yields the total number of pennies.
30. Between 6×10^{12} and 1.2×10^{13} stars

CHAPTER 1

Assessment *(continued)*

Critical Thinking

23. **Formulating Hypotheses** Suppose you want to know if objects with different masses fall to the ground at different rates. State a hypothesis about falling objects.

24. **Designing Experiments** Explain how you can test the hypothesis in Question 23. What will be the manipulated variable in your experiment? What will be the responding variable?

25. **Calculating** A triathlete enters a race in which he swims 500 meters, runs 3000 meters, and cycles 10.0 kilometers. What is the total distance of the race in kilometers?

26. **Using Models** Explain how a map of your town is an example of a model. How does this model help you plan a trip to an unfamiliar place?

27. **Using Graphs** Use the data in the table below to create a line graph. Plot distance on the vertical axis. Plot driving time on the horizontal axis. Calculate the slope of the line. If speed is the ratio of distance to time, what is the average driving speed of the trip?

Driving Distance and Time

City	Distance From Start (km)	Driving Time From Start (h)
New York City, N.Y.	750	9.5
Cleveland, Ohio	1300	16.25
Chicago, Ill.	1900	23.25
Omaha, Nebr.	2100	26.25
Cheyenne, Wyo.	2900	36.25
Salt Lake City, Utah	3600	45
San Francisco, Calif.	4800	60

Math Skills

28. **Calculating** If a thermometer outside your classroom indicates a temperature of 61 degrees Fahrenheit, what is the temperature in degrees Celsius? In kelvins?

29. **Problem Solving** Suppose you have a large coffee can full of pennies. How can you estimate how much money the can contains without counting all the coins? (*Hint:* What is the relationship between the mass of pennies and the number of pennies?)

30. **Calculating** The Milky Way galaxy contains between 200 and 400 billion stars. Estimate the number of stars in a cluster of 30 galaxies similar in size to the Milky Way. Your answer should consist of a low estimate and a high estimate, both expressed in scientific notation.

Concepts in Action

31. **Designing Experiments** A zookeeper notices that elephants become restless shortly before an earthquake. The zookeeper forms a hypothesis that, just before an earthquake occurs, an elephant detects a sound that humans are unable to hear. How could this hypothesis be tested?

32. **Making Judgments** You see an advertisement on television for an over-the-counter medication that has been "scientifically proven to work." How could you find out if this claim is true?

33. **Writing in Science** Write a paragraph describing how advances in technology have affected your life. (*Hint:* The first sentence should state the paragraph's main idea.)

Performance-Based Assessment

Designing Experiments Grocery stores carry many brands of household detergents. Design an experiment to compare a more expensive brand of detergent with a less expensive one. Is one brand better for some purposes than the other?

Go Online PHSchool.com
For: Self-grading assessment
Visit: PHSchool.com
Web Code: cca-0015

Concepts in Action

31. The zookeeper could test his hypothesis by installing an instrument that can detect sounds that are too low or too high in frequency for humans to hear. Sounds detected by the instrument could then be compared to the elephant's behavior and the timing of earthquakes.
32. You could test the claim by finding out what has been reported or written about the medication advertised. You could do an Internet search, query the manufacturer, or query a doctor.
33. Students may describe how certain advances in technology have made their lives more convenient. For example, advances in computer technology (such as faster processors and modems) have made it easier for people to communicate, access information, study, shop, and entertain.

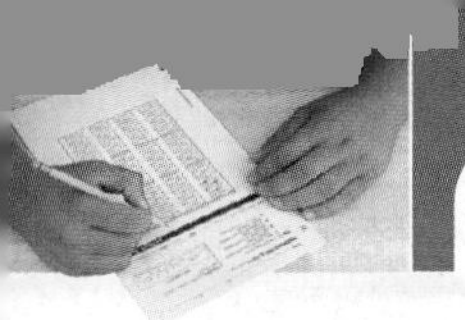

Standardized Test Prep

Test-Taking Tip

Calculating

Checking units is a very important part of problem solving. Keep these tips in mind when solving problems involving unit conversions:

- A conversion factor is a ratio of equivalent measurements.
- Write horizontal fractions to help keep track of conversion factors. For example, write $\frac{32\ g}{cm^3}$ as opposed to 32 g/cm^3.
- Line up conversion factors so that the unit you are converting cancels.
- If you have to square or cube a unit, make sure you square or cube the entire conversion factor.
- Make a reality check of your answer. If the units are wrong, your calculations are probably wrong. Also, verify that the numerical answer is reasonable.

Practice using these tips in Questions 2 and 4.

Choose the letter that best answers the question or completes the statement.

1. In a controlled experiment,
(A) there are multiple responding variables.
(B) the responding variable is kept constant.
(C) the manipulated variable is kept constant.
(D) the responding variable is deliberately changed.
(E) only one variable at a time is deliberately changed.

2. The speed of an object indicates how far it travels in a given amount of time. If an electron travels 2.42×10^8 meters in 2.00 seconds, what is the speed of this electron in cm/s?
(A) 1.21×10^8 cm/s
(B) 4.84×10^8 cm/s
(C) 1.21×10^{10} cm/s
(D) 2.42×10^{10} cm/s
(E) 4.84×10^{10} cm/s

3. A doctor measures the temperature of a patient to be 101°F. What is this temperature in kelvins?
(A) 38.3 K (B) 73.8 K
(C) 214 K (D) 311 K
(E) 346 K

4. The density of seawater is 1.024×10^3 kg/m^3. What is the density of seawater in g/cm^3?
(A) 102.4 g/cm^3
(B) 1.024×10^{-6} g/cm^3
(C) 1.024 g/cm^3
(D) 3.072×10^3 g/cm^3
(E) 1.024×10^9 g/cm^3

5. A student conducts an experiment by dropping a basketball and a box of cereal of the same weight from the top of a building. The student measures the time it takes for each object to strike the ground. What was the student's hypothesis?

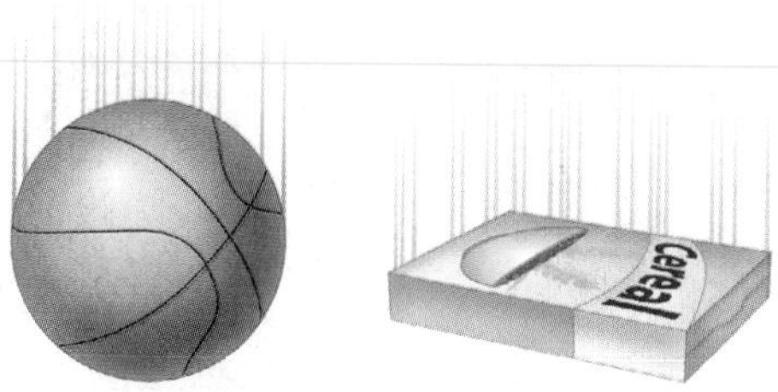
Cereal

(A) A basketball weighs more than cereal.
(B) Curved objects travel through the air faster than flat objects.
(C) Heavier objects travel through the air faster than lighter objects.
(D) Gravity pulls on objects of the same weight with the same force.
(E) Heavier objects strike the ground with a greater force than lighter objects.

6. If two variables are directly proportional, then
(A) an increase in one variable causes a decrease in the other variable.
(B) the product of the two variables is constant.
(C) the ratio of the two variables is constant.
(D) neither variable is the controlled variable.
(E) both variables are constant.

Standardized Test Prep

1. E **2.** C **3.** D
4. C **5.** B **6.** C

Performance-Based Assessment

Students may think of different ways to evaluate/measure the responding variable (how effectively a detergent cleans) in their experiments. Another important aspect of the experimental design is how to make the stains a controlled variable, for in order for a comparison of two cleaning agents to be exact, they must be tested on uniformly stained surfaces.

Go Online
PHSchool.com

Your students can independently test their knowledge of the chapter and print out their test results for your files.

CHEMISTRY

Interactive Textbook

The Interactive Textbook, found both online and on CD-ROM, includes the following materials.

Activities and Labs

Worksheets for each activity and lab are available as PDF files with clickable safety symbols.

Colorful Visuals

All art and relevant photographs from the Student Edition can be accessed in the Interactive Textbook.

Self Assessment

Provides additional assessment opportunities and questions:

- Interactive Reading Checkpoint questions
- Interactive Figure caption questions
- Chapter Pretests with hints
- Printable Chapter Assessments
- Standardized Test Prep

My Notes

Students can enter answers for questions or make notes about what they are learning.

References

Provides a drop-down menu of resources:

- Skills and Reference Handbook
- Glossary

Careers

Information on science careers is available through the Career page on www.PHSchool.com.

CHEMISTRY UNIT PREVIEW

Chemistry

As I worked on the chemistry chapters of this book, I was reminded of three good reasons why you should study chemistry in high school.

First, learning chemistry will increase your overall understanding of science. You'll find out how scientists use scientific methods to expand the frontiers of knowledge. In the lab, you will have an opportunity to experience these same methods for yourself.

Second, in today's world, it's useful to know chemistry. In fact, you certainly know some chemistry already. You have heard of the substances water, oxygen, and sugar. These are all chemicals. You may know a little bit about atoms and molecules. You'll learn much more about all of these topics when you study chemistry.

Third, chemistry will help you appreciate important issues in the world around you. You'll learn about such issues as water pollution, the use of fossil fuels, and the impact of forest fires. As you take the time to appreciate chemistry and its applications, I hope you'll enjoy the subject as much as I do.

David V. Frank

Fireworks Display in Sydney, Australia ▶
When fireworks explode, they produce colorful displays of light.

32

Go Online PHSchool.com

For students, the PHSchool.com Web site contains interactive data-sharing labs, interactive self-assessments, and science-related links. The PHSchool.com Web site also provides teachers with curriculum support, reference links, a way to create state-specific lesson plans, and instructions on how to create a Web page.

Go Online NSTA SCILINKS

NSTA SciLinks provides student worksheets for specific topics with additional teacher support.

Chemistry 33

Discovery Channel School — Video Field Trip

Use the following videos to help students understand the concepts in each chapter.

Chapter 1 Science Skills
Cracking the Case
Describes how forensic scientists analyze evidence left at the scene of a crime.

Chapter 2 Properties of Matter
Fresh-Squeezed Water
Shows and discusses equipment that is used to distill seawater into fresh water.

Chapter 3 States of Matter
Up, Up, and Away
Features hot-air balloons and discusses how they ascend and descend.

Chapter 4 Atomic Structure
Go For Gold
Discusses how some properties of gold are related to the structure of gold and how the surface of gold can be viewed with an electron microscope.

Chapter 5 The Periodic Table
You Are What You Eat
Discusses what scientists can learn from studying mummies, including finding clues to what they ate.

Chapter 6 Chemical Bonds
Good Conduct
Shows how silicon is refined and processed into chips and discusses how doping silicon increases its conductivity.

Chapter 7 Chemical Reactions
Taming the Flames
Shows how firefighters use a combination of chemistry and courage to put out wildfires.

Chapter 8 Solutions, Acids, and Bases
Suspended in Blood
Explains how the red blood cells, white blood cells, and platelets in your blood play a crucial role in keeping your body healthy.

Chapter 9 Carbon Chemistry
Clean Energy
Provides a closer look at fuel cells, a clean-energy technology that may power the cars of the future.

Chapter 10 Nuclear Chemistry
Nuclear Medicine
Explains how nuclear radiation and radioisotopes are used in the detection and treatment of many cancers.

Go Online — SCIENCE NEWS®

Students can find current information about specific discoveries in science from *Science News.*

Go Online — PLANETDIARY

Planet Diary contains current geological, astronomical, meteorological, and environmental news from around the world. Additional information and activities are included in the Phenomena Backgrounders.

Careers in Chemistry

The educational requirements for the chemistry-related careers on these two pages range from a high-school diploma to a master's degree.

Toxicologist

Connection to Chapter 5
Characteristics Good at written and oral communications, detail-oriented, computer literate
Preparation Courses in biology, human anatomy and physiology, environmental science
Employers Government agencies (USFDA and EPA), pharmaceutical companies, universities

Forensic Chemist

Connection to Chapter 2
Characteristics Curious, analytical, accurate record keeper, impartial, detail-oriented, capable of preparing evidence for presentation in court as well as testifying as an expert witness
Preparation Courses in biology, physics, English composition, metallurgy. Some states require several years of forensic laboratory experience.
Employers Local, state, and federal governments, universities, forensic laboratories, hospitals

Food Science Technician

Connection to Chapter 4
Characteristics Good at written and oral communications, analytical, able to work independently or as part of a team, computer literate
Preparation Courses in chemistry, biochemistry, microbiology, food engineering, basic business principles, statistics
Employers United States Food and Drug Administration (FDA), food processing industry, universities

Careers in Chemistry

What do the people on these pages have in common? They all use chemistry on the job. From toxicologists to firefighters, there are many exciting chemistry careers to choose from.

Toxicologist
Toxicologists determine the effects natural and synthetic chemicals may have on people, other organisms, and the environment. Toxicologists conduct experiments to find out whether certain chemicals are dangerous or safe to use. They also determine how much of a given chemical could be harmful.
Educational requirements Four-year bachelor of science degree, majoring in chemistry

Food Science Technician
Food science technicians help to ensure that the food you eat is healthful, safe, and flavorful. They use their knowledge of chemistry to develop new or better ways of preserving, processing, packaging, and storing foods. Some food service technicians analyze food content to determine levels of vitamins, fat, carbohydrates, or protein.
Educational requirements
Four-year college degree, majoring in chemistry

Forensic Chemist
Forensic chemists help law enforcement officials solve crimes. At a crime scene, a forensic chemist carefully gathers all the physical evidence and brings it back to the laboratory for analysis and identification. Physical evidence may include fibers, paints, glass, and stains.
Educational requirements
Master's degree in chemistry

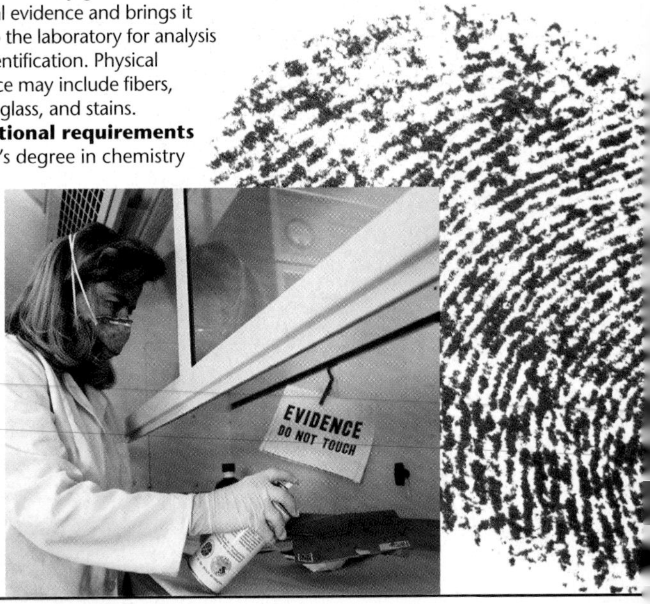
EVIDENCE
DO NOT TOUCH

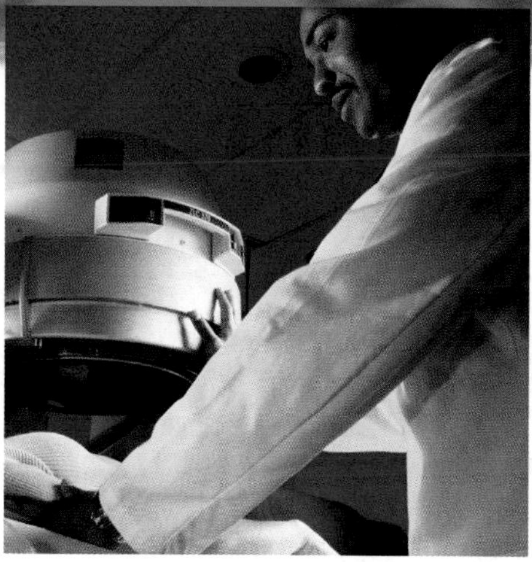

Nuclear Medicine Technologist
Nuclear medicine technologists apply their knowledge of nuclear chemistry to help diagnose diseases and disorders. They prepare and administer radioactive substances and use radiation detection devices to trace these substances in the body. Nuclear medicine technologists work directly with patients and closely with nuclear medicine physicians.
Educational requirements Two-year community or junior college degree, or a one-year certificate in nuclear medicine technology

Firefighter
Firefighters are highly trained professionals who respond to fires, hazardous chemical spills, and medical emergencies. When responding to a fire or spill, firefighters have to know what effects different chemicals have in different situations.
Educational requirements
High-school diploma

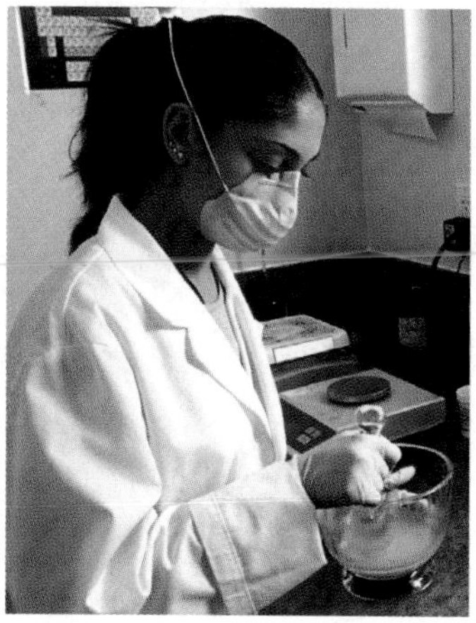

Pharmacist
A pharmacist dispenses drugs prescribed by physicians and dentists and gives information to patients about the drugs and their uses. Pharmacists understand the uses, effects, and composition of drugs, including their chemical properties and biological side effects.
Educational requirements Two years of college, four-year college of pharmacy program, internship, and passage of a state board examination

Go Online PHSchool.com
For: Career links
Visit: PHSchool.com
Web Code: ccb-1000

Nuclear Medicine Technologist

Connection to Chapter 10
Characteristics Good at written and oral communications, computer literate
Preparation Courses in human anatomy and physiology, physics, mathematics, medical technology, medical ethics, CPR certification, equipment certification
Employers Medical centers and hospitals, independent imaging centers, research centers

Firefighter

Connection to Chapter 7
Characteristics Demonstrate physical dexterity and strength, be mentally alert and a team player
Preparation 18–31 years of age, have corrected 20/20 vision, score well on the examination given by local governments. Many fire departments now require an Emergency Medical Technician (EMT) certificate as a condition of employment.
Employers Local, state, and federal governments

Pharmacist

Connection to Chapter 8
Characteristics Accurate record keeper, good at written and oral communications, conscientious, detail-oriented, desire to help others
Preparation Courses in mathematics, biology, and physics
Employers Hospitals and medical centers, independent pharmacies, drug companies, universities

Go Online PHSchool.com

Career Teaching Strategy
You can have students find out more about chemistry-related careers by looking for information in the library or on the Internet. Students can then construct a table that lists the position, describes the nature of the work, educational and training requirements, employment outlook, working conditions, and other necessary information.

CHAPTER 2

Planning Guide

Use these planning tools

Easy Planner
Teacher Express

SECTION OBJECTIVES	STANDARDS NATIONAL (See p. T18.)	STANDARDS STATE	ACTIVITIES and LABS
2.1 Classifying Matter, pp. 38–44 1 block or 2 periods **2.1.1 Classify** pure substances as elements or compounds. **2.1.2 Describe** the characteristics of an element and the symbols used to identify elements. **2.1.3 Describe** the characteristics of a compound. **2.1.4 Distinguish** pure substances from mixtures. **2.1.5 Classify** mixtures as heterogeneous or homogeneous. **2.1.6 Classify** mixtures as solutions, suspensions, or colloids.	A-1, A-2, G-1, G-2, G-3		**SE** Inquiry Activity: What Properties Could You Use to Describe Materials? p. 37 **L2** **TE** Teacher Demo: Transmission Versus Scattering, p. 43 **L2**
2.2 Physical Properties, pp. 45–51 1 block or 2 periods **2.2.1 Describe** physical properties of matter. **2.2.2 Identify** substances based on their physical properties. **2.2.3 Describe** how properties are used to choose materials. **2.2.4 Describe** methods used to separate mixtures. **2.2.5 Describe** evidence that indicates a physical change is taking place.	A-1, A-2, B-2, E-2, F-1		**SE** Quick Lab: Comparing Heat Conductors, p. 46 **L2** **TE** Teacher Demo: Comparing Melting Points, p. 48 **L2** **TE** Build Science Skills: Applying Concepts, p. 50 **L2** **LM** Investigation 2B: Determining the Densities of Liquids **L1**
2.3 Chemical Properties, pp. 54–58 1 block or 2 periods **2.3.1 Describe** chemical properties of matter. **2.3.2 Describe** clues that indicate that a chemical change is taking place. **2.3.3 Distinguish** chemical changes from physical changes.	A-1, A-2, B-3		**SE** Quick Lab: Identifying a Chemical Change, p. 56 **L2** **SE** Forensics Lab: Using Properties to Identify Materials, pp. 60–61 **L2** **TE** Teacher Demo: Oxygen Is Needed, p. 55 **L2** **LM** Investigation 2A: Recognizing Chemical and Physical Changes **L2**

Ability Levels	
L1	For students who need additional help
L2	For all students
L3	For students who need to be challenged

Components

SE	Student Edition	RSW	Reading & Study Workbook	CUT	Chapter & Unit Tests	T	Transparencies
TE	Teacher's Edition	MSPS	Math Skills & Problem Solving Workbook	CTB	Computer Test Bank	iT	Interactive Textbook
LM	Laboratory Manual			TP	Test Prep Resources	P	Presentation Pro CD-ROM
PLM	Probeware Lab Manual			DC	Discovery Channel Videotapes & DVDs	GO	Internet Resources

RESOURCES PRINT and TECHNOLOGY	SECTION ASSESSMENT
RSW Section 2.1 L1 MSPS Section 2.1 L2 T Chapter 2 Pretest L2 Section 2.1 L2 P Chapter 2 Pretest L2 Section 2.1 L2 SCILINKS GO Mixtures L2	SE Section 2.1 Assessment, p. 44 iT Section 2.1
RSW Section 2.2 L1 RSW Math Skill L2 DC Fresh-Squeezed Water L2 T Section 2.2 L2 P Section 2.2 L2 SCIENCE NEWS GO Properties of matter L2	SE Section 2.2 Assessment, p. 51 iT Section 2.2
RSW Section 2.3 L1 T Section 2.3 L2 P Section 2.3 L2 SCILINKS GO Chemical and physical changes L2	SE Section 2.3 Assessment, p. 58 iT Section 2.3

Go Online

Go online for these Internet resources.

PHSchool.com
Web Code: cca-1020
Web Code: cch-1020

NSTA SCILINKS
Web Code: ccn-1021
Web Code: ccn-1023

SCIENCE NEWS®
Web Code: cce-1022

Materials for Activities and Labs

Quantities for each group

STUDENT EDITION

Inquiry Activity, p. 37
rubber band, copper wire, steel paper clip, wooden toothpick, graphite pencil filler

Quick Lab, p. 46
2 plastic foam cups, scissors, metric ruler, metal rod, wooden rod, 2 liquid crystal thermometers, hot water, clock or watch with second hand

Quick Lab, p. 56
3 test tubes; test-tube rack; glass-marking pencil; 3 10-mL graduated cylinders; solutions of copper sulfate, calcium chloride, and sodium chloride

Forensics Lab, pp. 60–61
2 spot plates, glass-marking pencil, 5 laboratory spatulas, cornstarch, baking soda, baking powder, wash bottle of water, vinegar, iodine solution, sample from crime scene, sample from suspect's shoe

TEACHER'S EDITION

Teacher Demo, p. 43
2 beakers, water, iodine solution, table salt, stirring rods, milk, fish tank, flashlight, white paper

Teacher Demo, p. 48
water, ethanol, foam cups, freezer, large beaker, thermometer

Build Science Skills, p. 50
a mixture of salt, sand, and iron filings; beaker; magnet; plastic bag; water; funnel; filter paper

Build Science Skills, p. 52
tap water, bottled water, distilled water

Teacher Demo, p. 55
2 small candles, matches, large beaker

Chapter Assessment

CHAPTER ASSESSMENT

SE Chapter Assessment, pp. 63–64
CUT Chapter 2 Test A, B
CTB Chapter 2
iT Chapter 2
PHSchool.com GO
Web Code: cca-1020

STANDARDIZED TEST PREP

SE Chapter 2, p. 65
TP Diagnose and Prescribe

Interactive Textbook

Interactive Textbook with assessment at PHSchool.com

CHAPTER

2 Before you teach

From the Author

David Frank
Ferris State University

Big Ideas

Chemistry, at its heart, is the study of matter, although the focus of the study can vary among composition, structure, properties, and reactions. In this chapter, students will be introduced to matter through a discussion of properties that students can observe. In later chapters, students will study theories that explain the properties of matter, including the kinetic theory and the atomic theory.

Matter and Change In Section 2.1, students learn how the composition of a material can be used to classify the material as a pure substance or a mixture, and how the distribution of materials within a mixture can be used to classify the mixture as homogeneous or heterogeneous.

In this text, *material* is used to describe a particular type of matter, pure substance or mixture. The term *substance* is synonymous with *pure substance.* Thus, *substance* is used to refer to only elements and compounds.

In Sections 2.2 and 2.3, students are introduced to some properties that can be used to describe materials. Terms such as *viscosity* and *malleability* may be unfamiliar, but students should be familiar with the behaviors that they describe from such experiences as pouring ketchup or bending a paper clip. In Sections 2.2 and 2.3, students also begin to distinguish physical from chemical changes.

Take the opportunity to show students the relationships among different topics. For example, air is primarily a mixture of oxygen and nitrogen, while water is a compound of oxygen and hydrogen. A physical change occurs when oxygen and nitrogen are mixed. A difference in boiling points can be used to separate the mixture. A chemical change occurs when oxygen and hydrogen react and form water. A difference in physical properties cannot be used to separate water into its component elements.

Because Chapter 2 is an introductory chapter, many of the topics introduced in this chapter will be addressed in greater detail in later chapters: melting and boiling in Chapter 3, atoms in Chapter 4, elements in Chapter 5, chemical changes in Chapter 7, and solutions in Chapter 8.

Chemistry Refresher

Classifying Matter 2.1

The system for classifying matter presented in Section 2.1 is the first of many classification systems students will encounter in the chemistry unit. Students will also study solids, liquids, and gases; metals, nonmetals, and metalloids; acids, bases, and salts; and classes of organic compounds, as well as radioactive and nonradioactive isotopes. In Section 2.1, substances are classified as pure substances or mixtures. The key difference between pure substances and mixtures is uniformity of composition. The composition of a pure substance is constant. The composition of a mixture can vary widely.

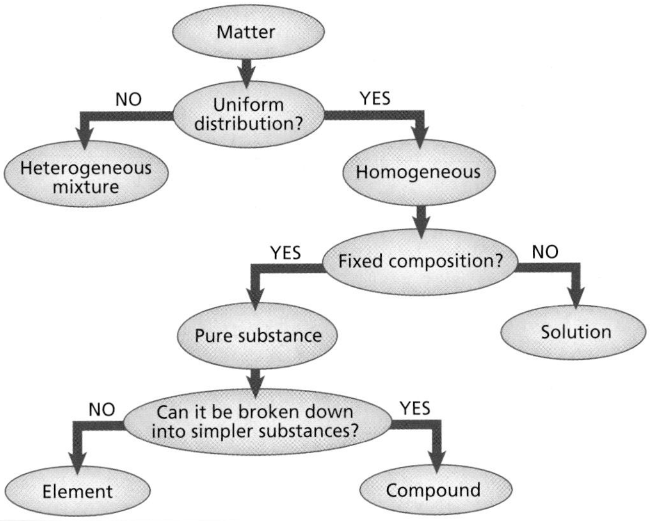
Matter
NO
Uniform distribution?
YES
Heterogeneous mixture
Homogeneous
YES
Fixed composition?
NO
Pure substance
Solution
NO
Can it be broken down into simpler substances?
YES
Element
Compound

The key difference between heterogeneous mixtures and homogeneous mixtures is uniformity of distribution. Chemists agree that solutions are homogeneous mixtures. But they do not always agree on the classification of suspensions and colloids. Some classify suspensions and colloids as heterogeneous mixtures. Some classify colloids as homogeneous mixtures. Some say that a colloid falls somewhere between a solution and a suspension.

Properties of Solutions, Colloids, and Suspensions

Property	Solution	Colloid	Suspension
Particle type	ions, atoms, small molecules	large molecules or particles	large particles or aggregates
Particle size (approximate)	0.1–1 nm	1–100 nm	100 nm and larger
Effect of light	no scattering	scattering	scattering
Effect of gravity	does not separate	does not separate	separates into layers
Filtration	cannot separate	cannot separate	can separate
Uniformity	homogeneous	borderline	heterogeneous

Go Online PDLinks NSTA

For: Teaching methods for properties of matter
Visit: www.SciLinks.org/PDLinks
Web Code: ccn-0299

Criteria used to distinguish among types of mixtures are helpful but not 100% definitive. For example, the particles in a colloid are supposed to remain dispersed, but many people classify dust and paint as colloids even though dust can settle out of the air and paint sometimes needs to be stirred. Also, a solution is supposed to be transparent, but that description would not fit a concentrated solution of iodine in alcohol.

Address Misconceptions

All of the particles in mixtures and solutions are similar in size. If this were true, mixtures could not be separated by filtration. For a strategy to overcome this misconception, see **Address Misconceptions** on **page 50.**

Classifying Properties 2.2 and 2.3

Students may focus on properties related to a specific sample (mass, volume, and shape) rather than properties that depend on the type of material used in the object. The terms used to describe these two classes of properties are extrinsic and intrinsic, respectively. This chapter focuses on intrinsic physical and chemical properties. Intrinsic properties such as viscosity, malleability, and density do not vary with the size of the sample.

It can be difficult to classify some properties as chemical or physical. An argument can be made that taste and smell are chemical properties because their detection depends on interactions between chemicals and sensory receptors in the mouth and nose. A substance dissolving in a solvent may be classified as a physical change or a chemical change depending on whether the substance dissociates (table salt), disperses (sucrose), or ionizes (hydrogen chloride) as it dissolves. (These processes are described in Section 8.1.)

Address Misconceptions

There is no distinction between chemical and physical changes. However, comparing the properties of substances before and after a change can indicate whether the change is physical or chemical. For a strategy to overcome this misconception, see **Address Misconceptions** on **page 58.**

Build Reading Literacy

Preview

Skim Ahead to Understand Text Organization

Strategy Get an advance idea of how the text is organized and activate prior knowledge. This prereading strategy involves skimming the titles, headings, visuals, and boldfaced text. Like checking a roadmap before beginning a trip, previewing helps the reader to recall familiar material and to prepare to learn new material. Before students begin to read, select a portion of Chapter 2 for them to preview, such as pp. 38–44.

Example

1. Ask students to look at the chapter title, section titles, and heads. Tell them to notice whether the terms and concepts mentioned are familiar or unfamiliar.
2. Have students look at the Reading Focus for the specific section to be previewed.
3. Ask students to compare the key concepts and the boldfaced statements in the section.
4. Have students look at the visuals in the section and (where possible) relate each to a specific heading.
5. You may wish to have students prepare a study guide using the headings, key concept questions, and vocabulary as categories in a chart showing the section organization. Have students read the selected pages in depth, filling in the chart with details as they read.

See p. 54 for a script on how to use the preview strategy with students. For additional Build Reading Literacy strategies, see pp. 41 and 48.

ASSESS PRIOR KNOWLEDGE

Use the Chapter Pretest below to assess students' prior knowledge. As needed, review these Science Concepts with students.

Review Science Concepts

Section 2.1 Review different kinds of quantities to be measured, such as temperature, volume, and mass, and the units used to describe each quantity.

Section 2.2 Encourage students to recall what derived units are. For example, review how to use mass and volume to calculate density.

Section 2.3 Have students review the definition of chemistry. Also review with students the types of topics that chemists study.

CHAPTER

2 Properties of Matter

CONCEPTS — in Action —

How do science concepts apply to your world? Here are some questions you'll be able to answer after you read this chapter.

- How do the properties of different materials affect the way clothes are cleaned? *(Section 2.1)*
- Why doesn't every batch of salsa taste equally "hot"? *(Section 2.1)*
- How does fog reduce a driver's ability to see the road ahead? *(Section 2.1)*
- Why does a cook use a wooden spoon to stir a pot of soup? *(Section 2.2)*
- Why does a banana change color as it ripens? *(Section 2.3)*

Discovery Channel School **Video Field Trip**

Fresh-Squeezed Water

- What methods are used to purify water? *(page 52)*

Parts of the Guggenheim Museum Bilbao in ▶ Spain are covered with titanium—a strong, elastic metal that reflects light.

Chapter Pretest

1. What instrument would you use to measure temperature? *(A thermometer)*

2. Which of the following is a unit of volume? *(d)*
- **a.** Gram
- **b.** Atmosphere
- **c.** Meter
- **d.** Liter

3. What characteristic of matter can you measure using a graduated cylinder? *(Volume)*

4. The sides of a cube are 2 cm by 2 cm. What is the volume of the cube? *(8 cm^3)*

5. What additional quantity would you need to calculate the density of the cube described in Question 4? *(The cube's mass)*

6. Which of the following topics is not studied in chemistry? *(d)*
- **a.** Composition of matter
- **b.** Reactions of substances
- **c.** Properties of materials
- **d.** Motion of large objects

Chapter Preview

Inquiry Activity

What Properties Could You Use to Describe Materials?

Procedure

1. Your teacher will provide you with samples of rubber, copper, steel, wood, and carbon. On a sheet of paper, list the materials, leaving room to write your description of each.
2. Determine and record the properties or characteristics of the materials by touching, manipulating, smelling, and looking at them.

Think About It

1. **Comparing and Contrasting** List one or more properties of each material that can be used to distinguish it from all the others.
2. **Observing** Write a description of one of the materials that could be used to clearly identify it.

Discovery Channel School **Video Field Trip**

Fresh-Squeezed Water

Encourage students to view the Video Field Trip "Fresh-Squeezed Water."

ENGAGE/EXPLORE

Inquiry Activity

What Properties Could You Use to Describe Materials? L2

Purpose In this activity, students begin to identify various properties of matter that can be used to describe materials.

Address Misconceptions

Students may confuse the properties of objects with the properties of materials. Show students plastic and metal paper clips. Point out that the shape of an object is not a property of a material, but the ability to be shaped can be.

Skills Focus Classifying

Prep Time 10 minutes

Materials rubber band, copper wire, steel paper clip, wooden toothpick, graphite pencil filler

Advance Prep You may use other objects containing the five materials, or objects made of different materials, but each material in the set must have a distinguishing property.

Class Time 10 minutes

Teaching Tips

- Identify the materials for the students (rubber band, copper wire, steel paper clip, wooden toothpick, and graphite pencil filler).
- Ask students leading questions such as "Is the material rigid or flexible?" "Is the material easily torn or broken?" and "Is the material easily stretched?"
- Some students may be more successful at this activity if you provide blank tables (with columns labeled Material and Observations) in which to record their observations.

Expected Outcome Students should observe a set of properties for each material and identify properties that can distinguish the materials.

Think About It

1. Possible distinguishing properties are rubber's elasticity, copper's color, steel's shininess, wood's brittleness, and graphite's slipperiness.
2. A possible answer for copper is a reddish solid that is flexible enough to be shaped into a narrow wire, which can be bent.

Visual, Kinesthetic

1 FOCUS

Objectives

2.1.1 **Classify** pure substances as elements or compounds.

2.1.2 **Describe** the characteristics of an element and the symbols used to identify elements.

2.1.3 **Describe** the characteristics of a compound.

2.1.4 **Distinguish** pure substances from mixtures.

2.1.5 **Classify** mixtures as heterogeneous or homogeneous.

2.1.6 **Classify** mixtures as solutions, suspensions, or colloids.

Reading Focus

Build Vocabulary — L2

Paraphrasing To help students understand the definitions of vocabulary terms, you may replace less familiar words in a definition with a more familiar word or phrase. For example, you can replace *distributed* in the definition of a homogeneous mixture with "spread out," or *shattering* in the definition of malleability with "breaking into pieces."

Reading Strategy — L2

a. Substance **b.** Compound
c. and d. Homogeneous mixture or heterogeneous mixture

2 INSTRUCT

Address Misconceptions — L2

Some students may associate the term *material* exclusively with solids because they can see and hold solid materials. They may have difficulty recognizing that liquids and gases are also matter. Challenge this misconception by pointing to the Materials list for the lab on p. 60 and asking students to identify the liquids.
Verbal

2.1 Classifying Matter

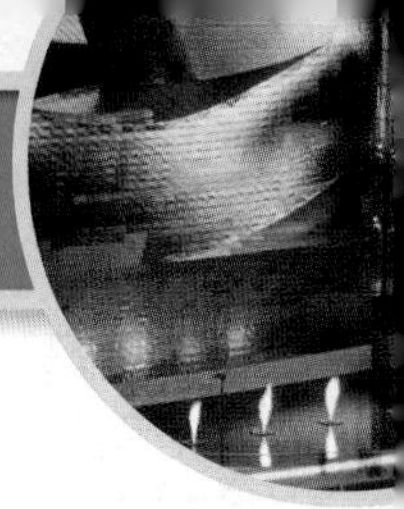

Reading Focus

Key Concepts

- Why are elements and compounds classified as pure substances?
- How do mixtures differ from pure substances?
- What is the main difference among solutions, suspensions, and colloids?

Vocabulary

- pure substance
- element
- atom
- compound
- heterogeneous mixture
- homogeneous mixture
- solution
- suspension
- colloid

Reading Strategy

Summarizing Copy the diagram below. As you read, complete the classification of matter.

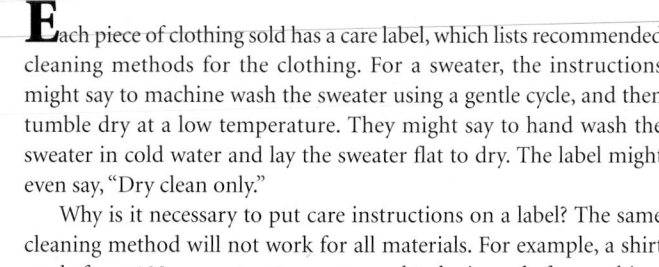

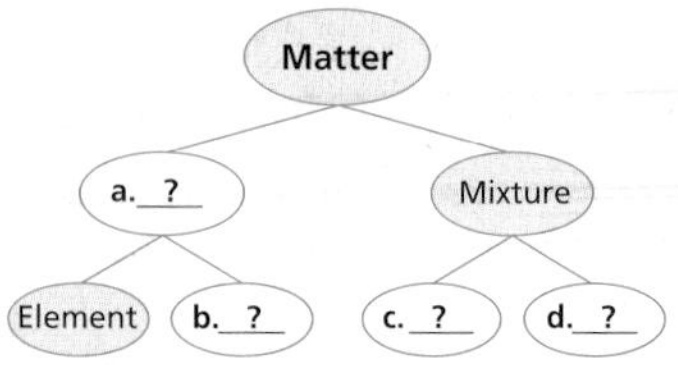
Matter
a. ?
Mixture
Element
b. ?
c. ?
d. ?

Each piece of clothing sold has a care label, which lists recommended cleaning methods for the clothing. For a sweater, the instructions might say to machine wash the sweater using a gentle cycle, and then tumble dry at a low temperature. They might say to hand wash the sweater in cold water and lay the sweater flat to dry. The label might even say, "Dry clean only."

Why is it necessary to put care instructions on a label? The same cleaning method will not work for all materials. For example, a shirt made from 100 percent cotton may need to be ironed after washing. But a shirt made from a cotton and polyester blend may come out of the dryer wrinkle free. A wool jacket often needs to be dry cleaned because wool can shrink when washed in water.

The tendency to wrinkle when washed is a property of cotton. The tendency not to wrinkle when washed is a property of polyester. The tendency to shrink when washed is a property of wool. Cotton, wool, and polyester have different properties because they have different compositions. The word *composition* comes from a Latin word meaning "a putting together," or the combining of parts into a whole. Based on their compositions, materials can be divided into pure substances and mixtures.

100% SHETLAND WOOL
DRY CLEAN OR HAND WASH IN MILD SOAP LAY FLAT TO DRY

Figure 1 You can use the care labels on clothing to sort laundry into batches for cleaning. The care label shown is for a wool sweater that needs to be dry cleaned or washed by hand.

Section Resources

Print
- ***Reading and Study Workbook With Math Support,*** Section 2.1
- ***Math Skills and Problem Solving Workbook,*** Section 2.1
- ***Transparencies,*** Chapter Pretest and Section 2.1

Technology
- ***Interactive Textbook,*** Section 2.1
- ***Presentation Pro CD-ROM,*** Chapter Pretest and Section 2.1
- ***Go Online,*** NSTA SciLinks, Mixtures

Pure Substances

Matter that always has exactly the same composition is classified as a **pure substance,** or simply a substance. Table salt and table sugar are two examples of pure substances. Every pinch of salt tastes equally salty. Every spoonful of sugar tastes equally sweet. **Every sample of a given substance has the same properties because a substance has a fixed, uniform composition.** Substances can be classified into two categories—elements and compounds.

Elements

Although there are millions of known substances, there are only about 100 elements. An **element** is a substance that cannot be broken down into simpler substances. Imagine cutting a copper wire into smaller and smaller pieces. Eventually you would end up with extremely tiny particles called copper atoms. An **atom** is the smallest particle of an element. **An element has a fixed composition because it contains only one type of atom.**

No two elements contain the same type of atom. In Chapter 4, you will find out more about atoms, including how the atoms of one element differ from the atoms of every other element.

Examples of Elements At room temperature (20°C, or 68°F), most elements are solids, including the elements aluminum and carbon. You have seen aluminum foil used to wrap food. Most soft drink cans are made from aluminum. Carbon is the main element in the marks you make with a pencil on a piece of paper. Some elements are gases at room temperature. The elements oxygen and nitrogen are the main gases in the air you breathe. Only two elements are liquids at room temperature, bromine and mercury, both of which are extremely poisonous. Figure 2 shows four elements and their symbols.

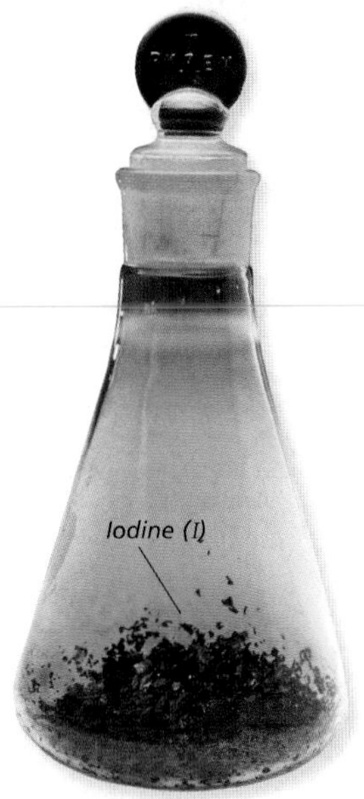
Iodine (I)

Aluminum (Al)
Gold (Au)
Carbon (C)

Figure 2 Aluminum, carbon, and gold are elements that you can see in common objects, such as cans, pencils, and rings. Mixtures containing iodine are used to prevent and treat infections. **Analyzing Data** ***Which of these elements has a symbol that is not related to its name in English?***

Pure Substances
FYI

Samples of pure substances almost always contain impurities, some that are unintentional, some intentional. For example, table salt is not pure sodium chloride. It contains between 0.006% and 0.01% potassium iodide.

Elements
FYI

Sometimes an atom is defined as "the smallest particle of an element that has the properties of the element." However, an atom of copper has none of the properties associated with bulk copper, such as malleability, ductility, or density.

Build Science Skills L2

Observing Have students look at the elements in Figure 2. Ask, **What are some characteristics of the elements in Figure 2?** *(Gold is yellow and shiny. Aluminum is gray and shiny. Carbon is dull and black. Iodine is a dark purple solid.)* Follow up on their observations by asking students to hypothesize about why the iodine sample is in a closed container. *(At room temperature, iodine evaporates and forms a purple gas, which is visible in the container. The gas is poisonous.)*
Visual

Customize for English Language Learners

Sharing Experiences
Encourage multilingual students to describe what a particular element is called in their native language. This exercise will be most useful for those elements that have been known for centuries or millennia. (Examples include carbon, mercury, sulfur, iron, copper, tin, zinc, silver, gold, and lead.) Use this information as a springboard for discussing the element names given in the text.

Answer to . . .

Figure 2 *Gold*

Section 2.1 (continued)

Integrate Language Arts L2

Have students research and explain the origin of element symbols (other than Au) that are not abbreviations for element names in English. Examples include silver (Ag), lead (Pb), tin (Sn), antimony (Sb), and mercury (Hg).
Verbal, Portfolio

Compounds

FYI

When the terms *element, atom, compound,* and *molecule* are defined in an introductory section, the definition of a molecule is often both too broad and too narrow. Molecules are not the smallest particle of all compounds, and many elements exist in nature as molecules. For this reason, in this text, the formal definition of molecule does not appear until Chapter 6, the chapter on bonding, where it can be defined accurately. (The term *molecule* is introduced informally in Section 3.3 when water molecules are described.)

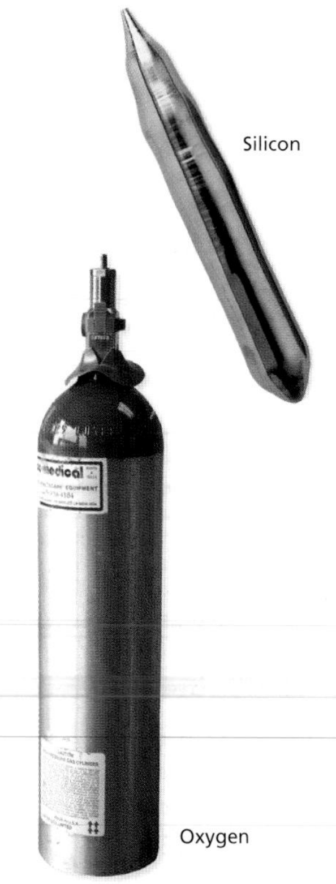
Silicon
Oxygen

Figure 3 Elements have different properties than their compounds. Silicon is a gray solid and oxygen is a colorless gas, which can be stored in a metal tank. Silicon and oxygen combine to form silicon dioxide—a colorless, transparent solid found in most grains of sand.

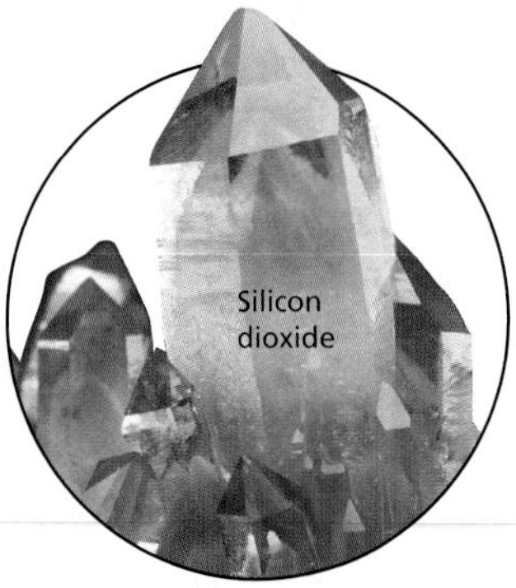
Silicon dioxide

Symbols for Elements In 1813, Jöns Berzelius, a Swedish chemist, suggested that chemists use symbols to represent elements. Many of the symbols he assigned to elements are still used. Each symbol has either one or two letters. The first letter is always capitalized. If there is a second letter, it is not capitalized.

It is easy to see why C and Al are used to represent carbon and aluminum. But why does gold have the symbol Au? The symbols that Berzelius chose were based on the Latin names of the elements. The Latin name for gold is *aurum.*

The symbols allow scientists who speak different languages to communicate without confusion. For example, nitrogen is known as *azote* in France, as *stickstoff* in Germany, and as *nitrógeno* in Mexico. But scientists who speak English, French, German, and Spanish all agree that the symbol for the element nitrogen is N.

Sometimes an element's name contains a clue to its properties. For example, the name hydrogen comes from the Greek words *hydro* and *genes,* meaning "water" and "forming."

Compounds

Water is composed of the elements hydrogen and oxygen. When electricity passes through water, bubbles of oxygen and hydrogen gas form and rise to the surface of the water. If the gases are collected in a container and a flame is brought near the mixture, the hydrogen and oxygen react and form water. Water is classified as a compound. A **compound** is a substance that is made from two or more simpler substances and can be broken down into those simpler substances. The simpler substances are either elements or other compounds.

The properties of a compound differ from those of the substances from which it is made. For example, oxygen and hydrogen are gases at room temperature, but water is a liquid. Hydrogen can fuel a fire, and oxygen can keep a fire burning, but water does not burn or help other substances to burn. In fact, water is one of the substances commonly used to put out fires.

Figure 3 shows another example of how properties change when elements join and form compounds. Silicon dioxide is a compound found in most light-colored grains of sand. It is a colorless, transparent solid. Yet, silicon dioxide is made from a colorless gas (oxygen) and a gray solid (silicon). Silicon is used to make chips for computers.

A compound always contains two or more elements joined in a fixed proportion. For example, in silicon dioxide, there are always two oxygen atoms for each silicon atom. (*Di-* means "two.") In water, there are always two hydrogen atoms for each oxygen atom.

Reading Checkpoint *What happens if electricity passes through water?*

Facts and Figures

Electrolysis of Water Early chemists were able to use heat to break down many compounds into their constituent elements. Because water cannot be decomposed by this method, water was classified as an element until chemists were able to use electric current to break down water into hydrogen and oxygen. (The decomposition of water into hydrogen and oxygen will not occur unless ions are added to the water because there are not enough ions in pure water to conduct an electric current.)

Salsa
• 4 or 5 plum tomatoes
• 3–5 fresh Serrano chili peppers
• 12 sprigs of cilantro
• large garlic clove
• small white onion
• 1½ teaspoons fresh lime juice
• ¾ teaspoon salt

Figure 4 The ingredients shown are used to make one kind of salsa, which is an example of a heterogeneous mixture.

Mixtures

Suppose you are making salsa using the ingredients shown in Figure 4. You have a choice. You can use exactly the amounts listed in the recipe, or you can adjust the ingredients according to your own taste. You might have to prepare the recipe a few times before deciding if you have just the right amount of each ingredient.

Mixtures tend to retain some of the properties of their individual substances. But the properties of a mixture are less constant than the properties of a substance. **The properties of a mixture can vary because the composition of a mixture is not fixed.** The type of pepper and the quantity of pepper used in a salsa recipe determine the "hotness" of a batch of salsa. Chili peppers contain a compound called capsaicin (kap SAY uh sin) that can cause a burning sensation in your mouth. The amount of capsaicin varies among types of peppers. Cayenne peppers, for example, contain more capsaicin than do jalapeño peppers.

No matter how well you stir a batch of salsa, the ingredients will not be evenly distributed. There may, for example, be more onion in one portion of the salsa than another. Mixtures can be classified by how well the parts of the mixture are distributed throughout the mixture.

Heterogeneous Mixtures If you look at a handful of sand from a beach, the sand appears to be all the same material. However, if you use a hand lens, you will notice that the sample of sand is not the same throughout. Figure 5 shows that grains of sand vary in size. Also, some grains are light in color and some are dark. Sand is an example of a heterogeneous mixture. Heterogeneous (het uh roh GEE nee us) comes from the Greek words *hetero* and *genus*, meaning "different" and "kind." In a **heterogeneous mixture,** the parts of the mixture are noticeably different from one another.

Figure 5 Sand is a heterogeneous mixture. The spoon is stainless steel, which is a homogeneous mixture. **Interpreting Photographs** ***Explain how viewing sand through a hand lens helps show that sand is a heterogeneous mixture.***

Mixtures

Build Reading Literacy L1

Compare and Contrast Refer to page **226D** in **Chapter 8**, which provides the guidelines for comparing and contrasting.

Have students read pp. 41–44 and gather information on different classifications of mixtures. Then, have students create a chart that compares and contrasts each type of mixture.
Visual

Integrating Language Arts L2

Have students consider the difference between hot food (as in warm versus cold) and hot food (as in spicy versus mild). Encourage students to suggest examples of dishes other than salsa that are hot in the second, spicy sense. Some students may want to record a family recipe for a "hot" dish. Have them identify the ingredient(s) that can be varied to control the "hotness" of the mixture.
Logical

Build Science Skills L2

Observing Have students look at samples of sand with a hand lens. Explain that the composition of sand can vary from beach to beach because the rocks and shells from which sand forms have different compositions. Ask, **How can you tell that sand is a heterogeneous mixture?** *(The grains of sand vary in color and size.)* (A sample of sand that contains only ground-up shells would probably be classified as homogeneous.)
Visual

Facts and Figures

Capsaicinoid Content Capsaicin (8-methyl-N-vanillyl-6-nonenamide) is the most abundant of a group of compounds called capsaicinoids. These compounds are found in the seeds and membranes of chili peppers. When they are ingested, they affect pain receptors in the mouth and throat. Because capsaicin is an oil, and oil and water do not mix, drinking water spreads the oil to more parts of the mouth and increases the burning sensation.

The capsaicinoid content of a pepper is measured in Scoville units. Wilbur Scoville developed the method for measuring the "hotness" of chili peppers in 1912. He mixed ground chilies with a sugar and water solution and diluted the mixture until tasters no longer reported a burning sensation. The greater the dilution needed, the higher the assigned number of Scoville units. Fifteen Scoville units is equivalent to one part per million.

Answer to . . .

Figure 5 *More details are visible in the magnified sand, making it easier to observe the different parts of the mixture.*

Reading Checkpoint *Bubbles of oxygen and hydrogen form and rise to the surface of the water.*

Data Analysis

Do the Contents of Two Cans of Mixed Nuts Meet FDA Regulations? L2

Answers

1. Both brands contain the same six types of nuts, but the amount of each type of nut varies.
2. There are 344.79 g in Brand A and 350.32 g in Brand B. The percents by mass in Brand A are: 44.2% peanuts, 13.64% almonds, 16.79% Brazil nuts, 13.4% cashews, 5.77% hazelnuts, and 6.21% pecans. The percents by mass in Brand B are: 54.8% peanuts, 8.90% almonds, 5.59% Brazil nuts, 21.06% cashews, 4.82% hazelnuts, and 4.82% pecans.
3. Yes. Both brands contain more than four types of nuts other than peanuts. The percent of each nut by mass is within the 2% to 80% range.
4. The ingredients are listed in order by total mass. The ingredient with the largest total mass is listed first.

For Extra Help L1

Have students answer Question 3 by calculating 2% and 80% of each total mass and checking to see if any of the masses fall outside that range.
Logical

Solutions, Suspensions, and Colloids

FYI

Many alloys are not true solutions. Sterling silver, a mixture of silver and copper, is an example. Silver and copper are completely soluble in all proportions when molten. However, solid sterling silver is a two-phase alloy with pockets of silver and pockets of a 71.9% silver and 28.1% copper mixture.

Go Online NSTA SCILINKS

Download a worksheet on mixtures for students to complete, and find additional teacher support from NSTA SciLinks.

Data Analysis

Do the Contents of Two Cans of Mixed Nuts Meet FDA Regulations?

The Food and Drug Administration (FDA) has two main areas of concern about food. First, and most important, the FDA ensures that food sold in the United States is safe to eat. Second, the FDA ensures that the information on a food label accurately describes a food product.

What can you assume when you see the label "mixed nuts" on a can of nuts? According to the FDA regulations, a can labeled *mixed nuts* must contain at least four types of shelled nuts other than peanuts. The mass of each type of nut must be not less than 2 percent of the total mass and not more than 80 percent of the total mass.

Contents of Two Cans of Mixed Nuts

Type of Nut	Mass in Brand A	Mass in Brand B
Peanut	152.39 g	191.96 g
Almond	47.02 g	31.18 g
Brazil nut	57.88 g	19.60 g
Cashew	46.20 g	73.78 g
Hazelnut	19.90 g	16.90 g
Pecan	21.40 g	16.90 g

1. **Comparing and Contrasting** How are the two brands of mixed nuts alike? How are they different?
2. **Calculating** What is the percent by mass of each type of nut in each can?
3. **Drawing Conclusions** Do the contents of each can meet the FDA regulations? Explain.
4. **Inferring** On the Brand A label, the nuts are listed in this order: peanuts, Brazil nuts, almonds, cashews, pecans, and hazelnuts. What do you think determines the order?

Go Online NSTA SCILINKS

For: Links on mixtures
Visit: www.SciLinks.org
Web Code: ccn-1021

Homogeneous Mixtures If you collect water from both the shallow end and the deep end of a swimming pool, the water samples will appear the same. The water in a swimming pool is a homogeneous (hoh moh GEE nee us) mixture of water and substances that dissolve in water. In a **homogeneous mixture,** the substances are so evenly distributed that it is difficult to distinguish one substance in the mixture from another. A homogeneous mixture appears to contain only one substance. The serving spoon in Figure 5 is made of stainless steel—a homogeneous mixture of iron, chromium, and nickel.

Solutions, Suspensions, and Colloids

It isn't always easy to tell a homogeneous mixture from a heterogeneous mixture. You may need to observe the properties of a mixture before you decide. The size of the particles in a mixture has an effect on the properties of the mixture. **Based on the size of its largest particles, a mixture can be classified as a solution, a suspension, or a colloid.**

Solutions If you place a spoonful of sugar in a glass of hot water and stir, the sugar dissolves in the water. The result is a homogeneous mixture of sugar and water. When substances dissolve and form a homogeneous mixture, the mixture that forms is called a **solution.** The windshield wiper fluid in Figure 6 is a solution. So is tap water.

Facts and Figures

Regulatory Agencies Responsibility for protecting the food supply is shared among the FDA, the Department of Agriculture, and the EPA, which regulates pesticides. Food that is adulterated or mislabeled may be voluntarily destroyed or recalled, or seized by court order. The FDA is responsible for establishing standards for identity, quality, and fill of container. If standards have been set for a product, such as mixed nuts, the product must comply with those standards. Food labels must include a statement of identity (usual or common name), the net quantity of the contents, the name and place of business of the supplier, and a list of ingredients in descending order by mass. The goal is to have honest and informative labels.

A

B

C

Figure 6 The liquids shown represent three categories of mixtures. **A** Windshield wiper fluid is a solution. **B** Muddy water collected from a swamp is a suspension. **C** Milk is a colloid.
Comparing and Contrasting *Based on appearance, how are a solution and a colloid similar?*

Liquid solutions are easy to recognize. They do not separate into distinct layers over time. If you pour a liquid solution through a filter, none of the substances in the solution are trapped in the filter. You can see through solutions that are liquids because light passes through them without being scattered in all directions. These three properties of liquid solutions can be traced to the size of the particles in a solution. The particles in a solution are too small to settle out of the solution, be trapped by a filter, or scatter light.

Suspensions Have you ever seen the instruction "Shake well before using" on a bottle? This instruction is a clue that the material in the bottle is a suspension. A **suspension** is a heterogeneous mixture that separates into layers over time. For example, if you shake up a container of sand and water, the sand mixes with the water and forms a suspension. Over time, the suspended particles of sand settle to the bottom of the container.

You could use a filter to separate the sand from the water. The water would pass through the filter, but the sand would remain in the filter paper. Suspended particles settle out of a mixture or are trapped by a filter because they are larger than the particles in a solution. The worker in Figure 7 is using a mask to filter out particles of plastic foam that are suspended in air. Because larger particles can scatter light in all directions, suspensions are cloudy.

Reading Checkpoint *What happens to suspended particles over time?*

Figure 7 When a surfboard is sanded, particles of plastic become suspended in air. The worker wears a mask to keep from breathing in the particles.

Teacher Demo

Transmission Versus Scattering L2

Purpose Students observe light pass through different mixtures.

Materials 2 beakers, water, iodine solution, table salt, stirring rods, milk, fish tank, flashlight, white paper

Procedure Demonstrate that a solution can have color and still transmit light. Fill two beakers halfway with water. Add a small amount of iodine solution to one beaker and stir. Add table salt to the second beaker. Ask students to describe the color of each mixture and state whether it is clear. Demonstrate transmission of light versus scattering. Fill the tank with water. Turn off the lights. Shine a flashlight through the tank so that it lights up the white paper placed behind the tank. Add some milk to the water and stir. Shine the light through the tank again. (These behaviors of light are discussed in detail in Section 18.3.)

Expected Outcome Although the salt solution is colorless and the iodine solution is colored, both transmit light. Light passes through the water in the tank and makes a bright spot on the paper. With milk added, the light is scattered so that the spot is much less distinct.
Visual

Use Visuals L1

Figure 7 To emphasize that suspended particles settle out over time, ask, **What will happen to the particles of plastic suspended in the air?** *(The particles will eventually settle out.)* Discuss with students the dangers of inhaling suspended particles. Ask, **How does a mask prevent the worker from inhaling particles of plastic?** *(The particles in suspensions can be separated by filtration. The mask is a filter.)*
Visual

Answer to . . .

Figure 6 *The solution and the colloid both appear homogeneous.*

Reading Checkpoint *Suspended particles settle out of a mixture.*

Build Science Skills L3

Classifying Have interested students research categories of colloids such as gels, foams, aerosols, and emulsions. Have students find out how scientists distinguish different types of colloids. Have them identify household examples of each type.
Visual, Portfolio

3 ASSESS

Evaluate Understanding L2

Have students make a game of concentration using the terms in the chapter and their definitions. Have groups of students write each term on separate index cards and the definition of each term on a second set of index cards. To play the game, students should shuffle all the cards together and then lay them face down in a grid. Each student takes turns flipping over two index cards. If the cards match, the student can remove the cards from the grid. If the cards do not match, the student places the cards face down. After all of the cards are gone, the student who has removed the most cards wins the match.

Reteach L1

Use Figure 6 as a visual aid to summarize the key differences among different types of mixtures.

Writing in Science

Students should specify which ingredients are required for the cereal to qualify for a particular label and suggest a range for ingredients such as dried fruit or nuts. (Students could choose another edible mixture, such as canned vegetable soup.)

Interactive Textbook If your class subscribes to the Interactive Textbook, use it to review key concepts in Section 2.1.

Answer to . . .

Figure 8 *High beams*

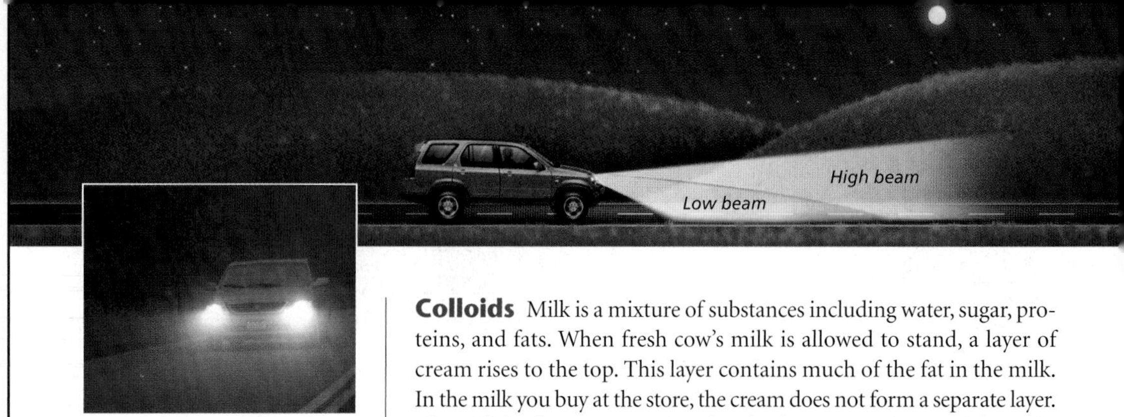
High beam
Low beam

Figure 8 The photograph shows how water droplets in fog scatter the light from high beams. The drawing compares the areas lit by high beams and low beams. **Interpreting Diagrams** ***Which beams normally make a larger area of a road visible?***

Colloids Milk is a mixture of substances including water, sugar, proteins, and fats. When fresh cow's milk is allowed to stand, a layer of cream rises to the top. This layer contains much of the fat in the milk. In the milk you buy at the store, the cream does not form a separate layer. The milk has been processed so that the fat remains dispersed throughout the milk. The result is homogenized milk, which is a colloid.

A **colloid** contains some particles that are intermediate in size between the small particles in a solution and the larger particles in a suspension. Like solutions, colloids do not separate into layers. You cannot use a filter to separate the parts of a colloid.

Fog is a colloid of water droplets in air. Figure 8 shows how fog affects which headlights a driver uses. Automobiles have headlights with low beams for normal driving conditions and high beams for roads that are poorly lit. With the high beams, a driver can see a bend in the road or an obstacle sooner. But the high beams are not useful on a foggy night because the water droplets scatter light back toward the driver and reduce visibility. With the low beams, much less light is scattered. The scattering of light is a property that can be used to distinguish colloids and suspensions from solutions.

Section 2.1 Assessment

Reviewing Concepts

1. Why does every sample of a given substance have the same properties?
2. Explain why the composition of an element is fixed.
3. Describe the composition of a compound.
4. Why can the properties of a mixture vary?
5. On what basis can mixtures be classified as solutions, suspensions, or colloids?

Critical Thinking

6. **Predicting** If you added salt instead of sugar to a pitcher of lemonade, how would this change the properties of the lemonade?
7. **Interpreting Visuals** Explain why silicon dioxide cannot be the only compound in the sample of sand shown in Figure 5.
8. **Inferring** Fresh milk is a suspension. After fresh milk is homogenized, it is a colloid. What happens to the size of the drops of fat in milk when milk is homogenized?

Writing in Science

Writing Instructions Pick a cereal that is an obvious mixture. Write rules that could be used to control the cereal's composition. Use the FDA rules for mixed nuts as a model.

Section 2.1 Assessment

1. A pure substance has a fixed composition.
2. An element contains only one kind of atom.
3. Compounds contain two or more elements joined in a fixed proportion.
4. Because the composition of a mixture is not fixed
5. Mixtures can be classified as solutions, suspensions, or colloids based on the size of their largest particles.
6. The lemonade would taste salty instead of sweet.
7. Silicon dioxide is colorless. There must be at least one other compound in the sample to account for the dark-colored grains.
8. Large drops are broken down into smaller drops, which can remain dispersed throughout the milk.

2.2 Physical Properties

Reading Focus

Key Concepts

- What are some examples of physical properties?
- How can knowing the physical properties of matter be useful?
- What processes are used to separate mixtures?
- When does a physical change occur?

Vocabulary

- physical property
- viscosity
- conductivity
- malleability
- melting point
- boiling point
- filtration
- distillation
- physical change

Reading Strategy

Building Vocabulary Copy the table. As you read, write a definition for each property.

Physical Property	Definition
Viscosity	a.__?__
Malleability	b.__?__
Melting point	c.__?__

If there are pitchers of ice water and lemonade on a picnic table, how do you know which liquid is in each pitcher? It's easy! The lemonade is yellow. Lemonade also has a tart taste that is hard to miss. A yellow color and a tart taste are two properties of lemonade.

Examples of Physical Properties

A **physical property** is any characteristic of a material that can be observed or measured without changing the composition of the substances in the material. **Viscosity, conductivity, malleability, hardness, melting point, boiling point, and density are examples of physical properties.**

Viscosity Suppose you knock over an open bottle of vinegar and an open jar of honey at exactly the same time. In the time it takes for the vinegar bottle to empty, the honey will scarcely start to flow. The tendency of a liquid to keep from flowing—its resistance to flowing—is called its **viscosity**. The greater the viscosity, the slower the liquid moves. Thick liquids, such as corn syrup and the honey in Figure 9, have a high viscosity. Thin liquids, such as vinegar, have a low viscosity.

The viscosity of a liquid usually decreases when it is heated. For example, a spoonful of cooking oil will spread more quickly across the bottom of a heated frying pan than across the bottom of a cold pan.

Why is the viscosity of a liquid important? Consider the motor oil used to keep the parts of an automobile engine from wearing away as they move past one another. The motor oil must not be too thick in cold weather or too thin in hot weather.

Figure 9 The object in the photograph is called a honey dipper. Honey is an example of a liquid with a high viscosity.

Section Resources

Print

- ***Laboratory Manual,*** Investigation 2B
- ***Reading and Study Workbook With Math Support,*** Section 2.2 and **Math Skill:** Melting and Boiling Points
- ***Transparencies,*** Section 2.2

Technology

- ***Interactive Textbook,*** Section 2.2
- ***Presentation Pro CD-ROM,*** Section 2.2
- ***Go Online,*** *Science News,* Properties of matter

Section 2.2

1 FOCUS

Objectives

2.2.1 **Describe** physical properties of matter.

2.2.2 **Identify** substances based on their physical properties.

2.2.3 **Describe** how properties are used to choose materials.

2.2.4 **Describe** methods used to separate mixtures.

2.2.5 **Describe** evidence that indicates a physical change is taking place.

Reading Focus

Build Vocabulary L2

LINCS Have students use the LINCS strategy to learn and review the terms *viscosity, conductivity,* and *malleability.* In LINCS exercises, the students **L**ist what they know about each term, **I**magine a picture that describes the word or phrase, **N**ote a reminding "sound-alike" word (such as *visible, train conductor,* and *mallet*), **C**onnect the terms to the sound-alike word by making up a short story, and then perform a brief **S**elf-test.

Reading Strategy L2

a. The tendency of a liquid to resist flowing **b.** The ability of a solid to be hammered without shattering **c.** The temperature at which a substance changes from a solid to liquid

2 INSTRUCT

Examples of Physical Properties

FYI

The text mentions that lemonade can be identified by its taste. Remind students that taste should never be used to identify an unknown substance and that no substances, known or unknown, should ever be ingested in a lab.

Quick Lab

Comparing Heat Conductors L2

Objective
After completing this activity, students will be able to
- distinguish a material that is a good conductor of heat from a material that is a poor conductor of heat.

Skills Focus **Observing, Inferring**

Prep Time 10 minutes

Advance Prep Acquire wood and metal rods of similar length from the metal or woodworking classroom, a crafts shop, or a home repair shop. Liquid crystal thermometers may be purchased at a pet or aquarium supply store. You may want to cut the cups and attach the thermometers to the rods in advance to save class time. Thermometers can be attached to the rods with their own adhesive backing or taped on. Heat enough water to fill each foam cup about 3/4 full.

Class Time 20 minutes

Safety Remind students to handle the setup carefully to prevent burns after the hot water is added.

Teaching Tips
- You may need to provide tape to attach thermometers to the rods.
- Construct a blank data table on the board, an overhead transparency, or a computer and have each group enter its data in this table. All data can then be pooled and averaged for greater accuracy.

Expected Outcome Metal will conduct heat faster than wood.

Analyze and Conclude
1. Metal is a better conductor. Students should cite the differences in temperature over time as evidence.
2. Metal is not the best choice for this purpose. Because metals are good conductors, the contents of the cup will cool quickly as heat is transferred to the surroundings.
3. Depending on what rods are used, possible sources of error are different lengths, different diameters, and different densities of the materials.
Kinesthetic, Logical

Quick Lab

Comparing Heat Conductors

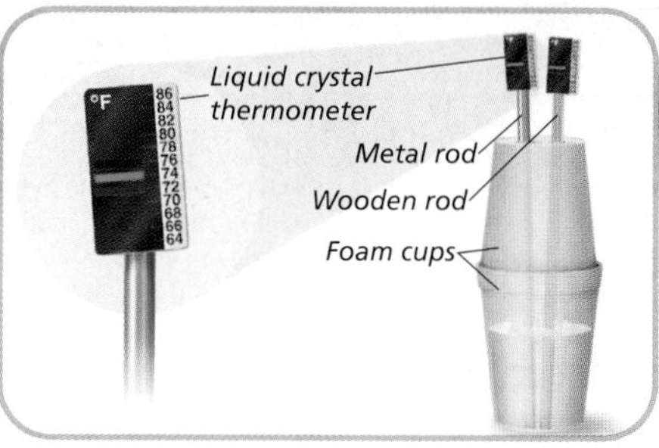
°F
86
84
82
80
78
76
74
72
70
68
66
64
Liquid crystal thermometer
Metal rod
Wooden rod
Foam cups

Materials
2 plastic foam cups, scissors, metric ruler, metal rod, wooden rod, 2 liquid crystal thermometers, hot water, clock or watch with second hand

Procedure
1. Make a data table with a column for time and a column to record the temperature of each rod.
2. Cut 3 cm off the top of one cup. Turn the cup upside down. Use the metal rod to make two holes about 3 cm apart in the bottom.
3. Attach a thermometer to each rod as shown.
4. Insert both rods so they will just touch the bottom of the second cup. Lay the cup with the rods on the table. Do not touch the rods and thermometers during the experiment.
5. Ask your teacher to add hot water to the intact cup until it is about three fourths full.
6. Hold the cup with the hot water firmly as you place the cup with the rods on top of it. **CAUTION** *Be careful not to overturn the cup.*
7. Observe and record the temperatures every minute for five minutes.

Analyze and Conclude
1. **Comparing and Contrasting** Is metal or wood a better conductor of heat? Explain.
2. **Applying Concepts** Is a metal cup a good container for keeping a drink hot for as long as possible? Give a reason for your answer.
3. **Evaluating** Describe any variables, other than the type of material, that were not controlled in this lab.

Conductivity Which spoon should you choose for stirring a pot of soup heating on the stove—a metal spoon or a wooden spoon? If one end of a metal object is heated, the other end will soon feel hot. A material's ability to allow heat to flow is called **conductivity.**

Materials that have a high conductivity, such as metals, are called conductors. If a material is a good conductor of heat, it is usually also a good conductor of electricity. Wood is not a good conductor of heat. You can stir hot soup with a wooden spoon without worrying about burning your hand because the wooden spoon stays cool to the touch.

Malleability The ancient gold objects in Figure 10 were found in a tomb in Greece. A goldsmith made the medallions by tapping gold with a small hammer and punch. Gold can be shaped in this way because it is malleable. **Malleability** (mal ee uh BIL uh tee) is the ability of a solid to be hammered without shattering. Most metals are malleable. By contrast, an ice cube breaks into small pieces when struck with a hammer. So does ordinary glass when hit by a fast-moving object such as a baseball. Solids that shatter when struck are brittle.

Reading Checkpoint *Why would a cook use a wooden spoon to stir hot soup?*

Figure 10 Because gold is both malleable and beautiful, it is often used to make jewelry. These ancient gold medallions were made to form a necklace.

Customize for Inclusion Students

Visually Impaired
Provide students who have visual impairments with samples of two different nontoxic solids that have approximately the same mass. By handling the samples, students can infer their relative densities from their volumes.

Provide samples of materials with a range of hardness. Have students do scratch tests to determine an order of hardness. Students should be able to feel any indentations on the surfaces of the softer materials.

Hardness One way to compare the hardness of two materials is to see which of the materials can scratch the other. The blade of a typical kitchen knife, for example, can scratch a copper sheet because stainless steel is harder than copper. The stainless steel in a knife blade is a hard solid that can be shaped into a sharp cutting edge. The material used to sharpen the blade must be harder than stainless steel. Diamond is the hardest known material. Some of the grinding wheels used to sharpen steel contain small grains of diamond. The man in Figure 11 is carving a canoe from a soft wood—Western red cedar.

Figure 11 This Tlingit carver is using an adze to carve a canoe from Western red cedar. Red cedar is a relatively soft wood.

Melting and Boiling Points If you leave a tray of ice cubes on your kitchen counter, the ice cubes will melt. The temperature at which a substance changes from solid to liquid is its **melting point.** For water, this change normally occurs at 0°C. If you heat water to cook pasta, the water will normally start to boil at 100°C. The temperature at which a substance boils is its **boiling point.** Figure 12 shows the melting point and the boiling point for some substances.

Density Density can be used to test the purity of a substance. Recall that density is the ratio of the mass of a substance to its volume. At room temperature, silver has a density of 10.5 g/cm^3. If a coin has a density of 9.9 g/cm^3 at room temperature, either the coin is not made from silver or the coin contains substances in addition to silver.

Density can be used to test the purity of methanol. Methanol is a fuel burned in some racing motorcycles. The American Motorcycle Association (AMA) requires racers to use fuel that is at least 99.65 percent pure. Race officials may collect a sample of fuel and measure its temperature and density. Then they compare the measured density to the expected density of methanol at that temperature. These spot checks keep racers from adding substances to the fuel that will give them an unfair advantage in a race.

Melting and Boiling Points of Some Substances

Substance	Melting Point	Boiling Point
Hydrogen	−259.3°C	−252.9°C
Nitrogen	−210.0°C	−195.8°C
Ammonia	−77.7°C	−33.3°C
Octane (found in gasoline)	−56.8°C	125.6°C
Water	0.0°C	100.0°C
Acetic acid (found in vinegar)	16.6°C	117.9°C
Table salt	800.7°C	1465°C
Gold	1064.2°C	2856°C

Figure 12 The table lists the melting points and boiling points for several substances. **Analyzing Data** ***Which of these substances are liquids at room temperature (20°C, or 68°F)?***

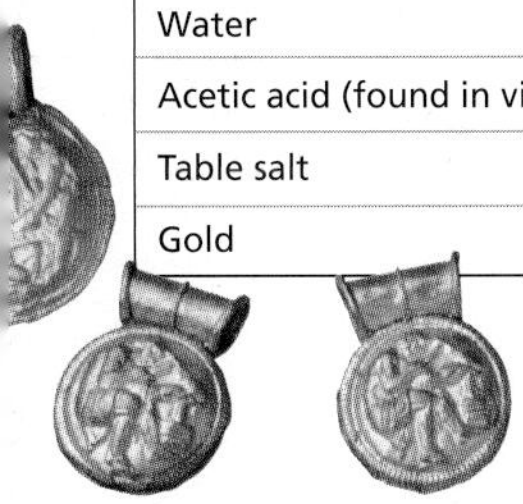

Use Visuals L1

Figure 10 Gold is the most malleable metal. Ancient Greek jewelry was often hammered to a thickness of 0.1 to 0.15 mm. Ask, **What properties of gold can you identify from Figure 10?** *(Gold is a shiny, yellow solid that can be shaped into small, detailed pieces.)* The medallions shown in Figure 10 were found in the Lazlo region of central Italy and were likely made between the eighth and sixth centuries B.C. Ask, **Given the age of this jewelry, what other property could you say gold exhibits?** *(Gold is durable.)*
Visual

Integrate Earth Science L2

There are different scales for describing hardness. The Brinell and Rockwell scales are based on the indentation made by an object. The Brinell hardness number is based on indentation depth. The Rockwell hardness number is based on indentation area. On a scale that measures resistance to abrasion, only two substances are rated above 10: cubic boron nitride (cBN), 19, and diamond, 42.5. Have students find out about hardness scales and describe how they are used to characterize rocks and minerals.
Logical, Portfolio

FYI

Boiling points depend on both temperature and pressure. In Chapter 3, students will study the effect of pressure on boiling points.

Facts and Figures

Specific Gravity The AMA race officials described in the text are using a hygrometer to test specific gravity. Specific gravity is the ratio of the mass of a solid or liquid to the mass of an equal volume of distilled water at 4°C. Because specific gravity is a ratio of values that have identical units, it does not have units. (Density is discussed in greater detail in Chapter 1.)

Answer to . . .

Figure 12 *Octane, water, and acetic acid*

Reading Checkpoint *A wooden spoon is a poor conductor of heat.*

Using Physical Properties

Build Reading Literacy

L1

Outline Refer to page **156D** in **Chapter 6**, which provides the guidelines for an outline.

Have students read pp. 48–50 and gather information on identifying, choosing, and separating substances based on their physical properties. Then, have students use the headings as major divisions in an outline. Have students refer to their outlines when answering the questions in the Section 2.2 Assessment.
Visual

Teacher Demo

Comparing Melting Points

L2

Purpose Students observe the differences in melting points of two substances.

Materials water, ethanol, foam cups, freezer, large beaker, thermometer

Procedure Tell students that you will demonstrate that the melting points of two substances differ. The night before, place a foam cup filled with water and a second foam cup filled with ethanol in the freezer. During class, pull both cups out of the freezer. Have students note that the water is frozen, but the ethanol is not. Remove the ice from the cup and add it to the large beaker. Add a small amount of water and allow the ice to begin melting. While the temperature of the ice water is leveling off, have a volunteer measure the temperature of the ethanol. Compare that temperature to the temperature of the ice water.

Expected Outcome Because most freezers do not cool to temperatures below the melting point of ethanol, –114.7°C, the ethanol will remain a liquid. After some of the ice has melted, the temperature of the solid-liquid system will stop decreasing and level off. This is the melting point of water, 0°C. The temperature of the chilled ethanol is below 0°C.
Visual

Using Physical Properties

People use data about physical properties to solve many different types of problems. **Physical properties are used to identify a material, to choose a material for a specific purpose, or to separate the substances in a mixture.**

Using Properties to Identify Materials The steps used to identify a material are similar to the steps used to test for purity. The first step is to decide which properties to test. The second step is to do tests on a sample of the unknown. The final step is to compare the results with the data reported for known materials.

The identification of a material can be a crucial step in solving a crime. A detective collects red paint chips from the scene of a hit-and-run accident. He asks a chemist at the crime lab to use the chips to identify the model of the missing vehicle. Because paint is a mixture of substances, the chemist can do tests that distinguish one type of red paint from another. The technician compares the data she collects to an FBI database. The database contains information about the paints used on different makes and models of cars. Once the detective knows the make and model, he uses a database of registered owners to create a list of possible suspects.

Using Properties to Choose Materials Properties determine which materials are chosen for which uses. For example, you wouldn't want shoelaces made from wood. Shoelaces must be flexible, that is, they must be able to bend without breaking. They must also be durable, that is, they must be able to withstand repeated use. Laces in hiking boots like those in Figure 13 are usually nylon or leather.

People don't consider just one property when choosing a material for a particular application. They look at a set of properties. For example, the How It Works box on page 49 explains how the properties of wax are used when clay molds are made for casting metal sculptures.

Figure 13 Shoelaces for hiking boots are sometimes made from leather. So are some belts and shoes. **Making Generalizations** ***What properties of leather would make it a suitable material for all three types of objects?***

Facts and Figures

Identifying Substances Sometimes a single property is not sufficient to positively identify a substance. Iron, nickel, and cobalt, which are often found together in nature, look quite similar. The density of iron is 7.87 g/cm^3. The density of nickel is 8.90 g/cm^3. The density of cobalt is 8.86 g/cm^3. Measurements of mass made on the type of balance found in most school labs would be precise enough to distinguish iron from cobalt or nickel, but not precise enough to distinguish cobalt from nickel.

Making a Sculpture

A process called lost-wax casting is used to make metal sculptures. Different stages of the process depend on physical properties of wax, clay, and metal. Wax can be carved and molded. Clay becomes brittle when baked at a high temperature. When melted, most metals form homogeneous mixtures, which can be poured into molds.

Interpreting Diagrams ***Why is it important that wax has a low melting point?***

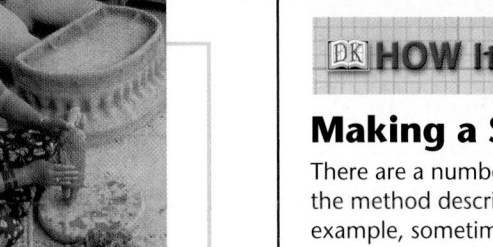

Preparing clay molds
This artist from Nepal in southern Asia is preparing molds for lost-wax casting. She is applying layers of clay to a wax model.

Wax model

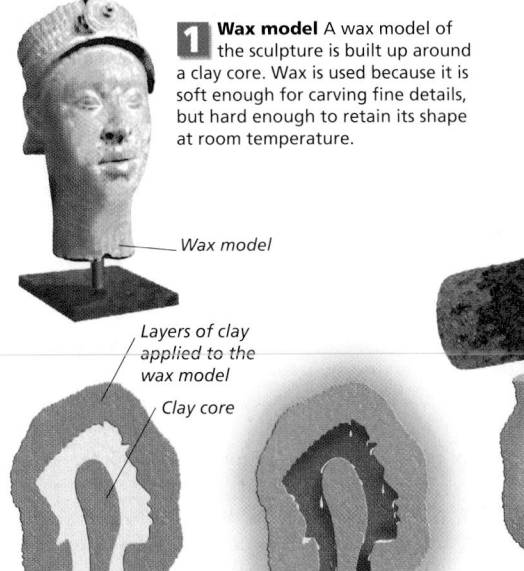

1 Wax model A wax model of the sculpture is built up around a clay core. Wax is used because it is soft enough for carving fine details, but hard enough to retain its shape at room temperature.

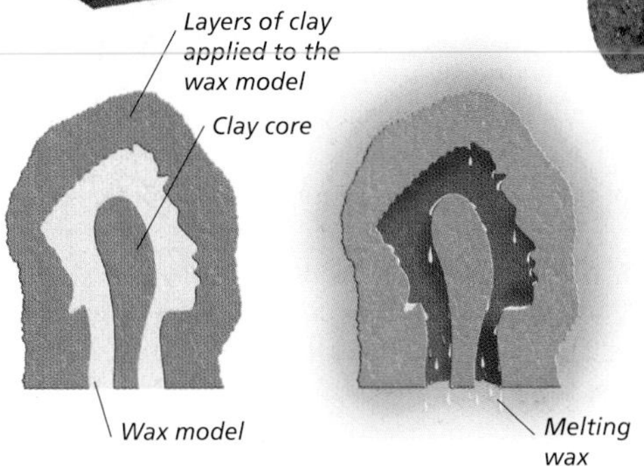
Layers of clay applied to the wax model
Clay core
Wax model
Melting wax

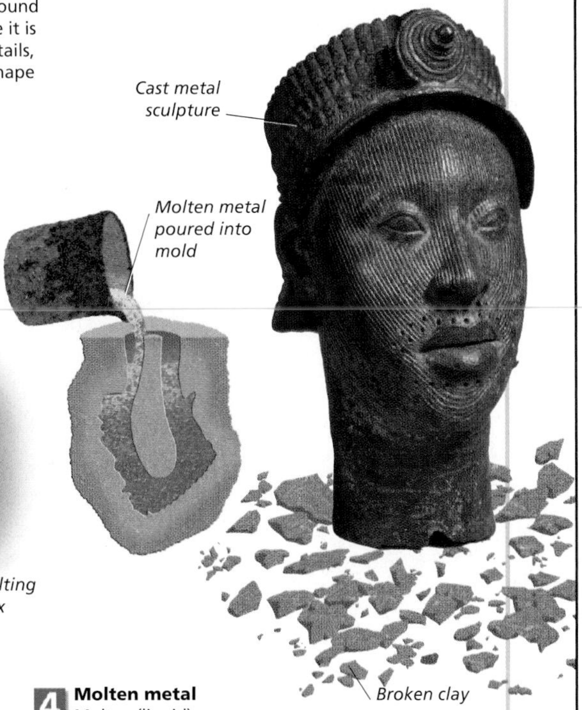
Cast metal sculpture
Molten metal poured into mold
Broken clay

2 Clay mold Clay is applied to the wax model in layers of increasing coarseness, and left to dry. The inner, finer layers capture every detail of the sculpture in a smooth mold. The outer, coarser layers (clay mixed with sand) provide strength.

3 Melting wax The clay-covered wax model is then baked in a kiln. Because wax has a low melting point, the wax model melts away inside the clay, leaving a hardened shell mold. This clay mold is then used to make the final sculpture.

4 Molten metal Molten (liquid) metal is poured into the clay mold and left to cool and harden. For this sculpture of an African head, a mixture of copper, zinc, and lead was used.

5 Metal sculpture When the metal has cooled, the clay shell is broken open to reveal the finished metal sculpture.

Making a Sculpture L2

There are a number of variations to the method described in the text. For example, sometimes there is no clay core. The lost-wax method of casting can also be used to make replicas of existing sculptures.

Many other molding and casting techniques also take advantage of the physical properties of different substances to maximize the quality of the final product. For example, the properties of some types of rubber make them ideal materials for molds. Rubber molds are flexible enough that the cast can be pulled out without breaking the mold, yet strong enough to preserve fine details in the final product. Because of their durability, rubber molds can be reused many times.

Interpreting Diagrams The wax must melt away when the model is heated in a kiln.
Logical

For Enrichment L3

Because an imprint made in wet sand will hold its shape, filling the imprint with melted wax or wet plaster will produce a cast of the object pressed into the sand. This sculpting technique is called a sand mold. Have students find out about sand molds and use them to make candles or plaster casts of their footprints or handprints.
Visual, Portfolio

Use Community Resources L2

Arrange for a sculptor or jewelry maker to visit the class. Have the artist describe the molding and casting techniques he or she uses. Before the visit, have students prepare questions about how the artist chooses materials based on their physical properties.
Interpersonal

Answer to . . .

Figure 13 *Flexibility and durability*

Using Properties to Separate Mixtures

Build Science Skills L2

Applying Concepts ACTIVITY

Purpose In this activity, students use properties to separate the components of a mixture.

Materials a mixture of table salt, sand, and iron filings; beaker; magnet; plastic bag; water; funnel; filter paper

Class Time 20 minutes

Procedure Encourage students to consider properties that can be used to separate each material from the other two materials in the mixture. Then, have students design a procedure to complete the separation.

Expected Outcome Students can collect the iron filings using a magnet covered with a plastic bag. They can add water to the mixture to dissolve the salt. They can use a filter to collect the sand. Students can collect the salt by letting the water evaporate for a few days.
Visual, Portfolio

Address Misconceptions L2

Students may think that all the particles in mixtures are similar in size. This is true for solutions and colloids, but not for suspensions. Challenge this misconception by displaying common devices used to filter mixtures (such as a sieve, a colander, and a coffee filter) and discussing the mixtures these devices are used to separate. The size of the holes in a filter determines whether filtration can be used to separate a suspension. Hole size also determines whether all the particles in a colloid pass through the filter or all the particles are trapped in the filter. Either way, the end result is that the colloid is not separated by filtration.
Verbal

Figure 14 These Americorps students are looking for artifacts at the San Diego Presidio—a fort that was built in 1769. As the students sift dirt through a screen, small objects buried in the dirt collect on the screen.
Applying Concepts ***How could changing the size of the holes in a screen change the number of objects found?***

Using Properties to Separate Mixtures

Some properties can be used to separate mixtures. **Filtration and distillation are two common separation methods.**

Filtration One way to make a pot of tea is to pour hot water over loose tea leaves. Some compounds in the tea leaves, such as caffeine, dissolve in the water. You can separate the hot tea from the loose leaves by pouring the mixture through a strainer. Using a strainer is a type of filtration. **Filtration** is a process that separates materials based on the size of their particles. Particles of the compounds that dissolve are small enough to pass through the strainer, but the tea leaves themselves are too large to pass through the strainer. The drip method of brewing coffee also uses a filter to separate the brewed coffee from the coffee grounds.

The students in Figure 14 are using a wire screen to locate small objects buried in the sand at an archaeological site. Particles of dirt are small enough to pass through the holes in the screen, but objects such as broken bits of pottery are too large to pass through the screen.

Distillation How can you separate the parts of a solution when all the particles in a solution are small enough to pass through a filter? Sometimes distillation can work. **Distillation** is a process that separates the substances in a solution based on their boiling points.

One practical use of distillation is to provide fresh water for submarines. Most submarines can store only enough fresh water to last about ten days. Each submarine has equipment that can convert seawater into fresh water. The water is heated until it changes from a liquid to a gas. The gas is cooled until it changes back to a liquid, which is collected in a separate container. Boiling can separate fresh water from seawater because water has a much lower boiling point than the compounds dissolved in seawater. These compounds are left behind in the original container.

Go Online SCIENCE NEWS

For: Articles on properties of matter
Visit: PHSchool.com
Web Code: cce-1022

Reading Checkpoint *How can loose tea leaves be removed from a pot of brewed tea?*

Facts and Figures

Tea Tea contains compounds called polyphenols, which are often referred to as tannins. There are health claims made for both black and green tea. The health claims made for green tea are related to the concentration of polyphenols. During the processing of black tea, most of the polyphenols are oxidized. Oxidation of polyphenols is limited during the processing of green tea. (The tea dumped into Boston harbor on December 16, 1773, was green tea, which outsold black tea in the Colonies.)

Go Online SCIENCE NEWS

Science News provides students with current information on properties of matter.

Recognizing Physical Changes

The change of water from a liquid to a gas during boiling is a physical change. A **physical change** occurs when some of the properties of a material change, but the substances in the material remain the same. For example, if you slowly heat butter in a pan, it changes from a solid to a liquid, but the substances in the butter do not change. Two other examples of physical changes are crumpling a piece of paper and slicing a tomato. Crumpling and slicing are actions that change the size and shape of a material, but not its composition.

Some physical changes can be reversed. You can freeze water, melt the ice that forms, and then freeze the water again. You can use an iron to remove the wrinkles from a cotton shirt. You can braid hair, unbraid the hair, and then braid it again. Some physical changes cannot be reversed. You would not expect to reconstruct a whole tomato from tomato slices or to replace the peel on a peeled orange. Figure 15 shows one physical change that can be reversed and one that cannot be reversed.

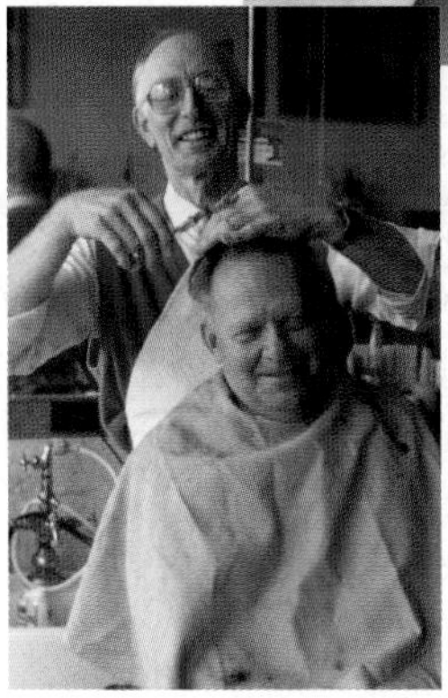

Figure 15 Braiding hair and cutting hair are examples of physical changes. Braiding is a reversible change. Cutting cannot be reversed.

Section 2.2 Assessment

Reviewing Concepts

1. List seven examples of physical properties.
2. Describe three uses of physical properties.
3. Name two processes that are used to separate mixtures.
4. When you describe a liquid as thick, are you saying that it has a high or a low viscosity?
5. Explain why sharpening a pencil is an example of a physical change.
6. What allows a mixture to be separated by distillation?

Critical Thinking

7. **Designing Experiments** How could you find out whether copper is harder or softer than the plastic used in a plastic cup?
8. **Inferring** Why would you expect the materials used to make pot holders to be poor conductors of heat?
9. **Applying Concepts** Silicon dioxide is a solid at room temperature and methanol is a liquid. Which substance has the higher melting point?

Connecting Concepts

Organizing Data In what order are the substances arranged in Figure 12? Use what you studied about organizing data in Section 1.4 to explain why this order is useful. Explain why you might choose a different order if you had similar data for 500 substances.

Recognizing Physical Changes

FYI

If butter heated in a pan begins to brown, this is a sign that a chemical change is starting to occur. Students are asked to compare the possible changes to heated butter in Question 5 of the Section 2.3 Assessment.

3 ASSESS

Evaluate Understanding L2

Tell students that a layer of fat rises to the top in a pot of chicken soup. Ask, **How can the cook remove the fat?** *(Skim the fat from the surface or freeze the soup and remove the solid fat layer.)*

Reteach L1

Use the How It Works feature on p. 49 to review with students the importance of examining physical properties when choosing a material. Discuss why the physical properties of wax, clay, and metal determine what roles they play in the making of a sculpture.

Connecting Concepts

The substances are ordered from lowest to highest melting point, which groups them into gases, liquids, and solids at room temperature. With a larger database, alphabetical order would be more useful for retrieving the data.

Interactive Textbook

If your class subscribes to the Interactive Textbook, use it to review key concepts in Section 2.2.

Section 2.2 Assessment

1. Students may list hardness, viscosity, conductivity, density, malleability, melting point, and boiling point. Students may also list color, taste, flexibility, and durability.
2. Identify materials, choose a material for a specific purpose, or separate the substances in a mixture
3. Filtration and distillation
4. A thick liquid has a high viscosity.
5. The shape and size of the pencil change, but the composition of the pencil remains the same.
6. A difference in boiling points allows mixtures to be separated by distillation.
7. By scratching the cup with an object made of copper
8. Pot holders are designed to prevent the transfer of heat from a cooking utensil.
9. Silicon dioxide

Answer to . . .

Figure 14 *With smaller holes, more objects would collect on the screen.*

Reading Checkpoint *Loose tea leaves can be removed by filtration.*

CONCEPTS — in Action —

Getting a Fresh Start L2

Background

Aeration is of great importance during waste-water treatment because of the organic compounds in sewage. Aeration is also important when the water source is groundwater because of the likely concentration of dissolved carbonates. Water that contains dissolved calcium and magnesium compounds is called hard water because deposits of these salts can accumulate in water and lessen the effectiveness of soap. Water softeners replace calcium and magnesium compounds with sodium compounds, which do not cause the same problems.

Build Science Skills L2

Observing

Purpose Students observe that water can taste different depending on its source and on its purity.

Materials tap water, bottled water, distilled water

Class Time 10 minutes

Procedure Have students taste samples of tap water, bottled water, and distilled water. Have them describe any differences or similarities they taste.

Safety Use only water that is intended for consumption.

Expected Outcome Students will be able to observe that the taste that they associate with water is due to substances dissolved in the water, and not to the water itself.
Kinesthetic, Visual

CONCEPTS in Action

Getting a Fresh Start

Water found in nature is never 100 percent pure. There are always substances dissolved in the water. Some of these substances, as well as bacteria and particles of dirt, must be removed before the water is fit to drink.

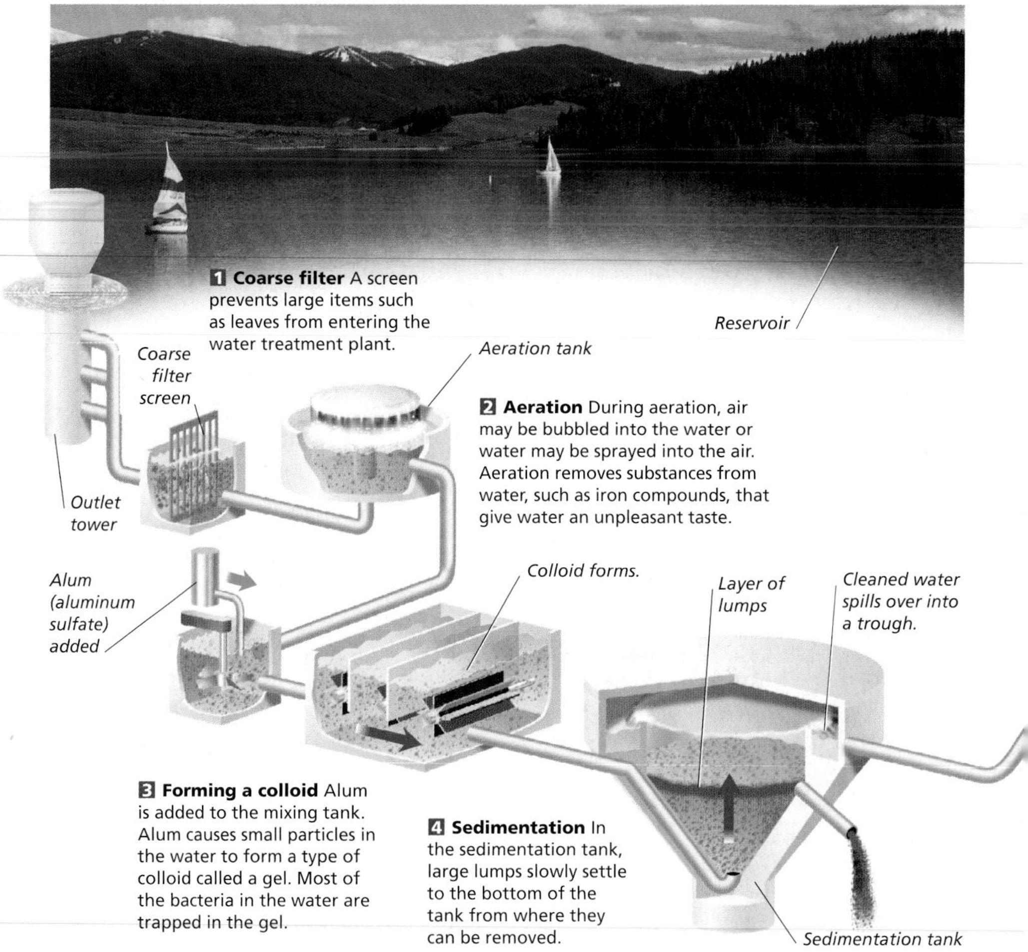
1 Coarse filter A screen prevents large items such as leaves from entering the water treatment plant.
Reservoir
Aeration tank
Coarse filter screen
2 Aeration During aeration, air may be bubbled into the water or water may be sprayed into the air. Aeration removes substances from water, such as iron compounds, that give water an unpleasant taste.
Outlet tower
Colloid forms.
Alum (aluminum sulfate) added
Layer of lumps
Cleaned water spills over into a trough.
3 Forming a colloid Alum is added to the mixing tank. Alum causes small particles in the water to form a type of colloid called a gel. Most of the bacteria in the water are trapped in the gel.
4 Sedimentation In the sedimentation tank, large lumps slowly settle to the bottom of the tank from where they can be removed.
Sedimentation tank

Water from the ground About half of the drinking water in the United States comes from natural underground sources. Although this groundwater is filtered as it passes through rocks and sand, it sometimes contains high levels of dissolved minerals or chemical pollutants. So groundwater is purified using a modified version of surface water filtration.

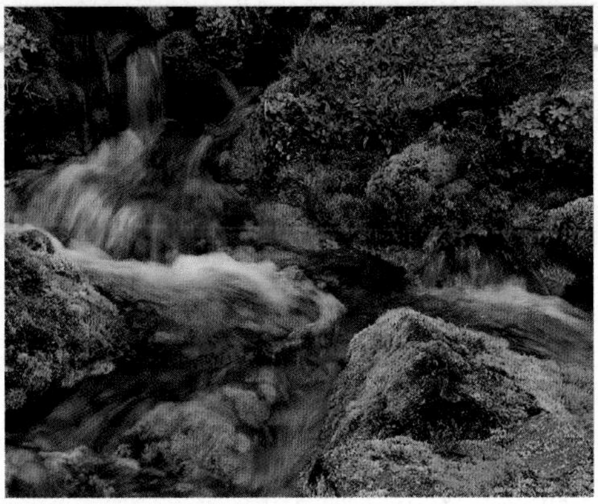

5 Sand and gravel filter Next, the water trickles through sand and gravel filter beds, which trap the remaining suspended particles. Because the filter beds can become clogged, they are washed every 24 hours.

6 Carbon filter The water is sometimes passed through a carbon filter. This filter removes tiny amounts of dissolved impurities, and improves the water's taste and color.

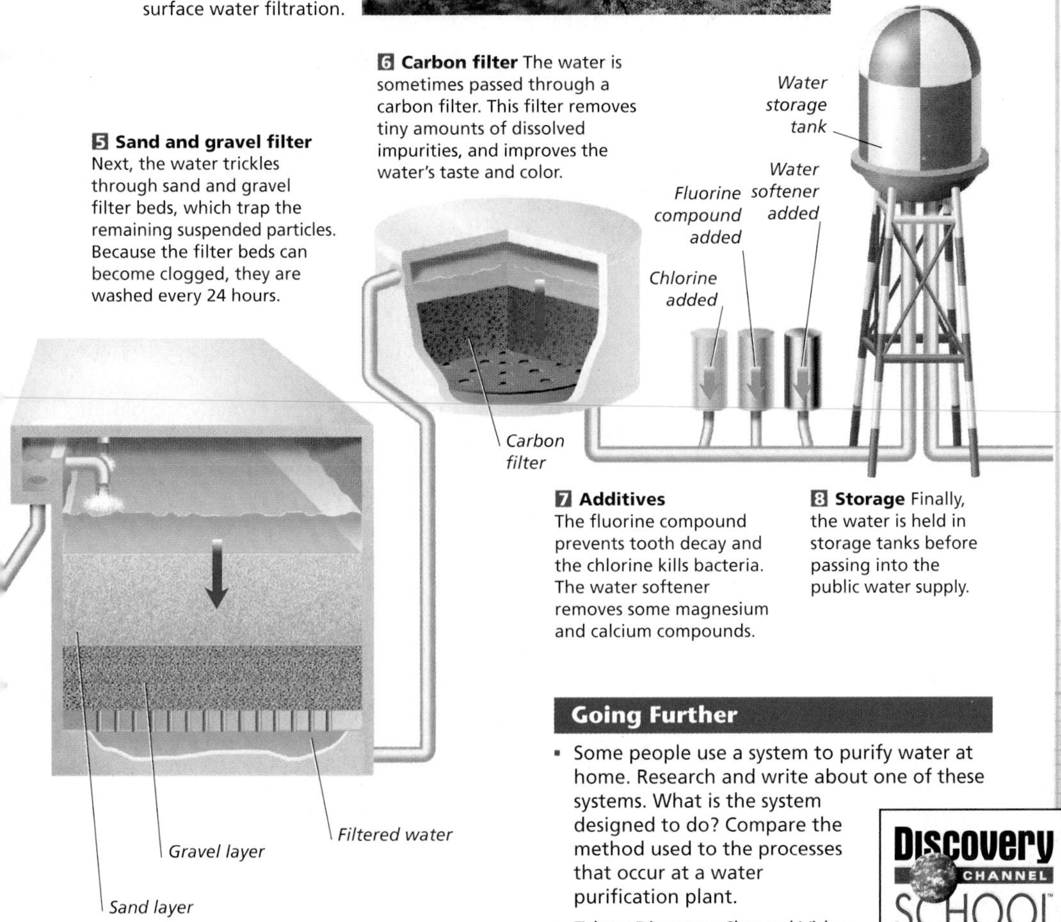
Water storage tank
Water softener added
Fluorine compound added
Chlorine added
Carbon filter
Filtered water
Gravel layer
Sand layer

7 Additives The fluorine compound prevents tooth decay and the chlorine kills bacteria. The water softener removes some magnesium and calcium compounds.

8 Storage Finally, the water is held in storage tanks before passing into the public water supply.

Going Further

- Some people use a system to purify water at home. Research and write about one of these systems. What is the system designed to do? Compare the method used to the processes that occur at a water purification plant.
- Take a Discovery Channel Video Field Trip by watching "Fresh-Squeezed Water."

Discovery Channel School **Video Field Trip**

Going Further

Most home water purification systems use activated charcoal (AC) filters or reverse osmosis (RO). Neither system removes all contaminants. Activated charcoal is an extremely porous solid with a large surface area on which substances are absorbed. Activated charcoal is effective for removing volatile organic compounds, pesticides, some metals, and chlorine. Sometimes bacteria grow on the filter. The surface of the activated charcoal may become saturated and ineffective before the consumer replaces the filter.

During reverse osmosis, normal household water pressure forces water through a semipermeable membrane. Reverse osmosis is useful for removing lead and other transition metals, asbestos, and many dissolved organic compounds. Reverse osmosis is a slow, wasteful process that uses three to nine gallons per gallon of purified water. (Some people use RO systems in their fish tanks.)

In parts of the world without municipal treatment plants, UV light is used to kill waterborne pathogens. **Verbal**

Video Field Trip

Fresh-Squeezed Water

After students have viewed the Video Field Trip, ask them the following questions: **Why did the people on Catalina Island need to convert seawater to fresh water?** *(They were running out of drinkable water.)* **What is a semipermeable membrane?** *(A semipermeable membrane is a material that has microscopic holes to allow water to pass through while blocking salts and viruses.)* **What is reverse osmosis?** *(During reverse osmosis, water under high pressure passes through a semipermeable membrane, which removes dissolved salts and other unwanted substances.)* **Why is NASA also interested in desalination methods?** *(Being able to recycle the water on board a spacecraft reduces the amount and the weight of water that must accompany the astronauts on their voyages.)*

Section 2.3

1 FOCUS

Objectives

2.3.1 **Describe** chemical properties of matter.

2.3.2 **Describe** clues that indicate that a chemical change is taking place.

2.3.3 **Distinguish** chemical changes from physical changes.

Reading Focus

Build Vocabulary L2

Word-Part Analysis Have students look up the words *flammable, inflammable,* and *nonflammable.* Have them find two meanings of the prefix *in-* to explain why the terms are confusing. Ask them to consider why it is very important to know what each term means. *(Inflammable and flammable are synonyms. The prefix* in- *can mean "not," or "into" as in "burst into flames." It is important to use the correct meanings when writing or interpreting fire safety warnings.)*

Reading Strategy L2

a. Copper roof changing color from red to green when exposed to moist air
b. Formation of carbon dioxide gas when vinegar is added to baking soda
c. Formation of cottage cheese curds when acid is added to milk

2 INSTRUCT

Observing Chemical Properties

Build Reading Literacy L1

Preview Refer to page **36D** in this chapter, which provides the guidelines for previewing.

Before they read the section, have students skim the headings, visuals, and boldfaced material to preview how the text is organized.
Visual

FYI

If the combustion of paraffin is not complete, carbon monoxide will form. Combustion as a type of reaction is addressed in Chapter 7. Combustion of fossil fuels is discussed in Chapter 9.

2.3 Chemical Properties

Reading Focus

Key Concepts

- When can chemical properties be observed?
- What observations might indicate that a chemical change has occurred?
- What is the difference between chemical and physical changes?

Vocabulary

- chemical property
- flammability
- reactivity
- chemical change
- precipitate

Reading Strategy

Relating Text and Visuals Copy the table. Find examples of the clues for recognizing chemical changes in Figures 19 and 20.

Clue	Example
Change in color	a. ?
Production of gas	b. ?
Formation of precipitate	c. ?

How would you describe candles like the ones in Figure 16? You might describe their color or their hardness. Or, you might observe that the candles float on water, and conclude that the density of candle wax is less than that of water. Color, hardness, and density are physical properties. But there is something else about the candles that may seem even more obvious to you: the fact that the candles are burning. The ability to burn is not a physical property because you cannot observe burning without changing the composition of the material that is burning. As a candle burns, new substances form.

Observing Chemical Properties

Most candles are made from paraffin, which is a mixture of compounds containing carbon and hydrogen. As a candle burns, the compounds combine with oxygen in the air to form water and carbon dioxide. (Carbon dioxide is the gas that gives a carbonated beverage its fizz.) The ability to burn is a chemical property. A **chemical property** is any ability to produce a change in the composition of matter. **Chemical properties can be observed only when the substances in a sample of matter are changing into different substances.** Flammability and reactivity are two examples of chemical properties.

Flammability Materials that burn can be used as fuel. Sometimes, people use burning newspapers to start a fire in a fireplace. Gasoline is the fuel burned in most automobiles. The chemical property that paper and gasoline share is their flammability. **Flammability** is a material's ability to burn in the presence of oxygen.

Figure 16 When candles burn, new substances form. The ability to burn is a chemical property.

Section Resources

Print
- ***Laboratory Manual,*** Investigation 2A
- ***Reading and Study Workbook With Math Support,*** Section 2.3
- ***Transparencies,*** Section 2.3

Technology
- ***Interactive Textbook,*** Section 2.3
- ***Presentation Pro CD-ROM,*** Section 2.3
- ***Go Online,*** NSTA SciLinks, Chemical and physical changes

Sometimes flammability is not a desirable property. For example, there are laws that regulate the flammability of fabrics. The fabrics used in children's sleepwear must have a low flammability. These fabrics are described as flame-resistant because they are difficult to ignite. If they do ignite, they burn slowly.

Reactivity The property that describes how readily a substance combines chemically with other substances is **reactivity.** Nitrogen and oxygen are the main gases in air. Oxygen is a highly reactive element. Nitrogen has an extremely low reactivity.

Oxygen reacts easily with most other elements. Figure 17 shows the rust that forms when oxygen reacts with iron and water. Rust is a brittle, reddish-brown compound. A rusty chain or bolt is more likely to break than a new chain or bolt because rust is weaker than iron. Because iron is highly reactive, you would not choose iron to make decorative objects, such as jewelry or coins.

Many uses of nitrogen depend on its low reactivity. For example, seawater is often stored in steel tanks located below the lowest deck of a ship. The seawater helps to keep the ship stable in the water. Over time, rust forms in the tanks because iron in the steel reacts with oxygen dissolved in the water. Researchers in Japan have developed a way to reduce the amount of rust produced. They pump nitrogen gas into the tanks, and the nitrogen displaces the dissolved oxygen.

Reading Checkpoint *Which element is more reactive—oxygen or nitrogen?*

Go Online NSTA SCILINKS

For: Links on chemical and physical changes
Visit: www.SciLinks.org
Web Code: ccn-1023

Figure 17 This automobile must have been exposed to air and water for many years. **Drawing Conclusions** ***What evidence is there that parts of the automobile contained iron?***

Teacher Demo

Oxygen Is Needed L2

Purpose Students observe that air is needed for a candle to burn.

Materials 2 small candles, matches, large beaker

Procedure Tell students that the flammability of a material is tested in air. Light two candles with a match. Carefully place a large beaker over one of the candles and have students observe what happens. Remove the beaker and relight the candle to show that it can still burn. Discuss how a scientist might test the hypothesis that oxygen is the gas in air that supports burning.

Expected Outcome After the beaker is placed over the candle, the flame dies out. The other candle continues to burn. To demonstrate that oxygen is the gas that supports burning, the scientist could try burning the candle in pure samples of the gases in air.
Visual, Logical

Build Science Skills L2

Designing Experiments Challenge students to describe a material that they could test for flammability without changing its composition. *(The material would have to be nonflammable.)* Help students by asking them how they would test the material for flammability and what the results of the test would be. Explain that the absence of an observed event is useful data.
Verbal

Go Online NSTA SCILINKS

Download a worksheet on chemical and physical changes for students to complete, and find additional teacher support from NSTA SciLinks.

Customize for English Language Learners

Paired Brainstorming
Have students work in pairs to think of other items—besides cars, chains, or bolts—that rust. Examples include bicycle frames, door and gate hinges, and old nails. Strengthen discussion skills by having students share their examples with the class. Encourage them to comment on what these items have in common. Although many items made from iron are coated with paint to prevent rusting, paint does chip and items containing iron will rust if left outdoors unprotected from the elements.

Answer to . . .

Figure 17 *The amount of rust is evidence that much of the automobile was made of iron.*

Reading Checkpoint *Oxygen*

Recognizing Chemical Changes

Quick Lab

Identifying a Chemical Change L2

Objective
After completing this activity, students will be able to
- recognize evidence of a chemical change.

Skills Focus **Observing, Drawing Conclusions**

Prep Time 20 minutes

Advance Prep To prepare 1-M solutions of calcium chloride, sodium chloride, and copper sulfate, dissolve 1 mole of each salt (111.0 g $CaCl_2$; 58.5 g NaCl; or 249.69 g $CuSO_4{\bullet}5H_2O$) in approximately 800 mL of distilled or deionized water in a 1-L volumetric flask. Once a salt has dissolved, add enough water to make a 1000-mL solution. Stir the solution. Provide each group with 25 mL of each solution in a wash bottle, which is the easiest container for students to handle. Be sure to label each container with its contents.

Class Time 20 minutes

Safety Remind students to wash their hands thoroughly at the end of the lab, to be careful when handling glassware, and to dispose properly of chemical wastes.

Teaching Tips
- Review how to pour a liquid from a graduated cylinder and accurately read the volume.

Expected Outcome A precipitate of calcium sulfate will form in test tube A. The other two combinations will show no evidence of a chemical change.

Analyze and Conclude
1. Formation of a precipitate indicated that a chemical change occurred in test tube A.
2. No, formation of a precipitate is evidence for a chemical change, but it is not conclusive.
Visual, Logical

Quick Lab

Identifying a Chemical Change

Materials

3 test tubes; test-tube rack; glass-marking pencil; 3 10-mL graduated cylinders; solutions of copper sulfate, calcium chloride, and sodium chloride

Procedure

1. Construct a data table with columns labeled Test Tube, Contents, and Observations.
2. Label the test tubes A, B, and C.
3. Pour 5 mL of copper sulfate solution into test tube A. Pour 5 mL of calcium chloride solution into test tube B. Pour 5 mL of sodium chloride solution into test tube C. **CAUTION** *Do not allow the solutions to touch your skin. They may cause irritation.*
4. Add 5 mL of calcium chloride solution to test tube A. Add 5 mL of sodium chloride solution to test tube B. Add 5 mL of copper sulfate solution to test tube C.
5. Examine the test tubes for evidence of a chemical change. Record your observations.
6. Pour the contents of the test tubes into the sink. Rinse out the test tubes and flush the contents down the drain. **CAUTION** *Wash your hands thoroughly with soap or detergent before leaving the laboratory.*

Analyze and Conclude

1. **Inferring** In which test tube(s) did a chemical change occur? Explain your answer.
2. **Evaluating** Can you be sure that a chemical change occurred? Explain your answer.

Recognizing Chemical Changes

Figure 18 shows what happens to banana peels as bananas ripen. The color change in a banana peel is caused by chemical changes that are taking place in the cells of the banana. A **chemical change** occurs when a substance reacts and forms one or more new substances. Chemical changes occur when a cake bakes in an oven, leaves on trees change color, and food is digested in your stomach.

How can you recognize a chemical change? You have to look for clues. For example, when food spoils, it often gives off an unpleasant odor. **Three common types of evidence for a chemical change are a change in color, the production of a gas, and the formation of a precipitate.**

Figure 18 As a banana ripens, chemical changes cause the peel to change color from green to yellow. In a banana that is overly ripe, different chemical changes cause the peel to turn brown. ***Observing*** ***Based on your experience, what other properties of a banana change as it ripens?***

Facts and Figures

Banana Science There are four stages of banana development: growth, maturation, ripening, and senescence. During ripening, bananas produce increased amounts of ethylene gas, which triggers chemical changes. The peel changes color and becomes more permeable, the pulp softens, starches break down into sugar, and compounds responsible for flavor and aroma are produced. Once ripening begins, the process cannot be stopped. Ripening occurs whether the banana is attached or detached from the parent plant.

A Change in Color Over time, a shiny silver bracelet that is exposed to air will darken. As a match burns, it shrivels up and turns black. The new copper roof and the old copper roof in Figure 19 have different colors. In each of these examples, a change in color is a clue that a chemical change has produced at least one new substance.

Production of a Gas Figure 20A shows what happens when you mix vinegar with baking soda. Bubbles of carbon dioxide form immediately. A similar chemical change happens when you use baking powder as an ingredient in a cake recipe. Baking powder is a mixture of baking soda and one or more acids that react when wet. As the cake bakes, the bubbles of carbon dioxide expand and cause the cake to rise.

Formation of a Precipitate Another chemical change you can observe in the kitchen is the curdling of milk. If you add lemon juice or vinegar to milk, small bits of white solid will separate from the liquid. Any solid that forms and separates from a liquid mixture is called a **precipitate.** When an acid is added to milk, proteins in the milk undergo a chemical change that alters their structure, causing them to stick together in clumps. They form the precipitate shown in Figure 20B.

Reading Checkpoint *What happens when you add vinegar to baking soda?*

Figure 19 When copper is exposed to moist air, it forms a thin coating called a patina. A new copper roof has a reddish color. The green patina on an old copper roof is a mixture of copper compounds.
Predicting ***Would a patina form faster in a rainy climate or in a dry climate?***

A

B

Figure 20 The formation of a gas or a precipitate can be a clue to chemical change. **A** Carbon dioxide gas forms when vinegar is mixed with baking soda. **B** The curds in cottage cheese form when an acid is added to milk.

Use Visuals L1

Figure 20 Emphasize that the best way to determine if a chemical change is taking place is to compare materials before and after the reaction. Ask, **Describe baking soda and vinegar before they are mixed.** *(Baking soda is a white solid, and vinegar is a clear solution.)* **What clue indicates that a chemical change is taking place?** *(There is production of a gas.)* **When you see no obvious clues to a chemical change, can you be certain that a chemical change has not occurred?** *(No)*
Visual

Facts and Figures

Acids in Action When acid is added to milk, one of the proteins in milk (casein) coagulates. The milk may thicken (as in buttermilk or yogurt) or separate into solid curds and liquid whey (as in cottage cheese). This process is called curdling. Acids may be added directly to the milk or produced by bacteria. Adding rennin (a coagulating enzyme) produces larger curds.

Single-action baking powder contains three dry ingredients: an acid (e.g., cream of tartar), a base (e.g., baking soda), and filler (e.g., cornstarch). When water is added, the acid and base react. Double-action baking powders contain two acids, one that reacts faster than the other. Recipes that use baking soda have another ingredient that provides the acid.

Answer to . . .

Figure 18 *Students may say that the banana becomes softer and that its odor increases.*

Figure 19 *In a rainy climate*

Reading Checkpoint *Bubbles of carbon dioxide form.*

Is a Change Chemical or Physical?

Address Misconceptions **L2**

Students often have trouble distinguishing chemical from physical changes. Explain that the composition of *some* substances must change during a chemical change, but the composition of *all* substances must remain the same during a physical change.
Verbal

FYI

The release of heat or light is sometimes listed as a clue for a chemical change, but energy changes occur with both physical and chemical changes. Exothermic and endothermic changes are discussed in Sections 3.3 (Phase Changes) and 7.3 (Energy Changes in Reactions).

3 ASSESS

Evaluate Understanding **L2**

Have students list three clues that indicate that a chemical change is taking place and give an example of each. Then, have them exchange their work with a partner and discuss examples of physical changes that also exhibit these clues.

Reteach **L1**

Use Figures 18, 19, and 20 to review the clues that indicate that a chemical change is taking place.

Connecting Concepts

Students might argue that observation and experimentation are the key steps in a scientific method for determining whether a change is physical or chemical.

Interactive Textbook If your class subscribes to the Interactive Textbook, use it to review key concepts in Section 2.3.

Answer to . . .

Figure 21 *Malleability increases.*

Figure 21 A blacksmith uses a hammer to shape a horseshoe that has been heated. Although the color of the iron horseshoe changes, no chemical change is occurring. **Inferring** ***Other than color, what physical property of iron is affected by heating?***

Is a Change Chemical or Physical?

It is not always easy to distinguish a chemical change from a physical change. Even if you observe a color change, a gas, or a precipitate, you cannot be sure that a chemical change has taken place. When the iron horseshoe in Figure 21 is heated, its color changes from gray to red. Despite this change in color, the iron is still iron. When water boils on a stove, the bubbles of gas that rise to the surface are still water.

Before you decide whether or not a chemical change has occurred, ask yourself this question: Are different substances present after the change takes place? If not, then the change is physical, not chemical. **When matter undergoes a chemical change, the composition of the matter changes. When matter undergoes a physical change, the composition of the matter remains the same.**

Section 2.3 Assessment

Reviewing Concepts

1. Under what conditions can chemical properties be observed?
2. List three common types of evidence for a chemical change.
3. How do chemical changes differ from physical changes?
4. Explain why the rusting of an iron bar decreases the strength of the bar.
5. A pat of butter melts and then burns in a hot frying pan. Which of these changes is physical and which is chemical?

Critical Thinking

6. **Comparing and Contrasting** Compare the properties of a raw egg to those of a hard-boiled egg.
7. **Classifying** If you spill household bleach on denim jeans, you will observe that the area of the spill no longer has a blue color. Is this change chemical or physical? Give a reason for your answer.
8. **Inferring** Gold and platinum are often used to make jewelry. What can you infer about the reactivity of these elements?

Connecting Concepts

Scientific Methods Section 1.2 listed typical steps scientists use. Which steps might you use to decide whether a change is physical or chemical? Explain.

Section 2.3 Assessment

1. When the substances in a sample of matter are changing into different substances
2. A change in color, the production of a gas, or the formation of a precipitate
3. A chemical change produces new substances. A physical change produces no new substances.
4. When iron rusts, the compound that forms is brittle.
5. Melting is a physical change. Burning is a chemical change.
6. The raw egg is a viscous liquid. The egg white is cloudy and the yolk is orange. The hard-boiled egg is a soft solid. The egg white is opaque and the yolk is yellow.
7. Because the bleach has caused the denim to change color, the change is likely to be a chemical change.
8. Because jewelry is designed to last a long time, the reactivity of gold and platinum must be relatively low.

issues in SCIENCE

What Should Be Done With Arsenic-Treated Wood?

Termites are among the organisms that attack untreated wood. In 1950, United States suppliers of lumber began to treat wood with a mixture of copper, chromium, and arsenic (CCA). The mixture slows the damage to wood by poisoning the attacking organisms. Outdoor structures such as decks and porches were made from CCA-treated wood. By 2002, more than 95 percent of treated lumber sold for use outdoors contained CCA.

Arsenic is a poison that has been linked with certain types of cancer. Arsenic can be absorbed through the skin or ingested in water or food. Consumers were especially concerned about children touching CCA-treated wood and then placing their unwashed fingers in their mouths. Some consumers asked the Environmental Protection Agency (EPA) to ban the use of CCA. In 2002, the chemical and home-improvement industries agreed to stop producing CCA-treated wood for home use.

The Viewpoints

Old CCA-Treated Wood Does Not Need to Be Removed

The EPA did not recommend tearing down existing structures made from CCA-treated wood. A panel of Florida doctors reported that they found no studies linking cancer in children and exposure to CCA-treated wood. They concluded that the amount of arsenic that children could absorb from treated wood is small compared to the amount of arsenic that occurs naturally in soil.

There are risks associated with disposing of treated wood. Burning arsenic-treated wood produces ash with high levels of arsenic. The ash would poison a person who inhaled, ingested, or touched it. The only acceptable method of disposal is in landfills, which are rapidly filling. Also, arsenic from landfills can end up in groundwater.

Old CCA-Treated Wood Needs to Be Removed

A report produced by one state's Department of Environmental Protection concluded that there is a serious risk for children exposed to arsenic from treated wood. The level of arsenic remains high for 20 years in CCA-treated wood. The useful life of most treated wood products is about 20 years.

An area of CCA-treated wood the size of a four-year-old's hand contains about 120 times the amount of arsenic allowed in a 6-ounce glass of water. (The EPA limit for arsenic in drinking water is 10 parts per billion.) Rainwater penetrates wood and dissolves arsenic. The arsenic ends up on the surface of the wood or in the soil near the wood.

Research and Decide

1. **Defining the Issue** In your own words, describe the issue that needs to be resolved about existing structures made from CCA-treated wood.
2. **Analyzing the Viewpoints** List three arguments of those who don't think that existing structures made from CCA-treated wood need to be removed. List three arguments of those who want to remove existing structures made from CCA-treated wood.
3. **Forming Your Opinion** Should existing structures built from CCA-treated wood be removed? Which argument did you find most convincing?

Go Online PHSchool.com

For: More on this issue
Visit: PHSchool.com
Web Code: cch-1020

issues in SCIENCE

What Should Be Done With Arsenic-Treated Wood? L2

Background

Woods that are naturally resistant to attack, such as cedar and redwood, tend to be more expensive than timber treated with CCA. Alternatives to waterborne preservatives such as CCA included creosote and pentachlorophenol, or penta. Creosote is a smelly mixture of chemicals distilled from coal tar. Railroads began to treat railroad ties with creosote in 1889. Penta was generally applied in a 5% solution of petroleum solvents. Its use became limited after the price of oil rose in the 1970s. Because there are health risks associated with both penta and creosote, their use has been restricted since 1986.

After students answer Question 3, ask, **What evidence did the opponents and supporters of CCA removal have that you do not have? Explain how that evidence might have influenced your opinion.** *(The viewpoints as presented were based on opposing interpretations of scientific studies. Being able to see the actual data might have influenced their opinions.)*

Go Online PHSchool.com

Have students further research the issues related to this topic.

Answers

1. Are structures built from CCA-treated wood enough of a health hazard for children that the structures should be removed?

2. Old CCA-Treated Wood Does Not Need to Be Removed: The EPA has not recommended removal of the structures. No studies link cancer in children and exposure to CCA-treated wood. There are serious risks associated with disposal of the wood. **Old CCA-Treated Wood Needs to Be Removed:** The level of arsenic remains high over the lifetime of the wood. The level of arsenic in the wood is much higher than the level allowed in water. Rain causes arsenic to collect on the surface of the wood or in soil.

3. Students should provide a reason for their decision.

Forensics Lab

Using Properties to Identify Materials

L2

Objective
After completing this activity, students will be able to
- identify simple chemical changes.
- identify an unknown sample by comparing its properties to those of known materials.

Skills Focus **Observing, Inferring, Predicting**

Prep Time 10 minutes

Advance Prep Set out small, labeled containers of each of the materials to be tested for each group. Provide dropper bottles of water, vinegar, and iodine solution for each group. If you need to prepare iodine solution, mix 1 mL of concentrated tincture of iodine with 50 mL of water. Use baking powder for the crime scene sample and baking soda for the suspect's shoe sample.

Class Time 45 minutes

Safety Make sure that students wear aprons, goggles, and plastic disposable gloves throughout the lab. Caution students about the proper handling of the iodine solution because it is poisonous and can stain skin and clothing. Rinse iodine spills with water.

Questioning Strategies
Ask students: **What observations could indicate that a chemical change has taken place?** *(The release of a gas, the formation of a precipitate, or a color change can indicate that a chemical change has taken place.)* **Which test distinguishes baking soda from baking powder?** *(Addition of iodine solution causes bubbling with baking powder, but not with baking soda.)* **How could you use data from this lab to help you identify the unknown samples?** *(By comparing the test results of the known samples with the test results of the unknown samples)* **Why do you need to use different wells for each material?** *(To avoid contamination of materials being tested)*

Forensics Lab

Using Properties to Identify Materials

Forensic chemists test the physical and chemical properties of materials found at a crime scene. They also do similar tests on the materials found on a suspect's skin or clothing. These materials are often complex mixtures, such as soil, which contain many substances. In this lab, you will compare the properties of three known materials with two samples of "evidence." These samples represent evidence from a crime scene and evidence from a suspect's shoe. Although your materials and equipment are less complex than those used by forensic chemists, your overall method will be similar to the methods they use.

Problem Can the properties of materials that appear similar be used to tell them apart?

Materials
- 2 spot plates
- glass-marking pencil
- 5 laboratory spatulas
- cornstarch
- baking soda
- baking powder
- wash bottle of water
- vinegar
- iodine solution
- sample from crime scene
- sample from suspect's shoe

Skills Observing, Inferring, Predicting

Procedure

Part A: Properties of Known Substances

1. On a separate sheet of paper, copy the data table shown.
2. Use a glass-marking pencil to label 15 wells A through O on the spot plates. Make a mark next to each well, not in the well.
3. Use a spatula to place a small amount of cornstarch in wells A, B, and C. Record any physical properties of the cornstarch that you observe.
4. Use a clean spatula to place a small amount of baking soda in wells D, E, and F. Record any physical properties of baking soda you observe.
5. Using a clean spatula, place a small amount of baking powder in wells G, H, and I. Record any physical properties of baking powder you observe.
6. Fill wells A, D, and G with water. Record any changes you observe.

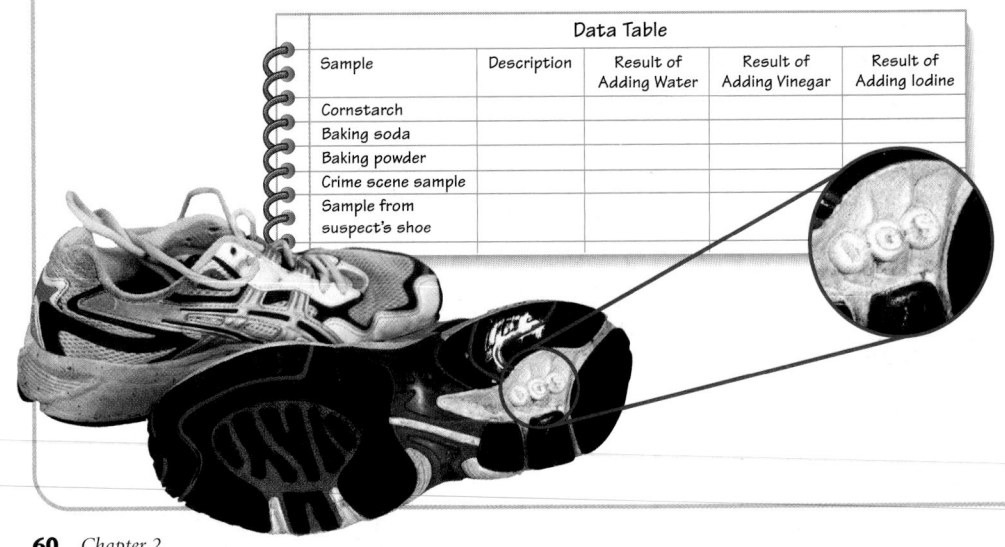

Data Table

Sample	Description	Result of Adding Water	Result of Adding Vinegar	Result of Adding Iodine
Cornstarch				
Baking soda				
Baking powder				
Crime scene sample				
Sample from suspect's shoe				

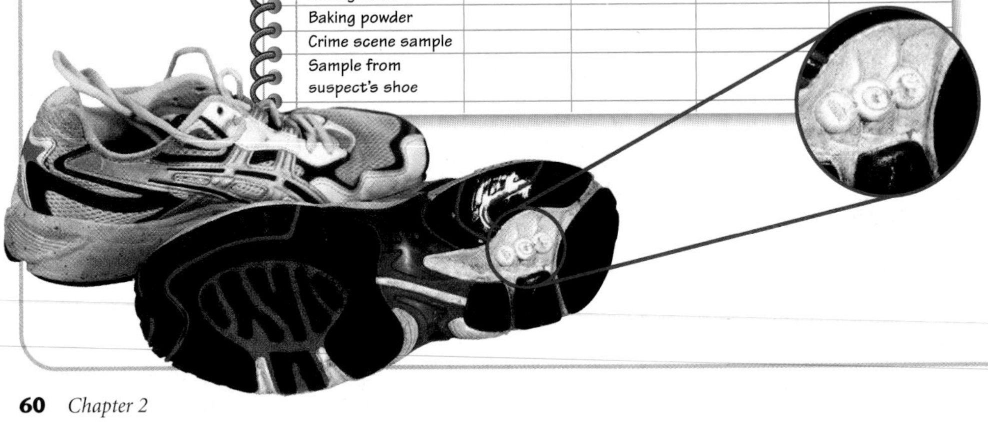

Sample Data Table

Sample	Description	Result of Adding Water	Result of Adding Vinegar	Result of Adding Iodine
Cornstarch	white powder	no change	no change	blue-black
Baking soda	white powder	dissolves	bubbles	no change
Baking powder	white powder	partly dissolves, bubbles	bubbles	bubbles
Crime scene sample	white powder	partly dissolves, bubbles	bubbles	bubbles
Sample from suspect's shoe	white powder	dissolves	bubbles	bubbles

7. Fill wells B, E, and H with vinegar. Record any changes you observe.
8. Add one drop of iodine solution to wells C, F, and I. Record any changes you observe. **CAUTION** *Iodine solution is corrosive and poisonous. It can stain skin and clothing. Rinse any iodine spills with water.*

Part B: Properties of Unknown Substances

9. **Predicting** Look at the sample from the crime scene and the sample from the suspect's shoe. Based on your observations, predict whether testing will show that the samples are identical. Record your prediction.
10. Use a clean spatula to place a small amount of the sample from the crime scene in wells J, K, and L. Record any physical properties of the sample that you observe.
11. Use a clean laboratory spatula to place a small amount of the sample from the suspect's shoe in wells M, N, and O. Record any physical properties of the sample that you observe.
12. Fill wells J and M with water. Record your observations.
13. Fill wells K and N with vinegar. Record your observations.
14. Add one drop of iodine solution to wells L and O. Record your observations.
15. Rinse all materials off the spot plates and flush them down the drain with at least ten times as much water. Dispose of your plastic gloves as directed by your teacher. **CAUTION** *Wash your hands thoroughly with soap or detergent before leaving the laboratory.*

Analyze and Conclude

1. **Analyzing Data** Were you able to use the ability to dissolve in water to distinguish all three materials? Explain.
2. **Drawing Conclusions** Are the samples from the suspect and from the crime scene identical?
3. **Evaluating and Revising** Did the data you collected support your prediction? Explain your answer.

Go Further Design an experiment to determine the effect of heating on the materials you tested in this lab. With your teacher's approval and supervision, carry out your experiment and use the data you collect to identify a sample of an unknown material.

Expected Outcome The crime scene sample and the sample from the suspect's shoe are not the same. The crime scene sample is baking powder and the sample from the suspect's shoe is baking soda.

Go Further

Check students' proposed procedures for safety before permitting them to carry out their experiments. Samples can be placed on a can lid with safely smoothed edges for heating over a Bunsen burner or hot plate. Cornstarch will visibly char when heated. The other materials will not undergo any visible changes.
Kinesthetic, Logical

Analyze and Conclude

1. The ability to dissolve in water distinguished cornstarch from baking soda and baking powder, but not baking soda from baking powder.
2. The results did not indicate that the sample from the crime scene (baking powder) has the same properties as the sample from the suspect's shoe (baking soda).
3. Yes or no (depending on the prediction made). Students should use evidence from the water and iodine solution tests to support their answers.
Visual, Logical

Study Guide

Study Tip

Structure Study Time
A good way to begin to study for a test is to figure out what topics will be covered and to what extent they will appear on the test. Tell students that they should structure their study time by studying each topic for an amount of time proportionate to its coverage in class or in the textbook. They should set time goals for themselves and take small breaks as a reward for accomplishing each goal.

Thinking Visually

a. Chemical change
b. Boiling, freezing, crumpling, slicing, braiding, or cutting
c. Burning

CHAPTER 2

Study Guide

2.1 Classifying Matter

Key Concepts

- Every sample of a given substance has the same properties because a substance has a fixed, uniform composition.
- An element has a fixed composition because it contains only one type of atom.
- A compound always contains two or more elements joined in a fixed proportion.
- The properties of a mixture can vary because the composition of a mixture is not fixed.
- Based on the size of its largest particles, a mixture can be classified as a solution, a suspension, or a colloid.

Vocabulary

pure substance, *p. 39*
element, *p. 39*
atom, *p. 39*
compound, *p. 40*
heterogeneous mixture, *p. 41*
homogeneous mixture, *p. 42*
solution, *p. 42*
suspension, *p. 43*
colloid, *p. 44*

2.2 Physical Properties

Key Concepts

- Viscosity, conductivity, malleability, hardness, melting point, boiling point, and density are examples of physical properties.
- Physical properties are used to identify a material, to choose a material for a specific purpose, or to separate the substances in a mixture.
- Filtration and distillation are two common separation methods.

Vocabulary

physical property, *p. 45*
viscosity, *p. 45*
conductivity, *p. 46*
malleability, *p. 46*
melting point, *p. 47*
boiling point, *p. 47*
filtration, *p. 50*
distillation, *p. 50*
physical change, *p. 51*

2.3 Chemical Properties

Key Concepts

- Chemical properties can be observed only when the substances in a sample of matter are changing into different substances.
- Three common types of evidence for a chemical change are a change in color, the production of a gas, and the formation of a precipitate.
- When matter undergoes a chemical change, the composition of the matter changes. When matter undergoes a physical change, the composition of the matter remains the same.

Vocabulary

chemical property, *p. 54*
flammability, *p. 54*
reactivity, *p. 55*
chemical change, *p. 56*
precipitate, *p. 57*

Thinking Visually

Concept Map Use information from the chapter to complete the concept map below.

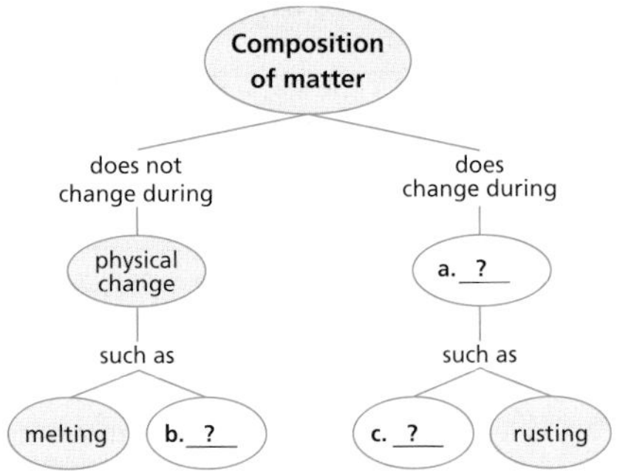
Composition of matter
does not change during
does change during
physical change
a. ?
such as
such as
melting
b. ?
c. ?
rusting

Chapter Resources

Print
- ***Chapter and Unit Tests,*** Chapter 2 Test A and Test B
- ***Test Prep Resources,*** Chapter 2

Technology
- ***Computer Test Bank,*** Chapter Test 2
- ***Interactive Textbook,*** Chapter 2
- ***Go Online,*** PHSchool.com, Chapter 2

CHAPTER 2

Assessment

Interactive textbook with assessment at PHSchool.com

Reviewing Content

Choose the letter that best answers the question or completes the statement.

1. Which of these substances is not an element?
   a. water b. hydrogen
   c. aluminum d. iron

2. Tap water is
   a. an element. b. a compound.
   c. a substance. d. a mixture.

3. When a homemade oil-and-vinegar salad dressing is left standing, it separates into layers. The salad dressing is a
   a. solution. b. suspension.
   c. colloid. d. compound.

4. Which of the following is not an example of a physical property?
   a. density b. flammability
   c. hardness d. melting point

5. Which material is a poor conductor of heat?
   a. iron b. silver
   c. wood d. copper

6. A material that can be hit without shattering is
   a. viscous. b. flammable.
   c. malleable. d. hard.

7. At room temperature, a substance with a melting point of 40°C is a
   a. solid. b. liquid.
   c. gas. d. mixture.

8. Which action involves a chemical change?
   a. making ice cubes
   b. adding sugar to tea
   c. cutting wrapping paper
   d. baking a cake

9. A substance that has little tendency to change into other substances is said to have low
   a. reactivity. b. density.
   c. viscosity. d. conductivity.

10. Formation of a precipitate is usually evidence of
    a. the separation of a mixture.
    b. a chemical change.
    c. the formation of a mixture.
    d. a physical change.

Understanding Concepts

11. Explain why the properties of a pure substance do not vary from sample to sample.

12. What is the difference between an element and a compound?

13. How does the composition of a mixture of hydrogen and oxygen differ from the composition of a compound containing hydrogen and oxygen?

14. Suppose all the grains in a sample of sand were exactly the same size. Could the sample still be a heterogeneous mixture? Explain your answer.

15. What allows a mixture to be separated by filtration?

16. Explain why viscosity is classified as a physical property.

17. Based on these pieces of pottery found in Grand Canyon National Park, would you describe pottery as a malleable or brittle material?

18. A sample of copper can be drawn into a thin wire. Is this property of copper a physical property or a chemical property? Explain.

19. Name one physical property and one chemical property of wood.

20. Why is breaking down a compound into its elements considered a chemical change?

21. List one physical change and one chemical change that occur when a candle burns.

22. Suppose you need to identify the material in an object without changing the object in any way. Should you use physical or chemical properties to identify the material? Explain your choice.

Homework Guide

Section	Questions
2.1	1–3, 11–15, 23, 24
2.2	4–7, 16–18, 25–29, 31, 35
2.3	8–10, 19–22, 30, 32–34

Assessment

Interactive Textbook If your class subscribes to the Interactive Textbook, your students can go online to access an interactive version of the Student Edition and a self-test.

Reviewing Content

1. a **2.** d **3.** b
4. b **5.** c **6.** c
7. a **8.** d **9.** a
10. b

Understanding Concepts

11. The properties of a substance are constant because the composition of a substance does not vary.
12. A compound can be broken down into simpler substances, but an element cannot.
13. The relative proportions of hydrogen and oxygen in the mixture can vary. The relative proportions of hydrogen and oxygen in the compound cannot vary.
14. Grains with identical sizes could contain different substances (which would be suggested by grains having different colors).
15. Some particles in the mixture are much larger than other particles in the mixture.
16. The viscosity of a substance can be determined without changing the substance into a different substance.
17. Pottery is brittle.
18. It is a physical property because the composition of copper does not change as its shape changes.
19. Students are likely to say that wood is a poor conductor of heat (physical) and wood is flammable (chemical).
20. Because a compound and its elements are different substances, a chemical change has taken place.
21. Students are likely to say that the melting of wax is a physical change and the burning of wax is a chemical change.
22. You should use physical properties because in order to determine chemical properties, you must change the material in the object.

Critical Thinking

23. No. The properties of a compound do not necessarily match the properties of the elements from which the compound is formed.
24. Possible questions: "Is the air dusty?" and "Does the air contain water droplets?"
25. Mass and volume are properties that vary from sample to sample of a substance.
26. No. Although the density of the solid matches the density of one of the substances in the table, isopropyl alcohol is a liquid at room temperature, not a solid.
27. No. Gold is too dense to float on water.
28. No. It is possible for two different substances to have the same density or for a mixture to have the same density of a substance.
29. You could measure the density of the bracelet and compare that value to the known density of pure gold.
30. You would have observed two common clues for a chemical change—a color change and the formation of a precipitate.

Concepts in Action

31. The syrup has a greater viscosity than the sap because it contains much less water, which has a low viscosity.
32. You can infer that hair is flammable.
33. Nitrogen has a low reactivity compared to oxygen.
34. The paint prevents the iron from coming in contact with oxygen and water. If the paint flakes off, the iron will start to rust.
35. The cheesecloth acts as a filter. The lemon juice can pass through, but the seeds cannot.

Go Online PHSchool.com

Your students can independently test their knowledge of the chapter and print out their test results for your files.

Assessment *(continued)*

Critical Thinking

23. **Applying Concepts** Ammonia is a compound of hydrogen and nitrogen that dissolves easily in water. Can you conclude that hydrogen and nitrogen dissolve in water? Explain your answer.

24. **Posing Questions** What information would you need to know about a sample of air before you could classify the sample as a solution, suspension, or colloid?

25. **Applying Concepts** Explain why you cannot use mass or volume alone to identify substances.

Use the table to answer questions 26 and 27.

Melting Points and Densities of Some Substances

Substance	Melting Point	Density
Aluminum	660.3°C	2.70 g/cm^3
Table salt	800.7°C	2.17 g/cm^3
Isopropyl alcohol	−89.5°C	0.78 g/cm^3
Bromine	−7.2°C	3.10 g/cm^3
Water	0.0°C	1.00 g/cm^3
Gold	1064.2°C	19.3 g/cm^3

26. **Analyzing Data** You have a solid with a density of 0.78 g/cm^3. Is it possible that this solid is one of the substances listed in the table? Explain.

27. **Using Tables** A solid, rectangular block of material floats on water. Is it possible that the block is pure gold? Explain your answer.

28. **Drawing Conclusions** At room temperature, two white solids have the same density. With just this information, is it possible to conclude that the two solids are the same material? Explain.

29. **Designing Experiments** How could you use density to show that a gold bracelet contains elements other than gold?

30. **Inferring** Suppose you mix two colorless liquids together and a green solid settles to the bottom of the container. Explain why you might be confident that a chemical change has taken place.

Concepts in Action

31. **Comparing and Contrasting** The photo shows maple sap being collected in a bucket. The sap is about 97% water and 3% sugar with traces of other compounds. Cans of 100% pure maple syrup contain about 34% water and 66% sugar. Which would have the greater viscosity—the maple sap or the maple syrup? Give a reason for your answer.

32. **Inferring** One of the general safety instructions for working in a laboratory is to tie back long hair, especially when using a lab burner. From this instruction, what can you infer about the flammability of hair?

33. **Applying Concepts** Why might valuable documents be stored in pure nitrogen instead of in air? Recall that air is a mixture of gases, including nitrogen and oxygen.

34. **Relating Cause and Effect** Explain why painting an iron railing can slow down the rate at which the railing rusts.

35. **Writing in Science** Cheesecloth is a type of cotton cloth used by cooks. Write a paragraph explaining why a cook might wrap a lemon wedge in cheesecloth before squeezing juice from the lemon. What process for separating mixtures is the cook using?

Performance-Based Assessment

Writing in a Journal Keep a journal for a day. List five physical changes and five chemical changes that you observe. Be sure to describe why you think each change is physical or chemical.

Go Online PHSchool.com

For: Self-grading assessment
Visit: PHSchool.com
Web Code: cca-1020

Performance-Based Assessment

Ask students to identify the criteria they used to classify the changes. Students may observe some events that will not be easy to classify. For example, a student might conclude that a chemical reaction occurs when a soft drink can is opened, because bubbles appear.

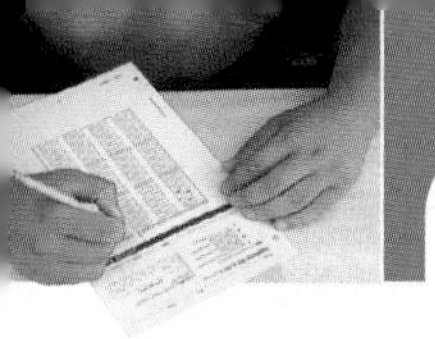

Standardized Test Prep

Test-Taking Tip

Using Models
For some test questions, you will be asked to decide what a visual model represents. Look at the model below. Notice that there are two types of particles shown and notice how the particles are distributed. Use what you observe to decide which answer is the best choice.

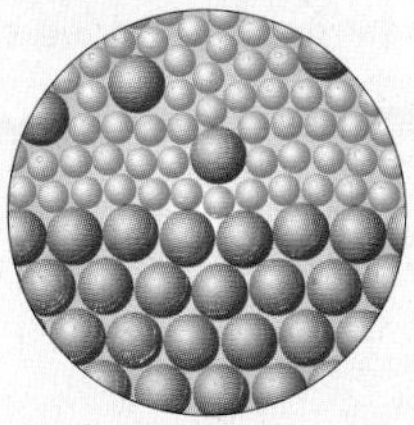

What type of matter does the model represent?
(A) a solution
(B) a colloid
(C) a suspension
(D) an element
(E) a homogeneous mixture

(Answer: C)

Choose the letter that best answers the question or completes the statement.

1. All pure substances
(A) contain only one type of atom.
(B) can be broken down into simpler substances.
(C) cannot be broken down into simpler substances.
(D) have a fixed composition.
(E) have a variable composition.

2. Which property can be used to separate a mixture by distillation?
(A) melting point
(B) boiling point
(C) density
(D) viscosity
(E) conductivity

3. During which of these events does a chemical change occur?
(A) Ice cubes melt.
(B) A pot of water boils.
(C) A heated iron bar turns red.
(D) A paper clip is bent.
(E) A cake rises in the oven.

4. You can be certain that a change is a chemical change if
(A) the change cannot be reversed.
(B) new substances form.
(C) bubbles are produced.
(D) a precipitate forms.
(E) there is a color change.

Use the drawings to answer Questions 5 and 6.

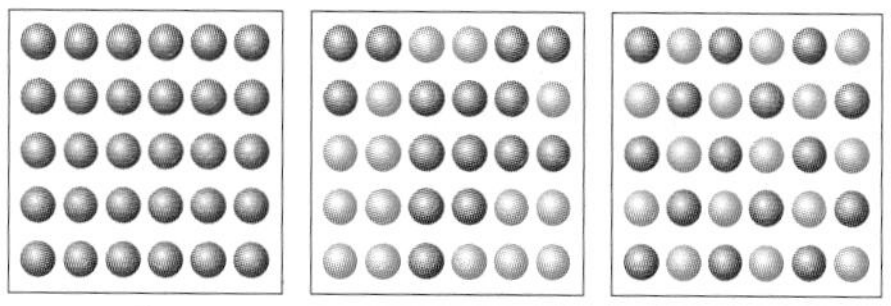

I II III

5. Which of the drawings could represent a homogeneous mixture?
(A) drawing I
(B) drawing II
(C) drawing III
(D) drawings I and III
(E) drawings II and III

6. Which of the drawings could represent an element?
(A) drawing I
(B) drawing II
(C) drawing III
(D) drawings I and III
(E) drawings II and III

Standardized Test Prep

1. D **2.** B **3.** E
4. B **5.** C **6.** A

CHAPTER 3

Planning Guide

Use these planning tools
Easy Planner
Teacher Express

SECTION OBJECTIVES	STANDARDS NATIONAL (See p. T18.)	STANDARDS STATE	ACTIVITIES and LABS
3.1 Solids, Liquids, and Gases, pp. 68–74 1 block or 2 periods **3.1.1** **Describe** the five states of matter. **3.1.2** **Classify** materials as solids, liquids, or gases. **3.1.3** **Explain** the behavior of gases, liquids, and solids, using kinetic theory.	A-1, B-2, B-5, F-5, G-1, G-2, G-3		**SE** Inquiry Activity: How Easy Is It to Compress Air and Water? p. 67 L2 **TE** Teacher Demo: Comparing Liquid Volume, p. 69 L2 **TE** Teacher Demo: Detecting the Motion of a Gas, p. 72 L2 **LM** Investigation 3B: Measuring Spaces Between Particles of Matter L1
3.2 The Gas Laws, pp. 75–81 1 block or 2 periods **3.2.1** **Define** pressure and gas pressure. **3.2.2** **Identify** factors that affect gas pressure. **3.2.3** **Predict** changes in gas pressure due to changes in temperature, volume, and number of particles. **3.2.4** **Explain** Charles's law, Boyle's law, and the combined gas law. **3.2.5** **Apply** gas laws to solve problems involving gases.	A-1, A-2, B-2, B-4, B-5, G-1, G-2, G-3		**SE** Quick Lab: Observing the Effect of Temperature on Gas Pressure, p. 79 L2 **TE** Build Science Skills: Observing, p. 75 L2 **TE** Teacher Demo: Changing Volume of a Balloon, p. 76 L2
3.3 Phase Changes, pp. 84–91 1 block or 2 periods **3.3.1** **Describe** phase changes. **3.3.2** **Explain** how temperature can be used to recognize a phase change. **3.3.3** **Explain** what happens to the motion, arrangement, and average kinetic energy of water molecules during phase changes. **3.3.4** **Describe** each of the six phase changes. **3.3.5** **Identify** phase changes as endothermic or exothermic.	A-1, A-2, B-2, B-5		**SE** Quick Lab: Observing Phase Changes, p. 90 L2 **SE** Exploration Lab: Investigating Changes in Temperature During Heating of Solids, pp. 92–93 L2 **TE** Teacher Demo: Energy Transfer, p. 86 L2 **LM** Investigation 3A: Performing a Fractional Distillation L2

Ability Levels	
L1	For students who need additional help
L2	For all students
L3	For students who need to be challenged

Components

SE	Student Edition	RSW	Reading & Study Workbook	CUT	Chapter & Unit Tests	T	Transparencies
TE	Teacher's Edition	MSPS	Math Skills & Problem Solving Workbook	CTB	Computer Test Bank	iT	Interactive Textbook
LM	Laboratory Manual			TP	Test Prep Resources	P	Presentation Pro CD-ROM
PLM	Probeware Lab Manual			DC	Discovery Channel Videotapes & DVDs	GO	Internet Resources

RESOURCES PRINT and TECHNOLOGY	SECTION ASSESSMENT
RSW Section 3.1 L1 MSPS Section 3.1 L2 T Chapter 3 Pretest L2 Section 3.1 L2 P Chapter 3 Pretest L2 Section 3.1 L2 SciLinks GO Kinetic theory L2	SE Section 3.1 Assessment, p. 74 Interactive Textbook iT Section 3.1
RSW Section 3.2 L1 RSW Math Skill L2 MSPS Section 3.2 L2 Discovery Channel School DC Up, Up, and Away L2 T Section 3.2 L2 P Section 3.2 L2 Science News GO Properties of matter L2	SE Section 3.2 Assessment, p. 81 Interactive Textbook iT Section 3.2
PLM Lab 1: Investigating Changes in Temperature During Heating of Solids L2 RSW Section 3.3 L1 T Section 3.3 L2 P Section 3.3 L2 SciLinks GO Phases of matter L2 PHSchool.com GO Data sharing L2	SE Section 3.3 Assessment, p. 91 Interactive Textbook iT Section 3.3

Go Online

Go online for these Internet resources.

PHSchool.com
Web Code: ccd-1030
Web Code: cca-1030

NSTA SciLinks
Web Code: ccn-1031
Web Code: ccn-1033

Science News
Web Code: cce-1032

Materials for Activities and Labs

Quantities for each group

STUDENT EDITION

Inquiry Activity, p. 67
syringe (sealed at narrow end), water

Quick Lab, p. 79
pan, metric ruler, empty beverage can, masking tape, hot plate, clock, tongs

Quick Lab, p. 90
250-mL Erlenmeyer flask, graduated cylinder, thermometer, dry ice

Exploration Lab, pp. 92–93
500-mL beaker, crushed ice, thermometer, hot plate, clock with second hand, test tube of lauric acid with thermometer, glass stirring rod, graph paper

TEACHER'S EDITION

Teacher Demo, p. 69
3 glass jars or bottles with lids, each having a noticeably different diameter but about the same volume; graduated cylinder; water

Teacher Demo, p. 72
spray can of air freshener, 3 stopwatches

Build Science Skills, p. 75
clay, CD case, textbook

Teacher Demo, p. 76
inflated balloons, refrigerator, warm place

Build Science Skills, p. 82
plastic bag (dry cleaner or thin garbage bag), string, hair dryers

Teacher Demo, p. 86
tray of ice cubes

Chapter Assessment

CHAPTER ASSESSMENT

SE Chapter Assessment, pp. 95–96
CUT Chapter 3 Test A, B
CTB Chapter 3
iT Chapter 3
PHSchool.com GO
Web Code: cca-1030

STANDARDIZED TEST PREP

SE Chapter 3, p. 97
TP Diagnose and Prescribe

Interactive Textbook

Interactive Textbook with assessment at PHSchool.com

CHAPTER 3

Before you teach

From the Author

David Frank
Ferris State University

Big Ideas

On Earth, matter is readily observed in three states: gas, liquid, and solid. The kinetic theory is used to explain the behavior of these states of matter, including what occurs within a sample of a substance as the substance changes from one state to another. The forces of attraction that hold solids and liquids together are also a key factor.

Matter and Change In Section 3.3, students build on knowledge from Chapter 2. They should realize that phase changes are physical changes because composition does not change during a phase change. You may need to stress that the molecules in ice, liquid water, and water vapor are identical. Only their arrangement is different. Because water is used as an example throughout the section, be sure that students do not assume that all substances have exactly the same properties as water. For example, substances that are normally gases at room temperature must have boiling points below 20°C.

Forces and Motion To understand the general properties of solids, liquids, and gases, students must envision the constant motion of atoms and molecules. To further understand gases, students need to know that gas pressure in an enclosed container is caused by particles colliding with the walls of their container. Section 3.2 focuses on the variables that affect the pressure of gases: temperature, volume, and number of particles. The section is organized so that you have options for presenting the relationships between the variables—qualitative descriptions of the factors that affect gas pressure, graphs of Charles's and Boyle's laws, and mathematical expressions.

Energy Energy is transferred between a system and its surroundings during a phase change. Students learn that the energy absorbed by material can overcome forces of attraction between particles in the material or increase the average kinetic energy of the particles.

Chemistry Refresher

States of Matter and Kinetic Theory 3.1

Solid, liquid, and gas are the common states of matter on Earth. However, almost all the matter in the observable universe exists as plasma. Plasma is formed when a gas is heated to temperatures near 10,000°C. At these temperatures, electrons can be lost during collisions between atoms or stripped by ionizing radiation. Because it contains mobile electrons, plasma can conduct an electric current. On Earth, plasma occurs mainly in lightning discharges and fluorescent lights. Not every substance can exist in every state. For example, some compounds that are solids at room temperature—e.g., mercury(II) oxide or sodium iodate—will decompose before they melt or boil.

Solids such as rubber, asphalt, and glasses are classified as amorphous solids because they lack the orderly internal structure found in crystalline solids. With the data supplied by improved instruments, scientists now know that glasses contain regions where the arrangement of particles is orderly.

The kinetic theory applies the laws of mechanics to individual atoms or molecules. It explains the physical properties of matter in terms of the motion of the particles. Two major contributors to the theory were James Joule (Count Rumford) and James Clerk Maxwell. The theory works best for gases (because the effect of attractive forces is minimal), but it can be applied to liquids and solids.

Address Misconceptions

Students may think that particles in gases have more kinetic energy than particles in liquids or solids. They are confusing how freely particles move with their speed of motion. For a strategy to overcome this misconception see **Address Misconceptions** on **page 73**.

The Gas Laws 3.2

Four variables are used to describe the behavior of a gas: temperature (T), pressure (P), volume (V), and amount. The amount of a gas is usually expressed as the number of moles (n). In 1662, Robert Boyle investigated the relationship between the volume and pressure of a gas. Using a J-shaped tube, Boyle measured gas pressure (indicated by the height of mercury) and gas volume at a constant temperature. His conclusions are now known as Boyle's law: $P_1V_1 = P_2V_2$.

Go Online PDLINKS NSTA

For: Teaching methods for states of matter
Visit: www.SciLinks.org/PDLinks
Web Code: ccn-0399

In 1787, Jacques Charles made a graph of volume versus temperature in degrees Celsius for a gas at constant pressure. The graph showed that volume increased as temperature increased, but it did not represent a direct relationship because the straight line did not pass through the (0, 0) point. When the line on the graph was extended beyond the data, the line crossed the x-axis at −273.15°C. This value is 0 K on the temperature scale developed by Lord Kelvin (William Thompson). As shown on the graph below, when Charles's data is plotted using kelvins instead of degrees Celsius, there is a direct relationship between the variables and Charles's law can be stated as $V_1/T_1 = V_2/T_2$.

Charles's Law

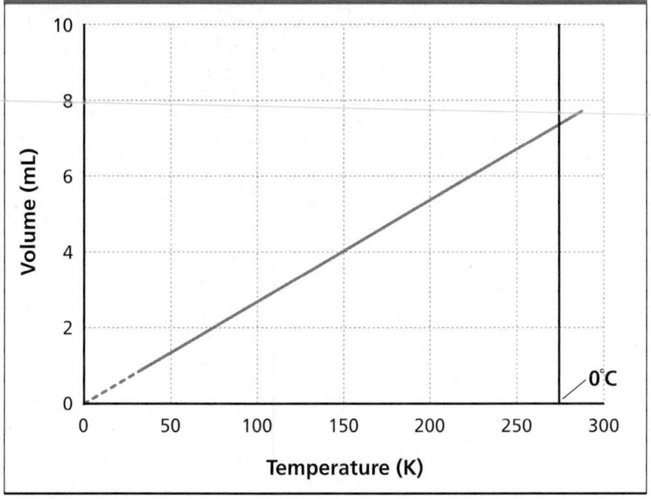

Volume (mL)
10
8
6
4
2
0
0
50
100
150
200
250
300
Temperature (K)
0°C

Address Misconceptions

Some students think that gases, such as those in air, do not have mass. But the particles in air must have mass to exert pressure. For a strategy to overcome this misconception see **Address Misconceptions** on **page 79.**

Boyle's law relates pressure and volume. Charles's law relates temperature and volume. In 1808, Joseph Gay-Lussac proposed the law that relates temperature and pressure: There is a direct relationship between the pressure of a gas and its kelvin temperature. The combined gas law describes all three laws, but it doesn't account for moles of a gas. Because gas pressure is due to the collision of particles, the number of particles in a sample of gas is key, not the type of particles. Amedeo Avogadro first stated this important idea as a hypothesis in 1811: Equal volumes of gases at the same temperature and pressure contain the same number of particles. The equation that relates all four variables—V, T, P, and n—is the ideal gas equation $PV = nRT$, where the ideal gas constant R equals 8.314 kPa•L/mol•K.

Phase Changes 3.3

A phase change involves the transfer of energy between a system and its surroundings. As a substance changes from a solid to a liquid to a gas, the degree of order in the system increases. When a phase change is from a more-ordered to a less-ordered state, energy must be absorbed by the system to overcome attractive forces. When the change is to a more-ordered state, energy is released by the system to the surroundings.

Build Reading Literacy

Predict

Previewing to Predict Content

Strategy Help students activate their prior knowledge about a topic and become actively engaged in reading. The process of making and confirming predictions also helps students correct their own misconceptions. Before students begin, have them focus on one topic in Chapter 3, such as the introductory paragraph on p. 68 and Describing the States of Matter on pp. 68–70.

Example

1. Introduce students to the topic by having them read the heading and subheadings.
2. Ask students what they think they will learn about the topic.
3. Have a student read aloud the first Key Concept under Reading Focus at the top of the page.
4. Have another student read aloud the Comparing and Contrasting instructions in the Reading Strategy.
5. Based on what they've read so far, ask students to predict the content of the section. Write their predictions on the board.
6. Have a student read aloud the boldfaced key statement on p. 68. Then, have other students read aloud the boldfaced terms on p. 69.
7. Discuss with students the predictions on the board. Allow them to revise the predictions if they wish.
8. Have students read through the section independently. Afterwards, ask which of their predictions were confirmed. Point out that there's nothing wrong with making an incorrect prediction. Predicting can help readers learn more about a topic.

See p. 77 for a script on how to use the predicting strategy with students. For additional Build Reading Literacy strategies, see pp. 69 and 85.

ASSESS PRIOR KNOWLEDGE

Use the Chapter Pretest below to assess students' prior knowledge. As needed, review these Science Concepts and Math Skills with students.

Review Science Concepts

Section 3.1 Review density, pure substances, homogeneous mixtures, and heterogeneous mixtures with students. Students may refer to the graphic organizer they completed in Section 2.1.

Section 3.2 Encourage students to review scientific methods, including forming and testing hypotheses. Discuss how developing a hypothesis is an important step in a scientific method.

Section 3.3 Have students review SI units for temperature and volume.

Review Math Skills

Formulas and Equations Students will need to know how to write equations and solve them for unknowns in order to solve problems involving gas laws.

Direct students to the **Math Skills** in the **Skills and Reference Handbook** at the end of the student text.

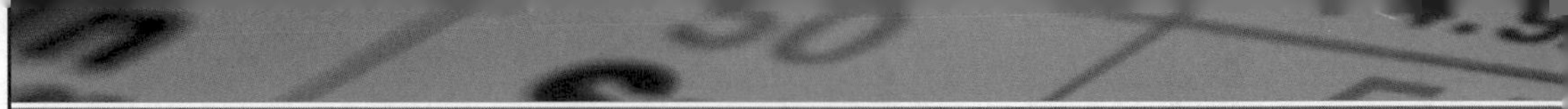

CHAPTER 3 States of Matter

CONCEPTS in Action

How do science concepts apply to your world? Here are some questions you'll be able to answer after you read this chapter.

- How can balloons have many different shapes? *(Section 3.1)*
- Why should you check the air pressure of tires before you go for a long drive? *(Section 3.2)*
- What controls the movement of air into and out of your lungs as you breathe? *(Section 3.2)*
- Why does pasta take longer to cook in Denver than in New Orleans? *(Section 3.3)*

Discovery Channel School **Video Field Trip**
Up, Up, and Away

- How is the altitude of a hot-air balloon controlled? *(page 82)*

When temperatures rise in the spring, ▶ the ice begins to melt on Bow Lake at Banff National Park in Alberta, Canada.

Chapter Pretest

1. What is the density of a sample whose mass is 12.02 g and whose volume is 6.01 mL? *(2.00 g/mL)*

2. Which of the following is an element? *(c)*
   a. Sand b. Water
   c. Gold d. Sugar

3. Differentiate heterogeneous from homogeneous mixtures. *(Heterogeneous mixture: parts are noticeably different; homogeneous mixture: parts are difficult to distinguish)*

4. Which of the following is not a step in a scientific method? *(b)*
   a. Developing a procedure to test a hypothesis
   b. Drawing a conclusion without any supporting evidence
   c. Forming a testable hypothesis
   d. Making observations

5. Identify tools needed to measure temperature and length. *(Thermometer and ruler)*

6. True or False: All of the following units are SI units: meter, pound, and kelvin. *(False)*

7. Density, mass, and volume are related by the equation *density = mass/volume.* What equation would you use to find volume if you knew the density and mass? *(volume = mass/density)*

8. Bromine boils at a temperature of 58.63°C. What is this temperature in kelvins? *(331.78 K)*

Chapter Preview

Inquiry Activity

How Easy Is It to Compress Air and Water?

Procedure

1. Insert a plunger into a syringe that is sealed at the narrow end. Push the plunger into the syringe as far as you can. Use the marks on the side of the syringe to read the volume of the air inside the syringe. Record this volume.
2. Remove the plunger. Fill the syringe with water by holding it under water in a large plastic container of water. **CAUTION** *Wipe up any spilled water right away to avoid slips and falls.*
3. While holding the syringe over the container, repeat Step 1. Record the volume of the water.

Think About It

1. **Comparing and Contrasting** Which was harder to compress, the air or the water? (To compress means to squeeze into a smaller volume.)
2. **Inferring** Based on your answer to Question 1, in which material are the particles closer together, in air or in water? Explain your answer.

DISCOVERY CHANNEL SCHOOL

Video Field Trip

Up, Up, and Away

Encourage students to view the Video Field Trip "Up, Up, and Away."

ENGAGE/EXPLORE

Inquiry Activity

How Easy Is It to Compress Air and Water? L2

Purpose In this activity, students will infer that gases are more easily compressed than liquids because there is more space between the particles in a gas than between the particles in a liquid.

Skills Focus **Comparing**

Prep Time 5 minutes

Materials syringe (sealed at narrow end), water

Advance Prep Obtain syringes from a scientific supply company. Remove the needles and seal the tip of each syringe by removing the plunger and dropping some nonwater-soluble glue into the head of the syringe.

Class Time 15 minutes

Safety Students should wear safety goggles and lab aprons.

Teaching Tips

- To keep track of the syringes, number them with an indelible marker before distributing them to students. As you distribute, record the syringe number and student's name. When you retrieve the syringes, check against the list.
- Demonstrate the proper handling of the syringe and plunger. Show students how to correctly read the markings on the syringes.
- Separate the plungers from the syringes before distributing them.
- Separate the plungers from the syringes, rinse them with distilled water, and allow them to air-dry before storing them.

Expected Outcome The plunger will be pushed farther into the air-filled syringe than into the water-filled syringe.

Think About It

1. The water was harder to compress.
2. The particles are closer together in water. Air can be compressed more easily than water because there is more space between the particles in air.
Visual, Logical

Section 3.1

1 FOCUS

Objectives

3.1.1 **Describe** the five states of matter.

3.1.2 **Classify** materials as solids, liquids, or gases.

3.1.3 **Explain** the behavior of gases, liquids, and solids, using kinetic theory.

Reading Focus

Build Vocabulary L2

Word Origins Explain to students that a Flemish chemist, Jan Baptista van Helmont (1577–1644), coined the word *gas*. Its origin is the Greek word *khaos*. Point out that the English word *chaos* refers to a disordered state. Relate this definition to the relative disorder of gases.

Reading Strategy L2

a. Definite shape b. Definite volume
c. Variable shape d. Variable volume

2 INSTRUCT

Describing the States of Matter

Use Visuals L1

Figure 1 Have students look at the magnified portion. Ask, **Why is the air bubble above the liquid in the tube?** *(Air is less dense than the liquid.)* **When might the tube in the middle of the level be used?** *(To see whether a shelf or counter is perfectly horizontal)* **When might the tube on the right be used?** *(To see whether a wall or doorframe is perfectly vertical)* If possible, bring in levels for students to observe and use.
Visual

3.1 Solids, Liquids, and Gases

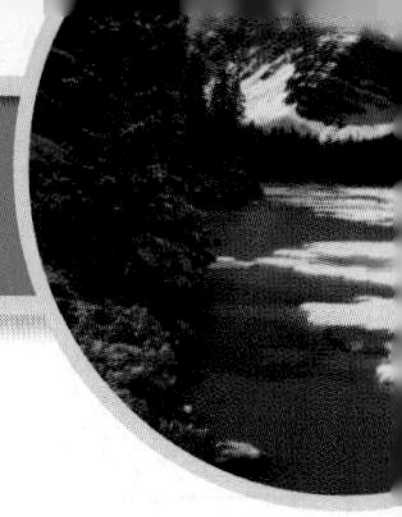

Reading Focus

Key Concepts

- How can shape and volume be used to classify materials?
- How can kinetic theory and forces of attraction be used to explain the behavior of gases, liquids, and solids?

Vocabulary

- solid
- liquid
- gas
- kinetic energy

Reading Strategy

Comparing and Contrasting Copy the diagram. As you read, replace each letter with one of these phrases: *definite volume, definite shape, variable volume,* or *variable shape.*

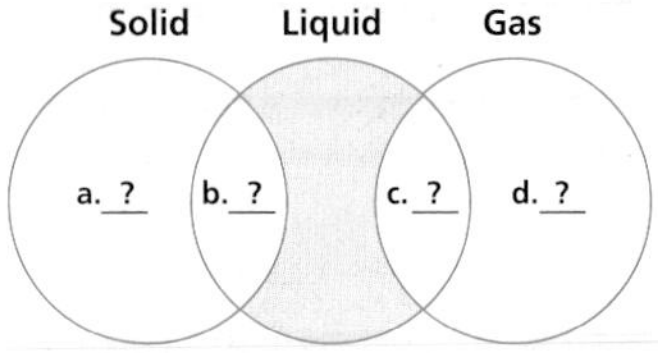

Solid
Liquid
Gas
a. ?
b. ?
c. ?
d. ?

Figure 1 Carpenters use a level to find out if a surface is perfectly horizontal. In the level shown, three clear plastic tubes are set into an aluminum frame. Each tube contains a liquid and a gas. **Classifying** ***What property could you use to distinguish the liquid or gas from the solids in a level?***

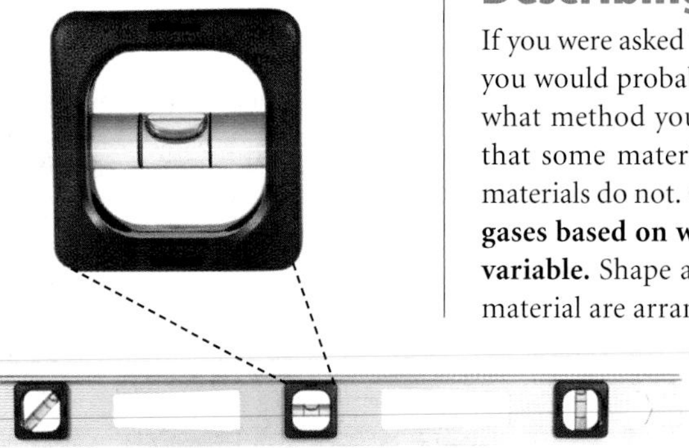

Do you recognize the object in Figure 1? It is a carpenter's level. A level can be used to see whether a surface is perfectly horizontal. The level has one or more transparent tubes inside a metal or wooden frame. Inside each tube is a clear liquid, such as alcohol, and an air bubble. When a carpenter places the level on a surface that is perfectly horizontal, the air bubble stays in the middle of the horizontal tube. The bubble moves to the high end of the tube if the surface is slanted.

The metal, alcohol, and air in a carpenter's level represent three states of matter. At room temperature, most metals are solids, alcohol is a liquid, and air is a gas. In this chapter, you will learn why the appearance and behavior of solids, liquids, and gases are different.

Describing the States of Matter

If you were asked to classify some materials as solids, liquids, or gases, you would probably find the task fairly easy. But could you describe what method you used to classify the materials? You might notice that some materials have a definite shape and volume and some materials do not. **Materials can be classified as solids, liquids, or gases based on whether their shapes and volumes are definite or variable.** Shape and volume are clues to how the particles within a material are arranged.

Section Resources

Print

- ***Laboratory Manual,*** Investigation 3B
- ***Reading and Study Workbook With Math Support,*** Section 3.1
- ***Math Skills and Problem Solving Workbook,*** Section 3.1
- ***Transparencies,*** Chapter Pretest and Section 3.1

Technology

- ***Interactive Textbook,*** Section 3.1
- ***Presentation Pro CD-ROM,*** Chapter Pretest and Section 3.1
- ***Go Online,*** NSTA SciLinks, Kinetic theory

Solids Think about these familiar objects: a pencil, a quarter, a book, and a cafeteria tray. What do these four objects have in common? They all have a recognizable shape and they all take up a certain amount of space. The materials in these objects are all in the solid state. **Solid** is the state of matter in which materials have a definite shape and a definite volume.

The term *definite* means that the shape and volume of a pencil won't change as you move the pencil from a desk drawer to a pencil case to a backpack. Changing the container doesn't change the shape or volume of a solid. However, the term *definite* doesn't mean that the shape or volume can never change. After all, you can change the shape of a pencil by sharpening it. You can change the shape of a copper wire by bending the wire.

Figure 2 shows the arrangement of atoms in a copper wire. The copper atoms are packed close together and are arranged in a regular pattern. Almost all solids have some type of orderly arrangement of particles at the atomic level.

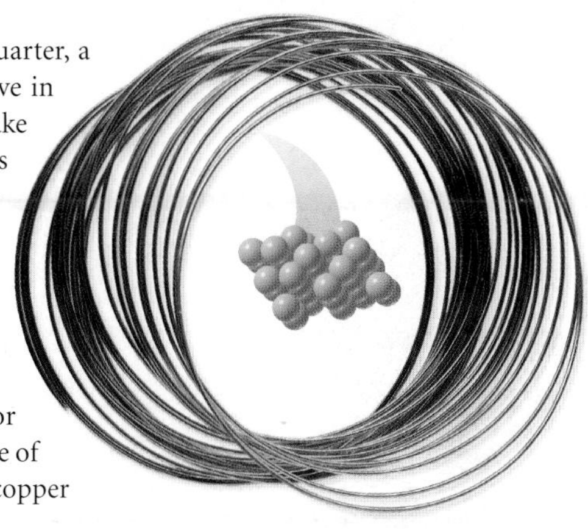

Figure 2 Samples of solid copper have definite volume. Copper atoms are packed close together in an orderly arrangement.

Liquids How good are you at estimating whether the juice remaining in an almost-empty bottle will fit in a glass? If your estimate is not accurate, you will run out of space in the glass before you run out of juice in the bottle.

Appearances can be deceiving. Imagine a narrow glass and a wide bottle side by side. Each contains exactly 350 milliliters of juice (about three quarters of a pint). There will seem to be more juice in the glass because the juice rises almost to the rim of the glass. There will seem to be less juice in the bottle because the juice forms a shallow layer. What can you learn about liquids from this comparison?

A liquid always has the same shape as its container and can be poured from one container to another. **Liquid** is the state of matter in which a material has a definite volume but not a definite shape.

Mercury exists as a liquid at room temperature. The drawing in Figure 3 shows the arrangement of atoms in liquid mercury. Compare this arrangement to the arrangement of copper atoms in Figure 2. The mercury atoms are close together but their arrangement is more random than the arrangement of atoms in copper.

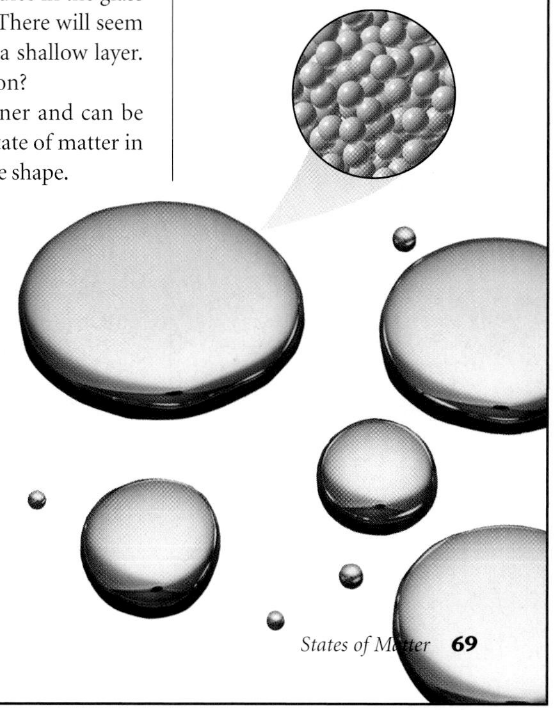

Figure 3 At room temperature, mercury is a liquid. Drops of mercury on a flat, clean surface have a round shape. Mercury in a container has the same shape as its container. **Comparing and Contrasting** ***Compare the arrangement of atoms in copper and mercury.***

Teacher Demo

Comparing Liquid Volume **L2**

Purpose Students observe that it is difficult to compare the volume of liquids in different containers because liquids take the shape of their containers.

Materials 3 glass jars or bottles with lids, each having a noticeably different diameter but about the same volume; graduated cylinder; water

Advance Prep Before class, use a graduated cylinder to add the same amount of water to each of the three containers. Pick a volume that will almost fill the narrowest container. To avoid evaporation, replace the lids on the containers.

Procedure Have students predict which container has the largest volume of water. Have volunteers use graduated cylinders to measure the amount of water in each container.

Expected Outcome If students' predictions are influenced by the height of the liquids in the containers, they will predict that the container with the narrowest diameter has the greatest volume. **Visual**

Build Reading Literacy **L1**

Relate Text and Visuals Refer to page **190D** in **Chapter 7**, which provides the guidelines for relating text and visuals.

Have students compare the drawings of a solid and a liquid in Figures 2 and 3 to the definitions for these states of matter. **Visual, Portfolio**

Customize for English Language Learners

Think-Pair-Share
Have students work in pairs to make a table describing solids, liquids, and gases. Remind students that they need to include in their descriptions information about shape, volume, and the arrangement of particles. An example of such a table would have Solids, Liquids, and Gases as column heads and Shape, Volume, and Arrangement of Particles as row heads. Students should title their tables States of Matter. Suggest that students list common examples of each state. Strengthen language skills by having students present their tables to the class.

Answer to . . .

Figure 1 *The liquid and gas have variable shapes.*

Figure 3 *In both copper and mercury, the atoms are close together, but the arrangement of atoms in mercury is less orderly (more random).*

Use Visuals L1

Figure 4 To help students distinguish a visual model of atoms from actual atoms, point out that the pink spheres represent helium atoms in a balloon. Ask, **Do the size and color of the spheres represent the actual size and color of helium atoms?** *(No, helium atoms are too small to see and helium is a colorless gas.)* Tell students that the actual distance between helium atoms in a balloon is about 10 times the diameter of a helium atom. Have students consider why illustrations cannot accurately represent such distances. **Visual, Logical**

FYI

In this chapter, plasma is not defined as an ionized gas because students are not introduced to ions until Chapter 6.

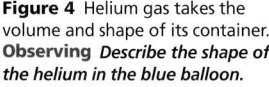

Gases If you were asked to name a gas, what would you say? Air, which is a mixture of gases, is probably the most obvious example. You might also mention natural gas, which is used as a fuel for heating homes. **Gas** is the state of matter in which a material has neither a definite shape nor a definite volume. (The adjective form of the word *gas* is *gaseous* (GAS e us), as in *gaseous state.*) A gas takes the shape and volume of its container.

The balloons in Figure 4 are filled with helium, a colorless gas that is less dense than air. Two of the balloons are teardrop-shaped and two are disk-shaped. The "shape" of the helium in a balloon is the same as the shape of the balloon itself. The volume of the helium in a balloon is equal to the volume of the balloon.

The helium atoms in a balloon are not arranged in a regular pattern, as shown in the drawing in Figure 4. They are at random locations throughout the balloon. There is more space between two helium atoms in a balloon than between two neighboring atoms in solid copper or liquid mercury.

Because of the space among helium atoms, a large amount of helium can be compressed into a metal cylinder. When helium flows from the cylinder into a balloon, the helium atoms spread out. If 200 balloons are filled from a single cylinder, the total volume of the balloons will be much larger than the volume of the cylinder.

Figure 4 Helium gas takes the volume and shape of its container. **Observing** ***Describe the shape of the helium in the blue balloon.***

Other States of Matter On Earth, almost all matter exists in a solid, liquid, or gaseous state. But ninety-nine percent of all the matter that can be observed in the universe exists in a state that is not as common on Earth. At extremely high temperatures, such as those found on the sun or other stars, matter exists as plasma. You will read more about the properties of plasmas in Chapter 10.

In the 1920s Satyendra Bose, a physicist from India, wrote a paper about the behavior of light. After Albert Einstein read the paper, he realized that the behavior described could apply to matter under certain conditions. Einstein made a bold prediction. He predicted that a fifth state of matter would exist at extremely low temperatures. At temperatures near −273°C, groups of atoms would behave as though they were a single particle. In 1995, scientists created this fifth state of matter, which is called a Bose-Einstein condensate (or BEC). It behaved as Einstein had predicted decades before.

Reading Checkpoint *How do atoms behave at temperatures near −273°C?*

Facts and Figures

Bose-Einstein Condensate In 1995, physicists at the University of Colorado at Boulder were the first to produce a BEC. The team of scientists, which included Eric Cornell and Carl Wieman, used lasers and magnets to cool about 2000 rubidium atoms to 20 billionths of a degree above absolute zero (−273.15°C). The rubidium atoms formed a tiny, almost stationary ball, which looked like a cherry pit with a diameter of 20 microns.

In 1997, Steven Chu, William Phillips, and Claude Cohen-Tannnoudji shared the Nobel Prize for Physics for their independent work using lasers to cool atoms. In 1985, Chu and his team had produced "optical molasses," an effect in which the movement of atoms was about one kilometers per hour instead of the expected 4000 kilometers per hour. At that speed the temperature of the sample was close to absolute zero.

Data Analysis

Why Was Mercury Used in Thermometers?

Until recently, mercury thermometers were used in homes and schools. When a thermometer broke, people were exposed to mercury. When broken thermometers were thrown away, they ended up in landfills. Mercury is a toxic substance that can harm humans and other organisms. Schools no longer use mercury thermometers and people are encouraged to replace their fever thermometers.

So why did people continue to use mercury thermometers long after they knew the dangers of mercury? Look at the data table. It lists some densities over a temperature range from 0°C to 150°C. The temperatures are given at 30-degree intervals.

1. **Using Tables** How does the density of mercury change as the temperature increases?
2. **Relating Cause and Effect** How does a change in density affect the volume of a mercury sample?

Density of Mercury

Temperature (°C)	Density (g/mL)	Volume of One Gram (mL)
0	13.60	0.07356
30	13.52	0.07396
60	13.45	0.07436
90	13.38	0.07476
120	13.30	0.07517
150	13.23	0.07558

3. **Calculating** If a thermometer contained a gram of mercury, how much would the volume of the mercury change when the temperature rose from 0°C to 30°C? From 30°C to 60°C? From 60°C to 90°C? From 90°C to 120°C?
4. **Drawing Conclusions** Why was mercury a better choice than water for the liquid in a thermometer? (*Hint:* Between 0°C and 30°C, the volume of a gram of water changes by 0.0042 mL. Between 30°C and 60°C, the volume changes by 0.0127 mL. Between 60°C and 90°C, the volume changes by 0.0188 mL.)
5. **Inferring** Why is the mercury in a thermometer stored in a narrow tube?

Kinetic Theory

Why, under ordinary conditions, is copper a solid, mercury a liquid, and helium a gas? To begin to answer that question, you need to know something about kinetic energy. An object that is moving has kinetic energy. The word *kinetic* comes from a Greek word meaning "to move." **Kinetic energy** is the energy an object has due to its motion.

The faster an object moves, the greater its kinetic energy is. A ball thrown at 85 miles (137 kilometers) per hour by the pitcher in Figure 5 has more kinetic energy than a ball thrown at 78 miles (125 kilometers) per hour. When a baseball is thrown, a batter can see that it is moving. But the batter cannot see that there is also motion occurring within the baseball. According to the kinetic theory of matter, particles inside the solid baseball are moving. Particles in the air that the baseball travels through are moving too.

The kinetic theory of matter says that all particles of matter are in constant motion. The theory was developed in the mid-1800s to explain the behavior of gases. It can also help to explain the behavior of liquids and solids.

Figure 5 The kinetic energy of a baseball depends on the speed at which the pitcher throws the ball.

Facts and Figures

Mercury Thermometer Daniel Fahrenheit invented the alcohol thermometer in 1709 and the mercury thermometer in 1714. He chose mercury because it remains a liquid over a wider range of temperatures than does water. The expansion rate of mercury is fairly uniform, mercury does not adhere to glass, and its color makes it easy to read.

Inhalation of mercury vapor can damage the nervous system and the respiratory system. To prevent mercury vapor from being inhaled when thermometers break, the Environmental Protection Agency, along with state and local agencies, has encouraged consumers to replace mercury fever thermometers. Alternatives to mercury thermometers include digital thermometers that use a change in the resistance in a thermoresistor and thermometers with sensors that detect infrared radiation.

Data Analysis

Why Was Mercury Used in Thermometers? L2

Answers

1. The density decreases.
2. As the density decreases, the volume increases.
3. 0.00040 mL; 0.00040 mL; 0.00040 mL; 0.00041 mL
4. Unlike with water, the change in volume for mercury is almost identical for each interval. (The expansion is linear.) Thus, the interval spacing between degree marks is consistent for mercury. (In addition, the liquid range for mercury is broader—from –38.9°C to 356.7°C.)
5. With such a small change in volume per degree, the mercury must be in a narrow tube for the difference in height to be observed and measured.

For Extra Help L1

Display a copy of the data table on the board. If students are having trouble answering Question 4, have a student record the incremental change in volume (calculated for Question 3) and change in temperature from row to row. This step should make it easier for students to see that the almost constant change in volume corresponds to a constant temperature interval. **Logical**

Kinetic Theory

FYI

The kinetic energy of an object is also affected by its mass. The greater the mass of an object, the greater its kinetic energy is. (This effect of mass and speed on kinetic energy is discussed in Section 15.1.)

Answer to . . .

Figure 4 *The helium in the blue balloon is star-shaped.*

Reading Checkpoint *Groups of atoms can behave as though they were a single particle.*

Explaining the Behavior of Gases

Teacher Demo

Detecting the Motion of a Gas L2

Purpose Students infer that particles in gases are in constant motion.

Materials spray can of air freshener, 3 stopwatches

Procedure Spray the air freshener at a distant corner of the room. Have students located in various parts of the room time how long it takes before they smell the gas. (The mist from the spray will evaporate.) Ask students to explain the results.

Expected Outcome Students will detect odor several moments after the air freshener is sprayed. Students should explain that they could smell the air freshener because the particles in a gas are in constant, random motion. That motion carried particles from the corner of the room to the students' locations.
Kinesthetic, Logical

Use Visuals L1

Figures 6 and 7 Have students compare the models of collisions shown in Figures 6 and 7. Ask, **How are the paths of billiard balls and helium atoms the same?** *(The paths of both are straight lines.)* **How is the motion of billiard balls different from the motion of helium atoms?** *(The motion of billiard balls is not constant or random.)* **What is a weakness of the model of helium atoms shown in Figure 7?** *(There are only two atoms to represent the billions of atoms that would be in such a jar.)*
Visual

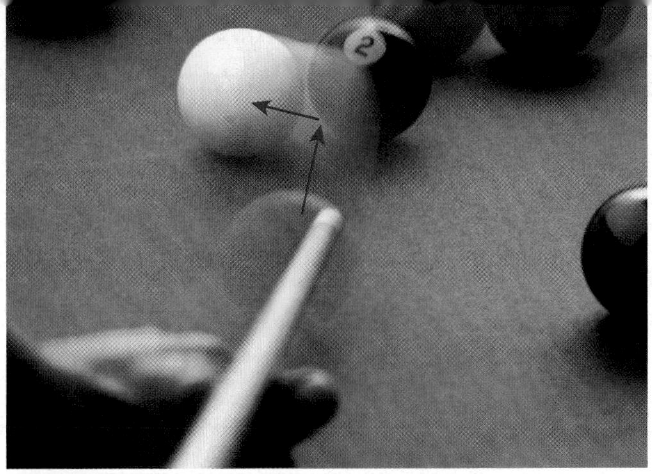

Figure 6 This photograph of billiard balls was taken just after the cue struck the white ball, which began to move. The white ball moved in a straight line until it collided with the dark blue ball. The collision caused the dark blue ball to start moving. The motion of billiard balls can be compared to the motion of particles in a gas.

Explaining the Behavior of Gases

You can compare the motion of the particles in a gas to the movement of balls during a game of billiards. When a cue strikes a billiard ball, as shown in Figure 6, the ball moves in a straight line until it strikes the side of the billiard table or another ball. When a moving ball strikes a ball at rest, the first ball slows down and the second ball begins to move. Kinetic energy is transferred during those collisions.

Motion in Gases Unlike billiard balls, the particles in a gas are never at rest. At room temperature, the average speed of the particles in a sample of gas is about 1600 kilometers per hour. The use of the term *average* is a clue that not all particles are moving at the same speed. Some are moving faster than the average speed and some are moving slower than the average speed.

Figure 7 shows the possible paths of two helium atoms in a container of helium gas. Notice that each atom moves in a straight line until it collides with the other atom or with a wall of the container. During a collision, one atom may lose kinetic energy and slow down while the other atom gains kinetic energy and speeds up. However, the total kinetic energy of the atoms remains the same.

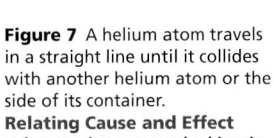

Figure 7 A helium atom travels in a straight line until it collides with another helium atom or the side of its container.
Relating Cause and Effect ***What can happen to the kinetic energy of two helium atoms when the atoms collide?***

The diagram in Figure 7 does not accurately compare the volumes of the atoms and the container. The volume of a helium atom is extremely small compared to the volume of its container. If there were a billion times a trillion helium atoms in a liter bottle, there would still be a large amount of space in the bottle.

Between collisions, why doesn't one particle in a gas affect the other particles in the gas? **There are forces of attraction among the particles in all matter.** If the particles are apart and moving fast, as in a gas, the attractions are too weak to have an effect. Under ordinary conditions, scientists can ignore the forces of attraction in a gas.

Facts and Figures

Mean Free Path The distance a particle of gas travels between collisions is called its mean free path. This distance varies with temperature and pressure. At 1 atmosphere of pressure and 25°C, the mean free path for a hydrogen molecule is 12.6×10^{-8} meters. For a nitrogen molecule, it is 6.76×10^{-8} meters. At 1 atmosphere of pressure and 25°C, a hydrogen molecule will collide with another molecule about 7.1×10^{11} times per second, while a nitrogen molecule will collide with another molecule about 1.42×10^{10} times per second. The shorter the mean free path is, the greater the number of collisions per second.

Kinetic Theory of Gases The kinetic theory explains the general properties of a gas. **The constant motion of particles in a gas allows a gas to fill a container of any shape or size.** Think about air in a tire. The walls of the tire keep the air contained. What if there is a hole in the tire? Because the particles in the air are in constant motion, some of the particles would travel to the hole and move out of the tire. The kinetic theory as applied to gases has three main points.

- Particles in a gas are in constant, random motion.
- The motion of one particle is unaffected by the motion of other particles unless the particles collide.
- Forces of attraction among particles in a gas can be ignored under ordinary conditions.

Reading Checkpoint *Describe the motion of particles in a gas.*

Explaining the Behavior of Liquids

The particles in liquids also have kinetic energy. So why does a liquid such as mercury have a definite volume at room temperature instead of expanding to fill its container? The average speed of a mercury atom is much slower than the average speed of a helium atom at the same temperature. A mercury atom has about 50 times the mass of a helium atom. This greater mass is only partly responsible for the slower speed. What other factor is responsible?

The particles in a liquid are more closely packed than the particles in a gas. Therefore, attractions between the particles in a liquid do affect the movement of the particles. A mercury atom in liquid mercury is like a student in the crowded hallway in Figure 8. The student's path may be blocked by students moving in the other direction. The student's ability to move is affected by interactions with other students.

In a liquid, there is a kind of tug of war between the constant motion of particles and the attractions among particles. This tug of war explains the general behavior of liquids. **A liquid takes the shape of its container because particles in a liquid can flow to new locations. The volume of a liquid is constant because forces of attraction keep the particles close together.** Because forces of attraction limit the motion of particles in a liquid, the particles in a liquid cannot spread out and fill a container.

Go Online NSTA SCiLINKS

For: Links on kinetic theory
Visit: www.SciLinks.org
Web Code: ccn-1031

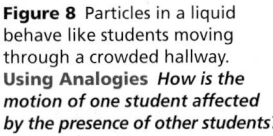

Figure 8 Particles in a liquid behave like students moving through a crowded hallway. **Using Analogies** ***How is the motion of one student affected by the presence of other students?***

Explaining the Behavior of Liquids

Build Science Skills L2

Using Analogies Have students think of analogies for the motion of particles in a liquid other than the analogy shown in Figure 8. Possible answers include dancers on a dance floor or bumper cars at an amusement park. Be sure students understand that the objects representing particles in the analogy should be in a confined space.
Logical

Address Misconceptions L2

Students may think that the particles in gases have more kinetic energy than the particles in liquids or solids. Students are confusing an increase in the ability of particles to move freely with an increase in average speed. Challenge this misconception by explaining that the particles in all substances at a given temperature have, on average, similar amounts of kinetic energy. Ask, **Why don't particles in a solid move as freely as particles in a gas at room temperature?** *(Strong forces of attraction among particles in the solid keep the particles vibrating around fixed locations within the solid.)*
Logical

Go Online NSTA SCiLINKS

Download a worksheet on kinetic theory for students to complete, and find additional teacher support from NSTA SciLinks.

Answer to . . .

Figure 7 *One atom may gain kinetic energy and speed up while the other atom loses kinetic energy and slows down.*

Figure 8 *A student's path may be blocked by students moving in the opposite direction.*

Reading Checkpoint *Particles in a gas are in constant, random motion.*

Section 3.1 (continued)

Explaining the Behavior of Solids

Build Science Skills L2

Using Models Fill a clear plastic box or tray with enough marbles to fill the bottom of the box. Gently move the box back and forth. Ask, **What state of matter does this model represent?** *(Solid)* **How are the particles in a solid like the marbles in this model?** *(Both the marbles and the particles in a solid are in fixed locations. They can only move back and forth.)* The marbles do not move until the box is shaken. **How well does this part of the model represent the behavior of particles in a solid?** *(Not well, because particles in a solid are constantly moving.)*
Visual

3 ASSESS

Evaluate Understanding L2

Have each student write a paragraph explaining how kinetic theory can be used to explain the general characteristics of solids, liquids, and gases.

Reteach L1

Review the properties of solids, liquids, and gases. Use Figure 1 to encourage students to think of practical applications in which the state of matter is important. For example, molten metals can be shaped in a mold, but a metal must be solid to be shaped by hammering.

Connecting Concepts

In a liquid, there is a tug of war between the motion of the particles and attractions among particles. With liquids at the same temperature, the deciding factor would be the strength of the attractive forces. An increase in these forces would decrease a liquid's ability to flow and increase its viscosity.

Interactive Textbook If your class subscribes to the Interactive Textbook, use it to review key concepts in Section 3.1.

Answer to . . .

Figure 9 *People remain in the same seats, but the positions of their bodies change.*

Figure 9 These photographs of an audience in a movie theater were taken at different times on the same day. The behavior of the audience can be compared to the behavior of particles in a solid. **Observing** ***What stayed the same and what changed between the photographs?***

Explaining the Behavior of Solids

You might compare the particles in a solid to a polite audience in a movie theater. While the movie is running, people stay in their seats. Although people move around in their seats, as shown in Figure 9, each person remains in essentially the same location during the movie. They have "fixed" locations in a total volume that does not change.

Solids have a definite volume and shape because particles in a solid vibrate around fixed locations. Vibration is a repetitive back-and-forth motion. Look back at the orderly arrangement of copper atoms in Figure 2. Strong attractions among the copper atoms restrict their motion and keep each atom in a fixed location relative to its neighbors. Each atom vibrates around its location but it does not exchange places with a neighboring atom.

Section 3.1 Assessment

Reviewing Concepts

1. How are shape and volume used to classify solids, liquids, and gases?
2. What does the kinetic theory say about the motion of atoms?
3. How is a gas able to fill a container of any size or shape?
4. Use kinetic theory and attractive forces to explain why a liquid has a definite volume and a shape that can vary.
5. Explain why a solid has a definite shape and volume.
6. How does the arrangement of atoms in most solids differ from the arrangement of atoms in a liquid?

Critical Thinking

7. **Using Analogies** Explain how the behavior of popcorn in a popcorn popper can be used as an analogy for the motion of gas particles.
8. **Applying Concepts** A hazardous chemical is leaking from a tank truck. Rescue workers need to evacuate people who live near the accident. Why are more people likely to be affected if the chemical is a gas, rather than a liquid?

Connecting Concepts

Viscosity Review the description of viscosity in Section 2.2. Use the tug of war between forces of attraction and kinetic energy to explain differences in viscosity among liquids at the same temperature.

Section 3.1 Assessment

1. Materials can be classified as solids, liquids, or gases based on whether their shapes and volumes are definite or variable.
2. All particles of matter are in constant motion.
3. The constant motion of gas particles allows a gas to fill a container of any shape and size.
4. Particles in a liquid can flow to new locations, but forces of attraction keep the particles close together.
5. The particles in a solid vibrate around fixed locations.
6. The atoms in most solids have a more orderly arrangement than the atoms in liquids, which are not restricted to fixed locations.
7. While popping occurs, the motion of the individual popcorn kernels is random and fairly continuous.
8. The particles of a gas have greater freedom of movement and will reach a wider area more quickly.

3.2 The Gas Laws

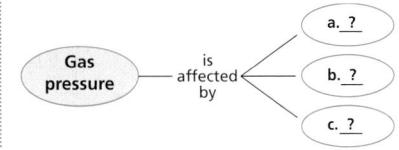

Reading Focus

Key Concepts

- What causes gas pressure in a closed container?
- What factors affect gas pressure?
- How are the temperature, volume, and pressure of a gas related?

Vocabulary

- pressure
- absolute zero
- Charles's law
- Boyle's law

Reading Strategy

Identifying Cause and Effect Copy the diagram. As you read, identify the variables that affect gas pressure.

Gas pressure — is affected by — a. ? / b. ? / c. ?

The woman in Figure 10 is taking a deep breath. This action helps reduce her breathing rate and increase the volume of air she inhales. When you inhale, the volume of your chest cavity increases and air moves into your lungs. When you exhale, the volume of your chest cavity decreases and air is pushed out of your lungs.

After you read this section, you will understand how changing the volume of your chest cavity causes air to move into and out of your lungs. Changes in the volume, the temperature, the pressure, and the number of particles have predictable effects on the behavior of a gas.

Pressure

At many hockey rinks, a layer of shatterproof glass keeps the puck away from the spectators. The force with which the puck hits the glass depends on the speed of the puck. The faster the puck is traveling, the greater the force is. The smaller the area of impact is, the greater the pressure produced. **Pressure** is the result of a force distributed over an area. If the edge of the puck hits the glass, it exerts more pressure than if the face of the puck hits the glass at the same speed.

The SI unit of pressure is derived from SI units for force and area. Force is measured in newtons (N) and area in square meters (m^2). When a force in newtons is divided by an area in square meters, the unit of pressure is newtons per square meter (N/m^2). The SI unit for pressure, the pascal (Pa), is shorthand for newtons per square meter. One pascal is a small amount of pressure. Scientists often express larger amounts of pressure in kilopascals. One kilopascal (kPa) is equal to 1000 pascals.

Figure 10 Taking a deep breath increases the volume of your chest cavity, which causes air to move into your lungs.

Section Resources

Print

- ***Reading and Study Workbook With Math Support***, Section 3.2 and **Math Skill:** The Combined Gas Law
- ***Math Skills and Problem Solving Workbook***, Section 3.2
- ***Transparencies***, Section 3.2

Technology

- ***Interactive Textbook***, Section 3.2
- ***Presentation Pro CD-ROM***, Section 3.2
- ***Go Online***, *Science News*, Properties of matter

Section 3.2

1 FOCUS

Objectives

3.2.1 **Define** pressure and gas pressure.

3.2.2 **Identify** factors that affect gas pressure.

3.2.3 **Predict** changes in gas pressure due to changes in temperature, volume, and number of particles.

3.2.4 **Explain** Charles's law, Boyle's law, and the combined gas law.

3.2.5 **Apply** gas laws to solve problems involving gases.

Reading Focus

Build Vocabulary L2

Paraphrase Replace less familiar words in a definition with more familiar words or phrases.

Reading Strategy L2

a. Temperature **b.** Volume **c.** Number of particles

2 INSTRUCT

Pressure

Build Science Skills L2

Observing ACTIVITY

Purpose Show the effect of area on pressure.

Materials clay, CD case, textbook

Advance Prep Prepare two flattened pieces of clay 3 cm thick.

Procedure Put the broad side of the CD case on a piece of clay with the book on top. After about 30 seconds, carefully remove the book and case. Then, put the case on the other piece of clay, narrow side down. Balance the book on the case for 30 seconds. (Place your hands on either side of the book as a precaution.) Remove the book and case. Ask, **How do the depths of the imprints compare?** *(The imprint is deeper when the case is placed on its edge.)* **What caused this difference?** *(Because the weight of the book was applied to a smaller area, the pressure was greater.)*

Expected Outcome When the same force is applied to a smaller area, the depth of the imprint increases.
Visual

Factors that Affect Gas Pressure

Teacher Demo

Changing Volume of a Balloon **L2**

Purpose Students observe the effect of temperature on the volume of a balloon.

Materials inflated balloons, refrigerator, warm place

Advance Prep One day ahead, inflate a balloon for each class. Place the balloons in a refrigerator overnight.

Procedure At the beginning of class, bring out a balloon and tell students where it has been. Ask, **Do you predict that the volume of the balloon will increase, decrease, or stay the same after the balloon has been in a warm place?** *(Increase)* Place the balloon in a warm place until shortly before the end of class. Make sure the balloon has room to expand, and that the temperature does not exceed 42°C. Ask, **What happened to the volume of the gas inside the balloon?** *(It increased.)* Explain that as temperature increases, the particles move faster, on average, which increases the pressure of the gas inside the balloon. The increased pressure causes the balloon to expand.

Expected Outcome The balloon's volume will increase as the temperature increases.
Visual, Logical

Use Visuals **L1**

Figure 11 Bring in a pressure gauge like the one in the photo. (The gauge measures how much the air pressure in the tire exceeds atmospheric pressure.) Have a volunteer note the units of pressure on the gauge. *(Pounds per square inch)* Explain that in the United States, pressure is not always measured in SI units. Ask, **Have you seen any other units used for pressure?** *(Students may have seen barometric pressure reported in inches of mercury.)* **Why is data from experiments measured and reported in SI units?** *(Scientists must use standard units so that their data can be shared with and tested by scientists in all countries.)*
Logical, Visual

An object does not need to be as large as a hockey puck to exert pressure when it collides with another object. Recall that the helium atoms in a balloon are constantly moving. The pressure produced by a single helium atom colliding with a wall is extremely small. However, there are more than 10^{22} helium atoms in a small balloon. When so many particles collide with the walls of a container at the same time, they produce a measurable pressure.

Collisions between particles of a gas and the walls of the container cause the pressure in a closed container of gas. The more frequent the collisions, the greater the pressure of the gas is. The speed of the particles and their mass also affect the pressure.

Reading Checkpoint *How does the frequency of collisions affect the pressure of a gas?*

Figure 11 The firefighter is using a pressure gauge to check the air pressure in a tire on a firetruck. If the tires on the truck have a 44.5-inch diameter, the pressure on a front tire should be about 125 pounds per square inch (psi).

Factors That Affect Gas Pressure

Think again about the collisions that produce gas pressure. What changes might affect the pressure of a gas in a container? The particles in the gas could move faster or slower. The gas could be moved into a larger or smaller container. You could add gas or remove gas from the container. **Factors that affect the pressure of an enclosed gas are its temperature, its volume, and the number of its particles.**

Temperature Suppose you are about to go on a long drive. The driver suspects that the air pressure in the automobile tires might be low. You check the pressure in each tire, using a pressure gauge like the one in Figure 11. You find that the measurements are well within the automobile manufacturer's guidelines. If you checked the tire pressures again after a few hours on the highway, would you be surprised to find that the pressure in the tires had increased?

The constant motion of tires on the highway causes the tires and the air in the tires to warm up. As the temperature rises, the average kinetic energy of the particles in the air increases. With increased kinetic energy, the particles move faster and collide more often with the inner walls of the tires. The faster-moving particles also hit the walls with greater force. The increase in the number of collisions along with the increase in the force of the collisions causes an increase in the pressure of the air in the tires. **Raising the temperature of a gas will increase its pressure if the volume of the gas and the number of particles are constant.**

Customize for Inclusion Students

Visually Impaired
Have students with visual impairments observe different air pressures in a bicycle tire. Bring a bicycle tire and a pump with a built-in gauge. Let out all of the air in the tire. Attach the pump to the inner tube valve. Read the pressure on the gauge and allow students to feel that the tire is completely flat. Pump up the tire to a third of the maximum recommended pressure (marked on the tire). Read the pressure on the gauge and allow students to feel the tire again. Pump up the tire to the maximum recommended pressure and allow students to repeat the observation. Discuss with students how the quantity of air in the tire affects the firmness of the tire.

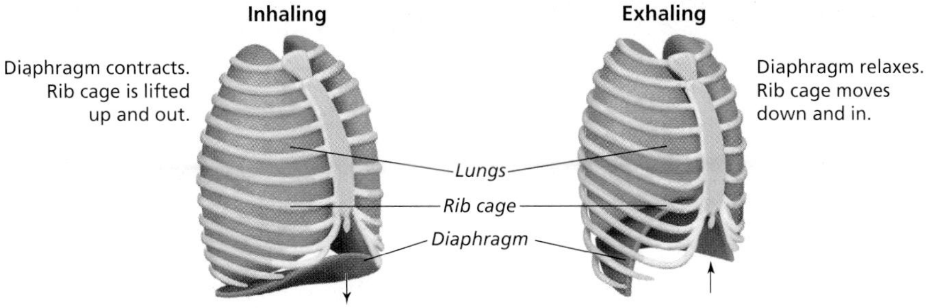
Inhaling
Exhaling
Diaphragm contracts. Rib cage is lifted up and out.
Diaphragm relaxes. Rib cage moves down and in.
Lungs
Rib cage
Diaphragm

Figure 12 Movement of a muscle called the diaphragm changes the volume of your chest cavity. The volume increases when you inhale and decreases when you exhale.
Interpreting Diagrams ***How does the movement of your rib cage affect the volume of your chest cavity?***

Volume Imagine that you have a plastic bottle that appears empty. If you twist the cap onto the bottle and then squeeze the bottle, what will happen? At first, the plastic will give a little, reducing the volume of the bottle. But soon you will feel pressure from inside the bottle resisting your efforts to further reduce the volume. The pressure you feel is a result of the increased pressure of the air trapped inside the bottle. As the volume is decreased, particles of trapped air collide more often with the walls of the bottle. **Reducing the volume of a gas increases its pressure if the temperature of the gas and the number of particles are constant.**

Figure 12 shows how the relationship between volume and pressure explains what happens when you breathe. As you inhale, a muscle called the diaphragm (DY uh fram) contracts. The contraction causes your chest cavity to expand. This temporary increase in volume allows the particles in air to spread out, which lowers the pressure inside the chest cavity. Because the pressure of the air outside your body is now greater than the pressure inside your chest, air rushes into your lungs.

When you exhale, your diaphragm relaxes and the volume of your chest cavity decreases. The particles in the air are squeezed into a smaller volume and the pressure inside your lungs increases. Because the pressure of the air inside your chest is now greater than the pressure of the air outside your body, air is forced out of your lungs.

Number of Particles You can probably predict what will happen to the pressure when you add more gas to a container. Think about a tire. Once the tire is inflated, its volume is fairly constant. So adding more air will increase the pressure inside the tire. The more particles there are in the same volume, the greater the number of collisions and the greater the pressure. At some point the rubber from which the tire is made will not be strong enough to withstand the increased pressure and the tire will burst. **Increasing the number of particles will increase the pressure of a gas if the temperature and the volume are constant.**

Go Online
SCIENCE NEWS

For: Articles on properties of matter
Visit: PHSchool.com
Web Code: cce-1032

Build Reading Literacy L1

Predict Refer to page **66D** in this chapter, which provides the guidelines for predicting.

List on the board examples of volume, temperature, and number of particles increasing or decreasing. Tell students to predict how each change will affect gas pressure in a closed container. Ask students to use the number of particle collisions to explain their predictions. As students provide their predictions and explanations, write the correct effect on pressure and the correct explanation on the board.
Logical, Portfolio

Go Online
SCIENCE NEWS

Science News provides students with current information on properties of matter.

Facts and Figures

Fainting Couches During the Victorian era, well-to-do households often had fainting couches. The tightly laced, whalebone corsets women wore restricted their ability to breathe deeply. As a result, they had low levels of oxygen in their blood, causing them to faint, or swoon. Today, Victorian fainting couches can be seen in historic houses or museums. Antique fainting couches and reproductions are available in some furniture and antique stores.

Answer to . . .

Figure 12 *The volume increases as the rib cage is lifted up and out. The volume decreases as the rib cage moves down and in.*

Reading Checkpoint *The more frequent the collisions, the greater the pressure of the gas is.*

Section 3.2 (continued)

Charles's Law

Build Science Skills L2

Using Tables and Graphs Have students analyze Figure 13. Have students look first at the graph for Charles's law. Point out the straight line with the positive slope. Ask, **What relationship does this line describe?** *(It describes a direct relationship between volume and temperature: As temperature increases, volume also increases.)* Ask, **Why is part of the line solid and part dashed?** *(The solid line represents actual data, while the dotted line is the extension of the collected data toward the zero point for volume.)* Have students refer to the Boyle's Law graph. Ask, **What happens to pressure as volume increases?** *(As volume increases, pressure decreases.)*
Visual, Logical

Build Math Skills L1

Line Graphs Students are likely to need help understanding why Charles's law does not apply when temperatures are expressed in degrees Celsius. Have students find the point on the graph where the temperature is 0°C and ask them to estimate the volume at that temperature. Then, tell them that the straight line must pass through (0, 0) for the responding variable to be directly proportional to the manipulated variable.
Logical, Portfolio

Direct students to the **Math Skills** in the **Skills and Reference Handbook** at the end of the student text for additional help.

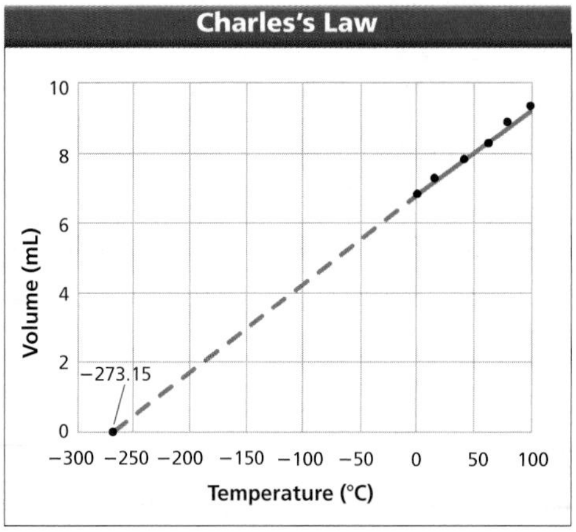

Charles's Law
Volume (mL)
10
8
6
4
2
0
−273.15
−300 −250 −200 −150 −100 −50 0 50 100
Temperature (°C)

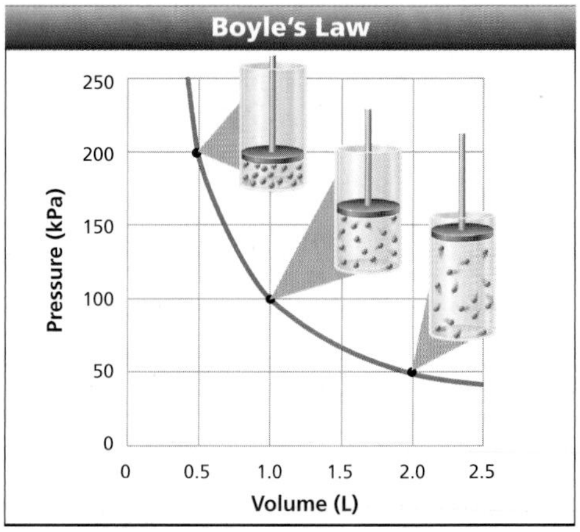

Boyle's Law
Pressure (kPa)
250
200
150
100
50
0
0 0.5 1.0 1.5 2.0 2.5
Volume (L)

Figure 13 These graphs compare the effects of temperature and volume on the pressure of a gas. Charles's law describes the direct relationship between the temperature and the volume. Boyle's law describes the inverse relationship between the volume and the pressure.
Controlling Variables ***For each graph, name the manipulated variable and the responding variable.***

Charles's Law

During his lifetime, the French physicist Jacques Charles (1746–1823) was known for his inventions, including the hydrogen balloon. Today, Charles is best known for his investigations of the behavior of gases. Charles collected data on the relationship between the temperature and volume of gases. When he graphed the data, the graph was a straight line, as shown in Figure 13. The graph shows that the volume of a gas increases at the same rate as the temperature of the gas.

Charles extended the line on his graph beyond the measured data to see what the temperature would have to be to produce a volume of 0 L. The temperature at the point where the line crossed the *x*-axis was −273.15°C. This temperature is equal to 0 K on the Kelvin temperature scale. A temperature of 0 K is called **absolute zero.** No scientist has produced a temperature of absolute zero in a laboratory, but some have come extremely close. As a gas cools to temperatures near 0 K, the gas changes to a liquid, a solid, or sometimes a Bose-Einstein condensate.

Charles's law states that the volume of a gas is directly proportional to its temperature in kelvins if the pressure and the number of particles of the gas are constant. Charles's law can be written as a mathematical expression in which T_1 and V_1 represent the temperature and volume of a gas before a change occurs. T_2 and V_2 represent the temperature and volume after a change occurs.

Charles's Law

$$\frac{V_1}{T_1} = \frac{V_2}{T_2}$$

The temperatures must be expressed in kelvins. If temperatures in degrees Celsius are used in the expression, the volume will not be directly proportional to the temperature.

Facts and Figures

Absolute Zero Based on the decrease in the volume of a gas as it cooled, scientists hypothesized that if an ideal gas were cooled to absolute zero (0 K on the Kelvin temperature scale or −273.15 on the Celsius scale), its volume would be zero. However, as actual gases are cooled, they reach temperatures at which they change to liquids or solids.

Theoretically, all motion of particles in matter should cease at absolute zero. But according to quantum mechanics, a substance will contain some energy of motion, regardless of its temperature. For that reason, substances cannot be cooled to absolute zero. However, Bose-Einstein condensates produced in laboratories exist at temperatures very close to absolute zero.

Boyle's Law

Robert Boyle, who was born in Ireland in 1627, was the first to describe the relationship between the pressure and volume of a gas. The graph in Figure 13 shows what happens when the volume of a cylinder containing a set amount of gas is decreased. What happens when the volume of the cylinder is reduced from 2.0 liters to 1.0 liter? The pressure of the gas in the cylinder doubles from 50 kilopascals to 100 kilopascals.

Boyle's Law

$$P_1V_1 = P_2V_2$$

Boyle's law states that the volume of a gas is inversely proportional to its pressure if the temperature and the number of particles are constant. Boyle's law can be expressed mathematically. P_1 and V_1 represent the pressure and volume of a gas before a change occurs. P_2 and V_2 represent the pressure and volume of a gas after a change occurs.

Reading Checkpoint *How is Boyle's law expressed mathematically?*

Quick Lab

Observing the Effect of Temperature on Gas Pressure

Materials

pan, metric ruler, empty beverage can, masking tape, hot plate, clock, tongs

Procedure

1. Fill a pan with cold water to a depth of 3 cm.
2. Use masking tape to cover half the opening of the can. **CAUTION** *Do not cover the entire opening with tape.*
3. Place the can on the hot plate and turn the hot plate to a high setting. Heat the can for 5 minutes and then turn off the hot plate.
4. Use tongs to remove the can from the hot plate and place it upside down in the pan of water as shown. The opening should be below the surface of the water. Observe the can as it cools.

Analyze and Conclude

1. **Inferring** How did the temperature of the air inside the can change when you heated the can? How did it change when you put the can in the water?
2. **Drawing Conclusions** What happened to the pressure of the air inside the can when you put the can in the cold water?
3. **Inferring** Did the air pressure outside the can change during the experiment?
4. **Formulating Hypotheses** What caused the change you observed in Step 4?

Facts and Figures

Experimental Evidence Robert Boyle was a founding member of The Royal Society, the oldest continuous scientific society in the world. The society's motto is *Nullius in Verba*, Latin for "Nothing in Words." The motto means that science should be based on experimental evidence, not debates.

Boyle's adherence to a scientific method was one of his most important contributions to science. He was among the first scientists to publish detailed experimental results, even results of unsuccessful experiments. In 1661, Boyle's *The Sceptical Chymist* was published. It disputed Aristotle's theories about elements. His 1662 publication of *The Spring and Weight of the Air* included experiments that led to Boyle's law. For these and earlier experiments, Boyle developed an improved vacuum pump, which required only one person to operate.

Boyle's Law

Quick Lab

Observing the Effect of Temperature on Gas Pressure

L2

Objective

After completing this activity, students will be able to

- predict the effect of temperature on the pressure of a gas.

Address Misconceptions

This lab helps dispel the misconception that a gas does not have mass. Explain that air pressure is the result of particles in air colliding with the can. The force of the collisions (and pressure) depends on the mass and speed of the particles.

Skills Focus **Inferring**

Prep Time 10 minutes

Materials pan, metric ruler, empty beverage can, masking tape, hot plate, clock, tongs

Advance Prep Ask students to contribute clean, empty beverage cans. Use dissecting pans, cake pans, or plastic dishpans.

Class Time 20 minutes

Safety Caution students not to touch the hot plate or the can once the hot plate has been turned on.

Expected Outcome The can will crack or collapse within one minute after being placed in cold water.

Analyze and Conclude

1. The temperature increased when the can was heated and decreased when it was placed in cold water.
2. The pressure decreased.
3. The air pressure outside the can did not change.
4. As the gas inside the can cooled, its pressure decreased until it could no longer offset the outside air pressure.

Answer to . . .

Figure 13 *For Charles's law, the manipulated variable is temperature and the responding variable is volume. For Boyle's law, the manipulated variable is volume and the responding variable is pressure.*

Reading Checkpoint $P_1V_1 = P_2V_2$

Build Math Skills L1

Formulas and Equations A gas has a pressure of 200 kPa in a 0.5-L container. Use Boyle's law to determine the pressure of the gas in a 2.0 container. *(50 kPa)* **Logical**

Direct students to the **Math Skills** in the **Skills and Reference Handbook** at the end of the student text for additional help.

The Combined Gas Law

Integrate Math L2

Have students show how the combined gas law can be used to derive Boyle's and Charles's laws. If temperature is constant, the temperature cancels out to reveal Boyle's law $P_1V_1 = P_2V_2$. Similarly, if volume remains constant, Charles's law of $P_1/T_1 = P_2/V_2$ is derived. **Logical**

Math Practice

Solutions L2

1. $V_2 = (P_1V_1/P_2) =$ (50 kPa)(5.0 L)/125 kPa = 2.0 L

2. $T_2 = (P_2T_1/P_1) =$ (825 kPa)(273 K)/388 kPa = 580 K

3. $T_2 = (V_2T_1/V_1) =$ (0.285 L)(283 K)/0.250 L = 323 K or 50°C **Logical**

For Extra Help L1

Remind students that before they solve a specific problem, they should determine which variable is not changing and remove that variable from the combined gas law. Then, they need to identify which of the variables is the unknown—V_2, T_2, or P_2—and rearrange the equation to solve for that variable. If students are having trouble rearranging the equation, provide students with the six possible forms of the equation. **Logical**

Additional Problems

1. A gas is stored at constant volume at a pressure of 137 kPa at 274 K. If the temperature rises to 296 K, what is the pressure? *(148 kPa)*

2. At constant temperature, the volume of a gas at 1000 kPa is changed from 100 L to 10 L. What is the new pressure? *(10,000 kPa)* **Logical**

The Combined Gas Law

The relationships described by Boyle's law and Charles's law can be described by a single law. The combined gas law describes the relationship among the temperature, volume, and pressure of a gas when the number of particles is constant.

Combined Gas Law

$$\frac{P_1V_1}{T_1} = \frac{P_2V_2}{T_2}$$

The combined gas law is used to solve many problems involving gases.

Math Skills

The Combined Gas Law

A cylinder that contains air at a pressure of 100 kPa has a volume of 0.75 L. The pressure is increased to 300 kPa. The temperature does not change. Find the new volume of air.

1 Read and Understand

What information are you given?

$P_1 = 100$ kPa $\quad P_2 = 300$ kPa $\quad V_1 = 0.75$ L

2 Plan and Solve

What unknown are you trying to calculate?

V_2

What expression can you use?

$$\frac{P_1V_1}{T_1} = \frac{P_2V_2}{T_2}$$

Cancel out the variable that does not change and rearrange the expression to solve for V_2.

$$P_1V_1 = P_2V_2 \qquad V_2 = \frac{P_1V_1}{P_2}$$

Replace each variable with its known value.

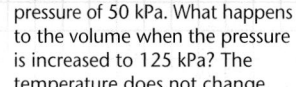

$$V_2 = 100 \text{ kPa} \times \frac{0.75 \text{ L}}{300 \text{ kPa}} = 0.25 \text{ L}$$

3 Look Back and Check

Is your answer reasonable?

Volume should decrease as pressure increases. The pressure tripled from 100 kPa to 300 kPa. The answer, 0.25 L, is one third the original volume, 0.75 L.

Math Practice

1. A gas has a volume of 5.0 L at a pressure of 50 kPa. What happens to the volume when the pressure is increased to 125 kPa? The temperature does not change.
2. Gas stored in a tank at 273 K has a pressure of 388 kPa. The safe limit for the pressure is 825 kPa. At what temperature will the gas reach this pressure?
3. At 10°C, the gas in a cylinder has a volume of 0.250 L. The gas is allowed to expand to 0.285 L. What must the final temperature be for the pressure to remain constant? (*Hint:* Convert from degrees Celsius to kelvins using the expression °C + 273 = K.)

Facts and Figures

Weather Balloons Large weather balloons are made of natural or synthetic rubber. They are filled with either helium or hydrogen. As the balloon expands, the thickness of the rubber decreases from about 0.051 mm to 0.0025 mm at the altitude when the balloon bursts. A balloon that is about 2 m in diameter at launch will be about 6 m in diameter after it expands. Balloons are launched twice a day at sites around the world.

Attached to the weather balloon is a radiosonde, an instrument that measures pressure, temperature, and relative humidity. Because the radiosonde can be reconditioned and used again, a parachute and mailing bag are also attached to the weather balloon. (The photograph in Figure 14 was taken at the National Weather Station in Maryland.)

It is harder for scientists to do a controlled experiment when they are studying events that occur in natural settings. Scientists need laws like the combined gas law to deal with situations in which multiple variables are changing. Balloons like the one in Figure 14 are used by scientists to gather data about Earth's atmosphere. The balloon is filled with hydrogen or helium. It carries a package of weather instruments up into the atmosphere. The instruments measure temperature, pressure, and water content at different levels in the atmosphere.

What will happen to the volume of the weather balloon as it rises through the atmosphere? Both pressure and temperature decrease as the altitude increases in Earth's atmosphere. A decrease in external pressure should cause the balloon to expand to a larger volume. A decrease in temperature should cause the balloon to contract to a smaller volume. Whether the balloon actually expands or contracts depends on the size of the changes in pressure and temperature.

Figure 14 These scientists are releasing a weather balloon into the atmosphere. The balloon is designed to burst when it reaches an altitude of about 27,400 meters. **Drawing Conclusions** ***What happens to the pressure inside a weather balloon as it rises?***

Section 3.2 Assessment

Reviewing Concepts

1. How is the gas pressure produced in a closed container of gas?
2. What three factors affect gas pressure?
3. How does increasing the temperature affect the pressure of a contained gas?
4. What happens to the pressure of a gas if its volume is reduced?
5. How does increasing the number of particles of a contained gas affect its pressure?

Critical Thinking

6. **Predicting** What happens to the pressure in a tire if air is slowly leaking out of the tire? Explain your answer.
7. **Comparing and Contrasting** What do Boyle's law and Charles's law have in common? How are they different?
8. **Applying Concepts** Some liquid products are sold in aerosol cans. Gas is stored in a can under pressure and is used to propel the liquid out of the can. Explain why an aerosol can should never be thrown into a fireplace or incinerator.

Math Practice

9. Two liters of hydrogen gas are stored at a pressure of 100 kPa. If the temperature does not change, what will the volume of the gas be when the pressure is decreased to 25 kPa?
10. You know that a gas in a sealed container has a pressure of 111 kPa at 23°C. What will the pressure be if the temperature rises to 475°C?

Use Visuals **L1**

Figure 14 The balloon will burst when it reaches an altitude of about 27,400 m. Ask, **What variables change as the balloon rises? How do they change?** *(Temperature and pressure both decrease.)* **How does each change affect the volume of the balloon?** *(Decreasing atmospheric pressure causes the balloon to expand. Decreasing temperature causes the balloon to shrink.)*
Visual, Logical

3 ASSESS

Evaluate Understanding **L2**

Have students look at the mathematical presentations of Charles's law on p. 78 and Boyle's law on p. 79 and describe the relationships in their own words.

Reteach **L1**

Write Charles's law and Boyle's law on the board. Have students quiz each other about the behavior of the responding variable when another variable increases or decreases.

Math Practice

Solutions
9. $V_2 = (P_1V_1/P_2) =$
(100 kPa)(2.0 L)/25 kPa = 8.0 L
10. $P_2 = (P_1T_2/T_1) =$
(111 kPa)(748 K)/296 K = 280 kPa

Interactive Textbook If your class subscribes to the Interactive Textbook, use it to review key concepts in Section 3.2.

Answer to . . .

Figure 14 *The pressure increases.*

Section 3.2 Assessment

1. Collisions between particles of a gas and the walls of the container cause the pressure in a closed container of gas.
2. Temperature, volume, and number of particles
3. Raising the temperature will increase the pressure if volume and number of particles are constant.
4. If the volume is reduced, the pressure of a gas increases if temperature and number of particles are constant.
5. Increasing the number of particles will increase the pressure if temperature and volume are constant.
6. Because the number of particles of air is reduced from the leak, the pressure will slowly decrease.
7. Both laws describe a relationship between two variables that affect a gas when other variables are constant. Charles's law shows how the volume of a gas is directly proportional to its temperature in kelvins. Boyle's law shows how the volume of a gas is inversely proportional to its pressure.
8. At a high temperature, the pressure in the gas might increase to the point where the can would explode.

CONCEPTS in Action

Riding on Air **L2**

Background

On August 27, 1783, Jacques Charles released his first hydrogen-filled balloon, which was about 4 m in diameter. He prepared the hydrogen by pouring sulfuric acid over scrap iron. Charles also made improvements to hot-air balloons, including a valve line that allowed operators to release gas from the balloon and a wicker basket (a nacelle), which was attached to the balloon by ropes. The first publication of Charles's work was by Joseph Gay-Lussac, who referred to Charles's work in an 1802 paper. Gay-Lussac also did ballooning. His altitude record of 7016 m (4.3 miles) stood for almost 50 years.

Build Science Skills **L2**

Observing ACTIVITY

Purpose Students will observe that heating air causes it to expand and become less dense.

Materials plastic bag (dry cleaner or thin garbage bag), string, hair dryers

Class Time 20 minutes

Procedure Organize students into groups of two or three. Have students tie a string around the closed end of the plastic bag and place evenly spaced paper clips around the open end as weights. Tell students to hold the open end of the plastic bag over the hair dryer (set on high) and let the bag fill with hot air. The plastic bag begins to rise as it fills with hot air. When the students feel the bag begin to rise, have them release the bag. Ask, **What causes the bag to rise?** *(The heated air inside the bag is less dense than the air outside the bag.)* **Use what happened to the plastic bag to explain how a hot-air balloon works.** *(A hot-air balloon rises because air in the balloon is heated.)*

Expected Outcome When the air inside the bag is heated, the bag begins to rise.
Visual, Group

CONCEPTS in Action

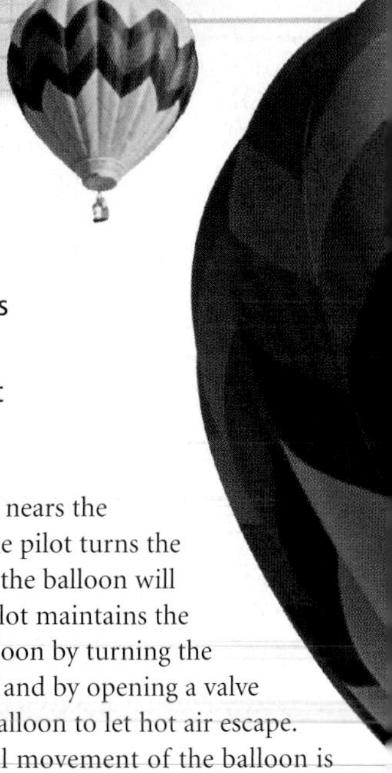

Riding on Air

Warm air is less dense than cold air. So if enough warm air is confined to a lightweight container, the container can rise through the surrounding colder air. This is the principle that allows a hot-air balloon to get off and stay off the ground.

When air is heated, the particles in the air gain energy and move faster on average. The particles also move farther apart, so a given volume of hot air contains fewer particles and has less mass than the same volume of cold air. This difference in density produces an upward force. In a hot-air balloon, the force is very small, equivalent to lifting about one tenth of a gram for each liter of air. A large volume of air is needed to support the mass of the balloon and any passengers. That is why hot-air balloons need to be large.

To heat the air, the pilot burns propane gas, which is stored under pressure in tanks. The bottom of the balloon's envelope (the skirt) is treated so that it is not flammable.

As the balloon nears the chosen altitude, the pilot turns the burner off so that the balloon will stop rising. The pilot maintains the altitude of the balloon by turning the burner on and off and by opening a valve at the top of the balloon to let hot air escape.

The horizontal movement of the balloon is much harder to control. The wind speed and wind direction vary at different altitudes. The pilot uses the burner and the valve to change the altitude of the balloon and take advantage of favorable winds. A hot-air balloon cannot land at the same spot from which it took off. The ground crew must drive to the landing site to collect the balloon and the passengers.

Taking Off and Landing

Launching and piloting a hot-air balloon is an activity that takes skill and patience.

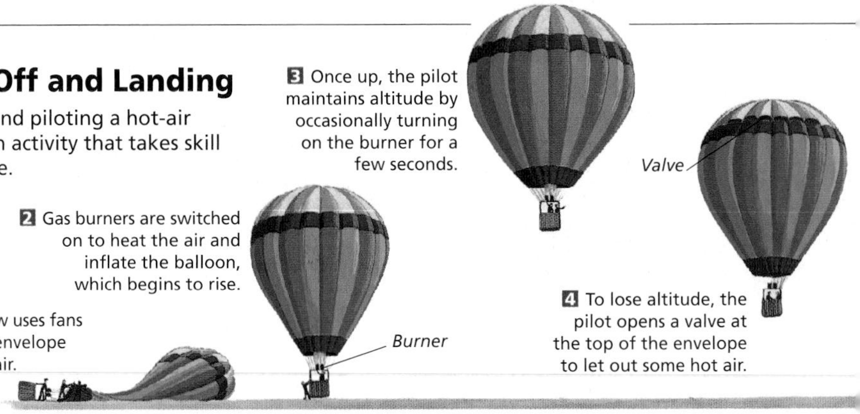
1 The crew uses fans to fill the envelope with cold air.
2 Gas burners are switched on to heat the air and inflate the balloon, which begins to rise.
Burner
3 Once up, the pilot maintains altitude by occasionally turning on the burner for a few seconds.
Valve
4 To lose altitude, the pilot opens a valve at the top of the envelope to let out some hot air.

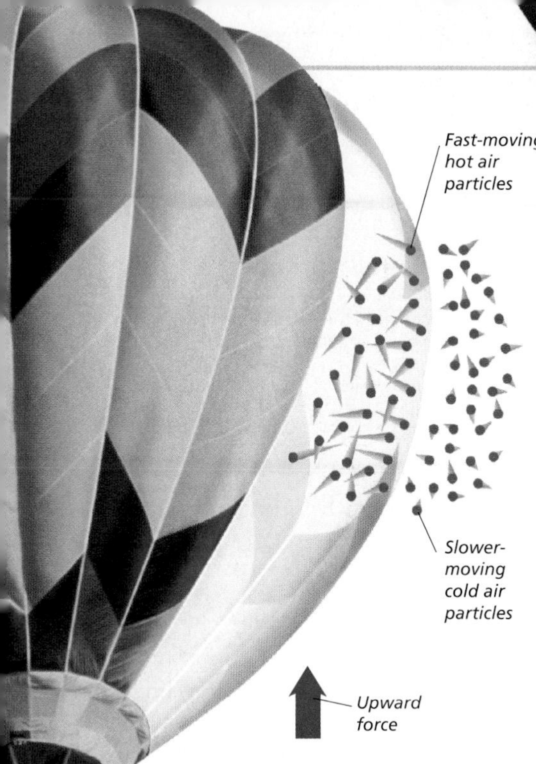
Fast-moving hot air particles
Slower-moving cold air particles
Upward force

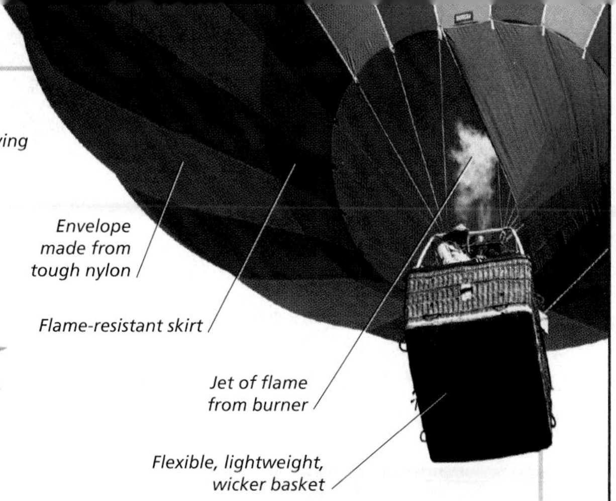
Envelope made from tough nylon
Flame-resistant skirt
Jet of flame from burner
Flexible, lightweight, wicker basket

Particle Pressure

Particles in hot air move faster and are farther apart than those in cold air, so hot air is less dense than cold air. With lower density, heated air rises over colder air.

Balloon Valve
The valve helps to control the balloon's altitude. When the valve is opened, some hot air is released from the top of the balloon. The hot air is replaced by cold air flowing into the base of the balloon. This exchange of cold air for hot air increases the mass of the balloon, causing it to descend until the pilot closes the valve.

5 The pilot selects a suitable place to land before opening the valve all the way.

6 The balloon slowly falls to the ground and collapses.

7 The crew gathers up the envelope.

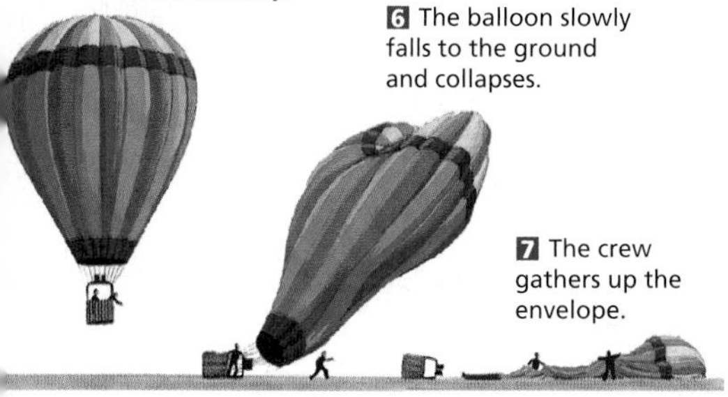

Going Further

- Write a paragraph comparing early hot-air balloons with modern balloons. Include the following information: the kind of materials used, the length of distances traveled, and the types of fuel used.
- Take a Discovery Channel Video Field Trip by watching "Up, Up, and Away."

Discovery Channel School **Video Field Trip**

Going Further

The Montgolfier hot-air balloon that first carried human passengers had an envelope made of cotton and paper coated with alum to reduce flammability. The fuel used was straw. The balloon flew from the center of Paris to the outskirts (a distance of about 9 kilometers) in 25 minutes on November 21, 1783. (Hot-air balloons were soon eclipsed by helium balloons or hydrogen balloons.) Modern passenger hot-air balloons were developed in the United States in the 1960s. Their envelopes are made of nylon and they use propane fuel. Hot-air balloons generally stay aloft for about an hour. (For long distance flights, balloonists generally use combination helium and hot-air balloons called Rozier balloons after Pilâtre de Rozier, a passenger on the first "manned" flight.) **Verbal**

Discovery Channel School

Video Field Trip

Up, Up, and Away

After students have viewed the Video Field Trip, ask them the following questions: **What gases have commonly been used in balloons that carry passengers?** *(Hot air, helium, and hydrogen)* **Why do the particles of a gas inside a balloon fill the entire balloon?** *(A gas has no particular size or shape and expands to fill the volume available.)* **What causes a hot-air balloon to lift off and rise from a surface?** *(Hot air inside the balloon is less dense than the cooler, denser air outside the balloon. The difference in density results in an upward force.)* In 1931, Auguste Piccard, a Swiss physicist and educator, built a balloon that could rise a distance of 16 miles. **Why did Piccard design the balloon so that it could become airborne when it was only partially filled?** *(Piccard knew the gas inside the balloon would continue to expand as the balloon floated up to greater heights because the outside air pressure decreased as the balloon rose.)* In Piccard's balloon, the pressure in the cabin was controlled as it is in planes that travel at great heights above Earth's surface. Air pressure in the cabin is kept higher than atmospheric pressure. **Why must the air pressure inside the cabin be controlled?** *(Atmospheric pressure decreases with altitude until it no longer can sustain respiration.)*

Section 3.3

1 FOCUS

Objectives

3.3.1 **Describe** phase changes.
3.3.2 **Explain** how temperature can be used to recognize a phase change.
3.3.3 **Explain** what happens to the motion, arrangement, and average kinetic energy of water molecules during phase changes.
3.3.4 **Describe** each of the six phase changes.
3.3.5 **Identify** phase changes as endothermic or exothermic.

Reading Focus

Build Vocabulary L2

Word-Part Analysis List on the board the following word parts and meanings: *-ion,* "the act of" or "the result of an action"; *-ic,* "related to or characterized by"; *endo-,* "inside"; *exo-,* "outside"; *therm,* "heat"; *-ize,* "to become." Have students identify these word parts in the vocabulary terms. Discuss the terms' meanings with students.

Reading Strategy L2

a. Liquid **b.** Liquid **c.** Gas **d.** Liquid **e.** Gas **f.** Gas

2 INSTRUCT

Characteristics of Phase Changes

Use Visuals L1

Figure 15 Note that water is one of the few substances that exist naturally as a solid, liquid, and gas under ordinary conditions. Have students look at the figure and read the caption. Ask, **Which two phases of water are visible in the photograph?** *(Solid and liquid)* **Where would the third phase most likely be found?** *(In the air)*
Visual, Logical

3.3 Phase Changes

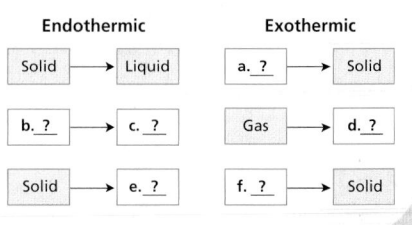

Reading Focus

Key Concepts

- What are six common phase changes?
- What happens to a substance's temperature and a system's energy during a phase change?
- How does the arrangement of water molecules change during melting and freezing?
- How are evaporation and boiling different?

Vocabulary

- phase change
- endothermic
- heat of fusion
- exothermic
- vaporization
- heat of vaporization
- evaporation
- vapor pressure
- condensation
- sublimation
- deposition

Reading Strategy

Summarizing Copy the diagram. As you read, complete the description of energy flow during phase changes.

Endothermic		Exothermic	
Solid →	Liquid	a. ? →	Solid
b. ? →	c. ?	Gas →	d. ?
Solid →	e. ?	f. ? →	Solid

Massive chunks of frozen water called icebergs are a common sight off the continent of Antarctica. A large iceberg like the one in Figure 15 contains enough fresh water to supply millions of people with water for a year. During the summer in southern Australia, fresh water is a scarce resource. People have proposed towing icebergs to Australia from Antarctica. The plan has not been implemented because the trip could take months to complete and much of the iceberg would melt along the way. In this section, you will find out what happens when a substance, such as water, changes from one state to another.

Characteristics of Phase Changes

When at least two states of the same substance are present, scientists describe each different state as a phase. For example, if an iceberg is floating in the ocean, there are two phases of water present—a solid phase and a liquid phase. A **phase change** is the reversible physical change that occurs when a substance changes from one state of matter to another.

Figure 15 The solid and liquid phases of water are visible in this photograph of an iceberg in the Amundsen Sea near Antarctica.

Section Resources

Print
- ***Laboratory Manual,*** Investigation 3A
- ***Reading and Study Workbook With Math Support,*** Section 3.3
Transparencies, Section 3.3

Technology
- ***Probeware Lab Manual,*** Lab 1
- ***Interactive Textbook,*** Section 3.3
- ***Presentation Pro CD-ROM,*** Section 3.3
- ***Go Online,*** NSTA SciLinks, Phases of matter; PHSchool.com, Data sharing

In Figure 16, a state of matter is listed at each corner of the triangle. Each arrow in the diagram represents a different phase change. Each pair of arrows represents a set of reversible changes. For example, the arrow starting at the solid phase and ending at the liquid phase represents melting. The arrow starting at the liquid phase and ending at the solid phase represents freezing.

Melting, freezing, vaporization, condensation, sublimation, and deposition are six common phase changes. All phase changes share certain characteristics related to energy and temperature.

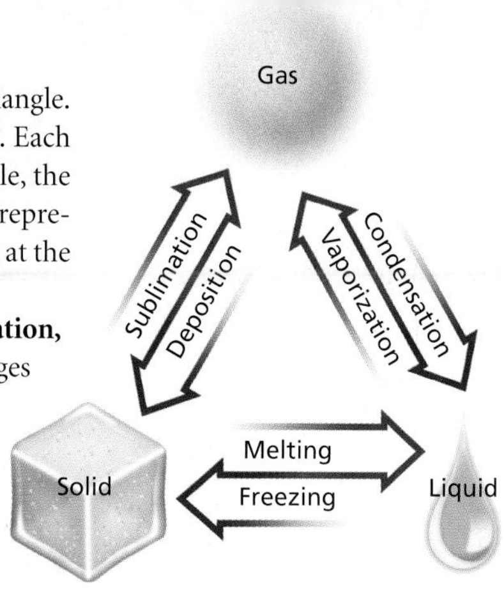

Gas
Sublimation
Deposition
Condensation
Vaporization
Melting
Freezing
Solid
Liquid

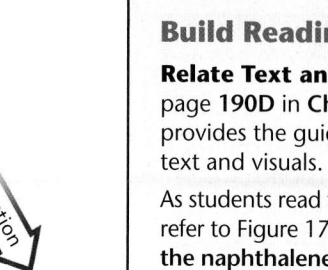

Figure 16 This diagram lists six physical changes that can occur among the solid, liquid, and gaseous phases of a substance. **Interpreting Diagrams** ***Explain why the changes are grouped into the pairs shown on the diagram.***

Temperature and Phase Changes One way to recognize a phase change is by measuring the temperature of a substance as it is heated or cooled. **The temperature of a substance does not change during a phase change.**

Naphthalene (NAF thuh leen) is a compound that is sometimes used in mothballs. Figure 17 is a graph of the data collected when a solid piece of naphthalene is slowly heated. Temperature readings are taken at regular intervals. At first the temperature rises as the solid naphthalene warms up. But at 80°C, the temperature of the naphthalene stops rising. The temperature remains at 80°C, which is the melting point of naphthalene, until melting is complete.

If liquid naphthalene is placed in an ice-water bath, the temperature of the liquid will drop until it reaches 80°C. It will remain at 80°C until all the liquid freezes. The temperature at which a substance freezes—its freezing point—is identical to the temperature at which it melts. The freezing and melting points of naphthalene are both 80°C.

If naphthalene is heated after it has completely melted, its temperature begins to rise again. The temperature keeps rising until it reaches 218°C, which is the boiling point of naphthalene. Until boiling is complete, the temperature remains at 218°C.

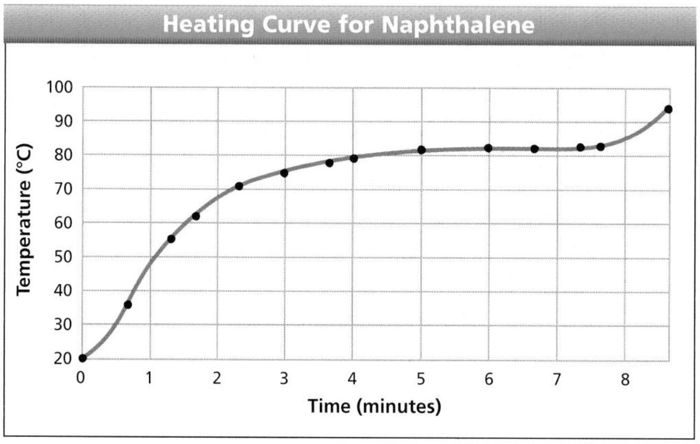

Heating Curve for Naphthalene
Temperature (°C)
100
90
80
70
60
50
40
30
20
0
1
2
3
4
5
6
7
8
Time (minutes)

Figure 17 This graph shows what happens to the temperature of a solid sample of naphthalene as the sample is slowly heated. **Using Graphs** ***What happened to the temperature in the interval between four and seven minutes?***

Build Reading Literacy L1

Relate Text and Visuals Refer to page **190D** in **Chapter 7,** which provides the guidelines for relating text and visuals.

As students read the section, have them refer to Figure 17. Ask, **In what state is the naphthalene at 20°C? In what state is the naphthalene at 90°C?** *(Solid, liquid)* **What are the melting and freezing points of naphthalene?** *(Both are 80°C.)* **What would the heating curve for naphthalene look like if the graph were extended beyond a temperature of 100°C?** *(The heating curve would rise until it reached the boiling point of naphthalene, which is 218°C.)*
Visual, Logical

FYI

The plateau on the graph in Figure 17 is not completely flat as it should be while a substance melts. This graph represents actual data collected in a lab. It is likely that there were some impurities in the naphthalene sample, which caused some minor fluctuation in the melting point.

Customize for English Language Learners

Build a Science Glossary
Direct students to Figure 16. Before they read, have them use the figure to make a list of the six terms in the arrows for a glossary. Students should add definitions for the terms to the glossary as they read the section. Encourage students to include examples of the six phase changes along with the definitions.

Answer to . . .

Figure 16 *The groupings represent pairs of reversible changes.*

Figure 17 *The temperature remained fairly constant.*

Integrate Biology L2

One of the main causes of frost damage in crops is ice-nucleating bacteria. These bacteria provide a nucleus around which ice can form. When ice forms on plants, it pierces their cell walls and causes the cells to desiccate, or dry out because water escapes from the cells. Have students search the Internet for information on ice-nucleating bacteria. Have students present what they learn in a pamphlet that offers suggestions on how to prevent frost damage from bacteria.
Verbal

Teacher Demo

Energy Transfer L2

Purpose Students observe that the phase change from ice to water is endothermic.

Materials tray of ice cubes

Procedure Place a tray of ice cubes on a counter at the beginning of class. As the ice begins to melt, ask students where the energy to melt the ice comes from.

Expected Outcome Students will observe that the ice melts. They will infer that the energy to melt the ice comes from the air and the counter because these materials are warmer than the ice.
Visual

Energy absorbed

Figure 18 This ice sculpture of a dog sled was carved at a winter fair in Fairbanks, Alaska. The ice sculpture will start to melt if the temperature rises above 0°C or sunlight shines directly on the ice.

Energy and Phase Changes During a phase change, energy is transferred between a substance and its surroundings. The direction of the transfer depends on the type of phase change. **Energy is either absorbed or released during a phase change.**

The ice sculpture in Figure 18 isn't going to last forever. When the temperature of the air rises above 0°C or when sunlight shines directly on the ice, an ice sculpture begins to melt. Melting is an example of an endothermic change. During an **endothermic** change, the system absorbs energy from its surroundings.

The amount of energy absorbed depends on the substance. For example, one gram of ice absorbs 334 joules (J) of energy as it melts. This amount of energy is the **heat of fusion** for water. Fusion is another term for melting. The heat of fusion varies from substance to substance.

One gram of water releases 334 joules of energy to its surroundings as it freezes, the same amount of energy that is absorbed when one gram of ice melts. Farmers use this release of energy to protect their crops. When farmers expect temperatures to drop slightly below 0°C, they spray the crops with water as shown in Figure 19. As water freezes, it releases heat. The flow of heat slows the drop in temperature and helps protect the crops from damage. Freezing is an example of an exothermic change. During an **exothermic** change, the system releases energy to its surroundings.

An understanding of phase changes can be useful in many situations. The How It Works box explains how the design of an ice rink in Utah allows the manager of the rink to control the hardness of the ice.

Energy released

Figure 19 Energy released as ice forms on these strawberry plants keeps the plants from freezing at temperatures slightly below 0°C. **Applying Concepts** ***Explain why a farmer would need to keep spraying the plants with water while the temperature remains below freezing.***

Reading Checkpoint *How much energy does one gram of ice absorb as it melts?*

Facts and Figures

Preventing Frost Damage For a frost control system to work, a farmer needs to start the sprinklers just before the temperature at ground level reaches 0°C. Placing a shallow pan of water in the lowest part of the field is an easy way to monitor the temperature. As soon as ice begins to form around the edge of the pan, the sprinklers should be turned on. The sprinklers should stay on until the temperature rises enough to start melting the ice.

This method of frost control is effective for strawberry plants down to about −6.6°C. When strawberries are in bloom, sprinklers are best started at 1.1°C. Blueberries with open blooms are safe from damage at temperatures as low as 0°C. Because of the cost of installation and operation, frost control systems are generally used for crops that can demand high unit prices, such as oranges, strawberries, Blueberries, and asparagus.

HOW It Works

Custom-Tailored Ice

At the Utah Olympic Oval the hardness of the ice can be controlled. The ice must be cold and hard for long speed-skating races, where the length of a skater's glide is important. For shorter races, the skaters need more traction, so the ice is made a little warmer and softer. **Interpreting Diagrams** ***What is the purpose of the sand layer?***

Speed Skater
This skater is racing at the Utah Olympic Oval, one of the world's most technically advanced ice rinks.

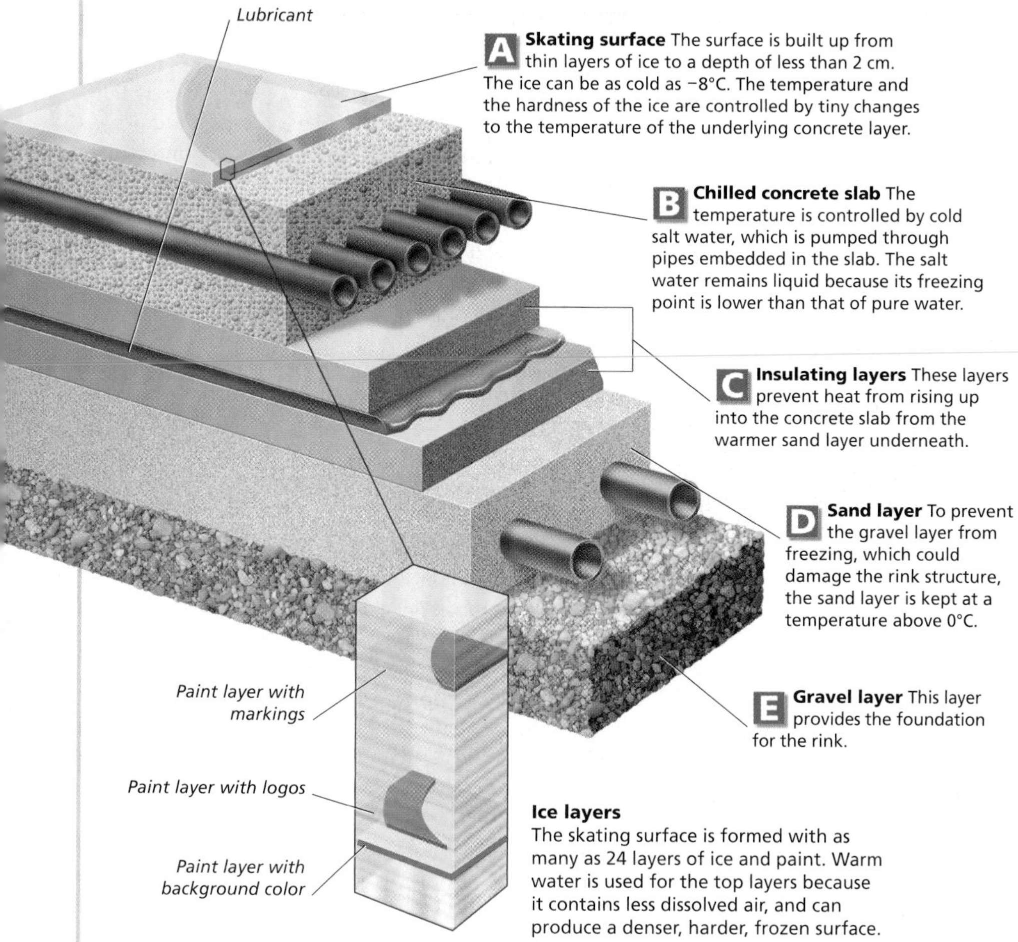
Lubricant
Paint layer with markings
Paint layer with logos
Paint layer with background color

A Skating surface The surface is built up from thin layers of ice to a depth of less than 2 cm. The ice can be as cold as −8°C. The temperature and the hardness of the ice are controlled by tiny changes to the temperature of the underlying concrete layer.

B Chilled concrete slab The temperature is controlled by cold salt water, which is pumped through pipes embedded in the slab. The salt water remains liquid because its freezing point is lower than that of pure water.

C Insulating layers These layers prevent heat from rising up into the concrete slab from the warmer sand layer underneath.

D Sand layer To prevent the gravel layer from freezing, which could damage the rink structure, the sand layer is kept at a temperature above 0°C.

E Gravel layer This layer provides the foundation for the rink.

Ice layers
The skating surface is formed with as many as 24 layers of ice and paint. Warm water is used for the top layers because it contains less dissolved air, and can produce a denser, harder, frozen surface.

HOW It Works

Custom-Tailored Ice L2

Skaters traveling at speeds up to 80 km/h will be slowed by a surface that is not smooth, level, and uniformly hard. The conditions of the ice at the Utah Olympic Oval, which was constructed for the 2000 Winter Olympics, can be changed overnight. For sprinters, the ice is softer so that their traction, or ability to grip the ice, is greater. A harder surface allows long-distance skaters to glide more easily across the ice.

Controlling the indoor climate is also important in maintaining the ice surface. The Utah Olympic Oval has two air-filtering systems and a dehumidifier that can reduce humidity to 3%. The air temperature varies only 3°C from the ice to the ceiling. Controlling the conditions above and below the ice allows for precise control of the ice surface.

Interpreting Diagrams The sand layer prevents the gravel layer from freezing and damaging the rink structure.
Visual, Logical

For Enrichment L3

Have students research playing surfaces used in other sports, such as football, tennis, and golf. Explain that different surfaces affect an athlete's performance. Students could compare the advantages and disadvantages of artificial turf and grass football fields; or cement, clay, and grass tennis courts. They could also find out how the length of grass affects shots at different locations on a golf course.
Logical

Answer to . . .

Figure 19 *Until the temperature rises above freezing, the farmer must continue to provide energy to keep the plants from freezing.*

Reading Checkpoint *334 joules*

Melting and Freezing

Use Visuals L1

Figure 20 Keeping food cool requires the transfer of energy. Ask, **What change occurs in the evaporator? Is this change exothermic or endothermic?** *(Liquid to gas; the change is endothermic because energy is absorbed from the food compartment)* **What change occurs in the condenser? Is this change exothermic or endothermic?** *(Gas is liquid; the change is exothermic because energy is released to the surroundings)*
Visual

FYI

Refrigeration is also discussed in Chapter 16, where the focus is on the need for work to be done for heat to flow from an area of lower temperature to an area at higher temperature. In this chapter, the focus is on the endothermic and exothermic phase changes.

Vaporization and Condensation

Use Community Resources L2

Invite an appliance repairperson to come to the class and speak about compounds used in air conditioner and refrigerator cooling coils. Suggest that the speaker describe the types of compounds used, how the compounds have changed over time, and whether there are any problems with the replacement compounds.
Interpersonal

Go Online NSTA SCiLINKS

Download a worksheet on phases of matter for students to complete, and find additional teacher support from NSTA SciLinks.

Go Online NSTA SCiLINKS

For: Links on phases of matter
Visit: www.SciLinks.org
Web Code: ccn-1033

Melting and Freezing

In water, hydrogen and oxygen atoms are combined in small units called molecules. Each water molecule contains two hydrogen atoms and one oxygen atom. **The arrangement of molecules in water becomes less orderly as water melts and more orderly as water freezes.**

Melting In ice, attractions between water molecules keep the molecules in fixed positions. When ice cubes are removed from a freezer and placed in an empty glass, heat flows from the air to the ice. As the ice gains energy, the molecules vibrate more quickly. At the melting point of water, 0°C, some molecules gain enough energy to overcome the attractions and move from their fixed positions. When all the molecules have enough energy to move, melting is complete. Any energy gained by the water after the phase change increases the average kinetic energy of the molecules, and the temperature rises.

Freezing When liquid water is placed in a freezer, energy flows from the water to the air in the freezer, and the water cools down. As the average kinetic energy of its molecules decreases, they move more slowly. At the freezing point of water, some molecules move slowly enough for the attractions between molecules to have an effect. When all the molecules have been drawn into an orderly arrangement, freezing is complete. Any energy removed from the ice after the phase change decreases the average kinetic energy of the molecules, and the temperature of the ice drops.

Often, people think of cold temperatures when they hear the term *freezing*. But substances that are solids at room temperature can freeze at temperatures that are quite high. For example, silicon freezes at 1412°C (2574°F). As a comparison, you can bake cookies at 177°C (350°F).

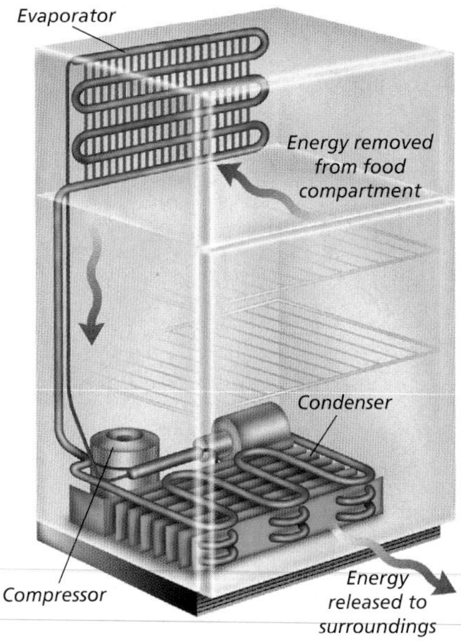
Evaporator
Energy removed from food compartment
Condenser
Compressor
Energy released to surroundings

Figure 20 In a refrigerator, a pair of phase changes keep the food cold. Energy from inside the food compartment is used to change a liquid to a gas in the evaporator. This energy is released when the compressed gas changes back to a liquid in the condenser.

Vaporization and Condensation

Figure 20 shows how food cools and stays cold in a refrigerator. The process depends on a substance that changes from a liquid to a gas to a liquid over and over again. During these phase changes, energy flows from the inside of the refrigerator to the outside.

The phase change in which a substance changes from a liquid into a gas is **vaporization.** Vaporization is an endothermic process. That is, a substance must absorb energy in order to change from a liquid to a gas. One gram of water gains 2261 joules of energy when it vaporizes. This amount of energy is the **heat of vaporization** for water. The heat of vaporization varies from substance to substance.

Facts and Figures

Chlorofluorocarbons Under the Clean Air Act, which became effective in November of 1995, it became illegal to release into the air compounds that harm Earth's ozone layer. Chlorofluorocarbons (CFCs) are among the banned substances. CFCs were used as refrigerants in cooling devices, such as refrigerators and air conditioners.

Because CFCs do not dissolve easily in water and are generally not very reactive, they tend to stay in the atmosphere once they are released. In the lower atmosphere, their presence causes few problems. However, these compounds move into the stratosphere where they are exposed to high energy radiation. This radiation causes the CFCs to react and release chlorine atoms. These chlorine atoms react with oxygen to form chlorine monoxide, which causes the ozone to decompose into oxygen. Hydrogen fluorocarbons (HFCs) have replaced CFCs in many cooling devices.

Scientists distinguish two vaporization processes—boiling and evaporation. **Evaporation takes place at the surface of a liquid and occurs at temperatures below the boiling point.**

Figure 21 Evaporation takes place at the surface of a liquid.

Evaporation If you go outside after a rain shower on a sunny, warm day, you may notice puddles of water. If you return to the same location after a few hours, the puddles may be gone. This disappearance of the puddles is due to evaporation. **Evaporation** is the process that changes a substance from a liquid to a gas at temperatures below the substance's boiling point.

Figure 21 shows what is happening as water evaporates from a small, shallow container. Some molecules near the surface are moving fast enough to escape the liquid and become water vapor. (A vapor is the gaseous phase of a substance that is normally a solid or liquid at room temperature.) The greater the surface area of the container, the faster the water evaporates.

What happens if the water is in a closed container? As the water evaporates, water vapor collects above the liquid. The pressure caused by the collisions of this vapor and the walls of the container is called **vapor pressure.** The vapor pressure of water increases as the temperature increases. At higher temperatures, more water molecules have enough kinetic energy to overcome the attractions of other molecules in the liquid.

Reading Checkpoint *How does the surface area of a liquid affect the rate of evaporation?*

Boiling As you heat a pot of water, both the temperature and the vapor pressure of the water increase. When the vapor pressure becomes equal to atmospheric pressure, the water boils. The temperature at which this happens is the boiling point of water.

The kinetic theory explains what happens when water boils. As the temperature increases, water molecules move faster and faster. When the temperature reaches 100°C, some molecules below the surface of the liquid have enough kinetic energy to overcome the attraction of neighboring molecules. Figure 22 shows that bubbles of water vapor form within the liquid. Because water vapor is less dense than liquid water, the bubbles quickly rise to the surface. When they reach the surface, the bubbles burst and release water vapor into the air.

Figure 22 Boiling takes place throughout a liquid. **Applying Concepts** ***Explain why the temperature of water does not rise during boiling.***

Build Science Skills L2

Designing Experiments The rate of evaporation is affected by surface area. Ask students to design an experiment using water in a beaker with gradations to test this statement. Have students identify the variables that will need to be controlled (type of liquid, volume of liquid, temperature of liquid, time). Ask, **What will the manipulated variable be?** *(Surface area)* **What will the responding variable be?** *(Rate of evaporation)* **How will you measure the rate of evaporation?** *(One acceptable answer is measuring the liquid level after a specified interval of time.)* Allow students to conduct approved experiments and summarize their results in a report.
Verbal, Logical

Address Misconceptions L2

Students often think that atoms and molecules expand as the temperature rises. Use water's expansion when it freezes to challenge this misconception. Explain that the space between water molecules is greater in ice than in liquid water because of the arrangement of molecules in ice. When ice melts, the space between molecules decreases and the volume decreases.
Logical

FYI

Eventually, no more vapor can collect above the liquid in a closed container. The water continues to evaporate, but some of the vapor condenses in return. This is an example of a dynamic equilibrium. Chemical (and physical) equilibrium is introduced in Chapter 7.

Water, especially tap water, contains dissolved gases such as oxygen and nitrogen. When water is heated, the solubility of these gases in water decreases, which causes small bubbles to form in heated water before it begins to boil.

Answer to . . .

Figure 22 *Energy absorbed by the system during boiling is used to overcome attractions among water molecules.*

Reading Checkpoint *The greater the surface area, the faster the water evaporates.*

Quick Lab

Observing Phase Changes L2

Objective
After completing this lab, students will be able to
- identify examples of condensation and sublimation.

Skills Focus Observing

Prep Time 15 minutes

Advance Prep Obtain dry ice from a local supplier or from a scientific supply house, ice cream wholesaler, or compressed gas dealer. Do not store dry ice in an airtight container. Leave a window open in your car if you have dry ice in the car. Use a hammer to carefully break the dry ice into pea-sized pieces.

Class Time 20 minutes

Safety Do not handle dry ice with bare hands. It damages skin tissue on contact. Wear safety goggles, a lab apron, and leather gloves when handling dry ice. Use forceps to dispense a pea-sized piece of dry ice into each flask. Caution students not to touch dry ice and to use care when handling glassware to avoid breakage. Provide only nonmercury thermometers.

Teaching Tips
- Do this lab after students have studied sublimation.
- If students are having trouble with Question 2, ask at what temperature water boils. If they are having trouble with Question 4, remind them that water vapor exists above the liquid.

Expected Outcome When dry ice is added to water, vigorous bubbling begins and a fog appears above the liquid.

For Enrichment L3

Challenge students to propose a way to have solid, liquid, and gaseous water together in the same test tube. One way is to place ice in liquid water in a closed container. Water vapor will collect above the surface of the water.
Visual, Logical

Quick Lab

Observing Phase Changes

Materials
250-mL Erlenmeyer flask, graduated cylinder, thermometer, dry ice

Procedure
1. Pour 150 milliliters of water into a 250-mL Erlenmeyer flask. Place a thermometer in the flask. **CAUTION** *Wipe up any spilled water right away to avoid slips and falls.*
2. Observe what happens after your teacher adds a small piece of dry ice to the flask. (Dry ice is solid carbon dioxide.) **CAUTION** *Dry ice can damage skin on contact. Do not touch the dry ice.*
3. Record the temperature of the water just after the dry ice is added and again after it is no longer visible.

Analyze and Conclude
1. **Observing** What happened when the dry ice was added to the water?
2. **Analyzing Data** Did adding the dry ice cause the water to boil? Explain your answer.
3. **Inferring** What was the source of the bubbles in the water?
4. **Formulating Hypotheses** What caused a cloud to form above the flask?
5. **Applying Concepts** What phase changes occurred in the flask?

The boiling point of a substance depends on the atmospheric pressure. The normal boiling point of water at sea level is 100°C. At higher elevations, the atmospheric pressure is lower. Do you know that Denver, Colorado, is called the mile-high city? This nickname is based on Denver's location at one mile above sea level. In Denver, the vapor pressure of water will equal atmospheric pressure at temperatures below 100°C. The boiling point of water in Denver can be as low as 95°C. Food does not cook as quickly at 95°C as it does at 100°C. Pasta takes longer to cook in Denver than in New Orleans, Louisiana, a city that is located near sea level.

Condensation Have you ever come out of a shower to find your bathroom mirror clouded over? The "cloud" on the mirror is caused by water vapor that cooled as it came in contact with the mirror. The water vapor transferred heat to the mirror and condensed into liquid water. **Condensation** is the phase change in which a substance changes from a gas or vapor to a liquid. This process is also responsible for the morning dew on the blades of grass in Figure 23. Condensation is an exothermic process.

Figure 23 Water vapor from the air condensed into drops of liquid water on these blades of grass.

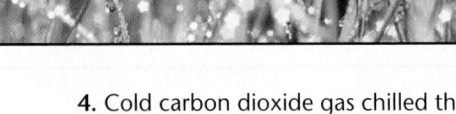

Analyze and Conclude
1. Bubbles formed in the water, and a fog formed above the water. The temperature of the water decreased.
2. No, because the water was not at 100°C when bubbles appeared.
3. Carbon dioxide gas from the dry ice
4. Cold carbon dioxide gas chilled the air above the water, causing water vapor to condense into tiny liquid droplets.
5. Sublimation of carbon dioxide and condensation of water occurred. Students may also mention vaporization of water.
Logical, Kinesthetic

Sublimation and Deposition

Directors of concerts and plays sometimes use dry ice to create a fog-like special effect. Dry ice is the common name for the solid form of carbon dioxide. At room temperature, dry ice can directly change from a solid to a colorless gas. **Sublimation** is the phase change in which a substance changes from a solid to a gas or vapor without changing to a liquid first. Sublimation is an endothermic change. As dry ice sublimes, the cold carbon dioxide vapor causes water vapor in the air to condense and form clouds.

Where does the name dry ice come from? Solid carbon dioxide does not form a liquid as its temperature rises. Suppose 100 steaks are shipped from Omaha, Nebraska, to a supermarket in Miami, Florida. The steaks will spoil unless they are kept cold during the trip. If regular ice is used, water collects in the shipping container as the ice melts. If the steaks are shipped in dry ice, the container and the steaks stay dry during the journey. Figure 24 shows another use of dry ice.

When a gas or vapor changes directly into a solid without first changing to a liquid, the phase change is called **deposition.** This exothermic phase change is the reverse of sublimation. Deposition causes frost to form on windows. When water vapor in the air comes in contact with cold window glass, the water vapor loses enough kinetic energy to change directly from a gas to a solid.

Figure 24 A technician at Tinker Air Force Base in Oklahoma hangs a mosquito trap. The trap is baited with dry ice because mosquitoes are attracted to carbon dioxide.

Section 3.3 Assessment

Reviewing Concepts

1. Name six common phase changes.
2. What happens to the temperature of a substance during a phase change?
3. How does the energy of a system change during a phase change?
4. What happens to the arrangement of water molecules as water melts and freezes?
5. What is the difference between evaporation and boiling?
6. Explain why sublimation and deposition are classified as physical changes.

Critical Thinking

7. **Applying Concepts** How can the mass of a pile of snow decrease on a sunny day when the air temperature does not rise above 0°C?
8. **Drawing Conclusions** At room temperature, table salt is a solid and acetone is a liquid. Acetone is the main ingredient in nail polish remover. What conclusion can you draw about the melting points of these materials?

Writing in Science

Steps in a Process Write a paragraph describing three steps that must occur for a water molecule to start on the surface of hot bath water and end up on the surface of a bathroom mirror. Note whether the phase changes that take place during the process are endothermic or exothermic. (*Hint:* Use words such as *first, next,* and *finally* to show the order of events.)

Section 3.3 Assessment

1. Melting, freezing, vaporization, condensation, sublimation, and deposition
2. The temperature of a substance does not change during a phase change.
3. Energy is either released or absorbed during a phase change.
4. The arrangement of molecules becomes less orderly as water melts and more orderly as water freezes.
5. Evaporation takes place at the surface of a liquid and occurs at temperatures below the boiling point.
6. A substance's identity does not change during sublimation or deposition.
7. When snow absorbs energy from sunlight, it either melts or sublimes.
8. Table salt must have a melting point above room temperature, and acetone must have a melting point below room temperature.

Sublimation and Deposition

Use Visuals L1

Figure 24 Have students examine Figure 24. Explain that the trap was hung as part of a study of West Nile virus, a mosquito-borne disease. Mosquitoes acquire the virus from infected birds and then transmit the virus to other animals and humans. Mosquitoes are collected and sent to a laboratory for identification by species and gender. Samples of similar female mosquitoes are blended and their RNA is analyzed for West Nile virus. Ask, **Why is dry ice used to bait the mosquito trap rather than gaseous carbon dioxide?** *(The large amount of carbon dioxide stored in dry ice is released slowly over time rather than all at once.)*
Logical

3 ASSESSMENT

Evaluate Understanding L2

Have students write the six terms that describe phase changes. Next to each term, students should describe the type of change. For example, for *melting*, students would indicate that the phase change is from a solid to a liquid. Tell students to include arrows pointing up to identify exothermic changes and arrows pointing down to identify exothermic changes.

Reteach L1

Use Figure 16 to review the six phase changes described in this section. Ask, **What do the phase changes with red arrows have in common?** *(They are all exothermic processes.)* **What do the phase changes with blue arrows have in common?** *(They are all endothermic processes.)*

Writing in Science

First, the water molecule on the surface of the bath water evaporates—an endothermic change. Next, random motion of the molecule carries it to the surface of the mirror. Finally, the molecule condenses on the mirror—an exothermic change.

Interactive Textbook If your class subscribes to the Interactive Textbook, use it to review key concepts in Section 3.3.

Exploration Lab

Investigating Changes in Temperature During Heating of Solids

L2

Objective

After completing this activity, students will be able to

- explain the constant temperature of a substance that is undergoing a phase change.

Address Misconceptions

Students might think the temperature should keep increasing as the ice melts. Ask them to predict the shape of the melting curve. After performing the lab, ask students to compare their predictions to the actual curves.

Skills Focus Measuring, Using Tables and Graphs

Prep Time 30 minutes

Advance Prep Buy crushed ice or crush it by placing ice cubes into a plastic bag and hitting them with a mallet while wearing goggles. Pour granular lauric acid into the test tubes and insert a thermometer into each test tube. Rather than discarding the lauric acid after the first class, leave the thermometers in the test tubes and allow the test tubes to cool to room temperature. The thermometers will be embedded in the solidified lauric acid.

Class Time 45 minutes

Safety Provide only nonmercury thermometers. Position hot plates away from the edges of tables. Place power cords behind the hot plates, where they are not likely to become entangled with arms or clothing. Once a hot plate is turned on, students should not touch it.

Teaching Tips

- Emphasize the importance of making an accurate measurement of the initial temperature of the ice.
- You may wish to save time by having some students perform Part A of the lab and others perform Part B. Students can then exchange data before making their graphs.
- To help students construct their graphs, show a sample graph on an overhead transparency. Include the grids for the horizontal and vertical axes, but not the data.
- You may wish to postpone the graphing of the results of Part A (Step 7) to the end of the lab, after all data have been collected.

Exploration Lab

Investigating Changes in Temperature During Heating of Solids

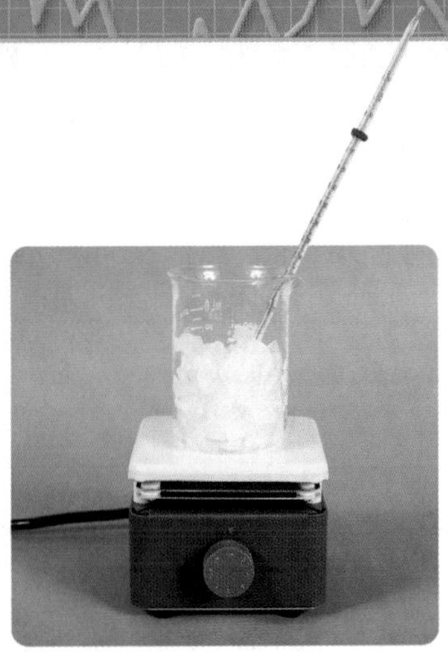

Lauric acid is a solid that is found in coconuts and processed foods that are made with coconut oil. Lauric acid is also used to make some soaps and cosmetics. In this lab, you will measure the temperature of ice and of lauric acid as these solids are heated and melt. You will graph the data you collect and compare the heating curves for ice and lauric acid.

Problem

What happens to the temperature of a substance during a phase change?

Materials

- 500-mL beaker
- crushed ice
- thermometer
- hot plate
- clock with second hand
- test tube of lauric acid with thermometer
- glass stirring rod
- graph paper

For the probeware version of this lab, see the Probeware Lab Manual, Lab 1.

Skills

Measuring, Using Graphs

Procedure

Part A: Heating Ice

1. On a sheet of paper, make a copy of the data table shown. Start with 11 blank rows, but leave space below your data table to add more rows, if necessary.
2. Fill a 500-mL beaker halfway with crushed ice. **CAUTION** *Use care when handling glassware to avoid breakage. Wipe up any spilled ice right away to avoid slips and falls.*
3. Place the beaker on a hot plate. Don't turn the hot plate on yet. Insert a thermometer into the ice. Because it takes several seconds for the thermometer to adjust to the temperature of its surroundings, wait 20 seconds and then measure the temperature of the ice. Record this temperature next to the 0 minutes entry in your data table.
4. Turn the hot plate to a low setting. **CAUTION** *Be careful not to touch the hot plate because contact with the hot plate could cause a burn.*
5. Observe and record the temperature at one-minute intervals until all the ice has changed to liquid water. Circle the temperature at which you first observe liquid water and the temperature at which all the ice has changed to liquid water.

Data Table

Time (minutes)	Temperature of Water (°C)	Temperature of Lauric Acid (°C)
0		
1		

Probeware Lab Manual Versions of this lab for use with probeware available from Pasco, Texas Instruments, and Vernier are in the Probeware Manual.

6. After all the ice has melted, make five more measurements of the temperature at one-minute intervals. Turn off the hot plate.
7. Graph your data with time on the horizontal axis and temperature on the vertical axis.

Part B: Heating Lauric Acid

8. Empty the water from the beaker into the sink. Fill the beaker halfway with cool tap water.
9. Place a test tube containing lauric acid and a thermometer into the beaker. If necessary, add or remove water so that the surface of the water in the beaker is above the surface of the lauric acid but below the opening of the test tube.
10. Place the beaker on the hot plate. After 20 seconds, measure the temperature of the water. Record this temperature next to the 0 minutes entry in your data table.
11. Repeat Steps 4 through 7 using the lauric acid instead of the ice. To keep the temperature the same throughout the water bath, use the glass stirring rod to stir the water after you take each temperature measurement.

Analyze and Conclude

1. **Using Graphs** Describe the shape of your graph for ice.
2. **Analyzing Data** What happened to the temperature of the ice-water mixture during the phase change?
3. **Drawing Conclusions** What happened to the energy that was transferred from the hot plate to the ice during the phase change?
4. **Comparing and Contrasting** Compare the shapes of the graphs for ice and for lauric acid. Compare the melting points of water and lauric acid.

Go Online PHSchool.com

For: Data sharing
Visit: PHSchool.com
Web Code: ccd-1030

Expected Outcome In Part A, if the readings are taken quickly enough, the first few temperature readings may be below 0°C. The temperature readings should remain at 0°C until all the ice has melted. The temperature should begin to rise once the ice has melted. Heating solid lauric acid raises its temperature to its melting point of 43.2°C. The temperature will begin to rise again after the lauric acid has melted.

Sample Data

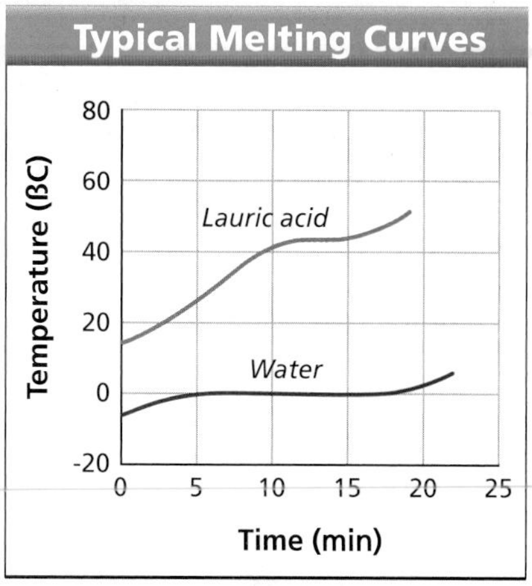
Typical Melting Curves
80
60
40
20
0
-20
0
5
10
15
20
25
Temperature (ßC)
Time (min)
Lauric acid
Water

Analyze and Conclude
1. The graph rises quickly to 0°C and remains horizontal at that temperature for a number of minutes. Then, it begins to rise again.
2. The temperature remained constant until the phase change was completed.
3. At first, the energy absorbed by the ice was used to overcome the forces of attraction holding water molecules in fixed positions. After all of the ice had melted, the energy absorbed increased the kinetic energy of the molecules in the liquid water.
4. The two graphs had similar shapes. However, ice melted at 0°C and lauric acid melted at about 43°C.
Logical

Go Online PHSchool.com

Have students pool and compare their data with students nationwide by visiting the Prentice Hall Web site at www.PHSchool.com.

Study Guide

Study Tip

Study With a Partner
On occasion, study with a friend. Quiz each other, compare notes from class lectures, go over homework answers, and discuss concepts that you need help with understanding.

Thinking Visually

a. and b. Condensation, freezing
c. Endothermic
d. Vaporization

Assessment

Interactive Textbook If your class subscribes to the Interactive Textbook, your students can go online to access an interactive version of the Student Edition and a self-test.

Reviewing Content

1. b	**2.** c	**3.** c
4. b	**5.** a	**6.** d
7. c	**8.** b	**9.** c
10. a		

CHAPTER 3

Study Guide

3.1 Solids, Liquids, and Gases

Key Concepts

- Materials can be classified as solids, liquids, or gases based on whether their shapes and volumes are definite or variable.
- The kinetic theory of matter states that all particles of matter are in constant motion.
- There are forces of attraction among the particles in all matter.
- The constant motion of particles in a gas allows a gas to fill a container of any shape or size.
- A liquid takes the shape of its container because particles in a liquid can flow to new locations. The volume of a liquid is constant because forces of attraction keep the particles close together.
- Solids have a definite volume and shape because particles in a solid vibrate around fixed locations.

Vocabulary

solid, *p. 69;* liquid, *p. 69;* gas, *p. 70;* kinetic energy, *p. 71*

3.2 The Gas Laws

Key Concepts

- Collisions between particles of a gas and the walls of the container cause the pressure in a closed container of gas.
- Factors that affect the pressure of an enclosed gas are its temperature, its volume, and the number of its particles.
- Raising the temperature of a gas will increase its pressure if the volume of the gas and the number of particles are constant.
- Reducing the volume of a gas increases its pressure if the temperature of the gas and the number of particles are constant.
- Increasing the number of particles will increase the pressure of a gas if the temperature and the volume are constant.
- The combined gas law can be expressed as

$$\frac{P_1V_1}{T_1} = \frac{P_2V_2}{T_2}$$

Vocabulary

pressure, *p. 75;* absolute zero, *p. 78;* Charles's law, *p. 78;* Boyle's law, *p. 79*

3.3 Phase Changes

Key Concepts

- Melting, freezing, vaporization, condensation, sublimation, and deposition are six common phase changes.
- The temperature of a substance does not change during a phase change.
- Energy is either absorbed or released during a phase change.
- The arrangement of molecules in water becomes less orderly as water melts, and more orderly as water freezes.
- Evaporation takes place at the surface of a liquid and occurs at temperatures below the boiling point.

Vocabulary

phase change, *p. 84;* endothermic, *p. 86;* heat of fusion, *p. 86;* exothermic, *p. 86;* vaporization, *p. 88;* heat of vaporization, *p. 88;* evaporation, *p. 89;* vapor pressure, *p. 89;* condensation, *p. 90;* sublimation, *p. 91;* deposition, *p. 91;*

Thinking Visually

Web Diagram Use information from the chapter to complete the web diagram on phase changes.

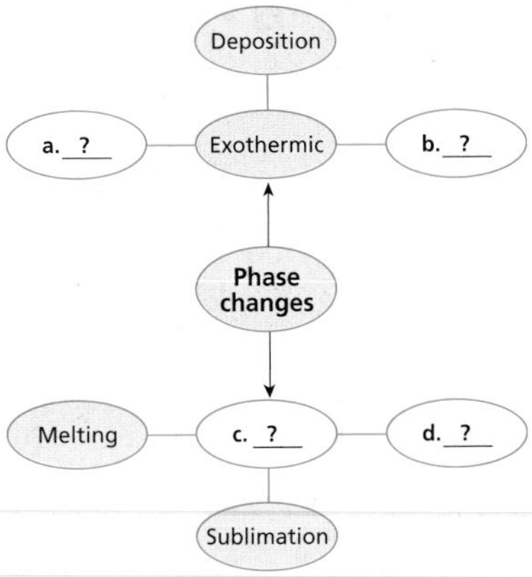
Deposition
a. ?
Exothermic
b. ?
Phase changes
Melting
c. ?
d. ?
Sublimation

Chapter Resources

Print
- ***Chapter and Unit Tests,*** Chapter 3 Test A and Test B
- ***Test Prep Resources,*** Chapter 3 ***Transparencies,*** Section 3.1

Technology
- ***Computer Test Bank,*** Chapter Test 3
- ***Interactive Textbook,*** Section 3.1
- ***Go Online,*** PHSchool.com, Chapter 3

CHAPTER 3

Assessment

Interactive textbook with assessment at PHSchool.com iText

Reviewing Content

Choose the letter that best answers the question or completes the statement.

1. Which state of matter has a definite volume but a variable shape?
   a. solid b. liquid
   c. gas d. vapor
2. In which state(s) of matter can materials take the shape of their containers?
   a. solid and liquid b. solid and gas
   c. liquid and gas d. liquid only
3. Which statement is true about the atoms in helium gas?
   a. They travel in circular paths.
   b. They have strong attractions to one another.
   c. They are not closely packed.
   d. They are arranged in an orderly pattern.
4. If the speed of an object increases, its kinetic energy
   a. decreases. b. increases.
   c. stays the same. d. is unpredictable.
5. The SI unit of pressure is the
   a. pascal. b. newton.
   c. square meter. d. psi.
6. Increasing which variable would decrease the pressure of a contained gas?
   a. temperature b. number of particles
   c. boiling point d. volume
7. Boyle's law relates pressure and
   a. temperature. b. number of particles.
   c. volume. d. mass.
8. Which of the following changes is exothermic?
   a. evaporation b. freezing
   c. boiling d. sublimation
9. The phase change that is the reverse of vaporization is
   a. freezing. b. melting.
   c. condensation. d. evaporation.
10. Which of these phase changes does NOT involve changing a liquid into a gas?
    a. sublimation b. vaporization
    c. evaporation d. boiling

Understanding Concepts

11. Provide an example of each of the three states of matter that exist at room temperature.
12. Compare and contrast liquid water and ice in terms of how definite their shapes and volumes are.
13. What three assumptions about particles in a gas are made by the kinetic theory?
14. Using the kinetic theory, explain why a liquid has a definite volume but a gas does not.
15. How do the way that atoms are arranged in liquid mercury and solid copper affect the movement of mercury and copper atoms?

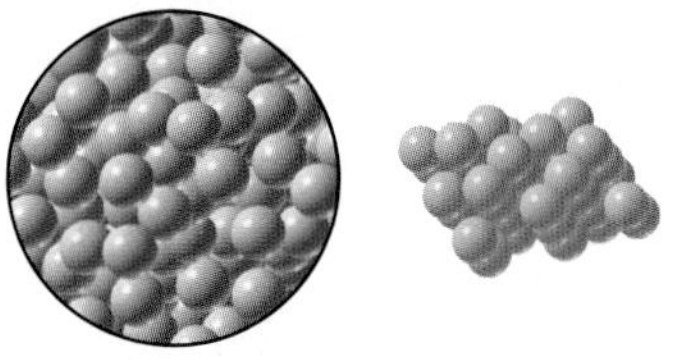

16. Using the kinetic theory, explain what causes gas pressure.
17. What three factors affect the pressure of a gas in a closed container?
18. If a piston moves downward in a cylinder, what happens to the volume and pressure of the gas in the cylinder? The temperature remains constant.
19. What happens to the speed of the particles inside an air-filled balloon if the temperature of the balloon increases?
20. Using the kinetic theory, explain why the pressure of a gas increases when its temperature increases.
21. How are the pressure and volume of a gas related?
22. How does an endothermic phase change differ from an exothermic phase change?
23. Compare the vapor pressure of water at 10°C with its vapor pressure at 50°C.
24. Explain why water has a different boiling point at an elevation of 3000 meters than it does at sea level.

Homework Guide

Section	Questions
3.1	1–4, 11–16, 33
3.2	5–7, 17–21, 27–28, 30–32, 35–36
3.2	8–10, 22–26, 29, 34, 37

Assessment (continued)

Understanding Concepts

11. Examples might include solid copper, liquid water, and the helium inside a balloon as a gas.
12. Both liquid water and ice have a definite volume. Ice has a definite shape, but liquid water does not.
13. The particles are in constant, random motion. The motion of one particle is unaffected by the motion of other particles unless the particles collide. Under ordinary conditions, forces of attraction between particles can be ignored.
14. The attractions between the particles in a liquid are strong enough to keep the particles close together. Without any significant attractions between particles in a gas, the particles are free to expand into any volume that is available.
15. The atoms in copper vibrate around fixed positions. The atoms in mercury can flow past one another.
16. Gas pressure is caused by collisions of atoms with their containers.
17. Temperature, volume, and the number of particles
18. The volume decreases and the pressure increases.
19. The particles in the air move faster, on average, when the temperature increases because they have more kinetic energy.
20. When the temperature of a gas increases, the particles have greater kinetic energy, on average, and move faster. Thus, atoms hit the walls of the container more often and with greater force, causing the pressure to increase.
21. The volume of a gas is inversely proportional to its pressure.
22. During an endothermic phase change, energy is absorbed by the system. During an exothermic phase change, energy is released by the system.
23. The vapor pressure of water is greater at 50°C than it is at 10°C.
24. Water boils when its vapor pressure becomes equal to atmospheric pressure. At 3000 m, the atmospheric pressure is lower than it is at sea level. Thus, vapor pressure equals atmospheric pressure at a lower temperature, and water boils at a lower temperature.

Critical Thinking

25. A balloon that is flexible will shrink. This observed change is not a phase change because helium is a gas before and after the change.
26. (a) Water melts and freezes at the same temperature. (b) Melting is an endothermic process. Freezing is an exothermic process.
27. Graph A
28. Graph A
29. Graph C

Math Skills

30. $P_1/P_2 = T_1/T_2$ or $P_1/T_1 = P_2/T_2$
31. 371 kPa
32. 1.8 L

Concepts in Action

33. There is almost no attraction between particles in a gas. They will quickly spread throughout the building. Because particles in a liquid strongly attract one another, they remain close together and don't spread throughout the building (unless the water quantity is large and there is no drain).
34. Because energy is being added but no increase in temperature occurs, a phase change is occurring in the can.
35. A decrease in pressure causes an increase in volume. A decrease in temperature causes a decrease in volume. Because the volume of the balloon increases, the decrease in pressure must affect the balloon more than the decrease in temperature.
36. The pressure increases.
37. Heating causes the water to vaporize. With continued heating, the pressure of the vapor increases because the volume of the confined vapor is constant. Eventually, the increased pressure causes the kernel to burst open.

Go Online PHSchool.com

Your students can independently test their knowledge of the chapter and print out their test results for your files.

CHAPTER 3

Assessment *(continued)*

Critical Thinking

25. **Classifying** If you take a helium balloon from inside a warm house to outside on a snowy day, what will happen to the balloon? Could you classify this change as a phase change? Explain your answer.

26. **Comparing and Contrasting** Compare the melting and freezing of water in terms of (a) the temperature at which these processes take place and (b) how energy is involved in these processes.

Use the graphs to answer Questions 27–29.

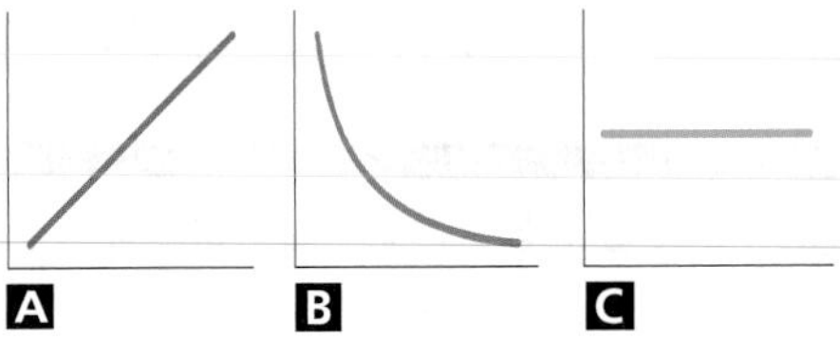

A
B
C

27. **Using Graphs** Which graph represents what happens to the pressure in a tire as air is added to the tire? Assume the temperature of the gas is constant.

28. **Using Graphs** Which graph represents what happens to the pressure in an aerosol can if the can is heated?

29. **Applying Concepts** Which graph represents temperature versus time during a phase change?

Math Skills

30. **Making Generalizations** The pressure of a gas is directly proportional to its temperature in kelvins. Using P_1, P_2, T_1, and T_2, write a mathematical equation that expresses this relationship.

31. **Calculating** An automobile tire has a pressure of 325 kPa when the temperature is 10°C. If the temperature of the tire rises to 50°C and its volume is constant, what is the new pressure?

32. **Calculating** A gas sample occupies 4.2 L at a pressure of 101 kPa. What volume will it occupy if the pressure is increased to 235 kPa?

Concepts in Action

33. **Using Models** If there is a gas leak in the basement of a building, you will soon notice an odor throughout the house. However, if there is a water leak in the basement, you will need to go to the basement to detect the leak. Use the kinetic theory to explain the differences.

34. **Inferring** A student examines a thermometer placed in a can containing a substance that is being heated. The temperature remains the same for several minutes, and then it starts to rise. Without looking in the can, how does the student know what is occurring in the can?

35. **Relating Cause and Effect** In Earth's atmosphere, pressure and temperature both decrease as altitude increases. Weather balloons expand as they rise. Which has more effect on the weather balloon, the decrease in pressure or the decrease in temperature? Explain your answer.

36. **Drawing Conclusions** In a car engine, air and gasoline vapors are mixed in a cylinder. A piston is pushed into the cylinder before a spark ignites the mixture of gases. When the piston is pushed into the cylinder, what happens to the pressure of the gases in the cylinder?

37. **Writing in Science** Unpopped popcorn kernels contain a small amount of water. Use what you know about vaporization and how gases behave to explain why popcorn pops when it is heated.

Performance-Based Assessment

Making a Poster The gas laws have many practical applications in cooking. Make a poster, including diagrams, that shows how two factors that affect gases affect cooking. Examples might include explaining why cakes rise while baking or why some recipes specify high-altitude temperatures and cooking times.

Go Online PHSchool.com

For: Self-grading assessment
Visit: PHSchool.com
Web Code: cca-1030

Performance-Based Assessment

Possible poster topics: Gas bubbles formed in cake batter increase in volume when the batter is heated, causing the cake to rise. Cake mixes often have instructions for baking at higher altitudes because the boiling point of water decreases at higher elevations. In a pressure cooker, the volume of air is constant. Heating the air increases both its temperature and pressure, and the food cooks in a shorter amount of time.

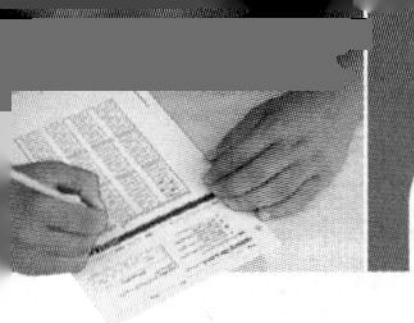

Standardized Test Prep

Test-Taking Tip

Watch For Qualifiers

The words *best* and *least* are examples of qualifiers. If a question contains a qualifier, more than one answer will contain correct information. However, only one answer will be complete and correct for the question asked. Look at the question below. Eliminate any answers that are clearly incorrect. Then choose the remaining answer that offers the best explanation for the question asked.

Choose the *best* explanation for why one particle in a gas does not affect other particles in a gas unless the particles collide.
(A) Particles in a gas are constantly moving.
(B) All the particles in a gas have the same kinetic energy.
(C) There are no forces of attraction among particles in a gas.
(D) There are billions of particles in a small sample of a gas.
(E) Particles in a gas are relatively far apart.

(Answer: E)

Choose the letter that best answers the question or completes the statement.

1. A material can be classified as a liquid if
(A) it has a definite shape and a definite volume.
(B) it has a definite shape and a variable volume.
(C) it has a variable shape and a definite volume.
(D) it has a variable shape and a variable volume.
(E) its particles vibrate around fixed locations.

2. Which statement *best* explains what must take place for water to boil?
(A) The water releases energy to its surroundings.
(B) Bubbles rise to the surface of the water.
(C) The vapor pressure of the water becomes equal to atmospheric pressure.
(D) Molecules at the surface of the water overcome the attractions of neighboring molecules.
(E) The temperature of the water increases.

3. Condensation is the phase change in which a substance changes from
(A) a solid to a gas.
(B) a solid to a liquid.
(C) a liquid to a solid.
(D) a liquid to a gas.
(E) a gas to a liquid.

4. Which of these statements about an enclosed gas is true? (Assume all quantities are constant except the two variables described in each statement.)
(A) Raising the temperature of a gas will increase its pressure.
(B) Increasing the volume of a gas will increase its pressure.
(C) Reducing the number of particles of a gas will increase its pressure.
(D) The volume of a gas is inversely proportional to its temperature in kelvins.
(E) The volume of a gas is directly proportional to its pressure.

Use the illustration to answer Question 5. Assume that the number of particles of gas in container A equals the number of particles of gas in container B.

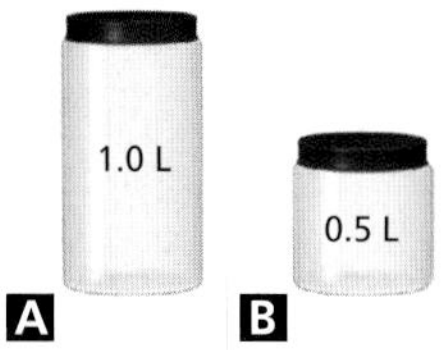
1.0 L
0.5 L
A
B

5. If the temperature is constant, the pressure in container B is
(A) one half the pressure in container A.
(B) twice the pressure in container A.
(C) equal to the pressure in container A.
(D) five times the pressure in container A.
(E) one fifth the pressure in container A.

6. During an endothermic phase change,
(A) the temperature of a substance rises.
(B) the temperature of a substance decreases.
(C) energy is transferred from a substance to its surroundings.
(D) a substance absorbs energy from its surroundings.
(E) there is no transfer of energy.

Standardized Test Prep

1. C **2.** C **3.** E
4. A **5.** B **6.** D

CHAPTER 4

Planning Guide

Use these planning tools
Easy Planner
Teacher Express

SECTION OBJECTIVES	STANDARDS NATIONAL (See p. T18.)	STANDARDS STATE	ACTIVITIES and LABS
4.1 Studying Atoms, pp. 100–105 1 block or 2 periods **4.1.1** **Describe** ancient Greek models of matter. **4.1.2** **List** the main points of Dalton's atomic theory and **describe** his evidence for the existence of atoms. **4.1.3** **Explain** how Thomson and Rutherford used data from experiments to produce their atomic models.	A-1, A-2, B-1, B-2, B-6, E-2, G-1, G-2, G-3		**SE** Inquiry Activity: How Can You Study Objects That Are Not Visible? p. 99 L2 **SE** Quick Lab: Investigating Charged Objects, p. 102 L2 **TE** Teacher Demo: Comparing Atomic Models, p. 104 L2
4.2 The Structure of an Atom, pp. 108–112 1 block or 2 periods **4.2.1** **Identify** three subatomic particles and **compare** their properties. **4.2.2** **Distinguish** the atomic number of an element from the mass number of an isotope, and use these numbers to **describe** the structure of atoms.	A-1, B-1, B-2, E-1, G-1, G-2, G-3		**TE** Teacher Demo: Particles and Numbers, p. 110 L2
4.3 Modern Atomic Theory, pp. 113–118 1 block or 2 periods **4.3.1** **Describe** Bohr's model of the atom and the evidence for energy levels. **4.3.2** **Explain** how the electron cloud model represents the behavior and locations of electrons in atoms. **4.3.3** **Distinguish** the ground state from excited states of an atom based on electron configurations.	A-1, A-2, B-1, B-2, G-1, G-2, G-3		**SE** Quick Lab: Comparing Excited States, p. 117 L2 **SE** Forensics Lab: Using Flame Tests, p. 119 L2 **TE** Teacher Demo: Electron Cloud Model, p. 116 L2 **LM** Investigation 4A: Constructing a Model of an Atom L2 **LM** Investigation 4B: Modeling an Electron Cloud L1

Ability Levels

L1	For students who need additional help
L2	For all students
L3	For students who need to be challenged

Components

SE	Student Edition	RSW	Reading & Study Workbook	CUT	Chapter & Unit Tests	T	Transparencies
TE	Teacher's Edition	MSPS	Math Skills & Problem Solving Workbook	CTB	Computer Test Bank	iT	Interactive Textbook
LM	Laboratory Manual			TP	Test Prep Resources	P	Presentation Pro CD-ROM
PLM	Probeware Lab Manual			DC	Discovery Channel Videotapes & DVDs	GO	Internet Resources

RESOURCES PRINT and TECHNOLOGY		SECTION ASSESSMENT
RSW Section 4.1	L1	**SE** Section 4.1 Assessment, p. 105
DC Go For Gold	L2	**iT** Section 4.1
T Chapter 4 Pretest	L2	
Section 4.1	L2	
P Chapter 4 Pretest	L2	
Section 4.1	L2	
SciLinks **GO** Atomic theory	L2	
RSW Section 4.2	L1	**SE** Section 4.2 Assessment, p. 112
RSW Math Skill	L2	**iT** Section 4.2
T Section 4.2	L2	
P Section 4.2	L2	
Science News **GO** Atomic chemistry	L2	
RSW Section 4.3	L1	**SE** Section 4.3 Assessment, p. 118
T Section 4.3	L2	**iT** Section 4.3
P Section 4.3	L2	
SciLinks **GO** Energy levels	L2	

Go Online

Go online for these Internet resources.

PHSchool.com
Web Code: cca-1040

Science News
Web Code: cce-1042

NSTA SciLinks
Web Code: ccn-1041
Web Code: ccn-1043

Materials for Activities and Labs

Quantities for each group

STUDENT EDITION

Inquiry Activity, p. 99
2 sealed, brown paper bags

Quick Lab, p. 102
transparent tape, metric ruler, scissors

Quick Lab, p. 117
fluorescent ("neon") markers, glow-in-the-dark toy, ultraviolet (UV) lamp

Forensics Lab, p. 119
solutions of calcium chloride, boric acid, potassium chloride, copper(II) sulfate, sodium chloride, and an unknown; Bunsen burner; nichrome wire loop; dilute solution of hydrochloric acid; wash bottle with distilled water

TEACHER'S EDITION

Teacher Demo, p. 104
3 clear, round bowls; flavored gelatin mix; canned blueberries; maraschino cherries

Build Science Skills, p. 106
modeling clay, plastic knives

Teacher Demo, p. 110
overhead projector, red and green gummy candies

Teacher Demo, p. 116
small, round balloon; large, round balloon; 10 beads with 4-mm diameter; 5 beads with 2-mm diameter

Chapter Assessment

CHAPTER ASSESSMENT

SE Chapter Assessment, pp. 121–122
CUT Chapter 4 Test A, B
CTB Chapter 4
iT Chapter 4
PHSchool.com GO
Web Code: cca-1040

STANDARDIZED TEST PREP

SE Chapter 4, p. 123
TP Diagnose and Prescribe

Interactive Textbook with assessment at PHSchool.com

CHAPTER 4

Before you teach

From the Author

David Frank
Ferris State University

Big Ideas

Once students have some understanding of the properties that are used to describe and classify matter, they need theories to explain why matter behaves in predictable ways. In Chapter 3, students used kinetic theory to explain the behavior of solids, liquids, and gases. The atomic theory presented in Chapter 4 will be used in Chapters 6 and 7 to explain bonding and chemical reactions.

Matter and Change In the nineteenth and early twentieth centuries, scientists refined models of the atom based on strong indirect evidence. Section 4.1 describes some of the methods scientists used to gather evidence about atomic structure. You can use Section 4.1 to help students understand the relationship between scientific laws (which summarize observed patterns in nature) and theories (which explain these observed patterns). Dalton's atomic theory is a case in point. In his theory, Dalton described properties of atoms that could explain the law of conservation of mass and the law of definite proportions.

Some people think that a theory must be discarded if evidence is discovered that contradicts the theory. More often, a theory is revised to account for new evidence. For example, the discovery of isotopes disproved Dalton's assumption that every atom of an element had the same mass. Subsequently, the atomic theory was revised to state that every atom of an element has the same number of protons, but not necessarily the same number of neutrons.

Forces and Motion The idea that oppositely charged particles attract and that similarly charged particles repel is a fundamental concept in science. The attraction of particles to a positive plate in Thomson's experiment demonstrated the negative charge of these particles (electrons). The repulsion of positively charged alpha particles in the gold foil experiment demonstrated that the nucleus of an atom has a positive charge.

Chemistry Refresher

Ancient Models of Atoms 4.1

Democritus of Abdera thought that the shapes and sizes of the atoms in a material determined the properties of the material. Atoms were seen as constantly moving in space, sometimes colliding and forming groups. Later, Aristotle gained authority for his idea that all substances were built up from only four elements because his proposals fit with the existing worldview throughout the Middle Ages. Much of alchemy was based on the theory that elements could be transformed into other elements through the qualities they possessed in common.

Evidence for Dalton's Theory 4.1

In 1802, John Dalton proposed the law of partial pressures of gases: A gas in a mixture of gases contributes the same pressure it would produce if it were the only gas in a container. In 1803, Dalton proposed the law of definite proportions, which states that elements form compounds in certain fixed ratios. Dalton's work with gas pressure and with the composition of compounds led him to consider the fundamental nature of matter. He presented his atomic theory in a series of lectures in 1807.

Dalton's Symbols for Some Elements

Symbol	Chemical Name	Symbol	Chemical Name
⊙	Hydrogen	●	Carbon
⦶	Azote (Nitrogen)	○	Oxygen

Subatomic Particles 4.1 and 4.2

J.J. Thomson studied the flow of current through gases in a sealed tube. He used a magnet to deflect the cathode rays. He could not use an electric field because the passage of the rays through the tube caused the gas to become a conductor. The conducting gas screened the particles in the rays from the effect of the external electric field. When Thomson removed almost all the gas from the tube, the effect of the field could be seen.

Address Misconceptions

Many students think that isotopes are different from "ordinary" or "regular" atoms. However, isotopes are atoms of an element that have differing nuclear compositions. For a strategy to overcome this misconception, see **Address Misconceptions** on **page 112.**

Go Online NSTA PD LINKS

For: Teaching methods for atomic structure
Visit: www.SciLinks.org/PDLinks
Web Code: ccn-0499

In 1909, Ernest Rutherford (who had worked with Thomson) asked Ernest Marsden (an undergraduate student from New Zealand) to find out whether any alpha particles were scattered by more than a few degrees as they passed through foil. Marsden used a sheet of gold foil that was only 0.00004 (4×10^{-5}) cm thick. After World War I, Rutherford experimented with bombarding nitrogen atoms with alpha particles. Some of the nitrogen atoms released hydrogen nuclei and transmuted into oxygen atoms. He concluded that these nuclei were released from the nitrogen nuclei and that they were fundamental particles. He is usually credited with naming these particles protons, after the Greek word *protos,* meaning "first." Although Rutherford predicted the existence of neutrons in 1920, it was his research assistant, James Chadwick, who provided the supporting evidence.

Electrons and Energy Levels 4.3

Address Misconceptions

Students may think that electrons travel around the nucleus in fixed orbits, like planets orbiting the sun. However, the exact path or location of an electron cannot be determined. For a strategy to overcome this misconception, see **Address Misconceptions** on **page 114**.

In a staircase, the distance between steps is (ideally) constant from step to step. In an atom, the difference in energy between energy levels is not constant. It decreases as the quantum number of the energy level (n) increases. The specific amount of energy that is absorbed or released when an electron moves between energy levels is called a *quantum* of energy. When the energy absorbed or released by an atom is light energy, the quanta are called *photons.*

Photon Emission as a Result of Energy Level Transitions

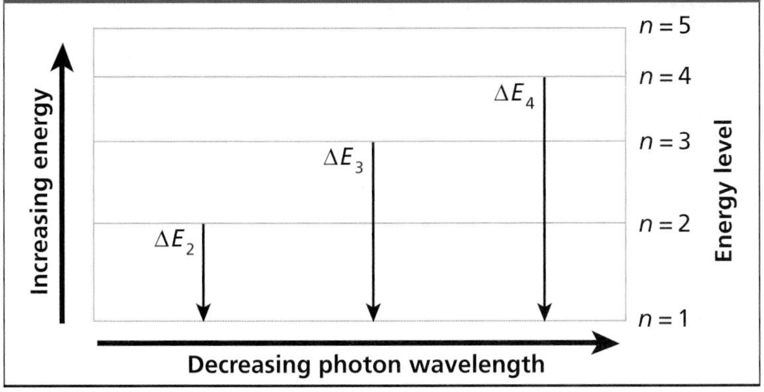
n = 5
n = 4
n = 3
n = 2
n = 1
ΔE4
ΔE3
ΔE2
Increasing energy
Energy level
Decreasing photon wavelength

Build Reading Literacy

Identify Main Idea/Details

Locating Topic Sentences in Paragraphs

Strategy Help students understand and remember the most important information about a topic. This strategy can be applied to short segments of text, such as a single paragraph or a subsection, to find the main idea and details that support the topic. Assign students a short passage to read, such as The Gold Foil Experiment on p. 104.

Example

1. Tell students that many paragraphs have a topic sentence that expresses the paragraph's main idea. Topic sentences are often the first or second sentence in the paragraph. Sometimes, however, they are the last sentence, or even a sentence in the middle of the paragraph.
2. Then, explain that the rest of the paragraph contains details, or additional facts and examples about the main idea.
3. Direct students' attention to a paragraph with a clearly stated topic sentence, and ask students which sentence best states the main idea of the paragraph.
4. Next, help students find sentences with details that explain more about the main idea.
5. Have students organize the main idea and details visually in a web format.
6. Have students work in pairs to identify the main idea and details in another passage and organize them in a web.

See p. 110 for a script on how to use the identify main ideas/details strategy with students. For additional Build Reading Literacy strategies, see pp. 103 and 113.

ASSESS PRIOR KNOWLEDGE

Use the Chapter Pretest below to assess students' prior knowledge. As needed, review these Science Concepts and Math Skills with students.

Review Science Concepts

Section 4.1 Encourage students to recall that compounds have fixed compositions. Remind students that an atom is the smallest particle of an element.

Section 4.2 Have students review the terms *mass, volume,* and *density* and the units used for each.

Section 4.3 Review two things that can happen when matter absorbs energy.

Review Math Skills

Scientific Notation Students will need to know how to use scientific notation to understand values for certain properties of subatomic particles.

Direct students to the **Math Skills** in the **Skills and Reference Handbook** at the end of the student text.

CHAPTER

4 Atomic Structure

CONCEPTS in Action

How do science concepts apply to your world? Here are some questions you'll be able to answer after you read this chapter.

- Which subatomic particle produces the images on many television screens and computer monitors? *(Section 4.2)*
- How does the type of hydrogen atom in water affect the properties of water? *(Section 4.2)*
- How do fireworks produce the colors you see when the fireworks explode? *(Section 4.3)*

Discovery Channel School **Video Field Trip**

Go For Gold

- What uses are there for objects that are not visible to the unaided eye? *(page 106)*

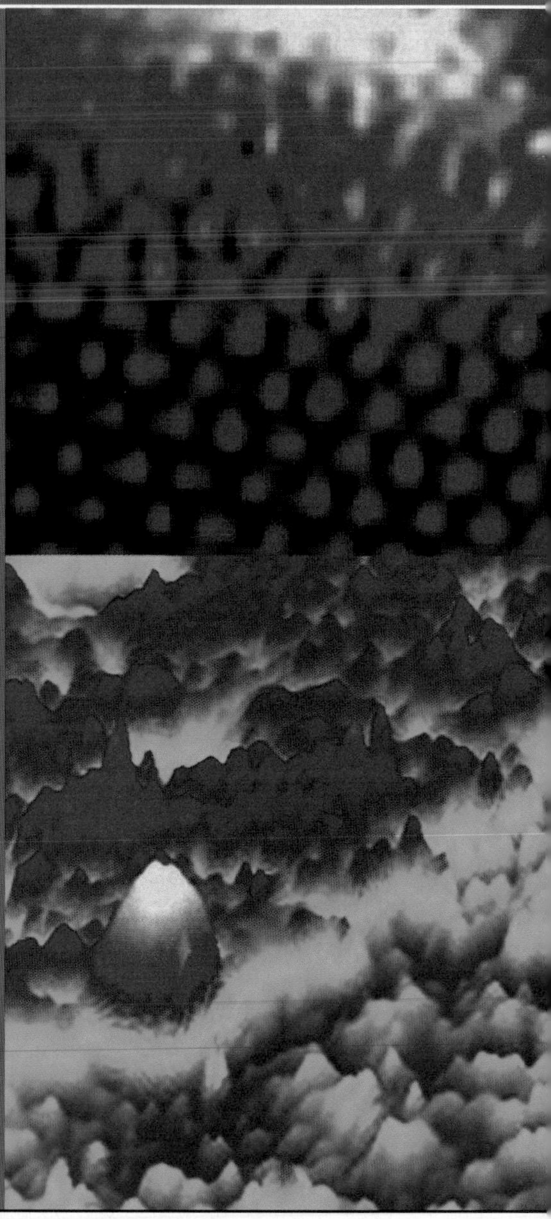

These images of carbon were magnified as ▶ much as 20 million times. Color was added to the images to highlight features. The upper left and right images are of graphite—the carbon used in pencils. The lower left image is of hollow spheres of carbon, one nanometer in diameter. The lower right image shows carbon tubes arranged in the shape of an A.

98 *Chapter 4*

Chapter Pretest

1. True or False: Compounds have fixed compositions. *(True)*
2. What is an atom? *(An atom is the smallest particle of an element.)*
3. Which of the following units is a unit of mass? *(c)*
   - **a.** mL **b.** °C
   - **c.** g **d.** cm
4. Volume is *(c)*
   - **a.** the straight-line distance between two points.
   - **b.** the quantity of matter in an object.
   - **c.** the amount of space taken up by an object.
   - **d.** a representation of an object or event.
5. What is density? *(Density is the ratio of the mass of a substance to its volume.)*
6. Which two of the following events can take place when a liquid absorbs energy? *(a and d)*
   - **a.** The average kinetic energy of the particles in the liquid increases.
   - **b.** The temperature decreases.
   - **c.** The liquid freezes.
   - **d.** The liquid changes to a gas.

Chapter Preview

Inquiry Activity

How Can You Study Objects That Are Not Visible?

Procedure

1. Make and record observations about the contents of two sealed bags. Use your senses of touch, smell, and hearing to help you make your observations.
2. **Predicting** Based on your observations, make a prediction about what objects could be in each bag. Decide whether there is a single object or more than one object in each bag.
3. Your teacher will list on the chalkboard all of the predictions from the class.

Think About It

1. **Inferring** What evidence did you use to predict what objects were in the bags and how many objects were in the bags?
2. **Evaluating and Revising** Record one of the predictions listed that fits your observations as well as or better than your own prediction.
3. **Designing Experiments** Propose an experiment that would test the prediction.

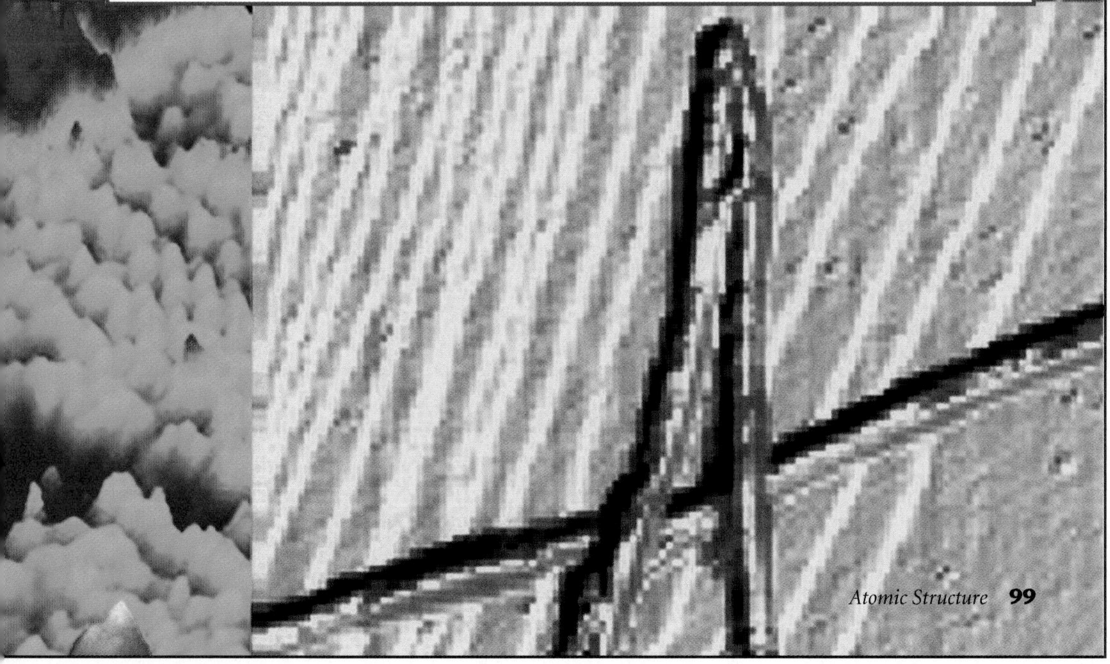

DISCOVERY CHANNEL SCHOOL **Video Field Trip**

Go For Gold

Encourage students to view the Video Field Trip "Go For Gold."

ENGAGE/EXPLORE

Inquiry Activity

How Can You Study Objects That Are Not Visible? L2

Purpose In this activity, students make inferences based on their observations and conclude that indirect evidence must be used to study the structure of objects that are too small to see.

Skills Focus **Observing, Inferring**

Prep Time 5 minutes

Materials 2 sealed, brown paper bags

Advance Prep Place a single type of small object in each bag. Possible objects that can be identified by properties other than sight are lemon slices (odor), pennies (shape), rubber bands (elasticity), sandpaper squares (texture), and bells (sound). Use a letter code to identify the object in each bag. Seal the bags before distributing them to students.

Class Time 10 minutes

Teaching Tips

- Use more than two types of objects so each group of students does not have an identical set.
- To model the study of atoms, ask students not to open the bags at the end of the activity.
- Ask students how they could apply what they have learned in this activity to the study of atoms, which are too small to see.

Expected Outcome Students should recognize that detailed observations can reveal information about objects and events that cannot be observed directly.

Think About It

1. Acceptable student answers may include sound, texture, hardness, smell, and how objects move inside the bags.
2. Students may choose a prediction that they did not record in Step 2 if this prediction is a better fit for the evidence they list for Question 1.
3. Answers should include a practical test that would clearly support or contradict the prediction chosen in Question 2.
Logical

1 FOCUS

Objectives

4.1.1 **Describe** ancient Greek models of matter.

4.1.2 **List** the main points of Dalton's atomic theory and **describe** his evidence for the existence of atoms.

4.1.3 **Explain** how Thomson and Rutherford used data from experiments to produce their atomic models.

Reading Focus

Build Vocabulary L2

Latin Plural Forms Explain that the word *nucleus* comes from a Latin word meaning "kernel." Explain that a kernel is a grain or seed. Ask students to discuss how the definition of the term *nucleus* relates to its Latin origin. *(Like the kernel of a nut, the nucleus is a small, massive center of the atom.)* Remind students that the plural of the word *nucleus* is *nuclei.*

Reading Strategy L2

a. Dalton **b.** Indivisible, solid spheres **c.** Thomson **d.** Negative charges evenly scattered through a positively charged mass of matter (plum pudding model) **e.** Deflection of alpha particles passing through gold foil

2 INSTRUCT

Ancient Greek Models of Atoms

Use Visuals L1

Figure 1 Have students examine the diagram in Figure 1 that lists the qualities of each of Aristotle's four elements. Ask, **What qualities did Aristotle use to describe air?** *(Air is a combination of hot and wet.)* **What element was a combination of dry and cold?** *(Earth)* **Is "wet and cold" an accurate description of water?** *(Wet describes water, but water isn't always cold.)*
Visual

4.1 Studying Atoms

Reading Focus

Key Concepts

- What was Dalton's theory of the structure of matter?
- What contributions did Thomson and Rutherford make to the development of atomic theory?

Vocabulary

- nucleus

Reading Strategy

Summarizing Copy the table. As you read, complete the table about atomic models.

Scientist	Evidence	Model
a. ___?___	Ratio of masses in compounds	b. ___?___
c. ___?___	Deflected beam	d. ___?___
Rutherford	e. ___?___	Positive, dense nucleus

Studying the structure of atoms is a little like studying wind. Because you cannot see air, you must use indirect evidence to tell the direction of the wind. You might notice which way fallen leaves move as they are pushed by the wind, and infer that the leaves and wind are moving in the same direction.

Atoms pose a similar problem because they are extremely small. Even with a microscope, scientists cannot see the structure of an atom. In this chapter, you will find out how John Dalton, J. J. Thomson, Ernest Rutherford, Niels Bohr, and other scientists used evidence from experiments to develop models of atoms.

Ancient Greek Models of Atoms

If you cut a piece of aluminum foil in half, you have two smaller pieces of the same shiny, flexible substance. You could cut the pieces again and again. Can you keep dividing the aluminum into smaller pieces? Greek philosophers debated a similar question about 2500 years ago.

The philosopher Democritus believed that all matter consisted of extremely small particles that could not be divided. He called these particles *atoms* from the Greek word *atomos,* which means "uncut" or "indivisible." He thought there were different types of atoms with specific sets of properties. The atoms in liquids, for example, were round and smooth, but the atoms in solids were rough and prickly.

Aristotle did not think there was a limit to the number of times matter could be divided. Figure 1 shows the model Aristotle used to describe matter. For many centuries, most people accepted Aristotle's views on the structure of matter. But by the 1800s, scientists had enough data from experiments to support an atomic model of matter.

Figure 1 Aristotle thought that all substances were built up from only four elements—earth, air, fire, and water. These elements were a combination of four qualities—hot, cold, dry, and wet. Fire was a combination of hot and dry. Water was a combination of cold and wet.

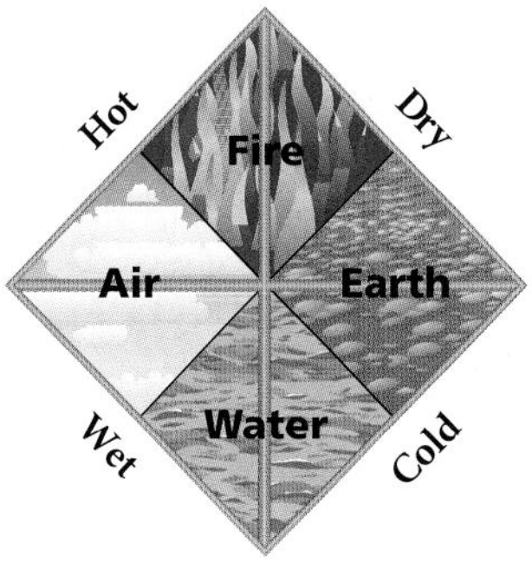
Hot
Dry
Fire
Air
Earth
Wet
Water
Cold

Section Resources

Print
- ***Reading and Study Workbook With Math Support,*** Section 4.1
- ***Transparencies,*** Chapter Pretest and Section 4.1

Technology
- ***Interactive Textbook,*** Section 4.1
- ***Presentation Pro CD-ROM,*** Chapter Pretest and Section 4.1
- ***Go Online,*** NSTA SciLinks, Atomic theory

Dalton's Atomic Theory

John Dalton was born in England in 1766. He was a teacher who spent his spare time doing scientific experiments. Because of his interest in predicting the weather, Dalton studied the behavior of gases in air. Based on the way gases exert pressure, Dalton correctly concluded that a gas consists of individual particles.

Evidence for Atoms Dalton gathered evidence for the existence of atoms by measuring the masses of elements that combine when compounds form. He noticed that all compounds have something in common. No matter how large or small the sample, the ratio of the masses of the elements in the compound is always the same. In other words, compounds have a fixed composition.

For example, when magnesium burns, as shown in Figure 2, it combines with oxygen. The product of this change is a white solid called magnesium oxide. A 100-gram sample of magnesium combines with 65.8 grams of oxygen. A 10-gram sample of magnesium combines with 6.58 grams of oxygen. The ratio of the mass of magnesium to the mass of oxygen is constant in magnesium oxide.

Dalton's Theory Dalton developed a theory to explain why the elements in a compound always join in the same way. **Dalton proposed the theory that all matter is made up of individual particles called atoms, which cannot be divided.** The main points of Dalton's theory are as follows.

- All elements are composed of atoms.
- All atoms of the same element have the same mass, and atoms of different elements have different masses.
- Compounds contain atoms of more than one element.
- In a particular compound, atoms of different elements always combine in the same way.

In the model of atoms based on Dalton's theory, the elements are pictured as solid spheres like those in Figure 3. Each type of atom is represented by a tiny, solid sphere with a different mass.

Recall that a theory must explain the data from many experiments. Because Dalton's atomic theory met that goal, the theory became widely accepted. Over time, scientists found that not all of Dalton's ideas about atoms were completely correct. But this did not cause later scientists to discard the atomic theory. Instead, they revised the theory to take into account new discoveries.

Reading Checkpoint *What did Dalton notice that all compounds have in common?*

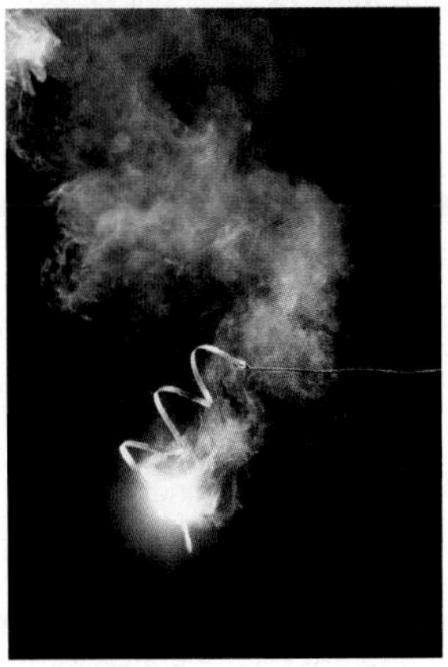

Figure 2 Magnesium reacts with oxygen to form the compound magnesium oxide. The ratio of magnesium to oxygen, by mass, in magnesium oxide is always about 3 : 2. **Observing** ***What color is magnesium oxide?***

Figure 3 Dalton made these wooden spheres to represent the atoms of different elements.

Dalton's Atomic Theory

Build Science Skills L2

Evaluating As students read Chapter 4, have them evaluate what portions of Dalton's model were accurate and what portions needed to be revised. *(Dalton did not discuss subatomic particles, which are smaller components of atoms. Atoms of the same element can have different masses.)*
Logical

Address Misconceptions L2

Many students have trouble differentiating compounds from mixtures. Remind students that Dalton noticed that the ratio of masses of elements in a compound is always the same. Compounds are distinguished from mixtures and solutions by their fixed compositions. Have students recall examples of mixtures and describe how their compositions can vary.
Verbal

Use Visuals L1

Figure 3 Have students examine the wooden spheres shown in Figure 3. Ask, **Why do you think there are holes in Dalton's wooden spheres?** *(One acceptable answer is that Dalton used the holes in the spheres to connect spheres together to construct models of compounds.)*
Visual, Logical

FYI

Not every scientist was convinced that Dalton had the physical evidence to support the assumption that elements are composed of indivisible particles called atoms. William Whewell (1784–1868) argued that particles could combine in fixed proportions in compounds, but still not be indivisible.

Customize for English Language Learners

Using Visual Aids
Have students draw simple illustrations for the models of atoms according to Dalton, Thompson, and Rutherford. Have them describe each model to a partner using the illustrations as a visual aid. Then, have each pair of students discuss the similarities and differences among the three models.

Answer to . . .

Figure 2 *White*

Reading Checkpoint *Dalton noticed that the ratio of masses of elements in a compound is always the same.*

Thomson's Model of the Atom

Quick Lab

Investigating Charged Objects **L2**

Objective
After completing this activity, students will be able to
- explain that like charges repel and unlike charges attract.

Skills Focus **Observing, Drawing Conclusions, Formulating Hypotheses**

Prep Time 5 minutes

Class Time 10 minutes

Expected Outcome Students will discover that the two pieces of tape are attracted to one another after they are pulled apart and then brought near one another.

Analyze and Conclude
1. The two pieces of tape have opposite charges because they attract when brought close together.
2. Possible answers include clothes that cling together when removed from a dryer, and the charge that builds up when a person walks across a carpet (which is demonstrated by the spark that occurs when the person touches a doorknob).
Kinesthetic, Logical

FYI

If you do not want to present all the experimental evidence for the atomic theory, be sure students understand attraction and repulsion of charged particles and Rutherford's nucleus model of the atom.

Quick Lab

Investigating Charged Objects

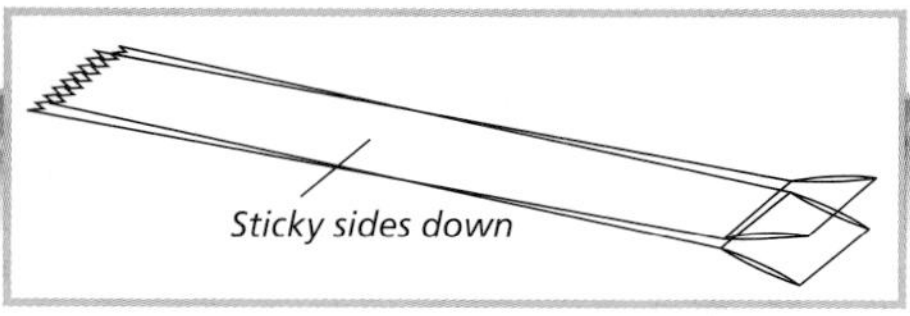
Sticky sides down

Materials

transparent tape, metric ruler, scissors

Procedure

1. Cut two 10-cm pieces of tape. Fold over 1 cm of tape at one end of each piece of tape to form a "handle."
2. Hold the pieces of tape by their folded ends so that they are hanging straight down. Then, without letting the pieces of tape touch, slowly bring their sticky sides close together. Record your observations.
3. Place one piece of tape on a clean surface with the sticky side facing down.
4. Place the second piece, sticky side down, directly over the first piece, as shown. Press down firmly so the pieces stick together.
5. Remove the joined strips from the table. Slowly peel the strips apart.
6. Bring the separated strips close together without touching. Record your observations.

Analyze and Conclude

1. **Drawing Conclusions** What can you conclude about the charges on the two pieces of tape after they are separated?
2. **Inferring** What other objects have you observed that became charged?

Thomson's Model of the Atom

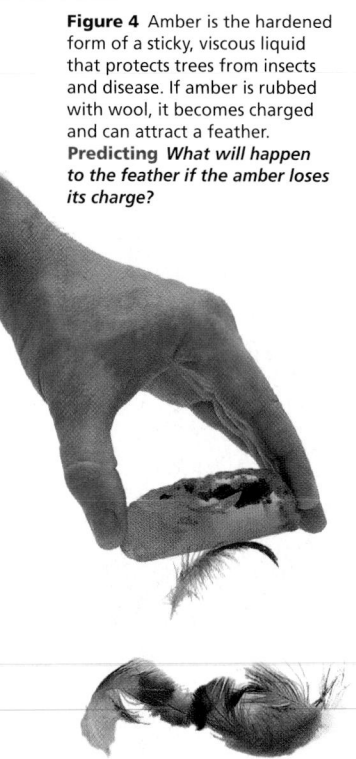

Figure 4 Amber is the hardened form of a sticky, viscous liquid that protects trees from insects and disease. If amber is rubbed with wool, it becomes charged and can attract a feather. **Predicting** ***What will happen to the feather if the amber loses its charge?***

When some materials are rubbed, they gain the ability to attract or repel other materials. Glass and the amber in Figure 4 have this property. Based on their behavior, such materials are said to have either a positive or a negative electric charge. Objects with like charges repel, or push apart. Objects with opposite charges attract, or pull together.

Some charged particles can flow from one location to another. A flow of charged particles is called an electric current. When you turn on an appliance such as a hair dryer, a current flows from the wall socket through the appliance. Joseph John Thomson (1856–1940), better known as J. J. Thomson, used an electric current to learn more about atoms.

Thomson's Experiments Thomson used a device like the one shown in Figure 5A. At the center of the device is a sealed glass tube from which most of the air has been removed. There is a metal disk at each end of the tube. Wires connect the metal disks to a source of electric current. When the current is turned on, one disk becomes negatively charged and the other disk becomes positively charged. A glowing beam appears in the space between the disks.

Thomson hypothesized that the beam was a stream of charged particles that interacted with the air in the tube and caused the air to glow. In one experiment Thomson did to test his hypothesis, he placed a pair of charged metal plates on either side of the glass tube, as shown in Figure 5B. The plates caused the beam to deflect, or bend, from its straight path. Thomson observed that the beam was repelled by the negatively charged plate and attracted by the positively charged plate.

Facts and Figures

Charge People have known for thousands of years that amber can attract other materials after it has been rubbed with fur. Plato even refers to these attractive powers of amber in one of his dialogues.

The labels *positive* and *negative* were arbitrarily assigned by Benjamin Franklin during his studies of electric charge and electric current. (He also was the first to use the terms *battery* and *conductor*.)

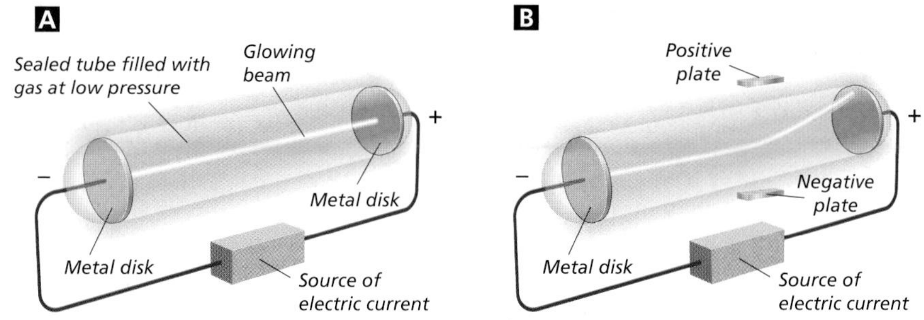
A
Sealed tube filled with gas at low pressure
Glowing beam
−
+
Metal disk
Metal disk
Source of electric current
B
Positive plate
−
+
Negative plate
Metal disk
Source of electric current

Figure 5 Thomson used a sealed tube of gas in his experiments. **A** When the current was on, the disks became charged and a glowing beam appeared in the tube. **B** The beam bent toward a positively charged plate placed outside the tube.
Inferring ***What was the charge on the particles in the beam?***

Evidence for Subatomic Particles Thomson concluded that the particles in the beam had a negative charge because they were attracted to the positive plate. He hypothesized that the particles came from inside atoms. He had two pieces of evidence to support his hypothesis. No matter what metal Thomson used for the disk, the particles produced were identical. The particles had about $\frac{1}{2000}$ the mass of a hydrogen atom, the lightest atom.

Thomson's discovery changed how scientists thought about atoms. Before his experiments, the accepted model of the atom was a solid ball of matter that could not be divided into smaller parts. **Thomson's experiments provided the first evidence that atoms are made of even smaller particles.** Thomson revised Dalton's model to account for these subatomic particles.

Thomson's Model An atom is neutral, meaning it has neither a negative nor a positive charge. How can an atom contain negative particles and still be neutral? There must be some positive charge in the atom. In Thomson's model of the atom, the negative charges were evenly scattered throughout an atom filled with a positively charged mass of matter. The model is called the "plum pudding" model, after a traditional English dessert.

You might prefer to think of Thomson's model as the "chocolate chip ice cream" model. Think of the chocolate chips in Figure 6 as the negative particles and the vanilla ice cream as the positively charged mass of matter. When the chocolate chips are spread evenly throughout the ice cream, their "negative charges" balance out the "positive charge" of the vanilla ice cream.

Reading Checkpoint *How do objects with the same charge behave when they come close to one another?*

Figure 6 A scoop of chocolate chip ice cream can represent Thomson's model of the atom. The chips represent negatively charged particles, which are spread evenly through a mass of positively charged matter—the vanilla ice cream.

FYI

Thomson used the speed of an electron, its angle of deflection, and the strength of the current to determine the charge-to-mass ratio of an electron. Robert Millikan determined the actual mass of an electron through his oil-drop experiment.

The current that flows through an appliance is an alternating current. The current Thomson used in his experiment was a direct current. Not all movement of charge is a current. Charge can flow to or from a balloon (or between a hand and a doorknob). With a current, charge must flow continuously (at least until the circuit is interrupted). The concepts of electric charge and current are addressed in depth in Chapter 20.

Use Community Resources L2

Have a physics or chemistry professor visit the class and demonstrate Thomson's experiment using a cathode ray tube. Encourage students to think of questions to ask about how the experiment demonstrates the properties of electrons.
Interpersonal, Visual

Build Reading Literacy L1

Compare and Contrast Refer to page **226D** in **Chapter 8**, which provides the guidelines for comparing and contrasting.

Have students read about the different atomic models described in Section 4.1. Then, have students create a chart that compares and contrasts each model.
Logical

Answer to . . .

Figure 4 *The feather will no longer be attracted to the amber and will drop to the ground.*

Figure 5 *Negative*

Reading Checkpoint *Objects with the same charge repel.*

Rutherford's Atomic Theory

FYI

Based on Figure 7, students might conclude that Marsden used a circular screen. The screen in the diagram represents multiple positions of a smaller screen that was moved from one position to another while data was collected. Alpha particles will be identified as helium nuclei in Chapter 10.

Teacher Demo

Comparing Atomic Models L2

Purpose Students will compare different atomic models.

Materials 3 clear, round bowls; flavored gelatin mix; canned blueberries; maraschino cherries

Procedure The day before, prepare the flavored gelatin mix. Divide the liquid gelatin evenly into the three bowls. Chill slightly. Drain the blueberries and add them to one of the bowls so that they are distributed as evenly as possible in the nearly gelled mix. Return the bowls to the refrigerator. Right before class, place a cherry in the center of the third bowl. Have students discuss which atomic models are represented by each bowl of gelatin.

Expected Outcome The gelatin alone represents Dalton's atomic model. The gelatin with blueberries represents Thomson's "plum-pudding" atomic model, with the berries representing electrons. The gelatin with the cherry represents Rutherford's atomic model. **Visual, Logical**

Go Online NSTA SciLinks

Download a worksheet on atomic theory for students to complete, and find additional teacher support from NSTA SciLinks.

Go Online NSTA SciLinks

For: Links on atomic theory
Visit: www.SciLinks.org
Web Code: ccn-1041

Rutherford's Atomic Theory

When you try something new, you may have expectations about the outcome. Does the outcome always meet your expectations or are you sometimes surprised? Scientists can also be surprised by the results of their experiments, but unexpected results can lead to important discoveries. This is what happened to Ernest Rutherford (1871–1937).

Rutherford's Hypothesis In 1899, Ernest Rutherford discovered that uranium emits fast-moving particles that have a positive charge. He named them alpha particles. In 1909, Rutherford asked one of his students, Ernest Marsden, to find out what happens to alpha particles when they pass through a thin sheet of gold.

Recall that in Thomson's model of the atom, the mass and positive charge are evenly spread throughout an atom. Based on this model, Rutherford hypothesized that the mass and charge at any location in the gold would be too small to change the path of an alpha particle. He predicted that most particles would travel in a straight path from their source to a screen that lit up when struck. Those few that did not pass straight through would be deflected only slightly.

The Gold Foil Experiment Marsden used the equipment shown in Figure 7. He aimed a narrow beam of alpha particles at the gold. The screen around the gold was made of a material that produced a flash of light when struck by a fast-moving alpha particle. By observing the flash, Marsden could figure out the path of an alpha particle after it passed through the gold.

Some of the locations of the flashes on the screen did not support Rutherford's prediction. More particles were deflected than he expected. About one out of every 20,000 was deflected by more than 90 degrees. Some of the alpha particles behaved as though they had struck an object and bounced straight back.

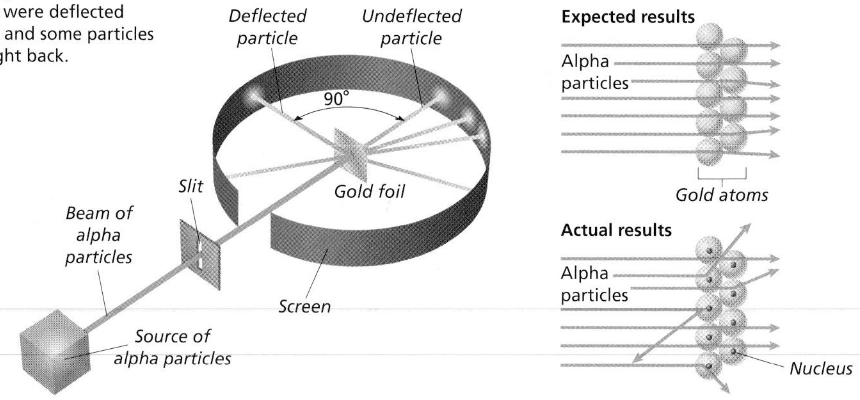
Deflected particle
Undeflected particle
90°
Slit
Gold foil
Beam of alpha particles
Screen
Source of alpha particles
Expected results
Alpha particles
Gold atoms
Actual results
Alpha particles
Nucleus

Figure 7 The path of an alpha particle can be detected by the location of a flash on a screen. Rutherford expected the paths of the positively charged alpha particles that were aimed at the thin gold foil to be affected only slightly by the gold atoms. But more particles were deflected than expected and some particles bounced straight back.

Facts and Figures

In His Own Words In a lecture Rutherford gave at Cambridge in 1936, he recalled his reaction when Geiger told him about alpha particles being scattered backward by the gold foil. Rutherford described his reaction. "It was almost as incredible as if you fired a 15-inch shell at a piece of tissue paper and it came back and hit you."

Discovery of the Nucleus The alpha particles whose paths were deflected must have come close to another charged object. The closer they came, the greater the deflection was. But many alpha particles passed through the gold without being deflected. From these results, Rutherford concluded that the positive charge of an atom is not evenly spread throughout the atom. It is concentrated in a very small, central area that Rutherford called the nucleus. The **nucleus** is a dense, positively charged mass located in the center of the atom. (The plural of *nucleus* is *nuclei.*)

Because Thomson's model no longer explained all the evidence, Rutherford proposed a new model. **According to Rutherford's model, all of an atom's positive charge is concentrated in its nucleus.** The alpha particles whose paths were deflected by more than 90 degrees came very close to a nucleus. The alpha particles whose paths were not bent moved through the space surrounding the nuclei without coming very close to any nucleus.

Figure 8 shows the inside of the Astrodome, a domed stadium in Houston, Texas. The roof of the stadium rises to a height of 202 feet above the center of the field. If an atom had the same volume as the stadium, its nucleus would have the volume of a marble. The total volume of an atom is about a trillion (10^{12}) times the volume of its nucleus.

Figure 8 The Houston Astrodome occupies more than nine acres and seats 60,000 people. If the stadium were a model for an atom, a marble could represent its nucleus. **Using Analogies** ***In the model, where would the marble have to be located in the stadium to represent the nucleus?***

Section 4.1 Assessment

Reviewing Concepts

1. What theory did Dalton propose about the structure of matter?
2. What evidence did J. J. Thomson provide about the structure of an atom?
3. What did Rutherford discover about the structure of an atom?
4. What evidence did Thomson have that his glowing beam contained negative particles?
5. Why was Dalton's model of the atom changed after Thomson's experiment?

Critical Thinking

6. **Comparing and Contrasting** Explain why scientists accepted Dalton's atomic theory but not the idea of an atom proposed by the Greek philosophers.
7. **Drawing Conclusions** If you observed a beam of particles being bent toward a negatively charged plate, what might you conclude?
8. **Relating Cause and Effect** In the Rutherford experiment, why weren't all the alpha particles deflected?

Writing in Science

Writing to Persuade Imagine you live in ancient Greece. Assume all you know about matter is what you can observe with your five senses. You have heard the views of both Democritus and Aristotle about matter. Write a paragraph supporting one of their views.

Section 4.1 Assessment

1. All matter is composed of individual particles called atoms, which cannot be divided.
2. Thomson provided the first evidence that atoms are made from even smaller particles.
3. All of the positive charge of an atom is concentrated in its nucleus.
4. The beam was attracted to a positively charged plate and repelled by a negatively charged plate.
5. Dalton assumed atoms were solid, indivisible particles. Thomson had evidence that smaller particles existed inside atoms.
6. Dalton had data from experiments to support his theory, whereas the Greeks did not have data.
7. The particles have a positive charge.
8. The nucleus is small compared with the atom as a whole. Very few of the alpha particles came close enough to a gold nucleus to be deflected.

Build Science Skills L2

Using Models Have students model the gold foil experiment by shooting marbles across the floor at an arrangement of widely spaced, small objects—such as beads that are glued to a flat surface—and recording the angle of the marbles that are deflected. Discuss the results of their experiment in light of Marsden's findings.

Kinesthetic, Interpersonal

Integrate Biology L2

Cells in most living organisms have a central structure called a nucleus. This organelle contains the cell's genetic, or hereditary, material. Ask, **How are an atom's nucleus and a cell's nucleus similar?** *(They are both central structures of a basic unit.)*

Logical

3 ASSESS

Evaluate Understanding L2

Ask groups of students to summarize Dalton's, Thompson's, and Rutherford's atomic theories. Have them come up with simple word phrases or mnemonic devices to help them easily distinguish among the three theories. For example, **D**ogs **S**ort **S**ocks = **D**alton's **S**olid **S**phere; **T**urtles **P**lay **P**ing-pong = **T**homson's **P**lum **P**udding; and **R**ats **P**oke **N**oodles = **R**utherford's **P**ositive **N**ucleus.

Reteach L1

Use the Science and History time line on p. 114 to present and discuss a summary of the three models.

Writing in Science

Students might argue that the properties Democritus assigned to atoms match observed properties of matter, such as smoothness and roughness. Students might argue that the properties Aristotle assigned to elements serve a similar purpose, and his system also seems to account for changes between types of matter.

Interactive Textbook If your class subscribes to the Interactive Textbook, use it to review key concepts in Section 4.1.

Answer to . . .

Figure 8 *The marble would have to be located in the center of the stadium.*

CONCEPTS — in Action —

Small-Scale Construction **L2**

Background

The diameter of one of the silicon gears is 50 microns (50,000 nanometers). Despite their relative sizes on the page, the silicon gear is much larger than the model of nanogears. (The atomic radius of a carbon atom is only 770 nanometers.)

In 1959, Richard Feynman suggested the possibility of nanometer-scale construction when he said, "The principles of physics, as far as I can see, do not speak against the possibility of maneuvering things atom by atom."

The uses for small-scale construction are potentially very diverse, though currently they are very limited. Biologists already use nanotechnology to make tiny labels for use in diagnostic and pharmaceutical research. Such molecular labels can be injected or absorbed in one part of the body and then traced as they travel throughout the body. One company has even made a sunscreen with nanometer-sized particles that scatter harmful light rays while transmitting visible light, which makes the cream clear instead of white.

Build Science Skills **L2**

Using Models ACTIVITY

Purpose Students will explore the difference between top-down and bottom-up methods of construction.

Materials modeling clay, plastic knives

Class Time 10 minutes

Procedure Have students use the top-down method to construct a model of a gear like the one shown in the dust mite photo. Consider bringing in samples of gears for students to observe. Then, have students use the bottom-up method to construct a model of the stick figure shown in the feature.

Expected Outcome Students will make a gear by starting with a lump of clay and then removing clay to shape the gear (a top-down construction method). They will make a stick figure by joining small pieces of clay together (a bottom-up method of construction).
Kinesthetic, Visual

CONCEPTS in Action

Small-Scale Construction

Some scientists and engineers think of atoms and molecules as construction materials for building very small objects.

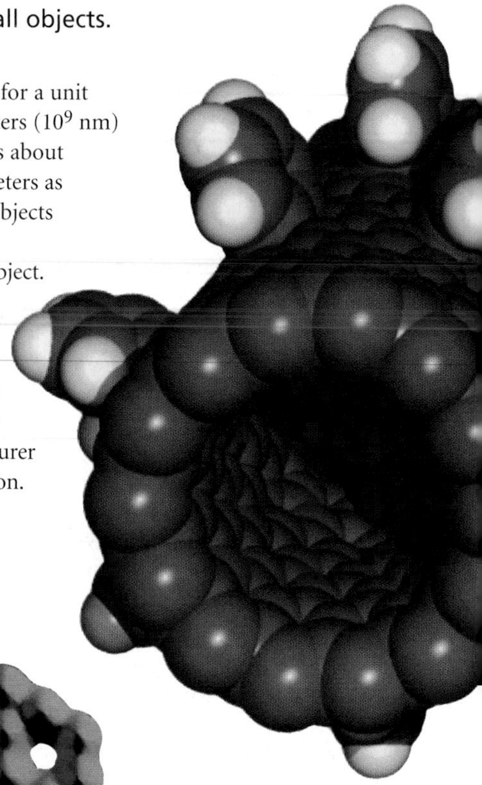

The field of science called nanotechnology is named for a unit of measurement—the nanometer. A billion nanometers (10^9 nm) can fit in one meter. The diameter of a human hair is about 80,000 nm. Scientists and engineers who use nanometers as measuring units are building miniature versions of objects such as motors.

There are two general methods for building any object. You can start with more material than you need and shape the object by removing matter or you can build up the object from smaller pieces. When you shape your nails with an emery board, you are using a top-down construction method. When you see "some assembly required" on the side of a box, the manufacturer expects you to use a bottom-up method of construction.

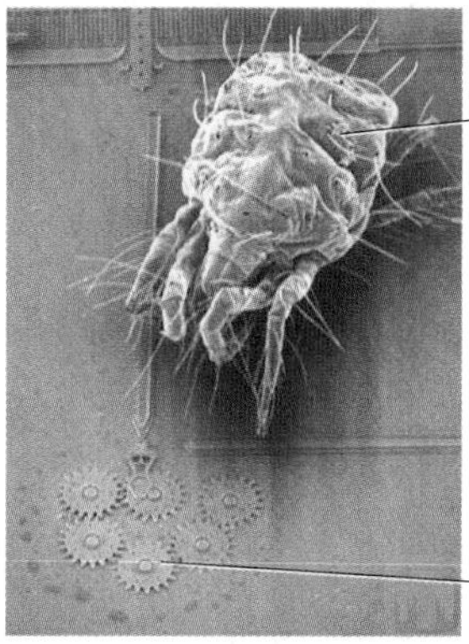
Dust mite
Silicon gear assembly

Building from the top down
Gears are toothed disks that are designed to fit together so that the motion of one gear controls the motion of another. These silicon gears are among the smallest objects ever made from the top down.

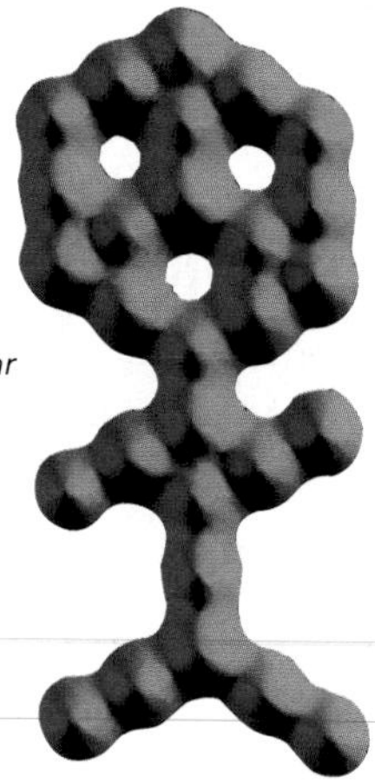

Building from the bottom up
With a scanning tunneling microscope, it is possible to move individual atoms or molecules. This figure, made of linked carbon monoxide molecules, is just five nanometers (0.000005 mm) tall. In 1990, scientists built this figure to demonstrate bottom-up construction methods.

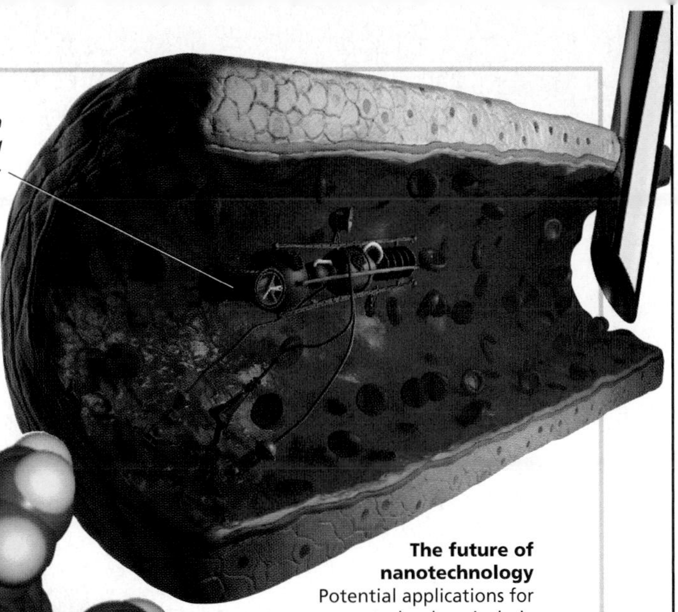
Futuristic model of a nanorobot performing surgery in a blood vessel.

The future of nanotechnology
Potential applications for nanotechnology include medical diagnostic tools and atomic-level electronic devices that assemble themselves. If such devices prove successful, perhaps someday the surgical robot will be built.

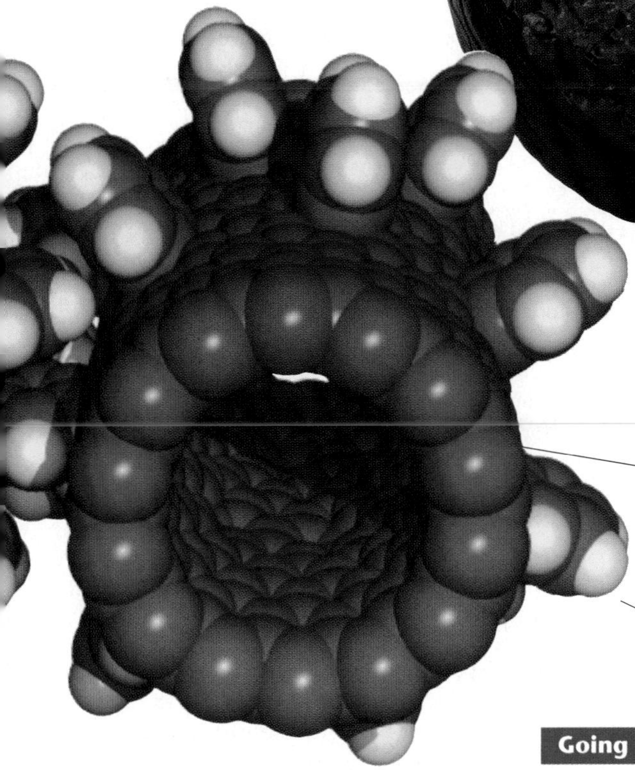
Sheet of carbon atoms rolled into a tube
Ring of carbon atoms with hydrogen atoms attached

Nanogears
This image of nanogears was produced with a computer program designed to make models of molecules. Hollow tubes (nanotubes) made from sheets of carbon atoms do exist. So do the rings containing carbon and hydrogen atoms, which are used for the "teeth" of the gears. But researchers need to figure out how to get the "teeth" to attach to the tubes.

Going Further

- Research proposed uses of nanotechnology. Make a poster describing one proposed use. Explain the advantage of using small objects in this application. What problems must be solved before the application can be used?
- Take a Discovery Channel Video Field Trip by watching "Go For Gold."

Discovery Channel School
Video Field Trip

Going Further

Possible uses include bar codes that attach to molecules and are used to monitor biological processes, devices that deliver drugs to specific locations in the body at specific times, and self-assembling products. One overall challenge is the construction of interfaces between humans and tiny devices.
Verbal, Visual

Discovery Channel School

Video Field Trip

Go For Gold

After students have viewed the Video Field Trip, ask them the following questions: **What did the ancient Egyptians know about how gold reacts with air?** *(They realized that gold does not react easily with air and does not corrode like many other metals.)* **Name a practical reason why temple roofs were often covered with gold in countries with hot climates.** *(Because gold is an excellent reflector of sunlight, it kept the interiors cooler than they would have been otherwise.)* **How do the properties of gold make it useful on space missions?** *(Gold is often used to coat space vehicles in order to reflect the intense sunlight. A thin layer of gold on the goggles used by astronauts reduces the intensity of light reaching the astronauts' eyes.)* **How can the arrangement of atoms on the surface of gold be observed?** *(Electron microscopes are designed to trace the arrangement of particles on a surface through the up-and-down movement of a probe tip.)*

1 FOCUS

Objectives

4.2.1 **Identify** three subatomic particles and **compare** their properties.

4.2.2 **Distinguish** the atomic number of an element from the mass number of an isotope, and use these numbers to **describe** the structure of atoms.

Reading Focus

Build Vocabulary — L2

Word-Part Analysis Have students look up the term *isotope* in a dictionary that provides word prefixes. Have them use the prefix *iso-* to help them understand the term. *(The prefix* iso- *means "same." Isotopes of an element have the same atomic number, but different numbers of neutrons.)*

Reading Strategy — L2

Most students will know that atoms are the "building blocks" of matter, and some may know that atoms contain subatomic particles. Students may say that they want to learn more about the structure of atoms.

2 INSTRUCT

Properties of Subatomic Particles

Use Visuals — L1

Figure 9 Have students examine the photo and the caption that describes it in Figure 9. Suggest some familiar objects that have a mass of 5 kg, such as a 12-pack of 16-ounce beverage containers. Ask, **If a proton's mass was 10 tons and an electron's mass was 5 kg, what mass would represent the mass of a neutron?** *(10 tons)* **Logical**

FYI

Different books use different conventions for symbols for subatomic particles. For example, some texts use only the letters *e, p,* and *n*. Others include a superscript zero on the *n* to indicate the lack of charge. Electrons, protons, and neutrons are not the only subatomic particles. Quarks will be discussed in Chapter 10.

4.2 The Structure of an Atom

Reading Focus

Key Concepts

- What are three subatomic particles?
- What properties can be used to compare protons, electrons, and neutrons?
- How are atoms of one element different from atoms of other elements?
- What is the difference between two isotopes of the same element?

Vocabulary

- proton
- electron
- neutron
- atomic number
- mass number
- isotopes

Reading Strategy

Monitoring Your Understanding Before you read, copy the table. List what you know about atoms and what you would like to learn. After you read, list what you have learned.

What I Know About Atoms	What I Would Like to Learn	What I Have Learned

Figure 9 This 45-foot-tall steel sculpture of a clothespin is in Philadelphia, Pennsylvania. Claes Oldenburg made the clothespin in 1976 from 10 tons of steel. If a proton had a mass of 10 tons, then an electron would have a mass of about 5 kilograms.

Beams like the ones Thomson produced create the images on many television screens. When a beam sweeps across the screen, spots on the screen light up in the same way the screen in the gold-foil experiment lit up when struck by an alpha particle. In a color television, there are three beams, one for each primary color of light—red, green, and blue. The particles in these beams are subatomic particles.

Properties of Subatomic Particles

By 1920, Rutherford had seen evidence for the existence of two subatomic particles and had predicted the existence of a third particle. **Protons, electrons, and neutrons are subatomic particles.**

Protons Based on experiments with elements other than gold, Rutherford concluded that the amount of positive charge varies among elements. Each nucleus must contain at least one particle with a positive charge. Rutherford called these particles protons. A **proton** is a positively charged subatomic particle that is found in the nucleus of an atom. Each proton is assigned a charge of 1+. Some nuclei contain more than 100 protons.

Electrons The particles that Thomson detected were later named electrons. *Electron* comes from a Greek word meaning "amber." An **electron** is a negatively charged subatomic particle that is found in the space outside the nucleus. Each electron has a charge of 1−.

Section Resources

Print
- ***Reading and Study Workbook With Math Support,*** Section 4.2 and **Math Skill:** Electrons and Orbitals
- ***Transparencies,*** Section 4.2

Technology
- ***Interactive Textbook,*** Section 4.2
- ***Presentation Pro CD-ROM,*** Section 4.2
- ***Go Online,*** *Science News,* Atomic chemistry

Properties of Subatomic Particles					
Particle	Symbol	Relative Charge	Relative Mass (proton = 1)	Actual Mass (g)	Model
Electron	e^-	1−	$\frac{1}{1836}$	9.11×10^{-28}	
Proton	p^+	1+	1	1.674×10^{-24}	
Neutron	n	0	1	1.675×10^{-24}	

Figure 10 This table lists the symbol, the relative charge, the relative mass, and the actual mass of an electron, a proton, and a neutron. The Model column shows the colors used in this book to represent the subatomic particles. **Calculating** ***What is the difference in actual mass between a proton and a neutron?***

Neutrons In 1932, the English physicist James Chadwick designed an experiment to show that neutrons exist. Chadwick concluded that the particles he produced were neutral because a charged object did not deflect their paths. A **neutron** is a neutral subatomic particle that is found in the nucleus of an atom. It has a mass almost exactly equal to that of a proton.

Comparing Subatomic Particles

Figure 10 summarizes some properties of protons, electrons, and neutrons. **Protons, electrons, and neutrons can be distinguished by mass, charge, and location in an atom.** Protons and neutrons have almost the same mass. But the data in Figure 10 show that it would take about 2000 electrons to equal the mass of one proton. Electrons have a charge that is equal in size to, but the opposite of, the charge of a proton. Neutrons have no charge. Protons and neutrons are found in the nucleus, but electrons are found in the space outside the nucleus.

Go Online SCIENCE NEWS

For: Articles on atomic chemistry
Visit: PHSchool.com
Web Code: cce-1042

Problem-Solving Activity

Designing an Atomic Exhibit

You work as a volunteer at the local science museum. You are asked to design an exhibit that compares the size of a lithium atom to the size of its nucleus. A lithium atom has a diameter of about 3×10^2 picometers. The nucleus of a lithium atom has a diameter of about 5×10^{-3} picometers. There are a trillion (10^{12}) picometers in a meter.

Defining the Problem State the problem in your own words. What decisions will you need to make before you can proceed?

Organizing Information How many times larger is the lithium atom than its nucleus? Find several objects that could represent the nucleus in your exhibit and measure their diameters.

Creating a Solution Pick one of the objects you measured to represent the nucleus in your atomic exhibit. Figure out how far away from the object you would have to place a marker so that people could visualize the relative sizes of the atom and the nucleus.

Presenting Your Plan Write a proposal to present to the committee that approves projects. Tell them where you would place the nucleus and where you would have to place the marker. Be prepared to explain why your exhibit needs the space you are requesting.

Comparing Subatomic Particles

Build Science Skills L2

Calculating Have students confirm the relative masses given in Figure 10 by dividing the mass given for an electron by the mass given for a neutron. *($9.11 \times 10^{-28}/1.675 \times 10^{-24} = 5.44 \times 10^{-4}$; $1/1836 = 5.45 \times 10^{-4}$)* These numbers are almost equal. Note that the masses given are in grams.
Logical

Problem-Solving Activity

Designing an Atomic Exhibit L2

Defining the Problem To design an exhibit that compares the size of a lithium atom to the size of its nucleus, students must decide what materials to use and where to locate the exhibit.

Organizing Information It is 60,000 times larger than its nucleus.

Creating a Solution If a standard marble with a 5/8-inch diameter (1.6 cm) represents the nucleus, the marker should be at a distance of 960 m to represent the outer limit of the atom.

Presenting Your Plan The proposal should explain why the exhibit requires at least two locations that are about a kilometer apart to make a model of the lithium atom in which the nucleus is the size of a marble. Encourage students to locate two familiar area landmarks that are the appropriate distance apart based on the item chosen for the nucleus.
Visual, Logical

For Extra Help L1

Be sure that students multiply by the conversion factor that has the given unit in the denominator and the desired unit in the numerator.
Logical

Customize for Inclusion Students

Visually Impaired
Provide visually impaired students with a tactile model that represents the difference in mass between a proton and an electron. Count out (or have a group of students count out) 1836 small beads and place them into a resealable plastic bag. Have them feel the difference in mass between the bag of 1836 beads and an identical bag containing only one bead. Point out that the masses they sense include the masses of the bags.

Go Online SCIENCE NEWS

Science News provides students with current information on atomic chemistry.

Answer to . . .

Figure 10 *0.001×10^{-24} g*

Atomic Number and Mass Number

FYI

The atomic mass unit will be introduced in Section 5.2, when atomic masses listed in the periodic table are discussed. The force that binds protons and neutrons together in the nucleus is called the strong nuclear force and is addressed in Chapter 10, as is the effect of the size of a nucleus on its stability.

Teacher Demo

Particles and Numbers L2

Purpose Students will observe the relationship between number of protons, number of neutrons, atomic number, and mass number.

Materials overhead projector, red and green gummy candies

Procedure Explain that the green candies represent neutrons and the red candies represent protons. Model a lithium-7 nucleus by placing a group of three red candies and four green candies on the overhead. Ask students to count the number of candies (particles) to determine the mass number of the lithium atom. Then, remove (subtract) the green candies (neutrons) to get the atomic number. Perform a similar demonstration with oxygen-16 (eight protons and eight neutrons) and boron-11 (five protons and six neutrons).

Expected Outcome Students should gain a familiarity with determining mass numbers and atomic numbers.
Visual

Build Reading Literacy L1

Identify Main Idea/Details Refer to page **98D** in this chapter, which provides the guidelines for identifying main ideas and details.

Have students read Atomic Number and Mass Number on p. 110. Ask them to identify the main idea of each paragraph. Point out that the main idea is usually within the first or second sentence of a paragraph. Encourage students to include this exercise in the notes they use to study.
Verbal

Everything scientists know about the nucleus and subatomic particles is based on how the particles behave. Scientists still do not have an instrument that can show the inside of an atom. But they do have microscopes that can show how atoms are arranged on the surface of a material. The How It Works box on page 111 describes one of those microscopes.

Reading Checkpoint *Which scientist demonstrated the existence of neutrons?*

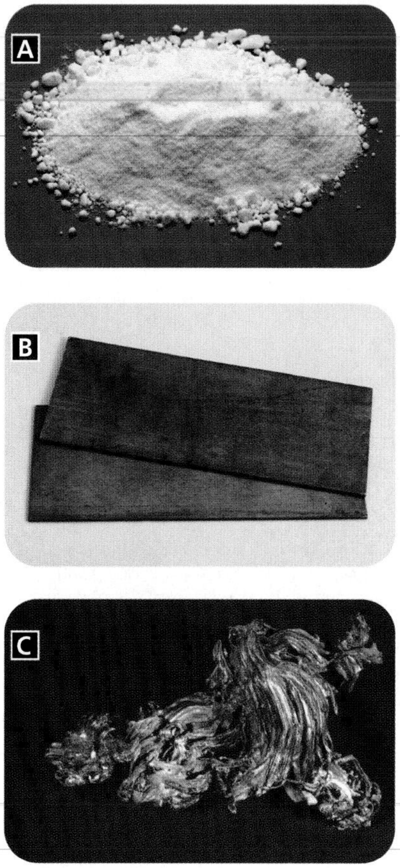

Figure 11 Each element has a different atomic number. **A** The atomic number of sulfur (S) is 16. **B** The atomic number of iron (Fe) is 26. **C** The atomic number of silver (Ag) is 47. **Applying Concepts** *How many protons are there in each atom of sulfur, iron, and silver?*

Atomic Number and Mass Number

Dalton predicted that the atoms of any element are different from the atoms of all other elements. With the discovery of subatomic particles, scientists were able to describe those differences.

Atomic Number The atoms of any given element always have the same number of protons. For example, there is one proton in the nucleus of each and every hydrogen atom. Therefore, hydrogen is assigned the atomic number 1. The **atomic number** of an element equals the number of protons in an atom of that element.

Hydrogen atoms are the only atoms with a single proton. **Atoms of different elements have different numbers of protons.** The sulfur shown in Figure 11A is assigned atomic number 16 because a sulfur atom has 16 protons. You can use atomic numbers to refer to elements, like names and symbols, because each element has a unique atomic number.

Each positive charge in an atom is balanced by a negative charge because atoms are neutral. So the atomic number of an element also equals the number of electrons in an atom. Each hydrogen atom has one electron. Each sulfur atom has 16.

Mass Number The atomic number tells you the number of protons in an atom's nucleus. It does not give you any information about the number of neutrons in an atom. For that information, you need to know the atom's mass number. The **mass number** of an atom is the sum of the protons and neutrons in the nucleus of that atom. An atom of aluminum with 13 protons and 14 neutrons has a mass number of 27. If you know the atomic number and the mass number of an atom, you can find the number of neutrons by subtracting.

Number of Neutrons

$$\text{Number of neutrons} = \text{Mass number} - \text{Atomic number}$$

DK HOW It Works

Scanning Tunneling Microscope

A probe is moved back and forth across the surface of a sample. When electrons jump, or tunnel, across the gap between the sample and the probe, an electric current is produced. A computer uses data about changes in the probe's position to produce an image of the sample's surface. **Interpreting Diagrams** ***How is the distance between the probe tip and the sample kept constant?***

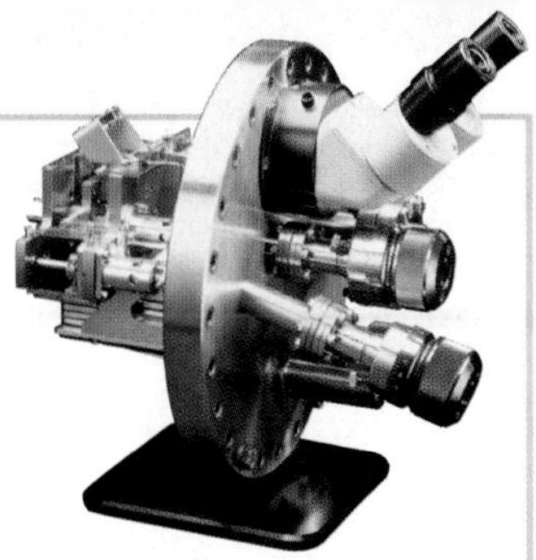

Scanning tunneling microscope
Modern scanning tunneling microscopes produce images of metal samples or biological specimens such as DNA.

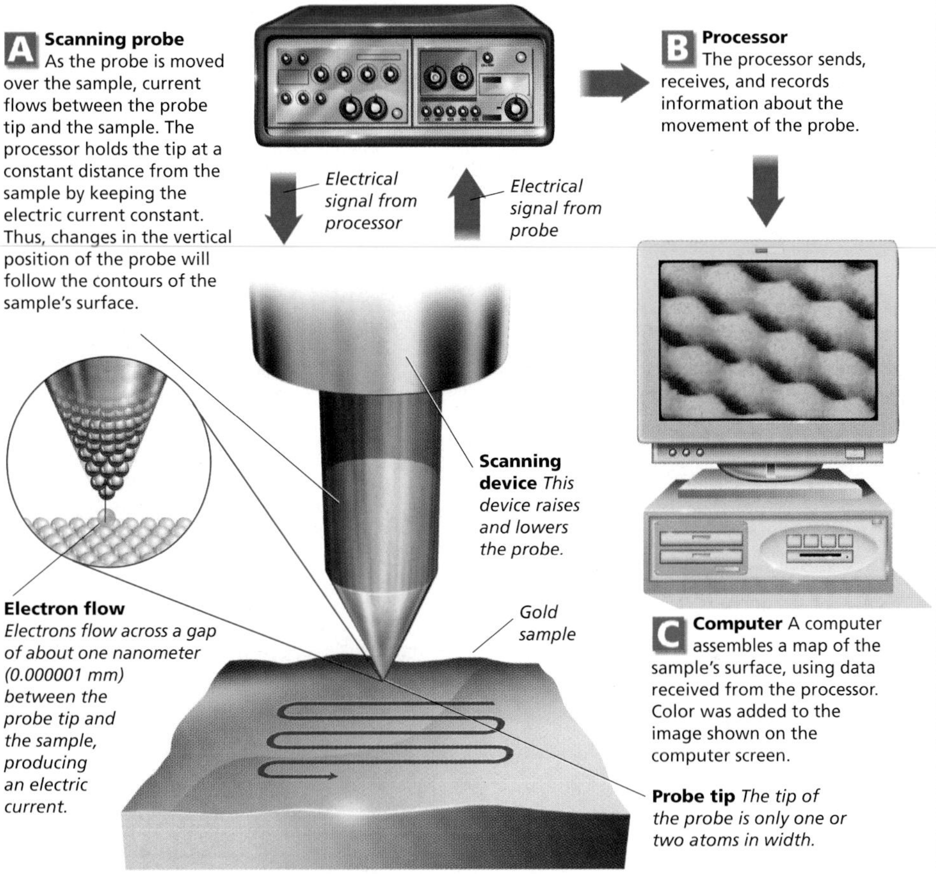

A Scanning probe As the probe is moved over the sample, current flows between the probe tip and the sample. The processor holds the tip at a constant distance from the sample by keeping the electric current constant. Thus, changes in the vertical position of the probe will follow the contours of the sample's surface.
B Processor The processor sends, receives, and records information about the movement of the probe.
Electrical signal from processor
Electrical signal from probe
Scanning device *This device raises and lowers the probe.*
Electron flow *Electrons flow across a gap of about one nanometer (0.000001 mm) between the probe tip and the sample, producing an electric current.*
Gold sample
C Computer A computer assembles a map of the sample's surface, using data received from the processor. Color was added to the image shown on the computer screen.
Probe tip *The tip of the probe is only one or two atoms in width.*

DK HOW It Works

Scanning Tunneling Microscope **L2**

The scanning tunneling microscope (STM) is used to obtain high-resolution images of solid surfaces. This technology allows scientists and researchers to view a three-dimensional profile of a surface, which can give information about surface textures and crystal structure. STM data is initially displayed as a black and white image that is colorized to highlight different features.

In 1986, Gerd Binnig of Germany and Heinrich Rohrer of Switzerland shared the Nobel Prize in Physics with Germany's Ernst Ruska for designing the scanning tunneling microscope.

Interpreting Diagrams The processor maintains a constant electric current between the probe tip and the sample, which keeps the distance between the tip and sample constant.
Logical

For Enrichment **L3**

Encourage students to explore the use of scanning tunneling microscopes in research on surface textures, crystal structure, or molecular shape. Have them present their findings to the class in the form of a poster.
Visual

Facts and Figures

Coining Terms The English physician William Gilbert (1544–1603) introduced the term *electric,* which is based on the Greek word for amber. (William Gilbert was the personal physician to Queen Elizabeth I and a pioneer in the study of magnetism. A unit of magnetic force is named for him.) Credit for naming the electron goes to G. Johnstone Stoney, an Irish physicist who suggested the name in 1891.

Answer to . . .

Figure 11 *There are 16 protons in a sulfur atom, 26 in an iron atom, and 47 in a silver atom.*

Reading Checkpoint *James Chadwick*

Section 4.2 (continued)

Isotopes

Build Science Skills

L2

Calculating Uranium-238 has a mass number of 238 with 146 neutrons in the nucleus. Uranium-235 has 143 neutrons in the nucleus. Ask, **What is the atomic number of uranium?** *(92)*
Logical

Address Misconceptions

L2

Many students think that isotopes are different from "ordinary" or "regular" atoms. To challenge this misconception, have students read the text on this page and examine the data presented in Figure 12. Ask, **How are the compositions of heavy water and ordinary water similar?** *(Both contain hydrogen and oxygen atoms.)* **What type of hydrogen atoms does ordinary water contain?** *(Hydrogen-1 atoms)* **What type of hydrogen atoms does heavy water contain?** *(Hydrogen-2 atoms)* **Compare the properties of heavy water and ordinary water.** *(They have different melting points, boiling points, and densities.)*
Logical

3 ASSESS

Evaluate Understanding

L2

Have students write three review questions for this section. Students should then break into groups of three or four and ask each other their questions.

Reteach

L1

Revisit Figure 10 to review the differences among protons, neutrons, and electrons.

Connecting Concepts

Students might say that "type of atom" refers to the atomic number of the atom or to the number of protons in the atom.

Interactive Textbook If your class subscribes to the Interactive Textbook, use it to review key concepts in Section 4.2.

Answer to . . .

Figure 12 *3.81°C*

Comparing Ordinary Water and Heavy Water

Property	Ordinary Water	Heavy Water
Melting point	0.00°C	3.81°C
Boiling point	100.00°C	101.42°C
Density (at 25°C)	0.99701 g/cm^3	1.1044 g/cm^3

Figure 12 Heavy water contains hydrogen-2 atoms, which have twice the mass of hydrogen-1 atoms. **Using Tables** ***At what temperature would a sample of heavy water freeze?***

Isotopes

In Dalton's atomic theory, all the atoms of a given element are identical. Every atom of a given element *does* have the same number of protons and electrons. But every atom of a given element *does not* have the same number of neutrons. **Isotopes** are atoms of the same element that have different numbers of neutrons and different mass numbers. **Isotopes of an element have the same atomic number but different mass numbers because they have different numbers of neutrons.**

For example, every atom of oxygen has 8 protons. Some oxygen atoms have 8 neutrons and a mass number of 16. Some oxygen atoms have 9 neutrons and a mass number of 17. Some oxygen atoms have 10 neutrons and a mass number of 18. When it is important to distinguish one oxygen isotope from another, the isotopes are referred to as oxygen-16, oxygen-17, and oxygen-18. All three oxygen isotopes can react with hydrogen to form water or combine with iron to form rust.

With most elements, it is hard to notice any differences in the physical or chemical properties of their isotopes. Hydrogen is an exception. Hydrogen-1 has no neutrons. (Almost all hydrogen is hydrogen-1.) Hydrogen-2 has one neutron, and hydrogen-3 has two neutrons. Because a hydrogen-1 atom has only one proton, adding a neutron doubles its mass. Water that contains hydrogen-2 atoms in place of hydrogen-1 atoms is called heavy water. Figure 12 compares some physical properties of ordinary water and heavy water.

Section 4.2 Assessment

Reviewing Concepts

1. Name three subatomic particles.
2. Name three properties you could use to distinguish a proton from an electron.
3. Which characteristic of an atom always varies among atoms of different elements?
4. How are the isotopes of an element different from one another?
5. What do neutrons and protons have in common? How are they different?
6. How can atoms be neutral if they contain charged particles?
7. What is the difference between atoms of oxygen-16 and oxygen-17?

Critical Thinking

8. **Comparing and Contrasting** What property do protons and electrons have that neutrons do not?
9. **Applying Concepts** Explain why it isn't possible for an atom to have a mass number of 10 and an atomic number of 12.

Connecting Concepts

Elements In Section 2.1, you were told that elements contain only one type of atom. How would you define "type of atom" to account for the existence of isotopes?

Section 4.2 Assessment

1. Proton, electron, and neutron
2. Mass, charge, and location in an atom
3. The atoms of any element have a different number of protons than the atoms of all other elements.
4. Isotopes of an element have the same atomic number but different mass numbers because they have different numbers of neutrons.
5. Protons and neutrons have almost the same mass and are both located in the nucleus of the atom. Protons are charged particles. Neutrons are neutral particles.
6. The positive charge of the protons in the nucleus is balanced by the negative charge of the electrons.
7. Each oxygen-17 atom has one more neutron than each oxygen-16 atom.
8. Protons and electrons are charged particles. Neutrons have no charge.
9. An atom with an atomic number of 12 has 12 protons. Because the mass number is the sum of the protons and neutrons, the mass number would need to be at least 12.

4.3 Modern Atomic Theory

Reading Focus

Key Concepts

- What can happen to electrons when atoms gain or lose energy?
- What model do scientists use to describe how electrons behave in atoms?
- What is the most stable configuration of electrons in an atom?

Vocabulary

- energy levels
- electron cloud
- orbital
- electron configuration
- ground state

Reading Strategy

Sequencing Copy the flowchart. After you read, complete the description of how a gain or loss of energy affects atoms.

Electrons and Energy Levels

a. ? → Excited state → b. ? → Emits energy

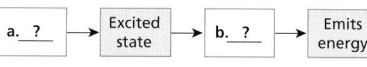

Have you ever wondered what produces the different colors in a fireworks display? Why does one explosion produce red light and another explosion produce green light? The people who make fireworks know that certain compounds will produce certain colors of light when they are heated. For example, compounds containing the element strontium produce red light when they are heated. Compounds containing barium produce green light.

You have seen two things that can happen when atoms absorb energy—an increase in kinetic energy or a phase change. But there is another possibility. The energy may be temporarily absorbed by the atom and then emitted as light. The colors in a fireworks display are a clue to how electrons are arranged in atoms.

Bohr's Model of the Atom

You may have seen diagrams of an atom that look like a solar system with planets revolving around a sun. These diagrams are based on a model of the atom that was developed by Niels Bohr (1885–1962), a Danish physicist who worked for a while with Rutherford. Bohr agreed with Rutherford's model of a nucleus surrounded by a large volume of space. But Bohr's model did something that Rutherford's model did not do. It focused on the electrons. A description of the arrangement of electrons in an atom is the centerpiece of the modern atomic model.

Figure 13 Fireworks are often displayed above the Lincoln Memorial in Washington, D.C. The red light was produced by a strontium compound.

Section Resources

Print

- ***Laboratory Manual,*** Investigations 4A and 4B
- ***Reading and Study Workbook With Math Support,*** Section 4.3
- ***Transparencies,*** Section 4.3

Technology

- ***Interactive Textbook,*** Section 4.3
- ***Presentation Pro CD-ROM,*** Section 4.3
- ***Go Online,*** NSTA SciLinks, Energy levels

Section 4.3

1 FOCUS

Objectives

4.3.1 **Describe** Bohr's model of the atom and the evidence for energy levels.

4.3.2 **Explain** how the electron cloud model represents the behavior and locations of electrons in atoms.

4.3.3 **Distinguish** the ground state from excited states of an atom based on electron configurations.

Reading Focus

Build Vocabulary L2

LINCS Have students use the LINCS strategy to learn the terms *energy levels, electron cloud, orbital, electron configuration,* and *ground state.* In LINCS exercises, students **L**ist what they know about each term, **I**magine a picture that describes the term, **N**ote a reminding "sound-alike" word, **C**onnect the terms to the sound-alike word by making up a short story, and then perform a brief **S**elf-test.

Reading Strategy L2

a. Electron moves to higher energy level.
b. Electron moves to lower energy level.

2 INSTRUCT

Bohr's Model of the Atom

Build Reading Literacy L1

Relate Text and Visuals Refer to page **190D** in **Chapter 7,** which provides the guidelines for relating text and visuals.

Have students read Bohr's Model of the Atom on pp. 113–116. Then, have students examine the diagram of Bohr's model in the time line on p. 115. Ask, **What do the circles around the nucleus represent?** *(They represent energy levels.)*
Visual

Address Misconceptions L2

Students may think that electrons travel around the nucleus in fixed orbits, like planets orbiting the sun. Challenge this misconception by having students compare Bohr's model and the electron cloud model. Explain that Bohr's model correctly introduced the concept of energy levels, but energy levels cannot be used to describe the actual location of an electron. The electron cloud model can be used to model the probability that an electron is in a certain location. The exact speed and location of a single electron cannot be determined.
Verbal

FYI

The usefulness of Bohr's model was limited. The model could be used to describe the behavior of the single electron in a hydrogen atom quite accurately. However, this model could not be applied to atoms with multiple electrons.

Integrate Space Science L2

Planets in the solar system travel in fixed orbits around the sun. Because most of the orbits are nearly circular, the difference between the distance to the sun when a planet is closest and when it is farthest away is not great (given the magnitude of distances in space). Pluto is an exception. Its orbit is so elliptical that there are times during Pluto's journey around the sun (249 Earth days) when it is closer to the sun than Neptune is. This switch in order of proximity to the sun lasts 20 years. It last happened between 1979 and 1999. Have students research when it will happen again.
Logical

Energy Levels In Bohr's model, electrons move with constant speed in fixed orbits around the nucleus, like planets around a sun. Each electron in an atom has a specific amount of energy. If an atom gains or loses energy, the energy of an electron can change. The possible energies that electrons in an atom can have are called **energy levels.**

To understand energy levels, picture them as steps in a staircase. As you move up or down the staircase, you can measure how your position changes by counting the number of steps you take. You might take one step up, or you might jump two steps down. Whether you are going up or down, you can move only in whole-step increments. Just as you cannot stand between steps on a staircase, an electron cannot exist between energy levels.

DK SCIENCE and History

Models of the Atom

The development of scientific ideas on the structure of atoms has passed several key milestones during the last 200 years.

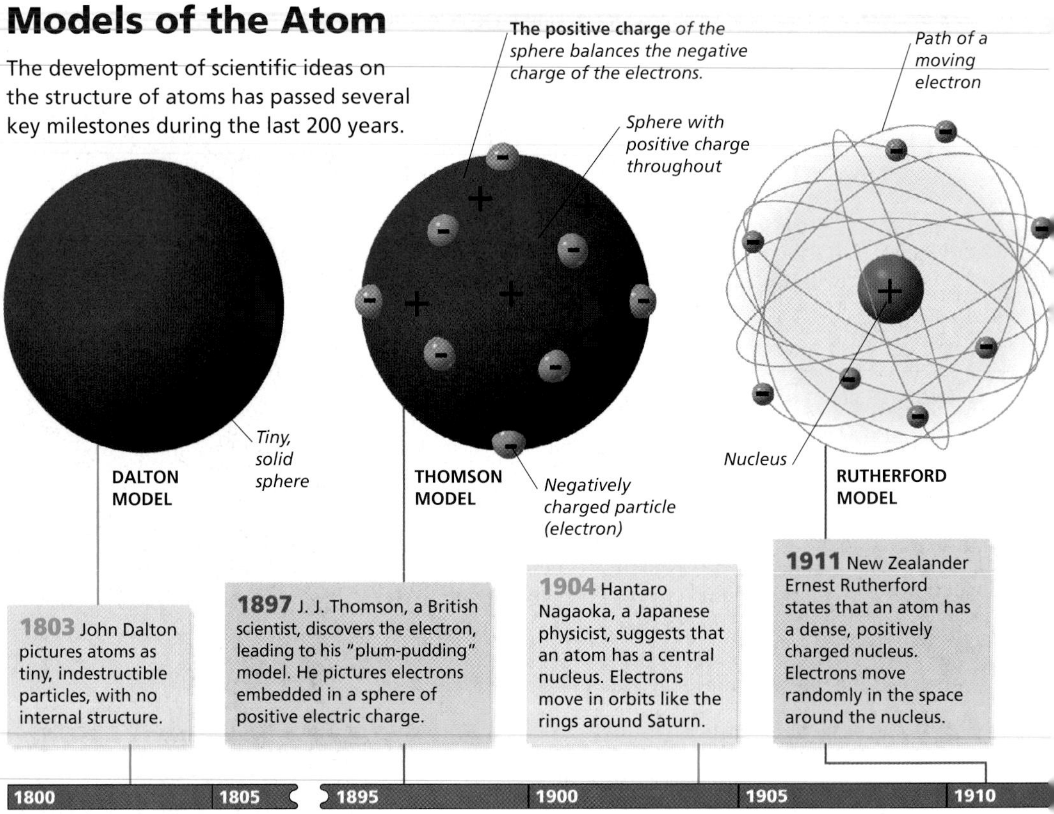

The positive charge of the sphere balances the negative charge of the electrons.
Path of a moving electron
Sphere with positive charge throughout
Tiny, solid sphere
DALTON MODEL
THOMSON MODEL
Negatively charged particle (electron)
Nucleus
RUTHERFORD MODEL
1803 John Dalton pictures atoms as tiny, indestructible particles, with no internal structure.
1897 J. J. Thomson, a British scientist, discovers the electron, leading to his "plum-pudding" model. He pictures electrons embedded in a sphere of positive electric charge.
1904 Hantaro Nagaoka, a Japanese physicist, suggests that an atom has a central nucleus. Electrons move in orbits like the rings around Saturn.
1911 New Zealander Ernest Rutherford states that an atom has a dense, positively charged nucleus. Electrons move randomly in the space around the nucleus.
1800
1805
1895
1900
1905
1910

Customize for English Language Learners

Think-Pair-Share
Have students work in pairs to think of structures that can serve as analogies for energy levels. Examples include rungs of a ladder, guitar frets, and the series of holes on a belt or shoe strap. Note, however, that in all of these models, the intervals are equal, which is not true of the intervals between energy levels. Provide pictures of dressers that have drawers of different sizes or bookshelves that have adjustable shelves, which might better model the intervals of energy levels. Strengthen discussion skills by having students share their examples with the class.

The landing at the bottom of the staircase is like the lowest energy level in an atom. Each step up represents a higher energy level. The distance between two steps represents the difference in energy between two energy levels. To continue the analogy, there would need to be a different staircase for each element because no two elements have the same set of energy levels.

An electron in an atom can move from one energy level to another when the atom gains or loses energy. An electron may move up two energy levels if it gains the right amount of energy. An electron in a higher energy level may move down two energy levels if it loses the right amount of energy. The size of the jump between energy levels determines the amount of energy gained or lost.

Writing in Science

Summary Select a scientist mentioned on the time line. Research and write a paragraph about the scientist's early years. What experiences led to his interest in science? Was he the first in his family to be interested in science? What subjects did he study at school?

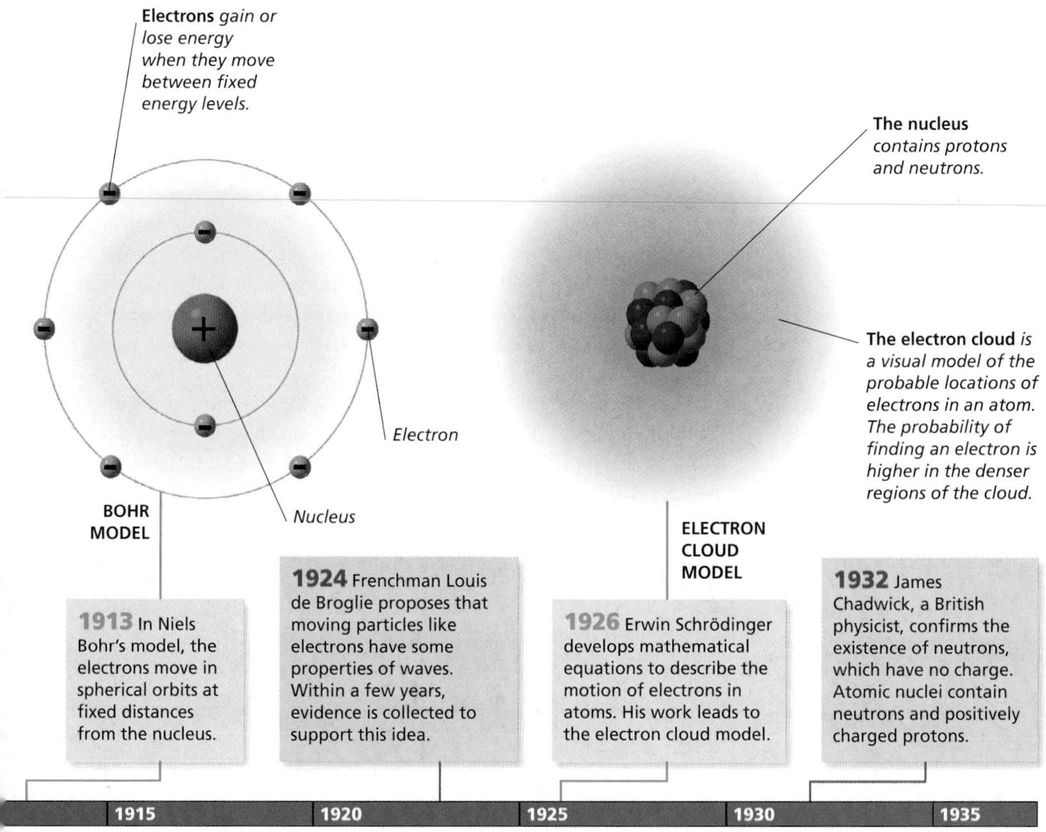

Electrons *gain or lose energy when they move between fixed energy levels.*
Electron
Nucleus
BOHR MODEL
The nucleus *contains protons and neutrons.*
The electron cloud *is a visual model of the probable locations of electrons in an atom. The probability of finding an electron is higher in the denser regions of the cloud.*
ELECTRON CLOUD MODEL
1913 In Niels Bohr's model, the electrons move in spherical orbits at fixed distances from the nucleus.
1924 Frenchman Louis de Broglie proposes that moving particles like electrons have some properties of waves. Within a few years, evidence is collected to support this idea.
1926 Erwin Schrödinger develops mathematical equations to describe the motion of electrons in atoms. His work leads to the electron cloud model.
1932 James Chadwick, a British physicist, confirms the existence of neutrons, which have no charge. Atomic nuclei contain neutrons and positively charged protons.
1915
1920
1925
1930
1935

FYI

In Section 6.1, students will learn that electrons sometimes gain enough energy to escape from an atom.

SCIENCE and History

Models of the Atom L2

Have groups of students build or draw models that represent the changes over time in scientists' understanding of atomic structure. Have them make a three-dimensional version of the time line shown and display it as a mobile or diorama. Have students note the time scale on the time line. Explain that the break between 1805 and 1895 allows the milestone in 1803 to be included.
Group, Visual

Writing in Science

There will be more information for some scientists than for others. The exercise focuses on early experiences because students will not understand most of what is written about the careers of these scientists. By pooling their research, students will see that scientists can emerge from diverse backgrounds.

Students may learn that Dalton was the son of a weaver and de Broglie was the son of a duke; that Dalton began his teaching career at the age of 12; that Schrödinger was an only child, but Rutherford had 11 siblings; or that Chadwick was shy and Rutherford charming.
Verbal

Use Community Resources L2

Have a female scientist visit the class to discuss the experiences that led to her interest in science. Have students prepare questions similar to those asked in the Writing in Science feature.
Interpersonal, Visual

Facts and Figures

De Broglie and Schrödinger In 1924, Louis de Broglie, a French graduate student, derived an equation that describes the wavelength of a moving particle. Using de Broglie's equation, an electron has a wavelength of about 2×10^{-10} cm. In 1926, Erwin Schrödinger, an Austrian physicist, wrote a mathematical equation to describe the location and energy of the electron in a hydrogen atom. When the equation is solved (using advanced calculus), it produces a series of wave functions that describe the behavior of electrons. The quantum mechanical model of atoms is based on these wave functions. Atomic physicists define an orbital as the space-dependent part of the Schrödinger wave function of an electron in an atom or molecule.

Electron Cloud Model

Build Science Skills L2

Using Models Have students examine the propeller in Figure 14. Ask, **How is the moving propeller similar to an electron cloud?** *(You cannot be sure at any specific moment where the propeller blades or electrons are located. However, the central part of the propeller and the nucleus of an atom are in fixed locations.)* **What other examples can you think of that could model the concept of an electron cloud?** *(Acceptable answers include a ceiling fan, or moths flying around a light bulb.)*
Visual

Teacher Demo

Electron Cloud Model L2

Purpose Students will use a model to describe the probable position of electrons.

Materials small, round balloon; large, round balloon; 10 beads with 4-mm diameter; 5 beads with 2-mm diameter

Procedure Put the 4-mm beads into the small balloon. Tell students that the small balloon represents the nucleus of a boron atom (five neutrons, five protons). Put the 2-mm beads into the large balloon. Explain that the beads represent electrons and the balloon represents the electron cloud. Slightly inflate the small balloon and push it completely into the large balloon. Inflate the large balloon and tie the end. Agitate the balloon so that the small beads are in constant motion.

Expected Outcome The precise location of a bead at a specific time is unknown, but the probability that it is in the large balloon is quite high.
Kinesthetic

Go Online NSTA SCI LINKS

For: Links on energy levels
Visit: www.SciLinks.org
Web Code: ccn-1043

Figure 14 When the propeller of an airplane is at rest, you can see the locations of the blades. When the propeller is moving, you see only a blur that is similar to a drawing of an electron cloud. ***Comparing and Contrasting*** ***Describe one difference between the motion of a propeller and the motion of an electron.***

Evidence for Energy Levels What evidence is there that electrons can move from one energy level to another? Scientists can measure the energy gained when electrons absorb energy and move to a higher energy level. They can measure the energy released when the electron returns to a lower energy level.

The movement of electrons between energy levels explains the light you see when fireworks explode. Light is a form of energy. Heat produced by the explosion causes some electrons to move to higher energy levels. When those electrons move back to lower energy levels, they emit energy. Some of that energy is released as visible light. Because no two elements have the same set of energy levels, different elements emit different colors of light.

Reading Checkpoint ***What determines the amount of energy gained or lost when an electron moves between energy levels?***

Electron Cloud Model

Like earlier models, Bohr's model was improved as scientists made further discoveries. Bohr was correct in assigning energy levels to electrons. But he was incorrect in assuming that electrons moved like planets in a solar system. Today, scientists know that electrons move in a less predictable way.

Scientists must deal with probability when trying to predict the locations and motions of electrons in atoms. An **electron cloud** is a visual model of the most likely locations for electrons in an atom. The cloud is denser at those locations where the probability of finding an electron is high. **Scientists use the electron cloud model to describe the possible locations of electrons around the nucleus.**

Figure 14 provides an analogy for an electron cloud. When the propeller of an airplane is at rest, you can count the number of blades. When the propeller is moving, the blades spin so fast that you see only a blur. You know that the blades are located somewhere in the blur, but at any specific moment in time you can't be exactly sure where each blade is located.

Facts and Figures

Emission and Absorption Spectra When the energy gained or lost by an atom is light energy, each frequency (or wavelength) of light corresponds to a movement of an electron between two energy levels in the atom. An element can be identified by the frequencies of light that are absorbed or emitted by its atoms because no two elements have the same set of energy levels. For example, the element helium was discovered on the sun in 1868 before it was discovered on Earth. The spectrum of light emitted by gases on the surface of the sun contained a yellow line that did not match a known element.

Go Online NSTA SCI LINKS

Download a worksheet on energy levels for students to complete, and find additional teacher support from NSTA SciLinks.

Quick Lab

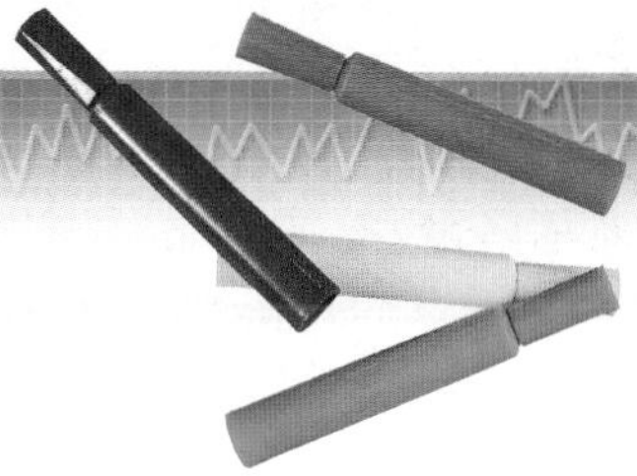

Comparing Excited States

Materials

fluorescent ("neon") markers, glow-in-the-dark toy, ultraviolet (UV) lamp

Procedure

1. Use the fluorescent markers to draw a picture on a piece of paper.
2. With the room darkened, observe your drawing under a UV lamp. **CAUTION** *Do not look directly at the light.* Remove the drawing from under the UV light and observe it again. Record your observations.
3. Observe the glow-in-the-dark toy under the UV light. Remove the toy from the light and observe it again. Record your observations.

Analyze and Conclude

1. **Observing** How did the glow of the toy differ from the glow of your drawing?
2. **Formulating Hypotheses** Use the concepts of ground and excited states to explain how UV light caused your drawing and the toy to glow.
3. **Drawing Conclusions** In which object, your drawing or the toy, do the atoms have excited states that are more stable, or less likely to change? Explain your answer.

Atomic Orbitals

The electron cloud represents all the orbitals in an atom. An **orbital** is a region of space around the nucleus where an electron is likely to be found. To understand the concept of an orbital, imagine a map of your school. Suppose you mark your exact location with a dot once every 10 minutes over a period of one week. The places you visit the most—such as your classrooms, the cafeteria, and the area near your locker—would have the highest concentration of dots. The places you visit the least would have the lowest concentration of dots.

The dots on your map are a model of your "orbital." They describe your most likely locations. There are some locations in your orbital that you may not visit every week—such as the principal's office or the auditorium. These locations may not be represented by a dot on your map. Despite such omissions, the dots on your map are a good model of how you usually behave in your orbital. **An electron cloud is a good approximation of how electrons behave in their orbitals.**

The level in which an electron has the least energy—the lowest energy level—has only one orbital. Higher energy levels have more than one orbital. Figure 15 shows the number of orbitals in the first four energy levels of an atom. Notice that the maximum number of electrons in an energy level is twice the number of orbitals. Each orbital can contain two electrons at most.

Figure 15 The table lists the number of orbitals in the first four energy levels of an atom. It also lists the maximum number of electrons in each energy level. **Inferring** *How many electrons can be in each orbital?*

Energy Levels, Orbitals, and Electrons

Energy Level	Number of Orbitals	Maximum Number of Electrons
1	1	2
2	4	8
3	9	18
4	16	32

Atomic Orbitals

Quick Lab

Comparing Excited States L2

Objective
After completing this activity, students will be able to
- explain how UV light causes objects to glow.
- use the persistence of light to compare excited states.

Skills Focus Observing, Formulating Hypotheses

Prep Time 5 minutes

Class Time 15 minutes

Safety Check the MSDS for the markers to make sure that they are low in VOCs (volatile organic compounds). Students should not look directly at UV light, which is harmful to the eyes. Demonstrate safe use of the UV lamps before allowing students to use them.

Teaching Tips
- Do this lab only after you teach ground state and excited states.

Expected Outcome Fluorescent ink will emit brilliant visible light under UV light. This fluorescence will instantly cease when the UV light is removed. Phosphorescent (glow-in-the-dark) objects will continue to emit visible light even after the UV light is removed.

Analyze and Conclude
1. The toy still glowed after the UV light was removed. The drawing did not.
2. The drawing and the toy absorbed energy from the UV light. When electrons moved to higher energy levels, the atoms were in an excited state. When electrons returned to lower energy levels, energy was released as visible light.
3. The fact that the toy's glow persisted suggests that the excited state of atoms in the toy was more stable than the excited state of atoms in the drawing.
Visual, Kinesthetic

FYI

According to the quantum mechanical model, an orbital is the mathematical function that describes the behavior of an electron in space.

Answer to . . .

Figure 14 *The propeller blades have a single, set path, and the blades stop moving when the engine is shut off.*

Figure 15 *Two*

Reading Checkpoint *The size of the jump between energy levels*

Electron Configurations

Use Visuals

L1

Figure 16 Extend the analogy of the gymnast on the balance beam by having students consider a gymnast doing an entire routine on equipment such as a balance beam, a pommel horse, parallel bars, or uneven bars. **In the analogy, when is the configuration of the gymnast like an atom in an excited state?** *(When the gymnast is in a precarious position, such as when the gymnast is not in direct contact with the equipment)* **In the analogy, when is the gymnast most like an atom in its ground state?** *(The gymnast is in her most stable position when she is standing on the floor.)*
Logical

3 ASSESS

Evaluate Understanding

L2

Have students draw and label a diagram that represents Bohr's model of an atom. Then, have students explain how the electron cloud model differs from Bohr's model.

Reteach

L1

Use the diagrams on p. 115 in the Science and History feature to review Bohr's model, energy levels, and electron clouds.

Writing in Science

The shelves in a bookcase can represent energy levels in an atom. If students know about potential energy, they may compare what happens to the energy of a book as it is moved between shelves to the difference in energy between electrons in different energy levels.

Interactive Textbook If your class subscribes to the Interactive Textbook, use it to review key concepts in Section 4.3.

Figure 16 A gymnast on a balance beam is like an atom in an excited state—not very stable.

Electron Configurations

How are the seats in your classroom arranged? Are they lined up neatly in rows, or are they grouped in clusters? A configuration is an arrangement of objects in a given space. Some configurations are more stable than others, meaning that they are less likely to change. The position of the gymnast on the balance beam in Figure 16 is not very stable because the beam is only 10 centimeters wide.

An **electron configuration** is the arrangement of electrons in the orbitals of an atom. **The most stable electron configuration is the one in which the electrons are in orbitals with the lowest possible energies.** When all the electrons in an atom have the lowest possible energies, the atom is said to be in its **ground state.**

For example, lithium is a silvery-white metal with an atomic number of 3, which means that a lithium atom has three electrons. In the ground state, two of the lithium electrons are in the orbital of the first energy level. The third electron is in an orbital of the second energy level.

If a lithium atom absorbs enough energy, one of its electrons can move to an orbital with a higher energy. This configuration is referred to as an excited state. An excited state is less stable than the ground state. Eventually, the electron that was promoted to a higher energy level loses energy, and the atom returns to the ground state. Helium, neon, argon, krypton, and xenon atoms returning from excited states to the ground state emit the light you see in "neon" lights.

Section 4.3 Assessment

Reviewing Concepts

1. When is an electron in an atom likely to move from one energy level to another?
2. What model do scientists use to describe how electrons move around the nucleus?
3. Describe the most stable configuration of the electrons in an atom.
4. What did Bohr contribute to modern atomic theory?
5. What does an electron cloud represent?

Critical Thinking

6. **Comparing and Contrasting** A boron atom has two electrons in the first energy level and three in the second energy level. Compare the relative energies of the electrons in these two energy levels.
7. **Making Judgments** Was Rutherford's model of an atom incorrect or incomplete? Explain your answer.
8. **Posing Questions** Apply what you know about charged particles to the modern model of the atom. Is there anything about the behavior of electrons in atoms that is unexpected? Explain your answer.

Writing in Science

Describing Energy Levels Use a bookcase as an analogy for the energy levels in an atom. Use the analogy to write a paragraph about electrons and energy levels. (*Hint:* Reread the staircase analogy on pages 114 and 115.)

Section 4.3 Assessment

1. Electrons are likely to move from one energy level to another when atoms gain or lose energy.
2. The electron cloud model
3. The most stable configuration is the one in which the electrons are in orbitals with the lowest possible energy.
4. Bohr contributed the idea that electrons have energy levels with specific amounts of energy.
5. An electron cloud represents the most probable locations of an electron in an atom.
6. The electrons in the second energy level will have more energy than the electrons in the first energy level.
7. Rutherford's description of an atom was correct, but incomplete. It did not provide as much information about the behavior of the electrons as later models.
8. Students may ask why the negatively charged electrons are not drawn into the nucleus by the positively charged protons.

Forensics Lab

Using Flame Tests

Forensic scientists use various approaches to distinguish different substances. In this lab, you will observe the flame colors of several substances and use the data to determine the identity of an unknown substance.

Problem How can the color of a flame be used to distinguish substances?

Materials

- solutions of calcium chloride, boric acid, potassium chloride, copper(II) sulfate, sodium chloride, and an unknown
- Bunsen burner
- nichrome wire loop
- dilute solution of hydrochloric acid
- wash bottle with distilled water

Skills Observing, Predicting, Using Data Tables

Procedure

Part A: Observing Flame Colors

1. Make a copy of the data table shown.

Data Table	
Solution	Flame Color
Calcium chloride	
Potassium chloride	
Boric acid	
Copper(II) sulfate	
Sodium chloride	
Unknown	
Identity of Unknown	

2. Light the Bunsen burner. **CAUTION** *Put on safety goggles and a lab apron. Tie back loose hair and clothing before working with a flame.*
3. Dip the wire loop into the calcium chloride solution and then place the loop in the flame as shown. Observe and record the color of the flame.
4. Clean the loop by dipping it into hydrochloric acid. Then, while holding the loop over a sink, rinse away the acid with distilled water. **CAUTION** *Keep hydrochloric acid away from your skin and clothing. Do not breathe in its vapor.*
5. Repeat Steps 3 and 4 with each of the other solutions. Be careful not to transfer any solution from one container to another. **CAUTION** *These chemicals are poisonous. Do not let them get on your skin.*

Part B: Examining an Unknown Solution

6. Obtain the unknown solution from your teacher.
7. Repeat Steps 3 and 4 using the unknown solution. Compare your observations with the other data you recorded to identify the unknown. **CAUTION** *Wash your hands thoroughly before leaving the laboratory.*

Analyze and Conclude

1. **Comparing and Contrasting** Is there a relationship between the color of the flame and the color of the solution?
2. **Formulating Hypotheses** How do these substances produce light of different colors?
3. **Drawing Conclusions** A forensic scientist does a flame test on a substance that was found at a crime scene. What might the scientist conclude if the flame turns green?

Go Further There is another test that you can use to distinguish elements by color. With your teacher supervising, dip a wire loop in borax. Heat the loop in a flame until the borax melts. Remove the loop from the flame and let the borax cool. It will form a clear glass bead. Dip the bead in a tiny sample of solid copper sulfate and return the loop to the flame for a few seconds. Remove the loop and observe the color of the bead as it cools.

Forensics Lab

Using Flame Tests L2

Objective
After completing this activity, students will be able to
- observe that different substances produce different colors when placed in a flame.

Skills Focus **Observing, Predicting, Using Data Tables, Drawing Conclusions**

Prep Time 20 minutes

Advance Prep Provide each lab group with a sample of each solution and unknown in a small, labeled container with a lid. Film canisters work well and they can be obtained free of charge from any photo shop. Prepare solutions that are about 0.1 M. Provide 0.1 M HCl in a glass container.

Class Time 40 minutes

Safety Students need to wear safety goggles and lab aprons. Review proper use of the Bunsen burner and appropriate safety precautions for using flames. Make sure long hair is tied back and loose clothing is not worn. Some of the substances are extremely toxic if ingested. Make sure students wash their hands thoroughly before leaving the laboratory.

Teaching Tips
- Demonstrate proper technique for performing flame tests and cleaning the wire loop between samples. Stress the importance of not contaminating one sample with another.
- Have students test the sodium chloride solution last because it can remain on the loop and make it difficult to see the other colors.
- Stress the importance of recording specific colors, for example, "fire-engine red" instead of simply "red."

Expected Outcome Students should be able to make accurate observations of flame colors and use them to identify their unknown solutions.

Sample Data
The following flame colors are characteristic: calcium: orange; potassium: violet; boron: light-green; copper: green; sodium: yellow-orange.

Go Further
The copper-glass bead will change from green to blue as it cools.
Kinesthetic, Visual

Analyze and Conclude
1. There is no relationship between flame color and solution color.
2. When the compounds are placed in the flame, atoms absorb energy and electrons move to higher energy levels. As these electrons move back to lower energy levels, they release energy as visible light. The color of light produced depends on the difference in energy between two specific energy levels in an atom.
3. The green flame indicates that the substance may contain copper, barium, or boron.
Visual, Logical

Study Guide

Study Tip

Organize New Information
Tell students to organize the key information from the chapter into one comprehensive document. They should consider creating an outline, a chart, a set of flashcards, a time line, or a concept map to help them visualize the relationships. For example, they might wish to organize all of the information in this chapter on an annotated time line. They could include drawings that illustrate each atomic model. They could also label the drawings with vocabulary terms and their definitions.

Thinking Visually

a. p^+
b. 1−
c. 0
d. 1
e. 1

CHAPTER 4

Study Guide

4.1 Studying Atoms

Key Concepts

- Dalton proposed the theory that all matter is made up of individual particles called atoms, which cannot be divided.
- Thomson's experiments provided the first evidence that atoms are made of even smaller particles.
- According to Rutherford's model, all of an atom's positive charge is concentrated in its nucleus.

Vocabulary

nucleus, *p. 105*

4.2 The Structure of an Atom

Key Concepts

- Protons, electrons. and neutrons are subatomic particles.
- Protons, electrons, and neutrons can be distinguished by mass, charge, and location in an atom.
- Atoms of different elements have different numbers of protons.
- Isotopes of an element have the same atomic number but different mass numbers because they have different numbers of neutrons.

Vocabulary

proton, *p. 108*
electron, *p. 108*
neutron, *p. 109*
atomic number, *p. 110*
mass number, *p. 110*
isotopes, *p. 112*

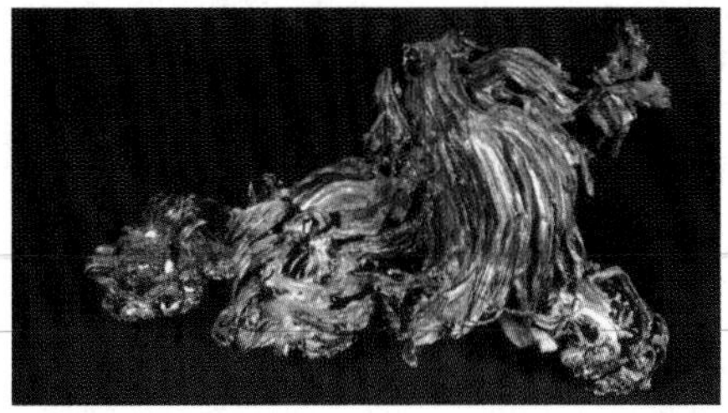

4.3 Modern Atomic Theory

Key Concepts

- An electron in an atom can move from one energy level to another when the atom gains or loses energy.
- Scientists use the electron cloud model to describe the possible locations of electrons around the nucleus.
- An electron cloud is a good approximation of how electrons behave in their orbitals.
- The most stable electron configuration is the one in which the electrons are in orbitals with the lowest possible energies.

Vocabulary

energy levels, *p. 114*
electron cloud, *p. 116*
orbital, *p. 117*
electron configuration, *p. 118*
ground state, *p. 118*

Thinking Visually

Table of Properties Use information from the chapter to complete the table below.

Particle	Proton	Electron	Neutron
Symbol	a. ?	e^-	n
Relative charge	1+	b. ?	c. ?
Relative mass	d. ?	$\frac{1}{1836}$	e. ?

Chapter Resources

Print
- ***Chapter and Unit Tests,*** Chapter 4 Test A and Test B
- ***Test Prep Resources,*** Chapter 4

Technology
- ***Computer Test Bank,*** Chapter Test 4
- ***Interactive Textbook,*** Chapter 4
- ***Go Online,*** PHSchool.com, Chapter 4

Assessment

Interactive textbook with assessment at PHSchool.com

Reviewing Content

Choose the letter that best answers the question or completes the statement.

1. One of the first people to state that matter is made up of atoms was
   a. Democritus. b. Aristotle.
   c. Dalton. d. Rutherford.
2. Dalton's model of an atom is best described as
   a. a solar system. b. a solid sphere.
   c. a plum pudding. d. an electron cloud.
3. Who provided the first evidence that atoms contain subatomic particles?
   a. Dalton b. Rutherford
   c. Thomson d. Bohr
4. Almost all the mass of an atom is located in its
   a. protons. b. electrons.
   c. electron cloud. d. nucleus.
5. An electron is a particle with
   a. a negative charge, found in the nucleus.
   b. a positive charge, found in the nucleus.
   c. no charge, found outside the nucleus.
   d. a negative charge, found outside the nucleus.
6. Which particle is the least massive?
   a. proton b. electron
   c. neutron d. nucleus
7. All atoms of an element have the same
   a. mass number. b. number of isotopes.
   c. atomic number. d. number of neutrons.
8. The number of neutrons in an atom equals the
   a. mass number minus atomic number.
   b. atomic number plus number of electrons.
   c. mass number plus atomic number.
   d. atomic number minus mass number.
9. The atomic number of sulfur is 16. How many electrons are there in an atom of sulfur-34?
   a. 16 b. 34
   c. 18 d. 50
10. Atoms emit energy as light when
    a. electrons move to a higher energy level.
    b. electrons move to a lower energy level.
    c. protons move to a higher energy level.
    d. protons move to a lower energy level.

Understanding Concepts

11. Why must indirect evidence be used to study the structure of atoms?
12. What evidence convinced Dalton that elements must be made of individual particles called atoms?
13. In Thomson's experiment, why was the glowing beam repelled by a negatively charged plate?
14. What evidence supported Thomson's hypothesis that the negative particles he observed came from inside atoms?
15. Compare the mass and volume of the nucleus to the total mass and volume of an atom.
16. Compare the relative masses of protons, neutrons, and electrons in an atom.
17. What is the difference between the atomic number of an atom and its mass number?
18. If the atomic number of an atom is 11, how many electrons does the atom have? Explain.
19. If an atom has an atomic number of 6 and a mass number of 14, how many protons, electrons, and neutrons are in the atom?
20. What part of Dalton's theory was modified after the discovery of isotopes?
21. Which isotope of oxygen is represented by the drawing—oxygen-16, oxygen-17, or oxygen-18? Assume that all the protons and neutrons in the nucleus are visible in the drawing. Give a reason for your answer.

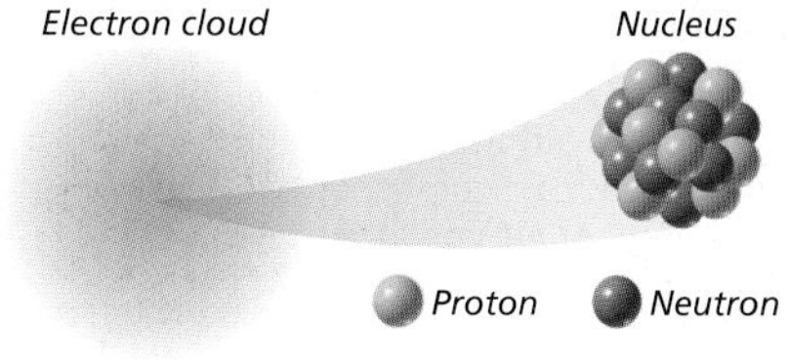

Electron cloud
Nucleus
Proton
Neutron

22. What is the main difference between Bohr's model of the atom and the atomic theory that is currently accepted?
23. What does it mean to say that an atom is in an excited state?

Homework Guide

Section	Questions
4.1	1–2, 11–14, 24–25, 34
4.2	3–9, 15–21, 26–33, 37
4.3	10, 22–23, 35–36

Assessment

Interactive Textbook If your class subscribes to the Interactive Textbook, your students can go online to access an interactive version of the Student Edition and a self-test.

Reviewing Content

1. a **2.** b **3.** c
4. d **5.** d **6.** b
7. c **8.** a **9.** a
10. b

Understanding Concepts

11. Atoms are too small to observe directly.
12. The ratio of the mass of elements in a compound is always the same.
13. The beam contained negatively charged particles, and like charges repel.
14. The particles were much less massive than the lightest known atom. The same particles were produced no matter which metal was used as the origin of the particles.
15. Almost all of the mass of an atom is located in the nucleus. The volume of the nucleus is much smaller than the volume of the atom as a whole.
16. Protons and neutrons have almost the same mass, which is about 2000 times greater than the mass of an electron.
17. The atomic number represents the number of protons or electrons in the atom. The mass number represents the number of protons and neutrons.
18. Because an atom must be neutral, it has 11 electrons to balance the charge on the 11 protons.
19. Six protons, six electrons, eight neutrons
20. All atoms of an element are identical.
21. Oxygen-17 because there are eight protons and nine neutrons
22. Bohr assumed that electrons traveled in orbits around the nucleus. Current atomic theory assumes that electrons do not travel in fixed paths.
23. One or more of the electrons in an atom have moved from the ground state to an orbital with a higher energy.

Critical Thinking

24. There are no external charged plates in setup A.
25. Because neutrons have no charge, the charged plates would not deflect the beam.
26. Carbon-14
27. A neutral particle is more difficult to detect than a charged particle because charged plates do not deflect its path.
28. The atom would have a negative charge, and atoms are neutral.
29. They are atoms of different elements because they have different numbers of protons. All atoms of a given element have the same number of protons.

Math Skills

30. 31 neutrons; 26 electrons
31. 19 protons, 19 electrons, 20 neutrons
32. Two protons and two neutrons

Concepts in Action

33. Iron-59 is different from other isotopes of iron because it contains 33 neutrons. It is the same as other isotopes because they all contain 26 protons.
34. Possible choices for the top-down analogy include a stone sculpture, a clay pot, or a carved wooden object, such as a totem pole. Choices for the bottom-up analogy include a brick wall, a bead necklace, a tile floor, or a patchwork quilt.
35. You cannot be certain because elements other than barium also may produce a green color.
36. Each element used in neon lights produces a distinctive color when its atoms are excited. If there are multiple colors, there must be multiple elements present.
37. With a scanning tunneling microscope, scientists can gather previously unavailable data about atoms, such as how atoms are arranged on the surface of materials. An electron microscope could not be developed until scientists knew that electrons existed.

Sn
51
78.96

Assessment *(continued)*

Critical Thinking

24. **Controlling Variables** Look at the drawing of the experimental setup in Figure 5A. Explain how the setup is a control for the setup in Figure 5B.

25. **Predicting** How would the results of Thomson's experiment change if the beam were a stream of neutrons instead of a stream of electrons?

26. **Interpreting Diagrams** The atomic number of carbon is 6. The atomic number of nitrogen is 7. The atomic number of oxygen is 8. Name the isotope represented by the drawing.

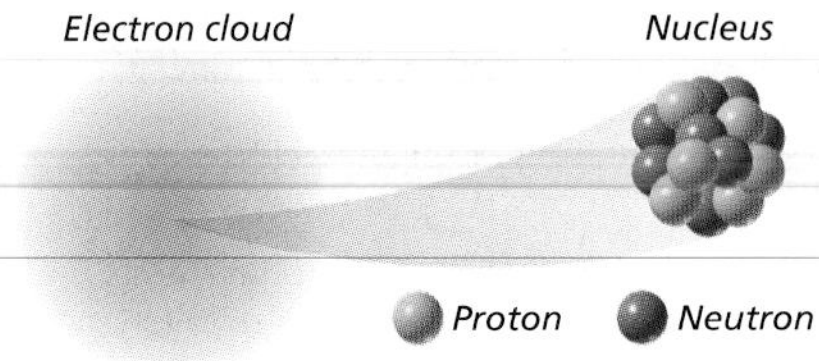
Electron cloud
Nucleus
Proton
Neutron

27. **Hypothesizing** Why were the proton and electron discovered before the neutron?

28. **Applying Concepts** Explain why a neutral atom cannot have one proton, one neutron, and two electrons.

29. **Classifying** The nucleus of an atom contains six neutrons and six protons. The nucleus of a second atom contains six neutrons and five protons. Are they atoms of different elements or isotopes of the same element? Explain your answer.

Math Skills

30. **Calculating** The atomic number for iron is 26. How many neutrons are in the nucleus of an iron atom with a mass number of 57? How many electrons does the iron atom have?

31. **Applying Concepts** If a potassium atom has an atomic number of 19 and a mass number of 39, how many protons, electrons, and neutrons are in the atom?

32. **Applying Concepts** A helium-4 atom has twice as many protons as a hydrogen atom. How many protons and how many neutrons are in the nucleus of a helium-4 atom?

Concepts in Action

33. **Comparing and Contrasting** The compound in blood that carries oxygen to cells throughout the body contains iron. Iron has an atomic number of 26. Iron-59 is used to diagnose disorders in the blood. How is iron-59 different from all other isotopes of iron? How is it the same?

34. **Using Analogies** Scientists working in the field of nanotechnology use either a top-down or bottom-up approach to construct tiny objects. Give an example of a visible structure that was made using the bottom-up approach and one that was made using the top-down approach.

35. **Inferring** If you see a green color when fireworks explode, can you be certain that the fireworks contained a barium compound? Give a reason for your answer.

36. **Relating Cause and Effect** Brightly colored neon lights consist of tubes filled with a gas. When an electric current passes through the tubes, different colors are emitted. Why might you conclude that the tubes in a multicolored display contain more than one element?

37. **Writing in Science** Better technology leads to an increase in scientific knowledge. An increase in knowledge allows for the invention of new technology. Write a paragraph discussing these statements. Use a scanning tunneling microscope as your example.

Performance-Based Assessment

Preparing a Survey Write ten questions you could ask to find out what people know about the modern model of an atom. Figure out the best order for the questions to test someone's knowledge fairly. Be prepared to explain your choices.

Go Online PHSchool.com

For: Self-grading assessment
Visit: PHSchool.com
Web Code: cca-1040

Performance-Based Assessment

Students should ask at least one question about the overall structure of an atom, the properties of subatomic particles, and the behavior of electrons. Students should be able to explain the order they have chosen.

Go Online PHSchool.com

Your students can independently test their knowledge of the chapter and print out their test results for your files.

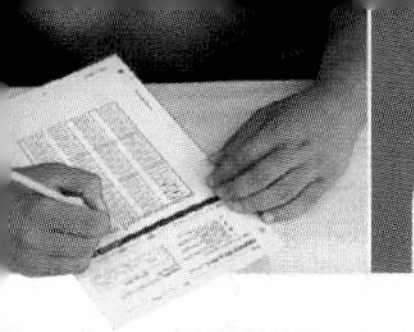

Standardized Test Prep

Test-Taking Tip

Using Data Tables
When presented with a question that is related to a data table, read the title of the table to see what type of data it contains. Then look at the headings of the columns and rows to see how the data are organized. The table below lists properties for subatomic particles. There is a row for each particle and a column for each property. Read the question to find out which data you will need to answer the question. In this case, you will need the data on relative charge.

Properties of Subatomic Particles

Particle	Symbol	Relative Charge	Relative Mass (proton = 1)
Electron	e^-	1−	$\frac{1}{1836}$
Proton	p^+	1+	1
Neutron	n	0	1

Which of the following statements is true?
(A) The charge on a proton is larger than the charge on an electron.
(B) The charge on a proton is smaller than the charge on an electron.
(C) The charge on a proton is identical to the charge on an electron
(D) The charge on a proton is equal in size but opposite to the charge on an electron.
(E) A proton is a neutral particle.

(Answer: D)

Choose the letter that best answers the question or completes the statement.

1. J. J. Thomson demonstrated that electrons
(A) have a negative electric charge.
(B) have a positive electric charge.
(C) are repelled by a positively charged object.
(D) are attracted to a negatively charged object.
(E) do not have an electric charge.

2. According to Dalton's atomic theory, an atom is
(A) made of smaller particles.
(B) a particle with a positive charge.
(C) the smallest particle of an element.
(D) in constant motion.
(E) a particle with a negative charge.

3. Electrons in the first energy level of an atom
(A) have no energy.
(B) have the lowest possible energy.
(C) have the highest possible energy.
(D) are in an excited state.
(E) are in an unstable state.

4. Most alpha particles pass through a thin layer of gold without deflection because gold atoms
(A) are filled with positively charged matter.
(B) have no overall charge.
(C) have a negatively charged nucleus.
(D) do not have a nucleus.
(E) have a dense nucleus surrounded by space.

Use the data table to answer Question 5.

Comparison of Oxygen Isotopes

Property	Oxygen-16	Oxygen-18
Protons	8	8
Neutrons	8	10
Electrons	8	8
Percentage in nature	99.757	0.205

5. What is the mass number of oxygen-18?
(A) 8
(B) 10
(C) 16
(D) 18
(E) 0.205

6. An electron configuration describes
(A) regions of space around the nucleus of an atom.
(B) possible energies that an electron can have.
(C) the arrangement of electrons in an atom.
(D) the emission of light from an excited atom.
(E) the number of possible orbitals in an atom.

Standardized Test Prep

1. A **2.** C **3.** B
4. E **5.** D **6.** C

CHAPTER 5

Planning Guide

Use these planning tools
Easy Planner
Teacher Express

SECTION OBJECTIVES	STANDARDS NATIONAL (See p. T18.)	STANDARDS STATE	ACTIVITIES and LABS
5.1 Organizing the Elements, pp. 126–129 1 block or 2 periods **5.1.1** **Describe** how Mendeleev arranged the elements in his table. **5.1.2** **Explain** how the predictions Mendeleev made and the discovery of new elements demonstrated the usefulness of his periodic table.	A-1, A-2, B-2, G-1, G-2, G-3		**SE** Inquiry Activity: How Much Data Do You Need to Identify a Pattern? p. 125 L2 **SE** Quick Lab: Making a Model of a Periodic Table, p. 128 L2
5.2 Modern Periodic Table, pp. 130–138 1 block or 2 periods **5.2.1** **Describe** the arrangement of elements in the modern periodic table. **5.2.2** **Explain** how the atomic mass of an element is determined and how atomic mass units are defined. **5.2.3** **Identify** general properties of metals, nonmetals, and metalloids. **5.2.4** **Describe** how properties of elements change across a period in the periodic table.	A-1, A-2, B-1, B-2		**SE** Quick Lab: Defining a Metal, p. 135 L2 **SE** Exploration Lab: Predicting the Density of an Element, pp. 150–151 L2 **TE** Teacher Demo: Period 3 Properties, p. 138 L2 **LM** Investigation 5A: Analyzing Patterns in the Periodic Table L2
5.3 Representative Groups, pp. 139–145 1 block or 2 periods **5.3.1** **Relate** the number of valence electrons to groups in the periodic table and to properties of elements in those groups. **5.3.2** **Predict** the reactivity of some elements based on their locations within a group. **5.3.3** **Identify** some properties of common A group elements.	B-1, B-2, B-3, C-1, C-5, F-1, F-3, F-5		**LM** Investigation 5B: Comparing Chemical Properties L1

Ability Levels		Components							
L1	For students who need additional help	SE	Student Edition	RSW	Reading & Study Workbook	CUT	Chapter & Unit Tests	T	Transparencies
L2	For all students	TE	Teacher's Edition	MSPS	Math Skills & Problem Solving Workbook	CTB	Computer Test Bank	iT	Interactive Textbook
L3	For students who need to be challenged	LM	Laboratory Manual			TP	Test Prep Resources	P	Presentation Pro CD-ROM
		PLM	Probeware Lab Manual			DC	Discovery Channel Videotapes & DVDs	GO	Internet Resources

RESOURCES PRINT and TECHNOLOGY		SECTION ASSESSMENT
RSW Section 5.1	L1	SE Section 5.1 Assessment, p. 129 iT Section 5.1
T Chapter 5 Pretest	L2	
Section 5.1	L2	
P Chapter 5 Pretest	L2	
Section 5.1	L2	
SciLinks GO Periodic table	L2	
PLM Lab 2: Predicting the Density of an Element	L2	SE Section 5.2 Assessment, p. 138 iT Section 5.2
RSW Section 5.2	L1	
RSW Math Skill	L2	
T Section 5.2	L2	
P Section 5.2	L2	
SciLinks GO Periodic law	L2	
RSW Section 5.3	L1	SE Section 5.3 Assessment, p. 145 iT Section 5.3
DC You Are What You Eat	L2	
T Section 5.3	L2	
P Section 5.3	L2	
Science News GO Elements	L2	

Go Online

Go online for these Internet resources.

PHSchool.com
Web Code: cca-1050

Science News
Web Code: cce-1053

NSTA SciLinks
Web Code: ccn-1051
Web Code: ccn-1052

Materials for Activities and Labs

Quantities for each group

STUDENT EDITION

Inquiry Activity, p. 125
stapled stack of paper with familiar phrases (some letters replaced with squares)

Quick Lab, p. 128
resealable plastic sandwich bag, different colored paint chip strips

Quick Lab, p. 135
forceps; magnesium; test tubes; test-tube rack; graduated cylinder; 20 mL 2 M HCl; small pieces of sulfur, aluminum, and silicon

Exploration Lab, pp. 150–151
unlined white paper, scissors, metric ruler, balance, forceps, silicon, tin, lead shot, 50-mL graduated cylinder, graph paper, periodic table

TEACHER'S EDITION

Teacher Demo, p. 138
6-volt battery, flashlight bulb with holder, 3 pieces of insulated wire with the ends stripped, 2.5-cm aluminum strip, small silicon chip, 2.5-cm piece of sulfur

Build Science Skills, p. 147
empty containers of fortified food products such as milk, juice, salt, and bread

Chapter Assessment

CHAPTER ASSESSMENT

SE Chapter Assessment, pp. 153–154
CUT Chapter 5 Test A, B
CTB Chapter 5
iT Chapter 5
PHSchool.com GO
Web Code: cca-1050

STANDARDIZED TEST PREP

SE Chapter 5, p. 155
TP Diagnose and Prescribe

Interactive Textbook

Interactive Textbook with assessment at PHSchool.com

CHAPTER 5

Before you teach

From the Author

David Frank
Ferris State University

Big Ideas

The arrangement of elements by atomic number produces a periodic table that reflects the underlying structure of atoms. Elements in a group have similar properties because they have the same number of valence electrons. Thus, the organization of the periodic table demonstrates the usefulness of the atomic theory taught in Chapter 4.

Matter and Change Mendeleev couldn't organize his table by atomic number because the subatomic structure of elements wasn't known in 1869. Instead, he arranged elements by atomic mass. Sometimes he had to violate this organizing principle by placing an element with a larger atomic mass before one with a smaller atomic mass so that elements with similar properties ended up in the same group. Because Mendeleev recognized that the periodic table was based on an actual pattern in nature, he had the confidence to leave blank spaces in his table when the known properties of elements didn't match those of the next available group. He even predicted properties for some missing elements. When germanium and gallium were discovered, their properties were a close match for the properties predicted for eka-silicon and eka-aluminum, which helped demonstrate the predictive power of the periodic law.

In Sections 5.2 and 5.3, specific elements are used to illustrate general trends. Some students may be overwhelmed by the amount of information provided. It is most important for students to know the general properties and locations of metals, nonmetals, and metalloids. Help them focus on the general properties of representative groups (for example, halogens are the most reactive nonmetals) rather than on the individual properties of fluorine, chlorine, and iodine.

Energy Although aluminum is the most abundant metal in Earth's crust, it was not commonly used until the late 1800s. Charles Hall developed an electrolytic process to recover the pure metal from its bauxite ore. Because this process is energy-intensive, recycling of aluminum helps conserve energy.

Chemistry Refresher

Organizing the Elements 5.1

After Lavoisier classified elements into metals, nonmetals, gases and earths in 1789, there were many attempts to find a rational system for organizing the elements. In 1829, Johann Döbereiner proposed a law of triads. A triad is a group of similar elements in which the properties of the middle element fall midway between the properties of the lighter and heavier elements as shown here for the atomic masses of alkali metals. Notice that the atomic mass of sodium (22.990) is close to the arithmetic mean of the atomic masses of lithium and potassium: $(6.941 + 39.098)/2 = 23.02$.

Element	Symbol	Atomic Mass
Lithium	Li	6.941
Sodium	Na	22.990
Potassium	K	39.098

In 1865, John Newlands arranged elements into seven columns in order of increasing atomic mass. The arrangement was inspired by the notes in a Western musical scale. Many modern chemists credit Newlands with the concept of periodicity, which he described in his law of octaves. However, he was not able to develop a useful system from his concept. In 1865, William Odling revised Newlands's system and produced a table that was similar to the one developed by Mendeleev. However, Odling did not explain the relationships shown in his table. In 1870, the German chemist Lothar Meyer published a plot of atomic volume vs. atomic mass, which showed a series of waves with sharp peaks at the beginning of each new period. Meyer is sometimes credited with an independent discovery of the periodic table. When Mendeleev prepared his table, he was not aware of the work of Newlands, Odling, or Meyer.

Address Misconceptions

Students may think that advances in science are always achieved by scientists working alone. They may not realize that most advances are the result of contributions by many scientists. For a strategy to overcome this misconception, see **Address Misconceptions** on **page 129.**

Go Online PDLinks NSTA

For: Teaching methods for the periodic table
Visit: www.SciLinks.org/PDLinks
Web Code: ccn-0599

Metalloids 5.2

Many periodic tables use a diagonal line to divide the metallic and nonmetallic regions of the periodic table. Elements that lie close to the line are described as having properties intermediate to those of metals and nonmetals. Because these borderline elements look like metals, they are often referred to as metalloids even though they do not exhibit all the general properties of metals. There is not universal agreement on which elements to classify as metalloids. Polonium is often classified as a metal and astatine is sometimes classified as a nonmetal. (The classification of metalloids presents similar issues as the classification of colloids—the intermediate category between solutions and suspensions.)

Diagonal Relationships 5.3

Using the first element in a group to refer to the group as a whole, as in The Boron Family, can be misleading because there can be significant differences between the properties of the first element and the properties of the rest of the group. Sometimes the first element has more in common with the second element of the neighboring group than with the second element in its own group. These cross-group relationships are called diagonal relationships. They exist between lithium and magnesium, beryllium and aluminum, and boron and silicon.

1A	2A	3A	4A
Li	Be	B	C
Na	Mg	Al	Si
K	Ca	Ga	Ge

Lithium and magnesium can serve as an example. Lithium is the only alkali metal to react with nitrogen in air to form a nitride. Magnesium reacts with nitrogen in air, too. Lithium carbonate and lithium hydroxide decompose when heated. So do magnesium carbonate and magnesium hydroxide. Carbonates and hydroxides of the other alkali metals are stable when heated. Many lithium compounds are less soluble in water than comparable compounds of other alkali metals. The lithium compounds are similar in solubility to magnesium compounds. Similarities between the chemistry of lithium and magnesium are mainly attributed to the similar sizes of their atoms and ions. (See the table of atomic and ionic radii in the Data Analysis on page 160.)

Build Reading Literacy

KWL (Know-Want-Learned)

What I Know/Want to Know/Learned Strategy To help students access prior knowledge, set a purpose for reading, recall what has been read, and link new information to prior knowledge. The KWL strategy has students create and complete a three-column chart similar to the one below. As students read, they complete the Learned column.

Know	Want to Know	Learned

Finally, students categorize information they learned in a box titled Information I Expect to Use.

Information I Expect to Use

Assign a section in Chapter 5, such as Classes of Elements, pp. 135–136, for students to read. Before they begin, have them create and complete the first two columns of the KWL chart.

Example

1. Draw a three-column KWL chart on the board for students to copy.
2. Have students complete the Know column with facts, examples, and other information they already know about the topic.
3. Tell students to complete the Want to Know column with questions about the topic that they want answers to. Students may scan the section to help them generate questions.
4. Have students read the section to learn more about the topic and determine answers to their questions. As they read, have them note answers in the Learned column, along with other facts, examples, and details they learned.
5. Below their KWL chart, have students draw an Information I Expect to Use box. Have them review the information in the Learned column and use it to complete the box with the useful categories of information.

See p. 144 for a script on how to use the KWL strategy with students. For additional Build Reading Literacy strategies, see pp. 126, 131, 136, and 143.

ASSESS PRIOR KNOWLEDGE

Use the Chapter Pretest below to assess students' prior knowledge. As needed, review these Science Concepts with students.

Review Science Concepts

Section 5.1 Have students recall how symbols are used to represent elements. Have them list examples of physical and chemical properties. Review three clues for recognizing a chemical change (a color change, production of a gas, formation of a precipitate).

Section 5.2 Ask students to recall that the atomic number of an element is the number of protons in an atom of the element and that each element has a different atomic number. Review the concept of isotopes and remind students that isotopes of an element have different numbers of neutrons.

Section 5.3 Have students review energy levels in preparation for a discussion of valence electrons. Ask students what they recall about the reactivity of elements such as oxygen and nitrogen.

CHAPTER

5 The Periodic Table

CONCEPTS in Action

How do science concepts apply to your world? Here are some questions you'll be able to answer after you read this chapter.

- How can a card game be a model for organizing elements? *(Section 5.1)*
- What do a piano keyboard and a periodic table of the elements have in common? *(Section 5.2)*
- Which element makes it possible for plants to capture the energy of sunlight and use it to make sugar? *(Section 5.3)*
- Why are aluminum cans such an important part of recycling programs? *(Section 5.3)*

Discovery CHANNEL SCHOOL

Video Field Trip

You Are What You Eat

- Can an element be both helpful and harmful to the human body? *(page 146)*

1.25
I'm RIPE PLEASE DON'T TOUCH
RASP BERRIES
2.00
PINT

At a farm stand, each product ▶ is displayed in its own bin, just as each element has a specific location in the periodic table.

Chapter Pretest

1. Which of the following is a symbol for an element? *(b)*
   - **a.** Aluminum
   - **b.** Al
   - **c.** al
   - **d.** AL

2. Is flammability a physical property or a chemical property? *(A chemical property)*

3. What happens to the composition of matter during a physical change? *(It remains the same.)*

4. What does the atomic number of an element represent? *(The number of protons in an atom of the element)*

5. Isotopes of an element have different numbers of *(a)*
   - **a.** neutrons.
   - **b.** electrons.
   - **c.** protons.
   - **d.** nuclei.

6. True or False: Electrons in atoms occupy orbitals in energy levels. *(True)*

7. Which element is more reactive, oxygen or nitrogen? *(Oxygen)*

Chapter Preview

Inquiry Activity

How Much Data Do You Need to Identify a Pattern?

Procedure

1. Your teacher will give you a stapled stack of paper. Look at the squares on the top sheet of paper. Try to figure out what familiar phrase you would see if all the squares were filled in. Record your prediction on the sheet.
2. Remove the top sheet and look at the second sheet. Again, try to figure out what letters belong in the squares. Record your prediction.
3. Continue this process until you have looked at all the sheets in the stack.

Think About It

1. **Observing** How did the information on the sheets change as you moved from the top to the bottom of the stack?
2. **Drawing Conclusions** How did the number of letters provided affect your ability to predict the phrase?
3. **Using Analogies** Describe another situation in which having more data makes it easier to recognize a pattern.

$ 2 50
SWEET

Discovery Channel School **Video Field Trip**

You Are What You Eat

Encourage students to view the Video Field Trip "You Are What You Eat."

ENGAGE/EXPLORE

Inquiry Activity

How Much Data Do You Need to Identify a Pattern? L2

Purpose In this activity, students identify a relationship between the amount of data available and the ability to recognize a pattern.

Skills Focus Predicting, Evaluating and Revising

Prep Time 15 minutes

Materials stapled stack of papers

Advance Prep Select a phrase that will be familiar to students. Draw a series of boxes on a sheet of paper to represent the letters of the phrase, leaving spaces between words. Make five copies of this sheet. Fill in two or three letters on the first copy. Add a few letters to each subsequent copy. Plan for two or three blanks on the fifth sheet. Give each student or group a stapled stack arranged in order of completeness with the least complete copy on top.

Class Time 10 minutes

Teaching Tips

- Before distributing the stacks, explain to students that they should not look ahead in the stack. For the activity to be successful, they must work with only one sheet at a time.

Expected Outcome Students' predictions will become increasingly accurate as they progress through the stack.

Think About It

1. There was more information.
2. Increasing the number of letters made it easier to predict the phrase.
3. In the suggested situations, the data must be limited to start. (If students are having trouble thinking of an example, ask what they can tell about a movie from a trailer or about a novel after reading one page.) **Logical**

For Enrichment L3

Use a numerical example to reinforce the need for enough data to reveal a pattern. Ask students to predict the next number in the sequence 3, 5, and 7. *(9)* Then say that the next number is 11. Ask what property the numbers 3, 5, 7, and 11 have in common. *(They are prime numbers.)* **Visual, Logical**

1 FOCUS

Objectives

5.1.1 **Describe** how Mendeleev arranged the elements in his table.

5.1.2 **Explain** how the predictions Mendeleev made and the discovery of new elements demonstrated the usefulness of his periodic table.

Reading Focus

Build Vocabulary L2

Word Forms Use the word *periodical* to help students understand the meaning of *periodic.* Explain that a periodical is published at regular intervals (weekly, monthly, or quarterly).

Reading Strategy L2

a. Mendeleev arranged the elements in order of increasing mass so that elements with similar properties were in the same column. **b.** Mendeleev used the properties of existing elements to predict properties of undiscovered elements. **c.** The close match between Mendeleev's predictions and the actual properties of new elements showed how useful his periodic table could be.

2 INSTRUCT

The Search for Order

Build Reading Literacy L1

Sequence Refer to **page 290D** in **Chapter 10**, which provides the guidelines for a sequence.

Have students create a flowchart showing the sequence of events described in the last two paragraphs on page 126. Ask, **Based on your sequence, what happened after Lavoisier grouped the known elements into four categories?** *(Scientists looked for different ways to classify the elements.)* **Verbal, Portfolio**

5.1 Organizing the Elements

Reading Focus

Key Concepts

- How did Mendeleev organize the elements in his periodic table?
- What evidence helped verify the usefulness of Mendeleev's table?

Vocabulary

- periodic table

Reading Strategy

Identifying Main Ideas Copy the table. As you read, write the main idea for each topic.

Topic	Main Idea
Mendeleev's proposal	a. ?
Mendeleev's prediction	b. ?
Evidence supporting Mendeleev's table	c. ?

In a video store, the latest movies are usually placed on the shelves in alphabetical order. Older movies are grouped into categories such as Action or Comedy. The manager has to choose a set of categories and then place each movie in the most appropriate location.

Scientists faced a similar challenge when they looked for a logical way to organize the elements. They had to decide what categories to use and where to place each element. An organized table of the elements is one of the most useful tools in chemistry. The placement of elements on the table reveals the link between the atomic structure of elements and their properties.

DRAMA
COMEDY

Figure 1 Older movies in video stores are placed into categories such as Drama or Comedy.

The Search for Order

Until 1750, scientists had identified only 17 elements. These were mainly metals, such as copper and iron. The rate of discovery increased rapidly as chemists began to investigate materials in a systematic way. As the number of known elements grew, so did the need to organize them into groups based on their properties.

In 1789, French chemist Antoine Lavoisier (la VWAH zee ay) grouped the known elements into categories he called metals, nonmetals, gases, and earths. For the next 80 years, scientists looked for different ways to classify the elements. But none of their systems provided an organizing principle that worked for all the known elements. A Russian chemist and teacher, Dmitri Mendeleev (Duh MEE tree Men duh LAY uff), would discover such a principle.

Section Resources

Print
- ***Reading and Study Workbook With Math Support,*** Section 5.1
- ***Transparencies,*** Chapter Pretest and Section 5.1

Technology
- ***Interactive Textbook,*** Section 5.1
- ***Presentation Pro CD-ROM,*** Chapter Pretest and Section 5.1
- ***Go Online,*** NSTA SciLinks, Periodic table

Mendeleev's Periodic Table

In the 1860s, Mendeleev was working on a textbook to use with his chemistry students. Because he needed to describe 63 elements, Mendeleev was looking for the best way to organize the information. He found a way to approach the problem while playing his favorite card game, a version of solitaire. In this game, the player sorts a deck of cards by suit and value. To finish the game, the player must end up with four columns, as shown in Figure 2. Each column contains cards of a single suit arranged in order by value.

Figure 2 A deck of cards can be divided into four suits—diamonds, spades, hearts, and clubs. In one version of solitaire, a player must produce an arrangement in which each suit is ordered from ace to king. This arrangement is a model for Mendeleev's periodic table.

Mendeleev's Proposal Mendeleev's strategy for organizing the elements was modeled on the card game. Mendeleev made a "deck of cards" of the elements. On each card, he listed an element's name, mass, and properties. He paid special attention to how each element behaved in reactions with oxygen and hydrogen. When Mendeleev lined up the cards in order of increasing mass, a pattern emerged. The key was to break the elements into rows, as shown in Figure 3.

Mendeleev arranged the elements into rows in order of increasing mass so that elements with similar properties were in the same column. The final arrangement was similar to a winning arrangement in solitaire, except that the columns were organized by properties instead of suits. Within a column, the masses increased from top to bottom. Mendeleev's chart was a periodic table. A **periodic table** is an arrangement of elements in columns, based on a set of properties that repeat from row to row.

Figure 3 This is a copy of a table that Mendeleev published in 1872. He placed the elements in groups based on the compounds they formed with oxygen or hydrogen. **Using Tables** ***How many elements did Mendeleev place in Group II?***

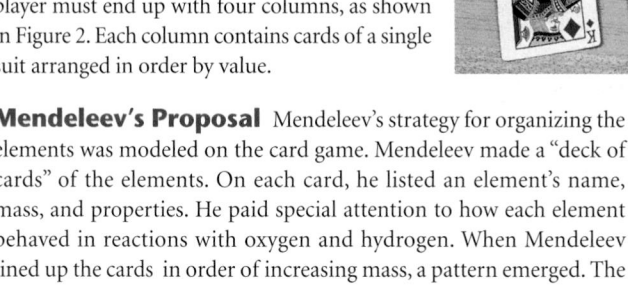

Group I	Group II	Group III	Group IV	Group V	Group VI	Group VII	Group VIII
H = 1							
Li = 7	Be = 9.4	B = 11	C = 12	N = 14	O = 16	F = 19	
Na = 23	Mg = 24	Al = 27.3	Si = 28	P = 31	S = 32	Cl = 35.5	Fe = 56, Co = 59, Ni = 59, Cu = 63.
K = 39	Ca = 40	— = 44	Ti = 48	V = 51	Cr = 52	Mn = 55	
(Cu = 63)	Zn = 65	— = 68	— = 72	As = 75	Se = 78	Br = 80	Ru = 104, Rh = 104, Pd = 106, Ag = 108.
Rb = 85	Sr = 87	Yt = 88	Zr = 90	Nb = 94	Mo = 96	— = 100	
(Ag = 108)	Cd = 112	In = 113	Sn = 118	Sb = 122	Te = 125	I = 127	— — — —
Cs = 133	Ba = 137	Di = 138	Ce = 140	—	—	—	
(—)	—	—	—	—	—	—	Os = 195, Ir = 197, Pt = 198, Au = 199.
—	—	Er = 178	La = 180	Ta = 182	W = 184	—	
(Au = 199)	Hg = 200	Tl = 204	Pb = 207	Bi = 208			
—	—	—	Th = 231	—	U = 240		

Integrate Social Studies **L2**

Lavoisier based his classification of elements on a vast amount of observed data. He used Boyle's definition of an element as a substance that chemists cannot separate into simpler substances. Most of the elements Lavoisier identified *were* elements, but his list did include heat, light, and five oxides that scientists had not been able to decompose. Have students consider what it means to "discover" an element by having them research and compare discovery dates for elements with the dates those elements were first isolated. (For example, beryllium was discovered in 1797, but it was not isolated until 1828.)
Verbal, Interpersonal

Mendeleev's Periodic Table

Use Visuals **L1**

Figure 3 Ask, **How is the table organized?** *(Elements are arranged in order of increasing mass.)* **What do the long dashes represent?** *(They represent undiscovered elements.)* **Why are masses listed with some of the dashes, but not with all of them?** *(Mendeleev was able to predict properties for some unknown elements based on the properties of neighboring elements.)*
Visual, Logical

FYI

In Section 5.1, the term *mass* is used as a shorthand for *atomic mass* because atomic mass is not defined until Section 5.2. Mendeleev was comparing the relative atomic masses of the elements. Mendeleev attended the first international chemistry congress in Karlsruhe in 1860. During that meeting, chemists agreed on a standard method for calculating atomic masses.

Customize for Inclusion Students

Learning Disabled
To reinforce the meaning of the word *periodic*, ask students to think of periodic activities in their own lives. Make a class list of these activities. Organize the list by time interval: daily, weekly, monthly, yearly, and so on. For example, students may have a weekly music lesson or a dance recital every six months. They celebrate a birthday once a year. You may also want to encourage students to think of periodic events that occur less frequently than once a year, for example, the Olympics or presidential elections.

Answer to . . .

Figure 3 *Mendeleev placed eight elements in Group II.*

Quick Lab

Making a Model of a Periodic Table **L2**

Objective
After completing this activity, students will be able to
- organize items in an array based on properties.
- predict where an additional item would fit in an incomplete array.

Skills Focus **Classifying, Inferring, Observing**

Prep Time 20 minutes

Materials resealable plastic sandwich bag, different colored paint chip strips

Advance Prep For each group, collect 4 strips with distinctly different colors. Make sure the color chips are about the same size after you cut off any printing number codes used to identify the shades. Remove one chip from each set. Place each set of chips in a bag.

Class Time 20 minutes

Expected Outcome Students are likely to organize chips of the same color in columns based on the intensity of the shades so that the pattern of colors repeats across the rows.

Analyze and Conclude
1. Students are likely to choose color and shade.
2. Color or intensity of shade repeats across each row.
3. Students should describe the color and approximate shade of the missing chip.
4. Both processes involve selecting properties to organize related items in a repeating pattern and predicting the properties of missing items. However, unlike the periodic table, the order of the columns in the color array can be arbitrary. **Visual, Logical**

Quick Lab

Making a Model of a Periodic Table

Materials
plastic bag containing color chips

Procedure
1. Remove the color chips from the bag and place them on a flat surface, color side up.
2. Identify a property that you can use to divide the chips into groups. Then, identify a second property that you can use to order the chips from top to bottom within a group.
3. Use the properties you chose to arrange the chips into a table with rows and columns. Your teacher deliberately left out a chip from each bag. Decide where to leave a gap in your table for the missing chip.

Analyze and Conclude
1. **Classifying** What property did you use to divide the color chips into groups? What property did you use to arrange the chips within a group from top to bottom?
2. **Making Generalizations** What pattern repeats across each row of your table?
3. **Predicting** Based on its location on your table, describe the missing chip.
4. **Comparing and Contrasting** Compare the process you used to construct your table to the process Mendeleev used to make his table. Describe similarities and differences.

Mendeleev's Prediction Mendeleev could not make a complete table of the elements because many elements had not yet been discovered. He had to leave spaces in his table for those elements. For example, Mendeleev placed bromine (Br) in Group VII because bromine and chlorine (Cl) have similar properties. This placement left four spaces in row 4 between zinc (Zn) and bromine. Mendeleev had only two elements, arsenic and selenium, to fill those spaces, based on their masses. He placed arsenic and selenium in the columns where they fit best and left gaps in the columns labeled Groups III and IV.

Mendeleev was not the first to arrange elements in a periodic table. He was not even the first to leave spaces in a periodic table for missing elements. But he was able to offer the best explanation for how the properties of an element were related to its location in his table.

An excellent test for the correctness of a scientific model, such as Mendeleev's table, is whether the model can be used to make accurate predictions. Mendeleev was confident that the gaps in his table would be filled by new elements. He used the properties of elements located near the blank spaces in his table to predict properties for undiscovered elements. Some scientists didn't accept these predictions. Others used the predictions to help in their search for undiscovered elements.

Reading Checkpoint *Why did Mendeleev place bromine in Group VII of his periodic table?*

Go Online NSTA SCI LINKS
For: Links to periodic table
Visit: www.SciLinks.org
Web Code: ccn-1051

Facts and Figures

Recognizing a Pattern Actions Mendeleev took while developing his table show that he realized the table represented a fundamental pattern in nature. First, he left gaps in the table for undiscovered elements. Second, he sometimes ignored accepted knowledge. For example, Berzelius had reported a formula of Be_2O_3 for beryllium oxide, which (if true) would mean that beryllium belonged in the third column. But, Mendeleev used beryllium to fill a space in the second column. Third, Mendeleev did not place all elements in order by atomic mass. He placed tellurium before iodine even though tellurium has a larger atomic mass.

Go Online NSTA SCI LINKS

Download a worksheet on the periodic table for students to complete, and find additional teacher support from NSTA SciLinks.

128 Chapter 5

Evidence Supporting Mendeleev's Table

Mendeleev named missing elements after elements in the same group. He gave the name eka-aluminum to the element that belonged one space below aluminum on the table. (*Eka* is a Sanskrit word meaning "one.") Mendeleev predicted that eka-aluminum would be a soft metal with a low melting point and a density of 5.9 g/cm^3.

In 1875, a French chemist discovered a new element. He named the element gallium (Ga) in honor of France. (The Latin name for France is *Gallia*.) Gallium is a soft metal with a melting point of 29.7°C and a density of 5.91 g/cm^3. Figure 4 shows a sample of gallium and a traffic signal that uses gallium compounds.

The properties of gallium are remarkably similar to the predicted properties of eka-aluminum. Scientists concluded that gallium and eka-aluminum are the same element. **The close match between Mendeleev's predictions and the actual properties of new elements showed how useful his periodic table could be.** The discovery of scandium (Sc) in 1879 and the discovery of germanium (Ge) in 1886 provided more evidence. With the periodic table, chemists could do more than predict the properties of new elements. They could explain the chemical behavior of different groups of elements.

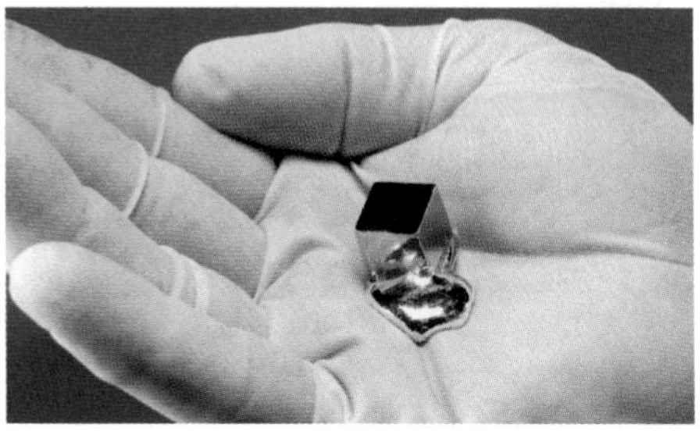

Figure 4 Gallium was discovered in 1875. Heat from a person's hand can melt gallium. In some traffic signals, there are tiny light emitting diodes (LEDs) that contain a compound of gallium. **Comparing and Contrasting** ***How does the melting point of gallium (29.7°C) compare to room temperature (about 25°C)?***

Section 5.1 Assessment

Reviewing Concepts

1. Describe how Mendeleev organized the elements into rows and columns in his periodic table.
2. How did the discovery of new elements such as gallium demonstrate the usefulness of Mendeleev's table?
3. Scientists before Mendeleev had proposed ways to organize the elements. Why were Mendeleev's efforts more successful?
4. What characteristic of solitaire did Mendeleev use as a model for his periodic table?
5. Why did Mendeleev leave spaces in his table?
6. In general, how can a scientist test the correctness of a scientific model?

Critical Thinking

7. **Inferring** Explain why it would not have been possible for a scientist in 1750 to develop a table like Mendeleev's.
8. **Predicting** How was Mendeleev able to predict the properties of elements that had not yet been discovered?

Writing in Science

Writing to Persuade Write a paragraph about Mendeleev's periodic table. Use the paragraph to convince a reader that the periodic table is extremely useful to scientists. (*Hint:* Use specific facts to support your argument.)

Section 5.1 Assessment

1. Mendeleev arranged the elements in rows in order of increasing mass so that elements with similar properties were in the same column.
2. The close match between Mendeleev's predictions and the actual properties of new elements showed how useful his periodic table could be.
3. Mendeleev provided an organizing principle that worked for all of the known elements.
4. In solitaire, cards are arranged into categories called suits and ordered by value.
5. In order to place elements with similar properties in the same column, Mendeleev needed to leave spaces for undiscovered elements.
6. The scientist tests whether the model can be used to make accurate predictions.
7. With only 17 known elements to work with, the scientist would not have had enough data.
8. Mendeleev based his predictions on the properties of nearby elements and other elements in the same column.

Address Misconceptions L2

Students may think that advances in science are always achieved by scientists working alone. They should realize that most advances are the result of many scientists working on different aspects of a problem. To help students overcome this misconception, have them research the Nobel Laureates in Chemistry and note how many times the prize was shared. Students could also look at the lists of authors in scientific journals.
Logical

FYI

The initial value reported for the density of gallium was 4.7 g/cm^3, but additional tests showed it to be 5.9 g/cm^3.

3 ASSESS

Evaluate Understanding L2

Assign each student to one of the four pages in Section 5.1. Have students write a review question related to the content of their assigned page. Invite students to take turns posing their questions to the class. Continue until everyone has had a turn, or until the questions become repetitive.

Reteach L1

Use Figure 3 to review Mendeleev's strategy for arranging the elements into rows and columns to form a periodic table.

Writing in Science

The paragraph should include information on how Mendeleev organized his table, why he left gaps in the table, the predictions he made based on the table, and how the discovery of gallium demonstrated the usefulness of the table.

Interactive Textbook If your class subscribes to the Interactive Textbook, use it to review key concepts in Section 5.1

Answer to . . .

Figure 4 *The melting point of gallium is slightly higher than room temperature.*

Reading Checkpoint *Mendeleev placed bromine in Group VII because bromine and chlorine have similar properties.*

1 FOCUS

Objectives

5.2.1 **Describe** the arrangement of elements in the modern periodic table.

5.2.2 **Explain** how the atomic mass of an element is determined and how atomic mass units are defined.

5.2.3 **Identify** general properties of metals, nonmetals, and metalloids.

5.2.4 **Describe** how properties of elements change across a period in the periodic table.

Reading Focus

Build Vocabulary L2

Vocabulary Knowledge Rating Chart Have students construct a chart with four columns labeled Term, Can Define or Use It, Heard or Seen It, and Don't Know. Have students copy the terms *period, group, periodic law, atomic mass unit, metals, transition metals, nonmetals,* and *metalloids* into column 1 and rate their term knowledge by putting a check in one of the other columns. Ask how many students actually know each term. Have them share their knowledge. Ask focused questions to help students predict text content based on the term, thus enabling them to have a purpose for reading. After students have read the section, have them rate their knowledge again.

Reading Strategy L2

a. and b. Students might ask the meaning of the term *atomic mass,* why two series of elements are placed below the main body of the table, why there are two numbering systems for the columns, or why Period 7 is incomplete. *(Student answers will vary depending on questions asked.)*

5.2 The Modern Periodic Table

Reading Focus

Key Concepts

- How is the modern periodic table organized?
- What does the atomic mass of an element depend on?
- What categories are used to classify elements on the periodic table?
- How do properties vary across a period in the periodic table?

Vocabulary

- period
- group
- periodic law
- atomic mass unit (amu)
- metals
- transition metals
- nonmetals
- metalloids

Reading Strategy

Previewing Copy the table below. Before you read, write two questions about the periodic table on pages 132 and 133. As you read, write answers to your questions.

Questions About the Periodic Table	
Question	**Answer**
a. ?	b. ?
c. ?	d. ?

Figure 5 shows a synthesizer keyboard with labels for the notes that correspond to the white keys. If you strike the key labeled middle C and then play the white keys in order from left to right, you will hear the familiar do-re-mi-fa-sol-la-ti scale. The next white note is a C that is an octave above middle C. An octave is the interval between any two notes with the same name. (The prefix *octa-* means "eight.") Because the scale repeats at regular eight-note intervals, the scale is an example of a periodic pattern.

The sounds of musical notes that are separated by an octave are related, but they are not identical. In a similar way, elements in the same column of the periodic table are related because their properties repeat at regular intervals. But elements in different rows are not identical. You can use the modern periodic table of elements to classify elements and to compare their properties.

G A B C D E F G A B
Middle C
D E F G A B C D E F

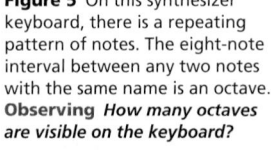

Figure 5 On this synthesizer keyboard, there is a repeating pattern of notes. The eight-note interval between any two notes with the same name is an octave. **Observing** *How many octaves are visible on the keyboard?*

Section Resources

Print
- ***Laboratory Manual,*** Investigation 5A
- ***Reading and Study Workbook With Math Support,*** Section 5.2 and **Math Skill:** Calculating Average Atomic Mass
- ***Transparencies,*** Section 5.2

Technology
- ***Probeware Lab Manual,*** Lab 2
- ***Interactive Textbook,*** Section 5.2
- ***Presentation Pro CD-ROM,*** Section 5.2
- ***Go Online,*** NSTA SciLinks, Periodic law

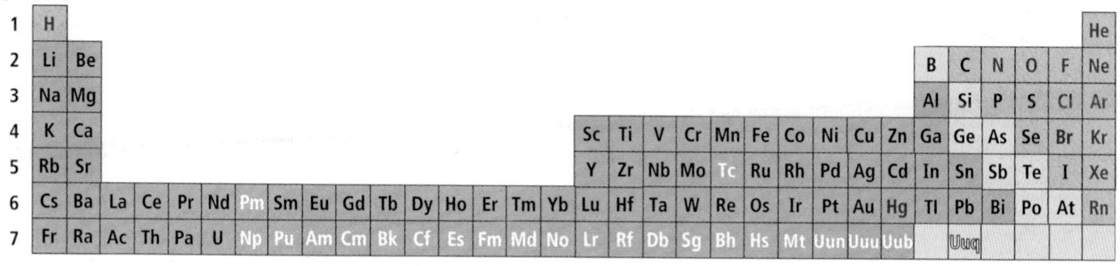
1 H He
2 Li Be B C N O F Ne
3 Na Mg Al Si P S Cl Ar
4 K Ca Sc Ti V Cr Mn Fe Co Ni Cu Zn Ga Ge As Se Br Kr
5 Rb Sr Y Zr Nb Mo Tc Ru Rh Pd Ag Cd In Sn Sb Te I Xe
6 Cs Ba La Ce Pr Nd Pm Sm Eu Gd Tb Dy Ho Er Tm Yb Lu Hf Ta W Re Os Ir Pt Au Hg Tl Pb Bi Po At Rn
7 Fr Ra Ac Th Pa U Np Pu Am Cm Bk Cf Es Fm Md No Lr Rf Db Sg Bh Hs Mt Uun Uuu Uub Uuq

Figure 6 This diagram shows one way to display a periodic table of the elements. There are 7 rows, or periods, in the table. There are 32 columns, or groups, in the table. **Comparing and Contrasting** ***Compare the numbers of elements in periods 1, 3, and 5.***

The Periodic Law

Mendeleev developed his periodic table before the discovery of protons. He did not know that all atoms of an element have the same number of protons. He did not know that atoms of two different elements could not have the same number of protons. **In the modern periodic table, elements are arranged by increasing atomic number (number of protons).** Figure 6 shows one way the known elements can be arranged in order by increasing atomic number.

Periods Each row in the table of elements in Figure 6 is a **period.** Period 1 has 2 elements. Periods 2 and 3 have 8 elements. Periods 4 and 5 have 18 elements. Period 6 has 32 elements. The number of elements per period varies because the number of available orbitals increases from energy level to energy level.

To understand the structure of the table, think about what happens as the atomic number increases. The first energy level has only one orbital. The one electron in a hydrogen atom and the two electrons in a helium atom can fit in this orbital. But one of the three electrons in a lithium atom must be in the second energy level. That is why lithium is the first element in Period 2. Sodium, the first element in Period 3, has one electron in its third energy level. Potassium, the first element in Period 4, has one electron in its fourth energy level. This pattern applies to all the elements in the first column on the table.

Groups Each column on the periodic table is called a **group.** The elements within a group have similar properties. **Properties of elements repeat in a predictable way when atomic numbers are used to arrange elements into groups.** The elements in a group have similar electron configurations. An element's electron configuration determines its chemical properties. Therefore, members of a group in the periodic table have similar chemical properties. This pattern of repeating properties is the **periodic law.**

Look at Figure 7 on pages 132 and 133. There are 18 groups in this periodic table. Some elements from Periods 6 and 7 have been placed below Period 7 so that the table is more compact.

Go Online NSTA SCiLINKS

For: Links on periodic law
Visit: www.SciLinks.org
Web Code: ccn-1052

2 INSTRUCT

The Periodic Law

Build Reading Literacy L1

Preview Refer to **page 36D** in **Chapter 2**, which provides the guidelines for using a preview strategy.

Have students preview the section (pp. 130–138), focusing their attention on headings, visuals, and boldfaced material. Ask, **Based on your preview, which figure in the section contains the most information?** *(Figure 7 on pp. 132–133)* **Based on your preview, name three classes of elements.** *(Metals, nonmetals, and metalloids)*
Visual, Verbal

Build Science Skills L2

Using Tables and Graphs Use the data in Figure 7 to show the advantage of arranging elements by atomic number instead of atomic mass. Make a large graph with atomic number on the horizontal axis and atomic mass on the vertical axis for elements 1 through 20. Draw straight lines between the points. Ask, **What does the graph show about the general relationship between atomic number and atomic mass?** *(As the atomic number increases, so does the atomic mass.)* **Are there any points on the graph that do not follow the pattern?** *(Yes, the atomic mass of element 18, argon, is greater than the atomic mass of element 19, potassium.)* Point out that arranging the elements strictly by increasing atomic mass would result in some elements with unlike properties being grouped together.
Visual, Logical

Go Online NSTA SCiLINKS

Download a worksheet on the periodic law for students to complete, and find additional teacher support from NSTA SciLinks.

Customize for English Language Learners

Simplify the Presentation
Tailor your teaching presentation of the section content to the less proficient English skills of your students. Do this by speaking directly and simplifying the words and sentence structures used to explain the material. For example, split a cause-and-effect sentence into two sentences labeled Cause and Effect. Use visual aids. For example, use the keyboard in Figure 5 to explain the interval of an octave. Use body language when appropriate to emphasize important words. For example, use a horizontal gesture when discussing periods and rows. Use a vertical gesture when describing groups and columns.

Answer to . . .

Figure 5 *3 octaves*

Figure 6 *There are 2 elements in Period 1, 8 in Period 3, and 18 in Period 5.*

Use Visuals **L1**

Figure 7 Begin by having students compare the layouts in Figures 6 and 7. Ask, **What is the major difference in the layouts?** *(Some elements from Periods 6 and 7 have been placed below the table.)* **How are the layouts alike?** *(Elements are arranged in order by atomic number. Elements with similar properties are in the same group and properties repeat in a predictable way from period to period.)* Return to Figure 7 when atomic masses are discussed on p. 134, and when ways to classify elements on the periodic table are introduced on p. 135. (The table shows two classification systems: the 1–18 numbering system approved by the International Union of Pure and Applied Chemistry (IUPAC), and a system in which two sets of groups numbered 1–8 are distinguished by A and B labels. Unless students ask, you may want to let students wonder about the A and B classification system, which will be addressed in the introduction to Section 5.3.)
Visual, Logical

FYI

Placement of the lanthanides and actinides below the main body of the table also serves to emphasize the similarities among these elements related to their electron configurations.

Periodic Table of the Elements

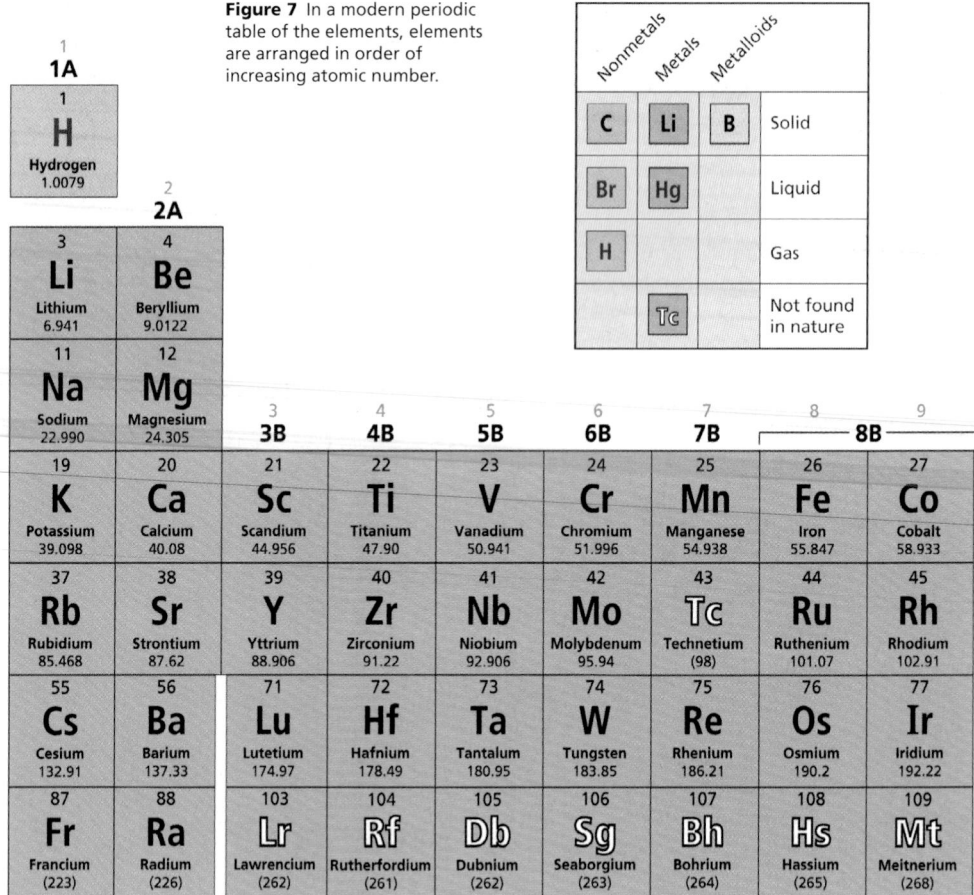

Figure 7 In a modern periodic table of the elements, elements are arranged in order of increasing atomic number.

	Nonmetals	Metals	Metalloids
Solid	C	Li	B
Liquid	Br	Hg	
Gas	H		
Not found in nature		Tc	

1 1A	2 2A	3 3B	4 4B	5 5B	6 6B	7 7B	8 8B	9 8B
1 H Hydrogen 1.0079								
3 Li Lithium 6.941	4 Be Beryllium 9.0122							
11 Na Sodium 22.990	12 Mg Magnesium 24.305							
19 K Potassium 39.098	20 Ca Calcium 40.08	21 Sc Scandium 44.956	22 Ti Titanium 47.90	23 V Vanadium 50.941	24 Cr Chromium 51.996	25 Mn Manganese 54.938	26 Fe Iron 55.847	27 Co Cobalt 58.933
37 Rb Rubidium 85.468	38 Sr Strontium 87.62	39 Y Yttrium 88.906	40 Zr Zirconium 91.22	41 Nb Niobium 92.906	42 Mo Molybdenum 95.94	43 Tc Technetium (98)	44 Ru Ruthenium 101.07	45 Rh Rhodium 102.91
55 Cs Cesium 132.91	56 Ba Barium 137.33	71 Lu Lutetium 174.97	72 Hf Hafnium 178.49	73 Ta Tantalum 180.95	74 W Tungsten 183.85	75 Re Rhenium 186.21	76 Os Osmium 190.2	77 Ir Iridium 192.22
87 Fr Francium (223)	88 Ra Radium (226)	103 Lr Lawrencium (262)	104 Rf Rutherfordium (261)	105 Db Dubnium (262)	106 Sg Seaborgium (263)	107 Bh Bohrium (264)	108 Hs Hassium (265)	109 Mt Meitnerium (268)

Lanthanide Series

57 La Lanthanum 138.91	58 Ce Cerium 140.12	59 Pr Praseodymium 140.91	60 Nd Neodymium 144.24	61 Pm Promethium (145)	62 Sm Samarium 150.4

Actinide Series

89 Ac Actinium (227)	90 Th Thorium 232.04	91 Pa Protactinium 231.04	92 U Uranium 238.03	93 Np Neptunium (237)	94 Pu Plutonium (244)

Atomic number	6
Element symbol	C
Element name	Carbon
Atomic mass	12.011

10	11 1B	12 2B	13 3A	14 4A	15 5A	16 6A	17 7A	18 8A
								2 He Helium 4.0026
			5 B Boron 10.81	6 C Carbon 12.011	7 N Nitrogen 14.007	8 O Oxygen 15.999	9 F Fluorine 18.998	10 Ne Neon 20.179
			13 Al Aluminum 26.982	14 Si Silicon 28.086	15 P Phosphorus 30.974	16 S Sulfur 32.06	17 Cl Chlorine 35.453	18 Ar Argon 39.948
28 Ni Nickel 58.71	29 Cu Copper 63.546	30 Zn Zinc 65.38	31 Ga Gallium 69.72	32 Ge Germanium 72.59	33 As Arsenic 74.922	34 Se Selenium 78.96	35 Br Bromine 79.904	36 Kr Krypton 83.80
46 Pd Palladium 106.4	47 Ag Silver 107.87	48 Cd Cadmium 112.41	49 In Indium 114.82	50 Sn Tin 118.69	51 Sb Antimony 121.75	52 Te Tellurium 127.60	53 I Iodine 126.90	54 Xe Xenon 131.30
78 Pt Platinum 195.09	79 Au Gold 196.97	80 Hg Mercury 200.59	81 Tl Thallium 204.37	82 Pb Lead 207.2	83 Bi Bismuth 208.98	84 Po Polonium (209)	85 At Astatine (210)	86 Rn Radon (222)
110 *Uun Ununnilium (269)	111 *Uuu Unununium (272)	112 *Uub Ununbium (277)		114 *Uuq Ununquadium				

*Name not officially assigned.

63 Eu Europium 151.96	64 Gd Gadolinium 157.25	65 Tb Terbium 158.93	66 Dy Dysprosium 162.50	67 Ho Holmium 164.93	68 Er Erbium 167.26	69 Tm Thulium 168.93	70 Yb Ytterbium 173.04
95 Am Americium (243)	96 Cm Curium (247)	97 Bk Berkelium (247)	98 Cf Californium (251)	99 Es Einsteinium (252)	100 Fm Fermium (257)	101 Md Mendelevium (258)	102 No Nobelium (259)

Integrate Language Arts L2

Elements 110, 111, 112, and 114 have not been named yet. Scientists can propose names for new elements, but the International Union of Pure and Applied Chemistry has final approval. Until new elements receive official names, chemists refer to them by their Latin-based atomic numbers. For example, element 114 is called ununquadium, Latin for one-one-four. Increase students' familiarity with the periodic table by having them identify some of the strategies used to name elements (scientists, geographic locations, mythological characters).
Verbal, Portfolio

Build Science Skills L2

Comparing and Contrasting For this activity, use a periodic table displayed in the classroom, or make copies of a periodic table that is a few years old to distribute to students. To illustrate the dynamic nature of science, have students compare Figure 7 to the older periodic table. Ask, **What differences do you notice between the two periodic tables?** *(Depending on when the older table was printed, the number of elements may vary and some elements in Period 7 may not have assigned names. Some values for atomic mass are likely to vary. A periodic table may include electron configurations for each element.)* Make a list of responses on the board. Then ask, **How will the periodic table change in the future?** *(Unnamed elements will be assigned official names and more elements may be discovered.)*
Visual, Verbal, Group

FYI

Although plutonium is classified as a synthetic element, traces of plutonium isotopes Pu-238 and Pu-239 appear at low concentrations (about one part per 1011) in pitchblende, a uranium ore. In 1971, Darlene Hoffman, a scientist at Los Alamos National Laboratory, discovered traces of Pu-244 in Precambrian rocks. Because this isotope has a half-life of about 82 million years, it probably existed when Earth formed.

Atomic Mass

Address Misconceptions L2

Students may not realize that all atoms of an element are isotopes. In other words, students may think that there is one "regular" atom and several variations called isotopes. Explain that a sample of an element found in nature contains a mixture of the different isotopes of that element. The symbols on the periodic table represent "average" atoms of elements. In fact, atoms with the atomic masses listed on the table do not exist. For example, there are no carbon atoms with an atomic mass of 12.011 amu. This value is a weighted average of the atomic masses of stable carbon isotopes. The value is close to the assigned value for carbon-12 because about 99% of a carbon sample is carbon-12 atoms.
Verbal, Logical

FYI

An atomic mass given in parentheses in Figure 7 is the mass number of the longest-lived isotope of an element that has no stable isotopes and for which the abundance of isotopes in nature shows great variability (or a complete absence in the case of technetium or promethium). Technetium and promethium have been detected in the spectra of stars.

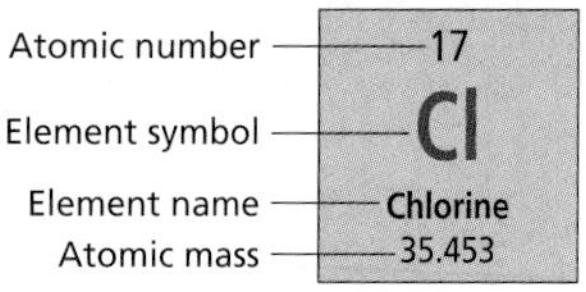
Atomic number
17
Element symbol
Cl
Element name
Chlorine
Atomic mass
35.453

Figure 8 This box provides four pieces of information about the element chlorine: its symbol, its name, its atomic number, and its atomic mass.

Atomic Mass

There are four pieces of information for each element in Figure 7: the name of the element, its symbol, its atomic number and its atomic mass. **Atomic mass is a value that depends on the distribution of an element's isotopes in nature and the masses of those isotopes.** You will use atomic masses when you study chemical reactions in Chapter 7.

Atomic Mass Units The mass of an atom in grams is extremely small and not very useful because the samples of matter that scientists work with contain trillions of atoms. In order to have a convenient way to compare the masses of atoms, scientists chose one isotope to serve as a standard. Recall that each isotope of an element has a different number of neutrons in the nuclei of its atoms. So the atoms of two isotopes have different masses.

Scientists assigned 12 atomic mass units to the carbon-12 atom, which has 6 protons and 6 neutrons. An **atomic mass unit** (amu) is defined as one twelfth the mass of a carbon-12 atom.

Isotopes of Chlorine In nature, most elements exist as a mixture of two or more isotopes. Figure 8 shows that the element chlorine has the symbol Cl, atomic number 17, and an atomic mass of 35.453 atomic mass units. (The unit for atomic mass is not listed in the periodic table, but it is understood to be the amu.) Where does the number 35.453 come from? There are two natural isotopes of chlorine, chlorine-35 and chlorine-37. An atom of chlorine-35 has 17 protons and 18 neutrons. An atom of chlorine-37 has 17 protons and 20 neutrons. So the mass of an atom of chlorine-37 is greater than the mass of an atom of chlorine-35.

Weighted Averages Your teacher may use a weighted average to determine your grade. In a weighted average, some values are more important than other values. For example, test scores may count more heavily toward your final grade than grades on quizzes or grades on homework assignments.

Figure 9 lists the atomic masses for two naturally occurring chlorine isotopes. If you add the atomic masses of the isotopes and divide by 2, you get 35.967, not 35.453. The value of the atomic mass for chlorine in the periodic table is a weighted average. The isotope that occurs in nature about 75% of the time (chlorine-35) contributes three times as much to the average as the isotope that occurs in nature about 25% of the time (chlorine-37).

Distribution of Chlorine Isotopes in Nature

Isotope	Percentage	Atomic Mass
Chlorine-35	75.78%	34.969
Chlorine-37	24.22%	36.966

Figure 9 This table shows the distribution and atomic masses for the two natural isotopes of chlorine. **Using Tables** *Which isotope occurs more often in nature?*

Reading Checkpoint *What is an atomic mass unit?*

Facts and Figures

Atomic Mass Units From the mid-1800s to 1960, oxygen was the standard for atomic masses. (Oxygen was likely chosen because it forms compounds with many elements.) After the discovery of isotopes, physicists and chemists began to use different standards. Physicists assigned the value 16.000 amu exclusively to oxygen-16. Other oxygen isotopes had different values. Chemists continued to use 16.000 amu as the average for all oxygen atoms. Although the differences between the standards were small, the situation was potentially confusing.

In 1961, chemists and physicists agreed on a unified standard based on the carbon-12 isotope, which is assigned a value of 12.000 amu. (Although the SI abbreviation for atomic mass unit was changed to u for unified when scientists adopted the unified atomic mass unit, the amu notation is still widely used.)

Classes of Elements

The periodic table in Figure 7 presents three different ways to classify elements. First, elements are classified as solids, liquids, or gases, based on their states at room temperature. The symbols for solids are black. The symbols for liquids are purple. The symbols for gases are red.

Second, elements are divided into those that occur naturally and those that do not. All but two elements with atomic numbers 1 through 92 occur on Earth. Elements with atomic numbers of 93 and higher do not occur naturally. The symbols for these elements are white. In Chapter 10, you will find out how elements that do not occur in nature are produced.

The third classification system puts elements into categories based on their general properties. **Elements are classified as metals, nonmetals, and metalloids.** In the periodic table, metals are located on the left, nonmetals are on the right, and metalloids are in between.

Metals The majority of the elements on the periodic table are classified as metals. In Figure 7, they are represented by blue boxes. **Metals** are elements that are good conductors of electric current and heat. Except for mercury, metals are solids at room temperature. Most metals are malleable. Many metals are ductile; that is, they can be drawn into thin wires.

Some metals are extremely reactive and some do not react easily. One way to demonstrate this difference is to compare the behavior of gold and the behavior of magnesium when these metals are exposed to the oxygen in air. Gold remains shiny because it does not react with the oxygen. Magnesium reacts with the oxygen and quickly dulls. Figure 10A shows one magnesium coil that is dull and one that is shiny. Figure 10B shows one use for a metal with a shiny surface.

Quick Lab

Defining a Metal

Procedure

1. Use forceps to put a piece of magnesium into a test tube in a test tube rack. Using a graduated cylinder, add 5 mL of hydrochloric acid to the test tube. **CAUTION** *Wear plastic gloves because the acid can burn skin or clothing.* Record your observations.
2. Repeat Step 1 with sulfur, aluminum, and silicon.

Analyze and Conclude

1. **Classifying** Based on their locations in the periodic table, classify the four elements as metals, metalloids, or nonmetals.
2. **Comparing and Contrasting** Compare the behavior of the metals with the acid to the behavior of the other elements with the acid.
3. **Forming Operational Definitions** Use your observations to write a definition of a metal.

A

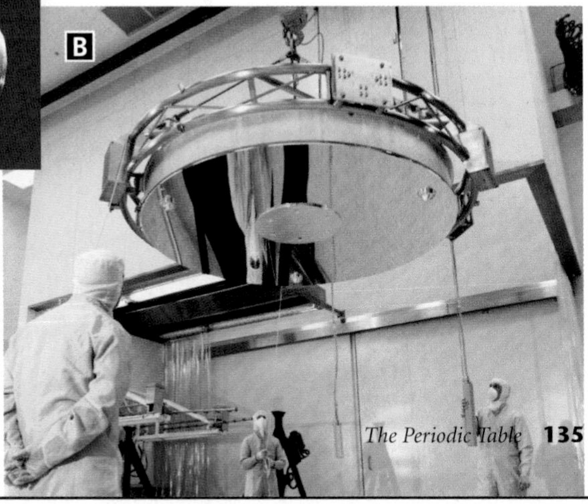
B

Figure 10 Magnesium and aluminum are typical metals. **A** When magnesium reacts with oxygen, a dull layer forms on its surface. The layer can be removed to reveal magnesium's shiny surface. **B** Many telescope mirrors are coated with aluminum to produce a surface that reflects light extremely well.

The Periodic Table **135**

Classes of Elements

Quick Lab

Defining a Metal L2

Objective
After completing this activity, students will be able to
- use a chemical property to distinguish metals.

Skills Focus Forming Operational Definitions

Prep Time 20 minutes

Materials forceps; magnesium; test tubes; test-tube rack; graduated cylinder; 20 mL 2 M HCl; small pieces of sulfur, aluminum, and silicon

Advance Prep Prepare 1 L of 2 M HCl: add 200 mL of 10 M HCl to a 1-L volumetric flask containing 750 mL of water and swirl gently to mix. Add water to bring the volume to 1 L. **CAUTION** *Wear safety goggles, a lab apron, and neoprene gloves.* Use concentrated HCl in a fume hood or other well-ventilated area. Never add water to acid.
Polish the magnesium lightly with steel wool to remove any magnesium oxide.

Class Time 20 minutes

Safety Remind students to use care in adding the acid and to rinse any acid off skin or clothing with water. **CAUTION** *The reaction of Mg in HCl will make the test tube hot.* Keep spill-control materials (baking soda or citric acid) nearby to clean up spills. Repeat as necessary to remove all acid contamination. Elemental sulfur may emit H_2S when dispersed in HCl. Test the sulfur beforehand in a fume hood or other well-ventilated area. Supply silicon as chips, not in powdered form, which is flammable. Neutralize the acid solutions with baking soda and wash them down the drain with excess water.

Teaching Tips
- Caution students not to get fingerprints on the Mg and Al samples.
- The complete reaction of Al and HCl will require more than 45 minutes. However, the results after 15 minutes will indicate how the materials react.

Expected Outcome

Element	Observation
Magnesium	Bubbles, test tube becomes hot, reaction complete in about 30 seconds, final solution clear.
Sulfur	No visible reaction
Aluminum	Slight bubbling in 5 minutes, test tube becomes warm after about 15 minutes, final mixture slightly cloudy with powdery gray precipitate.
Silicon	No visible reaction

Analyze and Conclude
1. Aluminum and magnesium are metals. Sulfur is a nonmetal and silicon is a metalloid.
2. Only the metals react with the acid.
3. A metal is a substance that reacts with HCl.
Logical

Answer to . . .

Figure 9 *Chlorine-35*

Reading Checkpoint *One-twelfth the mass of a carbon-12 atom*

Integrate Health L2

People who work under fluorescent lights or spend a lot of time viewing a computer screen sometimes choose pink lenses. Athletes participating in high-speed winter sports often use pink lenses because they help to increase contrast and depth perception when the available light is limited. Gray lenses are very common; they reduce the amount of light without changing its color. Have students research situations in which lenses with colors other than pink are used.
Verbal, Portfolio

Build Reading Literacy L1

Summarize Refer to **page 598D** in **Chapter 20**, which provides the guidelines for summarizing.

Have students write a summary of the text on pp. 135–136. Summaries should include information about each of the vocabulary terms on these pages. Ask, **Based on your summary, which class of elements has properties that fall between the properties of two other classes of elements?** *(Metalloids)*
Verbal, Portfolio

FYI

The important role metalloids play as semiconductors is addressed in Chapter 6.

The metals in groups 3 through 12 are called transition metals. **Transition metals** are elements that form a bridge between the elements on the left and right sides of the table. Transition elements, such as copper and silver, were among the first elements discovered. One property of many transition metals is their ability to form compounds with distinctive colors. The How It Works box on page 137 describes the use of transition elements in the production of colored glass.

Some transition elements have more properties in common than elements in other groups. This is especially true of elements in the lanthanide and actinide series. These elements are so similar that chemists in the 1800s had difficulty separating them when they were found mixed together in nature. A compound of erbium and oxygen was used to tint the lenses shown in Figure 11.

Figure 11 A compound of erbium (Er) and oxygen is used to tint glass pink.

Nonmetals In Figure 7, nonmetals are represented by yellow boxes. As their name implies, nonmetals generally have properties opposite to those of metals. **Nonmetals** are elements that are poor conductors of heat and electric current. Because nonmetals have low boiling points, many nonmetals are gases at room temperature. In fact, all the gases in the periodic table are nonmetals. The nonmetals that are solids at room temperature tend to be brittle. If they are hit with a hammer, they shatter or crumble.

Nonmetals vary as much in their chemical properties as they do in their physical properties. Some nonmetals are extremely reactive, some hardly react at all, and some fall somewhere in between. Fluorine in Group 17 is the most reactive nonmetal. It even forms compounds with some gases in Group 18, which are the least reactive elements in the table. The toothpaste in Figure 12 contains a compound of the nonmetal fluorine and the metal sodium. This compound helps to protect your teeth against decay.

Figure 12 Toothpaste contains a compound that helps to protect teeth from tooth decay. The compound is formed from the nonmetal fluorine and the metal sodium.

Metalloids In the periodic table in Figure 7, metalloids are represented by green boxes. **Metalloids** are elements with properties that fall between those of metals and nonmetals. For example, metals are good conductors of electric current and nonmetals are poor conductors of electric current. A metalloid's ability to conduct electric current varies with temperature. Pure silicon (Si) and germanium (Ge) are good insulators at low temperatures and good conductors at high temperatures.

Reading Checkpoint *Which type of metals tend to form compounds with distinctive colors?*

Facts and Figures

Fluoride in Toothpaste According to FDA regulations, toothpaste can contain sodium fluoride, sodium monofluorophosphate, or stannous fluoride at concentrations of 850 to 1150 ppm total fluorine. A package of toothpaste sold commercially cannot contain more than 276 mg of fluorine. Because too much fluoride can have adverse affects on health, people should rinse away excess toothpaste. There must be a warning on toothpaste packages to keep the product out of the reach of children under 6 years of age. Young children need to be supervised when they brush their teeth until they have learned how to minimize ingestion of the toothpaste.

HOW It Works

Making Glass

For more than 4500 years, people have made glass from sand. The float-glass process shown below is used to make large sheets of glass for windows, while molds are used to make glass bottles. **Interpreting Diagrams** ***How is air used in making glass bottles?***

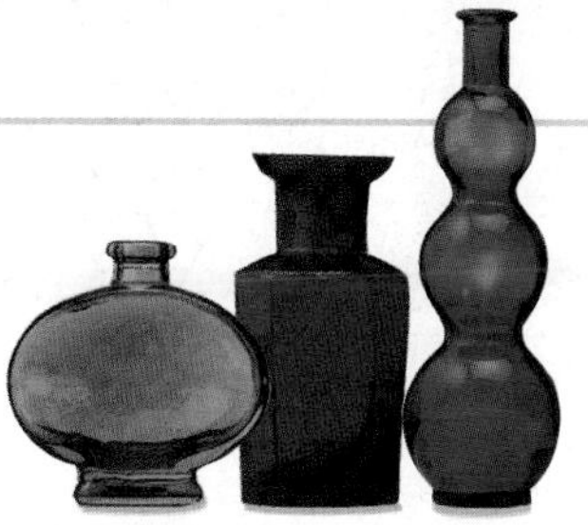

Colored glass
Metallic elements are mixed with the raw ingredients to produce colored glass. Iron or chromium is added for green, copper or gold for red, and cobalt for blue.

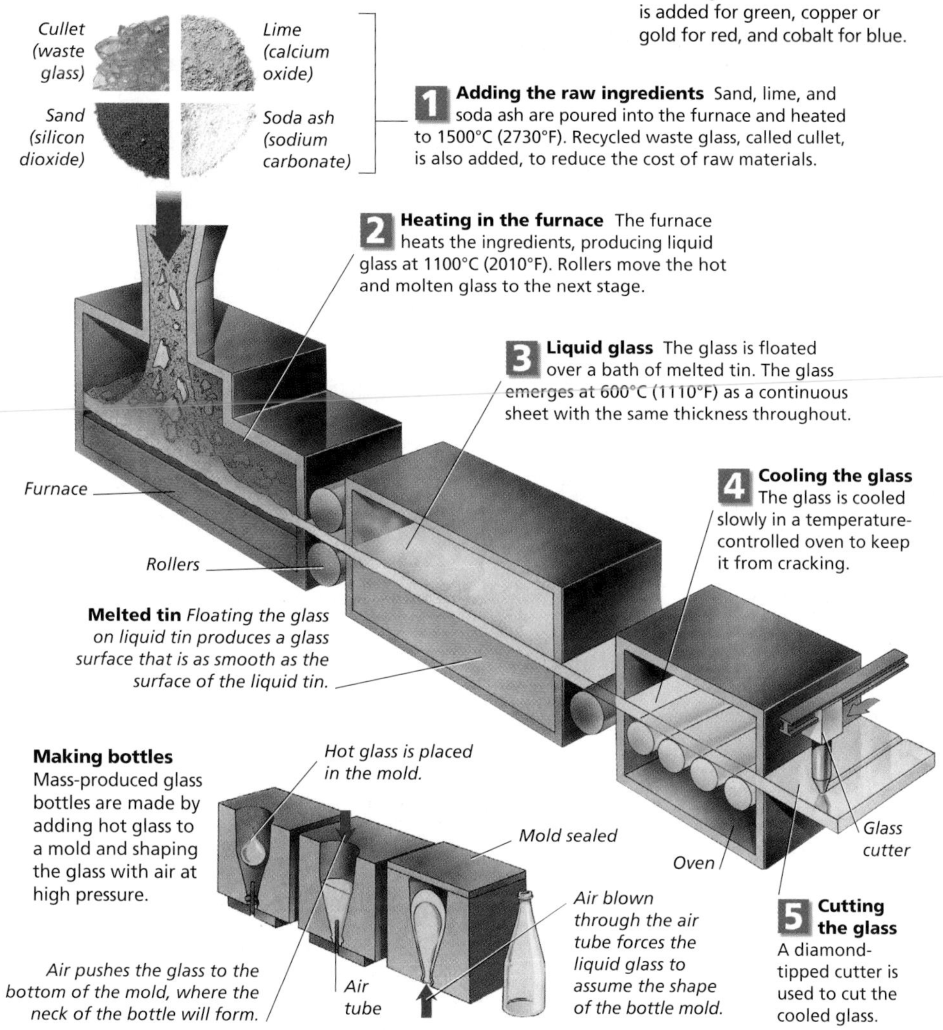
Cullet (waste glass)
Lime (calcium oxide)
Sand (silicon dioxide)
Soda ash (sodium carbonate)
1 Adding the raw ingredients Sand, lime, and soda ash are poured into the furnace and heated to 1500°C (2730°F). Recycled waste glass, called cullet, is also added, to reduce the cost of raw materials.
2 Heating in the furnace The furnace heats the ingredients, producing liquid glass at 1100°C (2010°F). Rollers move the hot and molten glass to the next stage.
3 Liquid glass The glass is floated over a bath of melted tin. The glass emerges at 600°C (1110°F) as a continuous sheet with the same thickness throughout.
4 Cooling the glass The glass is cooled slowly in a temperature-controlled oven to keep it from cracking.
Furnace
Rollers
Melted tin Floating the glass on liquid tin produces a glass surface that is as smooth as the surface of the liquid tin.
Making bottles Mass-produced glass bottles are made by adding hot glass to a mold and shaping the glass with air at high pressure.
Hot glass is placed in the mold.
Mold sealed
Oven
Glass cutter
Air blown through the air tube forces the liquid glass to assume the shape of the bottle mold.
5 Cutting the glass A diamond-tipped cutter is used to cut the cooled glass.
Air pushes the glass to the bottom of the mold, where the neck of the bottle will form.
Air tube

HOW It Works

Making Glass L2

Float-glass plants are among the largest buildings in the world. Giant bins hold the raw materials for making glass. Huge roof ventilators and stacks release the intense heat needed to produce the liquid glass. The glassmaking operation is continuous, with the fires burning constantly. Often a glass plant will produce various tints of glass that are used in different applications.

Interpreting Diagrams Air at high pressure is used to force the liquid glass to take the shape of the mold.
Visual, Verbal

For Enrichment L3

Interested students can research and report on the work of glassblowers and compare their techniques for shaping glass with the molding process that is described on p. 137. Have students use the library to find books, magazine articles, and videos to help in their research.
Verbal, Portfolio

FYI

Tell students that showing the raw ingredients of glass as four equal segments of a pie is not meant to reflect their actual percentages in the mixture. Adding soda ash saves energy because sodium carbonate lowers the melting temperature of the mixture. Running the glass over rollers instead of the molten tin produces an uneven surface.

Answer to . . .

Reading Checkpoint *Transition metals*

Variation Across a Period

Teacher Demo

Period 3 Properties — L2

Purpose Students observe differences in electrical conductivity among three Period 3 elements.

Materials 6-volt battery, flashlight bulb with holder, 3 pieces of insulated wire with the ends stripped, 2.5-cm aluminum strip, small silicon chip, 2.5-cm piece of sulfur

Advance Prep Use the battery, flashlight bulb with holder, and the wires to make an open circuit.

Procedure Touch the free ends of the two wires to each end of the aluminum strip. Have students observe the bulb. Repeat for silicon and sulfur.

Expected Outcome The material used to complete the circuit determines the brightness of the light. For aluminum, the bulb is bright; for silicon, the bulb is dim; for sulfur, the bulb does not light. Students should conclude that the Period 3 elements become less metallic from left to right across the period.
Visual, Logical

3 ASSESS

Evaluate Understanding — L2

Ask students to identify the general properties of metals, nonmetals, and metalloids.

Reteach — L1

Use Figure 13 to illustrate how the properties of elements change from left to right across a period in the periodic table.

Writing in Science

Student answers should reflect the fact that all the isotopes of an atom occupy the same place on the periodic table, despite their different mass numbers.

Interactive Textbook If your class subscribes to the Interactive Textbook, use it to review key concepts in Section 5.2.

Answer to . . .

Figure 13 *Chlorine*

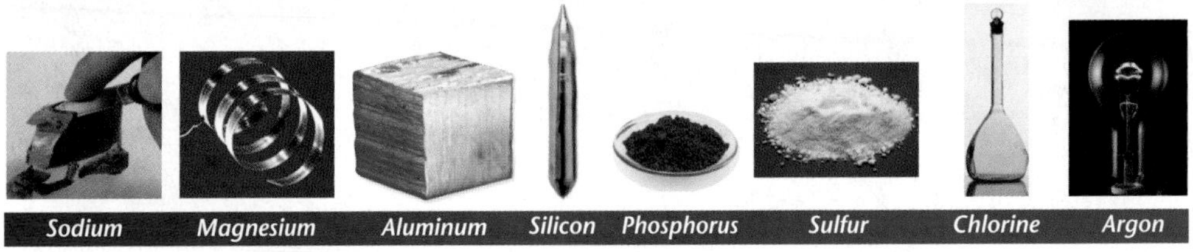
Sodium
Magnesium
Aluminum
Silicon
Phosphorus
Sulfur
Chlorine
Argon

Figure 13 From left to right across Period 3, there are three metals (Na, Mg, and Al), one metalloid (Si), and four nonmetals (P, S, Cl, and Ar). Many light bulbs are filled with argon gas. **Observing** *Which other element in Period 3 is a gas?*

Variation Across a Period

The properties within a period change in a similar way from left to right across the table, except for Period 1. **Across a period from left to right, the elements become less metallic and more nonmetallic in their properties.** The most reactive metals are on the left side of the table. The most reactive nonmetals are on the right in Group 17. The Period 3 elements shown in Figure 13 provide an example of this trend.

There are three metals, a metalloid, and four nonmetals in Period 3. If you were unwise enough to hold a piece of sodium in your hand, it would react quickly and violently with the water on your moist skin. But magnesium will not react with water unless the water is hot. Aluminum does not react with water, but it does react with oxygen.

Silicon is the least reactive element in Period 3 (except for argon). Under ordinary conditions, phosphorus and sulfur do not react with water, but they do react with oxygen. They also react with chlorine, which is a highly reactive nonmetal. Chlorine must be handled with as much care as sodium. Argon hardly reacts at all.

Section 5.2 Assessment

Reviewing Concepts

1. What determines the order of the elements in the modern periodic table?
2. Describe the periodic law.
3. What two factors determine the atomic mass of an element?
4. Name three categories that are used to classify the elements in the periodic table.
5. What major change occurs as you move from left to right across the periodic table?

Critical Thinking

6. **Formulating Hypotheses** The atomic mass of iodine (I) is less than the atomic mass of tellurium (Te). But an iodine atom has one more proton than a tellurium atom. Explain how this situation is possible.
7. **Applying Concepts** Explain how you know that no new element with an atomic number less than 100 will be discovered.
8. **Comparing and Contrasting** Compare the reactions with water of the elements sodium and magnesium.

Writing in Science

Explanatory Paragraph The word *isotope* comes from the Greek words *isos,* meaning "equal," and *topos,* meaning "place." Write a paragraph explaining how the isotopes chlorine-35 and chlorine-37 occupy the same place in the periodic table.

Section 5.2 Assessment

1. In the modern periodic table, elements are arranged by increasing atomic number.
2. Properties of elements repeat in a predictable way when atomic numbers are used to arrange elements into groups.
3. Atomic mass is a value that depends on the distribution of an element's isotopes in nature and the masses of those isotopes.
4. Metals, nonmetals, and metalloids
5. The elements become less metallic and more nonmetallic in their properties.
6. Answers may include that the tellurium isotopes that are most abundant have many neutrons in their nuclei or that all tellurium atoms have more neutrons than iodine atoms.
7. The atomic number of an element corresponds to the number of protons in the element's atoms. The atomic number must be a whole number. All the places between 1 and 100 are already filled with existing elements.
8. Sodium reacts quickly and violently with water at room temperature. Magnesium will not react unless the water is hot.

5.3 Representative Groups

Reading Focus

Key Concepts

- Why do the elements in a group have similar properties?
- What are some properties of the A groups in the periodic table?

Vocabulary

- valence electron
- alkali metals
- alkaline earth metals
- halogens
- noble gases

Reading Strategy

Monitoring Your Understanding Copy the table below. As you read, record an important fact about each element listed.

Element	Important Fact
Magnesium	a. ?
Aluminum	b. ?
Chlorine	c. ?

Why is hydrogen located on the left side of the periodic table with the active metals? It is a nonmetal gas that seems to have more in common with the nonmetals in Group 17. Hydrogen's location is related to its electron configuration, not its properties.

Valence Electrons

Did you wonder why there are two numbering schemes on the periodic table in Figure 7? When the A groups are numbered from 1 through 8, they provide a useful reminder about the electron configurations of the elements in those groups. The number of an A group matches the number of valence electrons in an electron configuration for an element in that group. A **valence electron** is an electron that is in the highest occupied energy level of an atom. These electrons play a key role in chemical reactions. Properties vary across a period because the number of valence electrons increases from left to right.

Elements in a group have similar properties because they have the same number of valence electrons. These properties will not be identical because the valence electrons are in different energy levels. Valence electrons explain the location of hydrogen. Because hydrogen has a single valence electron, it is grouped with other elements, such as lithium, that have only one valence electron.

Figure 14 Because hydrogen is flammable, it can be used as a fuel in automobiles like this one. An engine that burns hydrogen has a key advantage over an engine that burns gasoline. Only water is produced when hydrogen burns.

Section Resources

Print

- ***Laboratory Manual,*** Investigation 5B
- ***Reading and Study Workbook With Math Support,*** Section 5.3
- ***Transparencies,*** Section 5.3

Technology

- ***Interactive Textbook,*** Section 5.3
- ***Presentation Pro CD-ROM,*** Section 5.3
- ***Go Online,*** *Science News,* Elements

Section 5.3

1 FOCUS

Objectives

5.3.1 **Relate** the number of valence electrons to groups in the periodic table and to properties of elements in those groups.

5.3.2 **Predict** the reactivity of some elements based on their locations within a group.

5.3.3 **Identify** some properties of common A group elements.

Reading Focus

Build Vocabulary L2

Concept Map Have students construct a concept map with eight branches and title it Groups in the Periodic Table. As students read, they can add the names of groups to each branch, the group's number of valence electrons, elements in the group, and some properties of these elements.

Reading Strategy L2

Possible answers: **a.** Magnesium plays a key role in the production of sugar in plants. Mixtures of magnesium and other metals can be as strong as steel, but much lighter. **b.** Aluminum is the most abundant metal in Earth's crust. Much less energy is needed to purify recycled aluminum than to extract aluminum from bauxite. **c.** Chlorine is a highly reactive, nonmetal gas that is used to kill bacteria in water.

2 INSTRUCT

Valence Electrons

Integrate Space Science L2

Hydrogen exhibits metallic properties under extreme conditions. Scientists have theorized for decades that metallic hydrogen exists in the core of planets such as Jupiter. Interior pressure on Jupiter is millions of times greater than the pressure at the surface of Earth. At this pressure, electrons flow easily between hydrogen molecules. Have students do research and write a paragraph that compares and contrasts the cores of Jupiter and Earth, according to the current state of scientific knowledge.

Verbal, Portfolio

The Alkali Metals

Use Visuals L1

Figure 15 Ask students to study the two photos and the column of elements in Figure 15. Ask, **What properties of sodium are shown in the photos?** *(Sodium is a soft solid at room temperature with a metallic luster when first exposed to air. Sodium is extremely reactive and it reacts violently with water to form hydrogen gas.)* Point out to students that the reactivity of the alkali metals increases from the top of the group to the bottom. Ask, **Which alkali metals are less reactive than cesium but more reactive than lithium?** *(Sodium, potassium, and rubidium)*
Visual, Logical

Build Science Skills L2

Communicating Results Explain to students that Robert Bunsen and Gustav Kirchoff discovered cesium in 1840 and rubidium in 1841 by burning the substances and observing the color of the flames. Have students research the origin of the terms *cesium* and *rubidium.* Have students explain why these names are appropriate. *(Cesium comes from the Latin word* caesium, *which means "heavenly blue." Rubidium comes from the Latin word* rubidus, *which means "dark red." The names describe the colors of light emitted when the elements are burned.)*
Logical

FYI

Francium has been described as the most unstable element among the first 103 elements. Its longest-lived isotope, francium-223, has a half-life of only 22 minutes. The estimate is that there is only about one ounce of francium on Earth at any moment.

Go Online SCIENCE NEWS

Science News provides students with current information on elements.

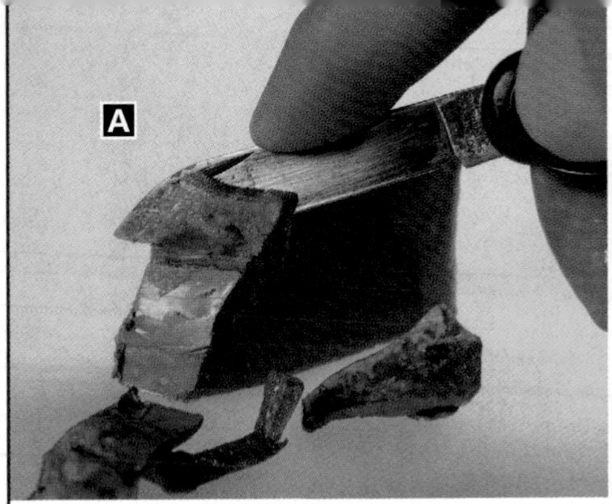
A

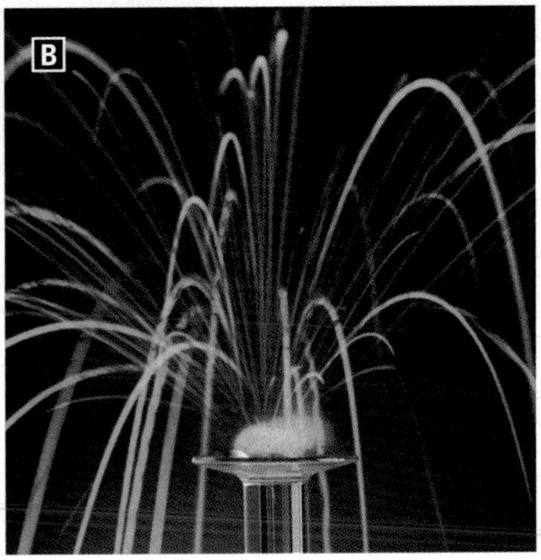
B

Group 1A

3	Li	Lithium
11	Na	Sodium
19	K	Potassium
37	Rb	Rubidium
55	Cs	Cesium
87	Fr	Francium

Figure 15 The element sodium is an alkali metal **A** Unlike most metals, sodium is soft enough to cut with a knife. **B** When sodium reacts with water, enough energy is released to ignite the hydrogen that is produced. **Predicting** *What happens when potassium comes in contact with water?*

The Alkali Metals

The elements in Group 1A are called **alkali metals.** These metals have a single valence electron and are extremely reactive. Because they are so reactive, alkali metals are found in nature only in compounds. The most familiar of these compounds is table salt—a compound of sodium and chlorine (sodium chloride). Sodium chloride can be obtained through the evaporation of seawater or from large salt deposits on the surface of Earth or underground.

Not all the elements in a group are equally reactive. Sodium is more reactive than lithium, potassium is more reactive than sodium, and rubidium is more reactive than potassium. **The reactivity of alkali metals increases from the top of Group 1A to the bottom.**

Sodium is about as hard as cold butter and can be cut with a sharp knife, as shown in Figure 15A. Sodium melts at about 98°C and has a lower density than water. A piece of sodium may be able to float on water, but Figure 15B shows that it won't be there for long. The sodium reacts violently with water and releases enough energy to ignite the hydrogen gas that is produced. Sodium and potassium are stored under oil to keep them from reacting with the oxygen and water vapor in air. Cesium is so reactive that it reacts with water at temperatures as low as −115°C. Cesium is usually stored in a sealed glass tube containing argon gas.

Go Online SCIENCE NEWS
For: Articles on elements
Visit: PHSchool.com
Web Code: cce-1053

Reading Checkpoint *How many valence electrons does an alkali metal have?*

Customize for English Language Learners

Compare/Contrast Chart
After students have read about Groups 1A and 2A, create a chart on the board with the title Alkali Metals vs. Alkaline Earth Metals. Separate the chart into two columns labeled Similarities and Differences. Ask for student responses to help you fill in the chart. After all correct answers have been recorded, keep the chart displayed as a reference for students.

The Alkaline Earth Metals

The elements in Group 2A are called **alkaline earth metals.** All alkaline earth metals have two valence electrons. Metals in Group 2A are harder than metals in Group 1A. The melting point of magnesium is 650°C, which is much higher than the melting point of sodium—98°C.

Differences in reactivity among the alkaline earth metals are shown by the ways they react with water. Calcium, strontium, and barium react easily with cold water. Magnesium will react with hot water, but no change appears to occur when beryllium is added to water. Magnesium and calcium have essential biological functions and they provide materials used in construction and transportation.

Group 2A
4 **Be** Beryllium
12 **Mg** Magnesium
20 **Ca** Calcium
38 **Sr** Strontium
56 **Ba** Barium
88 **Ra** Radium

Magnesium Magnesium plays a key role in the process that uses sunlight to produce sugar in plants like the one in Figure 16. The compound at the center of this process is chlorophyll (KLAWR uh fil), and at the center of chlorophyll is magnesium. A mixture of magnesium and other metals can be as strong as steel, but much lighter. Reducing overall mass without sacrificing strength is an important consideration in transportation. The frames of bicycles and backpacks often contain magnesium.

Calcium Your body needs calcium to keep your bones and teeth strong. Calcium carbonate—a compound of calcium, carbon, and oxygen—is the main ingredient in chalk, limestone, coral, and the pearl in Figure 16. Your toothpaste may contain the compound calcium carbonate because this hard substance can polish your teeth. The plaster cast in Figure 16 contains calcium sulfate, which is a compound of calcium, sulfur, and oxygen.

Figure 16 Chlorophyll molecules in spinach contain magnesium. An oyster shell and a pearl are both made from calcium carbonate. A plaster cast contains the compound calcium sulfate.

Spinach plant

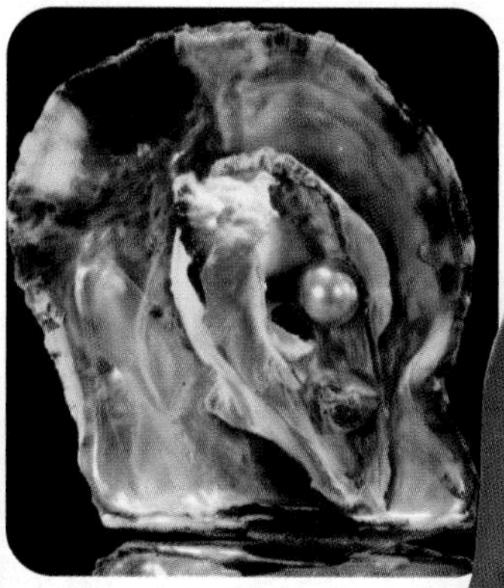

Oyster shell with pearl

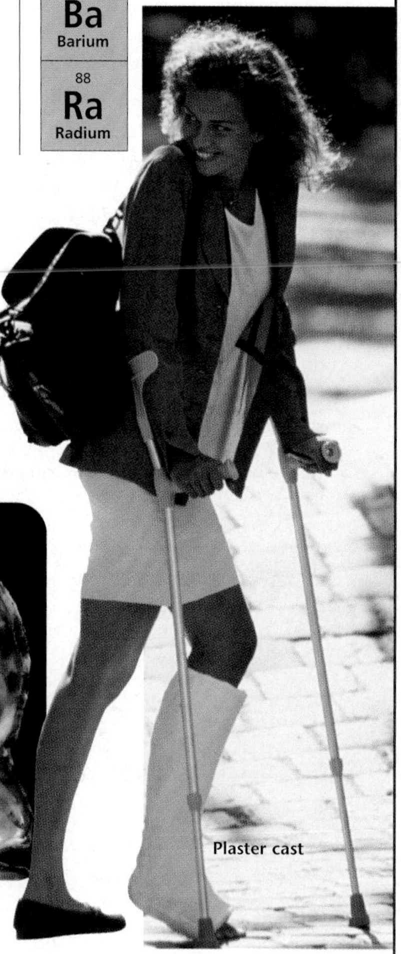

Plaster cast

The Alkaline Earth Metals

FYI

The mineral gypsum is heated to produce a white powdery substance called plaster of Paris. When water is added to plaster of Paris, heat is released as the plaster quickly hardens. During the process, the plaster expands by about 0.3–0.6%. A plaster cast is often replaced by a sturdier, more lightweight fiberglass cast after the swelling around an injury subsides.

Egyptians used plaster to join blocks of stone in pyramids. Romans made plaster casts of Greek statues. In the 1700s, wooden houses in Paris were often covered in plaster to protect against fire. This measure was taken in response to the destruction of London by fire in 1666.

Answer to . . .

Figure 15 *When potassium reacts with water, enough energy is released to ignite the hydrogen that is produced.*

Reading Checkpoint *An alkali metal has one valence electron.*

The Boron Family

Use Community Resources **L2**

Invite a representative from a community recycling program or a commercial recycler to speak to your class about the importance of recycling materials such as aluminum. Have students ask questions about the kinds of materials that are recycled and how the recycling process is different for each of them. They may also ask how recycling has changed over the past 10 years and what changes are expected in the future.
Interpersonal, Portfolio

The Carbon Family

Integrate Math **L2**

Tell students that silicon dioxide is the most abundant substance in Earth's crust. It is, of course, a compound of the elements silicon and oxygen. Point out to students that only eight elements make up 98.5% of Earth's crust: oxygen (46.6%), silicon (27.7%), aluminum (8.1%), iron (5.0%), calcium (3.6%), sodium (2.8%), potassium (2.6%), and magnesium (2.1%). Have students work in pairs to create a circle graph that shows this data. Remind students that they may need to combine some elements under a category labeled Other. If students need help constructing a circle graph, you may want to refer them to the **Math Skills** in the **Skills and Reference Handbook** at the end of the student text.
Visual, Logical

The Boron Family

Group 3A contains the metalloid boron, the well-known metal aluminum, and three less familiar metals (gallium, indium, and thallium). All these elements have three valence electrons.

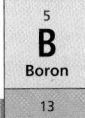

Aluminum is the most abundant metal in Earth's crust. It is often found combined with oxygen in a mineral called bauxite (BAWKS eyet). Aluminum is less reactive than sodium and magnesium. It is strong, lightweight, malleable, and a good conductor of electric current.

More than 10 percent of the aluminum produced is used as packaging. Some aluminum is used in window screens, window frames, and gutters. Parts of cars and airplanes are also made from aluminum. People are encouraged to recycle aluminum because the energy needed to purify recycled aluminum is only about 5 percent of the energy needed to extract aluminum from bauxite.

A compound of boron, silicon, and oxygen is used to make a type of glass that does not shatter easily when it undergoes a rapid change in temperature. Glass that contains boron is used to make laboratory glassware, such as the flasks in Figure 17. It is also used in cookware that can go directly from the oven to the refrigerator.

Figure 17 These students are using flasks made from glass that contains boron. This type of glass does not shatter as easily as glass without boron.

Group 3A

5	B	Boron
13	Al	Aluminum
31	Ga	Gallium
49	In	Indium
81	Tl	Thallium

Group 4A

6	C	Carbon
14	Si	Silicon
32	Ge	Germanium
50	Sn	Tin
82	Pb	Lead

Figure 18 The clay used to make this pottery contains compounds called silicates. These compounds always contain silicon and oxygen. They usually contain aluminum and often contain other elements such as iron.

The Carbon Family

Group 4A contains a nonmetal (carbon), two metalloids (silicon and germanium), and two metals (tin and lead). Each of these elements has four valence electrons. Notice that the metallic nature of the elements increases from top to bottom within the group. In keeping with this trend, germanium is a better conductor of electric current than silicon.

Life on Earth would not exist without carbon. **Except for water, most of the compounds in your body contain carbon.** Reactions that occur in the cells of your body are controlled by carbon compounds. Carbon and its compounds are discussed in Chapter 9, Carbon Chemistry.

Silicon is the second most abundant element in Earth's crust. It is found as silicon dioxide in quartz rocks, sand, and glass. The clay used to produce the pottery in Figure 18 contains silicon compounds called silicates. Silicon carbide, a compound of silicon and carbon, is extremely hard. Saw blades tipped with silicon carbide last many times longer than ordinary steel blades.

Reading Checkpoint *Which Group 3A element is a nonmetal?*

The Nitrogen Family

Group 5A contains two nonmetals (nitrogen and phosphorus), two metalloids (arsenic and antimony), and one metal (bismuth). Like the groups on either side of it, Group 5A includes elements with a wide range of physical properties. Nitrogen is a nonmetal gas, phosphorus is a solid nonmetal, and bismuth is a dense metal. Despite their differences, all the elements in Group 5A have five valence electrons. Nitrogen and phosphorus are the most important elements in Group 5A.

When air is cooled, the oxygen condenses before the nitrogen because nitrogen has a lower boiling point than oxygen. Much of the nitrogen obtained from air is used to produce fertilizers, like the three shown in Figure 19. **Besides nitrogen, fertilizers often contain phosphorus.** Your body uses compounds containing nitrogen and phosphorus to control reactions and release energy from food.

Phosphorus exists as an element in several forms with different properties. White phosphorus is so reactive that it bursts into flame when it is in contact with oxygen. Red phosphorus is less reactive and is used to make matches ignite.

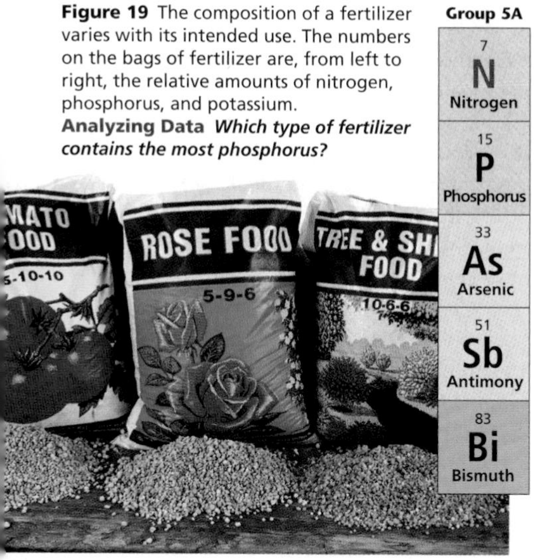

Group 5A
7
N
Nitrogen
15
P
Phosphorus
33
As
Arsenic
51
Sb
Antimony
83
Bi
Bismuth
ROSE FOOD
5-9-6
TREE & SH
FOOD
10-6-6
5-10-10

Figure 19 The composition of a fertilizer varies with its intended use. The numbers on the bags of fertilizer are, from left to right, the relative amounts of nitrogen, phosphorus, and potassium.
Analyzing Data *Which type of fertilizer contains the most phosphorus?*

Group 6A
8
O
Oxygen
16
S
Sulfur
34
Se
Selenium
52
Te
Tellurium
84
Po
Polonium

Figure 20 Sulfur is often found in nature in its elemental form—not combined with other elements.
Inferring *What does this information tell you about the reactivity of sulfur?*

The Oxygen Family

Group 6A has three nonmetals (oxygen, sulfur, and selenium), and two metalloids (tellurium and polonium). All the elements in Group 6A have six valence electrons.

Oxygen is the most abundant element in Earth's crust. Complex forms of life need oxygen to stay alive because oxygen is used to release the energy stored in food. Oxygen can be stored as a liquid under pressure in oxygen tanks. There must be no sparks or flames near an oxygen tank because materials that are flammable burn easily in pure oxygen.

Ozone is another form of the element oxygen. At ground level, ozone can irritate your eyes and lungs. At upper levels of the atmosphere, ozone absorbs harmful radiation emitted by the sun.

Sulfur was one of the first elements to be discovered because it is found in large natural deposits like the one in Figure 20. The main use of sulfur is in the production of sulfuric acid, a compound of sulfur, hydrogen, and oxygen. More sulfuric acid is produced in the United States than any other chemical. About 65 percent of the sulfuric acid produced is used to make fertilizers.

The Nitrogen Family

Build Reading Literacy L1

Identify Main Idea/Details Refer to **page 98D** in **Chapter 4**, which provides the guidelines for identifying main ideas and details.

Guide students in applying this strategy to the text on page 143. Tell students to look for the main idea of each paragraph and then list one or two supporting details. If the paragraph has no topic sentence, have students list two important facts from the paragraph.
Verbal, Portfolio

FYI

Of the 18 elements essential for plant growth, nitrogen, phosphorus, and potassium are most likely to be lacking. The numbers on the fertilizer packages shown in Figure 19 represent percent N, percent P_2O_5, and percent K_2O. (In the past, oxides were often used as standards for chemical comparisons.) Nitrogen and phosphorus are often present as nitrates and phosphates.

The Oxygen Family

Address Misconceptions L2

Students may think that the air they breathe is pure oxygen. Challenge this misconception by reminding students that air is a mixture of gases. Air is 78% nitrogen and 21% oxygen. Have students research what gases make up the remaining 1% of air. *(Answers should include carbon dioxide, water vapor, argon, and other noble gases.)*
Logical

Facts and Figures

Phosphorus The element phosphorus has 10 forms, which are usually grouped as white, red, and black phosphorus for simplicity. The white phosphorus forms are the least stable.

In 1680, Robert Boyle demonstrated that phosphorus ignited by friction could be used to light wooden splints that had been dipped in sulfur. There are two types of matches. In a strike-anywhere match, all of the required ingredients (often phosphorus sulfide and potassium chlorate) are in the match head. In a safety match, the ingredients are divided between the match head and a rough striking surface on the side of the matchbox. A safety match can be lit only when the tip is drawn across the striking surface, which contains phosphorus sulfide.

Answer to . . .

Figure 19 *Tomato food*

Figure 20 *Sulfur is not highly reactive under ordinary conditions.*

Reading Checkpoint *Carbon*

The Halogens

Build Reading Literacy L1

KWL Refer to **page 124D** in this chapter, which provides the guidelines for KWL (Know/Want to Know/Learned).

Teach this independent study skill as a whole-class exercise. **1.** Draw a three-column KWL chart on the board for students to copy. **2.** Have students complete the Know column with facts, examples, and other information that they already know about the Group 7A elements (the halogens). **3.** Tell students to complete the Want to Know column with questions about the halogens. **4.** Have students read p. 144 to learn more about the halogens. As they read, have them note answers to their questions in the Learned column, along with other facts, examples, and details they learned. **5.** Have students draw an Information I Expect to Use box below their KWL chart. Have them review the information in the Learned column and categorize the useful information in the box.
Verbal

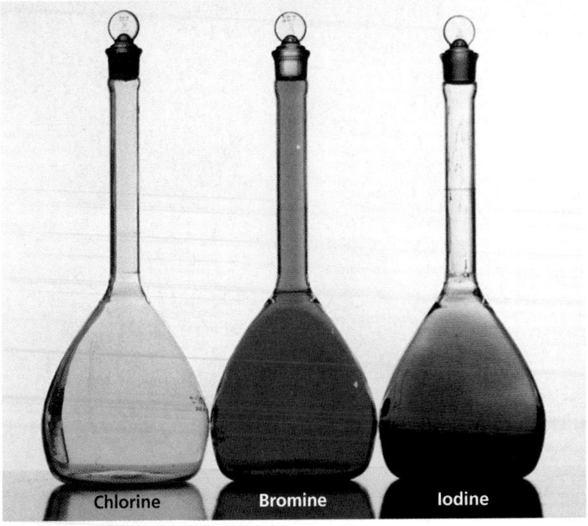
Chlorine
Bromine
Iodine

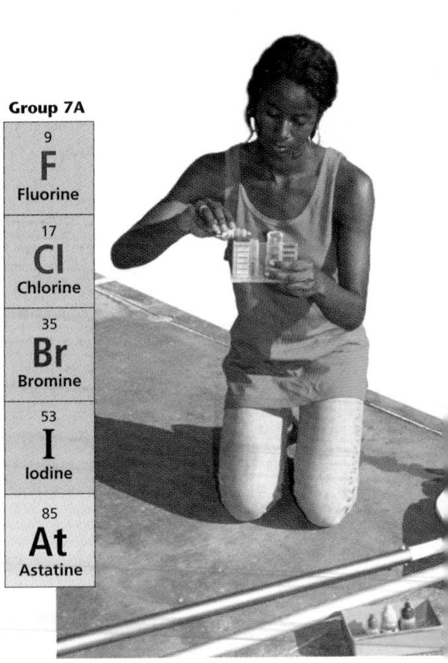
Group 7A
9
F
Fluorine
17
Cl
Chlorine
35
Br
Bromine
53
I
Iodine
85
At
Astatine

Figure 21 At room temperature, chlorine is a gas, bromine is a liquid, and iodine is a solid. Halogens react easily with metals, such as the iron in steel wool. At a swimming pool, the chlorine content must be tested frequently. **Applying Concepts** ***What process causes iodine vapor to collect in a flask of solid iodine?***

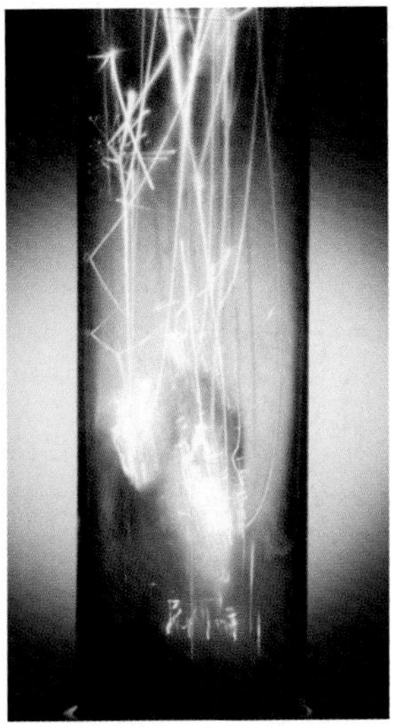

Chlorine reacting with steel wool

The Halogens

The elements in Group 7A are called **halogens.** Each halogen has seven valence electrons. Figure 21 shows the range of physical properties among the halogens. Fluorine and chlorine are gases, bromine is a liquid that evaporates quickly, and iodine is a solid that sublimes. **Despite their physical differences, the halogens have similar chemical properties.** They are highly reactive nonmetals, with fluorine being the most reactive and chlorine a close second. Halogens react easily with most metals. Figure 21 shows what happens when heated steel wool is plunged into chlorine.

Recall that a fluorine compound is used to prevent tooth decay. If you use pans with a nonstick coating to make omelets or muffins, you have seen another use of a fluorine compound. Have you ever noticed a sharp smell when adding bleach to a load of clothes? The smell comes from a small amount of chlorine gas that is released from a chlorine compound in the bleach. Chlorine is also used to kill bacteria in drinking water and swimming pools. The woman in Figure 21 is testing the level of chlorine in a swimming pool.

Your body needs iodine to keep your thyroid gland working properly. This gland controls the speed at which reactions occur in your body. Seafood is a good source of iodine. At a time when fresh fish was not available in all parts of the United States, people began to add iodine compounds to table salt. Salt that contains such compounds is called iodized salt.

Facts and Figures

Halogens The name astatine comes from the Greek *astatos,* meaning "unstable." Astatine is a radioactive element whose most stable isotope, At-210, has a half-life of only 8.1 h. Astatine is the most metallic of the halogens. It is usually classified as a metalloid, but is sometimes regarded as a nonmetal. Because of its rarity and instability, astatine has no practical uses.

Both bromine and iodine are volatile. Iodine comes from the Greek *ioeides,* meaning "violet colored." It is named for the color of iodine vapor, not the color of its solid crystals, which are dark gray.

The Noble Gases

The elements in Group 8A are called **noble gases.** Helium has two valence electrons. Each of the other noble gases has eight valence electrons. **The noble gases are colorless and odorless and extremely unreactive.** In Chapter 6, you will study the relationship between the electron configurations of the noble gases and their low reactivity.

It is not easy to discover a colorless, odorless gas. It is even harder if the gas rarely reacts. Scientists discovered argon when they noticed that the density of nitrogen collected from air did not match the density of nitrogen formed during chemical changes. In time, the scientists figured out that the "impurity" in atmospheric nitrogen was an unknown element.

An element that does not react easily with other elements can be very useful. For example, during one stage in the process of making computer chips, pure silicon is heated in a furnace at 1480°C. At this temperature, silicon reacts with both oxygen and nitrogen. So the heating must take place in an argon atmosphere.

Some light bulbs are filled with argon because the glowing filament in the bulb will not react with argon as it would react with oxygen. Using argon increases the number of hours the bulb can be lit before it burns out. All the noble gases except radon are used in "neon" lights like those shown in Figure 22.

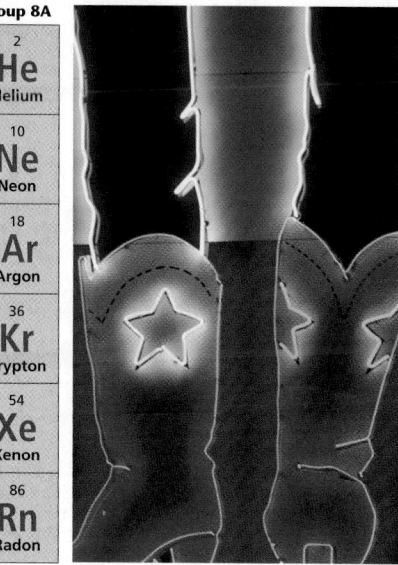

Group 8A
2 He Helium
10 Ne Neon
18 Ar Argon
36 Kr Krypton
54 Xe Xenon
86 Rn Radon

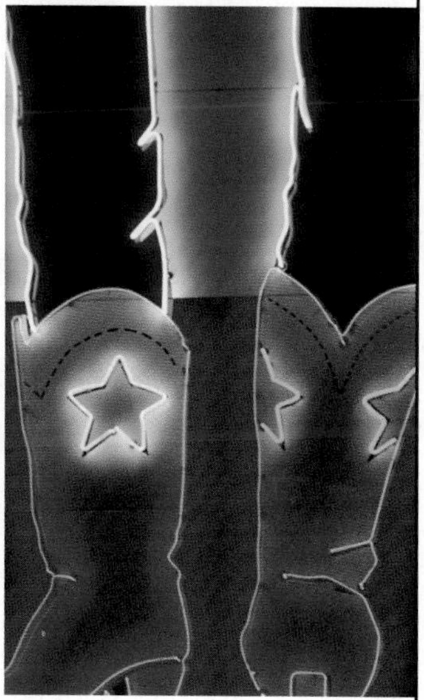

Figure 22 When electric current passes through noble gases, they emit different colors. Helium emits pink, neon emits orange-red, argon emits lavender, krypton emits white, and xenon emits blue.

Section 5.3 Assessment

Reviewing Concepts

1. Explain why elements in a group have similar properties.
2. What is the relationship between an alkali metal's location in Group 1A and its reactivity?
3. What element exists in almost every compound in your body?
4. Which Group 5A elements are found in fertilizer?
5. Which group of elements is the least reactive?
6. Why is hydrogen located in a group with reactive metals?
7. What biological function requires magnesium?
8. Why is aluminum recycled?
9. What is the main use of sulfur?
10. Why is chlorine added to drinking water?

Critical Thinking

11. **Comparing and Contrasting** In which class of elements is there a greater range of properties, the metals or the nonmetals? Give an example to support your answer.
12. **Making Generalizations** What happens to the reactivity of nonmetals within a group from the top of the group to the bottom?

Connecting Concepts

Using Physical Properties In Section 2.2, three ways to use physical properties are discussed. Find one example in Section 5.3 that illustrates each use. If necessary, reread pages 48 and 50.

Section 5.3 Assessment

1. They have similar properties because they have the same number of valence electrons.
2. The reactivity of alkali metals increases from the top of Group 1A to the bottom.
3. Carbon
4. Nitrogen and phosphorus
5. The noble gases (Group 8A)
6. Hydrogen is placed with other elements that have a single valence electron.
7. The process that uses sunlight to produce sugar in plants
8. The energy needed to purify recycled aluminum is only about 5% of the energy needed to extract aluminum from bauxite.
9. To produce sulfuric acid
10. Chlorine is added to drinking water to kill bacteria.
11. Accept all answers that are supported by reasonable arguments. Students may choose nonmetals and say that they display a greater range of physical properties and reactivity.
12. The reactivity of nonmetals decreases from the top to the bottom of a group.

The Noble Gases

Build Science Skills L2

Inferring Hold up an incandescent light bulb and tell students that the filament in the light bulb is made of tungsten, which emits light when it is heated to a high temperature. Explain that a light bulb with a tungsten filament contains small amounts of gases, such as argon, that do not react easily. Ask, **Why isn't air used in the light bulb?** *(The heated filament would burn in air, which contains oxygen.)* **Visual, Logical**

3 ASSESS

Evaluate Understanding L2

Write the names of A group elements discussed in Section 3.3 on separate index cards. Distribute one card to each pair of students and have them add the following information to the card: chemical symbol, atomic number, group number and group name, number of valence electrons, physical state at room temperature, class of element (metal, nonmetal, or metalloid), and one or two properties of the element.

Reteach L1

Use the segments of the periodic table that appear throughout the section to review each A group. Emphasize how the metallic properties of elements increase from top to bottom within a group and how the number of valence electrons changes from left to right across the periodic table.

Connecting Concepts

Examples of Identifying Materials: Distinguish halogens by their states and colors at room temperature.

Examples of Choosing Materials: Using hard calcium carbonate to polish teeth; using argon to increase the life of a light bulb.

Examples of Separating Materials: Sodium chloride from seawater by evaporation; nitrogen from oxygen based on their boiling points.

Interactive Textbook If your class subscribes to the Interactive Textbook, use it to review key concepts in Section 5.3.

Answer to . . .

Figure 21 *Sublimation*

CONCEPTS in Action

Elemental Friends and Foes L2

Background

All packaged and processed food sold in the United States displays a label with nutritional information. The label is designed to be easy to read and to enable consumers to quickly find the information they need to make appropriate food choices.

The label contains a Daily Value percentage (%DV) for calorie-containing nutrients such as fats and carbohydrates, as well as for cholesterol, vitamins, and minerals. For vitamins and minerals, the %DV is based on the Reference Daily Intake (RDI) values established by the U.S. Food and Drug Administration.

On current food labeling, the %DV for vitamins and minerals is the percentage of RDI available in a single serving. For example, the RDI for magnesium is 400 milligrams. If a single serving of a certain brand of cereal contains 40 milligrams of magnesium, the %DV for magnesium is listed as 10%.

It is likely that the number of elements classified as essential will grow along with advancements in understanding of nutrition and the human body. For example, nickel is an essential element in some species, but has not yet been determined to be essential in humans.

CONCEPTS in Action

Elemental Friends and Foes

Some elements are essential for your health, and some are extremely harmful. You need to obtain the right amounts of the twenty-five essential elements through a balanced diet, and to reduce your exposure to the harmful elements.

Eating a variety of foods helps to ensure that all the elements needed by your body are available. The required elements can be classified as major, lesser, or trace elements. An element is classified based on its percentage by mass in the body.

The six major elements are hydrogen, oxygen, carbon, nitrogen, phosphorus, and calcium. These six major elements account for almost 99 percent of your body mass. Nearly every compound in your body contains carbon and hydrogen, and many contain oxygen too. The compounds that control all the chemical changes that take place in cells contain nitrogen. Calcium is essential for healthy bones and teeth. Phosphorus is found in your DNA and in the molecules that transfer energy within cells.

The lesser elements are iron, potassium, zinc, sodium, sulfur, chlorine, and magnesium. For each lesser element, there is a recommended amount that needs to be taken in daily. These amounts vary from 15 milligrams for zinc to 400 milligrams for magnesium. Lesser elements help your body build tissues and maintain other cell processes. For example, nerves and muscles require magnesium to function properly.

The trace elements are vanadium, chromium, molybdenum, manganese, cobalt, copper, boron, tin, silicon, selenium, fluorine, and iodine. The quantities required are tiny, but trace elements perform important functions. For example, red blood cells would not mature without cobalt.

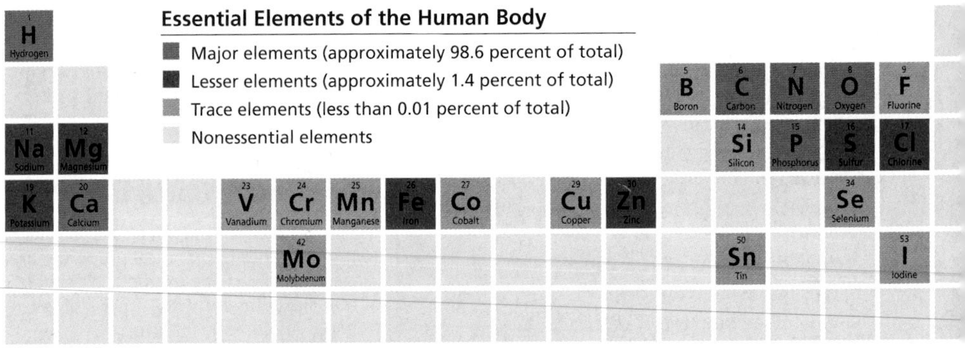

Essential Elements of the Human Body
Major elements (approximately 98.6 percent of total)
Lesser elements (approximately 1.4 percent of total)
Trace elements (less than 0.01 percent of total)
Nonessential elements
1 H Hydrogen
11 Na Sodium
12 Mg Magnesium
19 K Potassium
20 Ca Calcium
23 V Vanadium
24 Cr Chromium
25 Mn Manganese
26 Fe Iron
27 Co Cobalt
29 Cu Copper
30 Zn Zinc
42 Mo Molybdenum
5 B Boron
6 C Carbon
7 N Nitrogen
8 O Oxygen
9 F Fluorine
14 Si Silicon
15 P Phosphorus
16 S Sulfur
17 Cl Chlorine
34 Se Selenium
50 Sn Tin
53 I Iodine

Essential elements

The 25 elements essential to the human body are generally ingested as part of compounds found in food. The roles and functions of a few of these elements are shown here.

8 O Oxygen

Oxygen
This is the most abundant element in your body. The most important function of oxygen is to help release the energy stored in foods. You absorb oxygen from the air you breathe.

WATER

1 H Hydrogen

Hydrogen
Hydrogen is found in foods and in water, which accounts for more than 60 percent of body mass. Chemical reactions in cells take place in water.

6 C Carbon

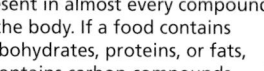

Carbon
Carbon is the second most common element in the human body. It is essential to life, because it is present in almost every compound in the body. If a food contains carbohydrates, proteins, or fats, it contains carbon compounds.

PASTA

26 Fe Iron

Iron
Iron is a very important trace element because it is part of hemoglobin. This compound transports oxygen through the blood to every cell in the body. Meat, fish, and leafy green vegetables, such as spinach, are good sources of iron.

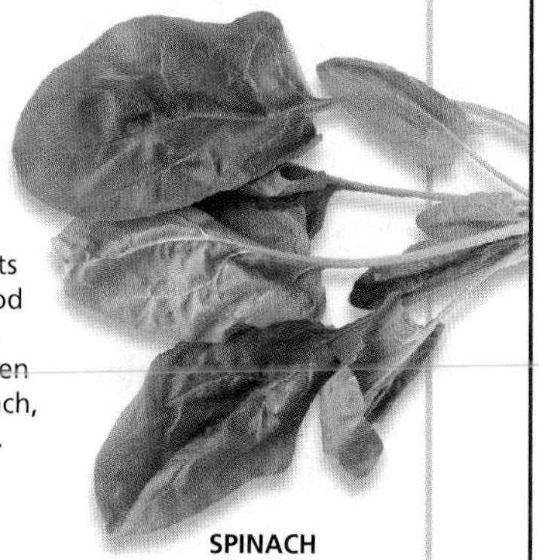
SPINACH

53 I Iodine

Iodine
Iodine is required in small amounts for the production of thyroxine by the thyroid gland. Thyroxine controls the rate of all chemical processes in the body. Fresh fish is a good source of iodine.

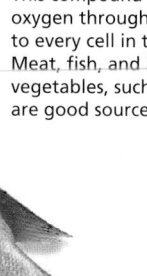

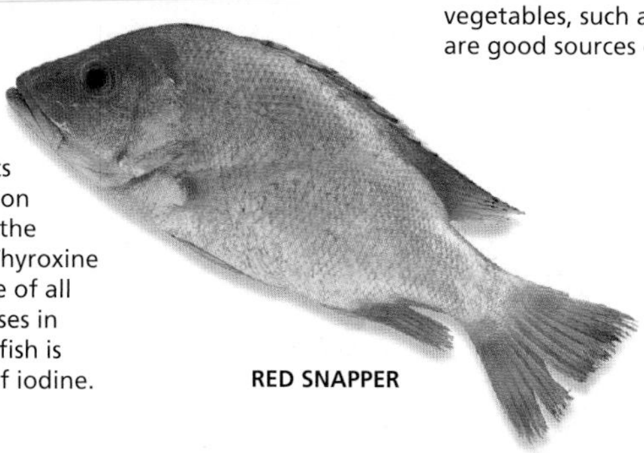
RED SNAPPER

GRAPES

23 V Vanadium

Vanadium
Vanadium can help control blood sugar levels. It also plays an important role in the formation of bones and teeth. Vanadium can be found in black peppercorns.

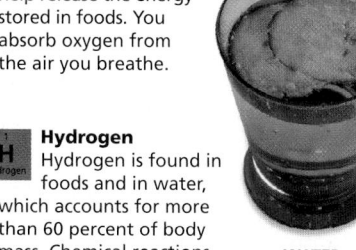

BLACK PEPPERCORNS

19 K Potassium

Potassium
Potassium is essential to muscle and nerve function, and helps keep the body's fluids in balance. It also stimulates the kidneys to remove body wastes. Potassium can be found in fruit and dairy products.

CHEESES

Build Science Skills L2

Drawing Conclusions

Purpose Students identify elements whose compounds are used to fortify foods.

Materials empty containers of fortified food products such as milk, juice, salt, and bread

Class Time 15 minutes

Procedure Explain that sometimes compounds of essential elements are added to foods so that people will have a sufficient amount of these elements in their diets. Tell students that to *fortify* means to enrich or increase the nutrient value of food. Pass the empty containers around. Have students look at the labels. Ask, **Which essential elements have been added to the foods?** *(Answers may include calcium, iron, and iodine.)* **Why are these elements essential?** *(Students' answers should include information from pp. 146 and 147.)*

Expected Outcome Students discover that compounds of calcium, iron, and iodine are likely to be added when food is fortified.
Logical, Visual

CONCEPTS
— in Action —

(continued)

Build Science Skills **L2**

Making Judgments Assign as a research topic one of the harmful elements—mercury, lead, or arsenic—to each student. Have students use the Internet or the library to find two or three recent newspaper or magazine articles related to the harmful effects of exposure to the element. Ask students to write a paragraph summarizing each article, and then write a paragraph explaining whether or not they think that more steps should be taken to protect people from exposure to the element.

Have a class discussion or debate in which students present their research findings and their viewpoints. Ask, **What are the harmful effects of the element you researched?** *(Sample answer: Exposure to lead can damage the central nervous system, kidneys, and digestive system.)* **What precautions for the use of this element are currently in place?** *(Sample answer: Lead is no longer allowed as a gasoline additive; regulations prohibit renting an apartment or house with peeling and flaking lead paint to families with young children; and lead levels in drinking water have been reduced.)* **Are these precautions sufficient? Explain your answer.** *(Sample answer: Yes, because these regulations have helped significantly reduce the number of children suffering from lead exposure. According to the Centers for Disease Control, this number decreased about 80% between the late 1970s and mid-1990s. An EPA document dated December 2002 reports that in 1978 nearly three to four million children were affected. In the 1990s, the number declined to about 890,000.)*
Interpersonal, Group

CONCEPTS in Action

Harmful Elements

Some elements should be avoided completely. These foes include metals, such as lead and mercury, and the metalloid arsenic. Harmful elements may enter the body in water, air, or food. Inside the body, nonessential elements may compete with essential elements and disrupt cell functions. Large amounts of harmful elements can stress the body's normal methods for eliminating toxins. Harmful elements can build up in body tissues.

For decades lead was used in paint and in gasoline to improve engine performance. These products are now lead free. The use of mercury in thermometers has been reduced and arsenic compounds are no longer used in pesticides.

Many trace elements are only helpful if ingested in the small recommended amounts. Larger quantities of most trace elements can be harmful, as can larger-than-required amounts of lesser elements, such as sodium.

82 **Pb** Lead

Lead
Too much lead in the bloodstream can lead to organ damage and learning difficulties, especially in young children. For this reason, the use of lead-based paint was banned in 1978. Children may still be a risk if they live in an older house with layers of peeling paint.

80 **Hg** Mercury

Mercury
Mercury is used in numerous industrial processes, but it is toxic and can damage the brain and nervous system. For this reason it should be handled with great care. It is particularly important to avoid inhaling mercury vapor.

33 **As** Arsenic

Arsenic
Arsenic has been known as a poison for centuries, yet compounds of arsenic were used to treat some diseases before the discovery of penicillin. Arsenic compounds are no longer used to protect crops from insect pests or to preserve wood. Drinking water can absorb arsenic as it flows over rocks. But the amount of arsenic in drinking water is limited by law to less than 50 micrograms in each liter of water.

Arsenic pesticide

Too much of a good thing

Many of the elements found in your body are needed in only very small amounts. Too much can often be harmful. The Food and Drug Administration provides guidelines on the safe daily quantities to take through food or supplements.

BEEF

30 Zn Zinc

Zinc
This trace element can be found in almost every cell of your body. Among other things, it helps to support a healthy immune system. Beef is a good source of zinc, but no more than 40 milligrams of zinc should be taken daily. Too much zinc can cause anemia by reducing iron uptake.

TABLE SALT

11 Na Sodium

Sodium
It is hard to avoid sodium in your diet because table salt contains a sodium compound (sodium chloride). Everybody needs some sodium each day to maintain water balance and nerve function. But too much sodium (more than 3 grams daily) can cause high blood pressure.

34 Se Selenium

Selenium
This trace element helps to maintain a healthy immune system. Brazil nuts are a good source of selenium, as are fruits and vegetables. While selenium supplements may be useful for some people, no more than 400 micrograms should be taken daily. Too much selenium can cause nerve damage.

BRAZIL NUTS

Going Further

- Choose a trace element other than vanadium, selenium, or iodine. Find out which foods are good sources of the element. Write a paragraph explaining how your diet meets or could be adjusted to meet your need for this element.
- Take a Discovery Channel Video Field Trip by watching "You Are What You Eat."

Discovery Channel School
Video Field Trip

Integrate Health L2

A person's diet must contain some sodium compounds so that important functions such as maintenance of appropriate water levels within cells and transmission of nerve impulses will occur. However, the level of sodium compounds in food (especially in processed foods) is so high that most people's intake of sodium compounds exceeds required levels. Have students research the possible adverse health effects of an excess of sodium in the body.
Verbal

Going Further

Chromium: black pepper, broccoli, asparagus, mushrooms, liver, raisins, nuts, brewer's yeast; molybdenum: legumes, leafy vegetables, grains; manganese: nuts, oatmeal, ginger, rice; cobalt: meat, dairy products, green leafy vegetables; silicon: whole grains, liver, red meat. (Tin exists in sufficient quantities in water, food, and air.)
Verbal, Portfolio

Discovery Channel School

Video Field Trip

You Are What You Eat

After students have viewed the Video Field Trip, ask them the following questions: **How did some ancient civilizations preserve their dead?** *(By embalming, or using preservatives)* **What are two types of information that scientists discover by examining mummies?** *(Student answers may include age, gender, diet, and cause of death.)* **What evidence led forensic scientists to suspect Tutankhamen, also known as King Tut, might not have died from natural causes?** *(X-rays showed bone damage to his skull probably caused by a blow to his head.)* **List features that scientists found in the bones of mummies in Chile.** *(Student answers may include bone deformation around the ear, bones with significant nitrogen deposits, and strong and healthy teeth.)* **What do forensic scientists suspect to be the causes of the features found in these mummies?** *(Fishing in cold waters could have caused the growth around the ears. Nitrogen deposits in their bones could have been caused by a diet rich in seafood. A diet of fish could explain the strong, healthy teeth.)*

Exploration Lab

Predicting the Density of an Element **L2**

Objective
After completing this activity, students will be able to
- state that density increases from the top to the bottom within a group in the periodic table.
- evaluate predictions of physical properties based on the periodic table.

Skills Focus Measuring, Predicting, Analyzing Data, Using Graphs and Tables

Prep Time 20 minutes

Advance Prep Place each of the elements into a separate small, labeled container. Select sample sizes that will fit in the available graduated cylinders.

Class Time 40 minutes

Safety Make sure that students wear safety goggles, disposable plastic gloves, and lab aprons and wash their hands before leaving the laboratory. Caution students about the proper handling of chemicals. If you cut pieces of tin for students to use, be sure to file the edges smooth. Do not discard lead.

Teaching Tips
- Review the proper techniques for accurate use of the balance. Also remind students to read volumes in a graduated cylinder at eye level and at the bottom of the meniscus.

Questioning Strategies
Ask, **Why is it necessary to subtract the mass of the weighing paper from the total mass of the weighing paper and the sample?** *(To obtain the mass of the sample)* **Why is it necessary to subtract the volume of water from the total volume of water and sample when determining the volume of the silicon, tin, and lead?** *(To obtain the volume of each sample)*

Expected Outcome The elements' densities increase from the top to the bottom of Group 4A, but not in a simple linear manner.

Exploration Lab

Predicting the Density of an Element

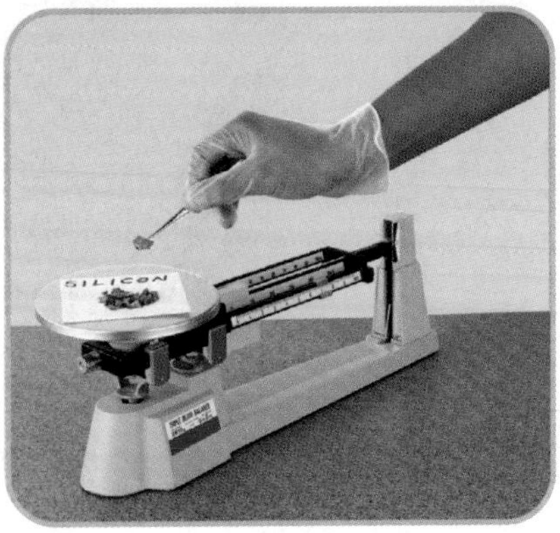
SILICON

Density is a useful property for identifying and classifying elements. In this lab, you will determine the densities of three elements in Group 4A—silicon, tin, and lead. Then you will use your data to predict the density of another element in Group 4A—germanium.

Problem Can the densities of elements within a group be used to help predict the density of another element in the group?

Materials
- unlined white paper
- scissors
- metric ruler
- balance
- forceps
- silicon
- tin
- lead shot
- 50-mL graduated cylinder
- graph paper
- periodic table

For the probeware version of this lab, see the Probeware Lab Manual, Lab 2.

Skills Measuring, Observing, Using Graphs, Calculating

Procedure

Part A: Measuring Mass
1. On a sheet of paper, make a copy of the data table shown.
2. Cut out three 10-cm × 10-cm pieces of paper from a sheet of unlined white paper. Label one piece of paper Silicon, the second Tin, and the third Lead. Find the mass of each piece of paper and record it in your data table.
3. Using forceps, place the silicon onto the paper labeled Silicon, as shown. Find the mass of the silicon and the paper. Record this mass in your data table. Then, subtract the mass of the paper from the mass of the silicon and paper. Record the mass of silicon in your data table. Set the paper containing the silicon aside for now.
4. Repeat Step 3 to find the masses of tin and lead.

Part B: Measuring Volume
5. Place 25 mL of water in the graduated cylinder. Measure the volume of the water to the nearest 0.1 mL. Record the volume (in cm^3) in your data table. (*Hint:* 1 mL = 1 cm^3)
6. Tilt the graduated cylinder and carefully pour the silicon from the paper into the graduated cylinder, as shown on page 151. Make sure that the silicon is completely covered by the water. Measure and record the volume of the water and silicon in your data table. Then, subtract the volume of water from the volume of the water and silicon. Record the result in your data table.
7. Repeat Steps 5 and 6 to find the volumes of tin and lead.

Data Table

Element	Mass of Paper (g)	Mass of Paper and Element (g)	Mass of Element (g)	Volume of Water (cm^3)	Volume of Water and Element (cm^3)	Volume of Element (cm^3)	Density of Element (g/cm^3)
Silicon							
Tin							
Lead							

Probeware Lab Manual Versions of this lab for use with Probeware available from Pasco, Texas Instruments, and Vernier are in the Probeware Manual.

Sample Data Table

Element	Density (g/cm^3)
Silicon	2.4
Tin	7.1
Lead	11.3
Germanium	4.6 (from student graph)

SILICON

Part C: Calculating Density

8. To calculate the density of silicon, divide its mass by its volume.

$$\text{Density} = \frac{\text{Mass}}{\text{Volume}}$$

Record the density of silicon in your data table.

9. Repeat Step 8 to find the densities of tin and lead.
10. Make a line graph that shows the relationship between the densities of silicon, tin, and lead and the periods in which they are located in the periodic table. Place the number of the period (from 1 to 7) on the horizontal axis and the density (in g/cm^3) on the vertical axis. Draw a straight line that comes as close as possible to all three points.
11. Germanium is in Period 4. To estimate the density of germanium, draw a dotted vertical line from the 4 on the horizontal axis to the solid line. Then, draw a dotted horizontal line from the solid line to the vertical axis. Read and record the density of germanium.
12. Wash your hands with warm water and soap before you leave the laboratory.

Analyze and Conclude

1. **Classifying** List lead, silicon, and tin in order of increasing density.
2. **Comparing and Contrasting** How does your estimate of the density of germanium compare with the actual density of germanium, which is 5.3 g/cm^3?
3. **Calculating** Use the formula for percent error (PE) to calculate a percent error for your estimate of the density of germanium.

$$\text{PE} = \frac{\text{Estimated value} - \text{Accepted value}}{\text{Accepted value}} \times 100$$

4. **Drawing Conclusions** How does the density of the elements change from silicon to lead in Group 4A?

Go Further Use reference books or sites on the Internet to research properties of Group 4A elements. Construct a graph that shows how another property, such as melting point or boiling point, varies among the Group 4A elements you explored. Determine whether knowing the values for three of the elements would allow you to accurately predict a value for the fourth element.

Analyze and Conclude

1. Silicon, tin, and lead
2. A typical student estimate for the density of germanium is 4.6 g/cm^3, which is a rough approximation of the actual value of 5.3 g/cm^3.
3. Student estimates are likely to be approximately 16% lower than the actual value.
4. From silicon to lead, the density of the elements increases.

Logical

Go Further

Students will discover that there also is a relationship, though slight, between position in the periodic table and other physical properties such as melting points and boiling points.
Visual, Logical

Study Guide

Study Tip

Organize Information
Tell students that organizing information will help them remember it more easily. Suggest that students write key information from the chapter on index cards or large self-stick notes and use them to create large concept maps.

Thinking Visually

a. Metalloids
b. Nonmetals
c. Liquids

CHAPTER 5

Study Guide

5.1 Organizing the Elements

Key Concepts

- Mendeleev arranged the elements into rows in order of increasing mass so that elements with similar properties were in the same column.
- The close match between Mendeleev's predictions and the actual properties of new elements showed how useful his periodic table could be.

Vocabulary

periodic table, *p. 127*

5.2 The Modern Periodic Table

Key Concepts

- In the modern periodic table, elements are arranged by increasing atomic number (number of protons). Each row on the table is a period. Each column is a group.
- Properties of elements repeat in a predictable way when atomic numbers are used to arrange elements into groups.
- Atomic mass is a value that depends on the distribution of an element's isotopes in nature and the masses of those isotopes.
- Elements are classified as metals, nonmetals, and metalloids. Metals are elements that are good conductors of electric current and heat. Nonmetals are poor conductors of electric current and heat. Metalloids are elements with properties that fall between those of metals and nonmetals.
- Across a period from left to right, the elements become less metallic and more nonmetallic in their properties.

Vocabulary

period, *p. 131*
group, *p. 131*
periodic law, *p. 131*
atomic mass unit (amu), *p. 134*
metals, *p. 135*
transition metals, *p. 136*
nonmetals, *p. 136*
metalloids, *p. 136*

5.3 Representative Groups

Key Concepts

- Elements in a group have similar properties because they have the same number of valence electrons.
- The alkali earth metals in Group 1A are extremely reactive. The reactivity of these metals increases from the top of the group to the bottom.
- Differences in reactivity among the alkaline earth metals in Group 2A are shown by the ways they react with water.
- Group 3A contains the most abundant metal in Earth's crust—aluminum. The energy needed to recycle aluminum is 5 percent of the energy needed to extract aluminum from bauxite.
- Group 4A contains the nonmetal carbon. Most compounds in your body contain carbon. Carbon compounds control reactions that occur in cells.
- Fertilizers usually contain the Group 5A elements nitrogen and phosphorus.
- Oxygen, in Group 6A, is the most abundant element in Earth's crust.
- Despite their physical differences, the halogens in Group 7A are all highly reactive nonmetals.
- The noble gases, in Group 8A, are colorless and odorless and extremely unreactive.

Vocabulary

valence electron, *p. 139*
alkali metals, *p. 140*
alkaline earth metals, *p. 141*
halogens, *p. 144*
noble gases, *p. 145*

Thinking Visually

Web Diagram Use information from the chapter to complete the web diagram below. The web relates states of matter at room temperature to categories of elements.

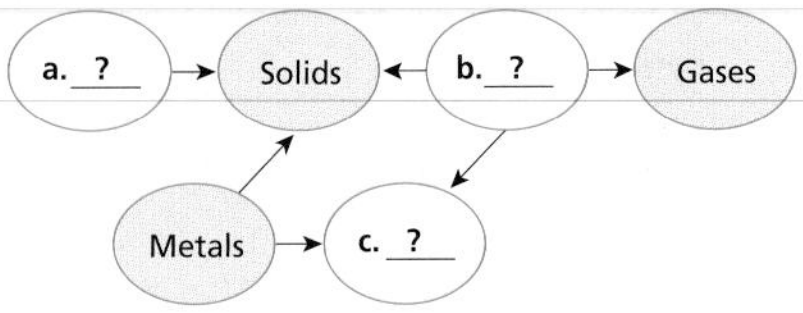
a. ?
Solids
b. ?
Gases
Metals
c. ?

Chapter Resources

Print

- ***Chapter and Unit Tests,*** Chapter 5 Test A and Test B
- ***Test Prep Resources,*** Chapter 5

Technology

- ***Computer Test Bank,*** Chapter Test 5
- ***Interactive Textbook,*** Chapter 5
- ***Go Online,*** PHSchool.com, Chapter 5

CHAPTER 5

Assessment

Interactive textbook with assessment at PHSchool.com

Reviewing Content

Choose the letter that best answers the question or completes the statement.

1. Mendeleev arranged the elements in his periodic table in order of
   a. atomic number. b. number of electrons.
   c. mass. d. number of neutrons.

2. Mendeleev's decision to leave gaps in his periodic table was supported by the discovery of
   a. electrons. b. protons.
   c. argon. d. gallium.

3. In a modern periodic table, elements are arranged in order of
   a. atomic number. b. number of isotopes.
   c. atomic mass. d. number of neutrons.

4. How many periods does the periodic table have?
   a. 18 b. 7
   c. 9 d. 8

5. An atomic mass unit is
   a. one twelfth the mass of a carbon-12 atom.
   b. the mass of a carbon-12 atom.
   c. the mass of a neutron.
   d. the mass of a proton.

6. An element that is shiny and conducts electric current is likely to be a
   a. gas. b. metal.
   c. metalloid. d. nonmetal.

7. Copper is an example of
   a. an alkali metal. b. an alkaline earth metal.
   c. a nonmetal. d. a transition metal.

8. Elements that have the same number of valence electrons are
   a. in the same period.
   b. in the same group.
   c. called noble gases.
   d. called transition metals.

9. The most reactive metals are the
   a. transition metals. b. alkaline earth metals.
   c. alkali metals. d. metalloids.

10. Which elements are all gases at room temperature?
    a. Group 1A b. Period 3
    c. Group 7A d. Group 8A

Understanding Concepts

11. What information did Mendeleev have about the elements he organized into a periodic table?

12. How did Mendeleev know where to leave the spaces in his table?

13. Why is the table of the elements shown in Figure 7 called a periodic table?

14. Why does the number of elements vary from period to period?

15. Explain how the atomic mass of an element is affected by the distribution of its isotopes in nature.

16. List three ways that the elements in the periodic table can be classified.

17. In general, what happens to the reactivity of elements in groups labeled A as atomic numbers increase across a period?

18. Why don't the elements within an A group in the periodic table have identical properties?

19. Why was it difficult to discover the noble gases?

Use this portion of the periodic table to answer Questions 20–23.

14 **Si** Silicon 28.086	15 **P** Phosphorus 30.974	16 **S** Sulfur 32.06	17 **Cl** Chlorine 35.453
32 **Ge** Germanium 72.59	33 **As** Arsenic 74.922	34 **Se** Selenium 78.96	35 **Br** Bromine 79.904

20. How many of the elements shown are metals? How many are nonmetals? How many are metalloids?

21. Which element is a liquid at room temperature and which is a gas at room temperature?

22. Which of the two halogens shown is more reactive? Give a reason for your answer.

23. Does selenium have more in common with sulfur or bromine? Explain your answer.

Homework Guide

Section	Questions
5.1	1–2, 11–12
5.2	3–7, 13–17, 20–21, 23–25, 38
5.3	8–10, 18–19, 22, 26–37, 39–40

Assessment

Interactive Textbook If your class subscribes to the Interactive Textbook, your students can go online to access an interactive version of the Student Edition and a self-test.

Reviewing Content

1. c **2.** d **3.** a
4. b **5.** a **6.** b
7. d **8.** b **9.** c
10. d

Understanding Concepts

11. Mendeleev knew their relative masses and properties.
12. Mendeleev placed elements in the groups where they logically belonged based on their properties.
13. The table is called a periodic table because the properties of the elements repeat at regular intervals from row to row.
14. The number of elements per period varies because the number of available orbitals increases as the energy level increases.
15. An atomic mass is a weighted average of the atomic masses of an element's isotopes. The distribution of the isotopes determines how much each isotope affects the weighted average.
16. Elements can be classified by their state at room temperature; by whether they exist in nature; and by whether they are metals, nonmetals, or metalloids.
17. Across a period from left to right, metals become less reactive and nonmetals become more reactive, excluding the elements in Group 8A.
18. Elements in the same A group do not have identical properties because their valence electrons are in different energy levels.
19. The noble gases were difficult to discover because they are colorless, odorless, and very rarely react.
20. 0 metals, 5 nonmetals, and 3 metalloids
21. Bromine is a liquid and chlorine is a gas.
22. Chlorine is more reactive than bromine because the reactivity of nonmetals increases from the bottom to the top of a group.
23. Selenium has more in common with sulfur because they are in the same group and have the same number of valence electrons.

Critical Thinking

24. There is not enough data for the solid because solids at room temperature can be metals, nonmetals, or metalloids. There is enough data for the gas because there are no gaseous metals or metalloids at room temperature.
25. Boron, with an atomic mass of 10.81
26. Three
27. Cesium is an extremely reactive metal; argon is an extremely unreactive nonmetal.
28. Halogens are always found in nature in compounds because halogens are highly reactive nonmetals.
29. Silicon
30. You would choose fluorine because it is much more likely to react than nitrogen is.
31. Elements X and Y are in Group 1 (1A) and Element Z is in Group 17 (7A).
32. Elements Y and Z are gases; element X is a solid.
33. Element Y is hydrogen, because hydrogen is the only gas in Group 1.

Concepts in Action

34. The beaker might shatter.
35. Students are likely to say nitrogen and phosphorus.
36. An element that is helpful in small quantities may be harmful when present in larger quantities. For example, trace amounts of selenium help maintain the immune system, but larger amounts can cause nerve damage.
37. The books would not fall apart if stored in a noble-gas atmosphere.
38. There is a repeating pattern of days and months on a calendar. However, Tuesdays do not necessarily have a different set of properties from Thursdays and there are no trends among Tuesdays equivalent to the trends in atomic mass or reactivity within a group in the periodic table.
39. Magnesium is required to produce chlorophyll, the green pigment in plants.
40. The essays should contain accurate information and make a reasonable argument for the value of the element.

CHAPTER 5

Assessment *(continued)*

Critical Thinking

24. **Classifying** If you know that an element is a solid at room temperature, do you have enough data to classify the element as a metal, metalloid, or nonmetal? If you know that the element is a gas at room temperature, do you have enough data? Explain your answers.
25. **Applying Concepts** An element on the periodic table has two naturally occurring isotopes. One isotope has an atomic mass of about 10 amu. The other isotope has an atomic mass of about 11 amu. What is the name of this element?
26. **Predicting** How many valence electrons would an element with atomic number 113 have?
27. **Applying Concepts** Why are samples of the alkali metal cesium usually stored in argon gas?
28. **Applying Concepts** Why are halogens found in nature only in compounds?
29. **Applying Concepts** Which element on the periodic table has chemical properties that are most similar to those of carbon?
30. **Designing Experiments** If you were trying to make a compound of the noble gas xenon, would you use nitrogen or fluorine? Explain your choice.

Use the table to answer Questions 31–33.

Properties of Elements X, Y, and Z

Element	Melting Point	Boiling Point	Valence Electrons
X	97.80°C	883°C	1
Y	−259.34°C	−252.87°C	1
Z	−101.5°C	−34.04°C	7

31. **Analyzing Data** In general, where would you find Elements X, Y, and Z on the periodic table?
32. **Classifying** Describe the state of each element at room temperature based on its melting and boiling points.
33. **Drawing Conclusions** Use your answers to Questions 31 and 32 to identify element Y. Explain your reasoning.

Concepts in Action

34. **Predicting** What might happen to a heated beaker made from glass that does not contain boron if the beaker were placed in a pan of ice water?
35. **Inferring** Based on the content of most fertilizers, name two elements other than carbon that are found in compounds in plants.
36. **Making Generalizations** Explain how the amount of a trace element an organism is exposed to affects the element's ability to help or harm an organism. Use the example of selenium. (*Hint:* Refer to the discussion on page 149.)
37. **Problem Solving** Sometimes old books fall apart when they are stored in air. Use what you know about the reactivity of elements to propose a way that old books could be kept from falling apart.
38. **Using Analogies** Explain how a calendar is similar to a periodic table and how it is different.
39. **Relating Cause and Effect** When corn plants have yellow leaves, it is a sign that the plants lack an essential element. Which element must be added to the soil to produce leaves with a healthy green color?
40. **Writing in Science** You write for a newsletter that has a feature called Element of the Month. It is your turn to write the feature. Pick an element that you think is worthy of attention. Write a brief essay and suggest a photo to be used with your feature.

Performance-Based Assessment

Design Your Own Periodic Table Make a version of the periodic table that presents the information provided in Figure 7 in a different, but useful, way.

Go Online PHSchool.com
For: Self-grading assessment
Visit: PHSchool.com
Web Code: cca-1050

Performance-Based Assessment

Students should be able to give reasons for their designs.

Go Online PHSchool.com

Your students can independently test their knowledge of the chapter and print out their test results for your files.

Standardized Test Prep

Test-Taking Tip

Narrowing the Choices
If after reading all the answer choices you are not sure which one is correct, eliminate those answers that you know are wrong. In the question below, first eliminate the answers that require a whole number. Then focus on the remaining choices.

6
C
Carbon
12.011

The number 12.011 is the
(A) atomic number for carbon.
(B) mass number for carbon.
(C) atomic mass of carbon-12.
(D) average atomic mass of carbon.
(E) percentage of carbon-12 in nature.

(Answer: D)

Choose the letter that best answers the question or completes the statement.

1. Which elements are as reactive as alkali metals?
(A) alkaline earth metals
(B) halogens
(C) noble gases
(D) transition metals
(E) metalloids

2. How many valence electrons do atoms of oxygen and sulfur have?
(A) 2
(B) 4
(C) 6
(D) 8
(E) 10

3. Moving across a period from left to right,
(A) elements become less metallic.
(B) elements become more metallic.
(C) elements become more reactive.
(D) elements become less reactive.
(E) elements have fewer valence electrons.

4. Which statement *best* describes nonmetals?
(A) Nonmetals are good conductors of heat and electric current.
(B) Nonmetals are brittle solids.
(C) Many general properties of nonmetals are opposite to those of metals.
(D) Nonmetals are located on the left side of the periodic table.
(E) All nonmetals are extremely reactive.

Use this portion of the periodic table to answer Questions 5–7.

13 Al Aluminum 26.982	14 Si Silicon 28.086	15 P Phosphorus 30.974
31 Ga Gallium 69.72	32 Ge Germanium 72.59	33 As Arsenic 74.922

5. Which list of elements contains only metalloids?
(A) aluminum and gallium
(B) silicon and germanium
(C) phosphorus and arsenic
(D) aluminum, silicon, and phosphorus
(E) gallium, germanium, and arsenic

6. Which elements did Mendeleev leave spaces for in his first periodic table?
(A) aluminum and phosphorus
(B) aluminum and germanium
(C) silicon and arsenic
(D) gallium and germanium
(E) gallium and aluminum

7. Which of the elements are among the most abundant in Earth's crust?
(A) silicon and phosphorus
(B) aluminum and phosphorus
(C) phosphorus and arsenic
(D) gallium and arsenic
(E) aluminum and silicon

Standardized Test Prep

1. B **2.** C **3.** A
4. C **5.** B **6.** D
7. E

CHAPTER 6

Planning Guide

Use these planning tools
Easy Planner
Teacher Express

SECTION OBJECTIVES	STANDARDS NATIONAL (See p. T18.)	STANDARDS STATE	ACTIVITIES and LABS
6.1 Ionic Bonding, pp. 158–164 1 block or 2 periods **6.1.1 Recognize** stable electron configurations. **6.1.2 Predict** an element's chemical properties using number of valence electrons and electron dot diagrams. **6.1.3 Describe** how an ionic bond forms and how ionization energy affects the process. **6.1.4 Predict** the composition of an ionic compound from its chemical formula. **6.1.5 Relate** the properties of ionic compounds to the structure of crystal lattices.	A-1, B-1, B-2, G-1		**SE** Inquiry Activity: What Can the Shape of a Material Tell You About the Material? p. 157 L2
6.2 Covalent Bonding, pp. 165–169 1 block or 2 periods **6.2.1 Describe** how covalent bonds form and the attractions that keep atoms together in molecules. **6.2.2 Compare** polar and nonpolar bonds, and **demonstrate** how polar bonds affect the polarity of a molecule. **6.2.3 Compare** the attractions between polar and nonpolar molecules.	A-1, A-2, B-2		**SE** Quick Lab: Analyzing Inks, p. 167 L2 **SE** Consumer Lab: Improving the Dyeing of Nonpolar Fabrics, pp. 184–185 L2 **TE** Teacher Demo: Modeling Overall Polarity, p. 168 L2 **TE** Teacher Demo: Surface Tension, p. 169 L2 **LM** Investigation 6B: Comparing Ionic and Covalent Compounds L1
6.3 Naming Compounds and Writing Formulas, pp. 170–175 1 block or 2 periods **6.3.1 Recognize** and **describe** binary ionic compounds, metals with multiple ions, and polyatomic ions. **6.3.2 Name** and **determine** chemical formulas for ionic and molecular compounds.	A-1, A-2, B-2, G-2		**SE** Quick Lab: Modeling Molecules, p. 173 L2 **LM** Investigation 6A: Playing the Ionic Compounds Card Game L2
6.4 The Structure of Metals, pp. 176–181 1 block or 2 periods **6.4.1 Describe** the structure and strength of bonds in metals. **6.4.2 Relate** the properties of metals to their structure. **6.4.3 Define** an alloy and **demonstrate** how the composition of an alloy affects its properties.	A-1, A-2, B-2, B-6, E-2, G-1, G-2, G-3		**TE** Teacher Demo: Comparing Bond Types, p. 177 L2 **TE** Teacher Demo: Bronze and Brass Tones, p. 180 L2

Ability Levels

- **L1** For students who need additional help
- **L2** For all students
- **L3** For students who need to be challenged

Components

SE Student Edition	**RSW** Reading & Study Workbook	**CUT** Chapter & Unit Tests	**T** Transparencies
TE Teacher's Edition	**MSPS** Math Skills & Problem Solving Workbook	**CTB** Computer Test Bank	**iT** Interactive Textbook
LM Laboratory Manual		**TP** Test Prep Resources	**P** Presentation Pro CD-ROM
PLM Probeware Lab Manual		**DC** Discovery Channel Videotapes & DVDs	**GO** Internet Resources

RESOURCES PRINT and TECHNOLOGY		SECTION ASSESSMENT
RSW Section 6.1	L1	**SE** Section 6.1 Assessment, p. 164
MSPS Section 6.1	L2	**iT** Section 6.1
T Chapter 6 Pretest	L2	
Section 6.1	L2	
P Chapter 6 Pretest	L2	
Section 6.1	L2	
SciLinks **GO** Ionic bonds	L2	
RSW Section 6.2	L1	**SE** Section 6.2 Assessment, p. 169
T Section 6.2	L2	**iT** Section 6.2
P Section 6.2	L2	
SciLinks **GO** Covalent bonding	L2	
RSW Section 6.3	L1	**SE** Section 6.3 Assessment, p. 175
RSW Math Skill	L2	**iT** Section 6.3
MSPS Section 6.3	L2	
T Section 6.3	L2	
P Section 6.3	L2	
SciLinks **GO** Chemical formulas	L2	
RSW Section 6.4	L1	**SE** Section 6.4 Assessment, p. 181
Discovery Channel School **DC** Good Conduct	L2	**iT** Section 6.4
T Section 6.4	L2	
P Section 6.4	L2	
Science News **GO** Metals	L2	

Go Online

Go online for these Internet resources.

PHSchool.com
Web Code: cca-1060

SCIENCE NEWS
Web Code: cce-1064

NSTA SciLinks
Web Code: ccn-1061
Web Code: ccn-1062
Web Code: ccn-1063

Materials for Activities and Labs

Quantities for each group

STUDENT EDITION

Inquiry Activity, p. 157
4 wood splints or small lab spatulas, sodium chloride, black construction paper, hand lens, alum, Epsom salts, sucrose

Quick Lab, p. 167
test paper, metric ruler, felt-tip markers, stapler, beaker, alcohol-water mixture, Petri dish

Quick Lab, p. 173
blue plastic-foam ball, black plastic-foam ball, 7 white gumdrops, toothpicks

Consumer Lab, pp. 184–185
tongs, 2 fabric test strips, hot dye bath containing methyl orange, clock or watch, paper towels, scissors, soap, hot iron(II) sulfate solution

TEACHER'S EDITION

Teacher Demo, p. 168
molecular model kit, 4 12-inch pieces of string or yarn, tape, overhead projector

Teacher Demo, p. 169
200-mL beaker, water, sewing needle, tweezers, dropper pipet

Teacher Demo, p. 177
salt lick (or rock salt), copper wire, hammer, goggles

Teacher Demo, p. 180
brass bell, bronze bell

Build Science Skills, p. 182
access to a library or the Internet, notepad for data collection

Chapter Assessment

CHAPTER ASSESSMENT

SE Chapter Assessment, pp. 187–188
CUT Chapter 6 Test A, B
CTB Chapter 6
iT Chapter 6
PHSchool.com GO
Web Code: cca-1060

STANDARDIZED TEST PREP

SE Chapter 6, p. 189
TP Diagnose and Prescribe

Interactive Textbook

Interactive Textbook with assessment at PHSchool.com

CHAPTER 6

Before you teach

From the Author

David Frank
Ferris State University

Big Ideas

The overriding theme of Chapter 6 is the principle that when the highest occupied energy level of an atom is filled with electrons, that atom tends to be stable. Except for elements in the first row of the periodic table, it takes eight electrons to fill the highest occupied energy level. For this reason, the principle is sometimes referred to as the octet rule. Because atoms of noble gases have an octet of valence electrons, these elements are extremely unlikely to react. Other elements must form bonds to achieve stable electron configurations.

Matter and Change Help students connect types of bonds to differences in properties among classes of substances. A good example is electrical conductivity. Covalent compounds do not conduct an electric current because their fundamental particles are neutral molecules with covalent bonds. Ionic compounds don't conduct in the solid state because their charged particles (ions) are fixed in position, but they do conduct as liquids because the ions are then free to move. Metals conduct even in the solid state due to their mobile electrons.

Forces and Motion Forces of attraction are the key to bond formation. Ionic bonds form because cations and anions attract one another. Covalent bonds form because the (positive) nuclei of two atoms are attracted to their shared electrons. Metallic bonds form because cations are attracted to a pool of shared valence electrons.

Energy The tendency for ionization energy to decrease from top to bottom within a group is related to another trend within groups—the increasing size of atomic radii. Valence electrons are shielded from the positive nucleus by all the nonvalence electrons. In larger atoms, such as cesium (Cs), there are more nonvalence electrons than in a smaller atom such as sodium (Na). So it takes less energy to remove an electron from cesium than from sodium. Ionization energy is important for explaining the behavior of metals. The ability to attract electrons is important for explaining the behavior for nonmetals.

Chemistry Refresher

Bond Strength in Ionic Compounds 6.1

An ionic compound forms when electrons are transferred from metal atoms to nonmetal atoms. The ions that form are in a three-dimensional array called a crystal lattice. Within the lattice, there are strong attractions between an ion and neighboring ions of opposite charge. The strength of the bonds depends on the arrangement of the ions, their sizes, and their charges. Crystals are classified by the angles at which the faces (sides) of the crystal meet and by how many of the edges on a face are of equal length. Most binary ionic compounds, such as sodium chloride, have cube-shaped crystals. In a cubic crystal, all of the edges on a face are of equal length and all the faces meet at a 90° angle. A unit cell (like the one shown below) is the smallest unit of a crystal that shows the arrangement of ions. For a given arrangement, the bond strength increases as the charges on the ions increase and as the distance between ions decreases (with smaller ionic radii).

Address Misconceptions

Objects become positively charged because they gain protons. However, electrons are the only subatomic particles that can be transferred during a chemical change. For a strategy to overcome this misconception, see **Address Misconceptions** on **page 159.**

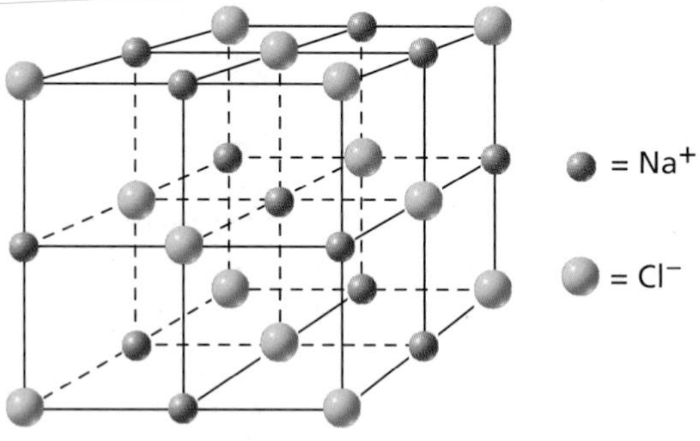
= Na^+
= Cl^-

Sodium Chloride Unit Cell

Electronegativity and Bond Types 6.2

Electronegativity is a quantity that describes an atom's ability to attract the electrons within a bond. Values for electronegativity are often based on values for ionization energy and electron affinity. Ionization energy is a measure of an atom's ability to lose electrons. Electron affinity is a measure of an atom's ability to gain electrons.

Go Online PD LINKS NSTA

For: Teaching methods for chemical bonds
Visit: www.SciLinks.org/PDLinks
Web Code: ccn-0699

Differences in electronegativity are used to predict the type of bond that will form between atoms of two elements. As the difference in electronegativity increases, the bond becomes more polar until the electrons are transferred and an ionic bond forms.

Electronegativity Values for Selected Elements

Li 1.0	Be 1.5	B 2.0	C 2.5	N 3.0	O 3.5	F 4.0
Na 0.9	Mg 1.2	Al 1.5	Si 1.8	P 2.1	S 2.5	Cl 3.0
K 0.8	Ca 1.0	Ga 1.6	Ge 1.8	As 2.0	Se 2.4	Br 2.8

Naming Compounds 6.3

The preferred method for naming ionic compounds of metals that have variable charge is the Stock system, which uses Roman numerals to represent the charge on the ion. However, an older system that uses a root word combined with different suffixes still persists for metals that have only two charges. In this older system, the suffix *-ous* is used for the ion with the lesser charge and the suffix *-ic* is used for the ion with the greater charge. Thus, an iron(II) ion is a ferrous ion and an iron(III) ion is a ferric ion. The older system does not indicate the actual charge on the ion.

Metallic Bonding 6.4

Address Misconceptions

Many students think that particles in solids cannot move. However, in all solids, particles constantly vibrate about a fixed position. For a strategy to overcome this misconception, see **Address Misconceptions** on **page 177.**

The valence electrons in a metal are often referred to as a "sea of electrons" because of their mobility. In general, the strength of a metallic bond increases with the number of valence electrons. A metal's melting point increases with bond strength. However, melting points for transition metals peak at Group 6B even though the number of valence electrons is still increasing across the period. According to quantum theory, valence electrons in metals are in a band of overlapping atomic orbitals. Properties of metals depend on electrons moving from lower to higher energy orbitals when energy is absorbed. The configuration in Group 6B metals is ideal because all the lower energy orbitals are filled while all the higher energy orbitals are unoccupied.

Build Reading Literacy

Outline

Understanding Text Structure

Strategy Help students focus on the text and not simply skim it. Outlining is a good strategy to apply to an entire section, if it is not excessively long, using the headings as major divisions. Outlining is best applied to sections in which the headings are parallel, and in which there are main headings and subheadings. Before you begin, choose a section for students to read and outline, such as Section 6.1, pp. 158–164.

Example

1. Before students read, have them preview the section's title and headings. Demonstrate and display how to make a skeleton outline for the section. Have students list the section title at the top level, the main headings as major divisions, and the subheadings at the next level.

I. Section Title
A. Main Heading
1. Subheading
a. detail
b. detail
c. detail

2. Have students copy the skeleton outline as they read, filling in details under each main heading and subheading of the outline.
3. Tell students not to outline sections that focus on the details of cycles or processes. Students can represent these by diagrams and flowcharts rather than outlining.
4. After reading, have students review the entire section and their outlines to make sure they have included all vocabulary definitions and key concepts as main ideas or details under the appropriate levels of their outlines.

See p. 171 for a script on how to use the outline strategy with students. For additional Build Reading Literacy strategies, see pp. 161, 166, and 179.

ASSESS PRIOR KNOWLEDGE

Use the Chapter Pretest below to assess students' prior knowledge. As needed, review these Science Concepts and Math Skills with students.

Review Science Concepts

Sections 6.1 and 6.2 Review the structure of atoms. Remind students that a particle with a negative charge will attract a particle with a positive charge. Encourage students to recall what they have learned about valence electrons and electron configurations. Students should be familiar with the organization of the periodic table.

Section 6.3 Review the locations of elements in the periodic table.

Section 6.4 Have students review the general properties of metals. Review the difference in composition between a substance and a mixture.

Review Math Skills

Ratios and Proportions Students will need to understand ratios and proportions in order to determine chemical formulas.

Direct students to the **Math Skills** in the **Skills and Reference Handbook** at the end of the student text.

CHAPTER

6 Chemical Bonds

CONCEPTS in Action

How do science concepts apply to your world? Here are some questions you'll be able to answer after you read this chapter.

- Why is titanium metal welded in an argon atmosphere? *(Section 6.1)*
- What causes a crystal of rock salt to shatter when it is struck? *(Section 6.1)*
- Why is water a liquid while carbon dioxide is a gas at room temperature? *(Section 6.2)*
- What advantage does jewelry made from a gold-silver alloy have over jewelry made from pure gold? *(Section 6.4)*

Discovery Channel School **Video Field Trip**
Good Conduct

- How does mixing other elements with silicon make silicon a better conductor of electric current? *(page 182)*

The calcium carbonate in shells ▶ and the silicon dioxide in sand are examples of compounds with different types of bonds.

156 *Chapter 6*

Chapter Pretest

1. Describe the structure of atoms. *(An atom consists of a dense, positively charged nucleus containing protons and neutrons, surrounded by space in which negatively charged electrons move.)*
2. True or False: Objects with opposite charges attract one another. *(True)*
3. What are valence electrons? *(Electrons in the highest occupied energy level of an atom)*
4. Which group in the periodic table contains elements that hardly react at all? *(The noble gases)*
5. Where on the periodic table are nonmetals generally found? *(The right side)*
6. How do the compositions of mixtures differ from those of substances? *(The composition of a mixture can vary. The composition of a substance is fixed.)*
7. What property is being described when someone says that a solid is easily hammered into sheets? *(b)*
- **a.** Conductivity
- **b.** Malleability
- **c.** Melting point
- **d.** Density

Chapter Preview

Inquiry Activity

What Can the Shape of a Material Tell You About the Material?

Procedure

1. Use a wood splint or small lab spatula to place a small sample of table salt on a sheet of black construction paper.
2. Use a hand lens to examine the sample. On a separate sheet of paper, sketch the shapes of some pieces in the sample.
3. Repeat Steps 1 and 2 with each of the compounds your teacher provides.

Think About It

1. **Observing** Compare the shapes of the pieces in the different compounds.
2. **Predicting** Could any differences you observed be used to identify a compound? Explain your answer.
3. **Formulating Hypotheses** What could be happening at the atomic level in compounds to produce the different shapes you observed?

Discovery Channel School

Video Field Trip

Good Conduct

Encourage students to view the Video Field Trip "Good Conduct."

ENGAGE/EXPLORE

Inquiry Activity

What Can the Shape of a Material Tell You About the Material? L2

Purpose In this activity, students begin to recognize that the shape of pieces of a compound could be related to its structure at the atomic level.

Skills Focus Observing, Comparing and Contrasting

Prep Time 10 minutes

Materials 4 wood splints or small lab spatulas, sodium chloride, black construction paper, hand lens, alum, Epsom salts, sucrose

Class Time 15 minutes

Safety Students should wear safety goggles, lab aprons, and disposable plastic gloves.

Teaching Tips

- Point out that if all the samples of a substance have a similar shape, the shape may be a property of the substance.
- Encourage students to think about the spatial arrangement of the particles in a substance.

Expected Outcome Each substance forms crystals with a particular and different shape.

Think About It

1. Sodium chloride crystals are cubes. Alum crystals are small and irregular "cuboids" shaped like a cube that is missing part of a side. Crystals of Epsom salts look like cylinders with one or both ends pointed. Sucrose crystals may appear oblong with slightly slanted ends.
2. Although the samples have distinctive shapes, the shapes are not sufficiently distinct to help a person identify each substance. (Many crystals have the same general shape.)
3. Students may hypothesize that the arrangement of particles at the atomic level might be responsible for the different crystal shapes.
Visual, Logical

1 FOCUS

Objectives

6.1.1 **Recognize** stable electron configurations.

6.1.2 **Predict** an element's chemical properties using number of valence electrons and electron dot diagrams.

6.1.3 **Describe** how an ionic bond forms and how ionization energy affects the process.

6.1.4 **Predict** the composition of an ionic compound from its chemical formula.

6.1.5 **Relate** the properties of ionic compounds to the structure of crystal lattices.

Reading Focus

Build Vocabulary L2

Word Forms Have students think of word forms related to *crystals* such as *crystalline* and *crystallize.* Have them discuss ways people commonly use these words—and the word *crystal*—and compare those usages to the way *crystals* is defined in Section 6.1.

Reading Strategy L2

a. Form a cation **b.** Form an anion

2 INSTRUCT

Stable Electron Configurations

Integrate Social Studies L2

In 1902, G.N. Lewis proposed "the theory of the cubical atom." He illustrated his theory with drawings of cubes with valence electrons placed at their corners. In his classic 1916 paper, "The Atom and the Molecule," Lewis simplified his diagrams by using dots to represent electrons and a symbol to represent the kernel of an atom.

Recreate the cube models for lithium and beryllium on the board or overhead projector. (Draw cubes with one and two corners circled, respectively.) Explain that each circle represents a valence electron. Then, have students refer to Figure 2 and draw their own cube models for boron, carbon, nitrogen, oxygen, and fluorine. **Logical, Visual**

6.1 Ionic Bonding

Reading Focus

Key Concepts

- When is an atom unlikely to react?
- What is one way in which elements can achieve stable electron configurations?
- How does the structure of an ionic compound affect its properties?

Vocabulary

- electron dot diagram
- ion
- anion
- cation
- chemical bond
- ionic bond
- chemical formula
- crystals

Reading Strategy

Sequencing Copy the concept map. As you read, complete the concept map to show what happens to atoms during ionic bonding.

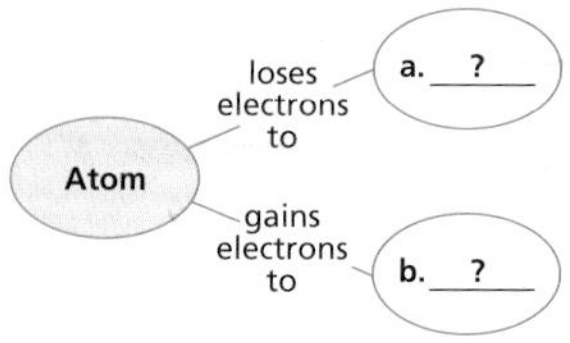
Atom
loses electrons to
a. ?
gains electrons to
b. ?

The handle of the titanium mug in Figure 1 was joined to the body by welding. The pieces were heated until their surfaces fused together. The welding of titanium does not take place in air. At the temperature at which welding occurs, titanium becomes hot enough to react with oxygen in the air, forming an oxide. The oxide makes the weld more brittle and likely to break. Because titanium does not react with a noble gas such as argon, the welding of titanium usually takes place in an argon atmosphere.

Argon's name is a reminder of its inactivity. It comes from the Greek word *argos,* which means "idle" or "inert." Why is argon very inactive yet oxygen is highly reactive? Chemical properties, such as reactivity, depend on an element's electron configuration.

Figure 1 The handle and body of this titanium mug were welded together in an argon atmosphere. If titanium is allowed to react with oxygen in air, the compound that forms makes the weld more brittle and more likely to break.

Stable Electron Configurations

The highest occupied energy level of a noble gas atom is filled. **When the highest occupied energy level of an atom is filled with electrons, the atom is stable and not likely to react.** The noble gases have stable electron configurations with eight valence electrons (or two in the case of helium).

The chemical properties of an element depend on the number of valence electrons. Therefore, it is useful to have a model of atoms that focuses only on valence electrons. The models in Figure 2 are electron dot diagrams. An **electron dot diagram** is a model of an atom in which each dot represents a valence electron. The symbol in the center represents the nucleus and all the other electrons in the atom.

Section Resources

Print

- ***Reading and Study Workbook With Math Support,*** Section 6.1
- ***Math Skills and Problem Solving Workbook,*** Section 6.1
- ***Transparencies,*** Chapter Pretest and Section 6.1

Technology

- ***Interactive Textbook,*** Section 6.1
- ***Presentation Pro CD-ROM,*** Chapter Pretest and Section 6.1
- ***Go Online,*** NSTA SciLinks, Ionic bonds

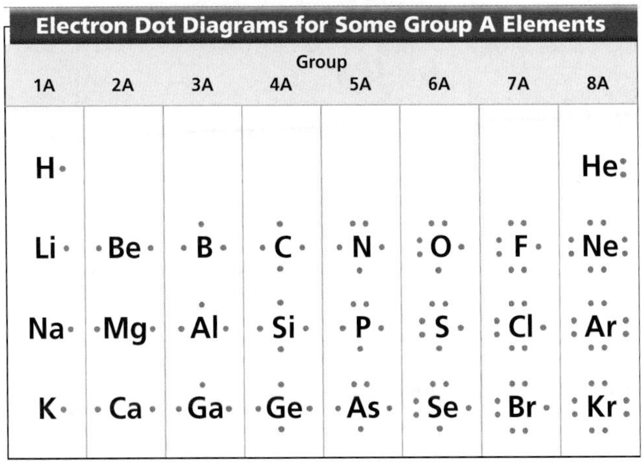

Electron Dot Diagrams for Some Group A Elements
Group
1A 2A 3A 4A 5A 6A 7A 8A
H He
Li Be B C N O F Ne
Na Mg Al Si P S Cl Ar
K Ca Ga Ge As Se Br Kr

Figure 2 In an electron dot diagram, each dot represents a valence electron. **Observing** ***How many valence electrons do sodium and chlorine have?***

Ionic Bonds

Elements that do not have complete sets of valence electrons tend to react. By reacting, they achieve electron configurations similar to those of noble gases. **Some elements achieve stable electron configurations through the transfer of electrons between atoms.**

Transfer of Electrons Look at the electron dot diagram for chlorine in Figure 2. A chlorine atom has one electron fewer than an argon atom. If the chlorine atom were to gain a valence electron, it would have the same stable electron arrangement as argon. Look at the electron dot diagram for sodium. A sodium atom has one more electron than a neon atom. If a sodium atom were to lose this electron, its highest occupied energy level would have eight electrons. It would then have the same stable electron arrangement as neon.

What happens at the atomic level when sodium reacts with chlorine? An electron is transferred from each sodium atom to a chlorine atom. Each atom ends up with a more stable electron arrangement than it had before the transfer.

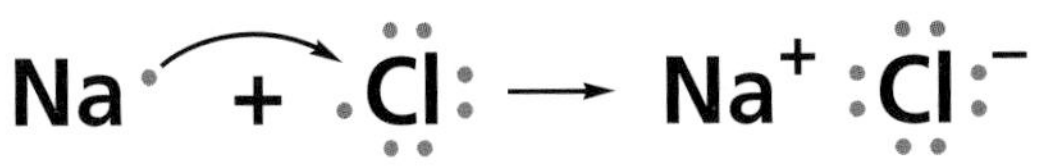

Na + Cl → Na+ Cl−

Formation of Ions When an atom gains or loses an electron, the number of protons is no longer equal to the number of electrons. The charge on the atom is not balanced and the atom is not neutral. An atom that has a net positive or negative electric charge is called an **ion.** The charge on an ion is represented by a plus or a minus sign. Notice the plus sign next to the symbol for sodium and the minus sign next to the symbol for chlorine.

Go Online NSTA SCILINKS

For: Links on ionic bonds
Visit: www.SciLinks.org
Web Code: ccn-1061

Build Science Skills L2

Predicting Emphasize that, except for hydrogen and helium, the dots in an electron dot diagram do not represent all of the electrons in an atom, just the valence electrons.

Have students look at Figure 2. Ask them to predict the electron dot diagrams for rubidium, strontium, indium, tin, antimony, tellurium, iodine, and xenon. *(These elements—Rb, Sr, In, Sn, Sb, Te, I, and Xe—have the same valence electron configurations as the elements directly above them in the periodic table.)*
Logical, Visual

Ionic Bonds

Address Misconceptions L2

Many students think that objects become positively charged because they gain protons. Challenge this misconception by explaining that electrons are the only subatomic particles that can be transferred from an atom during a chemical change. Have students recall how electrons can move to higher energy levels when an atom absorbs energy. Remind students of the location of protons in the nuclei of atoms.
Logical

FYI

Once an ion has been defined as a charged particle, the term *atom* can be reserved for the neutral particle.

Go Online NSTA SCILINKS

Download a worksheet on ionic bonds for students to complete, and find additional teacher support from NSTA SciLinks.

Customize for Inclusion Students

Visually Impaired
Have interested students listen to a recording of *Ionisation,* a musical work scored for percussion and sirens in 1931 by French-American composer Edgard Varèse (1883–1965). There is no melody or harmony, just blocks of sound produced by instruments including cymbals, maracas, and drums. The noises are supposed to represent what happens to electrons as ionization occurs. Let students state their reactions to the music. Ask them to discuss how appropriate the title is for this piece of music.

Answer to . . .

Figure 2 *Sodium has one valence electron. Chlorine has seven.*

Data Analysis

What Determines the Size of an Atom or Ion? L2

Answers

1. Within a period, the atomic radius decreases as the atomic number increases.
2. Within these groups, the atomic radius increases as the atomic number increases.
3. When the next higher energy level is occupied, there is a significant increase in the atomic radius.
4. The ionic radius for potassium is much smaller than its atomic radius. The ionic radius for bromine is much larger than its atomic radius.
5. With the loss of valence electrons, the radius decreases. With the addition of valence electrons, the radius increases.
6. An energy level that was occupied is no longer occupied and the size decreases.

For Extra Help L1

Explain that attractions between protons and electrons largely determine the atomic radius of a specific atom.
Verbal

FYI

Because an electron cloud does not have an outer edge, the radius for elements that form diatomic molecules is calculated by measuring the distance between the two nuclei in the molecule and dividing by two.

Data Analysis

What Determines the Size of an Atom or Ion?

Scientists use atomic radii to compare the sizes of atoms of different elements. Remember from mathematics that the radius of a sphere is the distance from the center of the sphere to its outer edge. The radius is half the diameter of the sphere. Because atomic radii are extremely small, these distances are expressed in units called picometers (pm). As a comparison, there are one billion (10^9) picometers in a millimeter.

The table shows the atomic radius and ionic radius for six metals and six nonmetals. You will use the data to relate the size of an element's atoms to the element's location on the periodic table. You also will use the data to compare the sizes of atoms and their ions.

Atomic and Ionic Radii

	1A	2A	6A	7A
Atomic radius	152	112	66	64
Element	Li	Be	O	F
Ionic radius	1+ 60	2+ 31	2– 140	1– 136
Atomic radius	186	160	103	99
Element	Na	Mg	S	Cl
Ionic radius	1+ 95	2+ 65	2– 184	1– 181
Atomic radius	227	197	117	114
Element	K	Ca	Se	Br
Ionic radius	1+ 133	2+ 99	2– 198	1– 195

1. **Using Tables** Within a period, what happens to the atomic radius as the atomic number of the elements increases?
2. **Using Tables** Within Groups 1A, 2A, 6A, and 7A, what happens to the atomic radius of elements as the atomic number increases?
3. **Inferring** How does adding an occupied energy level affect the atomic radius? (*Hint:* Lithium is a Period 2 element and sodium is a Period 3 element.)
4. **Comparing and Contrasting** Compare the atomic and ionic radii for potassium (K), and for bromine (Br).
5. **Making Generalizations** What happens to the radius of an atom when the atom loses electrons? When the atom gains electrons?
6. **Relating Cause and Effect** Explain the difference in size between a metal atom and its cation.

The ion that forms when a chlorine atom gains an electron has 17 protons and 18 electrons. This ion has a charge of 1– because it has one extra electron. The symbol for the ion is written Cl^{1-}, or Cl^- for short. An ion with a negative charge is an **anion** (AN eye un). Anions like the Cl^- ion are named by using part of the element name plus the suffix *–ide.* Thus, Cl^- is called a *chloride* ion.

A sodium ion has 11 protons and 10 electrons. Because it has one extra proton, the sodium ion has a charge of 1+. The symbol for the ion is written Na^{1+}, or Na^+ for short. An ion with a positive charge is a **cation** (KAT eye un). Naming a cation is easy. You just use the element name, as in the *sodium* ion.

Formation of Ionic Bonds Remember that a particle with a negative charge will attract a particle with a positive charge. When an anion and a cation are close together, a chemical bond forms between them. A **chemical bond** is the force that holds atoms or ions together as a unit. An **ionic bond** is the force that holds cations and anions together. An ionic bond forms when electrons are transferred from one atom to another.

Facts and Figures

Atomic and Ionic Radii The radius of an atom decreases from left to right across a period because valence electrons are shielded from the nucleus by electrons in lower energy levels. The amount of positive nuclear charge experienced by valence electrons is mainly determined by the difference in charge between the nucleus and the inner (or core) electrons. Because the number of core electrons does not change across a period, as the number of protons increases the charge experienced by valence electrons increases and the atomic radius decreases.

The radius of an anion is larger than the radius of its corresponding atom. Adding electrons to the highest occupied energy level increases the repulsions among electrons. The increase in repulsions causes the electrons to spread out more in space.

Ionization Energy An electron can move to a higher energy level when an atom absorbs energy. Cations form when electrons gain enough energy to escape from atoms. The energy allows electrons to overcome the attraction of the protons in the nucleus. The amount of energy used to remove an electron is called ionization energy. It varies from element to element. The lower the ionization energy, the easier it is to remove an electron from an atom.

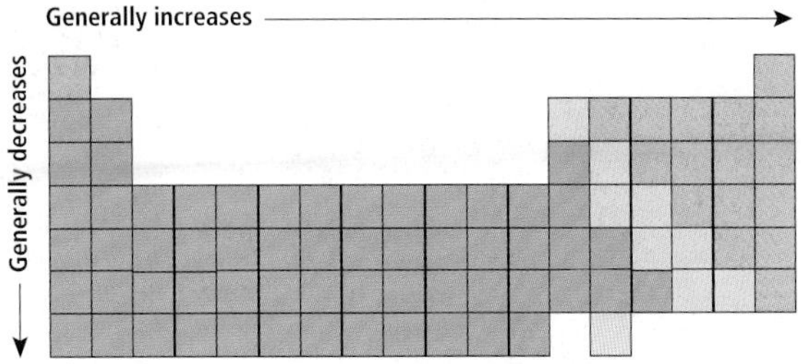

Generally increases
Generally decreases

Trends in Ionization Energy

Figure 3 Ionization energies generally increase from left to right across a period. ***Interpreting Diagrams*** *What is the trend for ionization energy within a group?*

Figure 3 shows two trends for ionization energy. Ionization energies tend to increase from left to right across a period. It takes more energy to remove an electron from a nonmetal than from a metal in the same period. Ionization energies tend to decrease from the top of a group to the bottom. In Group 1A, potassium has a lower ionization energy than sodium. So it is easier to remove an electron from potassium than from sodium, and potassium is more reactive than sodium.

Reading Checkpoint *What is ionization energy?*

Ionic Compounds

Compounds that contain ionic bonds are ionic compounds, which can be represented by chemical formulas. A **chemical formula** is a notation that shows what elements a compound contains and the ratio of the atoms or ions of these elements in the compound. The chemical formula for sodium chloride is NaCl. From the formula, you can tell that there is one sodium ion for each chloride ion in sodium chloride.

Based on the diagram in Figure 4, what would the formula for magnesium chloride be? A magnesium atom cannot reach a stable electron configuration by reacting with just one chlorine atom. It must transfer electrons to two chlorine atoms. After the transfer, the charge on the magnesium ion is 2+ and its symbol is Mg^{2+}. The formula for the compound is $MgCl_2$. The 2 written to the right and slightly below the symbol for chlorine is a subscript. Subscripts are used to show the relative numbers of atoms of the elements present. If there is only one atom of an element in the formula, no subscript is needed.

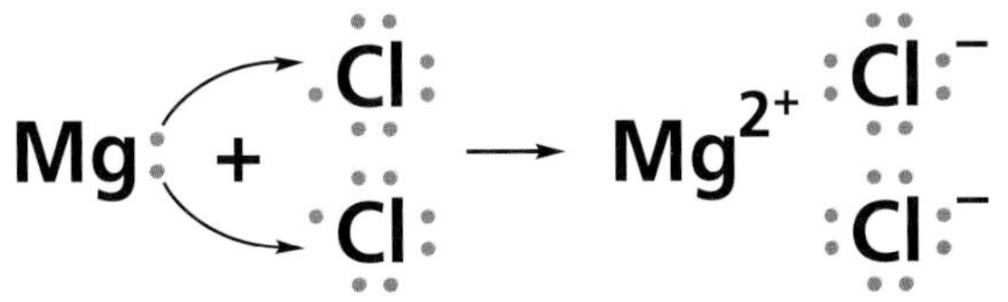

Mg
+
Cl
Cl
Mg
2+
Cl
−
Cl
−

Figure 4 Magnesium chloride forms when magnesium atoms transfer electrons to chlorine atoms. Magnesium chloride is used to control dust that is stirred up by traffic on unpaved roads.

Facts and Figures

Ionization Energy Ionization energy varies for each valence electron in an atom. These energies are referred to as first ionization energy, I_1, second ionization energy, I_2, and so forth. An I_2 is always greater than an I_1 for a given element because the second electron is being removed from a positively charged ion. Because the positive charge continues to increase with each subsequent removal of an electron, an I_3 is greater than an I_2.

FYI

Memory aids may help students distinguish cations and anions. Tell students that *cation* means "to go down," which might make them think of losing an electron, and that *anion* means "to go up," which might make them think of gaining an electron. Students could also think of related terms that start with the same letter, such as *cast off* for cation and *accept* for anion. Finally, students could associate the phrase A Negative ION with anion.

Use Visuals L1

Figure 3 Emphasize the difference between the trend in ionization energy across a period and the trend within a group. Ask, **According to Figure 3, which element has a greater ionization energy, sodium or magnesium?** *(Magnesium)* **Which element has a greater ionization energy, potassium or cesium?** *(Cesium)* **Logical**

Ionic Compounds

Build Reading Literacy L1

KWL Refer to page **124D** in **Chapter 5**, which provides the guidelines for a KWL.

Before students read Ionic Compounds, have students construct a KWL chart with three columns entitled, What I Know, What I Want to Know, and What I Learned. Have them fill out the final column after they have read pp. 161–164. **Intrapersonal**

Build Math Skills L1

Ratios and Proportions When elements combine to form compounds, they do so in specific whole number ratios. For example, water, or H_2O, has a hydrogen to oxygen ratio of 2:1. Ask students to calculate the following ratios: sodium to chlorine in sodium chloride, NaCl; magnesium to chlorine in magnesium chloride, $MgCl_2$; and sodium to oxygen in sodium oxide, Na_2O. *(1:1; 1:2; 2:1)* **Logical**

Direct students to the **Math Skills** in the **Skills and Reference Handbook** at the end of the student text for additional help.

Answer to . . .

Figure 3 *It generally decreases from top to bottom within a group.*

Reading Checkpoint *The amount of energy needed to remove an electron from an atom*

Integrate Earth Science L2

Geologists use a system to classify minerals similar to the one used by chemists to classify compounds. Ask students to use the library or Internet to find photographs of minerals that have cubic crystals (like sodium chloride) or hexagonal crystals (like ruby). Some students may also want to find examples of tetragonal, monoclinic, triclinic, and orthorhombic crystals.
Visual

Use Visuals L1

Figure 5 Have students examine Figure 5. Ask, **How are sodium ions represented in the figure?** *(Sodium ions are represented by the smaller, orange spheres.)* **How are chloride ions represented in the figure?** *(Chloride ions are represented by the larger, green spheres.)* **What do you notice about the pattern of the locations of positive and negative ions in the diagram?** *(No two neighboring ions have the same charge.)* **What similarity do you notice between the diagram and the photograph of sodium chloride crystals?** *(The structures in both the diagram and the photograph have a cubic shape.)*
Visual

Build Science Skills L2

Applying Concepts Help students understand the structure of a crystal lattice by encouraging them to think of three-dimensional analogies for lattices, such as scaffolding on a building or cups and saucers stacked on a tray in a restaurant.
Visual, Logical

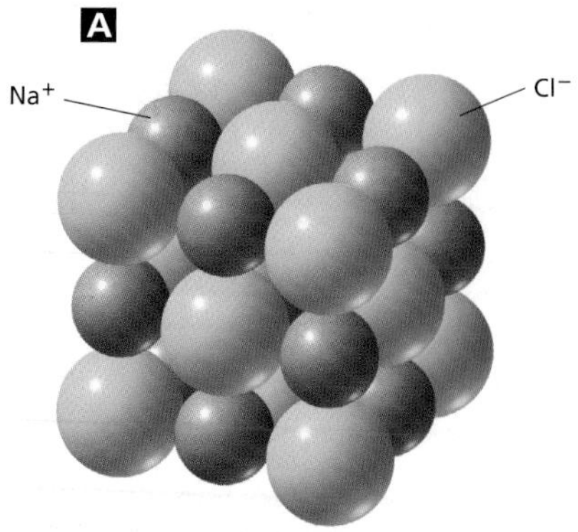
A
Na^+
Cl^-

B

Figure 5 The structure and shape of a crystal are related. **A** In a sodium chloride crystal, each ion is surrounded by six oppositely charged ions. **B** Sodium chloride crystals are shaped like cubes.

Crystal Lattices A chemical formula for an ionic compound tells you the ratio of the ions in the compound. But it does not tell you how the ions are arranged in the compound. If you looked at a sample of sodium chloride with a hand lens or microscope, you would be able to see that the pieces of salt are shaped like cubes. This shape is a clue to how the sodium and chloride ions are arranged in the compound.

Figure 5A shows that the ions in sodium chloride are arranged in an orderly, three-dimensional structure. Each chloride ion is surrounded by six sodium ions and each sodium ion is surrounded by six chloride ions. Each ion is attracted to all the neighboring ions with an opposite charge. This set of attractions keeps the ions in fixed positions in a rigid framework, or lattice. The repeating pattern of ions in the lattice is like the repeating pattern of designs on the wallpaper in Figure 6.

Solids whose particles are arranged in a lattice structure are called **crystals.** Compare the cubic shape of the sodium chloride crystals in Figure 5B to the arrangement of ions in Figure 5A. The shape of an ionic crystal depends on the arrangement of ions in its lattice. In turn, the arrangement of the ions depends on the ratio of ions and their relative sizes. Crystals are classified into groups based on the shape of their crystals. Crystals of ruby have a six-sided, hexagonal shape. The How It Works box on page 163 describes one way to make rubies.

Reading Checkpoint *What shape are sodium chloride crystals?*

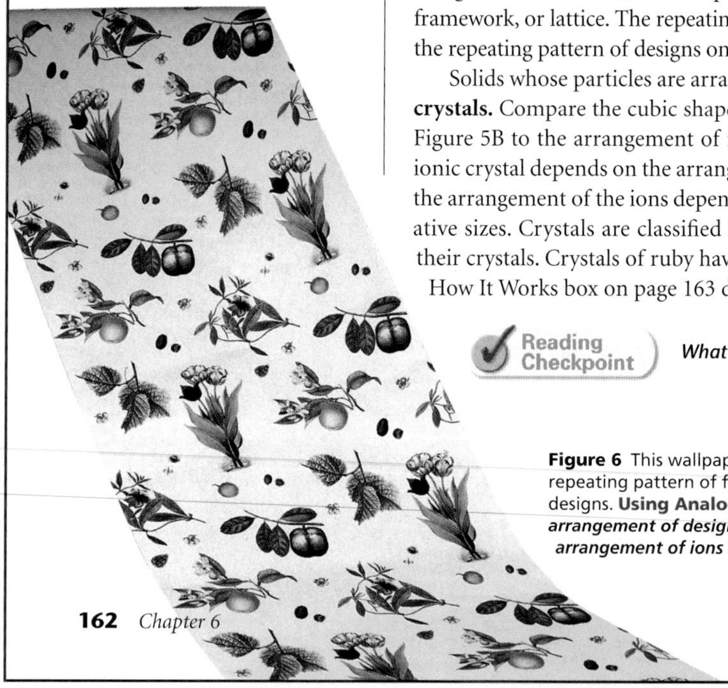

Figure 6 This wallpaper displays a repeating pattern of flower and fruit designs. **Using Analogies** *How is this arrangement of designs similar to the arrangement of ions in a crystal?*

Facts and Figures

Crystal Systems Crystals are classified into seven different crystal systems, which are described by geometric figures with six faces. The figures are distinguished by the angles at which the faces meet and by how many edges on a face are equal in length. Cubic: three equal edges, three 90° angles; tetragonal: two equal edges, three 90° angles; orthorhombic: no equal edges, three 90° angles; monoclinic: no equal edges, two 90° angles; triclinic: no equal edges, no 90° angles; hexagonal: two equal edges, two 90° angles, one 120° angle; rhombohedral: three equal edges, two 90° angles.

Synthetic Rubies

Rubies are mainly aluminum oxide, which is white. The substitution of a small percentage of chromium ions for aluminum ions gives rubies their distinctive red color. Because natural rubies are rare, rubies are often manufactured. **Interpreting Diagrams** ***What substances are in the mixture used to make rubies?***

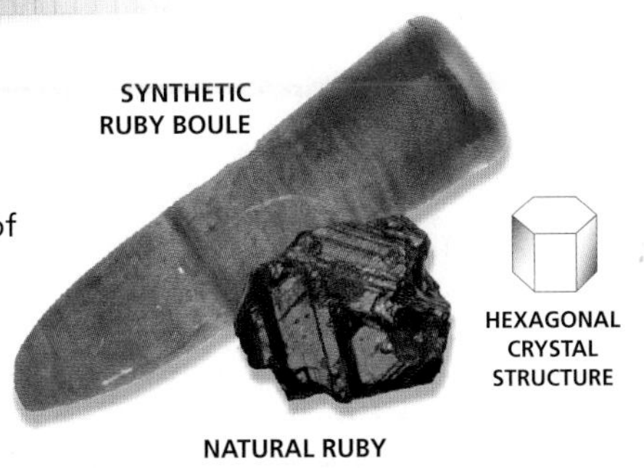
SYNTHETIC RUBY BOULE
HEXAGONAL CRYSTAL STRUCTURE
NATURAL RUBY

Synthetic ruby
A synthetic ruby boule has a hexagonal crystal structure identical to the natural ruby gemstone. Its shape is determined by the arrangement of ions in the crystal.

Making synthetic rubies
One way of making synthetic rubies is called the pulled-growth method. It was invented by Polish scientist Jan Czochralski (1885–1953).

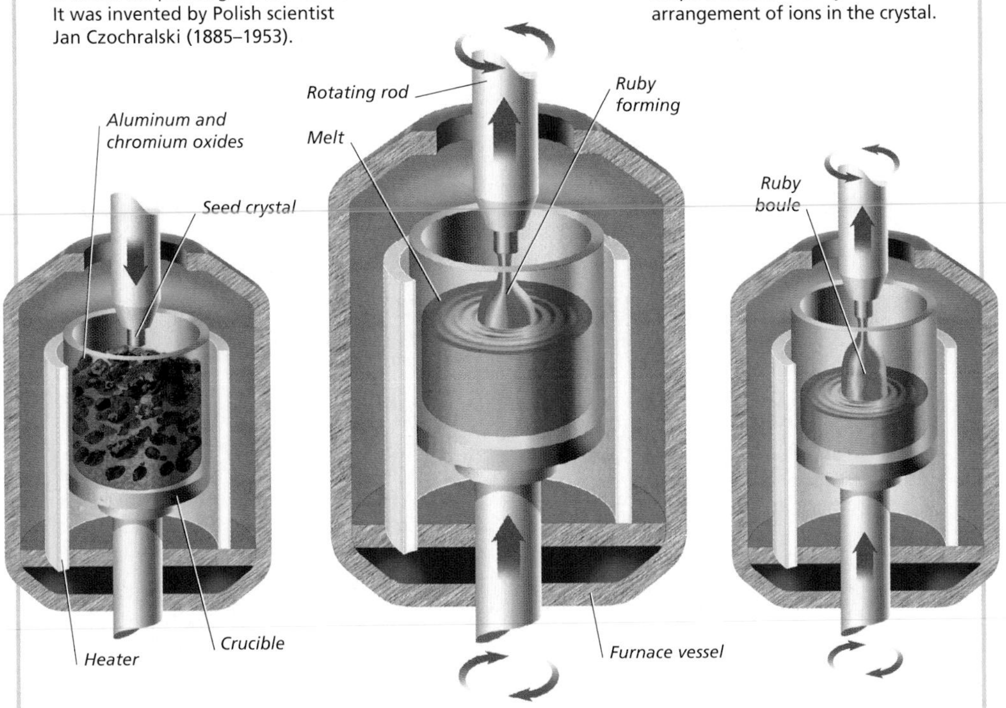
Aluminum and chromium oxides
Seed crystal
Heater
Crucible
Rotating rod
Melt
Ruby forming
Furnace vessel
Ruby boule

1 Seed crystal Aluminum oxide and chromium(VI) oxide are melted. A tiny piece of ruby, called a seed crystal, is attached to a rod and placed above the molten mixture (melt).

2 Lowering into the melt The rod is lowered until the seed crystal touches the melt. The rod is slowly lifted, and ions in the melt begin to attach themselves to the seed crystal to form a ruby.

3 Forming a boule As the rod is lifted higher, an oblong-shaped crystal called a boule grows from the end. Once cooled, the boule can be cut into different shapes.

Synthetic Rubies L2

Another technique used to create synthetic rubies was first used in 1902. It is called the Verneuil flame-fusion process. It differs from the more expensive Czochralski pulled-growth process described in the text in that the mixture of aluminum and chromium oxides is heated in open air with a flame instead of melted in a crucible.

The mineral corundum consists of aluminum oxide mixed with chromium, iron, or other mineral impurities. The color of a corundum crystal depends on the type and amount of impurities. Crystals of red corundum are called rubies, while crystals of other colors are called sapphires. In addition to the familiar use of synthetic rubies in jewelry, some lasers use synthetic rubies to produce light of a specific frequency.

Interpreting Diagrams Oxides of aluminum and chromium
Visual

For Enrichment L3

Interested students can make a poster presentation for the class explaining other methods for synthesizing gemstones. Some common methods besides the flame-fusion and pulled-growth methods include the flux-growth method, the solution-growth process, and horizontal crystallization.
Visual, Portfolio

Answer to . . .

Figure 6 *The pattern of design elements in the wallpaper repeats the way the arrangement of ions repeats in a crystal lattice.*

Reading Checkpoint *They are cubes.*

Section 6.1 (continued)

FYI

Real crystals are not perfect. Sites in a lattice may be vacant, sites may be occupied by impurities, and occupied sites may be squeezed in between regular sites in the lattice (an interstitial defect). In an ionic compound, a cation vacancy is balanced by a nearby anion vacancy or by an interstitial cation (which maintains an overall balance of charge). Crystal defects are largely responsible for how crystals fracture under stress.

Use Visuals L1

Figure 7 Have students compare the before-and-after diagrams. Ask, **When the hammer hits the crystal, what happens to the positions of the ions?** *(Ions with similar charge are pushed near one another.)* **How do objects with the same charge behave?** *(They repel.)* **Visual**

3 ASSESS

Evaluate Understanding L2

Have students describe the formation of anions, cations, and ionic bonds.

Reteach L1

Use the diagram at the bottom of p. 161 to review the formation of cations, anions, and ionic bonds.

Connecting Concepts

Potassium is more reactive than calcium because the amount of energy needed to remove a single valence electron from a potassium atom is much smaller than the amount of energy needed to remove two valence electrons from a calcium atom.

Interactive Textbook If your class subscribes to the Interactive Textbook, use it to review key concepts in Section 6.1.

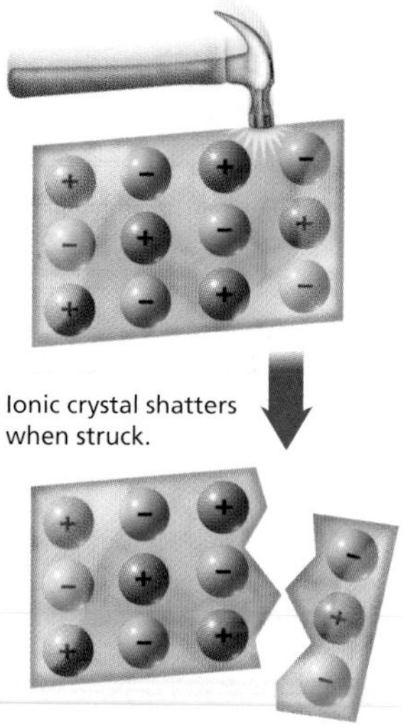
Hammer strikes crystal.
Ionic crystal shatters when struck.

Figure 7 When an ionic crystal is struck, ions are moved from their fixed positions. Ions with the same charge repel one another and the crystal shatters.

Properties of Ionic Compounds The properties of sodium chloride are typical of an ionic compound. It has a high melting point (801°C). In its solid state, sodium chloride is a poor conductor of electric current. But when melted, it is a good conductor of electric current. Sodium chloride crystals shatter when struck with a hammer. **The properties of an ionic compound can be explained by the strong attractions among ions within a crystal lattice.**

Recall that the arrangement of particles in a substance is the result of two opposing factors. The first factor is the attractions among particles in the substance. The second factor is the kinetic energy of the particles. The stronger the attractions among the particles, the more kinetic energy the particles must have before they can separate.

For an electric current to flow, charged particles must be able to move from one location to another. The ions in a solid crystal lattice have fixed positions. However, when the solid melts, the lattice breaks apart and the ions are free to flow. Melted, or molten, sodium chloride is an excellent conductor of electric current.

Rock salt contains large crystals of sodium chloride. If you tapped a crystal of rock salt sharply with a hammer, it would shatter into many smaller crystals. Figure 7 shows what happens to the positions of the ions when the crystal is struck. Negative ions are pushed into positions near negative ions, and positive ions are pushed into positions near positive ions. Ions with the same charge repel one another and cause the crystal to shatter.

Section 6.1 Assessment

Reviewing Concepts

1. When is an atom least likely to react?
2. Describe one way an element can achieve a stable electron configuration.
3. What characteristic of ionic bonds can be used to explain the properties of ionic compounds?
4. Use ionization energy to explain why metals lose electrons more easily than nonmetals.
5. Why is a rock salt crystal likely to shatter when struck?

Critical Thinking

6. **Making Generalizations** What will the ratio of ions be in any compound formed from a Group 1A metal and a Group 7A nonmetal? Explain your answer.
7. **Drawing Conclusions** Why do ionic compounds include at least one metal?
8. **Predicting** Based on their chemical formulas, which of these compounds is not likely to be an ionic compound: KBr, SO_2, or $FeCl_3$? Explain your answer.

Connecting Concepts

Reactivity of Metals Use what you know about how ionic bonds form to explain the difference in reactivity between potassium and calcium. If necessary, reread the description of Group 1A and Group 2A properties in Section 5.3.

Section 6.1 Assessment

1. When the highest occupied energy level of an atom is filled with electrons
2. Through the transfer of electrons between atoms
3. The strong attractions among ions within a crystal lattice
4. Metals have lower ionization energies than nonmetals. The lower the ionization energy, the easier it is to remove an electron from an atom.
5. When ions with the same charge are pushed close together, they repel one another.
6. The ratio will be one to one because a Group 1A metal loses one electron and a Group 7A nonmetal gains one electron to achieve a stable electron configuration.
7. One element in an ionic compound must form cations, but nonmetals tend to form anions.
8. SO_2 because sulfur and oxygen are both nonmetals and unlikely to form cations

6.2 Covalent Bonding

Reading Focus

Key Concepts

- How are atoms held together in a covalent bond?
- What happens when atoms don't share electrons equally?
- What factors determine whether a molecule is polar?
- How do attractions between polar molecules compare to attractions between nonpolar molecules?

Vocabulary

- covalent bond
- molecule
- polar covalent bond

Reading Strategy

Relating Text and Visuals Copy the table. As you read, look closely at Figure 9. Complete the table by describing each type of model shown.

Model	Description
Electron dot	a. ___?___
Structural formula	b. ___?___
Space-filling	c. ___?___
Electron cloud	d. ___?___

Plants absorb water through their roots from soil or from a solution containing nutrients, as in Figure 8. Carbon dioxide from the air enters the plants through small openings in their leaves. The plants use the energy from sunlight to convert water and carbon dioxide into a sugar. Energy is stored in the chemical bonds of the sugar.

The elements in sugar are carbon, oxygen, and hydrogen. All three are nonmetals, which have relatively high ionization energies. A transfer of electrons does not tend to occur between nonmetal atoms. So, how are two nonmetals able to form bonds?

Covalent Bonds

You and a friend are participating in a treasure hunt. The rules state that the first person to find all eight items on a list will win an 21-speed bicycle. After about an hour, you have found six of the items on the list and your friend has found the other two. You and your friend have incomplete sets of items. But if you are willing to share your items with your friend, together you will have a complete set of items and qualify for the prize. Of course, you will have to be willing to share the bicycle, too. When nonmetals join together, they display a similar sharing strategy.

Figure 8 When plants are grown in water instead of soil, you can see their roots. Plants absorb water through their roots and carbon dioxide through small openings in their leaves.

Section Resources

Print

- ***Laboratory Manual,*** Investigation 6B
- ***Reading and Study Workbook With Math Support,*** Section 6.2
- ***Transparencies,*** Section 6.2

Technology

- ***Interactive Textbook,*** Section 6.2
- ***Presentation Pro CD-ROM,*** Section 6.2
- ***Go Online,*** NSTA SciLinks, Covalent bonding

Section 6.2

1 FOCUS

Objectives

6.2.1 **Describe** how covalent bonds form and the attractions that keep atoms together in molecules.

6.2.2 **Compare** polar and nonpolar bonds, and **demonstrate** how polar bonds affect the polarity of a molecule.

6.2.3 **Compare** the attractions between polar and nonpolar molecules.

Reading Focus

Build Vocabulary L2

Concept Map Have students construct a concept map using the terms *atoms, molecules, ions, covalent bonds, ionic bonds, polar, nonpolar,* and *electrons.* Instruct students to place the terms in ovals and connect the ovals with lines on which linking words are placed. Students should place the main concept (Chemical Bonding) at the top or the center. As the distance from the main concept increases, the content should become more specific.

Reading Strategy L2

a. Dots represent valence electrons. **b.** A line represents a pair of shared valence electrons. **c.** Three-dimensional spheres represent atoms. **d.** Electron clouds represent atoms.

2 INSTRUCT

Covalent Bonds

Address Misconceptions L2

Many students do not differentiate among atoms, ions, and molecules in their sketches of particle models. Challenge this misconception by asking students to make drawings to represent an atom, a molecule, and an ion. Students should draw a single sphere for an atom, at least two spheres joined in some way for a molecule, and one sphere with either a plus or a minus charge for an ion.
Visual

Use Visuals **L1**

Figure 10 Have students examine Figure 10. Ask, **Why are the atoms in the models of diatomic molecules not complete spheres?** *(The space-filling models show that orbitals of atoms overlap when they form covalent bonds.)* Have students compare the space-filling models in Figure 10 to the data on atomic radii in the Data Analysis on p. 160. Ask, **Why are the spheres in the models of fluorine, chlorine, and bromine different sizes?** *(The different sizes of spheres model the different atomic radii of the atoms.)* **Logical**

Build Reading Literacy **L1**

Visualize Refer to page **354D** in **Chapter 12**, which provides the guidelines for visualizing.

After students have read about ionic and covalent bonds and the difference between polar and nonpolar bonds, encourage students to draw diagrams that demonstrate the differences between three types of bonding: nonpolar covalent, polar covalent, and ionic. **Visual, Portfolio**

FYI

Not all nonmetal elements exist as molecules. Of those that do, not all form diatomic molecules. Molecules of crystalline sulfur contain eight sulfur atoms, S_8. Molecules of white phosphorus contain four phosphorus atoms, P_4.

Based on the octet rule, a molecule of ozone, O_3, should contain one double bond and one single coordinate covalent bond (a bond in which one of the atoms donates an unshared pair of electrons). However, the measured bond lengths for the two bonds in an ozone molecule are identical. The bonds are hybrids—not strictly single bonds or double bonds.

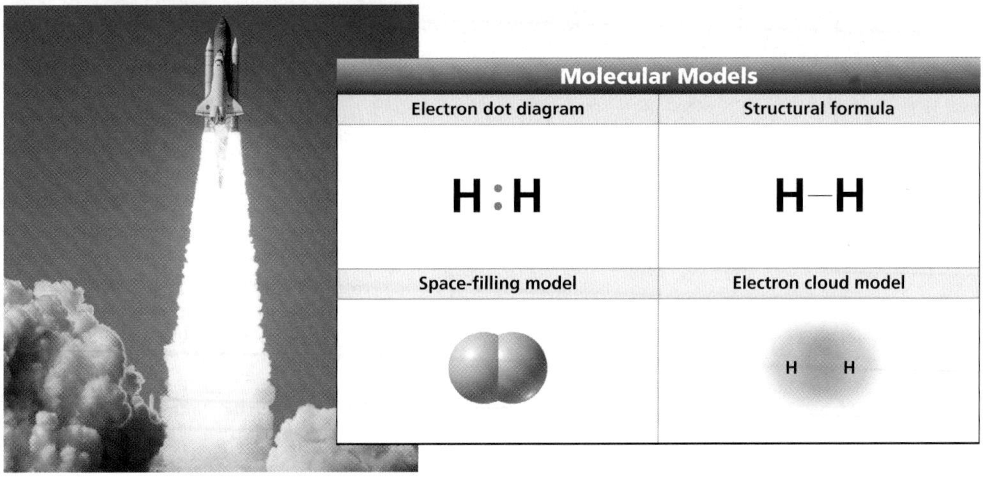
Molecular Models
Electron dot diagram
Structural formula
H:H
H–H
Space-filling model
Electron cloud model
H H

Figure 9 As a space shuttle lifts off, it leaves a water vapor trail. A reaction of hydrogen and oxygen produces the water. **Using Models** ***How is the bond between hydrogen atoms represented in each model of a hydrogen molecule?***

Sharing Electrons A hydrogen atom has one electron. If it had two electrons, it would have the same electron configuration as a helium atom. Two hydrogen atoms can achieve a stable electron configuration by sharing their electrons and forming a covalent bond. A **covalent bond** is a chemical bond in which two atoms share a pair of valence electrons. When two atoms share one pair of electrons, the bond is called a single bond.

Figure 9 shows four different ways to represent a covalent bond. In the electron dot model, the bond is shown by a pair of dots in the space between the symbols for the hydrogen atoms. In the structural formula, the pair of dots is replaced by a line. The electron cloud model and the space-filling model show that orbitals of atoms overlap when a covalent bond forms.

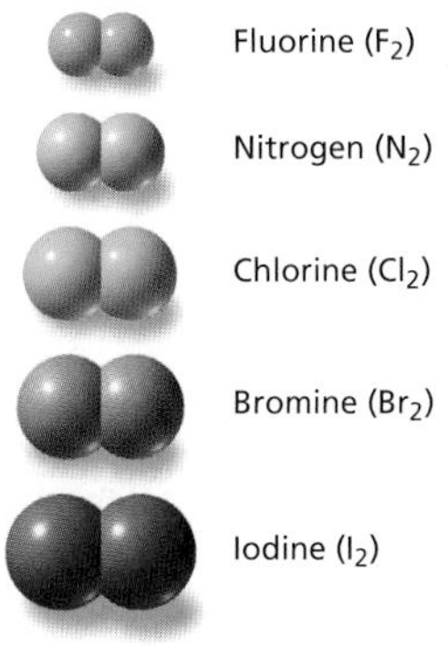
Fluorine (F_2)
Nitrogen (N_2)
Chlorine (Cl_2)
Bromine (Br_2)
Iodine (I_2)

Figure 10 These space-filling models represent diatomic molecules of five elements. **Using Models** ***How many atoms are in a diatomic molecule?***

Molecules of Elements Two hydrogen atoms bonded together form a unit called a molecule. A **molecule** is a neutral group of atoms that are joined together by one or more covalent bonds. The hydrogen molecule is neutral because it contains two protons (one from each atom) and two electrons (one from each atom). What keeps the hydrogen atoms together in the molecule? **The attractions between the shared electrons and the protons in each nucleus hold the atoms together in a covalent bond.**

A chemical formula can be used to describe the molecules of an element as well as a compound. The element hydrogen has the chemical formula H_2. The subscript 2 indicates that there are two atoms in a molecule of hydrogen.

Many nonmetal elements exist as diatomic molecules. *Diatomic* means "two atoms." Four of the models in Figure 10 are of halogens. A halogen atom has seven valence electrons. If two halogen atoms share a valence electron from each atom, both atoms have eight valence electrons.

Customize for English Language Learners

Think-Pair-Share
Have students work in pairs to think of situations that serve as analogies for ionic and covalent bonding. For example, if a jeweler lends an expensive piece of jewelry to a presenter at an awards show, a guard will accompany the presenter and stay as close as possible. This is similar to an ionic bond, in which a cation stays close to an anion to which it donates an electron. By contrast, students reading from one copy of the same book are like two atoms sharing a pair of electrons in a covalent bond. Strengthen discussion skills by having students share analogies with the class.

Quick Lab

Analyzing Inks

Materials

test paper, metric ruler, felt-tip markers, stapler, beaker, alcohol-water mixture, Petri dish

Procedure

1. Place the test paper on a clean surface. Use the ruler to draw the pencil line shown in the drawing. Use your markers to place color dots at the locations shown in the drawing.
2. With the ink marks on the outside, staple the two ends of the paper together to form a tube.
3. Pour the alcohol-water mixture into the beaker to a depth of 0.5 cm. Stand the paper in the beaker so that the dots are at the bottom. The paper should not touch the sides of the beaker. Invert the Petri dish over the beaker.
4. When the mixture reaches the top of the paper, remove the paper from the beaker. Unstaple the paper and lay it flat. Make a drawing of the results with each colored area labeled.

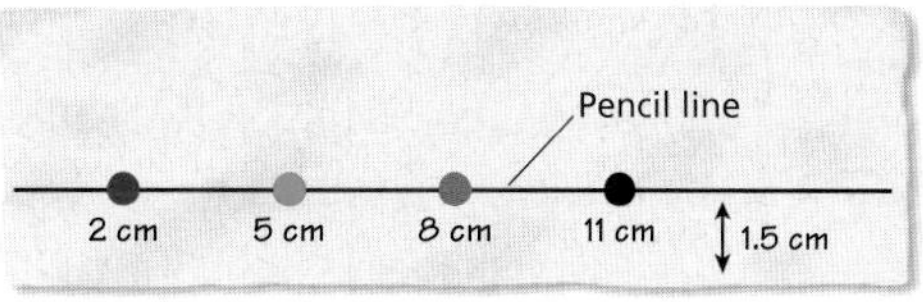

Pencil line
2 cm
5 cm
8 cm
11 cm
1.5 cm

Analyze and Conclude

1. **Observing** Which markers contained inks that were mixtures of colored substances?
2. **Formulating Hypotheses** How did some molecules in the ink move up the paper?
3. **Predicting** Assume that molecules in the test paper are more polar than molecules in the alcohol-water mixture. Would you expect the most polar molecules in ink to stick tightly to the paper or to move with the liquid? Explain.
4. **Designing Experiments** How could the procedure from this lab be used to identify a black ink whose composition is unknown?

Multiple Covalent Bonds Nitrogen has five valence electrons. If two nitrogen atoms shared a pair of electrons, each one would have only six valence electrons. If they shared two pairs of electrons, each atom would have only seven valence electrons. When the atoms in a nitrogen molecule (N_2) share three pairs of electrons, each atom has eight valence electrons. Each pair of shared electrons is represented by a long dash in the structural formula N≡N. When two atoms share three pairs of electrons, the bond is called a triple bond. When two atoms share two pairs of electrons, the bond is called a double bond.

Reading Checkpoint *What does the subscript 2 in the formula for a hydrogen molecule indicate?*

Unequal Sharing of Electrons

In general, elements on the right of the periodic table have a greater attraction for electrons than elements on the left have (except for noble gases). In general, elements at the top of a group have a greater attraction for electrons than elements at the bottom of a group have. Fluorine is on the far right and is at the top of its group. It has the strongest attraction for electrons and is the most reactive nonmetal.

Go Online NSTA SCILINKS

For: Links on covalent bonding
Visit: www.SciLinks.org
Web Code: ccn-1062

Unequal Sharing of Electrons

Quick Lab

Analyzing Inks **L2**

Objective

After completing this activity, students will be able to

- explain how differences in polarity can be used to separate the components of a solution.

Skills Focus Observing, Inferring

Prep Time 10 minutes

Advance Prep Provide each group with an 8-cm × 16-cm piece of test (chromatography) paper. The alcohol-water mixture is 70% isopropyl alcohol in water.

Class Time 20 minutes

Safety Provide only markers containing water-based inks or inks that are low in volatile organic compounds (VOCs). Make sure that there are no flames in the laboratory when alcohol is in use.

Teaching Tips

- Have students do this lab after they study polar molecules and attractions between molecules.
- Tell students not to touch the test paper with their bare hands because oil naturally present on their fingers will interfere with the results. They should wear plastic gloves.

Expected Outcome Most inks will contain more than one pigment.

Analyze and Conclude

1. In general, darker inks (such as brown or black) contain two or more red, blue, and yellow pigments.
2. Molecules that dissolved easily in the alcohol-water mixture moved up the paper with the mixture.
3. The most polar molecules would be found near the bottom of the paper because they are more strongly attracted to the paper than to the alcohol-water mixture.
4. If an unknown black ink produces a color pattern similar to one of the known inks, they are likely to be identical.
Visual, Logical

Go Online NSTA SCILINKS

Download a worksheet on covalent bonding for students to complete, and find additional teacher support from NSTA SciLinks.

Answer to . . .

Figure 9 *A pair of dots, a line, overlapping spheres, and overlapping electron clouds*

Figure 10 *Two*

Reading Checkpoint *The subscript 2 shows that there are two atoms in a hydrogen molecule.*

Teacher Demo

Modeling Overall Polarity **L2**

Purpose Students examine a model for molecular polarity.

Materials molecular model kit, 4 12-inch pieces of string or yarn, tape, overhead projector

Procedure Show students ball-and-stick models of a carbon dioxide molecule and a water molecule. Have them compare the linear shape of CO_2 with the bent shape of H_2O. Tie or tape one piece of string onto each of the oxygen atoms of the CO_2 model and onto each of the hydrogen atoms of the H_2O model. Place the CO_2 model on the overhead and demonstrate the effect of pulling the strings gently in opposite directions. Explain that this represents the canceling effect of opposing polar bonds (dipoles). Place the H_2O model on the overhead and demonstrate the effect of pulling the strings gently away from the oxygen atom in the direction of the bond angles. Explain that this represents the additive effect of polar bonds that are at an angle.

Expected Outcome The CO_2 model will stay in one place. The H_2O model will move in the direction of the hydrogen atoms.
Visual

Build Science Skills **L2**

Using Models Show students a ball-and-stick molecular model of ammonia, NH_3. Ask students to predict whether the molecule is polar or nonpolar and to give a reason for their choice. *(Ammonia is a polar molecule because its three bonds are oriented to one side of the central nitrogen atom. The polar bonds do not cancel out.)* Now show students a molecular model of sulfur trioxide, SO_3. Ask students to predict whether this molecule is polar or nonpolar and to explain their reasoning. *(Sulfur trioxide is a nonpolar molecule because its three bonds are oriented symmetrically in a plane around the central sulfur atom. The polar bonds cancel each other out.)*
Logical, Visual

Figure 11 Shared electrons in a hydrogen chloride molecule spend less time near the hydrogen atom than near the chlorine atom. ***Inferring*** ***Which element has a greater attraction for electrons—hydrogen or chlorine?***

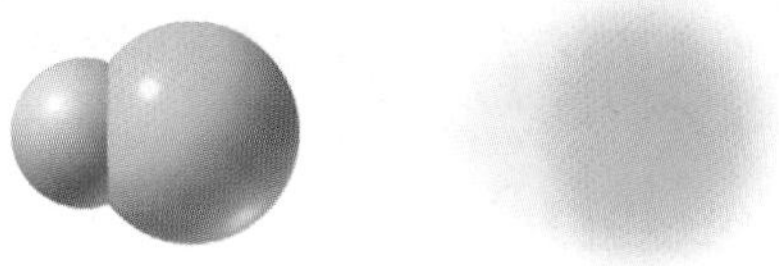
HCl

Polar Covalent Bonds In a molecule of an element, the atoms that form covalent bonds have the same ability to attract an electron. Shared electrons are attracted equally to the nuclei of both atoms. In a molecule of a compound, electrons may not be shared equally.

Figure 11 shows models of the molecule that forms when hydrogen reacts with chlorine. A chlorine atom has a greater attraction for electrons than a hydrogen atom does. In a hydrogen chloride molecule, the shared electrons spend more time near the chlorine atom than near the hydrogen atom. A covalent bond in which electrons are not shared equally is called a **polar covalent bond.** (One meaning of the term *polar* is "opposite in character, nature, or direction.")

When atoms form a polar covalent bond, the atom with the greater attraction for electrons has a partial negative charge. The other atom has a partial positive charge. The symbols δ– and δ+ are used to show which atom has which charge. (δ is the lowercase version of the Greek letter delta.)

Polar and Nonpolar Molecules Can you assume that a molecule that contains a polar covalent bond is polar? If a molecule has only two atoms, it will be polar. But, when molecules have more than two atoms, the answer is not as obvious. **The type of atoms in a molecule and its shape are factors that determine whether a molecule is polar or nonpolar.**

Compare the models of carbon dioxide and water in Figure 12. In carbon dioxide, there are double bonds between each oxygen atom and the central carbon atom. Because oxygen has a greater attraction for electrons than carbon does, each double bond is polar. However, the molecule is linear: all three atoms are lined up in a row. The carbon-oxygen double bonds are directly opposite each other. There is an equal pull on the electrons from opposite directions. The pulls cancel out and the molecule as a whole is nonpolar.

There are two single bonds in a water molecule. The bonds are polar because oxygen has a greater attraction for electrons than hydrogen does. Because the water molecule has a bent shape rather than a linear shape, the polar bonds do not cancel out. The two hydrogen atoms are located on the same side of the molecule, opposite the oxygen atom. The oxygen side of the molecule has a partial negative charge. The hydrogen side of the molecule has a partial positive charge.

CO_2
H_2O

Figure 12 In a carbon dioxide (CO_2) molecule, the polar bonds between the carbon atom and the oxygen atoms cancel out because the molecule is linear. In a water (H_2O) molecule, the polar bonds between the oxygen atom and the hydrogen atoms do not cancel out because the molecule is bent.

Facts and Figures

Surface Tension Refer back to the discussion in Section 3.3 about the effect of intermolecular attractions on the evaporation of water. Hydrogen bonds explain other properties of water, including its high surface tension. Because molecules on the surface are drawn inward by attractions from molecules beneath the surface, surface area is reduced. Surface tension explains why water drops bead up on a clean, waxed surface.

Attraction Between Molecules

In a molecular compound, there are forces of attraction between molecules. These attractions are not as strong as ionic or covalent bonds, but they are strong enough to hold molecules together in a liquid or solid. **Attractions between polar molecules are stronger than attractions between nonpolar molecules.**

Water molecules are similar in mass to methane (CH_4) molecules. Yet, methane boils at −161.5°C and water boils at 100°C because methane molecules are nonpolar and water molecules are polar. Each dashed line in Figure 13 represents an attraction between a partially positive hydrogen atom in one water molecule and a partially negative oxygen atom in another. Molecules on the surface of a water sample are attracted to molecules that lie below the surface and are pulled toward the center of the sample. These attractions increase the energy required for water molecules to evaporate. They raise the temperature at which vapor pressure equals atmospheric pressure—the boiling point.

Attractions among nonpolar molecules are weaker than attractions among polar molecules, but they do exist. After all, carbon dioxide can exist as solid dry ice. Attractions among nonpolar molecules explain why nitrogen can be stored as a liquid at low temperatures and high pressures. Because electrons are constantly in motion, there are times when one part of a nitrogen molecule has a small positive charge and one part has a small negative charge. At those times, one nitrogen molecule can be weakly attracted to another nitrogen molecule.

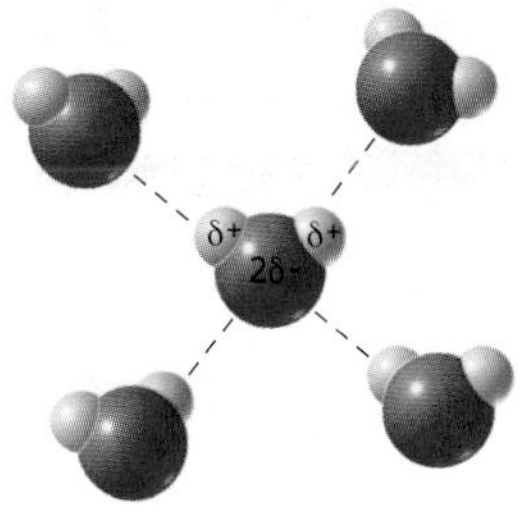
δ+
δ+
2δ−

Figure 13 Each dashed line in the drawing represents an attraction between a hydrogen atom and an oxygen atom. ***Interpreting Diagrams*** *In a water molecule, which atom has a partial negative charge? Which has a partial positive charge?*

Section 6.2 Assessment

Reviewing Concepts

1. What attractions hold atoms together in a covalent bond?
2. What happens to the charge on atoms when they form a polar covalent bond?
3. Name the two factors that determine whether a molecule is polar.
4. Compare the strength of attractions between polar molecules to the strength of attractions between nonpolar molecules.
5. What is a molecule?

Critical Thinking

6. **Applying Concepts** Which of these elements does not bond to form molecules: oxygen, chlorine, neon, or sulfur?
7. **Inferring** Why is the boiling point of water higher than the boiling point of chlorine?
8. **Using Diagrams** Based on their electron dot diagrams, what is the formula for the covalently bonded compound of nitrogen and hydrogen?

Connecting Concepts

Viscosity Review the description of the physical property viscosity in Section 2.2. Then write a paragraph explaining how attractions between molecules might affect the viscosity of a liquid.

Section 6.2 Assessment

1. The attractions between the shared electrons and the protons in each nucleus hold the atoms together in a covalent bond.
2. When atoms form a polar covalent bond, the atom with the greater attraction for electrons has a partial negative charge. The other atom has a partial positive charge.
3. The type of atoms in a molecule and its shape are factors that determine whether a molecule is polar or nonpolar.
4. Attractions between polar molecules are stronger than attractions between nonpolar molecules.
5. A neutral group of atoms that are joined together by one or more covalent bonds
6. Neon
7. Attractions between polar water molecules are stronger than attractions between nonpolar chlorine molecules.
8. NH_3

Attraction Between Molecules

Teacher Demo

Surface Tension L2

Purpose Students observe how surface tension can support a needle.

Materials 200-mL beaker, water, sewing needle, tweezers, dropper pipet

Procedure Fill the beaker with water. Using tweezers, gently place the needle on the water's surface so that surface tension supports it. Remove the needle, and place it in the water vertically so that it sinks. Pour the water out and collect the needle.

Expected Outcome Surface tension supports the needle.
Logical, Visual

3 ASSESS

Evaluate Understanding L2

Have students make a chart that compares and contrasts polar covalent bonds and nonpolar covalent bonds. Be sure students discuss the bonding atoms' attractions for electrons, partial charges, and attractions between molecules.

Reteach L1

Use Figures 11, 12, and 13 as visual aids while reviewing polar covalent bonds, nonpolar and polar molecules, and attractions between molecules.

Connecting Concepts

A greater attraction between molecules is likely to produce an increase in viscosity because the attractions would act in opposition to the motion of the molecules and reduce their ability to flow.

Interactive Textbook If your class subscribes to the Interactive Textbook, use it to review key concepts in Section 6.2.

Answer to . . .

Figure 11 *Chlorine*

Figure 13 *The oxygen atom has a partial negative charge. The hydrogen atoms have partial positive charges.*

Section 6.3

1 FOCUS

Objectives

6.3.1 **Recognize** and **describe** binary ionic compounds, metals with multiple ions, and polyatomic ions.

6.3.2 **Name** and **determine** chemical formulas for ionic and molecular compounds.

Reading Focus

Build Vocabulary — L2

Word-Part Analysis Ask students what words they know that have the prefix *poly-*. *(Polygon, polysyllabic, polyglot, polytechnic, and polygraph)* Give a definition of the prefix. *(Poly- means "many.")* Have students predict the meaning of the term *polyatomic ion*. *(A polyatomic ion is a covalently bonded group of atoms that has a positive or negative charge and acts as a unit.)*

Reading Strategy — L2

a. and b. Students should assume that any particle described as an ion has a charge. If they know the meaning of *poly-*, they may conclude that the ion contains three or more atoms.

2 INSTRUCT

Integrate Language Arts — L2

The production of lime through the decomposition of limestone (or any form of calcium carbonate) has been known for millennia, which is why there is a word for lime in many ancient languages. In Latin, this word is *calx*, which is the source for the name calcium. Have students research the origin of the phrase "in the limelight." *(Drummond developed limelight first as an aid to surveying. When lime was heated in a hydrogen-oxygen flame, it produced a bright, white light. In 1825, a light that Drummond placed on top of a hill in Belfast could be seen in Donegal about 105 km (66 miles) away. Limelight was first used in a theater in 1856, when a lens was placed in front of the limelight to produce a spotlight.)*
Logical

6.3 Naming Compounds and Writing Formulas

Reading Focus

Key Concepts

- What information do the name and formula of an ionic compound provide?
- What information do the name and formula of a molecular compound provide?

Vocabulary

- polyatomic ion

Reading Strategy

Predicting Copy the table. Before you read, predict the meaning of the term *polyatomic ion*. After you read, if your prediction was incorrect, revise your definition.

Vocabulary Term	Before You Read	After You Read
Polyatomic ion	a. ___?___	b. ___?___

Thomas Drummond was a Scottish surveyor and inventor. Around 1826, he discovered that a white solid called lime emits a bright light when heated to a high temperature. This discovery was extremely useful in the era before electric lighting. Limelight was used to produce a light that could be focused on a single spot on a stage. It also was used to produce lighthouse beams that could be seen from a great distance.

People have used mixtures of lime and water for centuries to whitewash houses and fences. The flowerpots in Figure 14 were coated with a lime wash to which paint pigments were added. Other names for lime are quicklime and unslaked lime. Having two or more names for a compound can be confusing. Also, names like lime or quicklime don't tell you much about the composition of a compound.

There is much less confusion when everyone is using the same name for a given compound. Chemists use a system for naming compounds that is based on composition. In this system, the chemical name for lime is calcium oxide and its chemical formula is CaO. This formula tells you that there is a one-to-one ratio of calcium ions to oxide ions in calcium oxide. The formula of a compound serves as a reminder of the composition of the compound.

Figure 14 These flowerpots were coated with a solution of lime and water. Paint pigments were mixed with the lime wash to produce the different colors. The chemical name for lime is calcium oxide.

Section Resources

Print

- ***Laboratory Manual,*** Investigation 6A
- ***Reading and Study Workbook With Math Support,*** Section 6.3 and **Math Skill:** Writing Formulas for Ionic Compounds
- ***Math Skills and Problem Solving Workbook,*** Section 6.3
- ***Transparencies,*** Section 6.3

Technology

- ***Interactive Textbook,*** Section 6.3
- ***Presentation Pro CD-ROM,*** Section 6.3
- ***Go Online,*** NSTA SciLinks, Chemical formulas

Figure 15 The brass vase on the left is coated with an oxide of copper that is red. Most of the surface of the plate on the right is coated with an oxide of copper that is black. **Classifying** ***How can you be sure that the oxides of copper are different compounds?***

Describing Ionic Compounds

Both of the objects in Figure 15 are coated with compounds of copper and oxygen. Based on the two colors of the coatings, copper and oxygen must form at least two compounds. One name cannot describe all the compounds of copper and oxygen. There must be at least two names to distinguish red copper oxide from black copper oxide. **The name of an ionic compound must distinguish the compound from other ionic compounds containing the same elements. The formula of an ionic compound describes the ratio of the ions in the compound.**

Binary Ionic Compounds A compound made from only two elements is a binary compound. (The Latin prefix *bi-* means "two," as in bicycle or bisect.) Naming binary ionic compounds, such as sodium chloride and cadmium iodide, is easy. The names have a predictable pattern: the name of the cation followed by the name of the anion. Remember that the name for the cation is the name of the metal without any change: sodium atom and sodium ion. The name for the anion uses part of the name of the nonmetal with the suffix *–ide:* iodine atom and iodide ion. Figure 16 shows the names and charges for eight common anions.

Common Anions

Element Name	Ion Name	Ion Symbol	Ion Charge
Fluorine	Fluoride	F^-	1−
Chlorine	Chloride	Cl^-	1−
Bromine	Bromide	Br^-	1−
Iodine	Iodide	I^-	1−
Oxygen	Oxide	O^{2-}	2−
Sulfur	Sulfide	S^{2-}	2−
Nitrogen	Nitride	N^{3-}	3−
Phosphorus	Phosphide	P^{3-}	3−

Figure 16 The table lists the element names, ion names, symbols, and charges for eight anions. The name of an anion is formed by adding the suffix *–ide* to the stem of the name of the nonmetal.

Describing Ionic Compounds

Address Misconceptions L2

Some students may think that a material's particles possess the same properties as the material. For example, they may think that the atoms that compose the copper oxides in Figure 15 are red or black. Challenge this misconception by noting that the black and red copper oxides both contain the same two elements—copper and oxygen—yet they are different colors.
Logical

FYI

The copper oxides differ in more than color. Copper(I) oxide melts at 1235°C and has a density of 6.0 g/cm³. Copper(II) oxide melts at 1446°C and has a density of 6.31 g/cm³.

Build Reading Literacy L1

Outline Refer to page **156D** in this chapter, which provides the guidelines for an outline.

Have students read the text on pp. 171–175 related to describing ionic and molecular compounds. Then, have students use the headings as major divisions in an outline. Have students refer to their outlines when answering the questions in the Section 6.3 Assessment.
Visual

Customize for Inclusion Students

Behaviorally Disordered
Have students work in groups and use index cards to create a classroom set of flashcards. Students can use the cards to support each other in small, noncompetitive study groups. Each card should contain information about a metal or nonmetal element that forms ions. One side of the card should list the name of an element (for example, chlorine), the formula for an ionic compound that contains the element (for example, NaCl), and four categories of color-keyed questions: Group in periodic table; Name of ion; Charge on ion; Other ion in compound. Color key the answers on the other side of the card. *(Halogens* or *7A; Chloride; 1−; Sodium)*

Answer to . . .

Figure 15 *They must be different compounds because their colors vary, and the properties of a compound should be consistent.*

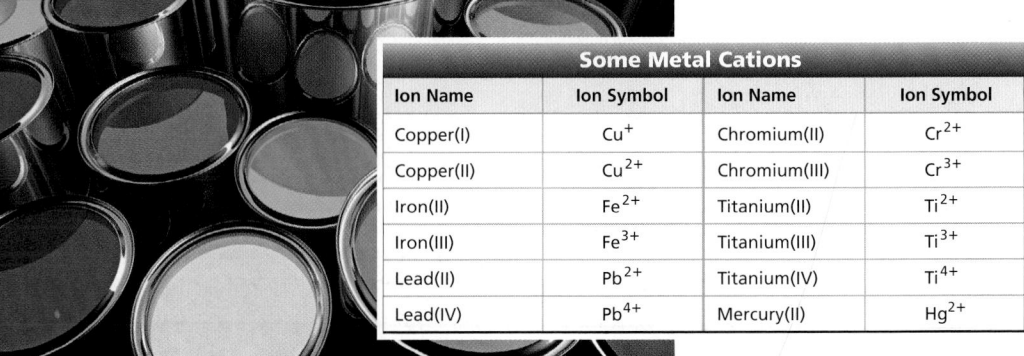

Use Visuals L1

Figure 18 Have students compare the two models of an ammonium ion. Have them discuss the advantages of each type of model. *(Both models show the number and types of atom in the ion. The electron dot diagram shows the valence electrons. The space-filling model shows the relative sizes of the atoms and how they are arranged in space.)* Point out that the brackets in the electron dot diagram indicate that the group of atoms as a whole, not any specific atom, has a positive charge. Ask, **What is the charge on an ammonium ion?** *(1+)* **How many covalent bonds are in an ammonium ion?** *(Four)* **How many valence electrons are involved in the bonds in the ammonium ion?** *(Eight)* **Visual**

FYI

Paint is a mixture of nonvolatile ingredients (the pigment and the binder) that are dispersed in a volatile liquid. A pigment is a substance that provides the color.

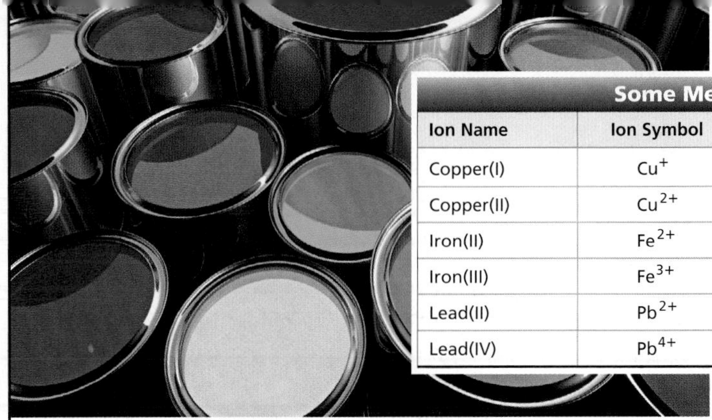

Some Metal Cations

Ion Name	Ion Symbol	Ion Name	Ion Symbol
Copper(I)	Cu^{+}	Chromium(II)	Cr^{2+}
Copper(II)	Cu^{2+}	Chromium(III)	Cr^{3+}
Iron(II)	Fe^{2+}	Titanium(II)	Ti^{2+}
Iron(III)	Fe^{3+}	Titanium(III)	Ti^{3+}
Lead(II)	Pb^{2+}	Titanium(IV)	Ti^{4+}
Lead(IV)	Pb^{4+}	Mercury(II)	Hg^{2+}

Figure 17 Many paint pigments contain compounds of transition metals. These metals often form more than one type of ion. The ion names must contain a Roman numeral. **Using Tables** ***How is the Roman numeral in the name related to the charge on the ion?***

Metals With Multiple Ions The alkali metals, alkaline earth metals, and aluminum form ions with positive charges equal to the group number. For example, the symbol for a potassium ion is K^{+}, the symbol for a calcium ion is Ca^{2+}, and the symbol for an aluminum ion is Al^{3+}.

Many transition metals form more than one type of ion. Notice the two copper ions listed in Figure 17, a copper(I) ion with a 1+ charge and a copper(II) ion with a 2+ charge. When a metal forms more than one ion, the name of the ion contains a Roman numeral to indicate the charge on the ion. These ion names can distinguish red copper(I) oxide from black copper(II) oxide. The formula for "copper one oxide" is Cu_2O because it takes two Cu^{1+} ions to balance the charge on an O^{2-} ion. The formula for "copper two oxide" is CuO because it takes only one Cu^{2+} ion to balance the charge on an O^{2-} ion.

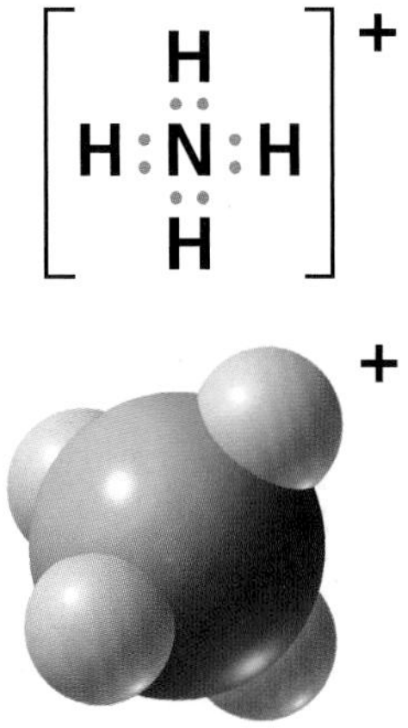

Ammonium ion
(NH_4^{+})

Figure 18 The atoms in an ammonium ion are joined by covalent bonds. The ion loses a valence electron as it forms. This loss leaves only 10 electrons to balance the charge on 11 protons.

Polyatomic Ions The electron dot diagram in Figure 18 describes a group of atoms that includes one nitrogen and four hydrogen atoms. It is called an ammonium ion. The atoms are joined by covalent bonds. Why does the group have a positive charge? The nitrogen atom has seven protons, and each hydrogen atom has one proton—eleven in total. But the group has only ten electrons to balance the charge on the protons—eight valence electrons and nitrogen's two inner electrons.

A covalently bonded group of atoms that has a positive or negative charge and acts as a unit is a **polyatomic ion.** The prefix *poly-* means "many." Most simple polyatomic ions are anions. Figure 19 lists the names and formulas for some polyatomic ions. Sometimes there are parentheses in a formula that includes polyatomic ions. For example, the formula for iron(III) hydroxide is $Fe(OH)_3$. The subscript 3 indicates that there are three hydroxide ions for each iron(III) ion.

Reading Checkpoint ***When are Roman numerals used in compound names?***

Quick Lab

Modeling Molecules

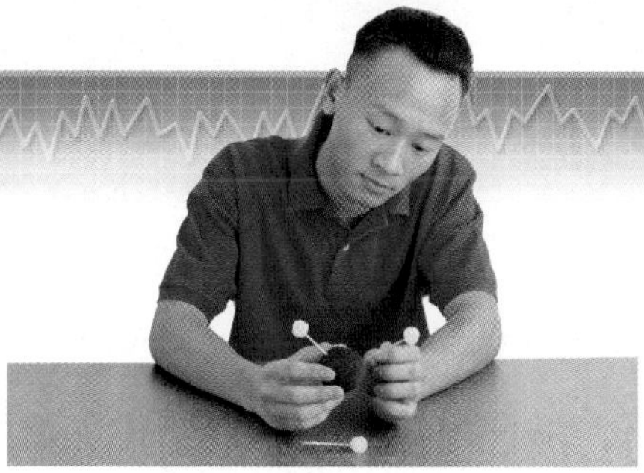

Materials

blue plastic-foam ball, black plastic-foam ball, 7 white gumdrops, toothpicks

Procedure

1. To make a model of an ammonia molecule (NH_3), insert a toothpick in each of 3 gumdrops. The gumdrops represent hydrogen atoms and the toothpicks represent bonds.
2. An ammonia molecule is like a pyramid with the nitrogen at the top and the hydrogen atoms at the corners of the base. Insert the toothpicks in the blue foam ball (nitrogen) so that each gumdrop is the same distance from the ball.
3. The hydrogen atoms in a methane molecule (CH_4) are equally spaced around the carbon. Use the black ball to make a model of methane.

Analyze and Conclude

1. **Comparing and Contrasting** Compare the shapes of the methane and ammonia molecules.
2. **Using Models** Why is carbon in the center of the methane molecule?

Writing Formulas for Ionic Compounds If you know the name of an ionic compound, you can write its formula. Place the symbol of the cation first, followed by the symbol of the anion. Use subscripts to show the ratio of the ions in the compound. Because all compounds are neutral, the total charges on the cations and anions must add up to zero.

Suppose an atom that gains two electrons, such as sulfur, reacts with an atom that loses one electron, such as sodium. There must be two sodium ions (Na^+) for each sulfide ion (S^{2-}). The formula for sodium sulfide is Na_2S. The 2− charge on one sulfide ion is balanced by the 1+ charges on two sodium ions.

Some Polyatomic Ions

Name	Formula	Name	Formula
Ammonium	NH_4^+	Acetate	$C_2H_3O_2^-$
Hydroxide	OH^-	Peroxide	O_2^{2-}
Nitrate	NO_3^-	Permanganate	MnO_4^-
Sulfate	SO_4^{2-}	Hydrogen sulfate	HSO_4^-
Carbonate	CO_3^{2-}	Hydrogen carbonate	HCO_3^-
Phosphate	PO_4^{3-}	Hydrogen phosphate	HPO_4^{2-}
Chromate	CrO_4^{2-}	Dichromate	$Cr_2O_7^{2-}$
Silicate	SiO_3^{2-}	Hypochlorite	OCl^-

Figure 19 This table lists the names and formulas of some polyatomic ions. Except for the ammonium ion, all the ions listed are anions. **Using Tables** ***Which element is found in all the anions whose names end in -ate?***

Quick Lab

Modeling Molecules **L2**

Objective

After completing this activity, students will be able to
- use physical models to compare the shapes of molecules.

Skills Focus **Using Models**

Prep Time 10 minutes

Advance Prep Plastic-foam balls are available from craft supply stores. If black and blue foam balls are not available, wrap other foam balls in colored foil, glue colored tissue paper around them, or spray-paint them to match the colors used in this book to represent atoms of carbon and nitrogen.

Class Time 20 minutes

Safety Tell students not to eat the gumdrops or anything else in the laboratory.

Expected Outcome Students will make tetrahedral (pyramidal) models of methane molecules.

Analyze and Conclude

1. The methane molecule is a tetrahedron (equal-sided triangular pyramid) and the ammonia molecule has a triangular shape.
2. The carbon atom is in the center because each of the four hydrogen atoms must bond to one carbon atom.
Visual, Kinesthetic

Build Science Skills **L2**

Inferring Molecules of NH_3 and NF_3 have the same shape, but bonds in NH_3 are shorter than bonds in NF_3. In other words, the hydrogen atoms are closer to the nitrogen atom in an ammonia molecule than the fluorine atoms are to the nitrogen atom in nitrogen trifluoride. Ask, **What does this data imply about the relative sizes of hydrogen and fluorine atoms?** *(The data confirms that a hydrogen atom has a smaller atomic radius than does a nitrogen atom.)* **Logical**

Answer to . . .

Figure 17 *The Roman numeral is equal to the charge on the ion.*

Figure 19 *Oxygen*

Reading Checkpoint *When the metal in the compound can form more than one type of ion*

Build Math Skills

L1

Positive and Negative Numbers
Remind students that the charges in an ionic compound must cancel each other. Ask, **How many atoms of a halogen would combine with one atom of an alkaline earth metal? Why?** *(Two atoms; the alkaline earth metal atom loses two electrons but each halogen atom needs only one electron to become stable.)* **Logical**

Direct students to the **Math Skills** in the **Skills and Reference Handbook** at the end of the student text for additional help.

Math Practice

Solutions

L2

1. It takes one calcium ion with a charge of 2+ to balance one oxide ion with a charge of 2−. The formula is CaO.
2. Two copper(I) ions, each with a charge of 1+, balance one sulfide ion with a charge of 2−. The formula is Cu_2S.
3. Two sodium ions, each with a charge of 1+, balance one sulfate ion with a charge of 2−. The formula is Na_2SO_4.
4. In the formula, Na represents the sodium ion and OH represents the hydroxide ion. The name of the compound is sodium hydroxide. **Logical**

For Extra Help

L1

Make sure the first step students take is to find the symbols and charges on the ions. Then, check that they are able to balance the charges.
Logical

Additional Problems

1. Write the formula for lithium oxide. *(Li_2O)*
2. Write the formula for iron(III) oxide. *(Fe_2O_3)*
Logical

Describing Molecular Compounds

FYI

There are two exceptions to the general rule for naming molecular compounds. Hydrogen is treated as though it were positioned between Group 5A and Group 6A, and oxygen is treated as though it were positioned after chlorine but before fluorine.

Math Practice

1. Write the formula for the compound calcium oxide.
2. Write the formula for the compound copper(I) sulfide.
3. Write the formula for the compound sodium sulfate.
4. What is the name of the compound whose formula is NaOH?

Math Skills

Writing Formulas for Ionic Compounds

What is the formula for the ionic compound calcium chloride?

1 Read and Understand

What information are you given?

The name of the compound is calcium chloride.

2 Plan and Solve

List the symbols and charges for the cation and anion.

Ca with a charge of 2+ and Cl with a charge of 1−

Determine the ratio of ions in the compound.

It takes two 1− charges to balance the 2+ charge. There will be two chloride ions for each calcium ion.

Write the formula for calcium chloride.

$CaCl_2$

3 Look Back and Check

Is your answer reasonable?

Each calcium atom loses two electrons and each chlorine atom gains one electron. So there should be a 1-to-2 ratio of calcium ions to chloride ions.

Describing Molecular Compounds

Like ionic compounds, molecular compounds have names that identify specific compounds, and formulas that match those names. With molecular compounds, the focus is on the composition of molecules. **The name and formula of a molecular compound describe the type and number of atoms in a molecule of the compound.**

Naming Molecular Compounds The general rule is that the most metallic element appears first in the name. These elements are farther to the left in the periodic table. If both elements are in the same group, the more metallic element is closer to the bottom of the group. The name of the second element is changed to end in the suffix *-ide*, as in carbon dioxide.

Go Online NSTA SCILINKS

For: Links on chemical formulas
Visit: www.SciLinks.org
Web Code: ccn-1063

Go Online NSTA SCILINKS

Download a worksheet on chemical formulas for students to complete, and find additional teacher support from NSTA SciLinks.

Two compounds that contain nitrogen and oxygen have the formulas N_2O_4 and NO_2. The names of these two compounds reflect the actual number of atoms of nitrogen and oxygen in a molecule of each compound. You can use the Greek prefixes in Figure 20 to describe the number of nitrogen and oxygen atoms in each molecule.

In an N_2O_4 molecule, there are two nitrogen atoms and four oxygen atoms. The Greek prefixes for two and four are *di-* and *tetra-*. The name for the compound with the formula N_2O_4 is dinitrogen tetraoxide. In an NO_2 molecule, there are one nitrogen atom and two oxygen atoms. The Greek prefixes for one and two are *mono-* and *di-*. So a name for the compound with the formula NO_2 is mononitrogen dioxide. However, the prefix *mono-* often is not used for the first element in the name. A more common name for the compound with the formula NO_2 is nitrogen dioxide.

Writing Molecular Formulas Writing the formula for a molecular compound is easy. Write the symbols for the elements in the order the elements appear in the name. The prefixes indicate the number of atoms of each element in the molecule. The prefixes appear as subscripts in the formulas. If there is no prefix for an element in the name, there is only one atom of that element in the molecule.

What is the formula for diphosphorus tetrafluoride? Because the compound is molecular, look for elements on the right side of the periodic table. Phosphorus has the symbol P. Fluorine has the symbol F. *Di-* indicates two phosphorus atoms and *tetra-* indicates four fluorine atoms. The formula for the compound is P_2F_4.

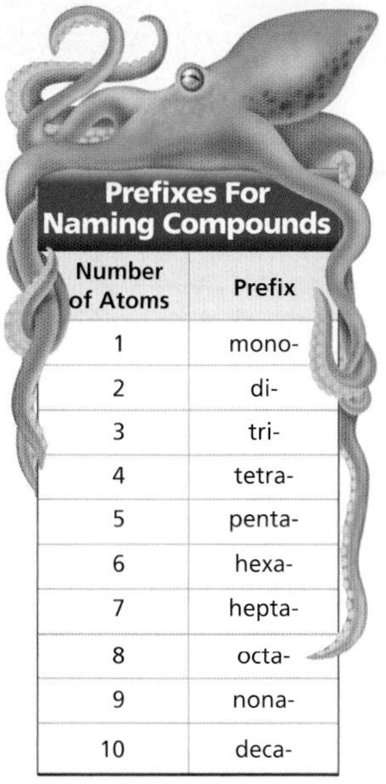

Prefixes For Naming Compounds

Number of Atoms	Prefix
1	mono-
2	di-
3	tri-
4	tetra-
5	penta-
6	hexa-
7	hepta-
8	octa-
9	nona-
10	deca-

Figure 20 These Greek prefixes are used to name molecular compounds. The prefix *octa-* means "eight," as in the eight tentacles of an octopus.

Section 6.3 Assessment

Reviewing Concepts

1. What does the formula of an ionic compound describe?
2. What do the name and formula of a molecular compound describe?
3. What suffix is used to indicate an anion?
4. Why are Roman numerals used in the names of compounds that contain transition metals?
5. What is a polyatomic ion?

Critical Thinking

6. **Applying Concepts** How is it possible for two different ionic compounds to contain the same elements?
7. **Calculating** How many potassium ions are needed to bond with a phosphate ion?

Math Practice

8. What are the names of these ionic compounds: LiCl, BaO, Na_3N, and $PbSO_4$?
9. Name the molecular compounds with these formulas: P_2O_5 and CO.
10. What is the formula for the ionic compound formed from potassium and sulfur?

Integrate Language Arts L2

To help students learn the prefixes used in molecular compounds, have them think of words they know that contain the Greek prefixes listed in Figure 20. If they are having trouble, encourage them to use a dictionary to find words. Examples include *monochrome, dichotomy, tricycle, tetrahedron, pentagon, hexadecimal, heptad, octave, nonagenarian,* and *decathlon.*
Verbal

3 ASSESS

Evaluate Understanding L2

Note that the process of writing molecular formulas is the reverse of the process for naming them. Have students write chemical formulas for three substances and chemical names for another three substances. Have students exchange the formulas and names with a partner to check and review their work.

Reteach L1

Use the tables on pp. 171–173 and the Math Skills on p. 174 to review naming and writing formulas for ionic compounds. Use the table on p. 175 to review naming and writing formulas for molecular compounds.

Math Practice

Solutions
8. Lithium chloride, barium oxide, sodium nitride, lead sulfate
9. Diphosphorus pentaoxide (pentoxide) and carbon monoxide
10. K_2S because it takes two potassium ions, each with a charge of 1+, to balance one sulfide ion with a charge of 2−

Interactive Textbook If your class subscribes to the Interactive Textbook, use it to review key concepts in Section 6.3.

Section 6.3 Assessment

1. The formula of an ionic compound describes the ratio of the ions in the compound.
2. The name and the formula of a molecular compound describe the type and number of atoms in a molecule of the compound.
3. *-ide*
4. The Roman numerals help distinguish the multiple ions of transition metals.
5. A covalently bonded group of atoms that has a positive or negative charge and acts as a unit
6. The explanation for binary compounds is that metals can form more than one type of cation. (Unless students have seen a more complete table of polyatomic ions, they are unlikely to know a second possible explanation: Some polyatomic ions contain the same elements, e.g., sulfate and sulfite ions.)
7. Three

Section 6.4

1 FOCUS

Objectives

6.4.1 **Describe** the structure and strength of bonds in metals.

6.4.2 **Relate** the properties of metals to their structure.

6.4.3 **Define** an alloy and **demonstrate** how the composition of an alloy affects its properties.

Reading Focus

Build Vocabulary L2

Vocabulary Knowledge Rating Chart Have students construct a chart with four columns labeled Term, Can Define It/Use It, Heard It/Seen It, and Don't Know. Have students copy the terms *metallic bond, metal lattice, alloy,* and *metallurgy* into the first column and rate their term knowledge by putting a check in one of the other columns. Ask how many students actually know each term. Have them share their knowledge. To provide a purpose for reading, ask focused questions to help students predict text content based on each term. After students have read the section, have them rate their knowledge again.

Reading Strategy L2

a. and b. Conductivity or malleability

2 INSTRUCT

Metallic Bonds

Integrate Social Studies L2

In the first light bulbs, air was removed from the light bulb to prevent combustion as the filament heated up. This solution was not ideal because atoms can sublime from the hot filament at very low pressures. With almost no air, atoms of the vaporized filament have uninterrupted paths to the inner walls of the bulb where they are deposited. The modern light bulb uses an argon atmosphere and a tungsten filament. This prolongs the life of the bulb because collisions between tungsten atoms and argon atoms can redirect tungsten atoms back toward the filament. Have interested students research the search for an effective filament. Students can present their findings in a poster or other visual display.
Visual

6.4 The Structure of Metals

Reading Focus

Key Concepts

- What are the forces that give a metal its structure as a solid?
- How do metallic bonds produce some of the typical properties of metals?
- How are the properties of alloys controlled?

Vocabulary

- metallic bond
- alloy

Reading Strategy

Relating Cause and Effect Copy the concept map. As you read, complete the map to relate the structure of metals to their properties.

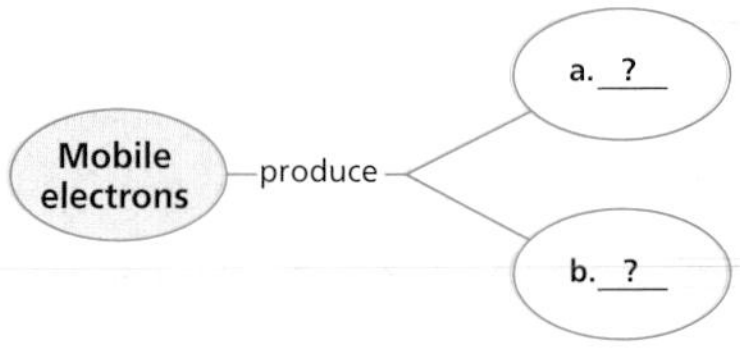
Mobile electrons
produce
a. ?
b. ?

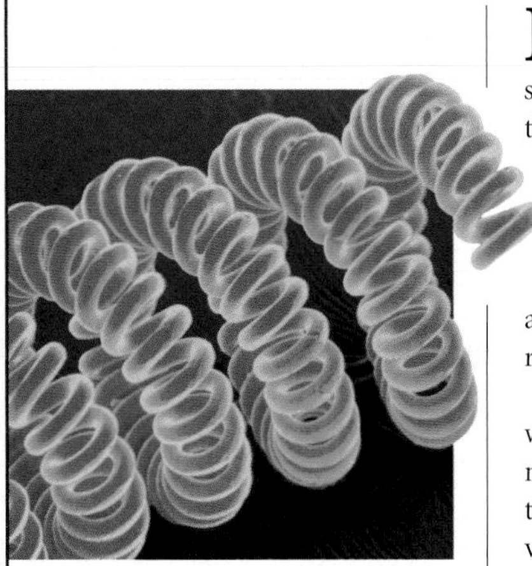

Figure 21 This photograph of the tungsten filament from a light bulb was taken with a scanning electron microscope. Color was added to the photo. The filament is magnified more than 100 times. The diameter of the wire is about 15 μm, or 0.0015 cm.

Light bulbs are easy to ignore unless a bulb burns out and you are searching for a replacement in the dark. But in the decades just before the year 1900, light bulbs were an exciting new technology. One challenge for researchers was to find the best material for the filaments in light bulbs. The substance had to be ductile enough to be drawn into a narrow wire. It could not melt at the temperatures produced when an electric current passes through a narrow wire. It had to have a low vapor pressure so that particles on the surface were not easily removed by sublimation.

The substance the researchers found was tungsten (W), a metal whose name means "heavy stone" in Swedish. Figure 21 shows a magnified view of the narrow coils in a tungsten filament. Tungsten has the highest melting point of any metal—3410°C—and it has the lowest vapor pressure. The properties of a metal are related to bonds within the metal.

Metallic Bonds

Metal atoms achieve stable electron configurations by losing electrons. But what happens if there are no nonmetal atoms available to accept the electrons? There is a way for metal atoms to lose and gain electrons at the same time. In a metal, valence electrons are free to move among the atoms. In effect, the metal atoms become cations surrounded by a pool of shared electrons. A **metallic bond** is the attraction between a metal cation and the shared electrons that surround it.

Section Resources

Print
- ***Reading and Study Workbook With Math Support,*** Section 6.4
- ***Transparencies,*** Section 6.4

Technology
- ***Interactive Textbook,*** Section 6.4
- ***Presentation Pro CD-ROM,*** Section 6.4
- ***Go Online,*** *Science News,* Metals

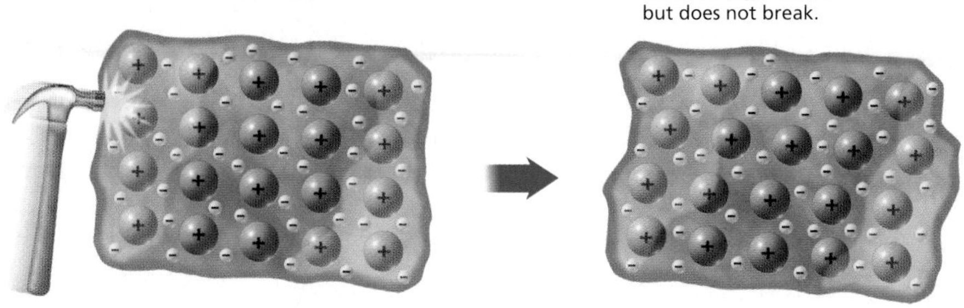
Hammer strikes metal.
Metal changes shape but does not break.

The cations in a metal form a lattice that is held in place by strong metallic bonds between the cations and the surrounding valence electrons. Although the electrons are moving among the atoms, the total number of electrons does not change. So, overall, the metal is neutral.

The metallic bonds in some metals are stronger than in other metals. The more valence electrons an atom can contribute to the shared pool, the stronger the metallic bonds will be. The bonds in an alkali metal are relatively weak because alkali metals contribute only a single valence electron. The result is that alkali metals, such as sodium, are soft enough to cut with a knife and have relatively low melting points. Sodium melts at 97.8°C. Transition metals, such as tungsten, have more valence electrons to contribute and, therefore, are harder and have higher melting points. Recall that tungsten melts at 3410°C.

Figure 22 In a metal, cations are surrounded by shared valence electrons. If a metal is struck, the ions move to new positions, but the ions are still surrounded by electrons. ***Classifying** What property of metals is displayed when a hammer strikes a metal?*

Explaining Properties of Metals

The structure within a metal affects the properties of metals. **The mobility of electrons within a metal lattice explains some of the properties of metals.** The ability to conduct an electric current and malleability are two important properties of metals.

Recall that a flow of charged particles is an electric current. A metal has a built-in supply of charged particles that can flow from one location to another—the pool of shared electrons. An electric current can be carried through a metal by the free flow of the shared electrons.

The lattice in a metal is flexible compared to the rigid lattice in an ionic compound. Figure 22 is a model of what happens when someone strikes a metal with a hammer. The metal ions shift their positions and the shape of the metal changes. But the metal does not shatter because ions are still held together by the metallic bonds between the ions and the electrons. Metallic bonds also explain why metals, such as tungsten and copper, can be drawn into thin wires without breaking.

Reading Checkpoint *What two important properties of metals can be explained by their structure?*

Customize for English Language Learners

Use a Cloze Strategy
Use a Cloze strategy for students with very limited English proficiency. Have students fill in the blanks in the following sentences while reading Explaining Properties of Metals. **The ______________ of ______________ within a metal lattice explains some of the properties of metal. The lattice in a metal is ______________ compared to the ______________ lattice in an ionic compound.** *(mobility; electrons; flexible; rigid)*

Teacher Demo

Comparing Bond Types L2

Purpose Students observe differences in the properties of substances with ionic bonds and metallic bonds.

Materials salt lick (or rock salt), copper wire, hammer, goggles

Procedure Take students outside to an open area. Allow them to examine the samples of rock salt and copper. Have students stand back a safe distance. While wearing goggles, hit each sample with a hammer against a hard surface, such as concrete. Allow students to observe how each sample looks after being pounded with a hammer.

Expected Outcome The rock salt shatters because sodium chloride is an ionic substance. The end of the copper wire can be pounded flat with a hammer because metals are malleable.
Visual

Explaining Properties of Metals

Use Visuals L1

Figure 22 Have students examine Figure 22. Ask, **How are the cations affected when the hammer strikes the metal?** *(The cations shift positions.)* **How are the metallic bonds between the cations and electrons affected when the hammer strikes the metal?** *(The metallic bonds are unaffected. Each cation is still surrounded by electrons.)*
Visual

Address Misconceptions L2

Many students think that particles in solids cannot move. Challenge this misconception by reminding students that the kinetic theory of matter says that all particles of matter are in constant motion. Ask, **Describe the motion of cations in a metal when the metal is not being struck by a hammer.** *(The cations vibrate, or move repeatedly back and forth, around fixed locations.)*
Logical

Answer to . . .

Figure 22 *Malleability*

Reading Checkpoint *The ability to conduct an electric current and malleability*

Alloys

Use Community Resources **L2**

Arrange for your class to visit the workshop of a jewelry maker, metalworker, blacksmith, or welder. Have students observe the types of equipment used to work with different metals. Ask questions regarding the artisan's choice of materials for different projects. Ask about the use of different alloys in metallurgy.
Interpersonal

FYI

There are different categories of alloys: true solutions, heterogeneous mixtures with two phases (a pure element and a compound), or intermetallic compounds with definite compositions.

SCIENCE and History

Milestones in Metallurgy **L2**

Ask students to choose one of the significant events in metallurgy history described in the time line. Have them do research in the library or on the Internet to find out more about the materials, applications, and people involved in their chosen topic. Have them present their findings to the class. Be sure that part of their presentation focuses on the specific properties of metals and alloys.
Verbal

Writing in Science

Henry Ford saw an automobile part made from vanadium steel when a French racer crashed at a European race meeting in 1905. He was impressed with the strength and low weight of the steel. American foundries did not have furnaces that could achieve the temperature required to produce the alloy. Ford found a small steel company in Ohio that was willing to experiment with the process and produce the alloy exclusively for Ford.
Verbal

Alloys

A friend shows you a beautiful ring that she says is made from pure gold. Your friend is lucky to have such a valuable object. The purity of gold is expressed in units called karats. Gold that is 100 percent pure is labeled 24-karat gold. Gold jewelry that has a 12-karat label is only 50 percent gold. Jewelry that has an 18-karat label is 75 percent gold.

The surface of an object made from pure gold can easily be worn away by contact with other objects or dented because gold is a soft metal. When silver, copper, nickel, or zinc is mixed with gold, the gold is harder and more resistant to wear. These gold mixtures are alloys. An **alloy** is a mixture of two or more elements, at least one of which is a metal. Alloys have the characteristic properties of metals.

SCIENCE and History

Milestones in Metallurgy

The science of metallurgy includes ways to extract metals from ores, refine metals, and use metals. Described here are some advances in metallurgy since 1850.

BESSEMER CONVERTER

BE 2789

Vanadium steel *This alloy becomes popular in car manufacturing because it is lightweight and strong.*

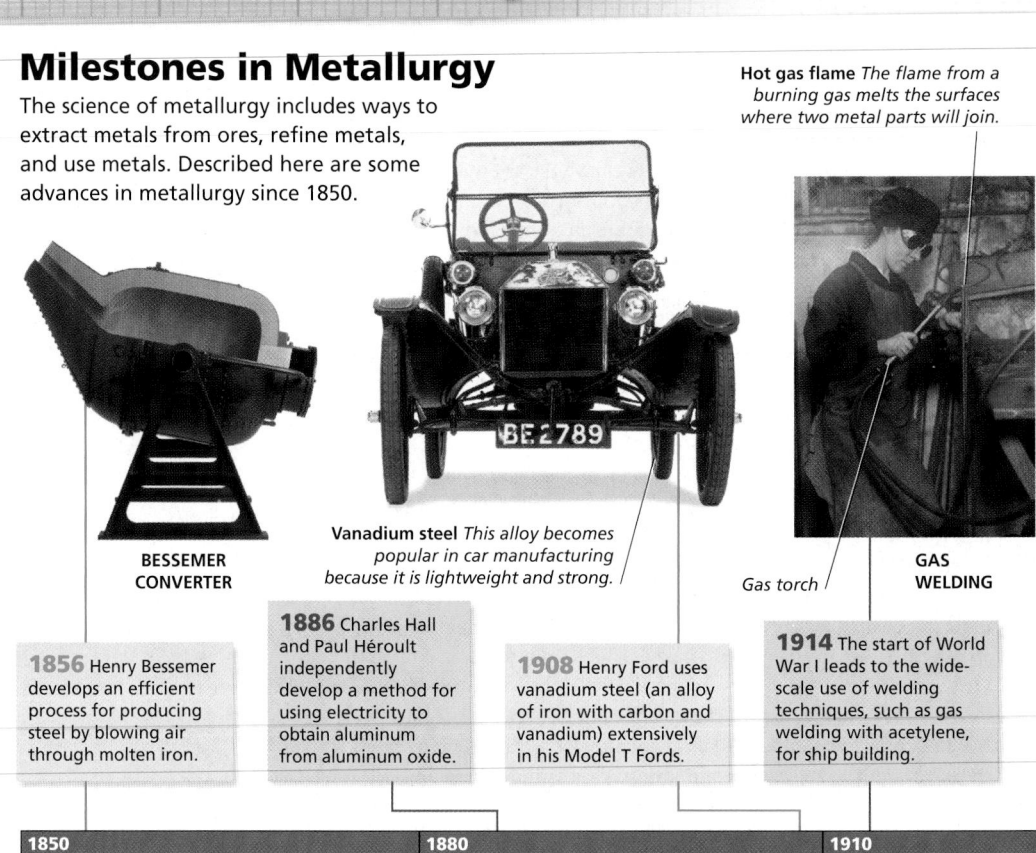

Hot gas flame *The flame from a burning gas melts the surfaces where two metal parts will join.*

Gas torch

GAS WELDING

1856 Henry Bessemer develops an efficient process for producing steel by blowing air through molten iron.

1886 Charles Hall and Paul Héroult independently develop a method for using electricity to obtain aluminum from aluminum oxide.

1908 Henry Ford uses vanadium steel (an alloy of iron with carbon and vanadium) extensively in his Model T Fords.

1914 The start of World War I leads to the wide-scale use of welding techniques, such as gas welding with acetylene, for ship building.

1850 | 1880 | 1910

Copper Alloys The first important alloy was bronze, whose name is associated with an important era in history—the Bronze Age. Metalworkers in Thailand may have been the first to make bronze. But people in other locations probably thought they were the first to make bronze. News didn't travel quickly in that era.

Metalworkers might have noticed that the metal they extracted by heating deposits of copper was not always the same. The difference in properties could be traced to the presence of tin. In its simplest form, bronze contains only copper and tin, which are relatively soft metals. Mixed together in bronze, the metals are much harder and stronger than either metal alone. **Scientists can design alloys with specific properties by varying the types and amounts of elements in an alloy.**

Writing in Science

Cause-Effect Paragraph
Write a paragraph about Henry Ford's decision to use vanadium steel for automobile parts. Where did Ford first see parts made from vanadium steel? What properties of this type of steel impressed Ford? Did Ford need to overcome any problems before going ahead with his plan?

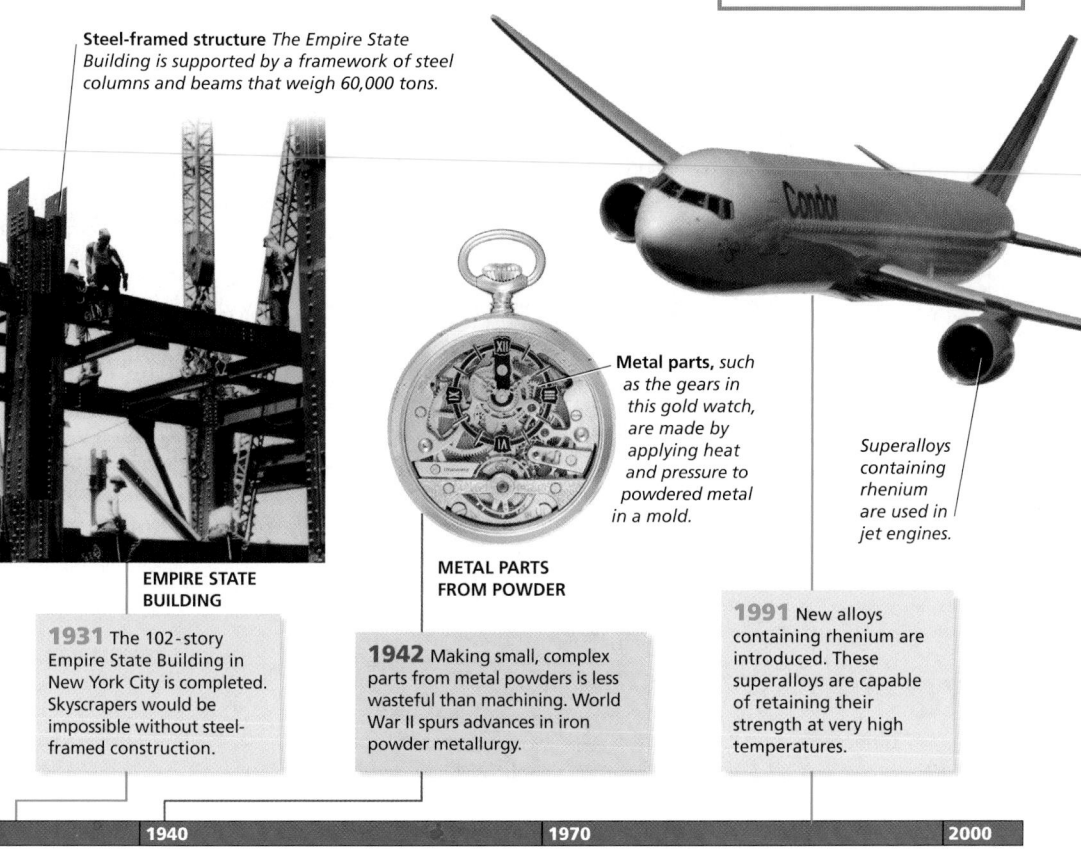

Steel-framed structure *The Empire State Building is supported by a framework of steel columns and beams that weigh 60,000 tons.*

EMPIRE STATE BUILDING

1931 The 102-story Empire State Building in New York City is completed. Skyscrapers would be impossible without steel-framed construction.

Metal parts, *such as the gears in this gold watch, are made by applying heat and pressure to powdered metal in a mold.*

METAL PARTS FROM POWDER

1942 Making small, complex parts from metal powders is less wasteful than machining. World War II spurs advances in iron powder metallurgy.

Condor

Superalloys containing rhenium are used in jet engines.

1991 New alloys containing rhenium are introduced. These superalloys are capable of retaining their strength at very high temperatures.

1940 | 1970 | 2000

Build Reading Literacy L1

Compare and Contrast Refer to page **226D** in **Chapter 8**, which provides the guidelines for comparing and contrasting.

Have students read the passage on copper alloys. Then, have students construct a chart that does the following: 1. Identify two copper alloys described in the text. 2. Make a list of properties the alloys have in common. 3. Make a list of properties that differ between the two alloys.
Visual

Facts and Figures

Bronze Bronze jewelry found in graves beneath the town of Ban Chiang in northeast Thailand has been dated to 3600 B.C., but this date is controversial. If correct, the site predates sites in Mesopotamia by several hundred years. Some copper alloys that contain little tin but are similar in color to bronze are labeled as bronzes to take advantage of the reputation of bronze as a hard, durable material.

Teacher Demo

Bronze and Brass Tones **L2**

Purpose Students observe the difference in tone between a brass bell and a bronze bell.

Materials brass bell, bronze bell

Procedure Allow students to examine each bell to see if they appear different in color or shininess. Ring each bell and allow students to note the difference in tone.

Expected Outcome In general, brass is shinier than bronze. A brass bell will have a duller tone that does not last as long as the clear, loud tone of a bronze bell. (Bell bronze contains about 80% copper and 20% tin, which is just the right composition to produce a hard, resonant material.)
Visual, Musical

Build Science Skills **L2**

Applying Concepts After students read about copper alloys, present the following problem to the class. **Imagine that you are going to make a wind chime in shop class as a gift. You have two choices of metals to use, brass or bronze. Which do you choose? Explain your answer.** *(Some students may choose brass because it is shinier and easier to shape into forms than bronze. Others may choose bronze because it has a clearer, louder tone and weathers better than brass.)*
Intrapersonal

Go Online SCIENCE NEWS®

Science News provides students with current information on metals.

Figure 23 This ancient statue of horses from Venice, Italy, and this modern French horn are both made from copper alloys. The statue is made from bronze, an alloy of copper and tin. The French horn is made from brass, an alloy of copper and zinc.

Bronze is hard and durable enough to be used for propellers on ships and for statues, such as the statue of horses in Figure 23. A bronze bell has a clear, loud tone that lasts for several seconds.

A brass bell has a duller tone that dies away quickly. Brass is another alloy of copper that has been known for centuries. In its simplest form, brass contains only copper and zinc. Although both bronze and brass are alloys of copper, they have distinctly different properties. Brass is softer than bronze and is easier to shape into forms such as the French horn in Figure 23. Brass is shinier than bronze but is likely to weather more quickly.

Steel Alloys The 1900s could be called the Age of Steel because of the skyscrapers, automobiles, and ships that were built from steel during the 1900s. Steel is an alloy of iron that contains small quantities of carbon, ranging from less than 0.2 percent to about 3 percent by mass. The smaller carbon atoms fit in the spaces between the larger iron atoms in the lattice. The carbon atoms form bonds with neighboring iron atoms. These bonds make the lattice harder and stronger than a lattice that contains only iron.

The properties of any particular type of steel depend on which elements other than iron and carbon are used and how much of those elements are included. Stainless steels contain more than 10 percent chromium by mass, but almost no carbon. Stainless steels are durable because chromium forms an oxide that protects the steel from rusting. But stainless steel is more brittle than steels that contain more carbon. The steel cables in the bridge in Figure 24 have to be strong enough to resist forces that might stretch the cables or cause them to break. The steel used contains sulfur, manganese, phosphorus, silicon, and 0.81 percent carbon.

Go Online SCIENCE NEWS®

For: Articles on metals
Visit: PHSchool.com
Web Code: cce-1064

Facts and Figures

Bronze Horses The origin of the gilded bronze horses of St. Mark's is unclear. The sculptures are not similar in style to other Greek or Roman sculptures of horses. Nor are they similar in composition. From chemical analyses, art historians know that the bronze is 98% copper, 1% tin, and 1% lead, which is an unusually high percent of copper. Art historians do know that the horses were cast in pieces that were welded together. The pieces were made using the lost wax method described in Chapter 2.

The horses can be traced from a triumphal arch in Rome to one in Constantinople. They were taken from Constantinople to Venice in 1204 (where they were placed on a balcony of the cathedral), then to Paris in 1797, and then back to Venice in 1815. For protection from air pollution, the horses are now stored inside the cathedral. A copy appears on the balcony.

Figure 24 The Golden Gate Bridge is a landmark in San Francisco, California. Its cables, towers, and deck contain steel. The steel in the cables needs to resist forces that pull on the cables. The steel in the towers needs to resist the compression forces caused by the weight of the cables, the deck, and the vehicles that travel across the bridge.
Drawing Conclusions ***Would the steel used for the cables and the steel used for the towers have the same composition? Give a reason for your answer.***

Other Alloys Airplane parts are made of many different alloys that are suited to particular purposes. The body of a plane is large and needs to be made from a lightweight material. Pure aluminum is lighter than most metals, but it bends and dents too easily. If a small amount of copper or manganese is added to aluminum, the result is a stronger material that is still lighter than steel.

For certain aircraft parts, even lighter materials are needed. Alloys of aluminum and magnesium are used for these parts. Magnesium is much less dense than most metals used to build structures. However, pure magnesium is soft enough to cut with a knife, and it burns in air. An aluminum-magnesium alloy keeps the advantages of magnesium without the disadvantages.

Section 6.4 Assessment

Reviewing Concepts

1. What holds metal ions together in a metal lattice?
2. What characteristic of a metallic bond explains some of the properties of metals?
3. How can scientists design alloys with specific properties?
4. Explain why the metallic bonds in some metals are stronger than the bonds in other metals.
5. Why are metals good conductors of electric current?
6. How does adding carbon to steel make the steel harder and stronger?

Critical Thinking

7. **Predicting** Which element has a higher melting point, potassium in Group 1A or calcium in Group 1B? Give a reason for your answer.
8. **Applying Concepts** Can two different elements form a metallic bond together?

Writing in Science

Compare-Contrast Paragraph Write a paragraph comparing the properties of ionic compounds and alloys. Relate their properties to the structure of their lattices.

Integrate Materials Science L2

The properties of an alloy that are determined by its composition include malleability, ductility, hardness, corrosion resistance, tensile strength (the ability to resist being pulled apart), shear strength (the ability to resist opposing forces that are not acting in a straight line), compressive strength (the ability to withstand pressures acting on a given plane), and elasticity (the ability to return to its original size and shape). Ask, **What properties of steel make it useful for the cables and towers of the Golden Gate Bridge?** *(Its high tensile strength makes steel a useful material for the cables, and its high compressive strength makes it a useful material for the towers.)* **Logical**

3 ASSESS

Evaluate Understanding L2

Have students write the names of the following elements on index cards: copper, gold, silver, nickel, zinc, tin, iron, carbon, and aluminum. On the other side of the cards, have students write common uses for these elements. (For example, alloys of aluminum and copper are used to make airplane parts.)

Reteach L1

Use Figure 22 to review how the structure within a metal affects the properties of a metal.

Writing in Science

In the rigid network of a crystal lattice, the charged particles are not free to flow unless the solid melts. When struck, the crystal shatters because ions with the same charge shift position in the lattice and repel. Thus, ionic solids are brittle and are poor conductors. In a metal lattice, the electrons are free to move and conduct a current. The lattice is malleable when struck because if a cation moves it is still surrounded by particles with an opposite charge.

Interactive Textbook If your class subscribes to the Interactive Textbook, use it to review key concepts in Section 6.4.

Section 6.4 Assessment

1. Metal ions are held together by the strong metallic bonds between the cations and the surrounding valence electrons.
2. The mobility of electrons within a metal lattice explains some of the properties of metals.
3. Scientists can design alloys with specific properties by varying the types and amounts of elements in an alloy.
4. The more valence electrons a metal can contribute, the stronger the bonds will be.
5. The valence electrons are free to move because they are not attached to a specific metal ion.
6. The smaller carbon atoms fit into spaces between the iron atoms and form bonds with neighboring iron atoms, which makes the lattice harder and stronger.
7. Calcium has a higher melting point because it contributes twice as many electrons to the metallic bonds.
8. Yes, alloys usually are mixtures of elements with metallic bonds.

Answer to . . .

Figure 24 *The compositions would probably be different because the forces acting on the cables and towers are different—tensile versus compressive, respectively.*

Chemical Bonds 181

CONCEPTS in Action

Chipping In **L2**

Background

The silicon crystal shown in the photo is called an ingot. Pure silicon ingots can be produced by the Czochralski pulled-growth method described on p. 163. Wafers cut from the ingot can be ground, polished, cleaned, etched, doped with elements such as phosphorus and boron, and sliced with a diamond saw to produce microchips.

Build Science Skills **L2**

Applying Concepts ACTIVITY

Purpose Students observe the importance of transistors in their lives.

Materials access to a library or the Internet, notepad for data collection

Class Time 20–30 minutes of research, one day of data collection, 20 minutes of class discussion

Procedure Have students use the library or the Internet to come up with a list of electronic devices that contain transistors. Have students record every time they use a device that contains a transistor, and the type of device. Have students compare their data in a class discussion.

Expected Outcome Devices that contain transistors include alarm clocks, watches, refrigerators, microwave ovens, washers, dryers, calculators, computers, radios, CD players, televisions, VCRs, DVD players, and video game consoles.
Intrapersonal, Kinesthetic

Chipping In

Tasks done by computers that filled an entire room in the 1950s are now done by devices the size of a credit card. This miniaturization in the electronics industry is due to semiconductors.

Semiconductors are solid substances, such as silicon, that have poor electrical conductivity at ordinary temperatures. Silicon has four valence electrons. In pure silicon, each atom forms single bonds with four other atoms. This arrangement leaves no electrons free to move through the silicon. The conductivity of silicon is greatly improved by adding small amounts of other elements to silicon, a process called doping.

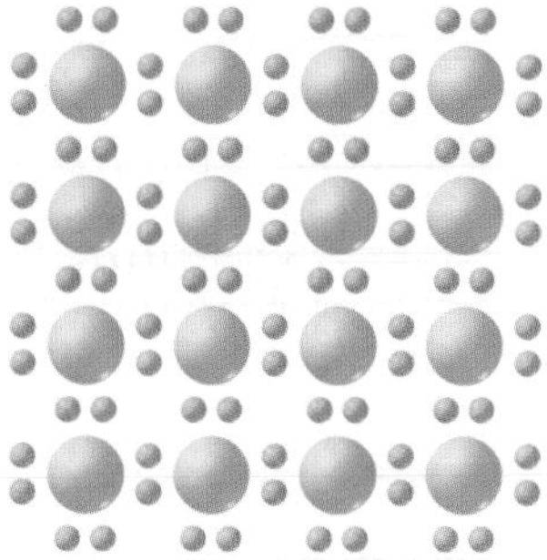
Pure Silicon

Doping
An element with five valence electrons, such as phosphorus, can be added to silicon. After a phosphorus atom bonds with four atoms, there is an extra electron that is free to move. Silicon doped with phosphorus is called *n*-type silicon because electrons have a negative charge. An element with three valence electrons, such as boron, can be added to silicon. Adding boron leaves holes to which electrons can move from neighboring atoms. Because the lack of an electron has the effect of a positive charge, silicon with boron is called *p*-type silicon.

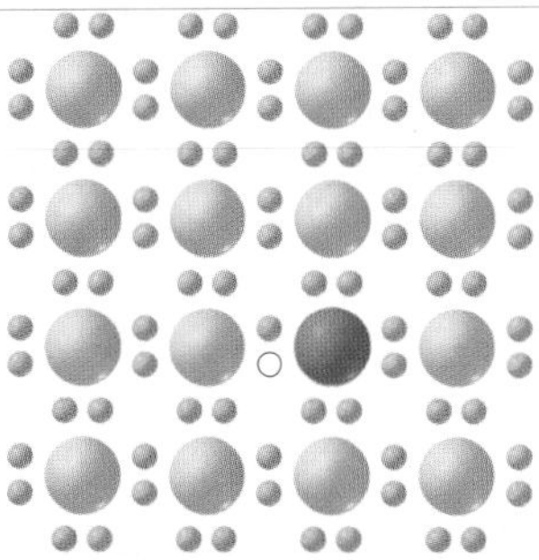
Silicon with boron

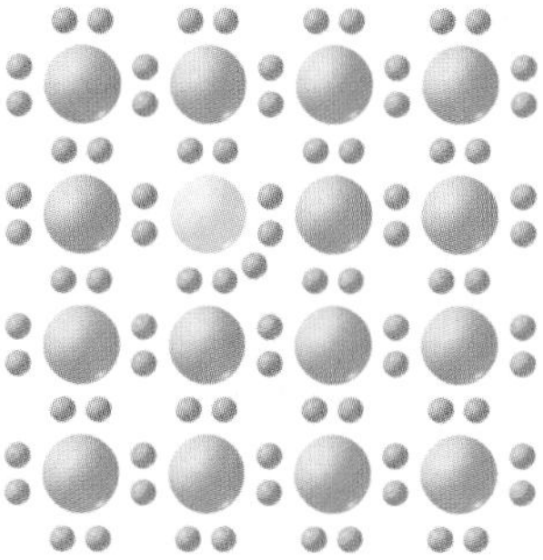
Silicon with phosphorus

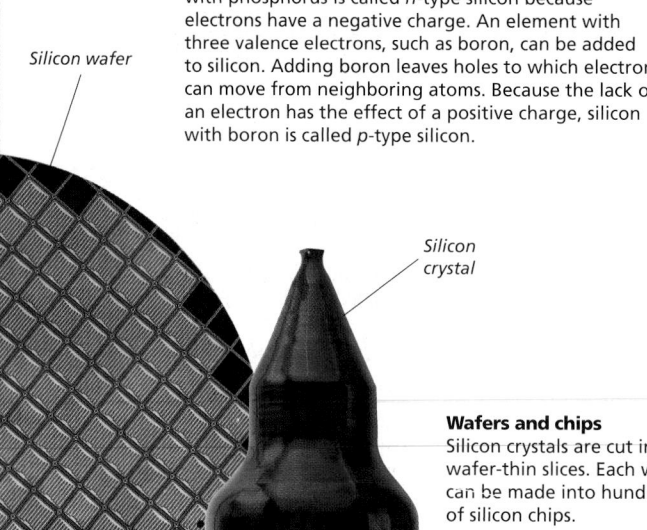

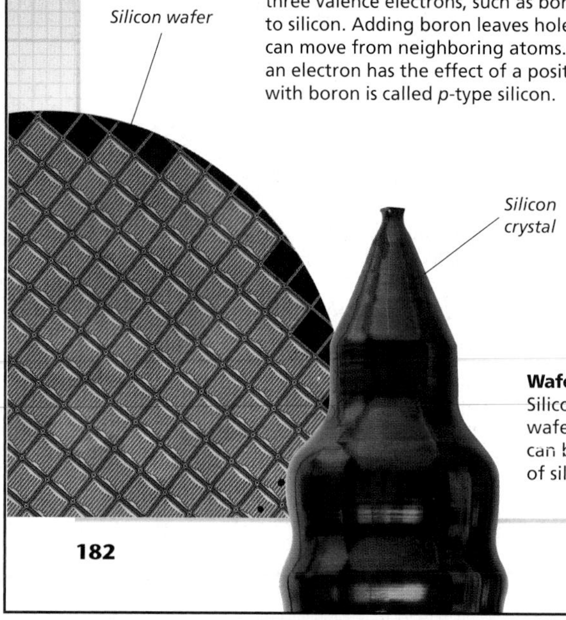
Silicon wafer
Silicon crystal

Wafers and chips
Silicon crystals are cut into wafer-thin slices. Each wafer can be made into hundreds of silicon chips.

Vacuum tube
Glass vacuum tubes used in early computers were fragile and took up space.

Integrated circuit on a silicon chip

Computer chip
In 1974, the first computer microchip contained 6000 transistors. Today, more than 40 million transistors can be placed on a single computer chip.

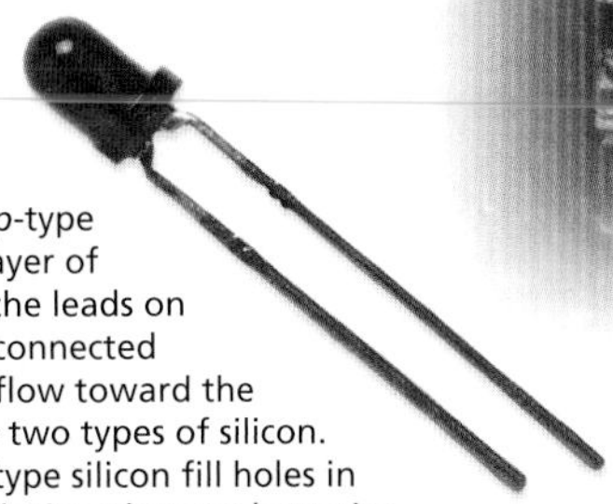

Diode
In a diode, a layer of *p*-type silicon is joined to a layer of *n*-type silicon. When the leads on a diode are correctly connected in a circuit, electrons flow toward the junction between the two types of silicon. Electrons from the *n*-type silicon fill holes in the *p*-type silicon. In devices that use batteries, a diode can keep electrons from flowing if the batteries are not inserted correctly. Some diodes emit light when the circuit is complete.

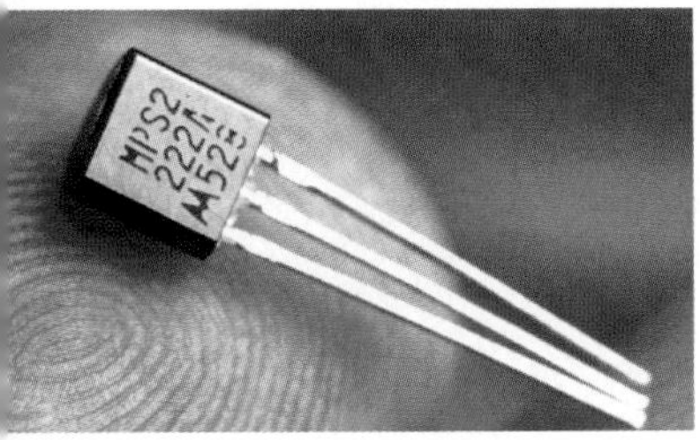

ransistor
ı a transistor, there are three layers of doped licon. There is a layer of *p*-type silicon andwiched between two layers of *n*-type licon or a layer of *n*-type silicon between wo layers of p-type silicon. Transistors are sed to amplify current. A small current pplied to the central layer of a transistor can roduce a larger current.

Going Further

- Research and write about the development of transistors. Why were researchers looking for a replacement for vacuum tubes? How did replacing vacuum tubes with transistors affect the size of radios and computers?
- Take a Discovery Channel Video Field Trip by watching "Good Conduct."

Discovery Channel School
Video Field Trip

Going Further

Transistors were developed to solve a problem with long distance telephone service. Until the 1950s, AT&T used vacuum tubes to amplify signals as they were transferred from one switch box to the next. Vacuum tubes were unreliable, used a lot of power, and produced a lot of heat.

After World War II, a team at Bell Laboratories in New Jersey (John Bardeen, Walter Brattain, and William Shockley) developed the transistor. In 1956, they shared the Nobel Prize in Physics. A transistor is a thin three-layer sandwich with a *p*-type semiconductor in the outer layers and an *n*-type in the middle (PNP), or an *n*-type semiconductor on opposite sides of a *p*-type (NPN).

Because transistors are so much smaller than vacuum tubes, devices such as radios, televisions, and computers were reduced in size when vacuum tubes were replaced with transistors.
Verbal

Discovery Channel School

Video Field Trip

Good Conduct

After students have viewed the Video Field Trip, ask them the following questions: **What is the main element in computer chips?** *(Silicon)* **What is the purpose of the seed crystal that is lowered into the rotating vat of molten silicon?** *(The atoms in the seed crystal form a lattice. As the molten silicon cools, silicon atoms follow this pattern as they form a much larger silicon crystal.)* **Why is pure silicon a poor conductor of electric current?** *(After each silicon atom forms four bonds with neighboring atoms, there are no free electrons to conduct electric current.)* **What happens when a boron atom is substituted in the lattice?** *(Boron has only three valence electrons, so holes [or the absence of an electron] are left to which electrons from neighboring atoms can move as they conduct electric current.)* **What happens when a phosphorus atom is substituted in the lattice?** *(A phosphorus atom has five valence electrons, so there is an extra electron that can freely move and conduct electric current.)* **How can the ability of pure silicon to conduct current at room temperature be increased?** *(Impurities, called dopants, can be added to increase the number of electrons or holes available to conduct an electric current.)*

Consumer Lab

Improving the Dyeing of Nonpolar Fabrics L2

Objective
After completing this activity, students will be able to
- relate the ability of fabrics to absorb and retain dyes to the polar or nonpolar character of their fibers.

Skills Focus Observing

Prep Time 40 minutes

Advance Prep Wear plastic gloves, a lab apron, and a dust mask when preparing the solutions. To prepare methyl orange dye solution, add 2.1 g Na_2SO_4 and 6–9 drops concentrated H_2SO_4 to 450 mL of water. Then, add 1.50 g methyl orange powder to the solution. Stir the solution. To prepare iron(II) sulfate solution, add 12.6 g $FeSO_4 \bullet H_2O$ to 450 mL water. Stir the solution. Place the solutions in 1-L beakers on hot plates and heat them in advance to near boiling. Arrange hot plates with the two solutions at several lab stations. Test fabrics that consist of a repeating pattern of wool, polyester, nylon, cotton, and various other natural and synthetic fibers may be obtained from a commercial fabric company. You may also make up your own test strips from fabric remnants.

Class Time 45 minutes, if different lab groups perform Parts A and B simultaneously. Alternatively, the work can be done by all groups over the course of two days.

Safety Review the safety information on the MSDS for methyl orange and iron(II) sulfate with students. Make sure students wear their goggles, gloves, and lab aprons at all times during the investigation. Emphasize the importance of protective clothing for this investigation. Any spills should be wiped up promptly to avoid slips and falls. The hot plates and furniture should be placed so that students will not bump into them as they move around. Do not use flames to heat the solutions. Advise students to wear old clothes suitable for painting on the day of this investigation. Stains from methyl orange may be permanent.

Consumer Lab

Improving the Dyeing of Nonpolar Fabrics

Most natural fibers, such as cotton and wool, consist of large molecules that have regions with a partial positive or partial negative charge. These polar molecules have a strong attraction for dyes that contain either polar molecules or ions.

The molecules in some manufactured fibers, such as nylon, are nonpolar molecules. These synthetic fibers are difficult to dye. Molecules of other synthetic fibers, such as polyester and rayon, have only a few polar regions. As you might suspect, polyester and rayon have intermediate attractions for dyes. In this lab, you will investigate a process for improving a fiber's ability to absorb and retain dye.

Problem
How can you increase the dye-holding capacity of nonpolar fibers?

Materials
- tongs
- 2 fabric test strips
- hot dye bath containing methyl orange
- clock or watch
- paper towels
- scissors
- soap
- hot iron(II) sulfate solution

Skills
Observing, Drawing Conclusions

Procedure

Part A: Dyeing Without Treatment
1. On a sheet of paper, copy the data table shown.
2. Use the tongs to immerse a fabric test strip in the methyl orange dye bath. **CAUTION** *The dye bath is hot. Do not touch the glass. The dye will stain skin and clothing.*
3. After 7 minutes, remove the strip from the dye bath. Allow as much of the dye solution as possible to drip back into the bath as shown on page 185. Rinse off the excess dye with water in the sink.
4. Place the strip on a paper towel to dry. Be careful to avoid splashes when transferring the strip between the dye bath and paper towel. Record your observations in your data table.
5. After the fabric strip is dry, test it for colorfastness, or the ability to hold dye. Cut the strip in half lengthwise and wash one half of the strip in the sink with soap and water.

Data Table

Dye Treatment	Dyeing of Fibers	Colorfastness of Fibers
Methyl orange		
Iron sulfate and methyl orange		

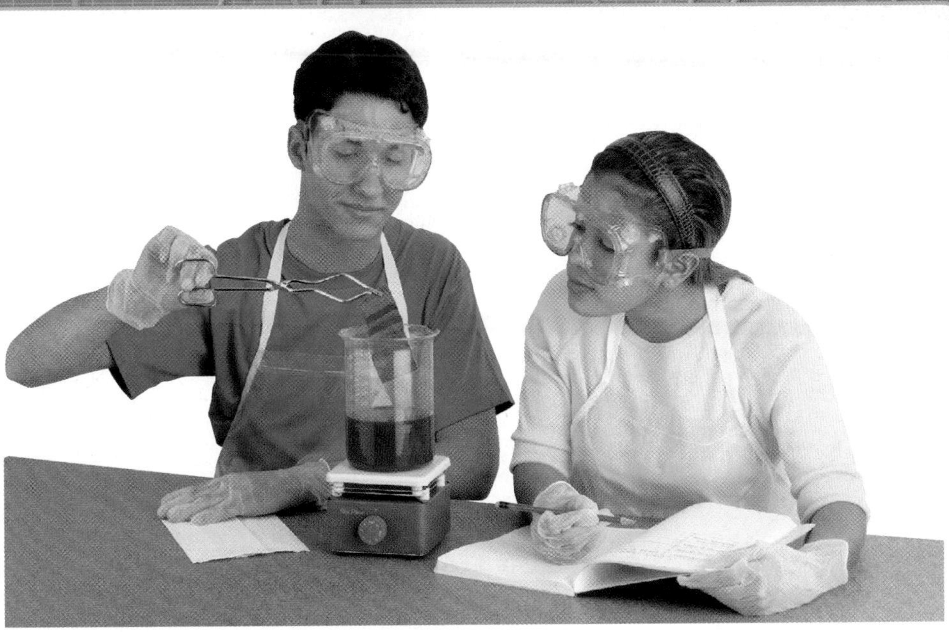

6. Allow the washed half-strip to dry and then compare the washed half to the unwashed half. Record your observations in your data table. Staple the half-strips to a sheet of paper and label each half-strip to indicate how you treated it.

Part B: Dyeing With Treatment

7. Use the tongs to place the second fabric strip in the iron(II) sulfate solution for 25 minutes. Then use tongs to lift the strip and allow it to drain into the iron(II) sulfate solution. Wring the strip as dry as possible over the solution. **CAUTION** *The strip will be hot. Allow it to cool before touching it. Wear plastic gloves.*
8. Repeat Steps 2, 3, and 4 using the strip that you treated with iron(II) sulfate.
9. To test the strip for colorfastness, repeat Steps 5 and 6.
10. Clean up your work area and wash your hands thoroughly with warm water and soap before leaving the laboratory.

Analyze and Conclude

1. **Comparing and Contrasting** How did the color of the untreated strip compare with the color of the treated strip?
2. **Comparing and Contrasting** How did the colorfastness of the untreated strip compare to the colorfastness of the treated strip?
3. **Applying Concepts** Silk blouses and shirts can be purchased in many intense colors. Why do you think silk is able to hold a variety of intense dyes?
4. **Drawing Conclusions** How does iron(II) sulfate affect the ability of a fabric to absorb dyes? (*Hint:* What kind of compound is iron(II) sulfate?)
5. **Predicting** A care label might say *Wash in cold water only.* What might happen to the color of a piece of clothing with this label if you washed the clothing in hot water?

Teaching Tips

- Explain the role of ionic and polar regions in the dyeing process. In Part A, students perform direct dyeing, which involves the ionic sites of the dye molecules attaching to ionic sites in the fabric. In Part B, ionic sites are introduced into the synthetic fibers so that more dye can bond to the fibers.
- Identify the different fibers in the fabric test strips for students.
- Make sure that the dye and iron(II) sulfate baths stay close to the boiling point, but do not let them boil, as they may spatter.

Expected Outcome Natural fibers absorb dye more easily and are more colorfast than synthetic fibers. Iron(II) sulfate treatment improves the dyeing and colorfastness of synthetic fibers.

Analyze and Conclude

1. Treatment increased the intensity of the colors for synthetic fibers.
2. In general, treatment improved colorfastness, especially in synthetic fabrics.
3. Silk is a natural fiber. Like most natural fibers, it has many polar regions that allow the dye to attach to the fibers.
4. Iron(II) sulfate is an ionic compound. Treatment with this compound adds ionic sites to the fabric, increasing its ability to bind dyes.
5. The hot water would remove more dye than would cold water, and the colors would run.

Visual, Kinesthetic

Sample Data Table

Dye Treatment	Dyeing of Fibers	Colorfastness of Fibers
Methyl orange	Intensity of color varies; wool is strongest, synthetics weakest.	Wool and cotton are colorfast; synthetic fibers are not.
Iron sulfate and methyl orange	Intensity of color varies, but increase in intensity is strongest in synthetics.	All fibers are colorfast.

Study Guide

Study Tip

Plan Ahead
Tell students to examine their schedules at least a week before the test. They should figure out how much time they will have available to study. Then, they should divide up that time and plan when they are going to study each topic covered on the test. They should review the most important topics first. That way, they can cut the time allotted for reviewing less important topics if they have less time for studying than expected.

Thinking Visually

a. Polar covalent bond
b. Nonpolar covalent bond

CHAPTER 6

Study Guide

6.1 Ionic Bonding

Key Concepts

- When the highest occupied energy level of an atom is filled with electrons, the atom is stable and not likely to react.
- Some elements achieve stable electron configurations through the transfer of electrons between atoms. An ionic bond forms when electrons are transferred from one atom to another.
- The properties of an ionic compound can be explained by the strong attractions among ions within a crystal lattice.

Vocabulary

electron dot diagram, *p. 158*
ion, *p. 159*
anion, *p. 160*
cation, *p. 160*
chemical bond, *p. 160*
ionic bond, *p. 160*
chemical formula, *p. 161*
crystals, *p. 162*

6.2 Covalent Bonding

Key Concepts

- The attractions between the shared electrons and the protons in each nucleus hold the atoms together in a covalent bond.
- When atoms form a polar covalent bond, the atom with the greater attraction for electrons has a partial negative charge. The other atom has a partial positive charge.
- The type of atoms in a molecule and its shape are factors that determine whether a molecule is polar or nonpolar.
- Attractions between polar molecules are stronger than attractions between nonpolar molecules.

Vocabulary

covalent bond, *p. 166*
molecule, *p. 166*
polar covalent bond, *p. 168*

6.3 Naming Compounds and Writing Formulas

Key Concepts

- The name of an ionic compound must distinguish the compound from other ionic compounds containing the same elements. The formula of an ionic compound describes the ratio of the ions in the compound.
- The name and formula of a molecular compound describe the type and number of atoms in a molecule of the compound.

Vocabulary

polyatomic ion, *p. 172*

6.4 The Structure of Metals

Key Concepts

- The cations in a metal form a lattice that is held in place by strong metallic bonds between the cations and the surrounding valence electrons.
- The mobility of electrons within a metal lattice explains some of the properties of metals.
- Scientists can design alloys with specific properties by varying the types and amounts of elements in an alloy.

Vocabulary

metallic bond, *p. 176*
alloy, *p. 178*

Thinking Visually

Concept Map Use information from the chapter to complete the concept map below.

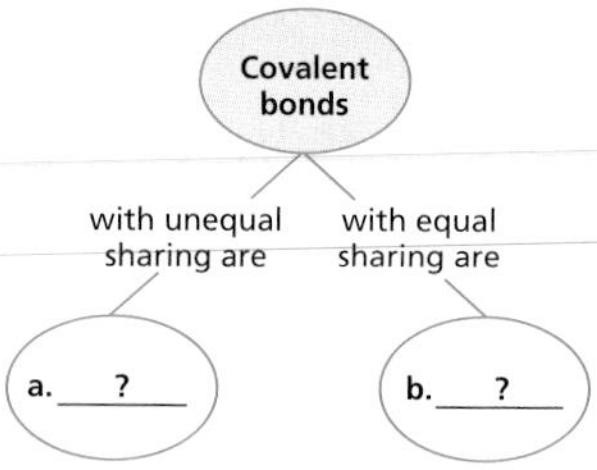
Covalent bonds
with unequal sharing are
with equal sharing are
a. ___?___
b. ___?___

Chapter Resources

Print
- ***Chapter and Unit Tests,*** Chapter 6 Test A and Test B
- ***Test Prep Resources,*** Chapter 6

Technology
- ***Computer Test Bank,*** Chapter Test 6
- ***Interactive Textbook,*** Chapter 6
- ***Go Online,*** PHSchool.com, Chapter 6

CHAPTER 6

Assessment

Reviewing Content

Choose the letter that best answers the question or completes the statement.

1. When an atom loses an electron, it forms a(n)
   a. anion. b. cation.
   c. polyatomic ion. d. neutral ion.
2. The charge on a chloride ion in $AlCl_3$ is
   a. 1+. b. 3+.
   c. 1−. d. 3−.
3. Which pair has the same electron configuration?
   a. Cl^- and Ar b. Cl^- and Ar^-
   c. Cl and Ar d. Cl^+ and Ar
4. A chemical bond that forms when atoms share electrons is always a(n)
   a. polar bond. b. ionic bond.
   c. metallic bond. d. covalent bond.
5. When two fluorine atoms share a pair of electrons, the bond that forms is a(n)
   a. polar covalent bond.
   b. ionic bond.
   c. nonpolar covalent bond.
   d. double bond.
6. The chemical formula for magnesium bromide is
   a. MgBr. b. $MgBr_2$.
   c. $Mg(II)Br_2$. d. Mg_2Br.
7. The compound with the formula $SiCl_4$ is
   a. silicon chloride. b. silicon chlorine.
   c. silicon(I) chloride. d. silicon tetrachloride.
8. The attraction among water molecules is stronger than the attraction among
   a. sodium and chloride ions.
   b. carbon dioxide molecules.
   c. the atoms in a polyatomic ion.
   d. atoms in a diatomic molecule.
9. Which type of solid is likely to be the best conductor of electric current?
   a. ionic compound b. covalent compound
   c. metal element d. nonmetal element
10. An alloy contains
    a. at least one metallic element.
    b. at least one nonmetallic element.
    c. only metallic elements.
    d. only nonmetallic elements.

Understanding Concepts

11. What is a stable electron configuration?
12. What does each dot in an electron dot diagram represent?
13. What process changes atoms into ions?
14. What keeps the ions in their fixed positions within a crystal lattice?
15. What are subscripts used for in chemical formulas?
16. Explain why a melted ionic compound is a good conductor of electric current, but a solid ionic compound is a poor conductor of electric current.
17. What distinguishes single, double, and triple covalent bonds?
18. Explain why the covalent bonds in molecules of elements are always nonpolar.
19. Explain why, in a covalent bond between oxygen and hydrogen, the hydrogen atom has a partial positive charge and the oxygen atom has a partial negative charge.
20. What is the name of the binary compound formed from potassium and iodine?
21. Write the formulas for the compounds called copper(I) chloride and copper(II) chloride.
22. Name the compounds represented by the space-filling models labeled A, B, and C.

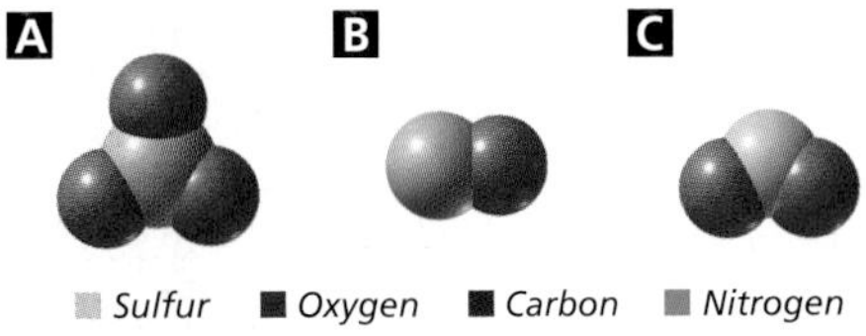

A
B
C
Sulfur
Oxygen
Carbon
Nitrogen

23. In general, what determines the strength of metallic bonds?
24. What properties of copper and tin change when these metals are mixed together to form bronze?
25. What advantage of magnesium is retained in magnesium alloys? What disadvantage is reduced?

Homework Guide

Section	Questions
6.1	1–3, 11–16, 26, 30, 33
6.2	4–5, 8, 17–19, 27, 34–35, 39–40, 42
6.3	6–7, 20–22, 28–29, 31–32, 36–38
6.4	9–10, 23–25, 41

Assessment

Interactive Textbook If your class subscribes to the Interactive Textbook, your students can go online to access an interactive version of the Student Edition and a self-test.

Reviewing Content

1. b 2. c 3. a
4. d 5. c 6. b
7. d 8. b 9. c
10. a

Understanding Concepts

11. In a stable electron configuration, the highest occupied energy level is filled with electrons.
12. Each dot represents a valence electron.
13. The transfer of electrons
14. Attractions between neighboring cations and anions keep the ions in fixed positions within the lattice.
15. A subscript is used to show the number of atoms of an element in a molecule or the ratio of ions in a crystal lattice.
16. When an ionic compound melts, ions can move away from their fixed locations in the crystal lattice.
17. Two atoms share two electrons in a single bond, four in a double bond, and six in a triple bond.
18. The covalent bonds in molecules of elements are always nonpolar because the atoms have the same attraction for electrons.
19. The oxygen atom has a greater attraction for electrons than the hydrogen atom does.
20. Potassium iodide
21. CuCl and $CuCl_2$
22. A is sulfur trioxide, B is carbon monoxide, and C is nitrogen dioxide
23. In general, the more valence electrons a metal has, the stronger the metal bonds are.
24. A mixture of copper and tin is harder and stronger than either metal in its pure form.
25. The advantage that is retained is that magnesium is a lightweight metal. The disadvantage that is reduced is that magnesium is a soft metal.

Critical Thinking

26. All three have the same electron configuration.
27. Molecules and polyatomic ions both contain covalent bonds.
28. Sulfur trioxide: polar covalent bonds; calcium oxide: ionic bonds; iodine: nonpolar covalent bonds
29. Sulfur dichloride, silver(I) sulfate, lithium fluoride, carbon disulfide, calcium hydroxide
30. Q is a metal. X and Z are nonmetals.
31. QX and Q_2Z
32. Cr_2Z_3
33. :F : Z : F:
34. Nonpolar covalent bond

Math Skills

35. 8
36. The ratio is two to one anions to cations.
37. BaF_2, Na_2O, $FeSO_4$, and $(NH_4)_2SO_4$

Concepts in Action

38. The correct formula is B.
39. Molecules of carbon dioxide are nonpolar. Molecules of water are polar. The attractive forces are much greater between polar molecules than between nonpolar molecules.
40. The carbonate ion is a polyatomic ion, which contains covalent bonds.
41. Phosphorus has five valence electrons compared to four valence electrons in silicon. The extra electrons are not needed to bond the atoms together and are free to move and carry the current.
42. Ideally, students should note that in both cases the electron will be sharing space with a second electron in orbitals that overlap. In the bond between hydrogen atoms, the electron will be equally attracted to both nuclei. In the bond between hydrogen and oxygen, the electron will have a greater attraction to the oxygen nucleus.

CHAPTER 6

Assessment *(continued)*

Critical Thinking

26. **Classifying** What does a fluoride ion have in common with a neon atom and a sodium ion?

27. **Comparing and Contrasting** How are molecules and polyatomic ions similar?

28. **Classifying** Classify the bonds in each of these compounds as ionic, polar covalent, or nonpolar covalent: SO_3, CaO, and I_2.

29. **Applying Concepts** Write the names for the compounds with these chemical formulas: SCl_2, Ag_2SO_4, LiF, CS_2, and $Ca(OH)_2$.

Use these diagrams to answer Questions 30–34.

A
B
C
X
Q
Z

30. **Using Models** Which of the three elements are metals and which are nonmetals?

31. **Applying Concepts** Element Q forms compounds with element X and with element Z. Write the formulas for these two compounds.

32. **Calculating** What would the formula be for a compound containing chromium(III) ions and ions of element Z?

33. **Applying Concepts** Draw an electron dot structure for a compound of fluorine and Z.

34. **Predicting** If an atom of X reacts with an atom of X, what kind of bond forms?

Math Skills

35. **Calculating** What is the total number of shared electrons in a carbon dioxide molecule?

36. **Making Generalizations** What is the ratio of anions to cations in a compound formed by a Group 2A metal and a Group 7A nonmetal?

37. **Applying Concepts** Write the formulas for barium fluoride, sodium oxide, iron(II) sulfate, and ammonium sulfate.

Concepts In Action

38. **Using Models** A solution of hydrogen peroxide (H_2O_2) and water is sometimes used to disinfect a cut. Which of the following formulas is the correct structural formula for hydrogen peroxide?

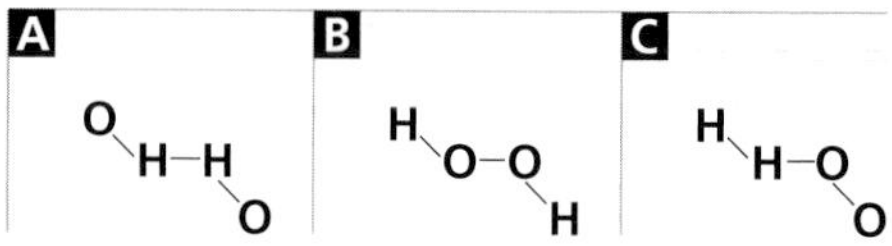
A
B
C

39. **Relating Cause and Effect** In a carbonated beverage, the main ingredients are water and carbon dioxide. Carbon dioxide gas is released when the bottle is opened. Why is water a liquid but carbon dioxide a gas at room temperature?

40. **Classifying** The shells shown on page 156 contain the compound calcium carbonate ($CaCO_3$). Explain how this compound can contain both ionic and covalent bonds.

41. **Relating Cause and Effect** How does adding some phosphorus to silicon make silicon a better conductor of electric current?

42. **Writing in Science** Compare what happens to the valence electron in a hydrogen atom when the atom bonds with another hydrogen atom and when the atom bonds with an oxygen atom.

Performance-Based Assessment

Designing an Advertisement You own a store that sells bronze bells. Design a quarter-page ad for your store to be published in your local directory of businesses. Write copy for your ad. Describe a photograph to use in the ad. Also supply a sketch showing how you want the copy and the photograph to be laid out on the page.

Go Online
PHSchool.com

For: Self-grading assessment
Visit: PHSchool.com
Web Code: cca-1060

Go Online
PHSchool.com

Your students can independently test their knowledge of the chapter and print out their test results for your files.

Performance-Based Assessment

The ad could include properties of bronze, such as hardness and durability. The ad should stress the sound produced by a bronze bell. (Have examples of ads in a local directory of businesses for students to look at. Students may want to research the cost of a quarter-page ad in the directory.)

Standardized Test Prep

Test-Taking Tip

Paying Attention to the Details
Sometimes two or more answers to a question are almost identical. If you do not read the answers carefully, you may select an incorrect answer by mistake. In the question below, all the answers include the correct elements in the correct order—metal before nonmetal. However, only one of the answers uses the correct rules for naming $CaCl_2$.

The name for the compound with the formula $CaCl_2$ is
(A) calcium(II) chloride.
(B) calcium chlorine.
(C) calcium dichloride.
(D) calcium chloride.
(E) monocalcium dichloride.

(Answer: D)

Choose the letter that best answers the question or completes the statement.

1. How many electrons does a Group 7A atom need to gain in order to achieve a stable electron configuration?
   (A) 0
   (B) 1
   (C) 2
   (D) 7
   (E) 8

2. What type of bond forms when electrons are transferred from one atom to another?
   (A) nonpolar covalent bond
   (B) ionic bond
   (C) polar covalent bond
   (D) polyatomic bond
   (E) metallic bond

3. Metallic bonds form between
   (A) cations and protons.
   (B) anions and protons.
   (C) cations and anions.
   (D) cations and electrons.
   (E) anions and electrons.

Use the table to answer Questions 4 and 5.

Some Ions and Their Symbols

Ion Name	Ion Symbol	Ion Name	Ion Symbol
Copper(I)	Cu^{+}	Nitrate	NO_3^{-}
Copper(II)	Cu^{2+}	Sulfate	SO_4^{2-}
Iron(II)	Fe^{2+}	Carbonate	CO_3^{2-}
Iron(III)	Fe^{3+}	Phosphate	PO_4^{3-}

4. What is the formula for copper(II) nitrate?
   (A) $CuNO_3$
   (B) $Cu_2(NO_3)_2$
   (C) $Cu(NO_3)_2$
   (D) Cu_2NO_3
   (E) $CuNO_2$

5. In the compound iron(II) carbonate, the ratio of iron(II) ions to carbonate ions will be
   (A) one to one.
   (B) two to one.
   (C) three to one.
   (D) one to two.
   (E) one to three.

6. All steels contain
   (A) copper and zinc.
   (B) copper and tin.
   (C) iron and chromium.
   (D) chromium and carbon.
   (E) iron and carbon.

7. What is the reason that water has a higher boiling point than expected?
   (A) Attractions among nonpolar water molecules are strong.
   (B) Water molecules have a linear shape.
   (C) Water molecules are not very massive.
   (D) There are strong attractions among polar water molecules.
   (E) There are no attractions among water molecules.

Standardized Test Prep

1. B **2.** B **3.** D
4. C **5.** A **6.** E
7. D

CHAPTER 7

Planning Guide

Use these planning tools
Easy Planner
Teacher Express

SECTION OBJECTIVES	STANDARDS NATIONAL (See p. T18.)	STANDARDS STATE	ACTIVITIES and LABS
7.1 Describing Reactions, pp. 192–198 1 block or 2 periods **7.1.1** **Interpret** chemical equations in terms of reactants, products, and conservation of mass. **7.1.2** **Balance** chemical equations by manipulating coefficients. **7.1.3** **Convert** between moles and mass of a substance using molar mass. **7.1.4** **Calculate** amounts of reactants or products by using molar mass, mole ratios, and balanced chemical equations.	A-1, A-2, B-2, B-3		**SE** Inquiry Activity: How Is Mass Conserved in a Chemical Change? p. 191 **L2** **SE** Quick Lab: Modeling a Mole, p. 196 **L2** **TE** Teacher Demo: Counting Particles, p. 195 **L2** **TE** Build Science Skills: Measuring and Calculating, p. 197 **L2**
7.2 Types of Reactions, pp. 199–205 1 block or 2 periods **7.2.1** **Classify** chemical reactions as synthesis, decomposition, single-replacement, double-replacement, or combustion reactions. **7.2.2** **Describe** oxidation-reduction reactions, and **relate** them to other classifications of chemical reactions.	A-1, A-2, B-1, B-2, B-3, F-1		**SE** Quick Lab: Identifying a Type of Reaction, p. 203 **L2** **TE** Teacher Demo: Exothermic Reaction, p. 200 **L2** **LM** Investigation 7A: Using Single-Replacement Reactions to Compare Reactivities **L2** **LM** Investigation 7B: Recognizing a Synthesis Reaction **L1**
7.3 Energy Changes in Reactions, pp. 206–209 1 block or 2 periods **7.3.1** **Describe** the energy changes that take place during chemical reactions. **7.3.2** **Classify** chemical reactions as exothermic or endothermic. **7.3.3** **Explain** how energy is conserved during chemical reactions.	B-2, B-3, B-5, F-1, F-5		**TE** Build Science Skills: Observing, p. 208 **L2**
7.4 Reaction Rates, pp. 212–215 1 block or 2 periods **7.4.1** **Explain** what a reaction rate is. **7.4.2** **Describe** the factors affecting chemical reaction rates.	A-1, A-2, B-3, C-1		**SE** Quick Lab: Observing the Action of Catalysts, p. 214 **L2** **TE** Build Science Skills: Calculating, p. 213 **L2** **TE** Teacher Demo: Temperature and Rate, p. 213 **L2**
7.5 Equilibrium, pp. 216–219 1 block or 2 periods **7.5.1** **Identify** and **describe** physical and chemical equilibria. **7.5.2** **Describe** the factors affecting chemical equilibrium.	A-1, A-2, B-2, B-3, C-1, E-1, G-1, G-3		**SE** Design Your Own Lab: Manipulating Chemical Equilibrium, pp. 220–221 **L2** **TE** Build Science Skills: Using Models, p. 216 **L2**

Ability Levels	
L1	For students who need additional help
L2	For all students
L3	For students who need to be challenged

Components							
SE	Student Edition	RSW	Reading & Study Workbook	CUT	Chapter & Unit Tests	T	Transparencies
TE	Teacher's Edition	MSPS	Math Skills & Problem Solving Workbook	CTB	Computer Test Bank	iT	Interactive Textbook
LM	Laboratory Manual			TP	Test Prep Resources	P	Presentation Pro CD-ROM
PLM	Probeware Lab Manual			DC	Discovery Channel Videotapes & DVDs	GO	Internet Resources

RESOURCES PRINT and TECHNOLOGY		SECTION ASSESSMENT
RSW Section 7.1	L1	SE Section 7.1 Assessment, p. 198
RSW Math Skill	L2	iT Section 7.1
MSPS Section 7.1	L2	
T Chapter 7 Pretest	L2	
Section 7.1	L2	
P Chapter 7 Pretest	L2	
Section 7.1	L2	
SCiLINKS GO Conservation of mass	L2	
SCIENCE NEWS GO Chemical reactions	L2	
RSW Section 7.2	L1	SE Section 7.2 Assessment, p. 205
T Section 7.2	L2	iT Section 7.2
P Section 7.2	L2	
SCiLINKS GO Chemical reactions, Oxidation and reduction	L2	
RSW Section 7.3	L1	SE Section 7.3 Assessment, p. 209
DC Taming the Flames	L2	iT Section 7.3
T Section 7.3	L2	
P Section 7.3	L2	
RSW Section 7.4	L1	SE Section 7.4 Assessment, p. 215
T Section 7.4	L2	iT Section 7.4
P Section 7.4	L2	
SCiLINKS GO Factors affecting reaction rate	L2	
RSW Section 7.5	L1	SE Section 7.5 Assessment, p. 219
T Section 7.5	L2	iT Section 7.5
P Section 7.5	L2	
SCiLINKS GO Factors affecting equilibrium	L2	

Go Online

Go online for these Internet resources.

PHSchool.com
Web Code: cca-1070

SCIENCE NEWS
Web Code: cce-1071

NSTA SCiLINKS
Web Code: ccn-1071
Web Code: ccn-1072
Web Code: ccn-1074
Web Code: ccn-1075
Web Code: ccn-1076

Materials for Activities and Labs

Quantities for each group

STUDENT EDITION

Inquiry Activity, p. 191
100-mL graduated cylinder, resealable quart-sized plastic bag, 10-cm × 10-cm piece of paper, effervescent antacid tablet, triple-beam balance

Quick Lab, p. 196
bolt, 2 nuts, 2 washers, balance

Quick Lab, p. 203
piece of zinc, copper(II) sulfate solution, 250-mL beaker, tongs, paper towel

Quick Lab, p. 214
5 test tubes, test-tube rack, marking pencil, dropper pipet, wood splint, platinum wire, 0.1 g manganese dioxide, 5 drops of copper(II) chloride solution, 0.1 g raw potato, graduated cylinder, 25 mL hydrogen peroxide

Design Your Own Lab, pp. 220–221
iodine-starch solution, 150-mL beaker, 4 dropper pipets, spot plate, ascorbic acid solution, chlorine bleach solution

TEACHER'S EDITION

Teacher Demo, p. 195
14 g graphite powder, small beaker, spatula, balance, a bag of rice, stack of paper plates

Build Science Skills, p. 197
copper wire, aluminum foil, water, sodium chloride, hydrogen peroxide, wire snips, metal spatulas, beakers, balances

Teacher Demo, p. 200
balance, evaporating dish, copper powder, ring stand, wire gauze, Bunsen burner, tongs

Build Science Skills, p. 208
beaker, water, thermometer, 1 tsp baking soda, 1 tsp calcium chloride

Build Science Skills, p. 210
fire extinguishers, fire extinguisher ratings

Build Science Skills, p. 213
clay, rulers, plastic knives

Teacher Demo, p. 213
2 chemical light sticks, 2 large beakers, hot water, ice water

Build Science Skills, p. 216
playing cards, watch

Chapter Assessment

CHAPTER ASSESSMENT
SE Chapter Assessment, pp. 223–224
CUT Chapter 7 Test A, B
CTB Chapter 7
iT Chapter 7
PHSchool.com GO
Web Code: cca-1070

STANDARDIZED TEST PREP
SE Chapter 7, p. 225
TP Diagnose and Prescribe

Interactive Textbook

Interactive Textbook with assessment at PHSchool.com

CHAPTER 7

Before you teach

From the Author

David Frank
Ferris State University

Big Ideas

This chapter covers a great deal of information regarding chemical reactions. Students are introduced to two basic conservation laws of chemical reactions: the law of conservation of mass and the law of conservation of energy. A classification scheme for reactions is discussed. Finally, students learn about reaction kinetics (rates) and chemical equilibrium, along with the factors affecting them.

Space and Time If reacting particles collide more frequently or with increased energy, then the rate of a chemical reaction increases. Factors that can make a reaction occur faster include temperature, surface area, stirring, concentration, and catalysts. To keep things simple, students are told that temperature affects the frequency of collision, but you should be aware that higher temperatures also increase the fraction of molecules with sufficient energy to react.

Matter and Change Because the number of reactions can appear overwhelming, students will find it helpful to see relationships between reactions by classifying them. By looking at the chemical equations, students can classify reactions as synthesis, decomposition, single-replacement, double-replacement, and combustion. By looking at electron transfers, students can classify some reactions as oxidation-reduction.

Students learn that the formation of a precipitate or a gas is evidence for a double-replacement reaction. In the next chapter, you may also wish to point out that the reaction between HCl and NaOH is also a double-replacement reaction. Furthermore, these categories overlap. For example, Mg burning in O_2 to produce MgO is an example of synthesis, combustion, and oxidation-reduction.

Energy Diagrams such as Figure 19 are important in understanding the energetics of a reaction. The relative location of the initial product and final reactant lines tells you if a reaction is exothermic or endothermic. The size of the "hump" in the middle is related to the rate at which the reaction takes place.

Chemistry Refresher

Describing Reactions 7.1

Chemical equations are used to describe reactions. The coefficients show the molar ratios of the reactants and products, and they can be changed in order to balance the equation. Chemical equations are balanced to show that mass is conserved in the chemical reaction.

Chemists use the mole, which is an amount containing 6.02×10^{23} particles, to count large numbers of small particles. The mass of one mole of a substance is called a molar mass. The molar mass of an element is the same as its atomic mass expressed in grams. A compound's molar mass is the sum of the atomic masses of its component elements expressed in grams. Molar mass is used to convert between molar and mass amounts of one substance. A mole ratio is used to convert between molar amounts of two different substances in a chemical reaction.

Address Misconceptions

Because reactants are changed into products, students may think that particles can be created or destroyed in ordinary chemical reactions. This is not the case—mass is conserved in all chemical reactions. For a strategy to overcome this misconception, see **Address Misconceptions** on **page 193.**

Types of Reactions 7.2

In a synthesis reaction, two or more substances react to form a single substance. The reverse of a synthesis reaction is a decomposition reaction. A single-replacement reaction is a reaction in which one element takes the place of another element in a compound. Potassium reacting with water is an example of a single-replacement reaction.

General equation for a single-replacement reaction:

$$A + BC \longrightarrow B + AC$$

Equation for potassium reacting with water:

$$2K + 2H_2O \longrightarrow H_2 + 2KOH$$

In a double-replacement reaction, two different compounds exchange positive ions and form two new compounds. In a combustion reaction, a substance reacts rapidly with oxygen, often generating light and heat. Any reaction involving a transfer of electrons can be classified as an oxidation-reduction (redox) reaction.

Go Online PDLinks

For: Teaching methods for chemical reactions
Visit: www.SciLinks.org/PDLinks
Web Code: ccn-0799

Energy Changes in Reactions 7.3

During a chemical reaction, chemical bonds in the reactants are broken and chemical bonds in the products are formed. Breaking bonds requires energy. Forming bonds releases energy. A chemical reaction can be classified as exothermic (releases energy to the surroundings) or endothermic (absorbs energy from the surroundings). Energy is conserved during chemical reactions; the total amount of energy before and after the reaction is the same.

Reaction Rates and Equilibrium 7.4 and 7.5

A reaction rate is the time-rate at which reactants change into products. Generally, reaction rates are increased by a rise in temperature, increased surface area or concentration of reactants, agitation, and catalysts. The effect of a catalyst on reaction energy is illustrated in the diagram below.

Reaction Energy—Catalyzed and Uncatalyzed

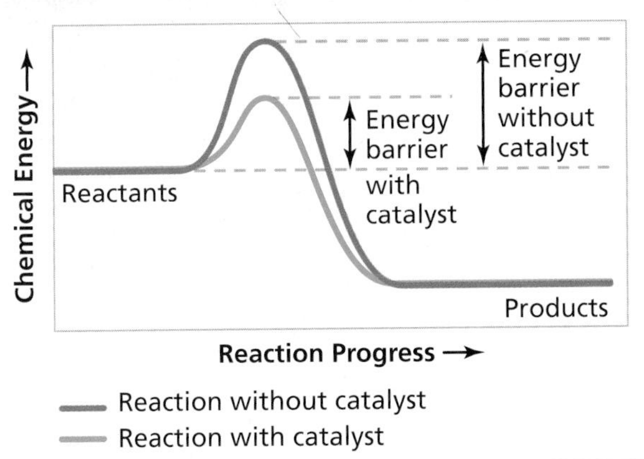
Chemical Energy →
Energy barrier without catalyst
Energy barrier with catalyst
Reactants
Products
Reaction Progress →
Reaction without catalyst
Reaction with catalyst

A system is in dynamic chemical equilibrium when there is no change in the concentrations of reactants and products, and reactants and products are forming simultaneously. This can take place only when the forward and reverse reactions occur at the same rate. Equilibria can also be physical in nature. For example, a physical equilibrium can exist between liquid water and water vapor inside a closed container.

Address Misconceptions

Students may think that a reaction at equilibrium has equal amounts of reactants and products. However, equilibrium describes the forward and reverse reaction rates, and not the relative amounts of reactants and products. For a strategy to overcome this misconception, see **Address Misconceptions** on **page 217.**

Henri Le Châtelier observed that when a system at equilibrium experiences a change, the equilibrium shifts in the direction that relieves the change. Factors affecting chemical equilibrium include shifts in temperature, pressure, and concentration.

Build Reading Literacy

Relate Text and Visuals

Use Graphic Elements to Clarify and Extend

Strategy Help students relate visuals to text, in order to clarify difficult concepts in the text or to understand information beyond that stated in the text. This strategy enables students to focus on their own thought processes as they actively make use of photos and illustrations as tools to support comprehension. Before students begin, choose a section in Chapter 7, such as Section 7.2, pp. 202–203.

Example

1. Have students keep their book closed as you read a few paragraphs aloud, including text that refers to a figure. You may want to think aloud as you read, saying, for example, "I wonder what that would look like?"

2. Then, have students open their book to the passage that you read. Tell them to reread it and then study the figure and its caption carefully. Ask what parts of the passage make more sense when students look at the figure.

3. Point out that visuals also sometimes communicate information that is not in the text. Have students identify any new information that can be learned from the figure.

4. Have students work in pairs, with one reading aloud through the next reference to a figure, and then both working together to discuss how the figure helps them understand the passage or provides additional information.

See p. 207 for a script on how to use the relate text and visuals strategy with students. For additional Build Reading Literacy strategies, see pp. 197, 204, 212, and 218.

ASSESS PRIOR KNOWLEDGE

Use the Chapter Pretest below to assess students' prior knowledge. As needed, review these Science Concepts and Math Skills with students.

Review Science Concepts

Section 7.1 Students should be familiar with chemical and physical properties. Review the information contained in a chemical formula. Have students review the terms *atom, mass, atomic mass,* and *chemical change.*

Section 7.2 Review the common types of evidence for a chemical change. Students should be familiar with the terms *precipitate, chemical change, element, compound, electron,* and *ion.*

Section 7.3 Encourage students to review chemical bond types, how they are named, and how they form. Students should be familiar with various forms of energy.

Sections 7.4 and 7.5 Be sure that students are familiar with the concepts of temperature, surface area, pressure, and concentration.

Review Math Skills

Formulas and Equations, Ratios and Proportions, and Conversion Factors Students need to interpret chemical formulas, balance chemical equations, and be familiar with the manipulation of conversion factors.

Direct students to the **Math Skills** in the **Skills and Reference Handbook** at the end of the student text.

CHAPTER

7 Chemical Reactions

CONCEPTS in Action

How do science concepts apply to your world? Here are some questions you'll be able to answer after you read this chapter.

- What happens to a piece of charcoal as it burns? *(Section 7.1)*
- How do air bags inflate? *(Section 7.2)*
- Why does a propane stove need a spark in order for the propane to ignite? *(Section 7.3)*
- How does a refrigerator keep food fresh? *(Section 7.4)*
- What changes take place inside a closed container of water? *(Section 7.5)*

Discovery Channel School **Video Field Trip**

Taming the Flames

- How do firefighters put out wildfires? *(page 210)*

Autumn leaves change color as a result of a series of chemical reactions.

Chapter Pretest

1. Which of the following is an example of a physical change? *(c)*
   - **a.** Wood burns and becomes ash.
   - **b.** A steel nail rusts over time.
   - **c.** Ice melts and becomes water.
   - **d.** Milk curdles when acid is added to it.

2. How do you find the atomic mass of an element? *(The atomic mass of each element is listed on the periodic table.)*

3. Which of the following characteristics can you determine about a substance based on its chemical formula? *(a)*
   - **a.** The number and types of atoms that make up the substance
   - **b.** The mass of an unknown sample of the substance
   - **c.** The melting point of the substance
   - **d.** The density and state of the substance at room temperature

4. Which conversion factor would you multiply 0.020 m by in order to express the quantity in centimeters? *(d)*
   - **a.** $\frac{1000\ \text{m}}{1\ \text{km}}$ **b.** $\frac{1\ \text{km}}{1000\ \text{m}}$
   - **c.** $\frac{1\ \text{m}}{100\ \text{cm}}$ **d.** $\frac{100\ \text{cm}}{1\ \text{m}}$

5. Which is the correct chemical formula for potassium hydroxide? *(b)*
   - **a.** POH **b.** KOH
   - **c.** P_5OH **d.** K_2OH

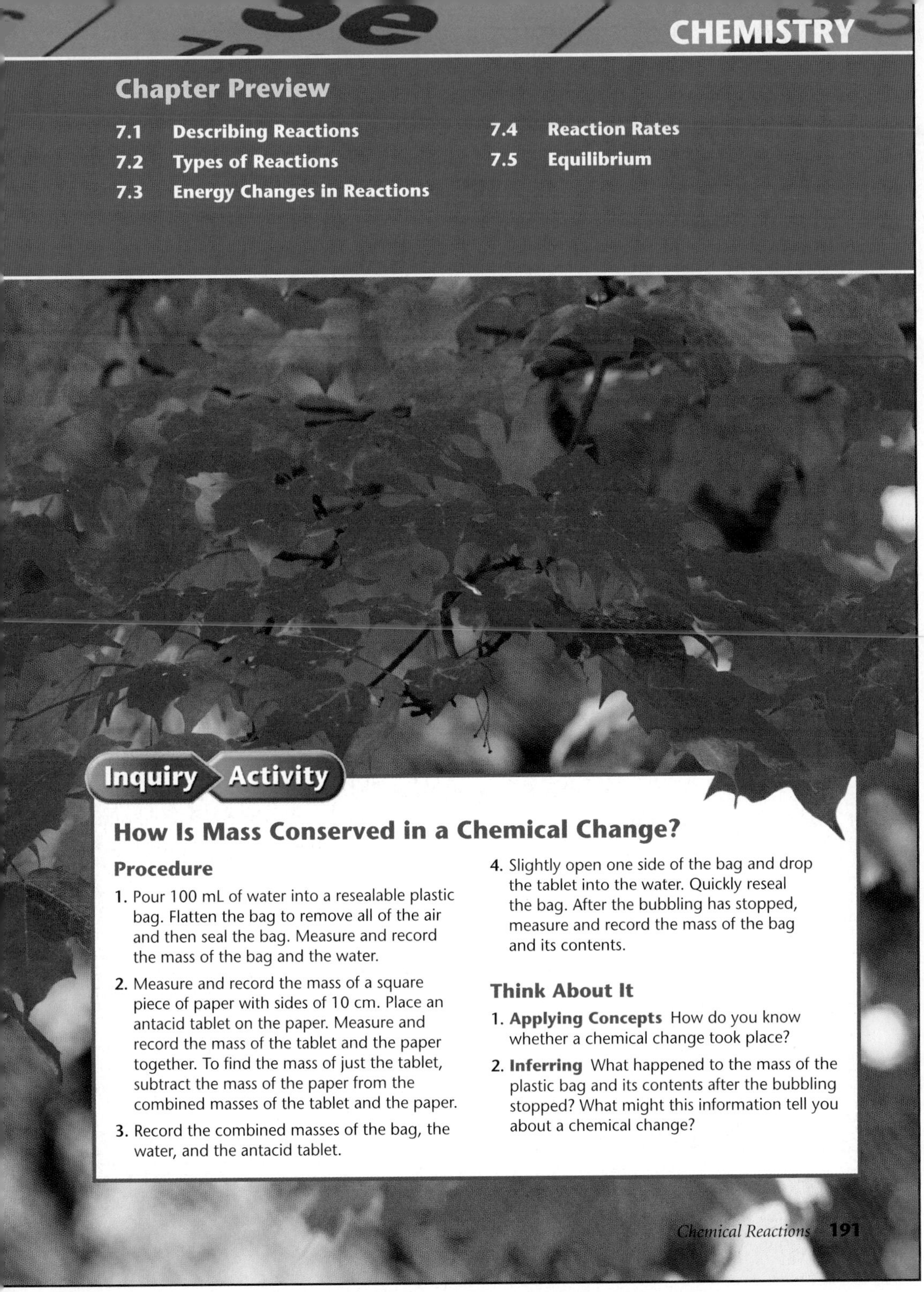
CHEMISTRY

Chapter Preview

Inquiry Activity

How Is Mass Conserved in a Chemical Change?

Procedure

1. Pour 100 mL of water into a resealable plastic bag. Flatten the bag to remove all of the air and then seal the bag. Measure and record the mass of the bag and the water.
2. Measure and record the mass of a square piece of paper with sides of 10 cm. Place an antacid tablet on the paper. Measure and record the mass of the tablet and the paper together. To find the mass of just the tablet, subtract the mass of the paper from the combined masses of the tablet and the paper.
3. Record the combined masses of the bag, the water, and the antacid tablet.
4. Slightly open one side of the bag and drop the tablet into the water. Quickly reseal the bag. After the bubbling has stopped, measure and record the mass of the bag and its contents.

Think About It

1. **Applying Concepts** How do you know whether a chemical change took place?
2. **Inferring** What happened to the mass of the plastic bag and its contents after the bubbling stopped? What might this information tell you about a chemical change?

Chemical Reactions **191**

Video Field Trip

Taming the Flames

Encourage students to view the Video Field Trip "Taming the Flames."

ENGAGE/EXPLORE

Inquiry Activity

How Is Mass Conserved in a Chemical Change? L2

Purpose In this activity, students begin to explain the law of conservation of mass as it applies to chemical reactions.

Address Misconceptions

This activity can help to remedy the misconception that gases do not have mass or weight.

Skills Focus **Observing, Inferring, Measuring**

Prep Time 10 minutes

Materials 100-mL graduated cylinder, resealable quart-sized plastic bag, 10-cm × 10-cm piece of paper, effervescent antacid tablet, triple-beam balance

Class Time 10 minutes

Safety Make sure that students tie back hair and loose clothing. Students should put on safety goggles, lab aprons, and plastic gloves before beginning the activity. Make sure that students wipe up any spilled water right away to avoid slips and falls.

Expected Outcome When dissolved in water, the antacid tablet produces bubbles of gas that inflate the bag. This process also produces a fizzing sound and causes the bag to become cooler to the touch.

Think About It

1. The formation of bubbles, the inflation of the bag, the bag getting cooler to the touch, and the fizzing sound provided evidence that a chemical change occurred.
2. The mass of the plastic bag and its contents remained the same. Students may infer that during a chemical change mass is not lost, but conserved.

Visual, Logical, Group

Section 7.1

1 FOCUS

Objectives

7.1.1 **Interpret** chemical equations in terms of reactants, products, and conservation of mass.

7.1.2 **Balance** chemical equations by manipulating coefficients.

7.1.3 **Convert** between moles and mass of a substance using molar mass.

7.1.4 **Calculate** amounts of reactants or products by using molar mass, mole ratios, and balanced chemical equations.

Reading Focus

Build Vocabulary L2

Concept Map Have students construct a concept map of the terms *reactants, products, chemical equations, coefficients,* and *moles.* Instruct students to place the terms in ovals and connect the ovals with lines on which linking words are placed. Students should place the main concept (Describing Reactions) at the top or center and use descriptive linking phrases to connect the terms.

Reading Strategy L2

Answers may vary. Possible answer:
a. How to balance chemical equations
b. An unbalanced equation can be balanced by changing the coefficients.
c. How to convert from mass to moles
d. The mass of a substance can be converted to moles by using the molar mass as a conversion factor.

2 INSTRUCT

Chemical Equations

Use Visuals L1

Figure 1 Have students examine the reaction taking place in the photo. **What clues show that a chemical reaction is taking place?** *(Energy is released in the form of heat and light.)* Mention that one of the reactants, O_2, and the product, CO_2, are colorless gases. **How might a scientist determine that oxygen gas is involved in this reaction?** *(He or she could attempt to burn charcoal in an oxygen-free environment.)*
Visual

7.1 Describing Reactions

Reading Focus

Key Concepts

- What is the law of conservation of mass?
- Why must chemical equations be balanced?
- Why do chemists use the mole?
- How can you calculate the mass of a reactant or product in a chemical reaction?

Vocabulary

- reactants
- products
- chemical equation
- coefficients
- mole
- molar mass

Reading Strategy

Monitoring Your Understanding Preview the Key Concepts, topic headings, vocabulary, and figures in this section. List two things you expect to learn. After reading, state what you learned about each item you listed.

What I Expect to Learn	What I Learned
a. ?	b. ?
c. ?	d. ?

What type of change is happening in Figure 1? When charcoal burns, it changes into other substances while producing heat and light. Burning is a chemical change. When a substance undergoes a chemical change, a chemical reaction is said to take place. In order to understand chemical reactions, you first must be able to describe them.

Figure 1 Burning is an example of a chemical reaction. When charcoal burns, the carbon in the charcoal reacts with oxygen in the air to produce carbon dioxide and heat.

Chemical Equations

A useful way of describing a change is to state what is present before and after the change. For example, suppose you wanted to show how your appearance changed as you grew older. You could compare a photo of yourself when you were younger with a photo that was taken recently.

A useful description of a chemical reaction tells you the substances present before and after the reaction. In a chemical reaction, the substances that undergo change are called **reactants.** The new substances formed as a result of that change are called **products.** In Figure 1, the reactants are the carbon in the charcoal and the oxygen in the air. The product of the reaction is carbon dioxide gas.

Using Equations to Represent Reactions During a chemical reaction, the reactants change into products. You can summarize this process with a word equation.

$$\text{Reactants} \longrightarrow \text{Products}$$

Section Resources

Print
- ***Reading and Study Workbook With Math Support,*** Section 7.1 and **Math Skill:** Balancing Chemical Equations
- ***Math Skills and Problem Solving Workbook,*** Section 7.1
- ***Transparencies,*** Chapter Pretest and Section 7.1

Technology
- ***Interactive Textbook,*** Section 7.1
- ***Presentation Pro CD-ROM,*** Chapter Pretest and Section 7.1
- ***Go Online,*** NSTA SciLinks, Conservation of mass; *Science News,* Chemical reactions

To describe the burning of charcoal, you can substitute the reactants and products of the reaction into the word equation as follows.

$$\text{Carbon} + \text{Oxygen} \longrightarrow \text{Carbon dioxide}$$

You can then simplify the word equation by writing the reactants and products as chemical formulas.

$$C + O_2 \longrightarrow CO_2$$

Now you have a chemical equation. A **chemical equation** is a representation of a chemical reaction in which the reactants and products are expressed as formulas. You can read the equation above as, "Carbon and oxygen react and form carbon dioxide," or, "The reaction of carbon and oxygen yields carbon dioxide."

Reading Checkpoint *What is a chemical equation?*

Conservation of Mass As a piece of charcoal burns, it gets smaller and smaller until it is finally reduced to a tiny pile of ash. Although the charcoal seems to disappear as it burns, it is actually being converted into carbon dioxide gas. If you measured the mass of the carbon dioxide produced, it would equal the mass of the charcoal and oxygen that reacted.

During chemical reactions, the mass of the products is always equal to the mass of the reactants. This principle, established by French chemist Antoine Lavoisier (1743–1794), is known as the law of conservation of mass. **The law of conservation of mass states that mass is neither created nor destroyed in a chemical reaction.** By demonstrating that mass is conserved in various reactions, Lavoisier laid the foundation for modern chemistry.

Figure 2 illustrates how a chemical equation can be restated in terms of atoms and molecules. The equation reads, "One atom of carbon reacts with one molecule of oxygen and forms one molecule of carbon dioxide." Suppose you have six carbon atoms. If each carbon atom reacts with one oxygen molecule to form one carbon dioxide molecule, then six carbon atoms react with six oxygen molecules to form six carbon dioxide molecules. Notice that the number of atoms on the left side of the equation equals the number of atoms on the right. The equation shows that mass is conserved.

Go Online SciLinks

For: Links on conservation of mass
Visit: www.SciLinks.org
Web Code: ccn-1071

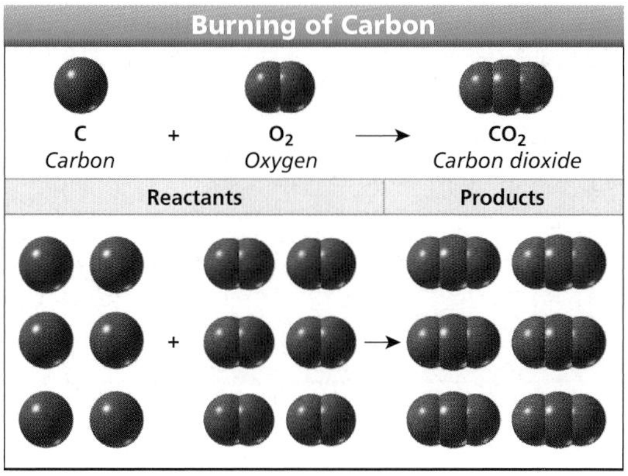

Burning of Carbon
C
Carbon
+
O2
Oxygen
CO2
Carbon dioxide
Reactants
Products

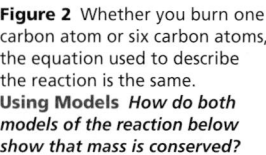

Figure 2 Whether you burn one carbon atom or six carbon atoms, the equation used to describe the reaction is the same. **Using Models** *How do both models of the reaction below show that mass is conserved?*

Address Misconceptions L2

Many students fail to recognize the conservation of particles that takes place during a chemical change. Challenge this misconception by having students count the numbers of carbon and oxygen atoms on both sides of the arrows in Figure 2. They should notice that both sides of the equation have the same number of each type of atom. Note that this chapter discusses only chemical reactions, not nuclear reactions (discussed in Chapter 10), in which mass is not conserved.
Visual

Build Math Skills L1

Formulas and Equations Have students write an equation for burning six carbon atoms in air to produce carbon dioxide. *($6C + 6O_2 \longrightarrow 6CO_2$)* Point out that while this equation is balanced, and represents the reaction of exactly six atoms of carbon and six molecules of oxygen, it is not the simplest equation for the reaction. Explain that a balanced chemical equation uses the simplest coefficients possible. Have students divide each coefficient by the greatest common factor, in this case 6, to get the simplest coefficients and the correctly balanced equation. *($C + O_2 \longrightarrow CO_2$)* **Logical**

Direct students to the **Math Skills** in the **Skills and Reference Handbook** at the end of the student text for additional help.

Go Online SciLinks

Download a worksheet on conservation of mass for students to complete, and find additional teacher support from NSTA SciLinks.

Customize for Inclusion Students

Visually Impaired
Provide students with molecular models that use different sizes or textures to identify the different types of atoms. Have them build molecular models that show the reaction for the burning of carbon. Then, have students use the models to demonstrate conservation of mass.

Answer to . . .

Figure 2 *In both models of the reaction $C + O_2 \longrightarrow CO_2$, the number of atoms of each element on the left equals the number of atoms of each element on the right.*

Reading Checkpoint *A chemical equation is a representation of a chemical reaction in which the reactants and products are expressed as formulas.*

Balancing Equations
Use Visuals L1

Figure 4 Have students use colored paperclips to model the different atoms of the reactants and products shown in Figure 4. As a class, go over the process of balancing the equation using the paperclips as a visual aid. Have students practice balancing the following equations by making lists of the numbers of each type of atom in the reactants and products as shown in Figure 4.

1. $Na + H_2O \longrightarrow NaOH + H_2$
($2Na + 2H_2O \longrightarrow 2NaOH + H_2$)
2. $HCl + CaCO_3 \longrightarrow CaCl_2 + CO_2 + H_2O$
($2HCl + CaCO_3 \longrightarrow CaCl_2 + CO_2 + H_2O$)
3. $Al + Cl_2 \longrightarrow AlCl_3$
($2Al + 3Cl_2 \longrightarrow 2AlCl_3$)

Students may find it helpful to make two or three models of each reactant and product and then try various combinations, listing and checking the balance of the atoms for each combination.
Visual

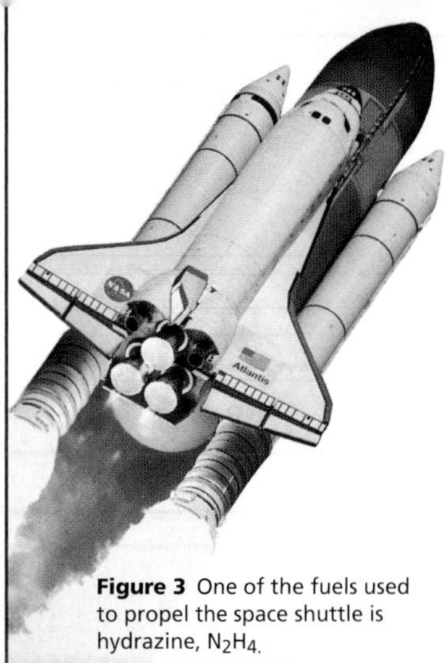

Figure 3 One of the fuels used to propel the space shuttle is hydrazine, N_2H_4.

Balancing Equations

Some reactions are powerful enough to propel spacecraft like the one shown in Figure 3. Many rocket fuels contain a compound called hydrazine, N_2H_4. When hydrazine burns in the presence of oxygen, the reaction produces nitrogen, water vapor, and heat. You can describe this reaction by writing a chemical equation.

$$N_2H_4 + O_2 \longrightarrow N_2 + H_2O$$

If you examine this equation carefully, you will notice that the number of atoms on the left side does not equal the number of atoms on the right. The equation is not balanced. **In order to show that mass is conserved during a reaction, a chemical equation must be balanced.**

You can balance a chemical equation by changing the **coefficients,** the numbers that appear before the formulas. In the unbalanced equation above, the coefficients are understood to be 1. When you change a coefficient, you change the amount of that reactant or product represented in the chemical equation. As you balance equations, you should never change the subscripts in a formula. Changing the formula changes the identity of that reactant or product.

The first step in balancing an equation is to count the number of atoms of each element on each side of the equation. As Figure 4A shows, the left side has two nitrogen atoms, four hydrogen atoms, and two oxygen atoms. The right side has two nitrogen atoms, two hydrogen atoms, and one oxygen atom. The hydrogen and oxygen atoms need to be balanced.

Figure 4 To balance a chemical equation, first count the atoms on each side of the equation. **Applying Concepts** ***Why must chemical equations be balanced?***

Burning of Hydrazine

$N_2H_4 + O_2 \longrightarrow N_2 + H_2O$

Reactants	Products
2 nitrogen atoms	2 nitrogen atoms
4 hydrogen atoms	2 hydrogen atoms
2 oxygen atoms	1 oxygen atom

A Unbalanced equation

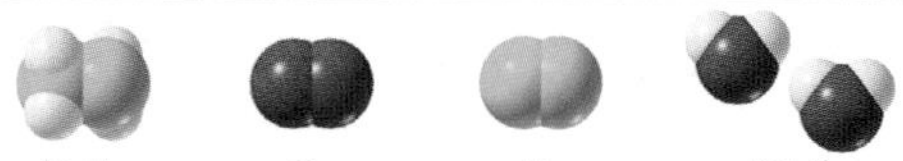

$N_2H_4 + O_2 \longrightarrow N_2 + 2H_2O$

Reactants	Products
2 nitrogen atoms	2 nitrogen atoms
4 hydrogen atoms	4 hydrogen atoms
2 oxygen atoms	2 oxygen atoms

B Balanced equation

The next step is to change one or more coefficients until the equation is balanced. You do not have to change the coefficients of N_2H_4 or N_2 because the nitrogen atoms are already balanced. However, the left side has more hydrogen and oxygen atoms than the right side, so you can try increasing the coefficient of water. Try changing the coefficient of water to 2. You then have four hydrogen atoms and two oxygen atoms on the right side, as shown in Figure 4B.

$$N_2H_4 + O_2 \longrightarrow N_2 + 2H_2O$$

The equation is now balanced. It tells you that each molecule of hydrazine requires one molecule of oxygen to react. It also tells you that when one molecule of hydrazine burns, it produces one molecule of nitrogen and two molecules of water.

Reading Checkpoint *What is a coefficient?*

Facts and Figures

Rocket Fuel In addition to hydrazine and solid fuels, another fuel used by the space shuttle is liquid hydrogen, H_2. The burning of rocket fuels must take place in the presence of oxygen, O_2. The oxygen is stored on the shuttle as liquid oxygen, also called LOX. The two substances react to produce water according to the equation $2H_2 + O_2 \longrightarrow 2H_2O$.

Math Skills

Balancing Chemical Equations

Write a balanced equation for the reaction between copper and oxygen to produce copper(II) oxide, CuO.

1 Read and Understand

What information are you given?

Reactants: Cu, O_2 Product: CuO

2 Plan and Solve

Write a chemical equation with the reactants on the left side and the product on the right.

$$Cu + O_2 \longrightarrow CuO$$

This equation is not balanced. Change the coefficient of CuO in order to balance the number of oxygen atoms.

$$Cu + O_2 \longrightarrow 2CuO$$

Change the coefficient of Cu in order to balance the number of copper atoms.

$$2Cu + O_2 \longrightarrow 2CuO$$

3 Look Back and Check

Is your answer reasonable?

The number of atoms on the left equals the number of atoms on the right.

Math Practice

1. Hydrogen chloride, or HCl, is an important industrial chemical. Write a balanced equation for the production of hydrogen chloride from hydrogen and chlorine.
2. Balance the following chemical equations.
   a. $H_2O_2 \longrightarrow H_2O + O_2$
   b. $Mg + HCl \longrightarrow H_2 + MgCl_2$
3. Ethylene, C_2H_4, burns in the presence of oxygen to produce carbon dioxide and water vapor. Write a balanced equation for this reaction.

Counting With Moles

How many shoes do you own? Because shoes come in twos, you would most likely count them by the pair rather than individually. The counting units you use depend on what you are counting. For example, you might count eggs by the dozen or paper by the ream.

Chemists also need practical units for counting things. Although you can describe a reaction in terms of atoms and molecules, these units are too small to be practical. **Because chemical reactions often involve large numbers of small particles, chemists use a counting unit called the mole to measure amounts of a substance.**

A **mole** (mol) is an amount of a substance that contains approximately 6.02×10^{23} particles of that substance. This number is known as Avogadro's number. In chemistry, a mole of a substance generally contains 6.02×10^{23} atoms, molecules, or ions of that substance. For instance, a mole of iron is 6.02×10^{23} atoms of iron.

Figure 5 Shoes are often counted by the pair, eggs by the dozen, and paper by the ream (500 sheets). To count particles of a substance, chemists use the mole (6.02×10^{23} particles).

Math Practice

Solutions **L2**

1. $H_2 + Cl_2 \longrightarrow 2HCl$
2. a. $2H_2O_2 \longrightarrow 2H_2O + O_2$
   b. $Mg + 2HCl \longrightarrow H_2 + MgCl_2$
3. $C_2H_4 + 3O_2 \longrightarrow 2CO_2 + 2H_2O$

Logical

For Extra Help **L1**

Only the coefficients, not the subscripts, should change. **Logical**

Direct students to the **Math Skills** in the **Skills and Reference Handbook** at the end of the student text for additional help.

Additional Problems

1. Balance the reaction of silicon with oxygen to form silicon dioxide.
($Si + O_2 \longrightarrow SiO_2$)
2. Balance $Fe + Cl_2 \longrightarrow FeCl_3$.
($2Fe + 3Cl_2 \longrightarrow 2FeCl_3$)

Logical, Portfolio

Counting With Moles

Teacher Demo

Counting Particles **L2**

Purpose Students see the efficiency of using molar mass to count particles.

Materials 14 g graphite powder, small beaker, spatula, balance, a bag of rice, stack of paper plates

Procedure Count out 1 mole of carbon atoms while a volunteer attempts to count out 1 mole of rice grains (100 grains of rice onto each paper plate). Write the molar mass of carbon on the board and weigh out 12.01 g of graphite. Have students note how few rice grains there are compared to 1 mole. Ask, **How large could 1 mole of rice grains be?** *(1 mole of rice grains could fill more than 10^{13} classrooms that are $10m \times 10m \times 4m$!)*

Expected Outcome Using molar mass to count is more efficient than counting particles one by one. **Visual, Logical**

Answer to . . .

Figure 4 *To show that mass is conserved during a chemical reaction*

Reading Checkpoint *A coefficient is a number that appears before a formula in a chemical equation.*

Chemical Reactions 195

Quick Lab

Modeling a Mole

L2

Objective
After completing this activity, students will be able to
- use the concept of moles to solve stoichiometric problems.

Skills Focus **Observing, Measuring, Predicting, Calculating**

Prep Time 5 minutes

Advance Prep Be sure the bolts, nuts, and washers are compatible.

Class Time 20 minutes

Expected Outcome Students will correctly assemble and predict the mass of the molecular model.

Analyze and Conclude
1. The mass of the molecule will equal the sum of the masses of all of its parts.
2. Students can make 10 models.
3. This answer will depend upon the mass of the nuts that are used. For example, if a nut has a mass of 10 g, then students would be able to make 10 models of the molecule.
Kinesthetic, Logical

For Enrichment

L3

Add bolts, washers, and nuts of different masses to the atom collection. Have students assemble a variety of new molecules with the same number of atoms but with different-sized pieces. They can determine whether the mass of the molecule changes and whether it is possible to assemble molecules that are different in structure but have the same mass.
Kinesthetic, Logical

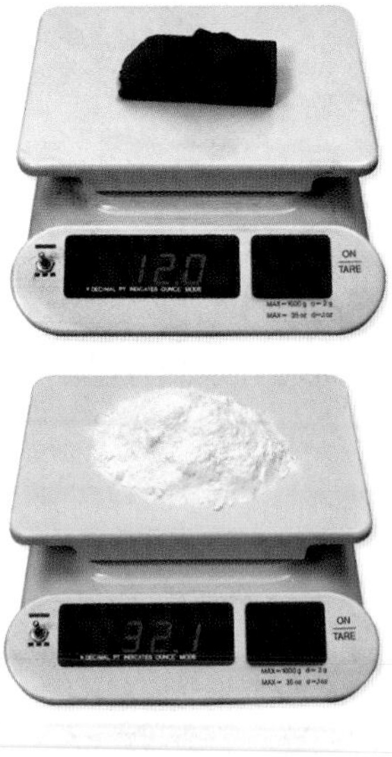

Figure 6 The molar mass of carbon is 12.0 grams. The molar mass of sulfur is 32.1 grams. **Inferring** ***If each of the carbon and sulfur samples contains one mole of atoms, why do the samples have different masses?***

Molar Mass A dozen eggs has a different mass than a dozen oranges. Similarly, a mole of carbon has a different mass than a mole of sulfur, as shown in Figure 6. The mass of one mole of a substance is called a **molar mass.** For an element, the molar mass is the same as its atomic mass expressed in grams. For example, the atomic mass of carbon is 12.0 amu, so the molar mass of carbon is 12.0 grams.

For a compound, you can calculate the molar mass by adding up the atomic masses of its component atoms, and then expressing this sum in grams. A carbon dioxide molecule is composed of one carbon atom (12.0 amu) and two oxygen atoms (2×16.0 amu = 32.0 amu). So carbon dioxide has a molar mass of 44.0 grams.

Mole-Mass Conversions Once you know the molar mass of a substance, you can convert moles of that substance into mass, or a mass of that substance into moles. For either calculation, you need to express the molar mass as a conversion factor. For example, the molar mass of CO_2 is 44.0 grams, which means that one mole of CO_2 has a mass of 44.0 grams. This relationship yields the following conversion factors.

$$\frac{44.0 \text{ g } CO_2}{1 \text{ mol } CO_2} \qquad \frac{1 \text{ mol } CO_2}{44.0 \text{ g } CO_2}$$

Suppose you have 55.0 grams of CO_2. To calculate how many moles of CO_2 you have, multiply the mass by the conversion factor on the right.

$$55.0 \text{ g } CO_2 \times \frac{1 \text{ mol } CO_2}{44.0 \text{ g } CO_2} = 1.25 \text{ mol } CO_2$$

You can check your answer by using the conversion factor on the left.

$$1.25 \text{ mol } CO_2 \times \frac{44.0 \text{ g } CO_2}{1 \text{ mol } CO_2} = 55.0 \text{ g } CO_2$$

Quick Lab

Modeling a Mole

Materials
bolt, 2 nuts, 2 washers, balance

Procedure

1. Measure and record the mass of one bolt, one nut, and one washer. Each piece of hardware will represent an atom of a different element.
2. Assemble the bolt, nuts, and washers together so that they form a model of a molecule known as BN_2W_2.
3. Predict the mass of BN_2W_2.
4. Test your prediction by finding the mass of your model.

Analyze and Conclude

1. **Analyzing Data** Did your prediction match the actual mass of your model? Explain.
2. **Calculating** How many models of your molecule can you make with 20 washers and as many nuts and bolts as you need?
3. **Calculating** How many models of your molecule can you make with 100 grams of nuts and as many bolts and washers as you need?

Chemical Calculations

Figure 7 A cake recipe tells you how much of each ingredient to use for each cake you bake. **Using Analogies** *How is a cake recipe like a chemical equation?*

Think about baking a cake like the one in Figure 7. The directions on a box of cake mix might tell you to add two eggs and one cup of water to the cake mix. Suppose you wanted to make three cakes. Although the directions don't tell you specifically how many eggs and how much water are required for three cakes, you could figure out the amounts. To make three cakes, you would need three times as much of each ingredient—six eggs, three cups of water, and three packages of cake mix.

Chemical equations can be read as recipes for making new substances. Figure 8 shows the balanced equation for the formation of water. You can read this equation as, "Two molecules of hydrogen react with one molecule of oxygen and form two molecules of water." In terms of moles, the equation reads, "Two moles of hydrogen react with one mole of oxygen and form two moles of water." To convert from moles to mass, you need to use the molar masses as conversion factors. Figure 8 shows how the same equation can also be read as, "4.0 grams of H_2 reacts with 32.0 grams of O_2 and forms 36.0 grams of H_2O."

How many grams of oxygen would you need to make 144 grams of water? **In chemical reactions, the mass of a reactant or product can be calculated by using a balanced chemical equation and molar masses of the reactants and products.** The chemical equation tells you how to relate amounts of reactants to amounts of products. Molar masses let you convert those amounts into masses.

Reading Checkpoint *How do you convert from moles to mass?*

Converting Mass to Moles To calculate how much oxygen is required to make 144 grams of water, you need to begin with a balanced chemical equation for the reaction.

$$2H_2 + O_2 \longrightarrow 2H_2O$$

The first step in your calculations is to determine how many moles of water you are trying to make. By using the molar mass of water, you can convert the given mass of water into moles.

$$144 \text{ g } H_2O \times \frac{1 \text{ mol } H_2O}{18.0 \text{ g } H_2O} = 8.00 \text{ mol } H_2O$$

Formation of Water

Equation	$2H_2$	+	O_2	→	$2H_2O$
Amount	2 mol		1 mol		2 mol
Molar Mass	2.0 g/mol		32.0 g/mol		18.0 g/mol
Mass (Moles × Molar Mass)	4.0 g	+	32.0 g	→	36.0 g

Figure 8 In a balanced chemical equation, the number of atoms of each element on the left equals the number of atoms of each element on the right. By using molar masses, you can show that the mass of the reactants equals the mass of the products.

Facts and Figures

Baking Reactions The reaction of sodium bicarbonate ($NaHCO_3$) under heat is one of the chemical reactions that make cakes and muffins rise. Cake recipes may call for baking soda (the common name for sodium bicarbonate) or baking powder (a mixture that contains sodium bicarbonate). When sodium bicarbonate is heated, it breaks down into simpler products according to the following equation.

$$2NaHCO_3 \longrightarrow Na_2CO_3 + H_2O + CO_2$$

The carbon dioxide produced by this reaction causes the cake to rise as it bakes. The CO_2 bubbles that become trapped give baked goods their spongy texture.

Build Science Skills L2

Measuring and Calculating ACTIVITY

Purpose Students calculate and measure out molar quantities of various samples.

Materials copper wire, aluminum foil, water, sodium chloride, hydrogen peroxide, wire snips, metal spatulas, beakers, balances

Class Time 10 minutes

Procedure Have students use the periodic table to determine the molar mass of Cu, Al, H_2O, NaCl, and H_2O_2. Ask them to calculate the mass of the following quantities: 0.5 mol Cu, 2 mol Al, 3 mol H_2O, 0.75 mol NaCl, and 1 mol H_2O_2. Have students wear goggles and work in groups to measure out each quantity. If supplies are limited, assign one quantity to each group.

Expected Outcome The molar mass for Cu is 63.55 g, for Al is 26.98 g, for H_2O is 18.02 g, for NaCl is 58.44 g, and for H_2O_2 is 34.02 g. Students should measure out 32 g Cu, 54 g Al, 54 g H_2O, 44 g NaCl, and 34 g H_2O_2.
Logical, Group

Chemical Calculations

Build Reading Literacy L1

Summarize Refer to page **598D** in **Chapter 20**, which provides the guidelines for a summary.

Have students read the text on pp. 197 and 198 related to chemical calculations. Then, have students summarize the steps required to determine the number of grams of oxygen needed to make 144 grams of water.
Logical

Answer to . . .

Figure 6 *Carbon and sulfur have different atomic masses. Therefore, the mass of one mole of carbon is different from the mass of one mole of sulfur.*

Figure 7 *A cake recipe tells you what ingredients and what amounts of each are required to make a cake. Similarly, a balanced chemical equation tells you what reactants and what relative amounts of each are required to form a product or set of products.*

Reading Checkpoint *You can convert moles of a substance into mass by multiplying by the molar mass of the substance.*

Section 7.1 (continued)

3 ASSESS

Evaluate Understanding

L2

Give students a chemical equation to analyze. Ask them to determine whether the equation is balanced, and to explain how conservation of mass applies. Then, have students write a problem that requires converting from mass of a reactant to mass of a product. Have students exchange their problem with a partner for him or her to solve.

Reteach

L1

Use Figure 2 to summarize the key concepts in this section, such as identifying reactants and products, balancing equations, understanding conservation of mass, and determining mole ratios. Have students determine the mole ratio of carbon to carbon dioxide in the balanced equation. *(1:1)*

Math Practice

Solutions

9. $2K + Br_2 \longrightarrow 2KBr$
10. $2Mg + O_2 \longrightarrow 2MgO$

Interactive Textbook

If your class subscribes to the Interactive Textbook, use it to review key concepts in Section 7.1.

Go Online SCIENCE NEWS

Science News provides students with current information on chemical reactions.

Go Online SCIENCE NEWS

For: Articles on chemical reactions
Visit: PHSchool.com
Web Code: cce-1071

Using Mole Ratios Remember the balanced chemical equation for the formation of water. You can read it as, "Two moles of hydrogen react with one mole of oxygen and form two moles of water." Because each mole of oxygen that reacts will yield two moles of water, you can write the following conversion factors, or mole ratios.

$$\frac{1 \text{ mol } O_2}{2 \text{ mol } H_2O} \qquad \frac{2 \text{ mol } H_2O}{1 \text{ mol } O_2}$$

The mole ratio on the left allows you to convert moles of water to moles of oxygen. Now you can calculate how many moles of oxygen are required to produce eight moles of water:

$$8.00 \text{ mol } H_2O \times \frac{1 \text{ mol } O_2}{2 \text{ mol } H_2O} = 4.00 \text{ mol } O_2$$

Converting Moles to Mass The last step is to convert moles of O_2 to grams of O_2 by using the molar mass of O_2 as a conversion factor.

$$4.00 \text{ mol } O_2 \times \frac{32.0 \text{ g } O_2}{1 \text{ mol } O_2} = 128 \text{ g } O_2$$

So, in order to produce 144 grams of H_2O, you must supply 128 grams of O_2. Notice that you used the concept of a mole in two ways to solve this problem. In the first and last step, you used a molar mass to convert between mass and moles. In the middle step, you used the mole ratio to convert moles of a product into moles of a reactant.

Section 7.1 Assessment

Reviewing Concepts

1. What is the law of conservation of mass?
2. Why does a chemical equation need to be balanced?
3. Why do chemists use the mole as a counting unit?
4. What information do you need to predict the mass of a reactant or product in a chemical reaction?
5. What is a mole ratio?

Critical Thinking

6. **Applying Concepts** The following equation describes how sodium and chlorine react to produce sodium chloride.

$$2Na + Cl_2 \longrightarrow 2NaCl$$

Is the equation balanced? Explain your answer.

7. **Calculating** Ammonia, NH_3, can be made by reacting nitrogen with hydrogen.

$$N_2 + 3H_2 \longrightarrow 2NH_3$$

How many moles of NH_3 can be made if 7.5 moles of H_2 react with enough N_2?

8. **Calculating** What mass of NH_3 can be made from 35.0 g of N_2?

Math Practice

9. Balance the following equation.

$$K + Br_2 \longrightarrow KBr$$

10. Write a balanced chemical equation for the formation of magnesium oxide, MgO, from magnesium and oxygen.

Section 7.1 Assessment

1. The law of conservation of mass states that mass is neither created nor destroyed.
2. A chemical equation must be balanced in order to demonstrate that mass is conserved.
3. Because chemical reactions often involve large numbers of small particles, the mole (6.02×10^{23} particles) is a practical counting unit for scientists to use.
4. In order to calculate the mass of a reactant or product in a chemical reaction, you need the molar mass of the reactant, the molar mass of the product, and a balanced chemical equation (which tells you the mole ratio between the reactant and product).
5. A mole ratio is a conversion factor that relates two substances that take part in a chemical reaction. A mole ratio can be determined from a balanced chemical equation.
6. Yes, there are two sodium atoms and two chlorine atoms on each side of the equation.
7. $7.5 \text{ mol } H_2 \times \frac{2 \text{ mol } NH_3}{3 \text{ mol } H_2} = 5.0 \text{ mol } NH_3$
8. Molar mass of N_2 is 28.0 g.
$35.0 \text{ g } N_2 \times \frac{1 \text{ mol } N_2}{28.0 \text{ g } N_2} = 1.25 \text{ mol } N_2$
Mole ratio of NH_3:N_2 is 2:1.
$1.25 \text{ mol } N_2 \times \frac{2 \text{ mol } NH_3}{1 \text{ mol } N_2} = 2.50 \text{ mol } NH_3$
Molar mass of NH_3 is 17.0 grams.
$2.50 \text{ mol } NH_3 \times \frac{17.0 \text{ g } NH_3}{1 \text{ mol } NH_3} = 42.5 \text{ g } NH_3$

7.2 Types of Reactions

Reading Focus

Key Concepts

- What are the general types of chemical reactions?
- How did the discovery of subatomic particles affect the classification of reactions?

Vocabulary

- synthesis reaction
- decomposition reaction
- single-replacement reaction
- double-replacement reaction
- combustion reaction
- oxidation-reduction reaction

Reading Strategy

Previewing Skim the section and begin a concept map like the one below that identifies types of reactions with a general form. As you read, add the general form of each type of reaction.

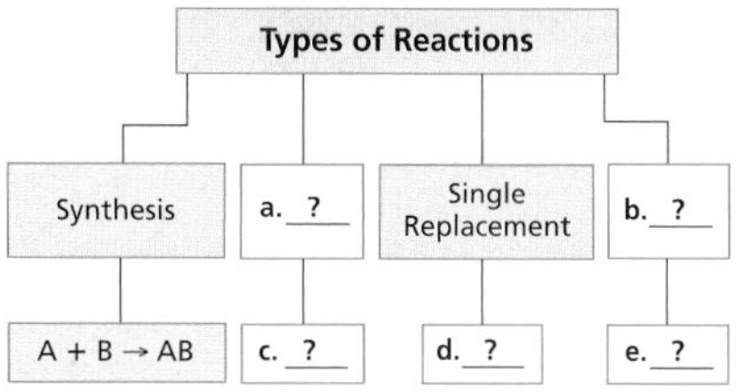

Types of Reactions
Synthesis
a. ?
Single Replacement
b. ?
A + B → AB
c. ?
d. ?
e. ?

The walls of the cave shown in Figure 9 are solid limestone. When hydrochloric acid is dropped on limestone, a chemical reaction occurs in which a gas is produced. Geologists can use this reaction to determine whether a rock sample contains the mineral calcium carbonate, $CaCO_3$. When a rock containing calcium carbonate reacts with hydrochloric acid, it fizzes. The bubbles contain carbon dioxide gas.

Many other reactions produce carbon dioxide. For example, heating limestone produces carbon dioxide. So does burning gasoline. However, just because two reactions have the same product, you cannot assume that they are the same type of reaction.

Classifying Reactions

Just as you can classify matter into different types, you can classify chemical reactions into different types. Reactions are often classified by the type of reactant or the number of reactants and products. **Some general types of chemical reactions are synthesis reactions, decomposition reactions, single-replacement reactions, double-replacement reactions, and combustion reactions.** Each type describes a different way in which reactants interact to form products.

Figure 9 The walls and other formations of Blanchard Springs Caverns in Arkansas contain the mineral calcium carbonate, $CaCO_3$.

Section Resources

Print

- ***Laboratory Manual,*** Investigations 7A and 7B
- ***Reading and Study Workbook With Math Support,*** Section 7.2
- ***Transparencies,*** Section 7.2

Technology

- ***Interactive Textbook,*** Section 7.2
- ***Presentation Pro CD-ROM,*** Section 7.2
- ***Go Online,*** NSTA SciLinks, Chemical reactions, Oxidation and reduction

Section 7.2

1 FOCUS

Objectives

7.2.1 **Classify** chemical reactions as synthesis, decomposition, single-replacement, double-replacement, or combustion reactions.

7.2.2 **Describe** oxidation-reduction reactions, and **relate** them to other classifications of chemical reactions.

Reading Focus

Build Vocabulary L2

Word Forms Ask students to write simple definitions of the words *synthesize, decompose,* and *replace*. Then, have students explain how these simple definitions relate to the terms *synthesis reaction, decomposition reaction, single-replacement reaction,* and *double-replacement reaction. (To synthesize is to combine and form a complex product, to decompose is to separate into basic parts, and to replace is to take or fill the place of.)*

Reading Strategy L2

a. Decomposition **b.** Double replacement **c.** $AB \longrightarrow A + B$
d. $A + BC \longrightarrow B + AC$
e. $AB + CD \longrightarrow AD + CB$

2 INSTRUCT

Classifying Reactions

Integrate Earth Science L2

Calcium carbonate in limestone rock is dissolved by water made acidic by carbon dioxide according to the following equation.

$$CaCO_3 + CO_2 + H_2O \rightleftharpoons Ca^{2+} + 2HCO_3^-$$

The reverse reaction deposits the calcium carbonate onto a limestone surface. (Note that reaction equilibrium is discussed in depth in Section 7.5.) In this way, water dripping in a limestone cave forms beautiful formations. Have students research cave formations. Ask, **What is the difference between stalactites and stalagmites?** *(Stalactites form on cave ceilings, while stalagmites form on cave floors.)*
Visual

Integrate Biology L2

Biologists often call the decay of organic matter *decomposition* even when the reactions that take place do not follow the general form AB ⟶ A + B. While both meanings of *decomposition* are derived from the idea of separating objects into simpler parts, chemists use this term to describe a reaction that leads to the breakdown of a single compound. **Logical**

Teacher Demo

Exothermic Reaction L2

Purpose Students observe a synthesis reaction.

Materials balance, evaporating dish, copper powder, ring stand, wire gauze, Bunsen burner, tongs

Procedure Measure and record on the board the mass of the evaporating dish. Measure out 10 g of copper powder and spread it evenly in the evaporating dish. Arrange the wire mesh on the ring stand so that it sits above the Bunsen burner. Place the evaporating dish on the wire mesh and light the Bunsen burner. Heat the copper powder in the evaporating dish for 10–15 minutes. Allow the evaporating dish and its contents to cool and then determine their total mass. Ask, **Was mass conserved in this reaction?** *(Students may answer no, based on the increase in mass.)* Have students calculate the mass of the synthesized product.

Expected Outcome The copper powder turns into black copper(II) oxide, and the product's mass is greater than the original mass of the copper powder. The additional mass comes from the oxygen, which is the other reactant in the synthesis reaction. **Visual, Logical**

Go Online NSTA SciLINKS

Download a worksheet on chemical reactions for students to complete, and find additional teacher support from NSTA SciLinks.

Figure 10 Sodium metal reacts vigorously with chlorine to form sodium chloride, NaCl. **Interpreting Photos** ***What evidence in this photograph tells you that a chemical reaction is taking place?***

Synthesis A **synthesis reaction** is a reaction in which two or more substances react to form a single substance. The reactants may be either elements or compounds. The product synthesized is always a compound. The general equation for a synthesis reaction is

$$A + B \longrightarrow AB$$

Figure 10 shows what happens when sodium reacts with chlorine. The product of this reaction is the compound sodium chloride, which appears as a whitish cloud of solid particles. You are probably more familiar with sodium chloride as table salt. You can describe the synthesis of sodium chloride with the following equation.

$$2Na + Cl_2 \longrightarrow 2NaCl$$

Another example of a synthesis reaction is hydrogen and oxygen reacting to form water.

$$2H_2 + O_2 \longrightarrow 2H_2O$$

This reaction is used to generate electricity for satellites and spacecraft.

Reading Checkpoint ***What is a synthesis reaction?***

Decomposition The opposite of synthesis is decomposition. A **decomposition reaction** is a reaction in which a compound breaks down into two or more simpler substances. The reactant in a decomposition reaction must be a compound. The products may be elements or compounds. The general equation for a decomposition reaction is

$$AB \longrightarrow A + B$$

When electricity passes through water, the water decomposes into hydrogen gas and oxygen gas. You can describe the decomposition of water by writing the following equation.

$$2H_2O \longrightarrow 2H_2 + O_2$$

Notice that this reaction is the opposite of the synthesis of water.

Another example of decomposition occurs in the making of cement. Cement factories use a giant kiln, or oven, to heat a mixture of clay and limestone. The heat causes the calcium carbonate in the limestone to decompose into lime, CaO, and carbon dioxide.

$$CaCO_3 \longrightarrow CaO + CO_2$$

The carbon dioxide escapes the kiln through a smokestack. The clay-and-lime mixture is cooled and ground into cement powder.

The How It Works box on page 201 describes a decomposition reaction that is used to make automobiles safer.

Go Online NSTA SciLINKS

For: Links on chemical reactions
Visit: www.SciLinks.org
Web Code: ccn-1076

Customize for English Language Learners

Discussion
Write the general equations for synthesis, decomposition, single-replacement, and double-replacement reactions on the board. Use word equations to explain what is happening in each reaction. For example, you might say, **In a synthesis reaction, chemical A reacts (combines) with chemical B to form a new chemical compound made up of the same elements as those in chemicals A and B.** Have students comment on how the equations are alike and how they are different. They may point out that the equation for synthesis appears to be the reverse of the equation for decomposition. Also, they may notice that the replacement reactions involve different particles changing places. Encourage students to use familiar words when describing their observations.

HOW It Works

Automobile Safety: Air Bags

Air bags are inflatable cushions built into a car's steering wheel or dashboard. In a crash, the bags inflate, protecting both the driver and the passenger. The whole process takes 0.04 second. **Interpreting Diagrams** ***What is the source of the gas that fills an air bag?***

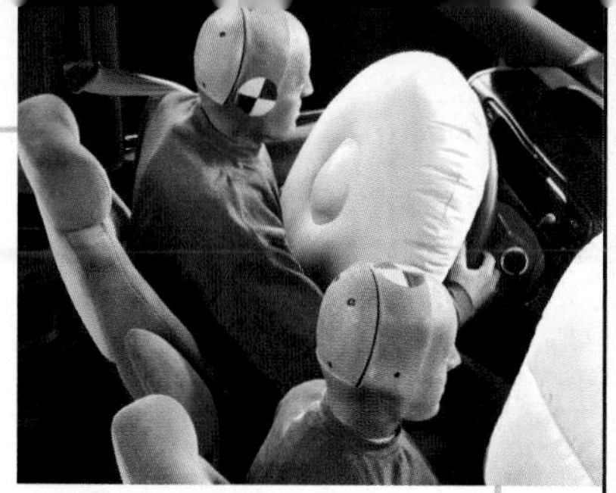

Testing air bags
Air bags have been shown to reduce the risk of serious injury in a head-on collision by 30 percent. New cars have air bags on both the driver and passenger sides.

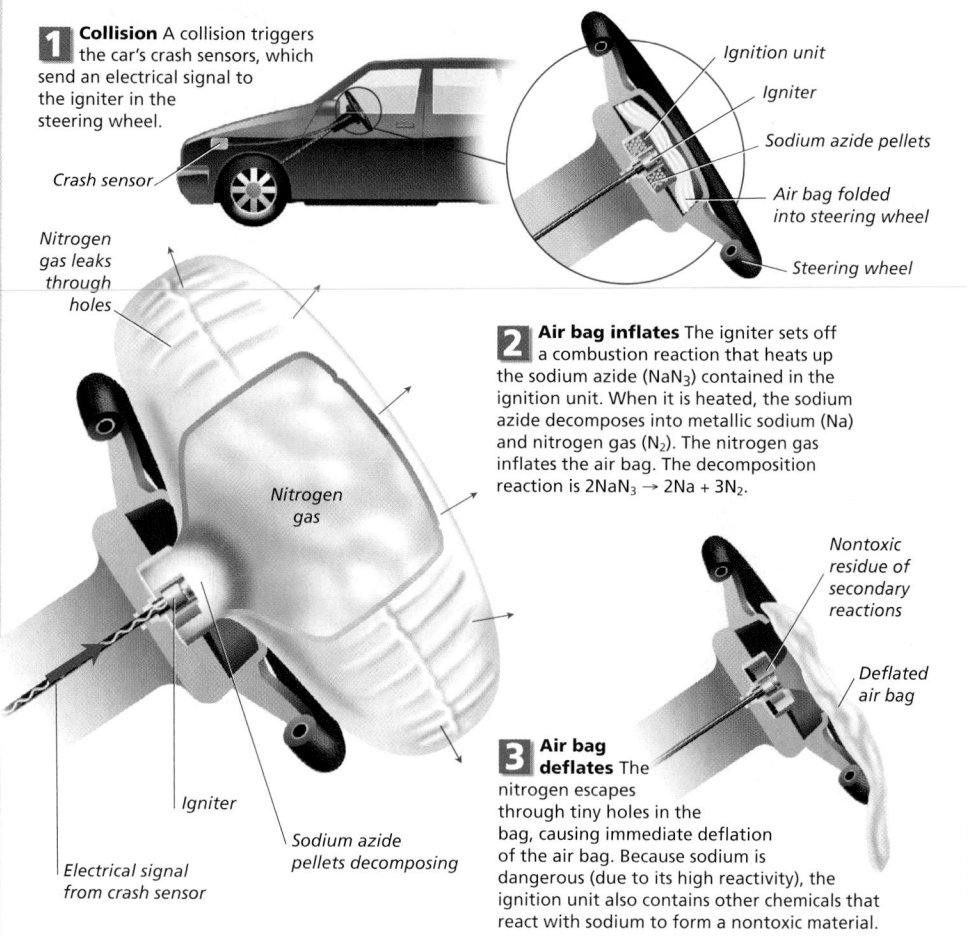

1 Collision A collision triggers the car's crash sensors, which send an electrical signal to the igniter in the steering wheel.

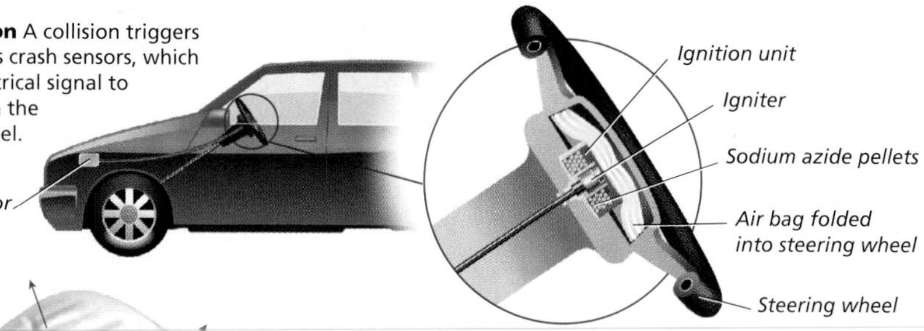

Crash sensor
Ignition unit
Igniter
Sodium azide pellets
Air bag folded into steering wheel
Steering wheel

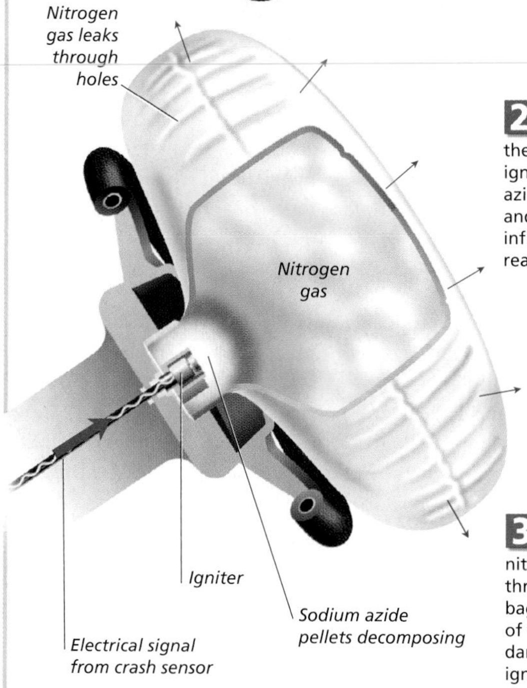

Nitrogen gas leaks through holes
Nitrogen gas
Igniter
Sodium azide pellets decomposing
Electrical signal from crash sensor

2 Air bag inflates The igniter sets off a combustion reaction that heats up the sodium azide (NaN_3) contained in the ignition unit. When it is heated, the sodium azide decomposes into metallic sodium (Na) and nitrogen gas (N_2). The nitrogen gas inflates the air bag. The decomposition reaction is $2NaN_3 \rightarrow 2Na + 3N_2$.

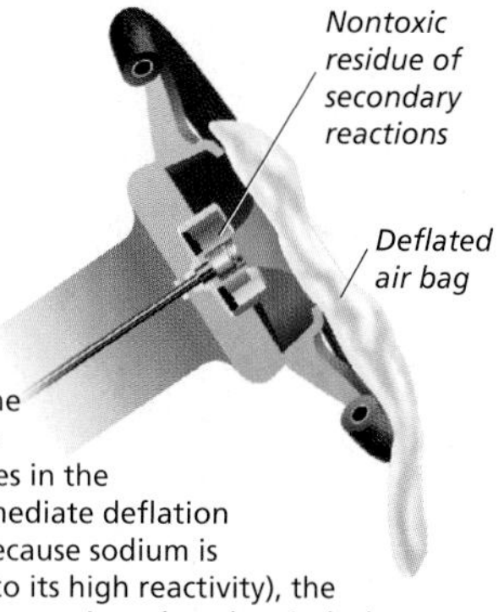

Nontoxic residue of secondary reactions
Deflated air bag

3 Air bag deflates The nitrogen escapes through tiny holes in the bag, causing immediate deflation of the air bag. Because sodium is dangerous (due to its high reactivity), the ignition unit also contains other chemicals that react with sodium to form a nontoxic material.

HOW It Works

Automobile Safety: Air Bags **L2**

The force of the reaction that inflates an air bag causes the air bag to break out of the steering wheel at up to 200 miles per hour. One way that manufacturers help the bag withstand the friction of this fast movement is by lubricating the bag with powders, such as talcum powder or cornstarch.

Interpreting Diagrams The source of the nitrogen gas that fills an air bag is the reacting sodium azide contained in the ignition unit. When the sodium azide pellets are heated, they decompose into sodium metal and nitrogen gas.
Visual

For Enrichment **L3**

Have students research the benefits and drawbacks of including air bags in automobiles. They may want to find out about the types of injuries caused and prevented by air bags as well as the types of injuries that air bags cannot prevent. **Verbal**

Address Misconceptions **L2**

Many students incorrectly think that the reactants are still present after a reaction has gone to completion. Challenge this misconception by discussing the reaction that takes place when an air bag inflates. After the class has read the feature on air bags, ask students where the nitrogen gas comes from when an air bag inflates. Explain that the nitrogen gas produced from the decomposition of solid sodium azide is exactly like the nitrogen gas in air. Apply this concept later when the class reads about single-replacement reactions that have solid reactants and products.
Verbal

Answer to . . .

Figure 10 *The formation of a cloudy substance and the release of energy (seen in the photo as light) are evidence that a chemical reaction is taking place.*

Reading Checkpoint *A synthesis reaction is a reaction in which two or more substances react to form a single substance.*

Use Visuals L1

Figure 11 Students may note that in the reaction between copper and silver nitrate, the water (part of the silver nitrate solution) doesn't appear as a reactant in the accompanying chemical equation in the text. Ask, **What evidence is there of a chemical change in Figure 11?** *(The solution changes color, and silver crystals form on the wire.)* Explain that when a compound dissociates in water, a physical change has taken place. The water and the dissolved substance remain chemically unchanged. The flask contains the same number of water molecules before and after the reaction takes place. Ask, **If you were to include water in the chemical equation, where would you place it?** *(Water would be on both sides of the equation with equivalent coefficients.)* Explain that just as in a math equation, you can cancel equivalent expressions that appear on both sides of the equation. **Visual**

Figure 11 A single-replacement reaction occurs when copper wire is submerged in a solution of silver nitrate. As the copper replaces the silver in the silver nitrate solution, the solution turns blue, and silver crystals form on the wire.

Single Replacement A **single-replacement reaction** is a reaction in which one element takes the place of another element in a compound. Single-replacement reactions have the general form

$$A + BC \longrightarrow B + AC$$

Suppose you dip a coil of copper wire into a solution of silver nitrate and water, as shown in Figure 11. A vivid chemical reaction takes place as the solution turns blue and the submerged part of the wire becomes coated with a silvery metal. In this reaction, the copper replaces the silver in silver nitrate to form copper(II) nitrate. The equation for this reaction is

$$Cu + 2AgNO_3 \longrightarrow 2Ag + Cu(NO_3)_2$$

Notice that one of the products is silver, which you can see adhering to the wire in Figure 12. The other product, copper(II) nitrate, gives the solution its blue color.

Recall that alkali metals are very reactive elements. Figure 12 shows potassium reacting with water. This is another example of a single-replacement reaction, as the element potassium replaces hydrogen in water to form potassium hydroxide, KOH.

$$2K + 2H_2O \longrightarrow H_2 + 2KOH$$

The heat produced by this chemical reaction causes the hydrogen gas to ignite explosively.

Figure 12 Potassium reacts with water in a single-replacement reaction that produces hydrogen gas and potassium hydroxide.

Reading Checkpoint *What is a single-replacement reaction?*

Facts and Figures

Activity Series Through experimentation, chemists can compile an activity series, a list of elements arranged in decreasing activity. The elements at the top of the list are the most reactive and will replace those elements at the bottom of the list when they are in compounds. For example, according to the activity series to the right, copper will replace silver in a single-replacement reaction, as in the reaction described in the text. Using the activity series, you could correctly predict that the following single-replacement reaction would take place.

$$Fe + CuSO_4 \longrightarrow FeSO_4 + Cu$$

Activity Series of Metals (Decreasing Reactivity ↓)
Potassium (K)
Calcium (Ca)
Magnesium (Mg)
Zinc (Zn)
Iron (Fe)
Lead (Pb)
Hydrogen (H)
Copper (Cu)
Silver (Ag)

Double Replacement A **double-replacement reaction** is one in which two different compounds exchange positive ions and form two new compounds. The general form of a double replacement reaction is

$$AB + CD \longrightarrow AD + CB$$

Notice that two replacements take place in this reaction. Not only is A replacing C, but C is also replacing A.

Solutions of lead(II) nitrate, $Pb(NO_3)_2$, and potassium iodide, KI, are both colorless. However, when these solutions are mixed, as shown in Figure 13, a yellow precipitate forms as a result of a double-replacement reaction. The equation for this reaction is

$$Pb(NO_3)_2 + 2KI \longrightarrow PbI_2 + 2KNO_3$$

The lead ions in $Pb(NO_3)_2$, trade places with the potassium ions in KI. The products are lead(II) iodide, PbI_2, which precipitates out of solution, and potassium nitrate, KNO_3, which remains in solution.

When geologists test the calcium carbonate content in a rock, they make use of the following double-replacement reaction.

$$CaCO_3 + 2HCl \longrightarrow CaCl_2 + H_2CO_3$$

One of the products of this reaction is calcium chloride, $CaCl_2$. The other product is carbonic acid, H_2CO_3, which decomposes into carbon dioxide gas and water.

$$H_2CO_3 \longrightarrow CO_2 + H_2O$$

150ml
NO. 14000

Figure 13 When potassium iodide solution is poured into a solution of lead(II) nitrate, a double-replacement reaction takes place. Lead(II) iodide forms as a yellow precipitate. **Comparing and Contrasting** ***How does a double-replacement reaction differ from a single-replacement reaction?***

Quick Lab

Identifying a Type of Reaction

Materials

piece of zinc, copper(II) sulfate ($CuSO_4$) solution, 250-mL beaker, tongs, paper towel

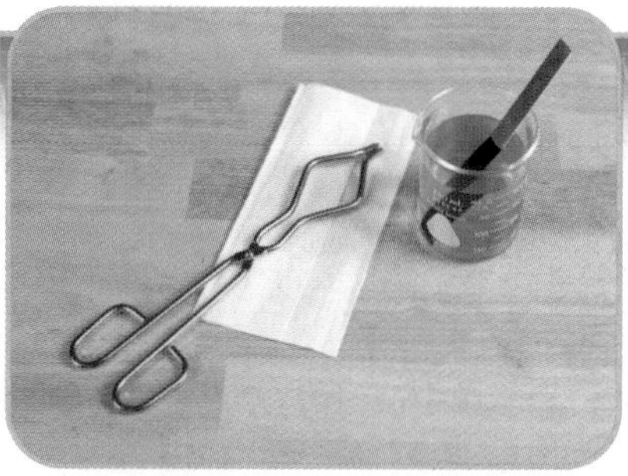

Procedure

1. Place the zinc in the beaker and add enough $CuSO_4$ solution to cover the zinc as shown. **CAUTION** *Be careful when using chemicals. Copper sulfate is toxic.*
2. After 5 minutes, carefully remove the zinc from the solution using the tongs and place the zinc on the paper towel to dry. Observe any changes that have occurred to the zinc and the solution of $CuSO_4$. **CAUTION** *Follow your teacher's instructions for disposal of used chemicals. Wash your hands with soap or detergent before leaving the laboratory.*

Analyze and Conclude

1. **Observing** What clues indicate that a chemical reaction has taken place?
2. **Applying Concepts** What were the reactants in this reaction? What were the products? Write a balanced chemical equation for the reaction.
3. **Classifying** Is this a single-replacement or double-replacement reaction? Explain.

Quick Lab

Identifying a Type of Reaction **L2**

Objective
After completing this activity, students will be able to
- determine whether a chemical reaction has occurred.
- identify a single-replacement reaction.

Skills Focus Observing, Predicting

Prep Time 10 minutes

Advance Prep Purchase zinc strips or cut a zinc sheet into 1" × 2" pieces. While wearing safety goggles and heavy gloves, file down all rough edges. To prepare 0.1 M $CuSO_4$: Dissolve 2.5 g $CuSO_4 \cdot 5H_2O$ in enough water to make 100 mL of solution. Be sure to take proper safety precautions.

Class Time 15 minutes

Safety Students should wear safety goggles, lab aprons, and disposable plastic gloves. They should tie back long hair and secure any loose clothing.

Expected Outcome The section of the zinc strip exposed to the $CuSO_4$ solution will have a distinct copper metal coating and the copper(II) sulfate solution will become darker and less blue in color.

Analyze and Conclude
1. The $CuSO_4$ solution turned less blue and the zinc became coated with reddish copper.
2. Zn and $CuSO_4$; Cu and $ZnSO_4$;
$Zn + CuSO_4 \longrightarrow Cu + ZnSO_4$
3. This is a single-replacement reaction because one element replaces another element in a compound. **Visual**

For Enrichment **L2**

Have students examine other single metal replacement reactions by placing copper and magnesium in $AgNO_3$, $CuSO_4$, $MgSO_4$, and $ZnSO_4$ solutions. The copper strip will react with $AgNO_3$, and the magnesium strip will react with $AgNO_3$, $CuSO_4$, and $ZnSO_4$. **Kinesthetic**

Answer to . . .

Figure 13 *In a double-replacement reaction, two different compounds exchange positive ions and form two new compounds.*

Reading Checkpoint *A reaction in which one element takes the place of another element in a compound*

Build Reading Literacy L1

Preview Refer to page **36D** in **Chapter 2**, which provides the guidelines for previewing.

Have students preview the text on pp. 204 and 205 related to oxidation and reduction reactions. They should note the headings, the bold-faced key ideas, and the chemical equations. Help students activate their prior knowledge by reviewing the role electrons play in ionic and covalent bonding.
Verbal

Reactions as Electron Transfers

Build Science Skills L2

Classifying Many kinds of reactions are also classified as redox reactions. For example, all combustion reactions are also redox reactions. The easiest reactions to identify as redox reactions contain pure elements. Have students search the section and identify these redox reactions, which have a product or a reactant that is an element.
($2Na + Cl_2 \longrightarrow 2NaCl$;
$2H_2 + O_2 \longrightarrow 2H_2O$;
$2H_2O \longrightarrow 2H_2 + O_2$;
$Cu + 2AgNO_3 \longrightarrow Cu(NO_3)_2 + 2Ag$;
$2K + 2H_2O \longrightarrow H_2 + 2KOH$;
$CH_4 + 2O_2 \longrightarrow CO_2 + 2H_2O$*)*
Logical

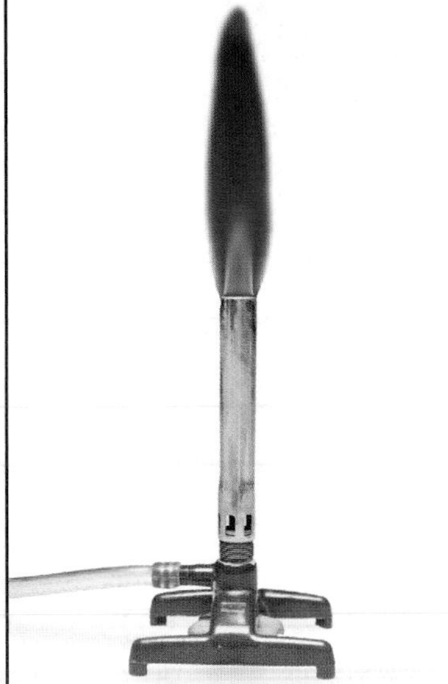

Figure 14 A Bunsen burner generates heat and light by the combustion of natural gas. **Interpreting Photos** *What reactants or products are visible in the reaction shown above?*

Combustion A **combustion reaction** is one in which a substance reacts rapidly with oxygen, often producing heat and light. The burning of natural gas, shown in Figure 14, is an example of combustion. The main component of natural gas is methane, CH_4. When methane burns in an unlimited supply of oxygen, the following reaction occurs.

$$CH_4 + 2O_2 \longrightarrow CO_2 + 2H_2O$$

The products of the reaction are carbon dioxide and water. The combustion of methane also generates both heat and light.

By now you know the chemical equation for the combustion of hydrogen.

$$2H_2 + O_2 \longrightarrow 2H_2O$$

Notice that you could also classify this reaction as the synthesis of water. The classifications for chemical reactions sometimes overlap.

Reactions as Electron Transfers

So far, you have learned that chemical reactions can be identified by the type of reactant or by the number of reactants and products. For example, in a combustion reaction one of the reactants must be oxygen. In a synthesis reaction, two or more reactants combine to form a single product.

As scientists learned more about the structure of the atom, they found different ways to describe how reactions take place. **The discovery of subatomic particles enabled scientists to classify certain chemical reactions as transfers of electrons between atoms.** A reaction in which electrons are transferred from one reactant to another is called an **oxidation-reduction reaction,** or redox reaction.

Oxidation For a long time, people have known that metals react with oxygen. Calcium, for instance, reacts with oxygen and forms calcium oxide (CaO), shown in Figure 15. Iron reacts with oxygen and forms rust, or iron(III) oxide (Fe_2O_3). These types of synthesis reactions, in which a metal combines with oxygen, traditionally have been classified as oxidations.

When calcium reacts with oxygen, the following reaction takes place.

$$2Ca + O_2 \longrightarrow 2CaO$$

Notice that while the atoms of both reactants (Ca and O_2) are neutral, the product of the reaction is a compound composed of ions (Ca^{2+} and O^{2-}). When calcium reacts with oxygen, each neutral calcium atom loses two electrons and becomes a calcium ion with a charge of 2+.

$$Ca \longrightarrow Ca^{2+} + 2e^-$$

Figure 15 Calcium oxide, or lime, is produced when calcium burns in the presence of oxygen. In this reaction, the calcium is oxidized and the oxygen is reduced.

204 *Chapter 7*

Facts and Figures

Corrosion of Metals Rust (Fe_2O_3) can result from oxygen and water coming into contact with iron. The corrosion of iron can result in the formation of many substances, including iron(II) oxide, FeO, and hydrated iron(III) oxide, $Fe_2O_3 \bullet nH_2O$. Iron is not the only metal that corrodes. Uncoated aluminum objects oxidize to form white Al_2O_3. Jewelry made of silver tarnishes over time, forming black Ag_2S. Copper pots often develop a distinctive green patina when exposed to the elements.

Any process in which an element loses electrons during a chemical reaction is called oxidation. A reactant is oxidized if it loses electrons. Note that the modern definition of oxidation is much broader than the original meaning. Oxygen doesn't always have to be present in order for an element to lose electrons. For example, when sodium reacts with chlorine, each neutral sodium atom loses one electron and becomes a sodium ion, Na^+.

Reduction As calcium atoms lose electrons during the synthesis of calcium oxide, the oxygen atoms gain electrons. As each neutral oxygen atom gains two electrons, it becomes an ion with a charge of 2−.

$$O + 2e^- \longrightarrow O^{2-}$$

The process in which an element gains electrons during a chemical reaction is called reduction. A reactant is said to be reduced if it gains electrons.

Oxidation and reduction always occur together. When one element loses electrons, another element must gain electrons. Note that oxidation-reduction reactions do not always involve complete transfers of electrons. For example, in the synthesis of water, hydrogen is oxidized as it partially loses electrons. Oxygen is reduced as it partially gains electrons.

Go Online NSTA SCILINKS

For: Links on oxidation and reduction

Visit: www.SciLinks.org

Web Code: ccn-1072

Section 7.2 Assessment

Reviewing Concepts

1. What are five general types of reactions?
2. How did the discovery of subatomic particles affect the classification of reactions?
3. The synthesis of water is described by the equation $2H_2 + O_2 \longrightarrow 2H_2O$. How is the decomposition of water related to this reaction? Explain, using a chemical equation.
4. Explain the difference between a single-replacement reaction and a double-replacement reaction.
5. Propane, C_3H_8, is frequently used in camping stoves. When propane undergoes combustion, what are the products formed?
6. Is the reaction represented by the following equation a redox reaction? Explain your answer.

$$2Hg + O_2 \longrightarrow 2HgO$$

Critical Thinking

7. **Predicting** What is the product of the synthesis reaction between magnesium and iodine? Explain your answer.
8. **Classifying** Identify these reactions as synthesis, decomposition, single replacement, double replacement, or combustion.
   a. $Pb(NO_3)_2 + 2HCl \longrightarrow PbCl_2 + 2HNO_3$
   b. $2C_2H_6 + 7O_2 \longrightarrow 4CO_2 + 6H_2O$
   c. $Ca + 2HCl \longrightarrow CaCl_2 + H_2$
   d. $2SO_2 + O_2 \longrightarrow 2SO_3$

Writing in Science

Explanatory Paragraph Write a paragraph explaining why the formation of water can be classified as a synthesis, combustion, or oxidation-reduction reaction.

3 ASSESS

Evaluate Understanding **L2**

Have students draw and label illustrations of different reactions on index cards. Have them exchange the cards and practice identifying each type of reaction.

Reteach **L1**

Make a chart of the number of reactants and products each reaction has.

Writing in Science

Synthesis: because two substances (oxygen and hydrogen) react to form a single substance (water); combustion: because the hydrogen reacts rapidly with oxygen, producing energy; and oxidation-reduction: because electrons are partially transferred from the hydrogen atoms to the oxygen

Interactive Textbook If your class subscribes to the Interactive Textbook, use it to review key concepts in Section 7.2.

Go Online NSTA SCILINKS

Download a worksheet on oxidation and reduction for students to complete, and find additional teacher support from NSTA SciLinks.

Answer to . . .

Figure 14 *None can be seen. (The natural gas is being fed through the tubing; the oxygen reacting with the gas is colorless; and the carbon dioxide and water produced are both colorless.) However, the energy released by the reaction can be seen in the blue flame.*

Section 7.2 Assessment

1. Synthesis reaction, decomposition reaction, single-replacement reaction, double-replacement reaction, and combustion reaction
2. The discovery of subatomic particles allowed scientists to classify certain reactions as transfers of electrons between atoms.
3. In the reaction $2H_2 + O_2 \longrightarrow 2H_2O$, water is formed from its elements. During the decomposition of water, water is broken down into its elements, according to the equation $2H_2O \longrightarrow 2H_2 + O_2$.
4. In a single-replacement reaction, an element replaces another element in one compound. In a double-replacement reaction, two elements replace each other in two different compounds.
5. Carbon dioxide and water
6. Yes, this is a redox reaction because electron transfer takes place. The charge of mercury changes from 0 to 2+ (oxidation). The charge of oxygen changes from 0 to 2− (reduction).
7. MgI_2. In ionic compounds, magnesium has a charge of 2+ and iodine has a charge of 1−.
8. a. Double replacement
   b. Combustion
   c. Single replacement
   d. Synthesis

Section 7.3

1 FOCUS

Objectives

7.3.1 **Describe** the energy changes that take place during chemical reactions.

7.3.2 **Classify** chemical reactions as exothermic or endothermic.

7.3.3 **Explain** how energy is conserved during chemical reactions.

Reading Focus

Build Vocabulary L2

Word-Part Analysis Tell students that the prefix *exo-* means *out* and the prefix *endo-* means *in*. Have students predict the meaning of the terms *exothermic reaction* and *endothermic reaction* given that the word root *thermo* means *heat*. *(An exothermic reaction gives off heat (energy), while an endothermic reaction takes in heat (energy).)*

Reading Strategy L2

a. Releases energy to the surroundings
b. Absorbs energy from surroundings

2 INSTRUCT

Chemical Bonds and Energy

Build Science Skills L2

Using Models Have students use molecular model kits to make ball-and-stick models for propane, C_3H_8. Explain that the sticks represent bonds and the balls represent atoms in the molecule. Have students count the number of bonds that will break in the combustion of a propane molecule.
Logical, Visual

7.3 Energy Changes in Reactions

Reading Focus

Key Concepts

- What happens to chemical bonds during a chemical reaction?
- What happens to energy during a chemical reaction?

Vocabulary

- chemical energy
- exothermic reaction
- endothermic reaction

Reading Strategy

Comparing and Contrasting Copy the Venn diagram. As you read, complete it to show the differences between exothermic and endothermic reactions.

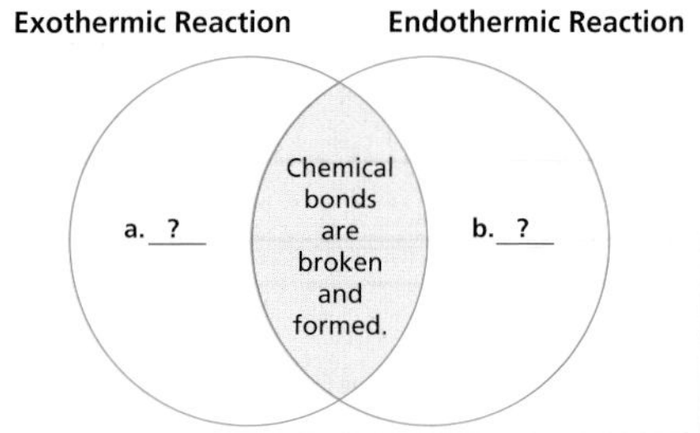

Exothermic Reaction
Endothermic Reaction
a. ?
Chemical bonds are broken and formed.
b. ?

If you've ever had a barbecue, you may have used a gas grill like the one shown in Figure 16. Many types of gas grills use propane, C_3H_8. You can think of a propane grill as the scene of a chemical reaction—specifically, a combustion reaction. The reactants are propane and oxygen, and the products are carbon dioxide and water. However, the description of this reaction is incomplete unless you consider the heat and light produced. Heat, after all, is the reason for using a propane grill.

Chemical Bonds and Energy

The heat produced by a propane grill is a form of energy. When you write the chemical equation for the combustion of propane, you can include "heat" on the right side of the equation.

$$C_3H_8 + 5O_2 \longrightarrow 3CO_2 + 4H_2O + \text{Heat}$$

This equation states that the heat released in the reaction came from the reactants. **Chemical energy** is the energy stored in the chemical bonds of a substance. A propane molecule has ten single covalent bonds (eight C—H bonds and two C—C bonds). The chemical energy of a propane molecule is the energy stored in these bonds. Likewise, oxygen, carbon dioxide, and water molecules all have energy stored in their chemical bonds.

Figure 16 Many portable barbecue grills burn propane gas.

Section Resources

Print
- ***Reading and Study Workbook With Math Support,*** Section 7.3
- ***Transparencies,*** Section 7.3

Technology
- ***Interactive Textbook,*** Section 7.3
- ***Presentation Pro CD-ROM,*** Section 7.3

Energy changes in chemical reactions are determined by changes that occur in chemical bonding. **Chemical reactions involve the breaking of chemical bonds in the reactants and the formation of chemical bonds in the products.** In the combustion of propane, the bonds in propane and oxygen molecules are broken, while the bonds in carbon dioxide and water molecules are formed.

Breaking Bonds As Figure 17 illustrates, each propane molecule reacts with five oxygen molecules. In order for the reaction to occur, eight C—H single bonds, two C—C single bonds, and five O═O double bonds must be broken. Breaking chemical bonds requires energy. This is why propane grills have an igniter, a device that produces a spark. The spark provides enough energy to break the bonds of reacting molecules and get the reaction started.

Forming Bonds Figure 17 also shows you that for each molecule of propane burned, three molecules of carbon dioxide and four molecules of water are formed. This means that six C═O double bonds and eight O—H single bonds are formed in the reaction. The formation of chemical bonds releases energy. The heat and light given off by a propane stove result from the formation of new chemical bonds. The bonds form as the carbon, hydrogen, and oxygen atoms in the propane and oxygen molecules are rearranged into molecules of carbon dioxide and water.

Reading Checkpoint *Does breaking chemical bonds require energy or release energy?*

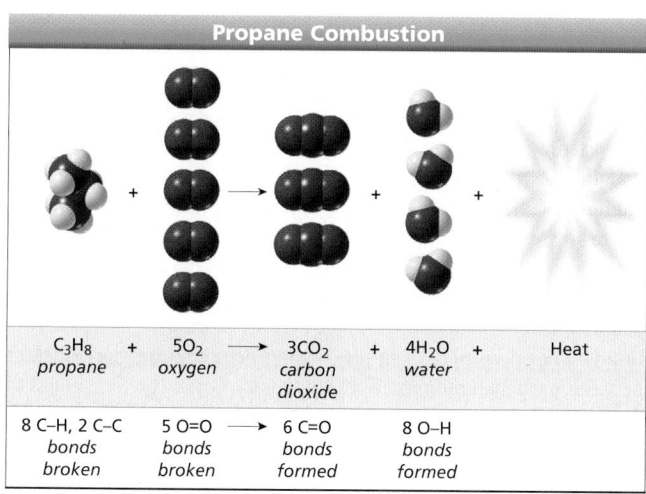

Propane Combustion

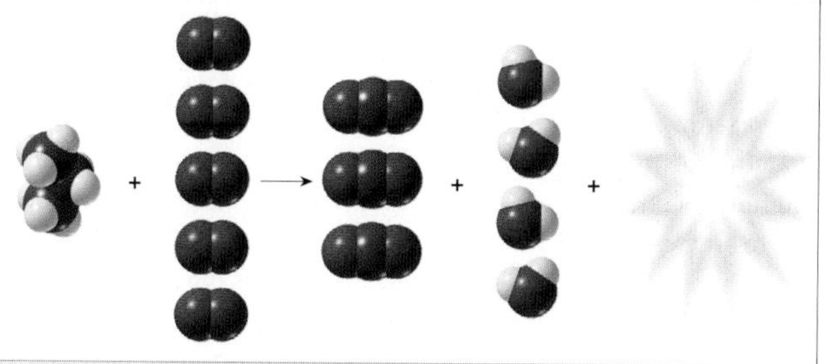

+
→
+
+

C_3H_8 *propane*	+	$5O_2$ *oxygen*	→	$3CO_2$ *carbon dioxide*	+	$4H_2O$ *water*	+	Heat
8 C–H, 2 C–C *bonds broken*		5 O=O *bonds broken*	→	6 C=O *bonds formed*		8 O–H *bonds formed*		

Figure 17 In order for the combustion of propane to occur, all the chemical bonds in the reactants (propane and oxygen) must be broken. The formation of the chemical bonds in the products completes the reaction. **Inferring** ***How does the chemical energy of the reactants compare to the chemical energy of the products in this reaction?***

Build Reading Literacy **L1**

Relate Text and Visuals Refer to page **190D** in this chapter, which provides the guidelines for relating text and visuals.

Have students read the text on pp. 206 and 207 related to energy changes in chemical reactions. Have students use Figures 16 and 17 to describe the path of energy that takes place in the barbecue scene. *(Energy stored in the bonds of the propane stored in the gas tank and the oxygen in the air is released during the combustion reaction. The heat released is absorbed by surroundings, which include the food on the grill.)*
Visual, Logical

Address Misconceptions **L2**

Many students associate combustion only with explosive reactions. Challenge this misconception by discussing ways in which a fire can burn without a great explosion. For example, simmering soup at low heat on a gas stove uses the combustion of methane. Explain that while combustion reactions are highly exothermic, they are not always accompanied by a blast.
Verbal

Customize for English Language Learners

Using Metaphors
Tell students that chemical energy in chemical reactions can be compared to money in starting a business. It takes money to purchase the merchandise. You can make that money back by selling the merchandise. If you have a product that sells well, you have a profitable business. But, if your merchandise does not sell well, you lose money. Have students come up with their own metaphors for chemical energy and share with the class.

Answer to . . .

Figure 17 *The chemical energy of the products is less than the chemical energy of the reactants.*

Reading Checkpoint *Breaking chemical bonds requires energy.*

Section 7.3 (continued)

Exothermic and Endothermic Reactions

Build Science Skills L2

Observing ACTIVITY

Purpose Students observe an exothermic process.

Materials beaker, water, thermometer, 1 tsp calcium chloride

Class Time 10 minutes

Procedure Have students fill a beaker with room temperature water and measure its temperature. Then, dissolve 1 tsp of calcium chloride in the water. Have students take the temperature of the solution and identify the process as endothermic or exothermic. Pour the waste solutions down the drain with excess water.

Safety Students should wear gloves and goggles for this activity.

Expected Outcome The temperature increases. The process is exothermic.
Logical, Visual, Group

Use Visuals L1

Figure 18 Have students examine the graphs. Ask, **As you go from left to right in each graph, what happens to the reactants?** *(They react to form the products.)* **What point on each graph represents the highest energy?** *(The energy is highest at each curve's peak.)* **What do the double-headed arrows represent?** *(The double-headed arrows represent the difference in chemical energy between the reactants and the products.)* **Which type of reaction has products with a greater amount of energy than the reactants?** *(The products in an endothermic reaction have a greater amount of chemical energy than the reactants.)*
Visual

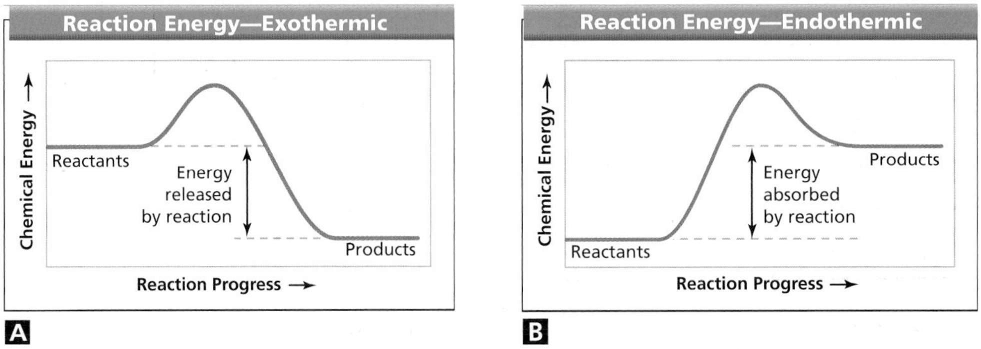
Reaction Energy—Exothermic
Chemical Energy →
Reactants
Energy released by reaction
Products
Reaction Progress →
A
Reaction Energy—Endothermic
Chemical Energy →
Products
Energy absorbed by reaction
Reactants
Reaction Progress →
B

Figure 18 In chemical reactions, energy is either released or absorbed. **A** In an exothermic reaction, energy is released to the surroundings. **B** In an endothermic reaction, energy is absorbed from the surroundings. **Using Graphs** ***How do the energy diagrams show that energy is conserved in chemical reactions?***

Exothermic and Endothermic Reactions

Recall that physical changes can release or absorb energy. During an exothermic change, such as freezing, energy is released to the surroundings. During an endothermic change, such as melting, energy is absorbed from the surroundings. Energy also flows into and out of chemical changes. **During a chemical reaction, energy is either released or absorbed.**

Exothermic Reactions A chemical reaction that releases energy to its surroundings is called an **exothermic reaction.** In exothermic reactions, the energy released as the products form is greater than the energy required to break the bonds in the reactants.

Combustion is an example of an extremely exothermic reaction. When 1 mole of propane reacts with 5 moles of oxygen, 2220 kJ (kilojoules) of heat is released. You can use this value to replace "heat" in the combustion equation written earlier.

$$C_3H_8 + 5O_2 \longrightarrow 3CO_2 + 4H_2O + 2220\ kJ$$

Figure 18A shows how chemical energy changes during an exothermic reaction. Notice that the chemical energy of the reactants is greater than the chemical energy of the products. The difference between these amounts of energy equals the amount of heat given off by the reaction.

In any reaction, the chemical energy reaches a peak before the reactants change into products. This peak represents the amount of energy required to break the chemical bonds of the reactants. Unless reacting particles collide with enough energy to break these bonds, the reaction will not occur. For example, at room temperature, the collisions between propane and oxygen molecules are not energetic enough to result in combustion. However, if you increase the temperature by adding a spark, some of the molecules around the spark move faster and are able to collide with enough energy to react.

Facts and Figures

Activation Energy Reactant particles must collide with enough speed in order to react. Activation energy is the energy required to start a chemical reaction. In an energy diagram, the activation energy is the difference in the energy of the reactants and the energy at the highest point of the curve. Methane gas in a gas stove reacts with oxygen in air to produce carbon dioxide and water. This combustion reaction provides the flame that heats food. However, simply exposing methane to air is not enough for the reaction to take place. Gas stoves have a pilot light or a sparking device that provides the activation energy needed for the reaction to occur. Once the gas is lit, the energy emitted from the exothermic reaction provides the activation energy for the continued burning of methane.

Endothermic Reactions A chemical reaction that absorbs energy from its surroundings is called an **endothermic reaction.** In an endothermic reaction, more energy is required to break the bonds in the reactants than is released by the formation of the products.

Figure 18B shows the energy diagram for an endothermic reaction. Notice that the energy of the products is greater than the energy of the reactants. The difference between these amounts of energy equals the amount of heat that must be absorbed from the surroundings.

When mercury(II) oxide is heated to a temperature of about 450°C, it breaks down into mercury and oxygen, as shown in Figure 19. The decomposition of mercury(II) oxide is an endothermic reaction that can be described by the following equation.

$$2HgO + 181.7\ kJ \longrightarrow 2Hg + O_2$$

Because heat is absorbed, the energy term appears on the left side of the equation. For every 2 moles of HgO that decomposes, 181.7 kJ of heat must be absorbed.

Figure 19 The orange-red powder in the bottom of the test tube is mercury(II) oxide. At about 450°C, mercury(II) oxide decomposes into oxygen gas (which escapes from the test tube) and mercury (droplets of which can be seen collecting on the sides of the test tube).

Conservation of Energy

In an exothermic reaction, the chemical energy of the reactants is converted into heat plus the chemical energy of the products. In an endothermic reaction, heat plus the chemical energy of the reactants is converted into the chemical energy of the products. In both cases, the total amount of energy before and after the reaction is the same. This principle is known as the law of conservation of energy. You will read more about how energy is conserved later.

Section 7.3 Assessment

Reviewing Concepts

1. What happens to chemical bonds as a chemical reaction occurs?
2. How do chemical reactions involve energy?
3. Is the combustion of propane endothermic or exothermic?
4. When propane reacts with oxygen, does the surrounding area become warmer or cooler?
5. Is energy created during an exothermic reaction? Explain.

Critical Thinking

6. **Inferring** Explain why methane does not react with oxygen at room temperature.
7. **Calculating** Methane reacts with oxygen in the following combustion reaction.

$$CH_4 + 2O_2 \longrightarrow CO_2 + 2H_2O$$

What bonds are broken when one molecule of methane reacts with two molecules of oxygen?

Connecting Concepts

Chemical Bonds Reread the descriptions of chemical bonds in Sections 6.1 and 6.2. Then, describe the decomposition of mercury(II) oxide. Specify which bonds are ionic and which bonds are covalent.

Conservation of Energy

Address Misconceptions L2

When examining a chemical equation, many students think that energy is being created or destroyed in the reaction. Unlike the situation with conservation of particles, the chemical equation does not clearly show conservation of energy. Challenge this misconception by having students refer to the energy diagrams in Figure 18 for a visual representation of the energy of the reactants and the products.
Visual

3 ASSESS

Evaluate Understanding L2

Have students sketch and label energy diagrams for exothermic and endothermic reactions. Have them discuss the energy diagrams in terms of breaking and forming bonds and conservation of energy.

Reteach L1

Compare and contrast the ways energy is notated in the equation on p. 206, in Figure 17, in Figure 18, and in the equation on p. 208.

Connecting Concepts

Mercury(II) oxide, or HgO, is an ionic compound. The decomposition of HgO can be described by the reaction $2HgO \longrightarrow 2Hg + O_2$. For each O_2 molecule formed by the decomposition of HgO, two ionic Hg—O bonds are broken and one covalent O═O double bond is formed.

Interactive Textbook If your class subscribes to the Interactive Textbook, use it to review key concepts in Section 7.3.

Section 7.3 Assessment

1. Chemical reactions involve the breaking of chemical bonds in the reactants and the formation of chemical bonds in the products.
2. During chemical reactions, energy is either released or absorbed.
3. The combustion of propane is exothermic because it releases energy.
4. Warmer. An exothermic reaction releases heat to the surrounding area.
5. No, energy is not created during an exothermic reaction. The energy released by an exothermic reaction was previously stored as chemical energy in the bonds of the reactants.
6. At room temperature, the collisions between methane molecules and oxygen molecules are not energetic enough to cause a reaction.
7. Four C—H single bonds and two O═O double bonds are broken when one molecule of methane burns.

Answer to . . .

Figure 18 *In Figure 18A, the chemical energy of the reactants equals the chemical energy of the products plus the energy released by the reaction. In Figure 18B, the chemical energy of the reactants plus the energy absorbed by the reaction equals the chemical energy of the products.*

CONCEPTS in Action

Firefighting L2

Background

Because fires require oxygen, fuel, and intense heat to burn, removing one or more of these components is the best way to put out a fire. Dousing a fire with water cools the fuel and makes it more difficult to heat to the ignition temperature. Backburning and firebreaks remove the fuel that a wildfire needs in order to spread. Smothering a fire reduces the amount of oxygen in the vicinity of the fire.

Build Science Skills L2

Applying Concepts

Purpose Students identify the types of fires that can occur in the home or laboratory and classify fire extinguishers used to control small fires.

Materials fire extinguishers, fire extinguisher ratings

Class Time 20 minutes

Procedure Tell students that different types of fire extinguishers made for home use can contain water, carbon dioxide, or a dry chemical material—such as sodium bicarbonate or potassium bicarbonate—that decomposes to produce carbon dioxide. Have students examine the different types of fire extinguishers and make note of their contents. Have them list the types of fires each type of extinguisher can put out. Have students apply what they have learned about combustion reactions to determine how each type of fire extinguisher works.

Expected Outcome Extinguishers that contain water can put out ordinary combustibles, such as paper or wood. Water extinguishers reduce the temperature of the fuel. Most dry chemical fire extinguishers can also put out flammable liquids and electrical fires. Dry chemical fire extinguishers smother the fire. Extinguisher ratings are as follows: A extinguishers put out paper and wood fires. B extinguishers put out flammable liquids. C extinguishers put out electrical fires.

Verbal, Logical, Group

CONCEPTS in Action

Firefighting

Uncontrolled fires threaten lives and property and can have a devastating effect on the environment. To fight fires, it is necessary to understand how they start, and what sustains them.

Fire is the result of combustion, a rapid reaction between oxygen and fuel. During combustion, fuel and oxygen react to form carbon dioxide, water, and heat. Most fires in rural areas, called wildfires, are caused by people being careless with campfires or cigarettes. Arson and lightning are also common causes. Usually the fire starts in an area of dry grass, which will ignite at a temperature of 150–200°C. Burning grass can create enough heat to ignite bushes, and these, in turn, may be tall enough to carry the flames into trees. (Wood has a higher ignition temperature, around 260°C.) Environmental conditions, such as drought that has left vegetation dry, and strong winds, can cause a small fire to spread. Wind also carries fire forward into new areas. Burning twigs and branches that become detached from trees can be blown into new areas of vegetation.

Dousing
Planes or helicopters are used to drop water or a fire-retardant slurry on a large fire. The slurry contains ammonium sulfate, $(NH_4)_2SO_4$, which helps smother the fire.

Firefighter
Firefighters wear protective clothing, helmets, and goggles. This firefighter also carries a shovel for digging trenches to stop a fire spreading.

Facts and Figures

Smothering a Fire Various reactions can take place in a fire depending on the type of fuel used. Pure carbon burns according to the following reaction.

$$C + O_2 \longrightarrow CO_2$$

Methane burns according to the following reaction.

$$CH_4 + 2O_2 \longrightarrow 2H_2O + CO_2$$

Draw students to the conclusion that reactions that involve burning have oxygen gas as a reactant. Ask them to speculate as to why covering a small burning object with a blanket can help put out the flames. Explain that smothering the flaming object with the blanket reduces the amount of oxygen available for the reactions.

Backburning
One way to stop a big fire is to start a smaller fire. This technique, called backburning, burns off vegetation between the fireline and the main fire. When the two fires meet, the blaze stops spreading because the land on either side has already been burned.

Boundary of Hanford site

Extent of fire

Smoke plume

Wildfire in Washington State
This satellite picture shows a forest fire that raged for two months in 2000 at the Department of Energy's site at Hanford. The fire was started by a vehicle fire and reached more than 500 square kilometers.

Firebreaks
In parts of the world where wildfires are common, strips of land are cleared of combustible vegetation to create firebreaks. Firefighters also dig firebreaks during fires to prevent fires from spreading.

Going Further

- Write a paragraph explaining how dousing, backburning, and firebreaks affect the chemical reactions involved in wildfires.
- Take a Discovery Channel Video Field Trip by watching "Taming the Flames."

Discovery Channel School **Video Field Trip**

Going Further

Dousing a wildfire with water deprives the combustion reaction of both oxygen and heat. (Although combustion is an exothermic reaction, heat is still required in order for the reacting particles to collide with enough energy to react, as seen in Figure 18A on p. 208.) Dousing with a chemical gel deprives the fire of oxygen. Both backburning and firebreaks keep wildfires from spreading by depriving the reaction of fuel such as wood and other vegetation.
Verbal

Use Community Resources **L2**

Have the class visit a fire station to learn more about fire prevention. Ask a firefighter to talk about the types of methods and chemicals used to prevent and extinguish fires.
Interpersonal

Video Field Trip
Taming the Flames

After students have viewed the Video Field Trip, ask them the following questions: **Describe how a fire burns, in terms of energy and chemical bonds.** *(The energy from the heat of the flames causes bonds in the fuel and oxygen to break and new bonds to form with the oxygen, releasing more energy to heat the reactants and keep the reaction going.)* **A fire requires heat, fuel, and oxygen to sustain it. List two things a firefighter can do to remove one of these three ingredients of a fire. Explain your answer.** *(Student answers may include firefighters can drop chemical gel on a fire to deprive it of oxygen, they can pour water on a fire to cool it and deprive it of oxygen, or they can dig trenches around the burning areas to deny the fire access to new fuel.)* **How do forest managers prevent large, uncontrollable forest fires by intentionally starting small, controlled fires?** *(Material such as leaves and needles, which could help produce large, uncontrollable fires, is cleared away by small, controlled fires. The flammable material that accumulates is called "duff.")*

1 FOCUS

Objectives

7.4.1 **Explain** what a reaction rate is.

7.4.2 **Describe** the factors affecting chemical reaction rates.

Reading Focus

Build Vocabulary L2

LINCS Have students use the LINCS strategy to learn and review the terms *reaction rate, surface area, concentration,* and *catalyst.* In LINCS exercises, students **L**ist what they know about each term, **I**magine a picture that describes the word, **N**ote a "sound-alike" word, **C**onnect the terms to the sound-alike word by making up a short story, and then perform a brief **S**elf-test.

Reading Strategy L2

a. Temperature **b.** Surface area
c. Stirring **d.** Concentration
e. Catalysts

2 INSTRUCT

Reactions Over Time

Build Math Skills L1

Ratios and Proportions
To help students understand reaction rate, review other rates that they might be familiar with. As an example of a rate, discuss speed as the ratio of distance traveled over time. In your discussion, be sure that students pay particular attention to the units (miles/hour, etc.). **Logical**

Direct students to the **Math Skills** in the **Skills and Reference Handbook** at the end of the student text for additional help.

Build Reading Literacy L1

Outline Refer to page **156D** in **Chapter 6**, which provides the guidelines for outlining.

Have students read the section. Then, have students use the headings as major divisions in an outline. Allow students to refer to their outlines when answering the questions in the Section 7.4 Assessment. **Visual**

7.4 Reaction Rates

Reading Focus

Key Concept

- What does a reaction rate tell you?
- What factors cause reaction rates to change?

Vocabulary

- reaction rate
- catalyst

Reading Strategy

Building Vocabulary Copy the partially completed web diagram at the right. Then, as you read, complete it with key terms from this section.

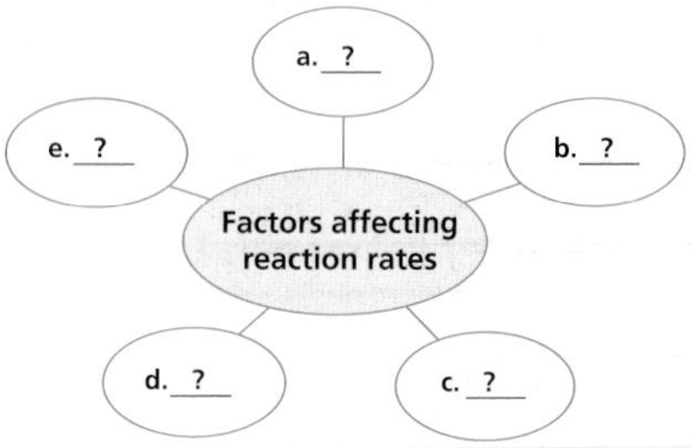

a. ?
b. ?
c. ?
d. ?
e. ?
Factors affecting reaction rates

You may have heard of athletes "burning Calories" when they exercise. A Calorie is a unit of energy used in the field of nutrition. The average banana, for instance, contains about 100 Calories. The cyclist in Figure 20 can use up, or burn, as many as 10,000 Calories during the course of a race. That adds up to a lot of bananas!

If you eat a banana, you provide your body with about 100 Calories to burn. This energy is released in a series of reactions that take place inside your body. A much faster way of releasing the energy contained in a banana is to burn it—outside the body—in a combustion reaction. In both cases, the total amount of energy released is the same. However, the time it takes for the energy to be released is different in each case.

Figure 20 A cyclist burns the Calories in a banana faster than a person walking would. But burning the banana outside the body would release the energy of the banana even faster.

Reactions Over Time

The progress of any chemical reaction can be measured over time. Different reactions have different durations. Some reactions, such as the explosion of TNT, happen almost instantaneously. Other reactions, such as tree leaves changing color during autumn, happen gradually.

Any change that happens over a period of time can be expressed as a rate. For example, speed is the rate that distance changes over time. A **reaction rate** is the rate at which reactants change into products over time. **Reaction rates tell you how fast a reaction is going.** That is, how fast the reactants are being consumed, how fast the products are being formed, or how fast energy is being absorbed or released.

Section Resources

Print
- ***Reading and Study Workbook With Math Support,*** Section 7.4
- ***Transparencies,*** Section 7.4

Technology
- ***Interactive Textbook,*** Section 7.4
- ***Presentation Pro CD-ROM,*** Section 7.4
- **Go Online,** NSTA SciLinks, Factors affecting reaction rate

Factors Affecting Reaction Rates

Recall that chemical reactions involve collisions between particles of reactants. The reaction rate depends on how often these particles collide. If the collisions occur more frequently, then the reaction rate increases. If the collisions occur less frequently, then the reaction rate decreases. Almost any reaction rate can be changed by varying the conditions under which the reaction takes place. **Factors that affect reaction rates include temperature, surface area, concentration, stirring, and catalysts.**

Temperature Suppose you are frying an egg in a frying pan. What happens if you increase the heat under the pan? The hotter the pan, the faster the egg will cook. Generally, an increase in temperature will increase the reaction rate, while a decrease in temperature will decrease the reaction rate. For instance, you store milk in a refrigerator to slow down the reactions that cause the milk to spoil. These reactions don't stop completely. Even milk stored in a refrigerator will eventually spoil. But the rate of spoiling decreases if the milk is kept cold.

Increasing the temperature of a substance causes its particles to move faster, on average. Particles that move faster are both more likely to collide and more likely to react. If the number of collisions that produce reactions increases, then the reaction rate increases.

Reading Checkpoint *How does temperature affect reaction rates?*

Surface Area Grain may not strike you as a dangerous material, but it can be explosive under the right conditions. The cause of the fire in Figure 21 was a combustion reaction between grain dust (suspended in the air) and oxygen. The rate of combustion was very rapid due to the small particle size of the grain dust.

The smaller the particle size of a given mass, the larger is its surface area. Imagine using a newspaper to cover the floor of a room. If you keep all the sections folded together, you can only cover a small area. However, if you separate the newspaper into pages and lay them out like tiles, you can cover a much larger area with the same mass of paper.

An increase in surface area increases the exposure of reactants to one another. The greater this exposure, the more collisions there are that involve reacting particles. With more collisions, more particles will react. This is why increasing the surface area of a reactant tends to increase the reaction rate.

Go Online NSTA SCILINKS

For: Links on factors affecting reaction rate
Visit: www.SciLinks.org
Web Code: ccn-1074

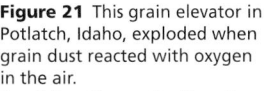

Figure 21 This grain elevator in Potlatch, Idaho, exploded when grain dust reacted with oxygen in the air.
Applying Concepts *How does surface area affect reaction rates?*

Factors Affecting Reaction Rates

Build Science Skills L2

ACTIVITY

Calculating

Purpose Students learn how to increase surface area.

Materials clay, rulers, plastic knives

Class Time 10 minutes

Procedure Have students make a clay cube, measure its dimensions, and calculate its surface area. Then, have students cut the clay cube in half and calculate the total surface area of the two pieces. Ask, **How does cutting the clay cube in half affect its surface area?** *(Surface area increases.)*

Expected Outcome The more pieces the clay cube is cut into, the greater the surface area becomes. **Logical, Visual**

Teacher Demo

Temperature and Rate L2

Purpose Students observe the effect of temperature on reaction rate.

Materials 2 chemical light sticks, 2 large beakers, hot water, ice water

Procedure Students will observe the same reaction taking place at two different temperatures. Fill one beaker with hot water and the other with ice water. Turn off the room lights. Place an activated light stick in each beaker. Explain that the light sticks glow due to a chemical reaction that gives off light.

Expected Outcome The light stick in hot water will glow more than the one in cold water. **Visual**

Go Online NSTA SCILINKS

Download a worksheet on factors affecting reaction rate for students to complete, and find additional teacher support from NSTA SciLinks.

Answer to . . .

Figure 21 *A surface area increase generally increases the reaction rate.*

Reading Checkpoint *Increasing the temperature generally increases the reaction rate.*

Customize for Inclusion Students

Visually Impaired
For visually impaired students, consider performing the above demonstration using a reaction that can be observed audibly. For example, place one effervescent tablet in a beaker of cold water and a second effervescent tablet in a beaker of hot water. Have students gather closely around the reaction, or find a way to amplify the reaction sounds. Students should be able to hear a difference in the rates of gas evolution.

Quick Lab

Observing the Action of Catalysts

L2

Objective
After completing this activity, students will be able to
- describe how a catalyst is able to promote a chemical reaction.

Address Misconceptions

Many students see the formation of a new substance with new properties as simply happening, rather than as a result of atoms rearranging. Catalysts can further confuse the issue because they aid the progress of a reaction without being changed by the reaction. Explain that in this Quick Lab, the same reaction takes place in all four test tubes. Use molecular models of hydrogen peroxide to show how the atoms in two H_2O_2 molecules are rearranged to form two water molecules, H_2O, and one molecule of oxygen, O_2.

Skills Focus **Observing, Formulating Hypotheses**

Prep Time 15 minutes

Advance Prep Provide a 3% solution of hydrogen peroxide (typical strength sold in stores) solution and 0.1 M $CuCl_2$ (clearly labeled). To make a 0.1 M solution of $CuCl_2$, dissolve 13.5 g $CuCl_2$ in enough water to make 1 L of solution.

Class Time 20 minutes

Safety Review the information in the MSDS for each compound with students before performing the lab. Make sure that students wear safety goggles, lab aprons, and plastic disposable gloves. Avoid skin contact with the compounds, as some are irritants. Students should wash their hands with soap or detergent before leaving the laboratory.

Expected Outcome The platinum wire, manganese dioxide, and raw potato catalyze the release of oxygen bubbles. Copper chloride does not.

Analyze and Conclude
1. The platinum wire produced moderate bubbling, MnO_2 produced vigorous bubbling, $CuCl_2$ produced no reaction, and potato produced foam.
2. MnO_2; potato
3. This test tube served as the control.
Visual, Group

Quick Lab

Observing the Action of Catalysts

Materials

5 test tubes, test-tube rack, marking pencil, dropper pipet, wood splint, platinum wire, 0.1 g manganese dioxide (MnO_2), 5 drops of copper(II) chloride ($CuCl_2$) solution, 0.1 g raw potato, graduated cylinder, 25 mL hydrogen peroxide (H_2O_2)

Procedure

1. Label the 5 test tubes from A to E with the marking pencil.
2. Put a small piece of platinum wire in test tube A. Add a tiny amount (about the tip of the wood splint) of MnO_2 to test tube B. Use the dropper pipet to put 5 drops of $CuCl_2$ in test tube C. Put a piece of potato in test tube D. Test tube E should remain empty for now. **CAUTION** *MnO_2 and $CuCl_2$ are toxic.*
3. Carefully add 5 mL of hydrogen peroxide to test tube A. **CAUTION** *Be careful when using chemicals.* Observe how fast the bubbles are produced.
4. Repeat Step 3 with test tubes B through E.

Analyze and Conclude

1. **Observing** What effect did the platinum wire, MnO_2, $CuCl_2$, and the potato have on the rate at which the bubbles were produced in the hydrogen peroxide?
2. **Comparing and Contrasting** Which catalyst(s) caused the reaction to go the fastest? The slowest?
3. **Inferring** Why did you put only hydrogen peroxide in test tube E?

Stirring You can also increase the exposure of reactants to each other by stirring them. For example, when you wash your clothes in a washing machine, particles of detergent react with particles of the stains on your clothes. This reaction would go slowly if you just left your clothes soaking in a tub of water and detergent. A washing machine speeds up the reaction by stirring the contents back and forth. Collisions between the particles of the reactants are more likely to happen. Stirring the reactants will generally increase the reaction rate.

Figure 22 The dye solution in the left beaker is more concentrated than the solution in the right. Increasing the concentration of the dye increases the rate of color change in the material.

Concentration Another way you can change the reaction rate is to change the concentration of the reactants. Concentration refers to the number of particles in a given volume. The more reacting particles that are present in a given volume, the more opportunities there are for collisions involving those particles. The reaction rate is faster.

Both of the beakers in Figure 22 contain a piece of material dipped in dye solution. Dyeing is a chemical reaction in which dye particles react with the particles of the material being dyed. The material dipped in the more concentrated dye becomes colored more quickly.

For gases, concentration changes with pressure. The greater the pressure of a gaseous reactant, the greater is its concentration, and the faster is the reaction rate.

Facts and Figures

Biological Catalysts
Catalysts that speed up reactions in biological systems are called enzymes. See Section 9.4 for a definition of *enzyme*. Enzymes help carry out many of the reactions that take place in the human body. For example, the enzyme lactase helps your body break down lactose, a carbohydrate found in milk. People with lactose intolerance do not produce enough lactase to properly digest milk products.

Catalysts Sometimes you can change a reaction rate by using catalysts. A **catalyst** is a substance that affects the reaction rate without being used up in the reaction. Chemists often use catalysts to speed up a reaction or enable a reaction to occur at a lower temperature. In the making of sulfuric acid, one of the steps involved is the reaction of sulfur dioxide with oxygen to form sulfur trioxide. This reaction happens very slowly without a catalyst such as vanadium(V) oxide.

$$2SO_2 + O_2 \xrightarrow{V_2O_5} 2SO_3$$

Since the catalyst is neither a reactant nor a product, it is written over the arrow. Because the catalyst is not consumed, it can be used to speed up the same reaction over and over again.

Recall that in order for a reaction to take place, the reacting particles must collide with enough energy to break the chemical bonds of those particles. As shown in Figure 23, a catalyst lowers this energy barrier. One way that a catalyst can do this is by providing a surface on which the reacting particles can come together. Imagine that you go to a party and make several new friends. By bringing people together, the party has made it easier for you to form those friendships. Similarly, a catalyst can "invite" reacting particles together so that they are more likely to react.

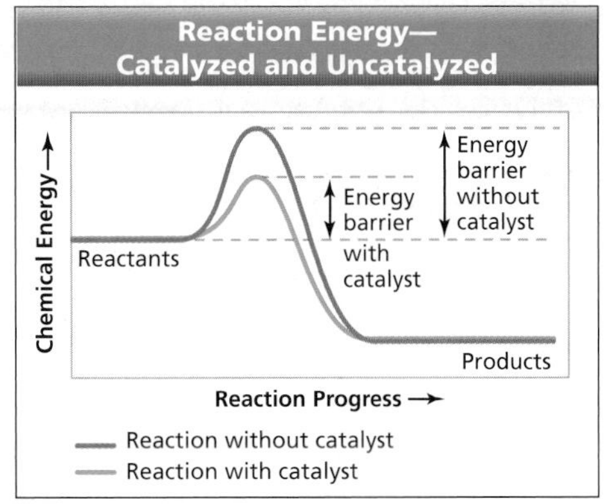

Reaction Energy—
Catalyzed and Uncatalyzed
Chemical Energy →
Energy barrier without catalyst
Energy barrier with catalyst
Reactants
Products
Reaction Progress →
Reaction without catalyst
Reaction with catalyst

Figure 23 The graph above shows how a catalyst lowers the amount of energy required for effective collisions between reacting particles.
Using Graphs ***In an exothermic reaction, how does a catalyst affect the amount of energy released?***

Section 7.4 Assessment

Reviewing Concepts

1. What does a reaction rate tell you?
2. What five factors affect reaction rates?
3. Explain why reactions take place faster at higher temperatures.
4. When you add baking soda to vinegar, the mixture fizzes as carbon dioxide gas is produced. Suppose you added water to the vinegar before you mixed it with the baking soda. What do you think would happen to the rate of carbon dioxide production?
5. How does a catalyst make a reaction go faster?
6. Platinum is a catalyst for the decomposition of hydrogen peroxide into water and oxygen.

$$2H_2O_2 \xrightarrow{Pt} 2H_2O + O_2$$

What would you expect to see if platinum were added to hydrogen peroxide solution?

Critical Thinking

7. **Applying Concepts** Explain why, if you want to store uncooked hamburger meat for a month, you put it in a freezer rather than a refrigerator.
8. **Evaluating** The reaction between magnesium and hydrochloric acid produces hydrogen. If you increase the concentration of HCl, the reaction takes place faster. Could HCl be considered a catalyst for this reaction? Explain your answer.

Writing in Science

Compare and Contrast Paragraph Write a paragraph explaining how temperature, concentration, surface area, and catalysts affect reaction rates.

Section 7.4 Assessment

1. How fast a chemical reaction is going
2. Temperature, concentration, surface area, stirring, and catalysts
3. Reacting particles move faster on average at higher temperatures. As a result, they collide with each other more often and with greater energy, and the reaction rate increases.
4. The CO_2 production would occur at a slower rate because you have diluted the vinegar. Decreasing the concentration of a reactant decreases the reaction rate.
5. A catalyst makes a reaction go faster by lowering the energy barrier required to break the bonds of the reacting particles.
6. You would see oxygen bubbles because platinum catalyzes the reaction.
7. A freezer is colder than a refrigerator, so the reactions responsible for spoiling the meat will take place more slowly in the freezer.
8. No, HCl cannot be considered a catalyst for the reaction because it is a reactant (and is used up during the reaction). A catalyst is neither a reactant nor a product.

Use Visuals — L1

Figure 23 Have students examine the effect of catalysts on energy barriers. Ask, **What do the two lines represent?** *(One line represents the chemical energy as the reaction with the catalyst progresses. The other line represents the chemical energy as the reaction without the catalyst progresses.)* **How does carrying out a reaction in the presence of a catalyst affect the energy barrier of the reaction?** *(The energy barrier for the reaction is less in the presence of the catalyst.)* **How does carrying out a reaction in the presence of a catalyst affect the energy of the reactants and products?** *(The energy of the reactants and products is unchanged by the presence of the catalyst.)* **Visual**

3 ASSESS

Evaluate Understanding — L2

Have students make flashcards that list the ways they could increase the rate of a reaction, with examples on the back of how each factor affects reaction rates. Have students quiz each other.

Reteach — L1

As a class, list five factors that affect reaction rate. Then, have students give an example of each and explain why the factor affects reaction rate.

Writing in Science

Factors that affect the rates of chemical reactions include temperature, concentration, surface area, and the presence of catalysts. Increasing the temperature, surface area of the reactants, or concentration of the reactants generally increases the reaction rate. Catalysts can speed up reactions by providing a surface on which the reacting particles can come together.

Interactive Textbook If your class subscribes to the Interactive Textbook, use it to review key concepts

Answer to . . .

Figure 23 *A catalyst does not affect the amount of energy released by the reaction. (The chemical energy of the reactants and the products does not change with the addition of a catalyst.) It does, however, lower the amount of energy required to break the chemical bonds of the reactants.*

1 FOCUS

Objectives

7.5.1 **Identify** and **describe** physical and chemical equilibria.

7.5.2 **Describe** the factors affecting chemical equilibrium.

Reading Focus

Build Vocabulary L2

Paraphrase To help students understand the vocabulary terms, paraphrase their definitions using words and phrases students are more familiar with. For example, explain that a system is in *equilibrium* when there is no overall change in amounts even though there is a great deal of movement back and forth. A *reversible reaction* is a chemical reaction that can go forward and backward at the same time.

Reading Strategy L2

1. Physical equilibrium 2. Chemical equilibrium B. Factors affecting chemical equilibrium 3. Concentration

2 INSTRUCT

Types of Equilibria

Build Science Skills L2

Using Models ACTIVITY

Purpose Students model dynamic equilibrium using playing cards.

Materials playing cards, watch

Class Time 10 minutes

Procedure Have one student use a watch to count seconds out loud one through six every six seconds. Have a second student pull cards from a deck and place them down in rows of six, one card down each second. After three rows of cards have been placed, have a third student begin to remove pairs of cards and place them on the deck every two seconds. Students will observe that the number of rows of cards does not change, because the cards are added and removed at the same rate.
Kinesthetic, Group

7.5 Equilibrium

Reading Focus

Key Concepts

- Under what conditions do physical and chemical equilibria occur?
- How do equilibrium systems respond to change?

Vocabulary

- equilibrium
- reversible reaction

Reading Strategy

Outlining As you read, make an outline of the most important ideas in this section.

I. Equilibrium
 A. Types of Equilibria
  1. ________
  2. ________
 B. ________
  1. Temperature
  2. Pressure
  3. ________

Suppose you're waiting in line for a toll booth at a bridge, like some of the cars shown in Figure 24. You notice that every time a car passes by a toll booth in the direction you are traveling, another car passes through the toll plaza in the opposite direction. The rate of cars entering equals the rate of cars exiting. As a result, the number of cars on either side of the toll plaza remains constant, although cars are continually entering and exiting the bridge.

Types of Equilibria

The traffic at a toll bridge is similar to a system in equilibrium. **Equilibrium** (plural *equilibria*) is a state in which the forward and reverse paths of a change take place at the same rate.

Recall that changes to matter are either physical or chemical. When opposing physical changes take place at the same rate, a physical equilibrium is reached. When opposing chemical changes take place at the same rate, a chemical equilibrium is reached.

Figure 24 About 190,000 vehicles pass through the toll plaza of New York City's Verrazano-Narrows Bridge every day.

Section Resources

Print
- ***Reading and Study Workbook With Math Support,*** Section 7.5
- ***Transparencies,*** Section 7.5

Technology
- ***Interactive Textbook,*** Section 7.5
- ***Presentation Pro CD-ROM,*** Section 7.5
- ***Go Online,*** NSTA SciLinks, Factors affecting equilibrium

Physical Equilibrium What happens when you pour some water into a jar and then close the lid? You might think that nothing happens at all. But in fact, some of the water undergoes a physical change by evaporating. As more water evaporates, some of the water vapor condenses. Eventually, the rate of evaporation equals the rate of condensation, and the system reaches equilibrium as shown in Figure 25.

When liquid water is in equilibrium with water vapor, you can describe the system by writing this equation.

$$H_2O(l) \rightleftharpoons H_2O(g)$$

Here, *l* stands for liquid and *g* stands for gas. The pair of arrows in this equation indicates that the forward change (evaporation) and the reverse change (condensation) are happening simultaneously and at the same rate. Both the forward and reverse changes are physical changes, so this equation represents a physical equilibrium. **When a physical change does not go to completion, a physical equilibrium is established between the forward and reverse changes.**

Pure Spring Water
H_2O molecules

Figure 25 Liquid water left in a closed container eventually reaches equilibrium with its vapor. **Interpreting Diagrams** ***What do the arrows represent in the diagram above?***

Chemical Equilibrium All the chemical equations you have seen so far have been written with single arrows, which suggest that all reactions go to completion in one direction. In reality, however, most reactions are reversible to some extent. A **reversible reaction** is a reaction in which the conversion of reactants into products and the conversion of products into reactants can happen simultaneously.

In the previous section, you read about the synthesis of sulfur trioxide from sulfur dioxide and oxygen. This is actually a reversible reaction that can be expressed as

$$2SO_2(g) + O_2(g) \rightleftharpoons 2SO_3(g)$$

If sulfur dioxide and oxygen are mixed in a closed container, the forward reaction will start to produce sulfur trioxide. However, once molecules of sulfur trioxide form, some of them will change back into the reactants by the reverse reaction. Eventually, the rate of the forward reaction (synthesis) will equal the rate of the reverse reaction (decomposition), and the system will reach equilibrium. **When a chemical reaction does not go to completion, a chemical equilibrium is established between the forward and reverse reactions.** During chemical equilibrium, the reactants change into products just as fast as the products change back into reactants.

Reading Checkpoint *What happens during chemical equilibrium?*

Go Online NSTA SCILINKS

For: Links on factors affecting equilibrium
Visit: www.SciLinks.org
Web Code: ccn-1075

Use Visuals L1

Figure 25 Have students examine the molecular models of water in the bottle of spring water. Ask, **In which states does water exist inside the bottle?** *(Liquid and vapor)* **Are the molecules of water in the liquid state chemically different than the molecules of water in the vapor state?** *(No, both states of water have the same chemical properties.)* Tell the students that the two states of water are at equilibrium. Ask, **What do you know about the rates of the forward and reverse processes?** *(At equilibrium, the forward and reverse processes occur at the same rate.)* **How is this modeled in Figure 25?** *(The arrows show the same number of molecules leaving the liquid as there are molecules entering the liquid.)* **Visual**

Address Misconceptions L2

Many students incorrectly associate equilibrium only with having equal amounts of reactants and products. Challenge this misconception by discussing the following example. A beaker at 0°C contains 2 g of ice and 8 g of water. The rate of melting equals the rate of freezing. Is the system at equilibrium? *(Yes)*
Verbal, Logical

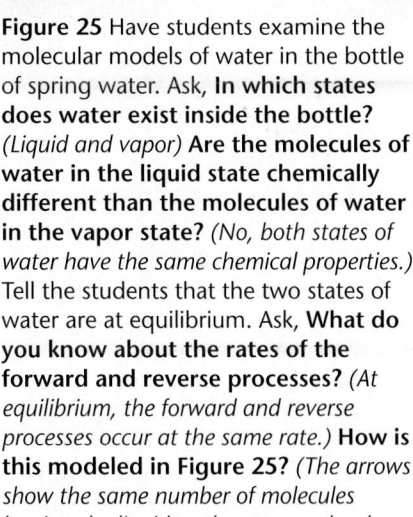

Go Online NSTA SCILINKS

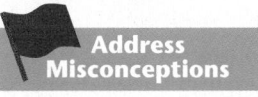

Download a worksheet on factors affecting equilibrium for students to complete, and find additional teacher support from NSTA SciLinks.

Customize for English Language Learners

Think-Pair-Share
Have students work in pairs to think of situations in which there is dynamic equilibrium. Examples include a doorman controlling the number of people who go in and out of an event, a clerk restocking the shelves at a grocery store, and a fountain consisting of a stream of water that pours into an overflowing vessel. Strengthen discussion skills by having students share their examples with the class. Encourage students to examine Figure 24 for an example of equilibrium in a real-world setting. Be sure that students understand that these examples are "open" systems, while dynamic equilibrium is a "closed" system.

Answer to . . .

Figure 25 *The arrows in the diagram shown represent opposing physical changes. The arrows pointing up represent evaporation, as liquid water changes into vapor. The arrows pointing down represent condensation, as the vapor changes into water.*

Reading Checkpoint *During chemical equilibrium, the reactants change into products at the same rate as the products change into reactants.*

Problem-Solving Activity

Recreating High Altitudes L2

Defining the Problem The problem is how to design a training facility that can recreate a high-altitude environment. The design will depend on what property of the air you wish to manipulate.

Organizing Information The equation $Hb + O_2 \rightleftharpoons HbO_2$ describes the hemoglobin-oxygen-oxyhemoglobin system. At high altitudes, the concentration of oxygen decreases, which shifts the equilibrium to the left. In response to the reduced oxyhemoglobin levels, the body produces more hemoglobin.

Creating a Solution The desired shift in the equilibrium happens when you lower the concentration of oxygen. One way you can do this is by reducing the pressure of the air inside the training facility. Another way to lower oxygen concentration is to change the composition of the air within the facility. This can be done by piping in air with a reduced fraction of oxygen. In the second solution, the facility can be operated at normal air pressure.

Presenting Your Plan Students might point out certain structural characteristics of their designs in their proposals. For example, a normal-pressure/low-oxygen facility would require a customized ventilation system that pipes in air with reduced oxygen levels. **Logical**

For Extra Help L1

Before they start, make sure students understand what the physical properties of air at a high altitude are. **Logical**

Factors Affecting Chemical Equilibrium

Build Reading Literacy L1

Reciprocal Teaching Refer to page **628D** in **Chapter 21**, which provides the guidelines for reciprocal teaching.

Have students read the section with a partner. One partner reads a paragraph out loud. Then, the other partner summarizes the paragraph's contents and explains the main concepts. The partners continue to switch roles with each new paragraph until they have finished the section. **Intrapersonal**

Problem-Solving Activity

Recreating High Altitudes

An important chemical equilibrium in your blood involves the reaction of hemoglobin (Hb) with oxygen (O_2) to form oxyhemoglobin (HbO_2).

$$Hb + O_2 \rightleftharpoons HbO_2$$

This equilibrium changes with altitude. As you move from lower to higher elevations, the concentration of oxygen in the air decreases, and the equilibrium shifts in the direction that produces less oxyhemoglobin. Your body responds to the shift by producing more hemoglobin. Studies have shown that athletes can improve their performance at sea level by living or training at high altitudes. Some training facilities are designed to recreate high altitudes. Imagine that you are asked to build such a facility.

Defining the Problem In your own words, state the problem you face.

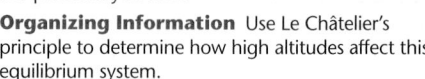

Organizing Information Use Le Châtelier's principle to determine how high altitudes affect this equilibrium system.

Creating a Solution The physical properties of the air inside the training facility include temperature, pressure, and composition. Figure out how to shift the equilibrium in the direction you want by changing one of these properties.

Presenting Your Plan Write a proposal to an athletic team that could benefit from using your training facility. Explain how your facility recreates a high-altitude environment.

Factors Affecting Chemical Equilibrium

Like reaction rates, chemical equilibria can change depending on the conditions of the reaction. While a reaction rate either increases or decreases in response to a change, an equilibrium shifts. That is, the equilibrium favors either the forward or the reverse reaction. **When a change is introduced to a system in equilibrium, the equilibrium shifts in the direction that relieves the change.** This rule was first observed by Henri Le Châtelier, shown in Figure 26. Today, the rule is known as Le Châtelier's principle.

The making of ammonia is an example of a process in which chemists apply Le Châtelier's principle. Ammonia is an important industrial chemical used to make fertilizers, cleaning agents, dyes, and plastics. The following equation describes the synthesis of ammonia.

$$N_2(g) + 3H_2(g) \rightleftharpoons 2NH_3(g) + \text{Heat}$$

Figure 26 French Chemist Henri-Louis Le Châtelier (1850–1936) published the first version of his principle of chemical equilibrium in 1884.

Suppose you have a system that contains nitrogen, hydrogen, and ammonia in equilibrium. By applying Le Châtelier's principle, you can predict how this system will be affected by changes in temperature, pressure, and concentration. In the ammonia plant shown in Figure 27, chemists must consider these same factors.

Temperature In the equation for the synthesis of ammonia, heat is written as a product. This tells you that the forward reaction is exothermic. In the reverse reaction, heat is a reactant. So the decomposition of ammonia is endothermic.

What would happen if you increased the temperature of a system that contained nitrogen, hydrogen, and ammonia? According to Le Châtelier's principle, if you added heat to the system, the equilibrium would shift in the direction that removes heat from the system. The system would favor the reverse reaction, which is endothermic. So by increasing the temperature, you would decrease the amount of ammonia.

Pressure Suppose you increased the pressure of the system. According to Le Châtelier's principle, if you increased the pressure, the equilibrium would shift in the direction that decreases the pressure of the system. In order to decrease pressure, the system would favor the reaction that produces fewer gas molecules. You can see that the left side of the equation has four gas molecules, while the right side has two. So by increasing the pressure, you would shift the equilibrium to the right, producing more ammonia.

Concentration A change in concentration of the reactants or products can also affect equilibrium. Suppose you removed ammonia from the nitrogen-hydrogen-ammonia system. Le Châtelier's principle tells you that the equilibrium would shift in the direction that produces ammonia. In order to produce ammonia, the system would favor the forward reaction.

Figure 27 Operating an ammonia plant at relatively low temperature, high pressure, and low ammonia concentration maximizes the amount of ammonia produced.

Section 7.5 Assessment

Reviewing Concepts

1. What happens when a physical change does not go to completion? What happens when a reaction does not go to completion?
2. Once a chemical reaction has reached equilibrium, how does the system respond to change?
3. What does the double-ended arrow indicate in the following chemical equation?

$$CaCO_3 \rightleftharpoons Ca^{2+} + CO_3^{2-}$$

4. For which of the following reactions are both reactants and products likely to be found when the reaction appears to be complete? Explain.

$$Mg + O_2 \longrightarrow 2MgO$$

$$HF + H_2O \rightleftharpoons H_3O^+ + F^-$$

Critical Thinking

5. **Inferring** Suppose the following reaction is allowed to come to equilibrium.

$$2NO_2(g) \rightleftharpoons N_2O_4(g)$$

How will increasing the pressure on this system affect the amount of N_2O_4 formed?

6. **Using Models** At 0°C, liquid water is in equilibrium with ice. Make a drawing of water molecules at this temperature, and describe what is happening.

Connecting Concepts

Phase Changes Write an equation for a system in which the sublimation and deposition of water have reached equilibrium. Use what you studied in Section 3.3 to explain what changes are happening.

Integrate Industry L2

The industrial synthesis of ammonia is called the Haber process and applies Le Châtelier's principle to maximize the efficiency of the production of ammonia according to the equation given in the text. Increasing the temperature increases the reaction rate, but shifts the equilibrium to the left. In order to shift the equilibrium back to the right, high pressure is applied. Ask, **What factors are used to shift equilibrium in the industrial synthesis of ammonia?** *(Temperature and pressure are used to shift equilibrium.)* **Logical**

3 ASSESS

Evaluate Understanding L2

Have students work in groups to perform a brief play that models a system in chemical or physical equilibrium.

Reteach L1

Compare the symbols used to show the movement of the water molecules with the double-arrow symbol used in a chemical equation that represents a reversible reaction. Ask students to discuss how these symbols are appropriate for describing equilibrium.

Connecting Concepts

$$H_2O(s) \rightleftharpoons H_2O(g)$$

In the forward change, ice is sublimating (changing into vapor). In the reverse change, water vapor is depositing (changing into ice). Because the system is in equilibrium, these opposite physical changes are taking place at the same rate.

Interactive Textbook If your class subscribes to the Interactive Textbook, use it to review key concepts in Section 7.5.

Section 7.5 Assessment

1. A physical equilibrium is reached between the forward and reverse changes. A chemical equilibrium is reached between the forward and reverse reactions.
2. The system shifts in the direction that relieves the change.
3. The reaction is reversible, meaning that both the forward and reverse reactions are taking place at the same time.
4. The second reaction. The double-ended arrow indicates a reaction that reaches equilibrium. This means that both reactants and products are present when the reaction appears to be complete.
5. Increasing the pressure of the system will cause the equilibrium to shift to the right, so as to decrease the total number of gas molecules. As a result, the amount of N_2O_4 in the system will increase.
6. In their drawings, students should differentiate between solid and liquid phases of the system. They could do this by using different colors, or by showing an orderly arrangement for solid water and a disorderly arrangement for liquid water. Students can model the phase changes by drawing arrows (as in Figure 25 on p. 217). Because the system is in equilibrium, half of the arrows should show melting and the other half should show freezing.

Design Your Own Lab

Manipulating Chemical Equilibrium **L2**

Objective
After completing this activity, students will be able to

- correctly predict the effect of changes in the concentrations of reactants or products on chemical equilibrium.

Skills Focus Formulating Hypotheses, Designing Experiments, Observing

Prep Time 30 minutes

Advance Prep To prepare 1 L of iodine-starch solution, combine 100 mL of commercial tincture of iodine (2% USP; do not use products labeled decolorized iodine, tincture of iodides, or 7% iodine solution) with 900 mL white vinegar or 1 M acetic acid and 2.5 mL of liquid laundry starch. Do not use spray starch or products labeled concentrated starch. If liquid starch is not available, prepare a stock starch solution by stirring 5 g of cornstarch into 30 mL of cold water to form a smooth suspension. Slowly pour this suspension into 500 mL of boiling water while stirring. Allow the starch solution to cool.

To prepare the ascorbic acid solution, dissolve 7.5 g of ascorbic acid in 1 L of water. To prepare 1 L of bleach solution, combine 250 mL of household chlorine bleach with 750 mL of water.

Class Time 45 minutes

Safety Before performing the lab, review with students the information in the MSDS for each chemical used. Make sure that students wear safety goggles, plastic gloves, and lab aprons.

Expected Outcome Addition of bleach or ascorbic acid shifts the position of equilibrium.

Design Your Own Lab

Manipulating Chemical Equilibrium

Chemical reactions tend to go to equilibrium. It is possible to shift the equilibrium by changing the conditions under which the reaction occurs. Factors that can affect chemical equilibrium include the concentration of reactants and products, temperature, and pressure. In this lab, you will observe a chemical reaction and use your observations to predict how one factor will shift the equilibrium of the reaction. Then, you will perform an experiment to test your prediction.

Problem How can you change the equilibrium of a chemical reaction?

Materials

- iodine-starch solution
- 150-mL beaker
- 4 dropper pipets
- spot plate
- ascorbic acid (vitamin C) solution
- chlorine bleach (sodium hypochlorite, NaOCl) solution

Skills Formulating Hypotheses, Designing Experiments, Observing

Procedure

Part A: Observing a Reversible Reaction

1. Pour 50 mL of iodine-starch solution into the 150-mL beaker. The dark color of this solution is due to the presence of iodine molecules (I_2) within the grains of starch. **CAUTION** *Handle iodine solutions with care. Iodine is toxic.*
2. Use a dropper pipet to transfer 3 drops of iodine-starch solution from the beaker to one well on the spot plate.
3. Use another clean dropper pipet to add one drop of ascorbic acid solution to the iodine-starch solution on the spot plate. Continue to add ascorbic acid solution to the mixture on the spot plate, one drop at a time, until the mixture becomes clear. When an iodine molecule reacts with ascorbic acid, the iodine molecule is reduced and breaks down into two colorless iodide ions ($2I^-$).

Sample Data Table			
Initial Solution	Solution Added	Quantity Added (mL)	Color of Resulting Mixture

4. Use the third clean dropper pipet to transfer one drop of colorless iodide solution to a second well on the spot plate.
5. Use the last clean dropper pipet to add bleach solution to the drop of colorless iodide solution, one drop at a time. Continue until the dark color of the iodine-starch solution reappears. **CAUTION** *Bleach can damage skin and clothing.* The chlorine bleach (NaOCl) oxidizes iodide ions (I^-), converting them to iodine molecules (I_2).
6. Write a chemical equation showing the equilibrium between iodine molecules and iodide ions. This equation does not need to be balanced. Label the two sides of your equation to indicate which substance appears dark and which appears colorless.

Part B: Design Your Experiment

7. **Predicting** Select one of the solutions used earlier that affects the equilibrium between iodine molecules and iodide ions. Record your prediction of the change you will observe in an iodine-starch solution as you add the solution that you selected.
8. **Designing Experiments** Design an experiment to test your prediction. Your experimental plan should describe in detail how you will perform your experiment.
9. Construct a data table like the sample data table shown, in which to record your observations. (*Note:* Your data table may not be exactly like the sample data table.)
10. Perform your experiment only after your teacher has approved your plan. Record your observations in your data table.
CAUTION *Wash your hands with soap or detergent before leaving the laboratory.*

Analyze and Conclude

1. **Analyzing Data** What factor did you investigate? How did it affect the equilibrium between iodine molecules and iodide ions?
2. **Predicting** How would you expect the equilibrium to change if you added more iodide ions to the mixture? Explain your answer.
3. **Calculating** When chlorine bleach (sodium hypochlorite, NaOCl) oxidizes iodide ions to iodine molecules, sodium hypochlorite is reduced to sodium chloride (NaCl) and water (H_2O). Write a balanced chemical equation for this reaction, beginning with the reactants sodium hypochlorite, iodide ions, and hydrogen ions (H^+).
4. **Drawing Conclusions** How does the addition of more product affect the chemical equilibrium of a reaction?

Go Further Design an experiment to determine whether other substances that are easily oxidized or reduced, such as iron ions, can reduce iodine to iodide, or oxidize iodide to iodine. Then, with your teacher's approval and supervision, perform your experiment.

Procedure

6. $I_2 \rightleftharpoons 2I^-$. The I_2 should be labeled "dark," and the $2I^-$ should be labeled "colorless."

Analyze and Conclude

1. Students should observe that increasing the quantity of chlorine bleach shifts the equilibrium toward iodine molecules, and increasing the quantity of ascorbic acid shifts the equilibrium toward iodide ions.
2. Adding iodide ions would shift the equilibrium toward the formation of more iodine.
3. $NaOCl + 2I^- + 2H^+ \longrightarrow I_2 + NaCl + H_2O$
4. Adding more product shifts the equilibrium toward the reactants in a reaction.
Logical, Kinesthetic

Go Further

Evaluate students' plans for clarity and safety before permitting students to proceed with their experiments. Results will depend on the substance chosen. The Fe^{3+} ion can oxidize iodine to iodide.
Logical, Kinesthetic

Study Guide

Study Tip

Make a List
Suggest that students write out a detailed list of everything they need to know for the test a day or two before they take the test. Creating the list is a thorough review in itself. Also, they can use the list to review for the test wherever they are—on their way to and from school, between classes, or during lunch—rather than having to carry around all of their notes and their textbooks.

Thinking Visually

a. Chemical equations
b. Released
c. Endothermic reactions

CHAPTER 7

Study Guide

7.1 Describing Reactions

Key Concepts

- The law of conservation of mass states that mass is neither created nor destroyed.
- In order to show that mass is conserved during a reaction, a chemical equation must be balanced.
- Because chemical reactions often involve large numbers of small particles, chemists use a unit called the mole to measure amounts of a substance.
- In chemical reactions, the mass of a reactant or product can be calculated by using a balanced chemical equation and molar masses.

Vocabulary

reactants, *p. 192;* products, *p. 192;* chemical equation, *p. 193;* coefficients, *p. 194;* mole, *p. 195;* molar mass, *p. 196*

7.2 Types of Reactions

Key Concepts

- The general types of chemical reactions are synthesis reactions, decomposition reactions, single-replacement reactions, double-replacement reactions, and combustion reactions.
- Scientists classify certain chemical reactions as transfers of electrons between atoms.

Vocabulary

synthesis reaction, *p. 200;* decomposition reaction, *p. 200;* single-replacement reaction, *p. 202;* double-replacement reaction, *p. 203;* combustion reaction, *p. 204;* oxidation-reduction reaction, *p. 204*

7.3 Energy Changes in Reactions

Key Concepts

- Chemical reactions involve the breaking of chemical bonds in the reactants and the formation of chemical bonds in the products.
- During a chemical reaction, energy is either released or absorbed.

Vocabulary

chemical energy, *p. 206;* exothermic reaction, *p. 208;* endothermic reaction, *p. 209*

7.4 Reaction Rates

Key Concepts

- Reaction rates tell you how fast a reaction is going.
- Factors that affect reaction rates include temperature, surface area, concentration, stirring, and catalysts.

Vocabulary

reaction rate, *p. 212;* catalyst, *p. 215*

7.5 Equilibrium

Key Concepts

- When a physical change does not go to completion, a physical equilibrium is established between the forward and reverse changes. When a chemical reaction does not go to completion, a chemical equilibrium is established between the forward and reverse reactions.
- When a change is introduced to a system in equilibrium, the equilibrium shifts in the direction that relieves the change.

Vocabulary

equilibrium, *p. 216;* reversible reaction, *p. 217*

Thinking Visually

Concept Map Use information from the chapter to complete the concept map below.

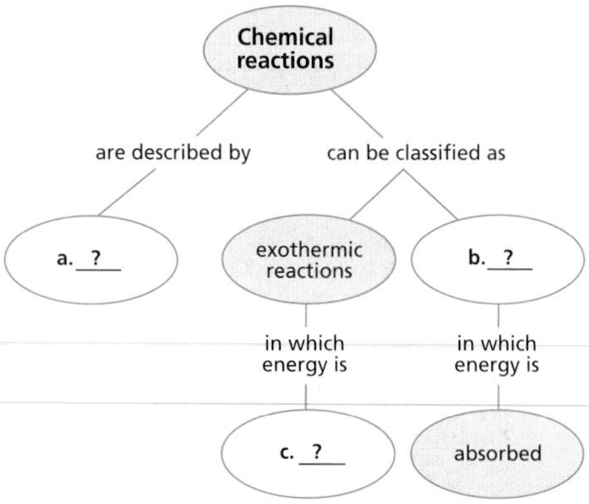

Chemical reactions
are described by
can be classified as
a. ?
exothermic reactions
b. ?
in which energy is
in which energy is
c. ?
absorbed

Chapter Resources

Print

- ***Chapter and Unit Tests,*** Chapter 7 Test A and Test B
- ***Test Prep Resources,*** Chapter 7

Technology

- ***Computer Test Bank,*** Chapter Test 7
- ***Interactive Textbook,*** Chapter 7
- ***Go Online,*** PHSchool.com, Chapter 7

CHAPTER 7

Assessment

Interactive Textbook with assessment at PHSchool.com

Reviewing Content

Choose the letter that best answers the question or completes the statement.

1. In the following equation, what are the reactants?
   $NaHCO_3 + HCl \longrightarrow NaCl + H_2O + CO_2$
   a. $NaHCO_3$ and HCl **b.** $NaHCO_3$ and NaCl
   c. HCl and NaCl **d.** NaCl, H_2O, and CO_2
2. Which of the following is a statement of the law of conservation of mass?
   a. Mass is created but not destroyed.
   b. Mass is destroyed but not created.
   c. Mass is neither created nor destroyed.
   d. Mass is both created and destroyed, depending on the chemical reaction.
3. The mass of a hydrogen atom is 1.0 amu, and the mass of a carbon atom is 12.0 amu. What is the molar mass of methane, CH_4?
   a. 13.0 amu **b.** 13.0 g
   c. 16.0 amu **d.** 16.0 g
4. In what type of reaction does one reactant form two or more products?
   a. synthesis **b.** decomposition
   c. single replacement **d.** double replacement
5. What particle is transferred from one atom to another in a redox reaction?
   a. electron **b.** neutron
   c. proton **d.** nucleus
6. Which of the following is a single replacement?
   a. $KOH + HCl \longrightarrow KCl + H_2O$
   b. $2Na + 2H_2O \longrightarrow H_2 + 2NaOH$
   c. $2C_2H_6 + 7O_2 \longrightarrow 4CO_2 + 6H_2O$
   d. $H_2O + CO_2 \longrightarrow H_2CO_3$
7. How are reactions related to chemical bonds?
   a. Bonds in the reactants are broken, and bonds in the products are formed.
   b. Bonds in the products are broken, and bonds in the reactants are formed.
   c. Bonds in both the reactants and products are broken.
   d. Bonds are formed in both the reactants and the products.
8. What type of reaction always releases energy?
   a. endothemic **b.** exothermic
   c. decomposition **d.** oxidation-reduction
9. In general, an increase in temperature
   a. increases reaction rate.
   b. decreases reaction rate.
   c. does not affect reaction rate.
   d. acts as a catalyst.
10. What takes place at chemical equilibrium?
   a. Reactants form more quickly than products.
   b. Products form more quickly than reactants.
   c. Reactants and products stop forming.
   d. Reactants and products form at the same rate.

Understanding Concepts

11. Write the following chemical equation in words.
   $CaCO_3 + \text{Heat} \longrightarrow CaO + CO_2$
12. Explain how a balanced chemical equation shows that mass is conserved.
13. Explain the following diagram in your own words.

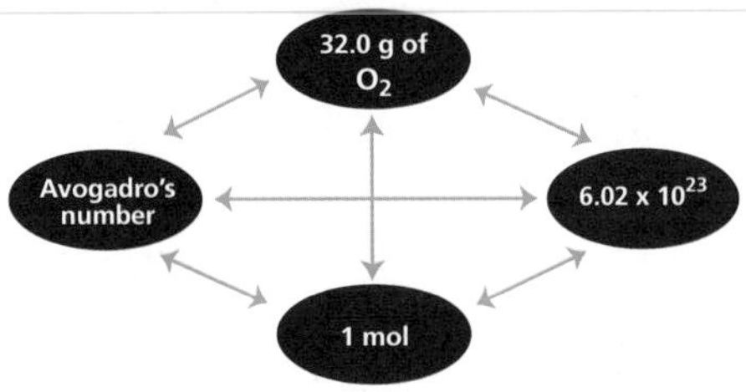

32.0 g of O2
Avogadro's number
6.02 x 10^23
1 mol

14. Compare oxidation and reduction.
15. Paper burns by combining with oxygen. Why doesn't paper burn every time it contacts oxygen?
16. Give an example of a chemical reaction that occurs slowly. Give another example of a chemical reaction that occurs quickly.

Answer Questions 17–18 based on the equation below.

$$C(s) + H_2O(g) + \text{Heat} \rightleftharpoons CO(g) + H_2(g)$$

17. How would you adjust the temperature to increase the amount of product?
18. Does the removal of hydrogen gas as it is produced shift the reaction to the left or the right?

Homework Guide

Section	Questions
7.1	1–3, 11–13, 19–20, 28–30
7.2	4–6, 14–16, 21–22
7.3	7–8, 23–24, 32
7.4	9, 17, 25–26, 31
7.5	10, 18, 27, 33

Assessment

Interactive Textbook If your class subscribes to the Interactive Textbook, your students can go online to access an interactive version of the Student Edition and a self-test.

Reviewing Content

1. a	**2.** c	**3.** d
4. b	**5.** a	**6.** b
7. a	**8.** b	**9.** a
10. d		

Understanding Concepts

11. Answers may vary. Sample answer: Calcium carbonate reacts under heat to produce calcium oxide and carbon dioxide.
12. A balanced chemical equation has the same number of atoms of each element on both sides, thus showing that mass is neither created nor destroyed.
13. Answers may vary. Sample answer: Avogadro's number equals 6.02×10^{23}, which is the number of particles contained in one mole, which is how many O_2 molecules are in 32.0 g of O_2. Any of the items in the concept web can be expressed in terms of one of the others.
14. In an oxidation reaction, an atom loses (or partially loses) electrons. In a reduction reaction, an atom gains (or partially gains) electrons.
15. In order for a reaction to occur, energy is required to break the chemical bonds of the reactants. At room temperature, there is not enough energy from the surroundings for paper to burst into flames, even though there is enough oxygen present in the air for it to react.
16. Answers will vary. Examples of slow reactions: formation of rust; tarnishing of silver; decomposition of wood or compost. Examples of fast reactions: burning of gasoline; browning of a cut apple; bleaching of clothing.
17. Increasing the temperature would shift the equilibrium to the right and increase the amount of product.
18. Removal of hydrogen would shift the equilibrium to the right.

Critical Thinking

19. When iron rusts, a color change is one indication that a chemical reaction has taken place. The product that forms (rust) has different properties than the reactants (iron, water, and oxygen).
20. The substances in the candle combine with oxygen to form gaseous products. The total mass of the reactants equals the total mass of the products.
21. A reaction that has two reactants and two products could be a single-replacement reaction, a double-replacement reaction, or a combustion reaction.
22. The burning of magnesium in oxygen could be classified as combustion, synthesis, or oxidation-reduction.
23. In order for chemical bonds to break, energy must be absorbed, so the process is endothermic.
24. In an endothermic reaction, the chemical energy of the reactants plus energy absorbed from the surroundings is converted into the chemical energy of the products. The total energy before and after the reaction is the same.
25. The surface area of B is greater than the surface area of A.
26. An increase in a reactant's surface area increases its exposure to other reactants. If A and B represent the same volume of a reactant, then the reacting particles in B have more opportunities for collisions that may result in reactions. The more collisions between reactants, the faster the reaction rate will be.
27. Both stirring and increasing reactant concentration increase the reaction rate. If you stopped stirring, it would slow down the reaction rate. Because two factors oppose each other (increasing concentration of a reactant and decreasing the stirring of reactants), the overall effect would depend on which factor produced a greater change in the reaction rate.

Math Skills

28. **a.** $2KI \longrightarrow 2K + I_2$
b. $2Na + 2H_2O \longrightarrow H_2 + 2NaOH$
c. $CH_4 + 2O_2 \longrightarrow CO_2 + 2H_2O$
29. 298 g
30. 0.459 mol

CHAPTER 7

Assessment *(continued)*

Critical Thinking

19. **Observing** Explain how you know that a chemical reaction takes place when iron rusts.

20. **Inferring** As a candle burns, its mass decreases. However, mass is conserved in this reaction. Explain this observation.

21. **Making Generalizations** In a certain chemical reaction, two reactants undergo change to form two products. Why can't you determine what type of reaction occurred from this information?

22. **Applying Concepts** Use the reaction that occurs when magnesium burns in oxygen to show how a reaction might be included in more than one category of reaction.

23. **Classifying** Is breaking bonds an endothermic process or an exothermic process? Explain.

24. **Inferring** Explain how energy is conserved in an endothermic reaction.

Use the diagram below to answer Questions 25–26.

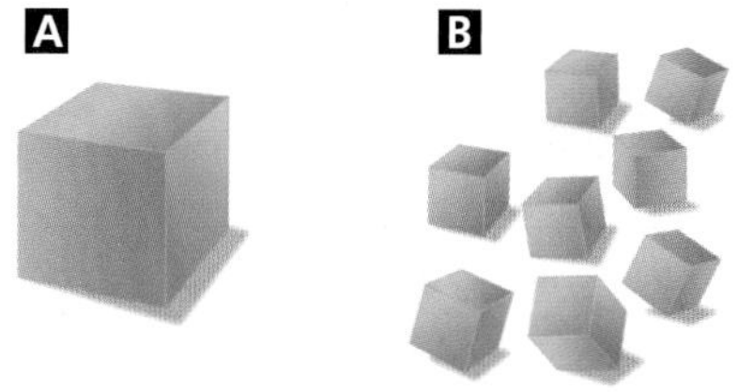
A
B

25. **Comparing and Contrasting** The volume of the cube in A equals the total volume of the cubes in B. Compare the surface areas of the cubes in A and B.

26. **Using Models** Use the diagram to explain how surface area affects reaction rates.

27. **Predicting** You are performing an experiment and want to increase the rate of reaction. You stop stirring the reactants and, instead, increase the concentration of one reactant. Can you expect the reaction to proceed at a faster rate? Explain.

Math Skills

28. **Applying Concepts** Balance each of the following chemical equations.
    a. $KI \longrightarrow K + I_2$
    b. $Na + H_2O \longrightarrow H_2 + NaOH$
    c. $CH_4 + O_2 \longrightarrow CO_2 + H_2O$

29. **Calculating** What mass of KBr is contained in 2.50 moles of the compound?

30. **Calculating** How many moles of Na_2CrO_4 are contained in 74.3 grams of the compound?

Concepts in Action

31. **Inferring** Kept at room temperature, batteries will eventually lose their charge. Why will keeping batteries in the freezer make them last longer?

32. **Drawing Conclusions** Octane, C_8H_{18}, is one of the compounds present in gasoline. The products of the burning of octane are water and carbon dioxide. In this reaction, which contain more energy, the bonds in the reactants or the bonds in the products? Explain.

33. **Writing in Science** Write a paragraph describing a chemical reaction that you have observed recently.

Performance-Based Assessment

Designing an Experiment Choose a chemical reaction that reaches equilibrium and includes at least one gas. Design an experiment that will show the effects of concentration, temperature, and pressure on the system. You will not actually perform the experiment, so you are not limited by the equipment available in your laboratory. Prepare a lab report that includes a hypothesis, all steps of the procedure, and any expected results.

Go Online
PHSchool.com
For: Self-grading assessment
Visit: PHSchool.com
Web Code: cca-1070

Concepts in Action

31. Lowering the temperature decreases the rate of reaction of the materials in the battery.
32. The burning of octane is exothermic—it releases energy. In an exothermic reaction, the chemical energy of the reactants equals the amount of energy released plus the chemical energy of the products. Therefore, the bonds in the reactants (octane and oxygen) contain more energy than the bonds in the products (water and carbon dioxide).
33. Students' answers may include word equations of common reactions, observations that can be interpreted as evidence of chemical change, or an inferred classification of the reaction.

224 Chapter 7

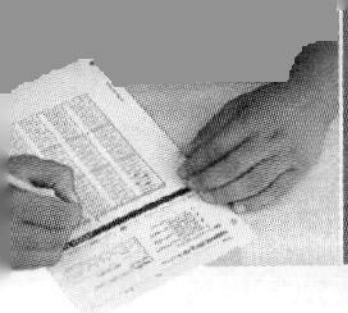

Standardized Test Prep

Test-Taking Tip

Calculating
When balancing chemical equations, follow these tips:

- Never change the subscript in any formula. Change only the coefficients.
- First, balance the atom that is most obviously unbalanced by placing a coefficient in front of the appropriate formula.
- Next, balance other atoms by placing coefficients in front of appropriate formulas.
- Finally, balance any atom that appears by itself in a formula (such as O_2, H_2, or Ca).
- Count the number of atoms of each element on both sides of the equation. If they are not equal, continue balancing.

Practice using these tips in Questions 1 and 3.

Choose the letter that best answers the question or completes the statement.

1. Balance this chemical equation.

$MgO + H_3PO_4 \longrightarrow Mg_3(PO_4)_2 + H_2O$
(A) $3MgO + 2H_3PO_4 \longrightarrow Mg_3(PO_4)_2 + 3H_2O$
(B) $3MgO + 2H_3PO_4 \longrightarrow Mg_3(PO_4)_2 + 2H_2O$
(C) $6MgO + 2H_3PO_4 \longrightarrow Mg_3(PO_4)_2 + 3H_2O$
(D) $6MgO + 2H_3PO_4 \longrightarrow 2Mg_3(PO_4)_2 + 6H_2O$
(E) $6MgO + 4H_3PO_4 \longrightarrow 2Mg_3(PO_4)_2 + 3H_2O$

Questions 2 and 3 refer to the following reaction.

$C_4H_{10} + O_2 \longrightarrow CO_2 + H_2O$

2. What type of reaction is described by this equation?
(A) synthesis
(B) decomposition
(C) combustion
(D) double replacement
(E) single replacement

3. Balance the equation for the reaction between butane (C_4H_{10}) and oxygen, and then determine how many grams of CO_2 are formed when 5.00 grams of C_4H_{10} react.
(A) 1.65 grams
(B) 3.79 grams
(C) 15.1 grams
(D) 20.0 grams
(E) 26.4 grams

4. Which equation describes a synthesis?
(A) $Ba(OH)_2 + 2HCl \longrightarrow BaCl_2 + 2H_2O$
(B) $CH_4 + 2O_2 \longrightarrow CO_2 + 2H_2O$
(C) $Zn + CuSO_4 \longrightarrow Cu + ZnSO_4$
(D) $2H_2 + O_2 \longrightarrow 2H_2O$
(E) $CaCO_3 \longrightarrow CaO + CO_2$

Use the energy diagram to answer Question 5.

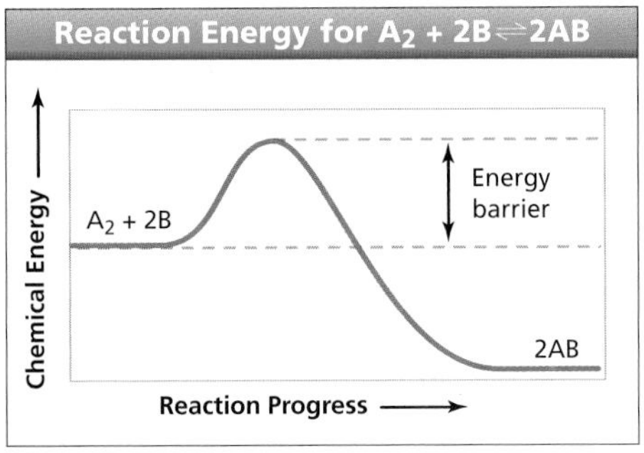

Reaction Energy for A2 + 2B ⇌ 2AB
Chemical Energy
A2 + 2B
Energy barrier
2AB
Reaction Progress

5. What effect would a catalyst have on the reaction $A_2 + 2B \rightleftharpoons 2AB$?
(A) It gives the products more energy.
(B) It makes the reaction endothermic.
(C) It gives the reacting particles more energy.
(D) It provides a new reaction pathway for the reactants.
(E) none of the above

6. The following equation shows the formation of ammonia (NH_3) from nitrogen (N_2) and hydrogen (H_2). This reaction is in equilibrium.

$N_2(g) + 3H_2(g) \rightleftharpoons 2NH_3(g) + \text{Heat}$

If the pressure of the system is decreased, the equilibrium will shift
(A) to the right because there are fewer moles of gas on the product side of the equation.
(B) to the left because there are more moles of gas on the reactant side of the equation.
(C) to the right because a drop in pressure brings the reactants together so they can react.
(D) to the left because a drop in pressure pulls the product molecules apart.
(E) in neither direction because pressure does not affect chemical equilibriums.

Standardized Test Prep

1. A 2. C 3. C
4. D 5. D 6. B

Performance-Based Assessment

Answers will vary. One of the reactions chosen might be the decomposition of hydrogen peroxide to form water and oxygen. For this reaction, increasing the pressure would shift the equilibrium to the left (in the direction of synthesis); increasing the temperature would shift the equilibrium to the right (in the direction of decomposition) as the reaction is endothermic; and removing oxygen from the system would decrease the concentration of products and shift the equilibrium to the right (in the direction of decomposition).

Go Online
PHSchool.com

Your students can independently test their knowledge of the chapter and print out their test results for your files.

CHAPTER 8

Planning Guide

Use these planning tools
Easy Planner
Teacher Express

SECTION OBJECTIVES	STANDARDS NATIONAL (See p. T18.)	STANDARDS STATE	ACTIVITIES and LABS
8.1 Formation of Solutions, pp. 228–234 1 block or 2 periods **8.1.1 Describe** how a substance can dissolve in water by dissociation, dispersion, or ionization. **8.1.2 Describe** how the physical properties of a solution can differ from those of its solute and solvent. **8.1.3 Identify** energy changes that occur during the formation of a solution. **8.1.4 Describe** factors affecting the rate at which a solute dissolves in a solvent.	A-1, A-2, B-2, B-3, B-6, F-1		**SE** Inquiry Activity: How Do Shaking and Heating Affect a Carbonated Beverage? p. 227 L2 **SE** Quick Lab: Comparing Heats of Solution, p. 232 L2 **TE** Teacher Demo: Freezing Points of Solutions, p. 231 L2
8.2 Solubility and Concentration, pp. 235–239 1 block or 2 periods **8.2.1 Define** solubility and **describe** factors affecting solubility. **8.2.2 Classify** solutions as unsaturated, saturated, or supersaturated. **8.2.3 Calculate** and **compare** and **contrast** solution concentrations expressed as percent by volume, percent by mass, and molarity.	B-2, E-1		**TE** Teacher Demo: Crystallization, p. 236 L2 **TE** Build Science Skills: Measuring, p. 237 L2 **LM** Investigation 8B: Comparing Solubilities and Rates of Dissolving L1
8.3 Properties of Acids and Bases, pp. 240–245 1 block or 2 periods **8.3.1 Define** acid and **describe** some of the general properties of an acid. **8.3.2 Define** base and **describe** some of the general properties of a base. **8.3.3 Identify** a neutralization reaction, and **describe** the reactants and products of neutralization. **8.3.4 Explain** how acids and bases can be defined as proton donors and proton acceptors.	A-1, A-2, B-2, B-3, F-1		**SE** Quick Lab: Using an Indicator, p. 243 L2 **SE** Exploration Lab: Preparing a Salt by Neutralization, pp. 254–255 L2 **TE** Teacher Demo: Neutralization Reaction, p. 244 L2 **LM** Investigation 8A: Comparing Antacids L2
8.4 Strength of Acids and Bases, pp. 246–249 1 block or 2 periods **8.4.1 Define** pH, and **relate** pH to hydronium ion concentration in a solution. **8.4.2 Distinguish** between strong acids and weak acids, and between strong bases and weak bases. **8.4.3 Define** buffer, and **describe** how a buffer can be prepared. **8.4.4 Explain** how electrolytes can be classified.	A-1, A-2, B-2, B-3, C-1, F-1, G-1, G-2, G-3		**SE** Quick Lab: Making a Battery, p. 248 L2

Ability Levels	
L1	For students who need additional help
L2	For all students
L3	For students who need to be challenged

Components

SE Student Edition	**RSW** Reading & Study Workbook	**CUT** Chapter & Unit Tests	**T** Transparencies
TE Teacher's Edition	**MSPS** Math Skills & Problem Solving Workbook	**CTB** Computer Test Bank	**iT** Interactive Textbook
LM Laboratory Manual		**TP** Test Prep Resources	**P** Presentation Pro CD-ROM
PLM Probeware Lab Manual		**DC** Discovery Channel Videotapes & DVDs	**GO** Internet Resources

RESOURCES PRINT and TECHNOLOGY		SECTION ASSESSMENT
RSW Section 8.1	L1	**SE** Section 8.1 Assessment, p. 234
T Chapter 8 Pretest	L2	**iT** Section 8.1
Section 8.1	L2	
P Chapter 8 Pretest	L2	
Section 8.1	L2	
SCILINKS **GO** Solutions	L2	
RSW Section 8.2	L1	**SE** Section 8.2 Assessment, p. 239
MSPS Section 8.2	L2	**iT** Section 8.2
RSW Math Skill	L2	
T Section 8.2	L2	
P Section 8.2	L2	
PLM Lab 3: Preparing a Salt by Neutralization	L2	**SE** Section 8.3 Assessment, p. 245
RSW Section 8.3	L1	**iT** Section 8.3
T Section 8.3	L2	
P Section 8.3	L2	
SCILINKS **GO** Bases	L2	
RSW Section 8.4	L1	**SE** Section 8.4 Assessment, p. 249
Discovery Channel School **DC** Suspended in Blood	L2	**iT** Section 8.4
T Section 8.4	L2	
P Section 8.4	L2	
SCILINKS **GO** pH	L2	

Go Online

Go online for these Internet resources.

PHSchool.com
Web Code: cca-1080

NSTA SCILINKS
Web Code: ccn-1081
Web Code: ccn-1083
Web Code: ccn-1084

Materials for Activities and Labs

Quantities for each group

STUDENT EDITION

Inquiry Activity, p. 227
plastic bottle of carbonated beverage, small balloon, bucket, hot water

Quick Lab, p. 232
2 large test tubes, 10-mL graduated cylinder, distilled water, thermometer, 1 g KCl, 5 mL 95% isopropyl alcohol solution, stirring rod

Quick Lab, p. 243
1/4 cup frozen blueberries, foam cup, spoon, 4 small plastic cups, 2 dropper pipets, lemon juice, white vinegar, window cleaner, baking soda

Quick Lab, p. 248
1 large fresh lemon, plastic knife, zinc strip, 2 copper strips, multimeter

Exploration Lab, pp. 254–255
3 dropper pipets, labels, 10-mL graduated cylinder, test tube rack, 2 10-mL test tubes, distilled water, hydrochloric acid, sodium hydroxide solution, 3 stirring rods, phenolphthalein solution, 2 25-mL beakers, pH paper, large watch glass, 100-mL beaker, hot plate

TEACHER'S EDITION

Teacher Demo, p. 231
2 trays, ice, rock salt, water, 2 small plastic containers (clear), thermometer

Teacher Demo, p. 236
beakers, 200 g sodium acetate trihydrate, distilled water, spatula, hot plate

Build Science Skills, p. 237
2 400-mL beakers, water, ice, hot plate, 2 70-mL test tubes, salt, scoop, 2 stirring rods, thermometer, weigh paper, balance, test tube tongs

Teacher Demo, p. 244
2 lemons, beaker, 0.1-M solution of NaOH, phenolphthalein solution (indicator), syringe, knife

Build Science Skills, p. 251
calcium hydroxide (pickling lime); 2 large, sealable jars; clear plastic cups; straws; stopwatches; jump ropes

Chapter Assessment

CHAPTER ASSESSMENT

SE Chapter Assessment, pp. 257–258
CUT Chapter 8 Test A, B
CTB Chapter 8
iT Chapter 8
PHSchool.com GO
Web Code: cca-1080

STANDARDIZED TEST PREP

SE Chapter 8, p. 259
TP Diagnose and Prescribe

Interactive Textbook

Interactive Textbook with assessment at PHSchool.com

CHAPTER 8

Before you teach

From the Author

David Frank
Ferris State University

Big Ideas

In this chapter, students are reintroduced to the homogeneous mixtures called solutions. Some characteristic properties result when solutions form, such as an increase in the boiling point and a decrease in the melting point of the solvent. Students then learn some of the properties of acids and bases, which have characteristic properties when dissolved in water.

Space and Time Point out to students that the factors that affect the rate of dissolving are similar to the factors that affect the rate of a chemical reaction. In both cases, the rates increase when collisions between particles take place more frequently. Thus, stirring, increased temperature, and increased surface area reduce the amount of time required to form a solution.

Matter and Change Take care to help students distinguish between the concentration of an acid and its strength. The concentration of an acid simply refers to how much is dissolved in water. The strength of an acid is related to the concept of equilibrium developed in the last chapter. A strong acid ionizes almost completely in water. A weak acid, however, reaches an equilibrium in which ionization occurs to only a small extent. A 1-M solution of the strong acid HCl, therefore, has a lower pH than a 1-M solution of CH_3COOH. However, the relatively dilute solution of 1.0×10^{-6} M HCl is still a strong acid, in spite of its relatively high pH, because the HCl still ionizes almost completely in water.

Forces and Motion The concept of polarity is applied in this chapter to the solution process. Due to the charges in both substances, ionic compounds are more likely to dissolve in polar substances than in nonpolar substances.

Energy The formation of a solution may be either endothermic or exothermic. This depends on the relative amount of energy used to break attractions between solute particles and solvent particles and the amount of energy released when new interactions between solute and solvent are formed.

Chemistry Refresher

Colligative Properties of Solutions 8.1

Dissolving a solute in a solvent results in a solution whose boiling point and freezing point are different than those of either the solute or the solvent. Colligative properties, such as freezing point depression and boiling point elevation, are properties of solutions that depend on the number of solute particles dissolved and not on the identity of the solute. Solutions of equal molarity do not necessarily have equal concentrations of solute particles. For example, 1 mole of a dissociating solute, such as NaCl, produces more particles in solution than 1 mole of a nondissociating solute, such as glucose. A third colligative property is osmotic pressure, or the pressure required to prevent the diffusion of pure solvent across a semipermeable membrane that separates a solution from the pure solvent.

Address Misconceptions

Many students do not differentiate between solvent and solute particles when learning about solutions. However, a solution's properties are determined by the different types of particles that constitute it. For a strategy to overcome this misconception, see **Address Misconceptions** on **page 229.**

Solubility 8.2

Solubility can be described as the amount of solute dissolved in a saturated solution. The solubility of one substance in another depends on several factors, including the polarity of the solvent, temperature, and pressure. Solutions can be described as unsaturated, saturated, or supersaturated. When a solute crystallizes out of a supersaturated solution, as shown above, the solution that remains is saturated.

Go Online PD LINKS NSTA
For: Teaching methods for solutions, acids, and bases
Visit: www.SciLinks.org/PDLinks
Web Code: ccn-0899

Describing Acids and Bases 8.3 and 8.4

Address Misconceptions

Some students may think that pure water is a good conductor of electricity. However, the number of ions in pure water is not great enough to carry an electric current. For a strategy to overcome this misconception, see **Address Misconceptions on page 249.**

Acids are compounds that produce hydronium ions (H_3O^+) in water. Bases are compounds that produce hydroxide ions (OH^-) when dissolved in water. Acids can also be classified as proton donors, while bases can be classified as proton acceptors. Both acids and bases are examples of electrolytes, or compounds that form ions when in solution. Students may have trouble grasping the difference between the concentration and strength of an acid or base. The concentration of hydronium ions in solution is described by pH. The degree to which ions form in solution is described by strength. For example, a very dilute strong acid will have few hydronium ions in solution, yet the acid is still classified as strong. Conversely, a very concentrated weak acid may have relatively many hydronium ions in solution, yet the acid is still classified as weak.

The pH Scale 8.4

The pH scale runs from 0 to 14, with 0 being very acidic, 7 being neutral, and 14 being very basic. Note that the pH scale is logarithmic, which means that solutions that differ by 1 pH unit have hydronium ion concentrations that differ by a factor of 10.

pH Values for Common Substances

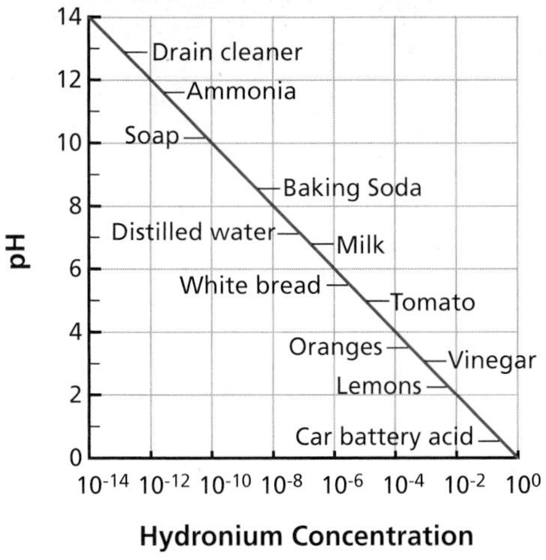
14
12
10
8
6
4
2
0
pH
Drain cleaner
Ammonia
Soap
Baking Soda
Distilled water
Milk
White bread
Tomato
Oranges
Vinegar
Lemons
Car battery acid
10^{-14} 10^{-12} 10^{-10} 10^{-8} 10^{-6} 10^{-4} 10^{-2} 10^{0}
Hydronium Concentration

The relationship between pH and hydronium ion concentration (given in molarity) is described by the following equation:

$$pH = -\log_{10} [H_3O^+]$$

Solutions can also be described by the pOH scale. A solution's pOH can be determined using the following equation:

$$pOH = -\log_{10} [OH^-]$$

The pOH scale is the opposite of pH scale. A very basic solution will have a low pOH, and a very acidic solution will have a high pOH.

Build Reading Literacy

Compare and Contrast

Identify Similarities and Differences

Strategy Help students read and understand material that discusses two or more related topics or concepts. This strategy helps students identify similarities and differences, thus enabling them to link prior knowledge with new information. Before students begin, assign a section in Chapter 8 for them to read, such as Section 8.2, pp. 235–239.

Example

1. Have students compare two or more topics or concepts under a section heading. Tell them that when they compare, they should focus on both similarities and differences. Remind them to look for these signal words:
- **Similarities:** *similar, similarly, also, just as, like, likewise, in the same way*
- **Differences:** *but, however, although, whereas, on the other hand, different, unlike*

2. Have students contrast two or more topics or concepts. Remind students that when they contrast, they should focus only on differences.

3. Have students create a chart or diagram comparing or contrasting two or more topics or concepts they read about in the section. Suggest that they create either a compare/contrast table or a Venn diagram to present their information.

See p. 241 for a script on how to use the compare and contrast strategy with students. For additional Build Reading Literacy strategies, see pp. 229, 236, and 246.

ASSESS PRIOR KNOWLEDGE

Use the Chapter Pretest below to assess students' prior knowledge. As needed, review these Science Concepts and Math Skills with students.

Review Science Concepts

Section 8.1 Go over atomic structure and the difference between ionic and molecular compounds. Review physical properties, including conductivity, freezing point, and boiling point. Be sure that students understand the difference between endothermic and exothermic processes.

Section 8.2 Encourage students to recall what they have learned about polar versus nonpolar substances. Review the concept of concentration and the use of units, such as liters, moles, and grams.

Section 8.3 Review chemical properties including reactivity. Encourage students to review different types of reactions, including double and single replacement reactions. Go over terms such as *proton, valence electron, ion,* and *positive* and *negative charge.*

Section 8.4 Review the definitions of chemical and physical equilibrium. Encourage students to recall how to describe a solution's concentration.

Review Math Skills

Line Graphs Students will need to know how to interpret line graphs in order to complete the Chapter 8 Assessment.

Direct students to the **Math Skills** in the **Skills and Reference Handbook** at the end of the student text.

CHAPTER 8

Solutions, Acids, and Bases

CONCEPTS in Action

How do science concepts apply to your world? Here are some questions you'll be able to answer after you read this chapter.

- How do road workers keep ice from building up on streets and highways? *(Section 8.1)*
- Why don't oil and water mix? *(Section 8.2)*
- What foods contain acids? *(Section 8.3)*
- Why do some people consume sports drinks? *(Section 8.4)*

Discovery Channel School **Video Field Trip**

Suspended in Blood

- How are nutrients delivered to your body's cells? *(page 250)*

When rainwater seeps through limestone ▶ rock in Earth's crust, calcium carbonate in the limestone dissolves in the water. After many years, a cave begins to form.

226 *Chapter 8*

Chapter Pretest

1. Describe the charge and location within an atom of the following subatomic particles: protons, electrons, and neutrons. *(Protons: positive; in the nucleus. Electrons: negative; in the electron cloud surrounding the nucleus. Neutrons: neutral; in the nucleus)*

2. True or False: Both molecular and ionic compounds contain covalent bonds. *(False)*

3. Conductivity, freezing point, and boiling point are all *(c)*

a. related to volume.
b. chemical properties.
c. physical properties.
d. related to mass.

4. Which of the following is always true of a polar covalent bond? *(a)*

a. One atom in the bond has a partial negative charge.
b. One atom in the bond is an ion.
c. Both atoms in the bond are of the same element.
d. Both atoms in the bond have partial positive charges.

5. How many moles are in 32.0 g of O_2 gas, which has a molar mass of 16.0 g? *(2.00 moles)*

6. Describe chemical equilibrium. *(Forward and reverse reactions take place at the same rate.)*

Properties of Liquid Solutions

The physical properties of salt are clearly different from the physical properties of water. But how do the properties of a saltwater solution compare to those of its solute and solvent? **Three physical properties of a solution that can differ from those of its solute and solvent are conductivity, freezing point, and boiling point.**

Conductivity Solid sodium chloride is a poor conductor of electric current. But when sodium chloride dissociates in water, the sodium and chloride ions are able to move freely. The ions in solution will then conduct an electric current. Hydrogen chloride gas is also a poor conductor of electric current. However, when hydrogen chloride ionizes in water, the resulting solution conducts an electric current.

Freezing Point and Boiling Point If you live in a cold climate, you are probably familiar with icy roads like the one in Figure 5. You may have seen snowplows or salt trucks spreading magnesium chloride, $MgCl_2$, or a similar ionic compound on these icy roads. When magnesium chloride dissolves in melting ice and snow, it dissociates into magnesium (Mg^{2+}) ions and chloride (Cl^-) ions. As Figure 6A shows, ice forms when water molecules are able to arrange themselves in a rigid, honeycomb-like structure. In Figure 6B, the presence of magnesium and chloride ions, which are attracted to the water molecules, interferes with the freezing process. The freezing point of water at sea level is 0°C. When icy roads are salted with magnesium chloride, the resulting solution can have a freezing point as low as −15°C.

A solute can also raise the boiling point of the solvent. For example, the coolant used in most car radiators is a solution containing water and ethylene glycol, $C_2H_6O_2$. Water at sea level boils at 100°C. Adding ethylene glycol to water raises the boiling point. The resulting solution helps prevent the engine from overheating. Because ethylene glycol also lowers the freezing point of water, the coolant does not freeze during spells of cold weather.

Figure 5 Salt spread on icy roads lowers the freezing point of water.

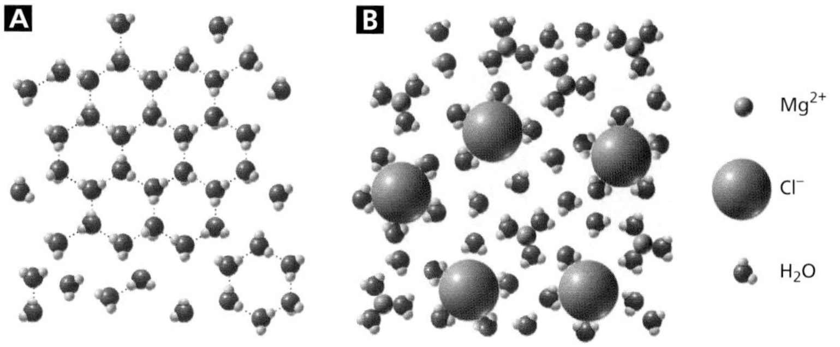
A
B
Mg2+
Cl−
H2O

Figure 6 The presence of solute particles affects how a solvent freezes. **A** Pure water freezes in a hexagonal pattern. **B** In water "salted" with $MgCl_2$, the dissociated Mg^{2+} and Cl^- ions disrupt the formation of ice crystals. **Using Models** ***How do the interactions between Mg^{2+} and H_2O differ from the interactions between Cl^- and H_2O?***

Properties of Liquid Solutions

Teacher Demo

Freezing Points of Solutions **L2**

Purpose Students observe the lower freezing point of a saltwater solution.

Materials 2 trays with sides at least 2 in deep, ice, rock salt, water, 2 small plastic containers (clear), thermometer

Procedure Explain to students that the water in an ice bath will remain at 0°C as long as some of the ice still remains. However, a saltwater solution in an ice bath will remain at an even lower temperature, depending on the concentration of the solution and the original temperature of the solid ice. Fill both trays with ice to a depth of 2 inches. Cover the ice of one of the trays with a generous amount of rock salt. Add water to both trays to a depth of 1 inch. Add one or two inches of water to each plastic container and place one of the containers in each ice water bath. Set the baths aside for the remainder of the class, checking them on occasion to see that they still contain unmelted ice. Add more ice if necessary. Have volunteers periodically check the temperatures of the two ice water baths. Check the contents of the plastic containers at the end of class.

Expected Outcome The water in the container placed in the ice water bath will remain liquid. The water in the container placed in the salt and ice water bath will freeze.
Visual

Facts and Figures

Structure of Ice The unusual structure of ice is due to the formation of hydrogen bonds between molecules and the angle between water's two O–H bonds. Because the formation of hydrogen bonds in place of weaker intermolecular forces releases energy, hydrogen bonding is energetically favorable. Thus, the open structure of ice maximizes the number of hydrogen bonds that can form among water molecules. Adding a solute prevents the water molecules from achieving this low energy structure.

Answer to . . .

Figure 6 *The Mg^{2+} ions are attracted to the oxygen atoms in the water molecules. The Cl^- ions are attracted to the hydrogen atoms in the water molecules.*

Reading Checkpoint *Sugar is a molecular compound that dissolves in water through dispersion.*

Heat of Solution

Quick Lab

Comparing Heats of Solution L2

Objective

After completing this activity, students will be able to
- determine whether a solution process is exothermic or endothermic.

Skills Focus Observing, Measuring, Classifying, Inferring

Prep Time 15 minutes

Class Time 15 minutes

Safety Caution students to use the stirring rod, not the thermometer, to stir the solutions. Do not use mercury thermometers. Have students observe safety symbols and wear safety goggles, plastic gloves, and lab aprons.

Teaching Tips
- Dispose of all waste solutions in the sink with excess water.

Expected Outcome The potassium chloride solution process is endothermic, and the temperature should fall. The alcohol solution process is exothermic, and the temperature should rise.

Analyze and Conclude

1. The temperature of the potassium chloride solution fell. The temperature of the alcohol solution rose.
2. The alcohol solution process is exothermic. The potassium chloride solution process is endothermic.
3. Assuming that the solute dissolved, students should infer that the amount of energy absorbed as the particles separated would be equal (or very similar) to the amount of energy released when the solution formed.

Visual, Logical

Go Online NSTA SciLinks

Download a worksheet on solutions for students to complete, and find additional teacher support from NSTA SciLinks.

Go Online NSTA SciLinks

For: Links on solutions
Visit: www.SciLinks.org
Web Code: ccn-1081

Heat of Solution

When sodium hydroxide, NaOH, dissolves in water, the solution becomes warmer. The solution releases energy to the surroundings. In contrast, when ammonium nitrate, NH_4NO_3, dissolves in water, the solution becomes colder. The solution absorbs energy from the surroundings. **During the formation of a solution, energy is either released or absorbed.**

Like chemical reactions, the solution process can be described as exothermic or endothermic. Dissolving sodium hydroxide in water is exothermic, as it releases heat. Dissolving ammonium nitrate in water is endothermic, as it absorbs heat. The How It Works box on page 233 describes how dissolving ammonium nitrate is used in cold packs.

In order for a solution to form, both the attractions among solute particles and the attractions among solvent particles must be broken. Breaking attractions requires energy. As the solute dissolves, new attractions form between solute and solvent particles. The formation of attractions releases energy. The difference between these energies is known as the heat of solution. For example, dissolving one mole of sodium hydroxide in water releases 44.5 kilojoules of heat. In this exothermic change, energy is released as NaOH and H_2O form new attractions. It is 44.5 kilojoules greater than the energy required to break the attractions among NaOH crystals and among H_2O molecules.

Reading Checkpoint *Does the breaking of attractions among solvent particles release energy or absorb energy?*

Quick Lab

Comparing Heats of Solution

Materials

2 large test tubes, 10-mL graduated cylinder, distilled water, thermometer, 1 g potassium chloride, 5 mL 95% isopropyl alcohol solution, stirring rod

Procedure

1. Add 5 mL of distilled water to each test tube. Measure and record the temperature of the water in each test tube to the nearest 0.2°C.
2. Remove the thermometer. Add the potassium chloride to one of the test tubes. Stir until the potassium chloride dissolves. **CAUTION:** *Use the stirring rod, not the thermometer, to stir the solution.*
3. Measure and record the final temperature of the solution. Rinse the thermometer.
4. Add 5 mL of the alcohol solution to the second test tube. Stir the mixture. Measure and record the final temperature.

Analyze and Conclude

1. **Observing** What happened to the temperature of each solution?
2. **Classifying** Which process was exothermic? Which was endothermic?
3. **Inferring** If there were no change in temperature during the formation of a solution, how would you explain this observation?

![DK] HOW It Works

Cold Packs

Instant hot and cold packs are often used by athletes to treat injuries. Hot packs are also used in cold weather to warm hands and feet. Both types of pack work through the action of chemicals that either release or absorb heat when they dissolve in water. One type of cold pack is shown below. **Inferring** ***How does shaking the pack after squeezing it affect the rate of dissolving?***

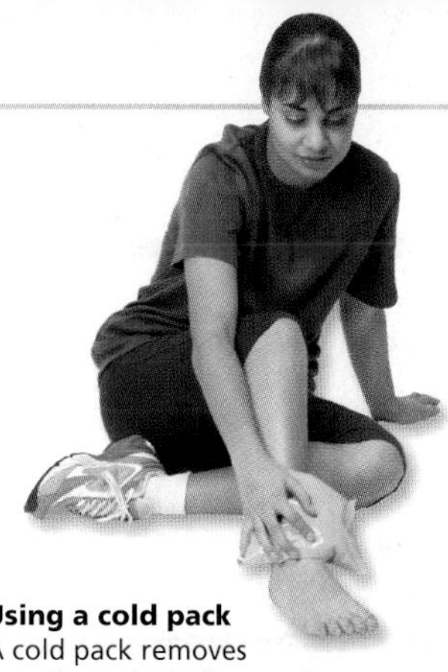

Using a cold pack
A cold pack removes heat from the inflammation around an injury. It also decreases the size of capillaries (small blood vessels) in the injured area, which reduces swelling and bruising.

A **Inside the pack** A cold pack consists of two sealed bags, one inside the other. The strong outer bag contains solid ammonium nitrate powder. The thin-walled inner bag contains water.

B **Squeezing the pack** When the pack is squeezed, the inner bag containing the water bursts. The water rushes into the outer bag where it dissolves the ammonium nitrate.

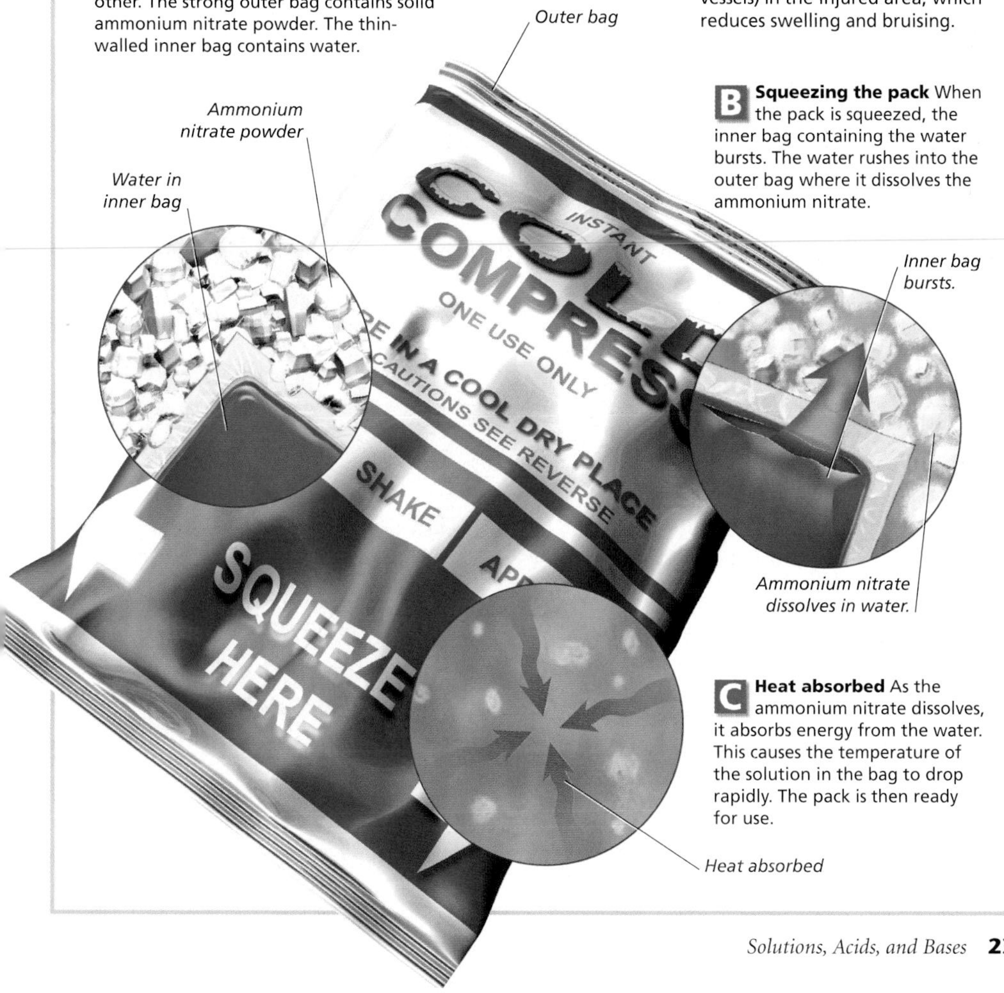
Outer bag
Ammonium nitrate powder
Water in inner bag
Inner bag bursts.
Ammonium nitrate dissolves in water.
Heat absorbed
INSTANT
COLD
COMPRESS
ONE USE ONLY
STORE IN A COOL DRY PLACE
CAUTIONS SEE REVERSE
SHAKE
SQUEEZE HERE

C **Heat absorbed** As the ammonium nitrate dissolves, it absorbs energy from the water. This causes the temperature of the solution in the bag to drop rapidly. The pack is then ready for use.

Facts and Figures

Instant Hot Packs Many hot packs use a mechanism similar to that of cold packs in order to produce the opposite effect. Hot packs can use calcium chloride, $CaCl_2$, or magnesium sulfate, $MgSO_4$, which have negative heats of solution. Both substances have other home uses. Calcium chloride is used to keep pickles crisp and magnesium sulfate is used as bath salts.

Another type of hot pack uses a supersaturated solution of sodium acetate, $NaC_2H_3O_2$. Clicking a disk in the pack causes the solute to crystallize, which is an exothermic process. These hot packs are reusable because placing the pack in boiling water causes the solute crystals to go back into solution.

Build Science Skills L2

Inferring Have students examine the description of what happens when NaOH dissolves in water. Tell them that the solute-solute attractions that are broken when NaOH dissociates are the ionic bonds between Na^+ and OH^- ions. Ask, **What solute-solute attractions are broken when molecular compounds dissolve through dispersion?** *(The intermolecular attractions between the solute molecules)*
Logical

![DK] HOW It Works

Cold Packs L2

The heat of solution for ammonium nitrate, NH_4NO_3, is 25.7 kJ/mol. This means that 25.7 kJ are absorbed when one mole, or about 80 g, of ammonium nitrate is dissolved in water. The amount of cooling that occurs depends on the amount of solid ammonium nitrate present in the cold pack.

Interpreting Diagrams Like stirring a mixture, shaking the bag moves more dissolved ions away from the surface of the solid ammonium nitrate and allows for more collisions between solute and solvent particles.
Visual

For Enrichment L3

Interested students can design a method for testing the effectiveness of different brands of hot or cold packs. They might compare how hot or cold each brand makes a sample of water. Alternatively, they might determine how long a desired temperature range is maintained by each brand.
Kinesthetic

Answer to . . .

Reading Checkpoint *Breaking attractions among solvent particles absorbs energy.*

Section 8.1 (continued)

Factors Affecting Rates of Dissolving

Address Misconceptions **L2**

The text states that increasing temperature speeds up the rate of dissolving. There are some exceptions to this rule. In the next section, students will read about the relationship between temperature and the solubility of gases. Gases (and some solids) are more soluble as the temperature of the solution decreases. Have students speculate as to how increasing the temperature of a solution affects the solubility of a gas. **Logical**

3 ASSESS

Evaluate Understanding **L2**

Have students draw illustrations that represent the terms *solvent, solute, dissociation, dispersion,* and *ionization* on index cards. Then, have students shuffle the cards and exchange them with a partner. The partner then tries to identify what each illustration represents.

Reteach **L1**

Use Figures 3, 4, and 6 to summarize key concepts about solutions, including dissociation, dispersion, and freezing point depression.

Connecting Concepts

Factors that affect chemical reaction rates include temperature, surface area, concentration, stirring, and catalysts. Rates of dissolving are affected by temperature, surface area, and stirring.

Interactive Textbook If your class subscribes to the Interactive Textbook, use it to review key concepts in Section 8.1.

Answer to . . .

Figure 7 *Increasing the temperature setting causes the detergent to dissolve at a faster rate.*

Crushed solid
Stirring
Heat

Figure 7 The rate of dissolving can be increased by reducing the particle size of the solute, by stirring, and by heating the solvent. ***Predicting*** ***How does changing the temperature setting on a washing machine affect how fast the detergent will dissolve?***

Factors Affecting Rates of Dissolving

You already know that sugar dissolves in water. But what do you know about the rate at which it dissolves? Like rates of chemical reactions, rates of dissolving depend on the frequency and energy of collisions that occur between very small particles. During a chemical reaction, collisions occur between particles of the reactants. During the formation of a solution, collisions occur between particles of the solute and solvent. **Factors that affect the rate of dissolving include surface area, stirring, and temperature.**

When a sugar cube dissolves in water, the dissolving takes place at the surfaces of the cube. The greater the surface area of a solid solute, the more frequent the collisions are between solute and solvent particles. More collisions result in a faster rate of dissolving. You can increase the surface area of a solid by dividing it into smaller particles. The more finely divided a solid solute, the faster it dissolves. For example, one gram of granulated sugar dissolves faster in water than a 1-gram sugar cube.

You can also make sugar dissolve faster by stirring the mixture. Stirring moves dissolved particles away from the surface of the solid, and allows for more collisions between solute and solvent particles.

Another way to speed up the rate of dissolving is to increase the temperature of the solvent. For example, sugar dissolves faster in warm water than it does in cold water. Increasing the temperature of a solvent causes its particles to move faster, on average. As a result, both the number of collisions and the energy of these collisions with solute particles increase. The solute goes into solution more quickly.

Section 8.1 Assessment

Reviewing Concepts

1. What are three ways that substances can dissolve in water?
2. What physical properties of a solution differ from those of its solutes and solvent?
3. How does the formation of a solution involve energy?
4. What factors affect dissolving rates?

Critical Thinking

5. **Comparing and Contrasting** Compare the processes by which sugar crystals and hydrogen chloride gas dissolve in water.
6. **Predicting** Suppose you put equal amounts of pure water and salt water into separate ice cube trays of the same size and shape. When you put both trays in the freezer, what would you expect to happen?

Connecting Concepts

Reaction Rates In Section 7.3, factors affecting chemical reaction rates are discussed. Find out which of these factors also affect rates of dissolving.

Section 8.1 Assessment

1. Dispersion, dissociation, and ionization
2. Conductivity, boiling point, and melting point
3. Breaking the attractions among solute particles and the attractions among solvent particles absorbs energy. Energy is released as new attractions form between solute and solvent particles.
4. Rates of dissolving are affected by temperature, surface area, and stirring.
5. Sugar crystals dissolve by dispersion, which means that the sugar molecules break away from the surface of the crystals as water molecules surround them. Hydrogen chloride gas dissolves in water by ionization, which means that a hydrogen proton is transferred from the hydrogen chloride molecule to a water molecule, forming a hydronium ion and a chloride ion.
6. The pure water would freeze before the saltwater because the salt would lower the freezing point of the water.

8.2 Solubility and Concentration

Reading Focus

Key Concepts

- How are solutions with different amounts of solute described?
- What factors determine the solubility of a solute?
- What are three ways to measure the concentration of a solution?

Vocabulary

- solubility
- saturated solution
- unsaturated solution
- supersaturated solution
- concentration
- molarity

Reading Strategy

Previewing Copy the table below. Before you read the section, rewrite the green topic headings as *how, why,* and *what* questions. As you read, write an answer to each question.

Question	Answer
What is solubility?	a. ___?___
b. ___?___	Solvent, temperature, and pressure
c. ___?___	d. ___?___

Have you ever prepared a pitcher of lemonade or iced tea? Fresh lemonade is a solution of water, lemon juice, and sugar. Water is the solvent. Lemon juice and sugar are the solutes.

You might be surprised at how much sugar can dissolve in water. However, there is a limit to the amount of sugar that can dissolve in a given amount of water. Once that limit is reached, no more sugar will dissolve, and you cannot make the solution taste any sweeter.

Solubility

The maximum amount of a solute that dissolves in a given amount of solvent at a constant temperature is called **solubility.** Solubilities are usually expressed in grams of solute per 100 grams of solvent at a specified temperature. Figure 8 lists the solubilities of some common substances in water at 20°C. Notice that table sugar is more soluble in water than table salt, which is more soluble than baking soda.

Knowing the solubility of a substance can help you classify solutions based on how much solute they contain. **Solutions are described as saturated, unsaturated, or supersaturated, depending on the amount of solute in solution.**

Solubility in 100 g of Water at 20°C

Compound	Solubility (g)
Table salt (NaCl)	36.0
Baking soda ($NaHCO_3$)	9.6
Table sugar ($C_{12}H_{22}O_{11}$)	203.9

Figure 8 At a given temperature, different solutes have different solubilities in water. **Calculating** *At 20°C, how much baking soda can dissolve in 200 grams of water?*

Section 8.2

1 FOCUS

Objectives

8.2.1 **Define** solubility and **describe** factors affecting solubility.

8.2.2 **Classify** solutions as unsaturated, saturated, or supersaturated.

8.2.3 **Calculate** and **compare** and **contrast** solution concentrations expressed as percent by volume, percent by mass, and molarity.

Reading Focus

Build Vocabulary L2

Word-Part Analysis Ask students what words they know that have the prefix *super-*. *(Superhero, supersonic, supervise)* Give a definition of the word part. (*Super-* means "above.") Have students predict the meaning of *supersaturated,* given that *saturated* means "unable to hold more." (*Supersaturated* means "holding an amount over the normal level.")

Reading Strategy L2

a. The maximum amount of solute that dissolves in a given amount of solvent at a given temperature
b. What factors affect solubility?
c. How is the concentration of a solution expressed?
d. Percent by volume, percent by mass, molarity

2 INSTRUCT

Solubility

Build Science Skills L1

Calculating Have students answer the following questions: Suppose you add 60 g of lead nitrate, $Pb(NO_3)_2$, to 100 g of water at 20°C. After you stir it, 8 g of lead nitrate remains undissolved. **What is the solubility of lead nitrate at 20°C?** *(52 g per 100 g of water)* **If you add 44 g of table salt to 100 g of water at 20°C, how many grams will remain undissolved?** *(8 g)*
Logical

Answer to . . .

Figure 8 *19.2 g*

Section Resources

Print
- ***Laboratory Manual,*** Investigation 8B
- ***Reading and Study Workbook With Math Support,*** Section 8.2 and **Math Skill:** Calculating the Molarity of a Solution
- ***Math Skills and Problem Solving Workbook,*** Section 8.2
- ***Transparencies,*** Section 8.2

Technology
- ***Interactive Textbook,*** Section 8.2
- ***Presentation Pro CD-ROM,*** Section 8.2

Build Reading Literacy L1

Outline Refer to page **156D** in **Chapter 6**, which provides the guidelines for outlining.

Have students read the section. Then, have them use the headings as major divisions in an outline. Have students refer to their outlines when answering the questions in the Section 8.2 Assessment. **Verbal**

Address Misconceptions L2

Some students think that when things dissolve they "disappear" and are no longer there. Challenge this misconception by reviewing the law of conservation of mass. Explain that mass is conserved in all ordinary chemical and physical processes, including solutes dissolving and coming out of solution. Have students examine the beakers on this page. Explain that even though you cannot see the solute in the first beaker, it is still there. Adding a crystal causes the solute to come out of solution and become visible again. **Visual**

Teacher Demo

Crystallization L2

Purpose Students observe crystallization of a solute from a supersaturated solution.

Materials beakers, 200 g sodium acetate trihydrate, distilled water, spatula, hot plate (An alternative to sodium acetate trihydrate is sodium thiosulfate hydrate.)

Procedure The day before, prepare a supersaturated solution consisting of 200 g sodium acetate trihydrate dissolved in 20 mL distilled water. Heat the solution until all of the solute has dissolved. Allow to cool overnight. (Consider preparing multiple solutions in case one crystallizes while it is cooling.) Tell the class that you have prepared a supersaturated solution. Add a crystal of sodium acetate to the cooled solution.

Expected Outcome Upon adding the crystal, the solute will crystallize out of solution and form a solid mass. Be prepared in case the beaker breaks due to expansion of the contents. Have students stand a safe distance away, and do not let students pick up broken glass if the beaker does break. **Visual**

Figure 9 A supersaturated solution is analogous to the overloaded man shown above. One wrong step, and he might drop all the boxes. In the photo sequence below, a single crystal of sodium acetate, $NaC_2H_3O_2$, is added to a supersaturated solution of sodium acetate in water. The excess solute rapidly crystallizes out of the solution.

Saturated Solutions Table sugar is very soluble in water. At 20°C, 203.9 grams of table sugar will dissolve in 100 grams of water. What will happen if you try to dissolve more than 203.9 grams of table sugar in the same amount of water? The extra sugar will not go into solution. The solution is already saturated. A **saturated solution** is one that contains as much solute as the solvent can hold at a given temperature. When a solution is saturated, the solvent is "filled" with solute. If you add more solute, it will not dissolve.

Unsaturated Solutions A solution that has less than the maximum amount of solute that can be dissolved is called an **unsaturated solution.** For example, many of the beverages you drink are unsaturated solutions of sugar in water. If you sweeten your lemonade with a spoonful of sugar, and the sugar dissolves, you know that the solution is unsaturated. As long as the amount of solute is less than the solubility at that temperature, the solution is unsaturated.

Supersaturated Solutions Have you ever tried to carry more books than you can easily manage? If you're not careful, you'll drop them all because the load is so unstable. Similarly, a solvent can sometimes dissolve more solute than you might expect, based on its solubility. Solubility is given at a specific temperature, such as 20°C. If you heat a solvent above that temperature, more solute may dissolve. If you then carefully cool the solvent back to 20°C without jarring it, you may be able to keep the extra solute in solution.

A **supersaturated solution** is one that contains *more* solute than it can normally hold at a given temperature. Supersaturated solutions are very unstable. If even a tiny crystal of the solute falls into a supersaturated solution, the extra solute can rapidly deposit out of solution, as shown in Figure 9.

Reading Checkpoint *How does a supersaturated solution differ from a saturated solution?*

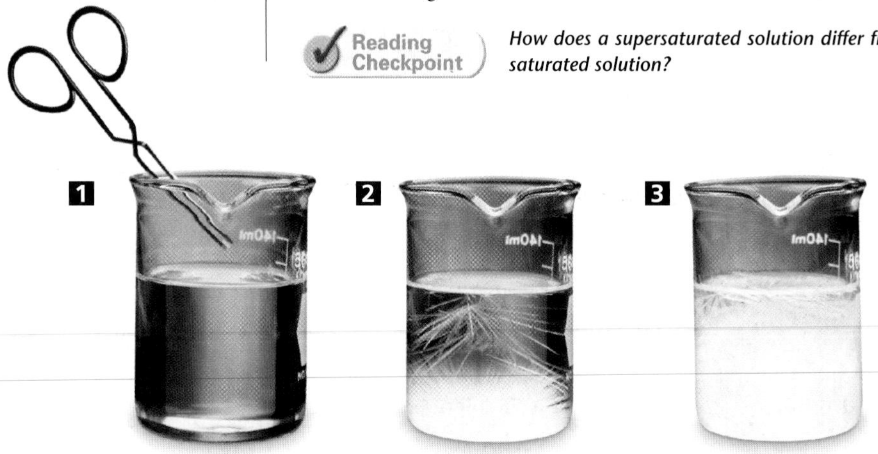
1
2
3

Customize for English Language Learners

Discussion

Students who are learning English can benefit from real-life examples that relate to science content. Encourage students to think of observations they may have made about factors that affect solubility. For example, perhaps they have seen that vinegar and oil salad dressing separates into layers. Also, they may have noticed that carbonated beverages taste "flat" when they are warm. Encourage students to share their observations with the class.

Factors Affecting Solubility

Have you ever had to clean oil or grease from your hands? If you rinse your hands in water alone, the oil remains on your hands. But if you use soapy water, you can easily rinse the oil off your hands. Oil is soluble in soapy water, but not in pure water. Solubility varies not only with the solvent used, but also with the conditions of the solution process. **Three factors that affect the solubility of a solute are the polarity of the solvent, temperature, and pressure.**

Figure 10 Generally, a solute is more likely to dissolve in a "like" solvent than an "unlike" solvent. **Classifying** ***How is saltwater an example of "like dissolving in like"?***

Solvent-Solute Combinations

Solvent Type	Solute Type	Will Solution Form?
Polar	Polar (or ionic)	More likely
Polar	Nonpolar	Not likely
Nonpolar	Polar (or ionic)	Not likely
Nonpolar	Nonpolar	More likely

Polar and Nonpolar Solvents Oil does not dissolve in water because oil molecules are nonpolar and water molecules are polar. A common guideline for predicting solubility is "like dissolves like." Solution formation is more likely to happen when the solute and solvent are either both polar or both nonpolar. Figure 11 illustrates how soapy water dissolves oil. A soap molecule has a polar end, which attracts water molecules, and a nonpolar end, which attracts oil. The soap molecules break up the oil into small droplets that are soluble in water.

Temperature When you add a large amount of sugar to cold tea, only a small amount dissolves. If you add the same amount of sugar to the same amount of hot tea, more sugar will dissolve. In general, the solubility of solids increases as the solvent temperature increases.

When a glass of cold water warms up to room temperature, bubbles form on the inside of the glass. These bubbles are gases that were dissolved in the water. They come out of the solution as the water temperature rises. Unlike most solids, gases usually become less soluble as the temperature of the solvent increases.

Pressure How do manufacturers produce a carbonated beverage? They use pressure to force carbon dioxide (CO_2) to dissolve in the liquid. Increasing the pressure on a gas increases its solubility in a liquid. The pressure of CO_2 in a sealed 12-ounce can of soda at room temperature can be two to three times atmospheric pressure.

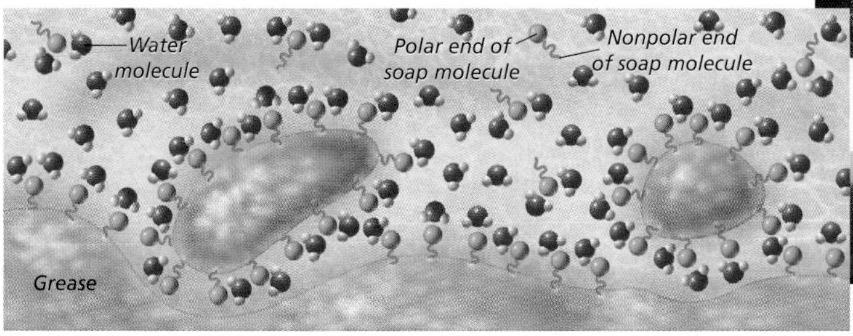
Water molecule
Polar end of soap molecule
Nonpolar end of soap molecule
Grease

Figure 11 Soaps and detergents are used to remove grease and oil stains. Soap molecules form attractions to both polar water molecules and nonpolar oil molecules. As the water flows away, it carries the oil with it.

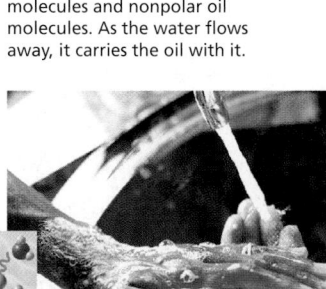

Factors Affecting Solubility

Build Science Skills L2

Measuring

ACTIVITY

Purpose Students approximate the solubility of sodium chloride at two different temperatures.

Materials For each group of students: 2 400-mL beakers, water, ice, hot plate, 2 70-mL test tubes, salt, scoop, 2 stirring rods, thermometer, weigh paper, balance, test tube tongs

Class Time 15–30 minutes

Procedure Have students make a 0°C ice water bath in one beaker. Then, have students heat water in the other beaker to 100°C. Have students measure 50 mL of room-temperature water into each test tube. Have them place one test tube in each bath. When the water in each test tube reaches 0°C and 100°C, respectively, have students add 10 g of salt to each test tube. They should then add salt in 1 g increments, stirring until all the salt is dissolved. Have them add salt until it no longer dissolves in the water. Have students record the total mass of salt added to each sample.

Safety Remind students to use caution when handling glassware and hot objects. Do not allow students to stir the solutions with the thermometers.

Expected Outcome Solubility of NaCl is 36 g in 100 mL at 0°C and 40 g in 100 mL at 100°C. **Kinesthetic, Logical**

Use Visuals L1

Figure 11 Have students examine Figure 11. Ask, **Which part of the soap molecule is polar?** *(The part represented by a sphere)* **Which substance is the polar end of the soap molecule attracted to?** *(Water)* **Visual**

Facts and Figures

Micelles and Soap When the nonpolar ends of soap molecules clump together in water in such a way that their polar ends radiate outward, they make a ball-shaped formation called a *micelle.* When a mixture of water and soap is mixed, the small micelles become suspended in the water. Because the micelles scatter light, soapy water is cloudy. The process for making soap is discussed in Section 8.3.

Answer to . . .

Figure 10 *NaCl contains positive and negative ions. Water contains atoms that have partial positive and negative charges.*

Reading Checkpoint *A supersaturated solution contains more solute than it can normally hold at a given temperature, while a saturated solution contains as much solute as the solvent can hold at a given temperature.*

Concentration of Solutions

Build Science Skills L2

Interpreting Diagrams Have students examine the label in Figure 12. Then, have students calculate the volume of real cranberry juice in 300 mL of Smith's Cranberry Juice. *(81 mL)*
Logical

Problem-Solving Activity

Putting the Fizz Into Carbonated Beverages L2

Defining the Problem The problem is how to find a supplier of carbon dioxide for adding carbonation to beverages and how to keep the levels of carbon dioxide in the beverages constant.

Organizing Information Examples of reactions that create carbon dioxide include reacting vinegar and baking soda, fermentation in yeast, cellular respiration in plants and animals, and combustion of carbon compounds. Students will need to find out what kinds of manufacturers produce large amounts of carbon dioxide gas. They will also need to find out how temperature, pressure, and type of solvent affect the solubility of gases.

Creating a Solution Students may choose a gas or petroleum company as a supplier. (CO_2 is also a by-product in fertilizer and fermentation processes.) Two factors that affect solubility of a gas in a liquid are temperature and pressure.

Presenting Your Plan Acceptable proposals should include reasons for choosing the supplier, such as low cost, facility of distribution, or quality of product. To regulate carbonation levels, the factory can manipulate the temperature and pressure at which CO_2 dissolves. The solubility of a gas increases as pressure increases and temperature decreases.
Logical

For Extra Help L1

Encourage students to be creative in their research. They do not have to limit their research to the library or Internet. Students may want to call a local restaurant that serves carbonated fountain drinks to find out where they get their carbon dioxide. They could also call or visit a local bottling company.
Interpersonal

SMITH'S
Cranberry Juice
Black River Falls, Wisconsin
Contains 27% Cranberry Juice
INGREDIENTS: Filtered Water, Cranberry Juice (Cranberry Juice from Concentrate and Cranberry Juice), High Fructose Corn Syrup, Ascorbic Acid (Vitamin C)

Figure 12 The juice squeezed from fruit is already a solution. Most bottled or canned juices are less-concentrated solutions of fruit juices, made by adding water. Percent by volume is a way to measure the concentration of one liquid dissolved in another.

Concentration of Solutions

How do you take your tea? Some people prefer their tea very concentrated, so they leave the tea bag in hot water for several minutes. Other people immerse the tea bag for only a minute or two, because they prefer their tea much less concentrated, or dilute. The resulting solutions differ in how much solute is present. The **concentration** of a solution is the amount of solute dissolved in a specified amount of solution. **Concentration can be expressed as percent by volume, percent by mass, and molarity.**

Percent by Volume Fruit juice bottles often have labels, such as the one in Figure 12, that state the percentage of "real juice" in the bottle. For example, if 27 percent of the total volume of liquid is fruit juice, the concentration of fruit juice is 27 percent by volume. Use the following equation to calculate concentration as a percent by volume.

$$\text{Percent by volume} = \frac{\text{Volume of solute}}{\text{Volume of solution}} \times 100\%$$

Percent by Mass Concentration expressed as a percent by mass is more useful when the solute is a solid. Percent by mass is the percent of a solution's total mass that is accounted for by a solute.

$$\text{Percent by mass} = \frac{\text{Mass of solute}}{\text{Mass of solution}} \times 100\%$$

Suppose you have 100 grams of a solution of sugar in water. After allowing the water to evaporate, 15 grams of sugar remain. So, the concentration of sugar in the solution was 15 percent by mass.

Problem-Solving Activity

Putting the Fizz Into Carbonated Beverages

You have been asked to find a supplier of carbon dioxide for a factory that produces carbonated beverages. You also must find out how to regulate the carbonation levels of the beverages produced.

Defining the Problem Describe your task in your own words.

Organizing Information Find examples of chemical reactions that produce carbon dioxide. What industries use such reactions? In addition, list and review the general factors affecting solubility.

Creating a Solution Choose a business or industry to supply your factory with carbon dioxide. Figure out how the solubility of a gas in a liquid varies under different conditions.

Presenting Your Plan Write a proposal to the manager of your factory. Explain your choice of a carbon dioxide supplier, and describe how to regulate carbonation levels of the beverages produced.

Facts and Figures

Molality Another way of describing solution concentration is called *molality*. Molality is defined as the number of moles of solute per kilogram of solvent, and is represented by a lower case *m*. The advantage of using molality over molarity to describe concentrations is that molality does not involve volume and thus does not change with changes in temperature. For this reason, molality is often used in calculations involving colligative properties (such as freezing point depression and boiling point elevation) that are observed over a range of temperatures.

Molarity Suppose you add 10 grams of sodium chloride to 100 milliliters of water. Then, in a different container, you add 10 grams of table sugar to 100 milliliters of water. Do the two solutions contain the same number of solute particles? No, they do not, because the two different solutes have different molar masses.

To compare the number of solute particles in solutions, chemists often use moles to measure concentration. Recall that a mole is the amount of a substance that contains approximately 6.02×10^{23} particles of that substance. **Molarity** is the number of moles of a solute dissolved per liter of solution. Use the following equation to calculate molarity.

$$\text{Molarity} = \frac{\text{Moles of solute}}{\text{Liters of solution}}$$

To make a 1-molar (1M) solution of sodium chloride in water, first calculate the molar mass of the solute. Sodium chloride, NaCl, has a molar mass of 58.5 grams. If 58.5 grams of sodium chloride is mixed with enough water to make one liter of solution, the resulting solution is 1-molar.

Table sugar, $C_{12}H_{22}O_{11}$, has a molar mass of 342 grams. To make a 1-molar solution of table sugar in water, 342 grams of table sugar must be added to enough water to make one liter of solution.

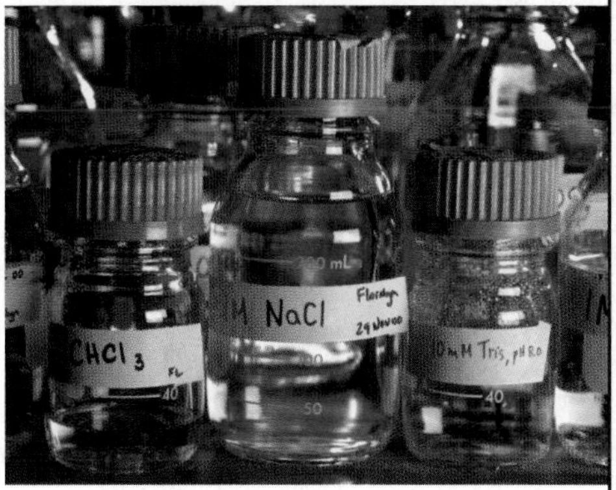

NaCl

Figure 13 A 1M NaCl solution contains 58.5 grams of NaCl per liter of solution. **Calculating** ***How much solute would you need to make to make one liter of a 0.2-molar solution of sodium chloride in water?***

Section 8.2 Assessment

Reviewing Concepts

1. What terms are used to describe solutions with different amounts of solute?
2. List three factors that affect solubility.
3. What are three ways to measure the concentration of a solution?
4. What is the effect of pressure on the solubility of a gas?
5. Compare a 2-molar solution of salt water with a 2-molar solution of sugar water. How are they similar? How are they different?

Critical Thinking

6. **Problem Solving** How would you figure out the solubility of an unknown solid in water?
7. **Inferring** Despite the name, dry cleaning does involve the use of liquid solvents. Why would a dry cleaner use both polar and nonpolar cleaning solvents?
8. **Calculating** Use the periodic table to find the mass of potassium nitrate (KNO_3) needed to make 1 liter of 1-molar solution.

Writing in Science

Compare and Contrast Paragraph Write a paragraph comparing the different ways that concentration can be expressed. (*Hint*: Describe what quantities must be measured for each type of concentration calculation.)

Build Math Skills L1

Calculating With Significant Figures Have students solve the following problems and express their answers using the correct significant figures. **What is the molarity of a solution consisting of 111 g of $CaCl_2$ dissolved in enough water to make 2.0 L of solution?** *(0.50 M)* **What volume of a 2.00-M solution KI in water contains 5.96 moles of solute?** *(2.98 L)*
Logical

Direct students to the **Math Skills** in the **Skills and Reference Handbook** at the end of the student text for additional help.

3 ASSESS

Evaluate Understanding L2

Have students write three math problems (with solutions) based on the equations given for percent by volume, percent by mass, and molarity. Have students take turns analyzing and solving the problems in class. Note that even incorrectly worded problems are useful because students can be asked to identify and correct the errors.

Reteach L1

Use the table on p. 235 to review solubility. Have students describe how much solute would be in an unsaturated, saturated, and supersaturated solution of each type of solute given in the table. For example, any amount less than 36.0 g of sodium chloride in 100 g of water would be an unsaturated solution.

Writing in Science

Concentration can be expressed in at least three different ways—percent by volume, percent by mass, and molarity. To determine percent by volume, you need to find the volume of solute and the volume of solution. To determine percent by mass, you need to find the mass of solute and the mass of solution. To determine molarity, you need to find the moles of solute and the volume of solution (in liters).

Interactive Textbook If your class subscribes to the Interactive Textbook, use it to review key concepts in Section 8.2.

Section 8.2 Assessment

1. Unsaturated, saturated, and supersaturated
2. Polarity of the solute and solvent, temperature, and pressure
3. Percent by volume, percent by mass, and molarity
4. It increases the solubility of a gas.
5. The molar concentrations of the solutions are identical; each contains the same number of moles of solute per liter of solution. The solutions differ in percent by mass concentration; the sugar water solution contains more grams of solute per gram of solution than the saltwater solution.
6. Measure the mass of a beaker containing 100 g of water. Add the unknown solid, while stirring, until no more dissolves. Measure the mass of the beaker and its contents again. Measure the temperature of the solution. The difference in mass is the solubility of the unknown solid in grams per 100 g of water.
7. To remove both polar and nonpolar stains
8. 101.1 g

Answer to . . .

Figure 13 *11.7 g*

Section 8.3

1 FOCUS

Objectives

8.3.1 **Define** acid and **describe** some of the general properties of an acid.

8.3.2 **Define** base and **describe** some of the general properties of a base.

8.3.3 **Identify** a neutralization reaction, and **describe** the reactants and products of neutralization.

8.3.4 **Explain** how acids and bases can be defined as proton donors and proton acceptors.

Reading Focus

Build Vocabulary L2

Concept Map Have students construct a concept map of the vocabulary terms used in this section. Instruct students to place the vocabulary terms in ovals and connect the ovals with lines on which linking words are placed. Students should place the main concept (Properties of Acids and Bases) at the top or the center. As they move away from the main concept, the content should become more specific.

Reading Strategy L2

b. A compound that produces hydronium ions when dissolved in water **d.** A compound that produces hydroxide ions when dissolved in water **f.** Any ionic compound that forms when an acid reacts with a base

2 INSTRUCT

Identifying Acids

Address Misconceptions L2

Many students think that all acids are harmful or that all harmful chemicals are acids. Challenge these misconceptions by asking, **What juices might contain acids?** *(Orange juice, lemon juice, and tomato juice are all acidic.)* **Do you know of any acid that exists normally in your body?** *(Stomach acid contains hydrochloric acid, which aids in digestion.)*
Verbal

8.3 Properties of Acids and Bases

Reading Focus

Key Concepts

- What are some general properties of acids and bases?
- What are the products of neutralization?
- What are proton donors and proton acceptors?

Vocabulary

- acid
- indicator
- base
- neutralization
- salt

Reading Strategy

Using Prior Knowledge Before you read, copy the table below and write your definition for each vocabulary term. After you read, write the scientific definition of each term and compare it with your original definition.

Term	Your Definition	Scientific Definition
Acid	a. ?	b. ?
Base	c. ?	d. ?
Salt	e. ?	f. ?

Figure 14 Soap making involves the use of a base such as sodium hydroxide or potassium hydroxide.

One of the chemicals used to make the soaps shown in Figure 14 is sodium hydroxide. In traditional soap making, sodium hydroxide is added to a mixture of melted animal or vegetable fats. As the mixture is brought to a boil, the sodium hydroxide reacts with the fats. The products of the reaction are glycerol (a colorless, syrupy liquid) and soap. After the glycerol is separated from the soap, the soap is purified. Other chemicals are then mixed with the soap to give it a particular scent and color.

Sodium hydroxide belongs to a class of compounds, known as bases, that share some physical and chemical properties. Bases are related to another class of compounds called acids. As you will discover, there are several differences among acidic solutions, basic solutions, and solutions that have properties of neither an acid nor a base.

Identifying Acids

An **acid** is a compound that produces hydronium ions (H_3O^+) when dissolved in water. Recall that when hydrogen chloride gas dissolves in water, it ionizes and forms hydronium ions and chloride ions.

$$HCl + H_2O \longrightarrow H_3O^+ + Cl^-$$

The solution that results is called hydrochloric acid. Figure 15 lists some common acids and their uses.

Section Resources

Print
- ***Laboratory Manual,*** Investigation 8A
- ***Reading and Study Workbook With Math Support,*** Section 8.3
- ***Transparencies,*** Section 8.3

Technology
- ***Probeware Lab Manual,*** Lab 3
- ***Interactive Textbook,*** Section 8.3
- ***Presentation Pro CD-ROM,*** Section 8.3
- ***Go Online,*** NSTA SciLinks, Bases

Common Acids		
Name	Formula	Use
Acetic acid	CH_3COOH	Vinegar
Carbonic acid	H_2CO_3	Carbonated beverages
Hydrochloric acid	HCl	Digestive juices in stomach
Nitric acid	HNO_3	Fertilizer production
Phosphoric acid	H_3PO_4	Fertilizer production
Sulfuric acid	H_2SO_4	Car batteries

Figure 15 The table lists names, formulas, and uses for several common acids. **Inferring** ***What products are formed when nitric acid ionizes in water?***

Acids have certain chemical and physical properties that are similar. **Some general properties of acids include sour taste, reactivity with metals, and ability to produce color changes in indicators.**

Sour Taste Foods that taste sour often contain acids. For example, lemons, grapefruits, limes, and oranges all contain citric acid. The vinegar used in salad dressings contains acetic acid, CH_3COOH. Dairy products that have spoiled contain butyric (byoo THIR ik) acid. While many of the foods you eat contain acids, you should never test an acid by tasting it.

Reactivity With Metals When you use aluminum foil to cover a bowl of leftover spaghetti sauce or other foods containing tomatoes, the foil often turns dark. The foil may also develop small holes, and the food may acquire a metallic taste. Tomatoes contain citric acid, which reacts with metals such as aluminum.

The reaction between an acid and a metal is an example of a single-replacement reaction. For example, when zinc is added to a test tube containing hydrochloric acid, bubbles form in the tube. The following equation describes the reaction.

$$Zn + 2HCl \longrightarrow H_2 + ZnCl_2$$

As the zinc replaces hydrogen in hydrochloric acid, hydrogen gas and zinc(II) chloride are produced.

Color Changes in Indicators An **indicator** is any substance that changes color in the presence of an acid or base. One of the most common indicators used is litmus, a kind of dye derived from plants called lichens (LY kens). Litmus paper, shown in Figure 16, is made by coating strips of paper with litmus. Blue litmus paper turns red in the presence of an acid. If you drop an unknown solution onto blue litmus paper and the litmus paper turns red, you can classify the solution as an acid.

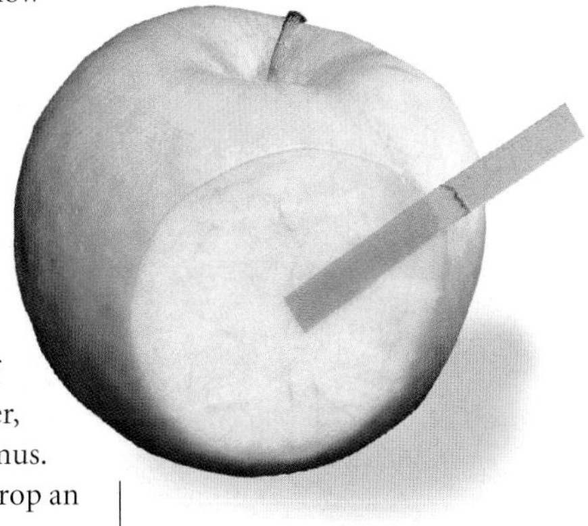

Figure 16 Litmus paper is an indicator that changes color in the presence of acids and bases. When blue litmus paper touches an acid, it turns red. Apples contain several acids, including malic acid, ascorbic acid (vitamin C), and citric acid.

Build Reading Literacy L1

Compare and Contrast Refer to page **226D** in this chapter, which provides the guidelines for comparing and contrasting.

Have students read the section. As they read, they should create lists of how acids and bases are similar and different.
Verbal

Customize for Inclusion Students

Behaviorally Disordered
Have students collect soil samples from various locations near the school and their homes. Have them note the types of plants that are found in the locations where they collected their samples. Provide students with water test kits so they can determine the pH of each sample. Have students determine if there is a correlation between the types of plants that grow in an area and the pH of the soil.

Answer to . . .

Figure 15 *NO_3^- and H_3O^+*

Identifying Bases

Build Science Skills L2

Observing Encourage students to bring in various products from home and test each product with litmus paper. Many of the following products contain acids: fruit juices, vinegar, carbonated beverages, milk, and fertilizers. Many of the following products contain bases: cleaning products, detergents, soaps, deodorants, and antacids. Avoid having students bring in corrosive products such as car batteries or drain cleaners. As a class, make a chart that classifies each product as acidic, neutral, or basic. **Visual**

Build Science Skills L2

Comparing and Contrasting Have students examine the table in Figure 17. Ask, **What do the bases listed in the table have in common?** *(They all contain OH^-, hydroxide ions.)* **How do the bases differ?** *(They have different cations and different numbers of hydroxide ions.)* **Logical**

Go Online NSTA SCILINKS

Download a worksheet on bases for students to complete, and find additional teacher support from NSTA SciLinks.

Go Online NSTA SCILINKS

For: Links on bases
Visit: www.SciLinks.org
Web Code: ccn-1083

Identifying Bases

Sodium hydroxide, NaOH, is an example of a base. A **base** is a compound that produces hydroxide ions (OH^-) when dissolved in water. When sodium hydroxide dissolves in water, it dissociates into sodium ions and hydroxide ions.

$$NaOH \longrightarrow Na^+ + OH^-$$

Figure 17 lists some common bases and their uses. Like acids, bases have certain physical and chemical properties that you can use to identify them. **Some general properties of bases include bitter taste, slippery feel, and ability to produce color changes in indicators.** Unlike acids, bases usually do not react with metals. However, low reactivity with metals is not considered a general property of bases. For example, sodium hydroxide reacts very vigorously with metals such as aluminum and zinc.

Bitter Taste Have you ever tasted unsweetened chocolate (sometimes called baking chocolate)? Without sugar, chocolate tastes bitter. Cacao beans contain a base called theobromine that gives unsweetened chocolate its bitter taste.

Many cough syrups and other liquid medicines contain similar bases. Fruit flavorings are often added to mask the taste of these basic solutions.

Slippery Feel Bases feel slippery. Wet soap and many cleaning products that contain bases are slippery to the touch. When wet, some rocks feel slippery because the water dissolves compounds trapped in the rocks, producing a basic solution.

Common Bases

Name	Formula	Uses
Aluminum hydroxide	$Al(OH)_3$	Deodorant, antacid
Calcium hydroxide	$Ca(OH)_2$	Concrete, plaster
Magnesium hydroxide	$Mg(OH)_2$	Antacid, laxative
Sodium hydroxide	$NaOH$	Drain cleaner, soap production

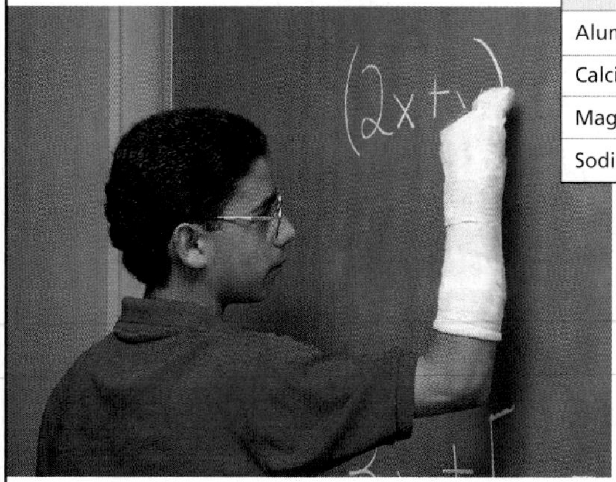

Figure 17 A base is a compound that produces hydroxide ions when dissolved in water. The plaster in this boy's cast contains a base. Bases are also commonly found in products used for cleaning.

Quick Lab

Using an Indicator

Materials

one quarter cup of frozen blueberries, foam cup, spoon, 4 small plastic cups, 2 dropper pipets, lemon juice, white vinegar, window cleaner, baking soda

Procedure

1. Place the blueberries in the foam cup and mash them with the spoon. Try to get as much juice out of the berries as possible. You will use the juice as an indicator.
2. Use the spoon to remove most of the crushed berries and discard them as directed by your teacher. Leave as much juice behind as possible.
3. Use a dropper pipet to place a few drops of lemon juice (which is acidic) in one of the plastic cups. Use a second pipet to add one drop of your indicator to the lemon juice. Swirl the cup. Record your observations.
4. Rinse out the pipets with water. Repeat Step 3, using vinegar and then window cleaner in place of lemon juice. Record your observations.
5. Place several drops of the indicator in the last plastic cup. Add a small pinch of baking soda to the cup. Swirl the cup. Record your observations.

Analyze and Conclude

1. **Classifying** Use your observations to determine how the color of blueberry juice changes in acids and bases.
2. **Drawing Conclusions** How does the blueberry indicator help you determine whether a material is an acid or a base?
3. **Inferring** Why does the color of the blueberry indicator change less when added to acids than when added to bases?

Color Changes in Indicators Bases turn red litmus paper blue. The litmus paper will change back to red if you drop an acidic solution on it.

Phenolphthalein (fee nol THAY leen) is another example of an acid-base indicator. In a solution containing a base, phenolphthalein is red. In a solution containing an acid, phenolphthalein is colorless.

Some flowers, like the hydrangeas shown in Figure 18, contain natural indicators. The color of the flowers depends on whether the plant is growing in acidic or basic soil. When hydrangeas grow in acidic soil, the flowers are bluish-purple. When hydrangeas grow in basic soil, the flowers are pink. By manipulating the acidity of the soil, gardeners can determine the color of the flowers.

Figure 18 Soil acidity can affect the color of flowers such as hydrangeas.

Reading Checkpoint *What color does litmus paper turn in a base?*

Facts and Figures

Litmus Paper Litmus paper contains a combination of several organic compounds that come from a species of lichen. Originally litmus was used as a dye. Today, some of these compounds are also used in perfume making and antibiotics.

Quick Lab

Using an Indicator L2

Objective
After completing this activity, students will be able to
- extract an indicator from blueberries and use it to classify substances as acids or bases.

Skills Focus Observing, Classifying, Drawing Conclusions, Inferring

Prep Time 15 minutes

Advanced Prep Provide ammonia-based window cleaner because alcohol-based window cleaner may not be basic.

Class Time 15 minutes

Safety Have students observe safety symbols and wear safety goggles and lab aprons.

Teaching Tips
- Have students dispose of crushed berries in the trash.
- Dispose of all waste solutions in the sink with excess water.

Expected Outcome The indicator will stay purple with lemon juice and vinegar. It will turn green with window cleaner and baking soda.

Analyze and Conclude
1. Lemon juice and vinegar contain acids and do not change the color of the indicator. Window cleaner and baking soda contain bases and change the color of the indicator to green.
2. It is purple in an acid and green in a base.
3. Blueberries contain acid. The indicator does not change color in an acid because it is already indicating an acid.
Visual, Logical

For Enrichment L3

Have students use their blueberry indicator on other substances, such as a carbonated beverage, deionized water, and a laundry detergent solution. Ask them if they can conclude that a substance, such as water, is acidic if it does not turn the indicator green. Have them test their inferences using litmus paper.
Visual, Logical

Answer to . . .

Reading Checkpoint *Blue*

Neutralization and Salts

Teacher Demo

Neutralization Reaction L2

Purpose Students observe a neutralization reaction.

Materials 2 lemons, beaker, 0.1-M solution of NaOH, phenolphthalein solution (indicator), syringe, knife

Procedure Tell students that the phenolphthalein solution is an indicator that is pink in the presence of bases. Pour a small amount of the 0.1-M NaOH solution in the beaker. Add a couple of drops of indicator. Have students note the pink color. Explain that you are going to try to turn one of the lemons pink by injecting it with the base and indicator. Use the syringe to inject the NaOH solution into one of the lemons. Wait a few moments and then cut open both lemons.

Safety Use caution when handling the base solution. Sodium hydroxide is corrosive. In case of spills, clean thoroughly with water. Have students wear safety goggles, plastic gloves, and lab aprons should they handle the demo materials. Do not allow students to handle the syringe.

Expected Outcome Both lemons will have their normal color. Explain that a neutralization reaction occurred. The base reacted with the acid in the lemons to produce a salt. You cannot use phenolphthalein to turn a lemon pink unless you add enough base to react with all of the acid in the lemon with some base left over. The amount of base required to neutralize a lemon depends on the amount of juice in the lemon and the amount of acid the juice contains. Pour a small amount of the base (with indicator) solution onto the cut face of one of the lemons to allow students to observe the pink color of the basic solution disappear as the base is neutralized.
Visual

Neutralization and Salts

When people eat fish, they sometimes squeeze lemon juice over the fish. Fish contains bases that can leave a bitter taste. Lemon juice contains acids, such as citric acid. By squeezing lemon juice over the fish, the citric acid reacts with the bases in the fish, and the fish tastes less bitter.

The reaction between an acid and a base is called **neutralization.** During neutralization, the negative ions in an acid combine with the positive ions in a base to produce an ionic compound called a **salt.** At the same time, the hydronium ions from the acid combine with the hydroxide ions from the base to produce water. **The neutralization reaction between an acid and a base produces a salt and water.**

For example, when hydrochloric acid reacts with sodium hydroxide, the following neutralization reaction occurs.

$$\underset{\text{acid}}{(H_3O^+ + Cl^-)} + \underset{\text{base}}{(Na^+ + OH^-)} \longrightarrow \underset{\text{water}}{2HOH} + \underset{\text{salt}}{(Na^+ + Cl^-)}$$

The products of the reaction are a salt made up of sodium and chloride ions, and water. If you let the water in the resulting solution evaporate, the sodium and chloride ions would begin to crystallize out of solution, forming table salt.

Table salt is the most common example of a salt compound. Other common salts are listed in Figure 19. For instance, baking soda, $NaHCO_3$, is produced during the neutralization reaction between sodium hydroxide and carbonic acid, H_2CO_3. The other product is water. The ocean contains many dissolved salts, including chlorides and sulfates of potassium, calcium, magnesium, and sodium. Many of these salts go into solution as seawater washes against rocks.

Figure 19 The common salts listed in the table can all be made by reacting an acid with a base. One of these salts, sodium carbonate, was used to make the glass for the vases shown below. **Inferring** ***Name an acid and a base that could react to form potassium chloride, KCl.***

Common Salts

Name	Formula	Uses
Sodium chloride	$NaCl$	Food flavoring, preservative
Sodium carbonate	Na_2CO_3	Used to make glass
Potassium chloride	KCl	Used as a salt substitute to reduce dietary intake of sodium
Potassium iodide	KI	Added to table salt to prevent iodine deficiency
Magnesium chloride	$MgCl_2$	De-icer for roads
Calcium carbonate	$CaCO_3$	Chalk, marble floors, and tables
Ammonium nitrate	NH_4NO_3	Fertilizer, cold packs

Facts and Figures

Differing Definitions The definitions for acids and bases given on the previous pages are similar to those described by Swedish physicist Svante Arrhenius in 1884. Note that acids do not necessarily contain hydronium ions and bases do not necessarily contain hydroxide ions. An alternative way of defining acids and bases was developed independently in 1923 by J. N. Brønsted and T. M. Lowry and is described on p. 245. A Brønsted-Lowry base is a proton acceptor, while a Brønsted-Lowry acid is a proton donor. The distinction is important when describing nonaqueous solutions.

Proton Donors and Acceptors

Recall that hydronium ions (H_3O^+) are produced when acids dissolve in water. When an acid and a base react in water, a proton from the hydronium ion from the acid combines with the hydroxide ion (OH^-) from the base to form water (H_2O). Acids lose, or "donate," protons. Bases "accept" protons, forming water, a neutral molecule. **Acids can be defined as proton donors, and bases can be defined as proton acceptors.** This definition allows you to classify a wider range of substances as acids or bases.

Based on the definitions of acids and bases that you read earlier in this section, water is neither an acid nor a base. However, using the proton-donor or proton-acceptor definition, water can act as either an acid or a base depending on the compound with which it reacts.

Figure 20 shows the ionization of hydrogen chloride and ammonia as they form solutions. In the first reaction, water acts as a base. It accepts a proton from hydrogen chloride and becomes a hydronium ion. In the second reaction, water acts as an acid. It donates a proton to the ammonia, which acts as a base. The resulting solution contains hydroxide ions and ammonium ions, NH_4^+.

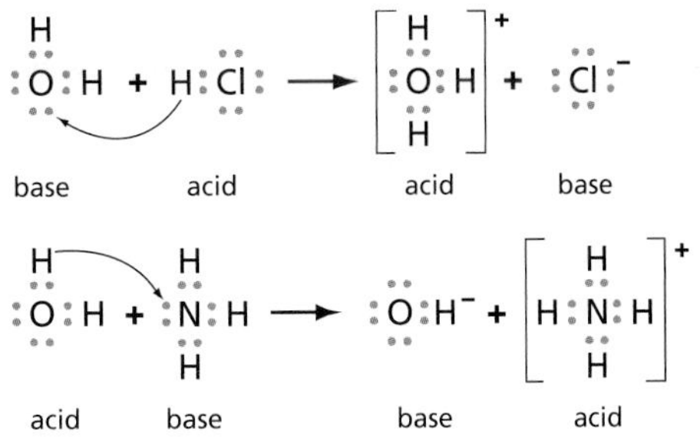
base
acid
acid
base
acid
base
base
acid

Figure 20 In the first reaction, water acts as a base, accepting a proton from hydrogen chloride. In the second reaction, water acts as an acid, donating a proton to the ammonia. ***Applying Concepts** What acts as the proton donor in the first reaction?*

Section 8.3 Assessment

Reviewing Concepts

1. List three general properties of acids.
2. List three general properties of bases.
3. What are the two products of a neutralization reaction?
4. What are the proton-donor and proton-acceptor definitions of acids and bases?
5. What ion is present in all common acid solutions?

Critical Thinking

6. **Using Analogies** Commercials for antacids often claim these products neutralize stomach acid. Antacids are bases. Think of an analogy for the way in which antacids neutralize acids.
7. **Applying Concepts** In the following equation, which reactant is a proton donor? Which is a proton acceptor?
$HNO_3 + H_2O \longrightarrow H_3O^+ + NO_3^-$

Connecting Concepts

Classifying Reactions Compare neutralization with the types of chemical reactions described in Section 7.2. To which type of reaction is neutralization most similar? Explain your choice.

Proton Donors and Acceptors

Use Visuals L1

Figure 20 Have students examine and read the caption for Figure 20. **How many reactions are represented in the figure?** *(2)* **How are atoms represented in this figure?** *(Atoms are represented by their chemical symbol and small, orange dots.)* **What do the small, orange dots represent?** *(Valence electrons)* **What do the positive and negative signs represent?** *(The charge of each ion)* **How can you tell which substance is the proton donor?** *(When that substance loses an H, a proton)* **What happens to a proton donor in this figure after it donates a proton?** *(It becomes a negative ion.)*
Visual

3 ASSESS

Evaluate Understanding L2

Have students write the equation for a neutralization reaction and label each reactant or product as an acid, base, salt, proton donor, or proton acceptor. Then, have them indicate the color each reactant and product would turn red and blue litmus paper.

Reteach L1

Use Figure 20 to summarize the key features of acids, bases, and neutralization reactions.

Connecting Concepts

Neutralization is an example of a double-replacement reaction. During neutralization, an acid and a base exchange positive ions, forming water and a salt.

Interactive Textbook If your class subscribes to the Interactive Textbook, use it to review key concepts in Section 8.3.

Section 8.3 Assessment

1. They taste sour, react with certain metals, and turn blue litmus paper red.
2. They taste bitter, feel slippery, and turn red litmus paper blue.
3. Water and a salt
4. Acids are proton donors, and bases are proton acceptors.
5. Hydronium (H_3O^+)
6. Acceptable answers include saying that it's like a positive number canceling out a negative number of the same value when added: $6+(-6)=0$
7. HNO_3 is the proton donor, and H_2O is the proton acceptor.

Answer to . . .

Figure 19 *Potassium hydroxide (KOH) and hydrogen chloride (HCl)*

Figure 20 *Hydrogen chloride*

Section 8.4

1 FOCUS

Objectives

8.4.1 **Define** pH, and **relate** pH to hydronium ion concentration in a solution.

8.4.2 **Distinguish** between strong acids and weak acids, and between strong bases and weak bases.

8.4.3 **Define** buffer, and **describe** how a buffer can be prepared.

8.4.4 **Explain** how electrolytes can be classified.

Reading Focus

Build Vocabulary L2

Word Meanings Ask students to brainstorm examples of product advertising that contain the terms *pH, electrolyte,* or *buffer.* *(Students may have heard of beauty products described as "pH-balanced," some sports beverages contain electrolytes, and many antacids contain buffers.)* Have students look up the definition of each term and speculate what is meant by the advertisers' claims. *(Answers may include that some deodorants differ in acidity, sports drinks contain ions in solution, and some antacids can be used to resist large changes in pH.)*

Reading Strategy L2

a. Ionizes almost completely when dissolved in water
b. Is a strong electrolyte
c. Dissociates almost completely when dissolved in water

2 INSTRUCT

Build Reading Literacy L1

Identify Main Idea/Details Refer to page **98D** in **Chapter 4**, which provides the guidelines for identifying main idea and details.

Have students read the section and make a list of the main headings on each page. Under each heading, have them identify the main idea of the passage. Have students refer to their lists when answering the questions in the Section 8.4 Assessment.
Verbal

8.4 Strength of Acids and Bases

Reading Focus

Key Concepts

- How is pH used to describe the concentration of acids and bases?
- How do strong acids and bases differ from weak acids and bases?
- Why are strong acids and bases good electrolytes?

Vocabulary

- pH
- buffer
- electrolyte

Reading Strategy

Comparing and Contrasting Copy the Venn diagram below. As you read, complete the diagram by comparing and contrasting acids and bases.

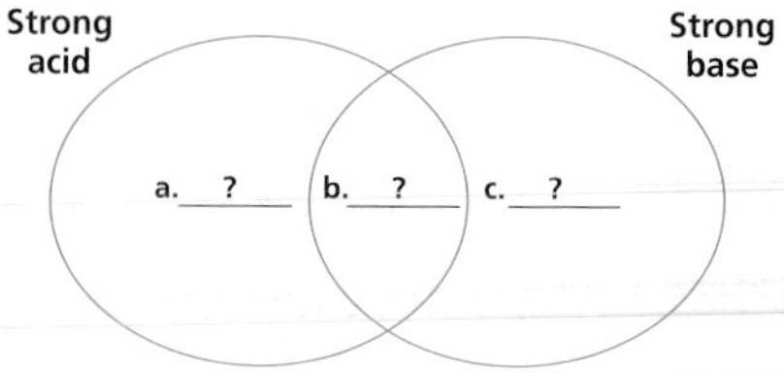

Strong acid
Strong base
a. ?
b. ?
c. ?

On a hot summer day, you might go swimming in a pool with some of your friends. As the water evaporates from your skin, you feel cooler and refreshed.

Have you ever thought about how the water in a swimming pool is made safe for swimming? You may have noticed the odor of chlorine at a backyard swimming pool or at larger municipal pools. Certain compounds of chlorine are dissolved in the water. These compounds prevent the growth of bacteria that could make you sick.

Figure 21 Sodium bicarbonate, or baking soda, is often added to swimming pools to regulate the acidity of the water.

The concentration of hydronium ions in solution must be carefully controlled in a swimming pool. If there are too many or too few hydronium ions, then the right compounds of chlorine will not be present. Figure 21 shows a pool maintenance worker adding sodium bicarbonate, $NaHCO_3$, to the water. Sodium bicarbonate can be used to lower the concentration of hydronium ions in solution.

How can you describe the acidity or basicity of a solution? One way is to determine the concentration of hydronium or hydroxide ions present in solution. Another way is to describe how readily those hydronium ions or hydroxide ions formed.

Section Resources

Print
- ***Reading and Study Workbook With Math Support,*** Section 8.4
- ***Transparencies,*** Section 8.4

Technology
- ***Interactive Textbook,*** Section 8.4
- ***Presentation Pro CD-ROM,*** Section 8.4
- ***Go Online,*** NSTA SciLinks, pH

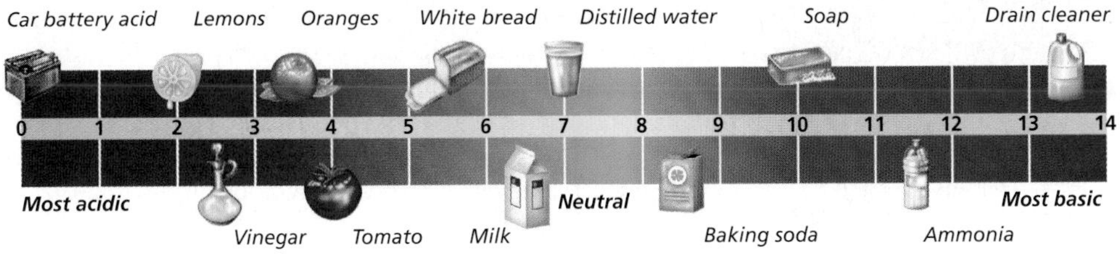
Car battery acid
Lemons
Oranges
White bread
Distilled water
Soap
Drain cleaner
0
1
2
3
4
5
6
7
8
9
10
11
12
13
14
Most acidic
Vinegar
Tomato
Milk
Neutral
Baking soda
Ammonia
Most basic

The pH Scale

Chemists use a number scale from 0 to 14 to describe the concentration of hydronium ions in a solution. It is known as the pH scale. The **pH** of a solution is a measure of its hydronium ion concentration. A pH of 7 indicates a neutral solution. Acids have a pH less than 7. Bases have a pH greater than 7.

Notice in Figure 22 that water falls in the middle of the pH scale. Water ionizes slightly according to the following reaction.

$$2H_2O \rightleftharpoons H_3O^+ + OH^-$$

The arrow pointing to the left is longer than the arrow pointing to the right to show that water contains more molecules than ions. Water is neutral because it contains small but equal concentrations of hydronium ions and hydroxide ions. At 25°C, the concentration of both H_3O^+ and OH^- in water is 1.0×10^{-7} M. Pure water has a pH of 7.

If you add an acid to water, the concentration of H_3O^+ increases and the concentration of OH^- decreases. Suppose you have a hydrochloric acid solution in which the concentration of H_3O^+ is 0.10 M (or 1.0×10^{-1} M). The solution has a pH of 1. **The lower the pH value, the greater the H_3O^+ ion concentration in solution is.**

If you add a base to water, the concentration of OH^- increases and the concentration of H_3O^+ decreases. Consider a sodium hydroxide solution in which the concentration of OH^- is 0.10 M. The concentration of H_3O^+ in this solution is 1.0×10^{-13} M, which corresponds to a pH of 13. **The higher the pH value, the lower the H_3O^+ ion concentration is.**

Reading Checkpoint *What is the pH of pure water?*

Strong Acids and Bases

Recall that some reactions go to completion while others reach equilibrium. When certain acids and bases dissolve in water, the formation of ions from the solute almost goes to completion. Such acids and bases are classified as *strong*.

Figure 22 The pH scale can help you classify solutions as acids or bases.
Comparing and Contrasting ***The desired pH range of chlorinated water in swimming pools is 7.2 to 7.8. How does the concentration of hydronium ions in this solution compare to that of lemon juice?***

Go Online NSTA SCiLINKS

For: Links on pH
Visit: www.SciLinks.org
Web Code: ccn-1084

The pH Scale

Use Visuals L1

Figure 22 Have students examine Figure 22 of the pH scale. Ask, **In which direction would you find substances that are more acidic?** *(To the left)* **Would a solution with a pH of 11 be an acid or a base?** *(A base)* **What is the pH of ammonia?** *(11.5)* **Compare the pH and acidity of oranges and tomatoes.** *(Oranges have a lower pH than tomatoes and are therefore more acidic.)* **Visual**

Build Math Skills L1

Exponents Many students have a hard time interpreting positive and negative exponents. Be sure that they understand that a value with a large negative exponent is significantly smaller than a value with a small negative exponent. **Logical**

Direct students to the **Math Skills** in the **Skills and Reference Handbook** at the end of the student text for additional help.

Strong Acids and Bases

Integrate Biology L2

Explain that the stomach contains a dilute solution of hydrochloric acid, HCl. Even though the solution is dilute, HCl is a strong acid, which means it ionizes completely in solution. Have students find out how this strong acid aids in digestion. Have them make a poster illustrating the stomach's role in digestion and explain how food is digested by stomach acid. *(Stomach acid works with enzymes to help break down proteins. Contraction of stomach muscles helps to mix the food, acid, and enzymes, turning food into a semiliquid.)* **Visual, Verbal**

Customize for English Language Learners

Think-Pair-Share
Have students work in pairs to think of other scales besides pH, and the quantities that they measure. Examples include temperature scales, hardness scales, and the Richter scale. Strengthen discussion skills by having students share their examples with the class. Encourage students to refer to Figure 22 and make comparisons between pH and other scales.

Go Online NSTA SCiLINKS

Download a worksheet on pH for students to complete, and find additional teacher support from NSTA SciLinks.

Answer to . . .

Figure 22 *Concentration of hydronium ions in lemon juice is greater.*

Reading Checkpoint *7*

Solutions, Acids, and Bases 247

Weak Acids and Bases

Quick Lab

Making a Battery

L2

Objective
After completing this activity, students will be able to
- make a battery using a lemon as a source for electrolytes.

Skills Focus **Observing, Predicting**

Prep Time 5 minutes

Advance Prep Use tin strips to cut copper and zinc into 2–5 cm strips. Strip the ends if using insulated wires. File down the rough edges of the metal strips. Wear heavy leather gloves when preparing the strips.

Class Time 10 minutes

Safety Have students observe safety symbols and wear lab aprons.

Teaching Tips
- Have students throw used lemons away.
- Clean used copper and zinc strips and save them for reuse.
- Current is the rate at which charge flows through a wire and is expressed in amps, while voltage is expressed in volts. Potential difference is a measure of the work required to carry positive charge from one point to another and is expressed in volts.

Expected Outcome The battery will probably produce less than 1 volt and a very small current, about 0.0001 amp. The actual voltage and current depend on how juicy the lemon is, how far apart the electrodes are placed, and how deep they go into the fruit.

Analyze and Conclude
1. There is no voltage when using two copper strips. Values between 0.5 V and 1 V are typical when using the copper and zinc strips.
2. A basic solution is also electrolytic and may provide a similar result.
Visual, Kinesthetic

For Enrichment

L3

Have students perform this lab with metals to determine which pairs of metals produce the greatest voltages. Then, refer them to a chemistry text to read about electronegativity. (Pairs of metals that are far apart in the electromotive series produce the greatest voltages.)
Kinesthetic

Quick Lab

Making a Battery

Materials

1 large fresh lemon, plastic knife, zinc strip, 2 copper strips, multimeter

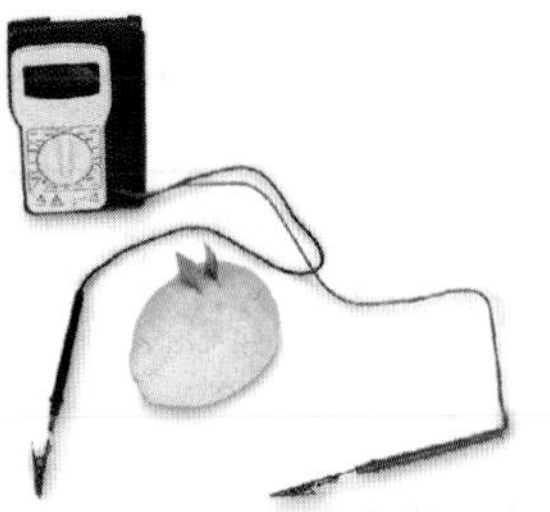

Procedure

1. Roll the lemon between your hands until it softens.
2. Use the knife to carefully cut two parallel slits in the lemon about 1 cm apart. Push the copper strips into the slits to a depth of 2 to 3 cm. Don't allow the strips to touch.
3. Attach the copper strips to the terminals of the multimeter. Observe the reading and record it.
4. Replace one of the copper strips with the zinc strip and repeat step 3.

Analyze and Conclude

1. **Observing** What was the reading on the multimeter when you used two copper strips? A copper and a zinc strip?
2. **Predicting** Lemon juice is acidic. Would a basic solution provide a similar result?

Strong Acids When hydrogen chloride dissolves in water, almost all of its molecules ionize. After the reaction, there are about the same number of hydronium ions in solution as there were molecules of HCl to begin with. The products do not reform reactant molecules. HCl is an example of a strong acid. **When strong acids dissolve in water, they ionize almost completely.** Other strong acids include sulfuric acid, H_2SO_4, and nitric acid, HNO_3.

Strong Bases When dissolved in water, sodium hydroxide almost completely dissociates into sodium and hydroxide ions. Sodium hydroxide is an example of a strong base. **Strong bases dissociate almost completely in water.** Other strong bases include calcium hydroxide, $Ca(OH)_2$, and potassium hydroxide, KOH.

Weak Acids and Bases

The citric acid in orange juice and the acetic acid in vinegar are *weak* acids. Toothpaste and shampoo contain *weak* bases. **Weak acids and bases ionize or dissociate only slightly in water.**

Weak Acids A solution of acetic acid, CH_3COOH, and water can be described by the following equation.

$$CH_3COOH + H_2O \rightleftharpoons CH_3COO^- + H_3O^+$$

The equilibrium favors the reactants over the products, so few ions form in solution. A weak acid forms fewer hydronium ions than a strong acid of the same concentration. This also means that a weak acid has a higher pH than a strong acid of the same concentration.

It is important to understand the difference between concentration and strength. Concentration is the amount of solute dissolved in a given amount of solution. Strength refers to the solute's tendency to form ions in water. You cannot assume that a strong acid has a low pH, because its concentration also affects pH. For instance, a dilute solution of HCl (a strong acid) can have a pH of 6. But a concentrated solution of acetic acid (a weak acid) can have a pH of 3.

Weak Bases Ammonia, NH_3, is a colorless gas with a distinctive smell. When it dissolves in water, very little of it ionizes. Equilibrium favors the reactants, so few NH_4^+ and OH^- ions are produced.

$$NH_3 + H_2O \rightleftharpoons NH_4^+ + OH^-$$

Buffers Weak acids and bases can be used to make buffers. A **buffer** is a solution that is resistant to large changes in pH. Buffers can be prepared by mixing a weak acid and its salt or a weak base and its salt. Because a buffer can react with both an acid and a base, its pH remains relatively constant.

Facts and Figures

Buffered Aspirin Many drugs contain buffers to offset the effects they might have upon ingestion. For example, acetylsalicylic acid is the ingredient in aspirin medication that relieves pain. Many of the kinds of aspirin available for consumer use are buffered to minimize the acidity of aspirin.

Electrolytes

Sports drinks, like the one shown in Figure 23, taste salty because they contain salts of elements such as sodium, potassium, and calcium. Salts are examples of electrolytes. An **electrolyte** is a substance that ionizes or dissociates into ions when it dissolves in water. The resulting solution can conduct electric current. The electrolytes in sports drinks help restore the balance of ions in your body.

Electrolytes can be classified as strong or weak. **Strong acids and bases are strong electrolytes because they dissociate or ionize almost completely in water.** For example, sodium hydroxide is a strong electrolyte that produces many ions in water. Salts are also strong electrolytes. When potassium chloride dissolves in water, it dissociates into potassium and chloride ions. In contrast, acetic acid is a weak electrolyte because it only partially ionizes.

Figure 23 Drinking sports drinks after exercising can restore the balance of ions in your body.

Batteries and other portable devices that produce electricity also contain electrolytes. Car batteries use lead plates in combination with the electrolyte sulfuric acid to produce electricity. Space shuttles use devices called fuel cells that provide electricity to power all the crafts' devices. Fuel cells use the strong base potassium hydroxide as an electrolyte. Instead of metal electrodes, the fuel cells use oxygen and hydrogen brought from Earth. At the same time that the fuel cells provide electrical energy to power a space shuttle, they also produce water that the crew can use.

Section 8.4 Assessment

Reviewing Concepts

1. How is pH related to the concentration of hydronium ions in solution?
2. What determines the degree to which an acid or base is weak or strong?
3. Are strong acids and bases good electrolytes? Explain why or why not.
4. Why is pure water neutral?
5. What is a buffer?

Critical Thinking

6. **Comparing and Contrasting** Explain how the concentration of an acid differs from the strength of an acid.
7. **Relating Cause and Effect** Suppose you add another liter of water to 1 liter of a 1-molar solution of hydrochloric acid. What happens to the number of hydronium ions in solution? What happens to the concentration?

Writing in Science

Explanatory Paragraph Explain the concept of a pH scale, and compare the pH values of acids, bases, and pure water. (*Hint:* Use examples from Figure 22 to help you describe the range of the pH scale.)

Electrolytes

Address Misconceptions **L2**

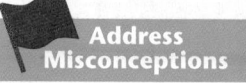

Many students think that pure water is a good conductor of electricity. Though pure water has some ions due to self-ionization, the number of ions in pure water is not great enough to carry an electric current. Explain that practically all water obtained from traditional sources contains electrolytes. Thus, it is very difficult to find water that will not conduct electricity. Even deionized water samples may have some dissolved ions depending on the effectiveness of the deionizer or the method of storage. **Verbal**

3 ASSESS

Evaluate Understanding **L2**

Encourage students to make a note card for each of the Key Concepts questions listed on p. 246. Then, ask them to make a note card that answers each question using one of the boldfaced key points in this section. Have them make three more sets of note cards using the vocabulary terms and their definitions. Encourage students to review the information on their cards.

Reteach **L1**

As a class, make a chart that lists what strong acids, strong bases, and strong electrolytes have in common. Do the same for weak acids, weak bases, and weak electrolytes.

Writing in Science

Acceptable answers include explaining that a pH scale allows you to describe how acidic or basic a solution is. Solutions with a pH lower than 7, such as vinegar, are acidic. Solutions with a pH higher than 7, such as household ammonia, are basic. Solutions with a pH of 7 (the same as pure water) are neutral.

Interactive Textbook If your class subscribes to the Interactive Textbook, use it to review key concepts in Section 8.4.

Section 8.4 Assessment

1. Solutions with a low pH have a high concentration of hydronium ions in solution and are acidic. Solutions with a high pH have a low concentration of hydronium ions in solution and are basic.
2. The degree to which an acid or base dissociates or ionizes when dissolved in water determines whether it is weak or strong.
3. Strong acids and bases are strong electrolytes because they dissociate or ionize almost completely when dissolved in water.
4. Pure water is neutral because it contains equal concentrations of hydronium and hydroxide ions.
5. A buffer is a solution that is resistant to large changes in pH.
6. The concentration of an acid is the amount of solute dissolved in a given amount of solution. The strength of an acid refers to the solute's tendency to form ions in water.
7. The number of hydronium ions stays the same. The concentration decreases because there are fewer ions per liter.

CONCEPTS in Action

River of Life L2

Background

When blood pH falls outside of the normal range, 7.35–7.45, a person may experience acidosis or alkalosis.

Acidosis occurs when blood has a pH as low as 7.2. It can arise from the blood having too much carbon dioxide due to poor breathing, production of acids due to high glucose levels in the urine (a symptom of diabetes), and loss of bicarbonate due to severe diarrhea. Alkalosis occurs when blood has a pH above 7.45. It can arise from the blood having too little carbon dioxide due to hyperventilation, the loss of stomach acid due to vomiting, and the presence of high levels of bicarbonate in fluids delivered intravenously (through an IV).

CONCEPTS in Action

River of Life

Just as rivers are used to transport products and raw materials, blood connects the body's living cells, delivering nutrients and carrying away wastes. The exact composition of this red liquid changes continuously as it flows through the body.

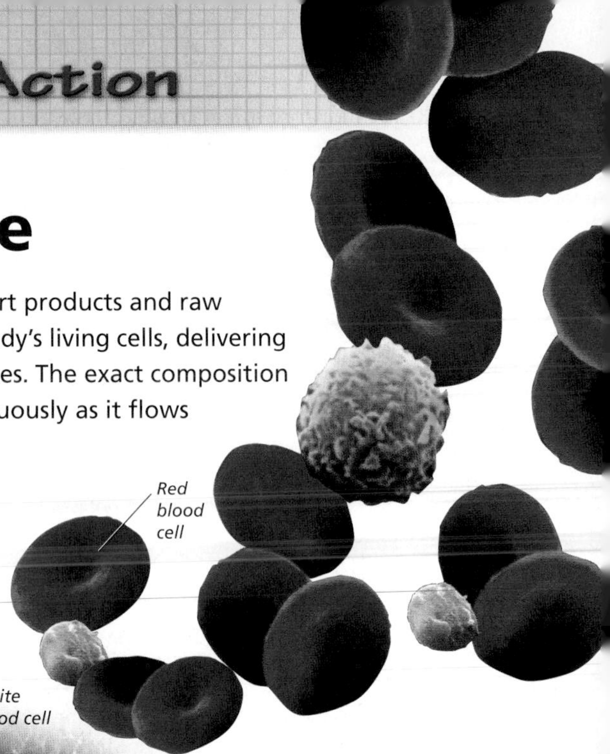
Red blood cell

Liquid tissue
Blood is a mixture of cells—red blood cells, white blood cells, and platelets—suspended in a water-based solution called plasma. Nutrients, vitamins, and minerals also travel in blood, dissolved in the plasma. The cells and other substances remain suspended in the blood because the heart's pumping action keeps the blood moving.

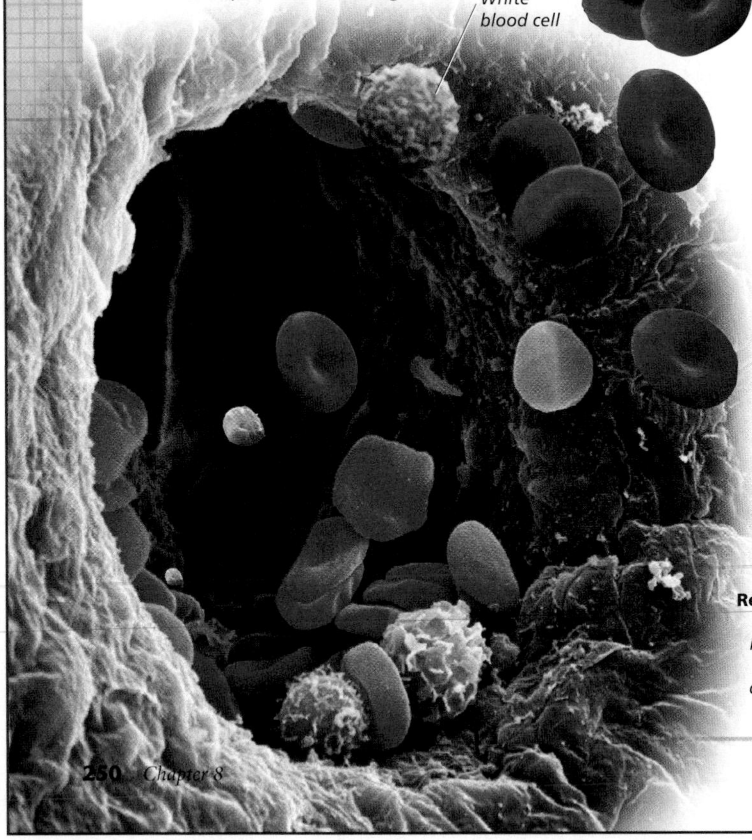
White blood cell

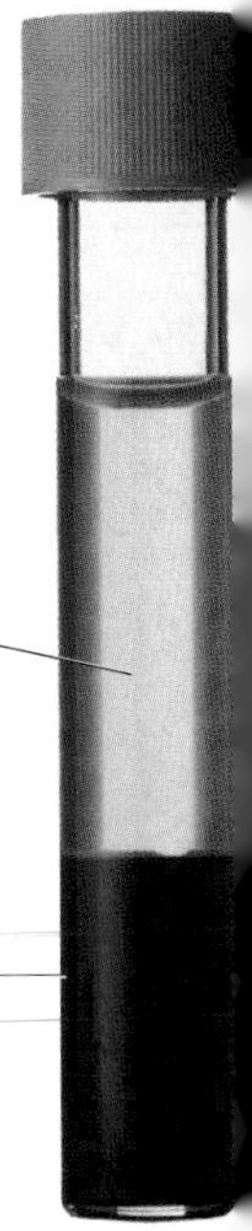

Blood components
When left to sit, blood separates into its parts. About 55 percent makes up the liquid top layer and 45 percent makes up the cellular layer below.

Plasma *This liquid part of the blood is about 90 percent water. The other 10 percent includes many dissolved substances, such as proteins and glucose.*

White blood cells and platelets *White blood cells help the body fight disease. Platelets help the blood to clot when bleeding occurs.*

Red blood cells *These cells contain the compound hemoglobin, which carries oxygen from the lungs to cells throughout the body.*

250 Chapter 8

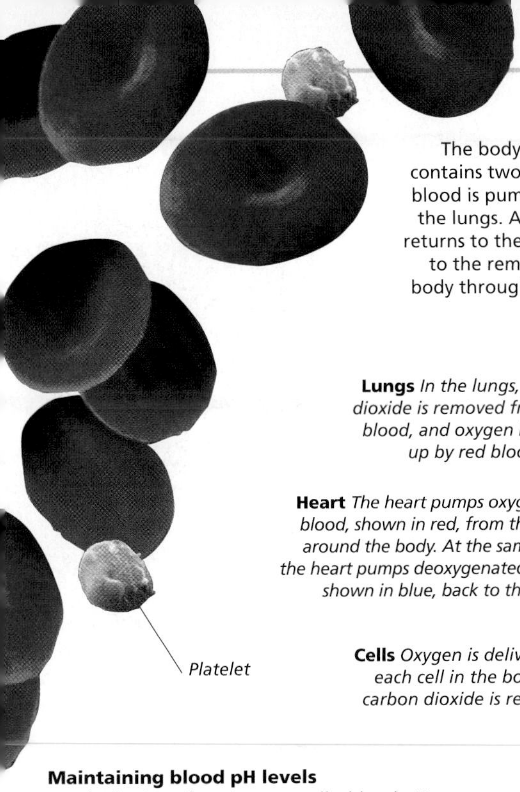
Platelet

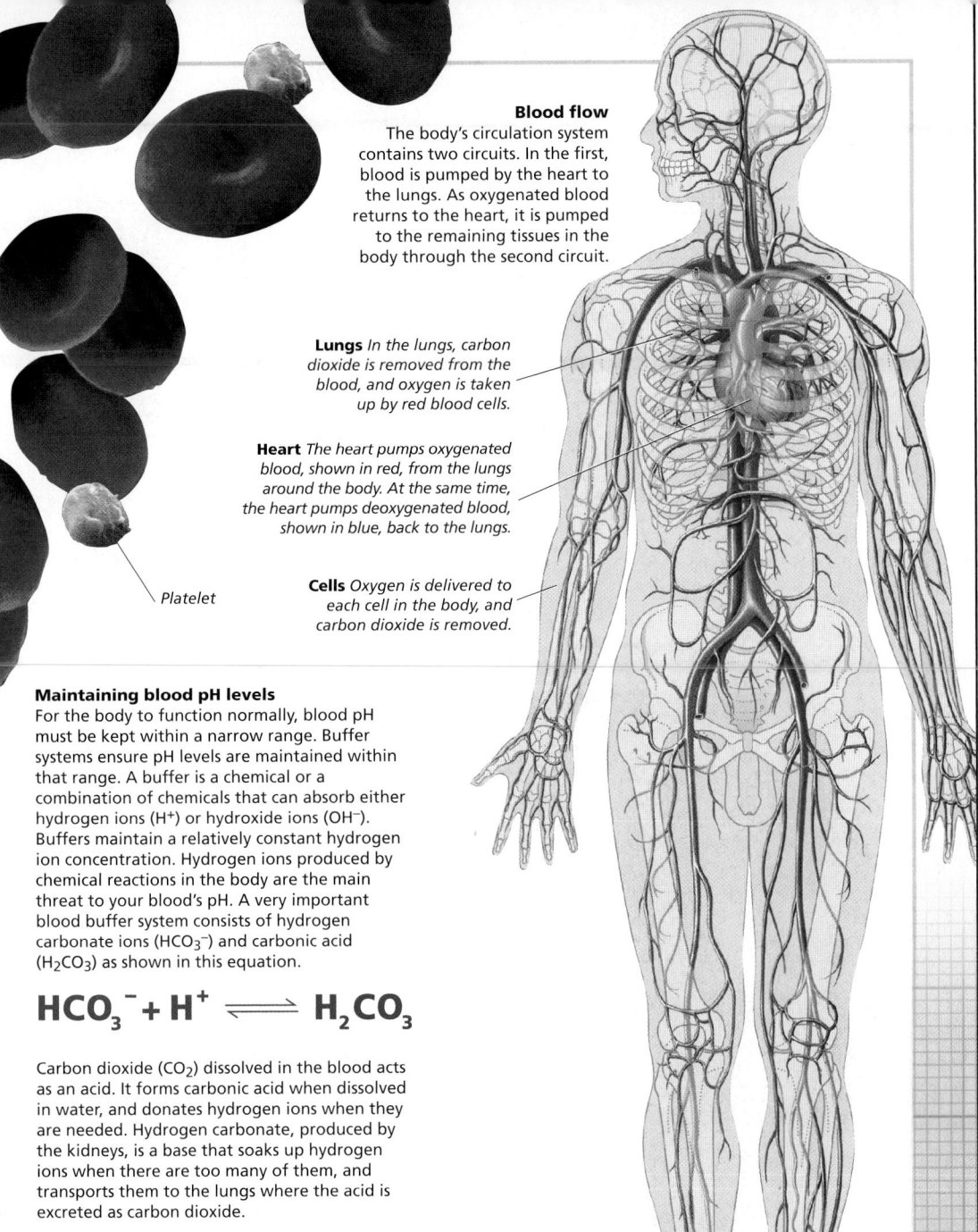

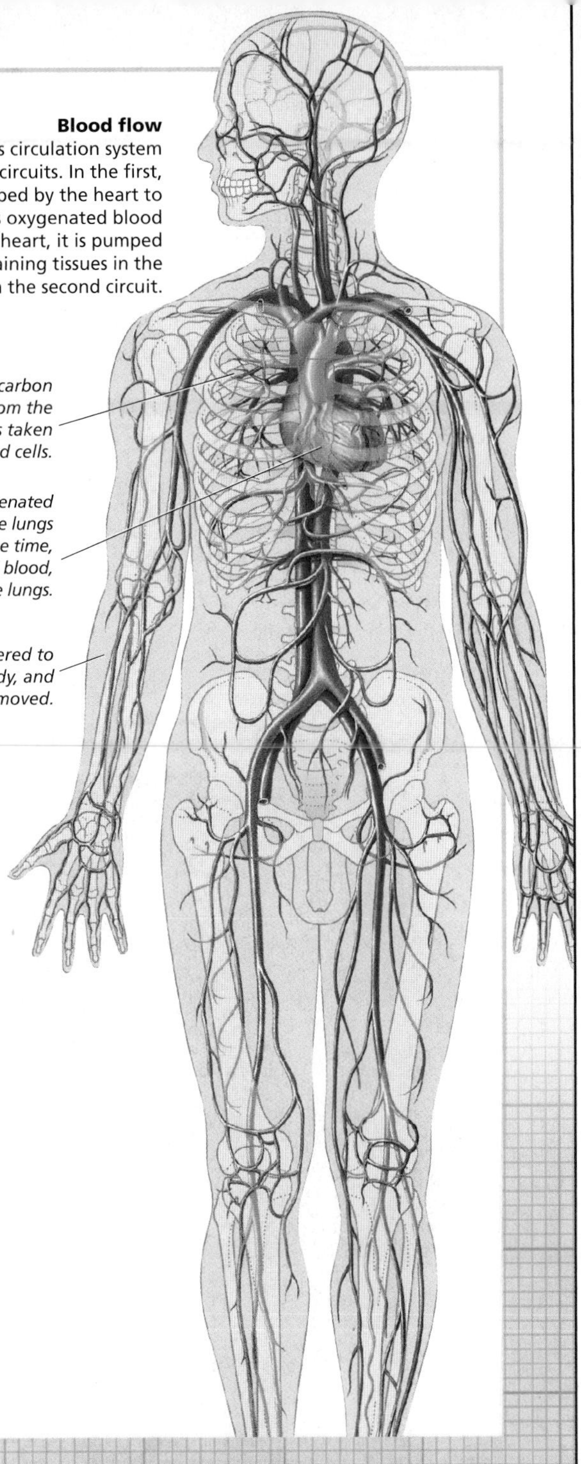
Blood flow
The body's circulation system contains two circuits. In the first, blood is pumped by the heart to the lungs. As oxygenated blood returns to the heart, it is pumped to the remaining tissues in the body through the second circuit.
Lungs *In the lungs, carbon dioxide is removed from the blood, and oxygen is taken up by red blood cells.*
Heart *The heart pumps oxygenated blood, shown in red, from the lungs around the body. At the same time, the heart pumps deoxygenated blood, shown in blue, back to the lungs.*
Cells *Oxygen is delivered to each cell in the body, and carbon dioxide is removed.*

Maintaining blood pH levels

For the body to function normally, blood pH must be kept within a narrow range. Buffer systems ensure pH levels are maintained within that range. A buffer is a chemical or a combination of chemicals that can absorb either hydrogen ions (H^+) or hydroxide ions (OH^-). Buffers maintain a relatively constant hydrogen ion concentration. Hydrogen ions produced by chemical reactions in the body are the main threat to your blood's pH. A very important blood buffer system consists of hydrogen carbonate ions (HCO_3^-) and carbonic acid (H_2CO_3) as shown in this equation.

$$HCO_3^- + H^+ \rightleftharpoons H_2CO_3$$

Carbon dioxide (CO_2) dissolved in the blood acts as an acid. It forms carbonic acid when dissolved in water, and donates hydrogen ions when they are needed. Hydrogen carbonate, produced by the kidneys, is a base that soaks up hydrogen ions when there are too many of them, and transports them to the lungs where the acid is excreted as carbon dioxide.

Build Science Skills **L2**

Applying Concepts ACTIVITY

Purpose In this activity, students test for the presence of carbon dioxide in breath and compare the carbon dioxide content of breath before and after exercise.

Materials calcium hydroxide (pickling lime); 2 large, sealable jars; clear plastic cups; straws; stopwatches; jump ropes

Class Time 25 minutes

Safety Caution students to only exhale through the straw. Limewater is corrosive. Have students wear safety goggles, plastic gloves, and lab aprons.

Procedure Prepare the day before a solution made of 1 tablespoon of pickling lime dissolved in 1 quart of water. Seal the jar and let it sit overnight. The next day, carefully pour off the clear liquid into a clean jar. Avoid transferring any of the white solid to the new jar. Seal the jar and save the limewater for the activity. Tell students that limewater turns cloudy in the presence of carbon dioxide. Pour into each test cup a small amount of limewater. Have students measure how long it takes for the solution to turn cloudy when they exhale into a straw submersed in the solution. Do not allow them to suck any of the limewater into the straw or into their mouths. Then, ask students to perform some sort of exercise. If you are able to go outside or to the gymnasium, students may jump rope for 5–10 minutes. If jump ropes are not available, students could walk briskly or do calisthenics for several minutes. Then, have students perform the test with a fresh solution of limewater.

Expected Outcome Limewater turns cloudy in the presence of carbon dioxide. The solution turns cloudy more quickly after exercise due to an increase in the levels of carbon dioxide in breath. **Kinesthetic**

(continued)

Using Blood

Build Science Skills L3

Inferring Explain that when a recipient's blood serum contains antibodies that react to the antigens on the surface of a donor's blood cells, it will produce a potentially fatal clumping of blood cells. Each blood type has a particular combination of antigens and antibodies. You can always receive blood of your own type. However, depending on your blood type, you may or may not be able to receive blood of another type. Give the following information to students.

- Type A blood has Type A antigens on its blood cells and anti-B antibodies in its serum.
- Type B blood has Type B antigens on its cells and anti-A antibodies in its serum.
- Type AB blood has both Type A and Type B antigens on its blood cells, but neither anti-A nor anti-B antibodies in its serum.
- Type O blood contains neither A nor B antigens on its cells but has both anti-A and anti-B antibodies in its serum. Ask, **Can you deduce which type of blood a person would need to donate to anyone?** *(People with Type O blood are universal donors.)* **Can you deduce which type of blood a person would need to have to be able to receive all other types?** *(People with Type AB blood are universal receivers.)*
Logical

Using Blood

Because blood is continuously replenished by the body, it can be taken from healthy people and made available for those who need it—whether because of blood loss in accidents or surgery, or to treat illnesses such as anemia or cancer.

Blood banks store blood from donors, or sometimes from a patient, for use during a planned surgery. Once collected, compounds are added to prevent clotting. Most blood is separated into components. For example, plasma can be stored at –18°C for up to 12 months, while platelets are stored at room temperature and must be used within 5 days.

Charles Drew
During the 1940s, physician and inventor Charles Drew developed methods for separating and storing blood on a large scale, providing the basis for today's Red Cross centers.

1900: Karl Landsteiner discovers three of the main blood groups (A, B, and O). The fourth group, AB, is discovered in 1902.

1932: First blood bank is established in Russia, followed in 1937 by the first United States hospital blood bank in Chicago.

1940: Charles Drew pioneers large-scale separation and storage of blood plasma.

1948: American Red Cross establishes a national blood collection and distribution program.

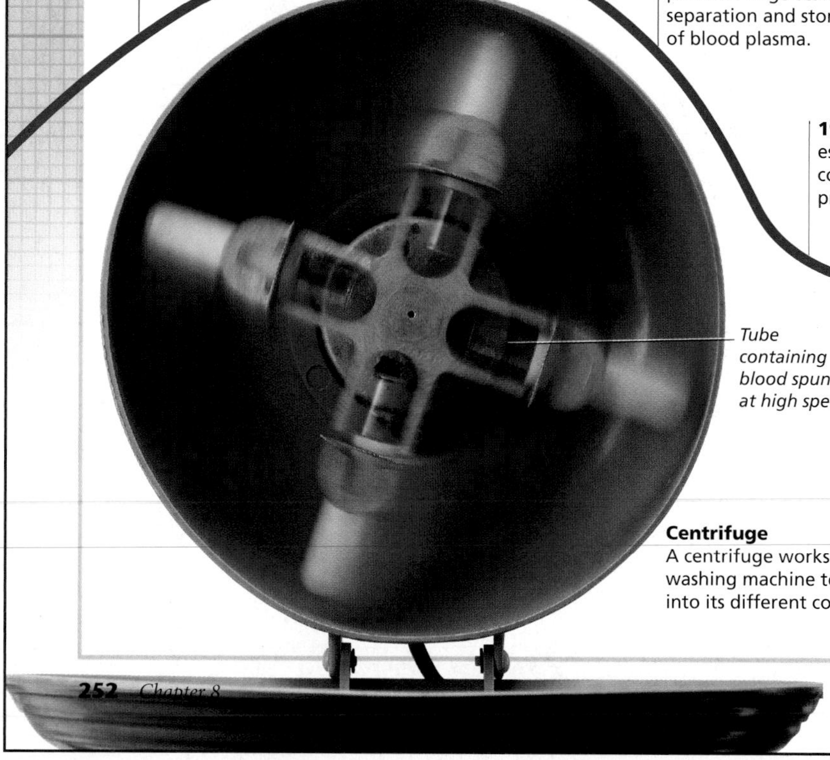
Tube containing blood spun at high speed

Centrifuge
A centrifuge works like the spin cycle on a washing machine to separate blood quickly into its different components.

Facts and Figures

Blood Types Some blood types are rarer than others. The following chart lists the approximate percentage of each blood type in the U.S. population.

Blood Type	Percentage of U.S. Population
O positive	38%
A positive	34%
B positive	9%
O negative	7%
A negative	6%
AB positive	3%
B negative	2%
AB negative	1%

Blood Transfusion

Each year, more than 4 million people in the United States receive a blood transfusion, either of whole blood or of a blood component, such as plasma or platelets. Before being stored, blood from a donor is tested to make sure it is safe.

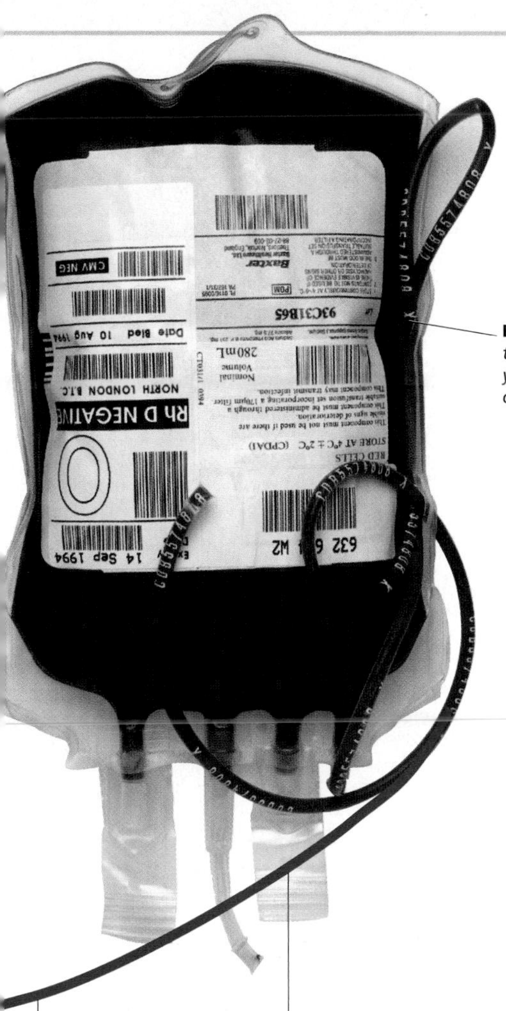

Blood bag *The use of whole blood in transfusions has been reduced in recent years but it is retained as a treatment option in cases of massive blood loss.*

Donated blood

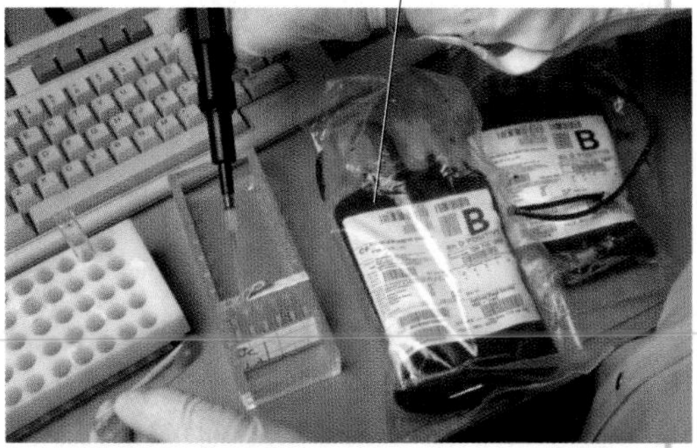

Crossmatching blood
Blood groups are used to determine which blood can be given to whom. Antigens, or molecular markers on the surface of red blood cells, determine the type of blood a person can safely receive in a transfusion. If blood of incompatible types is mixed, the red blood cells form clumps instead of mixing properly. These clumps can block blood vessels and even cause death.

1950: Plastic blood bags are introduced for blood storage, allowing blood to be frozen at lower temperatures and for longer periods.

1985: First HIV testing of donor blood is carried out, followed by other tests to protect transfusion patients from disease.

Going Further

- Research and write a paragraph about the work of Charles Drew. What methods did he use to prolong the storage time for whole blood? Why did he decide to separate whole blood into plasma and cells for storage?
- Take a Discovery Channel Video Field Trip by watching "Suspended in Blood."

Discovery Channel School **Video Field Trip**

Going Further

Acceptable answers include: Charles Drew (1904–1950) was a doctor and researcher who discovered that blood could be stored longer when the plasma was separated from the rest of the blood and then frozen. When the plasma is recombined with red blood cells, it can be used for blood transfusion. If blood is frozen without separating the cells from the plasma, the red blood cells will break down after two days. Drew also discovered that plasma could be safely given to patients regardless of their blood type or the type of the donor.
Verbal

Use Community Resources **L2**

Arrange for a medical technologist to visit the class. Have the medical technologist discuss the importance of blood type in using blood donations for transfusions. If possible, and following standard safety procedures, have the medical technologist perform a blood test on student volunteers to determine their blood type.
Interpersonal

Discovery Channel School **Video Field Trip**
Suspended in Blood

After students have viewed the Video Field Trip, ask them the following questions: **What are the most commonly found cells in blood?** *(Red blood cells)* **What is the function of red blood cells in the blood?** *(They pick up oxygen in the lungs and deliver it throughout the body.)* **How does the body use blood to dispose of the carbon dioxide that it produces?** *(Red blood cells absorb carbon dioxide on their way back to the lungs and release it there.)* **When you exercise, your body needs more oxygen. What changes occur that deliver the extra oxygen where it is needed?** *(You breathe faster and your heart beats faster. As a result, the blood picks up more oxygen in the lungs and moves faster to deliver the oxygen.)* **What are two other kinds of cells found in blood, and what is their function?** *(White blood cells attack invading bacteria, or germs, to help prevent disease. The blood also contains platelets that collect at cuts to block the flow of blood and to form a clot.)*

Exploration Lab

Preparing a Salt by Neutralization L2

Objective
After completing this activity, students will be able to
- perform a neutralization reaction.
- determine the indicating colors of an indicator.
- detect the occurrence of a neutralization reaction using an indicator.

Skills Focus **Observing, Measuring, Analyzing Data**

Prep Time 20 minutes

Advance Prep Prepare solutions of 1 M hydrochloric acid and 1 M sodium hydroxide. To help students keep track of their solutions, prepare sets of labeled test tubes for each group of students. Provide each group with about 8 mL of each solution. Provide phenolphthalein solution in a dropper bottle.

Class Time 60 minutes (2 class periods)

Safety Students should use caution with the acid and base solutions. Remind students never to taste anything (e.g., salt) in a lab. Hydrochloric acid and sodium hydroxide are corrosive. In case of spills, clean thoroughly with water. Caution students not to touch the hot plate or the heated beaker. Have students observe safety symbols and wear safety goggles, plastic gloves, and lab aprons.

Sample Data

Materials	Observations
1 mL	22 drops
HCl + phenolphthalein	clear
NaOH + phenolphthalein	pink
Drops of HCl used	88 drops
mL of HCl used	4 mL
Drops of NaOH used	88 drops
mL of NaOH used	4 mL
pH of final solution	7

Exploration Lab

Preparing a Salt by Neutralization

In this lab, you will prepare table salt by reacting hydrochloric acid (HCl) with sodium hydroxide (NaOH). To be sure that all of the acid and base have reacted, you will use phenolphthalein. You will first have to test the colors of this indicator with a known acid and base. After the acid and base have reacted, you will measure the pH of the solution with pH paper. Finally, you will evaporate the water and collect the sodium chloride.

Problem How can you produce a salt by neutralization?

Materials
- 3 dropper pipets
- labels
- 10-mL graduated cylinder
- test tube rack
- 2 10-mL test tubes
- distilled water
- hydrochloric acid
- sodium hydroxide solution
- 3 stirring rods
- phenolphthalein solution
- 2 25-mL beakers
- pH paper
- large watch glass
- 100-mL beaker
- hot plate

For the probeware version of this lab, see Probeware Lab Manual, Lab 3.

Skills Observing, Measuring, Analyzing Data

Procedure

Part A: Preparing for the Experiment

1. On a separate sheet of paper, copy the data table shown.

Data Table

Material(s)	Observation
1 mL	________ drops
HCl + phenolphthalein	________ (color)
NaOH+ phenolphthalein	________ (color)
Drops of HCl used	________ drops
mL of HCl used	________ mL
Drops of NaOH used	________ drops
mL of NaOH used	________ mL
pH of final solution	________

2. Place about 10 mL of distilled water in a 25-mL beaker. Set the graduated cylinder on the table and add distilled water to the 5-mL mark. Be sure that the *bottom* of the meniscus is on the 5-mL line.
3. To determine the number of drops in 1 mL, use a clean dropper pipet to add 1 mL of water to the graduated cylinder. Hold the dropper pipet straight up and down with the tip of the dropper pipet just inside the mouth of the cylinder. As your partner watches the liquid level in the cylinder, add drops of water one at a time while counting the drops. Continue adding drops until the liquid level reaches 6 mL. Record the number of drops in 1 mL.
4. Label one clean dropper pipet *Hydrochloric acid (HCl)* and the other *Sodium hydroxide (NaOH).*
5. Using the HCl dropper pipet, add 3 mL of hydrochloric acid to a clean test tube. **CAUTION** *Hydrochloric acid is corrosive. In case of spills, clean thoroughly with water.* Add 2 to 3 drops of phenolphthalein to the test tube. Use a clean stirring rod to mix the hydrochloric acid and indicator. Record your observations.
6. Using the dropper pipet labeled NaOH, add 3 mL of sodium hydroxide solution to a clean test tube. **CAUTION** *Sodium hydroxide is corrosive. In case of spills, clean thoroughly with water.* Add 2 to 3 drops of phenolphthalein to the test tube. Use a clean stirring rod to mix the sodium hydroxide solution and indicator. Record your observations.

Part B: Making the Salt

7. Using the HCl dropper pipet, add 4 mL of hydrochloric acid to a clean 25-mL beaker. Record the number of drops you used. Add 2 to 3 drops of phenolphthalein to the beaker.
8. Use the NaOH dropper pipet to add sodium hydroxide drop by drop to the beaker of hydrochloric acid and phenolphthalein, stirring constantly. Count the drops as you add them. As a pink color remains longer, add the drops more slowly.

9. Continue to add and count the drops of sodium hydroxide until a light pink color remains for at least 30 seconds. (Note: If you add too much sodium hydroxide, add a few more drops of hydrochloric acid until the color disappears.) Record any additional drops of hydrochloric acid that you added. Then, carefully add sodium hydroxide until one drop produces a lasting pink color. Record the total number of drops of sodium hydroxide used.
10. Use a piece of pH paper to determine the pH of the final solution. Record the pH. If the pH is higher than 7.0, add hydrochloric acid drop by drop, testing the pH with pH paper after each drop, until the pH is equal to 7.0. Record the pH and the total number of drops of HCl you added.
11. Use the solution in the beaker to fill the watch glass halfway.
12. Fill the 100-mL beaker about half full of water. Place the beaker on top of the hot plate.
13. Set the watch glass on top of the beaker.
14. Turn on the hot plate to a low setting. Adjust the heat as the water in the beaker warms. The water should simmer, but not boil.

CAUTION *Do not touch the hot plate or the beaker.* Heat until a solid is visible at the edges of the water in the watch glass and the water is nearly evaporated. Turn off the heat.

15. Allow the remaining water to evaporate. Observe the contents of the watch glass. Record your observations.
16. When the watch glass has cooled, dispose of the contents as directed by your teacher. Clean up your equipment. Wash your hands with soap and water.

Analyze and Conclude

1. **Comparing and Contrasting** What was the total amount of hydrochloric acid used to make the neutral solution? What was the total amount of sodium hydroxide? How do the amounts compare?
2. **Drawing Conclusions** What do you conclude about the concentrations of hydrochloric acid and sodium hydroxide in the solutions?
3. **Predicting** If the acid had been twice as concentrated as the base, how would your data have changed?

Teaching Tips

- When determining the number of drops in a milliliter, one student should place the tip of the dropper inside the opening of the graduated cylinder and count the drops while a second student kneels to examine the graduated cylinder at eye level.
- Students should read the level of the graduated cylinder while it is sitting on a flat surface. Remind students to read the bottom of the meniscus when making volume measurements.
- Show students how to label the pipets.
- The size of the beaker used in Step 12 depends on the size of the evaporating dish. A small evaporating dish may require a smaller beaker.
- Combine all waste solutions, and add acid or base until litmus indicates neutrality. Dispose of the neutral solution in the sink with excess water.

Expected Outcome It will take approximately the same number of milliliters of each solution to reach the pink endpoint.

Analyze and Conclude

1. See Expected Outcome. Students should recognize that they used equal volumes of base and acid.
2. The concentrations are the same.
3. It would have taken twice as much base to reach the color change.
Visual, Kinesthetic, Logical

Go Further

Have students perform a quantitative analysis to determine the identity of unknown solutions of NaOH. Prepare three solutions of NaOH (1 M, 0.5 M, and 0.1 M). Label them Solutions A, B, and C. Have students perform Steps 7–10 for each of the three unknown solutions. Using their results, they should identify each solution. It may be necessary to tell them which concentrations are expected.
Logical

Probeware Lab Manual Versions of this lab for use with probeware available from Pasco, Texas Instruments, and Vernier are in Probeware Lab Manual.

Study Guide

Study Tip

Customize Your Notes
Customizing your notes can help you remember important concepts. For example, if you like to draw, you may include illustrations that help you remember facts or terms. If you are better at organizing, use color coding or highlighting to link ideas or make facts more memorable.

Thinking Visually

a. Neutralization
b. Water
c. Salt

Assessment

Interactive Textbook If your class subscribes to the Interactive Textbook, your students can go online to access an interactive version of the Student Edition and a self-test.

Reviewing Content

1. d 2. a 3. d
4. b 5. a 6. c
7. c 8. b 9. a
10. d

Understanding Concepts

11. Increasing the temperature of a solvent decreases the solubility of a gas.
12. More energy is released when the solution forms than is absorbed when the solute and solvent molecules separate and break apart.
13. It provides more surface area that the solvent can contact.
14. An unsaturated solution contains less solute than it can hold at a given temperature; a saturated solution contains as much solute as it can hold at a given temperature; and a supersaturated solution contains more solute than it can hold at a given temperature.

CHAPTER 8

Study Guide

8.1 Formation of Solutions

Key Concepts

- Substances can dissolve in water in three ways—through dissociation, dispersion, and ionization.
- Three physical properties of a solution that can differ from those of its solute and solvent are conductivity, freezing point, and boiling point.
- During the formation of a solution, energy is either released or absorbed.
- Factors that affect the rate of dissolving include surface area, temperature, and stirring.

Vocabulary

solute, *p. 229;* solvent, *p. 229;* dissociation, *p. 229;* dispersion, *p. 230;* ionization, *p. 230*

8.2 Solubility and Concentration

Key Concepts

- Solutions are described as unsaturated, saturated, or supersaturated, depending on the amount of solute in solution.
- Three factors that affect the solubility of a solute are the type of bonding in the solute and solvent, temperature, and pressure.
- Concentration can be expressed as percent by volume, percent by mass, and molarity.

Vocabulary

solubility, *p. 235;* saturated solution, *p. 236;* unsaturated solution, *p. 236;* supersaturated solution, *p. 236;* concentration, *p. 238;* molarity, *p. 239*

8.3 Properties of Acids and Bases

Key Concepts

- Acids taste sour, react with certain metals, and turn blue litmus paper red. Bases taste bitter, feel slippery, and turn red litmus paper blue.
- The neutralization reaction between an acid and a base produces a salt and water.
- Acids can be defined as proton donors, and bases can be defined as proton acceptors.

Vocabulary

acid, *p. 240;* indicator, *p. 241;* base, *p. 242;* neutralization, *p. 244;* salt, *p. 244*

8.4 Strength of Acids and Bases

Key Concepts

- The lower the pH value, the greater the H_3O^+ ion concentration is. The higher the pH value, the lower the H_3O^+ ion concentration is.
- The strength of an acid or a base depends on the degree to which it dissociates or ionizes in water.
- Strong acids and bases are good electrolytes because they produce many ions in solution.

Vocabulary

pH, *p. 247;* buffer, *p. 248;* electrolyte, *p. 249*

Thinking Visually

Concept Map Use the information on acids and bases to complete the concept map below.

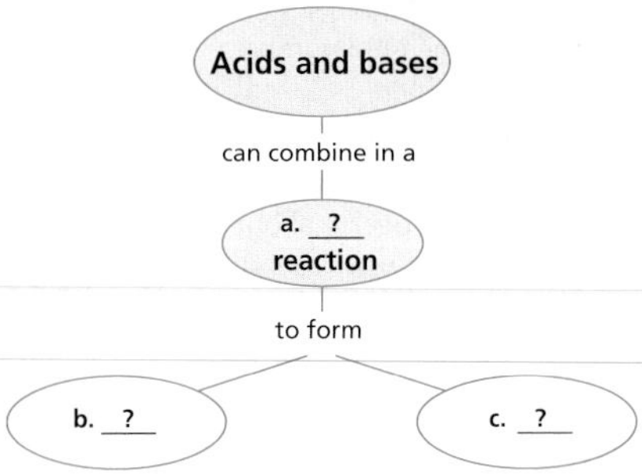
Acids and bases
can combine in a
a. ?
reaction
to form
b. ?
c. ?

Chapter Resources

Print
- ***Chapter and Unit Tests,*** Chapter 8 Test A and Test B
- ***Test Prep Resources,*** Chapter 8

Technology
- ***Computer Test Bank,*** Chapter Test 8
- ***Interactive Textbook,*** Chapter 8
- ***Go Online,*** PHSchool.com, Chapter 8

CHAPTER 8

Assessment

Interactive textbook with assessment at PHSchool.com iText

Reviewing Content

Choose the letter that best answers the question or completes the statement.

1. The parts of a solution are the
   a. salt and vapor. b. solvent and solid.
   c. solute and water. d. solute and solvent.
2. In a solution, the solute is the substance that
   a. dissolves in the solvent.
   b. is in the greatest quantity.
   c. is the liquid.
   d. is a solid.
3. Sugar dissolves in water through
   a. ionization. b. dissociation.
   c. neutralization. d. dispersion.
4. Ionic compounds produce ions in solution by
   a. ionization. b. dissociation.
   c. evaporation. d. dispersion.
5. The process by which some molecular compounds dissolve in water to form ions is
   a. ionization. b. dissociation.
   c. neutralization. d. dispersion.
6. The boiling point of a liquid solution is
   a. the same as the boiling point of the solvent.
   b. the same as the boiling point of the solute.
   c. higher than the boiling point of the solvent.
   d. lower than the boiling point of the solvent.
7. Which of the following is NOT characteristic of an acid?
   a. tastes sour
   b. reacts with metals
   c. turns litmus paper blue
   d. produces H_3O^+ ions in solution
8. The reaction between an acid and a base is called
   a. ionization. b. neutralization.
   c. dissociation. d. dispersion.
9. A solution of sodium hydroxide in water is most likely to have a pH close to
   a. 14. b. 7.
   c. 5. d. 3.
10. Substances that form ions when dissolved in water are
    a. solutions. b. molecules.
    c. polar. d. electrolytes.

Understanding Concepts

11. How does increasing the temperature of a solvent affect the solubility of a gas?
12. Explain why the temperature of water might increase when a solution forms.
13. Explain why crushing a solute increases the rate of solution.
14. Name and describe the three types of solutions.
15. Explain why oil does not dissolve in water.
16. Describe how you might increase the solubility of a solid in a liquid.
17. Explain how a solution can be both dilute and saturated.
18. Describe three different ways in which the concentration of a solution can be reported.
19. Define and give an example of an acid and of a base.
20. List the properties of acids and bases. Which of the properties would you use to safely test whether an unknown substance was an acid or a base?
21. If you add hydrochloric acid (HCl) to magnesium (Mg) metal, what will you observe? What products form in this reaction?
22. Identify each of the following compounds as an acid, base, or salt: LiOH, H_2CO_3, $Ba(OH)_2$, and KCl.
23. What determines the strength of an acid?
24. What happens when a solution of nitric acid (HNO_3) is added to a solution of potassium hydroxide (KOH)? What are the products?
25. Which of the following compounds can react with H_2SO_4 to form a salt? Name the salt(s) that would form. NaCl, $Ca(OH)_2$, HF, $AlCl_3$, H_2O, $Mg(OH)_2$

Homework Guide

Section	Questions
8.1	1–6, 12
8.2	11, 13–17
8.3	7–8, 18–21, 23–24
8.4	9–10, 22

Assessment (continued)

15. Oil is a nonpolar substance. Water is a polar substance. Water molecules attract one another much more than they attract the oil. Therefore, the water stays together and doesn't mix with the oil.
16. You could heat the liquid.
17. If the solute isn't very soluble, the solution can be saturated and still have very little solute in it, so it would be dilute.
18. Percent by volume (volume of solute divided by volume of solution multiplied by 100%), percent by mass (mass of solute divided by mass of solution multiplied by 100%), and molarity (moles of solute divided by liters of solution).
19. An acid produces hydronium ions in solution. Acceptable answers include hydrochloric acid, citric acid, and acetic acid. A base produces hydroxide ions in solution. Acceptable answers include sodium hydroxide, calcium hydroxide, and ammonia.
20. Acids taste sour, react with metals, and turn blue litmus paper red. Bases taste bitter, feel slippery, and turn red litmus paper blue. Acceptable answers include use of litmus paper.
21. You would observe bubbles of hydrogen gas forming on the metal. The products are magnesium chloride ($MgCl_2$) and hydrogen gas (H_2).
22. LiOH is a base, H_2CO_3 is an acid, $Ba(OH)_2$ is a base, and KCl is a salt.
23. The strength of an acid is determined by how completely it ionizes when dissolved in water.
24. A neutralization reaction occurs. The products are potassium nitrate and water.
25. $Ca(OH)_2$ and $Mg(OH)_2$. The salts would be calcium sulfate and magnesium sulfate.

Critical Thinking

26. NaCl is an ionic compound. When it is added to water, its ions dissociate. The ions are then pulled into solution by the polar water molecules. HCl is a polar molecular compound. When HCl is added to water, a proton is transferred from HCl to the water molecule, forming H_3O^+ and Cl^- ions. This process is an example of ionization.
27. (0.50 mol/L)(3.0 L)(342 g/mol) = 513 g
28. 9, because it is a base. If the pH were 4, it would be an acid and would be more likely to react with the metal.
29. X is a base. Z is an acid. Y could be water.

Math Skills

30. Potassium nitrate
31. It would be supersaturated.
32. 85 g

Concepts in Action

33. Acceptable answers may include the following steps: Obtain several different brands of antacids. Read the directions and measure out one dose of each antacid. Dissolve the doses in distilled water in separate beakers. Add to each beaker an indicator that changes color at a pH of about 7. Prepare a solution of HCl with a pH of 1, 2, or 3. Add hydrochloric acid to each beaker one drop at a time, counting the drops and stirring, until the indicator changes color and the color remains for at least 30 seconds. The antacid that requires the most drops is the most effective at neutralizing stomach acid. (Note: As some antacids are not very soluble in water, this experiment might require a "back titration," in which excess acid is added to dissolve all of the antacid, and the unreacted acid is then titrated with a base.)
34. Antacid A keeps stomach contents within the normal acid range. Antacid B changes stomach contents to a basic solution, which is not normal. The stomach contents must be acid to digest food. Antacid A is the more healthful choice.
35. Students should recognize that adding water to the acid will only dilute it and cause it to spread further. If workers sprinkled a powdered solid base over the acid, the base would dissolve and then neutralize the acid. An indicator could be used to determine if all the acid has been neutralized. The resulting mixture (containing water and a salt) could then be cleaned up safely like any other liquid spill.

Performance-Based Assessment

Acceptable displays include listing and illustrating the properties and examples of acids and bases discussed in this chapter. Acids and bases are used in a variety of ways to manufacture common items. Examples include sulfuric acid in the production of rayon, glue, and paper; nitric acid in the production of fertilizers, explosives, and nylon; and sodium hydroxide in the production of rayon, paper, and soap.

CHAPTER 8

Assessment *(continued)*

Critical Thinking

26. Comparing and Contrasting Compare what happens when NaCl and HCl are added to water.

27. Calculating The molar mass of sucrose, or table sugar, is 342 grams. Calculate how many grams of sucrose are required to make 3.0 liters of 0.50 M sucrose solution.

28. Applying Concepts A solution is an acid or a base, and it doesn't react with metal. Is its pH more likely to be 4 or 9? Explain your answer.

29. Inferring You have equal amounts of three colorless liquids, X, Y, and Z. An indicator is yellow in a pH of 8 or less and blue in a pH of 8 or more. The indicator turns blue in X and yellow in Y and Z. When you add liquid Z to X, the indicator turns yellow. When you add Z to Y, the solution remains yellow. Which liquid could be water?

Math Skills

Use the graph to answer Questions 30–32.

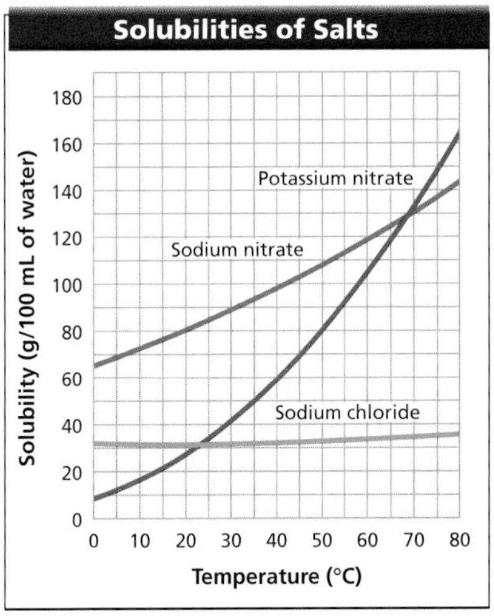
Solubilities of Salts
Solubility (g/100 mL of water)
180
160
140
120
100
80
60
40
20
0
Potassium nitrate
Sodium nitrate
Sodium chloride
0 10 20 30 40 50 60 70 80
Temperature (°C)

30. Using Graphs Which compound is the most soluble at 75°C?

31. Interpreting Diagrams What kind of solution would you have if it contained 50 grams of sodium chloride in 100 mL of water at 30°C?

32. Calculating How many grams of sodium nitrate would you need to make 100 mL of a saturated solution at 25°C?

Concepts in Action

33. Designing an Experiment Commercials often say that antacids "neutralize excess stomach acid." Stomach acid is hydrochloric acid with a pH of around 1–4 depending on what and how recently you have eaten. Design an experiment to test how effective various brands of antacids are at neutralizing stomach acid.

34. Making Judgments A single dose of antacid A changes the pH of stomach contents from 1 to 3. A single dose of antacid B changes the pH of stomach contents from 1 to 8. Which antacid would you choose to use? Explain your answer.

35. Writing in Science You are in charge of writing the directions for a safety workers' training manual. The manual tells workers what to do if a train carrying nitric acid derails and the acid spills. What are some things they could do to clean up the spill? Write the procedures in steps, explaining why each step is done.

Performance-Based Assessment

Making a Display Prepare a classroom display on the importance of acids and bases in daily life. Include information on the properties of acids and bases, as well as examples of where they are found in daily life. Research ways in which manufacturers use acids and bases to produce common items and include that information in your display.

Go Online
PHSchool.com

For: Self-grading assessment
Visit: PHSchool.com
Web Code: cca-1080

Standardized Test Prep

Test-Taking Tip

Some test questions may include a drawing of lab equipment. It is important that you carefully study the information presented in the question as well as the picture provided. Keep these tips in mind when answering a question with lab equipment drawings:

- Identify the equipment shown so you can determine what information the drawing can or cannot give you.
- Think of similar labs or questions you may have seen. These may help you determine the information available from the drawing.
- The drawings may not be drawn to scale. You must read and interpret the scales and increments carefully.
- Carefully read the question. You may not need all the information presented in the drawing or you may need more information than is presented in the drawing.

Practice using these tips in Question 6.

1. Which of the following will NOT increase the rate at which a solute dissolves in a solvent?
(A) increasing the surface area of the solute
(B) stirring the solvent
(C) increasing the temperature
(D) increasing the particle size of the solute
(E) agitating the mixture

2. At 20°C, a saturated solution contains 36 g of NaCl and 100 mL of water. All the solid is dissolved. What happens if the solution is slowly cooled to 0°C?
(A) It freezes.
(B) It becomes supersaturated.
(C) The pressure on it increases greatly.
(D) More NaCl could be dissolved in it.
(E) The NaCl reacts with the water.

3. Which pH indicates a solution of an acid?
(A) pH = 3
(B) pH = 7
(C) pH = 9
(D) pH = 14
(E) pH = 19

4. Which substance is a weak base?
(A) NaCl
(B) NH_3
(C) HCl
(D) HF
(E) KOH

5. What reaction occurs when a solution of hydrochloric acid, HCl, is mixed with a solution of calcium hydroxide, $Ca(OH)_2$?
(A) $Cl + Ca(OH) \longrightarrow HCa + Cl(OH)_2$
(B) $HCl + Ca(OH)_2 \longrightarrow H(OH)_2 + CaCl$
(C) $2HCl + Ca(OH)_2 \longrightarrow 2H_2O + CaCl_2$
(D) $2HCl + Ca(OH)_2 \longrightarrow H_2Ca + 2ClOH$
(E) $HCl + Ca(OH)_2 \longrightarrow$ no reaction occurs

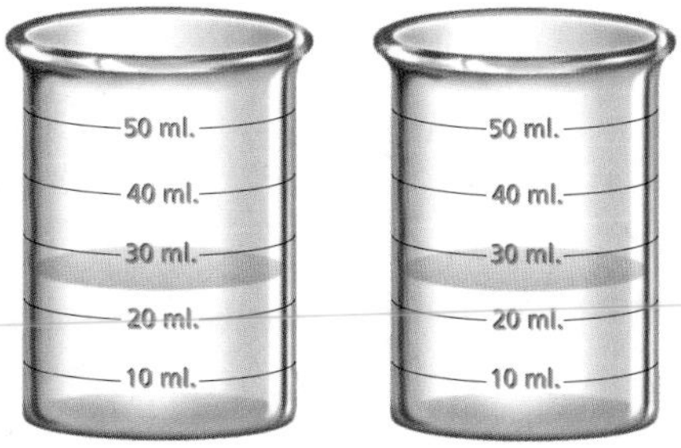
50 mL
40 mL
30 mL
20 mL
10 mL
50 mL
40 mL
30 mL
20 mL
10 mL

0.1 M HCl 0.1 M NaOH

6. If the contents of the two beakers shown above are mixed, the resulting solution
(A) will turn red litmus paper blue.
(B) will turn blue litmus paper red.
(C) will resist large changes in pH.
(D) will react with metals.
(E) will not change the color of red or blue litmus paper.

Standardized Test Prep

1. D **2.** B **3.** A
4. B **5.** C **6.** E

Go Online PHSchool.com

Your students can independently test their knowledge of the chapter and print out their test results for your files.

CHAPTER 9

Planning Guide

Use these planning tools
Easy Planner
Teacher Express

SECTION OBJECTIVES	STANDARDS NATIONAL (See p. T18.)	STANDARDS STATE	ACTIVITIES and LABS
9.1 Carbon Compounds, pp. 262–269 1 block or 2 periods **9.1.1 Relate** the structures of three forms of carbon to their properties. **9.1.2 Explain** why there are millions of different organic compounds. **9.1.3 Relate** the number and arrangement of carbon atoms in hydrocarbons to their properties. **9.1.4 Distinguish** unsaturated from saturated hydrocarbons. **9.1.5 Classify** hydrocarbons using structural formulas and names. **9.1.6 Describe** the formation, composition, and uses of three types of fossil fuels. **9.1.7 Distinguish** complete combustion from incomplete combustion of fossil fuels. **9.1.8 Describe** the effects of some products of the combustion of fossil fuels.	A-1, A-2, B-3, C-5, D-2, F-1, F-2, F-3, F-4, F-5, G-1, G-2, G-3		**SE** Inquiry Activity: Do All Carbon Compounds Have Similar Properties? p. 261 **L2** **SE** Quick Lab: Comparing Isomers, p. 265 **L2** **TE** Teacher Demo: Comparing Models of Molecules, p. 264 **L2** **TE** Teacher Demo: Fractional Distillation, p. 267 **L2**
9.2 Substituted Hydrocarbons, pp. 272–274 1 block or 2 periods **9.2.1 Classify** substituted hydrocarbons based on their functional groups. **9.2.2 Describe** some properties and reactions of five types of substituted hydrocarbons.	A-1, B-2, F-1, F-3, F-4, F-5		**TE** Teacher Demo: Modeling Functional Groups, p. 272 **L2**
9.3 Polymers, pp. 275–280 1 block or 2 periods **9.3.1 Distinguish** a monomer from a polymer. **9.3.2 Compare** three examples of synthetic polymers. **9.3.3 Describe** the structures and functions of four types of natural polymers.	B-2, C-1, C-2, C-5, G-1, G-3		**SE** Quick Lab: Distinguishing Sugars from Starches, p. 278 **L2** **LM** Investigation 9A: Testing for Nutrients in Foods **L2** **LM** Investigation 9B: Comparing Cross-Linked Polymers **L1**
9.4 Reactions in Cells, pp. 282–284 1 block or 2 periods **9.4.1 Compare** photosynthesis and cellular respiration. **9.4.2 Explain** how enzymes and vitamins help reactions take place in cells.	A-1, A-2, B-3, C-1, C-5, F-1		**SE** Consumer Lab: Comparing Vitamin C in Fruit Juices, p. 285 **L2** **TE** Teacher Demo: Photosynthesis and Cellular Respiration, p. 283 **L2** **TE** Teacher Demo: Denaturing an Enzyme, p. 284 **L2**

Ability Levels	
L1	For students who need additional help
L2	For all students
L3	For students who need to be challenged

Components

SE	Student Edition	RSW	Reading & Study Workbook	CUT	Chapter & Unit Tests	T	Transparencies
TE	Teacher's Edition	MSPS	Math Skills & Problem Solving Workbook	CTB	Computer Test Bank	iT	Interactive Textbook
LM	Laboratory Manual			TP	Test Prep Resources	P	Presentation Pro CD-ROM
PLM	Probeware Lab Manual			DC	Discovery Channel Videotapes & DVDs	GO	Internet Resources

RESOURCES PRINT and TECHNOLOGY	SECTION ASSESSMENT
RSW Section 9.1 L1 RSW Math Skill L2 Discovery Channel School DC Clean Energy L2 T Chapter 9 Pretest L2 Section 9.1 L2 P Chapter 9 Pretest L2 Section 9.1 L2 NSTA SCILINKS GO Fossil fuels L2	SE Section 9.1 Assessment, p. 269 Interactive Textbook iT Section 9.1
RSW Section 9.2 L1 MSPS Section 9.2 L2 T Section 9.2 L2 P Section 9.2 L2	SE Section 9.2 Assessment, p. 274 Interactive Textbook iT Section 9.2
RSW Section 9.3 L1 T Section 9.3 L2 P Section 9.3 L2 NSTA SCILINKS GO Polymers L2	SE Section 9.3 Assessment, p. 280 Interactive Textbook iT Section 9.3
RSW Section 9.4 L1 T Section 9.4 L2 P Section 9.4 L2 SCIENCE NEWS GO Organic chemistry and biochemistry L2	SE Section 9.4 Assessment, p. 284 Interactive Textbook iT Section 9.4

Go Online

Go online for these Internet resources.

PHSchool.com
Web Code: cca-1090
Web Code: cch-1090

NSTA SCILINKS
Web Code: ccn-1091
Web Code: ccn-1093

SCIENCE NEWS®
Web Code: cce-1094

Materials for Activities and Labs

Quantities for each group

STUDENT EDITION

Inquiry Activity, p. 261
sucrose (table sugar), cellulose (paper), isopropyl alcohol, polystyrene (foam cup), polypropylene (food storage container)

Quick Lab, p. 265
30 marshmallows, 70 raisins, 50 toothpicks

Quick Lab, p. 278
1 slice each of potato, ripe apple, and bread; 15 mL cornstarch; 15 mL table sugar; iodine in dropper bottle; 6 small paper plates

Consumer Lab, p. 285
apple juice, variety of other fruit juices, test tubes and rack, 10-mL graduated cylinder, methylene blue indicator, dropper pipet, stirring rods

TEACHER'S EDITION

Teacher Demo, p. 264
molecular model kit

Teacher Demo, p. 267
distillation apparatus with stand, 50 mL water, 50 mL ethanol, 60 mL mineral oil, hot plate, 60-mL beakers (6), concave glass beaker covers (3), shield, dropper pipets (5)

Build Science Skills, p. 270
100-mL beaker containing 1:1 mixture of sulfur powder and coal dust, plastic pipet, 100-mL graduated cylinder, stirring rod, distilled water, 100-mL beaker

Teacher Demo, p. 272
any appliance that has attachments with different functions

Teacher Demo, p. 283
methylene blue, water, 500-mL beaker, *elodea* sprig, straw

Teacher Demo, p. 284
potato, sharp knife, cutting surface, 3% hydrogen peroxide solution, water, 500-mL beakers (2), hot plate

Chapter Assessment

CHAPTER ASSESSMENT

SE Chapter Assessment, pp. 287–288
CUT Chapter 9 Test A, B
CTB Chapter 9
iT Chapter 9
PHSchool.com GO
Web Code: cca-1090

STANDARDIZED TEST PREP

SE Chapter 9, p. 289
TP Diagnose and Prescribe

Interactive Textbook

InteractiveTextbook with assessment at PHSchool.com

CHAPTER 9

Before you teach

From the Author

David Frank
Ferris State University

Big Ideas

So far, students have focused on three major areas of chemistry. In analytical chemistry, the composition of matter is the primary focus. In physical chemistry, laws and theories that describe the behavior of matter take center stage. Inorganic chemistry excludes most carbon compounds, but includes the elemental forms of carbon. In Chapter 9, students study a few organic compounds and get a glimpse of biochemistry, an area in which inorganic and organic compounds play key roles.

Space and Time At room temperature, there is no visible reaction between sucrose and oxygen to release energy stored in this sugar. So how is the energy released in cells at a temperature only slightly higher than room temperature? Protein catalysts allow reactions in cells to take place quickly at body temperature.

Matter and Change When students first encounter organic molecules, they may be intimidated by the complex structures. If possible, use three-dimensional models to support the structural formulas shown in the text. Once students understand how hydrocarbons are classified, they study a few examples of substituted hydrocarbons to see how functional groups affect the properties of organic compounds. Section 9.3 shows how functional groups link monomers in polymers.

Forces and Motion In Section 9.3, students see how the intermolecular forces of attraction they studied in Chapter 6 and applied to solutions in Chapter 8 can also be applied to polymers. Help students understand that concepts in chemistry hold true for all types of matter.

Energy In this chapter, students have numerous opportunities to apply what they learned about chemical reactions in Chapter 7. Students get to compare the exothermic combustion reactions of fossil fuels to the process in cells that releases energy from food—cellular respiration. They also get to see how cellular respiration and the endothermic process of photosynthesis are related through their reactants and products.

Chemistry Refresher

Organic Compounds 9.1

Chemists in the early 1800s thought that living things possessed a vital force that distinguished them from nonliving things, an idea known as *vitalism*. The term *organic* referred to substances found only in living organisms and *inorganic* referred to all other substances. Organic substances, chemists reasoned, could be used to produce inorganic substances. But inorganic substances lacked the vital force required to produce organic substances. In 1828, Friedrich Wöhler took the first step in disproving vitalism. During a systematic study of cyanates, he mixed two inorganic substances and produced the organic substance urea. Today the term *organic* refers to compounds containing carbon and hydrogen, often combined with a few other elements. In general, organic compounds contain carbon-to-hydrogen bonds, and inorganic compounds, such as carbides and carbonates, do not. There is rarely a one-to-one correlation between a chemical formula and an organic compound. (There are nine different compounds with the formula C_7H_{16}.)

Address Misconceptions

Students often explain the formula and structure of methane by saying that carbon needs four bonds. The type and number of bonds in a compound can be explained by the structures of the atoms that form the bonds. For a strategy to overcome this misconception, see **Address Misconceptions** on **page 263.**

The shape of a molecule depends on the bond lengths and bond angles between atoms. Bond length is the distance between the nuclei of bonded atoms. Bond lengths are usually reported in picometers (pm) or angstroms (Å). Generally, bond length decreases as the number of bonds between two atoms increases. The type of bond also affects the angle between atoms in the molecule. In all three examples shown, the arrangement of the hydrogen atoms minimizes repulsion between electron clouds.

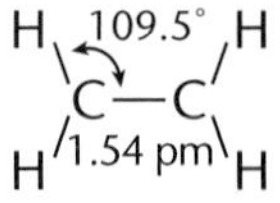
H
109.5°
H
C—C
H
1.54 pm
H

Ethane

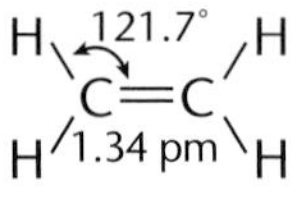
H
121.7°
H
C=C
H
1.34 pm
H

Ethene

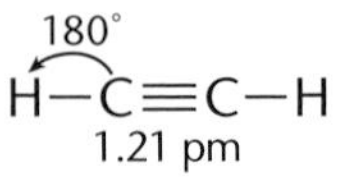
180°
H—C≡C—H
1.21 pm

Ethyne

Go Online PDLinks

For: Teaching methods for carbon chemistry
Visit: www.SciLinks.org/PDLinks
Web Code: ccn-0999

Naming Organic Compounds 9.2

The International Union of Pure and Applied Chemistry (IUPAC) established rules for naming organic compounds. In their system, names have a root that is based on the longest continuous chain of carbon atoms (or rings in aromatic hydrocarbons). A suffix is used for different classes of compounds (such as *-ol* for alcohols). Prefixes are used to indicate the location of branches or functional groups along the carbon chain. In the IUPAC system, isopropyl alcohol is 2-propanol. This name indicates that an –OH group is attached to the central carbon in a three-carbon chain.

Formation of Polymers 9.3

Polymers form by addition or condensation. The formation of polyethylene is an example of addition polymerization. Electrons in the double bond of an ethene molecule can form single bonds with carbon atoms in two other ethene molecules. In condensation polymerization, monomers are joined through a reaction that eliminates a small molecule. The illustration shows how water is eliminated when the carboxyl group of one amino acid joins to the amino group of a second amino acid. Each R represents a hydrocarbon chain.

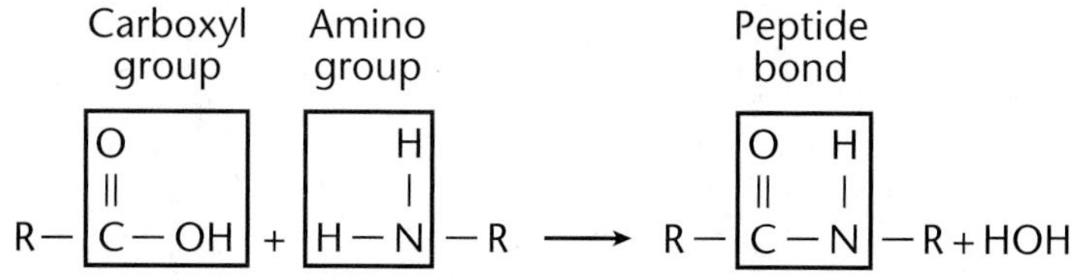

Carboxyl group
Amino group
Peptide bond

Reactions in Cells 9.4

Address Misconceptions

Students may confuse cellular respiration, respiration, and breathing. For a strategy to overcome this misconception, see **Address Misconceptions** on **page 283.**

Chemical reactions in cells are classified as catabolic or anabolic. Catabolic reactions break down compounds into simpler substances and release energy. Cellular respiration is a catabolic process. Anabolic reactions use energy to build complex molecules from simpler substances. Photosynthesis is an anabolic process. When chlorophyll molecules in plant cells absorb light, electrons in the molecules are promoted to higher energy levels. A series of carrier molecules transport these high-energy electrons to locations where the energy is used to build complex molecules, including carbohydrates.

Build Reading Literacy

Relate Cause and Effect

Understanding How and Why Things Occur

Strategy Help students read and understand relationships between events. Cause-effect relationships are integral to science, so it is very important that students understand the cause-effect relationships developed in the text. Before students begin, assign a passage in Chapter 9 for them to read, such as pp. 267–269 in Section 9.1.

Example

1. Remind students that a cause is what makes something happen and the effect is what happens as a result. Point out that in science, many actions cause other actions to occur.
2. Have students identify cause-effect relationships in the passage. Remind them that the text does not always directly state the cause-effect relationship, but in many cases clue words or phrases do point out such a connection: *because, so, since, results, therefore, cause, lead to.* For example, Rain is always slightly acidic *because* carbon dioxide dissolves in water droplets and forms carbonic acid.
3. Then, explain that causes and effects often occur in chains, with effects becoming causes of later effects. Have students find a cause-effect chain and show it in the form of a flowchart. (insufficient oxygen for complete combustion ⟶ carbon monoxide produced ⟶ inhaled and absorbed by blood ⟶ hemoglobin cannot carry oxygen to cells)

See p. 262 for a script on how to use the relate cause and effect strategy with students. For additional Build Reading Literacy strategies, see pp. 273, 275, and 282.

ASSESS PRIOR KNOWLEDGE

Use the Chapter Pretest below to assess students' prior knowledge. As needed, review these Science Concepts and Math Skills with students.

Review Science Concepts

Section 9.1 Review covalent bonding in general and the difference between single and double covalent bonds. Encourage students to recall the number of bonds carbon can form. Review how to interpret chemical formulas and chemical equations.

Sections 9.2 and 9.3 Have students review how physical properties, such as boiling points, are used to identify a substance. Discuss attractions between molecules.

Section 9.4 Review exothermic and endothermic reactions. Have students recall the role of a catalyst in a chemical reaction.

Review Math Skills

Data Tables Students will need to be familiar with analyzing data presented in tables about compounds and their properties.

Direct students to the **Math Skills** in the **Skills and Reference Handbook** at the end of the student text.

CHAPTER

9 Carbon Chemistry

CONCEPTS in Action

How do science concepts apply to your world? Here are some questions you'll be able to answer after you read this chapter.

- Why do homes that are heated with oil or natural gas often have carbon monoxide detectors? *(Section 9.1)*
- What makes the odor of rotten fish so different from the odor of roses? *(Section 9.2)*
- What do tires, a trash bag, and pasta have in common? *(Section 9.3)*
- How does your body release the energy stored in food? *(Section 9.4)*

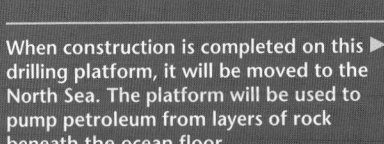

Discovery CHANNEL SCHOOL **Video Field Trip**

Clean Energy

- How are coal-burning power plants reducing air pollution? *(page 270)*

When construction is completed on this ▶ drilling platform, it will be moved to the North Sea. The platform will be used to pump petroleum from layers of rock beneath the ocean floor.

Chapter Pretest

1. What kind of bonds are found in molecules? *(Covalent bonds)*
2. How many electrons are shared in a double bond? *(4)*
3. How many bonds can a carbon atom form? *(4)*
4. Tell which of the following are formulas for a molecular compound. *(b and c)*
a. H_2 **b.** CO_2
c. CH_4 **d.** NaCl

5. In the following chemical equation, how many hydrogen atoms are in a molecule of the product? *(2)*
$2H_2 + O_2 \longrightarrow 2H_2O$
6. Which of these properties can be used to separate substances in a mixture? *(a)*
a. boiling point
b. hardness
c. malleability
d. flammability

7. True or False: Attractions between molecules are stronger than covalent bonds. *(False)*
8. True or False: An exothermic reaction releases energy. *(True)*
9. How does a catalyst affect the progress of a chemical reaction? *(It lowers the energy barrier, which increases the reaction rate.)*

Chapter Preview

Inquiry Activity

Do All Carbon Compounds Have Similar Properties?

Procedure

1. Examine samples of sucrose, cellulose, isopropyl alcohol, polystyrene, and polypropylene. All five compounds contain carbon and hydrogen. Sucrose, cellulose, and isopropyl alcohol contain oxygen, too.
2. Record a set of physical properties for each compound. Include some of the properties you studied in Chapter 2.

Think About It

1. **Making Generalizations** Is there any property you observed that you could use to classify a compound as a carbon compound?
2. **Formulating Hypotheses** Why does carbon form many more compounds than other elements do? (*Hint:* How many valence electrons does carbon have and what type of bonds does it form?)

Discovery Channel School **Video Field Trip**
Clean Energy

Encourage students to view the Video Field Trip "Clean Energy."

ENGAGE/EXPLORE

Inquiry Activity

Do All Carbon Compounds Have Similar Properties? L2

Purpose In this activity, students describe some carbon compounds and consider whether all organic compounds have similar properties.

Skills Focus **Observing, Classifying**

Prep Time 25 minutes

Materials sucrose (table sugar), cellulose (paper), isopropyl alcohol, polystyrene (foam cup), polypropylene (food storage container)

Class Time 20 minutes

Safety Isopropyl alcohol should be provided in closed, clear specimen bottles. Warn students not to open the bottles and have them wear safety goggles.

Teaching Tips

- Have students construct tables to record their observations of physical properties.

Expected Outcome Based on their observations, students should note the wide variation of properties among carbon compounds.

Think About It

1. There is no one property that distinguishes a compound as a carbon compound.
2. Carbon forms so many compounds because a carbon atom has four valence electrons available for bonding and can form single, double, and triple bonds.

Visual, Logical

Section 9.1

1 FOCUS

Objectives

9.1.1 **Relate** the structures of three forms of carbon to their properties.

9.1.2 **Explain** why there are millions of different organic compounds.

9.1.3 **Relate** the number and arrangement of carbon atoms in hydrocarbons to their properties.

9.1.4 **Distinguish** unsaturated from saturated hydrocarbons.

9.1.5 **Classify** hydrocarbons using structural formulas and names.

9.1.6 **Describe** the formation, composition, and uses of three types of fossil fuels.

9.1.7 **Distinguish** complete combustion from incomplete combustion of fossil fuels.

9.1.8 **Describe** the effects of some products of the combustion of fossil fuels.

Reading Focus

Build Vocabulary L2

Concept Map Have students make a concept map with the word *hydrocarbons* as the starting point. The diagram should include the following terms: *saturated hydrocarbons, unsaturated hydrocarbons, alkanes, alkenes, alkynes, aromatic hydrocarbons, branched chain, straight chain,* and *rings.*

Reading Strategy L2

a. Rigid three-dimensional network **b.** Widely spaced layers **c.** Hollow spheres with a surface of carbon atoms arranged in alternating hexagons and pentagons

2 INSTRUCT

Build Reading Literacy L1

Relate Cause and Effect Refer to page **260D** in this chapter, which provides the guidelines for relating cause and effect.

Have students read p. 262. Ask, **What caused scientists to change the definition of an organic compound?** *(Wöhler synthesized urea, an organic compound produced by many organisms.)* **Logical**

9.1 Carbon Compounds

Reading Focus

Key Concepts

- What are three forms of carbon?
- What factors determine the properties of a hydrocarbon?
- What are the three types of unsaturated hydrocarbons?
- What are the three main fossil fuels and the two primary products of their combustion?

Vocabulary

- organic compound
- network solid
- hydrocarbon
- saturated hydrocarbon
- isomers
- unsaturated hydrocarbon
- aromatic hydrocarbons
- fossil fuels

Reading Strategy

Previewing Copy the table below. Before you read, use the models in Figure 2 to describe the arrangement of carbon atoms in each form of carbon.

Forms of Carbon Compounds	
Diamond	a. ?
Graphite	b. ?
Buckminsterfullerene	c. ?

Until 1828, chemists divided compounds into compounds that chemists could produce and compounds that only organisms could produce. The compounds produced by *organisms* were called *organic* compounds. In 1828, a German chemist, Friedrich Wöhler, mixed silver cyanate, AgOCN, with ammonium chloride, NH_4Cl. He expected to make ammonium cyanate. Instead, he produced urea, $(NH_2)_2CO$, which is a product of reactions that occur in the livers of many organisms. Wöhler had synthesized an organic compound.

An **organic compound** contains carbon and hydrogen, often combined with a few other elements such as oxygen and nitrogen. There are millions of organic compounds—more than 90 percent of all known compounds. Remember that carbon has four valence electrons. So a carbon atom can form four single covalent bonds, or a double bond and two single bonds, or a triple bond and a single bond. Most of the bonds in organic compounds are carbon-to-carbon bonds or carbon-to-hydrogen bonds.

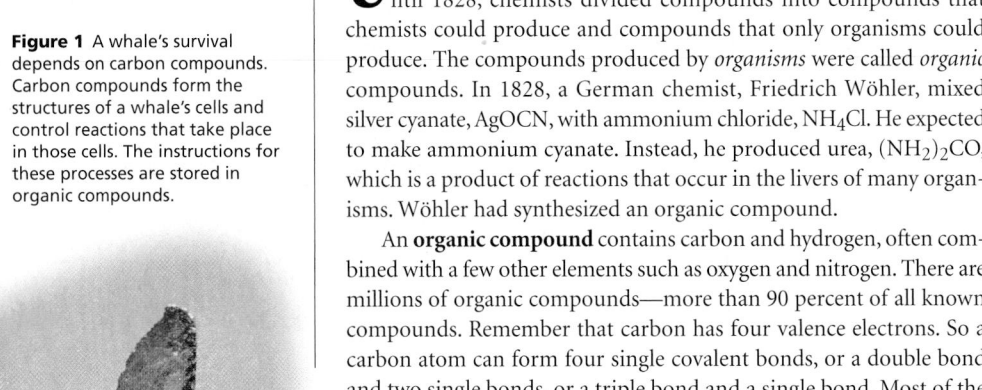

Figure 1 A whale's survival depends on carbon compounds. Carbon compounds form the structures of a whale's cells and control reactions that take place in those cells. The instructions for these processes are stored in organic compounds.

Section Resources

Print
- ***Reading and Study Workbook With Math Support,*** Section 9.1 and **Math Skill:** Balancing Equations for Organic Reactions
- ***Transparencies,*** Chapter Pretest and Section 9.1

Technology
- ***Interactive Textbook,*** Section 9.1
- ***Presentation Pro CD-ROM,*** Chapter Pretest and Section 9.1
- ***Go Online,*** NSTA SciLinks, Fossil fuels

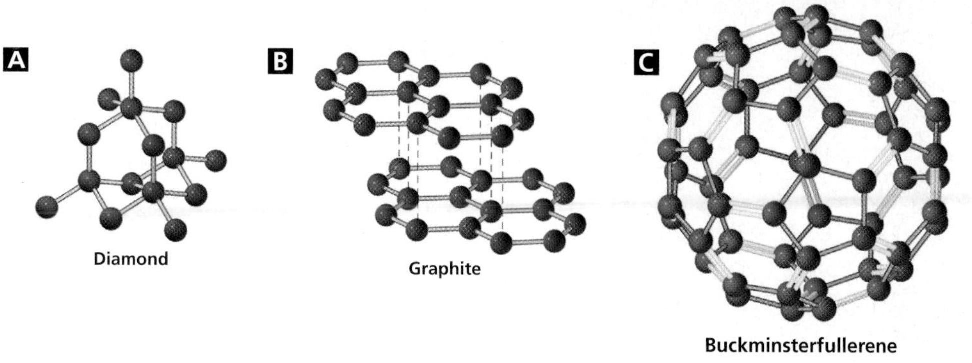
A
Diamond
B
Graphite
C
Buckminsterfullerene

Figure 2 There are several forms of carbon. **A** In diamond, carbon atoms are arranged in a rigid, three-dimensional network. **B** In graphite, the atoms are arranged in layers. **C** In fullerenes, carbon atoms are arranged in hollow spheres. **Predicting** ***Are the properties of fullerenes more like those of diamond or of graphite? Give a reason for your choice.***

Forms of Carbon

The element carbon exists in several forms with different properties. **Diamond, graphite, and fullerenes are forms of carbon.** In each form, there is a different arrangement of bonded carbon atoms.

Diamond Cutting, grinding, and drilling tools are often coated with diamond because no substance is harder than diamond. Diamond is an example of a network solid. In a **network solid,** all the atoms are linked by covalent bonds. A network solid is sometimes described as a single molecule. Figure 2A shows how the carbon atoms are linked in diamond. Covalent bonds connect each carbon atom in diamond to four other carbon atoms. The three-dimensional structure that results is rigid, compact, and strong. Diamond is harder than other substances because cutting a diamond requires breaking many covalent bonds.

Graphite A second form of carbon, graphite, has very different properties from diamond. It is extremely soft and slippery. Figure 2B shows how the carbon atoms in graphite are arranged in widely spaced layers. Within each layer, each carbon atom forms strong covalent bonds with three other carbon atoms. Between graphite layers the bonds are weak, which allows the layers to slide easily past one another. Because graphite is soft and slippery, it is a good lubricant for moving metal parts in machinery. Pencil "lead" is a mixture of graphite and clay. The layered structure of graphite explains why you can make pencil marks on paper and why the marks can be erased easily.

Fullerenes In 1985, researchers discovered a third form of carbon in the soot produced when some carbon compounds burn. Fullerenes are large hollow spheres or cages of carbon. These cages have since been found in meteorites. Figure 2C shows a model of a cage made from 60 carbon atoms. On the surface of the cage, the atoms form alternating hexagons and pentagons, like a soccer ball cover. The C_{60} molecule is called buckminsterfullerene after Buckminster Fuller, an architect who designed domes with similar geometric patterns.

Forms of Carbon

Use Visuals L1

Figure 2 Emphasize that the structures shown in A, B, and C all contain only carbon atoms. Ask, **What are the differences between the three forms of carbon?** *(Diamond has a rigid three-dimensional structure, graphite contains widely spaced layers, and fullerenes are hollow cages.)* **What types of bonds hold carbon atoms together in all three forms of carbon?** *(Covalent bonds)* **Visual**

Address Misconceptions L2

When students are asked why a methane molecule has the formula CH_4, a typical response is that carbon needs four bonds. Encourage them to consider a less anthropomorphic view. Have students recall that carbon has four valence electrons and that neon has eight valence electrons. When carbon atoms form four single covalent bonds, as in methane, they achieve the stable electron configuration of neon.
Logical

FYI

Charcoal, carbon black, and lamp black are classified as amorphous carbon because they do not have a regular crystalline structure.

Customize for English Language Learners

List-Group-Label
Encourage students to work independently or in groups to brainstorm words that make them think of the following forms of carbon: diamond, graphite, and fullerenes. Then, ask students to review the list of words and group them into logical categories (structure: rigid, hollow, layers; properties: slippery, hard, soft; uses: writing, cutting, jewelry). There must be at least three words in each group. Students can include a word in more than one group. They should label the groups to show how the words are related.

Answer to . . .

Figure 2 *Students may predict that fullerenes are likely to have properties more like diamond because of their three-dimensional structures. Or, they may (correctly) predict that fullerenes have properties more like graphite because their hollow structures are not rigid.*

Saturated Hydrocarbons

Integrate Language Arts L2

Tell students that one definition of *saturated* is "filled to capacity." So saturated can mean "the inability to contain, absorb, receive, or hold." For example, the ground may be saturated with water after a heavy rainstorm, meaning it can absorb no more water. Have students use these meanings to paraphrase the definition of the vocabulary term *saturated hydrocarbon. (Possible answer: In a saturated hydrocarbon, carbon atoms do not have the capacity to bond to additional hydrogen atoms.)*
Verbal

Teacher Demo

Comparing Models of Molecules L2

Purpose Students compare ball-and-stick models and structural formulas for methane and propane.

Materials molecular model kit

Procedure Write the structural formulas and chemical formulas for methane and propane on the board. Remind students that a structural formula provides more information than a molecular formula because it shows how the atoms are arranged in a molecule. Then, show students ball-and-stick models for methane and propane. Explain that a ball-and-stick model shows the angles between atoms in a molecule and the overall shape of the molecule. (Students may recall methane's tetrahedral shape from the Quick Lab in Section 6.3.) The bond angle between carbon and hydrogen is 109.5° in methane and propane.

Expected Outcome Students observe the similarities and differences between the structures of methane and propane molecules.
Visual, Logical

Figure 3 Microorganisms in the stomachs of a cow produce more than 500 liters of methane (CH_4) per day.

Saturated Hydrocarbons

Grass contains a compound called cellulose. Most organisms, including the grazing cows in Figure 3, cannot digest cellulose. However, microorganisms in cows' stomachs break down cellulose into smaller molecules that cows can digest. One of the products of this process is methane, CH_4, which is a hydrocarbon. A **hydrocarbon** is an organic compound that contains only the elements hydrogen and carbon. Methane is a saturated hydrocarbon. In a **saturated hydrocarbon,** all of the bonds are single bonds. A saturated hydrocarbon contains the maximum possible number of hydrogen atoms for each carbon atom. Another name for a saturated hydrocarbon is an alkane. Names of alkane compounds end in *–ane,* as in methane and propane.

Factors that determine the properties of a hydrocarbon are the number of carbon atoms and how the atoms are arranged. A hydrocarbon molecule can contain one carbon atom, as in methane, or more than 30 carbon atoms, as in asphalt. The carbon atoms can be arranged in a straight chain, a branched chain, or a ring.

Straight Chains Figure 4 lists the names, molecular formulas, structural formulas, and boiling points for four straight-chain alkanes. Recall that a molecular formula shows the type and number of atoms in a molecule of the compound. A structural formula shows how those atoms are arranged. The number of carbon atoms in a straight-chain alkane affects the state of the alkane at room temperature. Methane and propane are gases. Pentane and octane are liquids. The more carbon atoms, the higher the boiling point is.

Reading Checkpoint *What is another name for a saturated hydrocarbon?*

Figure 4 Molecules of ethane, propane, pentane, and octane have two, three, five, and eight carbon atoms, respectively. **Making Generalizations** ***How does increasing the number of carbon atoms affect the boiling point of a straight-chain alkane?***

Some Straight-Chain Alkanes

Name	Methane	Propane	Pentane	Octane
Molecular Formula	CH_4	C_3H_8	C_5H_{12}	C_8H_{18}
Structural Formula	H H–C–H H	H H H H–C–C–C–H H H H	H H H H H H–C–C–C–C–C–H H H H H H	H H H H H H H H H–C–C–C–C–C–C–C–C–H H H H H H H H H
Boiling Point	—161.5¡C	—42.1¡C	36.0¡C	125.6¡C

Facts and Figures

Naming Hydrocarbons Names of straight- and branched-chain hydrocarbons use prefixes to indicate the number of carbon atoms in the longest continuous chain. Except for *meth-* (1), *eth-* (2), and *prop-* (3), the prefixes used match those shown in Figure 20 on p. 175. For branched-chain hydrocarbons, the carbon atoms in the longest continuous chain are numbered beginning at one end of the chain. Prefixes that combine a numeral and a group designation are used to show the type and location of branches. Using this system, the official name for isobutane (shown in Figure 5) is 2-methylpropane.

Quick Lab

Comparing Isomers

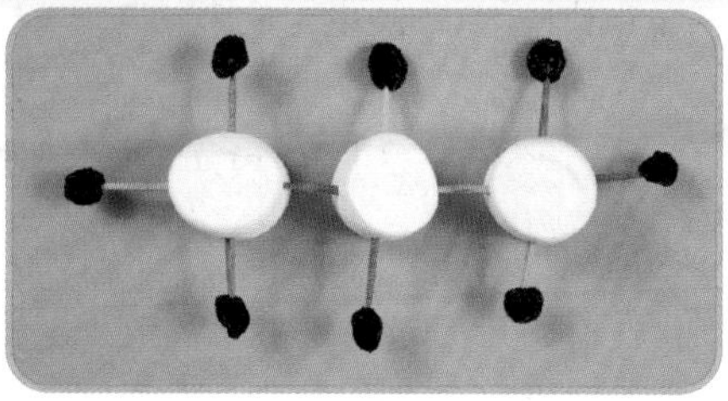

Materials

30 marshmallows, 70 raisins, 50 toothpicks

Procedure

1. Use marshmallows to represent carbon atoms, and raisins to represent hydrogen atoms, as in the model of propane shown. **CAUTION** *Do not eat anything in the laboratory.* Break the toothpicks in half to represent single bonds. Build models of five different isomers of hexane (C_6H_{14}).
2. For each model, attach all six carbon atoms first. Then attach hydrogen atoms until each carbon atom has four bonds.

Analyze and Conclude

1. **Using Models** Draw a structural formula for each isomer.
2. **Predicting** Would pentane (C_5H_{12}) or heptane (C_7H_{16}) have more isomers than hexane? Explain your answer.

Branched Chains Look at the butane and isobutane formulas in Figure 5. Both compounds have a molecular formula of C_4H_{10}, but their structural formulas are different. In isobutane, there is a branch at the point where a carbon atom bonds to three other carbon atoms.

Compounds with the same molecular formula but different structural formulas are **isomers.** Differences in structure affect some properties of isomers. Butane boils at –0.5°C, but isobutane boils at –11.7°C. The number of possible isomers increases rapidly each time an additional carbon atom is added to the chain. For example, octane (C_8H_{18}) has 18 isomers, while decane ($C_{10}H_{22}$) has 75.

Rings Figure 5 also shows the structural formula for cyclobutane. The carbon atoms in cyclobutane are linked in a four-carbon ring. Because each carbon atom forms bonds with two other carbon atoms, it can bond with only two hydrogen atoms. So cyclobutane (C_4H_8) molecules have two fewer hydrogen atoms than butane (C_4H_{10}) molecules. Most ring alkanes, or cyclic hydrocarbons, have rings with five or six carbons.

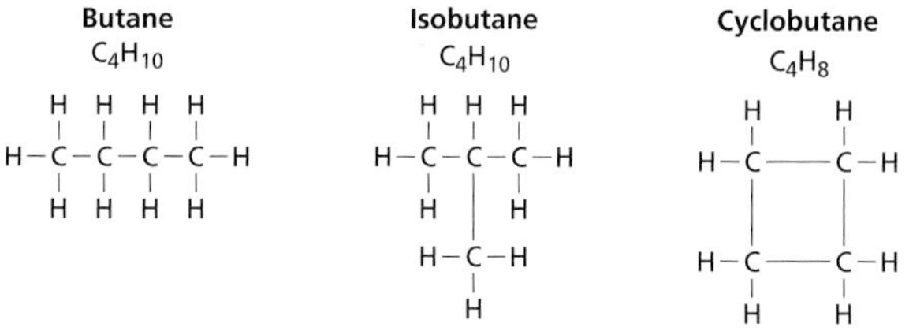
Butane
C4H10
Isobutane
C4H10
Cyclobutane
C4H8

Figure 5 Butane, isobutane, and cyclobutane represent three ways that carbon atoms are arranged in an alkane—in a straight chain, in a branched chain, and in a ring. **Classifying** ***Explain why butane and cyclobutane are not isomers.***

Facts and Figures

Hydrocarbons An isomer with branches often has a lower boiling point than its corresponding straight-chain isomer because less efficient packing results in weaker intermolecular forces. There is a strain on rings with only three or four carbon atoms because of the bond angles between the carbon atoms.

In general, unsaturated hydrocarbons are more reactive than saturated hydrocarbons because atoms or groups of atoms can be added to the molecule at the locations of double and triple bonds. Combustion reactions are the exception to this trend.

Quick Lab

Comparing Isomers **L2**

Objective
After completing this activity, students will be able to
- use structural formulas and models to describe the isomers of hexane.

Skills Focus **Observing, Predicting, Using Models**

Prep Time 10 minutes.

Materials 30 marshmallows, 70 raisins, 50 toothpicks

Advance Prep Set out raisins, marshmallows, and toothpicks in a central location.

Class Time 15–20 minutes

Safety Remind students never to eat anything in the laboratory.

Teaching Tips
- Display ball-and-stick models that are initially oriented with the branches at opposite ends. Rotate one model 180° to show that the structural formulas represent the same isomer.

Expected Outcome Students should be able to draw the structural formulas for the isomers of hexane.

Analyze and Conclude

1. There are five straight- and branched-chain isomers of hexane:

(1) C–C–C–C–C–C (hexane)

(2) C–C–C–C–C with C on the second carbon (2-methylpentane)

(3) C–C–C–C–C with C on the third carbon (3-methylpentane)

(4) C–C–C–C with C on the second and third carbons (2, 3-dimethylbutane)

(5) C–C–C–C with C above and below the second carbon (2, 2-dimethylbutane)

2. Heptane. The greater the number of carbon atoms, the greater the possibility for different lengths and locations of branches along a central chain.
Logical

Answer to . . .

Figure 4 *The boiling point increases.*

Figure 5 *Cyclobutane and butane do not have the same formula.*

Reading Checkpoint *Alkane*

Unsaturated Hydrocarbons

Integrate Social Studies L2

Friedrich August Kekulé claimed to have developed the model for the ring structure of benzene after he had a dream about a snake chasing its own tail. Have students find out more about this German chemist's work. Ask, **What other major contribution did Kekulé make to organic chemistry?** *(In 1854, he was one of the first to theorize that carbon forms four bonds.)*
Verbal

Integrate Health L2

The terms *saturated* and *unsaturated* are also used to describe fats. The term *fat* is commonly used to refer to the fats and oils that are obtained from animals and plants. (These fats are esters that form when fatty acids react with glycerol, an alcohol with three −OH groups.) There are three long hydrocarbon chains in each fat molecule. The chains contain an even number of carbon atoms (typically between 12 and 24). If the hydrocarbon chains contain only single bonds, then the fat is classified as a saturated fat. If there are one or more double or triple bonds in the hydrocarbon chains, then the fat is classified as an unsaturated fat. Unsaturated fats, such as corn oil and olive oil, are generally liquids at room temperature. Saturated fats, such as butter and bacon grease, tend to be solids at room temperature. A diet high in saturated fats has been linked to heart disease. Have students examine food labels to determine which types of foods contain saturated and unsaturated fats. You may also ask students to research whether cooking with unsaturated fats, such as olive oil, provides any health benefits other than preventing heart disease.
Visual

Unsaturated Hydrocarbons

A hydrocarbon that contains one or more double or triple bonds is an **unsaturated hydrocarbon.** These hydrocarbons are classified by bond type and the arrangement of their carbon atoms. **There are three types of unsaturated hydrocarbons—alkenes, alkynes, and aromatic hydrocarbons.**

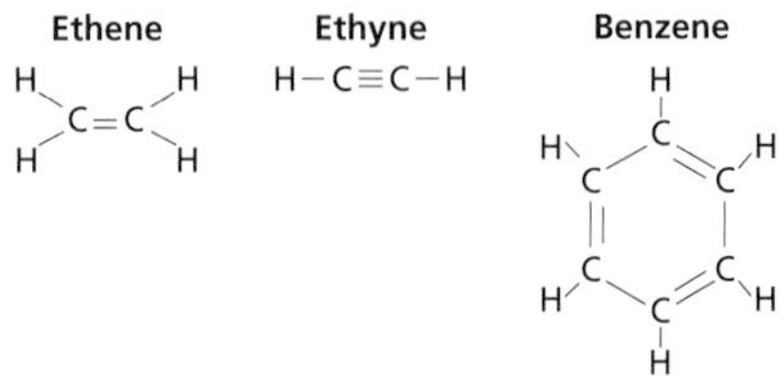
Ethene
Ethyne
H−C≡C−H
Benzene

Figure 6 There are three types of unsaturated hydrocarbons.
A Ethene is an alkene that controls the ripening of a tomato.
B Ethyne is an alkyne used in torches that cut metals or weld them together. **C** Kekulé figured out the ring structure of the aromatic hydrocarbon benzene.

A

Alkenes Many fruit-bearing plants produce ethene (C_2H_4), which controls the rate at which fruits, such as the tomato in Figure 6A, ripen. There is a double bond between the two carbon atoms in ethene. Hydrocarbons that have one or more carbon-carbon double bonds are alkenes. The names of alkenes end in *-ene.* Plastics used in trash bags and milk jugs are produced by reactions involving ethene.

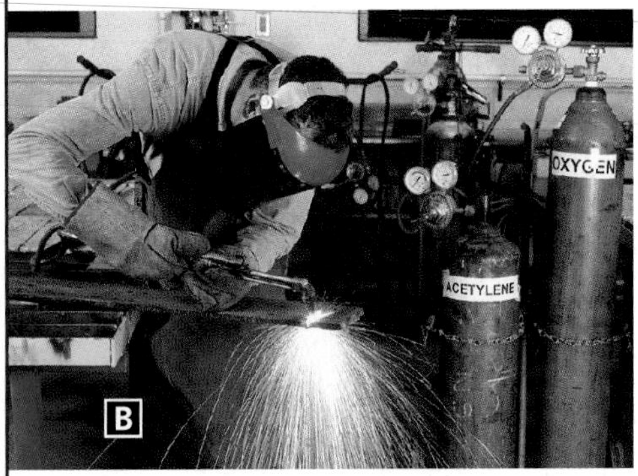
OXYGEN
ACETYLENE
B

Alkynes In 1895, Henry-Louis Le Châtelier reported that a flame produced when ethyne burned had a temperature about 1000°C higher than a flame produced when hydrogen burns. Ethyne (C_2H_2), also known as acetylene, is an alkyne. Alkynes are straight- or branched-chain hydrocarbons that have one or more triple bonds. Alkyne names end in *-yne.*

Alkynes are the most reactive hydrocarbon compounds. The welder in Figure 6B is burning a mixture of oxygen and acetylene in an oxyacetylene torch. The temperature of the flame produced approaches 3500°C. At that temperature, most metals can be melted and welded together. The acetylene and oxygen are stored under pressure in tanks.

C

3F A. KEKULE
1865 BENZEEN BENZENE C6H6
BELGIE-BELGIQUE

Aromatic Hydrocarbons The Belgian stamp in Figure 6C honors Friedrich Kekulé (1829–1896), who figured out that benzene (C_6H_6) is an unsaturated hydrocarbon with a ring structure. Although the formula shows alternating single and double bonds, the six bonds in the ring are identical. Six of the valence electrons are shared by all six carbon atoms. Hydrocarbons that contain similar ring structures are known as **aromatic hydrocarbons.** The name was chosen because many of these compounds have strong aromas or odors.

Reading Checkpoint *What is an unsaturated hydrocarbon?*

266 Chapter 9

A

Fossil Fuels

Some hydrocarbons were formed from plants and animals that lived in Earth's oceans and swamps millions of years ago. After those plants and animals died, they were buried under layers of rock and soil. High temperature and pressure deep in Earth's crust changed those remains into deposits of hydrocarbons called fossil fuels. **Fossil fuels** are mixtures of hydrocarbons that formed from the remains of plants or animals. **Three types of fossil fuels are coal, natural gas, and petroleum.** The type of fossil fuel produced depends on the origin of the organic material and the conditions under which it decays.

Coal The ferns in Figure 7A are similar to those that produced the coal in Figure 7B. Coal is a solid fossil fuel that began to form about 300 million years ago in ancient swamps. Giant tree ferns and other plants were buried in those swamps. After millions of years of pressure, the plant remains produced a mixture of hydrocarbons. Most of the hydrocarbons in coal are aromatic hydrocarbons with high molar masses. These compounds have a high ratio of carbon to hydrogen. So burning coal produces more soot than burning other fossil fuels does.

Natural Gas The second main fossil fuel, natural gas, formed from the remains of marine organisms. The main component of natural gas is methane—the same compound produced by cows as they digest grass. Natural gas also contains ethane, propane, and isomers of butane. Natural gas is distributed through a network of underground pipes. It is used for heating and cooking, and to generate some electricity. Deposits of natural gas are found along with deposits of coal and petroleum.

Petroleum The third main fossil fuel, petroleum, also formed from the remains of marine organisms. Petroleum, often known as crude oil, is pumped from deep beneath Earth's surface. It is a complex liquid mixture of hydrocarbons, mainly long-branched alkanes and alkenes. For petroleum to be useful, it must be separated into simpler mixtures, or fractions, such as gasoline and heating oil.

Figure 7 Fossil fuels form from the remains of plants and animals. **A** The ferns shown are similar to ferns that lived millions of years ago. **B** The imprints of ferns left on the lump of coal are evidence that the coal formed when plant remains were compressed under layers of rock and soil.

B

Go Online NSTA SciLinks

For: Links on fossil fuels
Visit: www.SciLinks.org
Web Code: ccn-1091

Fossil Fuels

Teacher Demo

Fractional Distillation **L2**

Purpose Students will observe fractional distillation of a mixture of organic compounds.

Materials distillation apparatus with stand, 50 mL water, 50 mL ethanol, 60 mL mineral oil, hot plate, 60-mL beakers (6), concave glass beaker covers (3), shield, dropper pipets (5)

Procedure Explain that fractional distillation is a method of separating mixtures using differences in boiling points. Measure 50 mL of water and 50 mL of ethanol in two different beakers and mix them together in the distillation chamber. Heat the mixture, keeping the temperature at about 85°C, just above the boiling point of ethanol and below the boiling point of water. Three times during the process, collect the distilled liquid (distillate) in a separate beaker, and cover the beaker. After you complete the distillation, place a drop of pure ethanol and a drop of pure water in a beaker of mineral oil. Next, place a drop from each beaker of distilled liquid into the mineral oil. Have students notice whether the drops float or how quickly they sink.

Safety Place a blast shield between the equipment and students. Use mitts or tongs to handle hot glass.

Expected Outcome The ethanol will collect more rapidly in the catch beaker. Pure ethanol floats in mineral oil, and pure water sinks. Students can infer the relative concentrations of ethanol and water in each distillate sample by the behavior of the drops in the mineral oil. **Visual**

Go Online NSTA SciLinks

Download a worksheet on fossil fuels for students to complete, and find additional teacher support from NSTA SciLinks.

Answer to . . .

Reading Checkpoint *A hydrocarbon that contains one or more double or triple bonds*

Build Science Skills **L2**

Problem Solving Tell students that they are given an unknown alkane. Have them use Figure 8 to answer the following question. Ask, **How could you determine if the alkane is one of the components of gasoline?** *(If its boiling point is between 40°C and 100°C, then the alkane may be a component of gasoline.)*
Visual, Logical

FYI

In industry documents that describe fractional distillation, there is variation in the names of the fractions collected, the length of the carbon chains in a fraction, and the temperature range at which a fraction is collected. There *is* agreement on how the process separates the numerous substances in petroleum into fractions.

Combustion of Fossil Fuels

Build Math Skills **L1**

Balancing Equations Remind students that only the coefficients in front of the formulas, and not the subscripts in the formulas, may be changed when they balance an equation. Have students practice balancing the equation for the complete combustion of ethane:

$C_2H_6 + O_2 \longrightarrow CO_2 + H_2O$

($2C_2H_6 + 7O_2 \longrightarrow 4CO_2 + 6H_2O$)

Then, have students determine the balanced equation for incomplete combustion of ethane.

($2C_2H_6 + 5O_2 \longrightarrow 4CO + 6H_2O$)
Logical

Direct students to the **Math Skills** in the **Skills and Reference Handbook** at the end of the student text for additional help.

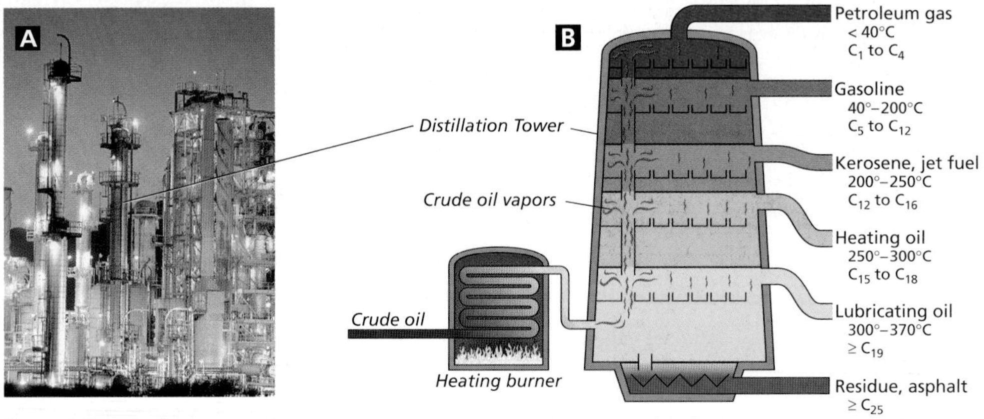
A
B
Distillation Tower
Crude oil vapors
Crude oil
Heating burner
Petroleum gas
< 40°C
C_1 to C_4
Gasoline
40°–200°C
C_5 to C_{12}
Kerosene, jet fuel
200°–250°C
C_{12} to C_{16}
Heating oil
250°–300°C
C_{15} to C_{18}
Lubricating oil
300°–370°C
≥ C_{19}
Residue, asphalt
≥ C_{25}

Figure 8 The petroleum pumped from underground deposits is a complex mixture of hydrocarbons. **A** At a refinery, petroleum is separated into mixtures called fractions. **B** The diagram shows some of the fractions that can be collected from a distillation tower. The labels provide data on the compounds within a fraction. For example, compounds in kerosene have from 12 to 16 carbon atoms and condense at temperatures between 200°C and 250°C. **Interpreting Diagrams** ***How many carbon atoms are there in the compounds in the petroleum gas fraction?***

The diagram in Figure 8B shows how petroleum is separated into fractions through a type of distillation called fractional distillation. When petroleum is heated in a distillation tower, most of the hydrocarbons vaporize. The vapors rise through the tower and condense as the temperature decreases. Compounds with higher boiling points condense first. They are collected near the bottom of the tower.

Combustion of Fossil Fuels

The energy released from fossil fuels through combustion is used to heat buildings, cook food, or for transportation. Recall that energy from the combustion of propane heats the air in a hot-air balloon.

$$C_3H_8 + 5O_2 \longrightarrow 3CO_2 + 4H_2O \text{ (complete combustion)}$$

The primary products of the complete combustion of fossil fuels are carbon dioxide and water. Burning fossil fuels increases the amount of carbon dioxide in the atmosphere. This increase may affect temperatures, amounts of rain, and sea levels worldwide. Some sulfur and nitrogen are in fossil fuels, and air contains nitrogen. So nitrogen oxides and sulfur dioxide are produced during the combustion of fossil fuels.

Incomplete Combustion In stoves and furnaces, there may not be enough oxygen available for complete combustion of all the fuel. So a deadly gas, carbon monoxide, is produced. This colorless, odorless gas can be inhaled and absorbed by blood. It keeps hemoglobin from carrying oxygen to cells. Safety experts recommend that homes heated with natural gas or heating oil have carbon monoxide detectors.

$$2C_3H_8 + 7O_2 \longrightarrow 6CO + 8H_2O \text{ (incomplete combustion)}$$

When fossil fuels undergo incomplete combustion in factories or power plants, they also produce tiny particles of carbon. Inhaling these particles can cause heart and lung problems.

Facts and Figures

Octane Number Octane ratings are used to compare blends of gasoline. Two substances found in gasoline are used as reference fuels: *n*-heptane and isooctane (2,2,4-trimethylpentane). Because *n*-heptane self-ignites when compressed, it burns too rapidly, causing a knocking sound in a poorly performing engine. Isooctane will not self-ignite if it is compressed before sparking. The octane rating describes a blend as though it contained only *n*-heptane and isooctane. With an octane rating of 89, gasoline performs as if it contained 89% isooctane and 11% *n*-heptane. With a higher octane rating, the possibility of knocking is lower.

Figure 9 This statue of George Washington was sculpted from marble in 1918. The photograph was taken in the 1990s. The damage was done by calcium carbonate in the marble reacting with sulfuric acid in acid rain.

Acid Rain The combustion of fossil fuels causes the acidity of rain to increase. Rain is always slightly acidic, with a pH of about 5.6, because carbon dioxide dissolves in water droplets and forms carbonic acid, H_2CO_3. Sulfur dioxide and nitrogen oxides released into the atmosphere also dissolve in water, forming sulfuric acid, H_2SO_4, and nitric acid, HNO_3. The pH of rain containing sulfuric acid and nitric acid can be as low as 2.7. These acids damage stone structures like the statue in Figure 9. They also damage metal and concrete.

Section 9.1 Assessment

Reviewing Concepts

1. Name three forms of carbon.
2. What two factors can affect the properties of a hydrocarbon?
3. Name the three categories of unsaturated hydrocarbons.
4. Name the three main fossil fuels.
5. What are the two primary products of the complete combustion of fossil fuels?
6. What are three ways that carbon atoms can be arranged in hydrocarbon molecules?

Critical Thinking

7. **Classifying** Why isn't carbon dioxide considered an organic compound?
8. **Applying Concepts** Draw structural formulas for the two branched-chain isomers of pentane, C_5H_{12}.

Connecting Concepts

Saturation Compare the way *saturated* and *unsaturated* are used in describing hydrocarbons to how they were used in describing solutions in Section 8.2.

Section 9.1 Assessment

1. Diamond, graphite, and fullerenes are forms of carbon.
2. Factors that determine the properties of a hydrocarbon are the number of carbon atoms and how the atoms are arranged.
3. The three types of unsaturated hydrocarbons are alkenes, alkynes, and aromatic hydrocarbons.
4. Three types of fossil fuels are coal, natural gas, and petroleum.
5. Carbon dioxide and water
6. As a straight chain, a branched chain, or a ring
7. Carbon dioxide does not contain any hydrogen atoms.
8.

```
C–C–C–C          C
  |              |
  C            C–C–C
                 |
                 C
```

(2-methylbutane) (2, 2-dimethylpropane)

Build Math Skills L1

Interpreting Equations Write the equations for the complete and incomplete combustion of propane on the board. Ask, **Why are there 5 moles of oxygen in the equation for the complete combustion, but 7 moles of oxygen in the equation for the incomplete combustion?** Let students figure out that the number of moles of methane is not the same in the two equations. Then, multiply the coefficients in the first equation by 2 to show that the amount of oxygen used is greater. **Logical**

Direct students to the **Math Skills** in the **Skills and Reference Handbook** at the end of the student text for additional help.

3 ASSESS

Evaluate Understanding

Have students make flashcards for the key concepts and vocabulary in this section. For example, for each type of unsaturated hydrocarbon, they can make a card that has an example and a definition. Students can use the flashcards to quiz one another.

Reteach L1

Use the structural formulas in the text on pp. 265 and 266 to review each type of hydrocarbon.

Connecting Concepts

In a saturated solution, the solvent contains the maximum amount of solute at a given temperature. A saturated hydrocarbon contains the maximum number of hydrogen atoms for each carbon atom. More solute can be added to an unsaturated solution. More hydrogen atoms can be added to an unsaturated hydrocarbon.

Interactive Textbook If your class subscribes to the Interactive Textbook, use it to review key concepts in Section 9.1.

Answer to . . .

Figure 8 *Molecules of compounds in petroleum gas contain one to four carbon atoms.*

CONCEPTS in Action

Breathing Easy L2

Background

The Department of Energy began The Clean Coal Technology Program in response to concerns about acid rain. The diagram illustrates some of the methods used to reduce emissions of nitrogen oxides and sulfur dioxide. (1) Sulfur that is not bonded to carbon is removed when coal is crushed and washed. (2) Jets of air keep limestone and crushed coal suspended so that the limestone can react with the sulfur dioxide. Because the temperature in the furnace is low and the amount of air is limited, most of the oxygen reacts with fuel, not nitrogen. (7) Smokestacks may contain electrostatic precipitators and scrubbers. As particles of ash pass through the precipitator, they gain a charge. They can be collected on a plate with an opposite charge. In one type of scrubber, limewater is sprayed into the stream of waste gases. The calcium hydroxide reacts with sulfur dioxide and forms solid calcium sulfate.

Build Science Skills L2

Observing

ACTIVITY

Purpose In this activity, students will use physical properties to separate a mixture of coal and sulfur.

Materials 100-mL beaker containing a 1:1 mixture of sulfur powder and coal dust, 100-mL graduated cylinder, stirring rod, distilled water, plastic pipet, 100-mL beaker

Class Time 10–15 minutes

Procedure Provide each group with a beaker containing 10 g of the sulfur-coal mixture. Have them add 30 mL of water to the beaker and mix using a stirring rod. Allow layers to form in the mixture. Next have students use a pipet to transfer the layer of water containing coal dust to a second beaker. Stir the mixture and allow layers to form again. Have students compare their activity to the process described in Step 1 of the diagram.

Safety Students should wear safety goggles and aprons.

CONCEPTS in Action

Breathing Easy

Coal-burning power stations produce more than half the electricity used in the United States. An average coal-burning power station emits about 10,000 tons of sulfur dioxide and the same amount of nitrogen oxides each year.

Oxides of sulfer and nitrogen cause smog and acid rain. They also can irritate your lungs. The United States has a Clean Coal Technology Program that encourages the development of technologies for reducing emissions of these harmful gases. The diagram shows steps in the process for reducing these emissions. The process begins when sulfur is washed from the surface of coal and ends when cleaner air is released into the atmosphere.

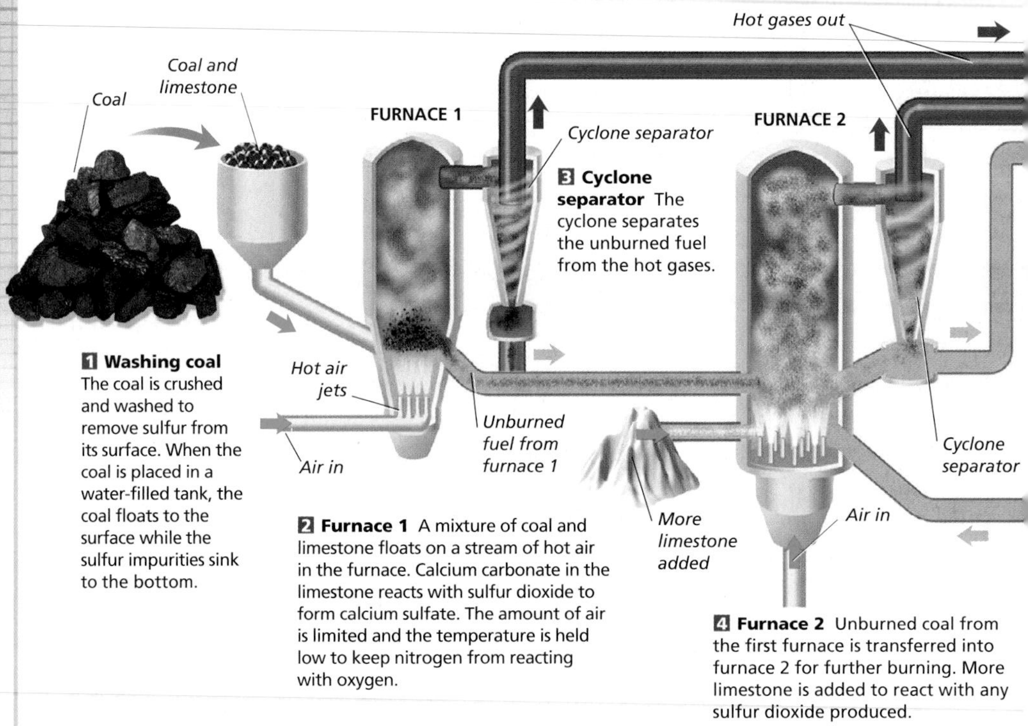

Hot gases out
Coal and limestone
Coal
FURNACE 1
Cyclone separator
FURNACE 2
3 Cyclone separator The cyclone separates the unburned fuel from the hot gases.
1 Washing coal The coal is crushed and washed to remove sulfur from its surface. When the coal is placed in a water-filled tank, the coal floats to the surface while the sulfur impurities sink to the bottom.
Hot air jets
Air in
Unburned fuel from furnace 1
More limestone added
Cyclone separator
Air in
2 Furnace 1 A mixture of coal and limestone floats on a stream of hot air in the furnace. Calcium carbonate in the limestone reacts with sulfur dioxide to form calcium sulfate. The amount of air is limited and the temperature is held low to keep nitrogen from reacting with oxygen.
4 Furnace 2 Unburned coal from the first furnace is transferred into furnace 2 for further burning. More limestone is added to react with any sulfur dioxide produced.

Facts and Figures

Catalytic Converters The combustion of petroleum products in internal combustion engines produces emissions that contribute to air pollution. In a vehicle's exhaust system, there is a catalytic converter. This device contains a mixture of catalysts for the oxidation of carbon monoxide and unburned hydrocarbons to carbon dioxide and water and the reduction of nitrogen oxides to nitrogen. The catalysts may be transition metals, such as platinum palladium, and rhodium; or oxides of transition metals, such as CuO and Cr_2O_3.

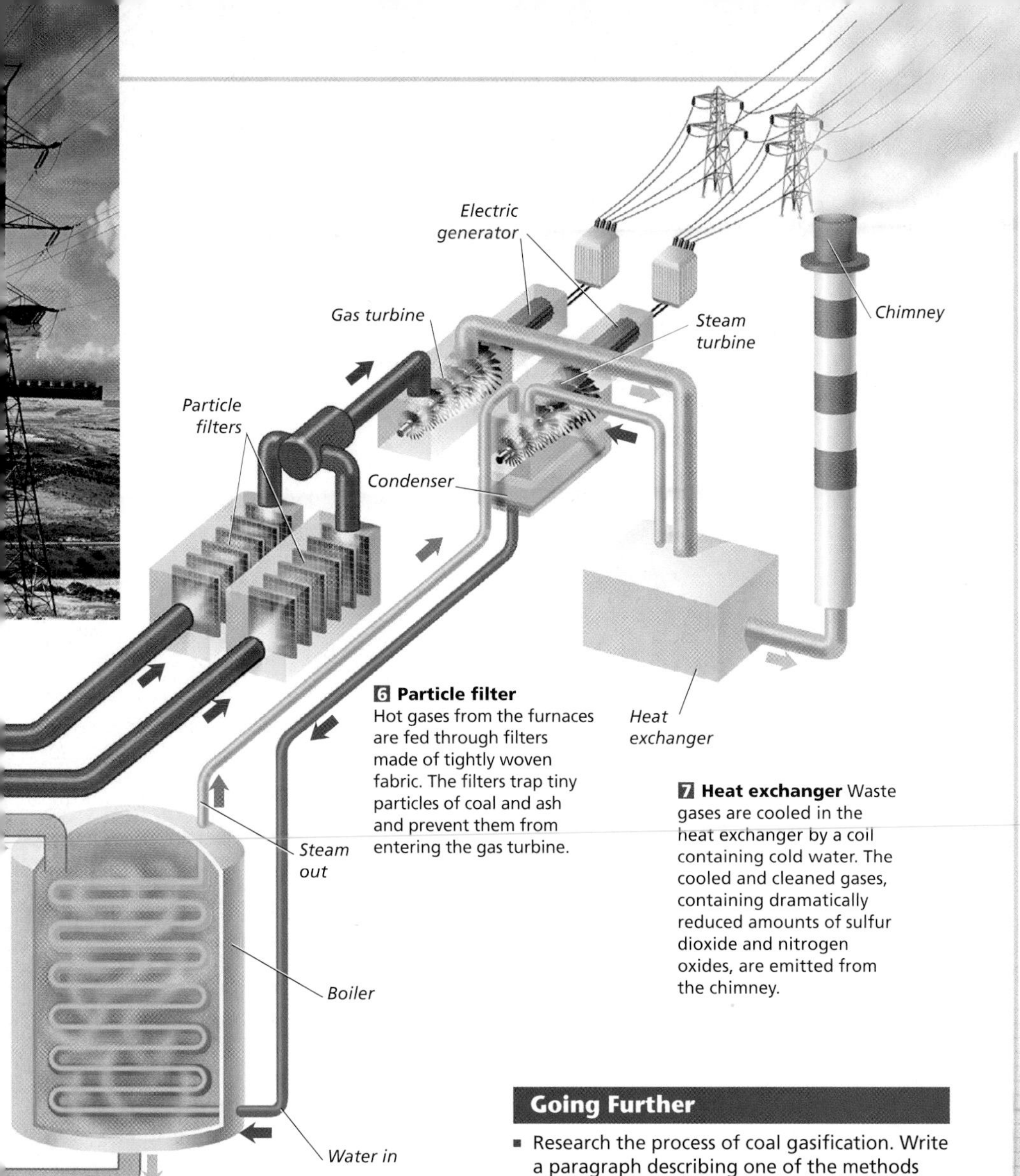
Electric generator
Gas turbine
Steam turbine
Chimney
Particle filters
Condenser
Heat exchanger
Steam out
Boiler
Water in

6 Particle filter Hot gases from the furnaces are fed through filters made of tightly woven fabric. The filters trap tiny particles of coal and ash and prevent them from entering the gas turbine.

7 Heat exchanger Waste gases are cooled in the heat exchanger by a coil containing cold water. The cooled and cleaned gases, containing dramatically reduced amounts of sulfur dioxide and nitrogen oxides, are emitted from the chimney.

5 Boiler Water from the condenser flows through pipes in the boiler. Hot gases from furnace 2 are fed into the boiler to heat the water. The steam created is used to spin a steam turbine. The exhaust gases are recycled back to furnace 2.

Going Further

- Research the process of coal gasification. Write a paragraph describing one of the methods used to convert coal into flammable gases. What gases are produced? What are the benefits of coal gasification? Are there any problems with the technology?
- Take a Discovery Channel Video Field Trip by watching "Clean Energy."

Discovery Channel School **Video Field Trip**

Expected Outcome Most of the sulfur will settle to the bottom of the first beaker while the coal dust floats. Any remaining sulfur will settle to the bottom of the second beaker. This activity demonstrates what happens when coal is crushed and washed prior to burning.
Visual, Kinesthetic

Going Further L3

The United States Department of Energy has funded research into coal gasification. They are encouraging the development of methods for converting solid coal into gases that can be used to generate power. During gasification, coal reacts with steam and oxygen at a high temperature and pressure. The methods produce a mixture of gases. Hydrogen and carbon monoxide are typical products. The hydrogen can be separated from the raw mixture and used directly as fuel or it can be combined with carbon monoxide to produce methane. Any carbon dioxide produced is captured for commercial applications or sequestered to prevent its release into the atmosphere.

If students search the Internet, they will find descriptions of multiple methods for coal gasification, and information on the advantages and drawbacks of the methods. The main advantages of coal gasification are a reduction in air pollution and an increase in efficiency (more energy produced from the same amount of coal). For now, drawbacks include the cost of equipment and a higher cost per kilowatt for power generation. Other drawbacks are the amount of water required and the amount of wastewater produced.
Verbal, Portfolio

Discovery Channel School

Video Field Trip

Clean Energy

After students have viewed the Video Field Trip, ask them the following questions: **What substances does a fuel cell use to produce energy? What form of energy is produced?** *(The fuel cell uses oxygen [from air] and hydrogen. The fuel cell produces electrical energy.)* **What technological advance made fuel cells more efficient?** *(The development of a new kind of membrane to separate the oxygen and hydrogen)* **Give one advantage that a fuel cell has over an internal combustion engine.** *(Student answers may include having no moving parts, producing only water as a product, and being quieter.)* **What advantage does a vehicle that uses a fuel cell have over a vehicle that uses batteries?** *(As long as fuel is provided, the fuel cell will continue to work.)* **If fuel cells are more efficient (that is, if they have a higher ratio of output energy to input energy) than internal combustion engines, why do most cars still have internal combustion engines?** *(Because of the large investment already made in internal engine technology)*

1 FOCUS

Objectives

9.2.1 **Classify** substituted hydrocarbons based on their functional groups.

9.2.2 **Describe** some properties and reactions of five types of substituted hydrocarbons.

Reading Focus

Build Vocabulary L2

Word Forms Before students read this section, have them look up the words *substitute* and *functional.* Then, have students write a prediction for the meanings of the terms *substituted hydrocarbon* and *functional group.* After students study the section, have them look at their predictions and discuss any differences between their predictions and the definitions in the text.

Reading Strategy L2

a. alcohol **b.** organic acid
c. organic base

2 INSTRUCT

Teacher Demo

Modeling Functional Groups L2

Purpose Students make an analogy between an appliance's attachments and functional groups.

Materials any appliance that has attachments with different functions

Procedure Demonstrate how the appliance works. Show students how each attachment performs a different function. Use these differences to explain how functional groups determine the properties of substituted hydrocarbons.

Safety Handle the appliance and its attachments according to the manufacturer's safety recommendations.

Expected Outcome Students will be able to compare the attachments of an appliance to functional groups in substituted hydrocarbons.
Visual, Logical

9.2 Substituted Hydrocarbons

Reading Focus

Key Concepts

- What functional groups are found in alcohols, organic acids, and organic bases?
- How are esters formed?

Vocabulary

- substituted hydrocarbon
- functional group

Reading Strategy

Monitoring Your Understanding Copy the table. As you read, complete the table by connecting each functional group with the type of compound that contains the functional group.

Functional Group	Type of Compound
–OH	a. ?
–COOH	b. ?
$-NH_2$	c. ?

The electric drill in Figure 10 can be used to drill holes, tighten a screw, or sand a rough surface. To change the function of the drill, you replace, or substitute, an attachment. A carbon atom in an organic compound can have four attachments. In a methane molecule (CH_4), the carbon atom has four identical attachments—its hydrogen atoms. When methane reacts with chlorine, chlorine atoms replace hydrogen atoms.

$$CH_4 + Cl_2 \longrightarrow CH_3Cl + HCl$$

Chloromethane and hydrogen chloride are products of the reaction between methane and chlorine. So are compounds with two, three, or four chlorine atoms. Organic compounds containing chlorine or other halogens are halocarbons. Almost all the halocarbons found on Earth were released from refrigerators, air conditioners, or aerosol sprays. Researchers have established that halocarbons containing chlorine and fluorine deplete Earth's protective ozone layer. The manufacture of chlorofluorocarbons has been restricted since 1990.

A hydrocarbon in which one or more hydrogen atoms have been replaced by an atom or group of atoms is a **substituted hydrocarbon.** The substituted atom or group of atoms is called a **functional group** because it determines the properties of the compound. Alcohols, organic acids, organic bases, and esters are substituted hydrocarbons.

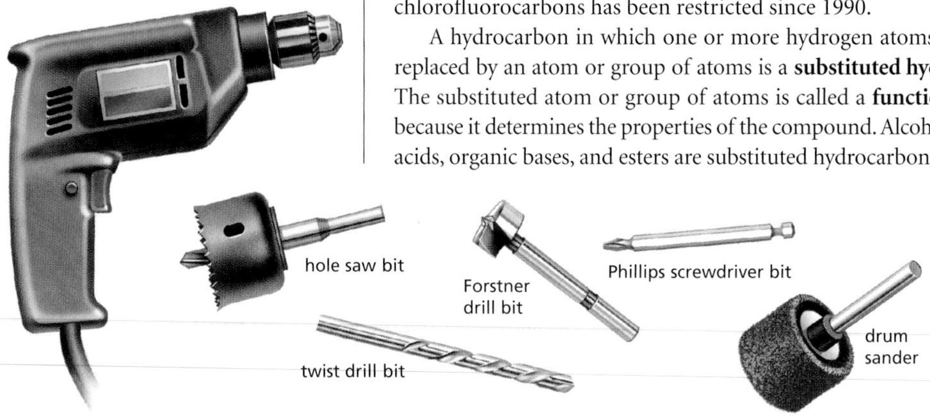

hole saw bit
Forstner drill bit
Phillips screwdriver bit
twist drill bit
drum sander

Figure 10 Hydrocarbons in which some hydrogen atoms have been replaced can be compared to an electric drill with attachments.
Inferring ***What determines the function of the drill, the drill itself or the attachments?***

Section Resources

Print
- ***Reading and Study Workbook With Math Support,*** Section 9.2
- ***Math Skills and Problem Solving Workbook,*** Section 9.2
- ***Transparencies,*** Section 9.2

Technology
- ***Interactive Textbook,*** Section 9.2
- ***Presentation Pro CD-ROM,*** Section 9.2

Data Analysis

Exploring Boiling Points of Chlorocarbons

Use the data given to construct a graph with *Number of Chlorine Atoms,* from 0 to 4, on the horizontal axis and *Boiling Point* on the vertical axis. Draw a smooth curve connecting the points.

Boiling Points of Methane and Its Substituted Chlorocarbons

Name	Formula	Boiling Point (°C)
Methane	CH_4	−161
Chloromethane	CH_3Cl	−24
Dichloromethane	CH_2Cl_2	?
Trichloromethane	$CHCl_3$	61
Tetrachloromethane	CCl_4	77

1. **Using Graphs** Predict the boiling point of dichloromethane.
2. **Relating Cause and Effect** What effect does increasing the number of chlorine atoms have on the boiling point?
3. **Formulating Hypotheses** Why is the boiling point of CH_3Br higher than the boiling point of CH_3Cl? (*Hint:* Compare the atomic masses for bromine and chlorine.)

Alcohols

Methanol, CH_3OH, is used as a fuel in some motorcycles. Ethanol, CH_3CH_2OH, is often mixed with gasoline to help the gasoline burn more completely. Methanol and ethanol are alcohols. The name of an alcohol ends in *-ol.* **The functional group in an alcohol is a hydroxyl group, –OH.** When a halocarbon reacts with a base, the products are an alcohol and salt.

$$CH_3Cl + NaOH \longrightarrow CH_3OH + NaCl$$

An alcohol can also be made by reacting an alkene with water.

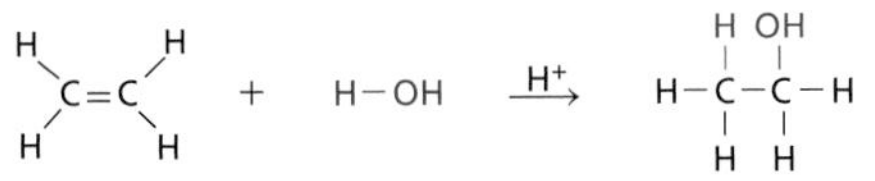

Ethene Water Ethanol

Organic Acids and Bases

The sharp, sour taste of a lemon comes from citric acid, an organic acid. **The functional group in organic acids is a carboxyl group, –COOH.** Names of organic acids end in *-oic.* Organic acids tend to have sharp tastes and strong odors. The simplest organic acid is methanoic acid, which is also known as formic acid. Vinegar is a solution of water and the organic acid ethanoic acid, which is usually referred to as acetic acid. If the ants in Figure 11 sprayed the formic acid they produce on your skin, your skin would itch or burn.

Methanoic acid

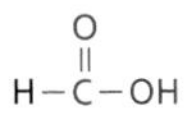

Ethanoic acid

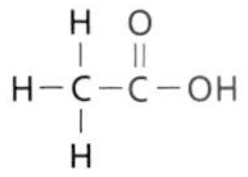

Figure 11 Birds sometimes will sit on an ants' nest and allow the ants to crawl over them. The methanoic acid sprayed by the ants is a natural pesticide that kills mites in the birds' feathers.

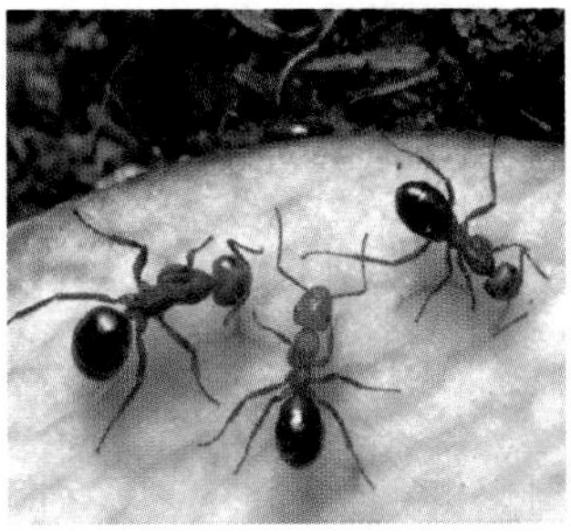

Customize for Inclusion Students

Learning Disabled
Make concept maps for each section and cover them with clear contact paper. Then, cut the maps into puzzle pieces. Provide students with the pieces and have them put the puzzle together. After students complete the puzzle, have them make flashcards with concept connections and added notes. For example, students may have cards with the names of compounds on one side and structural formulas on the other. They may also have key concept cards with an important word missing: ______ **form when organic acids react with alcohols.** The answer on the back of the card would be *Esters.*

Data Analysis

Exploring Boiling Points of Chlorocarbons L2

1. Acceptable answers include temperatures between −24°C and 61°C. (The boiling point of dichloromethane is 40°C.)
2. As the number of chlorine atoms increases, the boiling point increases.
3. Bromine is more massive than chlorine.

For Extra Help L1

Demonstrate how to use a curve on a graph to estimate the value of an unknown data point. Find the appropriate value on the horizontal axis. Use a ruler to intersect the curve above that value. Turn the ruler 90° and read the vertical value for the intersection point. **Visual**

Alcohols

Build Science Skills L2

Applying Concepts Ask students to predict the products for the complete combustion of methanol and ethanol. Then, have them write balanced equations for these reactions.

$$2CH_3OH + 3O_2 \longrightarrow 2CO_2 + 4H_2O$$
$$C_2H_5OH + 3O_2 \longrightarrow 2CO_2 + 3H_2O$$

Logical

FYI

There are multiple methods for the formation of alcohols, including fermentation and reduction of aldehydes and ketones.

Organic Acids and Bases

Build Reading Literacy L1

Compare and Contrast Refer to page **226D** in **Chapter 8,** which provides guidelines for comparing and contrasting.

Have students read the text on pp. 273–274 related to organic acids and bases. Ask, **How do organic acids and bases differ?** *(Organic acids have a carboxyl group, while organic bases have an amino group.)* **How are organic acids and bases similar?** *(They are substituted hydrocarbons with strong odors.)*
Verbal

Answer to . . .

Figure 10 *The attachments determine the specific function of the drill.*

Esters

Address Misconceptions L2

Students may not know that an object has an odor because molecules from substances in the object interact with chemoreceptors in the nose. Studying esters is a good way to challenge this misconception. Have students smell some fragrant objects, such as apples, bananas, or flowers. Explain that some of the compounds responsible for the odors are esters.
Logical, Kinesthetic

Use Community Resources L2

Have a pharmacist speak to the class about how functional groups determine the effect of a medicine. Have students ask how to find information on the chemical composition of active ingredients in prescription and over-the-counter drugs.
Interpersonal

3 ASSESS

Evaluate Understanding L2

Have students design and play a matching game that uses cards that identify the formulas and characteristics of each functional group described in the section.

Reteach L1

Use short phrases to summarize the characteristics of functional groups. For example, say that amines smell like rotten fish and esters have pleasant smells, like some flowers. Review other characteristics, such as chemical structure, for each functional group.

Connecting Concepts

Replacing a halogen with a hydroxyl group is a double-replacement reaction because the hydroxyl group and the halogen exchange places. The reaction of alkenes with water to produce an alcohol is a synthesis reaction because two reactants join to form one product.

Interactive Textbook If your class subscribes to the Interactive Textbook, use it to review key concepts in Section 9.2.

Figure 12 Many compounds in rose petals contribute to the fragrance of a rose. Some of these compounds are esters, which tend to have pleasant, sweet odors.

Do you know the smell of rotten fish? Then you've encountered a type of substituted hydrocarbon called an amine. Amines are organic bases. **The functional group in an amine is an amino group, $-NH_2$.** Amines are found in paints, dyes, and disinfectants. In Section 9.3 you will study the role organic bases play in the formation of organic compounds that are essential for life.

Esters

One group of substituted hydrocarbons accounts for the flavors of many foods and the pleasant odor of many flowers. These compounds are known as esters. **Esters form when organic acids react with alcohols.** The second product of the reaction is water. For example, ethanoic acid can react with methanol to produce methyl ethanoate (methyl acetate). The reaction is reversible.

Ethanoic acid + Methanol ⇌ Methyl ethanoate + Water

Esters are used in many processed foods to produce flavors such as strawberry, banana, and grape. Flowers like the roses in Figure 12 produce esters and other compounds with distinctive odors that attract insects for pollination. Sometimes, the compounds produced by the plant mimic compounds produced by the insect.

Section 9.2 Assessment

Reviewing Concepts

1. What functional groups are found in alcohols, organic acids, and organic bases?
2. Which types of compounds can react to produce esters?
3. What is a substituted hydrocarbon?
4. When a halocarbon reacts with a base, what products are produced?
5. What are two properties of organic acids?

Critical Thinking

6. **Classifying** An unknown compound has no noticeable odor. Explain why the compound is unlikely to be an organic acid, an organic base, or an ester.
7. **Inferring** What kind of organic compound gives a vitamin-C tablet its sour taste?
8. **Applying Concepts** Name one kind of substituted hydrocarbon you would expect to find in artificially flavored grape jelly.

Connecting Concepts

Types of Reactions Alcohols can be made by reacting halocarbons with bases, or alkenes with water. Review the general types of reactions presented in Section 7.2. Which types best describe the two methods for producing an alcohol? Explain your choices.

Section 9.2 Assessment

1. Alcohols have hydroxyl groups, organic acids have carboxyl groups, and organic bases have amino groups.
2. Esters form when organic acids react with alcohols.
3. A hydrocarbon in which a functional group has been substituted for a hydrogen atom
4. An alcohol and a salt
5. Organic acids contain carboxyl groups and have a sharp, sour taste and a strong smell.
6. Organic acids, organic bases, and esters tend to have noticeable smells.
7. An organic acid
8. An ester

9.3 Polymers

Reading Focus

Key Concepts
- What is one way that polymers can be classified?
- What are three examples of synthetic polymers?
- What are four types of polymers that organisms can produce?

Vocabulary
- polymer
- monomers
- carbohydrates
- nucleic acids
- amino acid
- protein

Reading Strategy
Identifying Main Ideas Before you read, copy the concept map. As you read, complete the map to summarize two main ideas about polymers.

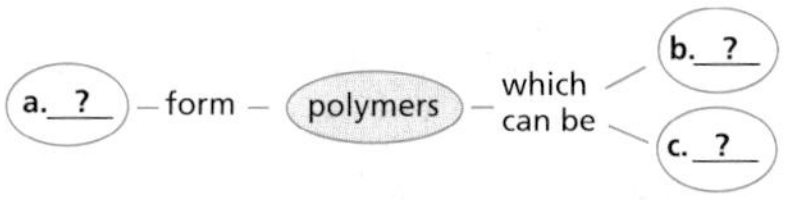
a. ?
form
polymers
which can be
b. ?
c. ?

Freight trains, like those in Figure 13, use different types of cars to transport goods. A flatcar with no sides or roof is used to haul steel beams. Grain is carried in covered hoppers, which have a hatch at the top and a chute at the bottom. Liquids travel in tank cars. The cars on a train may be all the same type or a mixture of different types. On average, about 100 cars are linked together behind the locomotive on a freight train.

Like freight trains, some molecules are built up from smaller units linked together. A **polymer** is a large molecule that forms when many smaller molecules are linked together by covalent bonds. The smaller molecules that join together to form a polymer are **monomers.** *Poly-* means "many." *Mono-* means "one." In some polymers, there is only one type of monomer. Other polymers have two or more kinds of monomers.

Polymers can be classified as natural polymers or synthetic polymers. Many important types of biological molecules are natural polymers. Organisms produce these polymers in their cells. Synthetic polymers are developed by chemists in research laboratories and manufactured in factories. Both types of polymers have industrial uses. For example, silk and cotton fabrics are woven from natural polymer fibers, while polar fleece is made from a synthetic polymer.

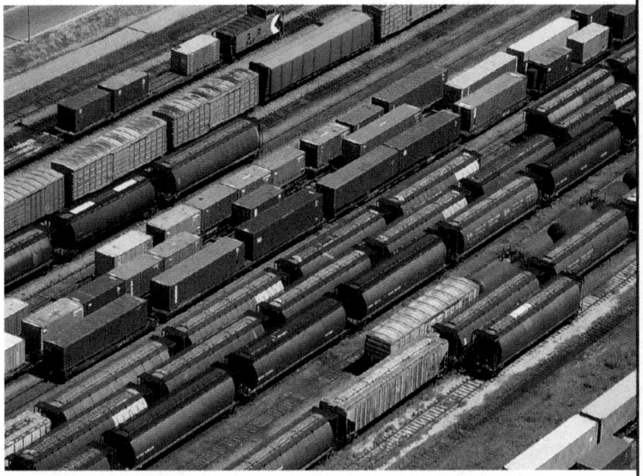

Figure 13 Couplers that interlock like the fingers of your hands connect one railroad car to another. Many cars can be joined together to form a train, because there is a coupler on both ends of a car. **Using Analogies** ***How is a polymer like a train?***

Section Resources

Print
- ***Laboratory Manual,*** Investigations 9A and 9B
- ***Reading and Study Workbook With Math Support,*** Section 9.3
- ***Transparencies,*** Section 9.3

Technology
- ***Interactive Textbook,*** Section 9.3
- ***Presentation Pro CD-ROM,*** Section 9.3
- ***Go Online,*** NSTA SciLinks, Polymers

Section 9.3

1 FOCUS

Objectives
9.3.1 **Distinguish** a monomer from a polymer.
9.3.2 **Compare** three examples of synthetic polymers.
9.3.3 **Describe** the structures and functions of four types of natural polymers.

Reading Focus

Build Vocabulary L2
Word-Part Analysis Have students break the vocabulary terms *polymer, monomer,* and *carbohydrate* into roots, prefixes, or suffixes. Students may need to use a dictionary to find the meanings of some parts. *(Monomer has the prefix* mono- *meaning "one." Monomers are the single units that make up polymers. Polymer has the prefix* poly- *meaning "many." Polymers contain many monomers. Carbohydrate has the prefix* carbo- *which means it contains carbon, and the suffix* -hydrate *which means it also contains the components of water—hydrogen and oxygen.)*

Reading Strategy L2
a. monomers
b. and **c.** natural/synthetic

2 INSTRUCT

Build Reading Literacy L1
Use Prior Knowledge Refer to page **2D** in **Chapter 1,** which provides guidelines for using prior knowledge.

Before students read, ask them to list different fibers used to make fabrics, such as wool and polyester. Have them discuss which fibers they think are natural and identify their sources.
Verbal, Intrapersonal

Answer to . . .

Figure 13 *Like a train, a polymer is made up of single units that are joined together.*

Synthetic Polymers

Use Visuals L1

Figure 14 Have students look at the objects in Figure 14. Ask, **What are some physical properties of rubber, nylon, and polyethylene?** *(Possible answer: Rubber resists wear. Nylon is durable and strong. High-density polyethylene is hard.)* **What are some ways that each of the polymers is used?** *(Possible answer: Rubber is used for tires and as an adhesive. Nylon is used for parachutes, windbreakers, fishing line, carpets, and rope. Polyethylene is used for milk bottles and plastic wrap.)*
Visual, Logical

Integrate Social Studies L2

Natural rubber collected from trees is soft and sticky. In 1839, Charles Goodyear found that when sulfur is added to rubber and the mixture is heated, the rubber is no longer sticky. Have students research other topics related to polymers. Possible topics include the discovery of nylon, the discovery of artificial silk (later called rayon) by Hilaire de Chardonnet, or the use of polymers in the film industry. Students may also want to research current efforts to recycle plastics, including the codes used on plastic products. Have students use posters or computer graphics to prepare a report on their research.
Verbal, Portfolio

Go Online NSTA SCILINKS

Download a worksheet on polymers for students to complete, and find additional teacher support from NSTA SciLinks.

A
B
C

Figure 14 Synthetic polymers are used to make tires, ropes, and plastic objects. **A** About half the rubber produced in the world is used to manufacture tires. **B** Nylon is a good choice for a rope because its fibers are strong and do not wear out easily. **C** The hard plastic shapes are made from a high-density polyethylene polymer. **Inferring** ***At room temperature, polymers are most likely to exist as which state of matter?***

Synthetic Polymers

The properties of a polymer depend on the type and number of monomers in the polymer. **Rubber, nylon, and polyethylene are three examples of compounds that can be synthesized.**

Rubber The sap collected from rubber trees in tropical regions contains rubber. So why would a chemist make synthetic rubber? The supply of natural rubber is limited. During World War II, the allies could not obtain natural rubber. Chemists worked hard to produce a synthetic rubber, using hydrocarbons from petroleum. Natural rubber and synthetic rubbers contain different monomers and have different properties. The tires in Figure 14A will resist wear and be less likely to leak if they are made of synthetic rubber. Rubber is used as an adhesive. The How It Works box on page 277 explains how adhesives work.

Nylon In the 1930s, Wallace Carothers was trying to produce a synthetic polymer to replace silk. The polymer he produced was nylon, which has properties not found in natural polymers. Nylon fibers are very strong, durable, and shiny. Nylon is used in parachutes, windbreakers, fishing line, carpets, and ropes like the one in Figure 14B.

Polyethylene Plastic milk bottles, plastic wrap, and the plastic shapes in Figure 14C are made of polyethylene. This polymer forms when ethene (or ethylene) molecules link head to tail. The number of carbon atoms in a polyethylene chain affects the properties of the polymer. The more carbon atoms in the chain, the harder the polymer is.

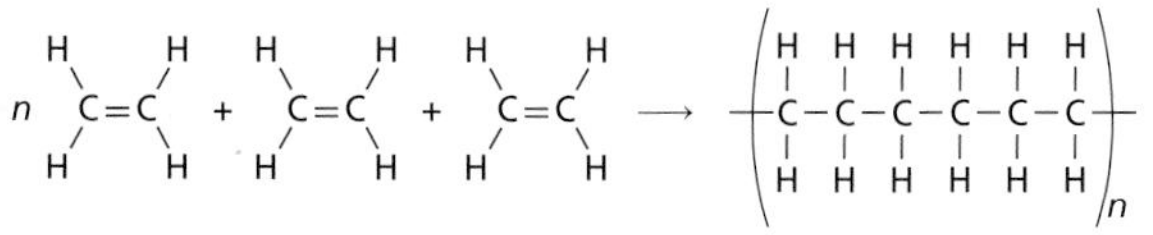

Reading Checkpoint *What determines the hardness of polyethylene?*

Go Online NSTA SCILINKS

For: Links on polymers
Visit: www.SciLinks.org
Web Code: ccn-1093

Customize for English Language Learners

Think-Pair-Share
Have students work in pairs to think of more analogies for polymers. Examples include beads in a necklace and links in a chain. Strengthen discussion skills by having students share their examples with the class.

Answer to . . .

Figure 14 *Polymers are most likely to be solids at room temperature.*

Reading Checkpoint *The hardness of polyethylene is determined by the number of carbon atoms in the chain. The more carbon atoms there are, the harder the polymer is.*

Synthetic Adhesives

Adhesion is the force of attraction between molecules of different substances whose surfaces are in contact. These forces are rarely strong enough to bind two surfaces together. An adhesive placed between the surfaces binds them together. Most adhesives are synthetic polymers. The diagram illustrates how some adhesives work. The adhesive remains liquid until the surfaces are in position. Then the adhesive sets. **Interpreting Diagrams** ***Explain the purpose of a stabilizer in an adhesive.***

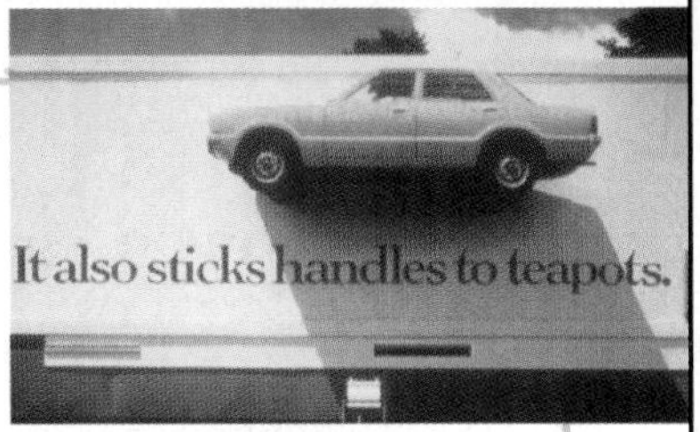
It also sticks handles to teapots.

Permanent adhesion
An epoxy resin was used to attach the automobile to the billboard. Epoxy resins are often stored in two parts that are mixed just before the epoxy is used. Strong binding forces in these adhesives make them heat- and water-resistant.

Temporary adhesion
The sticky strip on a reusable note is an adhesive containing tiny spheres. The spheres limit the amount of surface area that makes contact, so the note sticks lightly and repositions easily.

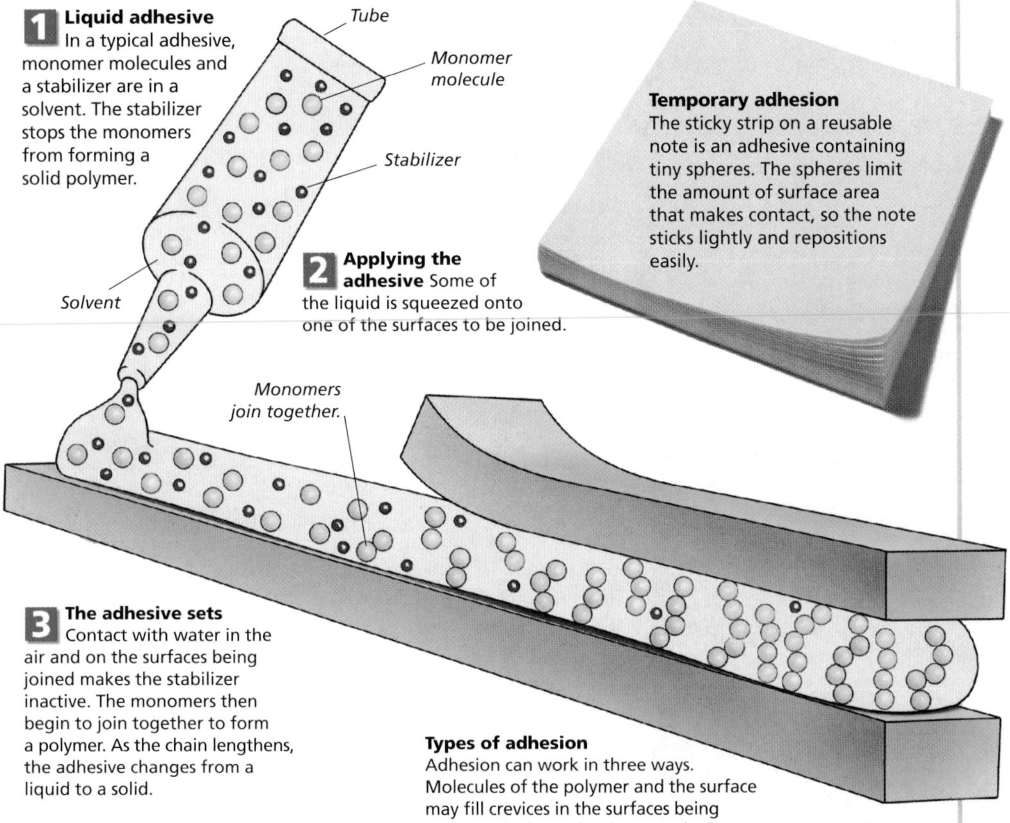
Tube
Monomer molecule
Stabilizer
Solvent
Monomers join together.

1 Liquid adhesive In a typical adhesive, monomer molecules and a stabilizer are in a solvent. The stabilizer stops the monomers from forming a solid polymer.

2 Applying the adhesive Some of the liquid is squeezed onto one of the surfaces to be joined.

3 The adhesive sets Contact with water in the air and on the surfaces being joined makes the stabilizer inactive. The monomers then begin to join together to form a polymer. As the chain lengthens, the adhesive changes from a liquid to a solid.

Types of adhesion
Adhesion can work in three ways. Molecules of the polymer and the surface may fill crevices in the surfaces being connected. The molecules may also be attracted to one another by intermolecular forces, or they may react by forming covalent bonds.

HOW It Works

Synthetic Adhesives L2

The invention of reusable notes began in 1968 when Dr. Spencer Silver was attempting to make a strong adhesive. One of the adhesives he produced was just strong enough to hold papers together, but it was weak enough that the papers could be separated without damage. Silver tried to develop a use for the weak adhesive, but it was his colleague, Art Fry, who realized the adhesive's potential. While singing in a choir, Fry was bothered by bookmarks slipping out of pages. By applying some of the weak adhesive to paper, Fry developed a reusable bookmark that could stick to pages without harming them. The adhesive is now used to produce the familiar, multi-colored reusable notes.

Interpreting Diagrams Stabilizers are used to prevent the adhesive monomers from forming a solid polymer.
Logical

For Enrichment L3

Have students work in pairs and devise an experiment to compare two types of commercially-available adhesives. Remind them to start by forming a hypothesis and writing a plan for their experiment. Suggest that they develop a number scale for reporting how well each adhesive binds two surfaces together. Materials may include paper, metal foil, or wooden craft sticks.
Kinesthetic, Logical

FYI

Although the terms are used interchangeably, *glue* refers to natural products and *adhesives* refers to synthetics.

Natural Polymers

Quick Lab

Distinguishing Sugars From Starches L2

Objective
After completing this activity, students will be able to
- use iodine to test for the presence of starch in foods.

Skills Focus Observing, Formulating Hypotheses, Inferring

Prep Time 15 minutes

Materials 1 slice each of potato, ripe apple, bread; 15 mL cornstarch; 15 mL table sugar; iodine in a dropper bottle; 6 small paper plates

Advance Prep Cut apples, potatoes, and bread into small cubes (about 1 cm^3). Place iodine solution in labeled dropper bottles.

Class Time 10–15 minutes

Safety Students should wear safety goggles and aprons. Remind students not to eat anything in the lab. If students slice their own apples and potatoes, remind them to be careful when handling sharp objects.

Teaching Tips
- Do not slice the apples and potatoes until right before class. Oxidation will cause them to turn brown, making it difficult to observe the results.
- Make sure that the apples are very ripe, but not rotten. In an unripe apple, all of the starch may not be converted to sugar, and students may get a positive result. Test one apple in advance.

Expected Outcome Iodine solution changes color in the presence of starch. Iodine will change from orange-rust to brown or blue-black with the cornstarch, potato, and bread. Iodine will not change color with the sugar or the apple.

Analyze and Conclude
1. Iodine will change color with starch, but not with a sugar.
2. The cornstarch, potato, and bread contain starch.
3. Possible answers include corn, flour, cereals, or any of the foods shown in Figure 15.
Visual, Logical

Quick Lab

Distinguishing Sugars From Starches

Materials

1 slice each of potato, ripe apple, and bread; 15 mL cornstarch; 15 mL table sugar; iodine in dropper bottle; 6 small paper plates

Procedure

1. Place one sample of each food on a paper plate. **CAUTION** *Never eat anything in a lab.*
2. Place 2 to 3 drops of iodine solution on the cornstarch. Record your observations.
3. Repeat Step 2 using sugar instead of cornstarch.
4. Place 2 to 3 drops of iodine on each of the other food samples. Record your observations.

Analyze and Conclude

1. **Classifying** How can an iodine solution be used to distinguish a sugar from a starch?
2. **Drawing Conclusions** Which of the food samples contained starch?
3. **Predicting** What other foods would turn dark when tested with iodine solution?

Natural Polymers

Almost all of the large molecules produced by organisms are polymers. **Four types of polymers produced in plant and animal cells are starches, cellulose, nucleic acids, and proteins.**

Starches Many animals are attracted to sweet-tasting foods. The compounds responsible for this sweetness are often sugars. Simple sugars have the formula $C_6H_{12}O_6$. They can exist as straight chains or rings. The simple sugars glucose and fructose can react to form sucrose (table sugar). Glucose monomers join to form starches as shown below.

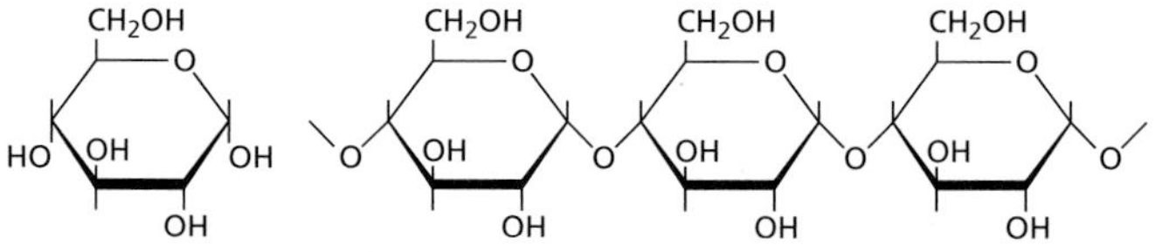

CH_2OH
O
HO
OH

Glucose **A type of starch found in plants**

Typically, a starch contains hundreds of glucose monomers. Plants store starches for food and to build stems, seeds, and roots. Flour for the bread, pasta, and tortillas shown in Figure 15 is made by grinding the seeds of grains, such as wheat and corn. Simple sugars, slightly more complex sugars such as sucrose, and polymers built from sugar monomers are all classified as **carbohydrates.**

Figure 15 All the foods shown contain starch, which is a polymer of the simple sugar glucose. ***Observing** Identify foods that you recognize in the photograph.*

Cellulose The carbohydrate cellulose is the main component of cotton and wood. It is the most abundant of all organic compounds found in nature. Cellulose molecules contain 3000 or more glucose monomers. Cellulose gives strength to plant stems and tree trunks. Most animals cannot digest cellulose.

Facts and Figures

Starchy Root Cassava is a starchy tuber that is a food staple for many people in South America, West Africa, and the Caribbean. Cassava is similar to the sweet potato, except that some varieties contain prussic acid. If not prepared by grating, pressing, and heating, cassava is toxic. Tapioca is a product of cassava roots.

278 Chapter 9

Nucleic Acids There are molecules in each cell of a plant or animal that store information about its structures and functions. These molecules are nucleic acids. **Nucleic acids** are large nitrogen-containing polymers found mainly in the nuclei of cells. There are two types of nucleic acid, deoxyribonucleic acid (DNA) and ribonucleic acid (RNA).

The monomers in a nucleic acid are nucleotides. Figure 16A shows the three parts of a DNA nucleotide. The yellow circle represents a phosphate group. The green pentagon represents deoxyribose sugar, which has a five-atom ring. The purple rectangle represents an organic base. The bases in DNA are adenine, thymine, cytosine, and guanine.

When two strands of DNA line up as shown in Figure 16B, an adenine base always pairs up with a thymine base, and a cytosine base always pairs up with a guanine base. These pairs of bases are arranged like the rungs of a ladder. The strands are held together by strong intermolecular attractions between hydrogen atoms on one strand and nitrogen or oxygen atoms on the other strand. Figure 16C shows how the strands twist around each other in a structure called a double helix. The order of the base pairs in a strand is a code that stores information that is used to produce proteins.

Reading Checkpoint *What are the two types of nucleic acids?*

A

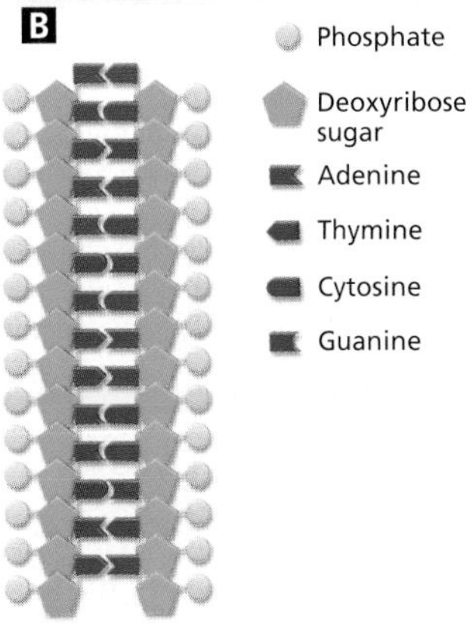
B
Phosphate
Deoxyribose sugar
Adenine
Thymine
Cytosine
Guanine

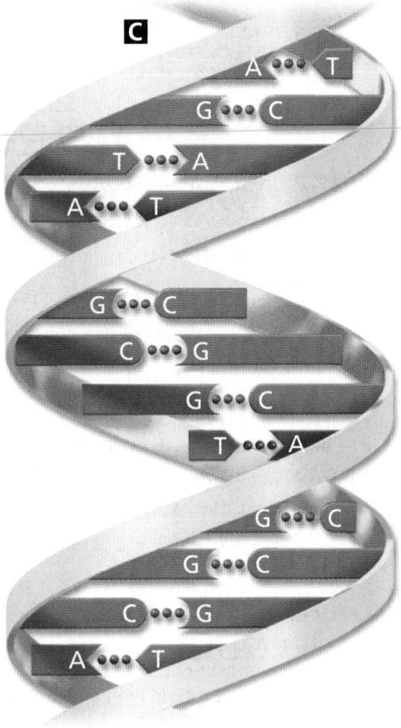
C
A T
G C
T A
A T
G C
C G
G C
T A
G C
G C
C G
A T

Figure 16 Nucleic acids are polymers that store the genetic information that gives the girls in the photograph their distinct physical characteristics. **A** The monomers in DNA have three components—a phosphate group, a sugar, and one of four organic bases. **B** Two strands of DNA are held together by intermolecular attractions between the organic bases. **C** The shape of DNA is like a twisted ladder. Phosphate-sugar chains form the sides of the ladder. The rungs of the ladder are pairs of bases.

Use Visuals **L1**

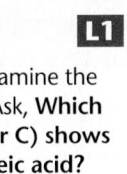

Figure 16 Have students examine the three-part diagram of DNA. Ask, **Which part of the diagram (A, B, or C) shows a single monomer of a nucleic acid?** *(Part A shows one nucleotide unit.)* **How are Parts B and C of the diagram related?** *(Part B shows two strands of the polymer, each containing many monomer units. Part C shows how the strands in Part B twist to form a double helix.)* Explain that the strands of DNA need to separate when DNA replicates (makes copies of itself). Ask, **If the strands were held together by covalent bonds instead of intermolecular attractions, how might this affect DNA replication?** *(Because covalent bonds are stronger than intermolecular attractions, more energy would be required to separate the strands.)*
Visual, Logical

FYI

RNA is different from DNA in several ways. The sugar in RNA is ribose instead of deoxyribose. RNA contains the base uracil instead of thymine. RNA has only one strand.

Answer to . . .

Figure 15 *Answers may include waffles, bread, pasta, oats, tortillas, rice, and cereal.*

Reading Checkpoint *RNA and DNA*

Build Science Skills L2

Comparing and Contrasting Have students compare and contrast proteins and nucleic acids. Ask, **What do these two types of polymers have in common?** *(Both have important biological functions, and the monomers of both are acids.)* **How do these two types of polymers differ?** *(The monomers in nucleic acids are nucleotides. The monomers in proteins are amino acids.)*
Logical

Integrate Health L2

Eggs, milk, meat, and fish usually contain all the essential amino acids. Individual plant foods do not. A strict vegetarian must eat a combination of foods to obtain all the essential amino acids. Have students research and prepare posters showing foods (such as beans and rice) that provide the complete set of essential amino acids.
Visual

3 ASSESS

Evaluate Understanding L2

Have students write down the following list of polymers: polyethylene, starch, cellulose, nucleic acids, and proteins. Then, have students identify the monomers for each polymer.

Reteach L1

Use the equation in the text on pp. 276 and 278 to compare a synthetic and a natural polymer.

Writing in Science

Paragraphs should include the following. Similarities: made up of smaller molecules called monomers that are linked together by covalent bonds. Differences: synthetic polymers are developed by chemists; organisms produce natural polymers.

Interactive Textbook If your class subscribes to the Interactive Textbook, use it to review key concepts in Section 9.3.

Answer to . . .

Figure 17 *Possible answers include: seafood, meat, beans, and nuts.*

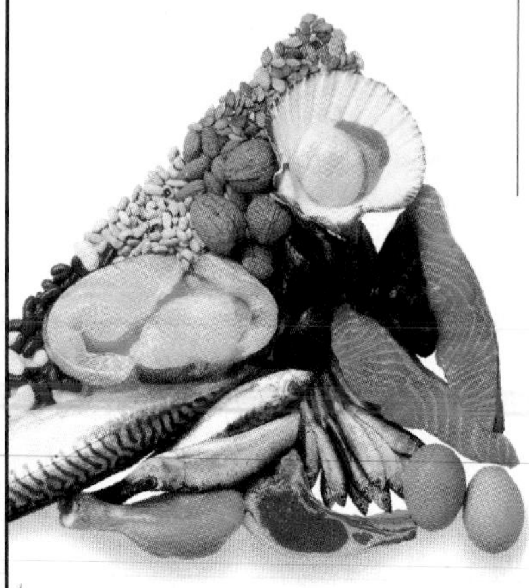

Figure 17 The foods shown are all good protein sources. ***Classifying*** *Group the foods into three or four categories.*

Proteins Recall that organic acids contain a –COOH group and organic bases, or amines, contain an $-NH_2$ group. There is one substituted hydrocarbon that contains both groups. An **amino acid** is a compound that contains both carboxyl and amino functional groups in the same molecule. There are about 20 amino acids that your body needs to function.

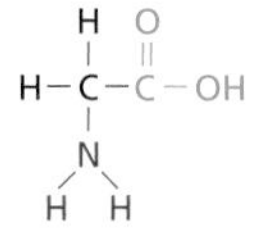

Glycine

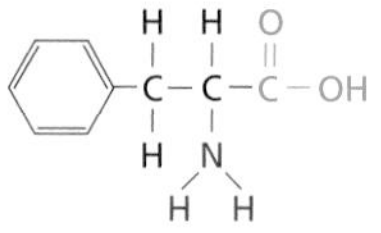

Phenylalanine

Your cells can manufacture some, but not all, of the amino acids. For example, your body can make glycine, but not phenylalanine. The essential amino acids that your body cannot make must come from foods like those in Figure 17.

Your cells use amino acids as the monomers for constructing protein polymers. A **protein** is a polymer in which at least 100 amino acid monomers are linked through bonds between an amino group and a carboxyl group. The instructions for making proteins are stored in DNA. Proteins make up the fibers of your muscles, your hair and fingernails, and the hemoglobin in your blood. Your body may contain as many as 300,000 different proteins.

Section 9.3 Assessment

Reviewing Concepts

1. Describe a way that polymers can be classified.
2. Name three synthetic polymers.
3. What are four types of polymers that can be found in the cells of organisms?
4. What are the three parts of a nucleotide?
5. What holds the bases together in DNA?
6. What two functional groups are found in amino acids?

Critical Thinking

7. **Using Analogies** Which natural polymers are like a train with identical freight cars and which are like a train with a mixture of different cars?
8. **Inferring** There is another system for classifying carbohydrates that uses the categories monosaccharides, disaccharides, and polysaccharides. Where would you place glucose, sucrose, and cellulose in this classification system? Give a reason for your answer.

Writing in Science

Compare-Contrast Paragraph Write a paragraph comparing natural and synthetic polymers in general. How are they similar? How are they different?

Section 9.3 Assessment

1. The two main types of polymers are natural and synthetic.
2. Rubber, nylon, and polyethylene
3. Starches, cellulose, nucleic acids, and proteins
4. Organic base, phosphate group, and a sugar
5. Strong intermolecular attractions
6. Amino acids contain a carboxyl group and an amino group.
7. Starches and cellulose are like trains with identical cars, and proteins and nucleic acids are like trains with a mixture of different cars.
8. Glucose is a monosaccharide because its molecules are single sugar units. Sucrose is a disaccharide because its molecules contain a glucose unit and a fructose unit linked together. Cellulose is a polysaccharide because it contains many glucose units linked together.

issues in SCIENCE Should People Conserve Fossil Fuels?

Many people depend on fossil fuels such as petroleum, or crude oil. Nearly 28 billion barrels of oil was consumed in 2002. More than 14 billion barrels was used to supply energy for automobiles, airplanes, and other means of transportation. Fractions of crude oil are also used to produce plastics, dyes, fertilizers, solvents, aerosols, explosives, paints, soaps, and medicines.

Scientists estimate that annual consumption of oil will increase to 38.6 billion barrels by 2020. Scientists disagree about how much of the remaining supply should be used. Some scientists say that there is more fossil fuels remaining than predicted and that there is no crisis. Others suggest that scientists must quickly develop alternative sources of energy for transportation, such as solar power, hydrogen fuel cells, or fuels made from plants. Alternative energy sources would reduce the use of fossil fuels and limit the amount of pollution during their combustion.

The Viewpoints

Fossil fuels are still abundant.

People can continue to use the known supply of fossil fuels at current rates for many years. New technology makes finding and extracting oil, coal, and natural gas easier. For example, in 1978 scientists thought there was about 648 billion barrels of oil remaining worldwide. However, with new discoveries and improved technology, optimists now think there may be as much as 3 trillion barrels remaining. Even if the use of oil increased, scientists would still have several hundred years to develop alternative fuels and new refining processes. In addition, technologies are reducing the amount of sulfur dioxide and nitrogen oxides released when fossil fuels are burned.

Fossil fuels must be conserved.

Advances in technology will serve only to speed up the rate at which oil is extracted from oil reserves. The amount of oil available for consumers will rise, and people will feel no need to conserve. At some point, production will decrease as supplies dwindle. The emissions produced when fossil fuels burn put society as a whole at risk. Despite more efficient methods of combustion, more than 6 billion tons of carbon dioxide was released into the atmosphere in 1997. Developing alternative sources of energy now will reduce pollution in the future. These alternatives also free fossil fuels for use in the production of plastics, paints, medicines, and other essential materials.

Research and Decide

1. **Defining the Issue** In your own words, describe the issue that needs to be resolved about the use of fossil fuels.
2. **Analyzing the Viewpoints** List three arguments made by those who think that fossil fuels do not need to be conserved. List three arguments made by people who think that fossil fuels must be conserved.
3. **Forming Your Opinion** Should people conserve fossil fuels? Did you find any convincing argument for or against conservation?
4. **Role-Playing** You manufacture a product that has parts made from synthetic polymers. The polymers are made from compounds found in oil. Your costs would increase without the polymers. Write a letter to your senator stating your point of view on funding alternative energy research.

Go Online PHSchool.com

For: More on this issue
Visit: PHSchool.com
Web Code: cch-1090

issues in SCIENCE

Should People Conserve Fossil Fuels? L2

Background

Industrialized societies are highly dependent on fossil fuels. These fuels provide the energy for heating, cooling, and lighting commercial and residential buildings; operating industrial machinery and home appliances; and transporting goods and people. A reduction in the supply of fossil fuels or an increase in their cost would have a major impact on the economy of an industrialized society. In these countries the availability and use of fossil fuels is an important domestic and foreign policy issue. The effect on the environment of the combustion of fossils fuels is also an important issue. So is the extraction, refining, and transporting of fossil fuels.

Answers

1. Should fossil fuels be conserved?
2. Acceptable answers against conservation include: Reserves are greater than previously thought; technology makes finding and extracting fuels easier; scientists have time to develop alternative technologies; technologies have reduced the emission of sulfur and nitrogen oxides when fossil fuels are burned. Acceptable answers in favor of conservation include: Advances in technology will increase the rate of consumption; eventually production will decrease; despite more efficient methods of combustion, tons of carbon dioxide are still released into the atmosphere.
3. Students should present arguments to support their decisions.
4. Acceptable answers will include persuasive reasoning to explain the chosen point of view.

Go Online PHSchool.com

Have students further research the issues related to this topic.

9.4 Reactions in Cells

Reading Focus

Key Concepts

- What energy conversion takes place during photosynthesis?
- How are photosynthesis and cellular respiration related?
- What molecules help cells function efficiently?

Vocabulary

- photosynthesis
- enzymes
- vitamins

Reading Strategy

Summarizing Copy the table. As you read, complete the table by recording a main idea for each heading.

Heading	Main Idea
Photosynthesis	a. ?
Cellular Respiration	b. ?
Enzymes and Vitamins	c. ?

Figure 18 Unlike a plant, this runner must get the energy he needs from the food he eats.

For thousands of years, people used whale oil and other animal fats as fuels for their lamps. As fats burn, they combine with oxygen and produce carbon dioxide and water. They also release energy in the form of heat and light. In a lamp, combustion takes place rapidly. In the cells of organisms, a more controlled version of the process releases energy stored in molecules. Some of the energy released helps maintain your internal body temperature at or close to 37°C.

Reactions that take place in cells follow the same rules as reactions that take place in a research laboratory or classroom. Some reactions go to completion and some reach an equilibrium point. Many reactions occur in solution and catalysts are often needed. Energy is transferred and energy is converted from one form to another. Photosynthesis and cellular respiration are two processes that allow organisms to meet their energy needs.

Photosynthesis

The sun is the primary source of energy for most plants and animals. During **photosynthesis,** plants chemically combine carbon dioxide and water into carbohydrates. The process requires light and chlorophyll, a green pigment in plants. This equation summarizes the process.

$$6H_2O + 6CO_2 + \text{Energy (light)} \longrightarrow C_6H_{12}O_6 + 6O_2$$

During photosynthesis, energy from sunlight is converted into chemical energy. Photosynthesis involves a complex series of chemical reactions. When all the reactions are complete, the energy from sunlight has been stored in the covalent bonds of molecules.

1 FOCUS

Objectives

9.4.1 **Compare** photosynthesis and cellular respiration.

9.4.2 **Explain** how enzymes and vitamins help reactions take place in cells.

Reading Focus

Build Vocabulary L2

Web Diagram Have students create a web diagram relating the terms *photosynthesis, cellular respiration, glucose, energy, carbohydrates, digestion,* and *polymers.*

Reading Strategy L2

a. During photosynthesis, energy from sunlight is converted into chemical energy.
b. During cellular respiration, the energy stored in products of photosynthesis is released.
c. Enzymes and vitamins are compounds that help cells function efficiently at normal body temperature.

2 INSTRUCT

Photosynthesis

Build Reading Literacy L1

Sequence Refer to page **290D** in **Chapter 10,** which provides guidelines for using a sequence.

Have students create a flowchart that follows a carbon atom through photosynthesis and cellular respiration. Have students mark where oxygen, water, and energy enter and exit the overall process.
Verbal

Integrate Biology L2

In green plants, chlorophyll a and b are the dominant light-absorbing pigments. These pigments and others contribute to the color of leaves and allow plants to absorb the energy of sunlight. Have interested students research chlorophyll's structure. *(Chlorophyll has a flat, star-shaped structure with a Mg^{2+} ion in the center.)*
Logical

Section Resources

Print

- ***Reading and Study Workbook With Math Support,*** Section 9.4
- ***Transparencies,*** Section 9.4

Technology

- ***Interactive Textbook,*** Section 9.4
- ***Presentation Pro CD-ROM,*** Section 9.4
- ***Go Online,*** *Science News,* Organic chemistry and biochemistry

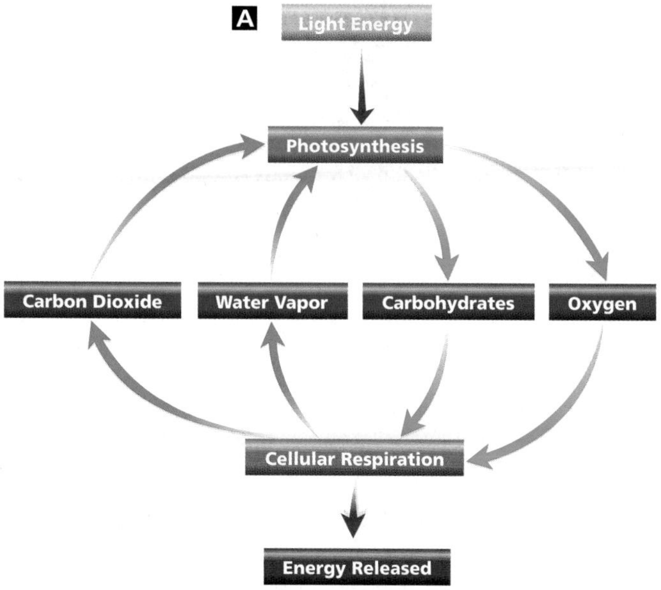
A
Light Energy
Photosynthesis
Carbon Dioxide
Water Vapor
Carbohydrates
Oxygen
Cellular Respiration
Energy Released

Figure 19 Products of cellular respiration are reactants during photosynthesis. **A** Cellular respiration and photosynthesis are two parts of the same cycle. **B** Plants can survive without people, but people cannot survive without plants.

B

Cellular Respiration

What does your body need energy for, besides maintaining a constant body temperature? Everything! It takes energy to laugh or cry, to heal a bone or a paper cut, to climb a rope or a staircase, or even to sleep. **During cellular respiration, the energy stored in the products of photosynthesis is released.** Like photosynthesis, cellular respiration is a complex series of reactions. This equation is a summary of the overall process.

$$C_6H_{12}O_6 + 6O_2 \longrightarrow 6H_2O + 6CO_2 + \text{Energy (heat)}$$

Figure 19 summarizes the relationship between photosynthesis and cellular respiration. Each process produces the reactants for the other process. Carbon dioxide and water are reactants in photosynthesis and products of cellular respiration. Carbohydrates and oxygen are reactants in cellular respiration and products of photosynthesis.

In the equation for cellular respiration, glucose is reacting with oxygen. The glucose can come from simple sugars or from starches because starch is a polymer of glucose. During digestion, starch breaks down into glucose. This process is an example of depolymerization. Fats are also a good source of energy. One gram of fat produces twice the energy of one gram of a carbohydrate.

Reading Checkpoint *Which produces more energy per gram, a carbohydrate or a fat?*

Go Online SCIENCE NEWS

For: Articles on organic chemistry and biochemistry
Visit: PHSchool.com
Web Code: cce-1094

Cellular Respiration

Address Misconceptions L2

Students may confuse cellular respiration, respiration, and breathing. Explain that cellular respiration is a chemical process that releases energy stored in molecules. During respiration, oxygen and carbon dioxide are exchanged between cells, blood, and air in the lungs. Breathing is the movement of air into and out of the lungs by inhalation and exhalation. **Verbal**

Teacher Demo

Photosynthesis and Cellular Respiration L2

Purpose Students learn about the products of photosynthesis and cellular respiration.

Materials methylene blue, water, 500-mL beaker, *elodea* sprig, straw

Procedure Explain that methylene blue turns orange in the presence of carbon dioxide. Place five drops of methylene blue in a beaker of water. Use the straw to blow into the water. After the solution changes color, remove the straw. Place an *elodea* sprig into the solution and place the beaker in sunlight. Have students notice the color change every five minutes for the next thirty minutes.

Safety Do not ingest any of the methylene blue.

Expected Outcome The solution turns orange when it absorbs carbon dioxide from exhaled air. As the elodea removes carbon dioxide from the solution, the color changes back to blue. **Visual**

Go Online SCIENCE NEWS

Science News provides students with current information on organic chemistry and biochemistry.

Customize for Inclusion Students

Gifted

Some organisms release the energy stored in compounds through an anaerobic process called fermentation. (Anaerobic means "in the absence of oxygen.") The products of the fermentation of carbohydrates are ethanol and carbon dioxide.

$$C_6H_{12}O_6 \longrightarrow 2CH_3CH_2OH + 2CO_2$$

Have students research and write a short report about fermentation. Suggest that they include information about common examples of fermentation. Many commercial products, including cheese, antibiotics, and vitamins, are produced by fermentation. Students might also want to research what causes lactic acid to build up in muscles and how athletes can reduce this process.

Answer to . . .

Reading Checkpoint *A fat*

Enzymes and Vitamins

Teacher Demo

Denaturing an Enzyme L2

Purpose Students will observe how enzyme activity is affected by temperature.

Materials potato, sharp knife, cutting surface, 3% hydrogen peroxide solution, water, 500-mL beakers (2), hot plate

Procedure Fill a beaker halfway with water and use the hot plate to boil the water. Cut a potato into small cubes (about 1 cm^3). Place some of the cubes in the boiling water and allow them to cook for several minutes. Fill a second beaker halfway with hydrogen peroxide solution. Place some of the raw cubes in the hydrogen peroxide solution. Have students observe the gas bubbles that form on the surface of the potato cubes. Explain that an enzyme in the potato is speeding up the reaction that decomposes hydrogen peroxide into water and oxygen. Explain that enzymes lose their ability to speed up reactions when they are damaged by an increase in temperature. Place some of the cooked potato cubes in the hydrogen peroxide and have students note that gas bubbles do not form (or form at a much slower rate). **Visual**

3 ASSESS

Evaluate Understanding L2

Have groups of students write four review questions with answers.

Reteach L1

Have students use Figure 19 to review the relationships between photosynthesis and cellular respiration.

Writing in Science

The masses of the vitamins in the pills are small (micrograms) compared to the masses of the minerals (milligrams).

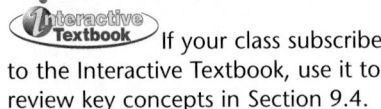

Interactive Textbook If your class subscribes to the Interactive Textbook, use it to review key concepts in Section 9.4.

Answer to . . .

Figure 20 *Soluble in water*

Figure 20 Lemons, limes, and oranges are sources of vitamin C. **Drawing Conclusions** *Is vitamin C soluble in fat or in water?*

Enzymes and Vitamins

Without some help, many of the reactions that take place in your cells would not happen fast enough to keep the cells alive. Your internal temperature should not vary more than a few degrees from 37°C. So you cannot increase the temperature to speed up a reaction in your cells. **Enzymes and vitamins are compounds that help cells function efficiently at normal body temperature.**

Enzymes Without enzymes, cells could not digest food or extract energy from food. **Enzymes** are proteins that act as catalysts for reactions in cells. Enzymes allow reactions to proceed faster at much lower temperatures than would normally happen. Your body uses thousands of enzymes to control reactions within your cells. Pepsin, for example, is an enzyme that breaks apart proteins. It works only in the acidic environment of the stomach. Some enzymes require a co-enzyme to function, often a metal ion or a water-soluble vitamin.

Vitamins In the 1800s, British sailors ate limes on long sea voyages. The limes were protection against scurvy, which causes severe pain and weakness. Limes contain vitamin C. **Vitamins** are organic compounds that organisms need in small amounts, but cannot produce. A vitamin that dissolves in water, such as vitamin C, gets eliminated from the body and must be replaced daily. A vitamin that dissolves in fats, such as vitamin A, can build up over time in body tissues. Taking excess amounts of fat-soluble vitamins may be harmful.

Section 9.4 Assessment

Reviewing Concepts

1. What happens to sunlight during photosynthesis?
2. Describe the relationship between photosynthesis and cellular respiration.
3. What molecules improve the efficiency of cell functions?
4. What happens to starch during digestion?
5. Why can't an increase in temperature be used to speed up reactions in cells?

Critical Thinking

6. **Formulating Hypotheses** Why must combustion in cells take place in multiple steps?
7. **Drawing Conclusions** Some bacteria do not require oxygen. How would the disappearance of plants affect these bacteria?
8. **Inferring** What affect could a lack of essential amino acids have on reactions in a person's body?

Writing in Science

Explanatory Paragraph Check the label on a package of multivitamins and minerals. Compare the masses of the minerals to the masses of the vitamins included in a single pill. Discuss any trend that you detect.

Section 9.4 Assessment

1. Sunlight is converted into chemical energy.
2. The products of one process are the reactants in the other.
3. Enzymes and vitamins
4. Starch is broken down into glucose, which can be used in cellular respiration.
5. The internal temperature should not vary more than a few degrees from 37°C.
6. Multiple steps allow the cells to release the energy stored in chemical bonds in smaller amounts, rather than all at once, which could cause the temperature in a cell to rise.
7. It's likely that these bacteria would not be affected because they do not require the oxygen that plants produce during photosynthesis.
8. Without these essential amino acids, the body would not be able to produce enzymes needed for cellular reactions.

Consumer Lab

Comparing Vitamin C in Fruit Juices

Various brands of juices claim to be good sources of vitamin C, but which juices are the best sources? Vitamin C is an organic acid called ascorbic acid. Like other acids, vitamin C reacts with indicators to produce a color change. This reaction can be used to determine the amount of vitamin C present in foods, such as fruit juices. In this lab, you will add an indicator to a sample of apple juice. The indicator will change color when all the vitamin C has reacted. Then you will test and compare the vitamin C content in other juices with the results for apple juice.

APPLE JUICE

Problem

Which juice provides the most vitamin C?

Materials

- apple juice
- a variety of other fruit juices
- test tubes and rack
- 10-mL graduated cylinder
- methylene blue indicator in dropper bottle
- stirring rods

Skills

Observing, Measuring, Analyzing Data

Procedure

Part A: Measuring Vitamin C in Apple Juice

1. On a sheet of paper, copy the data table.
2. Use a graduated cylinder to measure 10 mL of apple juice. Pour the juice into a test tube.
3. Add a drop of methylene blue indicator to the test tube. Stir until the color of the indicator disappears.
4. Add more indicator, one drop at a time, stirring after each addition. Count the drops you add. Stop adding the indicator when the last drop of indicator does not change color. Record the number of drops you used.

Data Table

Type of Juice	Number of Drops
Apple	

Part B: Measuring Vitamin C in Other Juices

5. Formulate and record a hypothesis about which juice will have the greatest amount of vitamin C. You will need to decide which variables must be kept the same, as well as how to account for bits of solid in some juices.
6. List the steps in your procedure and write the names of each of the juices to be tested in the left column of your data table.
7. Have your teacher check your procedure before you begin your experiment.

Analyze and Conclude

1. **Using Graphs** Make a bar graph of your data. Which juice required the most drops of indicator? Which required the least?
2. **Drawing Conclusions** Based on your data, which juice contained the most vitamin C? How did you reach this conclusion?
3. **Evaluating and Revising** What unexpected problems did you encounter? Explain how you could revise your procedure to avoid these problems.

Consumer Lab

Comparing Vitamin C in Fruit Juices L2

Objective
After completing this activity students will be able to
- use an indicator to compare the amount of vitamin C in fruit juices.

Skills Focus Formulating Hypotheses, Analyzing Data, Controlling Variables, Using Graphs and Charts

Prep Time 15–20 minutes

Advance Prep Place labeled containers of apple juice and other fruit juices, plus dropper bottles of methylene blue indicator solution, in a central location.

Class Time 20 minutes

Safety Students should wear safety goggles, aprons, and gloves. Remind students never to drink anything in the laboratory.

Expected Outcome In Part A, students will find that a permanent color change occurs after a certain number of drops of indicator are added to the juice. In Part B, students will produce write-ups that include a hypothesis; a discussion of variables and how they will be controlled; a procedure with directions; and a data table in which to record the data.

Analyze and Conclude
1. The graph and answers will vary depending on the samples tested.
2. The juice that required the most drops of indicator is the one that contains the most vitamin C.
3. Acceptable answers include that juices with large amounts of pulp were difficult to compare with clear juices with the same volume. (Students may suggest filtering those samples.) Students may also say that dark juices, such as prune juice or grape juice, obscured the color change. (Students might suggest diluting all samples with the same amount of distilled water.)
Visual, Logical, Portfolio

Going Further

Methylene blue reacts with all organic acids. Students can use it to find the total amount of organic acids in fruits and vegetables. With a blender and distilled water, they can make liquid samples to test. They must control the amount of food, the amount of water added, and the time of blending.
Visual, Logical

Study Guide

Study Tip

Organize New Information
After studying all of the sections in the chapter, have students examine connections between concepts in different sections. Use concept maps or web diagrams to study the relationships between carbon compounds, substituted hydrocarbons, polymers, and cellular reactions.

Thinking Visually

a. fossil fuels
b. c. d. in any order: petroleum, coal, natural gas

CHAPTER 9

Study Guide

9.1 Carbon Compounds

Key Concepts

- Diamond, graphite, and fullerenes are forms of carbon. Diamond is a network solid. Graphite forms layers that slide past one another. Fullerenes are large hollow spheres or cages of carbon.
- Factors that determine the properties of a hydrocarbon are the number of carbon atoms and how the atoms are arranged. Hydrocarbons can form a straight chain, a branched chain, or a ring.
- There are three types of unsaturated hydrocarbons—alkenes, alkynes, and aromatic hydrocarbons.
- Three types of fossil fuels are coal, petroleum, and natural gas. The primary products of the complete combustion of fossil fuels are carbon dioxide and water.

Vocabulary

organic compound, *p. 262;* network solid, *p. 263;* hydrocarbon, *p. 264;* saturated hydrocarbon, *p. 264;* isomers, *p. 265;* unsaturated hydrocarbon, *p. 266;* aromatic hydrocarbons, *p. 266;* fossil fuels, *p. 267*

9.2 Substituted Hydrocarbons

Key Concepts

- The functional group in an alcohol is a hydroxyl group, –OH. The functional group in an organic acid is a carboxyl group, –COOH. The functional group in an amine is an amino group, $-NH_2$.
- Esters form when organic acids react with alcohols.

Vocabulary

substituted hydrocarbon, *p. 272*
functional group, *p. 272*

9.3 Polymers

Key Concepts

- Polymers can be classified as natural polymers or synthetic polymers.
- Rubber, nylon, and polyethylene are three examples of compounds that can be synthesized.
- Four types of polymers produced in plant and animal cells are starches, cellulose, nucleic acids, and proteins.

Vocabulary

polymer, *p. 275;* monomers, *p. 275;* carbohydrates, *p. 278;* nucleic acids, *p. 279;* amino acid, *p. 280;* protein, *p. 280*

9.4 Reactions in Cells

Key Concepts

- During photosynthesis, energy from sunlight is converted into chemical energy.
- During cellular respiration, the energy stored in the products of photosynthesis is released .
- Enzymes and vitamins help cells function efficiently at normal body temperature.

Vocabulary

photosynthesis, *p. 282;* enzymes, *p. 284;* vitamins, *p. 284*

Thinking Visually

Concept Map Copy the concept map onto a sheet of paper. Use information from the chapter to complete it.

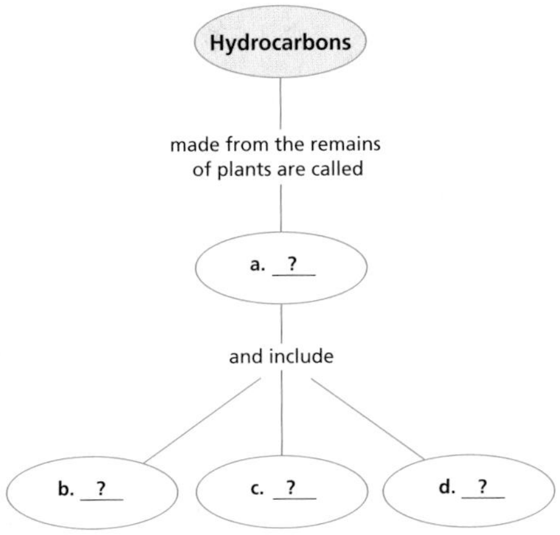

Hydrocarbons
made from the remains of plants are called
a. ?
and include
b. ?
c. ?
d. ?

Chapter Resources

Print
- ***Chapter and Unit Tests,*** Chapter 9 Test A and Test B
- ***Test Prep Resources,*** Chapter 9

Technology
- ***Computer Test Bank,*** Chapter Test 9
- ***Interactive Textbook,*** Chapter 9
- ***Go Online,*** PHSchool.com, Chapter 9

CHAPTER 9

Assessment

Interactive textbook with assessment at PHSchool.com

Reviewing Content

Choose the letter that best answers the question or completes the statement.

1. How many bonds can a carbon atom form?
   a. two b. four
   c. six d. seven

2. Two compounds that have the same molecular formula but different structural formulas are
   a. isomers. b. isotopes.
   c. alkanes. d. alkenes.

3. Which compound has a triple bond?
   a. alkene b. alkyne
   c. alkane d. alcohol

4. The primary products of complete combustion of fossil fuels are
   a. carbon monoxide and water.
   b. carbon dioxide and water.
   c. carbon dioxide and carbon monoxide.
   d. methane and water.

5. What is an organic compound with at least one hydroxyl group called?
   a. an organic acid
   b. an alkyne
   c. an organic base
   d. an alcohol

6. Amines all contain atoms of
   a. oxygen. b. nitrogen.
   c. sulfur. d. chlorine.

7. The monomers for protein molecules are
   a. ethene. b. nucleic acids.
   c. amino acids. d. ethanoic acids.

8. A nucleotide does not contain a(n)
   a. organic base.
   b. organic acid.
   c. sugar.
   d. phosphate group.

9. Reactions in cells take place at about
   a. 100°C. b. 0°C.
   c. 40°C. d. 60°C.

10. An enzyme is a
   a. protein. b. vitamin.
   c. lipid. d. carbohydrate.

Understanding Concepts

11. How did the synthesis of urea change the definition of an organic compound?
12. Why is diamond extremely hard but graphite is extremely soft?
13. What is a saturated hydrocarbon?
14. Why can an acetylene torch be used to weld metals together?
15. How are fossil fuels formed?
16. How are the hydrocarbons in petroleum separated into fractions?
17. Why is it important to make sure that there is plenty of air around a gas burner such as the one shown below?

18. How is acid rain produced?
19. What is a functional group?
20. Why is ethanol added to gasoline?
21. What types of substituted hydrocarbons can react to form esters?
22. Explain why natural and synthetic rubber have different properties.
23. What do cellulose and starch have in common?
24. What are the products of photosynthesis? What are the products of cellular respiration?
25. What role do enzymes play in cells?

Homework Guide

Section	Questions
9.1	1–4, 11–18, 26, 33–36, 39
9.2	5–6, 19–21, 27–28, 31–32
9.3	7–8, 22–23, 29, 37
9.4	9–10, 24–25, 30, 38

Assessment

Interactive Textbook If your class subscribes to the Interactive Textbook, your students can go online to access an interactive version of the Student Edition and a self-test.

Reviewing Content

1. b 2. a 3. b
4. b 5. d 6. b
7. c 8. b 9. c
10. a

Understanding Concepts

11. Because urea was synthesized in a laboratory, the definition of organic compounds changed from compounds produced by organisms to compounds containing carbon and hydrogen, often combined with a few other elements.
12. Diamond is hard because of its rigid, three-dimensional network structure. Graphite is soft because the bonds between graphite layers are weak.
13. A saturated hydrocarbon is a hydrocarbon that contains only single bonds.
14. The temperature of the flame in an oxyacetylene torch approaches 3500°C, a temperature high enough to melt most metals.
15. High temperatures and pressures changed the buried remains of plants and animals into mixtures of hydrocarbons.
16. The hydrocarbons are heated until they vaporize. The vapors rise in a distillation tower and condense as the temperature decreases. Those with higher boiling points condense first.
17. A lack of air can cause incomplete combustion, which produces carbon monoxide.
18. When fossil fuels are burned, sulfur dioxide and nitrogen oxides are produced. These oxides dissolve in water droplets, forming sulfuric acid and nitric acid.
19. A functional group is an atom or group of atoms that replace a hydrogen atom in a hydrocarbon.
20. Ethanol helps the gasoline burn more completely.
21. Organic acids and alcohols
22. They contain different monomers.
23. Both are polymers of glucose.
24. The products of photosynthesis are oxygen and carbohydrates. The products of cellular respiration are carbon dioxide and water.
25. Enzymes act as catalysts for reactions that take place in cells.

Chapter 9

Critical Thinking

26. No, because methane contains only one carbon atom, which eliminates the possibility of branching.
27. Double and triple bonds can be classified as functional groups because they affect the characteristic chemical properties of unsaturated compounds.
28. The compounds are classified as: alkane, alkyne, alcohol. The word endings identify the type of compound.
29. Students are likely to say that starches and proteins can be eaten. Silk, cotton, and rubber can be worn.
30. Acceptable answers include: Because vitamins are defined as substances that organisms cannot produce, strictly speaking, vitamin D should not be classified as a vitamin.

Math Skills

31. Alcohol 1
32. Alcohol 1 and Alkane 3
33. Alkane 1 is likely to have the fewest carbon atoms, and Alkane 3 is likely to have the most carbon atoms because the more carbon atoms an alkane has, the higher its boiling point.

Concepts in Action

34. You could test to see if the boiling point remains constant as the mixture boils or if the temperature changes (indicating more than one substance in the mixture).
35. There would be an immediate increase in carbon dioxide from combustion and a long-term increase because there would be fewer plants to absorb carbon dioxide for use in photosynthesis.
36. Possible answer: Because fossil fuels have been relatively inexpensive and plentiful, there has not been sufficient incentive to invest in alternative technologies.
37. Cells use the essential amino acids stored in ingested proteins as raw materials to manufacture proteins.
38. The termite has enzymes that allow the reaction to occur at the body temperature of a termite.
39. Sample answer: death of organisms; burial of remains; action of high temperatures and pressures over time; drilling or mining; fractional distillation; delivery to gas station; pumping into tank.

CHAPTER 9

Assessment *(continued)*

Critical Thinking

26. Predicting Does methane have isomers? Explain your answer.

27. Forming Operational Definitions Present an argument for classifying double and triple bonds as functional groups. (*Hint:* What is the role of a functional group in a compound?)

28. Classifying Based on their names, classify each of these compounds: octacosane, pentyne, and octanol. What information did the names provide that helped you classify the compounds?

29. Classifying Which natural polymers can be eaten for breakfast? Which natural polymers can be worn to school?

30. Applying Concepts When your skin is exposed to sunlight, cells in your skin produce vitamin D. Should vitamin D be classified as a vitamin? Give a reason for your answer.

Math Skills

Use this table to answer Questions 31–33.

Selected Properties of Fuels

Fuels	Melting Point (°C)	Boiling Point (°C)
Alcohol 1	6	228
Alcohol 2	26	83
Alkane 1	−183	−162
Alkane 2	−138	0
Alkane 3	−57	126

31. Analyzing Data Which fuel is a liquid across the greatest range of temperature?

32. Using Tables At 20°C, which fuels would be liquid?

33. Analyzing Data Look at the data for the three unknown alkanes. Which alkane is likely to have the fewest carbon atoms? Which is likely to have the most carbon atoms? Give a reason for your choices.

Concepts in Action

34. Designing Experiments You work at a refinery and want to know whether a fraction you have collected from a distillation tower is a single substance or a mixture. What kind of test could you do to find out?

35. Relating Cause and Effect What are two ways that a large forest fire might affect the amount of carbon dioxide in the atmosphere?

36. Making Judgments Why do you think progress in solar energy, wind power, and other alternative forms of energy has been slow?

37. Drawing Conclusions If the cells in your body can manufacture proteins, why are proteins an important part of a balanced diet?

38. Comparing and Contrasting When wood burns, the cellulose in wood is converted to carbon dioxide and water. The same products are produced when a termite digests wood, but the process occurs at a much lower temperature. Explain the difference in temperature.

39. Writing in Science Describe the series of events that starts with the death of a group of ancient ocean organisms and ends with filling the tank of an automobile with gasoline. (*Hint:* Consider making a flow chart of events first.)

Performance-Based Assessment

Animating a Process Make a flip book that begins with the sun providing energy for photosynthesis in a plant. It should proceed through photosynthesis, and then show how the products of photosynthesis are used in cellular respiration. Complete the book by showing the products of cellular respiration about to be used for photosynthesis.

Go Online PHSchool.com

For: Self-grading assessment
Visit: PHSchool.com
Web Code: cca-1090

Performance Based Assessment

Acceptable flip books should have pages showing the conversion of light energy to chemical energy, storage of chemical energy, and use of chemical energy in cellular respiration.

Go Online PHSchool.com

Your students can independently test their knowledge of the chapter and print out their test results for your files.

Standardized Test Prep

Test-Taking Tip

Make Logical Connections
A cause-and-effect statement may seem to be true when it is false. The statement may seem true because the descriptions of the cause and the effect are both accurate. However, there is no logical connection between the cause and the effect. In the question below, the opening phrase contains an accurate statement about body temperature. Most of the answers are accurate, too. But only one answer provides a logical effect of the statement in the opening phrase.

Because body temperature cannot vary more than a few degrees from 37°C,
(A) cellular respiration releases energy stored in covalent bonds.
(B) carbohydrates are good sources of energy.
(C) enzymes are required for reactions in cells.
(D) fats are good sources of energy.
(E) energy cannot be released in cells.

(Answer: C)

Choose the letter that best answers the question or completes the statement.

1. Benzene is classified as an aromatic hydrocarbon because
   (A) it has a strong odor.
   (B) it contains only carbon and hydrogen.
   (C) it is a compound found in coal.
   (D) it has an unsaturated ring structure.
   (E) it has a saturated ring structure.

2. How are photosynthesis and cellular respiration related?
   (A) They both occur in all living organisms.
   (B) They both consume more energy than they produce.
   (C) They both produce water and carbon dioxide.
   (D) Cellular respiration stores energy, and photosynthesis releases it.
   (E) Photosynthesis stores energy, and cellular respiration releases it.

3. Which type of compound forms when amino acids are linked together?
   (A) nucleic acid
   (B) protein
   (C) carbohydrate
   (D) organic acid
   (E) ester

4. What type of substituted hydrocarbon contains the functional group –OH?
   (A) halocarbon
   (B) alcohol
   (C) ester
   (D) organic base
   (E) organic acid

Use the diagram to answer Questions 5 and 6. The diagram shows a combustion apparatus used to identify hydrocarbons.

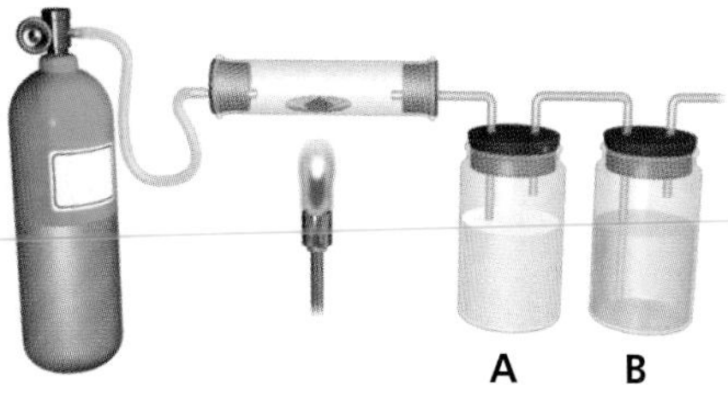
A
B

5. A sample of a hydrocarbon is in the glass tube. What gas is in the green tank?
   (A) nitrogen
   (B) carbon dioxide
   (C) oxygen
   (D) methane
   (E) acetylene

6. The containers labeled A and B absorb the primary products of the reaction that occurs in the tube. Those products are
   (A) carbon dioxide and water.
   (B) carbon monoxide and water.
   (C) oxides of sulfur and nitrogen.
   (D) sulfuric and nitric acid.
   (E) carbon dioxide and carbon monoxide.

Standardized Test Prep

1. D **2.** E **3.** B
4. B **5.** C **6.** A

CHAPTER 10

Planning Guide

Use these planning tools
Easy Planner
Teacher Express

SECTION OBJECTIVES	STANDARDS NATIONAL (See p. T18.)	STANDARDS STATE	ACTIVITIES and LABS
10.1 Radioactivity, pp. 292–297 1 block or 2 periods **10.1.1 Describe** the process of nuclear decay. **10.1.2 Classify** nuclear radiation as alpha particles, beta particles, or gamma rays. **10.1.3 Balance** nuclear equations. **10.1.4 Identify** sources of nuclear radiation, and **describe** how nuclear radiation affects matter. **10.1.5 Describe** methods of detecting nuclear radiation.	A-1, B-1, B-6, D-1, F-1, F-5, G-1, G-2, G-3		**SE** Inquiry Activity: What Happens When an Atom Decays? p. 291 L2 **TE** Teacher Demo: Stopping Radiation, p. 294 L2 **LM** Investigation 10B: Detecting Radiation L1
10.2 Rates of Nuclear Decay, pp. 298–301 1 block or 2 periods **10.2.1 Define** half-life, and **relate** half-life to the age of a radioactive sample. **10.2.2 Compare** and **contrast** nuclear reaction rates with chemical reaction rates. **10.2.3 Describe** how radioisotopes are used to estimate the age of materials.	A-1, A-2, B-1, B-3		**SE** Quick Lab: Modeling Half-Life, p. 300 L2 **TE** Teacher Demo: Predicting Decay, p. 299 L2 **LM** Investigation 10A: Modeling Radioactive Decay L2
10.3 Artificial Transmutation, pp. 303–305 1 block or 2 periods **10.3.1 Describe** and **identify** examples of transmutation. **10.3.2 Describe** how transuranium elements are synthesized. **10.3.3 Explain** how particle accelerators have been used in scientific research.	A-1, A-2, B-1, B-6, E-2, F-1, F-5, G-1, G-2, G-3		**SE** Quick Lab: Modeling Transmutation, p. 304 L2
10.4 Fission and Fusion, pp. 308–315 1 block or 2 periods **10.4.1 Compare** and **contrast** nuclear forces. **10.4.2 Describe** the process of nuclear fission. **10.4.3 Explain** how nuclear reactors are used to produce energy. **10.4.4 Describe** the process of nuclear fusion.	A-1, A-2, B-1, E-2, F-1, F-2, F-4, F-5, G-1, G-2, G-3		**SE** Exploration Lab: Modeling a Chain Reaction, pp. 316–317 L2 **TE** Teacher Demo: Nuclear Processes, p. 311 L2

Ability Levels

- **L1** For students who need additional help
- **L2** For all students
- **L3** For students who need to be challenged

Components

SE	Student Edition	**RSW**	Reading & Study Workbook	**CUT**	Chapter & Unit Tests	**T**	Transparencies
TE	Teacher's Edition	**MSPS**	Math Skills & Problem Solving Workbook	**CTB**	Computer Test Bank	**iT**	Interactive Textbook
LM	Laboratory Manual			**TP**	Test Prep Resources	**P**	Presentation Pro CD-ROM
PLM	Probeware Lab Manual			**DC**	Discovery Channel Videotapes & DVDs	**GO**	Internet Resources

RESOURCES PRINT and TECHNOLOGY	SECTION ASSESSMENT
RSW Section 10.1 **L1** **RSW Math Skill** **L2** **MSPS** Section 10.1 **L2** **T** Chapter 10 Pretest **L2** Section 10.1 **L2** **P** Chapter 10 Pretest **L2** Section 10.1 **L2** PLANETDIARY **GO** Radioactivity activity **L2**	**SE** Section 10.1 Assessment, p. 297 **iT** Section 10.1
RSW Section 10.2 **L1** **T** Section 10.2 **L2** **P** Section 10.2 **L2** NSTA SCiLINKS **GO** Half-Life **L2**	**SE** Section 10.2 Assessment, p. 301 **iT** Section 10.2
RSW Section 10.3 **L1** Discovery Channel School **DC** Nuclear Medicine **L2** **T** Section 10.3 **L2** **P** Section 10.3 **L2**	**SE** Section 10.3 Assessment, p. 305 **iT** Section 10.3
RSW Section 10.4 **L1** **T** Section 10.4 **L2** **P** Section 10.4 **L2** NSTA SCiLINKS **GO** Fission **L2**	**SE** Section 10.4 Assessment, p. 315 **iT** Section 10.4

Go Online

Go online for these Internet resources.

PHSchool.com
Web Code: cca-1100
Web Code: cch-1102

NSTA SCiLINKS
Web Code: ccn-1102
Web Code: ccn-1104

PLANETDIARY
Web Code: ccc-1101

Materials for Activities and Labs

Quantities for each group

STUDENT EDITION

Inquiry Activity, p. 291
green and purple beads

Quick Lab, p. 300
100 1-cm squares of wallpaper, large plastic bag, graph paper

Quick Lab, p. 304
periodic table, 2 sheets of unlined white paper, 32 green beads, 32 purple beads

Exploration Lab, pp. 316–317
20 dominoes, watch with a second hand (or stopwatch), metric ruler

TEACHER'S EDITION

Teacher Demo, p. 294
medical X-ray image or photograph of a medical X-ray image

Teacher Demo, p. 299
hot plate, 250-mL or 500-mL beaker, glass plate, popcorn, cooking oil

Build Science Skills, p. 307
500-mL beaker; sponges; shallow pans; food coloring; 1-cm strips of thin and thick cardboard, newspaper, and waxed paper; paper towels

Teacher Demo, p. 311
bubble solution, 2 bubble wands

Chapter Assessment

CHAPTER ASSESSMENT

SE Chapter Assessment, pp. 319–320
CUT Chapter 10 Test A, B
CTB Chapter 10
iT Chapter 10
PHSchool.com GO
Web Code: cca-1100

STANDARDIZED TEST PREP

SE Chapter 10, p. 321
TP Diagnose and Prescribe

Interactive Textbook

Interactive Textbook with assessment at PHSchool.com

CHAPTER 10

Before you teach

From the Author

David Frank
Ferris State University

Big Ideas

In the chapters leading to this one, students have focused on chemical changes. They have learned how electrons move around in these changes, as ionic or covalent bonds are broken or formed. In nuclear chemistry, students will study processes that take place when the nuclei of atoms are affected. Unlike the processes of earlier chapters, the numbers of neutrons and protons will change, and atoms of one element become atoms of another.

Space and Time Spontaneous nuclear decay processes follow first order kinetics. As a consequence, nuclear decays have a well-defined and constant half-life. One application of nuclear decay is to determine the ages of objects. Carbon-14 is incorporated into all living things, so carbon-14 dating is one method used for dating. Carbon-14 has a half-life of 5730 years. Radioisotopes with longer half-lives can be used to determine the age of rocks.

Matter and Change Students will first study the decay processes of a radioactive substance. Three types of nuclear radiation may be emitted: alpha particles, beta particles, or gamma rays. The first two types are associated with the change of an atom into an atom of another element or into a different isotope of the same element. Students will then study fission and fusion processes.

Forces and Motion Electrostatic forces, the attractions between particles of opposite charge and repulsions between particles of similar charge, have already been introduced. A student might wonder why a nucleus remains intact, given that it consists of positively charged protons and uncharged neutrons. Strong nuclear forces, which act over very short differences, keep these particles together.

Energy Compared to the physical and chemical changes that students have already studied, nuclear changes involve tremendous amounts of energy. During processes such as fusion, the products have less mass than the reactants, and large amounts of energy are released.

Chemistry Refresher

Nuclear Radiation 10.1

Radioactivity is the process in which an unstable atomic nucleus emits radiation in the form of particles and energy. The release of charged particles from a nucleus results in the formation of a different isotope with a different atomic number and/or atomic mass. Unlike stable isotopes, radioisotopes spontaneously decay into other isotopes.

Three common types of nuclear radiation are alpha particles, beta particles, and gamma rays. Nuclear radiation can ionize atoms. When cells of living tissue are exposed to nuclear radiation, they may no longer function properly. Nuclear radiation can be monitored using devices such as Geiger counters and film badges.

Address Misconceptions

Students may mistakenly think that gamma rays, X-rays, and visible light are unrelated. However, they are all part of a continuous magnetic spectrum, and for that reason, all three affect a photographic plate in the same way. For a strategy to overcome this misconception, see **Address Misconceptions** on **page 292.**

Half-Life and Radiocarbon Dating 10.2

The rate at which radioisotopes undergo nuclear decay is constant for each isotope under all conditions and depends on the number (fraction) of nuclei present. The amount of time required for half the atoms of a sample of a radioisotope to decay is called the half-life of the radioisotope.

Because the nuclear decay rate for a given radioisotope is constant, it can be used to measure the passage of time. Carbon-14 is a radioisotope commonly used for this purpose, through a method called radiocarbon dating. The small fraction of carbon atoms in the atmosphere that are carbon-14 has remained roughly constant for thousands of years. The carbon-14 is produced by the interaction of cosmic rays from outer space with Earth's atmosphere. All living organisms take in carbon, a certain percentage of which is carbon-14. When an organism dies, it no longer takes in carbon-14. The amount of carbon-14 in the dead organism decreases over time as the radioactive carbon undergoes beta decay to form nitrogen-14. Scientists can measure the ratio of carbon-14 to carbon-12 in the remains of the organism, and use this ratio to estimate how long ago the organism died.

Go Online PD LINKS NSTA

For: Teaching methods for nuclear chemistry
Visit: www.SciLinks.org/PDLinks
Web Code: ccn-1099

Artificial Transmutation 10.3

During nuclear decay, atoms of one element change into atoms of another element. This change is called transmutation. Scientists carry out artificial transmutations by bombarding atomic nuclei with high-energy particles. This process can be used to synthesize transuranium elements (elements with atomic numbers greater than 92), which are not usually found in nature.

Nuclear Forces and Reactions 10.4

Address Misconceptions

Students may incorrectly think that the sun is burning because the sun gives off heat and light. In fact, the light and heat from the sun are a result of nuclear reactions. For a strategy to overcome this misconception, see **Address Misconceptions** on **page 315.**

The subatomic particles in the nucleus are held together by strong nuclear forces. Repulsive electric forces between protons exist. In small nuclei, the strong nuclear forces are generally much greater than the electric forces. In very large nuclei, however, the opposing nuclear forces become similar in strength, resulting in an unstable nucleus.

A large, unstable nucleus may undergo nuclear fission, in which it splits into two smaller nuclei. Fission releases neutrons and a considerable amount of energy. In the presence of many unstable nuclei, fission can lead to a chain reaction, which can be either uncontrolled or controlled. An atomic bomb explosion is an example of an uncontrolled chain reaction. A controlled chain reaction occurs in the reactor of a nuclear power plant.

Another type of nuclear reaction is called fusion, in which two nuclei combine to form one larger nucleus. Fusion reactions release a tremendous amount of energy. The sun is powered by a fusion reaction in which hydrogen nuclei are fused together to form helium nuclei.

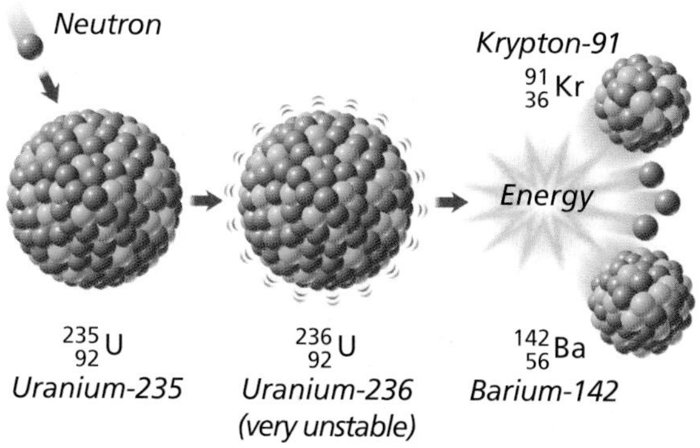

Neutron
Krypton-91
$^{91}_{36}Kr$
Energy
$^{235}_{92}U$
Uranium-235
$^{236}_{92}U$
Uranium-236
(very unstable)
$^{142}_{56}Ba$
Barium-142

Build Reading Literacy

Sequence

Ordering Events

Strategy Help students understand and visualize the steps in a process, or the order in which events occur. Sequences frequently involve cause-effect relationships. Readers can construct graphic organizers to help themselves visualize and comprehend a sequence. For most sequences, flowcharts are the graphic of choice. However, cycle diagrams are more appropriate for cycles. Before students begin, locate a description in the text of a several-step process or a chain of causes and effects, such as those in Section 10.4 related to a fission chain reaction (p. 311) or nuclear power generation (p. 314).

Example

1. Have students read the passage, thinking about what takes place first, second, third, and so on. Point out that the text will not always use order words such as *first, next, then,* and *finally*.
2. Review the passage, listing the steps or events in order.
3. If the passage describes a chain of steps or events, draw a flowchart on the board, having students tell the sequence of events, steps, or causes and effects, and writing each part of the process in a separate box.

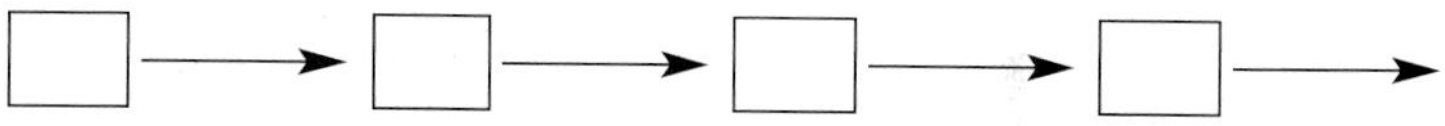

4. If the passage describes a cycle, use a cycle diagram to show the sequence.

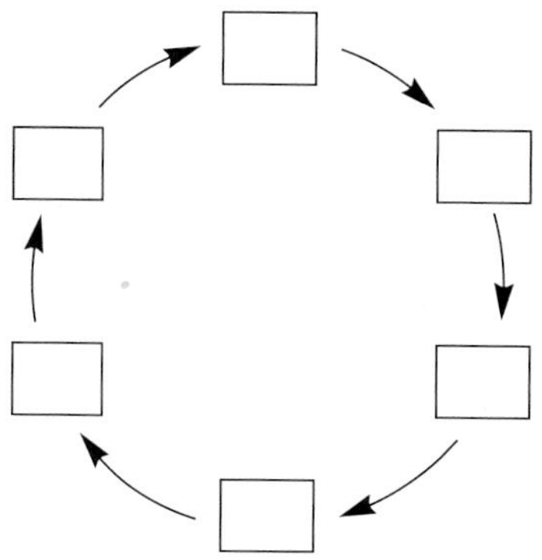

5. Have students locate additional examples of sequential relationships in the text or visuals of the chapter. Students can depict the steps or events using graphic organizers.

See p. 309 for a script on how to use the sequence strategy with students. For additional Build Reading Literacy strategies, see pp. 293 and 304.

ASSESS PRIOR KNOWLEDGE

Use the Chapter Pretest below to assess students' prior knowledge. As needed, review these Science Concepts and Math Skills with students.

Review Science Concepts

Section 10.1 Encourage students to recall what they have learned about balancing chemical equations. Review how chemical equations show conservation of mass.

Section 10.2 Encourage students to remember what they have learned about the rates of chemical reactions. To prepare students for a discussion of half-life, ask students to recall basic probability calculations.

Section 10.3 Review the different parts of the periodic table. Encourage students to recall the location of uranium and the elements heavier than uranium in the periodic table.

Section 10.4 Ask students to recall what they have learned about modern models of the atom.

Review Math Skills

Equations and Formulas Students will need to manipulate variables and constants to solve for unknowns in equations representing nuclear decay.

Direct students to the **Math Skills** in the **Skills and Reference Handbook** at the end of the student text.

CHAPTER 10 Nuclear Chemistry

CONCEPTS in Action

How do science concepts apply to your world? Here are some questions you'll be able to answer after you read this chapter.

- Why is radon gas dangerous? *(Section 10.1)*
- How can you measure the age of a rock? *(Section 10.2)*
- How does a smoke detector work? *(Section 10.3)*
- How does a nuclear reactor generate electricity? *(Section 10.4)*

Discovery Channel School **Video Field Trip**
Nuclear Medicine

- How can doctors diagnose certain types of cancer? *(page 306)*

A collision experiment in a particle accelerator can produce a variety of subatomic particles. Scientists can identify these particles based on the tracks left in a bubble chamber. ▶

Chapter Pretest

1. According to the law of conservation of mass, if element X has a molar mass of 3 g/mol, and element Y has a molar mass of 5 g/mol, what must be the total mass of products formed when one mole of the compound X_2Y decomposes? *(11 g)*

2. True or False: A reaction rate is the rate at which reactants change into products over time. *(True)*

3. If you tossed 128 coins in the air, about how many could you expect to land heads up? *(b)*
   - **a.** About 178 **b.** About 64
   - **c.** About 32 **d.** Almost none

4. Suppose you were to remove any coins that landed heads up, and then toss the remaining coins in the air. How many times could you expect to repeat this process until you had removed all of the coins? *(About 7 times)*

5. The element uranium belongs to *(d)*
   - **a.** Group 7A (halogens).
   - **b.** Group 8A (noble gases).
   - **c.** the lanthanide series.
   - **d.** the actinide series.

6. Which subatomic particles are found in the nucleus? *(Protons and neutrons)*

Chapter Preview

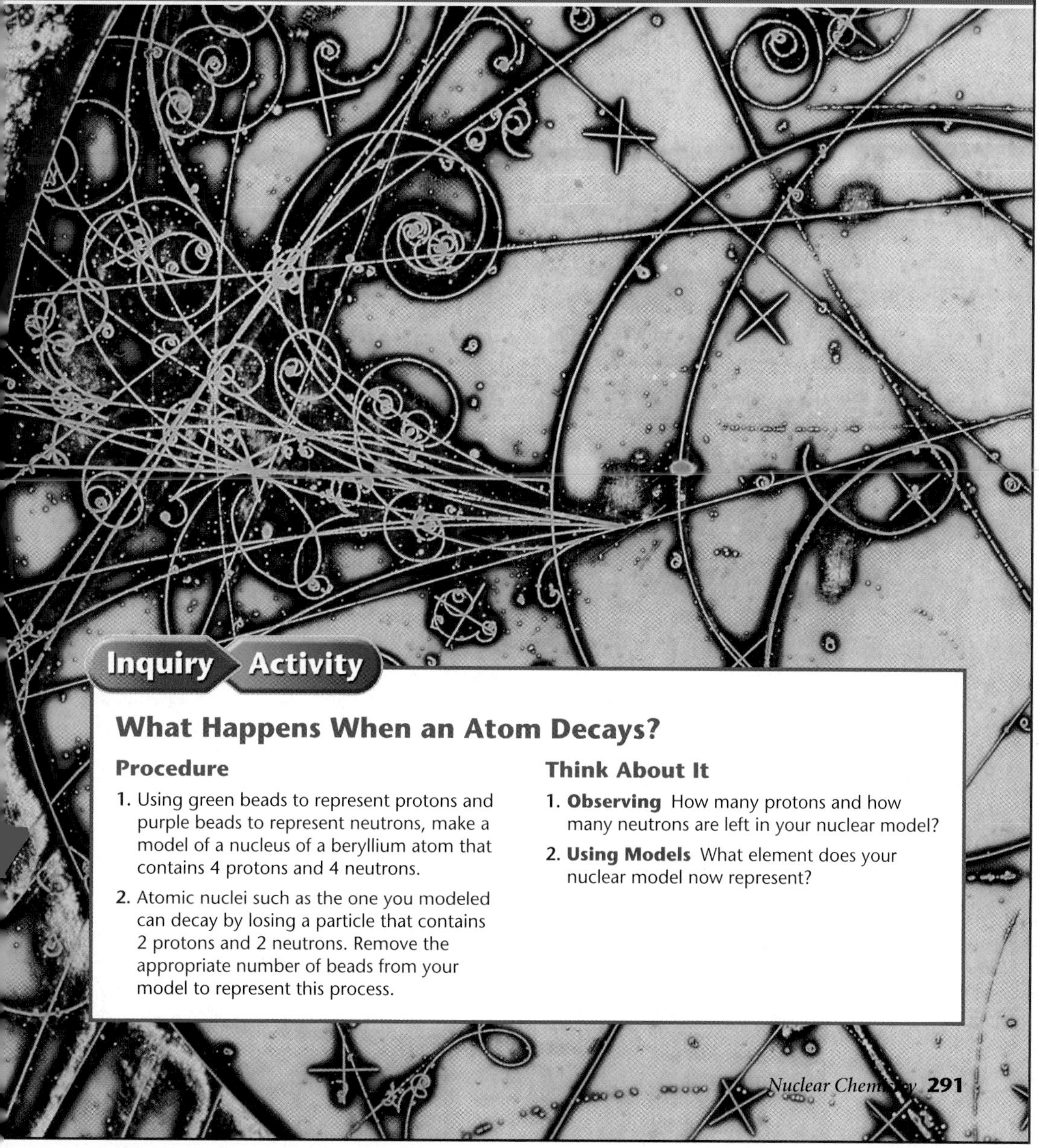

Inquiry Activity

What Happens When an Atom Decays?

Procedure

1. Using green beads to represent protons and purple beads to represent neutrons, make a model of a nucleus of a beryllium atom that contains 4 protons and 4 neutrons.
2. Atomic nuclei such as the one you modeled can decay by losing a particle that contains 2 protons and 2 neutrons. Remove the appropriate number of beads from your model to represent this process.

Think About It

1. **Observing** How many protons and how many neutrons are left in your nuclear model?
2. **Using Models** What element does your nuclear model now represent?

ENGAGE/EXPLORE

Inquiry Activity

What Happens When an Atom Decays? L2

Purpose In this activity, students begin to describe one mechanism of atomic decay that causes atoms to change from one element to another.

Address Misconceptions

Students may think that elements are unchangeable, and they may doubt that an atom of one element can change to another. Challenge this misconception by asking students to discuss the outcome of this activity. This activity demonstrates how elements can change, though it does not prove that such changes actually occur.

Skills Focus Using Models

Prep Time 5 minutes

Materials green and purple beads

Class Time 10 minutes

Expected Outcome The model will demonstrate the decay of $^{8}_{4}$Be to $^{4}_{2}$He by loss of an alpha particle (two protons and two neutrons).

Think About It

1. Two protons and two neutrons are left in the model.
2. The model represents helium.

Kinesthetic, Logical

Discovery Channel School

Video Field Trip

Nuclear Medicine

Encourage students to view the Video Field Trip "Nuclear Medicine."

Section 10.1

1 FOCUS

Objectives

10.1.1 **Describe** the process of nuclear decay.
10.1.2 **Classify** nuclear radiation as alpha particles, beta particles, or gamma rays.
10.1.3 **Balance** nuclear equations.
10.1.4 **Identify** sources of nuclear radiation, and **describe** how nuclear radiation affects matter.
10.1.5 **Describe** methods of detecting nuclear radiation.

Reading Focus

Build Vocabulary L2

Word-Part Analysis Point out the two vocabulary terms that contain the word *radiation (nuclear radiation, background radiation).* Explain that the word comes from a Latin word meaning "to spread out from a point."

Reading Strategy L2

Student answers may include:
a. Nuclear decay is the spontaneous change of one isotope into another. **b.** What are the types of nuclear radiation? **c.** What are the effects of nuclear radiation? **d.** One effect of nuclear radiation is the ionization of matter. **e.** How can nuclear radiation be detected? **f.** Nuclear radiation can be detected by a Geiger counter or film badge.

2 INSTRUCT

Nuclear Decay

Address Misconceptions L2

Many students think that gamma rays, X-rays, and visible light are unrelated. Point out that all three are different parts of the continuous electromagnetic spectrum. Explain that the photographic plate in Becquerel's experiment detected all three kinds of electromagnetic waves. Just as photographic film can detect visible light, it can detect X-rays and gamma rays emitted during nuclear decay. Students will read about the electromagnetic spectrum in Chapter 18.
Logical

10.1 Radioactivity

Reading Focus

Key Concepts

- What happens during nuclear decay?
- What are three types of nuclear radiation?
- How does nuclear radiation affect atoms?
- What devices can detect nuclear radiation?

Vocabulary

- radioactivity
- radioisotope
- nuclear radiation
- alpha particle
- beta particle
- gamma ray
- background radiation

Reading Strategy

Previewing Copy the table below. Before you read the section, rewrite the topic headings as *how, why,* and *what* questions. As you read, write an answer to each question.

Question	Answer
What is nuclear decay?	a. ____?____
b. ____?____	Alpha, beta, gamma
c. ____?____	d. ____?____
e. ____?____	f. ____?____

In 1896, French physicist Antoine Henri Becquerel (1852–1908) was experimenting with uranium salts. He hypothesized that the salts, which glow after being exposed to light, produced X-rays while they glowed. To test his hypothesis, Becquerel performed an experiment. First, he wrapped a photographic plate in paper. Then, he placed some uranium salts on the plate and set it outside in the sunlight, which caused the salts to glow. When Becquerel developed the plate, he got a foggy image. At the time, Becquerel thought that X-rays from the salts had penetrated the paper and fogged the plate.

Like any good scientist, Becquerel wanted to repeat his experiment, but a spell of bad weather forced him to wait. In the meantime, he left a wrapped photographic plate and uranium salts in a desk drawer. After several days, Becquerel decided to develop the plate without exposing the uranium to sunlight. To his surprise, he got the foggy image shown in Figure 1A. Later, Becquerel determined that the uranium salts had emitted rays that had never been observed before.

Figure 1 Due to rainy weather, Henri Becquerel postponed his intended experiment with uranium salts. **A** Without any exposure to sunlight, the salts still produced a foggy image on a photographic plate. **B** For his discovery of radioactivity, Becquerel shared the 1903 Nobel Prize for Physics with Marie and Pierre Curie.

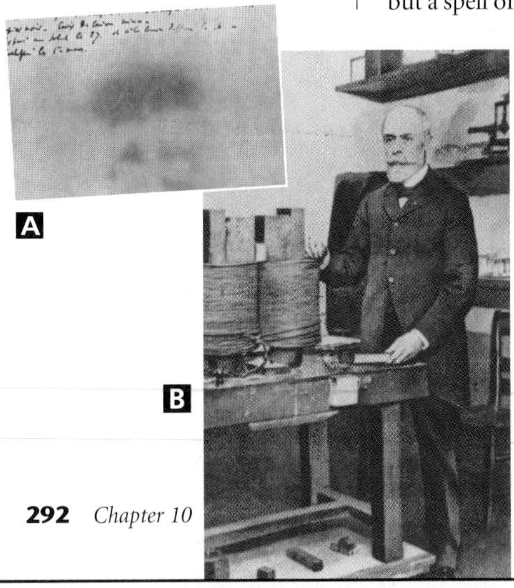
A
B

Nuclear Decay

Becquerel's experiment marked the discovery of radioactivity. **Radioactivity** is the process in which an unstable atomic nucleus emits charged particles and energy. Any atom containing an unstable nucleus is called a radioactive isotope, or **radioisotope** for short.

Section Resources

Print
- ***Laboratory Manual,*** Investigation 10B
- ***Reading and Study Workbook With Math Support,*** Section 10.1 and **Math Skill:** Nuclear Equations for Alpha Decay
- ***Math Skills and Problem Solving Workbook,*** Section 10.1
- ***Transparencies,*** Chapter Pretest and Section 10.1

Technology
- ***Interactive Textbook,*** Section 10.1
- ***Presentation Pro CD-ROM,*** Chapter Pretest and Section 10.1
- ***Go Online,*** *Planet Diary,* Radioactivity activity

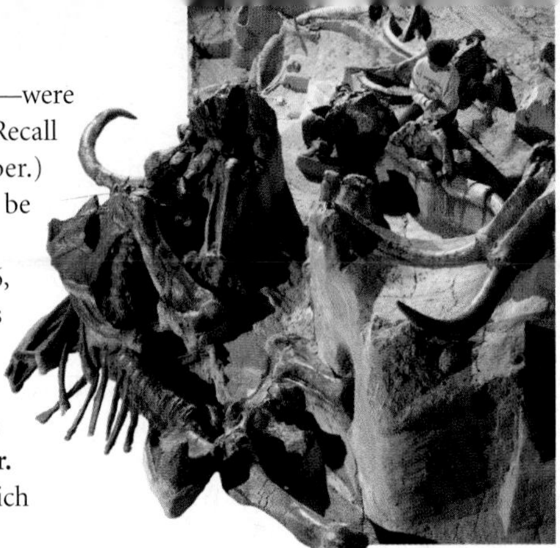

Radioisotopes of uranium—primarily uranium-238—were the source of radioactivity in Becquerel's experiment. (Recall that the name of an isotope includes its mass number.) Another common radioisotope is carbon-14, which can be found in fossils like the ones shown in Figure 2.

Unlike stable isotopes such as carbon-12 or oxygen-16, radioisotopes spontaneously change into other isotopes over time. When the composition of a radioisotope changes, the radioisotope is said to undergo nuclear decay. **During nuclear decay, atoms of one element can change into atoms of a different element altogether.** For example, uranium-238 decays into thorium-234, which is also a radioisotope.

Figure 2 About 26,000 years ago, more than 100 mammoths died at a sinkhole in Hot Springs, South Dakota. Scientists figured out how old the remains were by measuring amounts of the radioisotope carbon-14 contained in the mammoth bones.

Types of Nuclear Radiation

Scientists can detect a radioactive substance by measuring the nuclear radiation it gives off. **Nuclear radiation** is charged particles and energy that are emitted from the nuclei of radioisotopes. **Common types of nuclear radiation include alpha particles, beta particles, and gamma rays.** Figure 3 shows the properties of these three types of radiation.

Alpha Decay When a uranium-238 sample decays, it emits alpha particles. An **alpha particle** is a positively charged particle made up of two protons and two neutrons—the same as a helium nucleus. It has a 2+ charge. The common symbol for an alpha particle is $^{4}_{2}He$. The subscript is the atomic number (the number of protons). The superscript is the mass number (the sum of the numbers of protons and neutrons). Another symbol for an alpha particle is the Greek letter α.

Alpha decay, which refers to nuclear decay that releases alpha particles, is an example of a nuclear reaction. Like chemical reactions, nuclear reactions can be expressed as equations. The following nuclear equation describes the alpha decay of uranium-238.

$$^{238}_{92}U \rightarrow ^{234}_{90}Th + ^{4}_{2}He$$

In alpha decay, the product isotope has two fewer protons and two fewer neutrons than the reactant isotope. In the equation above, the mass number on the left (238) equals the sum of the mass numbers on the right (234 + 4). Also, the atomic number on the left (92) equals the sum of the atomic numbers on the right (90 + 2). In other words, the equation is balanced.

Alpha particles are the least penetrating type of nuclear radiation. Most alpha particles travel no more than a few centimeters in air, and can be stopped by a sheet of paper or by clothing.

Figure 3 Within a few years of Becquerel's discovery of radioactivity, Ernest Rutherford classified three types of nuclear radiation based on his own studies of uranium compounds. **Comparing and Contrasting** ***How do alpha particles, beta particles, and gamma rays differ in terms of charge? In terms of mass?***

Characteristics of Nuclear Radiation

Radiation Type	Symbol	Charge	Mass (amu)	Common Source
Alpha particle	α, $^{4}_{2}He$	2+	4	Radium-226
Beta particle	β, $^{0}_{-1}e$	1–	$\frac{1}{1836}$	Carbon-14
Gamma ray	γ	0	0	Cobalt-60

Types of Nuclear Radiation

Build Science Skills L2

Inferring Have students look at Figure 3, which shows the particles emitted in nuclear decay. Explain that a nucleus that emits an alpha particle gives up two protons and two neutrons (a helium nucleus). A nucleus that emits a beta particle (an electron) gives up a neutron but gains a proton, because a neutron decomposes into a proton and an electron during beta decay. Ask, **Which type of radioactive decay causes the largest change in the atomic number of a nucleus?** *(Alpha decay, which reduces the atomic number of the nucleus by two)*
Logical, Visual

Build Reading Literacy L1

Compare and Contrast Refer to page **226D** in **Chapter 8**, which provides the guidelines for comparing and contrasting.

Ask students to construct a compare/contrast table. Have them skim the sections on alpha decay, beta decay, and gamma decay. Then, ask students to describe similarities and differences of the decay types in their table.
Verbal, Visual

Customize for English Language Learners

Build a Science Glossary
Encourage English language learners to make a science glossary as they read the section. Suggest that they start with the vocabulary terms and then add any other new terms they encounter. Encourage students to copy the table in Figure 3 into their glossary, as these particles are key to understanding the chapter. Model how to divide words into parts such as prefix, root word, and suffix. Posting a list of suffixes and prefixes with their meanings in the classroom will help students when they encounter new words.

Answer to . . .

Figure 3 *Alpha particles have a charge of 2+; beta particles have a charge of 1−; gamma rays have no charge. Alpha particles have a mass of 4 amu; beta particles have a mass of* $\frac{1}{1836}$ *amu; and gamma rays have no mass.*

Use Visuals

L1

Figure 4 Emphasize that beta and gamma rays will pass through paper and that gamma rays will also pass through a thin sheet of aluminum. Ask, **What materials would effectively shield a radioactive source that emitted only beta particles?** *(Aluminum or concrete)* **Why might concrete be insufficient protection from gamma rays?** *(Some gamma rays will pass through concrete, and a concrete wall would have to be several meters thick to ensure that the gamma rays were effectively blocked.)* **Visual, Logical**

Teacher Demo

Stopping Radiation

L2

Purpose Demonstrate to students that radiation can be blocked to varying degrees by different materials.

Materials medical X-ray image or photograph of a medical X-ray image

Procedure Show students the medical X-ray image. Tell students that where the X-rays reached the film, it is black, and where the X-rays were completely blocked, the film is clear. When light shines through the clear part of the X-ray, it looks white. Ask, **Which blocks X-rays better, bone or soft tissue?** *(Bone, because the white area on the image means that the X-rays did not reach the film.)* **How can X-rays tell you about the thickness of bone?** *(Thick bone is really clear on the film or white in the image because it absorbs most of the X-rays. Thinner bone is light gray because some X-rays pass through the bone.)* **What do you think a metal object would look like on an X-ray image?** *(It would be white because it would block the X-rays.)*

Expected Outcome Students should be able to relate the penetrating power of X-rays to the penetrating power of nuclear radiation. **Visual, Verbal**

Go Online PLANETDIARY

Find links to additional activities and have students monitor phenomena that affect Earth and its residents.

Go Online PLANETDIARY

For: Radioactivity activity
Visit: PHSchool.com
Web Code: ccc-1101

Beta Decay When thorium-234 decays, it releases negatively charged radiation called beta particles. A **beta particle** is an electron emitted by an unstable nucleus. In nuclear equations, a beta particle is written as ${}^{0}_{-1}e$ or β. Because of its single negative charge, a beta particle is assigned an atomic number of −1. In Chapter 4, you learned that an electron has very little mass when compared with a proton. For this reason, a beta particle is assigned a mass number of 0.

How can an atomic nucleus, which has a positive charge, emit a negatively charged particle? During beta decay, a neutron decomposes into a proton and an electron. The proton stays trapped in the nucleus, while the electron is released. The following equation describes the beta decay of thorium-234.

$$^{234}_{90}\text{Th} \rightarrow {}^{234}_{91}\text{Pa} + {}^{0}_{-1}\text{e}$$

In beta decay, the product isotope has one proton more and one neutron fewer than the reactant isotope. The mass numbers of the isotopes are equal because the emitted beta particle has essentially no mass.

Due to their smaller mass and faster speed, beta particles are more penetrating than alpha particles. As Figure 4 illustrates, beta particles pass through paper, but can be stopped by a thin sheet of metal.

Reading Checkpoint *What is a beta particle?*

Gamma Decay Not all nuclear radiation consists of charged particles. A **gamma ray** is a penetrating ray of energy emitted by an unstable nucleus. Gamma radiation has no mass and no charge. Like X-rays and visible light, gamma rays are energy waves that travel through space at the speed of light.

Figure 4 The penetrating power of nuclear radiation varies with the type.
***Interpreting Diagrams** Which type of nuclear radiation is the most penetrating?*

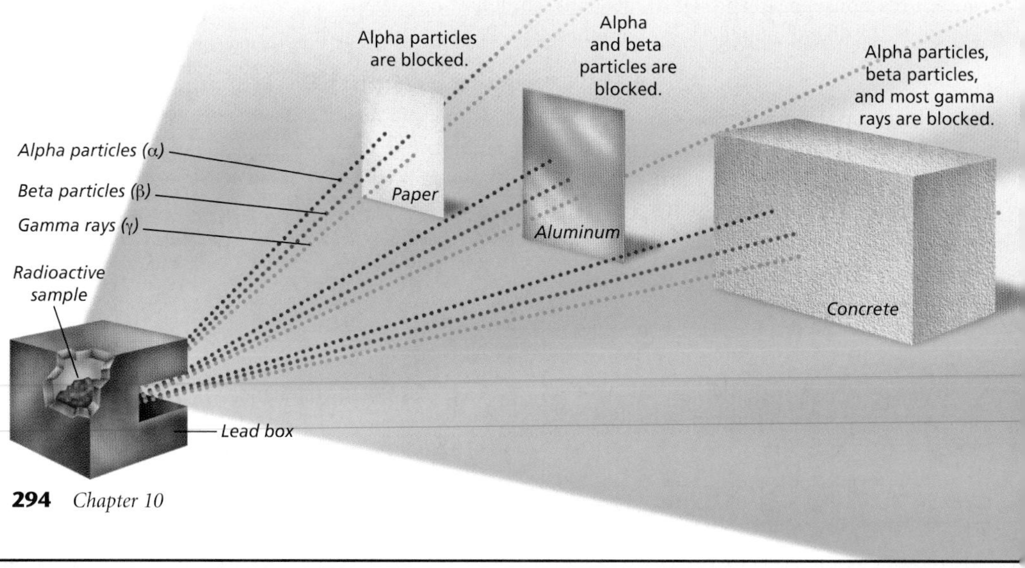

Alpha particles are blocked.
Alpha and beta particles are blocked.
Alpha particles, beta particles, and most gamma rays are blocked.
Alpha particles (α)
Beta particles (β)
Gamma rays (γ)
Radioactive sample
Paper
Aluminum
Concrete
Lead box

Facts and Figures

Explaining Energy The amount of energy emitted in alpha and gamma decay is equal to the energy difference of the nucleus before and after emission. However, this is not true in beta decay. Physicists had difficulty explaining this discrepancy, because the law of conservation of energy states that the total energy should remain unchanged during the process. In 1930, physicist Wolfgang Pauli proposed that an undetected particle, called the neutrino, was emitted along with the beta particles, accounting for some of the energy change in beta decay. In 1956, the neutrino was directly observed for the first time by American physicists Frederick Reines and Clyde Cowan.

Math Skills

Balancing Nuclear Equations

Write a balanced nuclear equation for the alpha decay of polonium-210.

1 Read and Understand

What information are you given?

Reactant isotope = polonium-210

Radiation emitted = ${}^{4}_{2}He$ (alpha particle)

Use the periodic table to obtain the atomic number of polonium.

Reactant isotope = ${}^{210}_{84}Po$

2 Plan and Solve

What unknowns are you trying to calculate?

Atomic number of product isotope, Z = ?

Mass number of product isotope, A = ?

Chemical symbol of product isotope, X = ?

What equation contains the given information?

$${}^{210}_{84}Po \rightarrow {}^{A}_{Z}X + {}^{4}_{2}He$$

Write and solve equations for atomic mass and atomic number.

$210 = A + 4$	$84 = Z + 2$
$210 - 4 = A$	$84 - 2 = Z$
$206 = A$	$82 = Z$

According to the periodic table, the element with an atomic number of 82 is lead, Pb. So, X is Pb. The balanced nuclear equation is shown below.

$${}^{210}_{84}Po \rightarrow {}^{206}_{82}Pb + {}^{4}_{2}He$$

3 Look Back and Check

Is your answer reasonable?

The mass number on the left equals the sum of the mass numbers on the right. The atomic number on the left equals the sum of the atomic numbers on the right. The equation is balanced.

Math Practice

1. Write a balanced nuclear equation for the alpha decay of thorium-232.
2. Write a balanced nuclear equation for the beta decay of carbon-14.
3. Determine the product of alpha decay for americium-241.
4. Determine the product of beta decay for strontium-90.

Math Practice

Solutions L2

1. ${}^{232}_{90}Th \longrightarrow {}^{A}_{Z}X + {}^{4}_{2}He$
$A = 232 - 4 = 228$
$Z = 90 - 2 = 88$
X = Ra
${}^{232}_{90}Th \longrightarrow {}^{228}_{88}Ra + {}^{4}_{2}He$

2. ${}^{14}_{6}C \longrightarrow {}^{A}_{Z}X + {}^{0}_{-1}e$
$A = 14 - 0 = 14$
$Z = 6 - (-1) = 7$
X = N
${}^{14}_{6}C \longrightarrow {}^{14}_{7}N + {}^{0}_{-1}e$

3. ${}^{241}_{95}Am \longrightarrow {}^{A}_{Z}X + {}^{4}_{2}He$
$A = 241 - 4 = 237$
$Z = 95 - 2 = 93$
X = Np
${}^{A}_{Z}X = {}^{237}_{93}Np$

4. ${}^{90}_{38}Sr \longrightarrow {}^{A}_{Z}X + {}^{0}_{-1}e$
$A = 90 - 0 = 90$
$Z = 38 - (-1) = 39$
X = Y
${}^{A}_{Z}X = {}^{90}_{39}Y$

Logical

For Extra Help L1

Remind students that when they write and solve the equation for atomic mass and atomic number, they must remember to change the sign of the constant when it is moved to the left side of the equation.
Logical

Direct students to the **Math Skills** in the **Skills and Reference Handbook** at the end of the student text for additional help.

Additional Problems

1. Write a balanced nuclear equation for the alpha decay of uranium-238.
(${}^{238}_{92}U \longrightarrow {}^{234}_{90}Th + {}^{4}_{2}He$)

2. Write a balanced nuclear equation for the beta decay of sodium-24.
(${}^{24}_{11}Na \longrightarrow {}^{24}_{12}Mg + {}^{0}_{-1}e$)

Logical, Portfolio

Answer to . . .

Reading Checkpoint *A beta particle is an electron emitted by an unstable nucleus.*

Figure 4 *Gamma rays are the most penetrating type of nuclear radiation shown in the diagram.*

Effects of Nuclear Radiation

Use Community Resources L2

Arrange to have someone from your state or local health department come to your class to talk about the hazards of radon. Have students prepare questions for the speaker in advance. The speaker can inform students about the possible dangers of radon in their homes and what kinds of tests are available. The speaker may also provide information on what the EPA considers to be safe radon levels. Have pairs or groups of students write thank-you notes to the speaker, incorporating a few of the facts that students learned from the presentation.
Interpersonal, Group

Integrate Earth Science L2

Radon is a naturally occurring radioactive element that is formed in the decay chain of uranium-238. Uranium can be found in almost all rocks and soil. Fortunately, in most areas the amount of uranium in rocks and soil is very small. Higher concentrations of uranium and its minerals are commonly found in light colored igneous rocks, granite, dark shale, phosphate-containing sedimentary rocks, and metamorphic rocks derived from these rocks. Soils derived from these rocks also have high uranium concentrations. Encourage students to work in small groups to research the concentrations of uranium in their community. They may use library resources, such as the Internet, to assist them in their research.
Group, Portfolio

Figure 5 The mineral autunite is an important source of uranium.

During gamma decay, the atomic number and mass number of the atom remain the same, but the energy of the nucleus decreases. Gamma decay often accompanies alpha or beta decay. For example, thorium-234 emits both beta particles and gamma rays (abbreviated as γ) as it decays.

$$^{234}_{90}\text{Th} \rightarrow {}^{234}_{91}\text{Pa} + {}^{0}_{-1}\text{e} + \gamma$$

Gamma rays are much more penetrating than either alpha particles or beta particles. It can take several centimeters of lead or several meters of concrete to stop gamma radiation.

Effects of Nuclear Radiation

You may not realize it, but you are exposed to nuclear radiation every day. Most of this is **background radiation,** or nuclear radiation that occurs naturally in the environment. Radioisotopes in air, water, rocks, plants, and animals all contribute to background radiation. Most rocks, such as the one in Figure 5, contain at least trace amounts of radioactive elements. Another source of background radiation is cosmic rays. Cosmic rays are streams of charged particles (mainly protons and alpha particles) from outer space. Collisions between cosmic rays and Earth's atmosphere shower the surface below with nuclear radiation. All this radioactivity may sound dangerous. However, background radiation levels are generally low enough to be safe.

When nuclear radiation exceeds background levels, it can damage the cells and tissues of your body. **Nuclear radiation can ionize atoms.** When cells are exposed to nuclear radiation, the bonds holding together proteins and DNA molecules may break. As these molecules change, the cells may no longer function properly.

Figure 6 Radon gas is produced underground as the uranium in rocks and soil decays. As the radon seeps up through the ground, it can get into buildings by passing through cracks or holes in their foundations. **Inferring** ***How would ventilation of the basement affect radon levels in the house shown below?***

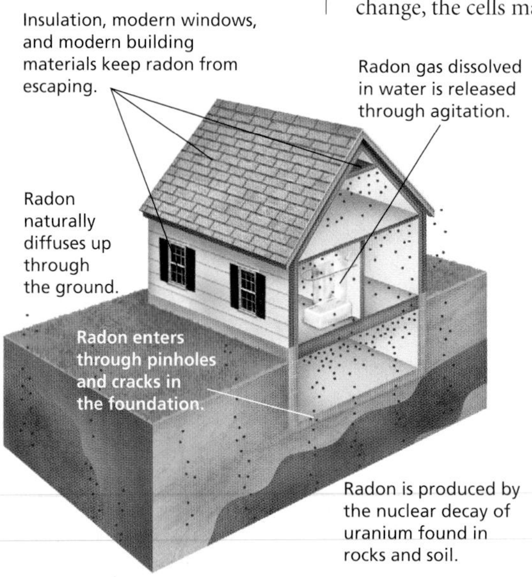
Insulation, modern windows, and modern building materials keep radon from escaping.
Radon gas dissolved in water is released through agitation.
Radon naturally diffuses up through the ground.
Radon enters through pinholes and cracks in the foundation.
Radon is produced by the nuclear decay of uranium found in rocks and soil.

Alpha particles, beta particles, and gamma rays are all forms of ionizing radiation. Alpha particles can cause skin damage similar to a burn, but they are not a serious health hazard unless an alpha-emitting substance is inhaled or eaten. For example, radon gas is a potentially dangerous natural source of alpha particles because it can be inhaled. Radon-222 is formed through a series of nuclear decays that begins with uranium-238 in rocks deep underground. As radon-222 is produced, it seeps upward toward the surface. It sometimes collects in the basements of buildings that lack proper ventilation, as shown in Figure 6. Prolonged exposure to radon-222 can lead to lung cancer.

Facts and Figures

Radon Radon is a colorless, odorless, tasteless gas. The most stable isotope, radon-222, is produced by the alpha decay of radium-226. The fact that radon may be a serious health hazard was not recognized until the late 1980s. Today, radon is considered by some to be the second leading cause of lung cancer in the United States, after smoking. Cigarette smokers who become exposed to radon are at particularly high risk of lung cancer.

There are three naturally occurring isotopes of radon. Radon-222 has the longest half-life, 3.82 days. Radon-220, with a half-life of 51.5 seconds, is formed in the decay chain of thorium-232. Radon-219, with a half-life of 3.92 seconds, is formed in the decay chain of actinium-227.

Answer to . . .

Figure 6 *Radon enters buildings from underground. Therefore, ventilating the basement of the house in Figure 6 would help reduce overall radon levels.*

296 Chapter 10

When exposure to nuclear radiation is external, the amount of tissue damage depends on the penetrating power of the radiation. For example, beta particles can damage tissues in the body more than alpha particles, but less than gamma rays. Gamma rays can penetrate deeply into the human body, potentially exposing all organs to ionization damage.

Detecting Nuclear Radiation

Although you can't see, hear, or feel the radioactivity around you, scientific instruments can measure nuclear radiation. **Devices that are used to detect nuclear radiation include Geiger counters and film badges.** A Geiger counter, shown in Figure 7, uses a gas-filled tube to measure ionizing radiation. When nuclear radiation enters the tube, it ionizes the atoms of the gas. The ions produce an electric current, which can be measured. The greater the amount of nuclear radiation, the greater the electric current produced in the tube is.

Recall that in Becquerel's experiment, nuclear radiation left an image on a photographic plate. Today, many people who work with or near radioactive materials wear film badges to monitor their exposure to nuclear radiation. A film badge contains a piece of photographic film wrapped in paper. The film is developed and replaced with a new piece periodically. The exposure on the film indicates the amount of radiation exposure for the person wearing the badge.

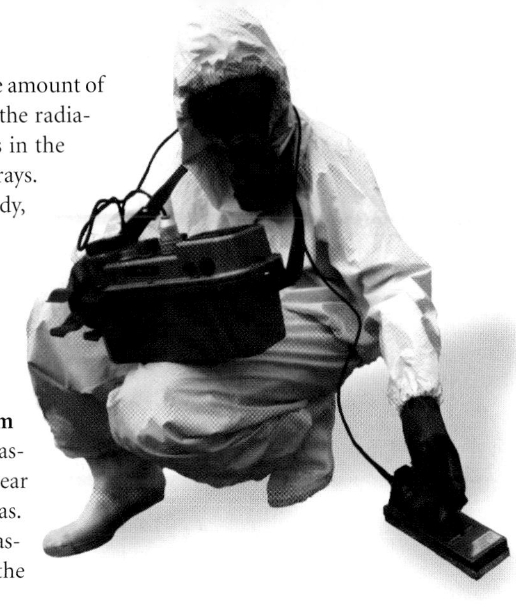

Figure 7 Wearing protective clothing, a firefighter uses a Geiger counter to test the ground for radioactivity. Firefighters sometimes help clean up accidents involving radioactive materials.

Section 10.1 Assessment

Reviewing Concepts

1. How does an element change during nuclear decay?
2. What are three types of nuclear radiation?
3. How are atoms affected by nuclear radiation?
4. What devices can be used to detect nuclear radiation?
5. How do types of nuclear radiation differ in electric charge?
6. Describe the penetrating power of each common type of radiation.
7. What is background radiation? List some of its sources.

Critical Thinking

8. **Predicting** What is the effect of beta decay on the composition of a nucleus?
9. **Inferring** Why do you think airplane pilots wear film badges?

Math Practice

10. Write a balanced nuclear equation for the alpha decay of radium-226.
11. Write a nuclear equation that describes the beta decay of hydrogen-3.

Detecting Nuclear Radiation

Use Visuals L1

Figure 7 Have students carefully examine the photograph. Ask, **Why is it important to wear protective clothing around radioactive materials?** *(Protective clothing keeps radioactive materials away from skin.)* Tell students that the EPA recommends heavy clothing as protection from beta radiation. Ask, **Does a Geiger counter protect against the effects of nuclear radiation?** *(No. The Geiger counter serves only as a monitoring device, not a shielding device.)* **Visual, Logical**

3 ASSESS

Evaluate Understanding L2

Randomly ask students to name the symbol or charge for each type of nuclear decay.

Reteach L1

Use Figure 4 to summarize the three different types of nuclear decay and how each type affects matter.

Math Practice

Solutions

10. $^{226}_{88}\text{Ra} \longrightarrow {}^{A}_{Z}\text{X} + {}^{4}_{2}\text{He}$

$A = 226 - 4 = 222$; $Z = 88 - 2 = 86$;

$\text{X} = \text{Rn}$; $^{226}_{88}\text{Ra} \longrightarrow {}^{222}_{86}\text{Rn} + {}^{4}_{2}\text{He}$

11. $^{3}_{1}\text{H} \longrightarrow {}^{A}_{Z}\text{X} + {}^{0}_{-1}\text{e}$

$A = 3 - 0 = 3$; $Z = 1 - (-1) = 2$;

$\text{X} = \text{He}$; $^{3}_{1}\text{H} \longrightarrow {}^{3}_{2}\text{He} + {}^{0}_{-1}\text{e}$

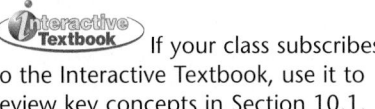

Interactive Textbook If your class subscribes to the Interactive Textbook, use it to review key concepts in Section 10.1.

Section 10.1 Assessment

1. During nuclear decay, atoms of one element can change into atoms of another element.
2. Three types of nuclear radiation are alpha particles, beta particles, and gamma rays.
3. Nuclear radiation can ionize atoms.
4. Geiger counters and film badges are two devices used to detect nuclear radiation.
5. Alpha particles have a charge of 2+; beta particles have a charge of 1−; gamma rays have no charge.
6. Alpha particles are the least penetrating. Most alpha particles can be stopped by a sheet of paper or by clothing. Beta particles pass through paper, but can be stopped by metal foil. Gamma rays, which are much more penetrating than either alpha particles or beta particles, can pass through several meters of concrete.
7. Background radiation is nuclear radiation that occurs naturally in the environment. Sources of background radiation include cosmic rays, and rocks and minerals that contain radioactive elements.
8. In beta decay, a neutron decomposes into a proton and an electron. Therefore, the mass number stays the same while the atomic number (the number of protons) increases by one. The net effect of beta decay is that the number of neutrons in the nucleus decreases by one and the number of protons increases by one.
9. Because they work at high altitudes, pilots are exposed to high levels of background radiation from cosmic rays. To monitor their radiation exposure, pilots wear film badges.

10.2 Rates of Nuclear Decay

Reading Focus

Key Concepts

- How do nuclear decay rates differ from chemical reaction rates?
- How do scientists determine the age of an object that contains carbon-14?

Vocabulary

- half-life

Reading Strategy

Identifying Details Copy the concept map below. As you read, complete it to identify details about radiocarbon dating.

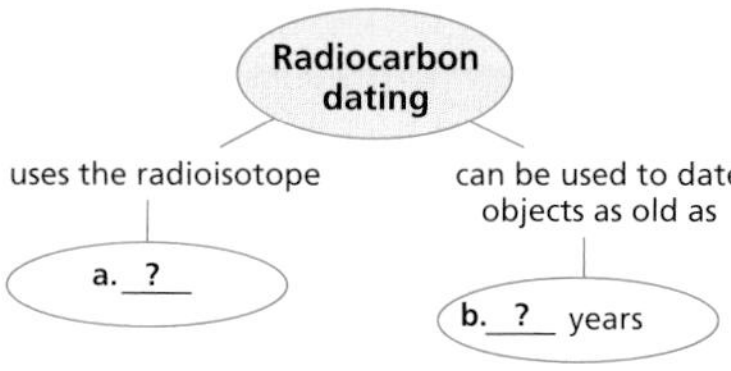
Radiocarbon dating
uses the radioisotope
can be used to date objects as old as
a. ?
b. ? years

A well-known theory is that early Americans were people from Siberia who crossed the Bering Strait into Alaska about 13,000 years ago. However, this theory has been challenged by recent scientific discoveries. In the 1990s, archaeologists working at a site in Cactus Hill, Virginia, found stone tools, charcoal, and animal bones that were at least 15,000 years old. Some of the artifacts were as much as 17,000 years old. The age of these artifacts suggests that the first Americans reached the continent much earlier than formerly thought. Some archaeologists have since revised their theories on the origin of America's earliest ancestors. One possible explanation is that the first Americans were people from Europe who crossed the Atlantic Ocean by using boats.

Figure 8 shows some of the artifacts from the Cactus Hill site. They certainly look very old, but the archaeologists needed to find out *how* old. One clue that can reveal the age of an object is how many radioactive nuclei it contains. Because most materials contain at least trace amounts of radioisotopes, scientists can estimate how old they are based on rates of nuclear decay.

Figure 8 These stone tools from the archaeological site in Cactus Hill, Virginia, are at least 15,000 years old. Scientists estimated the age of the site based on rates of nuclear decay.

1 FOCUS

Objectives

10.2.1 **Define** half-life, and **relate** half-life to the age of a radioactive sample.

10.2.2 **Compare** and **contrast** nuclear reaction rates with chemical reaction rates.

10.2.3 **Describe** how radioisotopes are used to estimate the age of materials.

Reading Focus

Build Vocabulary L2

Paraphrase Have students write a definition of *half-life* in their own words. After students read the section, ask them to draw a diagram that illustrates the definition.

Reading Strategy L2

a. Carbon-14
b. 50,000

2 INSTRUCT

Build Science Skills L2

Drawing Conclusions Ask students to look at Figure 8. Tell them that if the object is made of an organic (once-living) material, the object's carbon-14 content can be used to determine its age. Ask, **The tools shown in the photo are made of stone. Do you think the stone tools contain carbon-14?** *(No, stone is not an organic material.)* **The caption states that the objects are estimated to be 15,000 years old. If the stone tools were not used to determine this age, then what was?** *(The people who made the stone tools also made and used other, organic-based objects. These objects, perhaps made of cloth or wood, were used to determine the age.)*
Logical

Section Resources

Print
- ***Laboratory Manual,*** Investigation 10A
- ***Reading and Study Workbook With Math Support,*** Section 10.2
- ***Transparencies,*** Section 10.2

Technology
- ***Interactive Textbook,*** Section 10.2
- ***Presentation Pro CD-ROM,*** Section 10.2
- ***Go Online,*** NSTA SciLinks, Half-Life

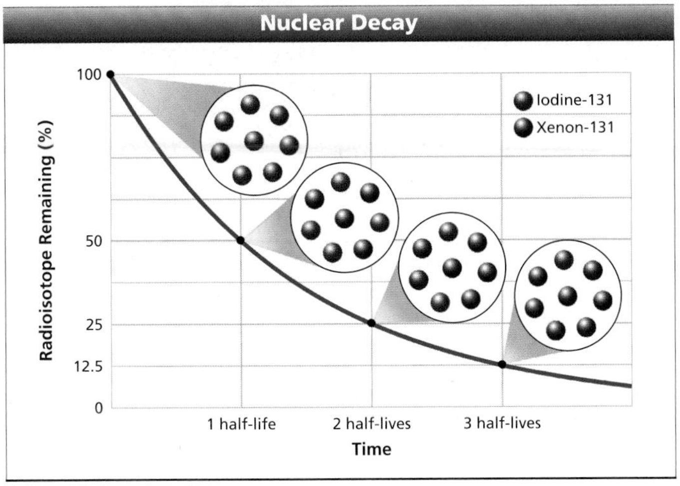
Nuclear Decay
Radioisotope Remaining (%)
100
50
25
12.5
0
Iodine-131
Xenon-131
1 half-life
2 half-lives
3 half-lives
Time

Figure 9 The half-life for the beta decay of iodine-131 is 8.07 days. After one half-life (8.07 days), half of a sample of iodine-131 will have decayed into xenon-131. After two half-lives (16.14 days), three quarters of the sample will have decayed.

Half-life

A nuclear decay rate describes how fast nuclear changes take place in a radioactive substance. Every radioisotope decays at a specific rate that can be expressed as a half-life. A **half-life** is the time required for one half of a sample of a radioisotope to decay. After one half-life, half of the atoms in a radioactive sample have decayed, while the other half remain unchanged. After two half-lives, half of the remaining half decays, leaving one quarter of the original sample unchanged. Figure 9 illustrates the nuclear decay rate of iodine-131. Iodine-131 has a half-life of 8.07 days. After two half-lives, or 16.14 days, the fraction of iodine-131 remaining is one quarter. After three half-lives, or 24.21 days, the fraction of iodine-131 remaining is one half of one quarter, or one eighth.

Half-lives can vary from fractions of a second to billions of years. Figure 10 lists the half-lives of some common radioisotopes. Uranium-238, for instance, has a half-life of 4.5 billion years. This means that in 4.5 billion years, there will be half as much uranium-238 on Earth as there is today. You could also say that 4.5 billion years ago, there was twice as much uranium-238 on Earth as there is today. **Unlike chemical reaction rates, which vary with the conditions of a reaction, nuclear decay rates are constant.** Regardless of the temperature, pressure, or surface area of a uranium-238 sample, its half-life is still 4.5 billion years.

Reading Checkpoint *What is a half-life?*

Figure 10 Nuclear decay rates are constant. A given radioisotope decays at a specific rate, or half-life. **Calculating** ***What isotope is produced by the nuclear decay of radon-222?***

Half-Lives and Radiation of Selected Radioisotopes

Isotope	Half-life	Nuclear Radiation Emitted
Radon-222	3.82 days	α
Iodine-131	8.07 days	β
Thorium-234	24.1 days	β, γ
Radium-226	1620 years	α, γ
Carbon-14	5730 years	β
Thorium-230	75,200 years	α, γ
Uranium-235	7.04×10^8 years	α, γ
Potassium-40	1.28×10^9 years	β, γ
Uranium-238	4.47×10^9 years	α

Half-Life

Use Visuals L1

Figure 9 Ask, **What happens to the amount of iodine-131 at the end of the first half-life?** *(Half of the iodine-131 atoms change into xenon-131 atoms.)* **Look at the line on the graph. Why is the line curved and not straight?** *(After each half-life, half of the remaining atoms have decayed. After one half-life, one half of the original atoms remain; after two half-lives, a fourth of the original atoms remain; and so on. After* n *half-lives, $(\frac{1}{2})^n$ of the original atoms remain. A graph of this relationship is a curve, not a straight line.)* **Visual**

Teacher Demo

Predicting Decay L2

Purpose Students learn that it is not possible to predict which atom decays in a radioactive sample.

Materials hot plate, 250-mL or 500-mL beaker, glass plate, popcorn, cooking oil

Procedure Place the beaker on the hot plate. Pour a small amount of cooking oil into the beaker and add popcorn to form a single layer 1 kernel thick. Put the glass plate on top of the beaker. Tell students that each kernel represents an atom that will decay. Explain to students that it is not possible to accurately predict which kernel will pop first. Tell students that when radioisotopes decay, they decay throughout the sample rather than in one particular area.

Safety Caution students to stand at a safe distance when you heat the cooking oil and pop the corn. Remind students never to eat anything in a laboratory.

Expected Outcome There will be no observable pattern to the order in which the kernels pop.
Visual, Logical

Customize for for Inclusion Students

Visually Impaired
Give students 75 metal washers. Have the students count out 40 washers and line them up in a single row. Explain that after the first half-life of a radioisotope, half of the atoms decay. Next, have them count out 20 washers and put them in a single row next to the first row of washers. Have them repeat this again for the second half-life with 10 washers, and then count out 5 washers for the third half-life. With all the rows even at the left, the students should be able to determine the shape of the "graph" by touching the right edge of each row. Inform students that in reality, exactly half of the particles do not decay each half-life, but that this process averages out to the half-life rate over a long period of time. However, reinforce that the general shape of the "graph" is accurate.

Answer to . . .

Figure 10 *Polonium-218. The equation is:*

$${}^{222}_{86}Rn \longrightarrow {}^{218}_{84}Po + {}^{4}_{2}He$$

Reading Checkpoint *A half-life is the time required for one half of a sample of a radioisotope to decay.*

Quick Lab

Modeling Half-Life L2

Objective
After completing this activity, students will be able to
- analyze data to calculate the "half-life" of a model radioactive element.

Address Misconceptions

Students may think that a half-life is half the time it takes for a radioactive substance to decay completely. This lab can help dispel this misconception.

Skills Focus **Analyzing Data, Calculating, Using Graphs**

Prep Time 20 minutes

Materials 100 1-cm squares of wallpaper, large plastic bag, graph paper

Advance Prep Use a paper cutter to cut up the wallpaper quickly.

Class Time 20 minutes

Teaching Tips
- Students can cut up the paper squares themselves.
- Explain to students that, on average, half the remaining squares will be removed each time Step 4 is repeated.
- Ask students: **How does this lab model radioactive decay?** *(Like the wallpaper squares, half the radioactive element decays during each half-life.)*

Expected Outcome Students will need to spill and remove paper squares six to nine times to remove all of the squares.

Analyze and Conclude
1. On average, half the squares will be removed in one spill and three-fourths of the squares will be removed in two spills.
2. Students' graphs should reflect the information in their data tables.
3. One year
Visual, Logical

Go Online NSTA SciLinks

Download a worksheet on half-life for students to complete, and find additional teacher support from NSTA SciLinks.

Quick Lab

Modeling Half-Life

Procedure

1. Put 100 1-cm squares of wallpaper in a large plastic bag. Construct a data table with 2 columns and 9 blank rows. Label the columns Spill Number and Number of Squares Returned.
2. Close the bag and shake it to mix up the squares. Then, spill them onto a flat surface.
3. Remove the squares that are face-side up. Record the number of squares remaining and return them to the bag.
4. Repeat Steps 2 and 3 until there are no squares left to put back into the bag.

Analyze and Conclude

1. **Analyzing Data** How many spills were required to remove half of the squares? To remove three fourths of the squares?
2. **Using Graphs** Graph your results. Plot spill number on the horizontal axis and the number of squares remaining on the vertical axis.
3. **Using Models** If each spill represents one year, what is the half-life of the squares?

Suppose you have a one-gram sample of iridium-182, which undergoes beta decay to form osmium-182. The half-life of iridium-182 is 15 minutes. After 45 minutes, how much iridium-182 will remain in the sample? To solve this problem, you first need to calculate how many half-lives will elapse during the total time of decay.

$$\text{Half-lives elapsed} = \frac{\text{Total time of decay}}{\text{Half-life}} = \frac{45\text{ min}}{15\text{ min}} = 3$$

After three half-lives, the amount of iridium-182 has been reduced by half three times.

$$\frac{1}{2} \times \frac{1}{2} \times \frac{1}{2} = \frac{1}{8}$$

So after 45 minutes, $\frac{1}{8} \times 1$ gram, or 0.125 gram, of iridium-182 remains while 0.875 gram of the sample has decayed into osmium-182.

Radioactive Dating

Now suppose you have a sample that was originally iridium-182, but three quarters of it have since decayed into osmium-182. Based on the fraction of iridium-182 left (one quarter), you can calculate the age of the sample to be two half-lives, or 30 minutes old.

The artifacts from Cactus Hill were dated by measuring levels of carbon-14, which has a half-life of 5730 years. Carbon-14 is formed in the upper atmosphere when neutrons produced by cosmic rays collide with nitrogen-14 atoms. The radioactive carbon-14 undergoes beta decay to form nitrogen-14.

$$^{14}_{6}\text{C} \rightarrow ^{14}_{7}\text{N} + ^{0}_{-1}\text{e}$$

Go Online NSTA SciLinks

For: Links on half-life
Visit: www.SciLinks.org
Web Code: ccn-1102

Facts and Figures

Radiocarbon Dating An American chemist, Dr. Willard F. Libby, developed this technique in the late 1940s. Radiocarbon dating is used to date once-living materials. The date when the organism died is the date when it stopped absorbing carbon-14.

Radiocarbon dating cannot be used to date the remains of organisms that died after the 1940s. Starting in the 1940s, the testing of nuclear bombs and use of nuclear reactors has dramatically increased the amount of carbon-14 and other radioisotopes in the environment.

Carbon reacts with oxygen in the atmosphere and forms carbon dioxide. As plants absorb carbon dioxide during photosynthesis, they maintain the same ratio of carbon-14 to carbon-12 as in the atmosphere. Likewise, animals have the same ratio of carbon isotopes as the plants they eat. When a plant or animal dies, however, it can no longer absorb carbon. From this point on, the organism's carbon-14 levels decrease as the radioactive carbon decays. **In radiocarbon dating, the age of an object is determined by comparing the object's carbon-14 levels with carbon-14 levels in the atmosphere.** For example, if the ratio of carbon-14 to carbon-12 in a fossil is half the ratio in the atmosphere, then the organism lived about 5730 years ago.

Because atmospheric carbon-14 levels can change over time, the calculated age of the fossil is not totally accurate. To get a more accurate radiocarbon date, scientists compare the carbon-14 levels in a sample to carbon-14 levels in objects of known age. Such objects might include trees (which can be dated by counting tree rings) or artifacts from a specific historical period.

Radiocarbon dating can be used to date any carbon-containing object less than 50,000 years old, such as the artifact in Figure 11. Objects older than 50,000 years contain too little carbon-14 to be measurable. To date objects thought to be older than 50,000 years, scientists measure the amounts of radioisotopes with longer half-lives than carbon-14. Geologists, for instance, use the half-lives of potassium-40, uranium-235, and uranium-238 to date rock formations. The older the rock, the lower are the levels of the radioisotope present.

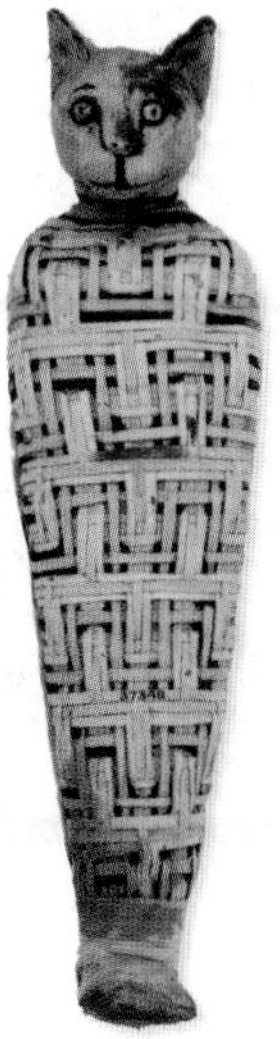

Figure 11 Radiocarbon dating has helped archaeologists learn more about ancient civilizations. Excavations in Abydos, a major archaeological site of ancient Egypt, have unearthed fascinating artifacts. This mummy case, containing the remains of a cat, is 1900 years old.

Section 10.2 Assessment

Reviewing Concepts

1. How are nuclear decay rates different from chemical reaction rates?
2. How can scientists determine the age of an object that contains carbon-14?
3. If a radioactive sample has decayed until only one eighth of the original sample remains unchanged, how many half-lives have elapsed?
4. What type of nuclear radiation is emitted when carbon-14 decays?

Critical Thinking

5. **Predicting** Can radiocarbon dating be used to determine the age of dinosaur fossils? Explain. (*Hint:* Dinosaurs roamed Earth more than 65 million years ago.)
6. **Inferring** All of the isotopes of radon have half-lives shorter than four days, yet radon is still found in nature. Explain why all the radon has not already decayed.
7. **Calculating** A certain isotope of technetium has a half-life of six hours. If it is given to a patient as part of a medical procedure, what fraction of the radioisotope remains in the body after one day?

Writing in Science

Explanatory Paragraph Archaeology is the study of past cultures. Explain how a concept in chemistry led to advances in archaeology.

Radioactive Dating

Build Science Skills L2

Measuring Ask students to choose a radioactive isotope for dating a hypothetical fossil. Tell students that archaeologists hypothesize that the fossil is about 20,000 years old. Have students look at the half-lives of radioisotopes in this section. Ask, **Which isotope would you recommend that the scientists first try?** *(Carbon-14)* **Why would that isotope be a good choice?** *(It is a good choice because the half-life of carbon-14 is 5370 years. The half-life of radium-226, at 1620 years, is too short. The half-life of thorium-230 is 75,200 years, which is too long. Using either of these could result in a less accurate measurement.)*
Logical, Verbal

3 ASSESS

Evaluate Understanding L2

Randomly ask students to determine the number of particles present after one, two, or three half-lives have passed from a specified initial number of particles.

Reteach L1

Use Figure 10 to review how different radioisotopes may be used to date objects of different ages. Emphasize that some radioisotopes with shorter half-lives are useful for dating young objects while radioisotopes with long half-lives are useful for dating old objects.

Interactive Textbook If your class subscribes to the Interactive Textbook, use it to review key concepts in Section 10.2.

Writing in Science

Half-life is a concept in nuclear chemistry that has led to profound advances in archaeology, the study of past cultures. A half-life is the time required for one half of a sample of a radioisotope to decay. Using radioisotopes such as carbon-14, scientists have been able to accurately date fossils and archaeological sites up to 50,000 years old.

Section 10.2 Assessment

1. Unlike chemical reaction rates, nuclear decay rates are constant.
2. The age of an object is determined by comparing the object's carbon-14 levels with carbon-14 levels in the atmosphere.
3. Three half-lives $(\frac{1}{2} \times \frac{1}{2} \times \frac{1}{2} = \frac{1}{8})$ have elapsed.
4. When a carbon-14 nucleus decays, it emits a beta particle.
5. Dinosaur fossils, about 65 million years old, are too old to be radiocarbon dated. Radiocarbon dating can only be used to date objects less than 50,000 years old.
6. Radon isotopes are still found in nature because they are continually formed by the decay of longer-lived radioisotopes.
7. Assuming the technetium is eliminated only by radioactive decay, then Half-Lives elapsed = Total time of decay/Half-Life = 24 hours/6 hours = 4. After four half-lives, the amount has been reduced by half four times. $(\frac{1}{2})^4 = \frac{1}{16}$

issues in SCIENCE

Should Archaeological Sites Be Protected From Development? L2

Background

Many places where people live today are the same places people have lived for hundreds or thousands of years. For example, a choice residential location today might be on a bluff overlooking a river. In the past, that same site might have been chosen because it was close to the river (a good source of food and water) and because it was easy to defend.

Answers

1. Answers will vary. One issue involved in the controversy surrounding the preservation of archaeological sites is the need for society to modernize. As communities modernize, they often seek new uses for existing land. However, defenders of archaeological sites would rather see these sites left undeveloped for the sake of scientific progress. Another issue is how much the community can benefit from the land. Protecting an archaeological site offers the benefits of scientific knowledge, education, and tourism. Developing an archaeological site offers the benefits of commerce, which may revitalize the community both socially and economically.

2. Advantages of protecting an archaeological site from development include advances in scientific research, educational opportunities for the community, and tourism. Disadvantages include lost economic and cultural opportunities.

3. Answers will vary based on which arguments students choose.

Go Online PHSchool.com

Have students further research issues related to this topic.

issues in SCIENCE

Should Archaeological Sites Be Protected From Development?

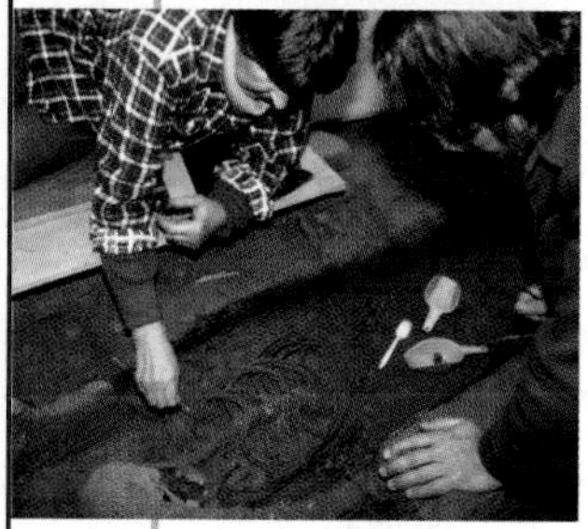

Some of the most important archaeological sites in the United States have been discovered accidentally by construction crews that were digging underground. In 1991, construction workers in New York City discovered the African Burial Ground. The burial ground was a cemetery used by African Americans more than 200 years ago. The federal government, which owned the land, continued with its original plan to construct an office building on the site. However, the government made sure to set aside part of the site for a memorial. It also declared the site a National Historic Landmark, and funded scientific research on the nearly 400 sets of skeletal remains found buried there.

In other cases of historic archaeological digs, local governments have protected the sites from commercial development. Such sites—including the Mammoth Site of Hot Springs, South Dakota, and the Miami Circle of Miami, Florida—are often declared historic parks or museums.

The Viewpoints

Archaeological Sites Should Be Protected From Development

Communities understand that preserving an archaeological site helps scientists learn about the past. That knowledge is precious. It is not worth sacrificing scientific progress in order to finish a construction project. If an important archaeological site is owned by a developer, the developer should be compensated fairly for the land. But from that point on, the site should be overseen by scientists so that it can be studied thoroughly. By preserving the entire site (instead of having to remove all its artifacts), scientists can better reconstruct the site's history. A well-preserved, well-managed site will also attract tourists, who will support the community's local businesses.

Archaeological Sites Should Not Be Protected From Development

As communities modernize, they often tear down old buildings and put up new ones. These new buildings provide housing and office space, and can inject new life into run-down neighborhoods. The discovery of ancient artifacts at a construction site should not stand in the way of progress. The land should serve the needs of the people who live there. Archaeologists should be allowed to remove artifacts that are found at the site for scientific study. But the site itself should not be made off-limits to developers. Building an office or apartment complex on the site would help local businesses much more than building a historical park.

Research and Decide

1. **Defining an Issue** In your own words, describe at least two major issues involved in the controversy surrounding the preservation of important archaeological sites.
2. **Analyzing the Viewpoints** List the key arguments expressed by the proponents and critics of building on archaeological sites. What are the advantages? What are the disadvantages?
3. **Forming Your Opinion** Should archaeological sites be protected from development? Which specific argument influenced you the most?

Go Online PHSchool.com

For: More on this issue
Visit: PHSchool.com
Web Code: cch-1102

10.3 Artificial Transmutation

Reading Focus

Key Concepts

- How do artificial transmutations occur?
- How are transuranium elements produced?

Vocabulary

- transmutation
- transuranium elements
- quark

Reading Strategy

Monitoring Your Understanding Preview the Key Concepts, topic headings, vocabulary, and figures in this section. List two things you expect to learn. After reading, state what you learned about each item you listed.

What I Expect to Learn	What I Learned
a. ___?___	b. ___?___
c. ___?___	d. ___?___

During the Middle Ages, a number of people, like the ones shown in Figure 12, were obsessed with the idea of changing lead into gold. For centuries, these early scientists, known as alchemists, tried to use chemical reactions to make gold. But no matter how many recipes they tried, the alchemists only succeeded in making compounds that contained lead. What were they doing wrong?

Figure 12 This painting of an alchemist's laboratory was made around 1570. The alchemists failed in their attempts to turn lead into gold.

Nuclear Reactions in the Laboratory

The alchemists were trying to achieve transmutation. **Transmutation** is the conversion of atoms of one element to atoms of another. It involves a nuclear change, not a chemical change.

Nuclear decay is an example of a transmutation that occurs naturally. Transmutations can also be artificial. **Scientists can perform artificial transmutations by bombarding atomic nuclei with high-energy particles such as protons, neutrons, or alpha particles.**

Early experiments involving artificial transmutation led to important clues about atomic structure. In 1919, a decade after he discovered the atomic nucleus, Ernest Rutherford performed the first artificial transmutation. Rutherford had been studying the effects of nuclear radiation on various gases. When Rutherford exposed nitrogen gas to alpha particles, he found that some of the alpha particles were absorbed by the nitrogen nuclei. Each newly formed nucleus then ejected a proton, leaving behind the isotope oxygen-17.

$$^{14}_{7}\text{N} + ^{4}_{2}\text{He} \rightarrow ^{17}_{8}\text{O} + ^{1}_{1}\text{H}$$

Note that $^{1}_{1}\text{H}$ represents a proton. Rutherford's experiment provided evidence that the nucleus contains protons.

Section Resources

Print
- ***Reading and Study Workbook With Math Support,*** Section 10.3
- ***Transparencies,*** Section 10.3

Technology
- ***Interactive Textbook,*** Section 10.3
- ***Presentation Pro CD-ROM,*** Section 10.3

Section 10.3

1 FOCUS

Objectives

10.3.1 **Describe** and **identify** examples of transmutation.
10.3.2 **Describe** how transuranium elements are synthesized.
10.3.3 **Explain** how particle accelerators have been used in scientific research.

Reading Focus

Build Vocabulary L2

Paraphrase Ask students to write the vocabulary words on a sheet of paper. Instruct students to write a definition, in their own words, for each term as they encounter the term while going through the chapter. After writing their own definition, they should also write a complete sentence with the term.

Reading Strategy L2

Possible answers: **a.** Examples of artificial transmutation **b.** Rutherford's transmutation of nitrogen-14 into oxygen-17; the synthesis of neptunium-239 **c.** Uses of transuranium elements **d.** Smoke detectors (americium-241); space probes (plutonium-238)

2 INSTRUCT

Nuclear Reactions in the Laboratory

Address Misconceptions L2

The alchemists of the Middle Ages never succeeded in turning lead into gold. This doesn't mean, however, that it is impossible. Modern scientists, including Glenn Seaborg in 1980, have reportedly turned lead into gold. However, this has only been done with very minute amounts of lead. Challenge students to find out why scientists do not manufacture gold for profit using transmutation. *(The process of using nuclear reactions to change lead into gold is more expensive than the worth of the gold. Currently, it is cheaper to mine gold ore.)*
Verbal

Transuranium Elements

Quick Lab

Modeling Transmutation L2

Objective
After completing this activity, students will be able to
- balance equations that describe simple nuclear reactions.

Skills Focus Calculating, Using Models

Prep Time 5 minutes

Class Time 15 minutes

Safety Caution students to avoid dropping beads on the floor where they may lead to slips and falls.

Expected Outcome The products are carbon-13 and oxygen-17.

Analyze and Conclude
1. The missing products were carbon-13 and oxygen-17. The models should show that the total number of protons and neutrons on the left side of the equation is the same as on the right. After counting the number of green beads (protons) in the missing product isotope, its identity can be determined by referring to the periodic table. The mass number of the missing product isotope is the sum of its protons and neutrons.
2. Use the following equation to check students' models.
$^{27}_{13}Al + ^{4}_{2}He \longrightarrow ^{30}_{14}Si + ^{1}_{1}H$
Visual

Build Reading Literacy L1

Visualize Refer to page **354D** in **Chapter 12**, which provides the guidelines for using visualization.

Have students keep their books closed. Tell them to listen carefully while you read the paragraph about synthesizing neptunium. Ask students to describe how they visualize what happens in the transmutation. Then, ask students to work in pairs and discuss how they visualized the process.
Visual

Quick Lab

Modeling Transmutation

Materials
periodic table, 2 sheets of unlined white paper, 32 green beads, 32 purple beads

Procedure
1. Use the periodic table to complete the following nuclear reaction. Then, write it on one of the sheets of paper.
$$^{10}_{5}B + ^{4}_{2}He \rightarrow ^{A}_{Z}X + ^{1}_{1}H$$
2. Count the number of protons and neutrons present in each reactant and product.
3. Using the green beads to represent protons and the purple beads to represent neutrons, make a model of each reactant and product below its symbol on the sheet of paper.
4. Repeat Steps 1 to 3 using the following nuclear reaction and the second sheet of paper.
$$^{14}_{7}N + ^{4}_{2}He \rightarrow ^{A}_{Z}X + ^{1}_{1}H$$

Analyze and Conclude
1. **Applying Concepts** What was the missing product in each of the equations? How did you know what the missing product was?
2. **Using Models** Make a model of the nuclear reaction between an alpha particle and an atom of aluminium-27. (*Hint:* One of the two products is a proton.)

Transuranium Elements

Elements with atomic numbers greater than 92 (uranium) are called **transuranium elements.** All transuranium elements are radioactive, and they are generally not found in nature. **Scientists can synthesize a transuranium element by the artificial transmutation of a lighter element.**

Neptunium was the first transuranium element synthesized. In 1940, scientists at the University of California, Berkeley, bombarded uranium-238 with neutrons, producing uranium-239. The uranium-239 underwent beta decay to form neptunium-239.

$$^{239}_{92}U \rightarrow ^{239}_{93}Np + ^{0}_{-1}e$$

Although most transuranium elements have only been produced for research, some are synthesized for industrial or consumer use. For example, americium-241 is a transuranium element used in smoke detectors. As americium-241 decays, it emits alpha radiation. This radiation ionizes the air inside a smoke detector to allow an electric current to flow. When smoke enters the smoke detector, it disrupts the current and the alarm goes off. Another useful transuranium element is plutonium-238. Figure 13 shows a space probe that runs on electrical energy generated by the decay of plutonium-238.

Reading Checkpoint *What is a transuranium element?*

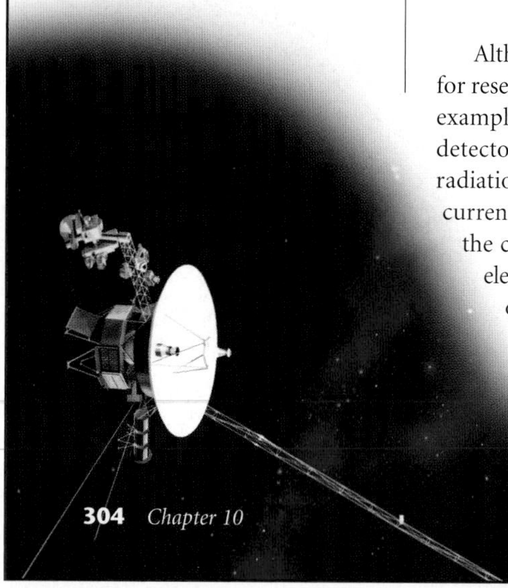

Figure 13 In 1977, the National Aeronautics and Space Administration (NASA) launched two identical spacecraft, Voyager 1 and Voyager 2. These spacecraft, which are still exploring the outer solar system, are powered by the alpha decay of plutonium-238. ***Inferring** What isotope is produced by the alpha decay of plutonium-238?*

Customize for Inclusion Students

Gifted
Challenge students to find the names of different types of subatomic particles besides protons, neutrons, and electrons. For example, have them research the six types of quarks. *(The six quarks are often called up, down, charmed, strange, top, and bottom.)* Then, have students find out when they were discovered and what properties are known about them. Have students create a presentation that explains the characteristics and discovery of several subatomic particles. *(Other subatomic particle types or categories include leptons, muons, tau particles, neutrinos, bosons, fermions, gluons, mesons, and baryons.)*

Particle Accelerators

In Rutherford's transmutation experiment, the radioactive element radium was used as a source of alpha particles. However, sometimes transmutations will not occur unless the bombarding particles are moving at extremely high speeds. In order to perform such transmutations, scientists use devices called particle accelerators. In a particle accelerator, charged particles can be accelerated to speeds very close to the speed of light. The fast-moving particles are guided toward a target, where they collide with atomic nuclei. With the help of particle accelerators, scientists have produced more than 3000 different isotopes.

Scientists also conduct collision experiments in order to study nuclear structure. Since the discoveries of the proton, neutron, and electron, more than 200 different subatomic particles have been detected. According to the current model of the atom, protons and neutrons are made up of even smaller particles called quarks. A **quark** is a subatomic particle theorized to be among the basic units of matter. Both protons and neutrons belong to a class of particles that are made up of three quarks. Six types of quarks are currently thought to exist. Two of these types were discovered at Fermi National Accelerator Laboratory, also known as Fermilab. Figure 14 shows one of the devices used at Fermilab to detect subatomic particles.

Figure 14 This particle detector records subatomic particles produced in the Tevatron, the most powerful particle accelerator in the world. The Tevatron is located at Fermilab in Batavia, Illinois.

Section 10.3 Assessment

Reviewing Concepts

1. How do scientists perform artificial transmutations?
2. How are transuranium elements produced?
3. How does artificial transmutation differ from nuclear decay?
4. Write the equation for the transmutation that occurs when an alpha particle combines with an oxygen-16 atom, emitting a proton.
5. Does fermium-257 undergo nuclear decay? Explain.

Critical Thinking

6. **Predicting** Bombarding a lithium-6 atom with a neutron produces helium-4 and another particle. What is that particle?
7. **Predicting** Curium was first synthesized by bombarding a target isotope with alpha particles, which produced curium-242 and a neutron. What was the target isotope? (*Hint:* Use the symbol $^{1}_{0}n$ to represent a neutron.)
8. **Inferring** Why can't the transuranium elements be made by exposing other elements to naturally occurring alpha radiation?

Writing in Science

Summary Write a brief summary of the first artificial transmutation, performed by Ernest Rutherford. (*Hint:* Your summary should describe an example of a nuclear reaction.)

Section 10.3 Assessment

1. By bombarding atomic nuclei with high-energy particles such as protons, neutrons, or alpha particles
2. By the artificial transmutation of lighter elements
3. Artificial transmutation is a nonnatural process in which a nucleus is bombarded with high-energy particles. Nuclear decay is a natural process in which an unstable nucleus emits charged particles and/or energy.
4. $^{16}_{8}O + ^{4}_{2}He \longrightarrow ^{19}_{9}F + ^{1}_{1}H$
5. Fermium-257, with an atomic number of 100, is a transuranium element and therefore undergoes nuclear decay.
6. Hydrogen-3
7. Plutonium-239
8. Because naturally occurring alpha particles do not have enough energy to be used in the synthesis of transuranium elements. The synthesis of transuranium elements requires high-energy particles.

Particle Accelerators

Build Science Skills **L2**

Inferring Ask students to read the first paragraph of Particle Accelerators. Ask, **What evidence supports the claim that most transuranium elements can exist only when atoms are bombarded with particles at very high speeds?** *(Transuranium elements generally do not occur in nature, so the conditions under which they are formed are not likely to be found in nature. Most transuranium elements have been produced only under conditions that can be achieved by using a particle accelerator.)*
Logical

3 ASSESS

Evaluate Understanding **L2**

Ask students to write three completed equations for transmutations. Have students take turns giving the reactants for the equation while another student determines the product with the correct number of protons and neutrons for each transmutation.

Reteach **L1**

Have students look at the transmutation equations in the section and ask them to explain how transmutation differs from nuclear decay.

Writing in Science

Rutherford performed the first artificial transmutation while studying the effects of nuclear radiation on gases. After he exposed nitrogen gas to alpha radiation, he observed that some of the alpha particles were temporarily absorbed by the nitrogen nuclei. Each newly formed nucleus then ejected a proton, leaving behind oxygen-17. In this transmutation, nitrogen-14 was converted into oxygen-17.

Interactive Textbook If your class subscribes to the Interactive Textbook, use it to review key concepts in Section 10.3.

Answer to . . .

Figure 13 *Uranium-234. The equation is:*

$^{238}_{94}Pu \longrightarrow ^{234}_{92}U + ^{4}_{2}He$

Reading Checkpoint *An element with an atomic number greater than 92*

CONCEPTS in Action

Nuclear Medicine L2

Background

PET (positron emission tomography) scanning can detect subtle changes in the body's metabolism and chemical reactions. The PET scanner detects radiation produced by a positron-emitting radioisotope injected into the body. Chemical compounds containing radioisotopes of carbon, nitrogen, or oxygen are commonly used as tracers.

Once the tracer enters the body, it travels through the bloodstream to the target organ. When the tracer reaches the target organ, the chemical that it is attached to begins taking part in the chemical reactions. Positrons, the antimatter equivalent of electrons, are released from the tracer and collide with electrons. Each collision annihilates a positron and an electron and releases two gamma rays. The PET scanner detects these gamma rays. The data is fed into a computer and a three-dimensional image is produced of the processes occurring in the target organ.

PET scans are used to evaluate a number of different medical conditions. They can be used to detect cancers, determine the extent to which cancer has spread, and determine the effectiveness of cancer treatment. PET scans can help diagnose brain conditions such as epilepsy and Alzheimer's disease. They can also evaluate cardiac conditions such as heart muscle function and coronary artery disease.

CONCEPTS in Action

Nuclear Medicine

Exposure to nuclear radiation is often harmful to the human body. However, scientists have also found nuclear radiation to be a powerful tool in the field of medicine.

Because radioisotopes are detectable by their radiation, they can be used as tracers that map out specific locations in the body. For example, the radioisotope iodine-131 is absorbed by the thyroid gland in the throat in the same way that iodine-127 is. If iodine-131 is injected into the body, the radiation it emits will show how well the thyroid gland is functioning.

Radioactive tracers can also be used to pinpoint the location of cancer cells. Cancer cells multiply rapidly and absorb glucose much faster than normal cells. If the glucose molecules are "tagged" with a radioactive tracer, such as flourine-18, the location of the cancer cells can be found by tracking areas of high glucose concentration.

Radioisotopes with short half-lives are chosen for medical uses. These isotopes decay so rapidly that after only a day or two, practically none of the isotope remains.

PET scanner
PET (positron emission tomography) scans use radioactive tracers to examine parts of the body, such as the brain. The patient receives an injection of radioactive tracer. The tracer produces gamma rays that are detected by the scanner.

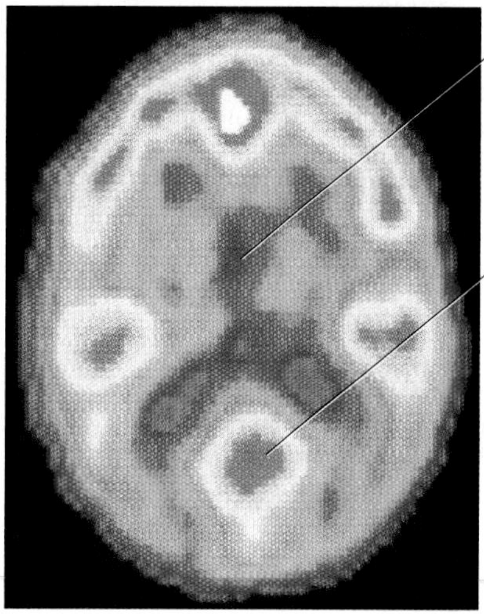

Tagged glucose is absorbed slowly in the blue areas, indicating normal tissue.

Red color shows greater glucose absorption in possibly cancerous areas.

PET scan of brain
This scan shows the level of activity in different areas of the brain. Glucose tagged with flourine-18 is absorbed more rapidly in areas of high brain activity and by cancer cells. Here, red shows the greatest activity and blue the least.

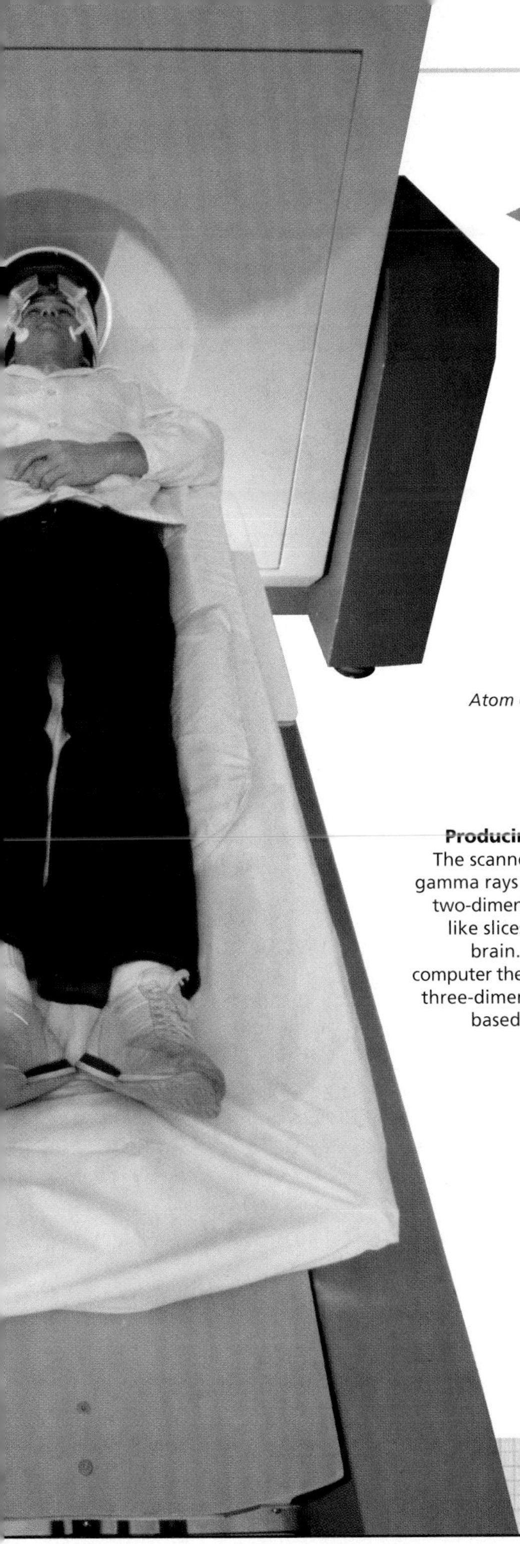

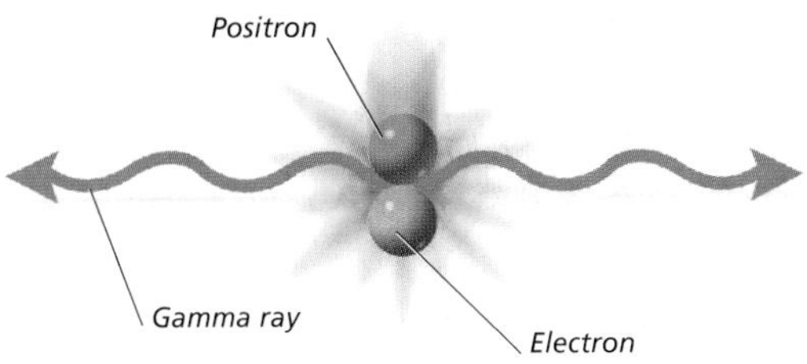
Positron
Gamma ray
Electron

Gamma rays
Gamma rays are produced when the tracer emits a positron. A positron is a particle with the mass of an electron but a charge of 1+. The positron is destroyed upon contact with an electron from a nearby atom in the body, and emits two gamma rays in opposite directions.

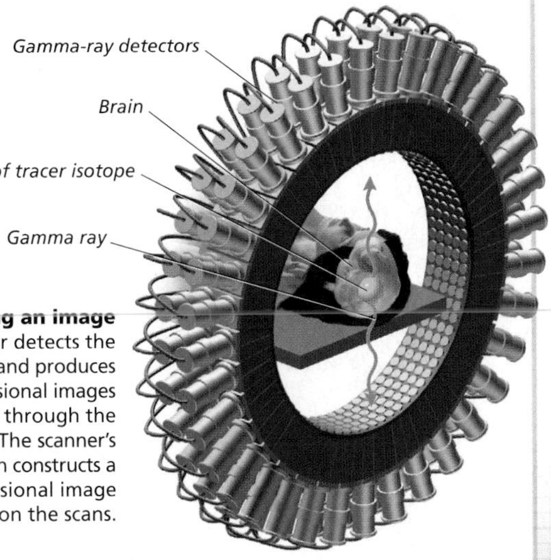
Gamma-ray detectors
Brain
Atom of tracer isotope
Gamma ray

Producing an image
The scanner detects the gamma rays and produces two-dimensional images like slices through the brain. The scanner's computer then constructs a three-dimensional image based on the scans.

Going Further

- Write a paragraph describing how radioactive tracers are used in medicine. Indicate what qualities make a particular radioisotope useful as a radioactive tracer in the human body.
- Take a Discovery Channel Video Field Trip by watching "Nuclear Medicine."

Discovery Channel School
Video Field Trip

Build Science Skills

L2

Using Models

ACTIVITY

Purpose Students model the radiation detected by a PET scanner.

Materials 500-mL beaker; sponges; shallow pans; food coloring; 1-cm strips of thin and thick cardboard, newspaper, and waxed paper; paper towels

Class Time 20 minutes

Advance Prep Fill the beaker with water and add several drops of food coloring. For each group, prepare a solution-soaked sponge placed flat in a pan.

Procedure Distribute several different strips to students and have them make a pattern on top of the sponge. Tell students to leave some areas of the sponge uncovered. Then, have students gently press the paper towel on top of the sponge for three seconds and remove it, placing the paper towel faceup next to the sponge. Ask, **How does the pattern on the paper towel compare to the pattern of squares on the sponge?** *(They are similar, but not identical. The waxed paper and heavy cardboard completely blocked the absorption of the solution. The newspaper did not block the absorption at all, and the light cardboard partially blocked the solution.)* **If the paper towel were a PET scan, which areas would show the most activity?** *(The areas that absorbed the most colored water.)* **Which areas would show the least?** *(The areas that absorbed the least.)*

Expected Outcome Students will gain a better understanding of how PET images are formed.
Logical, Kinesthetic

Going Further

Doctors can diagnose certain types of cancer by using radioactive tracers, or radioisotopes that are injected into a patient. The nuclear radiation emitted by the radioactive tracer is detected by imaging equipment such as a PET scanner. For a radioactive tracer to be practical, it must be readily absorbed by the organ(s) that doctors wish to study, and it must have a short half-life so as to minimize the patient's exposure to nuclear radiation.
Verbal, Portfolio

Discovery Channel School

Video Field Trip

Nuclear Medicine

After students have viewed the Video Field Trip, ask them the following questions: **What is nuclear medicine?** *(The use of small amounts of radioactive materials that enable a physician to look inside the body and to treat diseases such as some forms of cancer.)* **What did Marie and Pierre Curie discover?** *(Student answers may include: They discovered radium and polonium.)* **What did Irene Curie discover?** *(She discovered artificial radioactivity by determining that aluminum remained radioactive after being bombarded with radioactive particles.)* **If radioactive substances are used today to treat certain types of cancer, how was it possible for Marie Curie and Irene Curie to develop a form of cancer by working with radioactive substances?** *(When treating certain types of cancer, only small dosages of radioactivity are used. However, when Marie and Irene Curie did their research, they were in contact with large amounts of radioactive substances for prolonged periods of time.)*

1 FOCUS

Objectives

10.4.1 **Compare** and **contrast** nuclear forces.

10.4.2 **Describe** the process of nuclear fission.

10.4.3 **Explain** how nuclear reactors are used to produce energy.

10.4.4 **Describe** the process of nuclear fusion.

Reading Focus

Build Vocabulary L2

Word-Part Analysis Remind students that they can use what they know about word parts to figure out the meanings of words. Point out *fission* and *fusion.* Tell students that *-ion* means "the act of" or "the result of an act." Explain that *fiss-* comes from a Latin word meaning "split" and that *fus-* comes from another Latin word meaning "melted."

Reading Strategy L2

a. Is the splitting of a large nucleus into two smaller fragments **b.** Widely used as an energy source **c.** Is the fusing of two small nuclei into one larger nucleus **d.** Still being researched and developed as an alternate energy source

2 INSTRUCT

Nuclear Forces

Use Visuals L2

Figure 15 Have students carefully examine the illustration. Ask, **Why are there no electric forces between protons and neutrons?** *(Neutrons have no charge.)* **What force is able to overcome the electrostatic forces of repulsion that exist between protons in a nucleus?** *(The strong nuclear force)* **Visual, Logical**

10.4 Fission and Fusion

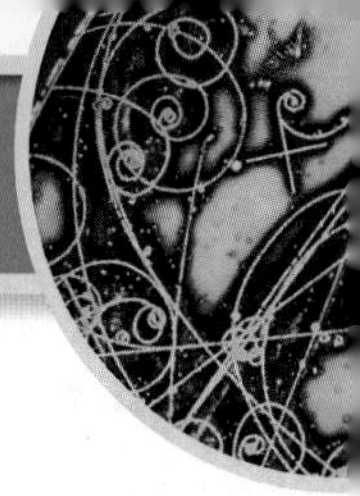

Reading Focus

Key Concepts

- Under what conditions does the strong nuclear force overcome electric forces in the nucleus?
- What property of fission makes it so useful?

Vocabulary

- strong nuclear force
- fission
- chain reaction
- critical mass
- fusion
- plasma

Reading Strategy

Comparing and Contrasting Copy the Venn diagram below. As you read, contrast fission and fusion by listing the ways they differ.

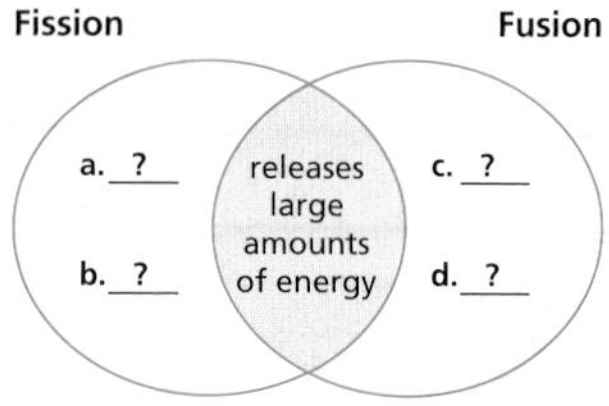
Fission
Fusion
a. ?
b. ?
releases large amounts of energy
c. ?
d. ?

Alternative energy sources may someday replace fossil fuels such as coal and oil. One alternative energy source that is widely used today is nuclear energy. Nuclear energy is the energy released by nuclear reactions.

Shortly after the discovery of radioactivity, scientists realized that atomic nuclei contained vast amounts of energy. By the late 1930s, scientists discovered that transmutations involved more than just the conversion of one element into another—they also involved the conversion of mass into energy.

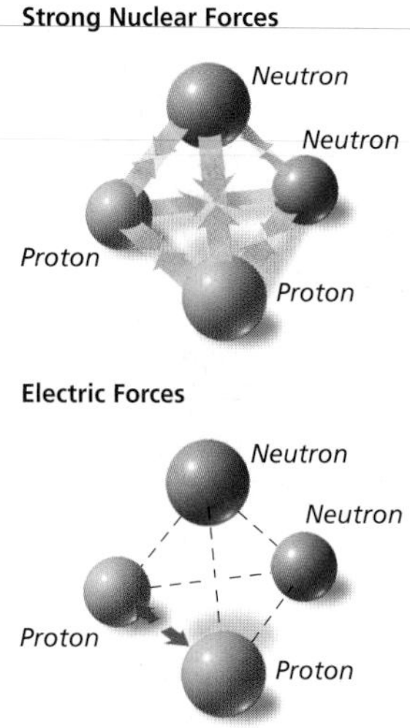
Strong Nuclear Forces
Neutron
Neutron
Proton
Proton
Electric Forces
Neutron
Neutron
Proton
Proton

Figure 15 Two kinds of forces act upon particles in the nucleus. Strong nuclear forces, which are attractive, act on protons and neutrons alike. Electric forces in the nucleus are repulsive, and act only among protons.
***Using Models** What atomic nucleus is represented above?*

Nuclear Forces

What holds the nucleus together? Remember that the protons in the nucleus are all positively charged, so they tend to repel one another. Clearly, there must be an attractive force that binds the particles of the nucleus. Otherwise, the protons would simply push one another away.

The **strong nuclear force** is the attractive force that binds protons and neutrons together in the nucleus. Because the strong nuclear force does not depend on charge, it acts among protons, among neutrons, and among protons and neutrons. **Over very short distances, the strong nuclear force is much greater than the electric forces among protons.** For example, at distances as short as the width of a proton, the strong nuclear force is more than 100 times greater than the electric force that repels protons. However, the strong nuclear force quickly weakens as protons and neutrons get farther apart. Figure 15 summarizes the forces acting on protons and neutrons in the nucleus.

Section Resources

Print
- ***Reading and Study Workbook With Math Support***, Section 10.4
- ***Transparencies***, Section 10.4

Technology
- ***Interactive Textbook***, Section 10.4
- ***Presentation Pro CD-ROM***, Section 10.4
- ***Go Online***, NSTA SciLinks, Fission

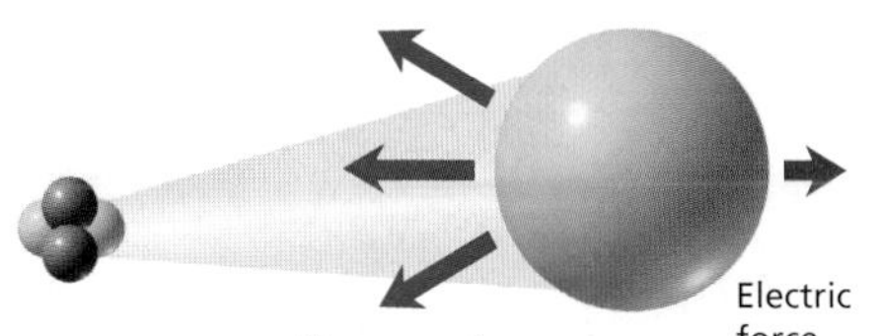
A Nuclear Forces Acting on a Proton of a Small Nucleus
Strong nuclear forces
Electric force

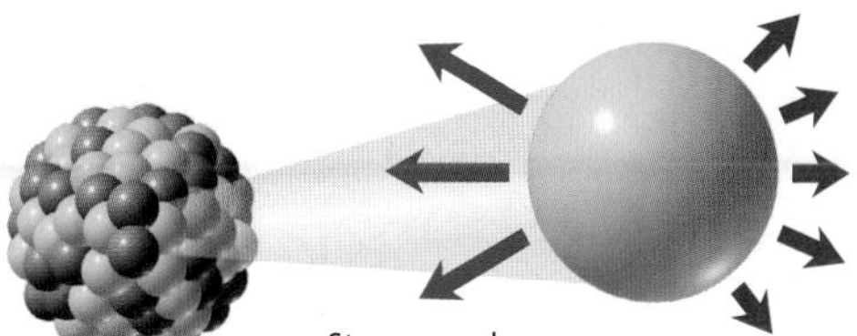
B Nuclear Forces Acting on a Proton of a Large Nucleus
Strong nuclear forces
Electric forces

Figure 16 The size of a nucleus affects how strongly it is bound together. **A** In a nucleus containing two protons and two neutrons, the strong nuclear forces easily overcome the electric force between the protons. **B** In a nucleus containing many protons and neutrons, the larger number of electric forces makes the nucleus less stable.

The Effect of Size on Nuclear Forces Electric forces in atomic nuclei depend on the number of protons. The greater the number of protons in a nucleus, the greater is the electric force that repels those protons. So in larger nuclei, the repulsive electric force is stronger than in smaller nuclei.

The effect of size on the strong nuclear force is more complicated. On one hand, the more protons and neutrons there are in a nucleus, the more possibilities there are for strong nuclear force attractions. However, as the size of the nucleus increases, the average distance between protons and neutrons increases. Because the strong nuclear force only acts over short ranges, the possibility of many attractions is never realized in a large nucleus. As a result, the strong nuclear force felt by one proton or neutron in a large nucleus is about the same as in a small nucleus, as shown in Figure 16.

Unstable Nuclei A nucleus becomes unstable, or radioactive, when the strong nuclear force can no longer overcome the repulsive electric forces among protons. While the strong nuclear force does not increase with the size of the nucleus, the electric forces do. There is, therefore, a point beyond which all elements are radioactive. All nuclei with 83 or more protons are radioactive.

Fission

In 1938, two German chemists, Otto Hahn and Fritz Strassman, performed a series of important transmutation experiments. By bombarding uranium-235 with high-energy neutrons, Hahn and Strassman hoped to produce more massive elements. Instead, their experiments produced isotopes of a smaller element, barium. Unable to explain their data, Hahn and Strassman turned to a colleague for help. In 1939, Lise Meitner, shown in Figure 17, and Otto Frisch, another physicist, offered a groundbreaking explanation for the experiments. The uranium-235 nuclei had been broken into smaller fragments. Hahn and Strassman had demonstrated nuclear fission. **Fission** is the splitting of an atomic nucleus into two smaller parts.

Figure 17 Austrian physicist Lise Meitner (1878–1968), shown here, and Otto Frisch were the first scientists to describe nuclear fission. Meitner correctly predicted that fission releases large amounts of energy.

Fission

Build Reading Literacy L1

Sequence Refer to page **290D** in this chapter, which provides guidelines for using a sequence.

Have students read the text on nuclear fission on pp. 309 and 310. Then, have students do the following:

1. Ask students to make a sketch similar to Figure 18. Tell students that they can use circles to represent the nuclei. Students should use larger circles to represent the uranium nuclei.
2. Have students label and describe what happens as a neutron strikes the uranium-235 nucleus and the steps that follow. Start with the neutron as Step 1. Each following step should be numbered in sequence.
3. Students' sketches should include as much detail as they find from the text, Figure 18, and the caption.

Visual, Portfolio

Integrate Language Arts L2

Tell students that scientists in several countries were instrumental to the understanding of nuclear fission. The English scientist James Chadwick discovered the neutron in 1932. In 1934, Italian scientists led by Enrico Fermi conducted experiments involving the slow-neutron bombardment of uranium. Fermi's results prompted German chemists Otto Hahn and Fritz Strassman, and Austrian physicist Lise Meitner, to further investigate the products formed when uranium is bombarded with neutrons. Meitner and Otto Frisch built on the results of this research and in 1939 described the fission process. Have students write a brief biography of one of the scientists who contributed to the understanding of nuclear fission.
Verbal

Customize for English Language Learners

Cloze Reading
Select and copy an appropriate paragraph from one of the sections, such as the second paragraph on p. 309. Leave the first and last sentences intact, since they are usually the introductory and concluding sentences. For the sentences in the middle, remove key vocabulary words and replace them with a blank. For example, leave blanks for *protons* and *neutrons* in the second sentence of this paragraph, for *proton* in the third sentence, and for *short* in the fourth sentence. Have students read the paragraph and fill in the blanks with the appropriate words. You may create a word bank for students to use when filling in the blanks.

Answer to . . .

Figure 15 *A helium nucleus*

Use Visuals
L1

Figures 18 and 19 Ask students to look at both figures. Ask, **Why do you think the uranium-236 atom is missing in Figure 19?** *(Uranium-236 is very unstable and does not last long before it splits into two smaller nuclei.)* **What happens to the amount of energy released during a chain reaction?** *(The amount of energy released increases as the chain reaction proceeds.)* **Visual**

Build Math Skills
L1

Formulas and Equations Ask students to examine the mass-energy equation and determine the units of measurement that *E* is equivalent to. Remind them that the SI units for mass and speed are, respectively, kg and m/s. (Units of *E* are equivalent to kg × (m/s)^2.) Also ask students to determine what the formula would be for calculating c. *($c = \sqrt{E/m}$)* **Logical**

Direct students to the **Math Skills** in the **Skills and Reference Handbook** at the end of the student text for additional help.

Go Online NSTA SCILINKS

Download a worksheet on fission for students to complete, and find additional teacher support from NSTA SciLinks.

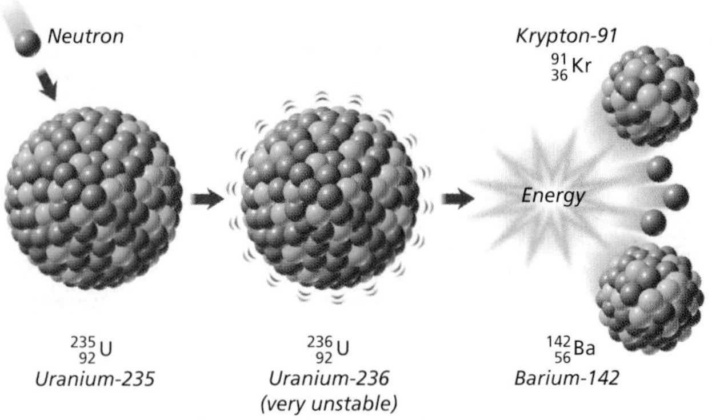

Neutron
Krypton-91
$^{91}_{36}Kr$
Energy
$^{235}_{92}U$
Uranium-235
$^{236}_{92}U$
Uranium-236
(very unstable)
$^{142}_{56}Ba$
Barium-142

Figure 18 The fission of uranium-235 yields smaller nuclei, neutrons, and energy. The nuclear equation for this reaction can be written as follows.

$$^{235}_{92}U + ^{1}_{0}n \rightarrow ^{91}_{36}Kr + ^{142}_{56}Ba + 3^{1}_{0}n + \text{energy}$$

Comparing and Contrasting ***How does fission differ from nuclear decay?***

Figure 18 illustrates the fission of a uranium-235 nucleus. Notice that one of the products of the reaction is energy. **In nuclear fission, tremendous amounts of energy can be produced from very small amounts of mass.** For example, the nuclear energy released by the fission of 1 kilogram of uranium-235 is equivalent to the chemical energy produced by burning more than 17,000 kilograms of coal.

Converting Mass Into Energy In the nuclear equation shown in Figure 18, the mass numbers on the left equal the mass numbers on the right. Yet when the fission of uranium-235 is carried out, about 0.1 percent of the mass of the reactants is lost during the reaction. This "lost" mass is converted into energy.

In 1905, more than 30 years before the discovery of fission, physicist Albert Einstein had introduced the mass-energy equation. It describes how mass and energy are related.

Mass–Energy Equation

$$E = mc^2$$

In the mass-energy equation, *E* represents energy, *m* represents mass, and *c* represents the speed of light (3.0×10^8 m/s). The conversion of a small amount of mass releases an enormous amount of energy. Likewise, a large amount of energy can be converted into a small amount of mass. The explosion of the first atomic bomb in 1945 offered a powerful demonstration of the mass-energy equation. The bomb contained 5 kilograms of plutonium-239. Fission of the plutonium produced an explosion that was equivalent to 18,600 tons of TNT.

Recall how the law of conservation of mass applied to chemical reactions. In nuclear reactions, however, the energies involved are much larger. To account for the conversion of mass into energy, a modified conservation law is used. According to the law of conservation of mass and energy, the total amount of mass and energy remains constant.

Go Online NSTA SCILINKS

For: Links on fission
Visit: www.SciLinks.org
Web Code: ccn-1104

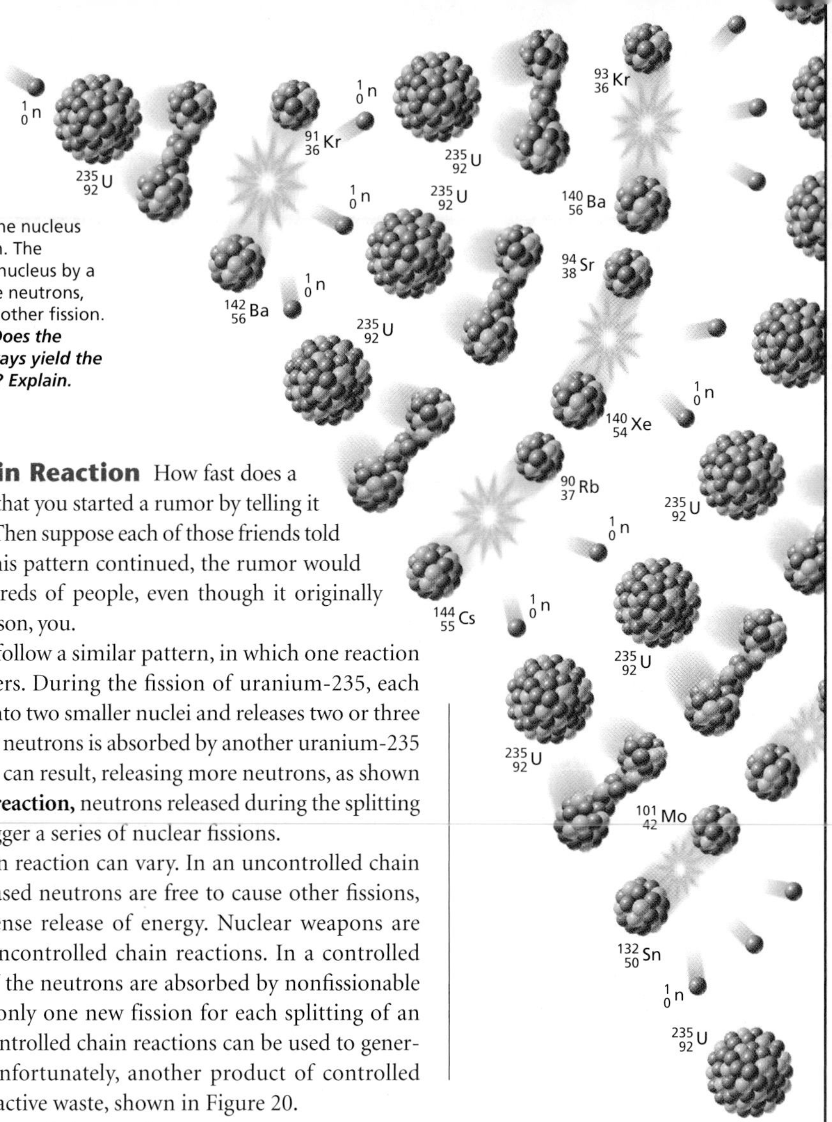
$^{1}_{0}n$
$^{235}_{92}U$
$^{91}_{36}Kr$
$^{142}_{56}Ba$
$^{93}_{36}Kr$
$^{140}_{56}Ba$
$^{94}_{38}Sr$
$^{140}_{54}Xe$
$^{90}_{37}Rb$
$^{144}_{55}Cs$
$^{101}_{42}Mo$
$^{132}_{50}Sn$

Figure 19 The fission of one nucleus can trigger a chain reaction. The splitting of a uranium-235 nucleus by a neutron yields two or three neutrons, each of which can cause another fission. **Interpreting Diagrams** ***Does the fission of uranium-235 always yield the same isotopes as products? Explain.***

Triggering a Chain Reaction How fast does a rumor spread? Imagine that you started a rumor by telling it to three of your friends. Then suppose each of those friends told three more friends. If this pattern continued, the rumor would quickly spread to hundreds of people, even though it originally started with just one person, you.

Nuclear fission can follow a similar pattern, in which one reaction leads to a series of others. During the fission of uranium-235, each reactant nucleus splits into two smaller nuclei and releases two or three neutrons. If one of these neutrons is absorbed by another uranium-235 nucleus, another fission can result, releasing more neutrons, as shown in Figure 19. In a **chain reaction,** neutrons released during the splitting of an initial nucleus trigger a series of nuclear fissions.

The speed of a chain reaction can vary. In an uncontrolled chain reaction, all of the released neutrons are free to cause other fissions, resulting in a fast, intense release of energy. Nuclear weapons are designed to produce uncontrolled chain reactions. In a controlled chain reaction, some of the neutrons are absorbed by nonfissionable materials, resulting in only one new fission for each splitting of an atom. The heat from controlled chain reactions can be used to generate electrical energy. Unfortunately, another product of controlled chain reactions is radioactive waste, shown in Figure 20.

In order to sustain a chain reaction, each nucleus that is split must produce, on average, one neutron that causes the fission of another nucleus. This condition corresponds to a specific mass of fissionable material, known as a critical mass. A **critical mass** is the smallest possible mass of a fissionable material that can sustain a chain reaction.

Reading Checkpoint *What is a chain reaction?*

Figure 20 A crane lowers drums of radioactive waste into a landfill in Hanford, Washington.

Teacher Demo

Nuclear Processes **L2**

Purpose Students observe a model of nuclear fission and fusion.

Materials bubble solution, 2 bubble wands

Procedure Dip the end of each wand into the solution and remove. Gently blow into the ring of each wand to make a bubble with a diameter a little larger than the ring, and catch the bubble on the wand. Bring the wands and the bubbles together. Press the bubbles together to form one large bubble, illustrating fusion. Pull the two frames farther apart to separate the bubble into two bubbles, one in each frame, simulating fission. When this is done a little faster small bubbles may be released, representing the released neutron. Discuss with students the strengths and weaknesses of this model.

Expected Outcome Students observe how to use bubbles to model nuclear fusion and nuclear fission. Students may point out that this demonstration does not model the neutron required to initiate fission.

Visual, Group

Facts and Figures

Natural Nuclear Reactor In 1972 when Francis Perrin uncovered evidence of a "natural nuclear reactor" in mines in Gabon, Africa, other scientists questioned his findings. They wanted to know how a natural nuclear reactor could exist when it required precise engineering work to construct one.

Further study showed that the expected proportions of uranium-238 (99.3%) and uranium-235 (0.7%), were not present in the Gabon mines. There was much less uranium-235. Scientists used this data and calculated that 1.7 billion years ago, the proportion of uranium-235 was 3%, enough for nuclear fission. Underground water helped create the right conditions for a chain reaction. Scientists think the natural nuclear reaction continued intermittently for at least a million years until the uranium-235 was mostly used up.

Answer to . . .

Figure 18 *Unlike nuclear decay, fission is generally not spontaneous. A neutron must be introduced in order for the fission of uranium-235 to occur. During the nuclear decay of uranium-235, however, no other reactants are necessary in order for the radioisotope to decay into thorium-231 and emit alpha radiation.*

Figure 19 *No. Fission of uranium-235 can produce a number of different combinations of product isotopes. Although fission results in the fragmentation of the nucleus into two parts, the composition of those two parts (and hence the number of neutrons released) can vary widely.*

Reading Checkpoint *A chain reaction is a nuclear reaction sequence in which neutrons released during the splitting of an initial nucleus trigger a series of nuclear fissions.*

SCIENCE and History

Nuclear Chemistry L2

Enrico Fermi and his research group achieved the first controlled nuclear chain reaction while the United States was fighting World War II. This was the first nuclear reactor. While this reactor was used for research, the main purpose of the reactor was to make plutonium for the atom bomb. After World War II, the U.S. population rose, and the growing population increased the demand for electricity. Scientists saw the potential of nuclear energy to help meet this demand. In 1951, electricity was produced using atomic power for the first time at a reactor in Idaho. The reactor produced enough electricity to light four light bulbs. Today, more than 400 nuclear power plants operate worldwide, with over 100 operating in the United States.

Have students research nuclear power plant safety and write a one-paragraph opinion about whether the benefits of nuclear power generation are worth the risks.
Verbal, Portfolio

Writing in Science

Possible answer: A number of groundbreaking scientific discoveries within the last 100 years have set the stage for nuclear energy. In 1905 (less than ten years after the discovery of radioactivity), Albert Einstein introduced his mass-energy equation, which described how very small amounts of mass could be converted into enormous amounts of energy. In 1938, Otto Hahn and Fritz Strassman performed the first nuclear fission (of uranium). A self-sustaining nuclear chain reaction was achieved just four years later. By 1951, scientists had developed nuclear fission into a promising source of electrical energy.
Verbal

Nuclear Energy from Fission Today, nuclear power plants generate about 20 percent of the electricity in the United States. In a nuclear power plant, controlled fission of uranium-235 occurs in a vessel called a fission reactor.

Unlike power plants that burn fossil fuels, nuclear power plants do not emit air pollutants such as oxides of sulfur and nitrogen. However, nuclear power plants have their own safety and environmental issues. For example, workers in nuclear power plants need to wear protective clothing to reduce their exposure to nuclear radiation. In addition, the fission of uranium-235 produces many radioactive isotopes with half-lives of hundreds or thousands of years. This radioactive waste must be

SCIENCE and History

Nuclear Chemistry

Over the last 100 years scientists have uncovered many secrets about the atomic nucleus. Developments have ranged from the synthesis of new elements to the harnessing of nuclear power as a viable energy source.

HENRI BECQUEREL

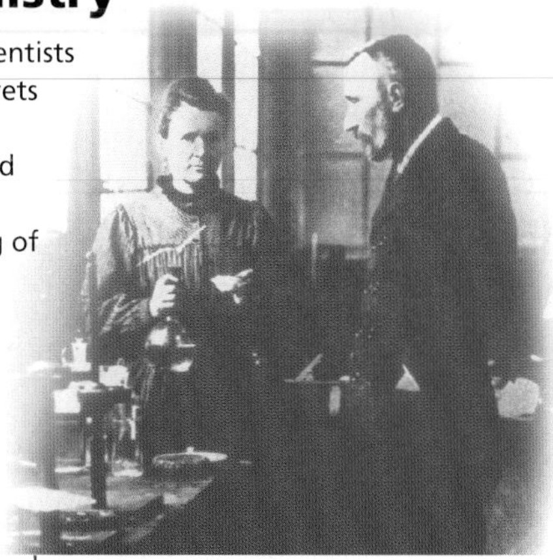

MARIE AND PIERRE CURIE AT WORK IN THEIR LABORATORY

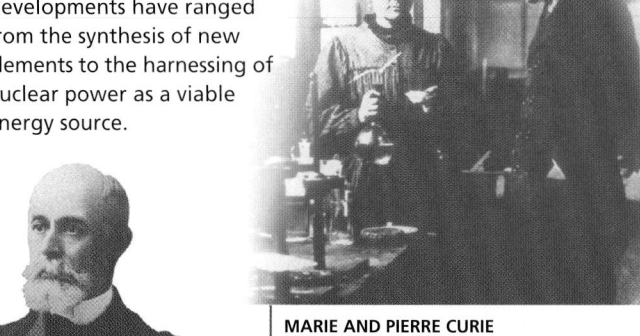

EQUIPMENT USED BY HAHN AND STRASSMANN

1896 French scientist Antoine Henri Becquerel discovers radioactivity in uranium.

1898 Marie and Pierre Curie discover the radioactive elements radium and polonium. By making radium available to other scientists, the Curies helped advance the study of radioactivity.

1905 Albert Einstein's mass-energy equation, $E = mc^2$, provides the basis for nuclear power.

1932 First atom smasher (subatomic particle accelerator) is used by John Cockcroft and Ernest Walton.

1938 Germans Otto Hahn and Fritz Strassmann produce nuclear fission by bombarding uranium-235 atoms with neutrons.

1890 | 1910 | 1930

isolated and stored so that it cannot harm people or contaminate the environment while it decays.

Another concern about nuclear power is that the operators of the plant could lose control of the reactor. For instance, if the reactor's cooling system failed, then a meltdown might occur. During a meltdown, the core of the reactor melts and radioactive material may be released. If the structure that houses the reactor is not secure, then the environment can become contaminated. In 1986, one of the reactors at the nuclear power station in Chernobyl, Ukraine, overheated during an experiment. A partial meltdown resulted, and large amounts of radioactive material were released into the atmosphere.

Writing in Science

Summary Write a paragraph about the history of nuclear energy based on some of the events in the time line below. (*Hint:* Before you write, use a flowchart to organize the events you wish to include.)

$\alpha = \frac{\hbar^2}{ec}$

ENRICO FERMI

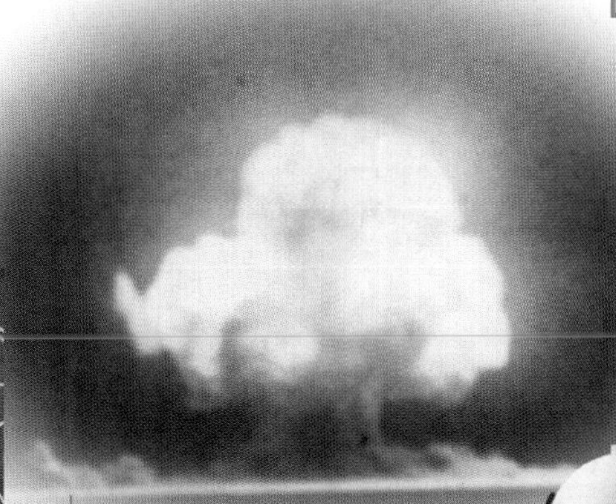

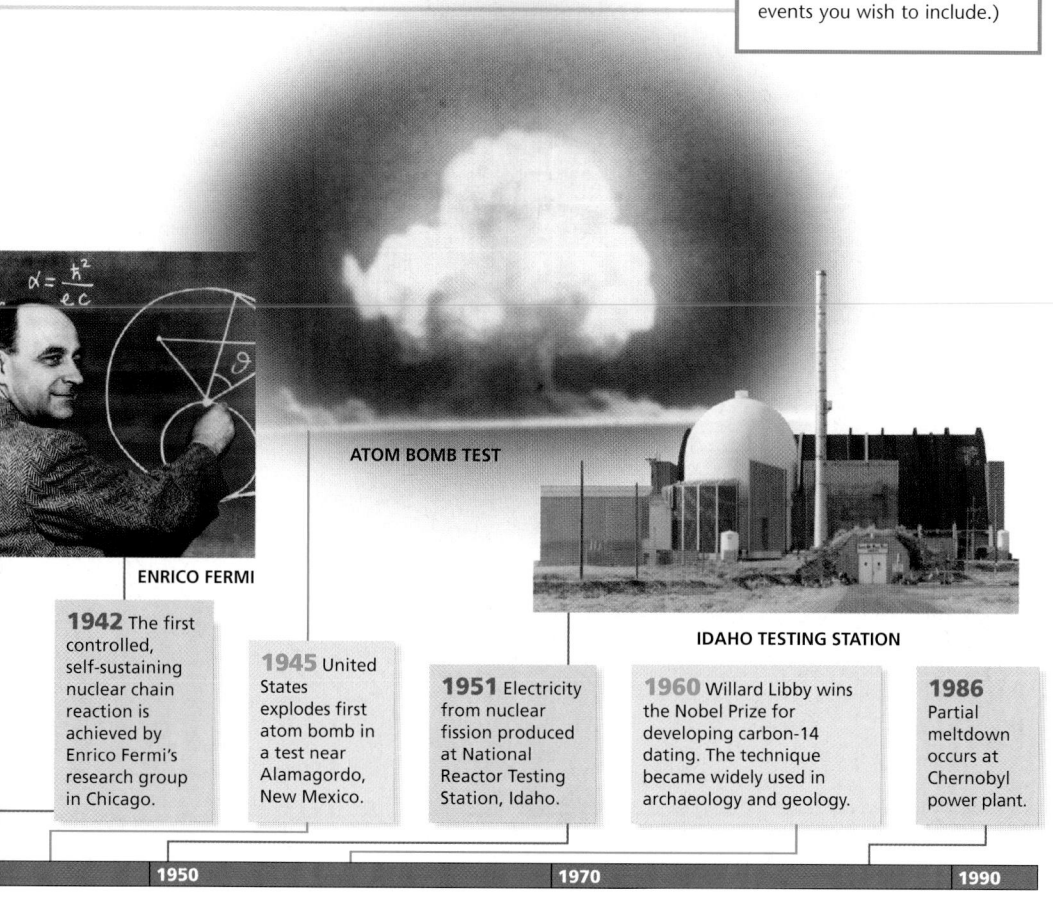

ATOM BOMB TEST

IDAHO TESTING STATION

1942 The first controlled, self-sustaining nuclear chain reaction is achieved by Enrico Fermi's research group in Chicago.

1945 United States explodes first atom bomb in a test near Alamagordo, New Mexico.

1951 Electricity from nuclear fission produced at National Reactor Testing Station, Idaho.

1960 Willard Libby wins the Nobel Prize for developing carbon-14 dating. The technique became widely used in archaeology and geology.

1986 Partial meltdown occurs at Chernobyl power plant.

1950 1970 1990

Use Community Resources

L2

Ask students to find out what percentage of the power in their state comes from nuclear power plants. Encourage them to use library resources, such as the Internet, to find statistics. If your state does not receive power from nuclear power plants, instruct students to find that information for another state. Ask students to make a diagram and write a brief summary of their findings.

Interpersonal, Portfolio

Nuclear Chemistry 313

DK HOW It Works

Nuclear Power Station L2

Background

Uranium-235, the fissionable material used in nuclear power plants, makes up only about 0.7% of all uranium found in nature. In order for a nuclear reactor to operate, about 3% of the uranium in the fuel rods must be uranium-235. Samples of uranium must be enriched so that they contain this higher percentage of uranium-235.

A bundle of fuel rods contains slightly more than the critical mass of uranium-235. Control rods are placed in the bundle in order to control when and how quickly the process of fission occurs.

Interpreting Diagrams In a nuclear power station, water is used to transfer the energy generated in the reactor core. Heat released in the core is absorbed by water in the steam generator. The steam produced is used to drive a turbine; the kinetic energy of the turbine is then converted into electrical energy. Water is also used as a coolant to condense the steam exiting the turbine. The steam condenses into liquid water and is piped back to the steam generator.
Visual

For Enrichment L3

The U.S. Navy uses nuclear reactors to power many different types of ships, ranging from submarines to aircraft carriers. Nuclear power is useful on ships that are at sea for long periods of time because the ships do not have to carry large quantities of fuel or refuel while they are on a mission. Ask students to research how nuclear reactors in ships differ from those in nuclear power stations.
Verbal

DK HOW It Works

Nuclear Power Station

Since the first nuclear bomb was exploded in 1945, scientists have found ways of utilizing the enormous power of nuclear fission for peaceful purposes. Nuclear power is now a major means of producing electricity. About 20 percent of electricity in the United States is generated this way. **Interpreting Diagrams** ***How is water used in a nuclear power station?***

Fission control
The fission reaction within the reactor core is controlled by neutron-absorbing control rods. Because they are still radioactive, the used rods are removed from the reactor core and stored in a pool, as shown above.

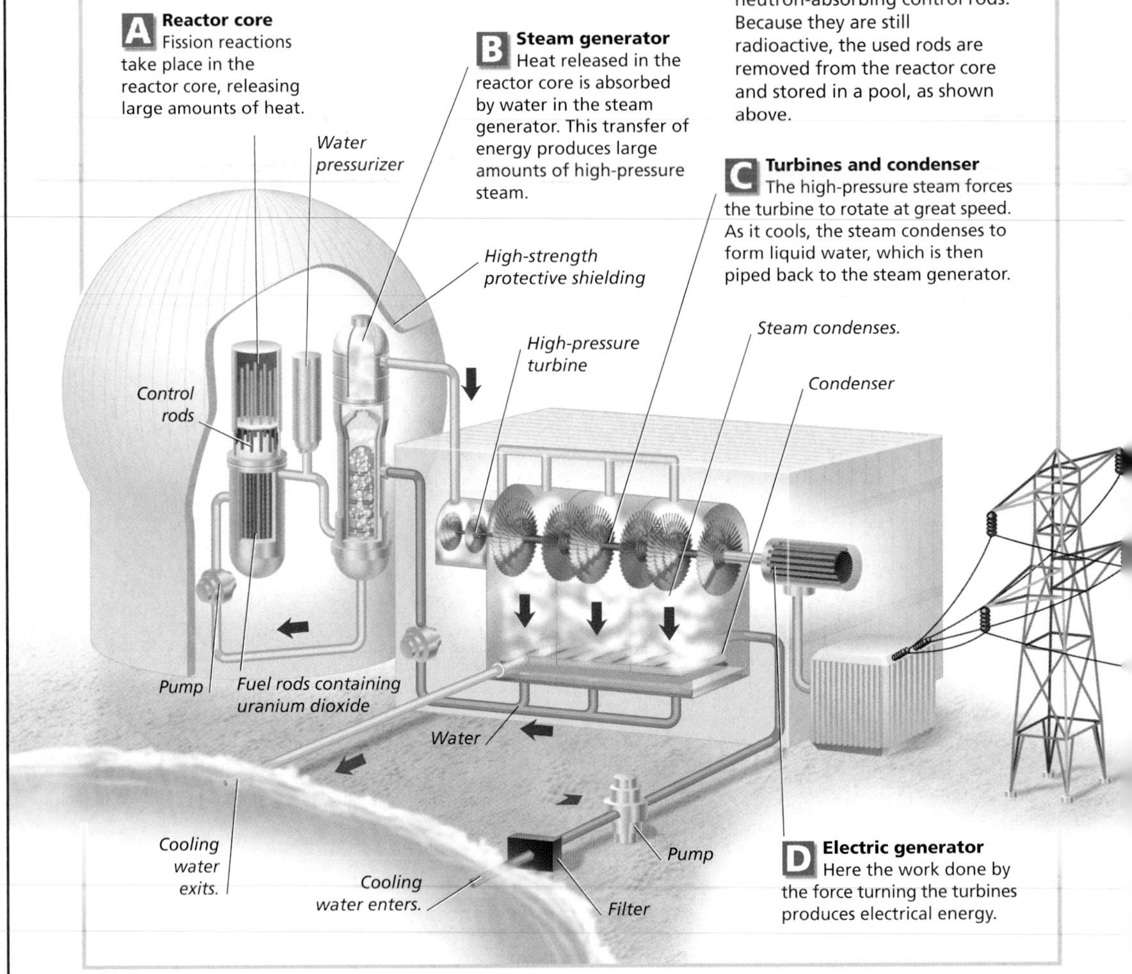
A Reactor core Fission reactions take place in the reactor core, releasing large amounts of heat.
B Steam generator Heat released in the reactor core is absorbed by water in the steam generator. This transfer of energy produces large amounts of high-pressure steam.
C Turbines and condenser The high-pressure steam forces the turbine to rotate at great speed. As it cools, the steam condenses to form liquid water, which is then piped back to the steam generator.
Water pressurizer
High-strength protective shielding
High-pressure turbine
Steam condenses.
Condenser
Control rods
Pump
Fuel rods containing uranium dioxide
Water
Cooling water exits.
Cooling water enters.
Pump
Filter
D Electric generator Here the work done by the force turning the turbines produces electrical energy.

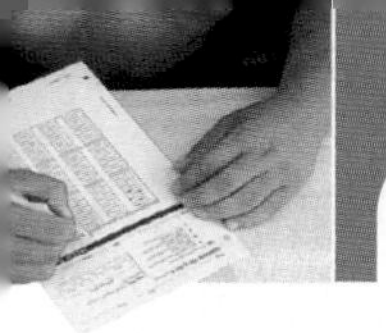

Standardized Test Prep

Test-Taking Tip

Evaluating and Revising
Frequently, a scientifically accurate answer choice may not answer the question that is being asked. Keep these tips in mind:

- Verify what the question is asking.
- Determine if an answer choice is a true statement or not.
- Determine if a true answer choice actually answers the question.
- Be cautious with inserted or deleted words that make a false statement seem accurate.

Practice using these tips in Question 5.

Choose the letter that best answers the question or completes the statement.

1. Which equation correctly shows beta decay?
   (A) $^{210}_{82}Pb \rightarrow ^{209}_{81}Tl + ^{0}_{-1}e + \gamma$
   (B) $^{210}_{82}Pb \rightarrow ^{209}_{83}Bi + ^{0}_{-1}e + \gamma$
   (C) $^{210}_{82}Pb \rightarrow ^{210}_{83}Tl + ^{0}_{-1}e + \gamma$
   (D) $^{210}_{82}Pb \rightarrow ^{210}_{83}Bi + \gamma$
   (E) $^{210}_{82}Pb \rightarrow ^{210}_{83}Bi + ^{0}_{-1}e + \gamma$

2. The half-life of radon-222 is 3.8 days. If a sample currently has 3.1 grams of radon-222, how much radon-222 did this sample have 15.2 days ago?
   (A) 12.4 grams (B) 47.1 grams
   (C) 49.6 grams (D) 57.8 grams
   (E) 92.7 grams

3. Radioactive decay of nuclei often involves several decays before a stable nucleus is formed. This is called a decay chain. What stable isotope is formed when radon-222 undergoes a decay chain of four alpha decays followed by four beta decays?
   (A) tungsten-206 (B) platinum-206
   (C) lead-206 (D) tungsten-214
   (E) lead-214

4. Which nucleus balances the following nuclear equation for the fission of uranium-235?
   $^{235}_{92}U + ^{1}_{0}n \rightarrow ^{90}_{38}Sr + ^{A}_{Z}X + 2\,^{1}_{0}n + \gamma$
   (A) $^{146}_{54}Xe$ (B) $^{146}_{52}Te$
   (C) $^{144}_{52}Te$ (D) $^{144}_{54}Xe$
   (E) $^{142}_{50}Sn$

5. Uranium-238 is less stable than oxygen-16. What accounts for this difference?
   (A) Uranium is a solid, while oxygen is a gas.
   (B) Unlike oxygen-16, uranium-238 has a nucleus in which repulsive electric forces surpass the strong nuclear forces.
   (C) Oxygen-16 has fewer electrons than uranium-238.
   (D) Uranium-238 has fewer neutrons than oxygen-16.
   (E) Unlike uranium-238, oxygen-16 has a nucleus in which the strong nuclear forces are overcome by repulsive electric forces.

6. The primary source of energy in stars is the fusion of hydrogen into helium. However, another reaction is believed to occur simultaneously. It is called the carbon-nitrogen-oxygen (CNO) cycle. In the diagram below, the symbol $^{0}_{+1}e$ represents a positron. A positron is a particle that has the same mass as an electron but a charge of 1+.

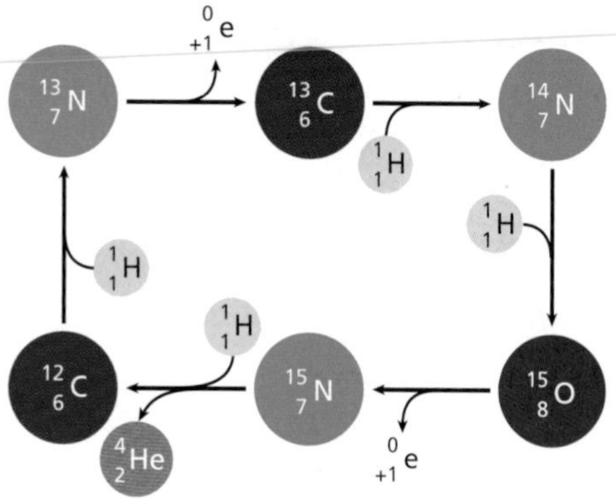

$^{13}_{7}N$
$^{0}_{+1}e$
$^{13}_{6}C$
$^{1}_{1}H$
$^{14}_{7}N$
$^{1}_{1}H$
$^{15}_{8}O$
$^{0}_{+1}e$
$^{15}_{7}N$
$^{1}_{1}H$
$^{12}_{6}C$
$^{4}_{2}He$
$^{1}_{1}H$

Which equation describes the CNO cycle?
   (A) $^{1}_{1}H \rightarrow ^{4}_{2}He + ^{0}_{+1}e$
   (B) $4\,^{1}_{1}H \rightarrow ^{4}_{2}He + 2\,^{0}_{+1}e$
   (C) $^{2}_{1}H + ^{3}_{1}H \rightarrow ^{4}_{2}He + ^{1}_{0}n$
   (D) $^{12}_{6}C \rightarrow ^{12}_{6}C + ^{4}_{2}He$
   (E) $^{12}_{6}C + ^{1}_{1}H \rightarrow ^{12}_{6}C + ^{4}_{2}He$

Standardized Test Prep

1. E **2.** C **3.** C
4. D **5.** B **6.** B

PHYSICS

The Interactive Textbook, found both online and on CD-ROM, includes the following materials.

Activities and Labs

Worksheets for each activity and lab are available as PDF files with clickable safety symbols.

Colorful Visuals

All art and relevant photographs from the Student Edition can be accessed in the Interactive Textbook.

Self Assessment

Provides additional assessment opportunities and questions:

- Interactive Reading Checkpoint questions
- Interactive Figure caption questions
- Chapter Pretests with hints
- Printable Chapter Assessments
- Standardized Test Prep

My Notes

Students can enter answers for questions or make notes about what they are learning.

References

Provides a drop-down menu of resources:

- Skills and Reference Handbook
- Glossary

Careers

Information on science careers is available through the Career page on www.PHSchool.com.

PHYSICS UNIT PREVIEW

Physics

Believe it or not, what physicists do every day is just an extension of what everyone does and experiences. From your first breath, you have been experimenting and interacting with the world around you.

Physics helps us understand so many phenomena. Learning physics lets us visit the outer edge of the universe as well as its tiniest corners and everything in between. Through many experiments, physicists have not only stretched our comprehension of the world, but have also helped us to understand what we can and can't do.

Welcome to this continuing adventure in physics. Part of any good adventure is not knowing exactly what will happen. I hope that at least some of what you learn will surprise you and make you think. Now that it is your turn to study physics, who knows what you might contribute!

Vasco da Gama Bridge ▶ The Vasco da Gama Bridge spans the water at Lisbon, Portugal. Large ships can pass under the bridge to reach the port.

322

Go Online PHSchool.com

For students, the PHSchool.com Web site contains interactive data-sharing labs, interactive self-assessments, and science-related links. The PHSchool.com Web site also provides teachers with curriculum support, reference links, a way to create state-specific lesson plans, and instructions on how to create a Web page.

Go Online NSTA SciLinks

NSTA SciLinks provides student worksheets for specific topics with additional teacher support.

Physics 323

Go Online

SCIENCE NEWS®

Students can find current information about specific discoveries in science from *Science News.*

Discovery Channel School

Video Field Trip

Use the following videos to help students understand the concepts in each chapter.

Chapter 11 Motion
Charting New Ground
Describes navigation without the benefit of maps and modern technology.

Chapter 12 Forces and Motion
Air Forces
Analyzes the motion of a parachutist.

Chapter 13 Forces in Fluids
Uplifting Experience
Features the forces and machine designs that make flight possible.

Chapter 14 Work, Power, and Machines
Pedal Power
Focuses on how cyclists get the most out of a compound machine.

Chapter 15 Energy
Physics of Fun
Uses the roller coaster to illustrate physics concepts.

Chapter 16 Thermal Energy and Heat
Powered by the Sun
Explores the use of solar energy.

Chapter 17 Mechanical Waves and Sound
Noise!
Focuses on noise pollution reduction.

Chapter 18 The Electromagnetic Spectrum and Light
Finding the Fakes
Shows forensic techniques being used to authenticate paintings.

Chapter 19 Optics
Traveling Light
Describes how fiber optics are used.

Chapter 20 Electricity
Current Computers
Examines how a computer stores, manipulates, and transfers information using miniature circuits.

Chapter 21 Magnetism
Magnetic Viewpoints
Explores the use of magnetic resonance imaging to make detailed images of the body.

Careers in Physics

Physics-related careers require a variety of skills and educational backgrounds. Here are just a few.

Computer Repair Technician

Connection to Chapter 20
Characteristics Independent worker, problem solver
Preparation Courses in electronics, basic understanding of mechanical equipment
Employers Professional and commercial equipment companies, computer and data processing services, computer stores

Aerospace Engineer

Connection to Chapter 13
Characteristics Creative, innovative, problem solver
Preparation Courses in mathematics, science, engineering
Employers Research and testing services, federal government, search and navigation equipment companies, aerospace companies

Camera Operator

Connection to Chapter 19
Characteristics Computer literate, artistic, patient, accurate, detail-oriented, good oral communicator, have good eyesight and hand-eye coordination
Preparation Courses in mathematics, training at a vocational institute, college, or university
Employers Motion picture companies, television stations, production companies

Careers in Physics

Many exciting career opportunities involve physics. Whether you want to become an electrician or an architect, you can put the ideas you read about in this unit to work toward a great career.

Computer Repair Technician
Computer repair technicians repair, maintain, and install mainframes, network servers, and personal computers. They also must be familiar with electronics, the technology that includes components such as electron tubes and photoelectric cells.
Educational requirements
Two-year community or junior college program in computer repair technology

Aerospace Engineer
If you have ever flown in an airplane, you have first-hand experience of the work of aerospace engineers. These professionals understand the principles of flight and are able to design, analyze, model, simulate, and test aircraft, spacecraft, missiles, and rockets. Aerospace engineers often specialize in areas such as propulsion, guidance, or navigation and control.
Educational requirements
Master's degree in physics, aerodynamics, or astronautics

Panasonic

Camera Operator
Lights—Camera—Action—Many motion picture camera operators hear this almost every day. Camera operators use lenses in their cameras and set up lights to photograph scenes. They also adjust the controls on the camera to produce high quality footage.
Educational requirements
High-school diploma

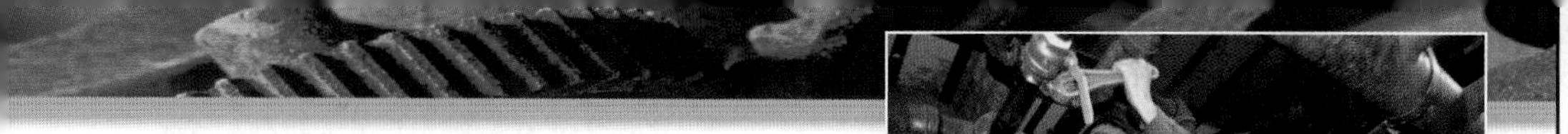

Architect
To find out what an architect does, all you have to do is look around you. Architects design all types of buildings, from houses to airport terminals to entire developments. Architects have to be able to predict how a building and its materials will hold up to a variety of forces.
Educational requirements Five-year bachelor of architecture program, three- to four-year master of architecture program for those with a degree in another discipline, internship, and passage of Architect Registration Examination

HVAC Technician
HVAC (heating, ventilation, and air conditioning) technicians install, maintain, and repair heating and cooling systems in homes and commercial buildings. HVAC technicians also make sure that ozone-depleting chemicals are not released into the environment.
Educational requirements Two-year community or junior college degree, with courses in mathematics, physics, chemistry, and mechanical drawing; refrigeration handler's license

Electrician
Electricians are responsible for installing, testing, and maintaining electrical systems. They also must adhere to the National Electrical Code and obey state and local building codes to safely install electrical systems.
Educational requirements Four- or five-year apprenticeship program and state license

Go Online
PHSchool.com
For: Career links
Visit: PHSchool.com
Web Code: ccb-2000

HVAC Technician

Connection to Chapter 16
Characteristics Able to troubleshoot, work independently, read and interpret blueprints, and have good hand-eye coordination.
Preparation Basic understanding of heating and cooling system design, understanding of microelectronics
Employers Contracting companies, manufacturers

Architect

Connection to Chapter 12
Characteristics Detail-oriented, artistic, analytical, creative, logical, computer literate, good at oral and written communications, able to work independently or as part of a team, able to conceptualize and understand spatial relationships
Preparation Courses in mathematics and design
Employers Architectural firms, government agencies

Electrician

Connection to Chapter 20
Characteristics Safety conscious, have stamina, good hand-eye coordination, ability to read and interpret blueprints
Preparation Courses in electronics
Employers Construction companies, maintenance companies

Go Online
PHSchool.com

Career Teaching Strategy
Have students use help-wanted ads from newspapers and the Internet to research physics-related jobs. Have students list the available physics-related positions, the qualifications necessary for each job, and the salaries being offered.

CHAPTER 11

Planning Guide

Use these planning tools
Easy Planner
Teacher Express

SECTION OBJECTIVES	STANDARDS NATIONAL (See p. T18.)	STANDARDS STATE	ACTIVITIES and LABS
11.1 Distance and Displacement, pp. 328–331 1 block or 2 periods **11.1.1 Identify** frames of reference and **describe** how they are used to measure motion. **11.1.2 Identify** appropriate SI units for measuring distances. **11.1.3 Distinguish** between distance and displacement. **11.1.4 Calculate** displacement using vector addition.	A-1, A-2, B-4		**SE** Inquiry Activity: How Does a Ramp Affect a Rolling Marble? p. 327 L2 **SE** Quick Lab: Comparing Distance and Displacement, p. 330 L2 **TE** Teacher Demo: Frames of Reference, p. 329 L2 **LM** Investigation 11A: Measuring Distance and Displacement L2
11.2 Speed and Velocity, pp. 332–337 1 block or 2 periods **11.2.1 Identify** appropriate SI units for measuring speed. **11.2.2 Compare** and **contrast** average speed and instantaneous speed. **11.2.3 Interpret** distance-time graphs. **11.2.4 Calculate** the speed of an object using slopes. **11.2.5 Describe** how velocities combine.	A-1, B-4, E-2, F-1, G-1, G-3		**SE** Exploration Lab: Investigating the Velocity of a Sinking Marble, p. 349 L2 **TE** Teacher Demo: Ticker Tape Car, p. 334 L2 **LM** Investigation 11B: Investigating Free Fall L1
11.3 Acceleration, pp. 342–348 1 block or 2 periods **11.3.1 Identify** changes in motion that produce acceleration. **11.3.2 Describe** examples of constant acceleration. **11.3.3 Calculate** the acceleration of an object. **11.3.4 Interpret** speed-time and distance-time graphs. **11.3.5 Classify** acceleration as positive or negative. **11.3.6 Describe** instantaneous acceleration.	A-1, A-2, B-4, D-1		**TE** Teacher Demo: Pendulum Accelerometer, p. 344 L2

Ability Levels	
L1	For students who need additional help
L2	For all students
L3	For students who need to be challenged

Components

SE	Student Edition	RSW	Reading & Study Workbook	CUT	Chapter & Unit Tests	T	Transparencies
TE	Teacher's Edition	MSPS	Math Skills & Problem Solving Workbook	CTB	Computer Test Bank	iT	Interactive Textbook
LM	Laboratory Manual			TP	Test Prep Resources	P	Presentation Pro CD-ROM
PLM	Probeware Lab Manual			DC	Discovery Channel Videotapes & DVDs	GO	Internet Resources

RESOURCES PRINT and TECHNOLOGY	SECTION ASSESSMENT
RSW Section 11.1 L1 **T** Chapter 11 Pretest L2 Section 11.1 L2 **P** Chapter 11 Pretest L2 Section 11.1 L2 SCLINKS **GO** Comparing frames of reference L2	**SE** Section 11.1 Assessment, p. 331 **iT** Section 11.1
RSW Section 11.2 L1 **RSW Math Skill** L2 **MSPS** Section 11.2 L2 **DC** Charting New Ground L2 **T** Section 11.2 L2 **P** Section 11.2 L2 SCLINKS **GO** Motion L2 PHSchool.com **GO** Data sharing L2	**SE** Section 11.2 Assessment, p. 337 **iT** Section 11.2
RSW Section 11.3 L1 **MSPS** Section 11.3 L2 **T** Section 11.3 L2 **P** Section 11.3 L2 SCLINKS **GO** Acceleration L2	**SE** Section 11.3 Assessment, p. 348 **iT** Section 11.3

Go Online

Go online for these Internet resources.

PHSchool.com
Web Code: ccd-2110
Web Code: cca-2110

NSTA SCLINKS
Web Code: ccn-2111
Web Code: ccn-2112
Web Code: ccn-2113

Materials for Activities and Labs

Quantities for each group

STUDENT EDITION

Inquiry Activity, p. 327
1-m long wooden board at least 10 cm wide, 6 identical textbooks, stopwatch, marble

Quick Lab, p. 330
graph paper, metric ruler

Exploration Lab, p. 349
clear shampoo, 100-mL graduated cylinder, 2 small marbles, stopwatch, forceps, masking tape, metric ruler, 10-mL graduated cylinder, long glass stirring rod, dropper pipet, graph paper

TEACHER'S EDITION

Teacher Demo, p. 329
tennis ball

Teacher Demo, p. 334
toy car, ticker tape, ticker timer (acceleration timer), masking tape

Build Science Skills, p. 340
handheld GPS receivers, 1 per group

Teacher Demo, p. 344
short pendulum (25 cm), turntable, lab stand, tape

Chapter Assessment

CHAPTER ASSESSMENT

SE Chapter Assessment, pp. 351–352
CUT Chapter 11 Test A, B
CTB Chapter 11
iT Chapter 11
PHSchool.com GO
Web Code: cca-2110

STANDARDIZED TEST PREP

SE Chapter 11, p. 353
TP Diagnose and Prescribe

Interactive Textbook

Interactive Textbook with assessment at PHSchool.com

CHAPTER 11

Before you teach

From the Author

Michael Wysession
Washington University

Big Ideas

Most of physics, and all of science, is concerned with motions. Before students can learn about the how (forces) and why (energy) of motions, they need to be able to describe them.

Space and Time In our local region of the universe, space has three spatial dimensions. Space is closely related to time, which is often considered to be a fourth dimension. In fact, large distances are measured in light-years, which are units of time.

Einstein demonstrated that all motions are relative, so a frame of reference within the three-dimensional space must be chosen. Distances, directions, and displacements are always measured relative to a frame of reference. Displacement is the combination of distance and direction.

Because it is important to describe motion over time, rates such as speed and velocity are often used. Velocity is the combination of speed and direction, analogous to the relation between displacement and distance. Acceleration is another common way to describe motion. Acceleration is the rate at which motion changes. Displacement, velocity, and acceleration are the most common examples of vectors.

Forces and Motion The motions of objects change when forces act upon them. Students need to be able to calculate these motions, and to be able to graph them. When there are no accelerations (no net forces), velocities are constant. These constant velocities plot as straight lines on a speed-time graph. When there are net forces, non-zero accelerations result in non-linear curves on a speed-time graph.

Matter and Energy Objects that appear to be motionless contain atoms that are continuously in motion—vibrating and colliding. Even pure electromagnetic energy such as light is in motion. Many of the following physics chapters explore the relations between matter and energy. In all cases, understanding and measuring how this matter and energy moves is a fundamental part of understanding the laws of the universe.

Physics Refresher

Distance and Displacement 11.1

For one-dimensional motion, the position of an object can be defined by a function $x(t)$. Displacement over a time interval can then be defined as $\Delta x = x_2 - x_1$. In more than one dimension, the displacement can be defined by a single vector function:

$$\mathbf{s}(t) = x(t)\mathbf{i} + y(t)\mathbf{j} + \ldots$$

In this equation, $\mathbf{s}(t)$ is the displacement as a function of time, $\mathbf{i}$ and $\mathbf{j}$ are unit vectors in the horizontal and vertical directions, respectively, and $x(t)$ and $y(t)$ are positions along the horizontal axis and vertical axis as functions of time.

Distance is how far an object travels on a path. Displacement is the straight-line distance from the start point to the end point.

Address Misconceptions

The location of an object can be described by stating its distance from a given point, ignoring direction. To describe position fully, you must specify both distance and direction. For a strategy to overcome this misconception, see **Address Misconceptions** on **page 330**.

Speed and Velocity 11.2

Velocity is defined as the rate of change of displacement. This can be expressed by the following differential equation:

$$\mathbf{v}(t) = d\mathbf{s}(t)/dt$$

Taking the derivative of displacement as shown above gives the instantaneous velocity at a point. The magnitude of this vector is the instantaneous speed.

Students may use the equation $\bar{v} = d/t$ to calculate average speed over a time interval, where $\bar{v}$ is the average speed, d is the distance traveled during a time interval, and t is the time interval.

Address Misconceptions

An object's speed is the same as its velocity. Velocity is a vector quantity that describes both speed and the direction of motion. For a strategy to overcome this misconception, see **Address Misconceptions** on **page 336**.

Go Online PD LINKS NSTA

For: Teaching methods for motion
Visit: www.SciLinks.org/PDLinks
Web Code: ccn-1199

Acceleration 11.3

Address Misconceptions

If an object is accelerating, then the object is speeding up. Acceleration is any change in velocity. This can be an increase in speed, a decrease in speed, or a change in direction. For a strategy to overcome this misconception, see **Address Misconceptions** on **page 343.**

Acceleration is defined as the rate of change of velocity. This can be expressed by the following differential equation:

$$\mathbf{a}(t) = d\mathbf{v}(t)/dt$$

Acceleration, like velocity and displacement, is a vector quantity having both magnitude and direction. Acceleration can be a change in speed, a change in direction, or both.

Taking the derivative of velocity as shown above gives the instantaneous acceleration at a point. For motion along a straight line, students may use the following equation $a = (v_f - v_i)/t$ to calculate average acceleration, where a is the average acceleration, v_f is the final speed, v_i is the initial speed, and t is the time interval. Note that if velocity of an object moving in the positive direction decreases during the time interval, $v_f < v_i$, and the average acceleration is negative.

Graphing Motion 11.2 and 11.3

Speed in one-dimensional motion can be shown on a graph of distance versus time, as shown in Figure A below. Constant speed appears on the graph as a straight line with finite, nonzero slope. The greater the absolute value of the slope, the greater the speed. A horizontal line represents zero velocity.

Acceleration in one-dimensional motion can be shown on a graph of distance versus time, or on a graph of speed versus time, as shown below right in Figure B. On a speed-time graph, constant speed is a horizontal line (with a slope of zero) and constant acceleration is a straight line with a nonzero slope. On a distance-time graph, constant acceleration appears as a curved line.

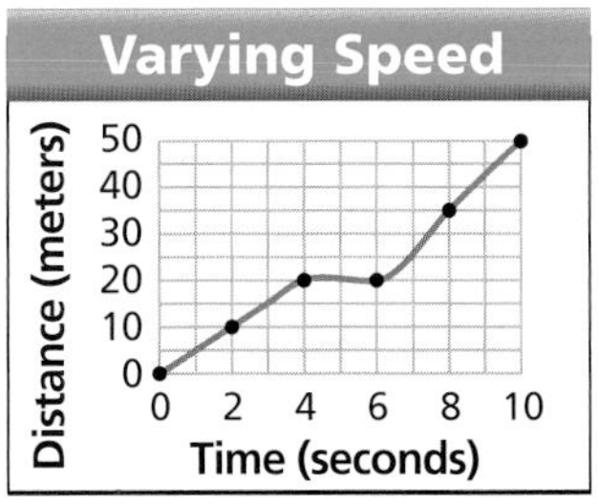

Varying Speed
Distance (meters)
50
40
30
20
10
0
0 2 4 6 8 10
Time (seconds)

▲ Figure A

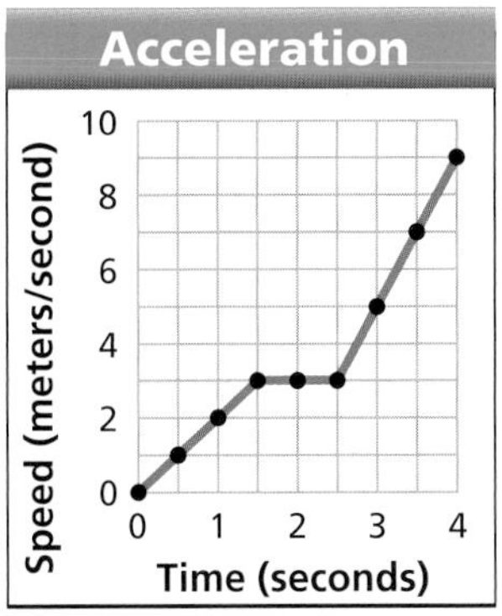

Acceleration
Speed (meters/second)
10
8
6
4
2
0
0 1 2 3 4
Time (seconds)

Figure B ▶

Build Reading Literacy

Monitor Your Understanding

Self-Questioning and Self-Adjusting While Reading

Strategy Help students read and understand difficult technical material. This strategy enables students to focus on their own thought processes as they actively question and apply fix-up strategies to improve comprehension. First, present the three steps in the example below, reviewing the fix-up strategies in Step 2. Then, before students begin, assign a section in Chapter 11, such as Section 11.2, pp. 332–337, for them to read. You might want to model the strategy with a paragraph or two before having students practice it on their own.

Example

1. Self-Question Have students read and think about the paragraphs under each heading, stopping often to ask themselves questions such as, "Do I understand this?" "Is this clear?" and "Does this answer my questions about ______?"

2. Identify Trouble Spots and Apply Fix-Up Strategies

- **Reread/Adjust Reading Pace** When students do not understand a paragraph, have them reread it slowly, making sure they understand each sentence before they continue.
- **Clarify** When students encounter a difficult paragraph, suggest they state what they do understand, talk through confusing points or steps in a process, or relate new information to concepts and examples that are already familiar to them.
- **Read Ahead/Use Visuals and Captions** Show students how to use visuals and captions to help clarify a process or a concept. Suggest that they can also read ahead to see whether a process or concept is discussed further as part of another concept.
- **Use Outside Resources** Point out, too, that students should seek assistance from friends, teachers, or other resources. Hearing additional examples or more than one person's explanation often aids comprehension.

3. Self-Check After students read, have them check their understanding by summarizing or retelling the main idea of a paragraph or section.

See p. 329 for a script on how to use the monitor your understanding strategy with students. For additional Build Reading Literacy strategies, see pp. 336 and 343.

CHAPTER

11 Motion

ASSESS PRIOR KNOWLEDGE

Use the Chapter Pretest below to assess students' prior knowledge. As needed, review these Science Concepts and Math Skills with students.

Review Science Concepts

Section 11.1 Review measurement. Remind students that measurements can be expressed in SI units or other units.

Section 11.2 Review graphing of scientific data. Remind students that graphs have different kinds of data on each axis. The slope of a line on a graph is the rise (change in vertical value) divided by the run (change in horizontal value).

Section 11.3 Further review graphing of scientific data. Remind students that data may form a straight line or a curve on a graph. The slope of a curved line at a given point is the slope of the straight line tangent to the graph at that point.

Review Math Skills

Conversion Factors, Averages, Line Graphs, Formulas and Equations, Significant Figures
Students will need to calculate velocity and acceleration and create graphs of motion as a function of time.

Direct students to the **Math Skills** in the **Skills and Reference Handbook** at the end of the student text.

CONCEPTS in Action

How do science concepts apply to your world? Here are some questions you'll be able to answer after you read this chapter.

- How can two people look at the same object, and only one of them see the object as moving? *(Section 11.1)*
- One person says that your school is 5 blocks from the library, and another person says the two buildings are 7 blocks apart. How can both people be right? *(Section 11.1)*
- What does a car's speedometer measure? *(Section 11.2)*
- When you drop a stone off a cliff, how fast does the stone fall? *(Section 11.3)*
- How can something that is slowing down be accelerating? *(Section 11.3)*

Discovery Channel School **Video Field Trip**
Charting New Ground

- How do ships stay on course? *(page 338)*

The time-lapse photo shows how ▶ the position of a gymnast changes from moment to moment.

Chapter Pretest

1. How many meters are in 28 km? *(28,000 m)*
2. Convert 35 km/h to a speed in m/s. *(9.7 m/s)*
3. Rearrange the following equation to solve for *d*: $v = d/t$. *($d = vt$)*
4. Rearrange the following equation to solve for v_f: $a = (v_f - v_i)/t$. *($v_f = at + v_i$)*
5. What are the SI units for distance and time? *(Meters and seconds)*
6. Which of the following describes the slope of a line? *(d)*
   - **a.** rise × run
   - **b.** run/rise
   - **c.** run − rise
   - **d.** rise/run
7. If a graph uses units of meters on the vertical axis and units of seconds on the horizontal axis, what would be the units of the slope of a line on the graph? *(m/s)*
8. Which of the following is true about a curved line on a graph? *(b)*
   - **a.** The slope is the same at every point.
   - **b.** The slope of the line may be different at every point.
   - **c.** The line has no slope.
   - **d.** The slope of the line is zero.

Chapter Preview

Inquiry Activity

How Does a Ramp Affect a Rolling Marble?

Procedure

1. Form a ramp by placing one end of a 1-meter-long board on a stack of six identical books.
2. Have your partner release a marble at the top of the ramp. Use a stopwatch to measure the time the marble takes to reach the bottom. Record this time.
3. **Predicting** How many books tall would the stack have to be to double the time needed for the marble to reach the ramp's bottom? Record your prediction.
4. Test your prediction. Remove one book from the stack and repeat Step 2. Continue this process until the time needed for the marble to roll down the ramp doubles.

Think About It

1. **Predicting** What would happen to the time needed for the marble to roll down the ramp if the ramp were nearly horizontal?
2. **Formulating Hypotheses** If you keep adding books to the stack, will the time needed for the marble to roll down the ramp decrease indefinitely? Explain your answer.

ENGAGE/EXPLORE

Inquiry Activity

How Does a Ramp Affect a Rolling Marble? L2

Purpose In this activity, students will begin to describe how the steepness of a ramp affects the motion of a rolling marble.

Skills Focus Measuring, Predicting

Prep Time 10 minutes

Materials 1-m long wooden board at least 10 cm wide, 6 identical textbooks, stopwatch, marble

Class Time 20 minutes

Safety Students must wear safety goggles. Ensure that the boards are smooth to prevent splinters.

Teaching Tips

- The boards should not be curved or warped so that the marbles do not roll off the sides of the ramps.

Expected Outcome Students will observe that the marble takes longer to descend when the steepness of the ramp is reduced.

Predicting Students may correctly predict that a height of three books would approximately double the time the marble takes to reach the bottom of the ramp.

Think About It

1. The time needed would be very long because the speed of the marble would be almost zero.
2. When the ramp is vertical, the marble is in free fall and the time required reaches a finite minimum value.
Kinesthetic, Group

Discovery Channel School **Video Field Trip**

Charting New Ground

Encourage students to view the Video Field Trip "Charting New Ground."

1 FOCUS

Objectives

11.1.1 **Identify** frames of reference and **describe** how they are used to measure motion.

11.1.2 **Identify** appropriate SI units for measuring distances.

11.1.3 **Distinguish** between distance and displacement.

11.1.4 **Calculate** displacement using vector addition.

Reading Focus

Build Vocabulary L2

Vocabulary Knowledge Rating Chart Before students read the section, have them rate their knowledge of the vocabulary terms for this section in a chart with the following headings: Term, Can Define or Use It, Have Heard or Seen It, Don't Know. After they have read the section, have them return to the chart and update it to reflect any increase in understanding.

Reading Strategy L2

a. Answers may vary. Sample answer: Frame of reference may mean the range of distances or area that you are considering in a problem. **b.** Frame of reference is a system of objects that are not moving with respect to one another. Frames of reference are important because they are needed to accurately describe motion.

2 INSTRUCT

Choosing a Frame of Reference

Use Visuals L1

Figure 1 Discuss Figure 1 with students after they read the section Choosing a Frame of Reference. Ask, **Describe the motion of the girl in the butterfly's frame of reference.** *(She would appear to bob up and down, exactly opposite the motion of the butterfly as seen from the girl's frame of reference.)* **Describe the motion of the butterfly in the butterfly's frame of reference.** *(The butterfly is at rest in the butterfly's frame of reference.)* **Which one is "really" moving, the butterfly or the girl?** *(It depends on the frame of reference.)* **Visual, Logical**

11.1 Distance and Displacement

Reading Focus

Key Concepts

- What is needed to describe motion completely?
- How are distance and displacement different?
- How do you add displacements ?

Vocabulary

- frame of reference
- relative motion
- distance
- vector
- resultant vector

Reading Strategy

Predicting Copy the table below and write a definition for *frame of reference* in your own words. After you read the section, compare your definition to the scientific definition and explain why the frame of reference is important.

Frame of reference probably means	Frame of reference actually means
a. ?	b. ?

On a spring day a butterfly flutters past. First it flies quickly, then slowly, and then it pauses to drink nectar from a flower. The butterfly's path involves a great deal of motion.

How fast is the butterfly moving? Is it flying toward the flower or away from it? These are the kinds of questions you must answer to describe the butterfly's motion. To describe motion, you must state the direction the object is moving as well as how fast the object is moving. You must also tell its location at a certain time.

Choosing a Frame of Reference

How fast is the butterfly in Figure 1 moving? Remember that the butterfly is moving on Earth, but Earth itself is moving as it spins on its axis and revolves around the sun. If you consider this motion, the butterfly is moving very, very fast!

To describe motion accurately and completely, a frame of reference is necessary. The necessary ingredient of a description of motion—a **frame of reference**—is a system of objects that are not moving with respect to one another. The answer to "How fast is the butterfly moving?" depends on which frame of reference you use to measure motion. How do you decide which frame of reference to use when describing the butterfly's movement?

Figure 1 You must choose a frame of reference to tell how fast the butterfly is moving.
Applying Concepts *Identify a good frame of reference to use when describing the butterfly's motion.*

328 *Chapter 11*

Section Resources

Print
- ***Laboratory Manual,*** Investigation 11A
- ***Reading and Study Workbook With Math Support,*** Section 11.1
- ***Transparencies,*** Chapter Pretest and Section 11.1

Technology
- ***Interactive Textbook,*** Section 11.1
- ***Presentation Pro CD-ROM,*** Chapter Pretest and Section 11.1
- ***Go Online,*** NSTA SciLinks, Comparing frames of reference

Figure 2 To someone riding on a speeding train, others on the train don't seem to be moving.

How Fast Are You Moving? How fast are the train passengers in Figure 2 moving? There are many correct answers because their motion is relative. This means it depends on the frame of reference you choose to measure their motion. **Relative motion** is movement in relation to a frame of reference. For example, as the train moves past a platform, people standing on the platform will see those on the train speeding by. But when the people on the train look at one another, they don't seem to be moving at all.

Which Frame Should You Choose? When you sit on a train and look out a window, a treetop may help you see how fast you are moving relative to the ground. But suppose you get up and walk toward the rear of the train. Looking at a seat or the floor may tell you how fast you are walking relative to the train. However, it doesn't tell you how fast you are moving relative to the ground outside. Choosing a meaningful frame of reference allows you to describe motion in a clear and relevant manner.

Measuring Distance

Distance is the length of a path between two points. When an object moves in a straight line, the distance is the length of the line connecting the object's starting point and its ending point.

It is helpful to express distances in units that are best suited to the motion you are studying. The SI unit for measuring distance is the meter (m). For very large distances, it is more common to make measurements in kilometers (km). One kilometer equals 1000 meters. For instance, it's easier to say that the Mississippi River has a length of 3780 kilometers than 3,780,000 meters. Distances that are smaller than a meter are measured in centimeters (cm). One centimeter is one hundredth of a meter. You might describe the distance a marble rolls, for example, as 6 centimeters rather than 0.06 meter.

Go Online NSTA SCILINKS

For: Links on comparing frames of reference
Visit: www.SciLinks.org
Web Code: ccn-2111

Customize for English Language Learners

Use Narrative
English language learners can better understand science content when it is framed in the context of a personal narrative. Have students use narrative to better understand displacement that isn't along a straight path. Pair ELL students and encourage them to narrate the route they take from the science classroom to the cafeteria, or another room in the school. As one student narrates, the other student may sketch a simple map, similar to the one on p. 331. Challenge students to mark the resultant vector on the map.

Teacher Demo

Frames of Reference L2

Purpose Students observe how motion can appear differently in different frames of reference.

Materials tennis ball

Procedure Stand at the front of the room, turned sideways, and toss the tennis ball straight up and then catch it. Ask, **Describe the path of the ball.** *(The ball travels straight up and down).* Tell students that to you, the ball also appears to travel straight up and down. Now, walk slowly across the front of the room as you toss the ball up and catch it. Ask, **Describe the path of the ball.** *(The ball travels up and down in an arc.)* Tell students that to you, the ball still appears to travel straight up and down.

Expected Outcome The description of motion depends on the frame of reference. **Kinesthetic, Visual**

Measuring Distance

Build Reading Literacy L1

Monitor Your Understanding Refer to page **326D** in this chapter, which provides guidelines for monitoring your understanding.

Have students read the passages Measuring Distance and Measuring Displacements (pp. 329–330). When they reach the bottom of p. 329, have them stop and write down the main ideas in the passage. Have them ask themselves, "Did I have any trouble reading this passage? If so, why?" Then, have them come up with their own strategies to improve their understanding. Have them use this strategy as they continue reading. **Intrapersonal, Verbal**

Go Online NSTA SCILINKS

Download a worksheet on comparing frames of reference for students to complete, and find additional teacher support from NSTA SciLinks.

Answer to . . .

Figure 1 *The ground would make a good frame of reference.*

Measuring Displacements Combining Displacements

Quick Lab

Comparing Distance and Displacement **L2**

Objective
After completing this activity, students will be able to
- distinguish between distance and displacement.

Address Misconceptions

This activity helps address the misconception that the distance an object travels and its displacement are the same. Challenge this misconception by discussing the answers to the Analyze and Conclude questions.

Skills Focus **Measuring**

Prep Time 10 minutes

Materials graph paper, metric ruler

Class Time 15 minutes

Teaching Tips
- Make sure that students read the metric side of the ruler if their rulers have both metric and English units.

Expected Outcome Students will be able to distinguish between distance, the length traveled between two points, and displacement, the length of the line between two points.

Analyze and Conclude
1. Displacement is always shorter than or equal to the distance because it is a straight line between two points, not always the actual path of motion.
2. The distance would be shorter if the path were more direct. The shortest path would be a diagonal line connecting Start and End, and it would be the same length as the displacement.
3. No, the displacement could not be shorter because it will always be the straight-line distance between the Start and End points.
Visual, Logical

Quick Lab

Comparing Distance and Displacement

Procedure
1. Draw a dot at the intersection of two lines near the bottom edge of a sheet of graph paper. Label the dot "Start."
2. Draw a second, similar dot near the top of the paper. Label this dot "End."
3. Draw a path from the Start dot to the End dot. Choose any path that stays on the grid lines.
4. Use a ruler to determine the distance of your path.
5. Use a ruler to determine the displacement from start to end.

Analyze and Conclude
1. **Observing** Which is shorter, the distance or the displacement?
2. **Evaluating and Revising** How could you have made the distance shorter?
3. **Inferring** If you keep the Start and End points the same, is it possible to make the displacement shorter? Explain your answer.

Measuring Displacements

To describe an object's position relative to a given point, you need to know how far away and in what direction the object is from that point. Displacement provides this information. **Distance is the length of the path between two points. Displacement is the direction from the starting point and the length of a straight line from the starting point to the ending point.**

Displacements are sometimes used when giving directions. Telling someone to "Walk 5 blocks" does not ensure they'll end up in the right place. However, saying "Walk 5 blocks north from the bus stop" will get the person to the right place. Accurate directions give the direction from a starting point as well as the distance.

Think about the motion of a roller coaster car. If you measure the path along which the car has traveled, you are describing distance. The direction from the starting point to the car and the length of the straight line from the starting point to the car describe displacement. After completing one trip around the track, the roller coaster car's displacement is zero.

Combining Displacements

Displacement is an example of a vector. A **vector** is a quantity that has magnitude and direction. The magnitude can be size, length, or amount. Arrows on a graph or map are used to represent vectors. The length of the arrow shows the magnitude of the vector. Vector addition is the combining of vector magnitudes and directions. **Add displacements using vector addition.**

Displacement Along a Straight Line When two displacements, represented by two vectors, have the same direction, you can add their magnitudes. In Figure 3A, the magnitudes of the car's displacements are 4 kilometers and 2 kilometers. The total magnitude of the displacement is 6 kilometers. If two displacements are in opposite directions, the magnitudes subtract from each other, as shown in Figure 3B. Because the car's displacements (4 kilometers and 2 kilometers) are in opposite directions, the magnitude of the total displacement is 2 kilometers.

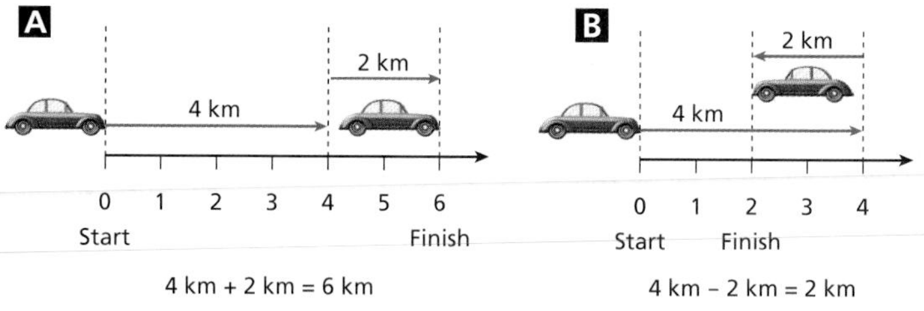

A
4 km
2 km
0 1 2 3 4 5 6
Start
Finish
4 km + 2 km = 6 km
B
4 km
2 km
0 1 2 3 4
Start
Finish
4 km - 2 km = 2 km

Figure 3 When motion is in a straight line, vectors add and subtract easily. **A** Add the magnitudes of two displacement vectors that have the same direction. **B** Two displacement vectors with opposite directions are subtracted from each other.

Displacement That Isn't Along a Straight Path

When two or more displacement vectors have different directions, they may be combined by graphing. Figure 4 shows vectors representing the movement of a boy walking from his home to school. He starts by walking 1 block east. Then he turns a corner and walks 1 block north. He turns once again and walks 2 blocks east. For the last part of his trip to school, he walks 3 blocks north. The lengths of the vectors representing this path are 1 block, 1 block, 2 blocks, and 3 blocks.

The boy walked a total distance of 7 blocks. You can determine this distance by adding the magnitudes of each vector along his path.

The vector in red is called the **resultant vector,** which is the vector sum of two or more vectors. In this case, it shows the displacement. The resultant vector points directly from the starting point to the ending point. If you place a sheet of paper on the figure and mark the length of the resultant vector, you see that it equals the length of 5 blocks. Vector addition, then, shows that the boy's displacement is 5 blocks approximately northeast, while the distance he walked is 7 blocks.

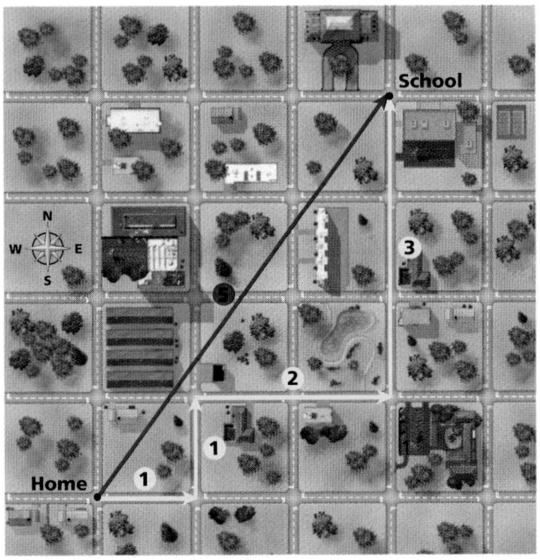
School
N
W
E
S
3
2
1
1
Home

Figure 4 Measuring the resultant vector (the diagonal red line) shows that the displacement from the boy's home to his school is two blocks less than the distance he actually traveled.

Section 11.1 Assessment

Reviewing Concepts

1. What is a frame of reference? How is it used to measure motion?
2. How are distance and displacement similar and different?
3. How are displacements combined?
4. A girl who is watching a plane fly tells her friend that the plane isn't moving at all. Describe a frame of reference in which the girl's description would be true.

Critical Thinking

5. **Using Analogies** Is displacement more like the length of a rope that is pulled tight or the length of a coiled rope? Explain.
6. **Making Judgments** Would you measure the height of a building in meters? Give reasons for your answer.
7. **Problem Solving** Should your directions to a friend for traveling from one city to another include displacements or distances? Explain.
8. **Inferring** The resultant vector of two particular displacement vectors does not equal the sum of the magnitudes of the individual vectors. Describe the directions of the two vectors.

Writing in Science

Compare-Contrast Paragraph Write a paragraph describing how the distance you travel from home to school is different from your displacement from home to school. (*Hint:* Make a simple sketch similar to Figure 4 and refer to it as you write.)

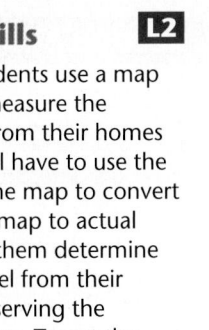

Build Science Skills L2

Measuring Have students use a map of the city or area to measure the straight-line distance from their homes to the school. They will have to use the scale information on the map to convert from distances on the map to actual distances. Then, have them determine the distances they travel from their home to school by observing the odometer of a car or bus. To get the distances traveled, they should subtract the odometer readings at their start points from the odometer readings when they arrive at the school. Have them compare the distances. In almost every case, the distance traveled should be greater than the straight-line distance on the map. **Logical**

3 ASSESS

Evaluate Understanding L2

Ask students to write a paragraph describing a situation in which the same motion appears differently from different frames of reference.

Reteach L1

Use Figure 4 to reteach the difference between displacement and distance traveled.

Writing in Science

Students' paragraphs should generally describe distances and directions they travel on the way to school. They should understand that displacement is determined by a straight-line distance from home to school. The total distance they travel will almost always be greater than the magnitude of the displacement, unless they travel in a single direction the whole time.

Interactive Textbook If your class subscribes to the Interactive Textbook, use it to review key concepts in Section 11.1.

Section 11.1 Assessment

1. A frame of reference is a set of objects that are not moving with respect to one another. Motion can only be described in comparison to a frame of reference.
2. Distance is the length of an object's actual path from a starting point to an ending point. Displacement is the length of a straight line from the starting point to the ending point.
3. Displacements are combined using vector addition.
4. If the plane is far away and flying directly toward or away from the girl, the plane would appear not to be moving. Also, the plane would not be moving in the frame of reference of the people on the plane.
5. Displacement is more like the length of a rope that is pulled tight; it measures the shortest distance between two points.
6. It makes sense to measure the height of a building in meters. Kilometers are too large and centimeters are too small.
7. You should use displacements. Displacements will tell your friend how far and which direction to go. Distances will only tell how far to go.
8. The vectors are at an angle to each other.

1 FOCUS

Objectives

11.2.1 **Identify** appropriate SI units for measuring speed.

11.2.2 **Compare** and **contrast** average speed and instantaneous speed.

11.2.3 **Interpret** distance-time graphs.

11.2.4 **Calculate** the speed of an object using slopes.

11.2.5 **Describe** how velocities combine.

Reading Focus

Build Vocabulary L2

Venn Diagram Have students draw a Venn diagram to show how the key terms of the section are related to each other. Student diagrams should show circles labeled Speed and Direction. The area in which the circles overlap should be labeled Velocity.

Reading Strategy L2

Answers may vary. Sample answers are shown below.
a. Average speed is distance divided by time. **b.** I could use this to calculate various speeds, like the average speed at which I travel getting to school.
c. Instantaneous speed is different from average speed **d.** You can't use a single speedometer reading to determine how long a trip will take. **e.** Velocity is not the same as speed. **f.** This could be useful in giving directions or in describing the path that you take on a walk.

2 INSTRUCT

Speed

Build Science Skills L2

Forming Operational Definitions An operational definition limits the meaning of a term to what is observed or measured in a particular situation. Ask, **What is an operational definition of speed for a skater on a circular track?** *(Sample answer: The amount of time it takes to circle the track one time, the number of times the skater could circle the track one time)* **What is an operational definition for a person walking down a street?** *(Sample answer: The number of meters traveled each second)*
Verbal, Logical

11.2 Speed and Velocity

Reading Focus

Key Concepts

- How are instantaneous speed and average speed different?
- How can you find the speed from a distance-time graph?
- How are speed and velocity different?
- How do velocities add?

Vocabulary

- speed
- average speed
- instantaneous speed
- velocity

Reading Strategy

Monitoring Your Understanding After you have finished reading this section, copy the table below. Identify several things you have learned that are relevant to your life. Explain why they are relevant to you.

What Is Relevant	Why It Is Relevant
a. ?	b. ?
c. ?	d. ?
e. ?	f. ?

Look out a window for a few minutes, and you will see things in motion. Some things are moving slowly. Perhaps you see a leaf floating through the air. Other things, such as a car or a bird, are moving fast. The growth rate of trees and grass is so slow that their motion cannot be detected with the unaided eye. The differences among these types of motion can be described in terms of speed.

Figure 5 The speed of an in-line skater is usually described in meters per second. The speed of a car is usually described in kilometers per hour.

Speed

To describe the speed of a car, you might say it is moving at 45 kilometers per hour. **Speed** is the ratio of the distance an object moves to the amount of time the object moves. The SI unit of speed is meters per second (m/s). However, just as with distances, you need to choose units that make the most sense for the motion you are describing. The in-line skater in Figure 5 may travel 2 meters in one second. The speed would be expressed as 2 m/s. A car might travel 80 kilometers in one hour. Its speed would be expressed as 80 km/h.

Two ways to express the speed of an object are average speed and instantaneous speed. **Average speed is computed for the entire duration of a trip, and instantaneous speed is measured at a particular instant.** In different situations, either one or both of these measurements may be a useful way to describe speed.

Section Resources

Print

- ***Laboratory Manual,*** Investigation 11B
- ***Reading and Study Workbook With Math Support***, Section 11.2 and **Math Skill:** Interpreting a Distance-Time Graph
- ***Math Skills and Problem Solving Workbook***, Section 11.2
- ***Transparencies,*** Section 11.2

Technology

- ***Interactive Textbook,*** Section 11.2
- ***Presentation Pro CD-ROM,*** Section 11.2
- ***Go Online,*** NSTA SciLinks, Motion; PHSchool.com, Data sharing

332 Chapter 11

Average Speed Describing the speed of a hiker isn't as easy as describing constant speed along a straight line. A hiker may travel slowly along rocky areas but then travel quickly when going downhill. Sometimes it is useful to know how fast something moves for an entire trip. **Average speed,** $\bar{v}$, is the total distance traveled, d, divided by the time, t, it takes to travel that distance. This can be written as an equation:

Average Speed

$$\text{Average speed} = \frac{\text{Total distance}}{\text{Total time}}, \text{ or } \bar{v} = \frac{d}{t}$$

During the time an object is moving, its speed may change, but this equation tells you the average speed over the entire trip.

Go Online NSTA SCILINKS

For: Links on motion
Visit: www.SciLinks.org
Web Code: ccn-2112

Math Skills

Calculating Average Speed

While traveling on vacation, you measure the times and distances traveled. You travel 35 kilometers in 0.4 hour, followed by 53 kilometers in 0.6 hour. What is your average speed?

1 Read and Understand

What information are you given?

Total Distance $(d) = 35 \text{ km} + 53 \text{ km} = 88 \text{ km}$

Total Time $(t) = 0.4 \text{ h} + 0.6 \text{ h} = 1.0 \text{ h}$

2 Plan and Solve

What unknown are you trying to calculate?

Average Speed $(\bar{v}) = ?$

What formula contains the given quantities and the unknown?

$$\bar{v} = \frac{d}{t}$$

Replace each variable with its known value.

$$\bar{v} = \frac{88 \text{ km}}{1 \text{ h}} = 88 \text{ km/h}$$

3 Look Back and Check

Is your answer reasonable?

Yes, 88 km/h is a typical highway speed.

Math Practice

1. A person jogs 4.0 kilometers in 32 minutes, then 2.0 kilometers in 22 minutes, and finally 1.0 kilometer in 16 minutes. What is the jogger's average speed in kilometers per minute?
2. A train travels 190 kilometers in 3.0 hours, and then 120 kilometers in 2.0 hours. What is its average speed?

Customize for English Language Learners

Create a Word Wall
Students can relate the concepts in this section to the vocabulary words by creating a word wall. Write the words *speed, average speed, instantaneous speed,* and *velocity* on the board. Then, as students work through the section, ask them to define each word in their own terms. Discuss their definitions and write acceptable definitions on the board next to each word. Students may also draw a graph or paste a magazine picture next to the corresponding word.

Math Practice

Solutions L2

1. $\bar{v}$ = (4.0 km + 2.0 km + 1.0 km)/(32 min + 22 min + 16 min) = (7.0 km)/(70 min) = 0.10 km/min
2. $\bar{v}$ = (190 km + 120 km)/(3.0 h + 2.0 h) = (310 km)/(5.0 h) = 62 km/h
Logical

For Extra Help L1

Remind students that all the values they plug into the equation must have appropriate units. They may have to convert some of the given units. Also remind students that the equation can be rearranged to solve for other variables. Show them how to rearrange to solve for *d* or *t*. **Logical`**

Direct students to the **Math Skills** in the **Skills and Reference Handbook** at the end of the student text for additional help.

Additional Problems

1. A car travels 85 km from Town A to Town B, then 45 km from Town B to Town C. The total trip took 1.5 hours. What was the average speed of the car? *(87 km/h)*
2. A bicyclist travels for 1.5 hours at an average speed of 32 km/h. How far does the bicyclist travel in that time? *(48 km)*
Logical, Portfolio

Use Community Resources L2

Have students contact their local or state department of transportation to find out about laws or guidelines for the assignments of speed limits. They may ask, "Are there specific maximum speed limits for residential areas?" or "What is the maximum speed limit for highways outside of city limits?" They may also ask the department representative what other factors are used in determining speed limits.
Interpersonal, Portfolio

Go Online NSTA SCILINKS

Download a worksheet on motion for students to complete, and find additional teacher support from NSTA SciLinks.

Graphing Motion

Teacher Demo

Ticker Tape Car L2

Purpose Students observe a technique that visually records motion.

Materials toy car, ticker tape, ticker timer (acceleration timer), masking tape

Procedure Place the car and the ticker on the ground in an open area. Thread the ticker tape through the ticker, then attach the ticker tape to the car with masking tape. Before you perform the demonstration, show the setup to the students and explain how the ticker works (the ticker marks the ticker tape at regular time intervals). Ask, **How will the marks appear on the tape when the car is moving at a constant speed?** *(The marks will be evenly spaced.)* Start the ticker and give the car a quick push. Turn off the ticker and cut off the used portion of the ticker tape. Have the students gather around the ticker tape and relate the marks on the ticker tape to the motion of the car that they observed.

Expected Outcome At first, the marks on the tape will be unevenly spaced (getting farther apart) because the car is accelerating. As the car slows down, the marks will get closer together again. When the car is at rest, many marks will be superimposed. If possible, demonstrate the car moving at a constant speed. When the car is moving at constant speed, the marks will be evenly spaced on the ticker tape. As an alternative, you can use probeware to plot the car's motion on a computer or graphing calculator, and then relate the graphs to the motion of the car.
Kinesthetic, Logical

Build Science Skills L2

Analyzing Data Use Figures 7A and 7B to demonstrate that speed is shown by the slope of the line on a distance-time graph. For Figure 7A, calculate the slope of the line on the board:

slope = rise/run = $(y_2 - y_1)/(x_2 - x_1)$
= (350 m − 100 m)/(14 s − 4 s)
= (250 m)/(10 s)
= 25 m/s

Then, have students calculate the speed represented by the three distinct portions on the graph in Figure 7C. *(25 m/s, 0 m/s, 37.5 m/s)*
Visual, Logical

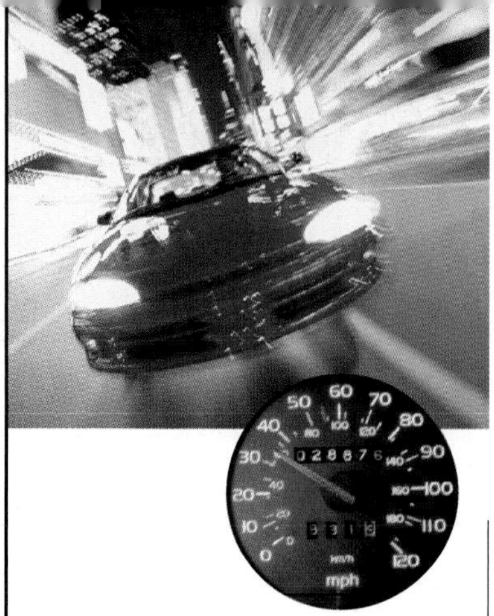

50 60 70
40 80
30 90
20 100
10 110
0 120
km/h
mph

Figure 6 The speedometer in a car measures the car's instantaneous speed. Note the scale markings are given both in km/h and miles per hour, mph.

Instantaneous Speed Average speed is useful because it lets you know how long a trip will take. Sometimes however, such as when driving on the highway, you need to know how fast you are going at a particular moment. The car's speedometer gives your instantaneous speed. **Instantaneous speed,** *v*, is the rate at which an object is moving at a given moment in time. For example, you could describe the instantaneous speed of the car in Figure 6 as 55 km/h.

Reading Checkpoint *What does a car's speedometer measure?*

Graphing Motion

A distance-time graph is a good way to describe motion. Figure 7 shows distance-time graphs for the motion of three cars. Recall that slope is the change in the vertical axis value divided by the change in the horizontal axis value. On these graphs, the slope is the change in the distance divided by the change in time. **The slope of a line on a distance-time graph is speed.** In Figure 7A, the car travels 500.0 meters in 20.0 seconds, or 25.0 meters per second. In Figure 7B, another car travels 250.0 meters in 20.0 seconds at a constant speed. The slope of the line is 250.0 meters divided by 20.0 seconds, or 12.5 meters per second. Notice that the line for the car traveling at a higher speed is steeper. A steeper slope on a distance-time graph indicates a higher speed.

Figure 7C shows the motion of a car that is not traveling at a constant speed. This car travels 200.0 meters in the first 8.0 seconds. It then stops for 4.0 seconds, as indicated by the horizontal part of the line. Next the car travels 300.0 meters in 8.0 seconds. The times when the car is gradually increasing or decreasing its speed are shown by the curved parts of the line. The slope of the straight portions of the line represent periods of constant speed. Note that the car's speed is 25 meters per second during the first part of its trip and 38 meters per second during the last part of its trip.

Figure 7 The slope of the line on a distance–time graph indicates the speed of the object. **Using Graphs** *If the car in Figure 7A required less time to travel a given distance, how would the slope change?*

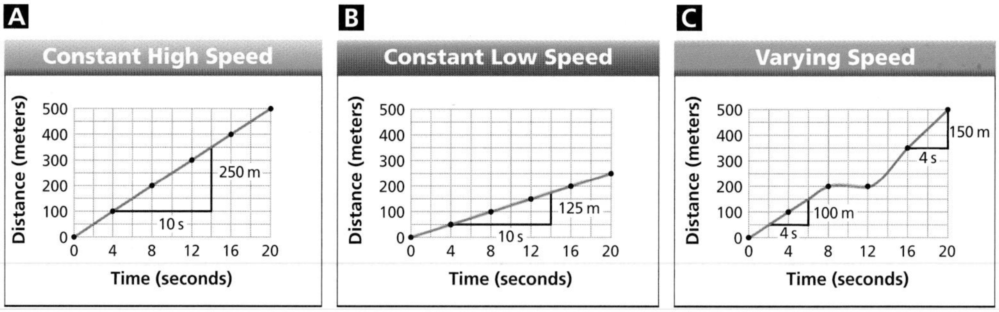

A
Constant High Speed
Distance (meters)
500
400
300
200
100
0
250 m
10 s
0 4 8 12 16 20
Time (seconds)
B
Constant Low Speed
Distance (meters)
500
400
300
200
100
0
125 m
10 s
0 4 8 12 16 20
Time (seconds)
C
Varying Speed
Distance (meters)
500
400
300
200
100
0
150 m
4 s
100 m
4 s
0 4 8 12 16 20
Time (seconds)

Facts and Figures

Speed Records According to the Guinness World Records, the fastest human sprinter is Tim Montgomery, who set a record of 100 m in 9.78 s in 2002. Fred Rompelberg set a record for the fastest speed on a bicycle when he rode 268.831 km/h (167.043 mph) in 1995. In 1972, the fastest recorded wind speed was clocked at 333 km/h (207 mph) in Thule, Greenland. The fastest speed in the universe is the speed of light. Light travels in a vacuum at 3.00×10^8 m/s (186,000 miles/second).

HOW It Works

Measuring Distance and Speed

Every car has a speedometer, which measures the car's speed, and an odometer, which measures the distance it has traveled. These devices work by counting the number of times the car's wheels turn (to give distance) and their rate of turning (speed).

Interpreting Diagrams ***What is the purpose of the worm gears?***

Digital Odometer
Some cars have a magnetic sensor that detects turns of the transmission shaft. The signal is transmitted to a computer, which calculates and displays the car's distance traveled.

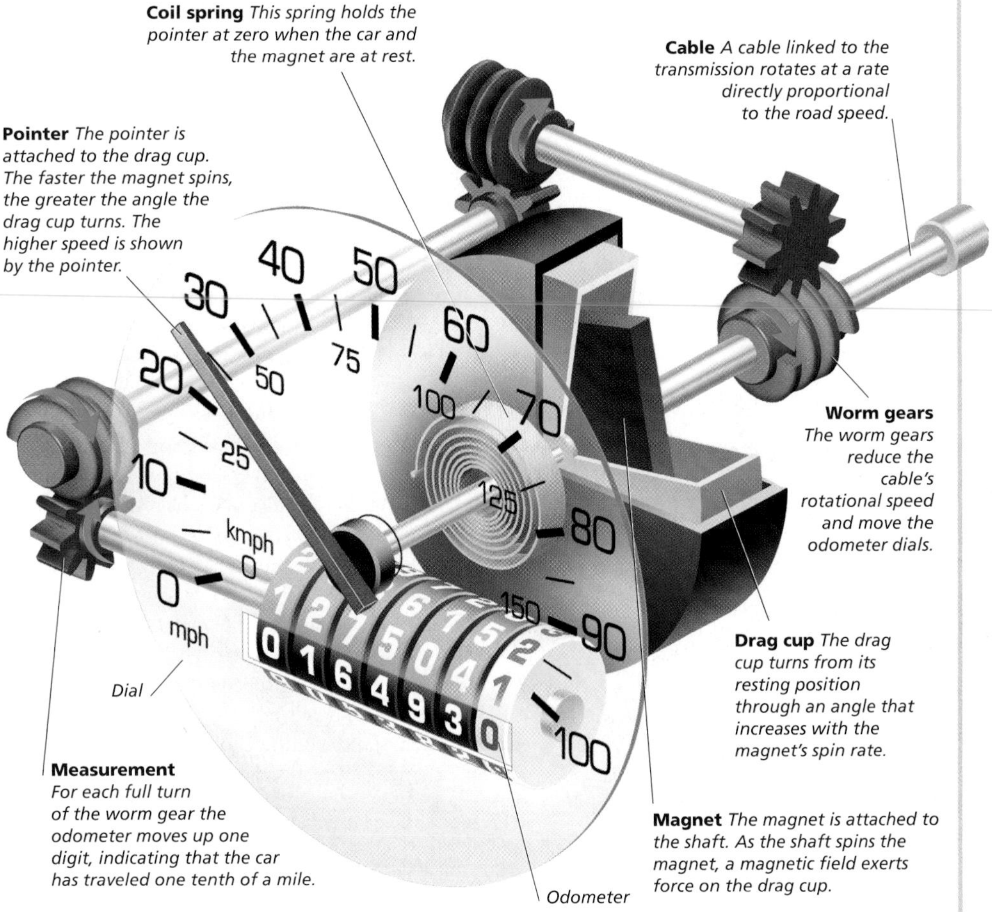

Coil spring *This spring holds the pointer at zero when the car and the magnet are at rest.*
Cable *A cable linked to the transmission rotates at a rate directly proportional to the road speed.*
Pointer *The pointer is attached to the drag cup. The faster the magnet spins, the greater the angle the drag cup turns. The higher speed is shown by the pointer.*
Worm gears *The worm gears reduce the cable's rotational speed and move the odometer dials.*
Drag cup *The drag cup turns from its resting position through an angle that increases with the magnet's spin rate.*
Dial
Measurement *For each full turn of the worm gear the odometer moves up one digit, indicating that the car has traveled one tenth of a mile.*
Odometer
Magnet *The magnet is attached to the shaft. As the shaft spins the magnet, a magnetic field exerts force on the drag cup.*

HOW It Works

Measuring Distance and Speed L2

The speedometer is an important part of any car. Knowing the speed of the car is important for following safety cautions on road signs.

By law, all cars must have a working odometer. It is against the law to change odometer readings or to operate a car in which the odometer is not working. The law prevents people from "rolling back" the odometers in order to increase the resale value of the car.

Interpreting Diagrams The worm gears convert the rotation of the cable into a much slower rotation that turns the odometer. The worm gears also change the direction of rotation so the shafts can be positioned to align with the odometer.
Logical, Visual

For Enrichment L3

Have students use a library or the Internet to research how speeds are measured on ships, airplanes, or spacecraft. Have them write a paragraph explaining their findings.
Verbal, Portfolio

Answer to . . .

Figure 7 *The slope of the line would increase.*

Reading Checkpoint *Instantaneous speed*

Velocity

Build Reading Literacy L1

Compare and Contrast Refer to page **226D** in **Chapter 8,** which provides guidelines for comparing and contrasting.

Have students compare and contrast speed and velocity. Ask students, **How are speed and velocity similar?** *(They both measure how fast something is moving.)* **How are speed and velocity different?** *(Velocity includes the direction of motion, while speed does not.)* **Is velocity more like distance or displacement? Why?** *(Velocity is more like displacement. Both velocity and displacement are vectors, including magnitude and direction.)*
Logical

Address Misconceptions L2

Students may think that an object's speed and its velocity are the same thing. On the board, draw a picture of an oval racetrack. Have students imagine a racecar traveling at a constant speed of 120 km/h around the track. Point to a place on the track where the car would be moving to the right. Ask students, **What is the speed of the racecar at this point?** *(120 km/h)* **In what direction is the racecar traveling at this point?** *(To the right)* **What is the velocity of the racecar at this point?** *(120 km/h to the right)* Now point to a point on the track where the car would be moving to the left. Ask students, **What is the speed of the racecar at this point?** *(120 km/h)* **In what direction is the racecar traveling at this point?** *(To the left)* **What is the velocity of the racecar at this point?** *(120 km/h to the left)* The speeds are the same at each point, but the velocities are different because the racecar is traveling in different directions.
Verbal, Visual

Figure 8 A cheetah's speed may be as fast as 90 km/h. To describe the cheetah's velocity, you must also know the direction in which it is moving.

Velocity

The cheetah is the fastest land animal in the world. Suppose a cheetah, running at 90 kilometers per hour, is 30 meters from an antelope that is standing still. How long will it be before the cheetah reaches the antelope? Do you have enough information to answer the question? The answer is no. Sometimes knowing only the speed of an object isn't enough. You also need to know the direction of the object's motion. Together, the speed and direction in which an object is moving are called **velocity.** To determine how long it will be before the cheetah reaches the antelope, you need to know the cheetah's velocity, not just its speed. **Velocity is a description of both speed and direction of motion. Velocity is a vector.**

Figure 8 shows a cheetah in motion. If you have ever seen a video of a cheetah chasing its prey, you know that a cheetah can change speed and direction very quickly. To represent the cheetah's motion, you could use velocity vectors. You would need vectors of varying lengths, each vector corresponding to the cheetah's velocity at a particular instant. A longer vector would represent a faster speed, and a shorter one would show a slower speed. The vectors would also point in different directions to represent the cheetah's direction at any moment.

A change in velocity can be the result of a change in speed, a change in direction, or both. The sailboat in Figure 9 moves in a straight line (constant direction) at a constant speed. The sailboat can be described as moving with uniform motion, which is another way of saying it has constant velocity. The sailboat may change its velocity simply by speeding up or slowing down. However, the sailboat's velocity also changes if it changes its direction. It may continue to move at a constant speed, but the change of direction is a change in velocity.

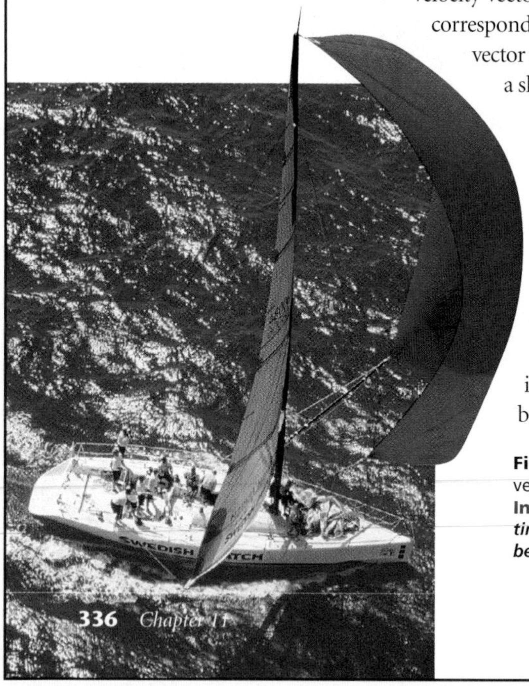

Figure 9 As the sailboat's direction changes, its velocity also changes, even if its speed stays the same. **Inferring** ***If the sailboat slows down at the same time that it changes direction, how will its velocity be changed?***

336 Chapter 11

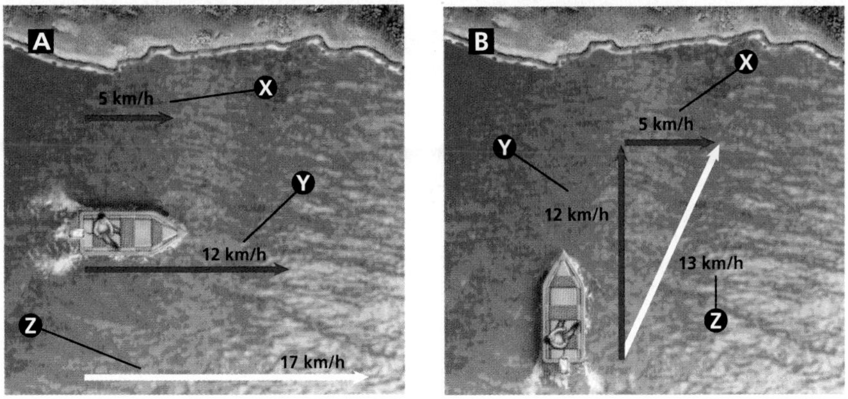
A
5 km/h
X
Y
12 km/h
Z
17 km/h
B
X
Y
5 km/h
12 km/h
13 km/h
Z

Figure 10 Vector addition is used when motion involves more than one velocity. **A** The velocity of the boat in the reference frame of the riverbank (17 km/h) is a combination of the relative velocities of the boat and the river. **B** You can determine the resultant velocity of the boat relative to the riverbank (13 km/h) by measuring from the tail of one vector to the head of the other.

Combining Velocities

Sometimes the motion of an object involves more than one velocity. **Two or more velocities add by vector addition.** The velocity of the river relative to the riverbank (X) and the velocity of the boat relative to the river (Y) in Figure 10A combine. They yield the velocity of the boat relative to the riverbank (Z). This velocity is 17 kilometers per hour downstream.

In Figure 10B, the relative velocities of the current (X) and the boat (Y) are at right angles to each other. Adding these velocity vectors yields a resultant velocity of the boat relative to the riverbank of 13 km/h (Z). Note that this velocity is at an angle to the riverbank.

Section 11.2 Assessment

Reviewing Concepts

1. What does velocity describe?
2. What shows the speed on a distance-time graph?
3. What is the difference between average speed and instantaneous speed?
4. How can two or more velocities be combined?

Critical Thinking

5. **Applying Concepts** Does a car's speedometer show instantaneous speed, average speed, or velocity? Explain.
6. **Designing Experiments** Describe an experiment you could perform to determine the average speed of a toy car rolling down an incline.
7. **Applying Concepts** Explain why the slope on a distance-time graph is speed. (*Hint:* Use the definition of *speed* on page 332 and the graphs in Figure 7.)

Math Practice

8. An Olympic swimmer swims 50.0 meters in 23.1 seconds. What is his average speed?
9. A plane's average speed between two cities is 600 km/h. If the trip takes 2.5 hours, how far does the plane fly? (*Hint:* Use the average speed formula in the form $d = \bar{v}t$.)

Combining Velocities

Use Visuals L1

Figure 10 Figure 10B shows two velocity vectors at right angles combining to form a single vector. You can use this opportunity to show students how to find the magnitude of resultant vectors.

Start by reminding students of the Pythagorean theorem:

$$a^2 + b^2 = c^2$$

for right triangles in which *a* and *b* are the legs and *c* is the hypotenuse. In this case, *a* is the speed of the boat, *b* is the speed of the river, and *c* is the resulting combined speed.

Do the following calculation on the board:

$$c = \sqrt{a^2 + b^2}$$
$$= \sqrt{(12 \text{ km/h})^2 + (5 \text{ km/h})^2}$$
$$= \sqrt{144 \text{ km}^2/\text{h}^2 + 25 \text{ km}^2/\text{h}^2}$$
$$= \sqrt{169 \text{ km}^2/\text{h}^2}$$
$$= 13 \text{ km/h}$$

When you have finished the calculation, point out that the result agrees with the speed shown in Figure 10B.

Visual, Logical

3 ASSESS

Evaluate Understanding L2

Ask students to write a paragraph describing how they could measure the average speed of a racecar on a racetrack. Also have them draw the velocity vectors at several locations for a racecar traveling at a constant speed around a circular track.

Reteach L1

Use the graphs in Figure 7 to reteach the concepts in the section.

Math Practice

Solutions L2

8. $\bar{v} = (50.0 \text{ m})/(23.1 \text{ s}) = 2.16 \text{ m/s}$
9. $d = \bar{v}t = (600 \text{ km/h})(2.5 \text{ h}) = 1500 \text{ km}$

Interactive Textbook If your class subscribes to the Interactive Textbook, use it to review key concepts in Section 11.2.

Answer to . . .

Figure 9 *Both the magnitude and direction of the velocity will change.*

Section 11.2 Assessment

1. Velocity describes both speed and direction of motion.
2. The slope of a line on a distance-time graph is equal to speed.
3. Average speed is calculated for the entire duration of a trip, whereas instantaneous speed is determined at a single moment.
4. Two or more velocities can be combined by vector addition.
5. A speedometer measures speed at the current moment, so it shows instantaneous speed, not average speed. Because a speedometer does not show direction it does not show velocity.
6. Students may describe how they could use a stopwatch to measure the time for the car to travel down the incline. The average speed would be calculated by dividing the distance traveled by the total time.
7. Slope is equal to the change in vertical value divided by the change in horizontal value. On a distance-time graph, the change in vertical value is a distance and the change in horizontal value is a time. Therefore, the slope is distance divided by time, which equals average speed.

CONCEPTS in Action

Navigation at Sea **L2**

Background

Before the invention of the compass, the most reliable source of information for navigators was the stars. Celestial navigation was useful not only at sea, but also in open deserts where there were few landmarks. The simplest examples of celestial navigation are the sighting of north using Polaris, the pole star, and crude approximations of east and west using sunrise and sunset. Early navigators at sea also often simply followed coastlines or tracked well-known ocean currents to keep from losing their way. The Polynesians were masters of navigation in the open sea, traveling long distances to pinpoint tiny islands in the South Pacific. The Polynesians are believed to have used the migratory paths of birds and the directions of waves as navigational clues.

CONCEPTS in Action

Navigation at Sea

For centuries, crossing the oceans was extremely perilous. There are few landmarks at sea to guide the sailor, and methods of measuring direction, speed, and distance were crude and often inaccurate.

The invention of the magnetic compass brought major advancement in navigation in the early 1100s. Although the compass allowed a sailor to maintain an accurate course, it did nothing to tell him where he actually was. For this, a frame of reference was needed, and the one adopted was the system of latitude and longitude. This system measures location in degrees north or south of the equator, and degrees east or west of Greenwich, England. Using a device called a sextant, latitude in the northern hemisphere was relatively easy to determine. Finding longitude was more difficult. The solution was to combine celestial observation and the use of a highly accurate sea-going clock that kept track of the time at a fixed location on Earth.

Sextant
This instrument was once an essential aid to navigation. With it, a sailor could accurately measure the angles of celestial bodies above the horizon. To take a reading, the observer looks through the telescope and moves the sextant's arm until an image of a star or the sun lines up with the horizon. The angle is then read off the scale.

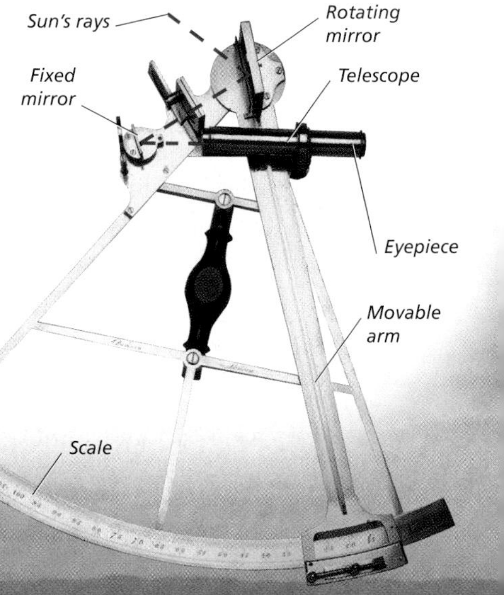

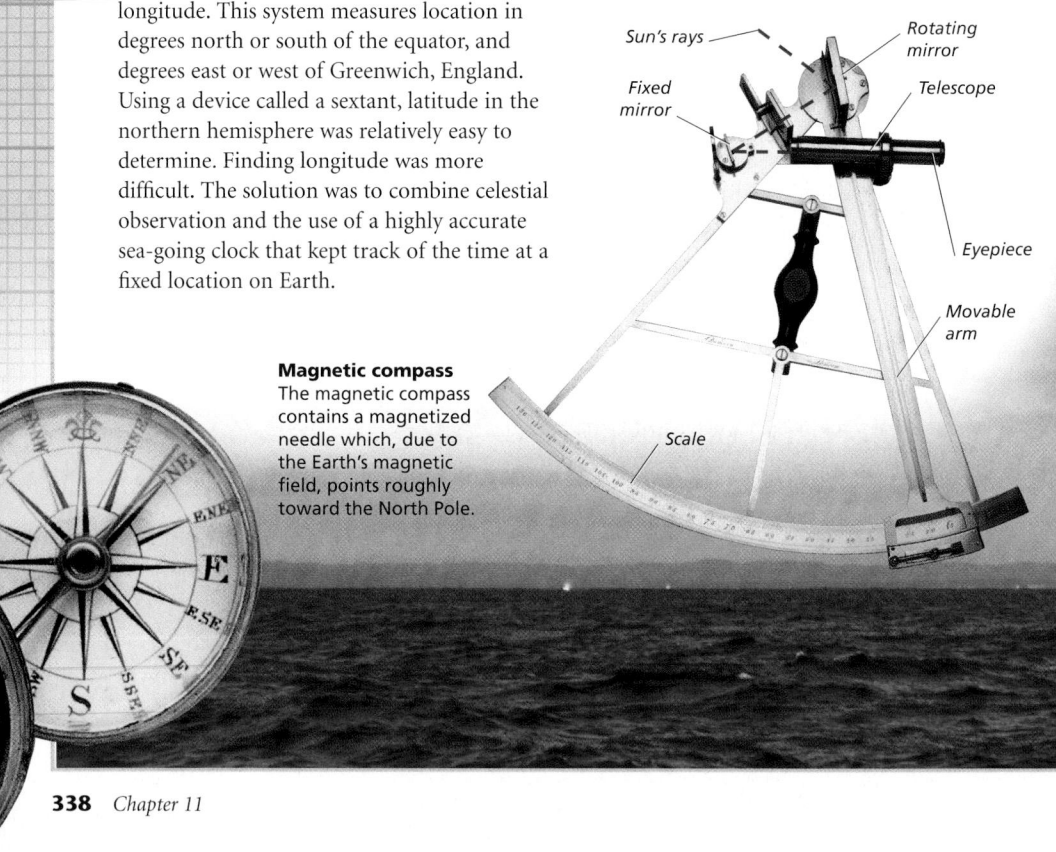

Sun's rays
Rotating mirror
Fixed mirror
Telescope
Eyepiece
Movable arm
Scale

NW
NE
ENE
E
ESE
SE
SSE
S

Magnetic compass
The magnetic compass contains a magnetized needle which, due to the Earth's magnetic field, points roughly toward the North Pole.

Finding location

Regular calculations of latitude and longitude have been the cornerstone of ocean navigation for about 300 years. A sextant and an accurate sea-going clock were needed to calculate both.

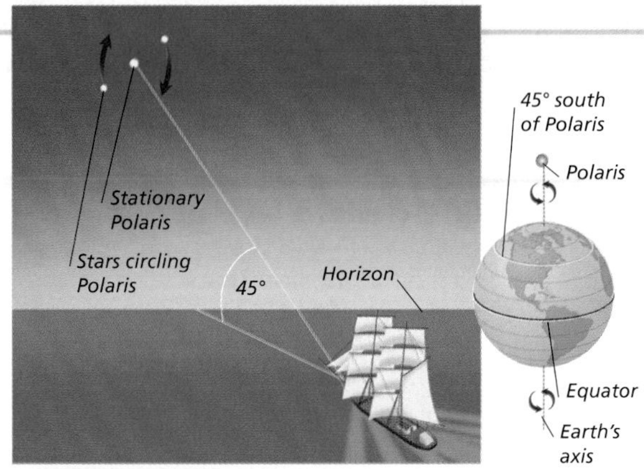

45° south of Polaris
Polaris
Stationary Polaris
Stars circling Polaris
45°
Horizon
Equator
Earth's axis

Determining latitude
To determine latitude is to find out how far north or south you are from the equator. In the northern hemisphere, latitude is measured with reference to Polaris. Using a sextant, you measure the angle of Polaris above the horizon, and this gives you your latitude, expressed in degrees. If Polaris is directly overhead, you must be at the North Pole (90° north latitude); if it is on the horizon, you must be at the equator (0°).

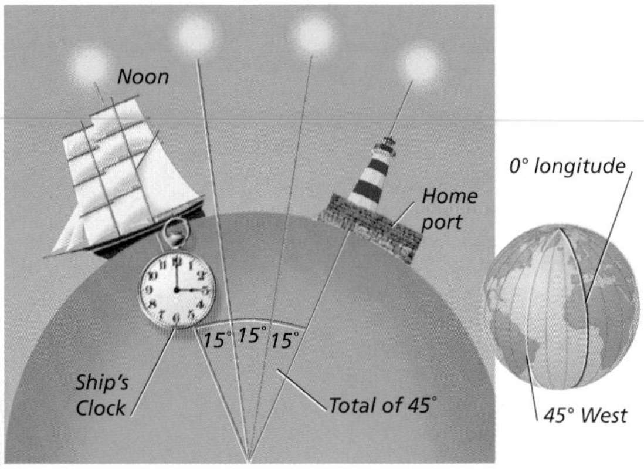

Noon
0° longitude
Home port
15°
15°
15°
Ship's Clock
Total of 45°
45° West

Determining longitude
To determine longitude is to find out how far east or west you are from Greenwich, England. To do this, while you are still in your home port, you set your sea-going clock for noon when the sun is at its highest point. Then, while you are at sea, you check the clock again when the sun is at its highest point. If the clock says 3 P.M., then you must have traveled 3 hours west of the port. Since the sun moves 15° per hour, 3 hours corresponds to 45° west.

Build Science Skills L2

Observing Have students go out on a clear night and locate Polaris, the pole star. Students may do this on their own, or you may have a class field trip. If you go as a group, also take a few pairs of binoculars and a telescope, if available. With a basic pair of binoculars, students can see many more stars, as well as many interesting celestial sights such as star clusters, the moons of Jupiter, and craters on Earth's moon. Teach students how to use the two stars at the end of the Big Dipper to locate Polaris. Then, follow the line from these two stars "up" away from the dipper (in the direction of the opening in the dipper; the actual direction will depend on the position of the dipper). The first bright star in the line is Polaris. Have students use a protractor and a ruler or other straight object to estimate Polaris' angle of elevation above the horizon. This angle should be equal to the latitude at which you are observing. Have students compare their estimates to the actual latitude.
Visual, Group, Portfolio

CONCEPTS — in Action —

(continued)

Build Science Skills L2

Measuring

ACTIVITY

Purpose After doing this activity, students will be able to use a handheld GPS receiver to find coordinates, mark waypoints, and navigate to a location.

Materials handheld GPS receivers, 1 per group

Advance Prep Clear data from all the GPS receivers. Set all receivers so they are using the same units for coordinates. If you are unfamiliar with operating a GPS receiver, review the manual and practice marking a few waypoints (waypoints are locations that you store in the memory of a GPS unit). Find several locations on the school grounds and write down the GPS coordinates for those locations (students will return to these locations in the activity).

Class Time 30 minutes

Procedure

1. Start by showing the class the basics of operating the GPS receiver. You may do this outdoors, or if you are in the classroom, put the receiver in simulator mode. Show students how to tell how strong the signals are, how to read the coordinates of their location, and how to mark a waypoint.

2. Start all groups at a single point. Have them acquire the coordinates at that location and mark a waypoint. Assign each group a different location and give them the coordinates (but do not tell them where the location is). Then, have them use the receivers to find their assigned locations. You may have them use the navigation feature of the receiver to find the location, or they may just use the coordinates. Have them mark a waypoint when they reach the location.

3. After they have found their location, have the group return and describe the location to you. Verify that it is close to the location that you intended. Check each group's receiver to see if their marked waypoints have the correct coordinates.

CONCEPTS in Action

Modern navigation

Today's sea navigators are fortunate by comparison with their predecessors. Instead of having to make complex calculations involving times and sextant angles, they can buy a global positioning system receiver. This modern receiver not only provides quick and accurate readings of latitude and longitude, but it also displays the ship's position on a digital chart.

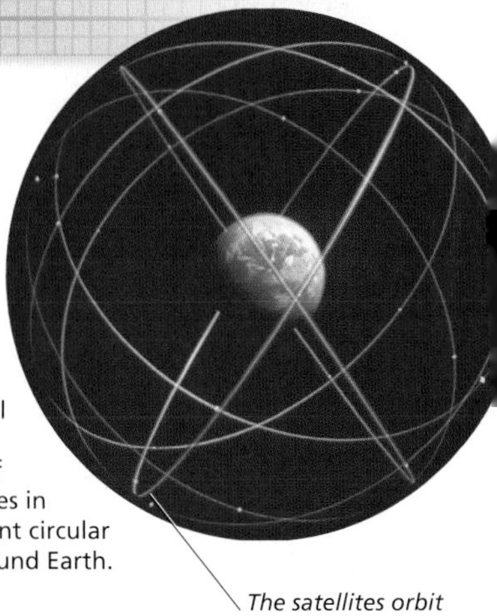

Satellite network The global network consists of 24 satellites in six different circular orbits around Earth.
The satellites orbit 20,200 km above Earth's surface.

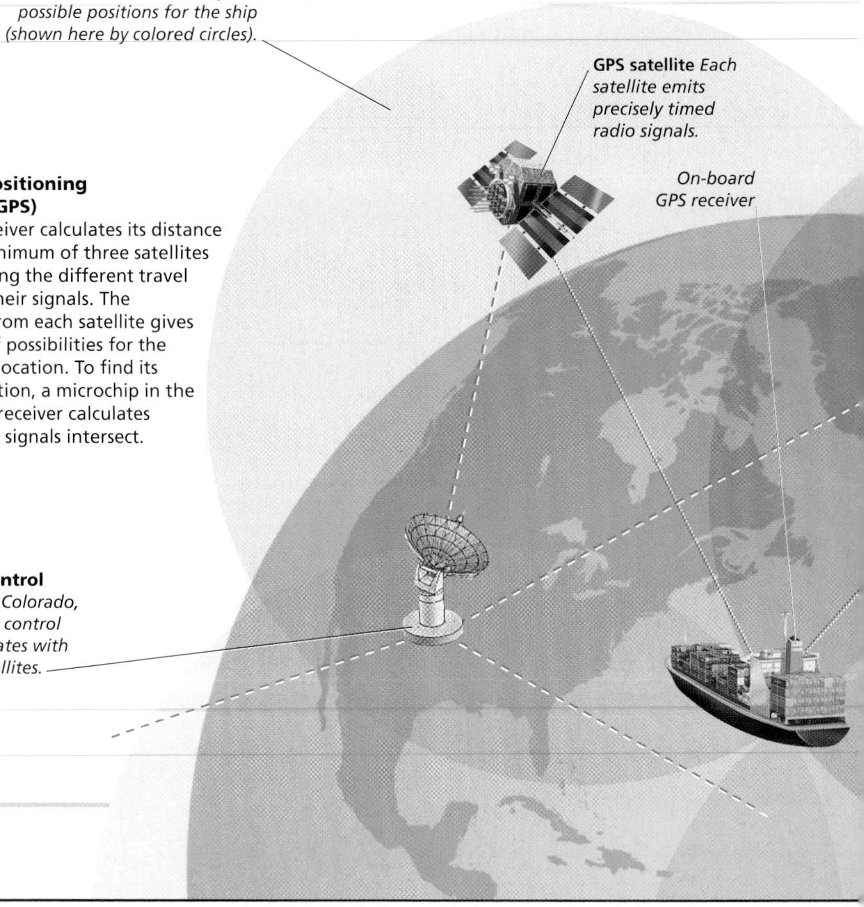

Range of positions *Each satellite transmits a range of possible positions for the ship (shown here by colored circles).*
GPS satellite *Each satellite emits precisely timed radio signals.*
On-board GPS receiver
Global Positioning System (GPS)
A GPS receiver calculates its distance from a minimum of three satellites by analyzing the different travel times of their signals. The distance from each satellite gives a range of possibilities for the receiver's location. To find its exact position, a microchip in the on-board receiver calculates where the signals intersect.
Master control *Located in Colorado, the master control communicates with all the satellites.*

Charting a course
A navigator normally keeps a record of the ship's movements on a chart. Positions obtained by GPS or other means are plotted on the chart, which can also be used to work out a compass bearing or a course for the next part of the voyage.

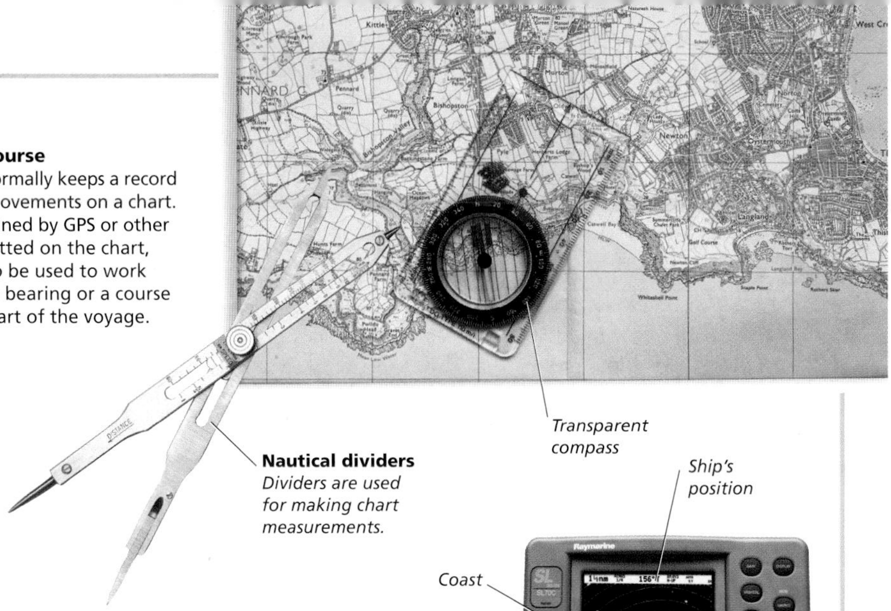
Transparent compass

Nautical dividers
Dividers are used for making chart measurements.

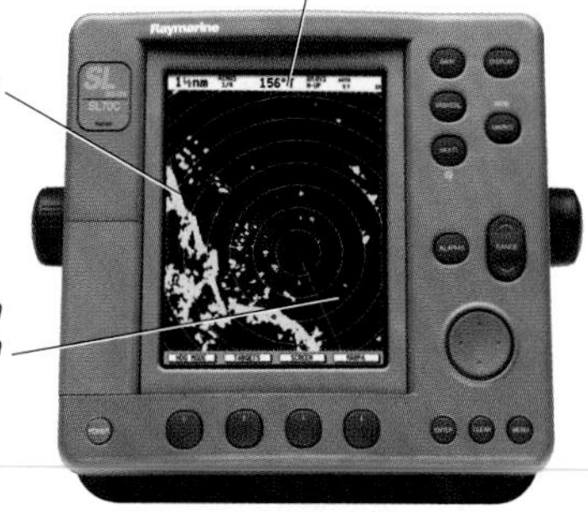
Ship's position
Coast
Open sea
Raymarine

Using radar
A radar set displays nearby land, boats, and other surface objects. It is useful for both navigation and collision avoidance, especially in foggy conditions.

GPS receiver
Today, receivers are made in a range of sizes down to handheld models. They usually give a position accurate to 100 meters, but enhanced units are accurate within 10 meters.

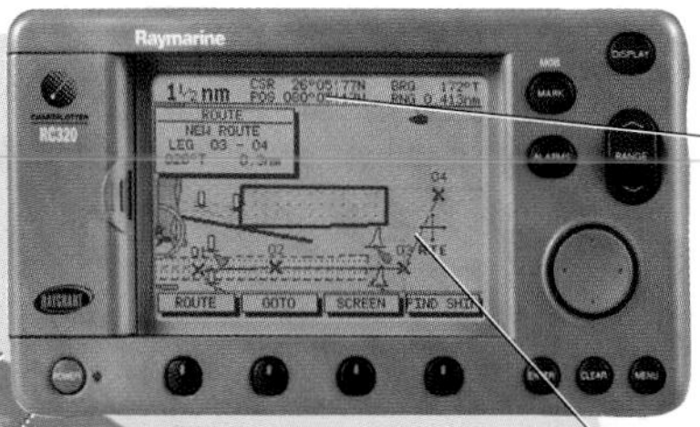
Raymarine
Position given by satellite
New route plotted on screen
ROUTE
GOTO
SCREEN
FIND SHIP
DISPLAY
CLEAR
MENU

Going Further

- Research the term *knots,* which is used for measuring a ship's speed. Write a paragraph to explain how speed was originally estimated on a ship by using knots.
- Take a Discovery Channel Video Field Trip by watching "Charting New Ground."

Discovery CHANNEL SCHOOL Video Field Trip

Expected Outcome Students may have trouble finding the locations at first. The GPS receivers may have varying degrees of accuracy, depending on the receiver and the outside conditions. Also, students may be confused if the axes of the coordinates do not align with the boundaries of the area. However, students should get used to operating the receiver and following the coordinates. Note that due to inaccuracies in GPS data and to differences in individual receivers, the locations that students find might not align perfectly with the locations that you found initially.
Kinesthetic, Group, Logical

Going Further

Students' paragraphs should describe how early navigators measured the speed of a ship by throwing a log or wooden panel overboard. The log or panel was tied with a rope that had knots tied at regular intervals. The speed of the ship (relative to the water) could be measured by counting the number of knots that passed over the edge of the ship in a certain time interval. Knots are still used as units of speed in navigation, although they are measured with more precise instruments. 1 knot = 1 nautical mile per hour = 6076 feet per hour = 1.15 mph.
Verbal

Discovery CHANNEL SCHOOL

Video Field Trip

Charting New Ground

After students have viewed the Video Field Trip, ask them the following questions: **What was the shape of Earth according to the ancient Greeks? What Earth dimension did they calculate using this shape?** *(They knew Earth was a sphere, and calculated its circumference.)* **What does latitude measure? Longitude?** *(Latitude measures how far north or south a location is. Longitude measures how far east or west a location is.)* **What did navigators notice about how high the sun rose at noon in northern regions? How could this be used to determine the position of their ships?** *(Navigators noticed that in northern regions the sun remained low in the sky even in the middle of the summer. The height of the sun at noon told navigators how far north they were. Some students may note that when the sun is low in the sky at noon in the Southern Hemisphere, this would indicate how far south you are.)* **How did navigators know how far west they were from their homeport in the 1700s?** *(The ship's clock would be set at the same time as the clock in the navigator's homeport. As the ship traveled west, the sun was lower in the sky when the clock read noon.)* **List two modern technologies that are now used in making maps.** *(Student answers may include aerial photography, satellites, and computers.)*

1 FOCUS

Objectives

11.3.1 **Identify** changes in motion that produce acceleration.
11.3.2 **Describe** examples of constant acceleration.
11.3.3 **Calculate** the acceleration of an object.
11.3.4 **Interpret** speed-time and distance-time graphs.
11.3.5 **Classify** acceleration as positive or negative.
11.3.6 **Describe** instantaneous acceleration.

Reading Focus

Build Vocabulary L2

Word Forms Point out other forms of the terms or parts of the terms. For example, in this section explain that *linear* contains the word *line* and means, "in a straight line," or more generally, "having to do with lines." Then have students predict what *nonlinear* might mean. *(It means not in a straight line or having to do with lines that are not straight.)*

Reading Strategy L2

a. Speed (or direction)
b. Direction (or speed)
c. m/s^2

2 INSTRUCT

What is Acceleration?

Use Visuals L1

Figure 11 Use the example of a bouncing basketball to introduce acceleration. Ask, **As the ball falls from the girl's hand, how does its speed change?** *(Its speed increases.)* **What happens to the speed of the ball as the ball rises from the ground back to her hand?** *(The speed decreases.)* **At what points does the ball have zero velocity?** *(When it touches the girl's hand and when it touches the floor)* **How does the velocity of the ball change when it bounces on the floor?** *(The speed quickly drops to zero, then quickly increases again. The ball also changes direction.)* **Visual, Logical**

11.3 Acceleration

Reading Focus

Key Concepts

- How are changes in velocity described?
- How can you calculate acceleration?
- How does a speed-time graph indicate acceleration?
- What is instantaneous acceleration?

Vocabulary

- acceleration
- free fall
- constant acceleration
- linear graph
- nonlinear graph

Reading Strategy

Summarizing Read the section on acceleration. Then copy and complete the concept map below to organize what you know about acceleration.

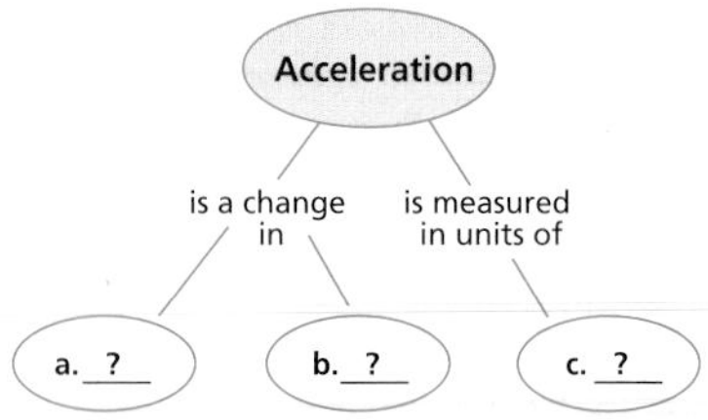
Acceleration
is a change in
is measured in units of
a. ?
b. ?
c. ?

Figure 11 The basketball constantly changes velocity as it rises and falls.

A basketball constantly changes velocity during a game. The player in Figure 11 dribbles the ball down the court, and the ball speeds up as it falls and slows down as it rises. As she passes the ball, it flies through the air and suddenly stops when a teammate catches it. The velocity of the ball increases again as it is thrown toward the basket.

But the rate at which velocity changes is also important. Imagine a basketball player running down the court and slowly coming to a stop. Now imagine the player running down the court and stopping suddenly. If the player stops slowly, his or her velocity changes slowly. If the player stops suddenly, his or her velocity changes quickly. The ball handler's teammates must position themselves to assist the drive or to take a pass. Opposing team members want to prevent the ball handler from reaching the basket. Each player must anticipate the ball handler's motion.

Velocity changes frequently, not only in a basketball game, but throughout our physical world. Describing changes in velocity, and how fast they occur, is a necessary part of describing motion.

What Is Acceleration?

The rate at which velocity changes is called **acceleration.** Recall that velocity is a combination of speed and direction. **Acceleration can be described as changes in speed, changes in direction, or changes in both. Acceleration is a vector.**

Section Resources

Print
- ***Reading and Study Workbook With Math Support,*** Section 11.3
- ***Math Skills and Problem Solving Workbook,*** Section 11.3
- ***Transparencies,*** Section 11.3

Technology
- ***Interactive Textbook,*** Section 11.3
- ***Presentation Pro CD-ROM,*** Section 11.3
- ***Go Online,*** NSTA SciLinks, Acceleration

342 Chapter 11

Changes in Speed We often use the word *acceleration* to describe situations in which the speed of an object is increasing. A television newscaster describing the liftoff of a rocket-launched space shuttle, for example, might exclaim, "That shuttle is really accelerating!" We understand that the newscaster is describing the spacecraft's quickly increasing speed as it clears its launch pad and rises through the atmosphere. Scientifically, however, acceleration applies to any change in an object's velocity. This change may be either an increase or a decrease in speed. Acceleration can be caused by positive (increasing) change in speed or by negative (decreasing) change in speed.

For example, suppose that you are sitting on a bus waiting at a stoplight. The light turns green and the bus moves forward. You feel the acceleration as you are pushed back against your seat. The acceleration is the result of an increase in the speed of the bus. As the bus moves down the street at a constant speed, its acceleration is zero. You no longer feel pushed toward your seat. When the bus approaches another stoplight, it begins to slow down. Again, its speed is changing, so the bus is accelerating. You feel pulled away from your seat. Acceleration results from increases or decreases in speed. As the bus slows to a stop, it experiences negative acceleration, also known as deceleration. Deceleration is an acceleration that slows an object's speed.

An example of acceleration due to change in speed is **free fall,** the movement of an object toward Earth solely because of gravity. Recall that the unit for velocity is meters per second. The unit for acceleration, then, is meters per second per second. This unit is typically written as meters per second squared (m/s^2). Objects falling near Earth's surface accelerate downward at a rate of 9.8 m/s^2. Each second an object is in free fall, its velocity increases downward by 9.8 meters per second. Imagine the stone in Figure 12 falling from the mouth of the well. After 1 second, the stone will be falling at about 9.8 m/s. After 2 seconds, the stone will be going faster by 9.8 m/s. Its speed will now be downward at 19.6 m/s. The change in the stone's speed is 9.8 m/s^2, the acceleration due to gravity.

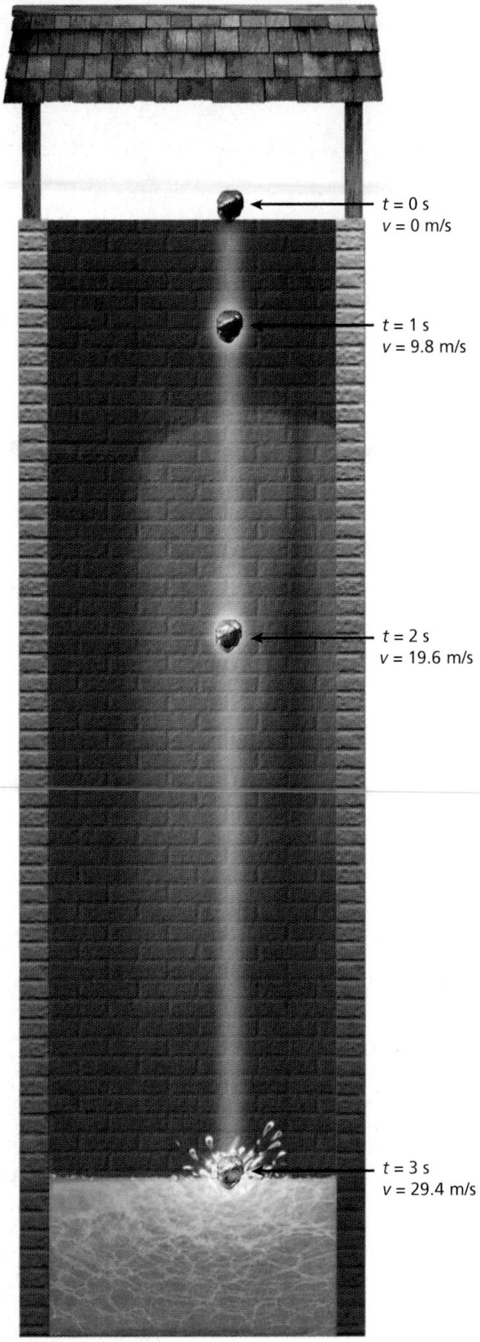

t = 0 s
v = 0 m/s
t = 1 s
v = 9.8 m/s
t = 2 s
v = 19.6 m/s
t = 3 s
v = 29.4 m/s

Figure 12 The velocity of an object in free fall increases 9.8 m/s each second.

Build Reading Literacy L1

Outline Refer to page **156D** in **Chapter 6,** which provides the guidelines for an outline.

Have students create an outline of Section 11.3 (pp. 342–348). Outlines should follow the head structure used in the section. Major headings are shown in green, and subheadings are shown in blue. Ask students, **Based on your outline, what are two types of changes associated with acceleration?** *(Changes in speed and changes in direction)* **Name two types of graphs that can be used to represent acceleration.** *(Speed-time graphs and distance-time graphs)*
Verbal, Logical

Address Misconceptions L2

Students may think that if an object is accelerating then the object is speeding up. Explain to students that this is true in common, everyday usage. But in scientific terms, acceleration refers to any change in velocity. Velocity is a vector including both speed and direction, so acceleration can be speeding up, slowing down, or even just changing direction.
Verbal

Use Visuals L1

Figure 12 Have students examine Figure 12. Ask, **How much time passes between each image of the falling rock?** *(1 s)* **How does the distance traveled change between successive time intervals?** *(The distance traveled increases.)* **How does the average speed change between successive time intervals?** *(The average speed increases.)*
Visual, Logical

Customize for Inclusion Students

Visually Impaired
Students who are visually impaired may grasp the concept of acceleration by considering the following scenario. When traveling in a closed car with your eyes closed, it is hard to tell how far you have traveled or how fast you are going. But you can feel accelerations. Ask, **How do you know when you are speeding up or slowing down?** *(When speeding up, it feels as if you are pressed against the back of the seat. When you are slowing down, it feels as if you are pulled forward against the seat belt.)* **How can you tell if you are changing direction?** *(You can feel yourself pulled to one side, away from the direction the car is turning.)*

Teacher Demo

Pendulum Accelerometer L2

Purpose Students observe how the displacement of a pendulum can be used as evidence of acceleration, and how a pendulum can show that acceleration is taking place during uniform circular motion.

Materials short pendulum (25 cm), turntable, lab stand, tape

Advance Prep Place the lab stand on the outer edge of the turntable. The stand should be tall enough to hold the pendulum so that it doesn't touch the turntable. Tape the base of the stand to the turntable.

Procedure Tell students that a pendulum can be used to provide evidence of acceleration. Acceleration causes displacement of the pendulum. Demonstrate this by walking forward and backward while holding a pendulum in one hand held in front of you. You will have to accelerate slightly as you walk; otherwise, the pendulum will start swinging. Ask students to describe the position of the pendulum when you stand still, walk forward, change direction, and walk backward. Show students the turntable, and tie the pendulum to the lab stand. Ask students to predict how the pendulum will be displaced when the turntable is spinning. Start the turntable spinning, and have students compare the observed displacement of the pendulum to their predictions.

Expected Outcome When you are holding the pendulum, the pendulum will be displaced toward you when you are walking forward and away from you when you are walking backward. When the turntable is spinning, the pendulum will be displaced away from the center of the turntable. This demonstrates that acceleration is taking place during uniform circular motion. The acceleration in this case is purely a change in direction.
Kinesthetic, Visual

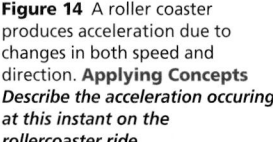

Figure 13 When you ride on a carousel, you accelerate because of the changing direction.

Changes in Direction Acceleration isn't always the result of changes in speed. You can accelerate even if your speed is constant. You experience this type of acceleration if you ride a bicycle around a curve. Although you may have a constant speed, your change in direction means you are accelerating. You also may have experienced this type of acceleration if you have ridden on a carousel like the one in Figure 13. A horse on the carousel is traveling at a constant speed, but it is accelerating because its direction is constantly changing.

Changes in Speed and Direction Sometimes motion is characterized by changes in both speed and direction at the same time. You experience this type of motion if you ride on a roller coaster like the one in Figure 14. The roller coaster ride starts out slowly as the cars travel up the steeply inclined rails. The cars reach the top of the incline. Suddenly they plummet toward the ground and then whip around a curve. You are thrown backward, forward, and sideways as your velocity increases, decreases, and changes direction. Your acceleration is constantly changing because of changes in the speed and direction of the cars of the roller coaster.

Similarly, passengers in a car moving at the posted speed limit along a winding road experience rapidly changing acceleration. The car may enter a long curve at the same time that it slows to maintain a safe interval behind another car. The car is accelerating both because it is changing direction and because its speed is decreasing.

Figure 14 A roller coaster produces acceleration due to changes in both speed and direction. **Applying Concepts** ***Describe the acceleration occuring at this instant on the rollercoaster ride.***

Constant Acceleration The velocity of an object moving in a straight line changes at a constant rate when the object is experiencing constant acceleration. **Constant acceleration** is a steady change in velocity. That is, the velocity of the object changes by the same amount each second. An example of constant acceleration is illustrated by the jet airplane shown in Figure 15. The airplane's acceleration may be constant during a portion of its takeoff.

Figure 15 Constant acceleration during takeoff results in changes to an aircraft's velocity that are in a constant direction.

Reading Checkpoint *What is constant acceleration?*

Calculating Acceleration

Acceleration is the rate at which velocity changes. **You calculate acceleration for straight-line motion by dividing the change in velocity by the total time.** If a is the acceleration, v_i is the initial velocity, v_f is the final velocity, and t is total time, this equation can be written as follows.

Acceleration

$$\text{Acceleration} = \frac{\text{Change in velocity}}{\text{Total time}} = \frac{(v_f - v_i)}{t}$$

Notice in this formula that velocity is in the numerator and time is in the denominator. If the velocity increases, the numerator is positive and thus the acceleration is also positive. For example, if you are coasting downhill on a bicycle, your velocity increases and your acceleration is positive. If the velocity decreases, then the numerator is negative and the acceleration is also negative. For example, if you continue coasting after you reach the bottom of the hill, your velocity decreases and your acceleration is negative.

Remember that acceleration and velocity are both vector quantities. Thus, if an object moving at constant speed changes its direction of travel, there is still acceleration. In other words, the acceleration can change even if the velocity is constant. Think about a car moving at a constant speed as it rounds a curve. Because its direction is changing, the car is accelerating.

To determine a change in velocity, subtract one velocity vector from another. If the motion is in a straight line, however, the velocity can be treated as speed. You can then find acceleration from the change in speed divided by the time.

Go Online NSTA SCiLINKS

For: Links on acceleration
Visit: www.SciLinks.org
Web Code: ccn-2113

Calculating Acceleration

Build Science Skills L2

Calculating Once students have learned the equation for acceleration, return to Figure 12 on p. 343. Apply the equation for acceleration to calculate the magnitude of the stone's acceleration in the first time interval:

$a = (v_f - v_i)/t$
$= (9.8\ m/s - 0\ m/s)/(1\ s) = 9.8\ m/s^2$

Then, have the students use the equation to calculate the acceleration of the stone for other time intervals. They should find that for every time interval, the magnitude of the acceleration is 9.8 m/s^2. **Logical**

Go Online NSTA SCiLINKS

Download a worksheet on acceleration for students to complete, and find additional teacher support from NSTA SciLinks.

Answer to . . .

Figure 14 *The roller coaster is accelerating; its speed is increasing (because it is falling) and its direction is changing (because the track is curved).*

Reading Checkpoint *Constant acceleration is a steady change in velocity.*

Math Practice

Solutions

1. $a = (v_f - v_i)/t = (0\ m/s - 10\ m/s)/20\ s = -0.5\ m/s^2$
2. $(v_f - v_i) = at = (9.0\ m/s^2)(4.0\ s) = 36\ m/s$
3. $v_i = 0$; $v_f = at = (9.8\ m/s^2)(2.0\ s) = 2.0 \times 10^1 m/s$
4. $v_f = 0$; $v_i = -at = -(9.8\ m/s^2)(2.5\ s) = -25\ m/s$ (the minus sign indicates that the velocity is in the direction opposite the acceleration)
Logical

For Extra Help **L1**

Students may have difficulty rearranging the equation to solve for other variables, especially for v_i or v_f. Write the procedure clearly on the board and describe each step. For example, to solve for v_f, 1) multiply both sides of the equation by t, then 2) cancel the t/t on the right side of the equation, then 3) add v_i to both sides of the equation. Afterwards, have students work in pairs and demonstrate the procedure for each other for the different variables. When you feel they understand the process, they can begin to solve problems that include numbers.
Logical

Direct students to the **Math Skills** in the **Skills and Reference Handbook** at the end of the student text for additional help.

Additional Problems

1. A sprinter accelerates from the starting block to a speed of 8.0 m/s in 4.0 s. What is the magnitude of the sprinter's acceleration? *(2.0 m/s²)*
2. A car is traveling at 14 m/s. Stepping on the gas pedal causes the car to accelerate at 2.0 m/s². How long does the driver have to step on the pedal to reach a speed of 18 m/s? *(2.0 s)*
Logical, Portfolio

Math Skills

Calculating Acceleration

A ball rolls down a ramp, starting from rest. After 2 seconds, its velocity is 6 meters per second. What is the acceleration of the ball?

1 Read and Understand

What information are you given?

Time = 2 s

Starting velocity = 0 m/s

Ending velocity = 6 m/s

2 Plan and Solve

What unknown are you trying to calculate?

Acceleration = ?

What formula contains the given quantities and the unknown?

$$a = \frac{(v_f - v_i)}{t}$$

Replace each variable with its known value.

$$\text{Acceleration} = \frac{(6\ \text{m/s} - 0\ \text{m/s})}{2\ \text{s}}$$

$$= 3\ \text{m/s}^2 \text{ down the ramp}$$

3 Look Back and Check

Is your answer reasonable?

Objects in free fall accelerate at a rate of 9.8 m/s². The ramp is not very steep. An acceleration of 3 m/s² seems reasonable.

Math Practice

1. A car traveling at 10 m/s starts to decelerate steadily. It comes to a complete stop in 20 seconds. What is its acceleration?
2. An airplane travels down a runway for 4.0 seconds with an acceleration of 9.0 m/s². What is its change in velocity during this time?
3. A child drops a ball from a bridge. The ball strikes the water under the bridge 2.0 seconds later. What is the velocity of the ball when it strikes the water?
4. A boy throws a rock straight up into the air. It reaches the highest point of its flight after 2.5 seconds. How fast was the rock going when it left the boy's hand?

Graphs of Accelerated Motion

You can use a graph to calculate acceleration. For example, consider a downhill skier who is moving in a straight line. After traveling down the hill for 1 second, the skier's speed is 4 meters per second. In the next second the speed increases by an additional 4 meters per second, so the skier's acceleration is 4 m/s². Figure 16 is a graph of the skier's speed. **The slope of a speed-time graph is acceleration.** This slope is change in speed divided by change in time.

Speed-Time Graphs The skier's speed increased at a constant rate because the skier was moving down the hill with constant acceleration. Constant acceleration is represented on a speed–time graph by a straight line. The graph in Figure 16 is an example of a **linear graph,** in which the displayed data form straight-line parts. The slope of the line is the acceleration.

Constant negative acceleration decreases speed. A speed-time graph of the motion of a bicycle slowing to a stop is shown in Figure 17. The horizontal line segment represents constant speed. The line segment sloping downward represents the bicycle slowing down. The change in speed is negative, so the slope of the line is negative.

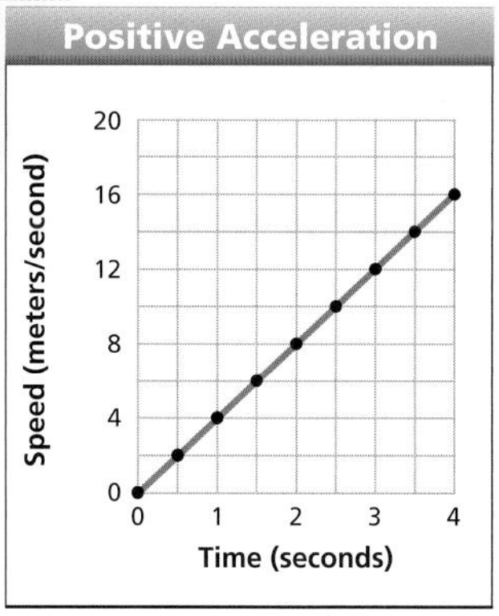

Positive Acceleration
Speed (meters/second)
20
16
12
8
4
0
0
1
2
3
4
Time (seconds)

Figure 16 The slope of a speed-time graph indicates acceleration. A positive slope shows that the skier's acceleration is positive.

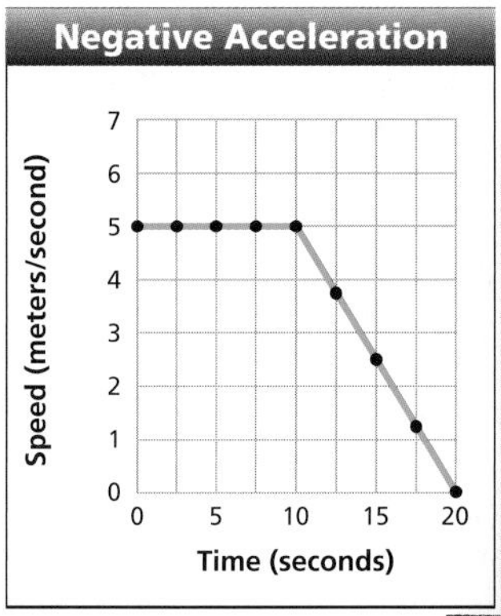

Negative Acceleration
Speed (meters/second)
7
6
5
4
3
2
1
0
0
5
10
15
20
Time (seconds)

Figure 17 The horizontal part of the graph shows a biker's constant speed. The part of the graph with negative slope shows negative acceleration as the mountain biker slows to a stop.

Motion 347

Graphs of Accelerated Motion

Build Math Skills **L1**

Finding Slope on a Graph Remind students that the slope of a line on a graph is found by dividing the difference of two points on the vertical axis by the corresponding points on the horizontal axis. The two points used to find the slope should be chosen as far apart on the line as possible.

Have students calculate the slope of the line on the graph in Figure 16. Tell them also to include the units in their calculation. *(4 m/s²)* Now have them calculate the slope of the line between 10 and 20 seconds on the graph in Figure 17. *(0.5 m/s²)*
Logical

Direct students to the **Math Skills** in the **Skills and Reference Handbook** at the end of the student text for additional help.

Use Visuals **L1**

Figure 17 Ask students the following questions about the speed-time graph in Figure 17. **What are the units on the vertical axis?** *(m/s)* **What are the units on the horizontal axis?** *(s)* **What would be the units of the slope of a line on this graph?** *(m/s/s, or m/s²)* Remind students that the bike represents the motion of a mountain biker in the photograph. Ask students, **Is the bike moving at time zero?** *(Yes)* **How fast is it moving at that time?** *(5 m/s)* **What happens to the bike after 10 seconds?** *(It starts to slow down.)* **How would you describe the acceleration of the bike from that point on?** *(The acceleration is constant and negative.)*
Visual, Logical

Section 11.3 (continued)

Instantaneous Acceleration

Integrate Math **L2**

Differential calculus is the branch of mathematics that physicists use when considering instantaneous quantities, such as instantaneous speed or instantaneous acceleration. When you use calculus to determine acceleration, you can take the difference in velocities over smaller and smaller time intervals until the time interval becomes, in effect, infinitely small. The slope of a curved line is equal to the slope of a line drawn tangent to a point on the plotted curve. Graphically, this is like finding the slope of a line connecting two points on a speed-time graph, but then moving the points closer and closer together until you have the slope of a line tangent to the curve at a single point on the graph. In this case, the slope of the line represents the instantaneous acceleration at that point.
Logical, Visual

3 ASSESS

Evaluate Understanding **L2**

Ask students to sketch a speed-time graph of a car starting from rest, accelerating up to the speed limit, maintaining that speed, then slowing again to a stop.

Reteach **L1**

Use the graphs on page 347 to reteach the concepts in the section. Ask students to identify which kind of acceleration cannot be shown on the graphs.
(A change in direction)

Math Practice

Solutions **L2**

8. $a = (v_f - v_i)/t =$
$(25 \text{ m/s} - 0 \text{ m/s})/(30.0 \text{ s}) =$
0.83 m/s^2

9. $a = (v_f - v_i)/t =$
$(30.0 \text{ m/s} - 25 \text{ m/s})/(10.0 \text{ s}) =$
0.50 m/s^2

Interactive Textbook If your class subscribes to the Interactive Textbook, use it to review key concepts in Section 11.3.

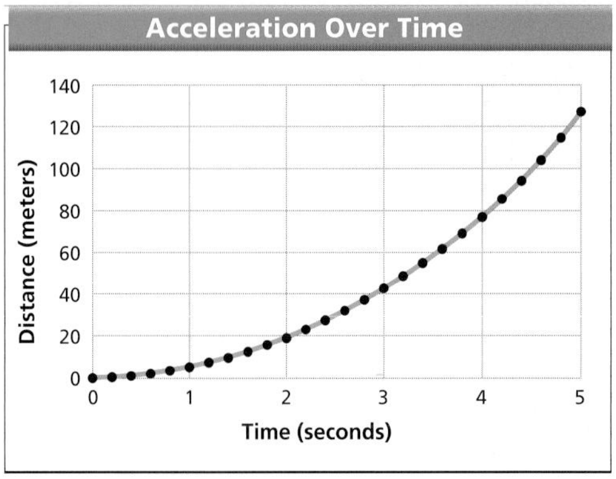

Acceleration Over Time
Distance (meters)
0
20
40
60
80
100
120
140
Time (seconds)
0
1
2
3
4
5

Figure 18 A distance-time graph of accelerated motion is a curve.

Distance-Time Graphs Accelerated motion is represented by a curved line on a distance-time graph. In a **nonlinear graph,** a curve connects the data points that are plotted. Figure 18 is a distance-time graph. The data in this graph are for a ball dropped from rest toward the ground.

Compare the slope of the curve during the first second to the slope of the curve during the fourth second. Notice that the slope is much greater during the fourth second than it is during the first second. Because the slope represents the speed of the ball, an increasing slope means that the speed is increasing. An increasing speed means that the ball is accelerating.

Instantaneous Acceleration

Acceleration is rarely constant, and motion is rarely in a straight line. A skateboarder moving along a half-pipe changes speed and direction. As a result, her acceleration changes. At each moment she is accelerating, but her instantaneous acceleration is always changing. **Instantaneous acceleration is how fast a velocity is changing at a specific instant.**

Acceleration involves a change in velocity or direction or both, so the vector of the skateboarder's acceleration can point in any direction. The vector's length depends on how fast she is changing her velocity. At every moment she has an instantaneous acceleration, even if she is standing still and the acceleration vector is zero.

Section 11.3 Assessment

Reviewing Concepts

1. Describe three types of changes in velocity.
2. What is the equation for acceleration?
3. What shows acceleration on a speed-time graph?
4. Define instantaneous acceleration.

Critical Thinking

5. **Comparing and Contrasting** How are deceleration and acceleration related?
6. **Applying Concepts** Two trains leave a station at the same time. Train A travels at a constant speed of 16 m/s. Train B starts at 8.0 m/s but accelerates constantly at 1.0 m/s^2. After 10.0 seconds, which train has the greater speed?
7. **Inferring** Suppose you plot the distance traveled by an object at various times and you discover that the graph is not a straight line. What does this indicate about the object's acceleration?

Math Practice

8. A train moves from rest to a speed of 25 m/s in 30.0 seconds. What is the magnitude of its acceleration?
9. A car traveling at a speed of 25 m/s increases its speed to 30.0 m/s in 10.0 seconds. What is the magnitude of its acceleration?

348 *Chapter 11*

Section 11.3 Assessment

1. Changes in velocity can be described as changes in speed, changes in direction, or changes in both (or, an increase in speed, a decrease in speed, or a change in direction).
2. $a = (v_f - v_i)/t$
3. The slope of the line on a speed-time graph gives the acceleration.
4. Instantaneous acceleration is how fast the velocity is changing at a specific instant.
5. Deceleration is a special case of acceleration in which the speed of an object is decreasing.
6. Train B ($v = v_o + at = 8.0 \text{ m/s} +$ $(1.0 \text{ m/s}^2)(10.0 \text{ s}) = 8.0 \text{ m/s} +$ $10.0 \text{ m/s} = 18 \text{ m/s}$)
7. The graph indicates that the object is accelerating.

Exploration Lab

Investigating the Velocity of a Sinking Marble

In this lab, you will graph the motion of a marble falling through shampoo.

Problem What does a distance-time graph look like for a marble falling through shampoo?

Materials

- clear shampoo
- 100-mL graduated cylinder
- 2 small marbles
- stopwatch
- forceps
- masking tape
- metric ruler
- 10-mL graduated cylinder
- long glass stirring rod
- dropper pipet
- graph paper

Skills Measuring, Observing, Using Tables and Graphs

Procedure

1. On a separate sheet of paper, make a copy of the data table shown.

Data Table		
Distance (mm)	First Marble Time (s)	Second Marble Time (s)

2. Wrap a small amount of masking tape around the tips of the forceps. This will allow you to grip the marble with them.
3. Measure the distance between the 10-mL gradations on the 100-mL graduated cylinder. Record the new distance in the first row of your data table.
4. Multiply this distance by 2 and write the result in the second row. For the third row, multiply the distance by 3. Continue until you have written distances in 10 rows.
5. Slowly pour 100 mL of clear shampoo into the 100-mL graduated cylinder.
6. Be ready to observe the marble as it falls through the shampoo. Grasp the marble with the forceps and hold the marble just above the shampoo-filled graduated cylinder.
7. Say "Go!" as you drop the marble into the shampoo. At the same moment, your partner should start the stopwatch.
8. Each time the lower edge of the marble reaches a 10-mL mark on the cylinder, say "Now." Your partner should note and record the time on the stopwatch.
9. Continue calling out "Now" each time the marble reaches a 10-mL mark until it comes to rest on the bottom of the cylinder. Say "Stop!"
10. Use the 10-mL graduated cylinder to add about 8 mL of water to the 100-mL graduated cylinder. Use the glass stirring rod to mix the water and shampoo gently but thoroughly.
11. With the dropper pipet, remove enough liquid from the graduated cylinder to decrease the volume to 100 mL.
12. Repeat Steps 6 through 9 using another marble.
13. Wash all supplies as instructed by your teacher.

Analyze and Conclude

1. **Using Tables and Graphs** Use the data you collected to make a distance-time graph for each of the two marbles.
2. **Observing** Explain the motion of the marbles as they fell through the shampoo. How did you show this motion on your graphs?
3. **Inferring** Based on your graphs, were the marbles accelerating? Explain your answers.
4. **Calculating** Use your data table to calculate the average speed of each marble.

Go Online PHSchool.com

For: Data sharing
Visit: PHSchool.com
Web Code: ccd-2110

Exploration Lab

Investigating the Velocity of a Sinking Marble

L2

Objective
After completing this activity, students will be able to
- use a distance-time graph to determine speed and acceleration.

Skills Focus Observing, Formulating Hypotheses, Using Tables and Graphs

Prep Time 10 minutes

Alternative Materials Corn syrup or mild laundry detergent can be used in place of shampoo.

Class Time 40 minutes

Safety Have students wear safety goggles to ensure shampoo does not enter their eyes.

Teaching Tips
- Tell students to pour the shampoo into the graduated cylinder so that as little as possible sticks to the side.

Expected Outcome The marble falls more quickly through diluted shampoo than through undiluted shampoo.

Sample Data

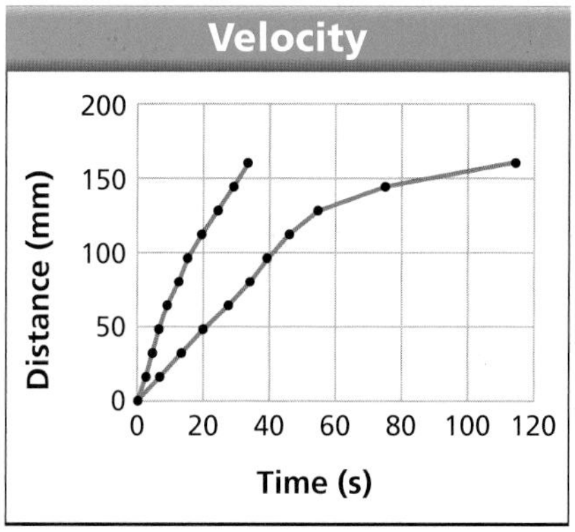
Velocity
Distance (mm)
200
150
100
50
0
0
20
40
60
80
100
120
Time (s)

Analyze and Conclude
1. The graph should be a nearly straight line for both marbles. The graph for the second marble will be steeper.
2. At first, the marbles fell at a nearly constant velocity, which is shown as a straight line on the distance-time graph. The second marble fell faster than the first marble. As the marbles approached the bottom of the cylinder, the viscosity of the shampoo caused them to slow down.
3. Answers will depend on the viscosity of the shampoo. In most cases, the marble did not accelerate because of the resistance from the viscous shampoo.
4. The speeds will depend on the type of shampoo used. Typical speeds are 2.5 mm/s and 6.0 mm/s for marbles falling in shampoo and diluted shampoo, respectively.
Logical, Kinesthetic

Go Online PHSchool.com

Students should see that the marbles have a nearly constant speed until they near the bottom of the graduated cylinder, where they begin to slow, but students' results will depend on their own data and the data on the site.

Study Guide

Study Tip

Schedule Study Time
Tell students to get into the habit of studying each day. They should set aside a block of time for reviewing their science notes. Tell students that focused daily study will reinforce what they learn in class and prepare them for test taking.

Thinking Visually

a. Velocity
b. Distance
c. Direction
d. Changes in both speed and direction

CHAPTER 11

Study Guide

11.1 Distance and Displacement

Key Concepts

- To describe motion accurately and completely, a frame of reference is needed .
- Distance is the length of the path between two points. Displacement is the direction from the starting point and the length of a straight line from the starting point to the ending point.
- Add displacements by using vector addition.

Vocabulary

frame of reference, *p. 328*
relative motion, *p. 329*
distance, *p. 329*
vector, *p. 330*
resultant vector, *p. 331*

11.2 Speed and Velocity

Key Concepts

- Average speed is computed for the entire duration of a trip, and instantaneous speed is measured at a particular instant.
- $\text{Average speed} = \dfrac{\text{Total distance}}{\text{Total time}}$
- The slope of a line on a distance-time graph is speed.
- Velocity is a description of both speed and direction of motion. Velocity is a vector.
- Two or more velocities add by vector addition.

Vocabulary

speed, *p. 332*
average speed, *p. 333*
instantaneous speed, *p. 334*
velocity, *p. 336*

11.3 Acceleration

Key Concepts

- Acceleration can be described as changes in speed, changes in direction, or changes in both. Acceleration is a vector.
- You calculate acceleration by dividing the change in velocity by the total time.

$$\text{Acceleration} = \frac{v_f - v_i}{t}$$

- The slope of a speed-time graph is the acceleration.
- Instantaneous acceleration is how fast a velocity is changing at a specific instant.

Vocabulary

acceleration, *p. 342*
free fall, *p. 343*
constant acceleration, *p. 345*
linear graph, *p. 347*
nonlinear graph, *p. 348*

Thinking Visually

Concept Map Copy the concept map below onto a sheet of paper. Use information from the chapter to complete the concept map.

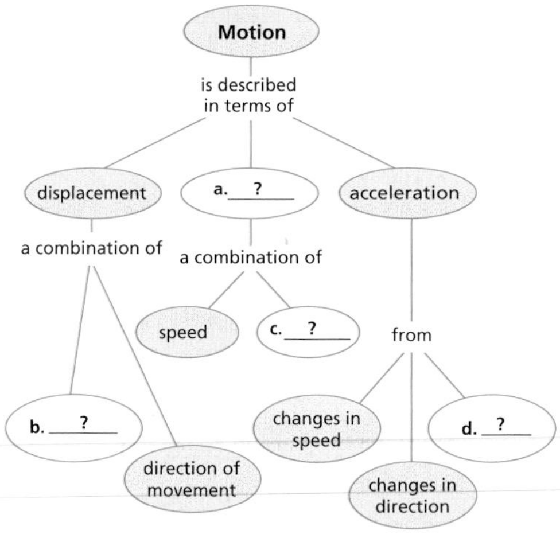
Motion
is described in terms of
displacement
a. ?
acceleration
a combination of
a combination of
speed
c. ?
from
b. ?
direction of movement
changes in speed
d. ?
changes in direction

Chapter Resources

Print
- ***Chapter and Unit Tests,*** Chapter 11 Test A and Test B
- ***Test Prep Resources,*** Chapter 11

Technology
- ***Computer Test Bank,*** Chapter Test 11
- ***Interactive Textbook,*** Chapter 11
- ***Go Online,*** PHSchool.com, Chapter 11

CHAPTER 11

Assessment

Interactive textbook with assessment at PHSchool.com iText

Reviewing Content

Choose the letter that best answers the question or completes the statement.

1. Motion is described with respect to a
   a. graph. b. displacement.
   c. slope. d. frame of reference.
2. Displacement is distance combined with
   a. direction. b. speed.
   c. velocity. d. magnitude.
3. Displacement vectors of 3 m and 5 m in the same direction combine to make a displacement vector that is
   a. 2 m. b. 0 m.
   c. 8 m. d. 15 m.
4. Average speed is the total distance divided by the
   a. average distance.
   b. average acceleration.
   c. total time.
   d. slope.
5. The slope of a distance-time graph is equal to the
   a. speed. b. acceleration.
   c. displacement. d. motion.
6. Velocity is
   a. the slope of a linear graph.
   b. acceleration divided by displacement.
   c. speed with direction.
   d. the same in all reference frames.
7. Two or more velocities can be combined by
   a. graphing the slope.
   b. using vector addition.
   c. calculating the instantaneous speed.
   d. determining the rate.
8. A ball just dropped is an example of
   a. constant speed.
   b. instantaneous speed.
   c. combining displacements.
   d. free fall.
9. Acceleration is equal to
   a. distance divided by time.
   b. change in speed divided by time.
   c. the slope of a distance-time graph.
   d. change in speed multiplied by time.
10. The rate at which velocity is changing at a given instant is described by
    a. instantaneous acceleration.
    b. average speed.
    c. constant speed.
    d. vector addition.

Understanding Concepts

11. Why is it necessary to choose a single frame of reference when measuring motion?
12. For what kinds of distances would you choose to make measurements in millimeters? In kilometers?
13. Light from a star travels to Earth in a straight line at a constant speed of almost 300,000 km/s. What is the acceleration of the light?
14. If two displacement vectors add to yield a total displacement of zero, what do you know about the two displacements?
15. How will the total distance traveled by a car in 2 hours be affected if the average speed is doubled?
16. How do you know that a speedometer tells you the instantaneous speed of a car?
17. On a distance-time graph, what would the curve describing constant speed look like?
18. A spider is crawling on a wall. First it crawls 1 meter up, then 1 meter to the left, and then 1 meter down. What is its total displacement?
19. A jogger travels 8.0 kilometers in 1.25 hours. What is the jogger's average speed?
20. You see a lightning bolt in the sky. You hear a clap of thunder 3 seconds later. The sound travels at a speed of 330 m/s. How far away was the lightning? (*Hint:* Assume you see lightning instantly.)
21. If a river current is 8.0 m/s, and a boat is traveling 10.0 m/s upstream, what is the boat's speed relative to the riverbank?
22. If an object is moving with constant velocity, what do you know about its acceleration?
23. If the plotted points on a speed-time graph do not form a straight line, what do you know about the object's acceleration?
24. Explain a situation in which you can accelerate even though your speed doesn't change.

Homework Guide

Section	Questions
11.1	1–3, 11–12, 14, 18–19, 35
11.2	4–7, 15–17, 20–21, 25–27, 29–30, 34
11.3	8–10, 13, 22–24, 28, 31–33

Assessment

Interactive Textbook If your class subscribes to the Interactive Textbook, your students can go online to access an interactive version of the Student Edition and a self-test.

Reviewing Content

1. d 2. a 3. c
4. c 5. a 6. c
7. b 8. d 9. b
10. a

Understanding Concepts

11. The motion appears to be different in different frames of reference.
12. Very small distances would be measured in millimeters. Very large distances would be measured in kilometers.
13. It has zero acceleration.
14. They are equal in length and opposite in direction.
15. The total distance would double.
16. A speedometer tells how fast an object is moving at a particular instant in time, which is the same as its instantaneous speed.
17. The curve of an object moving at constant speed would be a straight line on a distance-time graph.
18. 1 meter to the left
19. 6.4 km/h
20. 990 meters
21. 2.0 m/s
22. Acceleration is the change in velocity divided by the total time. If there is no change in velocity, then the acceleration is zero.
23. The object's acceleration is not constant.
24. Possible answer: moving in a circular motion with constant speed

Chapter 11

Critical Thinking

25. The velocities of 2 m/s forward and 2 m/s backwards cancel. An observer standing nearby would see the newspaper drop vertically to the ground.
26. Students' experiments should include measuring the track and measuring the time for the train to go around the track. They should also mention calculating the speed from these measurements.
27. The raft could be moving with a constant speed because the speed during each measured interval is the same.
28. 1400 m/s

Math Skills

29. For the first 10 seconds, the person is walking at a constant rate. For the next 10 seconds, the person is standing still.
30. 1.5 m/s
31. 0.75 m/s^2

Concepts in Action

32. The ship's final velocity is 600 m/s, less than its velocity in problem 28.
33. At each moment, the falling ball has an instantaneous acceleration that is the same as its constant downward acceleration of 9.8 m/s^2. The ball bouncing on the floor has a changing acceleration each time it hits the ground.
34. 5 km/h
35. Descriptions will vary but should include the up-and-down dribbling motion of the ball, the movement of the player down the court, and the projectile motion of the ball after it is shot toward the basket.

Go Online PHSchool.com

Your students can independently test their knowledge of the chapter and print out their results for your files.

CHAPTER 11

Assessment *(continued)*

Critical Thinking

25. **Applying Concepts** A girl moves at 2 m/s delivering newspapers. She throws a newspaper directly behind her at 2 m/s. In the frame of reference of someone standing nearby, what is the motion of the newspaper?
26. **Designing an Experiment** Design an experiment to measure the speed of a toy train going around a circular track.
27. **Analyzing Data** A raft floats downstream. After 1 minute it has moved 50.0 meters. After 2 minutes it has moved 100.0 meters. After 3 minutes it has moved 150.0 meters. Could the raft's speed be constant? Explain.
28. **Problem Solving** A rocket ship is moving through space at 1000 m/s. It accelerates in the same direction at 4 m/s^2. What is its speed after 100 seconds?

Math Skills

Use the following graph to answer Questions 29 and 30.

A Record of Typical Motion

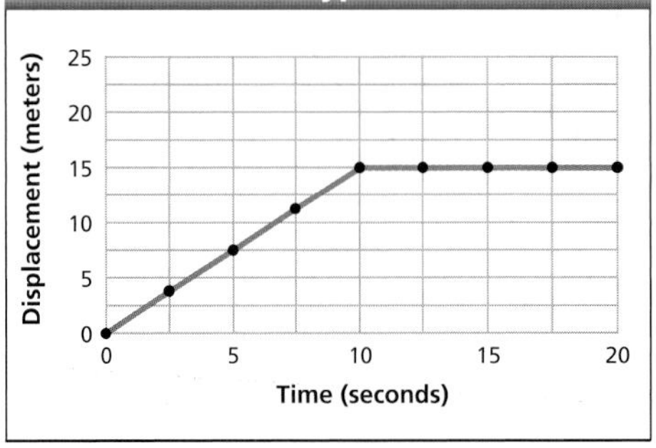

Displacement (meters)
25
20
15
10
5
0
0
5
10
15
20
Time (seconds)

29. **Using Graphs** The graph above shows the motion for a person walking down a street. Describe the history of the motion.
30. **Using Graphs** How fast is the person walking during the first 10 seconds?
31. **Calculating** A car starts from rest and increases its speed to 15 m/s in 20 seconds. What is the car's acceleration?

Concepts in Action

32. **Predicting** The propulsion system of the rocket ship described in problem 28 is tested. Its rockets are fired and the ship accelerates from rest at 5 m/s^2 for 2 minutes. How does the ship's final velocity compare with the ship's initial velocity in problem 28?
33. **Comparing and Contrasting** Compare the case of a rubber ball falling through the air and a rubber ball bouncing up and down on a hard floor. For which of these cases is the instantaneous acceleration always the same as the constant acceleration?
34. **Calculating** Two trains on parallel tracks are traveling in the same direction. One train starts 10 km behind the other. It overtakes the first train in 2 hours. What is the relative speed of the second train with respect to the first train?
35. **Writing in Science** Write a paragraph explaining how different reference frames affect descriptions of motion in the following scenario. A basketball player dribbles down the court at a constant speed and then shoots the ball into the basket. Describe the motion of the ball from the reference frame of a camera mounted directly behind the basket. Then, describe the motion of the ball from the reference frame of the basketball player. (*Hint:* Sketch displacement versus time graphs of the ball's motion based on each reference frame.)

Performance-Based Assessment

Creating a Table Use a table to present the distances and displacements between familiar places. In a third column include the average speed at which you travel between these places. Be sure to list the places in pairs, such as home and school, a park and the library, or your bed and front door. Estimate the displacement if you can't measure it.

Go Online PHSchool.com

For: Self-grading assessment
Visit: PHSchool.com
Web Code: cca-2110

Performance-Based Assessment

Students' tables should include several pairs of locations. In most cases, the distance traveled should be greater than the magnitude of the displacement between the locations. Students should use distance and time units appropriate to each pair of locations. Make sure the values for average speeds are realistic.

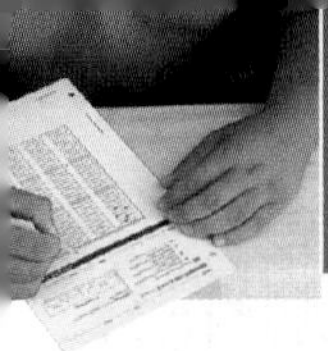

Standardized Test Prep

Test-Taking Tip

When answering a question with a graph, keep these tips in mind:

- Read the question thoroughly to identify what the question is asking.
- Study the name of the graph, if applicable. This may help you identify what information is available from the graph.
- Carefully examine the graph and take note of the axes labels.
- Identify the scale of the axes.
- Recall information, equations, definitions, relationships, and so forth that may be required to interpret the graph. For example, the slope of a distance-time graph is the speed of the object.
- Once you have chosen your answer, check it against the graph.

Determining Distance

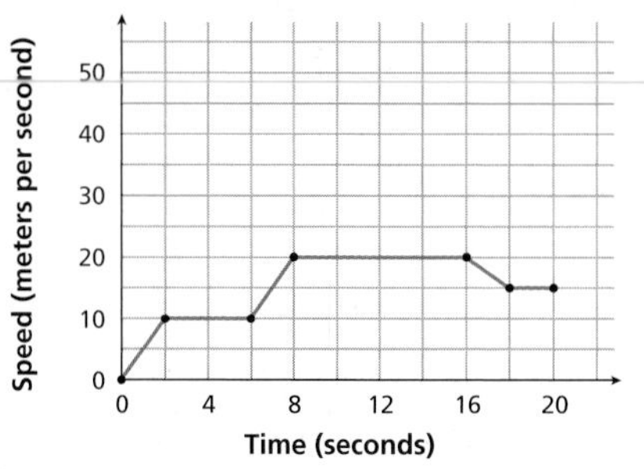
Speed (meters per second)
0
10
20
30
40
50
0
4
8
12
16
20
Time (seconds)

The graph above depicts motion in a straight line. During which time periods does acceleration occur?

(A) 0 s–2 s only
(B) 0 s–2 s and 6 s–8 s only
(C) 16 s–18 s only
(D) 0 s–2 s, 6 s–8 s, and 16 s–18 s only
(E) Acceleration occurs during the entire time period shown.

(Answer: D)

1. A delivery truck driver's round-trip route from the warehouse takes her 3 km east, then 1 km north, then 3 km west, and then 1 km south. Which of the following statements is FALSE?
(A) The displacement of the round trip is zero.
(B) The distance of the round trip is 8 km.
(C) After driving 3 km east, the magnitude of the distance and displacement are the same.
(D) After driving 3 km east and 1 km north, the magnitude of the distance and displacement are the same.
(E) none of the above

2. A runner completes a 10.0-km race in exactly 30 minutes. What is the runner's average speed in km/h? (60 minutes = 1 hour)
(A) 30.0 km/h (B) 20.0 km/h
(C) 15.0 km/h (D) 10.0 km/h
(E) 5.00 km/h

3. Which of the following is NOT a vector quantity?
(A) velocity
(B) displacement
(C) distance
(D) acceleration
(E) none of the above

4. Based on the speed-time graph shown at the left, what is the acceleration during the first 2 seconds?
(A) 1 m/s^2
(B) 2 m/s^2
(C) 4 m/s^2
(D) 5 m/s^2
(E) 10 m/s^2

5. A race car drives around a circular race track at constant speed. Which of the following statements is TRUE?
(A) A speed-time graph of the car's motion would be a horizontal line.
(B) A distance-time graph of the car's motion would be a straight line with a positive slope.
(C) The velocity of the car is constantly changing.
(D) The car is constantly accelerating.
(E) all of the above

Standardized Test Prep

1. D **2.** B **3.** C
4. D **5.** E

CHAPTER 12

Planning Guide

Use these planning tools
Easy Planner
Teacher Express

SECTION OBJECTIVES	STANDARDS NATIONAL (See p. T18.)	STANDARDS STATE	ACTIVITIES and LABS
12.1 Forces, pp. 356–362 1 block or 2 periods **12.1.1** **Describe** examples of force and **identify** appropriate SI units used to measure force. **12.1.2** **Explain** how the motion of an object is affected when balanced and unbalanced forces act on it. **12.1.3** **Compare** and **contrast** the four kinds of friction. **12.1.4** **Describe** how Earth's gravity and air resistance affect falling objects. **12.1.5** **Describe** the path of a projectile and **identify** the forces that produce projectile motion.	A-1, A-2, B-4, G-1		**SE** Inquiry Activity: What Starts an Object Moving? p. 355 L2 **SE** Quick Lab: Observing the Effects of Friction, p. 360 L2 **TE** Build Science Skills: Measuring, p. 357 L2
12.2 Newton's First and Second Laws of Motion, pp. 363–369 1 block or 2 periods **12.2.1** **Describe** Newton's first law of motion and its relation to inertia. **12.2.2** **Describe** Newton's second law of motion and use it to **calculate** acceleration, force, and mass values. **12.2.3** **Relate** the mass of an object to its weight.	A-1, A-2, B-4, F-1, G-1, G-2, G-3		**SE** Quick Lab: Investigating Inertia, p. 365 L2 **TE** Teacher Demo: Force and Acceleration, p. 365 L2 **TE** Teacher Demo: Newton's Second Law of Motion, p. 367 L2 **LM** Investigation 12A: Investigating Gravitational Acceleration and Fluid Resistance L2 **LM** Investigation 12B: Testing Galileo's Hypothesis L1
12.3 Newton's Third Law of Motion and Momentum, pp. 372–377 1 block or 2 periods **12.3.1** **Explain** how action and reaction forces are related according to Newton's third law of motion. **12.3.2** **Calculate** the momentum of an object and **describe** what happens when momentum is conserved during a collision.	B-4, G-1, G-2, G-3		**SE** Exploration Lab: Investigating a Balloon Jet, p. 383 L2 **TE** Build Science Skills: Predicting, p. 373 L2 **TE** Teacher Demo: Momentum, p. 374 L2
12.4 Universal Forces, pp. 378–382 1 block or 2 periods **12.4.1** **Identify** the forms of electromagnetic force that can both attract and repel. **12.4.2** **Identify** and **describe** the universal forces acting within the nucleus. **12.4.3** **Define** Newton's law of universal gravitation and **describe** the factors affecting gravitational force. **12.4.4** **Describe** centripetal force and the type of motion it produces.	A-1, A-2, B-1, B-4, E-2, G-1, G-2, G-3		**SE** Quick Lab: Investigating Force and Distance, p. 380 L2 **TE** Teacher Demo: Nuclear Forces, p. 379 L2

Ability Levels

- L1 For students who need additional help
- L2 For all students
- L3 For students who need to be challenged

Components

SE	Student Edition	RSW	Reading & Study Workbook	CUT	Chapter & Unit Tests	T	Transparencies
TE	Teacher's Edition	MSPS	Math Skills & Problem Solving Workbook	CTB	Computer Test Bank	iT	Interactive Textbook
LM	Laboratory Manual			TP	Test Prep Resources	P	Presentation Pro CD-ROM
PLM	Probeware Lab Manual			DC	Discovery Channel Videotapes & DVDs	GO	Internet Resources

RESOURCES PRINT and TECHNOLOGY		SECTION ASSESSMENT
RSW Section 12.1	L1	**SE** Section 12.1 Assessment, p. 362
T Chapter 12 Pretest	L2	**iT** Section 12.1
Section 12.1	L2	
P Chapter 12 Pretest	L2	
Section 12.1	L2	
SciLinks **GO** Forces	L2	
RSW Section 12.2	L1	**SE** Section 12.2 Assessment, p. 369
RSW Math Skill	L2	**iT** Section 12.2
MSPS Section 12.2	L2	
DC Air Forces	L2	
T Section 12.2	L2	
P Section 12.2	L2	
SciLinks **GO** Mass	L2	
PLM Lab 4: Investigating a Balloon Jet	L2	**SE** Section 12.3 Assessment, p. 377
RSW Section 12.3	L1	**iT** Section 12.3
MSPS Section 12.3	L2	
T Section 12.3	L2	
P Section 12.3	L2	
SciLinks **GO** Newton's laws	L2	
RSW Section 12.4	L1	**SE** Section 12.4 Assessment, p. 382
T Section 12.4	L2	**iT** Section 12.4
P Section 12.4	L2	
SciLinks **GO** Gravity	L2	

Go Online

Go online for these Internet resources.

PHSchool.com
Web Code: cca-2120

NSTA SciLinks
Web Code: ccn-2121
Web Code: ccn-2122
Web Code: ccn-2123
Web Code: ccn-2124

Materials for Activities and Labs

Quantities for each group

STUDENT EDITION

Inquiry Activity, p. 355
5 pennies

Quick Lab, p. 360
2 rubber erasers, sticky notes, scissors, metric ruler

Quick Lab, p. 364
index card, coin

Quick Lab, p. 380
balloon, bubble solution, bubble wand

Exploration Lab, p. 383
string (3 m in length), drinking straw, 4 long balloons, masking tape, stopwatch, meter stick, 2 threaded nuts, 2 chairs

TEACHER'S EDITION

Build Science Skills, p. 357
5-N spring scale, centimeter ruler, book, string, 5 objects (such as books) weighing from 1 to 5 newtons

Teacher Demo, p. 365
2 identical toy cars (or dynamics carts), 2 student volunteers, identical floor surface for each car

Teacher Demo, p. 367
wind-up toy car, 3 metal washers, tape

Build Science Skills, p. 370
sheet of paper, stopwatch, auditorium stage

Build Science Skills, p. 373
soccer ball, several heavy books

Teacher Demo, p. 374
water-filled balloons, pillow

Teacher Demo, p. 379
2 magnetic toy train cars or any 2 magnets, wide adhesive tape on a roll (or rubber band)

Chapter Assessment

CHAPTER ASSESSMENT

SE Chapter Assessment, pp. 385–386
CUT Chapter 12 Test A, B
CTB Chapter 12
iT Chapter 12
PHSchool.com GO
Web Code: cca-2120

STANDARDIZED TEST PREP

SE Chapter 12, p. 387
TP Diagnose and Prescribe

Interactive Textbook

Interactive Textbook with assessment at PHSchool.com

CHAPTER 12

Before you teach

From the Author

Michael Wysession
Washington University

Big Ideas

There are four distinct forces in our universe: gravitational, electromagnetic, and strong and weak nuclear forces. At the time of the big bang, these four forces were likely unified as a single force, but they fragmented as the universe expanded and cooled.

Space and Time Gravity is the most important force over large distances, and is responsible for large-scale motions in space. Gravity is the weakest of all the forces, but because it acts between all matter and because it decays at a moderate rate with distance, it is the most dominant force over large distances.

The strong and weak nuclear forces act between atomic particles. The strong force holds the nuclei of atoms together. The weak force is responsible for radioactive decay. These forces are immense at subatomic distances, but decay rapidly with distance.

The electromagnetic force is best known for effects such as electricity and magnetism. However, it also provides most of the everyday "forces" in our lives. Hold something up, and the electrons around the atoms of your hand are repelling the electrons around the atoms of the object you are holding. Pushing, pulling, hitting, and holding all result from the repelling electromagnetic forces supplied by the electrons on the outsides of the atoms of objects.

Forces and Motion The most important equation in all of science is likely $F = ma$, which says that when you push on an object, it accelerates. Push on a massive object, and it accelerates slowly. Push harder, and it accelerates faster. The most prevalent force on our planet's surface is the gravitational pull of Earth's mass. As a result, the most prevalent kind of motion is downward acceleration (i.e., things fall downhill).

Matter and Energy As Einstein showed, gravity is better viewed as a distortion of the fabric of space by matter. Very massive objects, like black holes and galaxies, create very large "warping" of the spatial dimensions of space. This explains why light from distant galaxies is bent around intervening galaxies.

Physics Refresher

Forces 12.1

A force, which can be simply defined as any push or pull, is the cause of acceleration (change in velocity). Force is a vector, that is, it has magnitude and direction. The SI unit of force is the newton (N), the amount of force that produces an acceleration of 1 m/s^2 on a 1 kg mass.

If all forces on an object are combined and the net force is zero, the object does not accelerate. If the net force is not zero, velocity remains constant.

Address Misconceptions

Some students may incorrectly think that only animate objects can exert a force. However, gravity is inanimate, as are many other forces. For a strategy to overcome this misconception, see **Address Misconceptions** on **page 358.**

Friction 12.1

Friction is the opposing force that touching objects experience as they move past one another. Static friction is the force of resistance to motion when two contacting surfaces are stationary. Kinetic friction (which includes sliding, rolling, and fluid friction) is the force of resistance that opposes the relative motion of two contacting surfaces moving past one another.

Laws of Motion 12.2 and 12.3

Newton's first law of motion says that an object at rest will remain at rest, and an object in motion will continue in motion with constant velocity unless it experiences a net force.

Newton's second law of motion says that an object's acceleration is directly proportional to the net force acting on it and

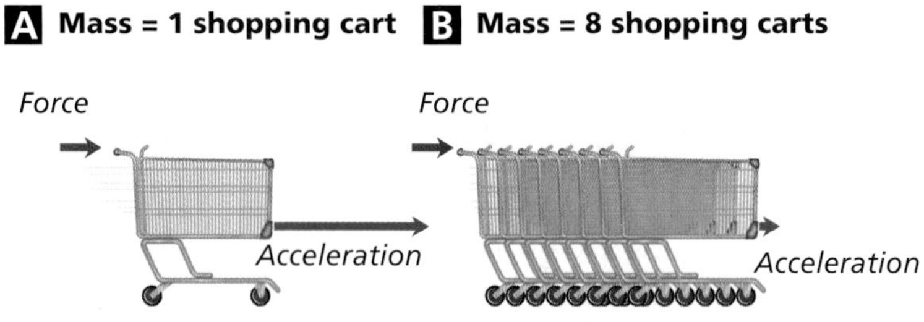
A Mass = 1 shopping cart
B Mass = 8 shopping carts
Force
Acceleration
Force
Acceleration

Acceleration depends on force and mass.

Go Online PD LINKS NSTA

For: Teaching methods for forces and motion
Visit: www.SciLinks.org/PDLinks
Web Code: ccn-1299

inversely proportional to its mass ($a = F/m$, $F = ma$). One application is the measurement of weight. Weight, W, is a force, while the gravity, g, is the acceleration ($W = mg$). On Earth's surface, g is approximately 9.8 m/s^2.

In the 1680s, Newton related the laws in his book *Philosophiae Naturalis Principia Mathematica.* He stated that force is proportional to change in momentum. Mathematically, this law is $F = m \times v$. A change in velocity is the same as acceleration, so this equation became $F = ma$.

Newton's third law of motion says that, when object A exerts a force on object B, object B exerts a force on object A that is equal in magnitude and opposite in direction.

Universal Forces 12.4

Three of the four universal forces are electromagnetic, strong nuclear, and weak nuclear. The range and relative strengths of the universal forces are summarized in the table below.

Universal Force Characteristics

Force	Relative Strength	Range
Strong nuclear	1	~10^{-15} m
Electromagnetic	10^{-2}	$\propto \frac{1}{r^2}$
Weak nuclear	10^{-13}	$< 10^{-18}$ m
Gravitational	10^{-38}	$\propto \frac{1}{r^2}$

The electromagnetic force consists of both the electric force and the magnetic force. These forces are found in regions in which there are electric and magnetic fields. Michael Faraday discovered that a changing magnetic field produces an electric field, and James Clerk Maxwell illustrated that a changing electric field produces a magnetic field.

The nucleus of an atom is held together by attractions among protons and neutrons called the strong nuclear force and the weak nuclear force. The strong nuclear force is greater than the electric repulsion of the protons' positive forces and therefore overcomes that repulsion, holding them together. The attraction due to the strong force, however, occurs over a very short distance, less than 3×10^{-15} m, or about three protons' width. The weak nuclear force is stronger than gravitational force.

Address Misconceptions

Some students may think that objects become positively charged because they have gained protons. What takes place is electron (not proton) transfer. Electrons have a negative charge. For a strategy to overcome this misconception, see **Address Misconceptions** on **page 379.**

Build Reading Literacy

Visualize

Forming Mental Pictures

Strategy Help students understand and recall complex text by forming mental pictures as they read. In some cases, visual elements of the text can aid students in visualizing; in other cases students must rely solely on text descriptions. Choose several paragraphs from Chapter 12, such as the four on p. 358. If possible, include at least one paragraph that has an accompanying figure and at least one other paragraph that refers to concepts or events that are not illustrated in visual elements, such as diagrams, charts, graphs, or photographs.

Example

1. Have students keep their books closed. Tell them to listen while you read and to visualize, or form mental pictures of, each object or action you read about.
2. Then, read a paragraph or so aloud, pausing frequently to demonstrate, by thinking aloud, how to visualize each thing described. When reading complex or technical text, pausing after each phrase will often be appropriate.
3. Tell students to continue visualizing. Slowly and clearly, read on. Then, select a logical stopping point and discuss with students the images they visualized.
4. If there is an accompanying figure, have students open to it and see how it compares with their visualizing. Point out that visuals in the text help readers picture what they are reading.
5. Have students work with partners to practice by taking turns reading and visualizing aloud. Tell them to expand on visuals that appear in the text and to describe their own mental images of ideas or events that are not shown in visuals.

See p. 368 for a script on how to use the visualize strategy with students. For additional Build Reading Literacy strategies, see pp. 357, 372, and 378.

ASSESS PRIOR KNOWLEDGE

Use the Chapter Pretest below to assess students' prior knowledge. As needed, review these Science Concepts and Math Skills with students.

Review Science Concepts

Section 12.1 Review with students what motion is and how it is measured. Encourage students to describe what a force is and what it can do.

Section 12.2 Ask students to review algebraic equations and exponents. Suggest that they observe physical forces in their everyday lives and be prepared to discuss how they think these forces affect motion.

Section 12.3 Encourage students to review the concepts of mass and velocity, making sure they do not confuse mass with weight or velocity with speed. Reinforce that mass and weight are not the same and that speed with direction is velocity.

Section 12.4 Review models of the atom if this concept has been covered. Remind students of their prior knowledge of gravitational force and forces that act between magnets and charged particles.

Review Math Skills

Formulas and Equations, Exponents, and Line Graphs
Students will need to work with equations and exponents to solve problems using Newton's second law of motion.

Direct students to the **Math Skills** in the **Skills and Reference Handbook** at the end of the student text.

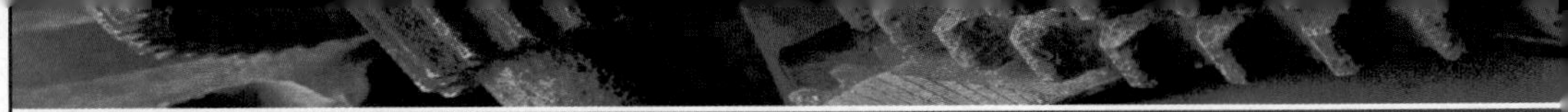

CHAPTER

12 Forces and Motion

CONCEPTS in Action

How do science concepts apply to your world? Here are some questions you'll be able to answer after you read this chapter.

- Why doesn't the pulling by each team in a tug of war always result in motion? *(Section 12.1)*
- Why do flying squirrels spread their arms and legs when they jump through the air? *(Section 12.1)*
- What happens to the forward motion of a passenger in a head-on auto accident? *(Section 12.2)*
- What brings the head of a hammer to a stop when you drive a nail into a board? *(Section 12.3)*
- What causes tides? *(Section 12.4)*

Discovery CHANNEL SCHOOL **Video Field Trip**
Air Forces

- What factors affect the fall of a sky diver? *(page 370)*

A kayaker maneuvers his way downstream using a paddle. ▶

Chapter Pretest

1. What is relative motion? *(Relative motion is movement in relation to a frame of reference.)*

2. What is the difference between distance and displacement? *(Distance is the length of a path between two points. Displacement is the direction from the starting point and the length of a straight line from the starting point to the ending point.)*

3. How is average speed calculated? *(Total distance is divided by total time.)*

4. On a distance-time graph, what does the slope represent? *(The slope represents the speed.)*

5. What is velocity? *(Velocity is speed with direction.)*

6. How is acceleration related to velocity? *(Acceleration is change in velocity, that is, any change in speed, direction, or both.)*

7. A backpack falls out of an open window. The backpack starts from rest and hits the ground 1.0 second later with a velocity of 9.8 m/s. What is the average acceleration of the backpack? *(c)*

a. 9.8 m/s **b.** 9.8 m
c. 9.8 m/s^2 **d.** All of the above

8. How are mass and weight different? *(Mass is a measure of inertia. Weight is the measure of the force of gravity acting on an object.)*

Chapter Preview

Inquiry Activity

What Starts an Object Moving?

Procedure

1. On a flat surface, arrange four pennies in a row so that they are touching one another.
2. Using your index finger, slide a fifth penny across the surface in line with the row of pennies so that it strikes a penny at one end of the row.

Think About It

1. **Observing** Describe how the row of pennies moves in response to the collision.
2. **Formulating Hypotheses** What do you think caused the pennies to move after the collision? Why didn't the pennies move before the collision?

DISCOVERY CHANNEL SCHOOL

Video Field Trip

Air Forces

Encourage students to view the Video Field Trip "Air Forces."

ENGAGE/EXPLORE

Inquiry Activity

What Starts an Object Moving? L2

Purpose
In this activity, students begin to use the concept of force to explain movement.

Address Misconceptions

Students may hold the misconception that only a moving object can exert force. To help dispel this misconception, after completing this activity ask students what caused the penny on the end of the row to move. Each penny exerts a force on the next, although only the last penny in the row moves.

Skills Focus Observing, Formulating Hypotheses

Prep Time 5 minutes

Materials 5 pennies

Advance Prep Checkers or game chips can be substituted for pennies.

Class Time 10 minutes

Safety Students should wear safety goggles. Caution students not to observe from a position in which the pennies move toward them.

Teaching Tips

- If students are having difficulty striking the row of coins head-on, they can tape a pair of rulers to the table on either side of the row of coins to create a linear track for the coins to travel along.

Expected Outcome As the row of coins is struck, the moving coin will stop at the head of the row while the coin at the far end of the row will move away.

Think About It
1. Only the coin at the far end of the row moved away.
2. During the collision, a force was transferred from one coin to the next in the row. Because no horizontal force was acting on the coins before the collision, they did not move at that time. Students may not articulate the abstract concept of a force well at this stage. Although students can reasonably be expected to start developing this concept, they may not express it in formally correct scientific language at this stage.
Visual

12.1 Forces

Reading Focus

Key Concepts

- How do forces affect the motion of an object?
- What are the four main types of friction?
- How do gravity and air resistance affect a falling object?
- In what direction does Earth's gravity act?
- Why does a projectile follow a curved path?

Vocabulary

- force
- newton
- net force
- friction
- static friction
- sliding friction
- rolling friction
- fluid friction
- air resistance
- gravity
- terminal velocity
- projectile motion

Reading Strategy

Relating Text and Visuals Copy the table below. As you read, look carefully at Figures 2, 3, and 5. Complete the table by describing the forces and motion shown in each figure.

Figure	Is Net Force 0?	Effect on Motion
2A	a. ?	b. ?
2B	c. ?	d. ?
3	e. ?	f. ?
5A	g. ?	h. ?
5B	i. ?	j. ?

Figure 1 The wind pushes against the man and his umbrella. The push from the wind is a force.

A powerful storm is approaching. The weather forecast calls for gale-force winds. Many people in the city decide to leave work early in order to get home before things get worse. As shown in Figure 1, a man pushes ahead into a strong wind and shields himself from the driving rain with an umbrella. The strong wind makes it very difficult for him to hold onto his umbrella. To keep the umbrella from being pulled from his hands, he tightly squeezes the umbrella handle. Elsewhere, a store owner attempts to bring in a folding sign that hasn't blown away because it is chained to a pole.

Wind is but one example of the many forces you experience every day. The study of forces is a very important part of physics. As you read this section you'll learn what forces are and how they make things move.

What Is a Force?

The man out in the storm is battling the forces of wind. A **force** is a push or a pull that acts on an object. **A force can cause a resting object to move, or it can accelerate a moving object by changing the object's speed or direction.** The force of the wind pushing against the man slows his speed. A strong gust could even change the direction in which he was moving.

Section 12.1

1 FOCUS

Objectives

12.1.1 **Describe** examples of force and **identify** appropriate SI units used to measure force.
12.1.2 **Explain** how the motion of an object is affected when balanced and unbalanced forces act on it.
12.1.3 **Compare** and **contrast** the four kinds of friction.
12.1.4 **Describe** how Earth's gravity and air resistance affect falling objects.
12.1.5 **Describe** the path of a projectile and **identify** the forces that produce projectile motion.

Reading Focus

Build Vocabulary L2

LINCS Have students use the LINCS strategy to learn and review the terms *force, friction, air resistance,* and *gravity.* In LINCS exercises, students **L**ist the parts that they know (list the word and its definition on an index card). **I**magine a picture (create a mental image of the term's meaning and describe the image using real words). **N**ote a sound-alike word (think of a familiar word that sounds like the term or part of it). **C**onnect the terms (make up a short story about each term's meaning that uses the sound-alike word). **S**elf-test (quiz themselves).

Reading Strategy L2

a. Yes **b.** No motion **c.** Yes **d.** No motion **e.** Yes **f.** No motion **g.** Yes **h.** No motion **i.** No **j.** Potted tree accelerates

2 INSTRUCT

What Is a Force?

Use Visuals L1

Figure 1 Emphasize that the wind acts as a force because it pushes against the man. Ask, **In what ways can the force of the wind alter the man's motion?** *(It can change the speed or direction of motion.)* **Will these changes cause the man to accelerate?** *(Yes)*
Visual

Section Resources

Print

- ***Reading and Study Workbook With Math Support,*** Section 12.1
- ***Transparencies,*** Chapter Pretest and Section 12.1

Technology

- ***Interactive Textbook,*** Section 12.1
- ***Presentation Pro CD-ROM,*** Chapter Pretest and Section 12.1
- ***Go Online,*** NSTA SciLinks, Forces

Measuring Force Forces are often easy to measure. In fact, if you've ever shopped at a grocery store, you may have measured forces using a spring scale like the one shown in Figure 2. The stretch of the spring in the scale depends on the amount of weight (a type of force) acting on it. As more fruit is placed on the scale, the spring is stretched farther and the scale reading increases.

Units of Force Force is measured in newtons, abbreviated as N. One **newton** is the force that causes a 1-kilogram mass to accelerate at a rate of 1 meter per second each second (1 m/s^2). In fact, 1 newton is equal to 1 kilogram-meter per second squared ($1 \text{ N} = 1 \text{ kg}\bullet\text{m/s}^2$). The newton is named after Sir Isaac Newton (1642–1727), the English scientist who explained how force, mass, and acceleration are related. You'll learn more about forces and mass in the next section.

Reading Checkpoint *What amount of force accelerates a 1-kilogram mass at 1 m/s^2?*

Representing Force You can use an arrow to represent the direction and strength of a force. The direction of the arrow represents the direction of the force. The length of the arrow represents the strength, or magnitude, of the force.

In Figure 2, the force arrows represent the weight of the items on the scale. Both arrows point down because weight always acts downward. The lengths of the arrows show you that more weight acts on the scale in Figure 2B than the one in Figure 2A.

A
B
HOBART
HOBART

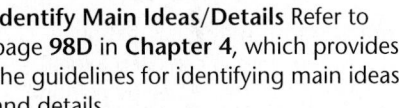

Figure 2 The downward force arrows represent the weight (a type of force) on the scales. The dial indicator gives a visual measure of the weight. **Calculating** *What is the approximate weight difference between the two scale readings?*

Combining Forces

Have you ever helped to push a car that has run out of gas? If you have, you were taking advantage of the fact that forces can be combined. The individual force of each person's push adds with the others into a larger force that allows you to move the car.

You can combine force arrows to show the result of how forces combine. That is, forces in the same direction add together and forces in opposite directions subtract from one another. The **net force** is the overall force acting on an object after all the forces are combined.

Build Science Skills L2

Measuring ACTIVITY

Purpose Students learn to measure force and sketch force arrows.

Materials 5-N spring scale, centimeter ruler, book, string, 5 objects (such as books) weighing from 1 to 5 newtons

Class Time 30 minutes

Procedure Have students pull each object at a slow, constant speed across a flat surface using the spring scale. They may need to attach the scale to the object using string. Students should record the force required to pull each object. Next, have them draw force arrows for each object. The arrows should be drawn to scale using a scale factor of 1 centimeter per newton of force.

Expected Outcome Students will draw scaled force arrows for each object. **Logical**

Combining Forces

Build Reading Literacy L1

Identify Main Ideas/Details Refer to page **98D** in **Chapter 4**, which provides the guidelines for identifying main ideas and details.

Ask students to explain the main concept in the first two short paragraphs under the head Combining Forces on p. 357. *(Forces can be combined.)* Encourage students to illustrate the main idea with a diagram. Ask, **What would be the effect on the direction of the net force if some of the people push the car forward while others push it backwards?** *(The net force would be in the direction of the people who were pushing with a greater force.)*
Logical, Portfolio

Customize for English Language Learners

Illustrate Content
You may assist English language learners by using diagrams, illustrations, or other visuals to explain the content of the lesson. Students may also benefit from keeping a "picture dictionary" with their own visuals to illustrate important concepts. For example, students may include diagrams to illustrate how forces combine and to show the meaning of *balanced force* and *unbalanced force.* This strategy can be especially helpful for students who are in the beginning stages of learning English. Students who have a greater mastery of English may also benefit from sharing their picture dictionaries with each other and explaining the concepts for which they have included visuals.

Answer to . . .

Figure 2 *The difference in weight between the two scale readings is about 3 pounds.*

Reading Checkpoint *The amount of force that accelerates 1 kg at 1 m/s^2 is one newton.*

Integrate Health **L2**

Figure 3 illustrates a group exercise (tug of war). Emphasize to students the value of regular exercise. According to the American Academy of Family Physicians, regular exercise reduces risk of some serious diseases including heart disease, diabetes, and obesity. Exercise also enhances flexibility so that body movement is easier. Regular exercise helps to relieve stress, increase energy and endurance, and—because it raises the rate at which the body burns calories—maintain a healthy weight.

Ask students to hypothesize why a person with normal (not high) blood pressure and a normal body weight is at lower risk for heart disease. *(That person's heart does not have to do extra work.)*
Verbal, Logical

Address Misconceptions **L2**

Some students may think that only people and animals can exert a force. You may dispel this fallacy by pointing out that moving automobiles or other moving vehicles are not living organisms. In addition, explain that the force of gravity is also inanimate. You could also use figures in the text to show that there are many examples all around students of forces that are not animate.
Visual, Logical

Use Visuals **L1**

Figure 4 Emphasize that the arrows in Figure 4 help students understand how forces combine. Tell students that the length of the arrows represents magnitude (size) of force. Ask, **When two arrows directly oppose one another and are different in size, what will be the direction of the net force?** *(The direction of the net force will be the same as the direction of the longer arrow.)* **How is the net force determined when two forces act in the same direction on an object?** *(The forces are added. The direction is the same as the forces.)* **Which of the combinations of forces shown in the figure would cause an object to move?** *(Only the unbalanced forces shown in A and B would cause the object to move.)*
Visual

Figure 3 In this tug of war, the two groups pull with equal forces in opposite directions. The forces combine by subtracting from each other.
Interpreting Photos *What is the net force acting on the rope?*

Balanced Forces Sometimes, the net force acting on an object is zero. Look at the tug of war in Figure 3. Each group pulls on the rope with the same amount of force, but they pull in opposite directions. Neither group wins the tug of war because the forces on the rope are balanced. Balanced forces are forces that combine to produce a net force of zero. **When the forces on an object are balanced, the net force is zero and there is no change in the object's motion.**

Examples of balanced forces are common. For example, imagine two people locked in an arm wrestling match. Although neither person's arm may be moving, a pair of equal and opposite balanced forces are acting. An unlimited number of individual forces can act on an object and still produce a net force of zero. As shown in Figure 3, the individual force exerted by each person still results in a zero net force on the rope.

Unbalanced Forces Often, the forces on an object are unbalanced. If you push hard against the side of a book that is resting on a table, the book will begin to move. This is an example of an unbalanced force. An unbalanced force is a force that results when the net force acting on an object is not equal to zero. **When an unbalanced force acts on an object, the object accelerates.**

Forces acting in opposite directions can also combine to produce an unbalanced force. When a team of people win a tug of war, they win by pulling with a greater force than the losing team. The two unequal forces act in opposite directions but combine to produce an unbalanced net force. The net force equals the size of the larger force minus the size of the smaller force. This unbalanced force causes the rope, the winning team, and the losing team to accelerate in the direction of the unbalanced force. Figure 4 shows several examples of how forces combine.

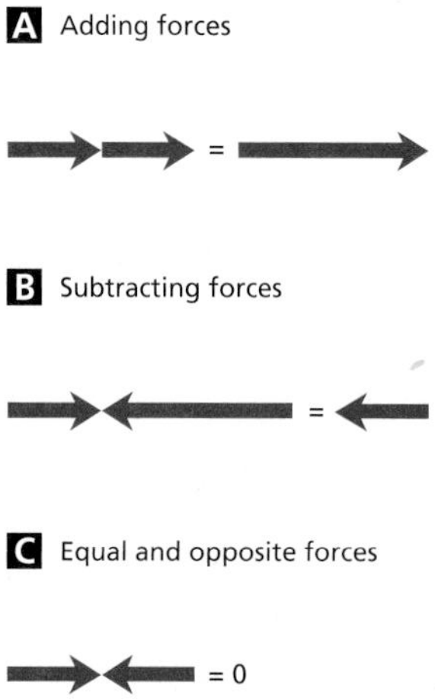
A Adding forces
=
B Subtracting forces
=
C Equal and opposite forces
= 0

Figure 4 Forces can add together or subtract from one another. **A** Two forces acting in the same direction add together. **B** Forces in opposite directions subtract from each other. **C** Forces that are equal in size and opposite in direction result in no net force.

Reading Checkpoint *What is the net force of a pair of balanced forces?*

Facts and Figures

Virtual Reality Forces A knowledge of balanced and unbalanced forces is important for virtual reality applications. Sensors detect the direction and magnitude of force exerted on an object by a user. The system then provides resistive force feedback to the user that corresponds to the desired virtual material. For example, the resistive force can be increased to simulate a stiff material such as hard rubber. The resistive force can be decreased to simulate a soft material such as a cloth.

Friction

All moving objects are subject to **friction,** a force that opposes the motion of objects that touch as they move past each other. Without friction, the world would be a very different place. In a frictionless world, every surface would be more slippery than a sheet of ice. Your food would slide off your fork. Walking would be impossible. Cars would slide around helplessly with their wheels spinning.

Friction acts at the surface where objects are in contact. Note that "in contact" includes solid objects that are directly touching one another as well as objects moving through a liquid or a gas. **There are four main types of friction: static friction, sliding friction, rolling friction, and fluid friction.**

Static Friction Imagine trying to push a large potted tree across a patio. Although you apply force to the pot by pushing on it, you can't get the pot to move. As shown in Figure 5A, the force of static friction opposes your push. **Static friction** is the friction force that acts on objects that are not moving. Static friction always acts in the direction opposite to that of the applied force.

You experience static friction every time you take a step. As you push off with each step, static friction between the ground and your shoe keeps your shoe from sliding.

Sliding Friction With the help of a friend, you push on the pot with enough force to overcome the static friction. The pot slides across the patio as shown in Figure 5B. Once the pot is moving, static friction no longer acts on it. Instead, a smaller friction force called sliding friction acts on the sliding pot. **Sliding friction** is a force that opposes the direction of motion of an object as it slides over a surface. Because sliding friction is less than static friction, less force is needed to keep an object moving than to start it moving.

Go Online NSTA SCiLINKS

For: Links on forces
Visit: www.SciLinks.org
Web Code: ccn-2121

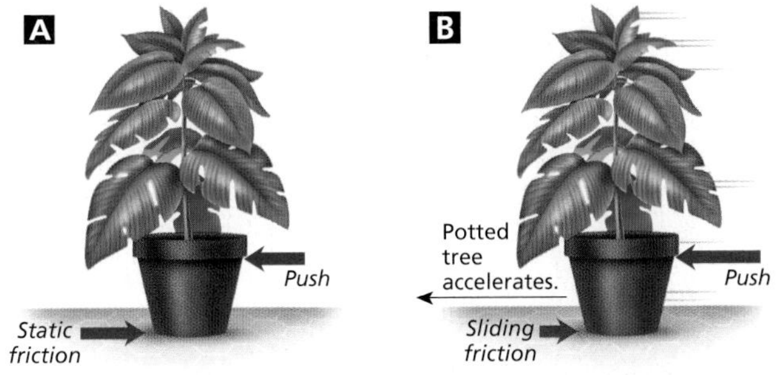
A
Push
Static friction
B
Potted tree accelerates.
Push
Sliding friction

Figure 5 Different types of friction act on moving and nonmoving objects. **A** Static friction acts opposite the direction of the force you apply to move the plant. The potted tree does not move. **B** When you push with more force, the potted tree begins to slide. Sliding friction acts to oppose the direction of motion.

Friction

Use Community Resources

L2

Ask a civil engineer to visit your class and talk about the effects of friction between road surfaces and the tires of a moving car. Have the engineer emphasize the necessity of friction in controlling a car. Suggest that the engineer explain to the students what happens when a car hydroplanes because of lack of friction between the tires and the surface of the road. Encourage students to ask questions about how engineers take friction into account when designing roads and bridges.
Interpersonal

Go Online NSTA SCiLINKS

Download a worksheet on forces for students to complete, and find additional teacher support from NSTA SciLinks.

Answer to . . .

Figure 3 *The net force on the rope is zero.*

Reading Checkpoint *The net force is zero.*

Quick Lab

Observing the Effects Of Friction

L2

Objective
After completing this activity, students will be able to
- describe the effect of friction on motion.

Skills Focus **Observing, Drawing Conclusions**

Prep Time 5 minutes

Materials 2 rubber erasers, sticky notes, scissors, metric ruler

Class Time 10 minutes

Teaching Tips
- Have students construct data tables in which to record their observations.
- You may need to show students how to arrange the erasers so that the ruler will strike both of them at the same time.
- Tell students to repeat the experiment if an eraser flips over or falls off the table.

Expected Outcome Students will observe that the sticky note increases the distance that the eraser slides.

Analyze and Conclude
1. The eraser with the sticky note attached slid farther.
2. The sticky note enabled one eraser to slide farther by reducing friction.
3. Friction produces a force that opposes motion. The greater the friction between two surfaces, the stronger that force is.
4. The erasers would slide farther if the force of friction were reduced by coating the erasers or the tabletop with a smoother material, or if the erasers were struck more firmly, providing a greater force in the direction of motion.
Logical

For Enrichment

L3

Students can use a spring scale to pull a mass across surfaces that provide more or less friction, to observe the difference between the forces required to overcome static and sliding friction. In general, more force is required to overcome static friction and begin sliding than to continue sliding at constant velocity.
Kinesthetic

Quick Lab

Observing the Effects of Friction

Procedure

1. Attach a sticky note to the widest side of a rectangular eraser. The note must cover the entire side of the eraser. Trim off excess paper with scissors.
2. Place the eraser from Step 1 note-side down, next to a second eraser so that one end of each eraser extends 2 cm over the edge of a table.
3. Use a ruler to strike both erasers firmly and evenly at the same time. Record the distance each eraser slides.
4. Repeat Steps 2 and 3 two more times. Calculate and record the average distance each eraser slides.

Analyze and Conclude

1. **Observing** Which eraser slid farther?
2. **Formulating Hypotheses** Why did the erasers slide different distances?
3. **Drawing Conclusions** How does friction affect the motion of a sliding object?
4. **Revising** What could you do to make the erasers slide even farther?

Rolling Friction When a round object rolls across a flat floor, both the object and the floor are bent slightly out of shape. This change in shape at the point of rolling contact is the cause of **rolling friction,** the friction force that acts on rolling objects. For a given set of materials, the force of rolling friction is about 100 to 1000 times less than the force of static or sliding friction. Because of this, professional movers often use wheeled dollies to move heavy objects.

Ball bearings like those shown in Figure 6 are often used to reduce friction in machines. A ball bearing is made up of a set of round balls located between two smooth surfaces. The balls roll as the surfaces move past each other. Friction is greatly reduced between the surfaces because rolling friction replaces sliding friction. Inline skates, skateboards, bicycles, and automobiles are just a few of the many machines that use ball bearings.

Fluid Friction Friction also acts on a submarine moving through water and on an airplane flying through air. Water and a mixture of gases such as air are known as fluids. The force of **fluid friction** opposes the motion of an object through a fluid. You feel fluid friction when stirring thick cake batter. The motion of the spoon through the batter is slowed by fluid friction. Fluid friction increases as the speed of the object moving through the fluid increases. Thus the faster you stir, the greater the friction is.

Fluid friction acting on an object moving through the air is known as **air resistance.** At higher speeds, air resistance can become a significant force. For this reason, bicyclists and speed skaters often wear slick racing suits to reduce air resistance.

Reading Checkpoint *What are two common examples of fluid friction?*

57MM

Figure 6 Ball bearings in these wheels greatly reduce friction by replacing sliding friction with rolling friction.

Facts and Figures

Friction and Tennis You may mention to the students that, if they have ever played tennis on a clay court, they may have discovered that clay courts are covered with a layer of fine sand. The sand granules act as ball bearings for a short distance and then cause the player to slide. Ask, **With clay courts, what types of friction is the player experiencing?** *(The player first experiences rolling friction when the sand granules are still rolling. The player then experiences sliding friction when the granules stop rolling and start sliding. The sliding friction is actually occurring between the grains of sand and the surface below the sand, as the sand sticks to the shoes of the player.)*

Gravity

Why do leaves fall to the ground? The answer is gravity. **Gravity** is a force that acts between any two masses. Gravity is an attractive force, that is, it pulls objects together. Earth's gravitational force exerts a force of attraction on every other object that is near Earth. That includes you—the force of Earth's gravity holds you on the ground. Note that the force of gravity does not require objects to be in contact for it to act on them. Unlike friction, gravity can act over large distances.

Earth's gravity acts downward toward the center of Earth. Fortunately, an upward force usually balances the downward force of gravity. What forces act on the boulder in Figure 7? Gravity pulls down on the boulder. An upward force supplied by the supporting rock acts upward and balances the downward gravitational force. Because the forces on the boulder are balanced, it remains at rest as it has for thousands of years.

Gravity
Supporting force

Figure 7 Earth exerts an attractive, downward force on this boulder.
Inferring *Because the boulder is at rest, what do you know about the net force acting on it?*

Falling Objects What forces affect the motion of a dollar bill dropped from the top of a tall building? Both gravity and air resistance affect the motion of a falling object. **Gravity causes objects to accelerate downward, whereas air resistance acts in the direction opposite to the motion and reduces acceleration.**

In Figure 8, a flying squirrel has jumped from a tree and is falling toward the ground. As you can see, the squirrel has positioned its body parallel to Earth's surface and spread its arms and legs. By doing this, the squirrel creates a very large surface area. The large area maximizes the force of air resistance acting to slow the squirrel's downward acceleration. Because of the squirrel's slower downward acceleration, it is able to travel farther through the air than would otherwise be possible.

As objects fall to the ground, they accelerate and gain speed. With increasing speed comes increasing air resistance. If an object falls for a long time, the upward force of air resistance becomes equal to the downward force of gravity. At this point, the forces acting on the object are balanced. Acceleration is zero and the object continues falling at a constant velocity. **Terminal velocity** is the constant velocity of a falling object when the force of air resistance equals the force of gravity. Read the Concepts in Action pages later in this chapter to learn how sky divers reach terminal velocity.

Gravity
Air resistance

Figure 8 This flying squirrel takes advantage of air resistance to slow its fall and increase the distance covered in the jump.

Gravity

Address Misconceptions **L2**

Students may think that no forces are acting on an object at rest. Help students see that this is false. Reinforce that resting objects have no *net force* acting on them. Show students that anything that has weight has at least two forces on it (if it is not in free fall). Forces of gravity pull the object downward toward Earth, and a reaction force pushes against that object, in accordance with Newton's third law of motion. Ask students to explain why a book which has weight (a type of force) rests on a desk without moving.
Visual, Logical

Use Visuals **L1**

Figure 8 The spread-out wings of the flying squirrel increase the air resistance that opposes the force of gravity, slowing the squirrel's fall. Have students examine the two force arrows in the figure. Ask, **What is the direction of the net force acting on the squirrel?** *(Downward)* **Why is the squirrel able to increase the distance covered when it jumps if the air resistance increases?** *(Because the squirrel's downward acceleration is slowed by the increased air resistance, the squirrel has more time to travel through the air. The squirrel's forward speed is not noticeably changed by the increased air resistance, and thus it travels a greater horizontal distance because it falls through the air a greater period of time.)*
Visual

Facts and Figures

Flying Squirrels Southern flying squirrels are found mostly from southern Ontario to the Gulf Coast. The length of an adult squirrel, including the tail, is about 23 to 25 cm, and its weight is usually between 55 and 110 g. Its fur is long, soft, and silky. On each side of the squirrel's body is a gliding membrane between the wrist of the front leg and the ankle of the hind leg. When the front and hind legs are extended, the membranes help the squirrel to glide in a motion that appears to be flying, giving the animal the name "flying squirrel." The tail acts as a rudder and helps to stabilize the squirrel as it glides.

Answer to . . .

Figure 7 *The net force on the boulder is zero.*

Reading Checkpoint *Answers may include stirring cake batter and air resistance.*

Projectile Motion

Use Visuals L1

Figure 9 Have students read the text under Projectile Motion. Then, ask questions to reinforce the idea that projectile motion is the result of the initial horizontal velocity and the vertical force of gravity. Ask, **Why does the yellow ball in Figure 9B continue downward at the same rate as the blue and green balls in Figure 9A?** *(They all accelerate downward by the force of gravity, approximately 9.8 m/s^2.)* **Why does the yellow ball (in 9B) continue horizontally?** *(The ball's initial horizontal velocity is not affected by the downward force of gravity.)*
Visual, Logical

3 ASSESS

Evaluate Understanding L2

Have students write a review question and its answer for each objective at the beginning of this section. Students should also be able to discuss the section objectives.

Reteach L1

Have students use Figure 4 to summarize the concepts of balanced and unbalanced forces. Use Figures 5 and 8 to review friction, gravity, and air resistance.

Connecting Concepts

Students' sketches should show constant horizontal velocity, steadily increasing downward velocity, and constant downward acceleration.

Interactive Textbook If your class subscribes to the Interactive Textbook, use it to review key concepts in Section 12.1.

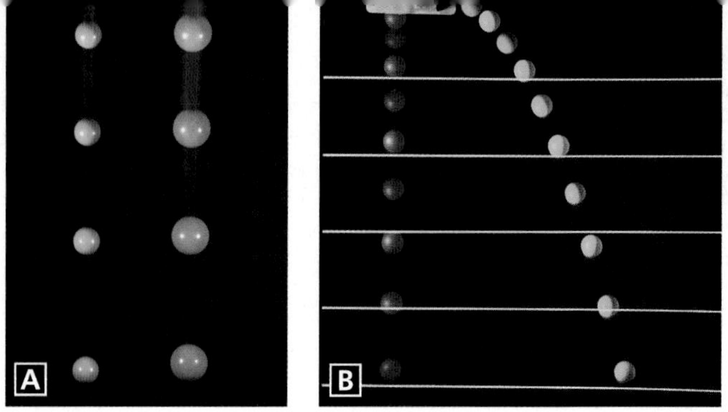
A
B

Figure 9 Gravity acts on falling objects. **A** Although their masses are different, the blue and green balls fall at the same rate. **B** The yellow ball is a projectile, following a curved path. ***Applying Concepts** What forces act on each of the falling balls?*

Projectile Motion

When you throw a ball forward, you'll notice that it actually follows a curved path. This curved path is an example of **projectile motion,** the motion of a falling object (projectile) after it is given an initial forward velocity. Air resistance and gravity are the only forces acting on a projectile.

Figure 9 shows the motion of two balls released at the same time. Figure 9A shows that balls of different mass fall at the same rate. In Figure 9B the curved path of the yellow ball is the result of the force of gravity and the initial horizontal velocity. **The combination of an initial forward velocity and the downward vertical force of gravity causes the ball to follow a curved path.** The two balls fall with the same acceleration and strike the ground at the same time.

Section 12.1 Assessment

Reviewing Concepts

1. How is the motion of an object affected when a force acts on it?
2. List the four types of friction.
3. How does air resistance affect the acceleration of a falling object?
4. Earth's gravitational force acts in what direction?
5. Describe why a projectile follows a curved path.

Critical Thinking

6. **Comparing and Contrasting** Compare the strengths of static, sliding, and rolling friction.
7. **Applying Concepts** Explain why falling leaves often do not fall in a straight-line path to the ground.
8. **Predicting** Two coins are knocked off a table at the same time by different forces. Which coin will hit the floor first?

Connecting Concepts

Velocity and Acceleration Make sketches of Figures 9A and 9B. Use them to relate the concepts of velocity and acceleration from Section 11.3 to falling objects. Add velocity and acceleration arrows at three locations on each sketch.

Section 12.1 Assessment

1. A force can set an object at rest into motion, or it can accelerate a moving object by changing its speed or direction.
2. Static friction, sliding friction, rolling friction, and fluid friction
3. It acts opposite the direction of motion and slows the acceleration of a falling object.
4. Downward toward the center of Earth
5. The combination of initial horizontal velocity and downward vertical force causes a projectile to follow a curved path.
6. The force of static friction is greater than that of sliding friction. The force of sliding friction is generally greater than that of rolling friction.
7. Varying air resistance acting on the leaf results in a fluttering motion.
8. Both coins hit the ground at the same time.

Answer to . . .

Figure 9 *Forces acting on both of the falling balls are air resistance and gravity. In addition, the projectile in Figure 9B was briefly acted on by the force that gave it its initial horizontal velocity.*

12.2 Newton's First and Second Laws of Motion

Reading Focus

Key Concepts

- How does Newton's first law relate change in motion to a zero net force?
- How does Newton's second law relate force, mass, and acceleration?
- How are weight and mass related?

Vocabulary

- inertia
- mass
- weight

Reading Strategy

Building Vocabulary Copy the table below. Then as you read the section, write a definition for each vocabulary term in your own words.

Vocabulary	Definition
Inertia	a. ?
b. ?	c. ?
d. ?	e. ?

Why do some cars accelerate faster than others? How does an ice skater glide far across the ice after pushing off only once? The answers to these questions involve the concepts of mass and inertia.

Aristotle, Galileo, and Newton

Modern scientists understand the relationships between force and motion. However, it took about 2000 years to develop this understanding.

Aristotle The ancient Greek scientist and philosopher Aristotle (384 B.C.–322 B.C.) made many scientific discoveries through careful observation and logical reasoning. He was not always correct. Aristotle incorrectly proposed that force is required to keep an object moving at constant speed. This error held back progess in the study of motion for almost two thousand years.

Galileo Italian scientist Galileo Galilei (1564–1642) experimented to find out about the world. By rolling balls down wooden ramps, he studied how gravity produces constant acceleration. Galileo concluded that moving objects not subjected to friction or any other force would continue to move indefinitely. Galileo's portrait and the title page from the book that presented his work are shown in Figure 10.

DISCORSI
E
DIMOSTRAZIONI
MATEMATICHE,
intorno à due nuoue scienze
Attenenti alla
MECANICA & i MOVIMENTI LOCALI,
del signor
GALILEO GALILEI LINCEO,
Filosofo e Matematico primario del Serenissimo
Grand Duca di Toscana.
Con una Appendice del centro di grauità d'alcuni Solidi.

IN LEIDA,
Appresso gli Elsevirii. M. D. C. XXXVIII.

Figure 10 Galileo's work helped correct misconceptions about force and motion that had been widely held since Aristotle's time.

Section Resources

Print

- ***Lab Manual,*** Investigations 12A and 12B
- ***Reading and Study Workbook With Math Support,*** Section 12.2 and **Math Skill:** Calculating Acceleration
- ***Math Skills and Problem Solving Workbook,*** Section 12.2
- ***Transparencies,*** Section 12.2

Technology

- ***Interactive Textbook,*** Section 12.2
- ***Presentation Pro CD-ROM,*** Section 12.2
- ***Go Online,*** NSTA SciLinks, Mass

Section 12.2

1 FOCUS

Objectives

12.2.1 **Describe** Newton's first law of motion and its relation to inertia.

12.2.2 **Describe** Newton's second law of motion and use it to **calculate** acceleration, force, and mass values.

12.2.3 **Relate** the mass of an object to its weight.

Reading Focus

Build Vocabulary L2

Vocabulary Rating Chart Have students make a four-column chart with the headings Term, Can Define or Use It, Heard or Seen It, and Don't Know. Have them put inertia, mass, and weight in the first column, rating their knowledge of each term by putting a checkmark in one of the other columns. Give students a purpose for reading by asking them to check their expectations as they read. Ask them to make another chart after they have read the section.

Reading Strategy L2

a. The tendency of an object to resist a change in its motion **b.** Mass **c.** The amount of matter an object contains as measured by its inertia **d.** Weight **e.** The force of gravity acting on an object

2 INSTRUCT

Aristotle, Galileo, and Newton

Integrate Social Studies L2

Aristotle did not correctly explain why an object falls toward Earth. Later, Galileo's observations led him to confirm that Earth is one of many planets, all governed by the same laws of gravity. Galileo prepared the way for Isaac Newton, whose laws are presented in this chapter. To demonstrate these ideas, have students further research the ideas Aristotle and Newton had on gravity. Then, drop an object to the floor, and have student volunteers play the roles of "Aristotle" and "Newton" and debate what caused the object to fall.
Verbal, Interpersonal

Build Science Skills L2

Inferring Before studying Newton's first law of motion, have students look at Figures 12A and 12B. Ask, **What would have happened to the test dummy if the air bag had not deployed and the dummy had not been wearing a seatbelt?** *(Students should infer from the photos that the dummy's forward motion continues after the crash, and that the dummy might have gone through the windshield.)* **Visual, Logical**

Newton's First Law of Motion

Use Visuals L1

Figures 12A and 12B Have students examine Figures 12A and 12B. Ask, **What is the effect of inertia on the car?** *(Inertia causes the mass of the car to continue forward, crushing the front of the car.)* **What effect does inertia have on the dummy?** *(After the car stops, the dummy continues to move forward until it is stopped by the air bag and seatbelt.)* **How is the mass of a passenger related to the passenger's inertia?** *(Passengers with greater mass have more inertia. It is harder to stop the forward motion of passengers with greater mass.)* **Visual, Logical**

Quick Lab

Investigating Inertia L2

Objective
After completing this activity, students will be able to
- use the concept of inertia to explain the movement of objects.

Address Misconceptions

This lab can help to correct the misconception that inertia refers to the tendency of objects to resist motion, rather than the tendency to resist a change in motion. Use student answers to Question 1 as the basis of a discussion about the nature of inertia.

Skills Focus Observing, Formulating Hypotheses

Prep Time 5 minutes

Materials index card, coin

Advance Prep Checkers may be substituted for coins.

Class Time 5 minutes

Expected Outcome Fast changes in the movement of the card can occur with little effect on the movement of the coin. When the card moves slowly, it carries the coin along.

Analyze and Conclude
1. In Step 1, the inertia of the coin resisted acceleration by the card. The force of friction was not strong enough to hold the coin in place on the accelerating card. In Step 2, the acceleration of the card was not as great. Therefore, the force of friction was strong enough to hold the coin in place on the card. In Step 3, the situation was identical to that in Step 2 at first. However, when the card suddenly stopped moving, the inertia of the coin was great enough to keep it moving in the same direction, in spite of the force of friction.
2. If the mass of the coin were greater, its inertia also would be greater. Therefore, the coin would again have resisted acceleration in Step 1 and moved with the card in Step 2 if the card was not moving too quickly. In Step 3, the coin would have continued moving longer after the card stopped moving. **Logical**

PHILOSOPHIÆ
NATURALIS
PRINCIPIA
MATHEMATICA.
IMPRIMATUR.
S. PEPYS, Reg. Soc. PRÆSES.

Figure 11 Isaac Newton published his work on force and motion in the book entitled *Principia.*

Newton In 1665, the plague broke out in London, forcing Isaac Newton to leave Trinity College in Cambridge, England, where he was a student. Over the next two years, Newton built on the work of scientists such as Galileo. He published his results many years later in a book entitled *Principia.* In this important work, Newton first had to define mass and force. He then introduced his laws of motion. Newton's portrait and the title page of *Principia* are shown in Figure 11.

Newton's First Law of Motion

Newton summarized his study of force and motion in several laws of motion. **According to Newton's first law of motion, the state of motion of an object does not change as long as the net force acting on the object is zero.** Thus, unless an unbalanced force acts, an object at rest remains at rest, and an object in motion remains in motion with the same speed and direction. For example, a soccer ball resting on the grass remains motionless until a force is applied to it in the form of a kick. The kicked ball begins rolling. Because friction between the grass and the ball acts on the ball as it rolls, the ball slows. The force of friction slows the ball and brings it to a stop.

Newton's first law of motion is sometimes called the law of inertia (in UR shuh). **Inertia** is the tendency of an object to resist a change in its motion. In other words, an object at rest tends to remain at rest, and an object in motion tends to remain in motion with the same direction and speed. Note that as the soccer ball sat motionless in the grass, the forces acting on it were balanced. The ball remained at rest until an unbalanced force acted on it. The ball has inertia.

Reading Checkpoint *How does a zero net force affect an object's motion?*

Figure 12

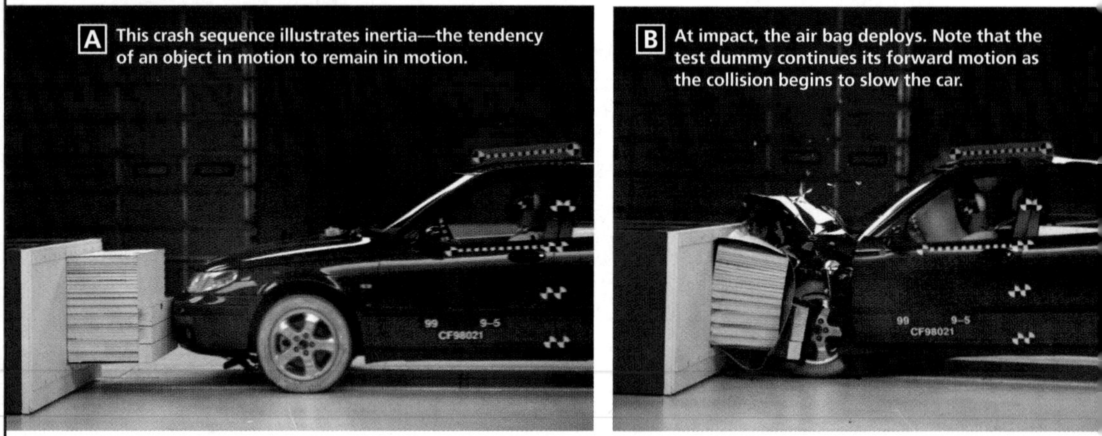

A This crash sequence illustrates inertia—the tendency of an object in motion to remain in motion.

B At impact, the air bag deploys. Note that the test dummy continues its forward motion as the collision begins to slow the car.

Think about what happens if you are in a moving car that is involved in a front-end collision. The collision makes the car stop suddenly. What happens to you? Because you have inertia, you continue moving forward. The series of photos in Figure 12 shows you how dangerous a front-end collision can be. If a seat belt and airbag had not restrained the test dummy, it would have crashed into the steering wheel and windshield with great force. The seat belt and airbag work by exerting force against the body of the dummy, opposing its forward motion.

Newton's Second Law of Motion

How do unbalanced forces affect the motion of an object? An unbalanced force causes an object's velocity to change. In other words, the object accelerates. For example, you apply a net force to a ball when you throw it. The harder you throw, the more the ball accelerates. In fact, the acceleration of the ball is directly proportional to the net force acting on it. If you double the force, the acceleration of the ball doubles as well. Newton also learned that the acceleration of an object depends upon its mass. **Mass** is a measure of the inertia of an object and depends on the amount of matter the object contains.

According to Newton's second law of motion, the acceleration of an object is equal to the net force acting on it divided by the object's mass. Thus, doubling the mass of an object cuts its acceleration in half. Newton was able to put these ideas into a single formula.

Newton's Second Law

$$\text{Acceleration} = \frac{\text{Net force}}{\text{Mass}}, \quad \text{or } a = \frac{F}{m}$$

Quick Lab

Investigating Inertia

Procedure

1. Place an index card on a flat table. Place a coin in the middle of the card. As quickly as you can, try to pull the card out from under the coin. Observe what happens to the coin.
2. Repeat Step 1 while moving the card slowly.
3. Repeat Step 1 again. This time, slowly accelerate the card, and then suddenly bring it to a stop.

Analyze and Conclude

1. **Applying Concepts** Use the concepts of inertia and friction to explain the behavior of the coin each time you moved the card.
2. **Predicting** How would your observations be different with a coin of greater mass? Test your predictions.

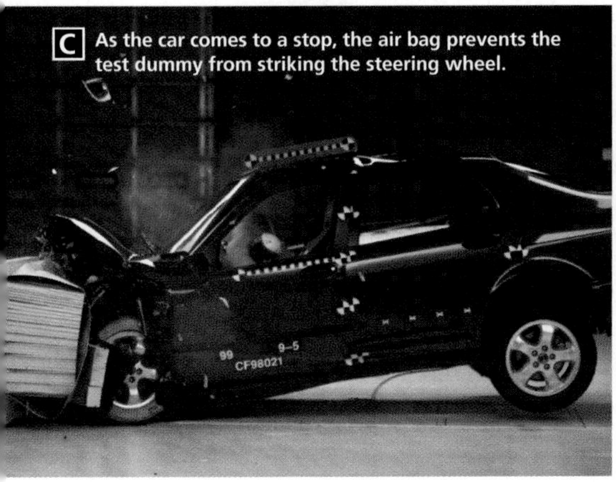

C As the car comes to a stop, the air bag prevents the test dummy from striking the steering wheel.

D Interpreting Photographs *What objects and devices absorb the energy of the crash?*

Newton's Second Law of Motion

Teacher Demo

Force and Acceleration L2

Purpose Students observe that acceleration is directly proportional to force applied

Materials 2 identical toy cars (or dynamics carts), 2 student volunteers, identical floor surface for each car

Procedure Tell students that the cars' masses are identical. Ask a student to push one car along the floor with little force. Have a second student push the other car with greater force.

Expected Outcome The car pushed with little force will accelerate very little. The car pushed with greater force will accelerate much more.
Visual, Group

Customize for Inclusion Students

Learning Disabled
Experiential and visual learning are good strategies for many learning-disabled students. Encourage students to do the following experiments to gain hands-on knowledge and to see the results themselves.

Use a wheeled toy to teach Newton's first and second laws of motion. Have students place a small object on the toy, push the toy forward, and suddenly stop the forward movement. Students will observe that the small object's inertia causes it to continue moving. Then allow students to push the wheeled toy with varying degrees of force. They will observe that when the mass does not change, acceleration varies in direct proportion to the force applied. In Section 12.3, students will learn Newton's third law by observing that, while they are standing on the floor, the floor exerts force in opposition to their weight.

Answer to . . .

Figure 12 *The crushing of the car's body absorbs much of the energy. The air bag and seatbelt also absorb crash energy.*

Reading Checkpoint *The object's motion does not change.*

HOW It Works

Crash-Test Dummies **L2**

Defining the way a body will respond to a crash is difficult because different parts of the human body behave in different ways in a crash. For that reason, developing a crash-test dummy that behaves like a human body in a crash has been difficult.

Early automotive crash test dummies were based on dummies used in aerospace. Because head, spine, and neck injuries can be life-threatening, dummies' heads, necks, and spines were a major focus of research. In 1973, dummies were improved. Injuries to lower extremities are rarely fatal, but they can reduce a person's quality of life. Further research and development of crash-test dummies will focus on lower extremities.

Interpreting Diagrams Forces from both the seatbelt and the air bag slow the dummy's movement.
Visual

For Enrichment **L3**

Have students research the methods used by the National Highway Traffic Safety Administration (NHTSA) to test a vehicle's crash worthiness and its likelihood of rolling over. Also have students create tables explaining the meaning of the star rating system used by the NHTSA. Select a method for students to use to present their findings to the class.
Logical

Use Community Resources **L2**

Arrange for a police officer to speak to your class about seatbelt safety laws. Have the officer reinforce the importance of seatbelts in preventing injury. The police department may have a video that could visually reinforce the concept of seatbelt safety and its relationship to Newton's first law of motion in sudden stops.
Logical, Visual

HOW It Works

Crash-Test Dummies

Dummies are used in simulated car crashes to study what might happen to passengers in a real crash. They are fitted with a range of measuring devices that track the motion of the dummies throughout the crash. By analyzing the data, scientists learn how injuries occur and how they can be prevented. **Interpreting Diagrams** ***What forces act on the crash-test dummy to slow its forward movement?***

Corner collision
One standard test involves crashing a car into a solid concrete wall at nearly 60 kilometers an hour. Other tests involve crashing a sled into the side or corner of the car.

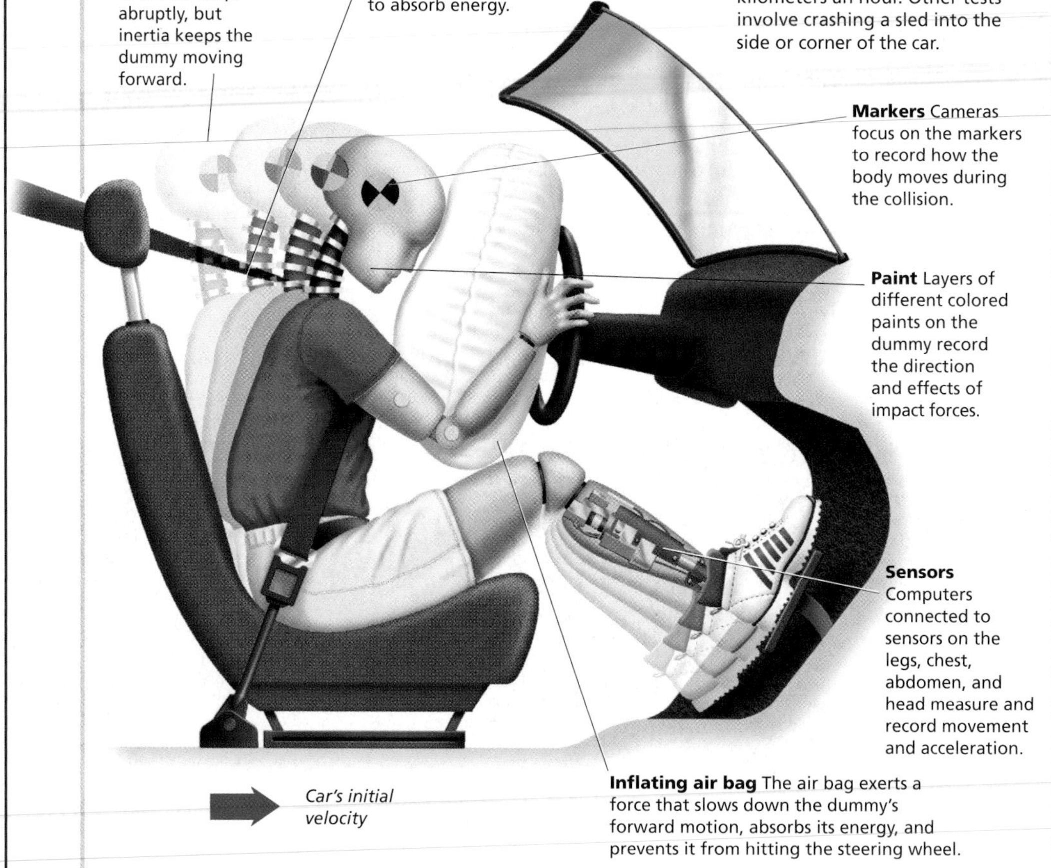
Impact Upon initial impact, the front of the car stops abruptly, but inertia keeps the dummy moving forward.
Seatbelt The seatbelt immediately tightens to slow down the dummy and to absorb energy.
Markers Cameras focus on the markers to record how the body moves during the collision.
Paint Layers of different colored paints on the dummy record the direction and effects of impact forces.
Sensors Computers connected to sensors on the legs, chest, abdomen, and head measure and record movement and acceleration.
Car's initial velocity
Inflating air bag The air bag exerts a force that slows down the dummy's forward motion, absorbs its energy, and prevents it from hitting the steering wheel.

Facts and Figures

Bike Helmets You may help your students understand that Newton's first law of motion is a reason for wearing helmets when cycling. During an accident, the foam padding in a helmet is deformed, absorbing the energy of the impact. Explain that each year, almost 400,000 children ages 14 and under are treated in emergency rooms for bicycle-related injuries. Head injuries account for more than two thirds of bicycle-related hospital admissions and more than half of bicycle-related deaths. If each child wore a bicycle helmet, between 39,000 and 45,000 head injuries, and between 18,000 and 55,000 scalp and face injuries could be prevented annually.

The acceleration of an object is always in the same direction as the net force. In using the formula for Newton's second law, it is helpful to realize that the units N/kg and m/s^2 are equivalent. The Math Skills box reinforces this relationship.

Note that Newton's second law also applies when a net force acts in the direction opposite to the object's motion. In this case, the force produces a deceleration that reduces the speed. This is the principle used by automobile seat belts. In a collision, the seat belt applies a force that opposes a passenger's forward motion. This force decelerates the passenger in order to prevent serious injury.

Math Skills

Newton's Second Law

An automobile with a mass of 1000 kilograms accelerates when the traffic light turns green. If the net force on the car is 4000 newtons, what is the car's acceleration?

1 Read and Understand

What information are you given?

Mass, $m = 1000$ kg

Force, $F = 4000$ N (in the forward direction)

2 Plan and Solve

What unknown are you trying to calculate?

Acceleration, $a = ?$

What formula contains the given quantities and the unknown?

$$\text{Acceleration} = \frac{\text{Net force}}{\text{Mass}},\ a = \frac{F}{m}$$

Replace each variable with its known value and solve.

$$a = \frac{4000\ \text{N}}{1000\ \text{kg}} = \frac{4\ \text{N}}{\text{kg}} = \frac{4\ \frac{\text{kg}\cdot\text{m}}{\text{s}^2}}{\text{kg}} = 4\ \text{m/s}^2$$

$a = 4\ \text{m/s}^2$ in the forward direction

3 Look Back and Check

Is your answer reasonable?

Powerful sports cars can accelerate at 6 m/s^2 or more. Thus, a smaller acceleration of 4 m/s^2 seems reasonable.

Math Practice

1. A boy pushes forward a cart of groceries with a total mass of 40.0 kg. What is the acceleration of the cart if the net force on the cart is 60.0 N?
2. What is the upward acceleration of a helicopter with a mass of 5000 kg if a force of 10,000 N acts on it in an upward direction?
3. An automobile with a mass of 1200 kg accelerates at a rate of 3.0 m/s^2 in the forward direction. What is the net force acting on the automobile? (*Hint:* Solve the acceleration formula for force.)
4. A 25-N force accelerates a boy in a wheelchair at 0.5 m/s^2 What is the mass of the boy and the wheelchair? (*Hint:* Solve Newton's second law for mass.)

Teacher Demo

Newton's Second Law of Motion L2

Purpose Students observe that acceleration is inversely proportional to mass. ($a = F/m$)

Materials wind-up toy car, 3 metal washers, tape

Procedure Have students wind the toy car completely and observe its motion along a flat surface. Next, have them tape metal washers to the car, wind it, and watch its motion along the flat surface again.

Expected Outcome Students will notice that the car's acceleration decreases because of the increased mass. **Visual**

Math Practice

Solutions L2

1. $a = F/m = 60.0\ \text{N}/40.0\ \text{kg} = 1.50\ \text{m/s}^2$

2. $a = F/m = 10{,}000\ \text{N}/5000\ \text{kg} = 2\ \text{m/s}^2$

3. $a = F/m$; $F = ma = 1200\ \text{kg} \times 3.0\ \text{m/s}^2 = 3600\ \text{N}$

4. $a = F/m$; $m = F/a = 25\ \text{N}/0.50\ \text{m/s}^2 = 50\ \text{kg}$

Logical

For Extra Help L1

Remind students that they first need to solve the equation $a = F/m$ for the unknown. Also ask students to identify all the known and unknown variables before using the equation. **Logical**

Direct students to the **Math Skills** in the **Skills and Reference Handbook** at the end of the student text for additional help.

Additional Problems

1. A 20-N net force acts on an object with a mass of 2.0 kg. What is the object's acceleration? *(10 m/s^2)*
2. A box has a mass of 150 kg. If a net force of 3000 N acts on the box, what is the box's acceleration? *(20 m/s^2)*
3. What is the acceleration of a 1000 kg car subject to a 500 N net force? *(0.5 m/s^2)*
Logical, Portfolio

Use Visuals L1

Figure 13 Use this figure to be sure that students understand the equation *F* = *ma* before asking the following question about the mass-acceleration ratio. Ask, **Why would one cart accelerate eight times as fast as the chain of eight carts with the same force applied in each case? Explain using the second-law equation.** *(If the force remains the same in the equation* F = ma, *then as mass increases, the acceleration has to decrease in proportion to the increase in mass.)* **How would the force have to change in order to have the same acceleration for eight carts as for one cart?** *(The force would have to be eight times greater.)* **How would another force directed to the left on the cart affect the cart's acceleration?** *(The acceleration would depend on the net force acting on the cart. The net force would be the force acting to the right minus the force acting to the left.)*
Visual

Build Reading Literacy L1

Visualize Refer to page **354D** in **Chapter 12,** which provides the guidelines for visualizing.

Tell students that forming a mental image of concepts they are learning helps them remember new concepts. For example, this section discusses weight in newtons, but students may think of weight in terms of pounds. Help students to visualize that the pound equals 4.448 newtons. Tell them, that in approximate weights, $\frac{1}{4}$ pound is slightly more than one newton. Encourage students to think of something the size of a pound, such as a pound of butter. If the butter is divided into four sticks, each stick is slightly more than the weight of one newton. Likewise, a quarter-pound hamburger could be called a "newton" burger.
Visual

Go Online NSTA SciLinks

Download a worksheet on mass for students to complete, and find additional teacher support from NSTA SciLinks.

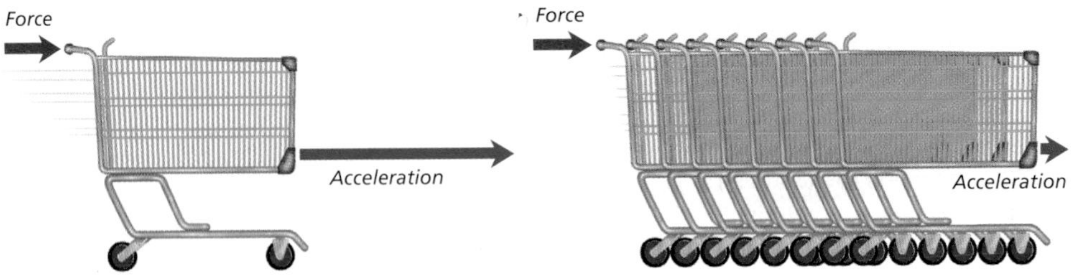
Force
Acceleration
Force
Acceleration

Figure 13 Acceleration depends directly on force and inversely on mass. Neglecting friction, when the same force acts, the single cart accelerates eight times faster than the chain of eight carts. **Predicting** ***How would the acceleration of a chain of two carts compare with the acceleration of a single cart if the same force acted on both?***

The shopping carts in Figure 13 further illustrate Newton's second law. What happens if you push on a single shopping cart? The unbalanced force causes the cart to accelerate. What happens when you push with the same force on a chain of eight shopping carts? The acceleration of the chain of carts is much less than that of the single cart. The chain of carts accelerates less because it has more mass.

Weight and Mass

Do you sometimes talk about weight and mass as if they were the same thing? Although related to each other, mass and weight are not the same. **Weight** is the force of gravity acting on an object. An object's weight is the product of the object's mass and acceleration due to gravity acting on it.

Weight Formula

$$\text{Weight} = \text{Mass} \times \text{Acceleration due to gravity}$$
$$W = mg$$

The weight formula is basically Newton's second law. However, weight (W) is substituted for force (F) and acceleration due to gravity (g) is substitutued for acceleration (a). In other words, $W = mg$ is a different form of $a = \frac{F}{M}$, that is when the equation is solved for force, $F = ma$. The value of g in the formula is 9.8 m/s^2.

In using the weight formula or Newton's second-law formula, make sure you use the correct units. The force (F or W) should be in newtons, the acceleration (a or g) in meters per second squared, and the mass (m) in kilograms. The following example shows how to use the weight formula.

If an astronaut has a mass of 112 kilograms, what is his weight on Earth where the acceleration due to gravity is 9.8 m/s^2?

$$\text{Weight} = \text{Mass} \times \text{Acceleration due to gravity}$$
$$= 112 \text{ kg} \times 9.8 \text{ m/s}^2$$
$$= 1100 \text{ kg·m/s}^2 = 1100 \text{ N}$$

Go Online NSTA SciLinks

For: Links on mass
Visit: www.SciLinks.org
Web Code: ccn-2122

A **Astronaut on Earth**
Mass = 88.0 kg; Weight = 863 N

B **Astronaut on Moon**
Mass = 88.0 kg; Weight = 141 N

Figure 14 Weight is a measure of the force of gravity acting on an object. **A** An astronaut with a mass of 88 kg weighs 863 N on Earth. **B** An astronaut with a mass of 88 kg weighs 141 N on the moon. **Calculating** ***If the same astronaut stood on Mars where the acceleration due to gravity is about 3.7 m/s^2, how much would the astronaut weigh?***

If you study the weight formula, you'll see that mass and weight are proportional. Doubling the mass of an object also doubles the object's weight. **Mass is a measure of the inertia of an object; weight is a measure of the force of gravity acting on an object.** Consider the same astronaut shown on Earth and on the moon in Figure 14. On the moon, the acceleration due to gravity is only about one sixth that on Earth. Thus, the astronaut weighs only about one sixth as much on the moon as on Earth. In both locations, the mass of the astronaut is the same.

Section 12.2 Assessment

Reviewing Concepts

1. State Newton's first law of motion in your own words.
2. What equation states Newton's second law of motion?
3. How is mass different from weight?

Critical Thinking

4. **Applying Concepts** Describe several examples of Newton's first and second laws that you observe during a normal day.
5. **Making Judgments** A steel ball is the same size as a wooden ball, but weighs twice as much. If both balls are dropped from an airplane, which of them will reach terminal velocity more quickly? Explain.

Math Practice

6. During a test crash, an air bag inflates to stop a dummy's forward motion. The dummy's mass is 75 kg. If the net force on the dummy is 825 N toward the rear of the car, what is the dummy's deceleration?
7. A bicycle takes 8.0 seconds to accelerate at a constant rate from rest to a speed of 4.0 m/s. If the mass of the bicycle and rider together is 85 kg, what is the net force acting on the bicycle? (*Hint:* First calculate the acceleration.)

3 ASSESS

Evaluate Understanding **L2**

Have students work in pairs to write three math problems (with solutions) based on Newton's second law, $a = F/m$. Then have them do the same for the weight equation, $W = mg$. Ask students to present their problems and solutions in class.

Reteach **L1**

Use Figure 12 to review inertia and its relationship to Newton's first law of motion. Use Figure 13 to review Newton's second law of motion. Use Figure 14 to review how Newton's second law is related to the weight formula.

Math Practice

Solutions **L2**

6. $a = F/m$ = 825 N/75 kg = 11 m/s^2, toward the rear of the car
7. $a = \delta v/t$ = (4.0 m/s)/(8.0 s) = 0.50 m/s^2; $F = ma$ = 85 kg x 0.50 m/s^2 = 43 N

Interactive Textbook If your class subscribes to the Interactive Textbook, use it to review key concepts in Section 12.2.

Section 12.2 Assessment

1. Students should paraphrase the following: According to Newton's first law of motion, the state of motion of an object does not change as long as the net force acting on the object is zero.
2. $a = F/m$
3. Mass is a measure of the inertia of an object; weight is a measure of the force of gravity acting on an object.
4. Students should cite examples in which objects at rest remain at rest or tend to continue moving (first law) and in which a net force acting on an object causes a change in the object's state of motion (second law).
5. The heavier steel ball will take longer to reach terminal velocity. A greater speed is needed to produce the air resistance required to balance the steel ball's greater weight. The steel ball must fall for a longer period of time in order to reach this greater speed.

Answer to . . .

Figure 13 *The two-cart chain would accelerate at half the rate of the single cart.*

Figure 14 *330 N*

CONCEPTS — in Action —

Terminal Speed **L2**

Background

The skydiver's weight, the gravitational force downward, is constant and is calculated with the formula $W = mg$. The variable g is 9.8 m/s/s, usually written 9.8 m/s^2. The opposing drag force, D, from the air, continues to increase until terminal velocity is reached. The drag force depends on the shape and position of the skydiver. Drag is calculated from a complex formula.

The skydiver's net force is weight minus drag, $W - D$. Using net force $W - D$ for F, acceleration is found as follows: $a = F/m = (W - D)/m$.

When weight equals drag, $W - D$ becomes zero; therefore, acceleration becomes zero. The skydiver stops accelerating and reaches maximum velocity, which is called terminal velocity.

Build Science Skills **L2**

Observing ACTIVITY

Purpose Students investigate air resistance and its effect on the rate of acceleration.

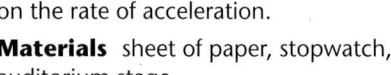

Materials sheet of paper, stopwatch, auditorium stage

Class Time 25 minutes

Procedure Have one student drop the flat sheet of paper from the auditorium stage while another times the paper's descent with the stopwatch. A third student can record the time.

Repeat the experiment, but this time have the student crumple the sheet of paper. Compare the descent times. Ask, **What variables remained constant and what variables changed?** *(Air resistance changed. Weight (mass) and acceleration due to gravity, g, remained the same.)* **Why are the times different?** *(A greater air resistance force acts on the flat sheet, causing it to fall more slowly.)* **If both the flat and crumpled sheets were dropped in a vacuum where there is no air resistance, what would happen?** *(The time it takes the sheet to fall would be the same.)*

Expected Outcome The increased force of air resistance acting on the flat sheet causes it to fall more slowly than the crumpled sheet.
Visual, Logical

CONCEPTS in Action

Terminal Speed

Imagine you are a sky diver about to step out of a plane and fall through the air. What forces will you experience during your fall? How can you use these forces to combine an exhilarating experience with a safe landing?

Upward drag force
Helmet for protection
Harness
Downward force of gravity

Sky diving relies on two principles of physics. First, if there is nothing to support you, the force of gravity will cause you to accelerate downward. Second, all fluids—including air—produce a drag force that opposes the motion of an object moving through the fluid. The speed of a falling object increases until the drag force equals the force of gravity. At this point, the net force is zero and the sky diver falls at a constant, terminal speed.

The actual terminal speed depends on several factors. For example, an object with greater mass has a greater gravitational force on it, increasing its terminal speed. Thinner air, such as air at very high altitudes, increases velocity by decreasing the drag force. A sky diver can also partially control the drag force, and terminal speed, by changing shape. Opening the parachute dramatically increases the drag force and lowers the terminal speed to about 4.5 meters per second—a speed suitable for landing.

The Sky Diving Sequence

No matter what the starting altitude, any sky dive consists of the same basic stages, starting with the jump from the plane.

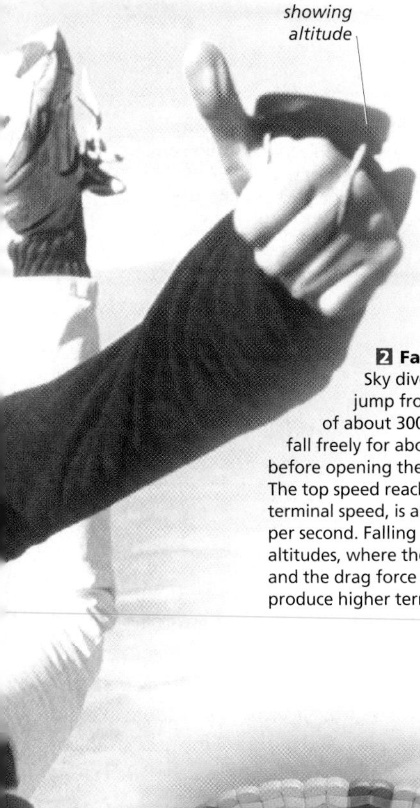
Alimeter showing altitude

Parachute

1 Jumping out Upon jumping, the sky diver begins accelerating at a rate of 9.8 meters per second per second in free fall. Within a few seconds she will reach maximum speed.

2 Falling freely Sky divers usually jump from a height of about 3000 meters and fall freely for about 45 seconds before opening the parachute. The top speed reached, known as terminal speed, is about 52 meters per second. Falling from very high altitudes, where the air is thinner and the drag force is less, can produce higher terminal speeds.

3 Slowing the fall Usually the parachute is fully open by the time the sky diver is 300 meters above the ground. The parachute causes rapid deceleration and allows the sky diver to make a steady descent, using the control lines to steer.

Sky diver lands standing up

4 Landing The sky diver pulls down on the control lines to achieve a safe and steady low-speed landing.

Going Further

- Research the development and use of the parachute and prepare a poster presentation of your findings. Be sure to include a development time line listing names and dates of significant contributions and advances.
- Take a Discovery Channel Video Field Trip by watching "Air Forces."

Discovery Channel School
Video Field Trip

Address Misconceptions

L2

Students may think that objects in a vacuum fall at a constant speed. Help them to realize that objects accelerate as they fall. Earth's gravitational acceleration in a vacuum is approximately 9.8 m/s/s, meaning that the velocity increases 9.8 m/s every second, or 9.8 m/s^2, as the object falls.

Without a vacuum, however, air resistance increases as the object falls until the object reaches terminal velocity. Reinforce that all objects in a vacuum accelerate at the same rate, but that they do not fall at a constant speed until they reach terminal velocity.
Logical

Going Further

Student poster presentations may include references to Leonardo da Vinci, Fauste Veranzio, and Joseph and Jacques Montgolfier.
Visual, Verbal

Discovery Channel School

Video Field Trip

Air Forces

After students have viewed the Video Field Trip, ask them the following questions: **What is the net force on the skydiver just before stepping out of the plane? Explain your answer.** (*Zero. The force of gravity is balanced by the force the aircraft exerts so that the skydiver is not yet accelerating.*) **How do the force of gravity and air resistance compare as the skydiver is falling and gaining speed? Explain your answer.** *(The force of gravity is greater than the air resistance because the gravitational force is downward and the air resistance is upward, resulting in a net force downward.)* **How does the force of air resistance change as the skydiver gains speed while falling?** *(The air resistance increases.)* **What happens to the skydiver's speed when the force of air resistance becomes equal to the force of gravity? Explain your answer.** *(The skydiver's speed stays the same. Gravity and air resistance balance each other. Because the net force is zero, there is no acceleration.)* **How does the force of air resistance change when the skydiver's parachute opens?** *(It suddenly increases.)*

1 FOCUS

Objectives

12.3.1 **Explain** how action and reaction forces are related according to Newton's third law of motion.

12.3.2 **Calculate** the momentum of an object and **describe** what happens when momentum is conserved during a collision.

Reading Focus

Build Vocabulary L2

Paraphrase Have students work with a partner to write an explanation in their own words for the law of conservation of momentum. They may do so by reading this section and by using what they have already learned about mass, inertia, and velocity. Have student groups read their explanation aloud. Encourage other students to react to the explanation they hear.

Reading Strategy L2

a. kg•m/s **b.** Mass (or velocity) **c.** Velocity (or mass)

Build Reading Literacy L1

Relate Text and Visuals Refer to page **190D** in **Chapter 7**, which provides the guidelines for relating text and visuals.

Ask questions that will help students understand how the visuals help clarify and extend concepts presented in the text. Point out Figure 15. Ask, **Describe the forces created when the bumper car strikes another car.** *(There is a force from each car toward the other car.)* **If a moving car hits a car at rest, will the car at rest exert a force on the moving car? Explain your answer.** *(Yes, according to Newton's third law, the car at rest exerts an equal and opposite force on the moving car.)*
Visual, Verbal

12.3 Newton's Third Law of Motion and Momentum

Reading Focus

Key Concepts

- What is Newton's third law of motion?
- What is needed for an object to have a large momentum?
- How is momentum conserved?

Vocabulary

- momentum
- law of conservation of momentum

Reading Strategy

Summarizing Read the section on momentum. Then copy and complete the concept map below to organize what you know about momentum.

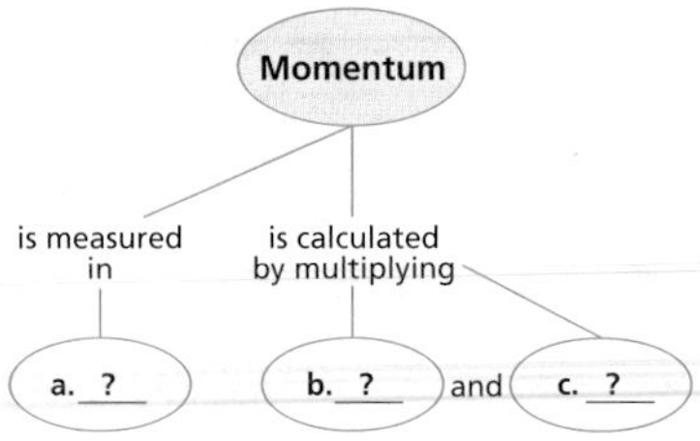

Momentum
is measured in
is calculated by multiplying
a. ?
b. ?
and
c. ?

Think physics the next time you go to an amusement park. There is no better place than an amusement park to see Newton's laws in action. As you experience sudden starts, stops, changes in direction, and possibly even free fall, you can be sure that the laws of physics control your motion. The bumper cars in Figure 15 illustrate momentum and Newton's third law of motion, the subjects of this section.

If you have ever driven a bumper car, you know your goal is to slam into another car head on. When you collide with the other car, you do so with enough force to jolt the other driver almost out of the seat. There are two parts to this collision, however—the collision also causes your own car to rebound sharply. Newton's third law of motion explains the behavior of the bumper cars during a collision.

Figure 15 When this bumper car collides with another car, two forces are exerted. Each car in the collision exerts a force on the other.

Section Resources

Print

- ***Reading and Study Workbook With Math Support,*** Section 12.3
- ***Math Skills and Problem Solving Workbook,*** Section 12.3
- ***Transparencies,*** Section 12.3

Technology

- ***Probeware Lab Manual,*** Lab 4
- ***Interactive Textbook,*** Section 12.3
- ***Presentation Pro CD-ROM,*** Section 12.3
- ***Go Online,*** NSTA SciLinks, Newton's laws

Newton's Third Law

A force cannot exist alone. Forces always exist in pairs. **According to Newton's third law of motion, whenever one object exerts a force on a second object, the second object exerts an equal and opposite force on the first object.** These two forces are called action and reaction forces.

Action and Reaction Forces The force your bumper car exerts on the other car is the action force. The force the other car exerts on your car is the reaction force. These two forces are equal in size and opposite in direction.

Pressing your hand against a wall also produces a pair of forces. As you press against the wall, your hand exerts a force on the wall. This is the action force. The wall exerts an equal and opposite force against your hand. This is the reaction force.

A similar situation occurs when you use a hammer to drive a nail into a piece of wood. When the hammer strikes the nail, it applies a force to the nail. This action force drives the nail into the piece of wood. Is there a reaction force? According to Newton's third law there must be an equal and opposite reaction force. The nail supplies the reaction force by exerting an equal and opposite force on the hammer. It is this reaction force that brings the motion of the hammer to a stop.

Action-Reaction Forces and Motion
Can you determine the action and reaction forces occurring in Figure 16? The swimmer uses her arms to push against the water and create an action force. The action force causes the water to move in the direction of the action force. However, the water also exerts its equal and opposite reaction force on the swimmer. The reaction force acts on the swimmer and pushes her forward through the water.

Unlike the swimmer in Figure 16, not all action and reaction forces produce motion. Pushing against the wall with your hand is an example of an action-reaction force pair that does not result in motion.

Action-Reaction Forces Do Not Cancel You may be wondering why the action and reaction forces acting on the swimmer in Figure 16 do not cancel each other and produce a net force of zero. The reason is that the action and reaction forces do not act on the same object. The action force acts on the water, and the reaction force acts on the swimmer. Only when equal and opposite forces act on the same object do they result in a net force of zero.

Reading Checkpoint *Why don't action and reaction forces cancel each other out?*

Go Online NSTA SciLinks

For: Links on Newton's laws
Visit: www.SciLinks.org
Web Code: ccn-2123

Figure 16 Action-reaction forces propel the swimmer through the water. The swimmer pushes against the water, and the water pushes the swimmer ahead.
Comparing and Contrasting ***Describe the magnitude and direction of the action and reaction forces acting on the swimmer.***

2 INSTRUCT

Newton's Third Law

Build Science Skills L2

Predicting ACTIVITY

Purpose Students use Newton's third law of motion to predict the effect of objects that hit against one another.

Materials soccer ball, several heavy books

Class Time 15 minutes

Procedure Ask students to use Newton's third law to predict the outcome of each activity before performing it. First, have students lift several heavy books above their heads and notice the downward force they feel against their hands. Next, place a soccer ball against a wall. Have a student kick the ball gently. The student should notice the opposing force he or she feels against his or her foot. Afterwards, have students discuss the origin of the forces they felt in each activity.

Expected Outcome Students will realize that the force they exerted on the books and ball caused an equal and opposite force against them.
Visual, Logical

Go Online NSTA SciLinks

Download a worksheet on Newton's laws for students to complete, and find additional teacher support from NSTA SciLinks.

Customize for English Language Learners

Use Interaction
One of the best ways to teach science content and language to all students, including English language learners, is to encourage verbal interaction, such as that which occurs in a group. You may help English language learners by using group activities in this section, as the section lends itself well to activities involving action-reaction forces. Since all force involves action-reaction, you may start with activities that make the concept easy to learn. For example, demonstrate that standing on the floor results in a reaction force of the floor, which is actually pushing back. Encourage students to work in groups to list other action-reaction forces.

Answer to . . .

Figure 16 *The action force is the force the swimmer exerts on the water. The equal and opposite reaction force is the force the water exerts on the swimmer.*

Reading Checkpoint *They do not cancel each other out because they act on different objects.*

Momentum

Teacher Demo

Momentum

L2

Purpose Students observe that force is related to the time during which an object's momentum changes.

Materials water-filled balloons, pillow

Procedure Before beginning the demonstration, explain to students that force can be written as a function of momentum and time: $F = m \times a = m \times (v/t) = (m \times v)/t$. Therefore, $F \times t = m \times v$, where momentum is $m \times v$, and $F \times t$ is the quantity known as impulse. Point out that force has an inverse relationship to time in the equation. Therefore, the longer the time period over which momentum change occurs, the smaller the force will be.

Take students outdoors to a paved area. Drop a water-filled balloon to the ground and let it burst on the pavement. Next, drop a water-filled balloon so that it lands on the pillow without bursting.

Safety Caution students to stand a safe distance away from you when you drop the balloons.

Expected Outcome Students should realize that when the balloon stops quickly, the momentum change occurs over a short time. This results in a large force acting on the balloon—the large force breaks the balloon. When the balloon lands on the pillow, its momentum change occurs over a much longer period of time. The balloon doesn't burst because the force acting on it is much less.
Visual, Logical

FYI

The coverage of momentum in this text is limited to linear momentum—angular momentum and conservation are not covered.Momentum is a vector quantity, having both magnitude and direction.

Momentum

Imagine a loaded shopping cart and a small glass marble are both slowly rolling toward you at the same speed. The marble is easier to stop. Intuitively, you know that a loaded shopping cart is harder to stop because it has a greater mass. If the marble were moving 100 times faster than the shopping cart, which would be easier to stop? **Momentum** is the product of an object's mass and its velocity. An object with large momentum is hard to stop. **An object has a large momentum if the product of its mass and velocity is large.** The momentum for any object at rest is zero. A huge rocket such as the space shuttle has zero momentum as it sits on the launch pad. A small 1-kilogram meteor traveling at the very high speed of 20 kilometers per second has a very large momentum.

DK SCIENCE and History

Amusement Park Rides

For more than one hundred years, engineers have been designing rides that subject riders to jarring motions, large accelerations, terrifying heights, soakings, or free falls.

Acceleration *Riders experience an acceleration toward the loop's center as they move around it.*
Start turret, 13 meters above the ground
LOOPING GRAVITY RAILWAY

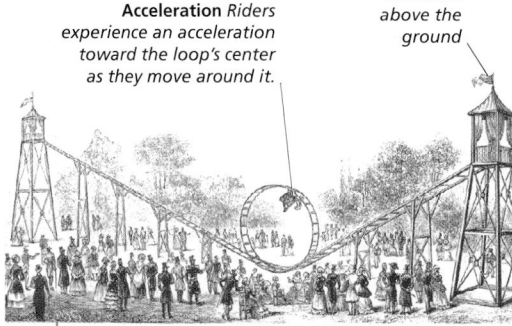

Maximum height *The first Ferris wheel is 80.5 m tall.*
Wood-paneled car *Each car has a mass of 13 tons and holds as many as 60 people.*
The ride *Passengers move at a speed of about 0.5 m/s.*
FERRIS WHEEL

1846 The first railway to turn its passengers upside down opens at a park in Paris, France.

1884 The first true roller coaster in America appears at Coney Island, New York.

1893 The George Ferris Giant Wheel, named after the inventor, debuts at the Columbian Exposition in Chicago. A ride costs 50 cents.

1900 Trolley companies build amusement parks to encourage weekend travel.

1845 | 1875 | 1905

You can calculate momentum by multiplying an object's mass (in kilograms) and its velocity (in meters per second).

Momentum Formula

$$\text{Momentum} = \text{Mass} \times \text{Velocity}$$

Momentum is measured in units of kilogram-meters per second.

Which has more momentum, a 0.046-kilogram golf ball with a speed of 60.0 meters per second, or a 7.0-kilogram bowling ball with a speed of 6.0 meters per second?

$$\text{Momentum}_{\text{golf ball}} = 0.046\ \text{kg} \times 60.0\ \text{m/s} = 2.8\ \text{kg•m/s}$$

$$\text{Momentum}_{\text{bowling ball}} = 7.0\ \text{kg} \times 6.0\ \text{m/s} = 42\ \text{kg•m/s}$$

The bowling ball has considerably more momentum than the golf ball.

Writing in Science

Explain a Sequence Write a paragraph about one of the amusement park rides shown on the time line. Describe the motion of the ride using Newton's laws of motion. (*Hint:* Before you write, use a diagram to analyze the forces acting on the ride at a particular moment.)

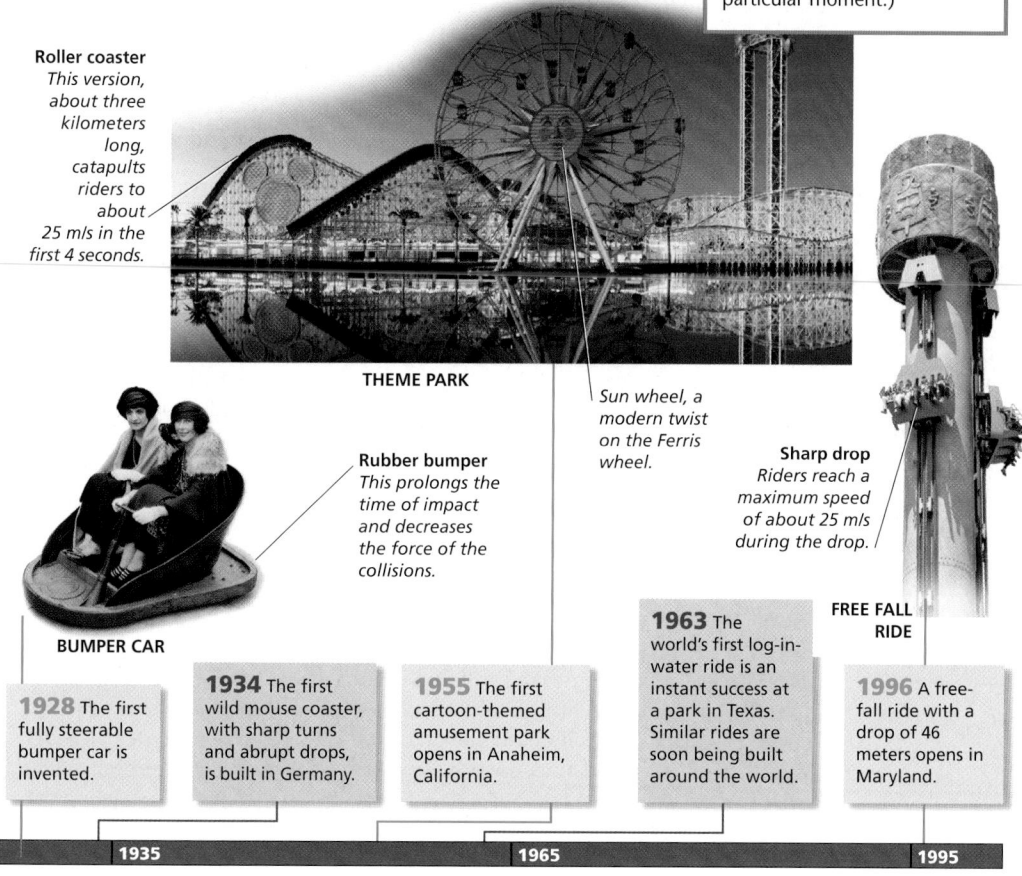

Roller coaster
This version, about three kilometers long, catapults riders to about 25 m/s in the first 4 seconds.
Sun wheel, a modern twist on the Ferris wheel.

THEME PARK

Rubber bumper
This prolongs the time of impact and decreases the force of the collisions.

BUMPER CAR

Sharp drop
Riders reach a maximum speed of about 25 m/s during the drop.

FREE FALL RIDE

1928 The first fully steerable bumper car is invented.

1934 The first wild mouse coaster, with sharp turns and abrupt drops, is built in Germany.

1955 The first cartoon-themed amusement park opens in Anaheim, California.

1963 The world's first log-in-water ride is an instant success at a park in Texas. Similar rides are soon being built around the world.

1996 A free-fall ride with a drop of 46 meters opens in Maryland.

1935 — 1965 — 1995

SCIENCE and History

Amusement Park Rides

L2

Have students read about the amusement park inventions shown in the timeline. Then, ask them what other science-related events they would add to the timeline. Suggestions may include these events: Orville and Wilbur Wright's first flight at Kitty Hawk, North Carolina, in 1903; Henry Ford's initial Model-T production in 1908; the opening of the 50-mile Panama Canal in 1914; or Charles Lindbergh's $33\frac{1}{2}$-hour, non-stop flight in a monoplane from New York to Paris in 1927. Then, ask students how all of the events in the timeline affected both science and society, including those events that students have added.
Verbal

Build Math Skills

L1

Equations and Formulas Many students have difficulty relating the description of a relationship given in the text with the equation used to solve problems. Have students read Momentum. Ask them to use the description from the text to write the momentum equation (Momentum = Mass × Velocity). Once they have written the equation, have them practice solving the equation for each of the three possible unknowns: momentum, mass, and velocity. Tell them that it is important to practice working with the units (kg•m/s). Refer students to the text samples on this page.
Logical, Portfolio

Direct students to the **Math Skills** in the **Skills and Reference Handbook** at the end of the student text for additional help.

Writing in Science

Explanations describing the forces and resulting motion that occur as a sequence of events will vary depending on which amusement park ride is chosen. Paragraphs should discuss forces, acceleration, and momentum.
Verbal, Portfolio

Conservation of Momentum

Use Visuals

L1

Figure 17 To help teach conservation of momentum, point out to students that each car's momentum is written on the car, and its velocity is written above the car. Ask students to describe the motion in 17A before and after the collision. *(The blue car, going in the same direction as the green car, but faster, catches the green car and collides with it. After the collision, part of the momentum from the blue car is transferred to the green car, but the total momentum is still the same.)* Ask, **What is the momentum of the blue car and the green car before and after the collision in 17A?** *(Before the collision, the blue car's momentum is 300,000 kg•m/s and the green car's momentum is 150,000 kg•m/s. After the collision, the blue car's momentum is 150,000 kg•m/s and the green car's momentum is 300,000 kg•m/s.)* **What is the sum of the momentum before and after the collision?** *(The total momentum is 450,000 kg•m/s before and after the collision.)* **How does this show conservation of momentum?** *(The total momentum doesn't change.)* Repeat the above questions for Figures 17B and 17C.
Visual, Logical

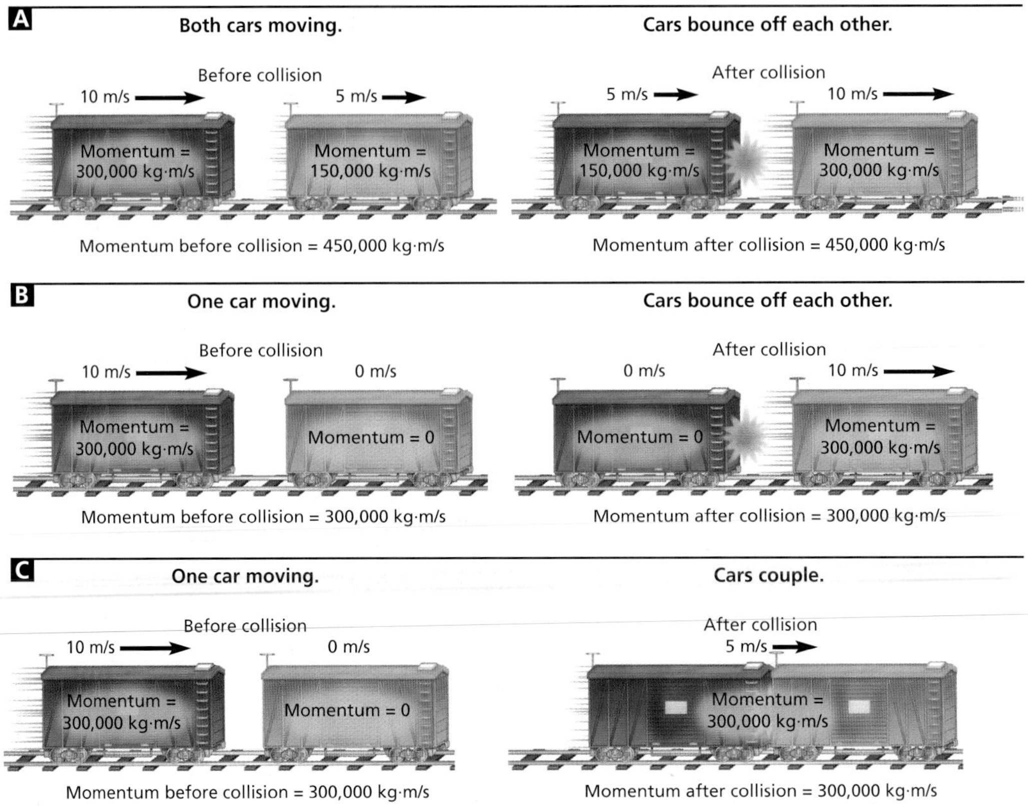

A
Both cars moving.
Before collision
10 m/s
5 m/s
Momentum = 300,000 kg·m/s
Momentum = 150,000 kg·m/s
Momentum before collision = 450,000 kg·m/s
Cars bounce off each other.
After collision
5 m/s
10 m/s
Momentum = 150,000 kg·m/s
Momentum = 300,000 kg·m/s
Momentum after collision = 450,000 kg·m/s
B
One car moving.
Before collision
10 m/s
0 m/s
Momentum = 300,000 kg·m/s
Momentum = 0
Momentum before collision = 300,000 kg·m/s
Cars bounce off each other.
After collision
0 m/s
10 m/s
Momentum = 0
Momentum = 300,000 kg·m/s
Momentum after collision = 300,000 kg·m/s
C
One car moving.
Before collision
10 m/s
0 m/s
Momentum = 300,000 kg·m/s
Momentum = 0
Momentum before collision = 300,000 kg·m/s
Cars couple.
After collision
5 m/s
Momentum = 300,000 kg·m/s
Momentum after collision = 300,000 kg·m/s

Figure 17 Three different collisions between equal-mass train cars are shown above. The different collisions between equal-mass train cars are shown above. In each collision, the total momentum of the train cars does not change—momentum is conserved. **Calculating** ***What is the mass of each train car?***

Conservation of Momentum

What happens to momentum when objects collide? Look at the collisions in Figure 17. Under certain conditions, collisions obey the law of conservation of momentum. In physics, the word *conservation* means that something has a constant value. That is, conservation of momentum means that momentum does not increase or decrease.

Imagine two trains colliding as shown in Figure 17A. If the two cars are part of a closed system, then momentum is conserved. A closed system means other objects and forces cannot enter or leave a system. Objects within the system, however, can exert forces on one another. According to the **law of conservation of momentum,** if no net force acts on a system, then the total momentum of the system does not change.

Thus, if we consider the two train cars as a closed system, the cars can exert forces on each other. But overall, the total momentum of the system is conserved. **In a closed system, the loss of momentum of one object equals the gain in momentum of another object—momentum is conserved.**

Data Analysis

Momentum

A class studied the speed and momentum of a 0.25-kilogram ball dropped from a bridge. The graph shows the momentum of the ball from the time it was dropped until the time it hit the river flowing below the bridge.

1. **Applying Concepts** At what time did the ball have zero momentum? Describe this point in the ball's motion.
2. **Using Graphs** At what time did the ball have the greatest momentum? What was the peak momentum value?
3. **Calculating** What is the ball's speed after 1.25 seconds? (*Hint:* Use the graph and the momentum formula.)

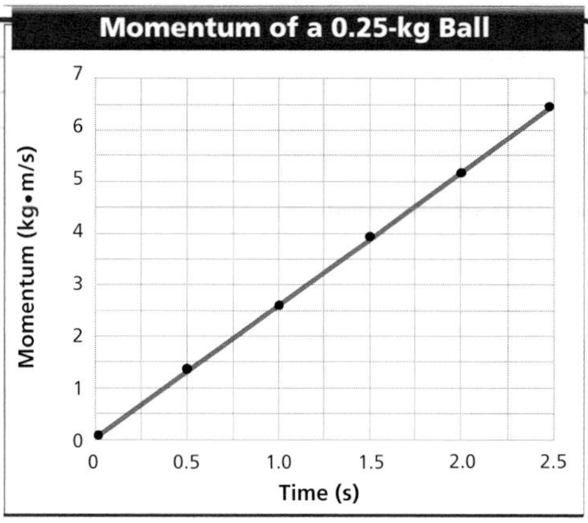

Momentum of a 0.25-kg Ball
Momentum (kg•m/s)
0
1
2
3
4
5
6
7
0
0.5
1.0
1.5
2.0
2.5
Time (s)

Three different closed systems are shown in Figure 17. Each system consists of two train cars with the same mass that collide. In Figures 17A and 17B, the train cars collide and then bounce apart. In Figure 17C, the cars collide and then join together. Examine the momentum of each train car before and after the collision. Note that the total momentum before and after each collision does not change. The momentum is conserved.

Section 12.3 Assessment

Reviewing Concepts

1. Using Newton's third law, explain what is meant by action and reaction pairs of forces.
2. State in your own words the formula for momentum.
3. What is a necessary condition for the conservation of momentum?
4. If an eagle and a bumblebee are traveling at 8 km/hr, which has more momentum? Explain.

Critical Thinking

5. **Applying Concepts** A friend tells you that a rowboat is propelled forward by the force of its oars against the water. First, explain whether the statement is correct, and then identify the action and reaction forces.
6. **Inferring** Explain how Newton's third law of motion is at work when you walk.
7. **Applying Concepts** Explain in terms of Newton's third law why someone who tries to jump from a canoe to a riverbank may fall into the water.

Writing in Science

Explanatory Paragraph Write a paragraph explaining why it is impossible to identify a single isolated force. State in your first sentence the main idea of Newton's third law of motion.

Section 12.3 Assessment

1. Whenever one object exerts a force on a second object, the second object exerts an equal and opposite force on the first object.
2. Momentum = Mass × Velocity
3. The objects involved must be part of a closed system.
4. Because the speeds are equal, the eagle's greater mass gives it more momentum.
5. It is incorrect because it is the force of the water against the oars that propels the boat forward. The oars pushing against the water is the action force, and the water pushing back against the oars is the reaction force.
6. As you walk, you bend your foot and push off against the ground. This action force produces the reaction force of the ground pushing against your shoe. The reaction force pushes you forward.
7. When you jump, you push against the canoe. However, the canoe also moves in the opposite direction of your jump. Because the canoe moves away, it produces a smaller reaction force on you. This small reaction force is not strong enough to propel you to the riverbank.

3 ASSESS

Evaluate Understanding **L2**

Ask students to write their own examples illustrating the key concepts of Newton's third law of motion, momentum, and conservation of momentum.

Reteach **L1**

Demonstrate a force acting on an object and ask the students to identify the action and reaction forces. Have them identify the direction of each force on the object on which it acts. Use Figure 17 to review momentum. Emphasize that momentum is mass times velocity.

Data Analysis

Momentum **L2**

Answers
1. At $t = 0$ s; the ball has zero momentum before it is released.
2. At $t = 2.5$ s; about 6.5 kg•m/s
3. $(m)(v) = 3.25$ kg•m/s
$v = (3.25 \text{ kg•m/s})/(0.25 \text{ kg})$
$v = 13$ m/s, upward
The speed is 13 m/s.

For Extra Help **L1**

Show students how they can locate the desired momentum value by moving their finger up the vertical axis until they reach the value. Then, they can move horizontally to the right until they hit the plotted line. Finally, they can move down to the horizontal axis and determine the time. For question 3, have students find the momentum for a time of 1.25 s. Then, demonstrate how students can find the ball's velocity by rewriting the momentum equation as velocity equals momentum divided by mass. **Logical**

Writing in Science

Student paragraphs will vary but must mention that forces always exist in pairs, and that according to Newton's third law, every action force has an equal and opposite reaction force.

Interactive Textbook If your class subscribes to the Interactive Textbook, use it to review key concepts in Section 12.3.

Answer to . . .

Figure 17 *30,000 kg*

Section 12.4

1 FOCUS

Objectives

12.4.1 **Identify** the forms of electromagnetic force that can both attract and repel.

12.4.2 **Identify** and **describe** the universal forces acting within the nucleus.

12.4.3 **Define** Newton's law of universal gravitation and **describe** the factors affecting gravitational force.

12.4.4 **Describe** centripetal force and the type of motion it produces.

Reading Focus

Build Vocabulary L2

Compare-Contrast Table Have students each make a table similar to the table on p. 378. Have students use *electromagnetic force, nuclear forces,* and *gravitational force* as the entries under the heading Force. For Relative Strength, have students use words such *as weak, weaker, weakest, strong, stronger,* and *strongest*. Suggest that students make this table as they read in order to help them learn the section's content.

Reading Strategy L2

a. Neutrons and protons **b.** Very short (decreases rapidly beyond the diameter of a few protons) **c.** Very strong (100 times stronger than electrical repulsion force at that distance) **d.** All particles **e.** Short **f.** Weaker than the strong nuclear force.

2 INSTRUCT

Electromagnetic Forces

Build Reading Literacy L1

Relate Cause and Effect Refer to page **260D** in **Chapter 9**, which provides the guidelines on relating cause and effect.

Encourage students to make a list of cause-and-effect relationships as they read about electromagnetic forces. Then, have students compare their lists. Students may list the behavior of charged objects when they approach one another, the clinging of clothes that have become charged, and the repulsion or attraction of magnetic poles. **Verbal, Logical**

12.4 Universal Forces

Reading Focus

Key Concepts

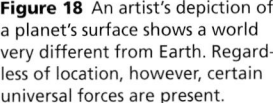

- What force can attract and repel?
- What force holds the nucleus together?
- What is Newton's law of universal gravitation?

Vocabulary

◆ electromagnetic force ◆ strong nuclear force ◆ weak nuclear force ◆ gravitational force ◆ centripetal force

Reading Strategy

Comparing and Contrasting Copy the table below. After reading the section, compare the two universal nuclear forces by completing the table.

Force	Acts on Which Particles?	Acts Over What Distance?	Relative Strength
Strong nuclear	a. ?	b. ?	c. ?
Weak nuclear	d. ?	e. ?	f. ?

If you could travel to a distant planet in another galaxy, what would you expect to find? The scene shown in Figure 18 is one possibility. Although this world looks so different from the one you know, some things on this distant planet would be familiar—the forces.

Observations of planets, stars, and galaxies strongly suggest four different forces exist throughout the universe. These forces are known as universal forces. The four universal forces are the electromagnetic, strong nuclear, weak nuclear, and gravitational. All the universal forces act over a distance between particles of matter, which means that the particles need not be in contact in order to affect one another. In addition, each of these forces is affected by the distance between the particles of matter.

Figure 18 An artist's depiction of a planet's surface shows a world very different from Earth. Regardless of location, however, certain universal forces are present.

378 Chapter 12

Electromagnetic Forces

Electric and magnetic force are two different aspects of the electromagnetic force. **Electromagnetic force** is associated with charged particles. **Electric force and magnetic force are the only forces that can both attract and repel.** To understand electric and magnetic forces, recall what you learned about charged particles in Chapter 4.

Section Resources

Print

- ***Reading and Study Workbook With Math Support,*** Section 12.4
- ***Transparencies,*** Section 12.4

Technology

- ***Interactive Textbook,*** Section 12.4
- ***Presentation Pro CD-ROM,*** Section 12.4
- ***Go Online,*** NSTA SciLinks, Gravity

Electric Forces Electric forces act between charged objects or particles such as electrons and protons. Objects with opposite charges—positive and negative—attract one another. Objects with like charges repel one another. Figure 19 shows that clothes often cling together when they are removed from a dryer. Some clothes, such as cotton socks, lose electrons easily and become positively charged. Other clothes, such as polyester shirts, gain electrons easily and become negatively charged. Because the oppositely charged particles attract one another, the clothes cling together.

Magnetic Forces Magnetic forces act on certain metals, on the poles of magnets, and on moving charges. Magnets have two poles, north and south, that attract each other. Two poles that are alike repel each other. If you have handled magnets, you know that when opposite magnetic poles are brought close, they almost seem to jump together. On the other hand, when two similar poles approach each other, you can feel them pushing apart.

Figure 20 shows a child's wooden train set whose cars are linked with magnets. Each car has a north pole on one end and a south pole on the other. Children quickly learn that if a train car won't stick to the one in front of it, the car must be turned around.

Figure 19 Clothes often acquire electric charges in the dryer. Clothes with opposite charges tend to cling together.

Reading Checkpoint *What type of force acts between particles with the same electrical charge?*

Nuclear Forces

Think about the nucleus of an atom, with its protons crammed into an incredibly small space. Because protons are positively charged, you would expect that an electric force of repulsion would break the nucleus apart. Scientists believe the nucleus would fly apart if there were not another, much stronger, attractive force holding the protons within the nucleus.

Two forces, the strong nuclear force and the weak nuclear force, act within the nucleus to hold it together. The strong nuclear force overcomes the electric force of repulsion that acts among the protons in the nucleus. The weak nuclear force is involved in certain types of radioactive processes.

LNER

Figure 20 A magnetic force of attraction holds the two train cars together.
Applying Concepts *How are the two magnetic poles of the magnets related?*

Strong Nuclear Force The **strong nuclear force** is a powerful force of attraction that acts only on the neutrons and protons in the nucleus, holding them together. The range over which the strong nuclear forces acts is approximately equal to the diameter of a proton (10^{-15} m). Although this force acts over only extremely short distances, it is 100 times stronger than the electric force of repulsion at these distances.

Address Misconceptions L2

Some students may think that for an object to become positively charged, it must gain one or more protons. Reinforce the concept that electron transfer leads to charged particles. Electrons have a negative charge. Therefore, gaining electrons makes an object more negative, and losing electrons makes an object more positive.
Logical

Nuclear Forces

Teacher Demo

Nuclear Forces L2

Purpose Students observe forces representing the strong force in an atom's nucleus and the electric force between protons.

Materials 2 magnetic toy train cars or any 2 magnets, wide adhesive tape on a roll (or rubber band)

Procedure Use the toy train cars or magnets to show students that like poles repel. With the cars touching each other, bind them together with adhesive tape. Be sure to tape the cars in such a way that the tape can be easily cut to free the cars. Tell students that the toy train cars are like protons, whose electric charges repel each other, and that the tape is like the strong nuclear force, overcoming the electric charge of the protons. Cut the tape and have students observe the energy released as the cars push away from each other. Relate this to the force released in a nuclear explosion when the nucleus of an atom is split.

Expected Outcome The students realize that the strong nuclear force in an atom's nucleus is stronger than the electric force between protons.
Visual, Logical

Customize for Inclusion Students

Physically Challenged
To accommodate students who have physical challenges, look for opportunities to include them in tasks that are suited to their motor skills. For example, have students with limited body movements explain the similarities in the way electrically charged particles attract and repel each other and the behavior of opposite magnetic poles. Then, provide them with bar magnets and ask them to demonstrate attractive and repulsive magnetic forces.

Answer to . . .

Figure 20 *The opposite poles, north and south, are touching one another.*

Reading Checkpoint *Electric force*

Gravitational Force

Quick Lab

Investigating Force and Distance L2

Objective
After completing this activity, students will be able to
- describe how the force of electrostatic attraction is affected by distance.

Skills Focus Observing, Formulating Hypotheses

Prep Time 5 minutes

Advance Prep Select a day when the relative humidity is moderate or low to perform this lab.

Class Time 5 minutes

Teaching Tips
- Demonstrate how to charge the balloon and hold it above the bubble.
- Some hair products will interfere with the balloon. In this case, have students rub the balloon against their clothes.

Expected Outcome The bubbles will be attracted to the charged balloon. The force of this attraction will increase as students bring the balloon closer to the bubbles.

Analyze and Conclude
1. There is very little electrical interaction between objects that are far apart. As the distance is decreased, the attraction between the two objects becomes stronger.
2. If the balloon were brought closer to the bubble, the force of attraction would increase and the bubble would move upwards toward the balloon.
Visual, Logical

Quick Lab

Investigating Force and Distance

Materials
balloon, bubble solution, bubble wand

Procedure
1. Inflate a balloon and then make a knot in its neck to close it. Rub the balloon back and forth against your hair to charge it.
2. Blow several bubbles into the air and hold the charged balloon above them. Observe how the distance between the balloon and the bubbles affects the speed at which the bubbles fall. **CAUTION** *Quickly wipe up any spilled bubble solution to avoid slips and falls.*
3. Try to temporarily suspend a bubble in the air without touching it with the balloon.

Analyze and Conclude
1. **Drawing Conclusions** How does the distance between two objects affect the force of attraction between them?
2. **Predicting** If a bubble were suspended below the balloon, what do you think would happen when you moved the balloon closer to the bubble?

Weak Nuclear Force The other powerful force in the nucleus is the weak nuclear force. As the name implies, the weak force is weaker in strength than the strong nuclear force. The **weak nuclear force** is an attractive force that acts only over a short range. The short range over which the weak nuclear force acts, about 10^{-18} meters, is less than the range of the strong nuclear force.

Gravitational Force

Gravity, the weakest universal force, is so much a part of your life that you probably take it for granted. You know from experience that objects fall toward Earth. It was Newton who discovered that gravity affects all objects in the universe. The same force acting on a falling apple is also acting on the moon to keep it in its orbit.

Gravitational force involves much more than just Earth's gravitational field. **Gravitational force** is an attractive force that acts between any two masses. **Newton's law of universal gravitation states that every object in the universe attracts every other object.**

Thus, Earth exerts a force on an apple, and the apple exerts an equal force on Earth. You exert a gravitational force on your textbook, and your textbook exerts an equal gravitational force on you. The reason you don't notice gravity pulling your textbook toward you is that your mass and the mass of the textbook are so small. It takes a huge mass such as Earth's to exert a large gravitational force. The attractive force of gravity acting between two objects is shown in Figure 21.

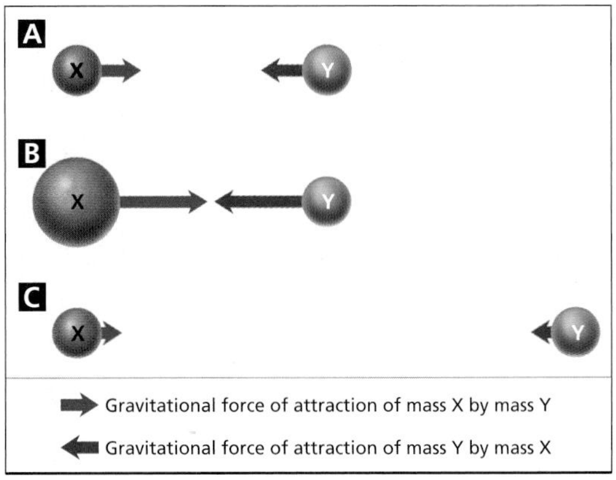
A
X
Y
B
X
Y
C
X
Y
Gravitational force of attraction of mass X by mass Y
Gravitational force of attraction of mass Y by mass X

Figure 21 Gravitational force depends upon mass and distance. **A** Two masses, X and Y, attract each other. **B** The larger mass of X results in a larger gravitational force. **C** Increasing the distance between the masses significantly reduces the gravitational force.

Facts and Figures

Law of Universal Gravitation Newton came to the conclusion that any two objects in the universe exert a gravitational force of attraction on each other. The force is directed along a line joining the objects' centers. Newton concluded that the gravitational attraction *(G)* is proportional to the product of the objects' masses (m_1 and m_2) and inversely proportional to the square of the distance *(d)* between them. That equation is $F = G(m_1 m_2/d^2)$. Because the value of *G* is very small, the gravitational force is only significant if one or both objects has a large mass and the distance between the objects is not very large. Earth's gravitational acceleration *g* is related to the equation of universal gravitation by the expression $g = g(m_e/d^2)$, where m_e is Earth's mass. In this case, the equation for universal gravitation reduces to the familiar equation $F = mg$.

Gravity Acts Over Large Distances The gravitational force between two objects is proportional to their masses and decreases rapidly as the distance between the masses increases. The greater the mass of the objects, the greater is the gravitational force. Gravitational force decreases with the square of the distance between the objects. As shown in Figures 21A and 21C, if the distance between masses doubles, the force of gravity is only one fourth as strong.

Gravity is the weakest universal force, but it is the most effective force over long distances. Gravity holds you on Earth. It keeps the moon in orbit around Earth, the planets in orbit around the sun, and the stars in orbit in their galaxies. The sun's mass is about 300,000 times the mass of Earth, so the sun's gravitational force is much stronger than that of Earth. The influence of the sun's gravitational force extends well beyond Earth. Pluto, which is almost 40 times farther from the sun than Earth is, has its orbit determined by the gravitational pull of the sun.

Reading Checkpoint *What factors affect gravitational force?*

Go Online NSTA SCINKS

For: Links on gravity
Visit: www.SciLinks.org
Web Code: ccn-2124

The Earth, Moon, and Tides How is the moon kept in orbit around Earth? Recall that the moon has inertia, so according to Newton's first law, it should continue to move along a straight path until acted upon by a force. That force is Earth's gravitational force, which acts continuously to pull the moon toward it, as shown in Figure 22.

Earth's gravitational attraction keeps the moon in a nearly circular orbit around Earth. It works in much the same way that a string tied to an eraser allows you to twirl the eraser in a circle over your head. As you twirl the eraser, the string exerts a centripetal force on the eraser. A **centripetal force** is a center-directed force that continuously changes the direction of an object to make it move in a circle. This center-directed force causes a continuous change in the direction of the eraser. The result is a circular path. The center-directed force of Earth's gravity pulls the moon into a nearly circular orbit around Earth.

Earth
Moon
Gravity
Motion of Moon

Figure 22 The moon's inertia and the gravitational pull of Earth result in a nearly circular orbit. The gravitational pull of the moon is the primary cause of Earth's ocean tides.

If you have spent time at the seashore, you have probably noticed that the level of the tide changes throughout the day. The gravitational pull from the moon produces two bulges in Earth's oceans. One bulge is on the side of Earth closest to the moon. The other bulge is on the side of Earth farthest from the moon. Earth rotates once per day beneath theses two bulges. This rotation results in two high and two low tides per day on Earth.

Build Science Skills L2

Observing Take students outside. Tie a string around an eraser, as described in the second paragraph of The Earth, Moon, and Tides. Ask a volunteer to twirl the eraser over his or her head. **CAUTION** *Make sure the students observing this demo stand far away from the student twirling the eraser.* Have students observe that the eraser follows a circular orbit. Remind students that inertia causes an object to resist change in motion. Explain that this means that the eraser would travel in a straight path if a force did not pull it into an orbit. Ask the volunteer to slowly twirl the eraser and then let go of the string. Have students observe what happens. Ask, **What force kept the eraser moving in a circular orbit?** *(The centripetal force from the string kept the eraser moving in a circular orbit.)* **What proof do you have that a centripetal force was acting on the twirling eraser to change its motion?** *(As soon as the string was released, the eraser moved in a straight line path.)* **As the eraser is twirled at a constant speed, is it accelerating? Explain your answer.** *(Yes, acceleration occurs because the eraser is constantly changing direction.)*
Visual, Logical

Use Visuals L1

Figure 22 Use Figure 22 to reinforce the concept of centripetal force and inertia, as discussed in Build Science Skills. Help students to see that gravitational pull is the centripetal (center-directed) force in planetary orbits. Ask, **What is the direction of the moon's velocity in Figure 22?** *(The moon's velocity is tangent to its circular path. At the instant shown, the direction of the moon's velocity is straight down toward the bottom of the page.)*
Visual, Logical

Go Online NSTA SCINKS

Download a worksheet on gravity for students to complete, and find additional teacher support from NSTA SciLinks.

Answer to . . .

Reading Checkpoint *Mass and distance*

Section 12.4 (continued)

3 ASSESS

Evaluate Understanding L2

Have students make a poster with information about electromagnetic forces, nuclear forces, and gravitational force. Students should include examples of each type of force along with sketches or diagrams that illustrate the main concepts.

Reteach L1

Ask students to list all examples of electromagnetic, nuclear, and gravitational forces they can think of, both from the text and from everyday examples. Have them explain the action of each of the forces they list.

Writing in Science

The electromagnetic force is both repulsive and attractive. The other three forces are only attractive. The electromagnetic force and the gravitational force act at all distances. The strong force and the weak force act only at very short distances.

Interactive Textbook If your class subscribes to the Interactive Textbook, use it to review key concepts in Section 12.4.

Satellites in Orbit Artificial satellites are launched into orbit by a rocket or space shuttle. Why doesn't a satellite in a high orbit need to fire rocket engines continuously to remain in orbit? Much like the moon, the satellite needs only the centripetal force provided by gravity and its inertia to maintain its orbit. Satellites in a low orbit, however, are slowed by friction with Earth's atmosphere. As a satellite loses speed, it loses altitude. Eventually the satellite reenters Earth's atmosphere and burns up.

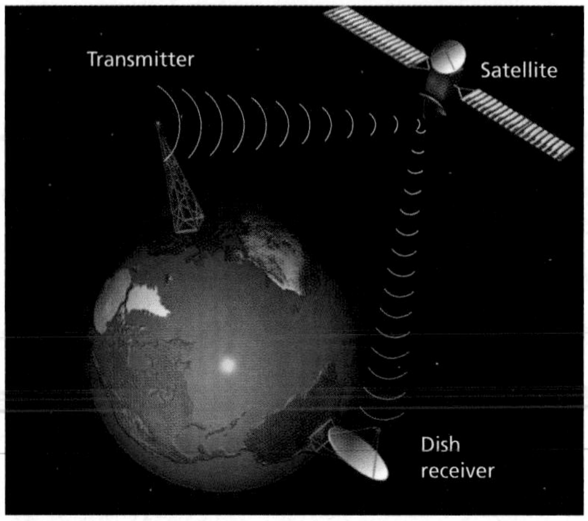
Transmitter
Satellite
Dish
receiver

Figure 23 Satellites are used to receive and transmit electromagnetic waves over great distances.

Uses of Satellites Currently, there are hundreds of artificial satellites orbiting Earth. These satellites perform many functions. They monitor Earth's weather, create detailed radar maps of Earth's surface, use telescopes to gaze deep into space, and study Earth's climate. Some satellites, like the one shown in Figure 23, receive and transmit radio and microwave signals. Numerous communication satellites are used to receive and transmit cell phone and satellite television signals.

The next time you watch an event on television transmitted by satellite from another part of the world, you should thank Isaac Newton. His work to discover the laws of motion and universal gravitation have led to the development of countless modern technologies.

Section 12.4 Assessment

Reviewing Concepts

1. Which universal force can repel as well as attract?
2. Which universal force acts to hold the nucleus together?
3. State in your own words what is meant by Newton's law of universal gravitation.
4. How does friction with the atmosphere affect the speed of an artificial satellite?

Critical Thinking

5. **Using Models** The moon in its orbit around Earth behaves like a ball at the end of a string being swung above your head. Explain the forces involved.
6. **Predicting** If the speed of an orbiting satellite decreases, how might you expect its orbit to change?
7. **Inferring** Explain how Newton's third law and his law of universal gravitation are connected.

Writing in Science

Compare-Contrast Paragraph Write a short paragraph comparing the similarities and differences of the universal forces. Discuss the distances over which the forces act and whether each force attracts, repels, or can do either.

Section 12.4 Assessment

1. Electromagnetic force is the only force that can both attract and repel.
2. The strong nuclear force acts within the nucleus to hold it together.
3. According to Newton's law of universal gravitation, every object in the universe attracts every other object.
4. Friction with the atmosphere slows artificial satellites in low orbit.
5. Earth's gravitational attraction acts as a centripetal force on the moon.
6. It would gradually be pulled closer to Earth and eventually fall out of orbit.
7. According to Newton's third law, whenever one object exerts a force on a second object, the second object exerts an equal and opposite force on the first object. Newton's law of gravitation is a special case of this in which the force is gravity.

Exploration Lab

Investigating a Balloon Jet

In this lab, you will examine the relationships among force, mass, and motion.

Problem How does a jet-powered device move?

Materials

- string, 3 m in length
- drinking straw
- 4 long balloons
- masking tape
- stopwatch
- meter stick
- 2 threaded nuts
- 2 chairs

For the probeware version of this lab, see the Probeware Lab Manual, Lab 4.

Skills Applying Concepts

Procedure

1. On a separate sheet of paper, make a copy of the data table shown.
2. Insert the string through the straw and tie each end of the string to the back of a separate chair. Pull the chairs apart until the string is tight and horizontal.
3. Blow up the balloon and then hold the balloon's opening closed. Record the length of the balloon. Have a classmate attach the balloon lengthwise to the straw using tape.
4. While continuing to hold the balloon's opening closed, slide the balloon jet to the end of the string as shown.
5. Release the balloon. Measure the time during which the balloon jet moves. Measure the distance that the balloon jet travels along the string. Record the distance and time values in the data table for 0 Nuts Used, Trial 1.
6. Repeat Steps 3 through 5 with a new balloon. Make sure to inflate the balloon to the same size as in Step 3. Record your results in the data table for 0 Nuts Used, Trial 2.
7. Repeat Steps 3 through 6 twice more with a new balloon. This time, tape two nuts to the balloon before releasing it. Record your results in the data table for 2 Nuts Used, Trials 1 and 2.
8. Calculate and record the average speed for each trial. The average speed is equal to the distance divided by the time.

Analyze and Conclude

1. **Applying Concepts** Use Newton's second and third laws to explain the motion of the balloon jet.
2. **Analyzing Data** How did adding mass (nuts) to the balloon jet affect its motion?

Data Table

Number of Nuts Used	Trial Number	Time (seconds)	Distance (centimeters)	Average Speed (cm/s)
0	1			
0	2			
2	1			
2	2			
Length of Inflated Balloon (centimeters)				

Exploration Lab

Investigating a Balloon Jet **L2**

Objective

After completing this activity, students will be able to

- use Newton's second and third laws of motion to explain the movement of a jet-powered device.
- use Newton's second and third laws of motion to describe how the mass of an object affects its acceleration in response to a force.

Address Misconceptions

Many students hold the misconception that a jet functions by pushing against the surrounding air. Point out that rockets work in the vacuum of outer space. Then, ask students to explain how they think the balloon jet moves. As the air in the balloon jet is pushed out the end, it produces an equal and opposite reaction in the balloon, which accelerates the balloon forward.

Skills Focus Measuring, Calculating, Applying Concepts

Prep Time 5 minutes

Class Time 45 minutes

Expected Outcome As the balloon is released it will accelerate along the length of the string. Adding the nuts to the mass of the balloon will reduce the time and distance that the balloon travels.

Analyze and Conclude

1. The jet's movement depends on Newton's third law of motion. The pressurized air inside the sealed balloon pushes outward in all directions, but as long as the air can't go anywhere, neither can the balloon. As soon as the air inside the balloon is allowed to escape, the force of the air on the opened end of the balloon no longer balances the force of air on the opposite end. The reaction to this action is the movement of the balloon in the opposite direction. Newton's second law of motion predicts that the balloon will accelerate at a rate that is directly proportional to the force of the compressed air, and inversely proportional to the balloon's mass.
2. Adding nuts increased the mass of the balloon jet, which reduced its acceleration.
Logical

Probeware Lab Manual Versions of this lab for use with probeware available from Pasco, Texas Instruments, and Vernier are in the Probeware Lab Manual.

Study Guide

Study Tip

Choose a Quiet Place
Tell students that being able to concentrate while studying will increase their comprehension. Therefore, a quiet place where they will not be distracted can help them to achieve a better grasp of the subject material and will make their study time more efficient.

Thinking Visually

a. Arrows
b. Newtons
c. Balanced
d. State of motion
e. Accelerate

Assessment

Interactive Textbook If your class subscribes to the Interactive Textbook, your students can go online to access an interactive version of the Student Edition and a self-test.

Reviewing Content

1. c	**2.** a	**3.** a
4. d	**5.** a	**6.** c
7. b	**8.** a	**9.** d
10. b		

CHAPTER 12

Study Guide

12.1 Forces

Key Concepts

- A force can cause a resting object to move, or it can accelerate a moving object by changing the object's speed or direction.
- When the forces on an object are balanced, there is no change in the object's motion. When an unbalanced force acts on an object, the object accelerates.
- There are four main types of friction: static friction, sliding friction, rolling friction, and fluid friction.
- Earth's gravity acts downward toward the center of Earth. Gravity causes objects to accelerate downward, whereas air resistance acts in the direction opposite to the motion and reduces acceleration.
- The combination of initial forward velocity and downward vertical force of gravity cause a projectile to follow a curved path.

Vocabulary

force, *p. 356;* newton, *p. 357;* net force, *p. 357;* friction, *p. 359;* static friction, *p. 359;* sliding friction, *p. 359;* rolling friction, *p. 360;* fluid friction, *p. 360;* air resistance, *p. 360;* gravity, *p. 361;* terminal velocity, *p. 361;* projectile motion, *p. 362*

12.2 Newton's First and Second Laws of Motion

Key Concepts

- According to Newton's first law of motion, the state of motion of an object does not change as long as the net force acting on the object is zero.
- According to Newton's second law of motion, the acceleration of an object is equal to the net force acting on it divided by the object's mass.
- $\text{Acceleration} = \frac{\text{Net force}}{\text{Mass}}$
- Weight = Mass × Acceleration due to gravity
- Mass is a measure of the inertia of an object; weight is a measure of the force of gravity acting on an object.

Vocabulary

inertia, *p. 364;* mass, *p. 365;* weight, *p. 368*

12.3 Newton's Third Law of Motion and Momentum

Key Concepts

- According to Newton's third law of motion, forces exist as equal and opposite force pairs.
- Momentum = Mass × Velocity
  An object has a large momentum if the product of its mass and velocity is large.
- Momentum is conserved in a closed system.

Vocabulary

momentum, *p. 374;* law of conservation of momentum, *p. 376*

12.4 Universal Forces

Key Concepts

- Electric and magnetic forces are the only forces that can both attract and repel.
- The strong and weak nuclear forces hold the nucleus together.
- Newton's law of universal gravitation states that every object in the universe attracts every other object.

Vocabulary

electromagnetic force, *p. 378;* strong nuclear force, *p. 379;* weak nuclear force, *p. 380;* gravitational force, *p. 380;* centripetal force, *p. 381*

Thinking Visually

Concept Map Use the information on forces from the chapter to complete the concept map below.

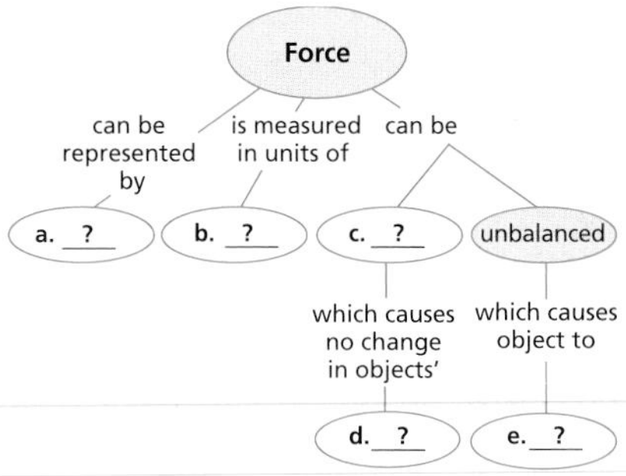
Force
can be represented by
is measured in units of
can be
a. ?
b. ?
c. ?
unbalanced
which causes no change in objects'
which causes object to
d. ?
e. ?

Chapter Resources

Print
- ***Chapter and Unit Tests,*** Chapter 12 Test A and Test B
- ***Test Prep Resources,*** Chapter 12

Technology
- ***Computer Test Bank,*** Chapter Test 12
- ***Interactive Textbook,*** Chapter 12
- ***Go Online,*** PHSchool.com, Chapter 12

CHAPTER 12

Assessment

Interactive textbook with assessment at PHSchool.com iText

Reviewing Content

Choose the letter that best answers the question or completes the statement.

1. Which is not a force?
   a. friction b. gravity
   c. momentum d. weight

2. You push on a box and are unable to move it. What force opposes your push?
   a. static friction b. rolling friction
   c. sliding friction d. air resistance

3. Air resistance depends on
   a. the velocity of a moving object.
   b. the weight of a moving object.
   c. the mass of a moving object.
   d. the inertia of a moving object.

4. What force besides gravity acts on a projectile?
   a. weak nuclear b. electrical
   c. magnetic d. air resistance

5. Newton's first law of motion is sometimes called the law of
   a. inertia. b. conservation.
   c. momentum. d. resistance.

6. A change in which of the following affects the weight of an object?
   a. momentum
   b. velocity
   c. acceleration due to gravity
   d. friction

7. Which represents Newton's second law?
   a. $v = \frac{d}{t}$ b. $a = \frac{F}{m}$
   c. $F = mv$ d. $F = 0$

8. For every action force there is a
   a. reaction force. b. net force.
   c. friction force. d. unbalanced force.

9. Momentum depends upon
   a. force only. b. velocity and friction.
   c. weight and mass. d. mass and velocity.

10. What force holds the nucleus together?
    a. magnetic
    b. strong nuclear
    c. gravitational
    d. centripetal

Understanding Concepts

11. Three forces act on a wooden crate that is initially at rest as shown below. Determine the net force acting on the crate and describe the resulting motion of the crate.

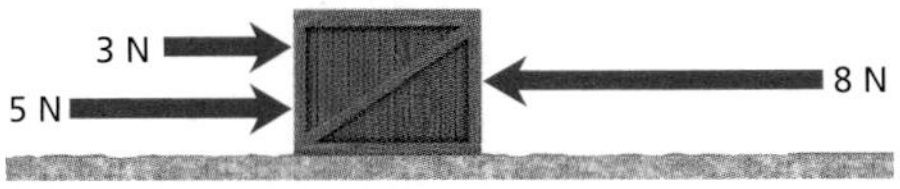

3 N
5 N
8 N

12. Suppose two 4-newton forces act on an object in the same direction. What is the net force on the object?

13. Five different forces act on an object. Is it possible for the net force on the object to be zero? Explain.

14. What happens to an object when an unbalanced force acts on it?

15. You push harder and harder on a box until it begins sliding across the floor. Which was the stronger of the forces acting on the box, static friction or sliding friction?

16. How do ball bearings reduce friction in machinery?

17. Explain why a falling object subjected to Earth's gravity does not continue to accelerate forever.

18. What is the difference between mass and weight?

19. What is an action-reaction pair?

20. What must you know to determine which of two vehicles traveling at the same velocity, has the greater momentum?

21. What force is responsible for your socks sticking together after they have been in a clothes dryer?

22. What particles do the strong and weak nuclear forces act on?

23. What force is responsible for the orbits of the planets in the solar system?

Homework Guide

Section	Questions
12.1	1–4, 11–17, 24, 28–29, 34–36
12.2	5–7, 18, 26–27, 30–31, 33
12.3	8–9, 19–20, 25, 32, 37
12.4	10, 21–23

Assessment (continued)

Understanding Concepts

11. The net force is zero and the crate does not move.
12. 8 N
13. Yes, all of the forces can cancel one another.
14. It accelerates.
15. Static friction
16. A machine part rubs against a rolling surface rather than a flat surface, thus reducing the size of the surfaces in contact and the amount of friction.
17. As the velocity of the falling object increases, the air resistance acting on it also increases. Eventually the opposing force of air resistance equals the object's weight, and the object reaches its terminal velocity.
18. Weight is a measure of the force of gravity acting on an object. Mass is the amount of matter an object contains as measured by its inertia.
19. When a force is exerted on an object, the object responds with an equal and opposite force. The forces generated in this way are called action-reaction pairs.
20. The mass of each vehicle
21. Electric force
22. Strong: protons and neutrons; weak: all particles
23. Gravitational force

Critical Thinking

24. The arrow follows a projectile path. It begins to fall as soon as it leaves the bow. Thus, if the arrow is aimed directly at the target, it will hit the target below the bull's-eye.
25. Newton's third law of motion describes the action and reaction forces that occur when the ball is struck by the racquet and when the ball strikes the wall. Newton's second law of motion describes the acceleration of the tennis ball when a force from the racquet or the wall is applied to it.
26. An object's weight is six times greater on Earth; however, its mass is the same in both locations.
27. 0.6 m/s^2; 5 kg
28. The inertia, mass, and weight of the 10-kg rock are 10 times greater than that of the 1-kg rock.
29. The air resistance is greatly increased when the top is down resulting in fewer miles per gallon.
30. Increasing the force applied to the object or decreasing the mass of the object will increase the acceleration of the object.

Math Skills

31. 0.25 m/s^2
32. 200 kg•m/s
33. 290 N

Concepts in Action

34. The fluid friction from the hovercraft's contact with the air is less than an ordinary boat's fluid friction from contact with the water.
35. The racer could be tested in a wind tunnel or out on a road. If the clothing is effective, the force on the racer in the wind tunnel will decrease. The racer's maximum speed on the road will increase.
36. Attach a spring scale to the box. Gradually increase the force applied by pulling on the spring scale. The smallest measured force on the spring scale that moves the box equals the force of static friction.
37. Student paragraphs will vary but should include the force applied at the drive wheels (supplied by the engine), the action-reaction force pair where the tires are in contact with the road, the air resistance (fluid friction), the rolling friction of the tires on the road, and the rolling friction of the ball bearings in the engine and wheels.

CHAPTER 12 Assessment *(continued)*

Critical Thinking

24. **Applying Concepts** When shooting an arrow at a target, why is it advisable to aim above the bull's-eye rather than directly at it?

25. **Inferring** When a tennis player practices by hitting a ball against a wall, which of Newton's laws of motion is the player making use of?

26. **Comparing and Contrasting** The moon's gravity is only one sixth that of Earth's. Explain how the weight and mass of an object differ between the two locations.

27. **Interpreting Graphs** The graph below shows the relationship between the force acting on an object and the acceleration of the object. What is the acceleration of the object when a 3-newton force acts on it? What is the object's mass?

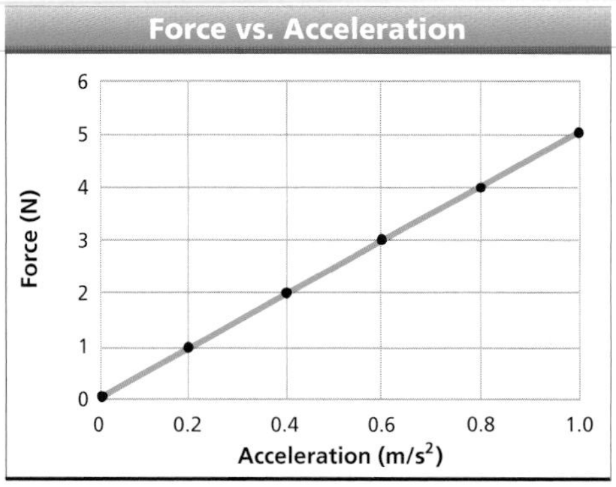

Force vs. Acceleration
Force (N)
0
1
2
3
4
5
6
Acceleration (m/s²)
0
0.2
0.4
0.6
0.8
1.0

28. **Comparing and Contrasting** Consider two rocks with masses of 1 and 10 kilograms. What is the relation between their inertias? Between their masses? Between their weights on Earth?

29. **Relating Cause and Effect** During a fuel-economy test of a sports car, the car achieved more miles per gallon of gasoline when its convertible top was up. Explain how the convertible top being up or down is related to the car's fuel economy.

30. **Applying Concepts** What are the two ways in which the acceleration of an object can be increased?

Math Skills

31. **Using Formulas** A 100-kg crate, sliding on a floor, is brought to a stop by 25-N force. What is the deceleration of the crate?

32. **Calculating** What is the momentum of an 80-kg runner moving at the speed of 2.5 m/s?

33. **Using Formulas** What is the weight on Earth of a girl with a mass of 30 kg? The acceleration due to gravity on Earth is 9.8 m/s^2.

Concepts in Action

34. **Inferring** Hovercraft, which move over water on a cushion of air, can achieve greater speeds than ordinary boats. Explain why this is possible.

35. **Making Judgments** Imagine that you have designed clothing for professional bicycle racers. How could you judge the effectiveness of the clothing at improving a racer's speed?

36. **Designing an Experiment** Explain how you could determine the force of static friction acting on a box that is resting on a rough floor.

37. **Writing in Science** Consider an automobile cruising at a constant speed on the highway. Write a paragraph summarizing the forces acting on the car. Be sure to include the force supplied by the engine and at least two types of friction acting on the car.

Performance-Based Assessment

Communicating Results Draw a cartoon that illustrates one of Newton's laws in an amusing way. You and your classmates might display your cartoons for the whole school to enjoy.

Go Online
PHSchool.com

For: Self-grading assessment
Visit: PHSchool.com
Web Code: cca-2120

Performance-Based Assessment

Drawings will vary but must properly illustrate one of Newton's laws.

Go Online
PHSchool.com

Your students can independently test their knowledge of the chapter and print out their test results for your files.

386 Chapter 12

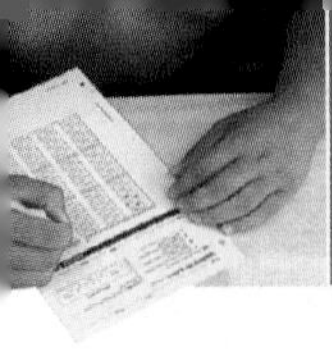

Standardized Test Prep

Test-Taking Tip

Using a Calculator
Keep the following tips in mind when solving problems that require a calculator. Write down the equation that you will be solving before using the calculator. Next, substitute the known values for each term in the equation. Then, enter the numbers into your calculator and calculate the answer. It is also important to become familiar with the order in which your calculator performs operations. Most calculators operate using an algebra-based operating system. If time permits, double-check your answer by performing the calculations a second time.

What is the acceleration of a 1200-kg car acted on by a net force of 250 N?

(A) 0.21 m/s^2 (B) 2.4 m/s^2
(C) 4.8 m/s^2 (D) 950 m/s^2
(E) 300,000 m/s^2

(Answer: A)

Choose the letter that best answers the question or completes the statement.

1. Which of the following correctly lists friction types (excluding fluid friction) from weakest to strongest?
   (A) sliding, static, magnetic
   (B) static, rolling, sliding
   (C) weak, strong, nuclear
   (D) rolling, sliding, static
   (E) static, sliding, rolling

2. Which statement about an object falling at terminal velocity is TRUE?
   (A) Unbalanced forces act on the object.
   (B) The net force acting on the object is zero.
   (C) The object is accelerating.
   (D) The object is traveling in a circular path.
   (E) No fluid friction acts on the object.

3. An object changes direction as it moves. Which of the following is FALSE?
   (A) The acting net force is not zero.
   (B) An unbalanced force acts on the object.
   (C) The object is accelerating.
   (D) A centripetal force must act on the object.
   (E) The object's inertia remains unchanged.

4. Which has the greatest momentum?
   (A) a huge boulder at rest
   (B) a small pebble that is tossed into the air
   (C) a baseball after it is hit with a bat
   (D) a small pebble at rest
   (E) a car traveling on a highway

Use the diagram below to answer Questions 5 and 6. The diagram shows how five forces act on a wooden crate as it slides across the floor.

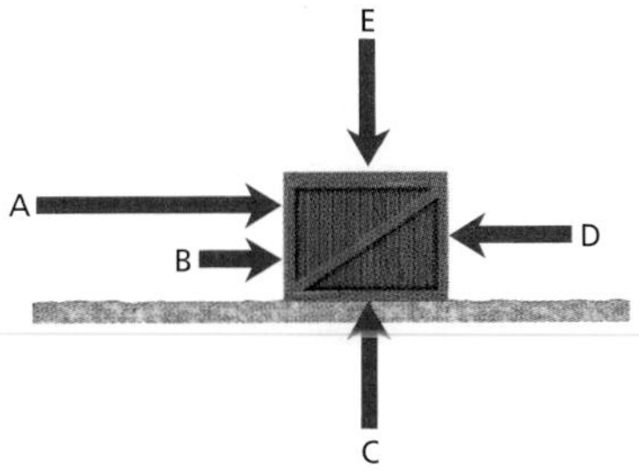
E
A
B
D
C

5. If A = 60 N, B = 20 N, C = 30 N, D = 30 N, and E = 30 N, which of the following statements is FALSE?
   (A) A net force of 50 N acts on the crate and the crate moves to the right.
   (B) The crate accelerates to the right.
   (C) The net force in the vertical direction is zero.
   (D) Force C represents the weight of the crate.
   (E) Forces C and E represent balanced forces acting in the vertical direction.

6. Which force represents the sliding friction force?
   (A) A
   (B) B
   (C) C
   (D) D
   (E) E

Standardized Test Prep

1. D 2. B 3. D
4. E 5. D 6. D

CHAPTER 13

Planning Guide

Use these planning tools
Easy Planner
Teacher Express

SECTION OBJECTIVES	STANDARDS NATIONAL (See p. T18.)	STANDARDS STATE	ACTIVITIES and LABS
13.1 Fluid Pressure, pp. 390–393 1 block or 2 periods **13.1.1** **Describe** and **calculate** pressure. **13.1.2** **Identify** appropriate SI units for measuring pressure. **13.1.3** **Describe** the relationship between water depth and the pressure it exerts. **13.1.4** **Describe** how forces from pressure are distributed at a given level in a fluid. **13.1.5** **Explain** how altitude affects air pressure.	A-1, B-4, G-1, G-2, G-3		**SE** Inquiry Activity: What Makes Something Sink or Float? p. 389 L2 **TE** Teacher Demo: Relating Cause and Effect, p. 391 L2
13.2 Forces and Pressure in Fluids, pp. 394–397 1 block or 2 periods **13.2.1** **Describe** how pressure is transmitted in a fluid according to Pascal's principle. **13.2.2** **Explain** how a hydraulic system works to change a force. **13.2.3** **Explain** how the speed and pressure of a fluid are related according to Pascal's principle.	B-4, G-1, G-2, G-3		**TE** Teacher Demo: Pascal's Principle, p. 394 L2 **LM** Investigation 13B: Investigating Siphons L1
13.3 Buoyancy, pp. 400–404 1 block or 2 periods **13.3.1** **Explain** the effect of buoyancy on the apparent weight of an object. **13.3.2** **Explain** the relationship between the volume of fluid displaced by an object and buoyant force acting on the object according to Archimedes' principle. **13.3.3** **Describe** the relationship among object density, fluid density, and whether an object sinks or floats in a fluid. **13.3.4** **Describe** the relationship among object weight, buoyant force, and whether an object sinks or floats in a fluid.	A-1, A-2, B-4, E-2, G-1, G-2, G-3		**SE** Quick Lab: Changing Buoyancy, p. 401 L2 **SE** Exploration Lab: Determining Buoyant Force, p. 405 L2 **TE** Teacher Demo: Volume Measurement, p. 403 L2 **LM** Investigation 13A: Investigating Sinking and Floating L2

Ability Levels

- **L1** For students who need additional help
- **L2** For all students
- **L3** For students who need to be challenged

Components

SE	Student Edition	**RSW**	Reading & Study Workbook	**CUT**	Chapter & Unit Tests	**T**	Transparencies
TE	Teacher's Edition	**MSPS**	Math Skills & Problem Solving Workbook	**CTB**	Computer Test Bank	**iT**	Interactive Textbook
LM	Laboratory Manual			**TP**	Test Prep Resources	**P**	Presentation Pro CD-ROM
PLM	Probeware Lab Manual			**DC**	Discovery Channel Videotapes & DVDs	**GO**	Internet Resources

RESOURCES PRINT and TECHNOLOGY	SECTION ASSESSMENT
RSW Section 13.1 **L1** **RSW Math Skill** **L2** **MSPS** Section 13.1 **L2** **T** Chapter 13 Pretest **L2** Section 13.1 **L2** **P** Chapter 13 Pretest **L2** Section 13.1 **L2**	**SE** Section 13.1 Assessment, p. 393 **iT** Section 13.1
RSW Section 13.2 **L1** **DC** Uplifting Experience **L2** **T** Section 13.2 **L2** **P** Section 13.2 **L2** SCI LINKS **GO** Bernoulli's Principle **L2**	**SE** Section 13.2 Assessment, p. 397 **iT** Section 13.2
PLM Lab 5: Determining Buoyant Force **L2** **RSW** Section 13.3 **L1** **T** Section 13.3 **L2** **P** Section 13.3 **L2** SCI LINKS **GO** Buoyancy **L2**	**SE** Section 13.3 Assessment, p. 404 **iT** Section 13.3

Go Online

Go online for these Internet resources.

PHSchool.com
Web Code: cca-2130

NSTA SCI LINKS
Web Code: ccn-2132
Web Code: ccn-2133

Materials for Activities and Labs

Quantities for each group

STUDENT EDITION

Inquiry Activity, p. 389
small, plastic bowl; wooden toothpick; piece of modeling clay; paper towel; water

Quick Lab, p. 401
clear plastic bottle with screw cap, dropper pipet, water

Exploration Lab, p. 405
string, rock, spring scale, can, plastic tub, sponge, paper towels, 100-g standard mass, wooden block tied to a fishing weight, 250-mL graduated cylinder

TEACHER'S EDITION

Teacher Demo, p. 391
1 shoe with large-area heel, 1 shoe with small-area heel (both shoes must fit the same student), 1 square of vinyl tile

Teacher Demo, p. 394
2 syringes (10 cc and 60 cc), 20 cm clear plastic tubing (4.8 mm ID), food coloring, water, 150-mL beaker, stirring rod

Build Science Skills, p. 399
clear straw, 1000-mL beaker or jar, several drops of dark food coloring, water

Teacher Demo, p. 403
small steel ball or irregularly shaped object, 500-mL beaker, 100-mL beaker, water

Chapter Assessment

CHAPTER ASSESSMENT

SE Chapter Assessment, pp. 407–408
CUT Chapter 13 Test A, B
CTB Chapter 13
iT Chapter 13
PHSchool.com GO
Web Code: cca-2130

STANDARDIZED TEST PREP

SE Chapter 13, p. 409
TP Diagnose and Prescribe

Interactive Textbook

Interactive Textbook with assessment at PHSchool.com

CHAPTER 13

Before you teach

From the Author

Sophia Yancopoulos
Manhattan College

Big Ideas

Fluids may initially seem a dry subject, but studying the ways that a fluid exerts force—as opposed to the ways that a solid behaves—has allowed us to send submarines underwater, fly airplanes, throw curve balls, and stop a car by lowering one foot on the brake pedal. A fluid behaves differently from a solid because the bonds between a fluid's atoms are weaker: Both liquids and gases are considered fluids.

Forces, Motion, and Energy When discussing forces in fluids, a key concept is pressure. Force is dependent on area, but pressure is not because it's equal to force distributed over area, allowing us to calculate, for example, the pressure of the atmosphere.

Three important force principles are discussed in this chapter. Archimedes' principle that the buoyant force on an object equals the weight of fluid it displaces can be tricky to grasp, because buoyancy is actually equal to the weight of the *volume* of fluid displaced.

In teaching Pascal's principle that fluids transmit pressure unchanged, it's important to emphasize that multiplying forces does not violate conservation of energy.

Bernouilli's principle that the internal fluid of a pressure decreases as its speed increases can be confusing unless it's clear that the internal pressure of a fluid is distinct from the pressure the fluid itself can exert on anything in its path.

Physics Refresher

Fluid Pressure 13.1

Pressure is a measure of force per unit area: $P = F/A$. In fluids (liquids and gases), gravitational force causes pressure to increase with the increasing depth of the fluid. You experience this in a swimming pool when you feel increased pressure on your eardrums deeper in the water. Recall that density equals mass divided by volume: $\rho = m/V$. Recall also that force equals mass times the acceleration due to gravity, g, and that volume is area times the depth of the fluid, h. Combining these with the equation relating pressure and force shows the relationship between pressure and depth of the fluid:

$$P = \rho h g$$

This equation shows that the pressure experienced by an object in a fluid depends only on the density of the fluid and the object's depth. It does not depend on the characteristics of the object.

Forces and Pressure in Fluids 13.2

Changes in pressure in a fluid are described by Pascal's principle: A change in pressure at any point in a fluid is transmitted equally and unchanged in all directions in the fluid. The figure below demonstrates this point:

Address Misconceptions

Students may mistakenly think that pressure is the same as force. However, pressure equals force per unit area. Force equals pressure multiplied by the area upon which the force is exerted. For a strategy to overcome this misconception, see **Address Misconceptions** on **page 391.**

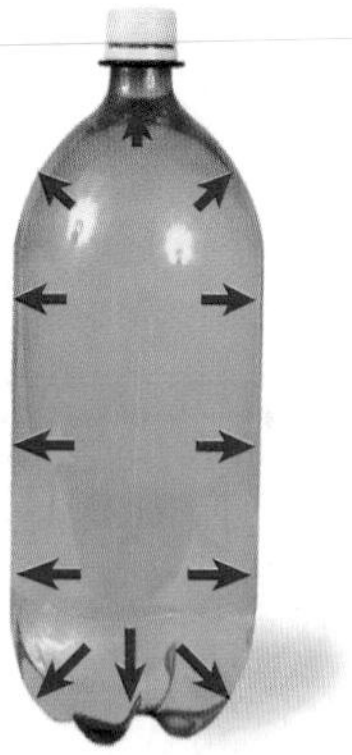

As shown by the length of the arrows in the figure, the forces exerted against the walls of the container are equal at a given depth.

Bernoulli's principle gives an important relationship for fluids in motion: As the speed of a fluid increases, pressure within the fluid decreases. The lift that enables an airplane to fly is primarily explained by this principle. The shape of a plane's wing

Go Online PDLINKS NSTA

For: Teaching methods for forces in fluids
Visit: www.SciLinks.org/PDLinks
Web Code: ccn-1399

causes air above the wing to travel faster than air below the wing. This results in a low-pressure area above the wing and a net upward force that lifts the plane.

Buoyancy 13.3

> **Address Misconceptions**
>
> *Students may incorrectly assume that the pressure a fluid exerts on an object in the fluid acts downward only.* Pascal's principle states that a change in pressure at any point in a fluid is transmitted equally and unchanged in all directions throughout the fluid. For a strategy to overcome this misconception, see **Address Misconceptions** on **page 395.**

An object that is floating or suspended in a fluid experiences both the downward force of gravity (its weight), as well as an upward force exerted by the fluid. This upward force is known as the buoyant force. The ancient Greek mathematician Archimedes stated that the buoyant force on an object is equal to the weight of the fluid displaced by the object. This can be shown mathematically by analyzing the forces on an object of height l submerged in a fluid. The buoyant force is the difference between the force of the fluid pressing down on the top of the object and the force of the fluid pressing up on the bottom of the object. The force acting on the top of the object is $F_{top} = P_{top}A$. The force at the bottom is $F_{bottom} = P_{bottom}A = P_{top} + \rho glA$. The buoyant force, then, is:

$$F_{buoyant} = \rho gV$$

This equation shows that the buoyant force is equal to the weight of the displaced fluid. It does not depend on the weight of the object. Consider the figure below.

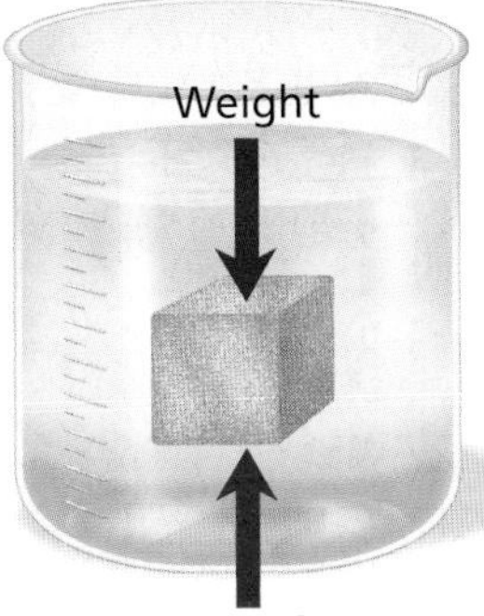

Weight
Buoyant force

In this figure, the weight of the object equals the buoyant force, so the object is suspended in the fluid. If the weight of the object were greater than the buoyant force, the object would sink. The buoyant force is also equal to the weight of the object when the object floats at the surface.

Build Reading Literacy

Anticipation Guide

Stimulating Interest in a Topic

Strategy Engage students actively with a selection by activating prior knowledge, arousing interest, and helping establish purposes for reading. The teacher generates a series of statements related to the topic of the passage for students to respond to and discuss before reading. Choose a passage from Chapter 13, such as Section 13.2, pp. 394–397, and prepare a set of statements ahead of time.

Example

1. Prior to class, read through the passage and identify major concepts and details.
2. Construct an anticipation guide as follows:
- Write 5–10 short, but thought-provoking, declarative statements about the most important concepts featured in the section.
- If students are likely to have misconceptions about the topic, be sure to include statements that address those misconceptions.
- The statements could be in either a true-false or an agree-disagree format.
- To the left of each statement, put a blank for student responses.

3. Before assigning the section to read, either display the guide on the board or on an overhead, or distribute individual worksheets. Students can respond to the statements individually or as a group.
4. Discuss students' responses, asking students to support their answers using examples from past experience or prior reading.
5. Then, have students read the section, evaluating the statements from the anticipation guide as they read.
6. After reading, revisit the guide, encouraging students to compare and contrast their prereading responses with their current ones. Have students quote information from the passage to support their decisions.

See p. 392 for a script on how to use the anticipation guide strategy with students. For additional Build Reading Literacy strategies, see pp. 395 and 402.

ASSESS PRIOR KNOWLEDGE

Use the Chapter Pretest below to assess students' prior knowledge. As needed, review these Science Concepts and Math Skills with students.

Review Science Concepts

Section 13.1 Review force and area and their related SI units. Remind students that force does not always result in motion. Encourage students to review rules for significant figures in answers involving division.

Section 13.2 Review balanced and unbalanced forces, net force, and weight. Encourage students to review Newton's laws of motion.

Section 13.3 Review with students the concepts of force, pressure, mass, weight, and density. Emphasize the similarities and differences between these concepts to help prevent confusion about buoyancy.

Review Math Skills

Formulas and Equations, Conversion Factors, Significant Figures Students will need to calculate and convert pressures and express answers with the correct number of significant figures.

Direct students to **Math Skills** in the **Skills and Reference Handbook** at the end of the student text.

CHAPTER 13 Forces in Fluids

CONCEPTS in Action

How do science concepts apply to your world? Here are some questions you'll be able to answer after you read this chapter.

- Why is a bicycle seat uncomfortable to sit on for long periods of time? *(Section 13.1)*
- Why do your ears pop when you drive up a mountain or fly in a plane? *(Section 13.1)*
- How are airplanes that weigh many tons able to fly through the air? *(Section 13.2)*
- Why do heavily loaded cargo ships float lower in the water than unloaded cargo ships? *(Section 13.3)*

Discovery Channel School

Video Field Trip

Uplifting Experience

- Why are airplane wings curved on the top? *(page 398)*

A kite is held aloft by the forces of the wind. ▶

Chapter Pretest

1. If two forces act in opposite directions on an object, how do you determine the net force on the object? *(Subtract the smaller force from the larger force.)*

2. What effect do balanced forces have on the motion of an object? *(The forces cause no change in the object's motion.)*

3. What effect do unbalanced forces have on the motion of an object? *(The object's speed increases in the direction of the greater force.)*

4. Which units could you use to describe the area of a chalkboard? *(b)*

a. Meters (m)
b. Square meters (m^2)
c. Cubic meters (m^3)

5. Which of the following defines weight? *(b)*

a. The amount of matter in an object
b. The force due to gravity acting on an object
c. The same as mass

6. A tennis ball has a volume of 125 cm^3 and a mass of 57 g. What is the ball's average density? *(Hint:* density = mass/volume*)* *(Ball's density = 0.46 g/cm³)*

7. The distance between a home and school is 6.35 km. What is this distance in meters? *(6350 m)*

8. Which of Newton's laws describes action-reaction forces? *(Newton's third law)*

Chapter Preview

Inquiry Activity

What Makes Something Sink or Float?

Procedure

1. **Predicting** Record your prediction of whether a wooden toothpick and a piece of clay will float in water.
2. To test your predictions, fill a bowl almost to its rim with water.
3. Place a wooden toothpick in the water. Shape a piece of clay into a cup and place it in the water. Record your observations.
4. Remove the clay from the water, dry it with a paper towel, and then tightly roll it into a small ball. Place the ball of clay in the water and record your observations.

Think About It

1. **Evaluating** Which of your predictions were correct?
2. **Observing** What effect did rolling the clay into a ball have on its ability to float?
3. **Formulating Hypotheses** What property of the clay did you change by rolling it into a small ball? Explain how this change affected the clay's ability to float.

DISCOVERY CHANNEL SCHOOL

Video Field Trip

Uplifting Experience

Encourage students to view the Video Field Trip "Uplifting Experience."

ENGAGE/EXPLORE

Inquiry Activity

What Makes Something Sink or Float? L2

Purpose In this activity, students begin to describe the effect of density on buoyancy.

ACTIVITY

Address Misconceptions

Students may hold the misconception that weight, rather than density, determines buoyancy. To help dispel this misconception, ask students whether larger pieces of wood and clay would have behaved in the same way as the small pieces observed in this activity.

Skills Focus Observing, Formulating Hypotheses

Prep Time 5 minutes

Materials small, plastic bowl; wooden toothpick; piece of modeling clay; paper towel; water

Class Time 15 minutes

Safety Students should wear safety goggles whenever they work in the laboratory.

Expected Outcome The toothpick and cup-shaped piece of clay will float. Rolled-up clay will sink.

Think About It

1. Students can be expected to predict correctly that the toothpick will float, but may be uncertain about whether the clay will float.
2. Rolling the clay into a ball caused it to sink.
3. Students may recognize that rolling the clay into a ball increases the density of the clay cup, but most will not be able to state at this stage that the density increases because the air enclosed in the clay cup is excluded when the clay is rolled up.

Visual, Logical

Section 13.1

1 FOCUS

Objectives

13.1.1 **Describe** and **calculate** pressure.

13.1.2 **Identify** appropriate SI units for measuring pressure.

13.1.3 **Describe** the relationship between water depth and the pressure it exerts.

13.1.4 **Describe** how forces from pressure are distributed at a given level in a fluid.

13.1.5 **Explain** how altitude affects air pressure.

Reading Focus

Build Vocabulary L2

LINCS Have students: **L**ist the words or parts of words that they know (for example, *press,* part of *pressure*). **I**magine a picture that creates a mental image of each term's meaning and describe the image in words (such as a column of water exerting force on a square unit area). **N**ote a reminding "sound-alike" word. **C**onnect the terms. (Make up a short story that includes the meanings of the terms.) **S**elf-test. (Quiz themselves.)

Reading Strategy L2

a. Definitions will vary and may involve the scientific or the nonscientific definition of pressure. **b.** Pressure is the amount of force per unit area. Students should contrast the scientific definition with the common definition.

2 INSTRUCT

Pressure

Use Visuals L1

Figure 1 Emphasize that pressure is affected by force and area. Ask, **If the weight is the same in both cases, why is the pressure not the same?** *(Pressure is the amount of force (weight) per unit area, not simply the amount of force.)* Ask, **Why is there greater pressure when the seat is smaller?** *(The pressure formula, P = F/A, shows that pressure is inversely proportional to the area on which the force is exerted. Thus, with a smaller surface area, the bicycle seat produces a greater pressure.)* **Visual**

13.1 Fluid Pressure

Reading Focus

Key Concepts

- How is pressure calculated?
- How does water pressure change with depth?
- How is pressure distributed at a given level in a fluid?
- How does air pressure change with altitude?

Vocabulary

- pressure
- pascal
- fluid

Reading Strategy

Using Prior Knowledge Before reading the section, copy the table below. In it, write the common definition of the word *pressure.* After you have read the section, write the scientific definition of *pressure* and contrast it to your original definition.

Meanings of *Pressure*	
Common definition	a. ?
Scientific definition	b. ?

Why is a theater seat so much more comfortable than a bicycle seat? One of the main reasons any seat is comfortable is the pressure it exerts on your body. As you read this chapter, you'll learn about pressure, and how fluids such as air and water can exert and transmit pressure.

Pressure

The comfort of the plush theater seats shown in Figure 1 is related to **pressure**—the result of a force distributed over an area. A theater seat's large padded seat and back offer a larger area to support your weight than a bicycle seat does. Thus, the theater seat exerts less pressure on you and is more comfortable than the bicycle seat.

Many other everyday situations also involve pressure. A sharp pencil easily pokes a hole through a sheet of paper, whereas the eraser end of the pencil does not. Why is this? The reason is the same—pressure.

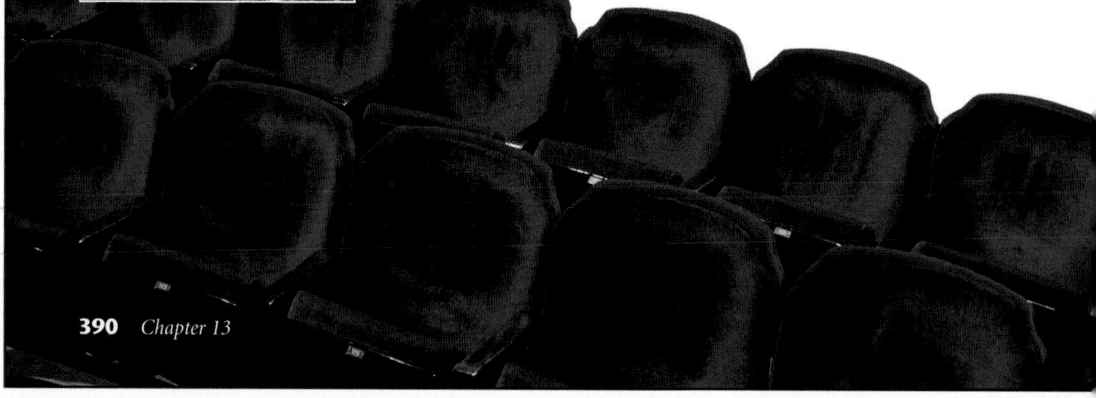

Figure 1 Because the theater exerts a supporting force over a larger area, it is more comfortable than the bicycle seat. ***Comparing and Contrasting*** ***What force acts on both seats?***

Section Resources

Print

- ***Reading and Study Workbook With Math Support,*** Section 13.1 and **Math Skill:** Graphing Air Pressure Data
- ***Math Skills and Problem Solving Workbook,*** Section 13.1
- ***Transparencies,*** Chapter Pretest and Section 13.1

Technology

- ***Interactive Textbook,*** Section 13.1
- ***Presentation Pro CD-ROM,*** Chapter Pretest and Section 13.1

The pencil point has a much smaller area than the eraser, so it exerts much greater pressure than the eraser. The greater pressure exerted by the pencil point allows it to pierce the paper easily.

To calculate pressure, divide the force by the area over which the force acts.

Pressure

$$\text{Pressure} = \frac{\text{Force}}{\text{Area}}$$

In the formula, force should be in newtons (N) and area should be in square meters (m^2). The resulting unit, newtons per square meter (N/m^2), is the SI unit of pressure, also known as a **pascal** (Pa). The pascal is named for French scientist Blaise Pascal (1623–1662). Pressures are often stated in units of kilopascals (kPa). Note that 1 kPa is 1000 Pa.

Consider a box with a weight of 2700 newtons resting on the ground. If the area of the box touching the ground is 1.5 square meters, what pressure does the box exert on the ground?

$$\text{Pressure} = \frac{\text{Force}}{\text{Area}} = \frac{2700\ \text{N}}{1.5\ \text{m}^2} = 1800\ \text{N/m}^2 = 1800\ \text{Pa} = 1.8\ \text{kPa}$$

Pressure in Fluids

A **fluid** is a substance that assumes the shape of its container. Both liquids and gases are fluids. Water, oil, gasoline, air, and helium are fluids. The particles that make up liquids and gases are shown in Figure 2.

Just as a person sitting in a seat exerts force and pressure, so does a fluid. Imagine a glass filled with water. The water flows to take the same shape as that of the glass. Because the water is in contact with the walls and bottom of the glass, it exerts pressure on these surfaces. The amount of pressure exerted depends on several factors.

Have you ever noticed what happens to the pressure exerted on your body as you swim downward in a pool? **Water pressure increases as depth increases. The pressure in a fluid at any given depth is constant, and it is exerted equally in all directions.** Surprisingly, the shape of a container and the area of its bottom surface do not affect fluid pressure. For a fluid that is not moving, depth and the type of fluid are the two factors that determine the pressure the fluid exerts.

Reading Checkpoint *How is fluid pressure related to fluid depth?*

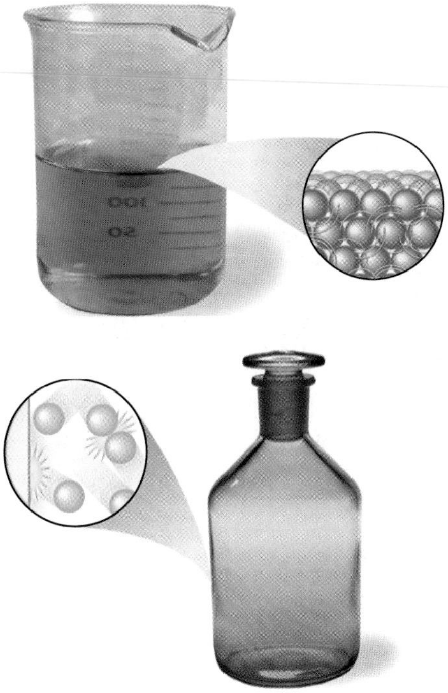

Figure 2 Both liquids and gases can flow and take on the shape of their containers. **A** Particles in a liquid are tightly packed together but are able to slide past one another. **B** Particles in a gas are far apart and travel in straight lines until they collide with another particle or object. **Inferring** *Based on the illustrations, can a gas be compressed into a smaller space?*

Teacher Demo

Relating Cause and Effect

L2

Purpose Students observe the effect different areas make in determining pressure.

Address Misconceptions

Students may mistakenly think that pressure is the same as force. Challenge this misconception by asking students to discuss the difference between pressure and force in this demo.

Materials 1 shoe with large-area heel, 1 shoe with small-area heel (both shoes must fit the same student),1 square of vinyl tile

Procedure Ask the student to put on both shoes and step on the vinyl tile. Have the student stand on one foot at a time on the tile. Have all of the other students observe the indentations made in the tile.

Expected Outcome The small-heeled shoe creates a deeper indentation in the tile. The deeper indentation is caused by the greater pressure exerted by the small-heeled shoe.
Visual, Logical

Pressure in Fluids

Build Math Skills

L1

Data Tables and Line Graphs Have students create a data table with various values of water pressure and area. (Water pressure increases by about $1\,kg/cm^2$ per 10 m of water.) Then, have them calculate the force for each pressure. They can use the data to create pressure/force and pressure/area line graphs.
Logical

Direct students to the **Math Skills** in the **Skills and Reference Handbook** at the end of the student text for additional help.

Customize for English Language Learners

Simplify the Presentation
Adapt your content presentation to the less proficient English skills of your ELL students. Use visual examples when appropriate to emphasize important concepts. For example, when describing how water pressure increases as depth increases, you might draw a picture of a jar containing a liquid. Near the top of the jar write *lower pressure.* Near the bottom of the jar write *higher pressure.*

Answer to . . .

Figure 1 *The weight of the person acts on each seat.*

Figure 2 *Yes. The space between gas particles allows a gas to be compressed into a smaller volume.*

Reading Checkpoint *Fluid pressure increases as fluid depth increases.*

Data Analysis

Planetary Atmospheres L2

Answers

1. Venus, 9120 kPa
2. Nitrogen
3. Mercury, 10^{-15} bar; Earth, 1 bar; Venus, 90.0 bar; Mars, 0.0070 bar
4. Pressure = Force/Area;
Force = Pressure × Area;
Force = 9120 kPa × 2.00 m^2 =
9.12×10^6 N/m^2 × 2.00 m^2 =
2.00×10^7 N
5. The helium-filled balloon would have the smallest volume on Venus because Venus has the greatest atmospheric pressure and the helium inside the balloon is compressible.

For Extra Help L1

Discuss scientific notation to help students read the atmospheric pressures in the table. Ask students to rewrite all the pressure values using scientific notation. Reinforce that atmospheric percentages could be understood by using a pie chart. Remind students to use the equation $F = PA$ when solving for force in newtons. **Logical**

Air Pressure and the Atmosphere

Build Reading Literacy L1

Anticipation Guide Refer to page **388D** in this chapter, which provides the guidelines for an anticipation guide.

Students should anticipate what will occur as a result of the principle's application. Display the following questions on the board or with an overhead projector before students read the text on pp. 392–393. Discuss student responses, then have them read the text. Ask students which of the following statements are true:

1. Air pressure increases as altitude increases. *(False)*
2. When your altitude increases, the pressure inside your ears equalizes with atmospheric pressure. *(True)*
3. When inside air pressure has equalized with atmospheric pressure, the balanced forces result in a net force of zero. *(True)*
4. Atmospheric pressure is exerting a large force on your body as you read this. *(True)*

After students have read the text, revisit the questions. **Verbal**

Data Analysis

Planetary Atmospheres

The layer of gases surrounding a planet is known as its atmosphere. All of the planets in our solar system have some form of atmosphere. The weight of an atmosphere creates atmospheric pressure at the planet's surface.

The table at the right gives data about the atmospheric composition and pressure for several of the planets.

1. **Interpreting Tables** Which planet listed in the table has the greatest atmospheric pressure?
2. **Interpreting Tables** What chemical substance exists in all but one of the atmospheres?

Planetary Atmospheres

Planet	Composition of Atmosphere	Atmospheric Pressure (kPa)
Mercury	Mixture of helium, sodium, and oxygen	10^{-12}
Earth	77% nitrogen, 21% oxygen, 1% argon	101.3
Venus	96% carbon dioxide, 3.5% nitrogen	9120
Mars	95% carbon dioxide, 2.7% nitrogen, 1.6% argon	0.71

3. **Converting Units** The bar is another unit of pressure (1 bar = 101.3 kPa). Convert each of the given pressures into bars.
4. **Using Formulas** How much force is exerted on a 2.00-square-meter area of Venus's surface?
5. **Predicting** On which planet would a helium-filled balloon have the smallest volume?

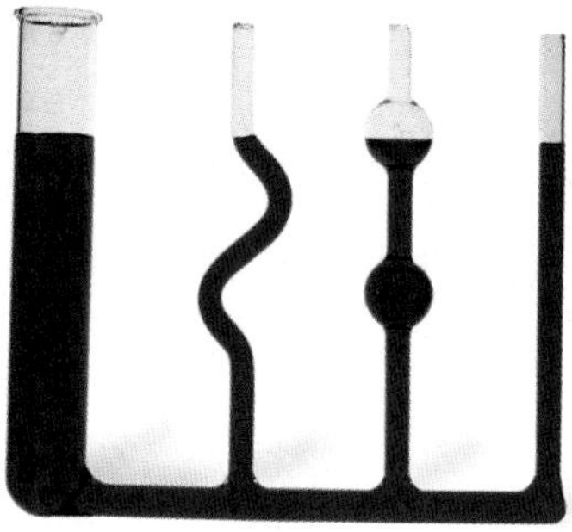

Figure 3 This Pascal vase is made up of several oddly shaped vases that are connected to one another at their base.
Drawing Conclusions ***What can you conclude from the fact that all of the fluid levels are the same?***

As you just learned, fluid pressure is determined by the type of fluid and its depth. Thus the amount of fluid, measured in terms of volume or weight, does not affect pressure. To prove this, imagine a large lake and a bathtub. Although they contain very different amounts of water, the pressure at a depth of 25 centimeters is the same in both the lake and the bathtub.

Note that each of the connected vases in Figure 3 contains a different amount of liquid. Yet, the liquid levels are all the same. Why is this? It is because pressure depends on depth, not amount. If the pressure at the bottom of all the vases were not the same, the water would flow until the pressures equalized.

Air Pressure and the Atmosphere

You live at the bottom of a vast ocean of fluid. Unlike fish, however, you live in an ocean of air. Air is a mixture of gases that make up Earth's atmosphere. Just as ocean water exerts pressure, so does Earth's atmosphere. The weight of Earth's atmosphere exerts a pressure of about 101 kPa at sea level.

Just as water pressure in a beaker increases with depth, air pressure increases with the depth of the atmosphere. Instead of saying they are at a certain depth in the atmosphere, however, people refer to their altitude above sea level. **Air pressure decreases as the altitude increases.**

Facts and Figures

Conversions for Pressure

Some conversion factors are:
1 Pa = 1 N/m^2
1 bar = 10^5 Pa
1 atm = 1.013×10^5 Pa
1 atm = 760 mm Hg

In other words, one bar is the force of 100,000 pascals, or 100,000 newtons acting on one square meter. Because one bar is a large measurement, a millibar (1 millibar = 0.001 bar = 100 Pa) is sometimes used to report air pressure. However, the millibar is often replaced with the term hectopascals (hPa), which is also equal to 100 pascals. To convert between inches of mercury, millibars, and hectopascals, use the relation that 0.02953 inches of mercury is equal to one millibar and equal to one hectopascal.

1
2
3
4

Have your ears ever popped while you were riding in an elevator, flying in a plane, or driving up to the mountains? In situations such as these, the outside air pressure changes more quickly than your ears can adjust. This creates a difference in pressure between the inside of your ear and the air outside. These unbalanced pressures equalize when air passes through a small tube within your ear. This is the popping sensation you feel.

You may be surprised to learn that as you read this, the atmosphere is exerting more than 1000 newtons of force on the top of your head. As shown in Figure 4, this is enough force to crush a can! Why then aren't you crushed by air pressure? Fortunately, the inside of your body also exerts pressure. You are not crushed like the can in Figure 4 because the pressure inside your body balances the air pressure outside. The balanced forces cancel, resulting in a net force of zero.

Figure 4 This series of photos (1–4) illustrates that the atmosphere can exert enough force to crush a metal can. A can containing a small amount of water is heated until the water boils. Then the can is capped and allowed to cool. As the can cools, the pressure inside the can becomes less than the pressure outside the can. The difference in pressure crushes the can.

Section 13.1 Assessment

Reviewing Concepts

1. What must you know to calculate pressure?
2. What is the relationship between the depth of water and the pressure it exerts?
3. How is pressure distributed at a given level in a fluid?
4. How does the pressure exerted by the atmosphere change as altitude increases?
5. Why don't you feel the pressure exerted by the atmosphere?

Critical Thinking

6. **Inferring** Some deep-sea fish have been known to explode as they are brought to the ocean's surface. How do pressure changes cause this to happen?
7. **Applying Concepts** A 500-N student stands on one foot. A 750-N student stands on two feet. If both students wear the same size shoe, which exerts the greater pressure?

Math Practice

8. A circus performer on a pair of stilts exerts a pressure of 32 kPa on the ground. If the performer stands on one stilt, what pressure does the stilt exert on the ground?
9. A book with a weight of 12 N rests on its back cover. If the back cover measures 21 cm by 28 cm, how much pressure does the book exert?

Build Science Skills L2

Controlling Variables Have students think about ways the demonstration shown in Figure 4 could be changed. Ask, **What are the variables in this demonstration?** *(The variables are the amount of water in the can, atmospheric pressure, and the temperature of the hot plate.)* **Which of these variables can be easily controlled?** *(Amount of water in the can and temperature of the hot plate)* **What are some possible effects of changing the controllable variables?** *(Increasing the amount of water will increase the time required to boil the water. Increasing the temperature of the hot plate will decrease the time needed to boil the water.)* **Logical, Visual**

3 ASSESS

Evaluate Understanding L2

Using the equation, $P = F/A$, have students work in pairs to write three math problems (with solutions) based on the pressure equation used in this section. Remember that even incorrectly worded problems are useful, as students can be asked to identify and correct the errors.

Reteach L1

Review the definitions of a fluid and pressure. Use Figure 3 to discuss how pressure in fluids is affected by depth and altitude.

Math Practice

Solutions L2

8. The pressure exerted when standing on one stilt is twice the pressure exerted when on two stilts.
Pressure = 2 × 32 kPa = 64 kPa

9. Pressure = Force/Area
Pressure = 12 N/(0.21 m × 0.28 m) = 12 N/0.0588 m^2 = 2.0 × 10^2 N/m^2 = 2.0 × 10^2 Pa

Interactive Textbook If your class subscribes to the Interactive Textbook, use it to review key concepts in Section 13.1.

Section 13.1 Assessment

1. Force and area are needed to calculate pressure.
2. Water pressure increases as depth increases.
3. At a given depth, pressure is constant and exerted equally in all directions.
4. Atmospheric pressure decreases as altitude above sea level increases.
5. You cannot feel atmospheric pressure acting on your body because the pressure inside your body balances the pressure outside.
6. Deep-sea fish have high internal body pressures in order to counteract the extreme water pressure that exists where they live. When the fish is suddenly brought to the surface, where the pressure is much less, its internal pressure can cause it to rupture or explode.
7. The 500-N student exerts greater pressure on area A than a 750-N student does on area 2A. (500 N/A > 750 N/2A).

Answer to . . .

Figure 3 *The pressure at the bottom of each vase section is the same. If the pressures differed, the fluid would flow and the levels would not be equal.*

Section 13.2

1 FOCUS

Objectives

13.2.1 **Describe** how pressure is transmitted in a fluid according to Pascal's principle.

13.2.2 **Explain** how a hydraulic system works to change a force.

13.2.3 **Explain** how the speed and pressure of a fluid are related according to Pascal's principle.

Reading Focus

Build Vocabulary L2

Word-Part Analysis Ask students what words they know that have the key word parts *hydro-* or *hydr-*. *(Hydrogen, hydrate, hydroelectric)* Explain that *hydraulic* contains the word parts *hydro-* or *hydr-*, which come from the Greek *hydor* ("water"). *Hydraulic* is also made of the word part *aulos* ("tube," "pipe").

Reading Strategy L2

a. Students will most likely predict that the foam balls will be blown apart from one another. Check that students provide reasons for their prediction. **b.** Reasons will likely include the force the air exerts on the foam balls as it blows past them.

2 INSTRUCT

Transmitting Pressure in a Fluid

Teacher Demo

Pascal's Principle L2

Purpose Students will observe the effects of Pascal's principle.

Materials 2 syringes (10 cc and 60 cc), 20 cm clear plastic tubing (4.8 mm ID), food coloring, water, 150-mL beaker, stirring rod

Procedure Attach the ends of the tubes to the syringes. Fill the system with water until the syringes are half full. Insert the plungers. Have students watch the water levels as you push first one plunger, then the other.

Expected Outcome Students will relate water level in the syringes to Pascal's principle. **Visual, Logical**

13.2 Forces and Pressure in Fluids

Reading Focus

Key Concepts

- How does Pascal's principle describe the transmission of pressure through a fluid?
- How does a hydraulic system work?
- How is the speed of a fluid related to the pressure within the fluid?

Vocabulary

- hydraulic system
- lift

Reading Strategy

Predicting Copy the table below. Then imagine two small foam balls hanging from strings at the same height with about three centimeters of space between them. Before you read the section, write a prediction about what will happen to the balls when you blow air through the space between them. Identify your reasons. After you have read the section, check the accuracy of your prediction.

Prediction	a. ?
Reason for prediction	b. ?

Suppose your teacher held a table tennis ball on an upward-pointing hair dryer. He then asked you to predict what would happen when the hair dryer was turned on and the ball was released. Did you predict that the ball would be blown up and away? If you did, you were wrong!

As shown in Figure 5, when the hair dryer was turned on, the table tennis ball was not blown away. Instead it was lifted up and suspended in the air stream above the hair dryer. Suppose your teacher then made the ball bob in the air stream by gently moving the hair dryer up and down. How was that possible? Read on to learn how fluids are able to transmit pressure and how moving fluids produce the pressure changes and forces that explain this demonstration.

Figure 5 The fast-moving stream of air from the blow dryer creates a column of low-pressure air. The table tennis ball is suspended in an area of low pressure.

Transmitting Pressure in a Fluid

As you learned in the previous section, a fluid exerts pressure equally in all directions at a given depth. You also know that the amount of pressure exerted by a fluid depends on the type of fluid and its depth. Apply these two concepts in the following thought experiment. Imagine a two-liter plastic soda bottle completely filled with water, with its cap tightly screwed on. The bottle is sitting upright on a table. Can you visualize and describe how the pressure forces act against the inside of the bottle?

Section Resources

Print
- ***Laboratory Manual,*** Investigation 13B
- ***Reading and Study Workbook With Math Support,*** Section 13.2
- ***Transparencies,*** Section 13.2

Technology
- ***Interactive Textbook,*** Section 13.2
- ***Presentation Pro CD-ROM,*** Section 13.2
- ***Go Online,*** NSTA SciLinks, Bernoulli's principle

Pascal's Principle The pressure forces acting on the bottle are shown in Figure 6A. Note that at any given depth, equal pressures act against the inside of the bottle. Note also that the pressure increases with depth. Now imagine what happens to the pressure inside the bottle if you tightly squeeze it at the middle. Will the pressure be greater at the point where you squeeze?

The pressure inside the squeezed bottle is shown in Figure 6B. Note that the pressure increases with depth, as it did before the bottle was squeezed. More important, note that the pressure increases equally throughout the water, not just at the point where you squeeze. Pascal discovered this phenomenon in the 1600s. His observation led to a general principle. **According to Pascal's principle, a change in pressure at any point in a fluid is transmitted equally and unchanged in all directions throughout the fluid.**

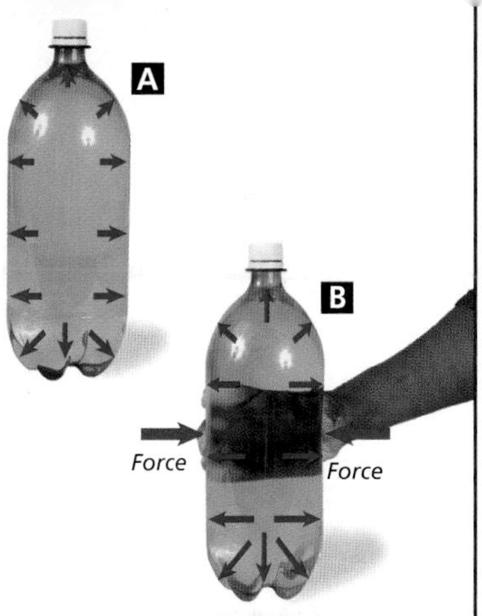

A
B
Force
Force

Figure 6 A change in pressure at any point in a fluid is transmitted equally and unchanged in all directions throughout the fluid. **A** Note that the forces exerted against the walls of the container are equal at a given depth. **B** When squeezed, the pressure is transmitted equally throughout the fluid.

Hydraulic Systems Hydraulics is the science of applying Pascal's principle. The dump truck in Figure 7A makes use of a hydraulic lift system. A **hydraulic system** is a device that uses pressurized fluid acting on pistons of different sizes to change a force.

Look at the diagram of a hydraulic system shown in Figure 7B. An input force is applied to the small piston, which pushes against the fluid sealed in the hydraulic system. Applying Pascal's principle, you know that the pressure produced by the small piston is transmitted through the fluid to the large piston. Thus, the pressure on both pistons is the same.

However, the pressure pushing against the large piston acts on a much larger area, which is the key to how the system works. **In a hydraulic lift system, an increased output force is produced because a constant fluid pressure is exerted on the larger area of the output piston.** This large output force is used to lift and dump the load. The amount the input force is increased depends on the areas of the pistons. If the large piston has eight times the area of the small piston, then the output force is eight times greater than the input force. Why is this? Recall that force is equal to the product of pressure and area. Because the pressure on each piston is the same, the difference in forces is directly related to the difference in areas.

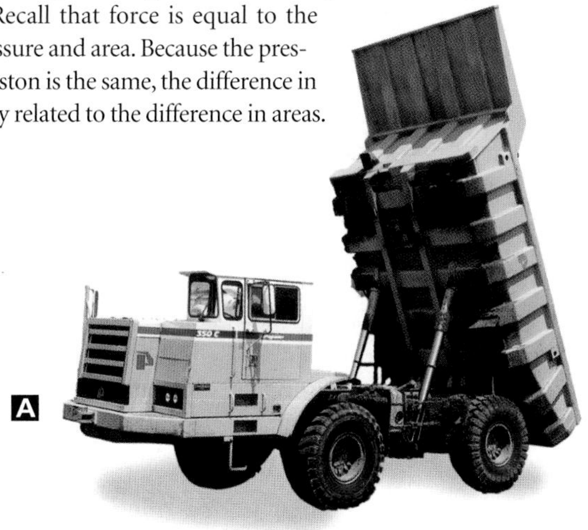

A

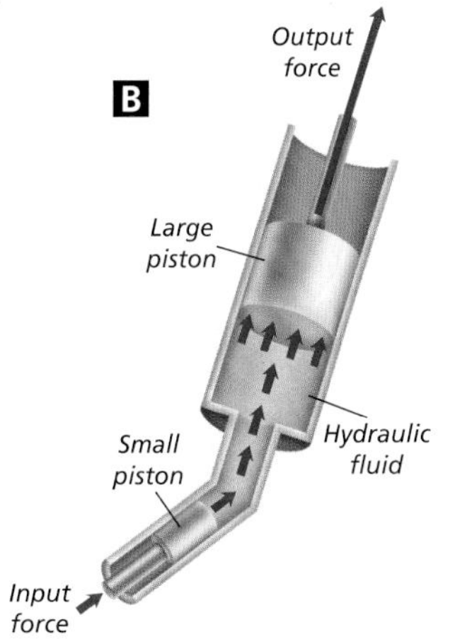

B
Output force
Large piston
Small piston
Hydraulic fluid
Input force

Figure 7 **A** The truck uses hydraulic-powered struts to lift its load and dump it on the ground. **B** The larger area of the output piston produces the increased force used to lift the load.

Address Misconceptions **L2**

Students may incorrectly assume that the pressure a fluid exerts on an object in the fluid acts downward only. Help them see that this is incorrect by having them place a table tennis ball at the bottom of a 1000-mL beaker partially filled with water. When they release the ball, it will quickly move to the top of the water because the force of the water pushes up, not down, on it.
Visual, Logical

Use Visuals **L1**

Figure 7 Emphasize Pascal's principle and how it applies to Figure 7. Ask, **Using Figure 7, explain how the truck's hydraulic system increases force.** *(The truck's hydraulic system uses a larger-area output piston to increase force. The force is increased because the pressure is applied over different areas. The force increases in direct proportion to the increased area, $F = PA$.)* **Based on Figure 7, approximately how many times larger is the output force than the input force?** *(Approximately five times)*
Visual, Logical

Build Reading Literacy **L1**

Relate Cause and Effect Refer to page **260D** in **Chapter 9**, which provides the guidelines for relating cause and effect.

Help students understand Pascal's principle by asking them to analyze the cause-and-effect relationships in a hydraulic system. Ask them to create a flowchart beginning with the input force of the small piston and ending with the output force of the large piston.
Logical

Customize for Inclusion Students

Visually Impaired
Students who are visually impaired may benefit from feeling the effects of pressure changes. Fill a plastic bottle with water, as shown in Figure 6 and use it to illustrate Pascal's principle, asking two students to help you. Have students describe the differences they feel in the bottles both before and after squeezing. Let one student feel the bottle while the other compresses it. Have them note that the pressure change occurs throughout the bottle no matter where the bottle is squeezed.

Bernoulli's Principle

Integrate Earth Science L2

Hurricane Damage Bernoulli's principle explains some of the devastating effects of a hurricane. When the high-speed winds of the hurricane pass over a building, the pressure quickly decreases. The difference in pressure between the inner and outer surfaces of the structure results in a strong upward force that can lift the roof off the building.
Verbal

Build Science Skills L2

Applying Concepts Divide the class into small groups. Provide each group with one of the following phenomena, and have them discuss how Bernoulli's principle applies to the situation.
(1) Wind speed increases as it flows over a mountain. *(Air pressure over mountains decreases.)* (2) Wind blows faster when it passes between high buildings in a city. *(Air pressure is lower between the buildings.)* (3) The upward draft of a fire in a chimney is better on a windy day. *(Decreased pressure above the chimney forces the smoke upward.)*
Logical, Portfolio, Group

Go Online NSTA SciLinks

Download a worksheet on Bernoulli's principle for students to complete, and find additional teacher support from NSTA SciLinks.

Figure 8 The airplane wing changes the flow pattern of the air it passes through. Note how air flowing over the top of the wing is diverted up and over the wing's curved surface.
Comparing and Contrasting ***How does the flow of air over the top of the wing (green arrows) compare with the flow of air under the wing (blue arrows)?***

Bernoulli's Principle

Try this simple experiment. Pick up a single sheet of paper and hold its top corners using both of your hands. Now position the paper directly in front of your mouth and blow as hard as you can over the top surface of the paper. Even though you are blowing over its top, the far end of the paper lifts upward.

The Swiss scientist Daniel Bernoulli (1700–1782) discovered the reason why the sheet of paper behaves as it does. **According to Bernoulli's principle, as the speed of a fluid increases, the pressure within the fluid decreases.** As the air blows across the top of the paper, the pressure exerted by the air decreases. Because the air below the paper is nearly motionless, it exerts a greater pressure. The difference in pressure forces the paper upward.

Bernoulli's principle explains the table tennis ball demonstration discussed earlier. The air from the dryer strikes the bottom of the ball and lifts it into the air. The pressure in this fast-moving air stream, however, is less than the pressure in the surrounding air. If the ball moves sideways out of the air stream, it encounters higher-pressure, slower-moving air. The higher-pressure air forces the ball back into the air stream coming from the hair dryer.

Bernoulli's principle has many applications in industry and explains many things in nature as well.

Reading Checkpoint *How is a fluid's speed related to the pressure it exerts?*

Wings and Lift The ability of birds and airplanes to fly is largely explained by Bernoulli's principle. As shown in Figure 8, the air traveling over the top of an airplane wing moves faster than the air passing underneath. This creates a low-pressure area above the wing. The pressure difference between the top and the bottom of the wing creates an upward force known as **lift.** The lift created in this way is a large part of what keeps the airplane aloft.

Go Online NSTA SciLinks

For: Links on Bernoulli's principle
Visit: www.SciLinks.org
Web Code: ccn-2132

Facts and Figures

Fluid Flow in Pipes Imagine water flowing from one pipe into another pipe with a smaller cross-sectional area. The amount of mass flowing through each pipe must be the same (conservation of mass). Thus, the water will flow faster in the smaller pipe in order to maintain the same mass flow rate. The product of the area and average velocity in pipe 1 equals the product of the area and average velocity in pipe 2, $A_1v_1 = A_2v_2$. As area increases, velocity decreases, and vice versa. Holding your finger partly over the end of a hose is an example of increased velocity due to decreased area.

The wings of birds produce lift in much the same way as an airplane wing. Unlike airplane wings, birds can flap their wings to produce forward movement and some lift.

Sometimes wings are used to create a downward force. Race cars often have an upside-down wing known as a spoiler mounted on the rear of the car. The downward force created by the spoiler pushes the tires down onto the road, giving the car better traction. Increased traction allows the car to go around corners at higher speeds.

Spray Bottles Figure 9 shows the design of a typical hose-end sprayer. This type of sprayer is often used to apply fertilizers and pesticides to lawns, plants, and trees. A concentrated solution of the chemical that is to be sprayed is placed in the solution chamber. The sprayer is then attached to a garden hose.

As water streams through the sprayer, it passes over the top of a small tube that reaches down into the solution chamber. The fast-moving water creates a low-pressure area at the top of the tube. The pressure difference between the solution chamber and the tube forces the concentrated solution up the tube. The solution then mixes with the water and is sprayed out of the end of the sprayer.

Figure 9 The design of a hose-end sprayer is based on Bernoulli's principle. Pressure differences draw the concentrated solution up into the fast-moving water stream.

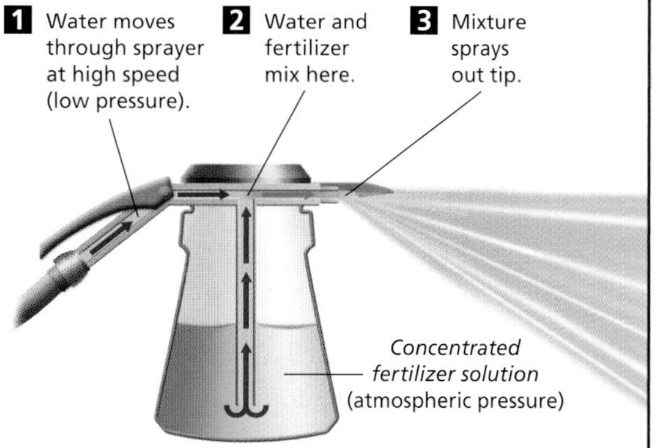
1 Water moves through sprayer at high speed (low pressure).
2 Water and fertilizer mix here.
3 Mixture sprays out tip.
Concentrated fertilizer solution (atmospheric pressure)

Section 13.2 Assessment

Reviewing Concepts

1. Describe Pascal's principle in your own words.
2. How is a hydraulic system able to increase force?
3. How are fluid speed and fluid pressure related?
4. How does an airplane wing produce lift?

Critical Thinking

5. **Predicting** Water is nearly incompressible. Air is easily compressed. Predict what will happen when an air-filled balloon is pulled to the bottom of a swimming pool.
6. **Applying Concepts** The area of an output piston is 25 times greater than the area of the input piston. If the input force is 40 newtons, what is the output force?
7. **Relating Cause and Effect** Two table tennis balls are suspended from strings so they hang at the same height with a small space between them. When a hair dryer is used to blow air between the two balls, the balls come together and touch. Explain why this occurs.
8. **Inferring** When cars pass one another in opposite directions on the highway, they tend to be forced together. Use Bernoulli's principle to explain why this happens.

Connecting Concepts

Net Force Review unbalanced forces in Section 12.1 and their relation to net force. Relate Bernoulli's principle to air flowing over an airplane wing and the creation of a net upward force.

3 ASSESS

Evaluate Understanding L2

Ask students at random to use either Bernoulli's principle or Pascal's principle to explain the operation of the following: sprayer (atomizer), airplane lift, and hydraulic jack.

Reteach L1

Use Figure 7 to review Pascal's principle and the application of constant fluid pressure in a hydraulic system. Use Figure 8 to summarize Bernoulli's principle, discussing how fast-moving air creates an area of lower pressure and results in lift.

Connecting Concepts

The pressure difference acting on the wing due to Bernoulli's principle results in different forces acting on the top and bottom of the wing. These forces are unbalanced (do not add to zero), resulting in a net upward force known as lift.

Interactive Textbook If your class subscribes to the Interactive Textbook, use it to review key concepts in Section 13.2.

Answer to . . .

Figure 8 *The air flowing over the top of the wing moves faster than the air flowing under the wing.*

Reading Checkpoint *As the speed of a fluid increases, the pressure within the fluid decreases.*

Section 13.2 Assessment

1. A change in pressure at any point in a fluid is transmitted equally and unchanged in all directions throughout the fluid.
2. The increased output force is produced because the fluid pressure is exerted on the larger area of the output piston.
3. As the speed of a fluid increases, the pressure within the fluid decreases.
4. Lift of a wing is largely explained by Bernoulli's principle. Air traveling faster over the top of the wing produces an area of reduced pressure. The resulting pressure difference between the top and bottom of the wing produces lift.
5. The water pressure increases with increasing depth in the pool, causing the air-filled balloon to be compressed.
6. Area of output piston/Area of input piston = 25; Input force = Output force/25 = 50 N/25 = 2 N; Output force = Input force × 25; Output force = 40 N × 25 = 1000 N
7. The moving air between the balls has a lower pressure than the surrounding, nonmoving air. The pressure difference forces the balls together.
8. Each moving car pulls a layer of air with it as it moves. When the cars pass, these two areas of moving, lower-pressure air meet, producing a pressure difference, which forces the cars toward each other.

CONCEPTS in Action

Airplane Motion L2

Background

The motion of an airplane is determined by the relationship of the four forces acting on it: thrust, drag, lift, and the plane's weight. When the plane cruises, all of the forces are balanced. The plane's horizontal movement is determined by thrust and drag. If thrust is greater than drag, the plane accelerates. If drag is greater than thrust, the plane slows down. The plane's vertical movement is determined by the plane's weight and lift. If lift is greater than weight, the plane rises. If weight is greater than lift, the plane falls.

The weight and thrust of an airplane are fixed quantities. The weight depends on the plane's mass, and the thrust depends on the plane's propulsion system. The lift and drag, however, change according to many factors. For example, both lift and drag increase as the square of the plane's velocity. If the plane's speed doubles, lift and drag quadruple. Also, lift and drag are directly proportional to air density. Because air density decreases with increased altitude, a plane experiences less lift the higher it goes. This explains why planes have a maximum height, known as a *flight ceiling*, at which they can travel.

CONCEPTS in Action

Airplane Motion

Four forces act on an airplane in flight. They are thrust, drag, lift, and weight. Lift and drag are known as aerodynamic forces because they result entirely from the plane's movement through the air.

Of the aerodynamic forces, lift is the least familiar. One source of lift is Bernoulli's principle. According to Bernoulli's principle, the pressure of a fluid such as air decreases as its speed increases. Because the air moving over the top of an airplane wing moves faster than the air moving beneath the wing, it creates a pressure difference that lifts the wing and hence the plane. Another source of lift is the slant of the wing. As the wing moves through the air, the wing forces air downward. According to Newton's third law of motion, this action must have a reaction. The reaction force also exerts an upward force on the wing.

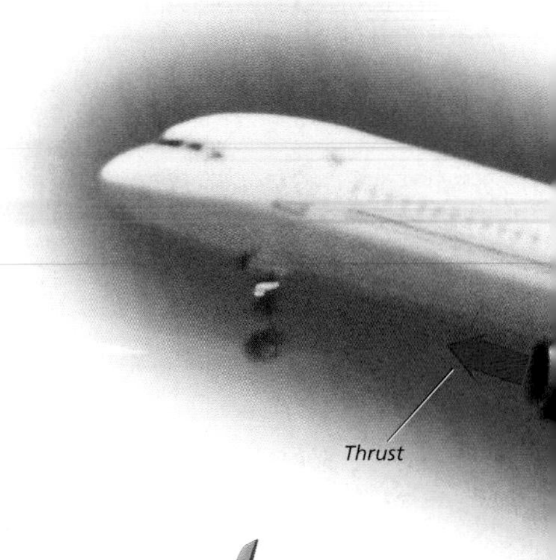
Thrust

Flight controls
In addition to the engines, the pilot has control over a number of other parts of the airplane that affect its motion through the air. These include the spoilers and flaps, and other parts of the wings and tail. These parts affect yaw (turning to left or right), pitch (tilting from back to front) and roll (one wing tilting up, and the other down).

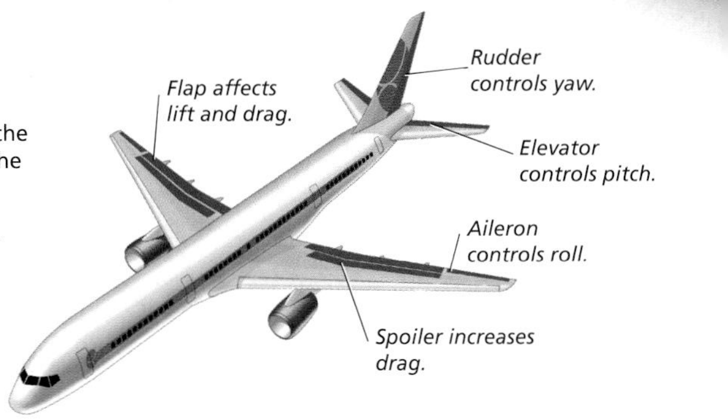
Flap affects lift and drag.
Rudder controls yaw.
Elevator controls pitch.
Aileron controls roll.
Spoiler increases drag.

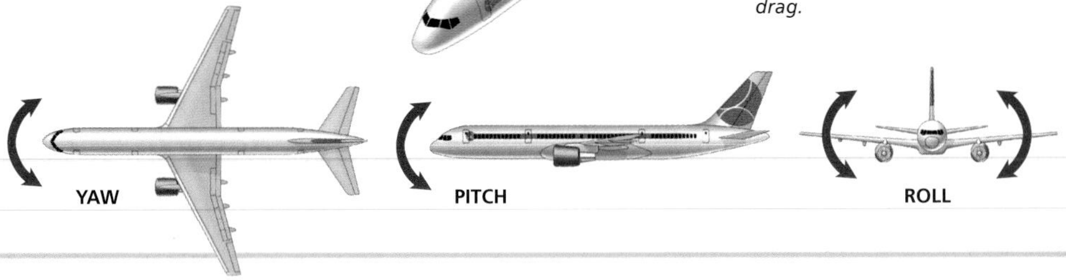
YAW
PITCH
ROLL

Air flow around wing
The movement of an airplane wing through the air causes air passing over the top of the wing first to be accelerated upward (upwash) and then rapidly downward (downwash). Overall, the wing produces a downward movement of the air, and the wing itself is pushed upward. The air flowing over the top of the wing has the lowest pressure. The result is an overall pressure difference that pushes the wing up.

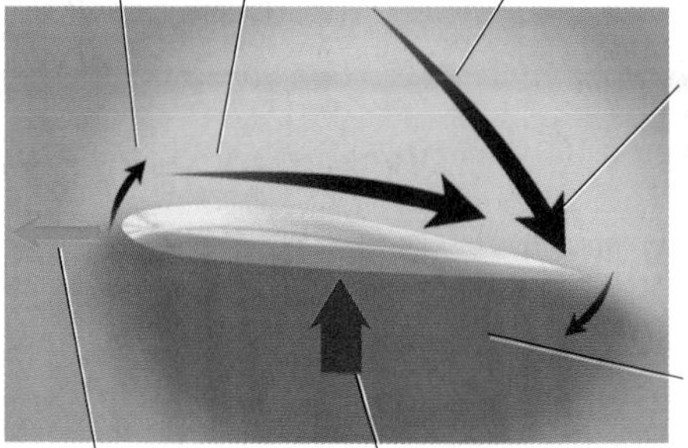

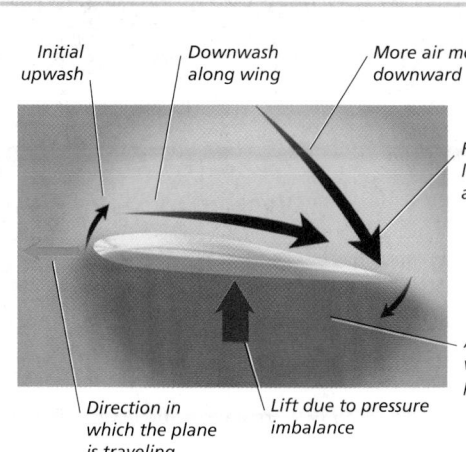

Initial upwash
Downwash along wing
More air moves downward (to fill void)
Fast-moving, low-pressure air
Air below wing under pressure
Direction in which the plane is traveling
Lift due to pressure imbalance

Engine generates thrust.
Lift
Wing generates lift.
Drag
Weight

Four forces acting on a plane
The engine produces thrust, which pushes the plane forward. Thrust is opposed by drag (air resistance), which increases with the airplane's speed. The thrust must create enough speed to generate lift. Lift is the upward force on the airplane caused by movement of its wings through the air. For the plane to become airborne, the lift must exceed the plane's weight.

Going Further

- Research the development of airplane engines since the early 1900s. Prepare a poster to present your findings. Include information on engine type, power or thrust produced, and a description of the plane the engine was used in.
- Take a Discovery Channel Video Field Trip by watching "Uplifting Experience."

Discovery Channel School
Video Field Trip

Build Science Skills L2

Designing Experiments

ACTIVITY

Purpose Students demonstrate Bernoulli's principle.

Materials clear straw, 1000-mL beaker or jar, several drops of dark food coloring, water

Class Time 45 minutes

Procedure Divide students into groups of two, and provide each group with the materials. Ask them to think about how the materials could be used to demonstrate Bernoulli's principle. Each group should develop a hypothesis, write a plan, and carry out their experiment. Afterwards, have each group of students write a description of their experiment, including an explanation of the results.

Expected Outcome Students will probably place the straw in a beaker filled with colored water. By blowing across the top of the straw, their partner will see the level of the water in the straw rise because of Bernoulli's principle.
Visual, Kinesthetic, Logical

Going Further

Poster presentations will vary considerably, but might include the development of vee, inline, radial, turboprop, and jet engines.
Visual

Discovery Channel School

Video Field Trip

Uplifting Experience

After students have viewed the Video Field Trip, ask them the following questions: **When you hold your hand with its front tilted slightly upward out of a car window, why do you feel an upward force?** *(You feel your hand pushed upward because it deflects air downward. The upward force can also be explained in terms of air flowing faster over the top of your hand and slower along the bottom.)* **How can the forces keeping an airplane in the air be explained in terms of how fast air moves around the wings?** *(The air moves faster over the top of the wings than under the bottom. This action produces lower pressure above the wings than below the wings, giving an upward net force.)* **How does the lift, or upward force on the plane, depend on the air speed of the plane?** *(The faster the plane moves the greater the lift. Students may note that this is why a plane must reach a particular take-off speed to be able to leave the ground.)* **What is the name of the shape and design that allows air to flow smoothly around a wing or other object moving through the air?** *(Streamlining)*

Section 13.3

1 FOCUS

Objectives

13.3.1 **Explain** the effect of buoyancy on the apparent weight of an object.

13.3.2 **Explain** the relationship between the volume of fluid displaced by an object and buoyant force acting on the object according to Archimedes' principle.

13.3.3 **Describe** the relationship among object density, fluid density, and whether an object sinks or floats in a fluid.

13.3.4 **Describe** the relationship among object weight, buoyant force, and whether an object sinks or floats in a fluid.

Reading Focus

Build Vocabulary L2

Word Forms Students benefit from knowing related forms of a key word tied to lesson concepts (for example, *buoyancy* and *buoyant*). Have students find the meaning of the root word *buoy* and build on it as they read p. 400.

Reading Strategy L2

a. Archimedes' Principle: The buoyant force on an object is equal to the weight of fluid it displaces.
b. Density and Buoyancy: Objects less dense than the fluid they are in float. Objects denser than the fluid they are in sink. When the buoyant force is equal to the weight, the object floats or is suspended. When the buoyant force is less than the weight, the object sinks.

2 INSTRUCT

Buoyant Force

Use Visuals L1

Figure 10 Remind students that pressure is exerted equally in all directions at a given level. Ask, **Why are the forces acting on the ball not all the same magnitude?** *(Different parts of the ball are at different depths. Water pressure increases as depth increases.)* **What determines the direction of the forces acting on the ball?** *(The forces are always perpendicular to the surface of the ball.)* **Visual, Logical**

13.3 Buoyancy

Reading Focus

Key Concepts

- What is the effect of buoyancy on the apparent weight of an object?
- How can you determine if an object will float or sink in a fluid?

Vocabulary

- buoyancy
- buoyant force
- Archimedes' principle

Reading Strategy

Summarizing Copy the table below. As you read about buoyancy, write a brief summary of the text following each green heading. Your summary should include only the most important information.

Section 13.3 Buoyancy
Buoyant Force Buoyant force is the apparent loss of weight of an object submerged in a fluid.
a. ?
b. ?

Have you ever stood in a pool and tried lifting a friend who was submerged in the water? If you have, you may recall how surprisingly easy your friend was to lift. Or perhaps you have gone swimming in a lake or bay where the very salty water made it easy to float on the surface. What forces make these two situations possible? In this section you'll learn the answers to these questions.

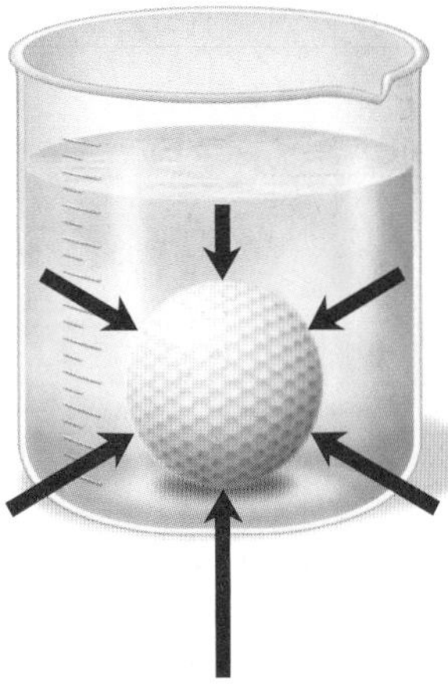

Figure 10 The forces from pressure acting on the bottom of this golf ball are greater than those acting on the top. This produces a net force—called the buoyant force—that acts upward on the ball.

Buoyant Force

You are easily able to lift a friend submerged in water because of buoyancy. **Buoyancy** is the ability of a fluid to exert an upward force on an object placed in it. **Buoyancy results in the apparent loss of weight of an object in a fluid.** In fact, every object in a fluid experiences buoyancy. When an object is submerged in water, the water exerts an upward force on the object, making it easier to lift. This upward force, which acts in the opposite direction of gravity, is called a **buoyant force.**

How is a buoyant force produced? To answer this question, examine the forces pressure exert on the submerged object in Figure 10. Because water pressure increases with depth, the forces pushing up on the bottom of the object are greater than the forces from pressure pushing down on the top of the object. All of the other non-vertical forces cancel one another out. The result is a net upward force—the buoyant force.

Section Resources

Print
- ***Laboratory Manual,*** Investigation 13A
- ***Reading and Study Workbook With Math Support,*** Section 13.3
- ***Transparencies,*** Section 13.3

Technology
- ***Probeware Lab Manual,*** Lab 5
- ***Interactive Textbook,*** Section 13.3
- ***Presentation Pro CD-ROM,*** Section 13.3
- ***Go Online,*** NSTA SciLinks, Buoyancy

Archimedes' Principle

Archimedes, an ancient Greek mathematician who died in 212 B.C., is credited with an important discovery that bears his name. According to **Archimedes' principle,** the buoyant force on an object is equal to the weight of the fluid displaced by the object.

When an object is submerged, it pushes aside, or displaces, a volume of fluid equal to its own volume. When an object floats on the surface of a fluid, it does not displace its entire volume. The floating object does, however, displace a volume equal to the volume of the part of the object that is submerged.

Density and Buoyancy

Density and buoyancy are closely related. Recall that density is the ratio of an object's mass to its volume. Densities are often expressed in the non-SI units of grams per cubic centimeter (g/cm^3). Water, for example, has a density of 1 g/cm^3, whereas steel has a density of 7.8 g/cm^3.

If an object is less dense than the fluid it is in, it will float. If the object is more dense than the fluid it is in, it will sink. Different fluids can also float or sink in one another. Oil, for example, floats on water because oil is less dense than water.

You can also determine if an object will float by analyzing the forces acting on it. As you can see in Figure 11, two forces act on every object in a fluid—weight and the buoyant force. The force of gravity, equal to the object's weight, acts downward on the object. The buoyant force, equal to the weight of the volume of displaced fluid, acts upward on the object. **When the buoyant force is equal to the weight, an object floats or is suspended. When the buoyant force is less than the weight, the object sinks.**

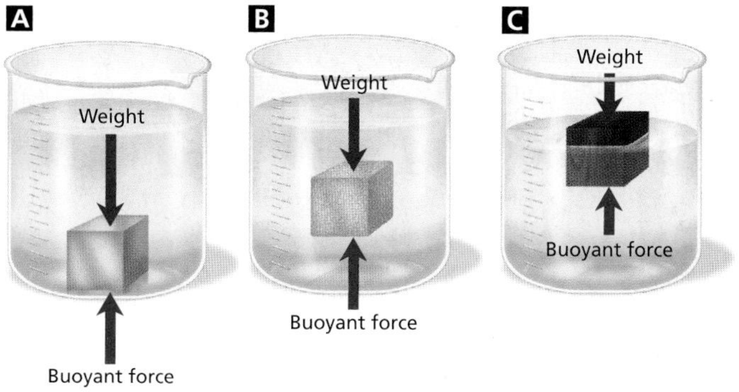

A
Weight
Buoyant force
B
Weight
Buoyant force
C
Weight
Buoyant force

Figure 11 The weight and buoyant force determines if an object sinks or floats. **A** The metal cube sinks because its weight is greater than the buoyant force. **B** Equal forces acting on this submerged cube allow it to be suspended in the fluid. **C** The partially submerged wood cube floats at a depth where the buoyant force and weight are equal.

Quick Lab

Changing Buoyancy

Procedure

1. Fill a plastic bottle with water up to its neck. Squeeze a dropper pipet's bulb and draw water into the pipet until it is about half full. Insert the pipet, bulb end up, into the bottle. The pipet should float at the water's surface.
2. Add water to the bottle until it is full. Tightly twist the cap onto the bottle. Trap as little air as possible in the bottle.
3. Observe what happens to the pipet as you squeeze, hold, and then release the bottle.

Analyze and Conclude

1. **Applying Concepts** Describe the changes in pressure during Step 3.
2. **Inferring** How did the volume of the air trapped inside the pipet change when the bottle was squeezed?
3. **Drawing Conclusions** Explain how squeezing and releasing the bottle caused the pipet to move up and down in the water.

Customize for English Language Learners

Think-Pair-Share
Students can work in pairs to explore the concept of buoyancy. First, have each pair of students study and discuss Figure 11. Next, have them write down what they have learned from the figure about buoyancy and Archimedes' principle. Finally, encourage students to explain the concepts presented in the figure to the class.

Density and Buoyancy

Quick Lab

Changing Buoyancy L2

Objective
After completing this lab, students will be able to
- describe the effect of a pressure change within a fluid system.

Address Misconceptions

Students may have the misconception that only movement of a fluid produces pressure. To help dispel this misconception, ask students if there is any pressure at all inside the bottle when it is not being squeezed. If they answer that there is not, ask what prevents the pressure of the atmosphere from collapsing the bottle.

Skills Focus **Observing, Inferring**

Prep Time 5 minutes

Materials clear plastic bottle with screw cap, dropper pipet, water

Advance Prep Provide long specimen forceps, if possible, so students can retrieve sunken dropper pipets without having to empty their bottles completely.

Class Time 20 minutes

Safety Caution students to wipe up any spilled water immediately.

Teaching Tips
- If the pipet sinks, tell students to remove it from the bottle, squeeze out some of the water, and return the pipet to the bottle.

Expected Outcome Squeezing the bottle causes the pipet to sink. When the bottle is released, the pipet rises.

Analyze and Conclude
1. The pressure increased when the bottle was squeezed, and returned to its original value when the bottle was released.
2. Squeezing the bottle caused the air bubble to become smaller.
3. When the air bubble in the pipet shrank, more water entered, increasing the mass and density of the pipet and its contents. This increase caused the pipet to sink. These changes were reversed when the bottle was released: The pressure was reduced, allowing the air bubble to enlarge, pushing water out of the pipet and increasing the buoyancy of the pipet.
Logical

Build Reading Literacy L1

Visualize Refer to page **354D** at the beginning of **Chapter 12,** which provides the guidelines for visualizing.

Encourage students to visualize the concepts of objects suspended or sinking in water. For example, suggest that they imagine themselves floating on a raft in a pool. Then, have them think what would happen if a friend also got on the raft. Would the raft continue to float, or would it sink further in the water? Encourage students to think about the weight and buoyant force on the raft. **Visual, Logical**

DK HOW It Works

Submarine L2

Submarines carry compressed air to use in the ballast tanks. At a constant temperature, the volume of a gas is inversely proportional to the pressure. The pressure of the compressed gas is therefore very high. Submarines have different methods that can be used for rising to the surface. One way is to blow the compressed, high-pressure air into the ballast tanks. Another method is to drive the submarine to the surface. This is done by positioning the diving planes so that the submarine's forward movement causes it to surface. The submarine then forces seawater out of the ballast tanks using low-pressure air.

Interpreting Diagrams Neglecting changes in the density of seawater, the buoyant force acting on the submerged submarine is constant and described by Archimedes' principle. By altering the submarine's weight relative to the constant buoyant force, the submarine is able to rise or drive.
Logical

For Enrichment L3

Students who need more of a challenge may design and construct a simple model submarine and present it to the class as an illustration of Archimedes' principle.
Verbal, Logical, Portfolio

Suspended An object that has the same density as the fluid it is submerged in will be suspended (it will float at any level) in the fluid. The buoyant force acting on the suspended object exactly equals the object's weight. Submarines and some fish are able to suspend themselves in water partly by adjusting their density. To learn more about submarines, read the How It Works box below.

Sinking If the shape of a ship's hull allows it to float, what causes a ship to sink? As you know, when the ship's weight becomes greater than the buoyant force acting on it, the ship will sink. This may occur when the ship damages its hull and takes on water. As water enters the hull, the ship displaces less water and the buoyant force decreases. If the damage is not fixed, the ship will eventually sink.

DK HOW It Works

Submarine

According to Archimedes' principle, the buoyant force on an object is equal to the weight of the fluid displaced by the object. Whereas the weight of an object acts downward, the buoyant force acts upward. **Interpreting Diagrams** ***When diving and surfacing, how do submarines make use of Archimedes' principle?***

Steering a submarine
The crew alters the buoyancy of the submarine to make it rise or sink. To steer the submarine through the water, crewmen also use the propeller and the rudder, and adjust the angle of the diving planes.

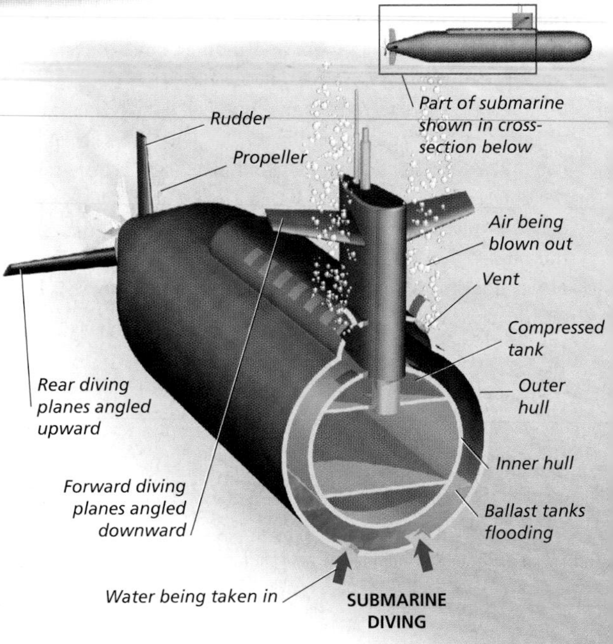

Part of submarine shown in cross-section below
Rudder
Propeller
Air being blown out
Vent
Compressed tank
Outer hull
Rear diving planes angled upward
Inner hull
Forward diving planes angled downward
Ballast tanks flooding
Water being taken in
SUBMARINE DIVING

A Negative buoyancy As long as it remains submerged, a submarine experiences a constant buoyant force. To overcome the buoyant force so the submarine can dive—that is, to achieve negative buoyancy—its weight must increase. This is done by flooding the ballast tanks, replacing air with water.

Facts and Figures

Archimedes Archimedes was born in the third century B.C., in Syracuse, a Greek city-state on the island of Sicily. He is considered by many to be one of the greatest mathematicians of all time. One of his most useful mathematical accomplishments was the discovery of the formula for a sphere's surface area ($S = 4\pi r^2$). He also discovered that the volume of a sphere is two-thirds the volume of a cylinder with the same radius. His discovery of the buoyant force on an object (Archimedes' principle) was set forth in the first of two books known as *On Floating Bodies.* Archimedes is also known for inventing a device, now known as Archimedes' screw, for easily raising water.

Floating You may be wondering why a piece of steel sinks, whereas a huge steel ship floats. A heavy steel ship floats because of the shape of its hull. The hull is shaped so that it displaces a large volume of water, creating a large buoyant force. The buoyant force created by the ship's hull is large enough to counteract the ship's tremendous weight.

Objects also float more easily in dense fluids. Why is this? As you know, the buoyant force acting on the object equals the weight of the volume of the fluid it displaces. For a given displacement, the denser the fluid is, the greater is the weight displaced. This greater displaced weight results in a greater buoyant force. This is why it is easier for a person to float in very salty water. The dense salty water produces a larger buoyant force when displaced by the person's body.

Go Online NSTA SCILINKS

For: Links on buoyancy
Visit: www.SciLinks.org
Web Code: ccn-2133

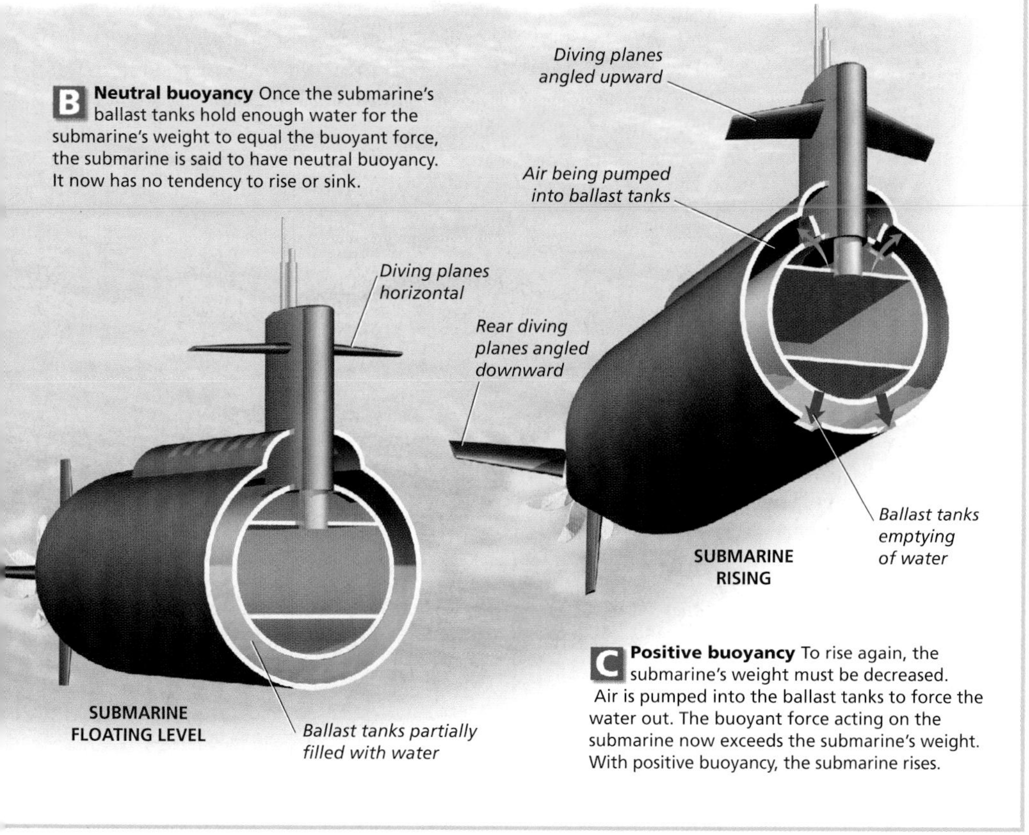
Diving planes angled upward
Air being pumped into ballast tanks
Diving planes horizontal
Rear diving planes angled downward
Ballast tanks emptying of water
SUBMARINE RISING
SUBMARINE FLOATING LEVEL
Ballast tanks partially filled with water

B Neutral buoyancy Once the submarine's ballast tanks hold enough water for the submarine's weight to equal the buoyant force, the submarine is said to have neutral buoyancy. It now has no tendency to rise or sink.

C Positive buoyancy To rise again, the submarine's weight must be decreased. Air is pumped into the ballast tanks to force the water out. The buoyant force acting on the submarine now exceeds the submarine's weight. With positive buoyancy, the submarine rises.

Facts and Figures

Densities Why does ice float in water? Why does a balloon filled with helium rise in air? Their densities answer these questions. When the densities of two objects are compared, the one with lower density will float or rise above the one with higher density.

The density of ice is about 920 kg/m^3, while the density of fresh water (at 4°C) is approximately 1,000 kg/m^3. Therefore, ice will float on water. In addition, the density of helium is approximately 0.178 kg/m^3, while the density of air (at sea level) is about 1.293 kg/m^3. Therefore, a balloon filled with helium will rise in the air.

Teacher Demo

Volume Measurement L2

Purpose Students observe an easy way to measure the volume of a solid object.

Materials small steel ball or irregularly shaped object, 500-mL beaker, 100-mL beaker, water

Procedure Have a student set the 100-mL beaker beside and under the spout of the 500-mL beaker. Then, have the student overfill the 500-mL beaker with water until some of the water spills into the 100-mL beaker. Empty the water out of the 100-mL beaker and return it to its position below the 500-mL beaker. Then, carefully add the steel ball or other object into the 500-mL beaker.

Expected Outcome The water that is displaced by the steel ball will pour into the smaller beaker. The volume of that displaced water equals the volume of the steel ball. **Visual, Logical**

Build Science Skills L2

Inferring Have students consider the explanation of *floating*. Ask, **How could the shape of a hull cause greater displacement of water?** *(Lead students to realize that it is density—mass divided by volume—that determines floating. If the volume is greater, the density is less because the same amount of mass is divided over a greater volume. An aluminum canoe is an example. If the same amount of aluminum were shaped into a cube, it would sink because it would be denser than the water. However, in the shape of a canoe, the volume becomes much greater, making the density much less and allowing it to float.)* **Logical**

Integrate Social Studies L2

Ask students to use the Internet to research ship museums. These museums often preserve and restore these vessels. Have students write a paragraph about the restoration of a particular ship at one of the museums. **Verbal, Portfolio**

Go Online NSTA SCILINKS

Download a worksheet on buoyancy for students to complete, and find additional teacher support from NSTA SciLinks.

Section 13.3 (continued)

Use Community Resources L2

Arrange for a submarine or ship crew member or a commercial diver to visit your class to discuss experiences related to buoyancy. Encourage students to write questions in advance. You may want to ask the students to write a paper for their portfolio on what they learned from the guest. **Verbal, Portfolio**

3 ASSESS

Evaluate Understanding L2

Ask students to explain the relationship among buoyant force, weight of fluid displaced, and the apparent weight of floating objects.

Reteach L1

Use Figure 11 and How It Works illustrations to review buoyancy, Archimedes' principle, and the way a submarine dives and rises.

Writing in Science

The paragraph should state that the weight of the sunken object is greater than the buoyant force acting on it, and that the weight of the floating object is equal to the buoyant force acting on it.

Interactive Textbook If your class subscribes to the Interactive Textbook, use it to review key concepts in Section 13.3.

Figure 12 The exposed green and red stripes on the ship's hull indicate that the ship is riding high in the water.
***Applying Concepts** How will the ship's level in the water change if it takes on additional cargo?*

The ability of a huge steel ship to float in water can also be explained in terms of density. As you know, a solid piece of steel sinks in water. A ship's shape, however, allows it to displace a very large volume of water relative to its weight. That is, the ship's shape increases its volume and decreases its density. As long as the ship's effective density is less than that of water, the ship floats.

The heavier the ship, the more water it must displace in order to float. The relationship between weight and the level a ship rides at in the water can be seen in Figure 12. If the cargo ship were completely loaded, it would need to displace more water in order to float.

Why do some balloons float in air whereas others do not? The answer has to do with density differences. Helium and hot air are both less dense than normal-temperature air. When a balloon is filled with either helium or hot air, a buoyant force from the displaced normal-temperature air acts on the balloon. If the size of the buoyant force is large enough, the balloon rises into the air.

Section 13.3 Assessment

Reviewing Concepts

1. How does buoyancy affect the apparent weight of an object in a fluid?
2. What determines if an object will float or sink in a fluid?
3. How does Archimedes' principle relate the buoyant force acting on an object and the volume of fluid displaced by the object?
4. How is the density of a floating object related to the density of the fluid it is floating in?

Critical Thinking

5. **Applying Concepts** An empty oil tanker displaces enough water to support its weight. Why doesn't the tanker sink when loaded with thousands of tons of oil?
6. **Inferring** A small object is able to float at any level when placed in water. What does this observation tell you about the object's density?
7. **Applying Concepts** A 350-N block of wood is thrown into a lake, where it floats. What is the buoyant force acting on it?

Writing in Science

Compare and Contrast Paragraph Write a paragraph comparing the forces acting on an object that floats in water and an object that sinks in water. Be sure to describe the relative sizes of the forces acting on each object. (*Hint:* Before you write, review the forces shown in Figure 11.)

Section 13.3 Assessment

1. Buoyancy results in the apparent loss of weight of an object in a fluid.
2. Floating: If an object is less dense than the fluid it is in, it will float. If the buoyant force is equal to the weight of the object, the object will float or be suspended. Sinking: If an object is more dense than the fluid it is in, it will sink. If the buoyant force is less than the weight of the object, the object will sink.
3. The buoyant force acting on an object is equal to the weight of fluid displaced by the object.
4. Floating objects have a density that is less than that of the fluid in which they are floating.
5. As the tanker is loaded with oil, its increased weight causes it to displace more water. This increased water displacement results in a greater buoyant force, which supports the loaded tanker.
6. The density of the object must be equal to the density of the water.
7. 350 N

Answer to . . .

Figure 12 *The ship will float at a lower level in the water if it takes on additional weight.*

Exploration Lab

Determining Buoyant Force

In this lab, you will analyze recorded data to determine the buoyant forces acting on objects.

Problem How does the buoyant force determine whether an object sinks?

Materials

string, rock, spring scale, can, plastic tub, sponge, paper towels, 100-g standard mass, wooden block tied to a fishing weight, 250-mL graduated cylinder

For the probeware version of this lab, see the Probeware Lab Manual, Lab 5.

Skills Measuring, Calculating

Procedure

1. Make a copy of the data table shown.
2. Tie one end of the string around the rock. Tie the other end to the spring scale. Suspend the rock from the spring scale and measure and record its weight in air in your data table.
3. Place the can in an upright position in the plastic tub. Completely fill the can with water. Wipe up any water that spills into the tub. **CAUTION** *Wipe up any water that spills on the floor to avoid slips and falls.*
4. Lower the rock into the water until it is completely submerged. Record in your data table the apparent weight in water of the submerged rock. Remove the rock from the can.
5. Without spilling any water, carefully remove the can from the tub. Pour the water from the tub into the graduated cylinder. Record the volume of displaced water in your data table.
6. Repeat Steps 2 through 5, first with the 100-g standard mass and then with the wooden block that is tied to a fishing weight.
7. To determine the buoyant force on each object, subtract its apparent weight in water from its weight in air. Record these values.
8. Calculate the weight of the water each object displaces. (*Hint:* 1.0 mL of water has a weight of 0.0098 N.) Record these weights.

Analyze and Conclude

1. **Observing** What force is responsible for the difference between the weight of each object in the air and its apparent weight in water?
2. **Analyzing Data** How is the buoyant force related to the weight of water displaced?
3. **Forming Operational Definitions** Define buoyant force and describe two ways you can measure it or calculate it.
4. **Drawing Conclusions** Explain what causes an object to sink or to float, using the terms *buoyancy, weight, force, density,* and *gravity.*

Data Table

Object	Weight in Air (N)	Apparent Weight in Water (N)	Buoyant Force (weight in air − apparent weight in water, N)	Volume of Displaced Water (mL)	Weight of Displaced Water (N)
Rock					
100-g standard mass					
Wood block with fishing weight					

Exploration Lab

Determining Buoyant Force L2

Objective
After completing this lab, students will be able to
- define the buoyant force as the difference between an object's weight in air and its apparent weight in water.
- state that the buoyant force on an object floating in water is equal to the weight of the water the object displaces.

Skills Focus **Measuring, Calculating**

Prep Time 10 minutes

Advance Prep If possible, supply a standard mass with a hook for ease of weighing. Attach enough mass to the wooden block to ensure that it will exert a measurable force on the spring scale when the block is in water.

Class Time 30 minutes

Teaching Tips
- Ask students why it was necessary to attach a weight to the wooden block. Explain that the weight is necessary to ensure that the wooden block will exert a measurable force on the spring scale when the block is in water.
- In Step 3, instruct students to overfill the can so some water pours over the top edge.

Expected Outcome The buoyant force on each object is equal to the weight of the water it displaces.

Analyze and Conclude
1. The difference is equal to the buoyant force that the water exerts on the object.
2. They are equal.
3. The buoyant force on an object is equal to the difference between its weight in air and its apparent weight in water. It is also equal to the weight of the water the object displaces.
4. An object will float when the upward force of buoyancy is greater than or equal to the downward force of gravity (the weight of the object). For the buoyant force to counteract the gravitational force, the object must weigh as much as or less than the volume of water it displaces. For this reason, floating objects have low densities.
Verbal, Logical

Sample Data Table

Object	Weight in Air (N)	Apparent Weight in Water (N)	Buoyant Force (weight in air − apparent weight in water, N)	Volume of Displaced Water (mL)	Weight of Displaced Water (N)
Rock	0.3	0.2	0.1	5.0	0.049
100-g standard mass	1.0	0.75	0.25	10.0	0.098
Wood block with fishing weight	1.8	1.5	0.3	25.0	0.24

Probeware Lab Manual Versions of this lab for use with probeware available from Pasco, Texas Instruments, and Vernier are in the Probeware Manual.

Study Guide

Study Tip

Focused Study
Chapters can be understood more easily with short, focused blocks of studying. There are several important principles to learn in the chapter (Pascal's, Bernoulli's, and Archimedes'). Trying to learn all of the principles at once is more likely to cause confusion.

Thinking Visually

a. Liquids (or gases) **b.** Gases (or liquids) **c.** Pressure = Force/Area **d.** Depth **e.** Altitude (or speed) **f.** Speed (or altitude) **g.** Pascals

CHAPTER 13

Study Guide

13.1 Fluid Pressure

Key Concepts

- Pressure $= \frac{\text{Force}}{\text{Area}}$
- Water pressure increases as depth increases.
- The pressure in a fluid at any given depth is constant and is exerted equally in all directions.
- Air pressure decreases as altitude increases.

Vocabulary

pressure, *p. 390*
pascal, *p. 391*
fluid, *p. 391*

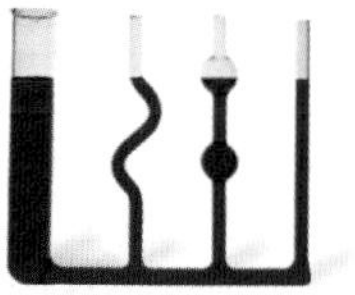

13.2 Forces and Pressure in Fluids

Key Concepts

- According to Pascal's principle, a change in pressure at any point in a fluid is transmitted equally and unchanged in all directions throughout the fluid.
- In a hydraulic lift system, an increased output force is produced by a constant fluid pressure exerted on the larger area of the output piston.
- According to Bernoulli's principle, as the speed of a fluid increases, the pressure within the fluid decreases.

Vocabulary

hydraulic system, *p. 395*
lift, *p. 396*

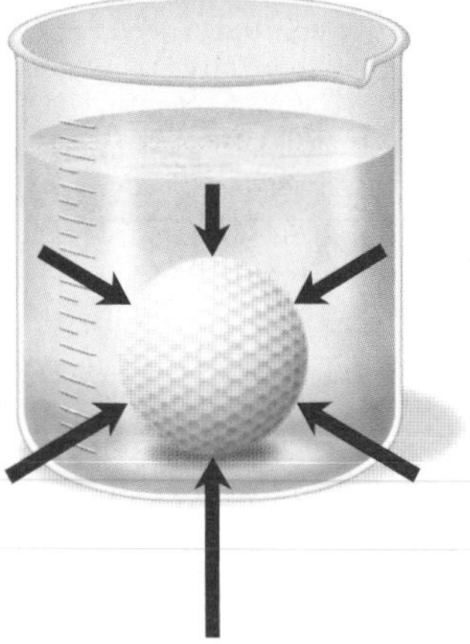

13.3 Buoyancy

Key Concepts

- Buoyancy results in the apparent loss of weight of an object in a fluid.
- If an object is less dense than the fluid it is in, it will float. If the object is more dense than the fluid it is in, it will sink.
- When the buoyant force is equal to the weight, an object floats or is suspended. When the buoyant force is less than the weight, the object sinks.

Vocabulary

buoyancy, *p. 400*
buoyant force, *p. 400*
Archimedes' principle, *p. 401*

Thinking Visually

Use the information from the chapter to complete the concept map below.

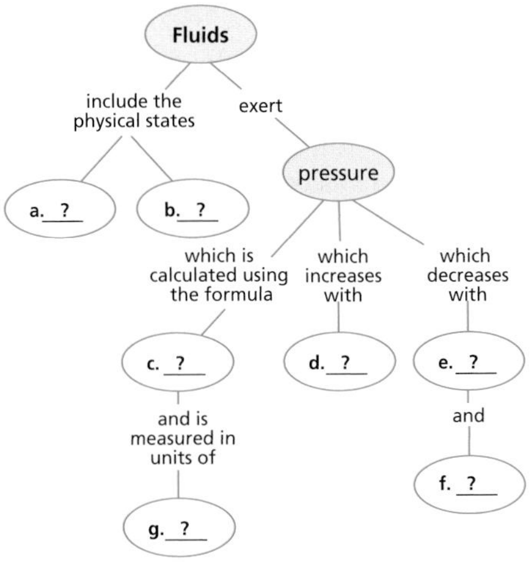

Fluids
include the physical states
exert
pressure
a. ?
b. ?
which is calculated using the formula
which increases with
which decreases with
c. ?
d. ?
e. ?
and is measured in units of
and
g. ?
f. ?

Chapter Resources

Print
- ***Chapter and Unit Tests,*** Chapter 13 Test A and Test B
- ***Test Prep Resources,*** Chapter 13

Technology
- ***Computer Test Bank,*** Chapter Test 13
- ***Interactive Textbook,*** Chapter 13
- ***Go Online,*** PHSchool.com, Chapter 13

CHAPTER 13

Assessment

Interactive textbook with assessment at PHSchool.com iText

Reviewing Content

Choose the letter that best answers the question or completes the statement.

1. A resting object exerts pressure equal to
   a. its mass times its contact area.
   b. its weight times its contact area.
   c. its mass divided by its contact area.
   d. its weight divided by its contact area.

2. Compared to the pressure exerted by a brick standing on its end, the pressure exerted by a brick resting on its side is
   a. the same. b. less.
   c. more. d. twice as much.

3. The amount of water pressure you experience while swimming in a pool depends on
   a. your buoyancy.
   b. the area of the pool.
   c. the volume of water in the pool.
   d. how deep you are in the water.

4. Which of the following is NOT true about the SI unit of pressure?
   a. It is used for fluids only.
   b. It is called a pascal.
   c. It is equal to one newton per square meter.
   d. It represents force per unit area.

5. Blaise Pascal discovered that changes in pressure
   a. are transmitted equally throughout a fluid.
   b. increase with depth of fluid.
   c. decrease with depth of fluid.
   d. depend on area.

6. In a hydraulic lift system, the output force is greater than the input force because
   a. a larger pressure acts on the output piston.
   b. a larger pressure acts on the input piston.
   c. the fluid pressure acts on areas of different sizes.
   d. of Bernoulli's principle.

7. Which of the following is NOT true about Bernoulli's principle?
   a. The pressure within a moving fluid is greater than the pressure within a nonmoving fluid.
   b. As a fluid's speed increases, the pressure within it decreases.
   c. When a moving fluid slows, the pressure within it increases.
   d. It helps explain the lift of an airplane.

8. The buoyant force acting on a submerged object is equal to
   a. the object's mass.
   b. the object's volume.
   c. the mass of the fluid displaced by the object.
   d. the weight of the fluid displaced by the object.

9. A partially submerged object floats when
   a. the object's weight is equal to the buoyant force.
   b. the object's mass is equal to the buoyant force.
   c. the object's weight is greater than the buoyant force.
   d. the buoyant force is downward.

10. A submarine changes depth by altering its
   a. speed. b. density.
   c. total area. d. shape.

Understanding Concepts

11. How is pressure different from force?

12. What are two characteristics of fluids?

13. State Archimedes' principle in your own words.

14. What two forces determine whether an object floats or sinks?

15. Why is it easier to float in salt water than in fresh water?

16. Why do helium-filled balloons rise in air?

17. Explain how a hydraulic lift operates.

18. Why is it easier to pull a submerged boat anchor to the surface than it is to lift it onto the boat?

19. Three different liquids and two equal-size cubes are placed in a beaker as shown. Which of the objects has the greater buoyant force acting on it?

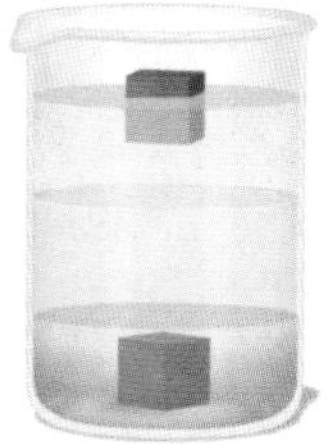

Assessment

Interactive Textbook If your class subscribes to the Interactive Textbook, your students can go online to access an interactive version of the Student Edition and a self-test.

Reviewing Content

1. d 2. b 3. d 4. a 5. a 6. c 7. a 8. d 9. a 10. b

Understanding Concepts

11. A force is a push or pull, whereas pressure is force per unit area.
12. Fluids flow and take on the shape of their containers.
13. The buoyant force on an object is equal to the weight of the fluid displaced by the object.
14. Weight and buoyant force
15. Salt water has a greater density and creates a greater buoyant force when displaced.
16. A helium-filled balloon is less dense than air, thus it rises (floats).
17. An input force to the input piston creates pressure within the hydraulic fluid. This fluid pressure is applied to the greater surface area of the output piston, creating a larger output force.
18. The buoyant force acting on the anchor submerged in the water is much greater than the buoyant force when the anchor is submerged in air.
19. The cube at the bottom has a greater buoyant force acting on it.

Homework Guide

Section	Questions
13.1	1–4, 11–12, 16, 20, 24, 26, 28–29
13.2	5–7, 17, 23, 27, 30–31
13.3	8–10, 13–15, 18–19, 21–22, 25

Critical Thinking

20. The weight of the rescuer is spread over a greater area, thus reducing the pressure acting on the ice. The reduced pressure makes it less likely that the rescuer will break through the ice.
21. Any experiment that will safely allow students to determine if the density of each gas is less than that of air is acceptable. Answers may include filling a balloon with each gas and observing whether it rises in the air.
22. The buoyant force provided by the water lessens the impact and weight acting on the weakened muscles.
23. Drawings should show that the inclined roofline of a house can cause the air flowing over the roof to speed up, much like the air flow over an airplane wing. The low-pressure, fast-moving air creates a pressure difference between the inside and outside of the house. This pressure difference can cause a house to explode.

Math Skills

24. 10 cm^3
25. 0.098 N
26. 520,000 Pa
27. 370,000 Pa

Concepts in Action

28. In general, the pressure at 200 m is four times greater than the pressure at 50 m. At any depth, the pressure on the bottom of the submarine is greater than the pressure on the top of the submarine.
29. The capped can will be crushed because the pressure outside the can is much greater than the pressure inside the can. The uncapped can will not be crushed because the pressure inside and outside the can is equal.
30. Pressing the brake pedal produces increased pressure in the hydraulic fluid. The increased fluid pressure acts on the larger-sized piston located at the brake, producing a larger force. This larger force is applied to the brake pad and is used to stop the car.
31. Explanations should discuss how the wing shapes cause air flowing over their tops to travel faster, thus creating an area of decreased pressure. The pressure difference between the top and bottom wing surfaces creates lift.

CHAPTER 13

Assessment *(continued)*

Critical Thinking

20. **Applying Concepts** In order to save someone who has fallen through the ice of a frozen lake, rescuers often reach the victim by crawling across the ice on their stomachs. Explain why the rescuers use this technique.

21. **Designing an Experiment** Your lab has two pressurized gas cylinders, each containing a different gas. Describe an experiment that could be used to determine whether each gas is less dense than air.

22. **Applying Concepts** For patients with muscles weakened due to injury, physical therapists recommend exercising in a swimming pool. Why is pool exercise preferred to exercise in a gym?

23. **Using Models** The high-speed winds of a hurricane sometimes cause houses to explode. Use a drawing to model the pressures acting on the house. Explain the areas of high and low pressure using Bernoulli's principle.

Math Skills

Use the illustration to answer Questions 24 and 25. The results of adding a small stone to a beaker that was filled to the brim with water is shown below.

100 mL
75
50
25
40 mL
30
20
10

24. **Converting Units** What is the volume of the stone in cm^3? (*Hint:* 1.0 mL = 1.0 cm^3)

25. **Calculating** If 1.0 cm^3 equals 1.0 mL, and 1.0 cm^3 of water has a mass of 1.0 g, calculate the buoyant force acting on the stone.

26. **Using Formulas** A 520-N ballet dancer is balanced on the toe of her shoe. If the toe has an area of 0.0010 m^2, what pressure does she exert on the floor?

27. **Using Formulas** A small hydraulic jack exerts a force of 2200 N. If the area of the jack's output piston is 0.0060 m^2, what is the pressure of the hydraulic fluid inside the jack?

Concepts in Action

28. **Comparing and Contrasting** Water exerts pressure on all sides of a submerged submarine. Compare and contrast the pressures acting on the submarine at a depth of 50 m to the pressures at a depth of 200 m.

29. **Predicting** An empty metal can is capped, attached to weights, and thrown into a deep ocean trench. A second, identical metal can is left uncapped, attached to weights, and thrown into the same trench. Both cans sink. Predict what will happen to each can and explain your reasons.

30. **Applying Concepts** When a driver presses on the brake pedal of a car, the car is easily brought to a stop. Explain how the car's hydraulic braking system transmits and increases the force applied to the brake pedal.

31. **Writing in Science** Explain how airplane wings and the wings of birds affect the air flowing over them to produce lift.

Performance-Based Assessment

Using Models Use what you have learned from this chapter to make a model boat out of a 10-cm-square piece of foil. Test your model boat in a tank of water to see how many pennies it can support before sinking. Compare the performance of your boat with those of your classmates. Suggest several design improvements based on your results.

Go Online
PHSchool.com

For: Self-grading assessment
Visit: PHSchool.com
Web Code: cca-2130

Performance-Based Assessment

Student model boat designs and results will vary. In general, boat shapes displacing the most water per unit depth submerged below the water line will support more pennies.

Go Online
PHSchool.com

Your students can independently test their knowledge of the chapter and print out their test results for your files.

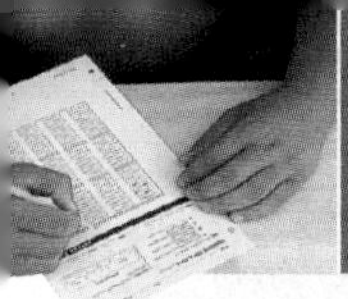

Standardized Test Prep

Test-Taking Tip

Simplify the Question

When reading a problem, it is important not to be confused by unnecessary information. It helps to rephrase the problem by ignoring the irrelevant information. Start with the question you are asked to answer. Then reread the problem and list only the information you need to answer the question. In the example below, you do not need to know water volume.

Beaker A contains 100 mL of water. Beaker B, which is smaller, contains 75 mL of water. The depth of water is the same in both beakers. Which of the following is TRUE?

(A) The volume is greater in beaker B.
(B) The pressure is greater at the bottom of beaker B than at the bottom of beaker A.
(C) The volume is equal in both beakers.
(D) The pressure is equal at the bottom of both beakers.
(E) The pressure is greater at the bottom of beaker A than at the bottom of beaker B.

(Answer: D)

Choose the letter that best answers the question or completes the statement.

1. During a storm, the wind exerts a 150-N force on a window that measures 1.00 m by 0.50 m. The outside air pressure is 101 kPa. What pressure, in pascals, does the wind exert on the window?
   (A) 75 Pa (B) 150 Pa
   (C) 1.5×10^3 Pa (D) 3.0×10^2 Pa
   (E) 3.0×10^5 kPa

2. Two identical beakers are both half filled with a liquid. Beaker A contains water and Beaker B contains a liquid that is denser than water. Which of the following is FALSE?
   (A) The pressure at the bottom of Beaker B is greater than that at the bottom of Beaker A.
   (B) The pressure within each fluid is exerted equally in all directions.
   (C) The mass of fluid in Beaker B is greater than the mass of fluid in Beaker A.
   (D) The volume of fluid in Beaker B is equal to the volume of fluid in Beaker A.
   (E) The volume of fluid in Beaker B is equal to the volume of fluid in Beaker A.

3. When air is blown between two balls suspended from strings, the balls come together and touch. This is explained by
   (A) Archimedes' principle.
   (B) Pascal's principle.
   (C) the Pauli exclusion principle.
   (D) Bernoulli's principle.
   (E) the hydraulic principle.

4. In a hydraulic system, the area of the output piston is three times larger than the area of the input piston. How is the output force related to the input force?
   (A) It is nine times smaller.
   (B) It is three times smaller.
   (C) They are both zero.
   (D) It is three times larger.
   (E) It is nine times larger.

Questions 5 and 6 refer to the diagram of an unknown substance in a beaker of water shown below.

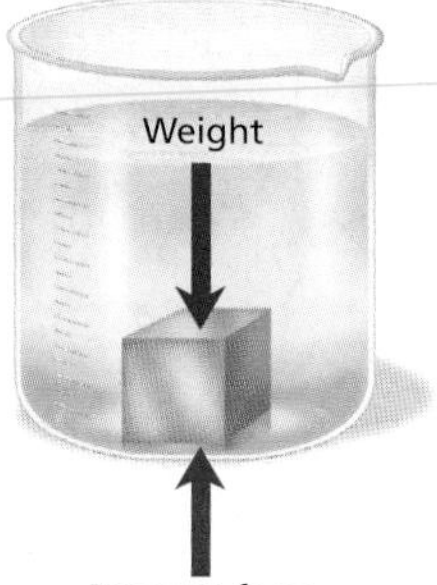
Weight
Buoyant force

5. How are the weight of the unknown object and the buoyant force acting on it related?
   (A) They are the same.
   (B) They are both equal to zero.
   (C) The weight is less than the buoyant force.
   (D) The buoyant force is more than the weight.
   (E) The weight is more than the buoyant force.

6. Which of the following is TRUE?
   (A) Forces from pressure act equally on all sides of the cube.
   (B) The unknown substance has a density greater than 1.0 g/cm^3.
   (C) The buoyant force equals the pressure.
   (D) The buoyant force is more than the weight.
   (E) The weight is equal to the buoyant force.

Standardized Test Prep

1. D **2.** D **3.** D
4. D **5.** E **6.** B

CHAPTER 14

Planning Guide

Use these planning tools
Easy Planner
Teacher Express

SECTION OBJECTIVES	STANDARDS NATIONAL (See p. T18.)	STANDARDS STATE	ACTIVITIES and LABS
14.1 Work and Power, pp. 412–416 1 block or 2 periods **14.1.1 Describe** the conditions that must exist for a force to do work on an object. **14.1.2 Calculate** the work done on an object. **14.1.3 Describe** and **calculate** power. **14.1.4 Compare** the units of watts and horsepower as they relate to power.	A-1, A-2, B-4, G-1, G-2, G-3		**SE** Inquiry Activity: How Do Ramps Help You Raise Objects? p. 411 L2 **TE** Teacher Demo: Work, p. 413 L2
14.2 Work and Machines, pp. 417–420 1 block or 2 periods **14.2.1 Describe** what a machine is and how it makes work easier to do. **14.2.2 Relate** the work input to a machine to the work output of the machine.			
14.3 Mechanical Advantage and Efficiency, pp. 421–426 1 block or 2 periods **14.3.1 Compare** a machine's actual mechanical advantage to its ideal mechanical advantage. **14.3.2 Calculate** the ideal and actual mechanical advantages of various machines. **14.3.3 Explain** why the efficiency of a machine is always less than 100%. **14.3.4 Calculate** a machine's efficiency.	A-1, A-2, G-1, G-2, G-3		**SE** Quick Lab: Using Friction to Change Mechanical Advantage, p. 424 L2 **SE** Consumer Lab: Determining Mechanical Advantage, pp. 438–439 L2 **TE** Teacher Demo: Mechanical Advantage, p. 423 L2
14.4 Simple Machines, pp. 427–435 1 block or 2 periods **14.4.1 Name, describe,** and **give an example** of each of the six types of simple machines. **14.4.2 Describe** how to determine the ideal mechanical advantage of each type of simple machine. **14.4.3 Define** and **identify** compound machines.	A-1, A-2		**SE** Quick Lab: Comparing Lever Arms, p. 429 L2 **TE** Teacher Demo: Inclined Planes, p. 430 L2 **LM** Investigation 14A: Comparing the Mechanical Advantage of Levers L2 **LM** Investigation 14B: Comparing Pulleys L1

Ability Levels
L1 For students who need additional help
L2 For all students
L3 For students who need to be challenged

Components

SE	Student Edition	**RSW**	Reading & Study Workbook	**CUT**	Chapter & Unit Tests	**T**	Transparencies
TE	Teacher's Edition	**MSPS**	Math Skills & Problem Solving Workbook	**CTB**	Computer Test Bank	**iT**	Interactive Textbook
LM	Laboratory Manual			**TP**	Test Prep Resources	**P**	Presentation Pro CD-ROM
PLM	Probeware Lab Manual			**DC**	Discovery Channel Videotapes & DVDs	**GO**	Internet Resources

RESOURCES PRINT and TECHNOLOGY	SECTION ASSESSMENT
RSW Section 14.1 L1 **RSW Math Skill** L2 **MSPS** Section 14.1 L2 **T** Chapter 14 Pretest L2 Section 14.1 L2 **P** Chapter 14 Pretest L2 Section 14.1 L2 NSTA SCILINKS **GO** Work L2	**SE** Section 14.1 Assessment, p. 416 **iT** Section 14.1
RSW Section 14.2 L1 **T** Section 14.2 L2 **P** Section 14.2 L2 NSTA SCILINKS **GO** Machines L2	**SE** Section 14.2 Assessment, p. 420 **iT** Section 14.2
RSW Section 14.3 L1 **MSPS** Section 14.3 L2 **T** Section 14.3 L2 **P** Section 14.3 L2 NSTA SCILINKS **GO** Mechanical advantage L2 **PHSchool.com GO** Data Sharing L2	**SE** Section 14.3 Assessment, p. 426 **iT** Section 14.3
RSW Section 14.4 L1 **MSPS** Section 14.4 L2 Discovery Channel School **DC** Pedal Power L2 **T** Section 14.4 L2 **P** Section 14.4 L2 NSTA SCILINKS **GO** Simple machines L2	**SE** Section 14.4 Assessment, p. 435 **iT** Section 14.4

Go Online

Go online for these Internet resources.

PHSchool.com
Web Code: ccd-2140
Web Code: cca-2140

NSTA SCILINKS
Web Code: ccn-2141
Web Code: ccn-2142
Web Code: ccn-2143
Web Code: ccn-2144

Materials for Activities and Labs

Quantities for each group

STUDENT EDITION

Inquiry Activity, p. 411
6 textbooks, 2 boards (1 long, 1 short), meter stick, spring scale, lab cart

Quick Lab, p. 424
6 books, board, 3 different kinds of shoes, 1-kg mass, spring scale

Quick Lab, p. 429
pencil, masking tape, spring scale, 500-g mass, meter stick

Consumer Lab, pp. 438–439
board with 2 nails, 4 thread spools (3 with different diameters), rubber band, masking tape, multispeed bicycle (1 or more per class), meter stick, thick leather glove

TEACHER'S EDITION

Teacher Demo, p. 413
a rigid object

Teacher Demo, p. 423
1 pulley, 10-N spring scale, 500-g mass, string

Teacher Demo, p. 430
long board, heavy box, small stepladder, spring scale

Build Science Skills, p. 437
1 bicycle with gears similar to that shown on pp. 436–437

Chapter Assessment

CHAPTER ASSESSMENT

SE Chapter Assessment, pp. 441–442
CUT Chapter 14 Test A, B
CTB Chapter 14
iT Chapter 14
PHSchool.com GO
Web Code: cca-2140

STANDARDIZED TEST PREP

SE Chapter 14, p. 443
TP Diagnose and Prescribe

Interactive Textbook

Interactive Textbook with assessment at PHSchool.com

CHAPTER 14

Before you teach

From the Author

Michael Wysession
Washington University

Big Ideas

This chapter ties together two fundamental aspects of physics: force and energy. Force applied over a distance to move an object equals work, and work is equal to the transfer of energy to that object by the action of a force.

Space and Time When an object is moved through space and time, we can quantify the results of that force. Moving the object against opposing forces (like friction or gravity) requires energy. The amount of energy expended (called work) is equal to the product of the force and the distance moved by the action of a force.

It is also helpful to know the rate at which energy is expended to move an object. Power is the rate at which energy is transferred to a system. Power is measured in watts, which are units of energy per time.

Forces and Motion Machines change the way forces are applied in order to do work. Some machines increase the distance over which an input force acts, allowing for smaller input forces. Some machines decrease the distance over which an input force acts, thus requiring larger input forces. Some machines change the direction of the force.

There are only a few types of simple machines: the pulley, wheel and axle, inclined plane, lever, screw, and wedge. Most machines in daily life are compound machines, which are combinations of two or more—and often many—simple machines.

Matter and Energy There is always an energy cost when doing work and using machines. Because of friction, the amount of energy applied to a system is always more than the amount of energy produced by the system. The missing energy goes into heat, or thermal energy, due to friction. The efficiency of a machine is the ratio of the work output to the work input.

Physics Refresher

Work 14.1

In physics, a force does work on an object if components of the force act in the direction of the object's movement. Work done (W) is defined as a product of the force or component of the force (F) and the distance moved (d) in the direction of the force. In equation form, Work = $(F \cos \theta)(d)$. Note that when the component of force is perpendicular to the direction, $\cos \theta$ is zero, and the work done is zero. Likewise, when the force is in the direction of motion, $\cos \theta = 1$, and work done is maximized. In this chapter, students consider only force in the direction of movement. The equation for work, then, is $W = F \times d$. The SI unit for work is newton-meter (N·m), or joule (J).

Address Misconceptions

Some students may think that any force on an object multiplied by the distance the object moves is work. However, work done by a force is defined as a product of the force and the displacement in the direction of the force. For a strategy to overcome this misconception, see **Address Misconceptions** on **page 413.**

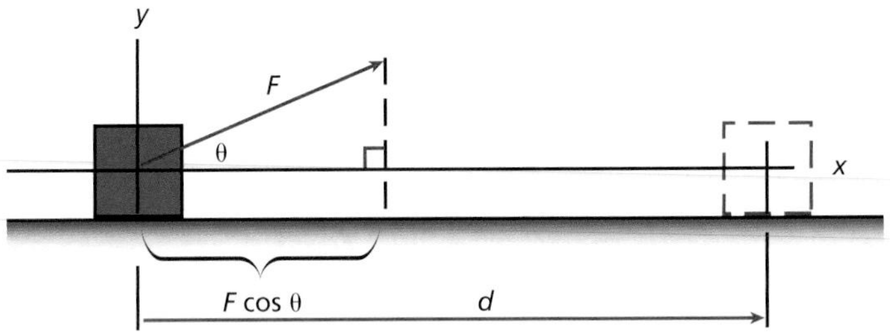
y
F
θ
x
F cos θ
d

Power 14.1

Power is the rate at which the work is done. The equation for power is $P = W/\Delta t$, where P = power, W = work, and Δt = difference in time. Substituting the definition of work into the equation for power yields another useful relationship.

$$P = W/\Delta t = Fd/\Delta t = Fv$$

Address Misconceptions

Some students may think that power is the same as force. However, power is the rate at which work is done. For a strategy to overcome this misconception, see **Address Misconceptions** on **page 414.**

Go Online PD LINKS NSTA

For: Teaching methods for work, power, and machines
Visit: www.SciLinks.org/PDLinks
Web Code: ccn-1499

In this equation, v = velocity. The SI unit for power is watt (W), described as 1 joule per second (1 J/s). Horsepower (hp) is another unit of power, where 1 hp = 746 W.

Work and Machines 14.2 and 14.4

Simple machines, whether a lever, a wheel and axle, an inclined plane, a wedge, a screw, or a pulley, take advantage of the inverse relationship of force and distance in the work equation, $W = Fd$. For example, the same work is done to lift a load whether a ramp is used or not. If a ramp is used, the distance through which the force is applied increases and the amount of force required decreases. If friction is neglected, the product Fd is constant and equals the work done (W) whether the ramp is used or not.

Mechanical Advantage 14.3

Mechanical advantage is a ratio of output force to input force (f_{out}/f_{in}) or input distance to output distance (d_{in}/d_{out}). The ratio d_{in}/d_{out} ignores the friction acting on the machine and is used to calculate ideal mechanical advantage (IMA). Because friction opposes the input force, the input force must increase to yield a desired output force. This results in the decreased mechanical advantage of any actual machine. In contrast, the ratio (f_{out}/f_{in}) is the actual mechanical advantage (AMA).

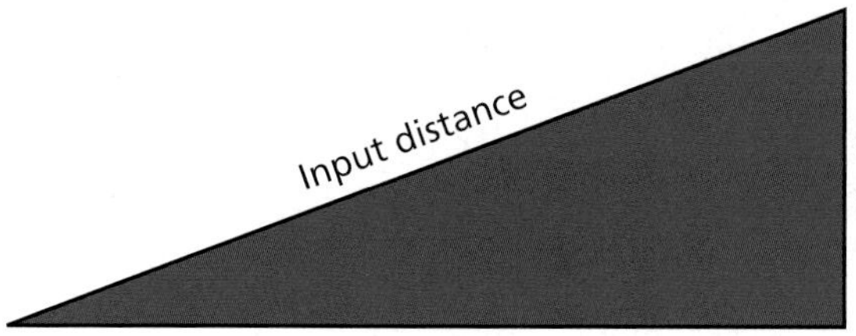
Input distance
Output distance
Ramp

Efficiency 14.3

Work is a measure of energy transfer. Therefore, if a machine were frictionless, then the input work would equal the output work, with 100% of the energy transferred. Because real machines are always subject to friction, the efficiency of real machines is always less than 100%. Friction dissipates energy in the form of heat and sound. The efficiency of a machine is a measure of how much work the machine puts out compared to how much work is put in. The ratio of work output to work input defines the ideal efficiency of a machine.

$$\text{Efficiency} = (\text{Work}_{out}/\text{Work}_{in})(100\%)$$

Build Reading Literacy

Think Aloud

Verbalize Thought Processes While Reading

Strategy Model cognitive and metacognitive processes that students can use to build meaning, self-correct, and monitor their own comprehension. Choose part of a section from Chapter 14, such as What Is Work? on pp. 412–413, and preview it. As you do so, imagine that you are reading these paragraphs for the first time, just as your students will be. Make a copy of the section, and on it write comments and questions that you can use as "think-aloud" models.

Example

1. Read several paragraphs aloud and have your students follow along silently. Have them listen to how you pause to check your own comprehension and to determine meaning at trouble spots. You might model some of the following strategies aloud as you read:

- Make a prediction, then revise or verify it.
- Describe mental pictures as they form.
- Connect new information with prior knowledge or related ideas; share an analogy.
- Verbalize confusing points and work out steps to clarify their meanings; adjust your reading pace if needed.

2. Select a logical stopping point. Then, have students read the next paragraph silently and apply similar strategies internally. Afterward, ask students to share the strategies they used. Repeat this step several times.

3. Have students work in pairs, taking turns applying think-aloud strategies to the next several paragraphs.

See p. 414 for a script on how to use the think-aloud strategy with students. For additional Build Reading Literacy strategies, see pp. 418, 422, and 431.

ASSESS PRIOR KNOWLEDGE

Use the Chapter Pretest below to assess students' prior knowledge. As needed, review these Science Concepts and Math Skills with students.

Review Science Concepts

Section 14.1 Review Newton's first and second laws. Encourage students to review the definition of force and the units used to represent it. Remind students how to break down a force vector into two component vectors at right angles to each other.

Section 14.2 Review the vector characteristics of force—magnitude and direction.

Section 14.3 Have students recall what they've learned about friction.

Section 14.4 Review geometric relationships related to circles and triangles. Tell students to keep these relationships in mind as they learn about simple machines.

Review Math Skills

Formulas and Equations Students will need to work with ratios and proportions, percents and decimals, and formulas and equations in order to solve equations related to mechanical advantage and efficiency.

Direct students to the **Math Skills** in the **Skills and Reference Handbook** at the end of the student text.

CHAPTER 14 Work, Power, and Machines

CONCEPTS in Action

How do science concepts apply to your world? Here are some questions you'll be able to answer after you read this chapter.

- Why can a snow blower remove snow faster than a person using a shovel? *(Section 14.1)*
- How can you lift a car using your hands? *(Section 14.2)*
- How does a nutcracker make it easier to crack a nut? *(Section 14.3)*
- Why are the trails up mountains constructed to be long and winding? *(Section 14.4)*

Discovery Channel School

Video Field Trip

Pedal Power

- Why do bicycles have gears? *(page 436)*

This powerful strip-mining shovel is able to remove tons of earth in a single load of its bucket. ▶

Chapter Pretest

1. According to Newton's first law, if no net force acts on an object, the object continues in motion with constant ________. *(a)*
   a. velocity **b.** force **c.** acceleration

2. A horizontal force on an object can be broken down into these components: 5 N north and 5 N east. If no other forces act on the object, in what direction will the object move? *(Northeast)*

3. Newton's second law states that the net force acting on an object equals the product of what two variables? *(Mass and acceleration)*

4. A machine produces an output force of 12.3 N when an input of 8.6 N is applied. What is the ratio of the machine's output force to its input force? *(1.4)*

5. A person exerts 22 N on a box. If a frictional force of 3 N opposes this force, what is the net force acting on the box? *(19 N)*

6. A machine has an output force of 57.3 N when a force of 32.6 N is used to operate the machine. What is the percentage increase of the force? *(176%)*

7. A small wheel has a radius of 32 cm, and a large wheel has a diameter of 128 cm. What is the ratio of the diameters of the large wheel to the small wheel? *(b)*
   a. 4 **b.** 2 **c.** 0.25 **d.** 0.5

Chapter Preview

Inquiry Activity

How Do Ramps Help You Raise Objects?

Procedure

1. Make a stack of five books.
2. Make a ramp by leaning a short board against the top of the book stack. Place a sixth book against the bottom edge of the board to keep the ramp from sliding down.
3. Measure and record the height and length of the ramp.
4. Use a spring scale to pull a laboratory cart up the ramp at constant speed. Record the force indicated on the spring scale.
5. Repeat Steps 2 through 4 using a longer board.

Think About It

1. **Comparing and Contrasting** Which ramp required a greater force to pull the cart? Which ramp required the cart to travel a greater distance?
2. **Predicting** How do you think the force needed to pull the cart would change if the cart accelerated up the length of the ramp?
3. **Formulating Hypotheses** Explain why a box that is too heavy to lift can often be pushed up a ramp.

Discovery CHANNEL SCHOOL **Video Field Trip**
Pedal Power

Encourage students to view the Video Field Trip "Pedal Power."

ENGAGE/EXPLORE

Inquiry Activity

How Do Ramps Help You Raise Objects? L2

Purpose In this activity, students begin to develop the idea that simple machines can reduce the force needed to accomplish a task by exerting a smaller force over a greater distance.

Address Misconceptions

Students may think that a ramp can reduce the amount of work done to accomplish a task. This lab can help to dispel that misconception. Use Question 1 as the basis of a discussion to point out that a longer ramp reduces the force required, but increases the distance over which the force must be applied. The work done by forces lifting the object is the same.

Skills Focus **Formulating Hypotheses**

Prep Time 15 minutes

Materials 6 textbooks, 2 boards (1 long, 1 short), meter stick, spring scale, lab cart

Class Time 20 minutes

Safety Sand the boards to remove any rough areas. Warn students to beware of splinters. Students should wear safety goggles.

Teaching Tips

- Depending on the range of your spring scales, you may need to place a mass in the cart to produce a measurable reading on the scale.
- The spring scale must be pulled parallel to the ramp so the force being measured is equal to and opposite the force of friction.

Expected Outcome Switching to the longer ramp reduces the force needed to raise the cart and increases the distance over which the force is applied.

Think About It

1. The shorter ramp; the longer ramp
2. A greater force would be needed to accelerate the cart up the ramp.
3. A heavy box can be pushed up a long ramp with less force than would be needed to lift the box because the ramp distributes the work done over a longer path.
Logical

Section 14.1

1 FOCUS

Objectives

14.1.1 **Describe** the conditions that must exist for a force to do work on an object.

14.1.2 **Calculate** the work done on an object.

14.1.3 **Describe** and **calculate** power.

14.1.4 **Compare** the units of watts and horsepower as they relate to power.

Reading Focus

Build Vocabulary L2

Table Encourage students to make a table to help them remember the definitions of *work* and *power*. These terms should go in the first column. Then, have students write the corresponding units, *joule* and *watt* (with *horsepower* in parentheses) in the second column, on the same row with the proper term. The third column is used for definitions of *work* and *power*.
Verbal

Reading Strategy L2

a. Up b. None c. No d. Horizontal
e. Horizontal f. Yes g. Diagonal
h. Horizontal i. Yes j. Up
k. Horizontal l. No

2 INSTRUCT

What Is Work?

Build Science Skills L2

Interpreting Photographs Tell students to imagine the action that occurs after the time shown in the photo. Ask, **Is work done on the weights when they are lowered, or dropped to the ground?** *(Yes)* **What force acts on and does work on the weights as they are lowered or dropped?** *(Gravity)*
Logical, Visual

14.1 Work and Power

Reading Focus

Key Concepts

- When does a force do work?
- How are work and power related?

Vocabulary

- work
- joule
- power
- watt
- horsepower

Reading Strategy

Relating Text and Visuals Copy the table shown at the right. As you read, look carefully at Figures 1 and 2 and read their captions. Complete the table by describing the work shown in each figure.

Figure	Direction of Force	Direction of Motion	Is Work Done?
1	a. ?	b. ?	c. ?
2A	d. ?	e. ?	f. ?
2B	g. ?	h. ?	i. ?
2C	j. ?	k. ?	l. ?

Figure 1 The weight lifter applies a large force to hold the barbell over his head. However, because the barbell is motionless, no work is done on the barbell. **Applying Concepts** ***Did the weight lifter do work on the barbell to lift it over his head?***

You are already familiar with the everyday meaning of work. Working at an after-school job, doing yard work at home, and completing your homework may all be common events in your life. In science, however, "work" means something very different.

Look at the weight lifter shown in Figure 1. He is exerting a large force in order to hold the heavy barbell over his head. You can tell from the look on his face that holding up the weight is hard work. However, a scientist would tell you that at this instant the weight lifter is actually doing no work on the nonmoving barbell. Read on to learn about the work that was done to lift the barbell overhead.

What Is Work?

Recall that an object begins moving only when an unbalanced force acts on it. In science, **work** is the product of force and distance. Work is done when a force acts on an object in the direction the object moves. For example, work is done by the weight lifter when he exerts an upward force to raise the barbell over his head.

Work Requires Motion Though it may seem surprising, the weight lifter in Figure 1 does no work on the barbell as he holds it over his head. Why is that? Because although force is applied to the barbell, the force does not cause the barbell to move. **For a force to do work on an object, some of the force must act in the same direction as the object moves. If there is no movement, no work is done.**

Section Resources

Print

- ***Reading and Study Workbook With Math Support,*** Section 14.1 and **Math Skill:** Calculating Work and Power
- ***Math Skills and Problem Solving Workbook,*** Section 14.1
- ***Transparencies,*** Chapter Pretest and Section 14.1

Technology

- ***Interactive Textbook,*** Section 14.1
- ***Presentation Pro CD-ROM,*** Chapter Pretest and Section 14.1
- ***Go Online,*** NSTA SciLinks, Work

Force
Direction of motion
This force does work.
This force does no work.
Force
Direction of motion
Force
Direction of motion

A Force and motion in same direction

B Part of force in direction of motion

C Lifting force not in direction of motion

Figure 2 The work done on an object depends on the size of the force acting in the direction of motion and on the distance the object moves. **A** When force and motion are in the same direction, the work done is maximized. **B** Only the horizontal part of the force does work to move the suitcase to the right. **C** Because the lifting force is not in the direction the suitcase moves, the force does no work on the suitcase.

Work Depends on Direction The amount of work done on an object, if any, depends on the direction of the force and the direction of the movement. For example, though you would never do this, imagine pulling a suitcase as shown in Figure 2A. Note that all of the force acts in the same direction as the suitcase moves—all of the force does work on the suitcase.

A force does not have to act entirely in the direction of movement to do work. Look at the forces and direction of motion shown as the suitcase is pulled in Figure 2B. The force acts upward and to the right along the handle, whereas the suitcase moves only to the right along the ground. Figure 2B shows that there is a horizontal portion of the force acting in the direction of motion. Only the horizontal part of the applied force—the part in the direction of movement—does work.

Any part of a force that does not act in the direction of motion does no work on an object. As shown in Figure 2C, the vertical lifting force does not act in the direction of motion. Thus, this vertical force does no work on the suitcase.

Calculating Work

Although the weight lifter in Figure 1 does no work while holding the barbell over his head, he did do work in lifting the barbell to the overhead position. The work done is calculated by multiplying the constant force acting in the direction of motion by the distance that the object moves.

Work

$$\text{Work} = \text{Force} \times \text{Distance}$$

Reading Checkpoint *How do you calculate work?*

Go Online NSTA SciLinks

For: Links on work
Visit: www.SciLinks.org
Web Code: ccn-2141

Address Misconceptions L2

Some students may think that any force acting on an object multiplied by the distance the object moves is work. To overcome this misconception, have a student walk across the room carrying a book. Explain that the force used to hold the book up does no work on the book because that force is not in the direction that the book moves. **Kinesthetic**

Calculating Work

Teacher Demo

Work L2

Purpose Students observe how work requires movement of an object in the direction of the applied force.

Materials a rigid object

Procedure Move the object in different ways as students describe the force acting on the object, the motion of the object, and whether work is done on the object. First, drop the object. *(The force is gravity acting downward; force and motion are in the same direction, so work is done.)* Next, press the object against the wall. *(Force is from the person pushing the object toward the wall; there is no motion; there is no work because there is no movement in the direction of force.)* Finally, push the object across a desk. *(Forces are the person pushing horizontally and gravity acting downward; there is only horizontal motion; there is work only in the horizontal direction.)*

Expected Outcome Students should see how the relationship between force and displacement determines whether work is done. **Visual, Logical**

Customize for English Language Learners

Use Context
ELL students may be confused by vocabulary terms such as *work* and *power*. For example, students are most likely familiar with the definition of work as "labor." However, it may not be initially clear what *work* means in a science context. Ask students to give examples of the word *work* as it pertains to a job. Then, provide examples of the term in a scientific sense. Guide students to then give their own examples of the term in a science context.

Go Online NSTA SciLinks

Download a worksheet on work for students to complete, and find additional teacher support from NSTA SciLinks.

Answer to . . .

Figure 1 *Yes*

Reading Checkpoint *Work = Force × Distance*

Build Reading Literacy L1

Think Aloud Refer to **page 410D** in this chapter, which provides guidelines for thinking aloud.

Set the example for this strategy by verbalizing your own thought processes while reading aloud Units of Work. Encourage student volunteers to read Using the Work Formula while quietly verbalizing their thought processes. Then, have a class discussion about the advantages students found in staying focused on a logical thought process when reading in this manner.
Intrapersonal, Auditory

What Is Power?

Address Misconceptions L2

Some students may think that power is the same as force. To overcome this misconception, have students think about the time needed for a person to push a heavy box across the room. Now imagine the person pushing the box across the floor in half the time. Point out that although this requires increased force and power, the two quantities are not the same. Increased force (in newtons) is needed to move the box at a faster rate, and more power (in watts) is required because the increased force was applied over a shorter period of time.
Logical

Build Science Skills L2

Applying Concepts Review with students the equations for both work and power. Ask, **Since *P* 5 *W*/*t* 5 *Fd*/*t* and since *d*/*t* 5 *v*, would *P* 5 *Fv*?** *(Yes, P = W/t = Fd/t = Fv.)* Ask, **If you use a snow blower and know the velocity of the expelled snow (in m/s) and the power output of the snow blower (in watts), can you calculate the force applied to the snow (in newtons?)** *(Yes, if you assume all the power is used for propelling the snow. If you know two of the three variables, P, F, or v, you can calculate the third. It is important, though, to use the correct units.)*
Logical

Figure 3 Power is the rate of doing work. Because the snow blower can remove more snow in less time, it requires more power than hand shoveling does.
Comparing and Contrasting *What is the source of power in each of the above photos?*

Units of Work When using SI units in the work formula, the force is in newtons, and distance is in meters. The product of force and distance results in the units of newton-meters, also known as joules. The **joule** (J) is the SI unit of work. When a force of 1 newton moves an object 1 meter in the direction of the force, 1 joule of work is done. The joule is named after James Prescott Joule (1818–1889), a British scientist famous for researching the relationship between work and heat.

Using the Work Formula It is easy to calculate the work done by a weight lifter who lifts a 1600-newton barbell over his head. Assume that the barbell is lifted to a height of 2.0 meters. To use the work formula, simply substitute the correct values into the formula and multiply.

$$\text{Work} = \text{Force} \times \text{Distance}$$

$$\text{Work} = 1600\ \text{N} \times 2.0\ \text{m}$$

$$\text{Work} = 3200\ \text{N}\cdot\text{m} = 3200\ \text{J}$$

What Is Power?

Often people are not just concerned about getting work done. They want it done fast, and that requires power. Power, like work, has a precise meaning in science.

Power is the rate of doing work. **Doing work at a faster rate requires more power. To increase power, you can increase the amount of work done in a given time, or you can do a given amount of work in less time.**

Figure 3 shows an example of what a difference in power means when performing a task such as snow removal. Work is required to move snow from one location to another. As you can see in Figure 3, a person using a shovel and a person using a snow blower can both do the work needed to remove the snow. Clearly, the snow blower can do the job much faster. The fact that the snow blower can do more work in less time means that it has more power.

You may have noticed that the size of the engine used by a machine is often an indication of its power. For example, compare the snow blower's small engine with the engine used by a truck pushing a snowplow. The truck's powerful engine allows it to remove snow at a very fast rate.

Reading Checkpoint *How does doing work at a faster rate affect the power required?*

Facts and Figures

Cassini-Huygens Spacecraft In 1997, NASA launched the Cassini-Huygens spacecraft on a mission to investigate Saturn, Venus, and Jupiter. The craft was loaded with instruments and cameras to help it complete this task. The Cassini spacecraft is the largest ever built and weighs nearly 5650 kg (6 tons). During launch, over 55 million joules of work were required for each kilometer that the spacecraft was lifted.

Calculating Power

You can calculate power by dividing the amount of work done by the time needed to do the work.

Power

$$\text{Power} = \frac{\text{Work}}{\text{Time}}$$

When using SI units in the power formula, work is in joules (J) and time is in seconds (s). The SI unit of power is the **watt** (W), which is equal to one joule per second. Thus, a 40-watt light bulb requires 40 joules each second that it is lit. This amount of power is also approximately equal to lifting your textbook a height of one meter in half a second.

Math Skills

Calculating Power

You exert a vertical force of 72 newtons to lift a box to a height of 1.0 meter in a time of 2.0 seconds. How much power is used to lift the box?

1 Read and Understand

What information are you given?

Force = 72 N Distance = 1.0 m

Time = 2.0 s

2 Plan and Solve

What formula contains the given quantities and the unknown?

$$\text{Power} = \frac{\text{Work}}{\text{Time}} = \frac{\text{Force} \times \text{Distance}}{\text{Time}}$$

Replace each variable with its known value and solve.

$$\text{Power} = \frac{72\text{ N} \times 1.0\text{ m}}{2.0\text{ s}} = 36\text{ J/s} = 36\text{ W}$$

3 Look Back and Check

Is your answer reasonable?

36 watts is not a lot of power, which seems reasonable considering the box was lifted slowly, through a height of only 1 meter.

Math Practice

1. Your family is moving to a new apartment. While lifting a box 1.5 m straight up to put it on a truck, you exert an upward force of 200 N for 1.0 s. How much power is required to do this?
2. You lift a book from the floor to a bookshelf 1.0 m above the ground. How much power is used if the upward force is 15.0 N and you do the work in 2.0 s?
3. You apply a horizontal force of 10.0 N to pull a wheeled suitcase at a constant speed of 0.5 m/s across flat ground. How much power is used? (*Hint:* The suitcase moves 0.5 m/s. Consider how much work the force does each second and how work is related to power.)

Calculating Power

Math Practice

Solutions **L2**

1. Work = Force × Distance = 200 N × 1.5 m = 300 J
Power = Work/Time = 300 J/1.0 s = 300 W
2. Work = Force × Distance = 15.0 N × 1.0 m = 15 J
Power = Work/Time = 15 J/2.0 s = 7.5 W
3. Work = Force × Distance = 10.0 N × 0.5 m = 5 J
Power = Work/Time = 5 J/1.0 s = 5 W
Logical

For Extra Help **L1**

Help students to learn 1 W = 1 J/s by relating the units to the variables in the power formula: Power = Work/Time. Have them write these units in their journals along with the work equation. **Logical, Visual**

Direct students to the **Math Skills** in the **Skills and Reference Handbook** at the end of the student text for additional help.

Additional Problems

1. A student rows a boat across a still pond, doing 3600 J of work on the oars in 60 seconds. What is the student's power output? (Power = Work/Time = 3600 J/60 s = 60 J/s = 60 W)
2. A truck pulls a trailer at a constant velocity for 100 m while exerting a force of 480 newtons for 1 minute (60 seconds). Calculate the power. (*Hint:* First calculate the work.) (Work = Force × Distance = 480 N × 100 m = 48,000 J; Power = Work/Time = 48,000 J/60 s = 800 J/s = 800 W)
Logical

Answer to . . .

Figure 3 *The woman provides the power needed to shovel the snow, whereas the gas-powered engine provides the power needed by the snow blower.*

Reading Checkpoint *Doing work at a faster rate requires more power.*

James Watt and Horsepower

Use Visuals L1

Figure 4 Ask students how the power that could be delivered by the 4 hp engine and the 4 work horses compares. *(Both can do roughly the same amount of work. See FYI note below.)* Then, remind them that 1 hp = 746 watts. Ask them to convert the 4 hp to power in watts. *(4 hp × 746 W/hp = 2984 W)* Then, relate the power of 1 hp to moving a stack of CDs. Because 1 newton is approximately equal to the weight of one compact disc in its case, 1 hp is enough power to move about 2,500 compact discs 1 meter in 1 second. **Visual**

FYI

Watt's horsepower value was based upon strong dray horses, which are about 50% more powerful than an average horse.

3 ASSESS

Evaluate Understanding L2

Have student work in pairs to write out two questions and answers about work and power. Then, ask students to form groups of four and quiz one another. Randomly select students to present their question and answer to the rest of the class.

Reteach L1

Use Figure 2 and its caption to summarize the key concepts related to work. Discuss how the force component in the direction of the motion and the force component not in the direction of the motion affect the work done.

Math Practice

Solutions

7. Work = Force × Distance
= 25 N × 1.5 m = 38 J

8. Power = Work/Time
= 100 J/2 s = 50 W

Interactive Textbook If your class subscribes to the Interactive Textbook, use it to review key concepts in Section 14.1.

Figure 4 Although the horse-drawn plow and the gasoline-powered engine get their power from different sources, both are capable of doing work at a rate of about four horsepower.

James Watt and Horsepower

Besides the watt, another common unit of power is the horsepower. One **horsepower** (hp) is equal to about 746 watts. The horsepower was first defined by Scottish scientist James Watt (1736–1819). Watt was looking for a way to compare the power outputs of steam engines he had designed. Horses were a logical choice for comparison as they were the most commonly used source of power in the 1700s. Watt did not want to exaggerate the power of his steam engines. Thus, after many experiments, he defined the horsepower based on the power output of a very strong horse. Figure 4 shows a comparison of two equivalent power sources.

Section 14.1 Assessment

Reviewing Concepts

1. What conditions must exist in order for a force to do work on an object?
2. What formula relates work and power?
3. How much work is done when a vertical force acts on an object moving horizontally?

Critical Thinking

4. **Applying Concepts** A desk exerts an upward force to support a computer resting on it. Does this force do work? Explain.
5. **Predicting** Two cars have the same weight, but one of the cars has an engine that provides twice the power of the other. Which car can make it to the top of a mountain pass first? Which car does more work to reach the pass?
6. **Comparing and Contrasting** You carry two heavy bags of groceries upstairs to your kitchen. Will you do more work on the bags if you carry them up one at a time? Explain.

Math Practice

7. How much work does a 25-newton force do to lift a potted plant from the floor to a shelf 1.5 meters high?
8. You lift a large bag of flour from the floor to a 1-meter-high counter, doing 100 joules of work in 2 seconds. How much power do you use to lift the bag of flour?

Section 14.1 Assessment

1. Some of the force must act in the same direction as the object moves.
2. Power = Work/Time
3. No work is done.
4. The supporting force does no work because the object it acts on (the computer) does not move.
5. The car with the more powerful engine will reach the top first. Both cars do the same amount of work to reach the top.
6. Carrying one bag at a time uses only half the force, but requires that the force be applied through twice the distance. The work done is the same in both cases.

14.2 Work and Machines

Reading Focus

Key Concepts

- How do machines make work easier?
- How are work input and work output related for a machine?

Vocabulary

- machine
- input distance
- output force
- work output
- input force
- work input
- output distance

Reading Strategy

Summarizing Copy the table shown. As you read, complete the table for each machine. After you read, write a sentence summarizing the idea that your table illustrates.

Machine	Increases or Decreases Input Force	Increases or Decreases Input Distance
Tire jack	a. ?	b. ?
Lug wrench	c. ?	d. ?
Rowing oar	e. ?	f. ?
Summary:	g. ?	

Two good friends, each one wearing her most glamorous dress, are on their way to a school dance when disaster strikes. Their car gets a flat tire! To fix it, they'll have to remove the flat tire and put on the spare tire. But won't loosening the lug nuts and lifting the car off of the ground require more force than they can exert just using their hands? How can they change the tire?

As shown in Figure 5, machines come to the rescue. Fortunately, all cars come with the tools designed to help you change a tire. With the help of a lug wrench and jack, which are actually simple machines, they'll have no problem changing the tire. Read on to learn how a car jack and a lug wrench alter forces to make changing a tire a relatively easy task.

Figure 5 All cars come equipped with simple machines designed to make changing a tire a fairly easy task.
Inferring *Does the jack used to lift the car increase or decrease the force applied to it?*

Machines Do Work

A **machine** is a device that changes a force. When using the jack, you apply a force to the jack handle. The jack changes this force and applies a much stronger force to lift the car. Because the jack increases the force you exert, it is a machine. **Machines make work easier to do. They change the size of a force needed, the direction of a force, or the distance over which a force acts.** Both the lug wrench and the jack allow a single person to apply enough force to accomplish tasks they would normally not be able to.

Section Resources

Print
- ***Reading and Study Workbook With Math Support,*** Section 14.2
- ***Transparencies,*** Section 14.2

Technology
- ***Interactive Textbook,*** Section 14.2
- ***Presentation Pro CD-ROM,*** Section 14.2
- ***Go Online,*** NSTA SciLinks, Machines

Section 14.2

1 FOCUS

Objectives

14.2.1 **Describe** what a machine is and how it makes work easier to do.

14.2.2 **Relate** the work input to a machine to the work output of the machine.

Reading Focus

Build Vocabulary L2

Paraphrase Paraphrasing can help students grasp the meaning of vocabulary terms. Encourage students to make a table with three columns. Ask them to write *machine, input distance, output force, work output, input force, work input,* and *output distance* in the first column; paraphrased meanings in the second column, and textbook definitions in the third column. Have students use the paraphrased terms to gain a better understanding of the text's definitions.

Reading Strategy L2

a. Decreases **b.** Increases **c.** Decreases **d.** Increases **e.** Increases **f.** Decreases **g.** Machines that decrease the applied force increase the distance the force is applied through and vice versa.

2 INSTRUCT

Machines Do Work

Address Misconceptions L2

Some students may think that all objects have a certain amount of force. For example, they may think that a moving object has force that allows it to move, and when the force runs out, the object stops moving. Challenge this misconception by relating it to machines. A machine needs an input force in order to perform work. The force is not already within the machine or a property of the machine.
Logical

Answer to . . .

Figure 5 *The jack increases the force applied to it.*

Build Reading Literacy **L1**

Relate Cause and Effect Refer to page **260D** in **Chapter 9**, which provides the guidelines for relating cause and effect.

Use Figure 6 to help students identify the cause-and-effect relationship between work done on and work done by a machine. *(The overall cause is the input work, and the overall effect is the output work.)* Show them also that the output force exerted (the force to lift the car) is greater than the input force, while the output distance (the distance the car is lifted) is less than the input distance. To be sure students understand the concepts, ask, **What is the input force in this example?** *(The force applied to the jack handle)* **What is the input distance?** *(The distance the jack handle moves through)* **What is the output force in this example?** *(It is the force exerted on the car.)* **What is the output distance?** *(It is the distance the car was lifted.)*
Logical, Visual

Go Online NSTA SciLinks

Download a worksheet on machines for students to complete, and find additional teacher support from NSTA SciLinks.

Figure 6 Turning the jack handle allows the man to raise the car. The distance moved by the handle is much greater than the distance the car is raised.
Comparing and Contrasting ***How does the force exerted on the jack handle compare with the force exerted by the jack on the car?***

Increasing Force How is a machine able to increase a force? Study what is happening in Figure 6. Each complete rotation of the jack handle applies a small force over a large distance. However, each rotation lifts the car only a very short distance. Thus a small force exerted over a large distance becomes a large force exerted over a short distance.

Raising a car using a machine such as a jack is similar to moving a stack of books by picking them up one at a time. Lifting the books one at a time takes less force. But there's a tradeoff—the total distance traveled is much greater. If a machine increases the distance over which you exert a force, then it decreases the amount of force you need to exert.

Increasing Distance Some machines decrease the applied force, but increase the distance over which the force is exerted. Look at the rowing shell in Figure 7. Each oar operates as a machine that pushes the boat through the water. The arrows show how pulling the end of each oar through a small distance moves the end of the oar in the water through a large distance. Increasing the distance the oar travels through the water helps you go fast. But again, there is a tradeoff. The increased travel of the oar through the water requires you to exert a greater force. A machine that decreases the distance through which you exert a force increases the amount of force required.

Changing Direction Some machines change the direction of the applied force. An example is shown in Figure 7. Pulling back on the handle of the oar causes its other end to move in the opposite direction. So not only can machines change the amount of force and the distance the force acts through, but they can also change the direction of the force.

Go Online NSTA SciLinks

For: Links on machines
Visit: www.SciLinks.org
Web Code: ccn-2142

Reading Checkpoint ***Give an example of a machine that changes the direction of an applied force.***

Customize for Inclusion Students

Hearing Impaired
Reinforce the lesson's content by providing a variety of visual examples. Be sure to spend time on all of the visual examples provided in the text. In addition, you may wish to provide other illustrations of machines that increase force, increase distance, or change direction. Label the illustrations so that students make the connection between the concept in the text and the visual example.

Work Input and Work Output

To row the boat in Figure 7, the rower pulls back on each oar handle and the other end of each oar pushes against the water. Work is done on the oars (the machine) by pulling on them, and the oars do work on the water to move the boat. Recall from Chapter 12 that friction acts against the motion of any object. **Because of friction, the work done by a machine is always less than the work done on the machine.**

Work Input to a Machine The force you exert on a machine is called the **input force.** The distance the input force acts through is known as the **input distance.** The work done by the input force acting through the input distance is called the **work input.** The work input equals the input force multiplied by the input distance.

Each oar in Figure 7 is a machine. For the oar, the input force is the force exerted on the handle and the input distance is the distance the handle moves. The work input is the work you do to move the handle. You can increase the work input by increasing the input distance, increasing the input force, or increasing both at once.

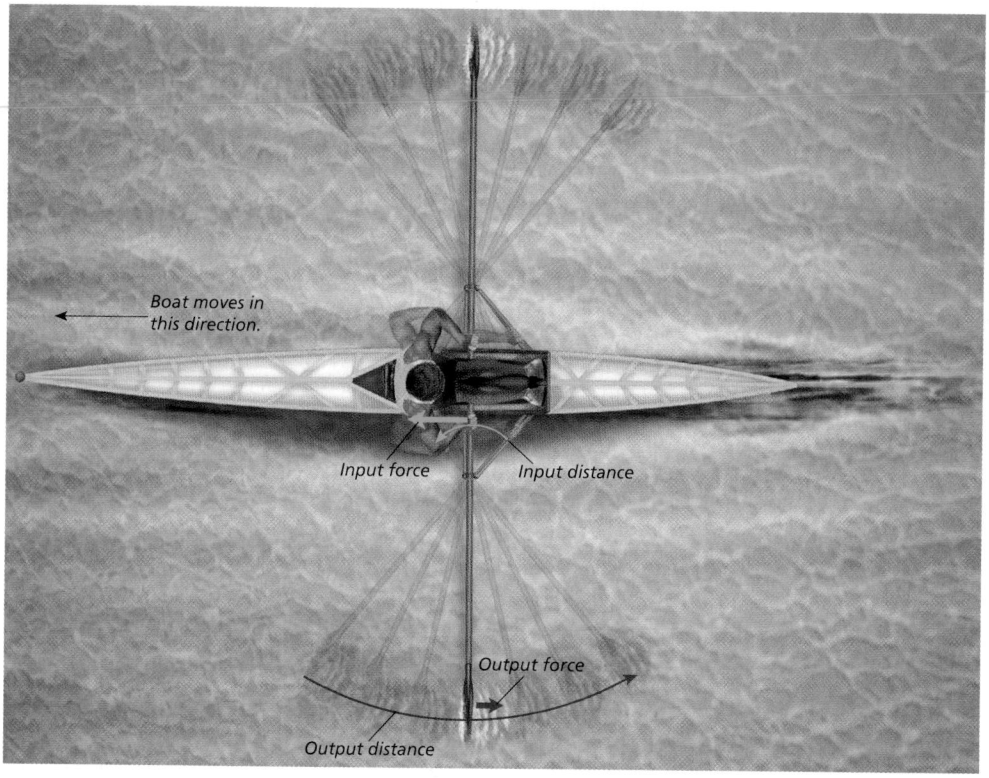

Boat moves in this direction.
Input force
Input distance
Output force
Output distance

Figure 7 The oars of the boat act as machines that increase the distance over which the force acts. **Predicting** *If the oar is pushed farther away from the boat, how will the force needed to pull the oar through the water change?*

Work Input and Work Output

Use Visuals **L1**

Figure 7 Have students look carefully at this figure to understand the relationships between input force, output force, distance, and mechanical advantage. Ask, **What is the input distance?** *(The input distance is the length of the path along which the oar handle moves. The path forms an arc.)* **How does the input distance compare to the output distance?** *(It is less.)* **What does this tell you about the mechanical advantage of the rowing setup?** *(The IMA is less than 1.)*
Visual, Logical

Build Science Skills **L2**

Calculating Using Figure 7, explain that, ignoring friction, if the rower uses 800 N of force to pull an oar's handle a distance of 0.5 m and the distance that the oar moves through in the water is 2 m, the force pushing against the water would be 200 N. Ask students to verify these values with calculations. *(Ignoring friction,* $W_{in} = W_{out}$; $F_{in}d_{in} = F_{out}d_{out}$; $800\ N \times 0.5\ m = 200\ N \times 2\ m$*)*
Visual, Logical

Facts and Figures

Perpetual Motion Machines Because of friction, building a machine that produces more energy than it uses is impossible. Nevertheless, each year, the United States Patent and Trademark Office receives applications for alleged perpetual motion machines. The office responds by requesting a working model. Three categories of perpetual motion machines are (1) those that create energy, (2) those that violate the rule that states, "the work done by a machine is always less than the work done on the machine," and (3) those that can run forever without requiring additional energy.

Answer to . . .

Figure 6 *The force exerted on the jack handle is much less than the force exerted by the jack on the car.*

Figure 7 *The required input force would increase.*

Reading Checkpoint *A jack changes the direction of the applied force because the input force is circular and the output force is vertical. Other examples include a crowbar, a seesaw, and a pulley.*

Work, Power, and Machines 419

3 ASSESS

Evaluate Understanding L2

Show students a pair of scissors or other simple mechanical device and ask them to identify the input force, distance, and work and the output force, distance, and work.

Reteach L1

Use Figure 7 to emphasize the relationship between input force, distance, and work and output force, distance, and work. Remind students that output work is always less than input work due to friction.

Connecting Concepts

The end of the oar in the water applies an action force to the water. According to Newton's third law, the water pushes back on the oar with an opposite reaction force. This reaction force propels the boat through the water. Fluid friction acts on the oar as it moves through the water, slowing its motion.

Interactive Textbook If your class subscribes to the Interactive Textbook, use it to review key concepts in Section 14.2.

Figure 8 The output work of the oars results from the oars pushing against the water so that the water pushes back against the oars. ***Observing*** *What evidence can you see in the photo that a force is acting on the water?*

Work Output of a Machine The force that is exerted by a machine is called the **output force.** The distance the output force is exerted through is the **output distance.** The **work output** of a machine is the output force multiplied by the output distance. Look back at Figure 7 one more time to see the output force, distance, and work for the oars. How are the input work and output work related? Although nearly equal, the output work is less than the input work because of friction. All machines use some amount of input work to overcome friction.

As the rowers pull on one end of each oar, the other ends push against the water as shown in Figure 8. The force of the oar on the water causes an equal and opposite reaction force to be exerted by the water on the oar. It is this reaction force that propels the boat through the water.

Can you increase the work output of the oar by positioning it differently? Unless the new position decreases friction, the answer is no. If there is no change in the work input, there cannot be an increase in the work output. The only way to increase the work output is to increase the amount of work you put into the machine. You cannot get more work out of a machine than you put into it!

Section 14.2 Assessment

Reviewing Concepts

1. How can using a machine make a task easier to perform?
2. How does the work done on a machine compare to the work done by a machine?
3. What changes can a machine make to a force?
4. A machine produces a larger force than you exert to operate the machine. How does the input distance of the machine compare to its output distance?
5. You do 200 J of work pulling the oars of a rowboat. What can you say about the amount of work the oars do to move the boat? Explain.
6. How can you increase the work output of a machine?

Critical Thinking

7. **Inferring** When you swing a baseball bat, how does the output distance the end of the bat moves compare with the distance you move your hands through? Why might this difference be useful?
8. **Applying Concepts** An advertisement for a new type of wrench claims it reduces the force needed to tighten a bolt. If the advertisement is correct, what do you know to be true about the input distance?

Connecting Concepts

Forces Recall what you learned about forces in Chapter 12. Explain how friction and Newton's third law of motion influence the movement of the oar as it is pulled by the rower shown in Figure 7.

Answer to . . .

Figure 8 *The movement of the water indicates that a force is acting on it.*

Figure 9 *The different areas are designed to accommodate different sized nuts and allow differing amounts of force to be used to crack a nut.*

Section 14.2 Assessment

1. Machines make work easier to do by altering the size of force needed, the direction of a force, or the distance over which a force acts.
2. Because of friction, the work done by a machine is always less than the work done on the machine.
3. Size of force; direction of force; distance through which a force acts
4. Because the output force is greater than the input force, the input distance must be greater than the output distance.
5. Less than 200 J of work are done to move the boat because some of the input work is lost to friction forces.
6. Increase the work input to the machine, or reduce any friction that limits work output.
7. The output distance is much greater than the input distance. The high speed of the bat end helps the batted ball to also acquire a high speed (and travel far).
8. If the input force is decreased, then the input distance must be increased.

14.3 Mechanical Advantage and Efficiency

Reading Focus

Key Concepts

- How does the actual mechanical advantage of a machine compare to its ideal mechanical advantage?
- Why is the efficiency of a machine always less than 100 percent?

Vocabulary

- mechanical advantage
- actual mechanical advantage
- ideal mechanical advantage
- efficiency

Reading Strategy

Building Vocabulary Copy the table below. Then as you read the section, write a definition for each vocabulary term in your own words.

Vocabulary	Definition
Mechanical advantage	a. ?
b. ?	c. ?
d. ?	e. ?
f. ?	g. ?

Try cracking a walnut by squeezing it in your hand. You'll find that you can't apply enough force to break the shell. Next try cracking the shell using a nutcracker. A nutcracker, which is a type of machine, is shown in Figure 9. If you squeeze the nutcracker near its pivot end, you still won't be able to crack the nut. When you squeeze the ends of the handles, however, a fairly small force cracks the shell apart. In this section you'll learn why a machine like the nutcracker is so sensitive to the location of the input force.

Mechanical Advantage

The relation of input force used to operate a machine and the output force exerted by the machine depends on the type of machine and how it is used. Thus the location of the nut in the nutcracker affects the force the nutcracker is able to exert.

The **mechanical advantage** of a machine is the number of times that the machine increases an input force. Suppose a nut is in the nutcracker at position A in Figure 9. In this position the nutcracker exerts a force on the nut about seven times greater than the force you exert on the nutcracker. In position A the nutcracker's mechanical advantage is about 7. However, if the nut is moved to position B, the mechanical advantage decreases to about 3.

A
B

Figure 9 A nutcracker is a machine capable of converting the input force applied to it into a larger force capable of cracking a nut. Because it increases force, the nutcracker has a mechanical advantage greater than 1. **Inferring** ***What might be the reason that the nutcracker has two different areas (A and B) to use for nut cracking?***

Section Resources

Print

- ***Reading and Study Workbook With Math Support,*** Section 14.3
- ***Math Skills and Problem Solving Workbook,*** Section 14.3
- ***Transparencies,*** Section 14.3

Technology

- ***Interactive Textbook,*** Section 14.3
- ***Presentation Pro CD-ROM,*** Section 14.3
- ***Go Online,*** NSTA SciLinks, Mechanical advantage; PHSchool.com, Data sharing

Section 14.3

1 FOCUS

Objectives

14.3.1 **Compare** a machine's actual mechanical advantage to its ideal mechanical advantage.
14.3.2 **Calculate** the ideal and actual mechanical advantages of various machines.
14.3.3 **Explain** why the efficiency of a machine is always less than 100%.
14.3.4 **Calculate** a machine's efficiency.

Reading Focus

Build Vocabulary L2

Vocabulary Knowledge Rating Chart Have students make a four-column chart with the headings Term, Can Define/Use It, Heard/Seen It, and Don't Know. Have them put vocabulary terms in the first column, rating their knowledge of each term by putting a checkmark in one of the other columns. Ask students what they expect this section will be about based on their understanding of the terms. Have them check those expectations as they read. Ask students to create another chart after they have read the section.

Reading Strategy

a. The number of times a machine increases force **b.** Actual mechanical advantage **c.** Ratio of output force to input force **d.** Ideal mechanical advantage **e.** The mechanical advantage of a machine if there were no friction **f.** Efficiency **g.** Percentage of work input that becomes work output

2 INSTRUCT

Mechanical Advantage

Use Visuals L1

Figure 9 Draw a sketch of the nutcracker on the board and ask students where the input force and the output force are for each position. Label the input and output arms for each position and return to the diagram when teaching ideal mechanical advantage.
Visual, Logical

Build Reading Literacy L1

Active Comprehension Refer to page **498D** in **Chapter 17**, which provides the guidelines for active comprehension.

Ask a student volunteer to read aloud the paragraphs at the top of pages 422 and 423 about actual and ideal mechanical advantage. Then, ask the class, **What more would you like to know about mechanical advantage?** Write students' questions on the board. Have students consider the questions as they finish reading. Allow time for discussion.
Verbal, Intrapersonal

Go Online NSTA SciLinks

Download a worksheet on mechanical advantage for students to complete, and find additional teacher support from NSTA SciLinks.

DK SCIENCE and History

Innovations of the Industrial Revolution L2

Have students read about the innovations of the Industrial Revolution. Then, ask them what general events they remember from history, social studies, literature, or other classes that they would add to the time line. Write these events on the board. Suggestions could be events such as the Declaration of Independence in 1776, the beginning of the U.S. Civil War in 1861, and the opening of the Panama Canal in 1914. Ask students how all events in the time line affected both science and society, including those you have added. Discuss any other scientific innovations, inventions, or discoveries that could be added to the time line.
Verbal

Writing in Science

Explanations will vary depending on which invention is chosen, but all students should correctly identify the simple machines involved in the invention's operation. Explanations should describe the proper sequence of events in the invention's motion and may mention input and output forces and distances.
Verbal, Logical

Go Online NSTA SciLinks

For: Links on mechanical advantage
Visit: www.SciLinks.org
Web Code: ccn-2143

Actual Mechanical Advantage The mechanical advantage determined by measuring the actual forces acting on a machine is the actual mechanical advantage. The **actual mechanical advantage** (AMA) equals the ratio of the output force to the input force.

Actual Mechanical Advantage

$$\text{Actual mechanical advantage} = \frac{\text{Output force}}{\text{Input force}}$$

A loading ramp is a machine used to move heavy items into a truck. For instance, a long inclined ramp decreases the input force needed to lift a refrigerator into a truck. The mechanical advantage of a ramp with a rough surface is less than that of a similar smooth ramp because a greater force is needed to overcome friction.

DK SCIENCE and History

Innovations of the Industrial Revolution

From the 1700s to the early 1900s, a stream of new machines and other inventions changed patterns of work and commerce forever.

Seed-free cotton collects here.
Waste material

COTTON GIN

Threads are interwoven here.

POWER LOOM

Chimney
Boiler

STEPHENSON'S ROCKET

1765 James Watt modifies the existing Newcomen steam engine to create a more efficient machine.

1793 Eli Whitney's cotton gin efficiently and quickly separates harvested cotton fiber from seeds. The process makes cotton manufacturing easier, and cotton farming profitable.

1807 The *Clermont*, Robert Fulton's river steamboat, makes its maiden voyage on the Hudson River.

1813 Francis Lowell and Paul Moody create the first power loom in America, based on an English design.

1829 Stephenson's Rocket, an early steam locomotive, wins a competition for locomotive speed in England.

1750 | 1775 | 1800 | 1825

Customize for English Language Learners

Use Personal Experience
ELL students can benefit by relating examples from their lives to material presented in the text. Encourage students to name machines they have used that increased mechanical advantage. You may review the examples of the nutcracker and the loading ramp. Students may also sketch an illustration or find a magazine photo of machines that increase mechanical advantage.

Ideal Mechanical Advantage What can be done to increase the actual mechanical advantage of a ramp? One way is to reduce the friction of the ramp. In fact, if any machine were frictionless, its mechanical advantage would be the maximum possible value. The **ideal mechanical advantage** (IMA) of a machine is the mechanical advantage in the absence of friction. **Because friction is always present, the actual mechanical advantage of a machine is always less than the ideal mechanical advantage.** Because friction reduces mechanical advantage, engineers often design machines that use low-friction materials and lubricants.

Reading Checkpoint *How does increased friction affect the actual mechanical advantage of a machine?*

Writing in Science

Explanatory Paragraph
Study the photo of one of the inventions shown in the time line. Write a paragraph in which you identify the simple machines used in the device and explain how these machines are used in the operation of the device.

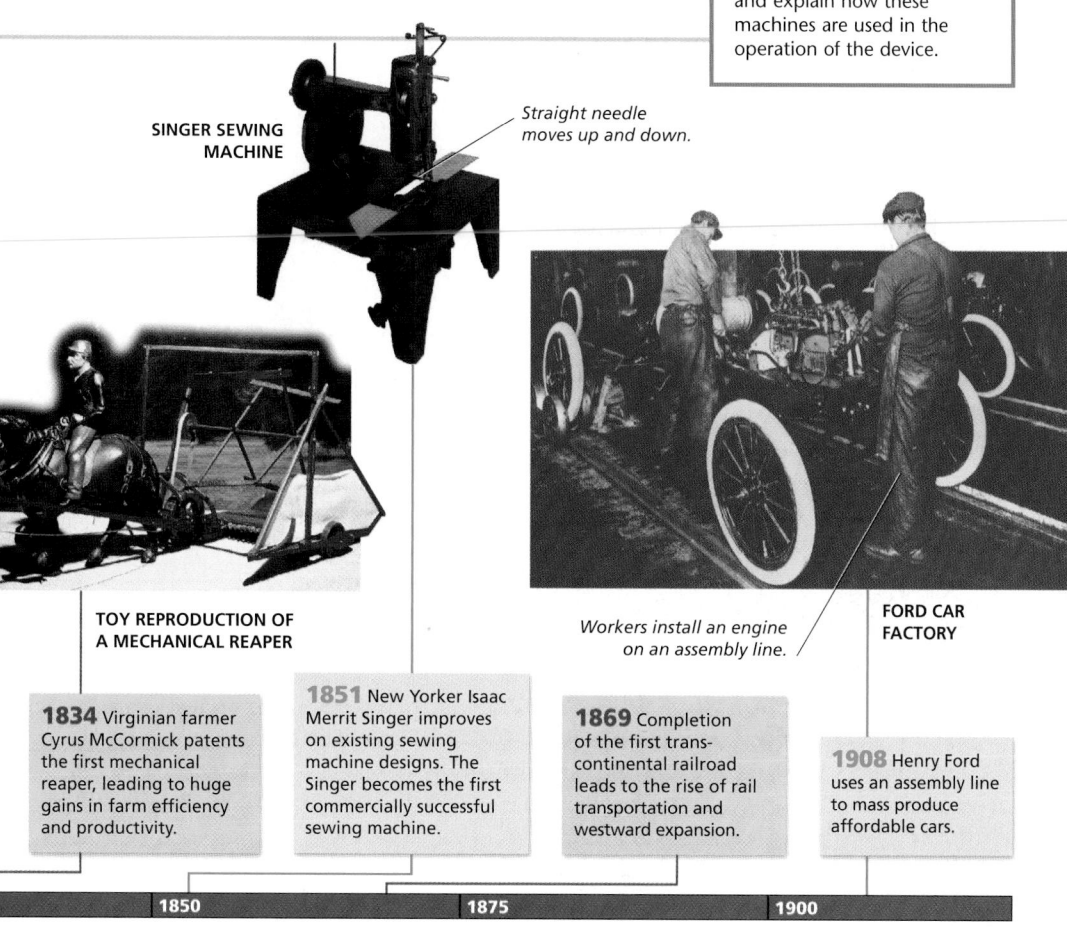

SINGER SEWING MACHINE

Straight needle moves up and down.

TOY REPRODUCTION OF A MECHANICAL REAPER

Workers install an engine on an assembly line.

FORD CAR FACTORY

1834 Virginian farmer Cyrus McCormick patents the first mechanical reaper, leading to huge gains in farm efficiency and productivity.

1851 New Yorker Isaac Merrit Singer improves on existing sewing machine designs. The Singer becomes the first commercially successful sewing machine.

1869 Completion of the first trans-continental railroad leads to the rise of rail transportation and westward expansion.

1908 Henry Ford uses an assembly line to mass produce affordable cars.

1850 1875 1900

Teacher Demo

Mechanical Advantage L2

Purpose Students learn about the concept of mechanical advantage.

Materials 1 pulley, 10-N spring scale, 500-g mass, string

Procedure Configure the pulley as shown in Figure 19A, p. 432. Attach the 500-g mass to one end of the string, and attach the spring scale to the other end of the string. Have students watch the scale as you use it to lift the mass. Show them that the force required equals the weight of the 500-g mass. Next, configure the pulley as shown in Figure 19B, p. 432. Demonstrate that the force needed to lift the 500-g mass is equal to half the weight of the mass. Explain to students that half the force was required because the mass is supported by two lengths of the string.

Expected Outcome Students should observe that the mechanical advantage using a fixed pulley is 1, and the mechanical advantage of a moveable pulley is 2.
Visual, Group

Build Science Skills L2

Designing Experiments Encourage students to work in teams to design and conduct experiments to test mechanical advantage. Suggest that they begin by brainstorming about possible simple machines they can test. For example, they could test a pair of pliers. Next, students should write a hypothesis and a plan for their experiment. All student plans should be approved by the teacher before they can be performed. Have students present their findings to the class.
Logical, Visual

Answer to . . .

Reading Checkpoint *Increased friction would decrease a machine's actual mechanical advantage.*

Calculating Mechanical Advantage

Quick Lab

Using Friction to Change Mechanical Advantage **L2**

Objective
After completing this activity, students will be able to
- explain how friction affects mechanical advantage and the force needed to perform work.

Address Misconceptions

Students may not think of friction as a force. Measuring a force that depends on friction can help to dispel this misconception.

Skills Focus **Measuring, Drawing Conclusions**

Prep Time 15 minutes

Advance Prep Provide smooth, splinter-free boards. Ask students to provide sneakers, slippers, and other footwear that vary in the friction they provide against a floor. All the shoes should be similar in weight.

Class Time 15 minutes

Safety Make certain that boards are free of rough or splintering edges.

Teaching Tips
- The spring scale must be pulled parallel to the board, as shown in the photo.

Ask, **How does friction affect the input force needed to accomplish a task?** *(Friction increases the force needed.)* **What work is accomplished by the force needed to overcome friction?** *(The additional force results in heating.)*

Expected Outcome Shoes with smoother soles will produce less friction, require less force, and provide more mechanical advantage.

Analyze and Conclude
1. Check students' answers.
2. Shoes with smoother soles that produce less friction will require less force and provide more mechanical advantage.
3. The shoe with the sole that provides the most traction required the most force. The additional force resulted in heating of the shoe and the ramp.
Visual, Logical, Group

Quick Lab

Using Friction to Change Mechanical Advantage

Materials

6 books, board, 3 different kinds of shoes, 1-kilogram mass, spring scale

Procedure

1. Create a stack of five books. Make a ramp by leaning the end of a board against the top of the stack. Place a sixth book at the bottom of the ramp to keep the board from sliding down off the stack of books.
2. Attach the spring scale to a shoe. Place the mass in the shoe. Suspend the shoe with the mass from the spring scale. Observe and record the force reading on the scale.
3. Place the shoe containing the mass on the bottom of the ramp as shown.
4. Use the spring scale to pull the shoe up the ramp at a slow constant speed. Observe and record the force reading on the spring scale.
5. **Predicting** Record your prediction of the force needed to pull the mass up the ramp in each of the other shoes. Investigate your predictions by repeating Steps 2 through 4 for each shoe.

Analyze and Conclude

1. **Calculating** Determine and record the actual mechanical advantage of the ramp for each shoe. To do this, divide the force measured in Step 2 by the force measured in Step 4.
2. **Comparing** Which shoe resulted in the largest mechanical advantage? The smallest mechanical advantage? Explain these results.
3. **Drawing Conclusions** Which shoe required the most force to pull it up the ramp? What did this additional force accomplish? Explain.

Figure 10 The cable supporting the gondola forms an inclined plane, a type of machine. The inclined plane is used to move people up to the top of the mountain.

Calculating Mechanical Advantage

Ideal mechanical advantage is easier to measure than actual mechanical advantage because it depends only on the locations of the forces and the distances over which they act. To calculate the ideal mechanical advantage of any machine, divide the input distance by the output distance. Remember that the effects of friction are neglected when calculating ideal mechanical advantage.

Ideal Mechanical Advantage

$$\text{Ideal mechanical advantage} = \frac{\text{Input distance}}{\text{Output distance}}$$

The gondola in Figure 10 makes use of the inclined plane formed by its supporting cable to more easily move people uphill. The increased horizontal distance (input distance) is greater than the vertical gain in height (output distance). Thus the inclined cable gives the gondola a mechanical advantage greater than 1.

Reading Checkpoint *What two quantities must you know in order to calculate ideal mechanical advantage?*

Math Skills

Calculating IMA

A woman drives her car up onto wheel ramps to perform some repairs. If she drives a distance of 1.8 meters along the ramp to raise the car 0.3 meter, what is the ideal mechanical advantage (IMA) of the wheel ramps?

1 Read and Understand

What information are you given?

Input distance = 1.8 m

Output distance = 0.3 m

2 Plan and Solve

What unknown are you trying to calculate?

IMA = ?

What formula contains the given quantities and the unknown?

$$\text{IMA} = \frac{\text{Input distance}}{\text{Output distance}}$$

Replace each variable with its known value and solve.

$$\text{IMA} = \frac{1.8\ \cancel{\text{m}}}{0.3\ \cancel{\text{m}}} = 6$$

3 Look Back and Check

Is your answer reasonable?

The IMA must be greater than 1 because the input distance is greater than the output distance. The calculated IMA of 6 seems reasonable.

Math Practice

1. A student working in a grocery store after school pushes several grocery carts together along a ramp. The ramp is 3 meters long and rises 0.5 meter. What is the ideal mechanical advantage of the ramp?
2. A construction worker moves a crowbar through a distance of 0.50 m to lift a load 0.05 m off of the ground. What is the IMA of the crowbar?
3. The IMA of a simple machine is 2.5. If the output distance of the machine is 1.0 m, what is the input distance?

Efficiency

Because some of the work input to a machine is always used to overcome friction, the work output of a machine is always less than the work input. The percentage of the work input that becomes work output is the **efficiency** of a machine. **Because there is always some friction, the efficiency of any machine is always less than 100 percent.**

Efficiency

$$\text{Efficiency} = \frac{\text{Work output}}{\text{Work input}} \times 100\%$$

Facts and Figures

Building the Egyptian Pyramids The mystery of how the pyramids of Giza were constructed still causes disagreement among scientists. The largest pyramid, known as the Great Pyramid, was originally about 147 m high. It was constructed using stone blocks, each having a mass of about 2200 kg. A prominent theory suggests that the ancient Egyptians built huge earthen ramps for hauling the blocks. However, the Egyptians would have needed very long ramps in order to do this. For example, a mechanical advantage of 20 would require ramps almost 3 km long.

Math Practice

Solutions L2

1. IMA = Input distance/Output distance; IMA = 3 m/0.5 m = 6
2. IMA = Input distance/Output distance; IMA = 0.50 m/0.05 m = 10
3. Input distance = (IMA)(Output distance); Input distance = (2.5)(1.0 m) = 2.5 m
Logical

For Extra Help L1

Write the formula for IMA on the board and review the algebra skills needed to solve the formula for any one of the three variables. **Logical**

Direct students to the **Math Skills** in the **Skills and Reference Handbook** at the end of the student text for additional help.

Additional Problems

1. If you exert 100 N on a jack to lift a 10,000 N car, what would be the jack's actual mechanical advantage? (AMA = Output force/Input force = 10,000 N/100 N = 100)
2. What is the ideal mechanical advantage of a 5-m-long ramp that rises 1 m off the ground at its end? (IMA = Input distance/Output distance = 5 m/1 m = 5)
Logical, Portfolio

Efficiency

Address Misconceptions L2

Some students may think that machines put out more work than people put in. In actuality, friction causes the work output of a machine to always be less than work input. Help students overcome this misconception by asking them to think about a hypothetical, perfect machine. Point out that even the slightest friction would decrease work output, and the efficiency would be less than 100%. Reinforce that although machines change forces, some of the input force is always lost to friction. **Logical**

Answer to . . .

Reading Checkpoint *You must know both the input distance and the output distance to calculate ideal mechanical advantage.*

Build Math Skills L1

Ratios and Proportions Reinforce the fact that no machine can be 100% efficient by having students relate that fact to the efficiency equation given on p. 425. Ask, **What is the maximum value the ratio (fraction) work output to work input can have?** *(The value must be < 1.)* **If a machine is 50% efficient, what is the value of the ratio (fraction) work output to work input?** *($\frac{1}{2}$)*
Logical
Direct students to the **Math Skills** in the **Skills and Reference Handbook** at the end of the student text for additional help.

3 ASSESS

Evaluate Understanding L2

Have students write a paragraph explaining ideal and actual mechanical advantage and how they are related to efficiency. Have students read their paragraph in class and ask the class to critique it.

Reteach L1

Bring in a nutcracker similar to the one in Figure 9 and use it to demonstrate the concept of mechanical advantage.

Math Practice

Solutions
8. Efficiency = (Work output/Work input) × 100% = (800 J/1000 J) × 100% = 80%
9. Efficiency = (Work output/Work input) × 100%, Work output = (Efficiency × Work input)/100% = (40% × 1000 J)/100% = 400 J

Interactive Textbook If your class subscribes to the Interactive Textbook, use it to review key concepts in Section 14.3.

Figure 11 The flow pattern of a smoke trail is analyzed by computers to determine the fluid friction forces (air resistance) acting on the vehicle. Engineers use these test data to optimize a vehicle's shape for maximum fuel efficiency.

Efficiency is usually expressed as a percentage. For example, if the efficiency of a machine is 75 percent, then you know that 75 percent of the work input becomes work output. If a machine requires 10.0 J of work input to operate, then the work output is 75% of 10.0 J.

$$\text{Work output} = \frac{\text{Work input} \times \text{Efficiency}}{100\%}$$

$$\text{Work output} = \frac{10.0\ \text{J} \times 75\%}{100\%} = 7.5\ \text{J}$$

Reducing friction increases the efficiency of a machine. Automobiles, for example, are designed so their wheels roll on bearings that contain many small steel rollers. Recall that rolling friction is less than sliding friction. Thus, the roller bearings reduce the friction of the rotating wheels. To further reduce the rolling friction, the roller bearings are also lubricated with grease.

As shown in Figure 11, the shapes of many cars are designed to minimize air resistance. The lower the air resistance, the more easily a car passes through the air. At highway speeds, more than 50% of the output work of the engine is used to overcome air resistance. Streamlining the car's body reduces the amount of work the engine must do to move the car at any speed.

Section 14.3 Assessment

Reviewing Concepts

1. Why is the actual mechanical advantage of a machine always less than its ideal mechanical advantage?
2. Why can no machine be 100% efficient?
3. You test a machine and find that it exerts a force of 5 N for each 1 N of force you exert operating the machine. What is the actual mechanical advantage of the machine?
4. How can two machines appear identical and yet not have the same actual mechanical advantage?
5. What information would you use to calculate the efficiency of a machine?

Critical Thinking

6. **Making Generalizations** When is the ideal mechanical advantage of a machine greater than 1?
7. **Applying Concepts** Suppose you are an inventor in 1900. You are constructing a bicycle of your own design. What could you do to ensure your bicycle efficiently changes the work input into forward motion?

Math Practice

8. You have just designed a machine that uses 1000 J of work from a motor for every 800 J of useful work the machine supplies. What is the efficiency of your machine?
9. If a machine has an efficiency of 40%, and you do 1000 J of work on the machine, what will be the work output of the machine?

Section 14.3 Assessment

1. The presence of friction results in the actual mechanical advantage of a machine always being less than its ideal mechanical advantage.
2. Because there is always some friction, the efficiency of any machine is always less than 100%.
3. Actual mechanical advantage = Output force/Input force = 5 N/1 N = 5
4. If the amount of friction acting on the machines differs, then the actual mechanical advantage of the machines will also differ.
5. Efficiency is calculated from work input and work output.
6. The IMA of a machine is greater than 1 whenever the output force is greater than the input force.
7. Answers will vary but should include the importance of keeping friction to a minimum.

14.4 Simple Machines

Reading Focus

Key Concepts

- What are the six types of simple machines?
- What determines the mechanical advantage of the six types of simple machines?

Vocabulary

- lever
- fulcrum
- input arm
- output arm
- wheel and axle
- inclined plane
- wedge
- screw
- pulley
- compound machine

Reading Strategy

Summarizing After reading the section on levers, complete the concept map below to organize what you know about first-class levers. Construct and complete similar concept maps for second- and third-class levers.

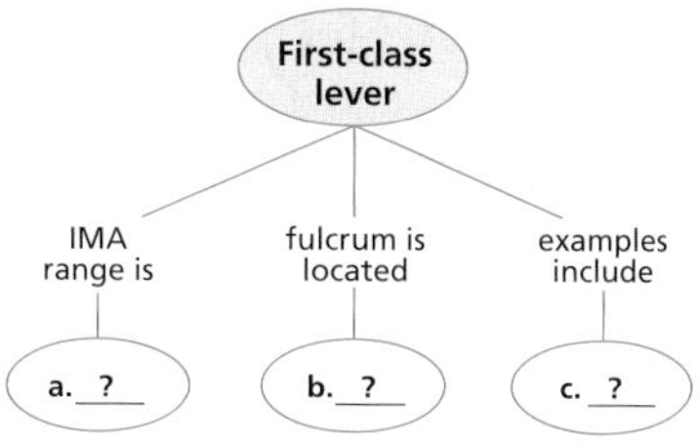

First-class lever
IMA range is
fulcrum is located
examples include
a. ?
b. ?
c. ?

What can you say about the workings of the strange contraption shown in Figure 12? Notice that a series of devices are arranged so that output of one device acts as the input of the next.

Many mechanical devices are combinations of two or more of the six different simple machines. **The six types of simple machines are the lever, the wheel and axle, the inclined plane, the wedge, the screw, and the pulley.** As you'll learn, you can tell a lot about a simple machine by its appearance. For several machines, you can even calculate the ideal mechanical advantage based solely on the locations of the forces involved.

Weekly Invention
Labor-Saving Auto Jack
WHEN REAR TIRE GOES FLAT, PULL STRING (A) AND FIRE PEANUT FROM CANNON (B) ~
ELEPHANT (C) SEES PEANUT AS IT LANDS ON PLATFORM (D)—HE WALKS DOWN RAMP AND HIS WEIGHT CAUSES HAND (E) TO JACK UP TIRE!
P.S. IF YOU GET A PUNCTURE IN FRONT TIRE, CALL A CAB.
A
B
C
D
E

Figure 12 The idea for this labor-saving auto jack comes from Rube Goldberg (1883–1970), a sculptor, author, and Pulitzer Prize-winning cartoonist.

Section Resources

Print

- ***Laboratory Manual,*** Investigations 14A and 14B
- ***Reading and Study Workbook With Math Support,*** Section 14.4
- ***Math Skills and Problem Solving Workbook,*** Section 14.4
- ***Transparencies,*** Section 14.4

Technology

- ***Interactive Textbook,*** Section 14.4
- ***Presentation Pro CD-ROM,*** Section 14.4
- ***Go Online,*** NSTA SciLinks, Simple machines

Section 14.4

1 FOCUS

Objectives

14.4.1 **Name, describe,** and **give an example** of each of the six types of simple machines.

14.4.2 **Describe** how to determine the ideal mechanical advantage of each type of simple machine.

14.4.3 **Define** and **identify** compound machines.

Reading Focus

Build Vocabulary L2

Concept Maps Have students expand on the concept maps used in the Reading Strategy by adding definitions for *fulcrum, IMA, input arm,* and *output arm* on the same page as the concept map.

Reading Strategy L2

a. less than 1 to greater than 1
b. between the input force and the output force **c.** seesaw, scissors, tongs

2 INSTRUCT

Address Misconceptions L2

Some students may think that the greater a machine's mechanical advantage, the faster the machine can complete the task. Remind students that other factors, such as friction, may influence whether the machine decreases the time required to complete a task. Also, reinforce that although the input force required by the machine may be decreased, there is a corresponding increase in the distance the force is applied over. Thus, decreased force does not necessarily mean the task can be completed more quickly.
Logical

Levers

Use Visuals L1

Figure 13 Point out to students the arrows designating input force and output force in the sketches. The locations of these arrows relative to the fulcrum illustrate the difference between the three classes of levers. Ask, **In which figure is the input force located between the fulcrum and the output force?** *(Figure 13C)* **What type of lever is this?** *(Third-class lever)* Then, help students relate each sketch to its accompanying photo.
Visual

Integrate Social Studies L2

For thousands of years, levers have been used for digging, cultivating land, and moving heavy objects. People in India and Egypt used levers to perform important tasks as long ago as 1500 B.C. Weighing scales that made use of levers were used around 5000 B.C. in Egypt. These scales functioned by placing weights at one end of a beam, and the object being weighed at the other end. This type of scale is similar to those used today in many doctors' offices.
Verbal

Use Community Resources L2

Arrange for a mechanical engineer to visit the classroom to discuss important ways in which levers (and other simple machines) are used in machinery. Ask the engineer to bring examples to class that illustrate how simple machines function. Encourage students, with the help of the engineer, to measure the dimensions of some of the simple machines brought to class and calculate mechanical advantage.
Interpersonal, Portfolio

Figure 13

Three Classes of Levers

A First-Class Lever

Output force
Input force
Fulcrum

The screwdriver is being used as a first-class lever with a mechanical advantage greater than 1. (Diagram is not drawn to scale.)

B Second-Class Lever

Input force
Output force
Fulcrum

The wheelbarrow has its output force located between the input force and the fulcrum. (Diagram is not drawn to scale.)

C Third-Class Lever

Fulcrum
Input force
Output force

The output distance of the broom is greater than the input distance the hands move through. (Diagram is not drawn to scale.)

Levers

Suppose you need to pry the lid off a can of paint. How can you make the task easier? A common solution is to slip the flat end of a screwdriver under the lid of the paint can and then to pry the lid off by pushing down on the screwdriver. This is an example of a **lever,** a rigid bar that is free to move around a fixed point. The fixed point the bar rotates around is the **fulcrum.** Levers are classified into three categories based on the locations of the input force, the output force, and the fulcrum.

The **input arm** of a lever is the distance between the input force and the fulcrum. The **output arm** is the distance between the output force and the fulcrum. **To calculate the ideal mechanical advantage of any lever, divide the input arm by the output arm.**

First-Class Levers Figure 13A shows a screwdriver being used as a first-class lever to open a paint can. The fulcrum in this case is actually the inside edge of the paint can. The position of the fulcrum identifies a first-class lever—the fulcrum of a first-class lever is always located between the input force and the output force.

Depending on the location of the fulcrum, the mechanical advantage of a first-class lever can be greater than 1, equal to 1, or less than 1. Examples of first-class levers include a seesaw, scissors, and tongs.

Customize for Inclusion Students

Gifted
Have students create a computer graphics presentation that compares the different classes of levers. The presentations should include photographs of various objects that are levers. Each object should have the input force, output force, and fulcrum labeled.

Second-Class Levers In a second-class lever the output force is located between the input force and the fulcrum. The wheelbarrow shown in Figure 13B is a second-class lever.

When you lift the handles of a wheelbarrow, it rotates around its fulcrum. Parts of the wheelbarrow near the fulcrum move through a smaller distance than those closer to the handle. Thus the input distance your hands move to lift the wheelbarrow is larger than the output distance the wheelbarrow moves to lift its load. The increased input distance means it takes less force from you to lift the load. The mechanical advantage of a second-class lever is always greater than 1.

Third-Class Lever The input force of a third-class lever is located between the fulcrum and the output force. As shown in Figure 13C, the output distance over which the third-class lever exerts its force is always larger than the input distance you move the lever through. Because of this, the mechanical advantage of a third-class lever is always less than 1. Baseball bats, hockey sticks, and golf clubs are all third-class levers.

Reading Checkpoint *Which classes of levers can have a mechanical advantage less than 1?*

Go Online NSTA SCiLINKS

For: Links on simple machines
Visit: www.SciLinks.org
Web Code: ccn-2144

Quick Lab

Comparing Lever Arms

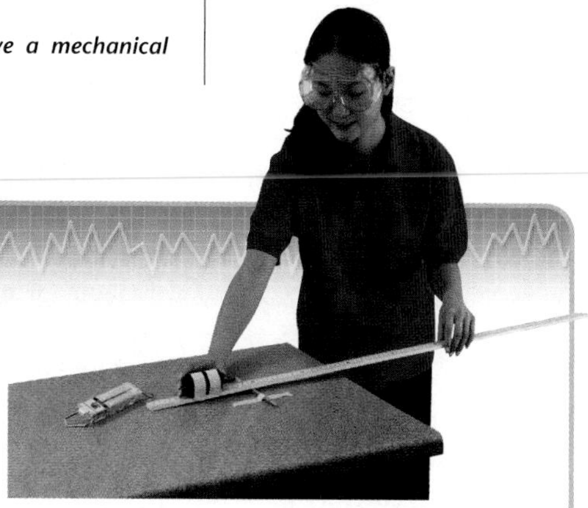

Materials

pencil, masking tape, spring scale, 500-g mass, meter stick

Procedure

1. Construct a data table with columns labeled Output Force, Output Arm, Input Force, Input Arm, and Mechanical Advantage.
2. Suspend the 500-g mass from the spring scale. Observe the force on the scale and record it as the output force.
3. Tape a pencil parallel to and near the edge of a table as shown. Tape the 500-g mass to the meter stick so it's centered on the 10-cm mark.
4. Position the 20-cm mark of the meter stick on the pencil as shown. Record the distance from the pencil to the center of the mass as the output arm.
5. Attach the spring scale at the 90-cm mark of the meter stick. Record the distance from the pencil to this mark as the input arm.
6. Pull straight down on the spring scale so the 500-g mass is lifted off of the table. Record the force on the spring scale as the input force.
7. Repeat Steps 5 and 6 with the spring scale located at the 80-cm, 70-cm, 60-cm, and 50-cm marks on the meter stick.

Analyze and Conclude

1. **Calculating** Calculate and record the mechanical advantage of the lever for each input arm.
2. **Using Graphs** Plot a graph of mechanical advantage versus the length of the input arm.
3. **Analyzing Data** How does changing the input arm affect the mechanical advantage?

Quick Lab

Comparing Lever Arms L2

Objective
After completing this activity, students will be able to
- describe the relationship between the input arm length and the mechanical advantage of a lever.

Skills Focus **Analyzing Data**

Prep Time 10 minutes

Class Time 20 minutes

Safety Students should wear safety goggles.

Teaching Tips
- Ask students to identify the fulcrum and the input and output arms and forces as they work.

Expected Outcome Graphs will indicate that the mechanical advantage is roughly proportional to the length of the input arm.

Analyze and Conclude
1. Student data should indicate that the mechanical advantage is roughly proportional to the length of the input arm.
2. Students should construct graphs that reflect a direct proportion between mechanical advantage and the length of the input arm.
3. The mechanical advantage is proportional to the length of the input arm.
Logical, Visual

For Enrichment L3

Have students determine and compare the ideal mechanical advantage of several tools that involve levers, such as scissors, metal-cutting shears, bolt cutters, a crowbar, and tire irons. **Logical, Visual**

Go Online NSTA SCiLINKS

Download a worksheet on simple machines for students to complete, and find additional teacher support from NSTA SciLinks.

Answer to . . .

Reading Checkpoint *First- and third-class levers can have a mechanical advantage less than 1.*

Wheel and Axle

Build Science Skills L2

Observing Have students first read the text about wheels and axles. Then ask, **Name some mechanical devices you have observed that you think use the wheel-and-axle principle.** *(Possible answers: cranks, wrenches, screwdrivers, clocks, bicycles, steering wheels and axles, automobile wheels with tires and their shafts, and any other rotating wheel and shaft run by a belt or by gears)*
Logical, Visual

Inclined Planes

Teacher Demo

Inclined Planes L2

Purpose Students gain appreciation for inclined-plane MA.

Materials long board, heavy box, small stepladder, spring scale

Procedure With a student's help, put one end of the board on the floor and the other end on the lowest step of the stepladder. Measure the height of that step from the floor, and record it on the board as "output distance." Measure the distance along the board, and record it on the board as "input distance." Calculate the IMA for the setup. *(IMA = input distance/output distance)* Now pull the box up along the board using the spring scale and record the force required. Repeat this process using two other steps on the ladder.

Ask students to compare the force required to the IMA of the board used as a ramp. *(The greater the IMA, the less force required.)* Then, write the equation $Fd = W$ on the board, and remind students that distance and force have an inverse relationship: as one increases the other decreases.

Expected Outcome The lowest step will give the largest mechanical advantage, because the divisor in the MA equation is the smallest. Students experience and comprehend that the greater the mechanical advantage, the less input force is needed to accomplish the work.
Visual, Group

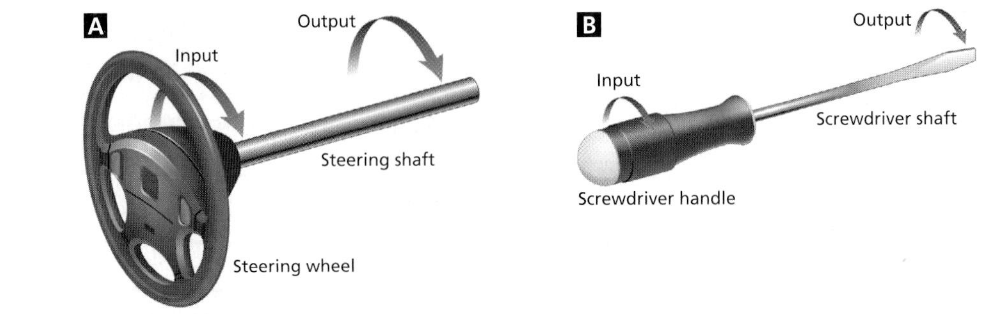
A
Input
Output
Steering shaft
Steering wheel
B
Input
Output
Screwdriver shaft
Screwdriver handle

Figure 14 A wheel and axle is a type of simple machine consisting of two disks or cylinders with different radii. **A** The steering mechanism used in a car is a wheel and axle. **B** When turning a screw with a screwdriver, the input force is applied to the larger-radius handle and the screw is turned by the smaller-radius shaft.

Wheel and Axle

Are you excited about "getting behind the wheel" of a car in a few years? To be scientifically correct, you'll actually be getting behind a wheel and axle, a type of simple machine. A **wheel and axle** is a simple machine that consists of two disks or cylinders, each one with a different radius. A steering wheel, as shown in Figure 14A, consists of a large wheel attached to a narrow axle.

The outer disk is the wheel and the inner cylinder is the axle. The wheel and the axle rotate together as a unit. In a car, the steering wheel the driver turns is the wheel, and the shaft that rotates with it is the axle.

Depending on the purpose of the machine, the input force can be exerted on the wheel or the axle. **To calculate the ideal mechanical advantage of the wheel and axle, divide the radius (or diameter) where the input force is exerted by the radius (or diameter) where the output force is exerted.** Though it may not appear so, a wheel and axle is similar to a lever, with the center of the two cylinders acting as the fulcrum.

A wheel and axle machine can have a mechanical advantage greater than 1 or less than 1. For a steering wheel, the driver applies force to the larger radius of the wheel. Because the input distance is larger than the output distance, a steering wheel has a mechanical advantage greater than 1.

Figure 15 This long and winding road acts like a type of simple machine known as an inclined plane. **Applying Concepts** *As the road becomes steeper, how does its mechanical advantage change?*

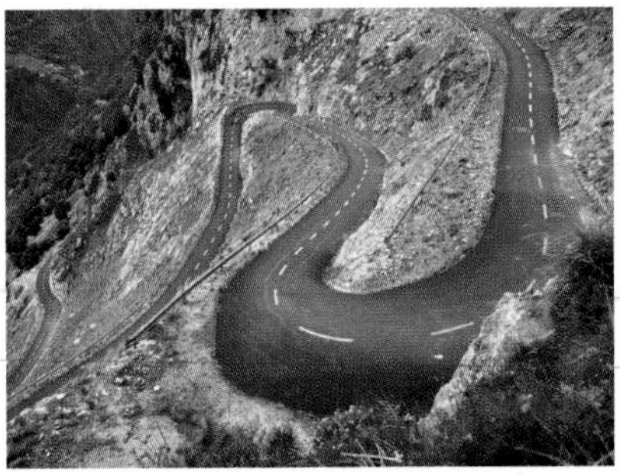

Inclined Planes

Imagine how hard it would be to walk straight up the side of a steep hill. By following the gentler slope of a winding trail, it is easier to walk up the hill. Why is that so? It is because the required input force is decreased when the input distance is greater than the output distance. Remember, however, that although it is easier to reach the top of a hill using the trail, you'll have to walk a longer distance. As shown in Figure 15, switchback roads are often used to make steep mountain passes easier for automobiles to climb.

Facts and Figures

The Earliest Wheels An early use of wheels is depicted in a rock drawing from ancient Sumeria, now part of southern Iraq. The pictograph, dating from 3500 B.C., shows wheels under a sled used for transporting objects.

430 Chapter 14

Gently sloping trails and roads are also a type of simple machine—an inclined plane. An **inclined plane** is a slanted surface along which a force moves an object to a different elevation. The ramp that makes a refrigerator easier to lift into a truck is an inclined plane. So are the wheelchair ramps used in front of buildings. The distance along the ramp is its input distance, whereas the change in height of the ramp is its output distance. **The ideal mechanical advantage of an inclined plane is the distance along the inclined plane divided by its change in height.** For example, a 6-meter-long ramp that gains 1 meter of height has an ideal mechanical advantage of 6.

Wedges and Screws

Wedges and screws are similar to inclined planes because both involve sloping surfaces. A key difference, however, is that wedges and screws have sloping surfaces that move.

Wedges A **wedge** is a V-shaped object whose sides are two inclined planes sloped toward each other. Figure 16 shows a type of wedge often used to split wood. A sledgehammer drives the wedge into the log. As the wedge is driven in, its sloping sides push the wood on either side a small distance apart. This gives a wedge a mechanical advantage greater than 1. The thinner a wedge is relative to its length, the less the wedge separates the wood fibers as it moves through the log. **A thin wedge of a given length has a greater ideal mechanical advantage than a thick wedge of the same length.** Other examples of wedges are a knife blade, which cuts best when its edge is sharp, and a zipper, which uses a wedge to separate and join the zipper's teeth.

Input Force
Output Force

Figure 16 The wedge being used to split the log consists of two inclined planes that slope toward each other. The inclined planes force the wood fibers apart as the wedge is driven into the log. **Relating Cause and Effect** ***What is the cause of the forces, exerted by the wedge, that split the log apart?***

Screws A **screw,** as shown in Figure 17, is an inclined plane wrapped around a cylinder. For two screws of the same length, the one whose threads are closer together moves forward less for each turn of the screw. **Screws with threads that are closer together have a greater ideal mechanical advantage.**

The thread on a screw is usually measured in threads per inch or threads per centimeter. A screw with fewer threads per inch takes fewer turns to drive into a piece of wood or other material. But the smaller mechanical advantage of the screw requires you to exert a greater input force in order to drive it in. Other common examples of the screw include nuts, which have the threads on the inside, and bolts.

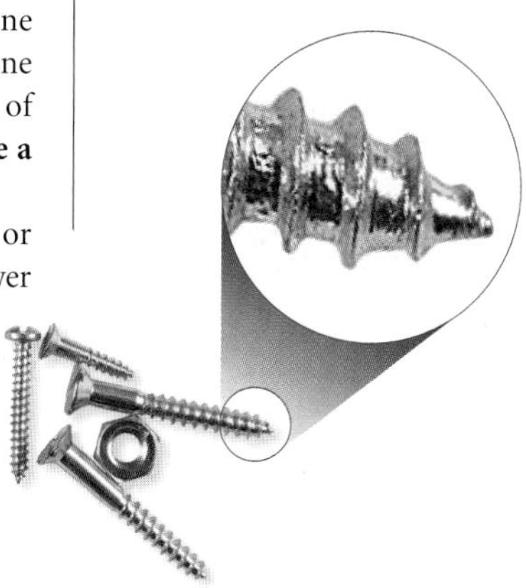

Figure 17 A screw is a simple machine made up of an inclined plane wrapped around a cylinder.

Reading Checkpoint *How is a screw similar to an inclined plane?*

Wedges and Screws

Build Reading Literacy L1

Use Prior Knowledge Refer to page **2D** in **Chapter 1,** which provides the guidelines for using prior knowledge.

Relate the content about wedges and screws to students' prior experiences. Some students will know from experience that screws with threads that are close together require less force to turn than those with threads that are farther apart. Tell students that the closely-spaced threads have longer inclined planes, giving them a greater mechanical advantage.
Logical, Visual

Use Visuals L1

Figure 16 Ask students to look at the wedge in Figure 16. Ask, **Why would a thin wedge give a greater MA than a thick wedge?** *(The length of the wedge is divided by the width of the opening to find the mechanical advantage. The smaller the number you divide by, the larger the answer will be.)*
Visual, Logical

Integrate History L2

In 1880, American inventor Herman Hollerith worked for the U.S. Census Bureau. Hollerith noted that the machines used to calculate census statistics were not sufficient for the task and invented the first census tabulator in 1884. The tabulator was a compound machine. (Compound machines will be covered on p. 435.) The machine was used for the 1890 census. It sorted and counted punched cards that were coded with census data. Encourage students to research how Hollerith's invention laid important groundwork for the creation of electronic computers. **Verbal**

FYI

Some screws, such as the one shown in Figure 17, make use of a wedge-shaped tip and wedge-faced threads. Most bolts and machine screws do not make use of these wedges.

Answer to . . .

Figure 15 *The mechanical advantage decreases as the road gets steeper.*

Figure 16 *The sledgehammer provides the input force needed to split the log apart.*

Reading Checkpoint *A screw is an inclined plane wrapped around a cylinder.*

Pulleys

Use Visuals

L1

Figure 19 Tell students to look at all three sketches in Figure 19. Ask, **What is the mechanical advantage of the pulley in 19A?** *(MA = 1)* **What is the MA in 19B?** *(MA = 2)* **What is the MA in 19C?** *(MA = 4)* Remind students that MA is the output force divided by the input force. Ask, **Does an MA of 4 mean that the pulley exerts 4 N of force for every 1 N of force put into it?** *(Yes)*
Visual, Logical

Build Science Skills

L2

Predicting Have students look at Figure 19C. Ask, **What would happen to the mechanical advantage of the pulley system if two more pulleys were added?** *(The mechanical advantage would change from 4 to 8 because each pulley adds two load-carrying rope sections to the system.)*
Logical, Visual

FYI

A pulley is an important tool used in rescue operations. Various types are used, depending on the emergency. Pulley systems (block and tackle) can be attached to fire trucks, the beams of buildings, or other anchor points and used to lower or raise objects or people. A type of pulley known as a snatch block has one sheave, or groove, and an opening on one side of the pulley's shell. A rope is threaded through the opening so that the pulley or the object can be pulled to the side. Other pulleys are attached to pivots to provide greater flexibility of movement.

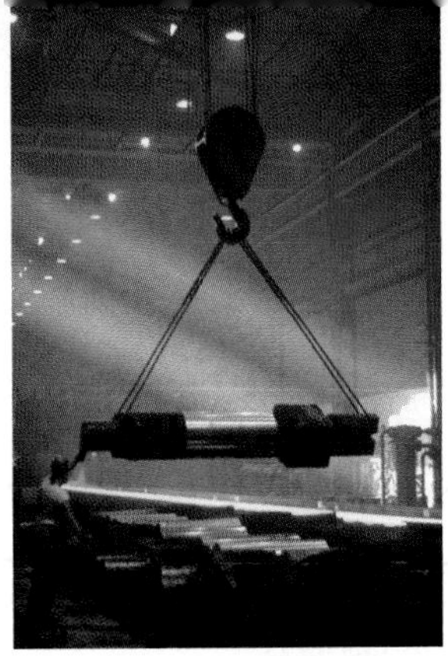

Figure 18 A worker watches as a pulley moves a large fabricated part through a factory. **Interpreting Photos** ***Based on what can be seen in the photograph, what is the approximate mechanical advantage of the pulley being used?***

Pulleys

A construction worker needs to lift a load of roofing materials onto the roof where he is working. Because it is easier and safer, he uses a pulley system to lift the load. The pulley system allows him to pull with less force than is needed to lift the load directly upward.

A **pulley** is a simple machine that consists of a rope that fits into a groove in a wheel. Pulleys produce an output force that is different in size, direction, or both, from that of the input force. **The ideal mechanical advantage of a pulley or pulley system is equal to the number of rope sections supporting the load being lifted.** Part of a pulley system is shown in Figure 18.

Fixed Pulleys A fixed pulley is a wheel attached in a fixed location. Fixed pulleys are only able to rotate in place. The direction of the exerted force is changed by a fixed pulley, but the size of the force is not. If you use the fixed pulley shown in Figure 19A, the rope or chain lifts the load up as far as you pull down the rope. Thus, the ideal mechanical advantage of a fixed pulley is always 1. Assuming friction forces are small, the input force and output force will be the same. Examples of fixed pulleys include the pulley at the top of a flagpole and the pulleys used to pull up blinds.

Figure 19

Three Types of Pulleys

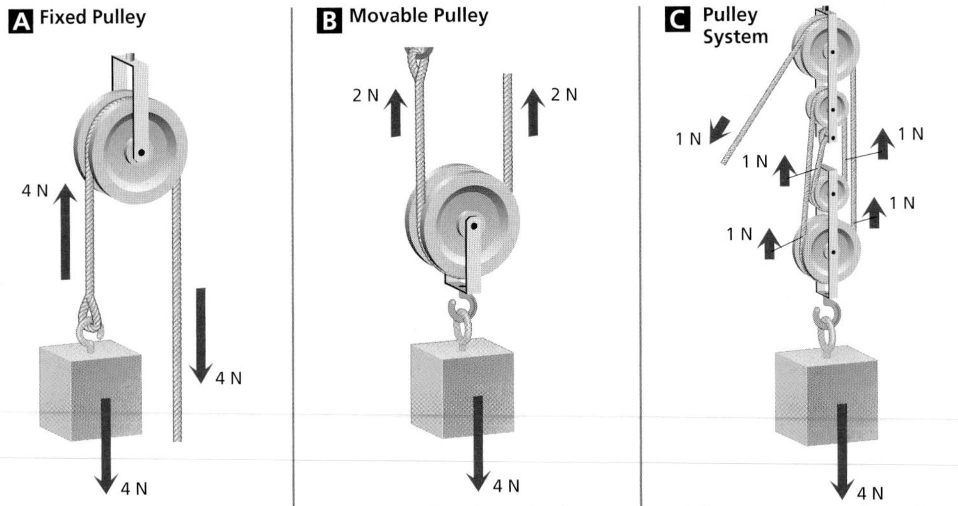
A Fixed Pulley
4 N
4 N
4 N
B Movable Pulley
2 N
2 N
4 N
C Pulley System
1 N
1 N
1 N
1 N
1 N
4 N

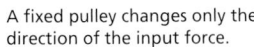

A fixed pulley changes only the direction of the input force.

Movable pulleys change both the direction and the size of the input force.

Pulley systems are made up of both fixed and movable pulleys.

Facts and Figures

Checks on Mechanical Advantage As the mechanical advantage of a pulley system increases, the distance that a load can be lifted per unit length of input distance moved through decreases proportionally. For example, a single pulley with an MA of 2 and a 44.5 N input force can lift an 89 N weight 15 cm when 30 cm of rope is pulled. By contrast, a double pulley system with twice the MA (4) and a 44.5 N input force can lift a 178 N weight. However, pulling 30 cm of rope will lift the weight only 7.5 cm (half the distance as the single pulley). Another limit to lifting ability is friction, which increases as more pulleys are added to the system. Friction reduces the ideal mechanical advantage to a lesser actual mechanical advantage.

Data Analysis

Pulley System Performance

A shipyard has many different pulleys and pulley systems in use. The pulleys are used to move large, heavy, fabricated ship sections through the manufacturing process. During an annual safety and performance inspection of three of the company's systems, a facility engineer collected the data shown in the graph. The data give the measured output forces for a range of given input forces.

1. **Using Graphs** What system requires the smallest input force to lift a 2500-N load?
2. **Calculating** Determine the actual mechanical advantage for each of the systems for a 2000-N input force.
3. **Applying Concepts** Which of the three systems shown in the graph consists of a single fixed pulley? Explain how you know.

Performance of Three Pulley Systems

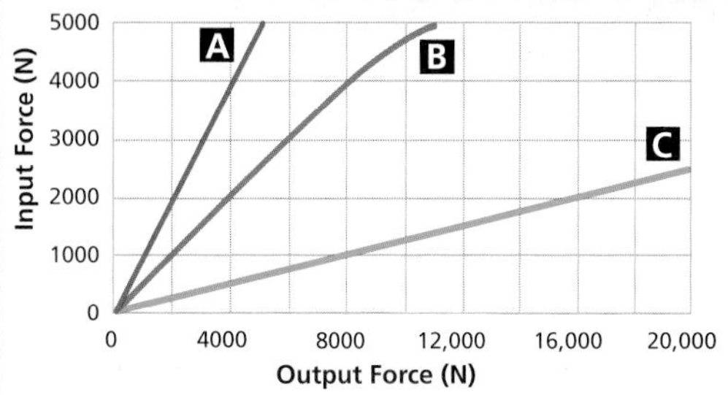

Input Force (N)
5000
4000
3000
2000
1000
0
0
4000
8000
12,000
16,000
20,000
Output Force (N)
A
B
C

4. **Inferring** Describe what happens to system B's output force as the input force increases above 4000 N. How does this affect the mechanical advantage of the system at higher loads? Offer a possible cause for the performance shown in the graph.
5. **Applying Concepts** Using the mechanical advantage value from Question 2, determine the output force of system A for an input force of 8000 N.

Movable Pulley As you can see in Figure 19B, a movable pulley is attached to the object being moved rather than to a fixed location. If you are pulling up on the rope on the right with a force of 10 newtons, then both sections of the rope pull up with the same force of 10 newtons. Thus, the pulley exerts a 20-newton output force from a 10-newton input force. The movable pulley in Figure 19B has a mechanical advantage of 2. Movable pulleys are used to reduce the input force needed to lift a heavy object. Sailors use movable pulleys to pull in sails, and skyscraper window washers stand on platforms suspended by movable pulleys.

Pulley System By combining fixed and movable pulleys into a pulley system, a large mechanical advantage can be achieved. The mechanical advantage that results depends on how the pulleys are arranged. The pulley system shown in Figure 19C has four segments of supporting rope. Ignoring friction, each one of the four segments supplies a lifting force as strong as the force you exert on the rope. Thus the output force is four times stronger than the input force. The pulley system has a mechanical advantage of 4. Using pulley systems in combination with other simple machines, large cranes are able to lift railroad locomotives!

Reading Checkpoint *How is it possible to achieve a large mechanical advantage using pulleys?*

Data Analysis

Pulley System Performance **L2**

Answers

1. C
2. A: AMA = Output force/input force = 2000 N/2000 N = 1; B: AMA = Output force/input force = 4000 N/2000 N = 2; C: AMA = Output force/input force = 16,000 N/2000 N = 8
3. System A could be a fixed pulley because it has a mechanical advantage of 1.
4. The output force begins to decrease relative to the required input force. At higher loads the mechanical advantage is decreased. Increased friction at higher loads could be a cause.
5. 8000 N

For Extra Help **L1**

Remind students that straight lines on a line graph indicate that the horizontal/vertical *(x/y)* ratio remains constant. Show that lines A and C remain straight and that B remains straight until it gets to 4000 N of input force.

For A, output force equals input force at any point. (A's MA = 1.) For B, output force is 2 times input force at any point until 4000 N. (B's MA = 2 for forces < 4000 N) For C, the output force is eight times the input force at any point. (C's MA = 8.)
Logical

Answer to . . .

Figure 18 *There appear to be seven rope segments supporting the load, thus the mechanical advantage of the pulley system is 7.*

Reading Checkpoint *By having several pulleys with numerous rope segments supporting the load, a large mechanical advantage can be achieved.*

DK HOW It Works

Elevator

L2

Around 1800, people used ropes made from plant fibers, along with steam and hydraulic power, to lift heavy loads. In 1853, Elisha Graves Otis introduced safety features that made it possible for passengers to ride in elevators. Electric motors were not used in elevator operation until the latter part of the nineteenth century.

Interpreting Diagrams It balances the weight of the elevator.
Visual

For Enrichment

L3

Students may research and give presentations to the class concerning new developments in various types of elevators. (*Hint:* Use "elevators" as an Internet search term to find helpful government sites on the subject.)
Verbal, Portfolio

DK HOW It Works

Elevator

Skyscrapers are vital to the economies of large cities with limited area for buildings. Stacking one floor on top of another produces a lot of floor space for offices. However, skyscrapers would be impractical without elevators. Elevators allow people to be transported hundreds of feet in the air. The cable elevator is the most popular type today. **Interpreting Diagrams** ***What is the purpose of the counterweight?***

Elevator motor
The elevator motor is needed to accelerate the car and compensate for the varying load.

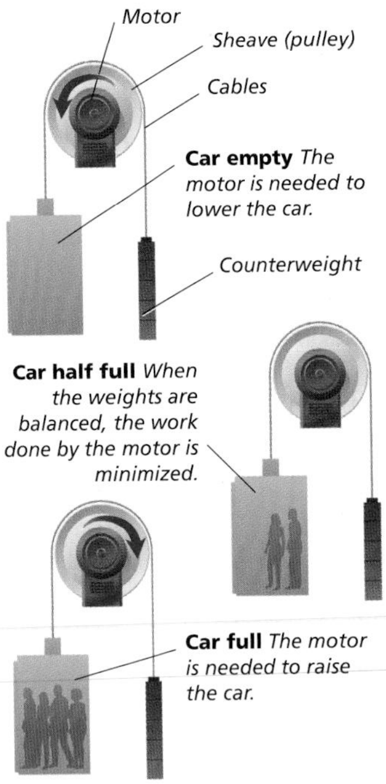
Motor
Sheave (pulley)
Cables
Car empty *The motor is needed to lower the car.*
Counterweight
Car half full *When the weights are balanced, the work done by the motor is minimized.*
Car full *The motor is needed to raise the car.*

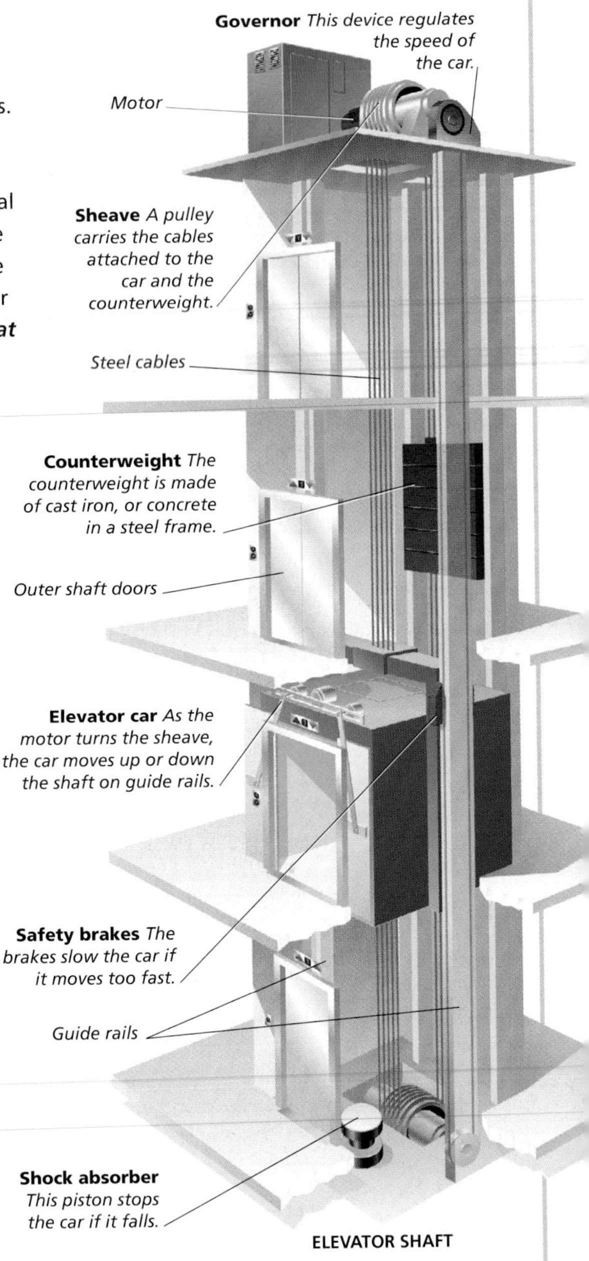
Governor *This device regulates the speed of the car.*
Motor
Sheave *A pulley carries the cables attached to the car and the counterweight.*
Steel cables
Counterweight *The counterweight is made of cast iron, or concrete in a steel frame.*
Outer shaft doors
Elevator car *As the motor turns the sheave, the car moves up or down the shaft on guide rails.*
Safety brakes *The brakes slow the car if it moves too fast.*
Guide rails
Shock absorber *This piston stops the car if it falls.*
ELEVATOR SHAFT

Compound Machines

Look closely at a pair of scissors. You'll notice they consist of a couple of simple machines. The edges are sharpened like wedges. The blades and the handles together function as levers. In fact, most of the machines you use every day are actually a combination of simple machines working together. A **compound machine** is a combination of two or more simple machines that operate together. Many familiar compound machines, such as a car, a washing machine, or a clock, are combinations of hundreds or thousands of simple machines.

Look at the complex mechanisms of the watch shown in Figure 20. How do these simple machines interact to accomplish their task of keeping time? In a compound machine, the output force of one simple machine becomes the input force for another machine. Inside the watch, a complex series of gears is designed so that one gear drives the next. Each gear acts as a continuous lever. These gears help keep accurate track of days, hours, minutes, and seconds.

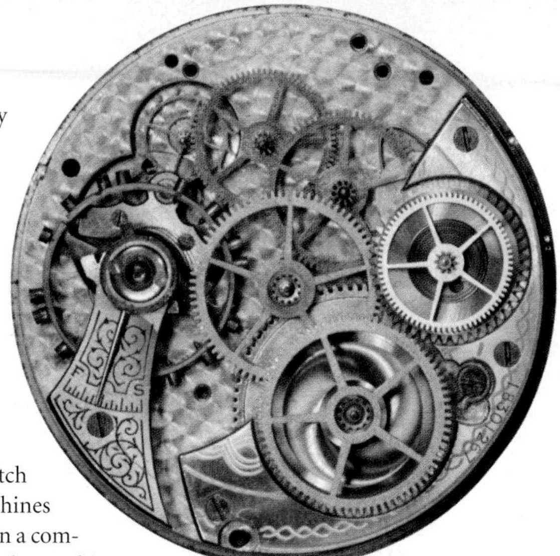

Figure 20 The complex workings of this watch consist of a series of machines. The output of one machine acts as the driving input for the next machine in the series.

Section 14.4 Assessment

Reviewing Concepts

1. Name six kinds of simple machines. Give an example of each.
2. Describe how to determine the ideal mechanical advantage of each type of simple machine.
3. How are the lever and the wheel and axle related to each other?
4. What is the ideal mechanical advantage of a ramp if its length is 4.0 m and its higher end is 0.5 m above its lower end?
5. Tightening a screw with a larger spacing between its threads requires fewer turns of a screwdriver than tightening a screw with smaller thread spacing. What is a disadvantage of the screw with larger thread spacing?
6. What class or classes of lever always have a mechanical advantage greater than 1?

Critical Thinking

7. **Making Generalizations** If you want to pry the lid off a paint can, will it require less force to use a long screwdriver or a short screwdriver? Explain.
8. **Calculating** When the pedals of a bicycle move through a distance of 0.25 m, the rear wheel of the bicycle moves 1.0 m. What is the ideal mechanical advantage of the bicycle?
9. **Applying Concepts** Explain why it could be useful for the mechanical advantage of a bicycle to be less than 1.

Writing in Science

Steps in a Process Write a paragraph describing the series of events that occur in the operation of a complex machine that you have used today.

Compound Machines

Use Visuals L1

Figure 20 Encourage students to look closely at the workings of the watch in Figure 20. Ask, **What type of simple machine do you see functioning as gears?** *(Wheel and axle)*
Visual

3 ASSESS

Evaluate Understanding L2

Ask students to identify simple machines in their everyday lives, making sure to name a machine for each of the six types. As a class, see how many different examples you can name.

Reteach L1

Bring in examples of each type of simple machine and demonstrate to the class how to use each one. Ask students to identify the input and output forces for each machine.

Writing in Science

Student paragraphs will vary, but should properly identify how the output of one machine acts as the input to the next machine in the series.

Interactive Textbook If your class subscribes to the Interactive Textbook, use it to review key concepts in Section 14.4.

Section 14.4 Assessment

1. Examples include: lever (crow bar), wheel and axle (screwdriver), inclined plane (ramp), wedge (axe), screw (machine screw), pulley (flag-raising pulley)
2. For each machine, IMA = Input distance/Output distance: lever (Input arm/Output arm), wheel and axle (Input radius/Output radius), inclined plane (Distance along plane/Change in height), wedge (Distance along wedge/Change in wedge thickness), screw (Distance screw is rotated through/Distance screw advances), pulley (Number of rope segments supporting the load)
3. A wheel and axle is like a lever in which the fulcrum is located at the center of the two concentric rotating cylinders.
4. IMA = Input distance/Output distance = 4.0 m/0.5 m = 8
5. The screw with the greater thread spacing has a smaller mechanical advantage, making it harder to turn.
6. Second-class levers
7. A long screwdriver requires less force to pry the lid off of the paint can because it has a longer input distance and a greater mechanical advantage.
8. IMA = Input distance/Output distance = 0.25 m/1 m = .25
9. A mechanical advantage less than 1 means the rider does not have to pedal much in order to make the bike travel a large distance over the ground.

CONCEPTS in Action

Gearing Up for Better Bikes L2

Background

Using gears to change speed is not a new idea. In a 1784 patent, James Watt described a "two-speed transmission." Although mechanics at that time were quite simple, wheels, axles, pulleys, and drive belts were already in use.

Until the mid-1800s, British patents were issued to agricultural machinery that had only two speeds. However, in the 1850s, patent requests began to arrive for three-speed systems.

Eventually, derailleur systems were developed. One of these systems is used on a bicycle with gears. As the text explains, "derailleurs are used to move the chain from one sprocket to another." Therefore, derailleurs make it possible for gears to change.

When comparing the output gear rotation to the input gear rotation, the ratio of the diameters or number of gear teeth of the gears determines the relative speeds. In other words, if the input gear has twice the diameter or twice the number of gear teeth of that of the output gear, the input gear would have half the speed of the output gear.

CONCEPTS in Action

Gearing Up for Better Bikes

The different gears on a bike allow you to change the distance the bike moves for each turn of the pedals. Cyclists use a low gear to climb hills and to accelerate. In a low gear, the chain connects a small front gear to a large back gear. A high gear is used for speed on level roads or for going downhill. In a high gear, the chain connects a large front gear to a small back gear.

Freewheels *These allow the bike to roll forward without the cyclist pedaling. When the bike is pedaled forward, a ratchet engages to drive the rear wheel.*
Sprockets, or cogs
Guide pulley
Chain *The chain needs to be the correct width to operate smoothly over the sprockets and chainwheels, and the correct length for optimum shifting performance.*
Rear derailleur *The guide pulley feeds the chain to the selected rear wheel sprocket. The tension pulley uses a spring to keep the entire chain assembly tight.*
Tension pulley

Derailleur Gears

The chain connecting the front chainwheel to the rear wheel sprocket serves as a belt to make the wheel turn faster than your feet. Wheel sprockets of various sizes are used to obtain different speeds. Derailleurs are used to move the chain from one sprocket to another.

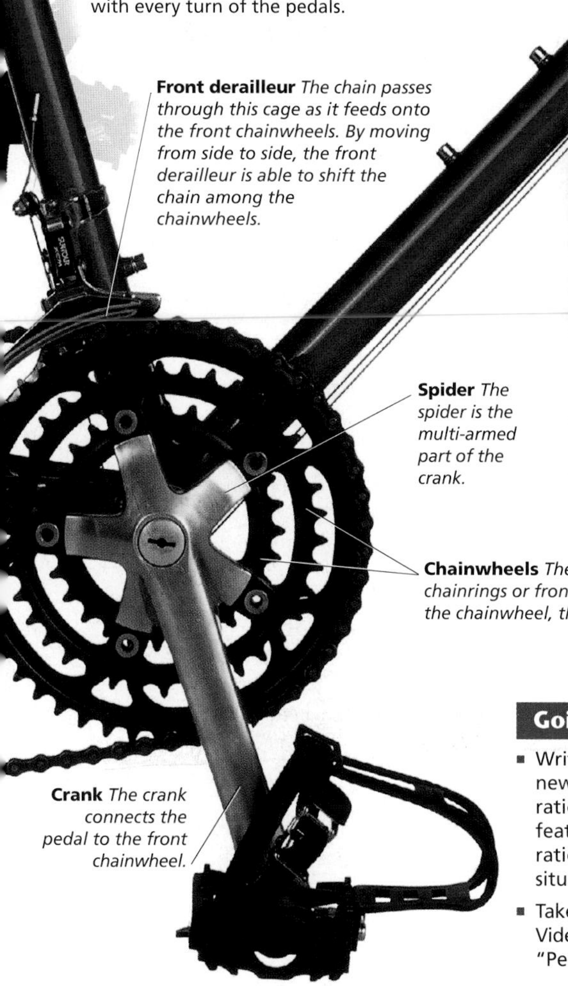

Bicycle gear ratios
The lowest gear ratio on the bike might be a front chainwheel with 13 teeth and a rear gear with 52 teeth. In this case, the rear wheel will turn once for every four turns of the chainwheel. Working up through the gears gradually changes this ratio, allowing the bike to travel farther with every turn of the pedals.

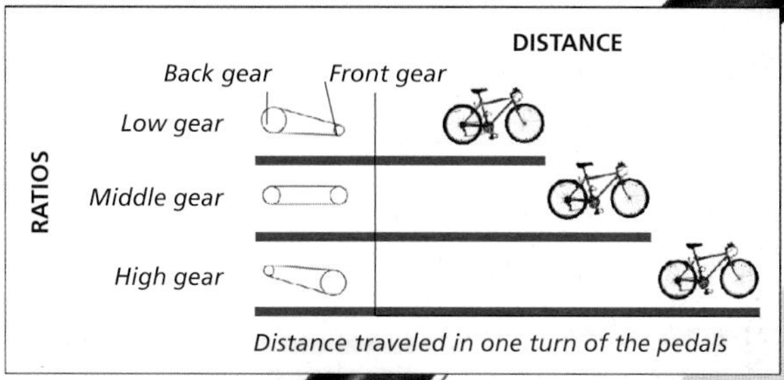
DISTANCE
Back gear
Front gear
Low gear
Middle gear
High gear
RATIOS
Distance traveled in one turn of the pedals

Front derailleur *The chain passes through this cage as it feeds onto the front chainwheels. By moving from side to side, the front derailleur is able to shift the chain among the chainwheels.*

Gearless bikes
Before the bicycle chain was invented, bicycle pedals were fixed to the axle of the front wheel. Today's track racers are also gearless (and brakeless), but only for the sake of fairness. This means that all of the bikes have the same mechanical advantage.

Spider *The spider is the multi-armed part of the crank.*

Chainwheels *These are also called chainrings or front sprockets. The larger the chainwheel, the higher the gear is.*

Crank *The crank connects the pedal to the front chainwheel.*

Going Further

- Write an instruction manual to explain how a new cyclist can make the best use of gear ratios. Use terms from this feature to describe which gear ratios are best for different situations and why.
- Take a Discovery Channel Video Field Trip by watching "Pedal Power."

Discovery Channel School
Video Field Trip

Build Science Skills L2

Inferring ACTIVITY

Purpose Students observe how the number of teeth on gears affects gear ratios.

Materials 1 bicycle with gears similar to that shown on pp. 436–437

Class Time 30 minutes

Procedure Point out the different gears on the bicycle. Have students work in pairs to count the number of teeth on each gear. One student can count as the other student records the numbers. Then, have the students calculate the different gear ratios for the bicycle and identify which is the highest and which is the lowest. Ask, **What does the gear ratio mean in terms of the pedal and wheel revolutions?** *(A high gear ratio means more wheel revolutions for each turn of the pedals.)* **Would a high or low gear ratio be good for climbing hills?** *(Low gear ratio)* **Would a high or low gear ratio be good for traveling along level ground?** *(High gear ratio)*

Safety Caution students to keep hands and clothing away from the chain and the gears.

Expected Outcome Students understand the relationship between number of gear teeth and gear ratios.
Logical, Visual

Going Further

Student instruction manuals will vary, but should discuss why low gears are good for hills and why high gears are good for flat roads. Manuals should also discuss how to properly select a high or low gear using the front and rear derailleurs.
Verbal, Logical

Discovery Channel School

Video Field Trip

Pedal Power

After students have viewed the Video Field Trip, ask them the following questions: **Why did early bicycle riders have to deal with being high above the ground while riding?** *(The early bicycles were designed with a very large front wheel, placing the rider high above the ground.)* **What properties must a bicycle frame have in order to be useful in long distance bicycle races such as the Tour de France?** *(The bicycle frame must be sturdy, reliable, and lightweight.)* **Why is the ability to move through the air with as little resistance from the wind as possible important to the movement of a racing bike?** *(Most of the energy the rider expends; 70% to 95% is used just to overcome wind.)* **In long distance bicycle races, one cyclist on the team may ride in front of another cyclist on the team for most of the race. How does this action help the second cyclist?** *(This reduces the amount of energy the second cyclist must expend to keep moving.)*

Consumer Lab

Determining Mechanical Advantage **L2**

Objectives After completing this activity, students will be able to
- determine the mechanical advantage of a pair of gears.
- select a pair of gears for a particular application on the basis of their mechanical advantage.

Skills Focus **Measuring, Calculating**

Prep Time 20 minutes

Advance Prep Each lab group will need a small board with two nails. A woodshop teacher can help you prepare the boards, which should be sanded smooth and splinter-free. Hammer two thin nails into each board approximately 15 cm apart so that the heads of the nails protrude approximately 3 to 4 cm above the surface to serve as axles for rotation of the interchangeable spools. Have students bring in enough bicycles to avoid delays as each group waits for a turn.

Class Time 55 minutes

Safety In Part B, make certain that students keep their hands out of the spokes and drive trains.

Teaching Tips
- In Step 4, tell students to measure the radii to the nearest tenth of a centimeter.
- In Step 5, you may need to show students that they can adjust the tension of the rubber band by wrapping it around the spools two or three times to ensure good traction. Tell students to round the number of revolutions to the nearest tenth of a revolution.
- In Step 9, tell students to measure the radii to the nearest tenth of a centimeter.
- In Step 10, show students how to hold the rear wheel off the floor so that they can hold the bicycle in place while shifting gears.
- In Step 12, the revolutions of the rear wheel can be more easily counted if students begin with the air valve at the bottom of the wheel.

Consumer Lab

Determining Mechanical Advantage

Many complex machines have an adjustable mechanical advantage. In this lab, you will learn how adjusting the mechanical advantage of a bicycle affects the bicycle's performance.

Pedal
Wheel

Problem
How does mechanical advantage affect the performance of a bicycle?

Materials
- board with two nails
- 4 thread spools, 3 with different diameters
- rubber band
- masking tape
- multispeed bicycle (one or more per class)
- meter stick
- thick leather glove

Skills
Measuring, Calculating

Procedure

Part A: Modeling the Mechanical Advantage of a Bicycle

1. On a separate sheet of paper, make a copy of the Data Table for part A.
2. Use a piece of masking tape to label each nail on the board. Label one nail *Pedals* and the other nail *Wheel.* To model the pedals and rear wheel of a bicycle, place a spool on each nail in the board and join the spools with a rubber band as shown.
3. Use a pencil to make a reference mark on the edge of each spool. These marks will help you observe the motion of the spools as they turn.
4. **Measuring** Use a ruler to measure the radius of each spool in your model. Record these measurements in your data table.
5. The pedal spool represents the pedals and the gears attached to them. The wheel spool represents the rear wheel and its gears. Using the reference marks, observe the wheel spool as you turn the pedal spool through five complete revolutions. Record the number of revolutions of the wheel spool in your data table.

Data Table: Part A

Pedal Spool Radius (cm)	Revolutions of Pedal Spool	Wheel Spool Radius (cm)	Revolutions of Wheel Spool	IMA
	5			
	5			
	5			

6. Replace the wheel spool with a spool of a different diameter. Repeat Steps 3 through 5 for each diameter of wheel spool.
7. **Calculating** The ideal mechanical advantage (IMA) of a bicycle is equal to the distance the pedals move divided by the distance the rear wheel moves. For your model,

$$\text{IMA} = \frac{5 \times \text{Pedal radius}}{\left(\begin{matrix}\text{Revolutions}\\ \text{of wheel}\end{matrix}\right) \times \left(\begin{matrix}\text{Wheel}\\ \text{radius}\end{matrix}\right)}$$

Calculate the mechanical advantage of each spool combination you used. Record these values in your data table.

Part B: Analyzing Bicycle Gears

Rear wheel radius
Pedal radius

8. On a separate sheet of paper, make a copy of the Data Table for part B.
9. **Measuring** Work in groups of three. Use a meter stick to measure the radius of the pedals and the rear wheel as shown. Record these measurements in your data table.
10. One person should hold the bicycle with its rear wheel slightly off the floor. While a second person turns the pedals, a third person should use the bicycle's gear shifters to place the chain on the smallest pedal gear and the largest rear wheel gear. CAUTION *Keep your hands out of the spokes, chain, and gears.*
11. One person should put on a heavy leather glove, while a second person holds the bicycle with its rear wheel slightly off the floor.
12. The third person should slowly turn the pedals through five complete revolutions. The person who is wearing the glove should gently hold the rear tire tread so that the wheel turns only as fast as the pedals force it to move. This person should also observe the position of the valve stem to count the number of revolutions of the rear wheel. Record the number of revolutions of the rear wheel in your data table.

Data Table: Part B

Size of Pedal Gear	Smallest	Smallest	Largest
Size of Rear Wheel Gear	Largest	Medium	Smallest
Pedal Radius (cm)			
Revolutions of Pedal	5	5	5
Rear Wheel Radius (cm)			
Revolutions of Rear Wheel			
IMA			

13. Repeat Steps 10 through 12, once using the smallest pedal gear and a mid-sized rear-wheel gear, and then again using the largest pedal gear and the smallest rear-wheel gear.
14. **Calculating** Use the equation in Step 7 to calculate the mechanical advantage of the bicycle for each gear combination you used. Record these values in your data table.

Analyze and Conclude

1. **Analyzing Data** Which combination of pedal and rear wheel gears provided the greatest mechanical advantage? The least advantage?
2. **Applying Concepts** To ride quickly on a level road, would you select a gear combination with a large mechanical advantage or a small one? Explain your answer.
3. **Drawing Conclusions** To decrease the force needed to ride a bicycle up a steep hill, would you select a gear combination with a large mechanical advantage or a small one? What size rear-wheel gear would you use to race on a flat road? Explain.

Go Online PHSchool.com

For: Data Sharing
Visit: PHSchool.com
Web Code: ccd-2140

Questioning Strategies Ask, **How do you measure the mechanical advantage of a wheel and axle?** *(The mechanical advantage of a wheel and axle is equal to the input radius divided by the output radius.)* **How would you measure the mechanical advantage of a bicycle?** *(The pedal radius divided by the rear wheel radius)* **When do you shift gears on a bicycle?** *(Gears are shifted when the effort required of the rider changes, for example when the rider begins to go up or down a hill.)* **How does shifting gears help you to ride a bicycle?** *(Varying the gear ratio enables the rider to exert the same force over a short distance for maximum power, or over a long distance for maximum speed.)*

Expected Outcome Increasing the size of the rear wheel gear relative to the pedal gear increases the mechanical advantage of the bicycle and reduces the distance the rear wheel moves for each turn of the pedals.

Sample Data The mechanical advantage of a typical multispeed bicycle gear train can vary from approximately 0.7 to 4.

Analyze and Conclude

1. The largest pedal gear and the smallest rear wheel gear provided the greatest mechanical advantage. The smallest pedal gear and the largest rear wheel gear provided the least mechanical advantage.
2. A large mechanical advantage would be best for riding quickly on a level road because it would produce the greatest number of turns of the rear wheel for each turn of the pedals.
3. A gear combination with a large mechanical advantage would be best for riding up a steep hill because it would exert the greatest force on the rear wheel. A small rear wheel gear would be best for racing on a flat road because it would cause the rear wheel to turn fastest and therefore cause the bicycle to move fastest. A large rear wheel gear would be best for uphill mountain biking because it would exert the greatest force on the rear wheel. **Logical**

Go Online PHSchool.com

Students should see that mechanical advantage is directly proportional to the radius of the pedal gear and inversely proportional to the radius of the rear wheel gear, but students' results will depend on their own data and the data on the site.

Work, Power, and Machines 439

Study Guide

Study Tip

Keep a Calendar
Encourage students to keep an assignment calendar and a "to do" list. Recommend that students take time each day to plan when they will work on each assignment, putting items from the "to do" list onto the calendar. Remind students to consider deadlines and to allow a realistic amount of time for each assignment.

Thinking Visually

a. watts
b. work
c. joules
d. force
e. newtons
f. meters

CHAPTER 14

Study Guide

14.1 Work and Power

Key Concepts

- Work = Force × Distance. Work is done on an object when a force acts in the same direction as the object moves.
- Power = Work ÷ Time. Power is the rate of doing work. Doing work faster requires more power.

Vocabulary

work, *p. 412*
joule, *p. 414*
power, *p. 414*
watt, *p. 415*
horsepower, *p. 416*

14.2 Work and Machines

Key Concepts

- Machines make work easier by changing the force needed, the direction of the force, or the distance over which the force acts.
- Work output (done by a machine) is always less than the work input (done on the machine).

Vocabulary

machine, *p. 417*
input force, *p. 419*
input distance, *p. 419*
work input, *p. 419*
output force, *p. 420*
output distance, *p. 420*
work output, *p. 420*

14.3 Mechanical Advantage and Efficiency

Key Concepts

- Friction is present in all machines. Because of friction, the actual mechanical advantage is always less than the ideal mechanical advantage.
- Actual mechanical advantage $= \frac{\text{Output force}}{\text{Input force}}$
- Ideal mechanical advantage $= \frac{\text{Input distance}}{\text{Output distance}}$
- Efficiency $= \frac{\text{Work output}}{\text{Work input}} \times 100\%$
- Because of friction, the efficiency of any machine is always less than 100 percent.

Vocabulary

mechanical advantage, *p. 421*
actual mechanical advantage, *p. 422*
ideal mechanical advantage, *p. 423*
efficiency, *p. 425*

14.4 Simple Machines

Key Concept

- The six types of simple machines are the lever, the wheel and axle, the inclined plane, the wedge, the screw, and the pulley.

Vocabulary

lever, *p. 428*
fulcrum, *p. 428*
input arm, *p. 428*
output arm, *p. 428*
wheel and axle, *p. 430*
inclined plane, *p. 431*
wedge, *p. 431*
screw, *p. 431*
pulley, *p. 432*
compound machine, *p. 435*

Thinking Visually

Concept Map Use information from the chapter to complete the concept map below.

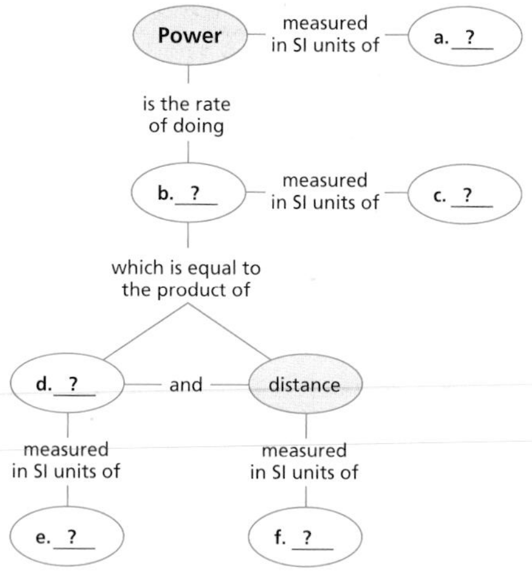

Power
measured in SI units of
a. ?
is the rate of doing
b. ?
measured in SI units of
c. ?
which is equal to the product of
d. ?
and
distance
measured in SI units of
measured in SI units of
e. ?
f. ?

Chapter Resources

Print
- ***Chapter and Unit Tests,*** Chapter 14 Test A and Test B
- ***Test Prep Resources,*** Chapter 14

Technology
- ***Computer Test Bank,*** Chapter Test 14
- ***Interactive Textbook,*** Chapter 14
- ***Go Online,*** PHSchool.com, Chapter 14

CHAPTER 14

Assessment

Interactive textbook with assessment at PHSchool.com iText

Reviewing Content

Choose the letter that best describes the question or completes the statement.

1. Work is the product of
   a. speed and force. b. force and distance.
   c. power and force. d. motion and force.

2. Which of the following is a unit of work?
   a. joule b. watt
   c. horsepower d. newton

3. How much work, in N•m, is done when a 10.0-N force moves an object 2.5 m?
   a. 0.25 N•m b. 2.5 N•m
   c. 25 N•m d. 4.0 N•m

4. Power is equal to work divided by
   a. time.
   b. force.
   c. distance.
   d. mechanical advantage.

5. If a machine has a mechanical advantage much larger than 1, its output force is
   a. much larger than its input force.
   b. much less than its input force.
   c. about the same as its input force.
   d. in the same direction as its input force.

6. How is the work output of a machine related to its work input?
   a. always less b. always greater
   c. always equal d. always zero

7. A machine with a 5-N input force and a 25-N output force has a mechanical advantage of
   a. 2. b. 5.
   c. 20. d. 125.

8. The mechanical advantage of a pulley system depends upon
   a. the diameter of the pulley wheels.
   b. the length of the rope.
   c. the number of sections of rope.
   d. the direction of the input force.

9. A screw can be considered a type of
   a. lever. b. inclined plane.
   c. pulley. d. compound machine.

10. Which is not a simple machine?
    a. wedge b. screw
    c. lever d. fulcrum

Understanding Concepts

11. Does an athlete do work on a trophy as she lifts it overhead? Is work done on the trophy as she stands still holding the trophy overhead? Explain.

12. What is the scientific definition of power?

Questions 13–15 refer to the illustration below.

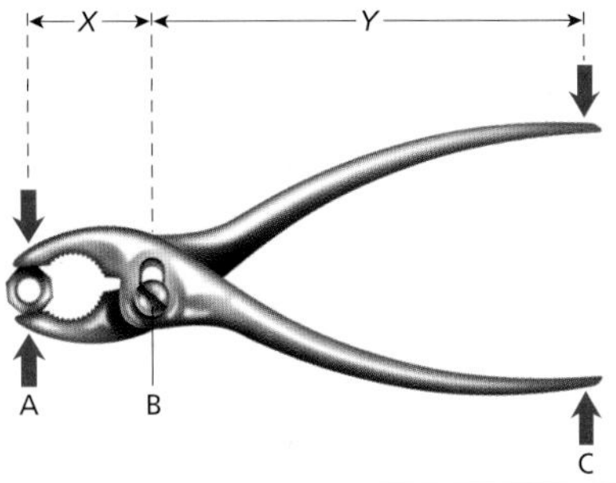

X
Y
A
B
C

13. Identify the position of the fulcrum.

14. If $X = 3.0$ cm and $Y = 15.0$ cm, what is the ideal mechanical advantage of the pliers?

15. If the output force is 50.0 N and the input force is 12.5 N, what is the actual mechanical advantage of the pliers?

16. A machine you designed has input and output arms that pivot around a fulcrum. When the input arm is pushed down through a short distance, the output arm moves down through a longer distance. Is the output force less than, equal to, or greater than the input force?

17. A machine has an efficiency of 60%. What happens to 60% of the work put into the machine, and what happens to the other 40%?

18. Identify the simple machines in a pair of scissors.

19. Why would you use a single fixed pulley to lift a box if the pulley's mechanical advantage is 1?

20. What determines the class of a lever?

21. Is a screw with fewer or more threads per centimeter easier to drive into a piece of wood? Explain.

Homework Guide

Section	Questions
14.1	1–4, 11–12, 28–29, 32
14.2	6, 16, 34
14.3	5, 7, 17, 27
14.4	8–10, 13–16, 18–26, 30–31, 33

Assessment

Interactive Textbook If your class subscribes to the Interactive Textbook, your students can go online to access an interactive version of the Student Edition and a self-test.

Reviewing Content

1. b 2. a 3. c
4. a 5. a 6. a
7. b 8. c 9. b
10. d

Understanding Concepts

11. Yes; no; Work is done as force is used to lift the trophy up through a distance. No work is done when a force is used to hold the trophy motionless overhead.
12. Power is the rate of doing work.
13. B
14. 5
15. 4
16. Less than
17. 60% of the work input becomes work output, while the other 40% of work input is lost to friction.
18. Two levers and two wedges
19. You would use a single fixed pulley whenever you want to change the required direction of input force.
20. The locations of the input force, output force, and fulcrum determine the class of a lever.
21. The greater the number of threads per centimeter a screw has, the greater its mechanical advantage is and the easier it is to drive in a piece of wood.

Critical Thinking

22. Examples will vary but may include a rowing oar, golf club, or baseball bat. Machines with a mechanical advantage less than 1 are useful when an increased output distance is advantageous.
23. The ramp has an IMA of 5 and the pulley system has an IMA of 4. The ramp requires a greater input distance but a smaller force to lift the load.
24. Friction occurs where objects are in contact as they move past one another. For a pulley, friction primarily occurs as the rope moves around the pulley and as the pulley rotates around its axis.
25. Steel bolt (screw), iron nail (wedge), screwdriver (wheel and axle)

Math Skills

26. 3
27. 29 N
28. 100 J
29. 60,000 J

Concepts in Action

30. A screwdriver used to drive a screw into a board acts as a wheel and axle. The length of the screwdriver does not affect its mechanical advantage when used as a wheel and axle. As a wheel and axle, the wide handle provides a greater mechanical advantage than the narrow handle does.
31. A faucet handle is a wheel and axle. The output force is larger than the input force.
32. Walking up the stairs requires 100 W of power, whereas the elevator requires 1000 W of power (both assuming 1000 N of force acting over a distance of 20 m). The elevator reaches the fifth floor 10 times faster than walking up the stairs.
33. Friction causes the work output to be less than the work input in each simple machine. The loss of useful work in each simple machine is additive, and sums to the total loss of useful work.
34. The lower gear increases the distance you pedal (increases input distance), but does so by making it easier to pedal (decreases input force needed to produce the output force required to climb the hill).

CHAPTER 14

Assessment *(continued)*

Critical Thinking

22 **Applying Concepts** Give an example of a useful machine you have seen that has a mechanical advantage less than 1. State how the machine is useful in terms of changing forces, distances, or directions.

23. **Comparing and Contrasting** A ramp 20 m long and 4 m high is used to lift a heavy box. A pulley system with 4 rope sections supporting the load is used to lift an identical box to a height of 4 m. Assume that friction can be ignored. Compare and contrast the input force and input distance needed to lift each box.

24. **Generalizing** In a pulley system, where is there likely to be friction that reduces the efficiency?

25. **Classifying** Classify each of these items as a type of simple machine: a steel bolt, an iron nail, and a screwdriver.

Math Skills

Use the illustration below to answer Questions 26 and 27.

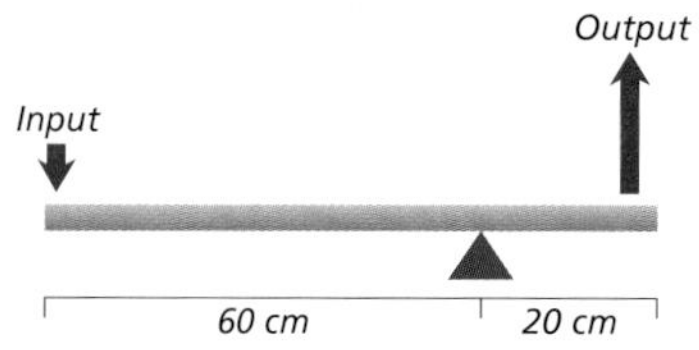
Output
Input
60 cm
20 cm

26. **Using Equations** The figure above shows the distances from the fulcrum to the input and output forces of a lever. Use these distances to calculate the ideal mechanical advantage of the lever.

27. **Using Equations** If the actual mechanical advantage is 2.9 and the input force is 10.0 N, what is the output force?

28. **Using Equations** How much work does a 50-N force do when lifting a box 2 meters?

29. **Calculating** How much work does a 1-kW motor do in one minute?

Concepts in Action

30. **Applying Concepts** Which would be the better choice for driving a screw into a board, a long screwdriver with a narrow handle, or a short screwdriver with a wide handle? Explain.

31. **Classifying** What type of simple machine is a water faucet handle? Is the output force larger or smaller than the input force?

32. **Comparing and Contrasting** A man weighing 1000 newtons walks from the ground floor to the fifth floor of a building, gaining 20 meters of height in 200 seconds. The next day he returns to the building, but this time uses the elevator. The elevator takes 20 seconds to reach the fifth floor. Compare and contrast the power and time requirements to reach the fifth floor.

33. **Relating Cause and Effect** In a bicycle, the output of one simple machine is the input of another. Why might you expect the efficiency of the bicycle to be less than the efficiency of each of the simple machines that is part of it?

34. **Writing in Science** Explain why you might shift into a lower gear to climb a hill on a bike. Your explanation should include a discussion of the input force and distance.

Performance-Based Assessment

Using Models Imagine you have a younger brother who weighs half as much as you do. Design a seesaw you could use together. Create a model of your seesaw design and label it to show the distances that you and your brother must sit from the fulcrum. Explain why you chose the fulcrum position as you did.

Go Online
PHSchool.com

For: Self-grading assessment
Visit: PHSchool.com
Web Code: cca-2140

Performance-Based Assessment

Student seesaw design will vary depending on the weights of the two people. Review student sketches for accuracy of fulcrum position. The product (Weight × Distance to fulcrum) should be the same on each side of the fulcrum.

Go Online
PHSchool.com

Your students can independently test their knowledge of the chapter and print out their test results for your files.

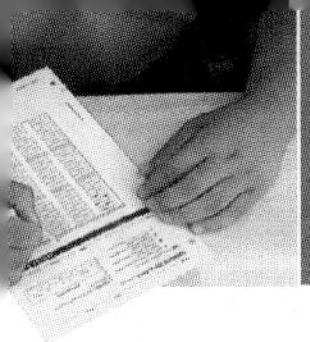

Standardized Test Prep

Test-Taking Tip

Questions with NEVER

Questions containing absolute negative qualifiers such as NEVER can be tricky. If the question lists statements, it helps to look at each statement and add NEVER just before the verb. For example, rephrase choice A below as "The input force NEVER equals the output force." Then try to find one example that disproves this statement. The input force and output force can be equal in a lever with the fulcrum in the center. Therefore, the statement is not true. Repeat this process for each choice until you find one that is true in all cases.

Which of the following is NEVER true?
(A) The input force equals the output force.
(B) The ideal mechanical advantage is 1.
(C) The actual mechanical advantage is 1.
(D) The efficiency is 100 percent.
(E) The efficiency is 50 percent.

(Answer: D)

Choose the letter that best answers the question or completes the statement.

1. An applied force acts upward on a moving wooden crate as shown below. Which of the following statements is TRUE?
   (A) The power used to move the crate is 150 W.
   (B) The force does no work on the crate.
   (C) The force does 150 J of work on the crate.
   (D) The force does 66 J of work on the crate.
   (E) The force accelerates the crate.

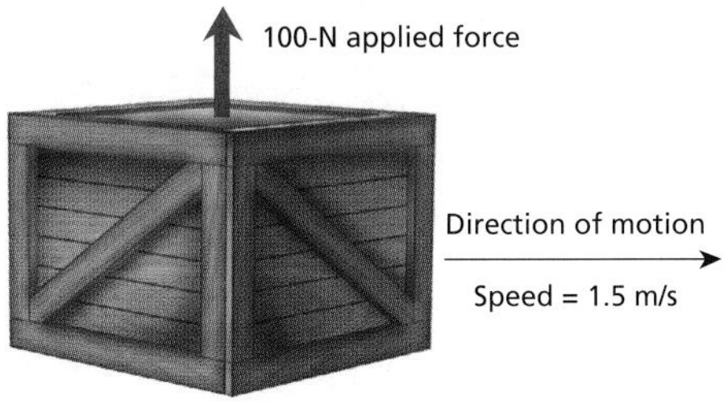
100-N applied force
Direction of motion
Speed = 1.5 m/s

2. A machine is used to lift boxes in a warehouse. Which change will increase the power of the machine?
   (A) decreasing the distance the boxes are lifted
   (B) decreasing the force exerted by the machine
   (C) increasing the friction inside the machine
   (D) decreasing the time it takes to lift the boxes
   (E) decreasing the work done by the machine

3. Which statement is NEVER true for a machine?
   (A) The output force is greater than the input force.
   (B) The machine changes a force.
   (C) The machine changes the direction of a force.
   (D) The machine changes the distance over which a force acts.
   (E) The work output equals the work input.

4. Which of the following will increase the actual mechanical advantage of a machine?
   (A) decreasing the output force
   (B) decreasing the friction
   (C) increasing the input force
   (D) decreasing the time required
   (E) increasing the time required

5. The diagram below represents a first-class lever. Which point(s) could be the fulcrum for this lever?
   (A) A only
   (B) B only
   (C) C only
   (D) A or C only
   (E) A, B, or C only

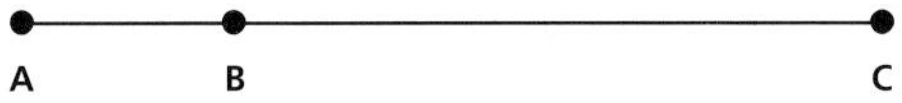
A
B
C

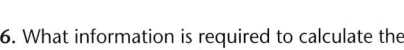

6. What information is required to calculate the actual mechanical advantage of a lever?
   (A) input arm and output arm
   (B) input distance and output distance
   (C) input force and output force
   (D) work input and work output
   (E) internal friction

Standardized Test Prep

1. B	**2.** D	**3.** E
4. B	**5.** B	**6.** C

CHAPTER 15

Planning Guide

Use these planning tools
Easy Planner
Teacher Express

SECTION OBJECTIVES	STANDARDS NATIONAL (See p. T18.)	STANDARDS STATE	ACTIVITIES and LABS
15.1 Energy and Its Forms, pp. 446–452 1 block or 2 periods **15.1.1 Describe** the relationship between work and energy. **15.1.2 Relate** kinetic energy to mass and speed and **calculate** these quantities. **15.1.3 Analyze** how potential energy is related to an object's position and **give examples** of gravitational and elastic potential energy. **15.1.4 Solve equations** that relate an object's gravitational potential energy to its mass and height. **15.1.5 Give examples** of the major forms of energy and **explain** how each is produced.	A-1, A-2, B-1, B-3, B-4, B-5, B-6		**SE** Inquiry Activity: How Can Energy Change Form? p. 445 L2 **SE** Quick Lab: Investigating Elastic Potential Energy, p. 450 L2 **TE** Teacher Demo: Burning a Peanut, p. 451 L2 **LM** Investigation 15A: Determining the Effect of Mass on Kinetic Energy L2
15.2 Energy Conversion and Conservation, pp. 453–459 1 block or 2 periods **15.2.1 Describe** conversions of energy from one form to another. **15.2.2 State** and **apply** the law of conservation of energy. **15.2.3 Analyze** how energy is conserved in conversions between kinetic energy and potential energy and **solve equations** that equate initial energy to final energy. **15.2.4 Describe** the relationship between energy and mass and **calculate** how much energy is equivalent to a given mass.	A-1, A-2, B-5, G-1, G-2, G-3		**SE** Quick Lab: Exploring Energy Conversion, p. 454 L2 **SE** Application Lab: Investigating a Spring Clip, p. 467 L2 **TE** Teacher Demo: Energy in a Pendulum, p. 456 L2 **LM** Investigation 15B: Determining the Kinetic Energy of a Pendulum L1
15.3 Energy Resources, pp. 462–466 1 block or 2 periods **15.3.1 Classify** energy resources as renewable or nonrenewable. **15.3.2 Evaluate** benefits and drawbacks of different energy sources. **15.3.3 Describe** ways to conserve energy resources.	A-1, A-2, B-5, D-1, F-2, F-3, F-4		**TE** Teacher Demo: Simple Solar Cell, p. 464 L2

Ability Levels

L1 For students who need additional help
L2 For all students
L3 For students who need to be challenged

Components

SE	Student Edition	**RSW**	Reading & Study Workbook	**CUT**	Chapter & Unit Tests	**T**	Transparencies
TE	Teacher's Edition	**MSPS**	Math Skills & Problem Solving Workbook	**CTB**	Computer Test Bank	**iT**	Interactive Textbook
LM	Laboratory Manual			**TP**	Test Prep Resources	**P**	Presentation Pro CD-ROM
PLM	Probeware Lab Manual			**DC**	Discovery Channel Videotapes & DVDs	**GO**	Internet Resources

RESOURCES PRINT and TECHNOLOGY		SECTION ASSESSMENT
RSW Section 15.1	L1	**SE** Section 15.1 Assessment, p. 452
RSW Math Skill	L2	**iT** Section 15.1
MSPS Section 15.1	L2	
T Chapter 15 Pretest	L2	
Section 15.1	L2	
P Chapter 15 Pretest	L2	
Section 15.1	L2	
NSTA SciLinks **GO** Potential and kinetic energy	L2	
PLM Lab 6: Investigating a Spring Clip	L2	**SE** Section 15.2 Assessment, p. 459
RSW Section 15.2	L1	**iT** Section 15.2
MSPS Section 15.2	L2	
Discovery Channel School **DC** Physics of Fun	L2	
T Section 15.2	L2	
P Section 15.2	L2	
NSTA SciLinks **GO** Energy	L2	
PHSchool.com **GO** Data sharing	L2	
RSW Section 15.3	L1	**SE** Section 15.3 Assessment, p. 466
MSPS Section 15.3	L2	**iT** Section 15.3
T Section 15.3	L2	
P Section 15.3	L2	
Science News **GO** Energy and energy resources	L2	

Go Online

Go online for these Internet resources.

PHSchool.com
Web Code: ccd-2150
Web Code: cca-2150

NSTA SciLinks
Web Code: ccn-2151
Web Code: ccn-2152

SCIENCE NEWS
Web Code: cce-2153

Materials for Activities and Labs

Quantities for each group

STUDENT EDITION

Inquiry Activity, p. 445
flashlight, solar calculator, wind-up toy; other items may be substituted if the three listed in the Procedure are not available. Alternatives include a wind-up alarm clock, electric alarm clock, jack-in-the-box, radio, or CD player.

Quick Lab, p. 450
basketball, tennis ball, meter stick

Quick Lab, p. 454
small steel ball of known mass, box lined with soft modeling clay, meter stick, graph paper

Application Lab, p. 467
clamp, spring clip, masking tape, metric ruler, 50-newton spring scale, graph paper

TEACHER'S EDITION

Teacher Demo, p. 451
peanut, paper clip, pliers, pan of water, matches, safety goggles

Teacher Demo, p. 456
pendulum bob and string, hook at top of board, chalk (or marker), level

Build Science Skills, p. 461
flexible track (like the bendable tracks used for toy cars), steel balls, books or wooden supports

Teacher Demo, p. 464
small solar array, small motor with fan, direct sunlight or bright light source

Chapter Assessment

CHAPTER ASSESSMENT

SE Chapter Assessment, pp. 469–470
CUT Chapter 15 Test A
Chapter 15 Test B
CTB Chapter 15
iT Chapter 15
PHSchool.com GO
Web Code: cca-2150

STANDARDIZED TEST PREP

SE Chapter 15, p. 471
TP Diagnose and Prescribe

Interactive Textbook

Interactive Textbook with assessment at PHSchool.com

CHAPTER 15 Before you teach

From the Author

Michael Wysession
Washington University

Big Ideas

Energy is continuously converting between many different forms. During these conversions, energy is never created or destroyed, and the total energy of a closed system is always constant. "The Conservation of Energy" is the underlying law of the universe.

Space and Time Most types of energy can be divided into two classes: energy of location (potential energy) and energy of motion (kinetic energy). Potential energy is the capacity to do work. An object can be given potential energy by moving it against an opposing force, like lifting it up against the force of gravity or pushing it into a compressing spring. Drop the object or release the spring, and work is done as the potential energy converts to kinetic energy.

Chemical energy can also be thought of as a kind of potential energy. Energy is required to bring atoms together to form chemical bonds. When these bonds are broken, energy is released.

Forces and Motion Kinetic energy is energy of motion. The most common type of KE is the motion of macroscopic objects. Kinetic energy is calculated as one half of the product of the mass of the object times the square of the object's velocity.

There are other forms of energy that involve motions, however. Thermal energy, or heat, is a measure of the vigor of motions of the atoms of a material. Electrical energy includes the motions of electrons through a conducting material. Electromagnetic energy involves the motion of electromagnetic waves (like light).

Matter and Energy As Einstein showed through the famous equation $E = mc^2$, mass is a form of energy. Because "c^2" is enormous, when mass is destroyed, it converts into a great deal of energy. Two types of nuclear energy, fission and fusion, can be used as sources of human energy needs. Nonrenewable energy sources are mined from the ground, and include uranium (nuclear fission), oil, gas, and coal. Renewable energy sources are derived from the sun, and include solar, wind, hydroelectric, and biomass.

Physics Refresher

Mechanical Energy 15.1

The total mechanical energy in a system is the sum of all kinetic energy and potential energy in the system. Kinetic energy is the energy that an object has due to its motion. Potential energy is the energy due to the relative position of objects in a system or due to the shape of an object (e.g., when an object is stretched or compressed).

The translational kinetic energy (kinetic energy due to motion in one direction) of an object is defined as follows:

Address Misconceptions

Students may mistakenly think that an object at rest has no energy. This is true of kinetic energy, but not of other forms of energy. For a strategy to overcome this misconception, see **Address Misconceptions** on **page 448.**

$$KE = \frac{1}{2}mv^2$$

In this equation, m is mass and v is velocity. Because the velocity is squared, kinetic energy is always positive. There are also other types of kinetic energy, such as vibrational kinetic energy.

Gravitational potential energy is the energy an object has due to its position in a gravitational field. Near Earth's surface, gravitational potential energy can be calculated with the following formula:

$$PE = mgh$$

In this equation, m is mass, g is the acceleration due to gravity, and h is the height relative to an arbitrary zero point.

Elastic potential energy is the energy an object has when it is stretched or compressed. It can also be the energy contained in a system of objects connected by a spring or springs.

Other Forms of Energy 15.1

The total mechanical energy of a system is the sum of kinetic energy and potential energy. However, the objects in a system may also contain energy that (ideally) does not play a role in the behavior of the system on a large scale. These forms of energy are called nonmechanical energy or internal energy. Many forms of internal energy turn out to be kinetic energy or potential energy when viewed at small scales.

Go Online PD LINKS NSTA

For: Teaching methods for energy
Visit: www.SciLinks.org/PDLinks
Web Code: ccn-1599

Energy Conversions 15.2

Energy often changes from one form to another. A classic example is the energy in a pendulum. When a pendulum bob is at its maximum displacement, the mechanical energy in the system is all in the form of gravitational potential energy. As the pendulum bob falls, the potential energy is converted to kinetic energy. When the pendulum bob swings through its lowest point, the mechanical energy in the system is all in the form of kinetic energy. As the pendulum bob rises on the other side, this kinetic energy is converted back to gravitational potential energy. Energy slowly escapes the system as it is converted to thermal energy (due to friction and air resistance).

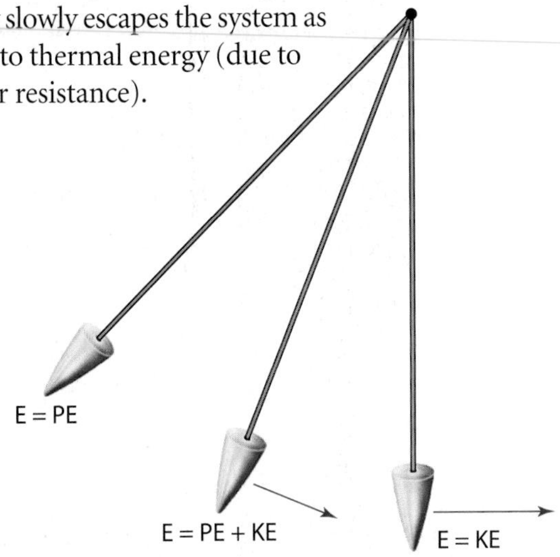
E = PE
E = PE + KE
E = KE

Conservation of Energy 15.2 and 15.3

Address Misconceptions

Students may incorrectly think that energy is truly lost in many energy transformations. In an energy transformation, some energy may be converted to non-mechanical forms of energy and some energy may leave the system, but total energy is always conserved. For a strategy to overcome this misconception, see **Address Misconceptions** on **page 457.**

The law of conservation of energy states that energy cannot be created or destroyed. Note that the law does not specify that *mechanical* energy is conserved, or that the total energy in a system is always the same. In all real systems, energy leaks out of the system, often in the form of thermal energy due to friction. Because mass and energy are equivalent, the law of conservation of energy is sometimes stated more generally as the law of conservation of mass and energy.

Energy conservation, as an economic or environmental issue, should not be confused with the law of conservation of energy. Energy conservation has to do with preservation of energy resources that can be harnessed and distributed for human use.

Build Reading Literacy

Directed Reading/Thinking Activity (DRTA)

Predict, Read, Confirm, Revise Predictions

Strategy Help students develop their own reading and thinking processes by setting their own purposes for reading. Select a section of Chapter 15 for students to read, such as Section 15.1, pp. 446–452. Before modeling the strategy with students, divide the targeted section into approximately four equal portions. Present the steps per the example below.

Example

1. Preview Tell students to survey the section by analyzing the titles, headings, visual elements, and boldfaced type. Have students also read the introductory and concluding paragraphs.
2. Predict/Generate Questions Ask students to hypothesize and predict what they will learn, and to formulate their own "teacher-type" questions to be answered; that is, of the type that a teacher might ask. List students' responses on the board.
3. Read/Evaluate and Refine Predictions Have students read a portion of the section. Pause afterward for students to evaluate their predictions. Discuss any answers they learned to their questions, and any prior misconceptions that were clarified. Ask students to formulate refined predictions and questions based on the new information.
4. Repeat the process for the remaining text portions.

See p. 455 for a script on how to use the directed reading/thinking activity (DRTA) strategy with students. For additional Build Reading Literacy strategies, see pp. 446 and 464.

ASSESS PRIOR KNOWLEDGE

Use the Chapter Pretest below to assess students' prior knowledge. As needed, review these Science Concepts and Math Skills with students.

Review Science Concepts

Section 15.1 Review the concept of work. Remind students that work equals force times distance, and that there must be movement in order for work to be done. Review speed and velocity. Review mass and weight. Remind students that weight is a force.

Section 15.2 Review friction and air resistance. Ask students to consider how friction affects the temperature of objects. Review conservation of momentum. Students will learn that energy is also a conserved quantity.

Section 15.3 Review power and efficiency. Remind students that work out does not always equal work in.

Review Math Skills

Scientific Notation, Multiplying and Dividing Exponents, Formulas and Equations, Squares and Square Roots Students will need these skills to solve problems involving kinetic energy, potential energy, and conservation of mechanical energy.

Direct students to the **Math Skills** in the **Skills and Reference Handbook** at the end of the student text.

CHAPTER 15 Energy

CONCEPTS in Action

How do science concepts apply to your world? Here are some questions you'll be able to answer after you read this chapter.

- Why does a basketball bounce higher than a slice of bread? *(Section 15.1)*
- How can an object from space damage a car? *(Section 15.2)*
- How do gulls use energy conversion to obtain food? *(Section 15.2)*
- How do pole vaulters propel themselves high into the air? *(Section 15.2)*
- How can the wind be used to light a bulb? *(Section 15.3)*

Discovery CHANNEL SCHOOL **Video Field Trip**

Physics of Fun

- How are roller coasters designed to be both safe and thrilling? *(page 460)*

This frog converts one form of energy into another as it leaps into the air. ▶

Chapter Pretest

1. How much work is done when a weightlifter holds a barbell motionless over his head? *(No work is done.)*
2. Calculate the work done on a 2-N mass when it is lifted to a height of 2 m. *(4 J)*
3. Calculate the average speed of a bicycle that travels 100 m in 20 s. *(5 m/s)*
4. Is weight a force? What is the formula for calculating weight? *(Yes. $W = mg$)*
5. How does the temperature of an object change when it is acted on by friction? *(The temperature increases.)*
6. True or False: In a closed system, the loss of momentum of one object equals the gain in momentum of another object. *(True)*
7. How is power related to work? *(Power is the rate at which work is done.)*
8. True or False: The amount of work done on a machine (work in) always equals the amount of work done by the machine (work out). *(False)*

Chapter Preview

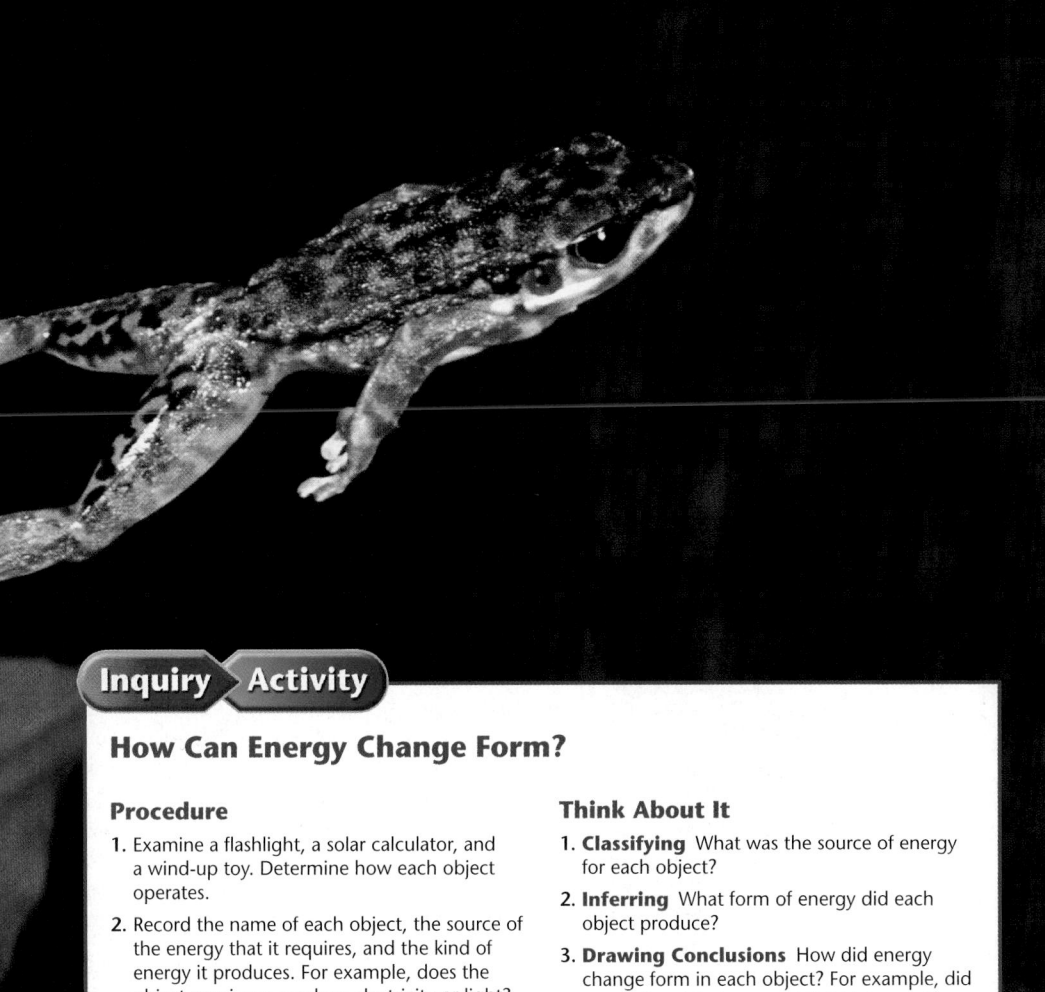

Inquiry Activity

How Can Energy Change Form?

Procedure

1. Examine a flashlight, a solar calculator, and a wind-up toy. Determine how each object operates.
2. Record the name of each object, the source of the energy that it requires, and the kind of energy it produces. For example, does the object require or produce electricity or light?

Think About It

1. **Classifying** What was the source of energy for each object?
2. **Inferring** What form of energy did each object produce?
3. **Drawing Conclusions** How did energy change form in each object? For example, did any of the objects convert light into another form of energy?

Energy 445

Discovery Channel School

Video Field Trip

Physics of Fun

Encourage students to view the Video Field Trip "Physics of Fun."

ENGAGE/EXPLORE

Inquiry Activity

How Can Energy Change Form? L2

Purpose
In this activity, students begin to distinguish different types of energy and describe energy transformations.

Skills Focus **Observing, Inferring, Formulating Hypotheses**

Prep Time 5 minutes

Materials
flashlight, solar calculator, wind-up toy; other items may be substituted if the three listed in the Procedure are not available.

Class Time 20 minutes

Teaching Tips

- Have students construct data tables to record their observations.
- Encourage students to focus on the idea that energy can change forms, rather than on correctly naming different types of energy.

Expected Outcome Students will identify the energy transformations that occur in various devices.

Think About It
1. At this stage, students may identify the energy source for a battery-powered flashlight as "electricity," rather than chemical energy. Similarly, they may fail to recognize that light, rather than "electricity," is the energy source for a solar calculator. A wind-up toy requires a form of mechanical energy (elastic potential energy).
2. At this stage, students can reasonably be expected to distinguish devices that produce mechanical, electrical, chemical energy, or light. A wind-up toy produces mechanical energy, a flashlight produces light, and a solar calculator produces electrical energy.
3. Students should be able to describe the energy conversion that each device performs. For example, they may say that a flashlight converts electrical energy to light, a wind-up toy converts one source of mechanical energy into another example of mechanical energy, and a solar calculator converts light into electrical energy.
Logical

1 FOCUS

Objectives

15.1.1 **Describe** the relationship between work and energy.

15.1.2 **Relate** kinetic energy to mass and speed and **calculate** these quantities.

15.1.3 **Analyze** how potential energy is related to an object's position and **give examples** of gravitational and elastic potential energy.

15.1.4 **Solve equations** that relate an object's gravitational potential energy to its mass and height.

15.1.5 **Give examples** of the major forms of energy and **explain** how each is produced.

Reading Focus

Build Vocabulary L2

Separating Compound Terms Almost all the vocabulary terms for this section are compound terms of the form *(modifier) + energy.* Have students list the word or words modifying *energy* in each term. For each modifier, have them state or guess its meaning. After they have read the section, have them check to see if their guesses were correct.

Reading Strategy L2

a. kinetic energy
b. the energy of motion
c. gravitational potential energy
d. elastic potential energy

2 INSTRUCT

Build Reading Literacy L1

Outline Refer to page **156D** in **Chapter 6,** which provides the guidelines for an outline.

Have students create an outline of the section (pp. 446–452). Outlines should follow the head structure used in the section. Major headings are shown in green, and subheadings are shown in blue. Ask, **Based on your outline, what are two types of potential energy?** *(Gravitational and elastic)* **List three other forms of energy.** *(Answers may include kinetic energy, mechanical energy, thermal energy, chemical energy, electrical energy, electromagnetic energy, or nuclear energy.)* **Verbal, Logical**

15.1 Energy and Its Forms

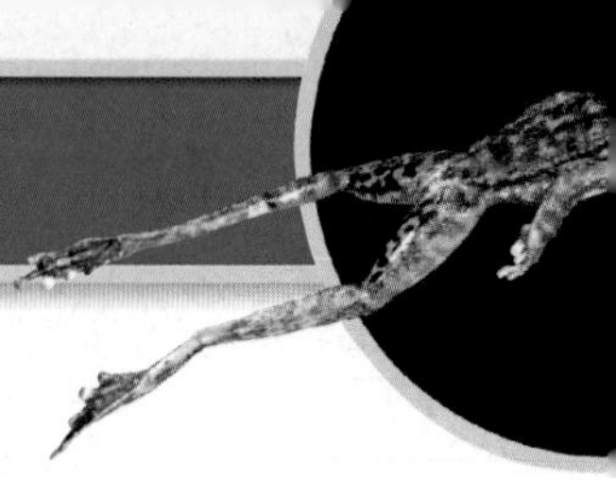

Reading Focus

Key Concepts

- How are energy and work related?
- What factors does the kinetic energy of an object depend on?
- How is gravitational potential energy determined?
- What are the major forms of energy?

Vocabulary

- energy
- kinetic energy
- potential energy
- gravitational potential energy
- elastic potential energy
- mechanical energy
- thermal energy
- chemical energy
- electrical energy
- electromagnetic energy
- nuclear energy

Reading Strategy

Building Vocabulary Copy the partially completed concept map below. Then, as you read, complete it with vocabulary terms and definitions from this section.

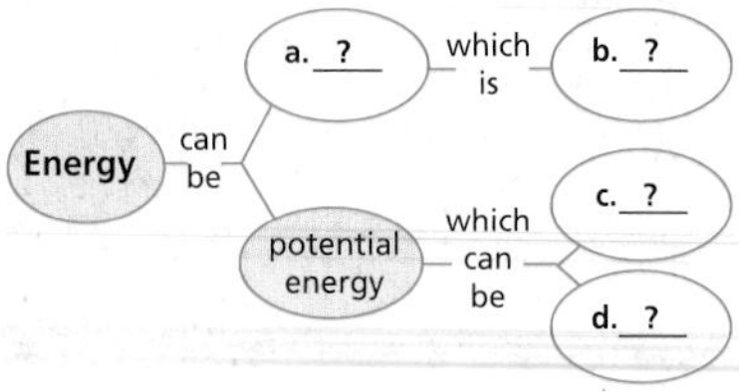
Energy
can be
a. ?
which is
b. ?
potential energy
which can be
c. ?
d. ?

The road that winds through the mountain valley was closed. Skiers were banned from the area. The sound of artillery fire echoed from the mountains. It seemed out of place in this picturesque scene of snow-covered peaks surrounding the valley. A moment of quiet followed the blast. Suddenly the snow broke loose with a menacing roar. Tumbling down the mountainside, the snow buried everything in its path. You can see in Figure 1 the enormous mass of accumulated snow that had hung above the valley. After the avalanche, the valley was quiet again. It is safe for skiers and hikers to return to the area.

This is the work of researchers at the Avalanche Control Section in Glacier National Park, Canada. These scientists monitor the snow as it builds up layer by layer on the park's upper peaks. They can predict when an avalanche is about to happen. With well-timed artillery shots, they make the avalanche happen at a time when the released energy cannot harm anyone.

Figure 1 In an avalanche, a mass of loose snow, soil, or rock suddenly gives way and slides down the side of a mountain.

Section Resources

Print
- ***Laboratory Manual,*** Investigation 15A
- ***Reading and Study Workbook With Math Support,*** Section 15.1 and **Math Skill:** Calculating Potential Energy
- ***Math Skills and Problem Solving Workbook,*** Section 15.1
- ***Transparencies,*** Chapter Pretest and Section 15.1

Technology
- ***Interactive Textbook,*** Section 15.1
- ***Presentation Pro CD-ROM,*** Chapter Pretest and Section 15.1
- ***Go Online,*** NSTA SciLinks, Potential and kinetic energy

Energy and Work

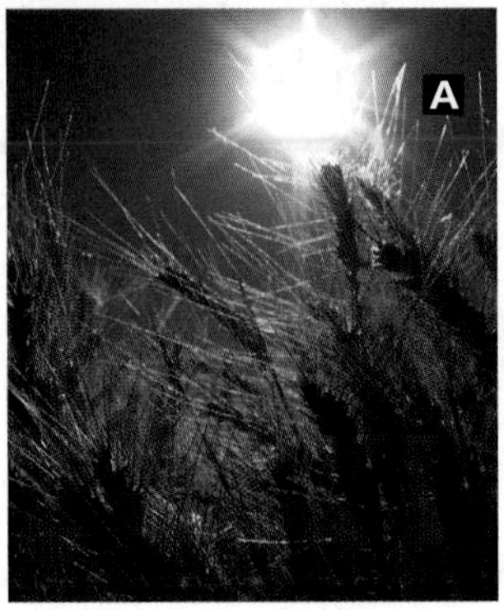
A

Where did the energy of the avalanche come from? Where did it go? Energy is known by the changes it causes. You can hear the roar of an avalanche and see the movement of the snow. Sound and motion are examples of energy in action. In order to define energy, you need to return to the definition of a related topic, work. Recall that work is done when a force moves an object through a distance. **Energy** is the ability to do work. In other words, energy is transferred by a force moving an object through a distance.

Work and energy are closely related. When work is done on an object, energy is transferred to that object. **Work is a transfer of energy.** Both work and energy are typically measured in joules (J). Recall that 1 joule equals 1 newton-meter, the work done when an object is moved 1 meter by a 1-newton force. Although energy can take many different forms, it can always be measured in joules.

Think about the work and energy involved in doing something as simple as carrying your backpack up a flight of stairs. You do work on the backpack by lifting it against the force of gravity. This work requires energy. The energy to do the work comes from your muscles. Your muscles receive energy from the food you eat. The energy contained in your food comes from plants that have used the energy of sunlight, or animals that have eaten such plants. Figure 2 shows some of the many forms of energy.

B

C

Figure 2 Energy has many different forms. **A** The sun gives off energy in the form of heat and light. **B** Plants convert sunlight into food that we can process and eat. **C** People convert food energy into muscle movement.
Applying Concepts ***How did the skiers in the photo obtain the energy to climb the mountain slope?***

Kinetic Energy

Many forms of energy can be classified into two general types: kinetic energy and potential energy. The energy of motion is called **kinetic energy.** The word kinetic comes from the Greek word *kinetos,* meaning "moving."

The kinetic energy of any moving object depends upon its mass and speed. To calculate the kinetic energy of an object in joules, multiply $\frac{1}{2}$ by the object's mass (m) in kilograms and the square of its speed (v) in meters per second.

Kinetic Energy

$$\text{Kinetic energy (KE)} = \frac{1}{2}mv^2$$

Notice that doubling the mass in the formula would double the kinetic energy. However, doubling the speed would quadruple the kinetic energy, since kinetic energy is proportional to the square of an object's speed.

Energy and Work

Integrate Health **L2**

The energy in food is often measured in units of Calories. A food Calorie is actually equal to 1 kcal, or 1000 conventional calories. A conventional calorie is the amount of energy required to raise the temperature of 1 gram of water by 1°C. A conventional calorie is equivalent to 4.184 J, so a food Calorie is equivalent to 4184 J.

The number of Calories in a food item is the amount of chemical energy that can be obtained from complete combustion of the food. Some of this energy is lost as heat when you digest the food. Once the food is digested, the remaining energy is available for you to do work. However, if you don't use all of the energy you get from food to do work, the extra energy may be stored in fat molecules. To avoid gaining fat, you should burn about as many food Calories as you take in each day.

Ask students, **If you ate a sandwich that provided you with a net of 450 Calories of energy, how many joules of work would you be able to do with that energy?** *(If your body were 100% efficient, about 1.9 million joules.)*

Ask students, **List some ways that your body uses energy.** *(Answers may include: walking, lifting, breathing, maintaining body temperature, digesting food)* You may also encourage students to look for Calorie information on food labels and to keep a tally of how many Calories they consume over the course of a day.
Logical, Portfolio

Kinetic Energy

Build Science Skills **L2**

Inferring Ask, **Why would tripling the speed at which a car is moving have a greater effect on its kinetic energy than tripling its mass?** *(Kinetic energy is directly proportional to mass, but it is proportional to the square of the object's speed. Tripling the mass would triple the kinetic energy, but tripling the velocity would make the kinetic energy nine times greater.)*
Logical

Customize for English Language Learners

Think-Pair-Share Have students work in pairs to think of examples of each of the forms of energy introduced in the section. If possible, group nonnative English speakers together with others who speak their native language. Encourage them to find examples from inside the classroom (for example, electromagnetic energy in the lights). Strengthen discussion skills by having students share their examples with the class.

Answer to . . .

Figure 2 *They obtained energy from the food they ate.*

Math Practice

L2

Solutions

1. $KE = \frac{1}{2}mv^2 =$ $(0.50)(70.0\ kg)(2.0\ m/s)^2 = 140\ J$
2. $KE = \frac{1}{2}mv^2 =$ $(0.50)(1400\ kg)(25\ m/s)^2 = 440{,}000\ J$
3. Rearranging the KE formula to solve for v, $v = \sqrt{2(KE)/m} = \sqrt{2(18{,}000\ J)/50.0\ kg} = 27\ m/s$

Logical

For Extra Help

L1

Help students solve for speed, *v*. First, show students how to rearrange the equation to solve for v^2.

$$v^2 = 2(KE)/m$$

Then, remind students to take the square root of both sides to solve for *v*.

$$v = \sqrt{2(KE)/m}$$

Logical

Direct students to the **Math Skills** in the **Skills and Reference Handbook** at the end of the student text for additional help.

Additional Problems

1. What is the kinetic energy of a 70.0-kg man walking at a speed of 4.0 m/s? *(560 J; Emphasize that this is not twice, but four times the kinetic energy of the man walking at 2 m/s in Math Practice Question 1.)*
2. A bicycle and rider with a combined mass of 150 kg have 300 J of kinetic energy while coasting. What is the speed of the bicycle? *(2 m/s)* **Logical, Portfolio**

Potential Energy

Address Misconceptions

L2

Students may think that an object at rest has no energy. While a stationary object has no kinetic energy, it can have potential energy if there are forces acting on it. If it is being pulled on by the force of gravity, it has gravitational potential energy. For example, a person sitting in a dunk tank has gravitational potential energy. As soon as the seat under him is pulled away, the force of gravity is no longer balanced by the opposing force of the seat. Work is done on the person as he falls into the water. Recall that energy is the ability to do work. Because work is done as the person falls, you know energy must have been present. **Logical**

Math Skills

Calculating Kinetic Energy

A 0.10-kilogram bird is flying at a constant speed of 8.0 m/s. What is the bird's kinetic energy?

1 Read and Understand

What information are you given?

Mass, $m = 0.10\ kg$ Speed, $v = 8.0\ m/s$

What unknown are you trying to calculate?

Kinetic energy of the bird, KE

2 Plan and Solve

What equation contains the given quantities and the unknown?

$$KE = \frac{1}{2}mv^2$$

Substitute the known values in the formula for KE.

$$KE = \frac{1}{2}(0.10\ kg)(8.0\ m/s)^2$$
$$= 3.2\ kg{\cdot}m^2/s^2 = 3.2\ J$$

3 Look Back and Check

Is your answer reasonable?

It seems reasonable because the bird has a low mass, so it would not have much kinetic energy.

Math Practice

1. A 70.0-kilogram man is walking at a speed of 2.0 m/s. What is his kinetic energy?
2. A 1400-kilogram car is moving at a speed of 25 m/s. How much kinetic energy does the car have?
3. A 50.0-kilogram cheetah has a kinetic energy of 18,000 J. How fast is the cheetah running? (*Hint:* Rearrange the equation to solve for *v*.)

Figure 3 When this musician pulls the string of her cello to one side, the string is stretched and gains potential energy.

Potential Energy

Potential energy is energy that is stored as a result of position or shape. The musician in Figure 3 adds energy to the cello string by plucking it. The energy is stored in the stretched string when the musician pulls it to one side. Then she releases the string and allows it to vibrate. The stored energy is converted into kinetic energy. You can also store energy just by picking up a book and holding it in the air. Let go of the book and that stored energy will turn into the kinetic energy of motion as the book falls to the floor. Plucking a string and lifting a book are two examples of stored energy—energy with the potential to do work. Two forms of potential energy are gravitational potential energy and elastic potential energy.

Gravitational Potential Energy

When you lift your gym bag up to the top seat of the bleachers, you do work to increase the potential energy of your bag. Potential energy that depends upon an object's height is called **gravitational potential energy.** This type of potential energy increases when an object is raised to a higher level.

The diver shown in Figure 4 is standing motionless at the end of a diving board, so she has no kinetic energy. But she does have energy—gravitational potential energy. She gained this potential energy by doing work—by climbing up the steps to the diving board. As always, the work done equals force (her weight) multiplied by distance (the height she climbs). You can use this work to calculate how much potential energy is gained.

An object's gravitational potential energy depends on its mass, its height, and the acceleration due to gravity. The gravitational potential energy an object gains is equal to its weight (mg) multiplied by its height (h).

Gravitational Potential Energy

$$\text{Potential energy (PE)} = mgh$$

To calculate gravitational potential energy in joules, the mass of the object is expressed in kilograms and the height of the object is expressed in meters. The acceleration due to gravity, g, has a value in SI units of 9.8 m/s^2 on Earth. Note that height is measured from the ground or floor or some other reference level. Therefore, gravitational potential energy is measured relative to that same reference level.

Gravitational potential energy is directly related to the mass of the object and its height relative to a reference level. Thus, doubling either the mass of the object or its height doubles its gravitational potential energy.

Suppose the diver at the top of a 10.0-meter-high diving platform has a mass of 50.0 kilograms. You can calculate her potential energy relative to the ground as follows.

$$\begin{aligned} PE &= mgh \\ &= (50.0\ \text{kg})(9.8\ \text{m/s}^2)(10.0\ \text{m}) \\ &= 4900\ \text{kg}\cdot\text{m}^2/\text{s}^2 = 4900\ \text{J} \end{aligned}$$

If, instead, the diver was standing on the ground, her height above the ground would be zero. Therefore, her gravitational potential energy relative to the ground would also be zero.

Reading Checkpoint *What is gravitational potential energy?*

Figure 4 This diver has gravitational potential energy as she stands at the end of a diving board. **Predicting** ***How would the diver's potential energy change if she stood on a platform twice as high as the one shown in the photo?***

Go Online NSTA SCILINKS

For: Links on potential and kinetic energy
Visit: www.SciLinks.org
Web Code: ccn-2151

Use Visuals L1

Figure 4 Use the figure to help students understand how gravitational potential energy depends on the reference level used to measure height. Ask, **Would the diver's gravitational potential energy change if there were only three-quarters as much water in the pool?** *(It depends on the reference level; if the reference level were the surface of the water, the answer would be* Yes.*)* **What is the diver's gravitational potential energy relative to the platform?** *(Zero)* **Why does it probably make more sense to measure the diver's potential energy relative to the water?** *(Because this measurement can be used to determine quantities such as how much kinetic energy the diver will have when she hits the water or how much energy she used to climb the platform.)*
Visual, Logical

Build Math Skills L1

Formulas and Equations Place a book on the top shelf of a bookshelf. Have students use a meter stick to determine the book's height and a balance to determine its mass. Then, have them calculate the book's gravitational potential energy. Ask students to identify each variable in the gravitational potential energy equation and state its value. Next, have students repeat the procedure with the book placed on another shelf of the bookshelf.
Logical

Direct students to the **Math Skills** in the **Skills and Reference Handbook** at the end of the student text for additional help.

Go Online NSTA SCILINKS

Download a worksheet on potential and kinetic energy for students to complete, and find additional teacher support from NSTA SciLinks.

Answer to . . .

Figure 4 *Her potential energy would double.*

Reading Checkpoint *Gravitational potential energy is the form of potential energy that depends on an object's mass, height, and the acceleration due to gravity.*

Quick Lab

Investigating Elastic Potential Energy L2

Objective
After completing this activity, students will be able to
- describe the energy conversions that occur when a small ball is dropped while on top of a large ball.
- apply the law of conservation of energy to practical situations.

Address Misconceptions

Students may think that the height of a ball's bounce is a fixed, inherent characteristic of the ball. This lab can help students overcome this misconception.

Skills Focus **Observing, Inferring**

Prep Time 5 minutes

Advance Prep Do the lab outdoors or in the gym because the tennis ball will bounce very high in Step 3. Any two highly elastic balls will work, as long as one has more mass and is considerably larger than the other.

Class Time 15 minutes

Safety Students should stand clear of the balls in Step 3.

Teaching Tips
- In Step 3, students should hold the basketball in one hand and balance the tennis ball with the other hand.

Expected Outcome The tennis ball should bounce about four times higher in Step 3 than it does alone.

Analyze and Conclude
1. It may bounce to a height of 60 to 80 cm in Step 2 and approximately 3 m in Step 3.
2. The mechanical energy after the bounce is less than the initial mechanical energy because the ball does not rise to the height from which it was dropped. Just before and just after the bounce, the gravitational potential energy is zero, so the difference in energy must be due to a difference in kinetic energy.
3. The tennis ball bounced much higher in Step 3 than it did in Step 2 and Step 1 for two reasons. First, the tennis ball had more kinetic energy in Step 3 than it did in Step 2 because it received some elastic potential energy from the basketball. Second, the mass of the tennis ball is much smaller than the mass of the basketball. Therefore, the tennis ball reached a greater velocity and bounced higher than it did in Step 2 and higher than the basketball did in Step 1.
Kinesthetic, Visual

For Enrichment L3

Students can use resources in the library or on the Internet to research the slingshot effect, which uses the gravitational potential energy of space probes as they pass by planets to accelerate the probes toward their targets. This effect is based on a principle similar to one used in this lab.
Verbal

Figure 5 A compressed bicycle shock absorber and a wound-up toy robot both have elastic potential energy.

Quick Lab

Investigating Elastic Potential Energy

Materials basketball, tennis ball, meter stick

Procedure
1. Drop the basketball from a height of 1 m. Use a meter stick to measure how high it bounces. Record your result.
2. Repeat Step 1 with the tennis ball.
3. Place the tennis ball on top of the basketball and drop both together from a height of 1 m. Record your observations.

Analyze and Conclude
1. **Observing** How high did the tennis ball bounce in Steps 2 and 3?
2. **Applying Concepts** From your observations of Step 2, how can you prove that the kinetic energy of the tennis ball just after a bounce is less than it was just before the bounce?
3. **Drawing Conclusions** Use the concepts of kinetic and potential energy to explain your observations of the tennis ball in Step 3.

Elastic Potential Energy The potential energy of an object that is stretched or compressed is known as **elastic potential energy.** Something is said to be elastic if it springs back to its original shape after it is stretched or compressed. Think back to the last time you stretched a rubber band between your fingers. By stretching the rubber band, you did work on it. Just like the musician did with her cello string, the energy you added was stored in the rubber band as potential energy. If you've ever broken a stretched rubber band, you may have felt a painful snap on your hand. The rubber band's elastic potential energy was converted into kinetic energy.

Elastic potential energy can also be stored in objects that are compressed, such as springs. Drop a slice of bread on the floor and it does not bounce noticeably. Why doesn't it? The bread is not very elastic. Drop a basketball on the floor and the basketball bounces back up. The compressed air in the ball forces the ball to spring back into shape after hitting the ground, propelling the ball back up. Other examples of elastic potential energy are shown in Figure 5.

Forms of Energy

All energy can be considered to be kinetic energy, potential energy, or the energy in fields such as those produced by electromagnetic waves. Some familiar examples are the chemical energy in fireworks, electrical energy in lightning bolts, and nuclear energy within the sun. **The major forms of energy are mechanical energy, thermal energy, chemical energy, electrical energy, electromagnetic energy, and nuclear energy.** Each of these forms of energy can be converted into other forms of energy.

Mechanical Energy The energy associated with the motion and position of everyday objects is **mechanical energy.** Don't be confused by the name, however. Mechanical energy is not limited to machines. Mechanical energy is the sum of an object's potential energy and kinetic energy. Speeding trains, bouncing balls, and sprinting athletes all have mechanical energy.

Mechanical energy does not include thermal energy, chemical energy, or other forms of energy associated with the motion or the arrangement of atoms or molecules. Most of these other forms of energy do involve kinetic or potential energy, but on an atomic scale. However, the mechanical energy of a speeding train and a sprinting athlete comes from the chemical energy of the train's fuel and the sprinter's body cells.

Thermal Energy Almost all of the matter around you contains atoms. These particles are always in random motion and thus have kinetic energy. The total potential and kinetic energy of all the microscopic particles in an object make up its **thermal energy.** When an object's atoms move faster, its thermal energy increases and the object becomes warmer. As Figure 6 shows, when objects are hot enough they can emit visible light.

Figure 6 Energy occurs in many forms. This molten metal is extremely hot. It contains a great deal of thermal energy. **Observing** ***What other kinds of energy are evident in this photograph?***

Chemical Energy The campers in Figure 7 are toasting marshmallows over a campfire. The source of energy for the fire is the energy stored in wood. When the wood is burned, energy is released and heats the marshmallows as well as the area around the campfire. The energy stored in wood is chemical energy. **Chemical energy** is the energy stored in chemical bonds. When bonds are broken, the released energy can do work. All chemical compounds, including fuels such as coal and gasoline, store energy. For example, cars can use the chemical energy stored in gasoline to move about. The gasoline is burned in the car's engine and some of its chemical energy is converted into mechanical energy to move the car.

Reading Checkpoint *What is chemical energy?*

Figure 7 This family is using the chemical energy of burning wood to produce thermal energy for heating marshmallows.

Forms of Energy

Teacher Demo

Burning a Peanut **L2**

Purpose To demonstrate that food contains chemical energy.

Materials peanut, paper clip, pliers, pan of water, matches, safety goggles

Safety Prior to conducting this demonstration, ask if there are any students with peanut allergies. As an alternative to a peanut, another nut could be used. Wear safety goggles and keep a fire extinguisher close at hand.

Procedure Make a small loop at one end of the paper clip to hold the peanut. Hold the other end of the paper clip with pliers. Place the peanut in the loop and hold it over the pan of water. Light the match and hold it to the peanut until the peanut starts to burn. The pan of water will catch and extinguish any pieces of the peanut that fall.

Expected Outcome The peanut should burn steadily for about a minute. This demonstrates that even a single peanut contains a large amount of chemical energy. You may make this demonstration quantitative by holding the peanut under a beaker containing 25 mL of water. You can measure the temperature change of the water and calculate the amount of energy released from the peanut.
Visual

FYI

Students may benefit from understanding that sound is a form of energy. When energy leaves a system during energy transfers, part of the energy is usually lost as sound. Students will study mechanical waves and sound in Chapter 17.

Facts and Figures

Sound as Energy Sound may also be considered a form of energy. Sound consists of longitudinal waves that carry energy through a medium. All waves carry energy from one place to another. As sound passes through a medium, particles in the medium are compressed or pulled apart. The motion of the particles and the collisions of particles with each other transfer kinetic energy along with the wave. The compressions produce areas of increased pressure that have elastic potential energy. Because sound waves carry kinetic and potential energy, sound can be considered a form of mechanical energy. Waves that depend on the vibration of particles in a medium are called *mechanical waves.* The only waves that do not require a medium are electromagnetic waves.

Answer to . . .

Figure 6 *Kinetic energy, gravitational potential energy, electromagnetic energy*

Reading Checkpoint *The energy stored in chemical bonds*

Build Science Skills L2

Classifying Ask students to classify the following types of energy as kinetic energy or potential energy when considered at an atomic or subatomic scale: thermal energy *(Kinetic)*, chemical energy *(Potential)*, nuclear energy *(Potential)*
Logical, Visual

3 ASSESS

Evaluate Understanding L2

Ask students to list at least two kinds of energy in the objects in each of the following examples:
A car driving *(Kinetic energy, chemical energy)*
A car battery *(Chemical energy, electrical energy)*
An apple falling *(Kinetic energy, gravitational potential energy, chemical energy)*
A spring-loaded mouse trap *(Elastic potential energy when set, kinetic energy when sprung)*

All of the above objects also have thermal energy, electromagnetic energy, and nuclear energy.

Reteach L1

Review Figures 3–8. For each figure, discuss the type of energy that the figure illustrates.

Math Practice

Solutions L2
8. PE = mgh =
$(60.0 \text{ kg})(9.8 \text{ m/s}^2)(74.8 \text{ m}) = 44{,}000 \text{ J}$
9. KE = $\frac{1}{2}mv^2$ =
$(0.50)(0.145 \text{ kg})(30.0 \text{ m/s})^2 = 65.3 \text{ J}$

Interactive Textbook If your class subscribes to the Interactive Textbook, use it to review key concepts in Section 15.1.

A
B

Figure 8 Two major forms of energy are electrical energy and electromagnetic energy. **A** Lightning bolts transfer electric charge. **B** Galaxies are giant structures in space that typically contain billions of stars. The stars give off enormous amounts of electromagnetic energy.

Electrical Energy Many devices you use every day use electricity, or electrical energy. **Electrical energy** is the energy associated with electric charges. Electric charges can exert forces that do work. Batteries, which convert chemical energy to electrical energy, are used to operate portable CD players, flashlights, and calculators. Electrical energy also occurs in nature. The powerful bolts of lightning shown in Figure 8A are produced by electrical energy.

Electromagnetic Energy The sun radiates electromagnetic energy into space and is the source, either directly or indirectly, of most of the world's energy supplies. **Electromagnetic energy** is a form of energy that travels through space in the form of waves. Visible light and X-rays are examples of electromagnetic energy. Because electromagnetic waves can travel long distances through air and space, they are often used for communication. The glowing galaxy in Figure 8B is emitting electromagnetic energy of many kinds.

Nuclear Energy The nucleus of an atom is held together by strong and weak nuclear forces, which can store an enormous amount of potential energy. The energy stored in atomic nuclei is known as **nuclear energy.** A nuclear power plant uses nuclear fission reactions to generate electricity. Nuclear fission is a process that releases energy by splitting nuclei apart. A second type of nuclear reaction, nuclear fusion, releases energy when less massive nuclei combine to form a more massive nucleus. The heat and light of the sun are produced by the fusion of hydrogen nuclei into helium nuclei.

Section 15.1 Assessment

Reviewing Concepts

1. Describe the relationship between work and energy.
2. How is the kinetic energy of an object determined?
3. What factors determine the gravitational potential energy of an object?
4. Give an example of each of the major forms of energy.
5. When you heat a pot of water over a flame, what form of energy is added to the water?

Critical Thinking

6. **Applying Concepts** What kind of energy is represented by an archer stretching a bow string?
7. **Applying Concepts** Can an object have both kinetic energy and potential energy at the same time? Explain.

Math Practice

8. A 60.0-kg person walks from the ground to the roof of a 74.8-m-tall building. How much gravitational potential energy does she have at the top of the building?
9. A pitcher throws a 0.145-kg baseball at a velocity of 30.0 m/s. How much kinetic energy does the ball have?

Section 15.1 Assessment

1. Energy is the ability to do work, and work is the transfer of energy.
2. By multiplying half an object's mass by the square of its speed
3. Its mass, the acceleration due to gravity, and its height relative to a reference level
4. Sample answers include a bouncing ball for mechanical energy, molten steel or fire for thermal energy, wood or gasoline for chemical energy, CD players or lightning for electrical energy, light for electromagnetic energy, and nuclear power plants for nuclear energy.
5. Thermal energy
6. Elastic potential energy
7. Yes. Kinetic energy and potential energy are not mutually exclusive. For example, a falling object has both kinetic energy and gravitational potential energy.

15.2 Energy Conversion and Conservation

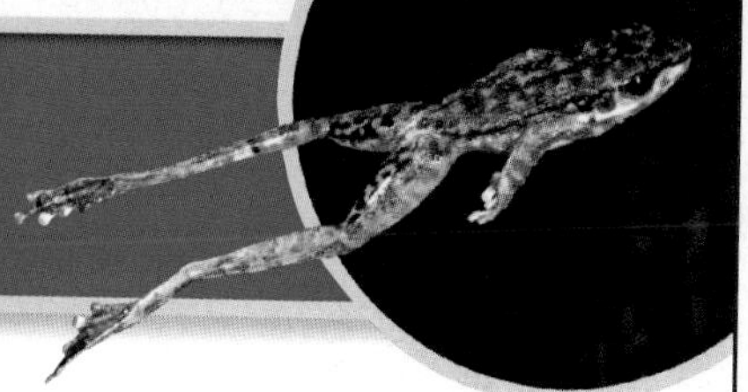

Reading Focus

Key Concepts
- Can energy be converted from one form into another?
- What is the law of conservation of energy?
- What energy conversion takes place as an object falls toward Earth?
- How are energy and mass related?

Vocabulary
- energy conversion

Reading Strategy
Relating Cause and Effect Copy the flowchart below. As you read, complete the chart to explain an energy conversion. Make two similar charts for pendulums and pole vaults.

Gull lifts oyster, increasing oyster's gravitational potential energy. → a. ? → b. ?

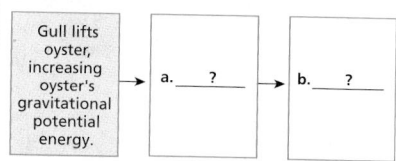

On October 9, 1992, people from Kentucky to New York reported seeing a bright streak of white light shooting across the night sky. Most observers, having seen "shooting stars" before, expected this one to quickly burn out and disappear. However, that did not happen. The shooting star, or meteor, continued streaking across the sky. After a few seconds, pieces of the meteor broke off, creating a series of smaller streaks of light. Eventually, the streaks disappeared from view. Although the event was interesting, most witnesses probably soon forgot about it.

However, the meteor was not soon forgotten by the owners of a red automobile in Peekskill, New York. Unfortunately for them, a large chunk of the meteor made it through Earth's atmosphere and struck their parked car. The car was badly damaged, as shown in Figure 9. Luckily, no one was in the car at the time, and so no one was hurt.

As the Peekskill meteor traveled through the atmosphere, some of its kinetic energy was converted into light and heat. The light made the meteor visible in the sky. The heat caused a large portion of the meteor to vaporize in the atmosphere. Upon impact, much of the meteor's remaining kinetic energy went into smashing the metal body of the car.

Figure 9 A meteor crashed into the rear of this car, causing considerable damage.

Section Resources

Print
- ***Laboratory Manual,*** Investigation 15B
- ***Reading and Study Workbook With Math Support,*** Section 15.2
- ***Math Skills and Problem Solving Workbook,*** Section 15.2
- ***Transparencies,*** Section 15.2

Technology
- ***Probeware Lab Manual,*** Lab 6
- ***Interactive Textbook,*** Section 15.2
- ***Presentation Pro CD-ROM,*** Section 15.2
- ***Go Online,*** NSTA SciLinks, Energy; PHSchool.com, Data sharing

Section 15.2

1 FOCUS

Objectives
15.2.1 **Describe** conversions of energy from one form to another.
15.2.2 **State** and **apply** the law of conservation of energy.
15.2.3 **Analyze** how energy is conserved in conversions between kinetic energy and potential energy and **solve equations** that equate initial energy to final energy.
15.2.4 **Describe** the relationship between energy and mass and **calculate** how much energy is equivalent to a given mass.

Reading Focus

Build Vocabulary L2
Paraphrasing Tell students that *conversion* means *a change from one form or state to another.* Prompt students to describe other situations where conversions take place, such as converting money from one currency to another or converting from one unit of measure to another. For each example, identify the previous form or state and the new form or state.

Reading Strategy L2
a. The gull drops the oyster, and the oyster's gravitational potential energy is converted into kinetic energy as the oyster falls. (Air resistance can be ignored.)
b. The oyster strikes a rock and breaks. Kinetic energy is converted into work (breaking the shell) and thermal energy. The kinetic energy and gravitational potential energy of the oyster are now zero.
c. Pull pendulum up (work converted to PE).
d. Pendulum swings down (PE converts to KE).
e. Pendulum swings up (KE converts into gravitational PE).
f. Pole-vaulter sprints (work increases KE).
g. Pole bends (KE converts to elastic PE).
h. Pole-vaulter accelerates up (PE converts to KE).

2 INSTRUCT

Energy Conversion

Quick Lab

Exploring Energy Conversion L2

Objective
After completing this activity, students will be able to
- describe the relationship between kinetic energy and velocity.

Address Misconceptions

Students may intuitively understand that faster objects have more kinetic energy than slower objects, but may hold the misconception that kinetic energy is roughly proportional to velocity. The strong effect of height—and therefore velocity—on crater diameter can help students overcome this misconception.

Skills Focus **Observing, Inferring, Calculating**

Prep Time 20 minutes

Advance Prep Boxes should be large enough for students to drop the balls into the boxes without missing them. A box about the size of a shoebox should be sufficient. Tell students the mass of the ball.

Class Time 25 minutes

Teaching Tips
- Have students construct data tables to record their observations.
- Remind students to measure the height of the ball from the surface of the clay, not from the floor or tabletop.
- Remind students to convert measurements to meters and kilograms in order to calculate energy in joules for Question 2.

Expected Outcome Students will observe that an increase in height will produce a larger crater.

Analyze and Conclude
1. Increasing the height increases the crater diameter.
2. Energies depend on the mass of the ball. $PE_{60\ cm} = 2 \times PE_{30\ cm}$ and $PE_{90\ cm} = 3 \times PE_{30\ cm}$.
3. Increasing kinetic energy results in a crater with a larger diameter.
Kinesthetic, Logical

Energy Conversion

The Peekskill meteor clearly shows that energy can change forms. **Energy can be converted from one form to another.** The process of changing energy from one form to another is **energy conversion.**

Not all energy conversions are as dramatic as the Peekskill meteor. Energy conversions are constantly taking place all around you, often without you noticing. Wind-up toys store elastic potential energy in a compressed spring. When the spring unwinds, potential energy is converted into the kinetic energy of the toy's moving parts. Light bulbs convert electrical energy into thermal energy and electromagnetic energy.

In some cases, energy is converted from one form into another in a series of steps. The striking of the match shown in Figure 10 is a good example. In lighting a match, your muscles use chemical energy moving your hand to strike the match against a rough area on the matchbox. Friction between the match and the matchbox converts some of the match's kinetic energy into thermal energy. The thermal energy triggers a chemical reaction on the match tip, releasing some of the match's stored chemical energy. The stored chemical energy is then converted into thermal energy and electromagnetic energy in the flame.

Figure 10 Energy is converted from one form to another as this match is lit.
Applying Concepts *What energy conversions take place when you turn on a battery-powered portable radio?*

Reading Checkpoint *What energy conversions occur in lighting a match?*

Quick Lab

Exploring Energy Conversion

Materials
small steel ball of known mass, box lined with soft modeling clay, meter stick, graph paper

Procedure
1. Construct a data table with 3 blank rows and 5 columns labeled Mass, Height, Diameter, Potential Energy, and Kinetic Energy.
2. Drop the ball into the box of clay from a height of 30 cm. Record this height.
3. Measure and record the diameter of the crater that the ball formed.
4. Repeat Steps 2 and 3, dropping the ball from 60 cm and 90 cm.
5. Graph your data. Plot the crater diameter on the vertical axis and height on the horizontal axis.

Analyze and Conclude
1. **Using Graphs** According to your graph, how are crater diameter and the height of the ball related?
2. **Calculating** For each height, calculate and record the initial potential energy of the ball.
3. **Drawing Conclusions** How are kinetic energy and crater diameter related? (*Hint:* The ball's kinetic energy when it hits the clay equals the potential energy it started with, *mgh*.)

Customize for Inclusion

Hearing Impaired
Clues about energy and energy transfers are often in the form of sounds. For example, you may be able to tell how fast a train is moving by how loud it sounds, how hard a baseball player hits the ball by the sound of the crack of the bat, or how angry someone is by the volume of one's voice. However, sounds are not the only clues to energy and energy transfers. Invite hearing-impaired students to consider and share what kinds of information they observe that tell them about how much energy people and objects have, and about energy transfers. For example, they may use visual clues such as light given off by the coil in a toaster to tell that the coil is hot.

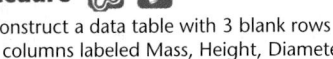

KOREA

Figure 11 Although speed skaters slide quickly over smooth ice, they are still slowed down by friction with the air and the surface of the ice.
Inferring *What are two ways that skaters can reduce friction?*

Conservation of Energy

When energy changes from one form to another, the total energy remains unchanged even though many energy conversions may occur. This is one of the most important concepts in science, the law of conservation of energy. **The law of conservation of energy states that energy cannot be created or destroyed.** According to the law of conservation of energy, energy can be converted from one form to another. However, in a closed system, the amount of energy present at the beginning of a process is the same as the amount of energy at the end. (In a closed system, nothing can enter or leave.)

You know that if you stop pedaling when you're riding a bike on a flat path, the bike will eventually come to a stop. The moving bike had kinetic energy. Where did the bike's kinetic energy go? The bike slowed down and stopped because of frictional forces acting over a distance. The work done by friction changes kinetic energy into thermal energy.

As a bicycle moves, it encounters friction with the ground and the air. Such friction causes a continual conversion of kinetic energy into thermal energy. Thus, as the bicycle slows, it gains thermal energy. So do the ground and the air. When the energy lost to frictional forces is accounted for, energy is conserved overall.

Recall that friction within machinery reduces efficiency. Friction is a major cause of energy consumption in cars and factories. All moving parts are subject to friction.

You can reduce friction but you can't avoid it. Friction is everywhere. Even the skaters in Figure 11 are subject to friction. Recall that objects moving through the air are slowed by air resistance. In many cases, most of a falling object's potential energy is converted into thermal energy because of air resistance.

You can ignore the effects of friction in many everyday situations. A marble dropped from one meter above the ground, for example, encounters so little air resistance that it can be ignored.

Go Online NSTA SciLinks

For: Links on energy
Visit: www.SciLinks.org
Web Code: ccn-2152

Conservation of Energy

Build Reading Literacy L1

Directed Reading/Thinking Activity (DRTA) Refer to page **444D** in this chapter, which provides the guidelines for a DRTA strategy.

Have students read only the main headings on pp. 455–457. Then, have them make predictions about the main ideas that will be presented in the passage. For example, they may predict that energy conversions in a pole vault involve kinetic energy, elastic potential energy, and gravitational potential energy. They may also form questions about the passage, such as "What kinds of energy conversions take place in a pendulum?" Record all ideas on the board. Have students read each subsection of the passage. After they have finished a subsection, pause and ask the students if they have any new predictions or questions, or if they want to modify any of their initial predictions. Repeat until the entire passage has been read. Finish by having students confirm which of their predictions were correct, and provide answers to questions that were addressed in the passage. **Verbal, Group**

Go Online NSTA SciLinks

Download a worksheet on energy for students to complete, and find additional teacher support from NSTA SciLinks.

Answer to . . .

Figure 10 *Chemical energy in the battery is converted into electrical energy in the radio. This electrical energy is converted into sound, a form of mechanical energy, and a small amount of thermal energy.*

Figure 11 *By wearing clothing and helmets that reduce air resistance; by staying low to the ice to reduce air resistance*

Reading Checkpoint *The kinetic energy of the hand is converted into thermal energy by friction. The increase in the match's thermal energy releases chemical energy stored on its tip, which is converted into thermal energy and electromagnetic energy in the form of a flame.*

Facts and Figures

Dark Energy and the Expanding Universe Recent studies suggest that the universe is expanding and that the expansion is accelerating. This finding appears to violate the law of conservation of energy because it requires increasing energy. However, Einstein's general theory of relativity included a "cosmological constant" that predicted this accelerated expansion. Many scientists did not accept this prediction, and even Einstein abandoned his idea. The first results suggesting expansion were released in 1998, and since then scientists have been racing to explain the phenomenon. Some scientists have reintroduced the cosmological constant, while others have proposed a type of "dark energy," previously undetected, that is driving the acceleration. This open question is sure to be an important subject of new theories and research in the twenty-first century.

Energy Conversions

Teacher Demo

Energy in a Pendulum L2

Purpose Students use the law of conservation of energy to predict and explain the motion of a pendulum.

Materials pendulum bob and string, hook at top of board, chalk (or marker), level

Procedure Tie the string to the pendulum bob and hang the pendulum in front of the board. The pendulum should reach at least 2/3 of the way down the board. When the pendulum is at rest, draw a vertical line directly behind the pendulum string. Use the level to draw a long horizontal line about 15 cm above the pendulum bob. Displace the pendulum to one side so that it is even with the horizontal line. Ask students to predict how high the pendulum will swing on the other side. Release the pendulum bob.

Let the pendulum swing until it no longer reaches the height of the horizontal line. Have students discuss what may have happened to the mechanical energy that was lost from the system.

Now have a student come to the board and hold a pencil at the intersection of the vertical line and the horizontal line. The pencil should be sticking straight out with the eraser against the board. The pencil will shorten the length of the pendulum in the second half of the pendulum's motion. Make sure the student holding the pencil is clear of the pendulum's path. Hold the pendulum bob as before and again ask students to predict how high the pendulum will swing on the other side. Release the pendulum bob, and observe.

Expected Outcome In both cases, the pendulum should initially rise to the height of the horizontal line. Discuss with students how this demonstrates the conservation of energy. After the pendulum swings for a while, it no longer rises to the height of the horizontal line because some of the kinetic energy is converted to thermal energy due to air resistance and friction at the support. Point out to students that total energy is still conserved, although mechanical energy is not.
Kinesthetic, Logical

Figure 12 Some gulls use energy conversion to obtain food by dropping oysters onto rocks. **Applying Concepts** ***Where is the oyster's potential energy greatest? Where is its kinetic energy greatest?***

Energy Conversions

One of the most common energy conversions is between potential energy and kinetic energy. **The gravitational potential energy of an object is converted to the kinetic energy of motion as the object falls.** That's what happens when an avalanche brings tons of snow from the top of a mountain to the valley floor. Similarly, when you release a compressed spring, the elastic potential energy of the spring is converted into kinetic energy as the spring expands. Conversions between kinetic and potential energy can happen in both directions, that is, from kinetic to potential energy, or from potential to kinetic energy.

Some gulls use energy conversion to obtain food. Oysters are a food source for gulls. However, it is difficult for a gull to break open an oyster's hard shell with its beak. Unfortunately for the oyster, gulls have learned a clever way to use gravitational potential energy, as shown in Figure 12. A hungry gull picks up an oyster and flies high into the air directly over some rocks. The gull does work on the oyster by raising it against the force of gravity, thereby increasing the oyster's potential energy. While over the rocks, the gull lets the oyster fall. As the oyster falls, its gravitational potential energy is converted into kinetic energy. The oyster picks up speed until it hits the rocks. The impact breaks open the shell. The gull then swoops down to enjoy its meal.

Energy Conversion in Pendulums At the lake, you grab a rope hanging from a tree branch. With a yell, you swing down toward the lake, and pick up speed until you land with a giant splash. A rope swing is an example of a pendulum. A pendulum consists of a weight swinging back and forth from a rope or string.

Pendulums were used in the first truly accurate clocks. The Dutch scientist Christiaan Huygens (1629–1695) made the first pendulum clock in 1656. Pendulum clocks such as the one shown in Figure 13 make use of the fact that the time it takes for a pendulum to swing back and forth once is precisely related to its length.

Kinetic energy and potential energy undergo constant conversion as a pendulum swings. At the highest point in its swing, the pendulum is momentarily motionless as it changes direction. At this point, the weight at the end of the pendulum has zero kinetic energy and maximum potential energy.

As the pendulum swings downward, potential energy is converted to kinetic energy. At the bottom of the swing, the pendulum has maximum kinetic energy and zero potential energy. The pendulum then moves upward again, repeating the process. Eventually, frictional forces slow down the pendulum. In a clock, a spring mechanism or hanging weights provide energy to keep the pendulum swinging despite the effects of friction.

Figure 13 Pendulum clocks use pendulums to maintain accurate time.

Energy Conversion in the Pole Vault The pole vault is a difficult track and field event that requires a combination of speed, strength, timing, and energy conversion. In the pole vault, an athlete uses a flexible pole to propel himself over a high bar. Look at the pole-vaulter's jump in Figure 14 and think about how energy changes during the jump.

In order to start the jump with as much kinetic energy as possible, the pole-vaulter sprints down the runway as fast as he can. At the end of his sprint, he plants the end of a long pole at the base of the high bar and propels himself into the air. The pole-vaulter's kinetic energy is partially converted into elastic potential energy as the pole bends. The pole springs back into shape, propelling the pole-vaulter upward, hopefully high enough to clear the bar.

As the pole-vaulter soars, his kinetic energy decreases while he gains gravitational potential energy. Once the highest point has been reached, his gravitational potential energy begins to convert back to kinetic energy. The pole-vaulter picks up speed as he falls back to the ground.

Reading Checkpoint *What energy changes occur in a pole vault?*

SPORT

Figure 14 A pole-vaulter converts kinetic energy into potential energy in order to propel himself high into the air. **Applying Concepts** ***At which point does a pole-vaulter have the most gravitational potential energy?***

Energy Conversion Calculations When friction is small enough to be ignored, and no mechanical energy is added to a system, then the system's mechanical energy does not change. Recall that mechanical energy is the total kinetic and potential energy of an object.

$$\text{Mechanical energy} = \text{KE} + \text{PE}$$

You can apply the law of conservation of energy to any mechanical process. A mechanical process can be any action, such as the motion of a pendulum, water falling in a waterfall, or a diver propelled by a diving board. In all of these processes, if friction can be neglected, the mechanical energy at the beginning equals the mechanical energy at the end. That is, total mechanical energy remains constant. This equality can be stated as follows.

Conservation of Mechanical Energy

$$(\text{KE} + \text{PE})_{\text{beginning}} = (\text{KE} + \text{PE})_{\text{end}}$$

The Math Skills box on the following page shows how the conservation of mechanical energy equation can be used.

Address Misconceptions **L2**

Students may think that energy is truly lost in many energy transformations. Apparent energy losses due to friction can be especially confusing. Instruct students to rub their hands together rapidly for a few seconds. Ask students, **How did rubbing your hands together change the temperature of your hands?** *(It increased the temperature.)* **Did your hands produce any sound when you rubbed them together?** *(Yes)* **Was the kinetic energy that you used to rub your hands together lost?** *(No)* **Into what forms of energy was the kinetic energy converted?** *(Thermal energy and sound)*
Kinesthetic, Logical

Use Visuals **L1**

Figure 14 Ask students, **What kind of energy does the pole-vaulter have before planting the pole?** *(Kinetic energy)* **Into what two forms of energy is the kinetic energy converted?** *(Elastic potential energy, gravitational potential energy)* **What two forms of energy does the pole-vaulter have when he lets go of the pole?** *(Kinetic energy, gravitational potential energy)* **Into what form of energy is the potential energy converted as the pole-vaulter falls?** *(Kinetic energy)* **What happens to the energy when the pole-vaulter hits the mat?** *(Some of it becomes sound, and some of it is absorbed into the mat and the pole-vaulter's body as thermal energy.)*
Visual, Logical

Answer to . . .

Figure 12 *Potential energy is greatest at maximum height; kinetic energy is greatest just before the oyster strikes the ground.*

Figure 14 *At the highest point in his vault.*

Reading Checkpoint *The pole-vaulter's kinetic energy from running is converted into the elastic potential energy of the pole and his own gravitational potential energy as he rises and the pole straightens. After the pole-vaulter reaches his maximum height, his gravitational energy is converted back into kinetic energy as he falls.*

Math Practice

Solutions L2

1. $(PE)_{beginning} = (KE)_{end} = \frac{1}{2}mv^2 = (0.50)(10\text{ kg})(60\text{ m/s})^2 = 18{,}000\text{ J}$
2. $(PE)_{beginning} = mgh = (70.0\text{ kg})(9.8\text{ m/s}^2)(3.0\text{ m}) = 2100\text{ J}$; At the beginning, KE = 0 and at the end, PE = 0, so $(PE)_{beginning} = (KE)_{end} = \frac{1}{2}mv^2$; Substituting the known values, $2100\text{ J} = (0.5)(70.0\text{ kg})(v^2)$; Solving for v, $v = \sqrt{(2)(2100\text{ J})/70.0\text{ kg}} = 7.7\text{ m/s}$
3. $(PE)_{beginning} = mgh = (1.0\text{ kg})(9.8\text{ m/s}^2)(0.04\text{ m}) = 0.4\text{ J}$; at the beginning, KE = 0; at the lowest point, PE = 0; therefore $(PE)_{beginning} = (KE)_{end} = 0.4\text{ J}$

Logical

For Extra Help L1

For most simple conservation of mechanical energy problems, the calculations depend on some form of the equation PE = KE, or $mgh = \frac{1}{2}mv^2$. If students are having difficulty with a particular problem, help them rearrange the equation to separate known and unknown variables before plugging in numbers.

Logical

Direct students to the **Math Skills** in the **Skills and Reference Handbook** at the end of the student text for additional help.

Additional Problems

1. If you throw a baseball straight up with a speed of 5 m/s, what will be the speed of the ball when it comes back to your hand? Ignore air resistance. *(5 m/s)*
2. A 1000-kg car is coasting at 10 m/s toward a hill that is 10 m high. Will the car make it to the top of the hill if the driver does not step on the gas pedal? *(No. Initial KE = 50,000 J. At a height of 10 m, PE would be about 100,000 J. The car could only reach a height of 5 m, ignoring friction.)*

Logical, Portfolio

Math Skills

Conservation of Mechanical Energy

At a construction site, a 1.50-kg brick is dropped from rest and hits the ground at a speed of 26.0 m/s. Assuming air resistance can be ignored, calculate the gravitational potential energy of the brick before it was dropped.

1 Read and Understand

What information are you given?

Mass, $m = 1.50\text{ kg}$ Final speed, $v = 26.0\text{ m/s}$

What unknown are you trying to calculate?

Gravitational potential energy of the brick before it was dropped, PE

2 Plan and Solve

What equations or formulas contain the given quantities and the unknown?

Because the brick falls without air resistance, the conservation of mechanical energy equation can be used.

$$(KE + PE)_{beginning} = (KE + PE)_{end}$$

You will also need to use the formula for kinetic energy (KE).

$$KE = \frac{1}{2}mv^2$$

Note that the KE at the beginning is zero because the brick has not yet begun to fall. Also, when the brick hits the ground, its potential energy is zero. Substitute these values into the conservation of energy formula.

$$(PE)_{beginning} = (KE)_{end}$$

Substitute the formula for KE.

$$PE = KE = \frac{1}{2}mv^2$$

Substitute the known values and calculate the PE.

$$PE = \frac{1}{2}(1.50\text{ kg})(26.0\text{ m/s})^2 = 507\text{ kg•m}^2/\text{s}^2 = 507\text{ J}$$

3 Look Back and Check

Is your answer reasonable?

Check the answer by finding the initial height of the brick, using PE = 507 J = mgh. Substituting in m and g gives h = 34.5 m. This is a reasonable height for an object in free fall to reach a speed of 26.0 m/s.

Math Practice

1. A 10-kg rock is dropped and hits the ground below at a speed of 60 m/s. Calculate the gravitational potential energy of the rock before it was dropped. You can ignore the effects of friction.
2. A diver with a mass of 70.0 kg stands motionless at the top of a 3.0-m-high diving platform. Calculate his potential energy relative to the water surface while standing on the platform, and his speed when he enters the pool. (*Hint:* Assume the diver's initial vertical speed after diving is zero.)
3. A pendulum with a 1.0-kg weight is set in motion from a position 0.04 m above the lowest point on the path of the weight. What is the kinetic energy of the pendulum at the lowest point? (*Hint:* Assume there is no friction.)

Facts and Figures

Quantization of Energy $E = mc^2$, Einstein's equation showing the equivalence of mass and energy, is probably the most famous equation in physics today. However, Max Planck's equation, $E = h\nu$, is also important. In this equation, E is energy, h is a constant called Planck's constant (6.63×10^{-34} J•s), and ν (the Greek letter "nu") is frequency. This equation encapsulates the idea that energy exists in discrete packets, called quanta.

Planck proposed this equation in 1900 to help explain blackbody radiation. Einstein provided further experimental support for this equation in 1905 when he used it to explain the photoelectric effect. The photoelectric effect is a result of the fact that light, like all forms of energy, comes in discrete packets. Light quanta are also called photons. Students will learn more about photons in Chapter 18.

Energy and Mass

Figure 15 Albert Einstein made important contributions to many areas of physics. His theory of special relativity showed that energy and mass are equivalent.

Physicist Albert Einstein (1879–1955), shown in Figure 15, developed his special theory of relativity in 1905. This theory included the now-famous equation $E = mc^2$. In Einstein's equation, E is energy, m is mass, and c is the speed of light. This seemingly ordinary equation has surprising consequences. **Einstein's equation, $E = mc^2$, says that energy and mass are equivalent and can be converted into each other.** In other words, energy is released as matter is destroyed, and matter can be created from energy.

Notice that the speed of light is squared in Einstein's equation. The speed of light is an extremely large number, 3.0×10^8 meters per second. Thus, a tiny amount of matter can produce an enormous amount of energy. Suppose 1 gram of matter were entirely converted into energy.

$$E = mc^2 = (10^{-3}\text{ kg}) \times (3 \times 10^8\text{ m/s}) \times (3 \times 10^8\text{ m/s})$$

$$= 9 \times 10^{13}\text{ kg}\cdot\text{m}^2/\text{s}^2 = 9 \times 10^{13}\text{ J}$$

In comparison, 1 gram of TNT produces only 2931 joules of energy. In nuclear fission and fusion reactions, however, large amounts of energy are released by the destruction of very small amounts of matter. Therefore, the law of conservation of energy has been modified to say that mass and energy together are always conserved.

Section 15.2 Assessment

Reviewing Concepts

1. Describe how energy can be converted from one form to another in a wind-up toy.
2. What does the law of conservation of energy state?
3. As an object falls in free fall, what energy change is taking place?
4. What did Einstein conclude about the relationship between energy and mass?
5. What type of energy change results when friction slows down an object?
6. Describe the energy of a playground swing at its highest position.

Critical Thinking

7. **Inferring** Why does a bouncing ball rise to a lower height with each bounce? What energy conversion is taking place?
8. **Applying Concepts** To begin a dive, a diver jumps into the air and then lands on the diving board, causing it to bend. What type of energy conversions occur as the board springs back and propels the diver up into the air?

Math Practice

9. A 0.15-kg ball is thrown into the air and rises to a height of 20.0 m. How much kinetic energy did the ball initially have?
10. A 125-g steel ball with a kinetic energy of 0.25 J rolls along a horizontal track. How high up an inclined track will the ball roll if friction can be ignored?

Energy and Mass

Build Science Skills L2

Calculating Have students use Einstein's mass-energy equation to calculate the energy equivalence of an electron ($m = 9.1 \times 10^{-31}$ kg) and of their own body. *(For an electron: $E = mc^2 = (9.1 \times 10^{-31}\text{ kg})(3.0 \times 10^8\text{ m/s})^2 = 8.2 \times 10^{-14}$ J; for a 50-kg student: $E = mc^2 = (50\text{ kg})(3 \times 10^8\text{ m/s})^2 = 5 \times 10^{18}$ J)*
Logical, Portfolio

3 ASSESS

Evaluate Understanding L2

Ask students to describe systems or situations in which energy conversions are taking place. They may use examples from the section or new examples. For each system, they should identify at least two forms of energy. They should also describe how energy is lost from the system, and say what form the energy takes after it has left the system.

Reteach L1

Review Figures 10–14. For each figure, discuss the energy conversions that are taking place. Identify what forms of energy are present before, during, and after the events shown in each figure.

Math Practice

Solutions L2

9. The ball's potential energy at the beginning and kinetic energy at its maximum height are zero. Using the conservation of energy formula, $(KE)_{beginning} = (PE)_{end}$, $(KE)_{beginning} = mgh = (0.15\text{ kg})(9.8\text{ m/s}^2)(20.0\text{ m}) = 29$ J
10. The ball's initial potential energy and its kinetic energy at the maximum height along the track are zero. Using the conservation of energy formula, $(KE)_{beginning} = (PE)_{end} = mgh$, solve for h. $h = KE/mg = 0.25\text{ J}/(0.125\text{ kg} \times 9.8\text{ m/s}^2) = 0.20$ m

Interactive Textbook If your class subscribes to the Interactive Textbook, use it to review key concepts in Section 15.2.

Section 15.2 Assessment

1. Elastic potential energy stored in the wound-up spring is converted to kinetic energy as the spring unwinds and the toy moves.
2. Energy cannot be created or destroyed.
3. Gravitational potential energy is converted into kinetic energy as the object falls.
4. Energy and mass are equivalent, and can be converted into one another.
5. Friction causes the conversion of kinetic energy to thermal energy.
6. The swing has maximum gravitational potential energy and no kinetic energy at its highest position.
7. Friction within the ball, between the ball and the ground, and between the ball and the air converts kinetic energy into thermal energy. Each bounce has less kinetic energy.
8. The elastic potential energy of the board is converted into both kinetic energy and gravitational potential energy (because the diver's height increases while the diver is still in contact with the board).

CONCEPTS in Action

Roller Coasters L2

Background

Most historians believe that roller coasters developed from ice slides used for recreation in sixteenth-century Russia. Some of these slides were over 70 feet high and stretched for hundreds of feet. Wheeled roller coasters became popular in France during the nineteenth century. Roller coasters became popular in the United States during the early twentieth century, epitomized by the many coasters at New York's Coney Island amusement park. Roller coasters had a resurgence in popularity in the 1960s, when many large wooden coasters were built, and in the 1970s, when many steel looping coasters were created. Today's largest and fastest roller coasters are made of steel. Some have vertical drops of over 300 feet and reach speeds of over 100 miles per hour. But many people still enjoy the rattle and creak of wooden coasters, too.

Roller Coasters

A roller coaster is a train powered by gravity. An initial store of potential energy is released dramatically during the ride.

A roller coaster's first hill, called the lift hill, is the highest point of the ride. As the coaster plunges down the first drop, its potential energy is converted into kinetic energy, the energy of motion. Later, some of this kinetic energy is converted back into potential energy as the coaster's speed decreases during a climb. Over the course of the ride, the coaster's total mechanical energy (potential plus kinetic energy) gradually decreases. This change occurs due to friction from the rails and the air, which causes the coaster's mechanical energy to be converted into heat. By the end of the ride, all the potential energy created on the lift hill has been lost as heat.

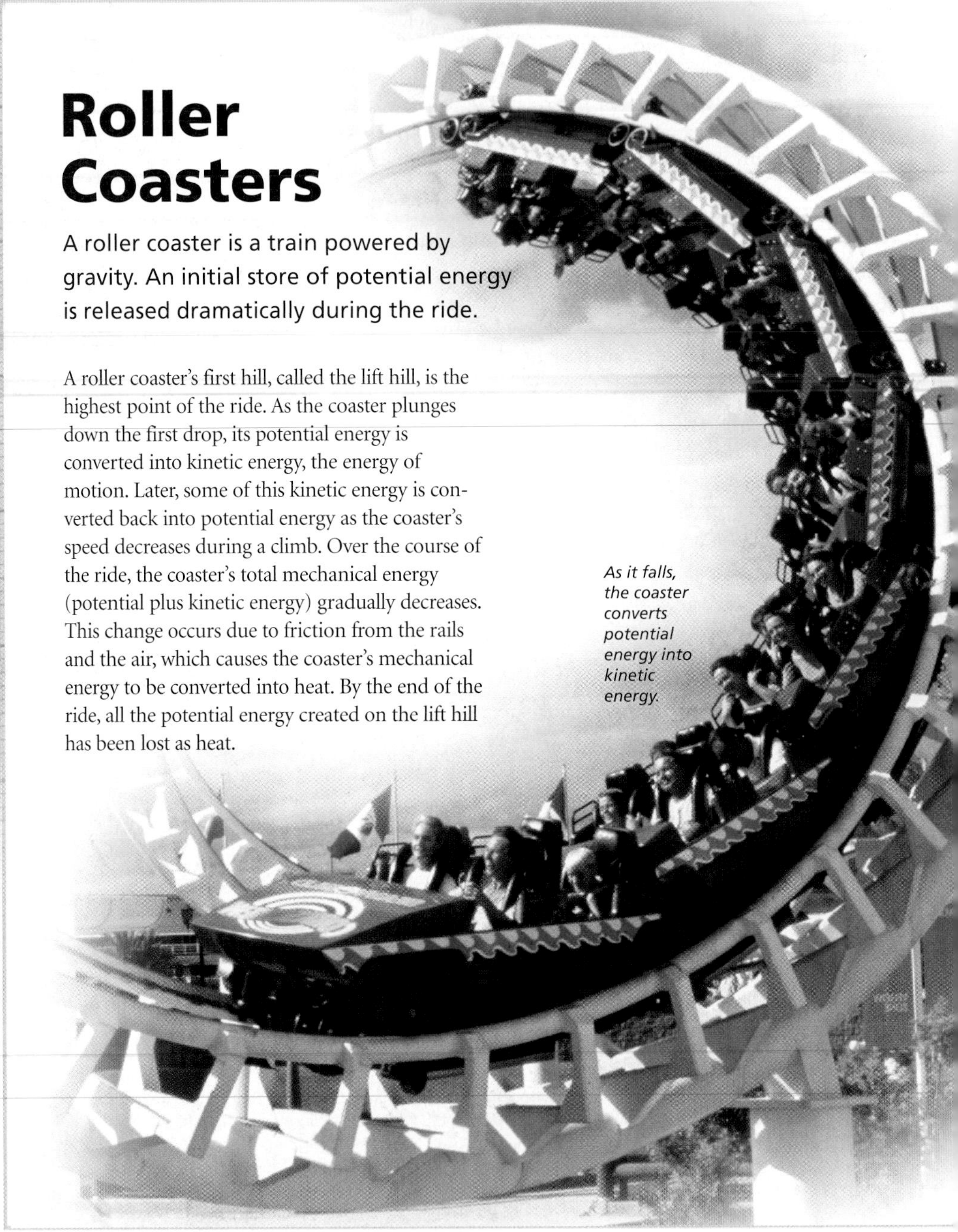

As it falls, the coaster converts potential energy into kinetic energy.

Releasing energy

A roller coaster goes through a series of exchanges between potential and kinetic energy.

A cable *pulls cars to the top of the lift hill. During the climb, the coaster builds up potential energy.*
Potential energy *rapidly turns into kinetic energy during the first plunge.*
Kinetic energy *reaches a maximum as the coaster reaches the bottom of the first hill.*
The second loop *has a lower peak than the first because the coaster's energy is reduced by friction.*

Design and safety

The job of a roller coaster designer is to make sure that a ride is terrifying but safe. Some people are concerned that designers are providing riders with greater thrills at the expense of their safety. Safety experts say that the risk of injury is small, but it is important to pay attention to restrictions regarding height and medical conditions.

Coaster forces
During a ride, you are kept in your seat by the safety bar and by the force of the seat pushing on you. The coaster also exerts large forces on the track, which must be inspected daily for structural damage.

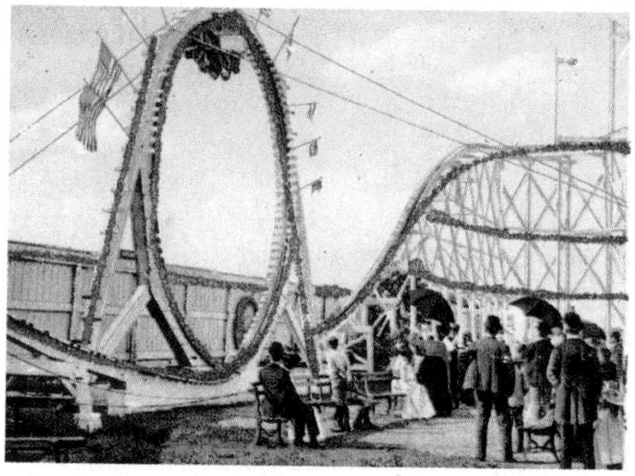

Acceleration
An early loop ride at Coney Island subjected riders to about 12 g's (12 times the acceleration due to gravity). For safety reasons, most modern rides do not exceed 5 g's.

Going Further

- Select an amusement park ride that you enjoy. Use library or Internet resources to discover the principles of physics that allow this ride to work. Write a paragraph or draw a diagram explaining what you have learned.
- Take a Discovery Channel Video Field Trip by watching "Physics of Fun."

Discovery Channel School
Video Field Trip

Build Science Skills **L2**

Using Models

ACTIVITY

Purpose After doing this activity, students will be able to build a physical model to determine properties of a roller coaster and realize that to complete a loop, a ball must have sufficient KE going into the loop.

Materials flexible track (like the bendable tracks used for toy cars), steel balls, books or wooden supports

Class Time 15 minutes

Procedure

1. Have students lay out a piece of track flat on the floor, and elevate one end on a stack of books or wooden supports. Have students bend the flat portion of the track so that it makes a vertical loop.
2. Have students start a steel ball rolling near the top of the elevated end. They should not push the ball, and they should start the ball in the same position for each trial. Have them experiment with the height of the loop. Then, have them find the greatest height that still allows the ball to stay in constant contact with the track while completing the loop.
3. Have students estimate the kinetic energy needed to make it around the top of the tallest loop. (*Hint*: Subtract the PE at the top of the loop from the initial PE.)

Expected Outcome The amount of kinetic energy needed to complete the loop depends on the height of the loop and the shape of the loop.
Kinesthetic, Portfolio

Going Further

Besides roller coasters, students may wish to consider a variety of spinning amusement park rides such as carousels, Ferris wheels, and tilting rides. These rides involve inertia and centripetal force. Other types of rides include bumper cars, pendulum-type rides, and tower freefall-type rides. The physics of these rides varies, but generally relates to Newton's laws of motion, the conservation of energy, and/or the conservation of momentum.
Verbal, Visual

Discovery Channel School

Video Field Trip

Physics of Fun

After students have viewed the Video Field Trip, ask them the following questions: **How does a roller coaster get to the top of the first hill?** *(It is pulled up by a chain and motor mechanism.)* **How does the roller coaster continue to move after the first hill?** *(By gravity. Students' answers may also include that potential energy is converted to kinetic energy as the roller coaster's height decreases, and back again to potential energy on the next hill.)* **When does the roller coaster have the most potential energy?** *(At the tops of hills. Students may additionally comment that the potential energy is greatest at the top of the first hill.)* **What happens to the roller coaster's potential energy as it goes down a hill?** *(It is converted into kinetic energy.)* **Why are the frames of modern roller coasters made out of steel, instead of the wooden frames that were once used?** *(Steel can support the stronger forces produced by the roller coaster. Also, it can be shaped into many different forms.)*

Section 15.3

1 FOCUS

Objectives

15.3.1 **Classify** energy resources as renewable or nonrenewable.

15.3.2 **Evaluate** benefits and drawbacks of different energy sources.

15.3.3 **Describe** ways to conserve energy resources.

Reading Focus

Build Vocabulary — L2

Word-Part Analysis Ask students what words they know that contain the key word parts *geo-* and *bio-*. *(Answers may include* geology, geometry; biology, biography.*)* Ask them to give a definition of each word part. *(geo- means "Earth" and bio- means "life.")*

Reading Strategy — L2

a. Nonrenewable energy resources include oil, natural gas, and coal. They exist in limited quantities.
b. Renewable energy resources include hydroelectric, solar, geothermal, wind, biomass, and nuclear fusion.
c. Energy resources can be conserved by reducing energy needs and by increasing energy efficiency.

2 INSTRUCT

Nonrenewable Energy Resources

Use Visuals — L1

Figure 16 Have students examine Figure 16. Ask, **What energy resource is being extracted in the figure?** *(Crude oil)* **Does it require energy to pump crude oil from underground and to process crude oil into more useful forms of fuel, such as gasoline?** *(Yes)* **If it requires energy to pump and process oil, then how can oil be a useful source of energy?** *(The amount of energy that the oil provides is greater than the energy required to extract it.)* **Of the forms of energy that you learned in Section 1, what form of energy does the oil contain?** *(Chemical energy)*
Visual, Logical

15.3 Energy Resources

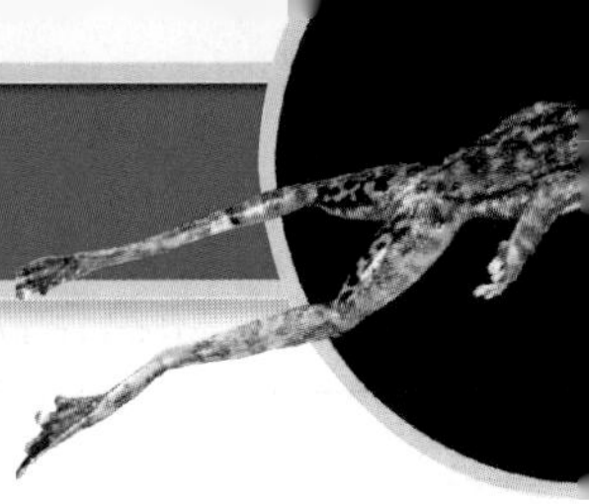

Reading Focus

Key Concepts

- What are the major nonrenewable and renewable sources of energy?
- How can energy resources be conserved?

Vocabulary

- nonrenewable energy resources
- fossil fuels
- renewable energy resources
- hydroelectric energy
- solar energy
- geothermal energy
- biomass energy
- hydrogen fuel cell
- energy conservation

Reading Strategy

Identifying Main Ideas Copy the table below. As you read, write the main idea for each heading.

Heading	Main Idea
Nonrenewable energy resources	a. ___?___
Renewable energy resources	b. ___?___
Conserving energy resources	c. ___?___

From the alarm clock that wakes you up each morning to the light that you turn off before you sleep, you depend on energy resources to operate many different devices to get you through each day. Energy resources can be classified as either renewable or nonrenewable.

Figure 16 Crude oil is pumped out of the ground or ocean floor. It is then refined and turned into gasoline, fuel oil, and other oil products.

Nonrenewable Energy Resources

Nonrenewable energy resources exist in limited quantities and, once used, cannot be replaced except over the course of millions of years. **Nonrenewable energy resources include oil, natural gas, coal, and uranium.** Such resources are currently being used much faster than they can be replaced, creating concern about how long they will last.

Oil, natural gas, and coal are known as **fossil fuels** because they were formed underground from the remains of once-living organisms. Currently, fossil fuels account for the great majority of the world's energy use. These fuels are not distributed evenly throughout the world. For example, about 60 percent of known oil supplies are located in a small area in the Middle East. The United States has just 2 percent of the world's oil supplies but about 25 percent of the world's coal supplies. Fossil fuels are relatively inexpensive and are usually readily available, but their use creates pollution.

Section Resources

Print
- ***Reading and Study Workbook With Math Support,*** Section 15.3
- ***Math Skills and Problem Solving Workbook,*** Section 15.3
- ***Transparencies,*** Section 15.3

Technology
- ***Interactive Textbook,*** Section 15.3
- ***Presentation Pro CD-ROM,*** Section 15.3
- ***Go Online,*** *Science News,* Energy and energy resources

Renewable Energy Resources

Renewable energy resources are resources that can be replaced in a relatively short period of time. Most renewable energy resources originate either directly or indirectly from the sun. The sun and Earth are constantly releasing large amounts of energy. This energy could be used for generating electric power, heating buildings or other purposes. **Renewable energy resources include hydroelectric, solar, geothermal, wind, biomass, and, possibly in the future, nuclear fusion.** The challenge for engineers and scientists is to find efficient ways to make these energy resources inexpensive and convenient.

Hydroelectric Energy Energy obtained from flowing water is known as **hydroelectric energy.** As water flows downhill, its gravitational potential energy is converted into kinetic energy. This kinetic energy can be used to turn turbines that are connected to electric generators.

Some hydroelectric power plants simply depend upon the natural flow of water in a river. But most modern plants, such as the one shown in Figure 17, rely on dams built across rivers. A dam blocks the flow of water, storing potential energy that is converted into kinetic energy when the water is released. The major advantages of hydroelectric energy include its low cost to produce and lack of pollution. Dams, however, cause a variety of environmental problems. For example, dams hamper the run of fish upriver for spawning. Also, in the United States many of the most suitable sites for hydroelectric plants are already in use.

Figure 17 Hoover Dam was built across the Colorado River on the Arizona-Nevada border. This 221-meter-tall structure can generate over 2 million kilowatts of power. **Applying Concepts** ***What type of energy conversion is involved in a hydroelectric plant?***

Data Analysis

World Energy Use

Which energy resources are most commonly used around the world? How is energy use changing over time? The table shows total world energy use in 1991 and 2000. Energy use is measured in British thermal units, or Btu (1 Btu = 1055 J). Note that petroleum includes oil and related fuels.

1. **Using Tables** What was the world's largest source of energy in 1991? In 2000?
2. **Analyzing Data** In general, how did usage change from 1991 to 2000?
3. **Graphing** Make a circle graph of world energy use by source for the year 2000.

World Energy Use ($\times 10^{15}$ Btu)

Source	1991	2000
Petroleum	136.47	154.28
Coal	88.35	94.22
Natural gas	76.03	90.15
Hydroelectric power	23.13	27.80
Nuclear fission	21.29	25.66
Other	1.82	2.99

4. **Analyzing Data** What percentage of world energy use in 2000 was accounted for by fossil fuels?
5. **Predicting** How might total world energy use be different in 2020? Explain.

Customize for English Language Learners

Incorporating Personal Narratives
Tell students a story about a time in your life when you were lacking in a commonly available energy resource or a convenience that depends on energy resources (for example, during a power outage or when your car broke down). Ask students specific questions about how you could have changed your behavior to deal with the situation, for example, "What could I use for lights at night?" or "How could I get to work?" Encourage students to tell their own stories about similar situations. To close the discussion, you may point out that some of the ways people deal with unusual or emergency conditions are also ways that people could reduce energy use in everyday life.

Renewable Energy Resources

Integrate Earth Science L2

While hydroelectric power itself is a clean and renewable resource, hydroelectric dams block the regular flow of rivers, flooding areas upstream to create large reservoirs. Dam construction often receives public support not only because it provides power, but also because it creates lakes that provide recreational opportunities. The reservoir creates a new aquatic ecosystem, but it also destroys the ecosystem that was there for a long time before the dam was built. Have students use a library or the Internet to research the effects of dams on landscapes and ecosystems. Have them write a report arguing for or against the construction of large dams.
Verbal, Portfolio

Data Analysis

World Energy Use L2

1. Petroleum in both years
2. Each type of energy use increased between 1991 and 2000.
3. Students' circle graphs should reflect the following approximate percentages of world energy use by source: petroleum (39%), coal (24%), natural gas (23%), hydroelectric power (7%), nuclear fission (6%), other (1%).
4. Approximately 86%
5. Based on the trend between 1991 and 2000, students will likely predict that total world energy use will be significantly higher in 2020 than it was in 2000. They may also predict that the percentage of energy resources in the "other" category (which includes most renewable energy resources) will increase by 2020.

Logical

For Extra Help L1

Tell students to scan the data vertically to answer Question 1 and horizontally to answer Question 2. For Questions 3 and 4, review the calculation of percentages. Tell students that they must first find the total world energy use for the year 2000 by adding all the numbers in the right-hand column. **Logical**

Answer to . . .

Figure 17 *Gravitational potential energy to kinetic energy and kinetic energy to electric energy*

Teacher Demo

Simple Solar Cell L2

Purpose Demonstrate energy conversions and renewable resources.

Materials small solar array, small motor with fan, direct sunlight or bright light source

Procedure Attach the wires from the motor to the solar array. Place the solar array in direct sunlight or under a bright light source.

Expected Outcome The motor will spin and the fan blades will rotate. Ask students to describe the energy transformations, starting with the light and ending with the motion of the blades. *(Electromagnetic energy from light is converted to electrical energy in the solar cell. The motor converts this electrical energy into kinetic energy, which turns the fan.)*
Kinesthetic, Logical

Use Community Resources L2

Have students contact the local electric company and ask what kind of power plant(s) it uses. Have students ask if the company uses any renewable energy resources, such as wind, solar, or geothermal energy.
Interpersonal, Portfolio

Build Reading Literacy L1

Compare and Contrast Refer to page **226D** in **Chapter 8,** which provides the guidelines for comparing and contrasting.

Have students compare and contrast renewable energy resources. Ask, **How are all renewable energy sources similar?** *(They can be replaced in a short time; most originate from the sun; most are nonpolluting.)* Ask, **Which renewable energy sources are derived from the kinetic energy of natural materials?** *(Hydroelectric, wind)*
Logical

Go Online SCIENCE NEWS

Science News provides students with current information on energy and energy resources.

A
B

Figure 18 Solar and geothermal energy plants use renewable resources to generate electricity. **A** A solar electric plant uses solar cells to convert sunlight into electricity. **B** A geothermal plant in California uses Earth's thermal energy to generate electricity. **Comparing and Contrasting** ***What are some similarities and differences between solar energy and geothermal energy?***

Solar Energy Sunlight that is converted into usable energy is called **solar energy.** Passive solar designs use sunlight to heat a building without using machinery. For example, sunlight passing through the windows of a house may be absorbed by thick walls that then radiate thermal energy to warm the house.

In an active solar energy system, sunlight heats flat collection plates through which water flows. The heated water may be used directly for the building's hot water needs, or it may be used to heat the house. Sunlight can also be converted directly into electrical energy by means of solar cells, also known as photovoltaic cells. Many small devices such as calculators now run on solar cells. A few large solar electric plants, like the one shown in Figure 18A, use mirrors that concentrate sunlight to produce electricity.

The benefits of solar energy depend on the climate. Solar energy is nonpolluting, but for areas where cloudy days are frequent, solar energy is less practical.

Geothermal Energy **Geothermal energy** is thermal energy beneath Earth's surface. In some regions, especially near volcanoes, geothermal energy is used to generate electicity. The geothermal power plant in Figure 18B pumps water into the ground, where it turns into steam. The steam is then used to drive electric generators. Geothermal energy is nonpolluting, but is not widely available.

Other Renewable Resources Sunlight causes plants to grow, converting electromagnetic energy into chemical energy. The chemical energy stored in living things is called **biomass energy.** Biomass can be converted directly into thermal energy. For example, many people around the world burn wood or peat to heat their homes or for cooking. Also, agricultural wastes such as corn stalks can be converted into a high-energy alcohol fuel that can be added to gasoline for cars.

A **hydrogen fuel cell** generates electricity by reacting hydrogen with oxygen. Hydrogen fuel cells can be used to convert energy from renewable resources. For example, hydrogen fuel can be extracted from water using electricity from solar cells. The end product of fuel cells is water, so they offer a nonpolluting means for transporting energy.

A form of hydrogen is also the most likely raw material for another future source of energy, nuclear fusion. The process of fusion will probably produce little pollution or radioactive waste. Scientists have been working on sustained fusion for years, but many challenges remain.

Go Online SCIENCE NEWS

For: Articles on energy and energy resources
Visit: PHSchool.com
Web Code: cce-2153

Reading Checkpoint *What is biomass energy?*

Facts and Figures

Extreme Solar Energy The British-American physicist Freeman Dyson is famous for his inventive ideas related to the Search for Extraterrestrial Intelligence (SETI). In 1959, Dyson proposed a theoretical device, now called a Dyson sphere, that an advanced civilization could use to capture nearly all of the energy radiated from a star.

Dyson believed that while a moderately technological civilization like our own is limited to the energy resources found on our home planet, a highly advanced technological civilization (particularly one capable of interstellar travel) would have more extreme energy needs. Therefore, they would eventually come up with a device similar to the Dyson sphere. Dyson suggested that scientists searching for extraterrestrial life should look for evidence of Dyson spheres because they would be sure signs of an advanced civilization.

464 Chapter 15

HOW It Works

Wind Turbine

Wind turbines convert the kinetic energy in the horizontal movement of wind into rotational energy of the turbine's rotor shaft. Rotational energy is then converted into electrical energy using an electric generator. The output of a wind turbine depends on the turbine's size and the wind's speed. **Interpreting Diagrams** ***What is the purpose of the gearbox?***

Wind farm
Enormous wind farms like this one in California can generate as much power as a large power plant (without any air pollution).

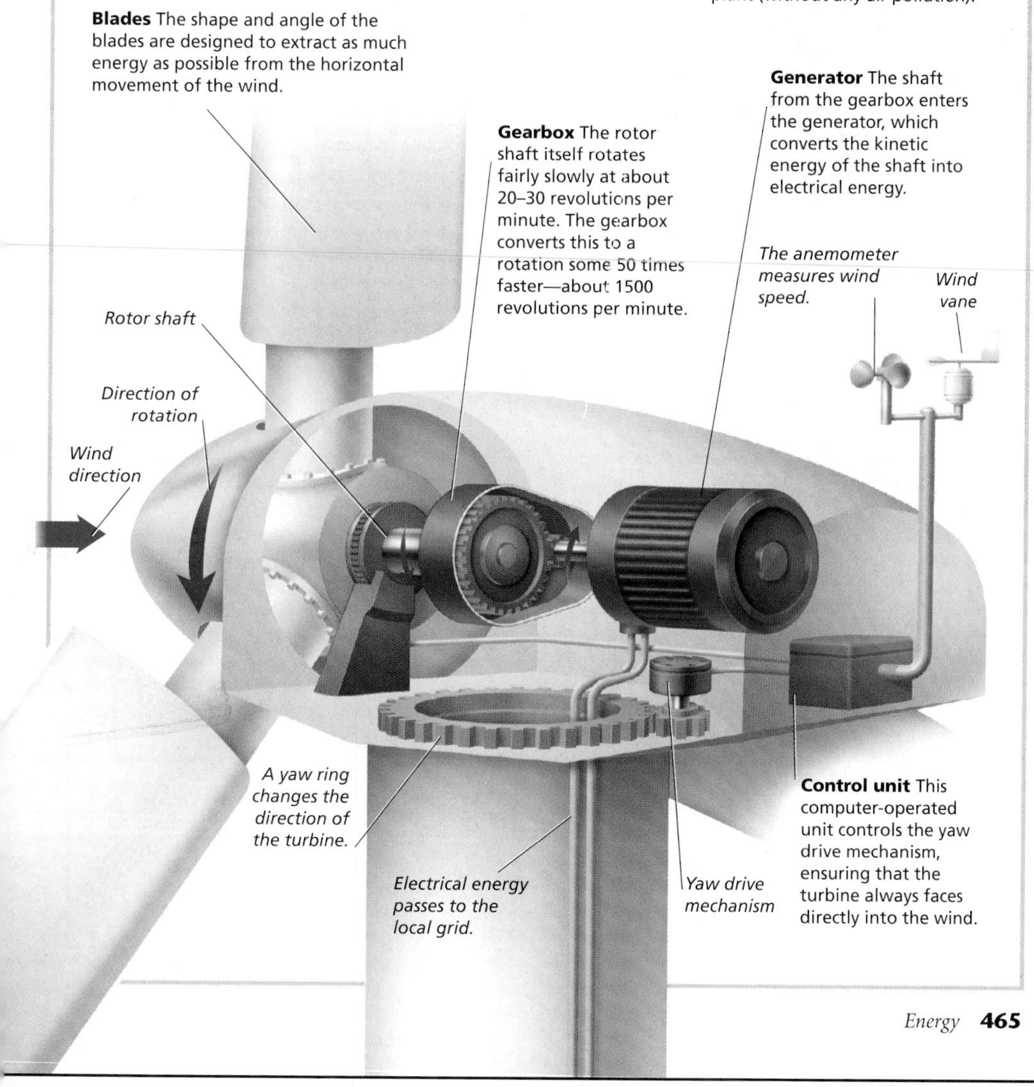
Blades The shape and angle of the blades are designed to extract as much energy as possible from the horizontal movement of the wind.
Gearbox The rotor shaft itself rotates fairly slowly at about 20–30 revolutions per minute. The gearbox converts this to a rotation some 50 times faster—about 1500 revolutions per minute.
Generator The shaft from the gearbox enters the generator, which converts the kinetic energy of the shaft into electrical energy.
The anemometer measures wind speed.
Wind vane
Rotor shaft
Direction of rotation
Wind direction
A yaw ring changes the direction of the turbine.
Electrical energy passes to the local grid.
Yaw drive mechanism
Control unit This computer-operated unit controls the yaw drive mechanism, ensuring that the turbine always faces directly into the wind.

HOW It Works

Wind Turbine L2

Humans have used wind as a source of power for many centuries. Perhaps the earliest example is the use of sails to power ships. Windmills were used in the Middle East and China to pump water or grind grains as early as 500 A.D. The earliest windmills turned on a vertical axis, rather than a horizontal axis as most do today. Windmills played an important role in the development of the American West, as they provided power to pump water from underground sources to support livestock and crops. The use of wind turbines to generate electricity developed in tandem with the increasing use of electricity in the late nineteenth and early twentieth centuries. Today, wind provides less than one % of the electric power used in the United States. However, proponents of wind power estimate that wind could provide up to ten times our current total use of electricity.

Wind power is essentially a type of solar power because wind is driven by uneven heating of air near Earth's surface by the sun. This also means that wind is a free and renewable resource. Because there are no chemical or nuclear reactions involved in generating electricity from wind, wind power produces no pollution.

Interpreting Diagrams The purpose of the gearbox is to increase the rotational speed of the shaft.
Logical

For Enrichment L3

The most extensive wind resources on Earth are found over the oceans. Have students research large offshore wind farms currently in use or in development. They may write a report or prepare a presentation for the class about their findings.
Verbal, Portfolio

Answer to . . .

Figure 18 *Both solar energy and geothermal energy are renewable energy resources that are nonpolluting and can be used to produce electricity or heat. The source of solar energy is the sun, while that of geothermal energy is heat from Earth. The factors that influence their availability differ as well.*

Reading Checkpoint *The chemical energy stored in living things*

Section 15.3 (continued)

Conserving Energy Resources

Address Misconceptions L2

Some students may think that energy comes from a specific source, such as food or a power company. Point out that objects always have some gravitational potential energy (with respect to some reference point), and that any moving object has kinetic energy. The forms of energy discussed in this section can be harnessed and distributed on a large scale, often by converting them to electrical energy. **Verbal**

Build Science Skills L2

Analyzing Data Have students examine a monthly electricity bill to find the energy usage. Show students that kW-h = power × time = (work/time) × time = work. Explain that work has the same units as energy. Ask students to convert the usage from kilowatt-hours to joules (1 kW-h = 1000 W-h × 3600 s/h = 3.6×10^6 J).
Logical, Portfolio

3 ASSESS

Evaluate Understanding L2

Ask students to state the fundamental difference between renewable and nonrenewable energy resources and then list at least three examples of each.

Reteach L1

Have each student review an energy resource. Have them work in pairs and discuss the pros and cons of the resource that they reviewed.

Writing in Science

Encourage students to use a library or the Internet to research energy conservation and alternative energy resources.

Interactive Textbook If your class subscribes to the Interactive Textbook, use it to review key concepts in Section 15.3.

Answer to . . .

Figure 19 *By reducing the total number of vehicles*

CRES
Butterfield

Figure 19 Mass transportation systems include buses, trains, and streetcars such as the one shown here. **Inferring** ***How can the use of mass transportation save energy?***

Conserving Energy Resources

Fossil fuel supplies may become increasingly scarce and expensive in the future. An important way to make these energy resources last longer is to use them more slowly. **Energy resources can be conserved by reducing energy needs and by increasing the efficiency of energy use.** Finding ways to use less energy or to use energy more efficiently is known as **energy conservation.**

It's easy to forget that the energy you use often comes at the expense of resources that are being used up forever. People can reduce the use of these resources by making energy-saving decisions, for example turning off lights when they are not being used. Because conventional cars consume an enormous amount of energy, the decisions that people make about transportation are very important. Walking or biking on short trips and carpooling can save considerable energy. Using mass transportation, such as the streetcar shown in Figure 19, can also reduce energy use.

Making appliances, cars, and even light bulbs more energy efficient is a way of reducing energy use while still enjoying its benefits. Much has already been done to make appliances more energy efficient. Light bulbs have been developed that provide superior lighting at a lower energy cost. The technology for further improvement, including more fuel-efficient cars, is already known in many cases. However, the initial cost of energy efficiency can be an obstacle for manufacturers and for consumers. Energy-efficient purchases often cost more initially, but can save money in fuel costs over time.

Section 15.3 Assessment

Reviewing Concepts

1. List the major nonrenewable and renewable sources of energy.
2. What could be done to make present energy resources last longer?
3. Why are coal, oil, and natural gas called fossil fuels?

Critical Thinking

4. **Applying Concepts** You are looking for the best place to build a hydroelectric plant along a river. Would you locate the plant along a steep or flat section of the river? Explain.
5. **Comparing and Contrasting** How are passive and active solar energy systems different?
6. **Applying Concepts** Describe three ways that you used energy resources today.

Writing in Science

Writing to Persuade Suppose you are an energy planner who is concerned about the possibility of future shortages of electricity. Write a paragraph describing one or two proposals that you think would help to avoid this potential problem.

Section 15.3 Assessment

1. Nonrenewable: oil, natural gas, coal, and uranium; Renewable: solar, hydroelectric, wind, biomass, geothermal, and possibly nuclear fusion in the future
2. Use nonrenewable energy resources more slowly by reducing energy use and increasing energy efficiency.
3. They are each made from remains of ancient organisms.
4. Steep, because the faster moving water has more kinetic energy and thus can generate more power
5. Passive solar systems convert sunlight to thermal energy without the use of machinery. Active solar systems use machinery to convert sunlight into thermal energy or electricity.
6. Student answers may include turning on an electric light, listening to the radio, taking a shower, using a computer, and so forth.

Application Lab

Investigating a Spring Clip

There are many ways to use potential energy. A spring clip is a device used to hold weights on a barbell. The spring clip stores energy when you compress it. In this lab, you will determine how the distance you compress a spring clip is related to the force you apply and to the spring's potential energy.

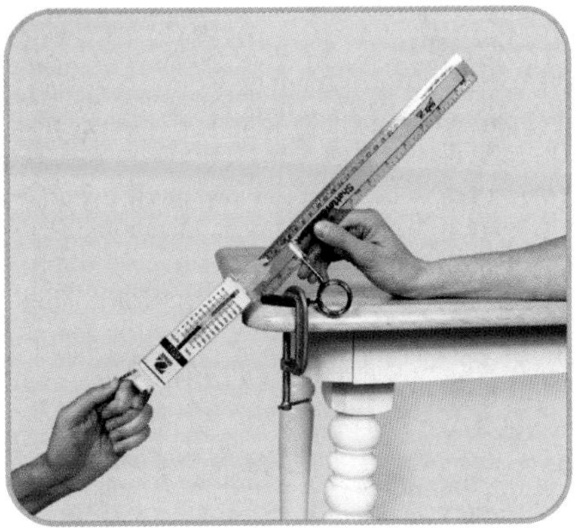

Problem How does the force you apply to a spring clip affect its elastic potential energy?

Materials

- clamp
- spring clip
- masking tape
- metric ruler
- 50-newton spring scale
- graph paper

For the probeware version of this lab, see the Probeware Lab Manual, Lab 6.

Skills Measuring, Using Tables and Graphs

Procedure

1. Make a data table with three columns. Label the columns Force (N), Position of Handle (cm), and Total Distance Moved (cm).
2. Using the clamp, firmly attach one handle of the spring clip to a tabletop, with the other handle facing up and away from the table as shown. **CAUTION** *Be careful not to pinch your fingers with the clamp or spring clip.*
3. Remove the plastic cover from the upper handle of the spring clip. Hook the spring scale to the spring clip handle as shown and use masking tape to secure it. Have your teacher check your setup for safety before proceeding.
4. Have a classmate hold the ruler next to the spring clip as shown. Record the starting position of the handle. (The reading on the spring scale should be zero.)
5. Slowly pull the spring scale down at a right angle to the upper handle until the upper handle moves 0.1 cm. Record the force and the position of the upper handle. Slowly release the scale back to the starting position.
6. Repeat Step 5, this time pulling the handle 0.2 cm from the starting position.
7. Repeat Step 5 a few more times, pulling the handle 0.1 cm farther each time. Continue until the spring scale reaches its maximum force.
8. Calculate the total distance the handle moved each time you pulled it and record these values in your data table. Graph your data. Place distance on the horizontal axis and force on the vertical axis.

Analyze and Conclude

1. **Using Graphs** What is the approximate relationship between the total distance you compressed the spring clip and the force you applied to it?
2. **Classifying** What type of energy transfer did you use to compress the spring clip? What type of energy did the spring clip gain when it was compressed?
3. **Drawing Conclusions** What relationship exists between the distance the spring clip was compressed and its potential energy? (*Hint:* The elastic potential energy of the spring clip equals the work done on it.)

Go Online PHSchool.com

For: Data sharing
Visit: PHSchool.com
Web Code: ccd-2150

Probeware Lab Manual Versions of this lab for use with probeware available from Pasco, Texas Instruments, and Vernier are in the Probeware Lab Manual.

Application Lab

Investigating a Spring Clip

L2

Objective
After completing this activity, students will be able to
- describe the relationship between an applied force and the resulting change in elastic potential energy.

Skills Focus **Observing, Measuring, Using Tables and Graphs**

Prep Time 15 minutes

Advance Prep Spring clips can be purchased from department or sporting-goods stores. C-clamps can be purchased from hardware stores.

Class Time 45 minutes

Safety Students should wear safety goggles. Check students' setups in Step 2 to make sure that the spring clip is securely clamped to the table and will not come loose when compressed. Masking tape placed as shown in the photograph will prevent the spring scale from becoming a projectile if a student accidentally releases it.

Teaching Tips
- Make sure that students do not exceed the limits of the spring scale. If it is stretched too far, it may not work properly in the future.

Expected Outcome There should be a linear relationship between force and distance. As distance increases, force increases.

Analyze and Conclude
1. As the distance increased, the force increased. The relationship between force and distance is directly proportional.
2. Students did work to compress the spring clip. This action increased the elastic potential energy of the spring clip.
3. The greater the distance the spring clip was compressed, the greater its elastic potential energy.
Kinesthetic, Logical

Go Online PHSchool.com

Students should see a direct relationship between applied force and elastic potential energy, but their results will depend on their own data and the data on the site.

Study Guide

Study Tip

Take Control
Tell students to make a list of all the things they need to do. Suggest that they divide their workload into manageable chunks.

Thinking Visually

a. Electrical
b. The energy associated with electric charges
c. Chemical
d. Possible answers include wood, gasoline, food items, and so forth.
e. Energy that travels through space in the form of waves
f. Possible answers include visible light and X-rays.
g. The energy stored in atomic nuclei
h. The total kinetic and potential energy of all the microscopic particles in an object
i. Possible answers include molten metal and fire.

Assessment

Interactive Textbook If your class subscribes to the Interactive Textbook, your students can go online to access an interactive version of the Student Edition and a self-test.

Reviewing Content

1. a	**2.** b	**3.** a
4. d	**5.** c	**6.** d
7. a	**8.** b	**9.** c
10. c		

CHAPTER 15

Study Guide

15.1 Energy and Its Forms

Key Concepts

- Work is the transfer of energy.
- The kinetic energy of any moving object depends on its mass and speed.
- An object's gravitational potential energy depends on its mass, its height, and the acceleration due to gravity.
- The major forms of energy are mechanical energy, thermal energy, chemical energy, electrical energy, electromagnetic energy, and nuclear energy.

Vocabulary

energy, *p. 447*
kinetic energy, *p. 447*
potential energy, *p. 448*
gravitational potential energy, *p. 449*
elastic potential energy, *p. 450*
mechanical energy, *p. 450*
thermal energy, *p. 451*
chemical energy, *p. 451*
electrical energy, *p. 452*
electromagnetic energy, *p. 452*
nuclear energy, *p. 452*

15.2 Energy Conversion and Conservation

Key Concepts

- Energy can be converted from one form to another.
- The law of conservation of energy states that energy cannot be created or destroyed.
- The gravitational potential energy of an object is converted to the kinetic energy of motion as the object falls.
- Einstein's equation shows that energy and mass are equivalent, and can be converted into each other.

Vocabulary

energy conversion, *p. 454*

15.3 Energy Resources

Key Concepts

- Nonrenewable energy resources include oil, natural gas, coal, and uranium.
- Renewable energy resources include hydroelectric, solar, geothermal, wind, biomass, and, possibly in the future, nuclear fusion.
- Energy resources can be conserved by reducing our energy needs and by increasing the efficiency of energy use.

Vocabulary

nonrenewable energy resources, *p. 462*
fossil fuels, *p. 462*
renewable energy resources, *p. 463*
hydroelectric energy, *p. 463*
solar energy, *p. 464*
geothermal energy, *p. 464*
biomass energy, *p. 464*
hydrogen fuel cell, *p. 464*
energy conservation, *p. 466*

Thinking Visually

Comparing and Contrasting Copy the partially completed table below. Complete it to compare the major forms of energy.

Form of Energy	Definition	Example
Mechanical	Energy of motion and position of everyday objects	Bouncing ball
a. ___?___	b. ___?___	Lightning
c. ___?___	Energy stored in chemical bonds	d. ___?___
Electromagnetic	e. ___?___	f. ___?___
Nuclear	g. ___?___	Fission
Thermal	h. ___?___	i. ___?___

Chapter Resources

Print
- ***Chapter and Unit Tests,*** Chapter 15 Test A and Test B
- ***Test Prep Resources,*** Chapter 15

Technology
- ***Computer Test Bank,*** Chapter Test 15
- ***Interactive Textbook,*** Chapter 15
- ***Go Online,*** PHSchool.com, Chapter 15

CHAPTER 15

Assessment

Interactive textbook with assessment at PHSchool.com iText

Reviewing Content

Choose the letter that best answers the question or completes the statement.

1. The energy of a moving object is
   a. kinetic energy. b. potential energy.
   c. chemical energy. d. nuclear energy.

2. If the speed of an object doubles, its kinetic energy
   a. doubles. b. quadruples.
   c. stays the same. d. is halved.

3. An example of an object having elastic potential energy is
   a. a stretched spring. b. books on a shelf.
   c. a moving arrow. d. a falling oyster.

4. An example of electromagnetic energy is
   a. a falling rock. b. a stretched spring.
   c. a speeding train. d. sunlight.

5. Energy stored in the bonds between atoms is called
   a. kinetic energy. b. mechanical energy.
   c. chemical energy. d. thermal energy.

6. Mechanical energy is
   a. found in machinery only.
   b. usually measured at the atomic level.
   c. the sum of the chemical and thermal energy of an object.
   d. the sum of the kinetic and potential energy of an object.

7. An example of the conversion of gravitational potential energy into kinetic energy is
   a. a falling raindrop.
   b. a gasoline-powered engine.
   c. striking a match.
   d. a hockey puck sliding on ice.

8. The law of conservation of energy states that
   a. energy cannot be converted from one form to another.
   b. energy cannot be created or destroyed.
   c. energy resources must be used efficiently.
   d. energy is constantly being lost to friction.

9. Which of the following energy resources accounts for most of the world's present energy use?
   a. uranium b. solar energy
   c. fossil fuels d. wind energy

10. Most renewable energy originates from
   a. fossil fuels. b. the ground.
   c. the sun. d. uranium.

Understanding Concepts

11. What is energy?

12. How are kinetic energy and potential energy different?

13. How does the potential energy of an object change when its height is tripled?

14. Look at the graphs below. One of the graphs is a plot of kinetic energy vs. mass for a set of objects with different masses, all moving at the same speed. The other graph is a plot of kinetic energy vs. speed for a set of objects with the same mass, all moving at different speeds. Identify each graph and explain how can you tell which graph is which.

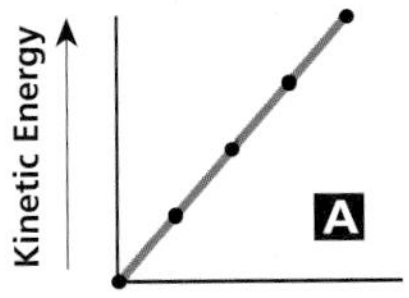
Kinetic Energy
A

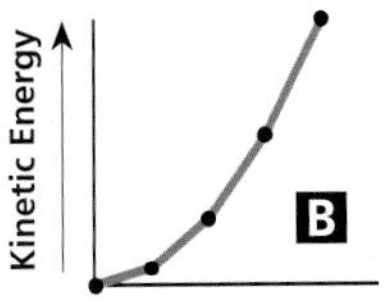
Kinetic Energy
B

15. What happens to the atoms of an object if its thermal energy is increased?

16. Explain the energy conversions that occur as a basketball falls, hits the ground, and bounces back up. Ignore frictional forces.

17. What force is acting when the kinetic energy of a moving object is converted into thermal energy?

18. Explain how energy is converted as a pendulum swings.

19. Is mechanical energy always conserved? Explain why or why not.

20. Explain the meaning and the importance of the formula $E = mc^2$.

21. Why are coal, oil, and natural gas considered to be nonrenewable energy resources?

22. What is the source of geothermal energy?

Homework Guide

Section	Questions
15.1	1–6, 11–15, 23–24, 26–29, 32
15.2	7–8, 16–20, 25, 30–31, 33
15.3	9–10, 21–22, 34–36

Assessment (continued)

Understanding Concepts

11. Energy is the ability to do work.
12. Kinetic energy is the energy of motion of a moving object. Potential energy is energy stored due to the position or shape of an object.
13. Its potential energy is also tripled because potential energy is proportional to an object's height relative to a reference level.
14. Graph A is the kinetic energy vs. mass plot because kinetic energy is directly proportional to mass. Graph B is the kinetic energy vs. speed plot because kinetic energy is proportional to the square of speed.
15. The object's atoms move faster.
16. Gravitational potential energy is converted into kinetic energy as the ball falls. The kinetic energy is converted into elastic potential energy when the ball hits the ground and is compressed. The elastic potential energy is converted back into kinetic energy as the ball springs back into shape and is propelled upward. Finally, the ball's kinetic energy is converted into gravitational potential energy as the ball rises.
17. Friction
18. The point from which the pendulum weight is released is its maximum height, and this position has maximum potential energy. As the pendulum swings downward, gravitational potential energy is converted into kinetic energy. At the bottom of the swing, the pendulum reaches its maximum kinetic energy. Relative to this height, it has zero potential energy. The pendulum then moves upward, and its kinetic energy is converted back into gravitational potential energy. As the result of friction resistance, some energy is also converted into thermal energy during each swing.
19. No. Mechanical energy is not conserved when friction exists.
20. This formula shows that energy and mass are equivalent, and that energy can be converted into mass and mass can be converted into energy. A tiny amount of mass is equivalent to a large amount of energy.
21. They are all fossil fuels that formed over millions of years and cannot be quickly replaced.
22. Geothermal energy comes from the heat below Earth's surface.

Critical Thinking

23. $KE = 1/2mv^2 =$
$(0.500)(100.0 \text{ kg})(10{,}000 \text{ m/s})^2 =$
5.00×10^9 J

24. Step 1: Use the scale to find the mass of the ball. Step 2: Put the ball on top of a vertically oriented compressed spring. Step 3: Release the spring and measure how high the ball is propelled into the air. Step 4: Use the equation for gravitational potential energy to find the energy of the ball at its peak. Step 5: Apply the law of conservation of energy. The gravitational potential energy of the ball equals the elastic potential energy of the spring.

25. $(KE + PE)_{150m} = (KE + PE)_{63m}$
$KE_{150m} = 0$; $PE_{150m} =$
$(0.15 \text{ kg})(9.8 \text{ m/s}^2)(150 \text{ m}) = 220$ J;
$PE_{63m} = (0.15 \text{ kg})(9.8 \text{ m/s}^2)(63 \text{ m}) =$ 93 J
$(0 + 220 \text{ J}) = (KE_{63m} + 93 \text{ J})$
$KE_{63m} = 220 \text{ J} - 93 \text{ J} = 130$ J

Math Skills

26. $KE = 1/2mv^2$; units for KE are $\text{kg}\bullet(\text{m/s})^2 = \text{kg}\bullet\text{m}^2/\text{s}^2$
$PE = mgh$; units for PE are $\text{kg}\bullet(\text{m/s}^2)\bullet\text{m} = \text{kg}\bullet\text{m}^2/\text{s}^2$
Note that 1 $\text{kg}\bullet\text{m/s}^2$ is a newton, so the units for KE and PE are newton-meters, or joules.

27. Ball 1, 32.0 J; Ball 2, 1.00 J; Ball 3, 24.0 J

28. Ball 2, with a gravitational potential energy of 197 J

29. Ball 2, with a kinetic energy of 197 J

Concepts in Action

30. The graph of kinetic energy should start high and gradually decrease as the ball reaches its maximum height. Then, the curve should rise again until the ball hits the ground. The potential energy graph should be the reverse, with maximum values when kinetic energy is lowest and a value of zero when the ball is on the ground.

31. The frictional force of the air is converting the gravitational potential energy into thermal energy.

32. $PE = mgh =$
$(200.0 \text{ kg})(9.8 \text{ m/s}^2)(3.00 \text{ m}) = 5900$ J

33. At the top of the loop, the car's gravitational potential energy is a maximum and its kinetic energy is a minimum. As the car moves downward, it picks up speed as gravitational potential energy is converted into kinetic energy. The car's kinetic energy is highest and gravitational potential energy is lowest at the bottom of the loop.

34. Advantages include lack of noise and lack of pollution. A disadvantage is its dependence on the availability of the sun. Solar energy is not available at night, unless it has been stored from the daytime. Some regions do not have enough sunny days to make solar energy practical.

35. The kinetic energy of the wind can be used to turn the arms of a turbine, which can generate electricity when connected to a generator.

36. Students should state the law of conservation of energy in their own words. Their example should either account for the thermal energy lost due to friction or focus on an example where friction is negligible.

CHAPTER 15

Assessment *(continued)*

Critical Thinking

23. Calculating A small meteoroid is approaching Earth. It has a mass of 100.0 kg and a speed of 10.0 km/s. How much kinetic energy does the meteoroid have? (*Hint:* 1 km = 1000 m)

24. Designing an Experiment Design an experiment to find out how much elastic potential energy is in a compressed spring. In addition to the spring, you may use a small metal ball, a ruler, and a scale for measuring mass.

25. Calculating A 0.15-kg ball is dropped from the top of a 150-m building. What is the kinetic energy of the ball when it passes the sixteenth floor at a height of 63 m? (Ignore air resistance.)

Math Skills

26. Converting Units Using mass in kg, velocity in m/s, and height in m, show that the formulas for kinetic energy and gravitational potential energy result in energy values with the same units. What is the energy unit called?

Questions 27–29 refer to the data in the table below.

Three balls are thrown vertically into the air from different heights above the ground. The data for each ball are shown in the table below.

Data Table

Object	Mass (kg)	Initial Upward Speed (m/s)	Initial Height Above Ground (m)
Ball 1	1.00	8.00	15.00
Ball 2	2.00	1.00	10.00
Ball 3	3.00	4.00	5.00

27. Calculating How much kinetic energy does each ball have when it is thrown?

28. Analyzing Data Which ball has the greatest gravitational potential energy when it reaches its maximum height? (*Hint:* Find the total energy for each ball.)

29. Predicting Which ball hits the ground with the most kinetic energy?

Concepts in Action

30. Using Graphs A soccer ball is kicked from the ground into the air. Describe two graphs that show how the potential energy and kinetic energy change between the time the ball is kicked and when it lands. (*Hint:* Make time the *x*-axis.)

31. Inferring When a falling object reaches a speed called terminal velocity, its speed no longer increases. The object is losing gravitational potential energy but not gaining kinetic energy. Since energy must be conserved, where must the gravitational potential energy be going?

32. Calculating Suppose a 200.0-kilogram dolphin is lifted in the air to be placed into an aquarium tank. How much energy is needed to lift the dolphin 3.00 meters into the air?

33. Applying Concepts How is energy converted as a car moves between the top and the bottom of a roller coaster loop?

34. Making Judgments What are some advantages and disadvantages of solar energy?

35. Applying Concepts How can electricity be obtained from the wind?

36. Writing in Science Using your own words, write a brief summary of the law of conservation of energy. Include an example from your everyday life.

Performance-Based Assessment

Applying Concepts Identify one practical way that your family or school could reduce energy use. Find out how much energy is currently being used for the purpose you choose, and estimate how much energy your suggestion could save. Write a brief summary of your recommendations.

Go Online
PHSchool.com

For: Self-grading assessment
Visit: PHSchool.com
Web Code: cca-2150

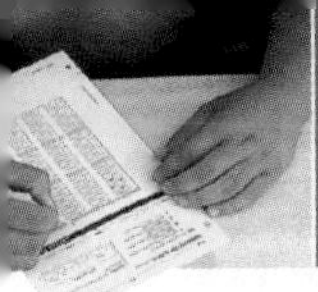

Standardized Test Prep

Test-Taking Tip

Avoiding Careless Mistakes
Students often make mistakes when they fail to examine a test question and possible answers thoroughly. Read the question carefully and underline key words that may change the meaning of the question, such as *not, except, excluding,* and so on. After choosing an answer, reread the question to check your selection.

Which statement about work and energy is NOT correct?
(A) Both can be expressed in joules.
(B) Energy is the ability to do work.
(C) Work done is always equal to energy input.
(D) Energy input is always greater than work output.
(E) Energy is transferred in order to accomplish work.

(Answer: C)

Choose the letter that best answers the question or completes the statement.

1. Which form of energy does a plant store when light is transformed during photosynthesis?
   (A) chemical energy
   (B) thermal energy
   (C) mechanical energy
   (D) electrical energy
   (E) nuclear energy

2. Which of the following is NOT an example of kinetic energy being converted to potential energy?
   (A) a basketball player jumping for a rebound
   (B) releasing a compressed spring
   (C) squeezing a rubber ball
   (D) pulling a sled up a hill
   (E) a swing moving upward

3. A 50.0-kg wolf is running at 10.0 m/sec. What is the wolf's kinetic energy?
   (A) 5 J (B) 500 J
   (C) 5000 J (D) 250 J
   (E) 2500 J

4. Friction causes kinetic energy to be converted into
   (A) potential energy.
   (B) thermal energy.
   (C) mechanical energy.
   (D) electrical energy.
   (E) chemical energy.

5. Which of the following is NOT considered a renewable energy resource?
   (A) geothermal energy
   (B) biomass
   (C) hydroelectric energy
   (D) uranium
   (E) wind energy

Use the figure below to answer Questions 6 and 7.

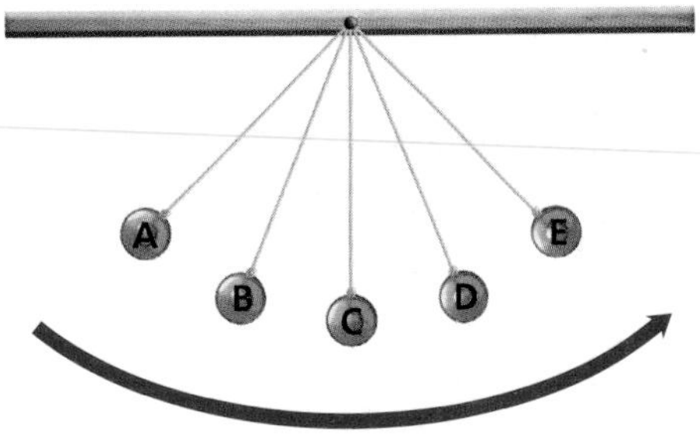
A
B
C
D
E

A pendulum weight is released in position A. The weight moves through positions B, C, D, and E.

6. At which location(s) does the pendulum have maximum potential energy?
   (A) A and B
   (B) B and D
   (C) C only
   (D) D and E
   (E) A and E

7. At which location(s) does the pendulum have maximum kinetic energy?
   (A) A and B
   (B) B and D
   (C) C only
   (D) D and E
   (E) A and E

Standardized Test Prep

1. A 2. B 3. E
4. B 5. D 6. E
7. C

Performance-Based Assessment

Students should focus on a specific energy conservation measure, such as replacing incandescent light bulbs with a more efficient alternative. They can estimate daily energy use of an electrical device by multiplying the device's power rating in watts by the approximate number of hours the device is used each day. If they choose an option related to space heating or cooling, they should also consider seasonal variations in use.

Go Online PHSchool.com

Your students can independently test their knowledge of the chapter and print out their results for your files.

CHAPTER 16

Planning Guide

Use these planning tools
Easy Planner
Teacher Express

SECTION OBJECTIVES	STANDARDS NATIONAL (See p. T18.)	STANDARDS STATE	ACTIVITIES and LABS
16.1 Thermal Energy and Matter, pp. 474–478 1 block or 2 periods **16.1.1 Explain** how heat and work transfer energy. **16.1.2 Relate** thermal energy to the motion of particles that make up a material. **16.1.3 Relate** temperature to thermal energy and to thermal expansion. **16.1.4 Calculate** thermal energy, temperature change, or mass using the specific heat equation. **16.1.5 Describe** how a calorimeter operates and **calculate** thermal energy changes or specific heat using calorimetry measurements.	A-1, A-2, B-2, B-5, G-1, G-2, G-3		**SE** Inquiry Activity: What Happens When Hot and Cold Liquids Mix? p. 473 L2 **SE** Quick Lab: Cooling Air, p. 476 L2 **SE** Design Your Own Lab: Using Specific Heat to Analyze Metals, p. 493 L2 **TE** Teacher Demo: Calorimetry, p. 478 L2
16.2 Heat and Thermodynamics, pp. 479–483 1 block or 2 periods **16.2.1 Describe** conduction, convection, and radiation and **identify** which of these is occurring in a given situation. **16.2.2 Classify** materials as thermal conductors or thermal insulators. **16.2.3 Apply** the law of conservation of energy to conversions between thermal energy and other forms of energy. **16.2.4 Apply** the second law of thermodynamics in situations where thermal energy moves from cooler to warmer objects. **16.2.5 State** the third law of thermodynamics.	A-1, A-2, B-2, B-5, B-6, D-1, G-1, G-2, G-3		**SE** Quick Lab: Observing Convection, p. 481 L2 **TE** Teacher Demo: Conductors and Insulators, p. 480 L2 **TE** Build Science Skills: Applying Concepts, p. 482 L2 **LM** Investigation 16A: Determining the Effect of Surface Area on Heat Transfer L2 **LM** Investigation 16B: Explaining How a Flame Can Boil Water in a Paper Cup L1
16.3 Using Heat, pp. 486–492 1 block or 2 periods **16.3.1 Describe** heat engines and **explain** how heat engines convert thermal energy into mechanical energy. **16.3.2 Describe** how the different types of heating systems operate. **16.3.3 Describe** how cooling systems, such as refrigerators and air conditioners, operate. **16.3.4 Evaluate** benefits and drawbacks of different heating and cooling systems.	A-1, B-3, B-5, F-4, G-1, G-2, G-3		**TE** Teacher Demo: Cooling by Evaporation, p. 490 L2

Ability Levels	
L1	For students who need additional help
L2	For all students
L3	For students who need to be challenged

Components							
SE	Student Edition	RSW	Reading & Study Workbook	CUT	Chapter & Unit Tests	T	Transparencies
TE	Teacher's Edition	MSPS	Math Skills & Problem Solving Workbook	CTB	Computer Test Bank	iT	Interactive Textbook
LM	Laboratory Manual			TP	Test Prep Resources	P	Presentation Pro CD-ROM
PLM	Probeware Lab Manual			DC	Discovery Channel Videotapes & DVDs	GO	Internet Resources

RESOURCES PRINT and TECHNOLOGY		SECTION ASSESSMENT
PLM Lab 7: Using Specific Heat to Analyze Metals	L2	SE Section 16.1 Assessment, p. 478
RSW Section 16.1	L1	iT Section 16.1
RSW Math Skill	L2	
MSPS Section 16.1	L2	
T Chapter 16 Pretest	L2	
Section 16.1	L2	
P Chapter 16 Pretest	L2	
Section 16.1	L2	
SciLinks GO Specific heat	L2	
RSW Section 16.2	L1	SE Section 16.2 Assessment, p. 483
Discovery School DC Powered by the Sun	L2	iT Section 16.2
T Section 16.2	L2	
P Section 16.2	L2	
SciLinks GO Thermodynamics	L2	
RSW Section 16.3	L1	SE Section 16.3 Assessment, p. 492
MSPS Section 16.3	L2	iT Section 16.3
T Section 16.3	L2	
P Section 16.3	L2	
Science News GO Heat	L2	

Go Online

Go online for these Internet resources.

PHSchool.com
Web Code: cca-2160

Science News®
Web Code: cce-2163

NSTA SciLinks
Web Code: ccn-2161
Web Code: ccn-2162

Materials for Activities and Labs

Quantities for each group

STUDENT EDITION

Inquiry Activity, p. 473
2 plastic foam cups, glass stirring rod, thermometer, 2 100-mL graduated cylinders

Quick Lab, p. 476
round balloon, 2-L plastic bottle, metric tape measure, plastic bucket, ice

Quick Lab, p. 481
100-mL beaker, cold water, dropper pipet, hot water, food coloring, paper towel

Design Your Own Lab, p. 493
10 steel bolts, balance, 50-cm length of string, clamp, ring stand, boiling water bath (shared with class), thermometer, 500-mL graduated cylinder, ice water, foam cup with lid, aluminum nails, crushed can

TEACHER'S EDITION

Teacher Demo, p. 478
plastic foam cup with lid, thermometer, water, iron bolt (~75 g)

Teacher Demo, p. 480
a block of wood, an aluminum pie plate, a metal spoon, a plastic spoon, a silk or cotton handkerchief, a metal screwdriver

Build Science Skills, p. 482
putty (enough to make 1 golf ball-sized ball per student), table or desktop

Build Science Skills, p. 484
a box with black interior, a box with white interior, clear plastic wrap, 2 beakers, 2 thermometers

Teacher Demo, p. 490
paper towels, water, tape, hand-held or electric fan, thermometer

Chapter Assessment

CHAPTER ASSESSMENT

SE Chapter Assessment, pp. 495–496
CUT Chapter 16 Test A, B
CTB Chapter 16
iT Chapter 16
PHSchool.com GO
Web Code: cca-2160

STANDARDIZED TEST PREP

SE Chapter 16, p. 497
TP Diagnose and Prescribe

Interactive Textbook

Interactive Textbook with assessment at PHSchool.com

CHAPTER 16

Before you teach

From the Author

Michael Wysession
Washington University

Big Ideas

Thermal energy, temperature, and heat are all related, but they describe very different quantities. Every object (including a student!) has a great amount of thermal energy, which consists of the sum of the kinetic and potential energies of all of the particles that make up the object. An object's temperature is determined by the level of kinetic energy of its particles. Heat is thermal energy that is transferred from one object to another.

Space and Time At all levels of the universe (atoms, planets, galaxies), thermal energy naturally flows from hot regions to cold regions. This law is often referred to as entropy. The implication of entropy is that energy in the universe will eventually dissipate so that, far in the future, stars will no longer be able to form.

There is a limit to how cold an object can get, called absolute zero. The temperature of empty space is actually a few degrees above absolute zero, due to the presence of microwave energy left over from the big bang.

Forces and Motion Thermal energy flows from hot regions to cold regions in three ways: by radiation, by conduction, and by convection. With radiation, electromagnetic waves radiate away from a hot region. Conduction involves the propagation of heat through matter by collisions between particles. With convection, the particles in a material move, carrying thermal energy with them. In the presence of gravity, convection involves the flow of hot material up and cold material down. Large-scale motions on and within Earth are caused by convection: flow of air in the atmosphere, water in the ocean, and rock and metal within the mantle and core.

Matter and Energy When the thermal energy of matter increases, its temperature increases in relation to a particular material's specific heat. Most matter expands when it becomes hotter, a process called thermal expansion. Heat engines and heat pumps use thermal properties of liquids and gases to do work. Heat engines rely on the expansion of gases when they combust or are heated. Heat pumps rely upon the absorption of heat by liquids when they vaporize.

Physics Refresher

Thermal Energy and Temperature 16.1

The internal energy of an object is the total energy of atoms and molecules within it. This text uses the term *thermal energy* instead of *internal energy*. Thermal energy may include the average potential energy of interacting atoms as well as average kinetic energy. Average kinetic energy generally increases as the temperature increases, and there is a close relation between average kinetic energy and temperature. The precise relation depends on the material. For a monatomic gas, the average kinetic energy per atom of gas at absolute temperature T is given by

$$\mathrm{KE}_{\mathrm{avg}} = \frac{3}{2}kT,$$

where k is Boltzmann's constant. For a diatomic gas, the moving particles are molecules having an average kinetic energy $\frac{5}{2}kT$ per molecule. In solids and liquids this relationship can be more complex.

Transfer of Thermal Energy 16.2

Convection transfers thermal energy by the motion of the particles in a fluid from one place to another. A fluid that is heated expands, becoming less dense than the surrounding fluid. The difference in densities causes the warm, less dense fluid to rise and the cooler, denser fluid to sink.

In conduction, the particle collisions transfer thermal energy on average from particles with greater kinetic energy to particles with lower kinetic energy.

Address Misconceptions

Students may assume that the phrase heat transfer *shows that heat is a moving substance.* Heat is a transfer of thermal energy that may or may not involve a movement of particles. For a strategy to overcome this misconception, see **Address Misconceptions** on **page 475**.

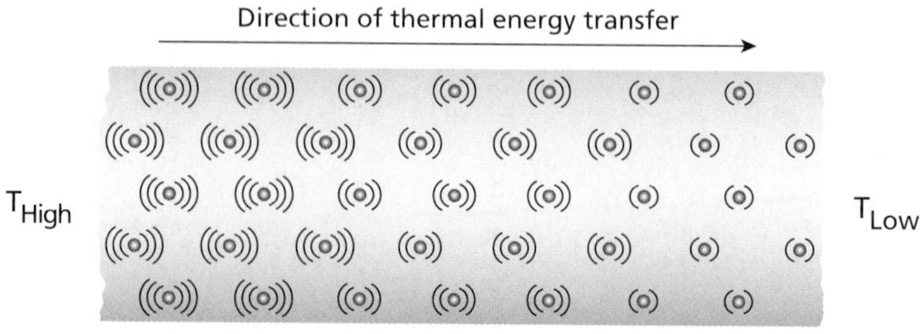
Direction of thermal energy transfer
T_{High}
T_{Low}

Conduction

Go Online PD LINKS NSTA

For: Teaching methods for thermal energy and heat
Visit: www.SciLinks.org/PDLinks
Web Code: ccn-1699

Radiation transfers energy by means of electromagnetic waves, which can travel through empty space. Absorption of radiation by matter increases the matter's thermal energy, while emission of radiation decreases the thermal energy of the matter.

Thermodynamics 16.2 and 16.3

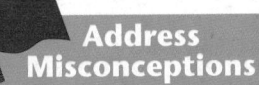

Address Misconceptions

Students may assume that all of the energy added to a system by heating it will increase the system's thermal energy. Heat may also be converted into work or internal energy (in a phase change). For a strategy to overcome this misconception, see **Address Misconceptions** on **page 482**.

In addition to the three laws of thermodynamics is the so-called "zeroth" law, which states that if an object is in thermal equilibrium with two other objects, those two objects are in thermal equilibrium with each other. This condition allows a definition of a temperature scale, which assigns the same temperature to all three objects.

In the operation of a heat engine, all of the energy can be accounted for using the first law of thermodynamics. But the energy that must be given up is considered waste energy if it cannot spontaneously be transferred back to the high-temperature source. The measure of the increased disorder that results from making energy less useable is called entropy. Another statement of the second law is that the total entropy for the system and its surroundings spontaneously increases for all macroscopic processes.

Entropy changes take place in all matter, but these changes become smaller as the temperature of matter decreases. The temperature at which no entropy change (that is, no change in the disorder of the system) would occur is defined as absolute zero. This is one way of expressing the third law of thermodynamics.

Uses of Heat 16.3

In many types of heat engines, a quantity of matter (water and steam in a steam engine, a gasoline-air mixture in a gasoline engine) is heated. The three common features of all heat engines are 1) energy is transferred to the chamber by heat from a region at a higher temperature, 2) work is done in the chamber, and 3) thermal energy is transferred from the chamber to a region of lower temperature. In a refrigerator, the process is reversed: Work is done to transfer thermal energy from a region at a cooler temperature to a region at a high temperature.

Build Reading Literacy

Make Inferences

Reading Between the Lines

Strategy Help students fill in information not found in the text by drawing on prior knowledge and using context clues. To use this strategy, students must identify their prior knowledge, recognize clues in the text, and make connections between their prior knowledge and text clues to make an inference.

Choose a passage such as the last two paragraphs on p. 474. The passage should contain concepts that the author refers to but does not explain completely. You may wish to photocopy the paragraphs and highlight examples for your own reference prior to oral reading.

Example

1. Read aloud or have students read aloud a portion of the chosen text. Point out an example of the author's referring to something without explaining it completely. Tell students that texts often do not define everything because they assume that the reader has a certain amount of background knowledge.
2. Model this strategy by thinking aloud. First, mention facts you already know that are directly related to the subject, either from your own experience or from what you have read about it previously in the text.
3. Next, read text clues aloud and point out what those clues tell about the concept.
4. Then, explain what you understand about the text by combining your prior knowledge and text clues.
5. Have students read the next paragraph or two silently, applying the strategies to make an inference. Discuss their inferences.
6. Repeat this process, having students work with partners to find other opportunities to make inferences in the chapter.

See p. 475 for a script on how to use the make inferences strategy with students. For additional Build Reading Literacy strategies, see pp. 480 and 486.

PHYSICS
Chapter 16

ASSESS PRIOR KNOWLEDGE

Use the Chapter Pretest below to assess students' prior knowledge. As needed, review these Science Concepts and Math Skills with students.

Review Science Concepts

Section 16.1 Review work, kinetic energy, and thermal energy. Remind students of the Celsius and Kelvin temperature scales used in science. Review how matter consists of atoms, ions, and molecules.

Section 16.2 Review efficiency of machines and the law of conservation of energy. Remind students of the definition of absolute zero.

Section 16.3 Review the states of matter. Review chemical energy and energy conversions.

Review Math Skills

Scientific Notation, Calculating with Significant Figures, Formulas and Equations Students will need to manipulate 4-variable formulas to calculate specific heat.

Direct students to the **Math Skills** in the **Skills and Reference Handbook** at the end of the student text.

CHAPTER 16 Thermal Energy and Heat

CONCEPTS in Action

How do science concepts apply to your world? Here are some questions you'll be able to answer after you read this chapter.

- When a car has been warmed by the sun, why is the metal door hotter than the plastic bumper? *(Section 16.1)*
- Why doesn't hot air burn your unprotected arm when you reach into an oven? *(Section 16.2)*
- Why does a bicycle pump heat up when you pump up a tire? *(Section 16.2)*
- Why must a car engine have a cooling system? *(Section 16.3)*
- Can you cool a kitchen by leaving the refrigerator door open? *(Section 16.3)*

Discovery Channel School **Video Field Trip**

Powered by the Sun

- What energy-saving strategies are used in a solar-heated home? *(page 484)*

34027

As this locomotive steams along, it uses thermal energy to do the work of climbing a hill. ▶

Chapter Pretest

1. True or False: Degrees Celsius and kelvins are units of temperature. *(True)*
2. What kind of energy is released when bonds between atoms are broken? *(Chemical energy)*
3. True or False: Thermal energy is the total potential and kinetic energy of the microscopic particles in an object. *(True)*
4. The change of state from liquid to gas is called ______________. *(vaporization)*
5. Which of the following is the energy of a moving object? *(d)*
   a. Mechanical energy
   b. Chemical energy
   c. Potential energy
   d. Kinetic energy
6. The principle that energy cannot be created or destroyed is known as the law of ______________. *(conservation of energy)*
7. Define work. *(Work is a transfer of energy.)*
8. If the input work for a simple machine is 21.0 J, and the output work is 7.0 J, the efficiency of the machine is ______________. *(c)*
   a. 3.0%
   b. 0.33%
   c. 33%
   d. 30%

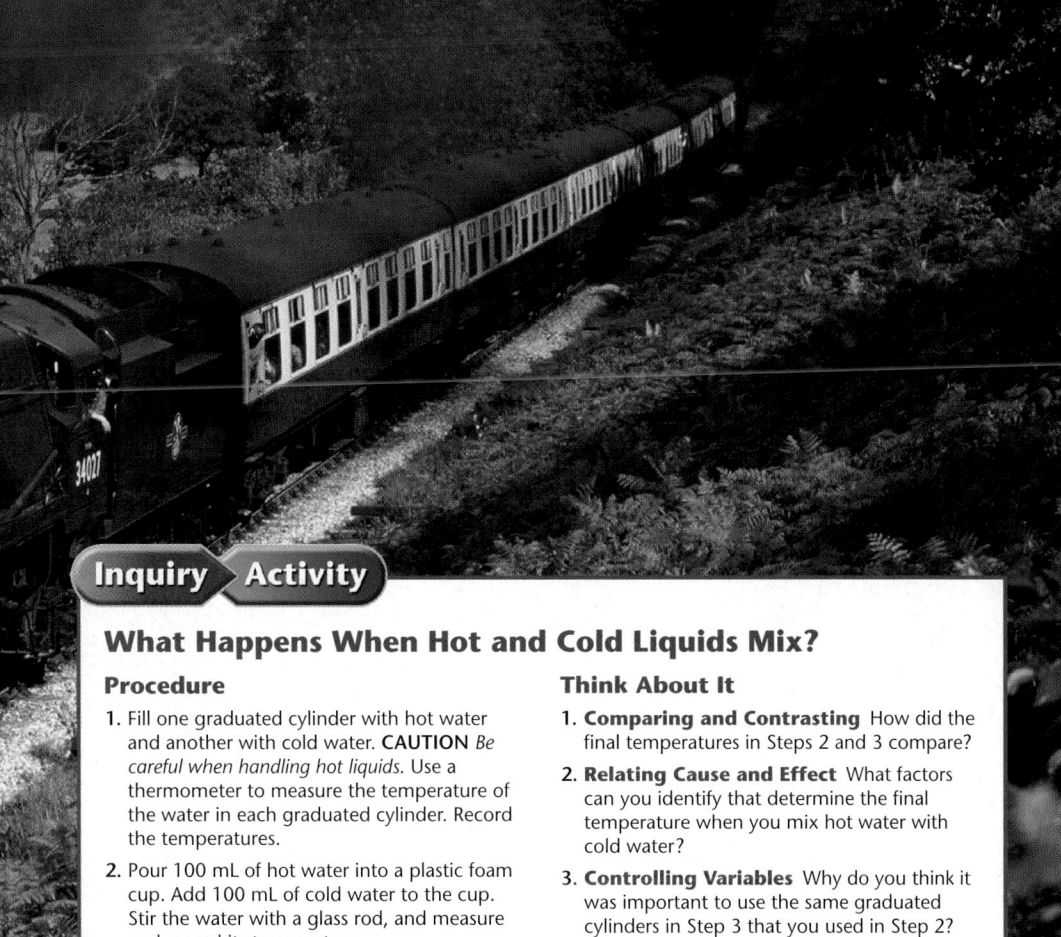

Chapter Preview

Inquiry Activity

What Happens When Hot and Cold Liquids Mix?

Procedure

1. Fill one graduated cylinder with hot water and another with cold water. **CAUTION** *Be careful when handling hot liquids.* Use a thermometer to measure the temperature of the water in each graduated cylinder. Record the temperatures.
2. Pour 100 mL of hot water into a plastic foam cup. Add 100 mL of cold water to the cup. Stir the water with a glass rod, and measure and record its temperature.
3. Repeat Step 2, this time adding 50 mL of cold water to 100 mL of hot water.

Think About It

1. **Comparing and Contrasting** How did the final temperatures in Steps 2 and 3 compare?
2. **Relating Cause and Effect** What factors can you identify that determine the final temperature when you mix hot water with cold water?
3. **Controlling Variables** Why do you think it was important to use the same graduated cylinders in Step 3 that you used in Step 2?

Discovery Channel School — **Video Field Trip**

Powered by the Sun

Encourage students to view the Video Field Trip "Powered by the Sun."

ENGAGE/EXPLORE

Inquiry Activity

What Happens When Hot and Cold Liquids Mix? L2

Purpose Students recognize that the final temperature of a mixture depends on the masses and temperatures of the substances that are mixed.

Address Misconceptions

Students may think that because the temperature of the cold water added is the same for both mixtures, the final temperature should be similar. To help remedy this misconception, ask what else may affect the final temperature.

Skills Focus **Observing, Inferring, Measuring**

Prep Time 15 minutes

Materials 2 plastic foam cups, glass stirring rod, thermometer, 2 100-mL graduated cylinders

Class Time 20 minutes

Safety Students should use tongs or wear heat-resistant gloves when handling hot glassware. Use non-mercury thermometers.

Teaching Tips

- Hot and cold tap water should be sufficient to show the desired results. Water could be cooled in a freezer to increase the temperature difference.
- Students should stir the mixtures before measuring the temperature.
- Students should do the first trial rapidly so that the water temperatures are the same for both trials.

Expected Outcome The cup that received 100 mL of cold water will be cooler.

Think About It

1. The mixture to which 50 mL of cold water was added had a higher temperature.
2. Students may cite the temperatures and "amounts" of water added. They may also say that energy or heat changed the temperature of the water.
3. Using the same source of hot and cold water ensures that the temperatures used will be close to the same in both trials.
Logical, Group

1 FOCUS

Objectives

16.1.1 **Explain** how heat and work transfer energy.

16.1.2 **Relate** thermal energy to the motion of particles that make up a material.

16.1.3 **Relate** temperature to thermal energy and to thermal expansion.

16.1.4 **Calculate** thermal energy, temperature change, or mass using the specific heat equation.

16.1.5 **Describe** how a calorimeter operates and **calculate** thermal energy changes or specific heat using calorimetry measurements.

Reading Focus

Build Vocabulary L2

Concept Map Have students construct a concept map of the vocabulary terms in this section. Instruct students to place the terms in ovals and connect the ovals with lines on which linking words are placed. Students should place the main concept (Thermal Energy and Matter) at the top. As they move away from the main concept, the content should become more specific.

Reading Strategy L2

Sample answers: **a.** A pitcher of juice **b.** Why did Rumford conclude that heat is not a form of matter? **c.** The brass was hot enough to make water boil only during drilling, so the heat must be related to the motion of the drill. **d.** How is specific heat related to temperature? **e.** The lower a material's specific heat, the more its temperature rises when a given amount of energy is absorbed by a given mass.

2 INSTRUCT

Work and Heat

FYI

It is common usage to talk about heat flowing. More precisely, it is thermal energy that flows. It is always correct to use "heat" as a verb; using "heat" as a noun should be avoided.

16.1 Thermal Energy and Matter

Reading Focus

Key Concepts

- In what direction does heat flow spontaneously?
- What is the temperature of an object related to?
- What two variables is thermal energy related to?
- What causes thermal expansion?
- How is a change in temperature related to specific heat?
- On what principle does a calorimeter operate?

Vocabulary

- heat
- temperature
- absolute zero
- thermal expansion
- specific heat
- calorimeter

Reading Strategy

Previewing Copy the table below. Before you read, preview the figures in this section and add two more questions to the table. As you read, write answers to your questions.

Questions About Thermal Energy and Matter	Answers
Which has more thermal energy, a cup of tea or a pitcher of juice?	a. ___?___
b. ___?___	c. ___?___
d. ___?___	e. ___?___

In the 1700s, most scientists thought heat was a fluid called *caloric* that flowed between objects. In 1798, the American-born scientist Benjamin Thompson (1753–1814), also known as Count Rumford, challenged this concept of heat. Rumford managed a factory that made cannons. Figure 1 shows how a brass cylinder was drilled to make the cannon barrel. Water was used to cool the brass so that it did not melt. Rumford observed that the brass became hot as long as the drilling continued, producing enough heat to boil the water. Soon after the drilling stopped, however, the water stopped boiling. When the drilling resumed, the water again came to a boil. Based on his observations, Rumford concluded that heat could not be a kind of matter, but instead was related to the motion of the drill.

Figure 1 Count Rumford supervised the drilling of brass cannons in a factory in Bavaria. From his observations, Rumford concluded that heat is not a form of matter.

Work and Heat

A drill is a machine that does work on the cannon. Remember that no machine is 100 percent efficient. Some of the work done by the drill does useful work, but some energy is lost due to friction. Friction causes the moving parts to heat up. The more work done by the drill, the more that friction causes the cannon to heat up.

Heat is the transfer of thermal energy from one object to another because of a temperature difference. **Heat flows spontaneously from hot objects to cold objects.** Heat flows from the cannon to the water because the cannon is at a higher temperature than the water.

Section Resources

Print
- ***Reading and Study Workbook With Math Support,*** Section 16.1 and **Math Skill:** Calculating with Specific Heat
- ***Math Skills and Problem Solving Workbook,*** Section 16.1
- ***Transparencies,*** Chapter Pretest and Section 16.1

Technology
- ***Probeware Lab Manual,*** Lab 7
- ***Interactive Textbook,*** Section 16.1
- ***Presentation Pro CD-ROM,*** Chapter Pretest and Section 16.1
- ***Go Online,*** NSTA SciLinks, Specific heat

Temperature

How do you know something is hot? You might use a thermometer to measure its temperature. **Temperature** is a measure of how hot or cold an object is compared to a reference point. Recall that on the Celsius scale, the reference points are the freezing and boiling points of water. On the Kelvin scale, another reference point is **absolute zero**, which is defined as a temperature of 0 kelvins.

Temperature is related to the average kinetic energy of the particles in an object due to their random motions through space. As an object heats up, its particles move faster, on average. As a result, the average kinetic energy of the particles, and the temperature, must increase.

Why does heat flow from a high to a low temperature? One way that heat flows is by the transfer of energy in collisions. On average, high-energy particles lose energy, and low-energy particles gain energy in collisions. Overall, collisions transfer thermal energy from hot to cold objects.

Thermal Energy

Recall that thermal energy is the total potential and kinetic energy of all the particles in an object. **Thermal energy depends on the mass, temperature, and phase (solid, liquid, or gas) of an object.**

Thermal energy, unlike temperature, depends on mass. Suppose you compare a cup of tea and a teapot full of tea. Both are at the same temperature, so the average kinetic energy of the particles is the same in both containers. However, there is more thermal energy in the teapot because it contains more particles.

Now consider how thermal energy varies with temperature. You can do this by comparing a cup of hot tea with a cup of cold tea. In both cases, the tea has the same mass, and the same number of particles. But the average kinetic energy of particles is higher in the hot tea, so it also has greater thermal energy than the cold tea.

Figure 2 shows the particles in a cup of hot tea and in a pitcher of lemonade. The tea is at a higher temperature because its particles move a little faster, on average. But they are only moving slightly faster, and the pitcher of lemonade has many more particles than the tea. As it turns out, the pitcher of lemonade has more thermal energy than the cup of hot tea.

Reading Checkpoint — *What is thermal energy?*

A

B

Figure 2 Thermal energy depends on mass and temperature. **A** The tea is at a higher temperature than the lemonade because its particles have a higher average kinetic energy. **B** The lemonade is at a lower temperature, but it has more thermal energy because it has many more particles. **Inferring** *In which liquid are water particles moving faster, on average?*

Build Reading Literacy — L1

Make Inferences Refer to page **472D** in this chapter, which provides the guidelines for making inferences.

Students' understanding often depends on how they apply prior knowledge toward making inferences about new situations. Have students read the two paragraphs at the bottom of p. 474. Invite students to describe situations that are similar to the drill heated by friction. Then, ask students to make an inference: **Based on what you have read, why do your hands feel warmer after you rub them together?** *(Some of the work done is lost to friction, and so is converted to thermal energy.)*
Logical

Temperature

Address Misconceptions — L2

Students may assume from common-use phrases such as *heat transfer* and *heat flow* that heat is a moving substance. Emphasize that heat is a flow, or transfer, of thermal energy from one object or material to another, just as work is a transfer of mechanical energy. While convection involves the movement of particles of a fluid from one place to another, there is obviously no flow of matter when thermal energy is transferred from one solid to another. An amount of heat, like an amount of work, refers to how much energy is transferred.
Verbal

Thermal Energy

Use Visuals — L1

Figure 2 Stress that the particles in both liquids are mostly water molecules, and that these are not simple spheres. Ask, **In what ways can a water molecule move?** *(Each molecule can move to the sides in three dimensions, rotate, and stretch along its molecular bonds.)* Point out that some kinetic energy is present in each of these motions, and this affects the overall temperature of the liquid.
Visual

Customize for English Language Learners

Reading/Learning Log
Concepts such as heat, temperature, and thermal energy are easy to misunderstand and confuse with each other. Be sure that English language learners have a clear understanding of these concepts by having them construct a Reading/Learning Log. Have students write what they understand in the left column, and what they still have questions about in the right column.

Answer to . . .

Figure 2 *The average speed of water particles is greater in the tea because the average kinetic energy is greater.*

Reading Checkpoint — *Thermal energy is the total potential and kinetic energy of all the particles in an object.*

Thermal Contraction and Expansion

Quick Lab

Cooling Air — L2

Objective
After completing this activity, students will be able to
- describe the effect of temperature on the volume of a gas.

Skills Focus Measuring, Comparing and Contrasting

Prep Time 20 minutes

Materials round balloon, 2-L plastic bottle, metric tape measure, plastic bucket, ice

Advance Prep The circumference of the balloon can be found by wrapping a string around the balloon and then measuring the length of the string.

Class Time 20 minutes

Safety Students should wear safety goggles and lab aprons and must wipe up any spills immediately to avoid falls.

Teaching Tips
- Students can calculate the volume of the balloon from its circumference by approximating the shape of the balloon as a sphere and using the equation $C = 2\pi r$ to find the radius. The volume is then given by $V = \frac{4}{3}\pi r^3$. Make sure students include the bottle to determine the total volume of the enclosed air.

Expected Outcome The balloon contracts as the air in the bottle cools.

Analyze and Conclude
1. The volume decreased when cool.
2. Cooling the air inside the bottle and balloon reduced the kinetic energy of its particles, and therefore the pressure on the balloon, causing it to contract.
Visual, Logical

Specific Heat

Build Science Skills — L2

Analyzing Data Have students examine the specific heat values in Figure 3. Ask, **Which substance requires nearly 1 J of energy to raise the temperature of 1 g by 1°C?** *(Air)* **What amount of energy would be required to raise the temperature of 2.00 g of water by 1.00°C?** *(4.18 × 2.00 = 8.36 J)* **Logical**

Quick Lab

Cooling Air

Procedure
1. Inflate a round balloon and then stretch its opening over the mouth of a 2-L bottle. Use a tape measure to measure and record the balloon's circumference.
2. Put a dozen ice cubes into a plastic bucket. Add cold water to the bucket to a depth of 15 cm. Submerge the bottom of the bottle in the ice water and tape the bottle in place.
3. After 10 minutes, measure and record the circumference of the balloon.

Analyze and Conclude
1. **Observing** How did the volume of air in the balloon change?
2. **Inferring** Explain why the air behaved as it did.

Thermal Contraction and Expansion

If you take a balloon outside on a cold winter day, it shrinks. Can you explain why? As temperature decreases, the particles that make up the air inside the balloon move more slowly, on average. Slower particles collide less often and exert less force, so gas pressure decreases and the balloon contracts. This is called thermal contraction.

If you bring the balloon inside, it expands. **Thermal expansion** is an increase in the volume of a material due to a temperature increase. **Thermal expansion occurs when particles of matter move farther apart as temperature increases.** Gases expand more than liquids and liquids usually expand more than solids. A gas expands more easily than a liquid or a solid because the forces of attraction among particles in a gas are weaker.

Thermal expansion is used in glass thermometers. As temperature increases, the alcohol in the tube expands and its height increases. The increase in height is proportional to the increase in temperature. In an oven thermometer, a strip of brass and a strip of steel are bonded together and wound up in a coil. As the coil heats up, the two metals expand at different rates, and the coil unwinds. This causes the needle to rotate on the temperature scale.

Reading Checkpoint *What is thermal expansion?*

Specific Heat

When a car is heated by the sun, the temperature of the metal door increases more than the temperature of the plastic bumper. Do you know why? One reason is that the iron in the door has a lower specific heat than the plastic in the bumper. **Specific heat** is the amount of heat needed to raise the temperature of one gram of a material by one degree Celsius. If equal masses of iron and plastic absorb the same heat, the iron's temperature rises more. **The lower a material's specific heat, the more its temperature rises when a given amount of energy is absorbed by a given mass.**

Specific heat is often measured in joules per gram per degree Celsius, or J/g•°C. Figure 3 gives specific heats for a few common materials. It takes 4.18 joules of energy to raise the temperature of 1.00 gram of water by 1.00 degree Celsius. How much energy is needed to heat 2.00 grams of water to the same temperature? You would have to add twice as much energy, or 8.36 joules.

Specific Heats of Selected Materials

Material (at 100 kPa)	Specific Heat (J/g•°C)
Water	4.18
Plastic (polypropylene)	1.84–2.09
Air	1.01
Iron	0.449
Silver	0.235

Figure 3 Specific heat is the heat needed to raise the temperature of 1 gram of material by 1°C. **Analyzing Data** *Which material in the table has the highest specific heat? The lowest?*

Facts and Figures

Thermal Contraction One of the few exceptions to thermal expansion is water near its freezing point. Over most temperature ranges, water increases in volume as its temperature increases, but between 0°C and 4°C water actually contracts as it gets warmer. This unusual behavior occurs because hydrogen bonding between water molecules in ice arranges them in a way that occupies a greater volume than in liquid water. This results in ice being less dense than liquid water. In the winter, when a pond begins to freeze, the denser, warmer water sinks to the bottom, and the cooler, less dense ice floats. This forms a layer of warmer water at the bottom of the pond, in which fish are able to live.

The heat (Q) absorbed by a material equals the product of the mass (m), the specific heat (c), and the change in temperature (ΔT).

Specific Heat

$$Q = m \times c \times \Delta T$$

In this formula, heat is in joules, mass is in grams, specific heat is in J/g•°C, and the temperature change is in degrees Celsius.

Go Online NSTA SCILINKS

For: Links on specific heat
Visit: www.SciLinks.org
Web Code: ccn-2161

Math Skills

Calculating Specific Heat

An iron skillet has a mass of 500.0 grams. The specific heat of iron is 0.449 J/g•°C. How much heat must be absorbed to raise the skillet's temperature by 95.0°C?

1 Read and Understand

What information are you given?

Mass of iron, $m = 500.0$ g

Specific heat of iron, $c = 0.449$ J/g•°C

Temperature change, $\Delta T = 95.0$°C

2 Plan and Solve

What unknown are you trying to calculate?

Amount of heat needed, $Q = ?$

What formula contains the given quantities and the unknown?

$$Q = m \times c \times \Delta T$$

Replace each variable with its known value.

$$Q = 500.0 \text{ g} \times 0.449 \text{ J/g•°C} \times 95.0\text{°C}$$

$$= 21{,}375 \text{ J} = 21.4 \text{ kJ}$$

3 Look Back and Check

Is your answer reasonable?

Round off the data to give a quick estimate.

$Q = 500 \text{ g} \times 0.5 \text{ J/g•°C} \times 100\text{°C} = 25 \text{ kJ}$

This is close to 21.4 kJ, so the answer is reasonable.

Math Practice

1. How much heat is needed to raise the temperature of 100.0 g of water by 85.0°C?
2. How much heat is absorbed by a 750-g iron skillet when its temperature rises from 25°C to 125°C?
3. In setting up an aquarium, the heater transfers 1200 kJ of heat to 75,000 g of water. What is the increase in the water's temperature? (*Hint:* Rearrange the specific heat formula to solve for ΔT.)
4. To release a diamond from its setting, a jeweler heats a 10.0-g silver ring by adding 23.5 J of heat. How much does the temperature of the silver increase?
5. What mass of water will change its temperature by 3.0°C when 525 J of heat is added to it?

Build Math Skills L1

Formulas and Equations Students should become familiar with rearrangements of the formula $Q = m \times c \times \Delta T$, so that any one of these quantities can be calculated in terms of the other three. Have students rearrange the equation in order to calculate specific heat $c = Q/(m \times \Delta T)$, mass $m = Q/(c \times \Delta T)$, and temperature $\Delta T = Q/(m \times c)$.
Logical, Portfolio

Direct students to the **Math Skills** in the **Skills and Reference Handbook** at the end of the student text for additional help.

Math Practice

Solutions L2

1. $Q = m \times c \times \Delta T$
$= (100.0 \text{ g})(4.18 \text{ J/g•°C})(85.0\text{°C})$
$= 35.5$ kJ
2. $Q = m \times c \times \Delta T$
$= (750 \text{ g})(0.449 \text{ J/g•°C})(125\text{°C} - 25\text{°C})$
$= (750 \text{ g})(0.449 \text{ J/g•°C})(100\text{°C}) = 34$ kJ
3. $\Delta T = Q/(m \times c)$
$= 1{,}200{,}000 \text{ J}/(75{,}000 \text{ g} \times 4.18 \text{ J/g•°C})$
$= 3.8$°C
4. $\Delta T = Q/(m \times c)$
$= 23.5 \text{ J}/(10.0 \text{ g} \times 0.235 \text{ J/g•°C})$
$= 10.0$°C
5. $m = Q/(\Delta T \times c)$
$= 525 \text{ J}/(3.0\text{°C} \times 4.18 \text{ J/g•°C}) = 42$ g

Logical

For Extra Help L1

Make sure students start by writing out the equation required to solve each problem. Then, check that they are able to solve the equation for the unknown variable using basic algebra skills.
Logical

Additional Problems

1. Gold has a specific heat of 0.13 J/g•°C. If a sample of gold with a mass of 250 g undergoes a temperature increase of 4.0°C, how much heat does it absorb? *(130 J)*
2. A piece of iron at a temperature of 145.0°C cools off to a temperature of 45.0°C. If the iron has a mass of 10.0 g and a specific heat of 0.449 J/g•°C, how much heat is given up? *(449 J)*

Logical, Portfolio

Go Online NSTA SCILINKS

Download a worksheet on specific heat for students to complete, and find additional teacher support from NSTA SciLinks.

Answer to . . .

Figure 3 *Silver has the lowest specific heat. Water has the highest specific heat.*

Reading Checkpoint *Thermal expansion is the increase in volume of a material due to a temperature increase.*

Measuring Heat Changes

Teacher Demo

Calorimetry
L2

Purpose Students observe a calorimeter measuring changes in thermal energy.

Materials plastic foam cup with lid, thermometer, water, iron bolt (~75 g)

Procedure Place the iron bolt in a freezer for one hour prior to the demonstration. Fill the cup two-thirds full with room-temperature water and record its temperature. Place the cold iron in the water and cover the cup. After three minutes, record the temperature of the water. Ask students what they can infer about the bolt's initial temperature.

Safety Wipe up spills immediately.

Expected Outcome Students should conclude that the bolt was colder than the water. **Visual, Group**

3 ASSESS

Evaluate Understanding
L2

Ask students to write a summary paragraph relating thermal energy, temperature, and heat.

Reteach
L1

Use Figure 2 to summarize key concepts about thermal energy.

Math Practice

Solutions

10. $Q = m \times c \times \Delta T = (1000.0\text{ g}) \times (0.39\text{ J/g}\cdot{}^\circ\text{C}) \times (45.0 - 25.0{}^\circ\text{C}) = 7800\text{ J}$

11. $\Delta T = Q/(m \times c) = 18{,}200\text{ J}/(100.0\text{ g})(4.18\text{ J/g}\cdot{}^\circ\text{C}) = 43.5{}^\circ\text{C}$

Interactive Textbook If your class subscribes to the Interactive Textbook, use it to review key concepts in in Section 16.1.

Answer to . . .

Figure 4 *The stirrer keeps temperature uniform.*

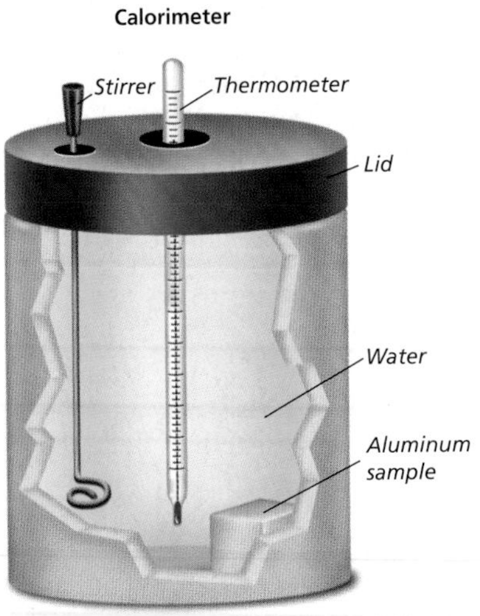

Calorimeter
Stirrer
Thermometer
Lid
Water
Aluminum sample

Figure 4 A calorimeter is used to measure specific heat. A sample to be tested is heated and placed in the calorimeter. The lid is put on and the temperature change is observed. **Hypothesizing** *Why does the calorimeter need a stirrer?*

Measuring Heat Changes

A **calorimeter** is an instrument used to measure changes in thermal energy. **A calorimeter uses the principle that heat flows from a hotter object to a colder object until both reach the same temperature.** According to the law of conservation of energy, the thermal energy released by a test sample is equal to the thermal energy absorbed by its surroundings. The calorimeter is sealed to prevent thermal energy from escaping.

Figure 4 shows how a calorimeter can be used to measure the specific heat of aluminum. A known mass of water is added to the calorimeter. The mass of the sample of aluminum is measured. The aluminum is heated and then placed in the water. The calorimeter is sealed. As the aluminum cools off, the water is stirred to distribute thermal energy evenly. The water heats up until both the aluminum and the water are at the same temperature. The change in temperature of the water is measured. The thermal energy absorbed by the water is calculated using the specific heat equation. Since this same amount of thermal energy was given off by the sample of aluminum, the specific heat of aluminum can be calculated.

Section 16.1 Assessment

Reviewing Concepts

1. In what direction does heat flow on its own spontaneously?
2. How is the temperature of an object related to the average kinetic energy of its particles?
3. Name two variables that affect the thermal energy of an object.
4. What causes thermal expansion of an object when it is heated?
5. How do the temperature increases of different materials depend on their specific heats?
6. What principle explains how a calorimeter is used to measure the specific heat of a sample material?

Critical Thinking

7. **Applying Concepts** Why is it necessary to have regularly spaced gaps between sections of a concrete sidewalk?
8. **Predicting** An iron spoon and silver spoon have the same mass. Which becomes hotter when both are left in hot tea for one minute? (*Hint:* Use the specific heats given in Figure 3.)
9. **Calculating** If it takes 80.0 joules to raise the temperature of a material by 10.0°C, how much heat must be added to cause an additional increase of 20.0°C?

Math Practice

10. The specific heat of copper is 0.39 J/g•°C. How much heat is needed to raise the temperature of 1000.0 g of copper from 25.0°C to 45.0°C?
11. A peanut burned in a calorimeter transfers 18,200 joules to 100.0 g of water. What is the rise in the water's temperature? (*Hint:* Rearrange the specific heat formula to solve for ΔT.)

Section 16.1 Assessment

1. Heat flows spontaneously from hot objects to cold objects.
2. Temperature is related to the average kinetic energy of the particles in an object due to their random motions through space.
3. Mass of the object, temperature
4. Particles of matter tend to move farther apart as temperature increases.
5. The lower a material's specific heat, the more its temperature increases when equal amounts of thermal energy are added to equal masses.
6. A calorimeter uses the principle that heat flows from a hotter object to a colder object until both reach the same temperature.
7. The gaps provide space for concrete slabs to expand into so they do not buckle.
8. Both spoons absorb the same energy and have the same mass. Because silver has a lower specific heat (0.235 J/g•°C) than iron (0.449 J/g•°C), the silver becomes hotter.
9. Doubling the temperature change doubles the energy required, so 160 joules must be added.

16.2 Heat and Thermodynamics

Reading Focus

Key Concepts

- Why is conduction slower in gases than in liquids or solids?
- In what natural cycles do convection currents occur?
- How does an object's temperature affect radiation?
- What are the three laws of thermodynamics?

Vocabulary

- conduction
- thermal conductor
- thermal insulator
- convection
- convection current
- radiation
- thermodynamics
- heat engine
- waste heat

Reading Strategy

Building Vocabulary Copy the table below. As you read, add definitions and examples to complete the table.

Definitions	Examples
Conduction: transfer of thermal energy without transfer of matter	Frying pan handle heats up.
Convection: a. ___?___	b. ___?___
Radiation: c. ___?___	d. ___?___

To bake cookies, you put cookie dough on a baking sheet and pop it in the oven. When the timer goes off, you use oven mitts to pull out the baking sheet. Why isn't your bare arm burned by the hot air in the oven? One reason is that air is not a very good conductor of thermal energy.

Conduction

Conduction is the transfer of thermal energy with no overall transfer of matter. Conduction occurs within a material or between materials that are touching. To understand conduction, look at the Newton's cradle in Figure 5. When a ball is pulled back and released, you might expect all of the balls to move to the right after the impact. Instead, most of the kinetic energy is transferred to one ball on the end. Similarly, in conduction, collisions between particles transfer thermal energy, without any overall transfer of matter.

Recall that forces are weak among particles in a gas. Compared to liquids and solids, the particles in gases are farther apart. **Conduction in gases is slower than in liquids and solids because the particles in a gas collide less often.** In most solids, conduction occurs as particles vibrate in place and push on each other. In metals, conduction is faster because some electrons are free to move about. These free electrons collide with one another and with atoms or ions to transfer thermal energy.

Figure 5 Conduction is the transfer of thermal energy without transferring matter. This device, called Newton's cradle, helps to visualize conduction. After one ball strikes the rest, most of the kinetic energy is transferred to one ball on the end.

Section Resources

Print
- ***Laboratory Manual,*** Investigations 16A and 16B
- ***Reading and Study Workbook With Math Support,*** Section 16.2
- ***Transparencies,*** Section 16.2

Technology
- ***Interactive Textbook,*** Section 16.2
- ***Presentation Pro CD-ROM,*** Section 16.2
- ***Go Online,*** NSTA SciLinks, Thermodynamics

Section 16.2

1 FOCUS

Objectives

16.2.1 **Describe** conduction, convection, and radiation and **identify** which of these is occurring in a given situation.

16.2.2 **Classify** materials as thermal conductors or thermal insulators.

16.2.3 **Apply** the law of conservation energy to conversions between thermal energy and other forms of energy.

16.2.4 **Apply** the second law of thermodynamics in situations where thermal energy moves from cooler to warmer objects.

16.2.5 **State** the third law of thermodynamics.

Reading Focus

Build Vocabulary L2

Word-Part Analysis Ask students what words they know that have the key word parts *therm, con, duct,* and *radia. (Thermal energy, conductor,* and *radiator)* Give a definition of a word part. *(Therm* means "heat," *con* means "with," *duct* means "to lead," and *radia* means "rays.") Give additional examples that share the word parts in question. *(Thermometer, contact, deduct, radio)*

Reading Strategy L2

a. The transfer of thermal energy by the movement of particles in a fluid **b.** Hot air circulates in an oven. **c.** The transfer of energy by waves moving through space **d.** Heating coil of an electric stove glows.

2 INSTRUCT

Conduction

Use Visuals L1

Figure 5 Use the Newton's cradle to reinforce why energy is transferred more efficiently by conduction in a liquid or solid. Ask, **How could the balls be arranged to demonstrate conduction in a gas?** *(The balls could be detached and spread on a table. When one ball is rolled toward any of the others, collisions would occur only occasionally and without order.)*
Visual

Teacher Demo

Conductors and Insulators L2

Purpose To show the similarities and differences between types of thermal conductors and insulators.

Materials a block of wood, an aluminum pie plate, a metal spoon, a plastic spoon, a silk or cotton handkerchief, a metal screwdriver

Procedure Place the objects on a windowsill that is well-exposed to sunlight. Leave half of each object lying in the sunlight and the other half lying in the shade. Place the screwdriver so that the half of the metal shaft nearest the handle is in the shade. Leave the objects in the sunlight for at least 30 minutes. Have each student pick up each object by the end that has been in shade. Have them note carefully any difference between the temperatures of the two ends of each object.

Safety Remind students that the parts of the objects that have been in sunlight may be very hot.

Expected Outcome The pie plate, the metal spoon, and the shaft of the screwdriver are all metals, and so are good thermal conductors. The parts of these objects that have been in the shade should feel warm. The wood, handkerchief, plastic spoon, and handle of the screwdriver are thermal insulators, and should not feel very warm.
Kinesthetic, Group

Convection

Build Reading Literacy L1

Sequence Refer to page **290D** in **Chapter 10**, which provides the guidelines for a sequence.

Convection involves a sequence of steps. Have students describe the convection of warm air as a sequence of events, starting with "air heated by sunlight." *(The sequence may resemble the following: 1) The temperature of the air increases. 2) The air expands. 3) The less dense air rises while cooler, denser air sinks.)*
Logical

Figure 6 The arrows show how thermal energy is conducted away from the heat source in a metal frying pan. **Predicting** ***Would it be safe to touch the handle of the wooden spoon?***

Thermal Conductors Figure 6 shows a frying pan on a hot stove. The bottom of the pan heats up first. The metal handle heats up last. You can see that the flames do not directly heat the handle. The handle heats up because the metal is a good thermal conductor.

A **thermal conductor** is a material that conducts thermal energy well. A wire rack in a hot oven can burn you because the metal conducts thermal energy so quickly. Pots and pans often are made of copper or aluminum because these are good conductors.

A thermal conductor doesn't have to be hot. Why does a tile floor feel colder than a wooden floor? Both floors are at room temperature. But the tile feels colder because it is a better conductor and transfers thermal energy rapidly away from your skin.

Thermal Insulators Why is it safe to pick up the wooden spoon shown in Figure 6? Wood heats up slowly because it is a poor conductor of thermal energy. A material that conducts thermal energy poorly is called a **thermal insulator.**

Air is a very good insulator. A double-pane window has an air space contained between two panes of glass. The air slows down conduction to reduce heat loss in winter and to keep heat out of a building in summer. More expensive windows use argon gas, which is an even better insulator than air. Wool garments and plastic foam cups are two more examples of insulators that use trapped air to slow down conduction.

Convection

Convection is the transfer of thermal energy when particles of a fluid move from one place to another. Look at the people building a wall with sandbags in Figure 7A. The moving sandbags are like the particles in a fluid. The wall grows taller as more and more sandbags arrive. In much the same way, particles in a fluid can transfer thermal energy from a hot area to a cold area.

Figure 7 Convection is the transfer of thermal energy by the movement of particles in a fluid.
A Passing sandbags along a line is like transferring thermal energy by convection.
B The arrows show convection of air in an oven.
Predicting ***Which part of the oven should have the highest temperature?***

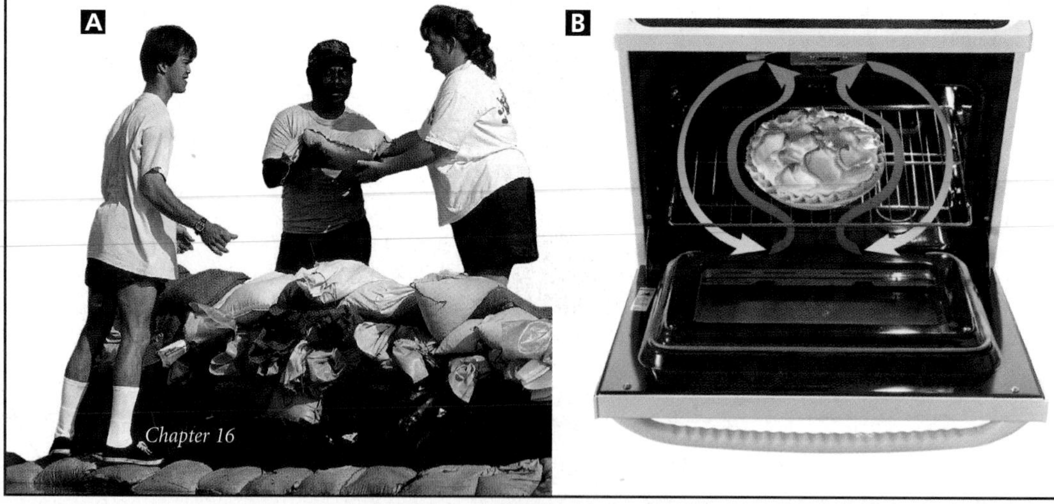
A
B
Chapter 16

Customize for Inclusion Students

Learning Disabled
Learning-disabled students may process information in different ways, depending on their individual learning preferences and strengths. Some may respond better to visual stimuli, while others may learn best through the aural or kinesthetic modes. In presenting information for these students, involve as many modalities as possible. For example, teach conduction by placing a stainless steel spoon and a plastic spoon in warm water. Have students observe the spoons and compare the way they feel when they are removed from the water. In similar ways, involve students' aural, visual, and kinesthetic senses to reinforce your explanation of scientific concepts.

Baking instructions sometimes tell you to use the top rack of an oven. Figure 7B shows why the temperature is lower at the top of the oven. When air at the bottom of the oven heats up, it expands and becomes less dense than the surrounding air. Due to the difference in density, the hot air rises. The rising air cools as it moves away from the heat source. As a result, the coolest air is at the top of the oven.

Air circulating in an oven is an example of a convection current. A **convection current** occurs when a fluid circulates in a loop as it alternately heats up and cools down. In a heated room, convection currents help keep the temperature uniform throughout the room. **Convection currents are important in many natural cycles, such as ocean currents, weather systems, and movements of hot rock in Earth's interior.**

Radiation

At a picnic, you might use a charcoal grill to cook food. When you stand to the side of the grill, heat reaches you without convection or conduction. In much the same way, the sun warms you by radiation on a clear day. The space between the sun and Earth has no air to transfer thermal energy. **Radiation** is the transfer of energy by waves moving through space. Heat lamps used in restaurants are a familiar example of radiation.

All objects radiate energy. As an object's temperature increases, the rate at which it radiates energy increases. In Figure 8, the electric heating coil on a stove radiates so much energy that it glows. If you are close to the heating coil, you absorb radiation, which increases your thermal energy. In other words, it warms you up. The farther you are from the heating coil, the less radiation you receive, and the less it warms you.

Reading Checkpoint *What is radiation?*

Quick Lab

Observing Convection

Procedure

1. Fill a 100-mL beaker halfway with cold water.
2. Fill a dropper pipet with hot water colored with food coloring. Wipe the pipet with a paper towel so no food coloring is on the outside of the pipet.
3. Insert the tip of the pipet into the cold water, halfway between the surface of the water and the bottom of the beaker.
4. Slowly squeeze the pipet bulb. Observe the water in the beaker from the side.

Analyze and Conclude

1. **Observing** Describe the motion of the colored hot water in the beaker.
2. **Inferring** Explain why the hot water behaved as it did.
3. **Predicting** How would colored cold water move in a beaker of hot water?

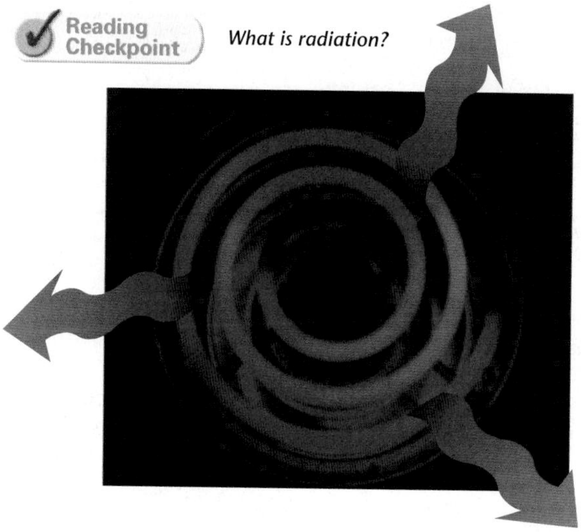

Figure 8 A heating coil on a stove radiates thermal energy. The changing color of the red arrows indicates that the farther you are from the coil, the less radiation you receive.

Facts and Figures

Blackbody Radiation Radiation itself has no temperature because it does not consist of matter. Matter, however, can emit and absorb radiation. This changes the thermal energy, and thus the temperature, of an object. A good emitter of radiation is also a good absorber of radiation. Because black surfaces absorb radiation best, a perfect absorber and emitter of radiation is called an *ideal blackbody* or *blackbody.* Blackbodies emit radiation at all wavelengths with a characteristic curve that depends on the temperature of the object. By comparing the color and brightness of the light emitted by an unknown radiating object to a blackbody with known properties, the temperature of the unknown object can be determined.

Quick Lab

Observing Convection L2

Objective
Students will learn to
- use the concept of convection to describe fluid motion.

Skills Focus **Observing, Predicting**

Prep Time 10 minutes

Advance Prep Provide a 500-mL beaker of hot water with several drops of food coloring.

Class Time 20 minutes

Safety Turn off the hot plate at the start of the activity. Remind students not to touch anything that is hot, to handle glassware carefully, and to wear safety goggles and lab aprons.

Teaching Tips
- Remind students to release the colored water slowly, so that its movement will depend only on its temperature.

Expected Outcome The colored water should float to the top of the beaker.

Analyze and Conclude
1. It rose to the top of the beaker and formed a visible layer there.
2. The warm water rose to the top due to convection.
3. The cold water would sink.
Visual, Logical

Radiation

Address Misconceptions L2

Students may confuse the term *radiation* as it is used here with radiation from nuclear decay. Explain that in both types of radiation, energy spreads outward, or radiates, from a source. But nuclear decay such as alpha decay can also transfer mass. In thermal radiation, the mass of an object does not change because only energy is transferred.
Verbal

Answer to . . .

Figure 6 *Yes, because wood is not a good thermal conductor.*

Figure 7 *Hot air rises and cools, so the highest temperature is at the bottom of the oven, where the heat source is.*

Reading Checkpoint *Radiation is the transfer of energy through space without the help of matter to carry it.*

Thermodynamics

Build Science Skills L2

Applying Concepts ACTIVITY

Purpose Students apply the concept of conservation of energy.

Materials putty (enough to make 1 golf ball-sized ball per student), table or desktop

Class Time 10 minutes

Procedure Have students roll putty into balls about the size of a golf ball. Students hold the putty balls 2–3 feet above a table or desk and then drop them, noting the changes that occur.

Expected Outcome The potential energy of the putty ball held above the table will be converted to kinetic energy when the ball is released. Finally, it will stick to the table, and so undergo a decrease in kinetic and potential energy. According to the first law of thermodynamics, none of the energy is lost. Some of the mechanical energy is applied to changing the shape of the putty ball. The rest is converted to increasing the thermal energy of both the putty and the table, though increased thermal energy may not be detectable due to the small amount of energy involved. **Logical**

Address Misconceptions L2

Students may assume that adding energy to a system by heating it will only increase the system's thermal energy. Explain that work may be done, or internal energy may increase (during a phase change). Sometimes the added heat is mostly used to increase the thermal energy of the system, and little work is done. Demonstrate this effect by placing a sealed bottle of apple juice on a sunny windowsill. Only a small amount of work will be done because of the rigid walls of the bottle, but the temperature of the juice will increase. Work is negligible compared to the amount of energy added to the juice. **Kinesthetic**

Go Online NSTA SciLinks

Download a worksheet on thermodynamics for students to complete, and find additional teacher support from NSTA SciLinks.

Go Online NSTA SciLinks

For: Links on thermodynamics
Visit: www.SciLinks.org
Web Code: ccn-2162

Thermodynamics

The study of conversions between thermal energy and other forms of energy is called **thermodynamics.** Count Rumford made a good start in this field. But many scientists still believed that heat was a kind of matter. Then in 1845, James Prescott Joule (1818–1889) published his results from a convincing experiment.

Joule carefully measured the energy changes in a system. Recall that a system is any group of objects that interact with one another. Joule's system included a falling weight that turned a paddle wheel in a container of water. As the weight fell, the paddle churned a known mass of water. The water heated up due to friction from the turning paddle. Joule carefully measured the work done by the falling weight. He found that the work almost exactly equaled the thermal energy gained by the water. Joule is often given credit for discovering the first law of thermodynamics. That is the law of conservation of energy applied to work, heat, and thermal energy.

Outside air at 20°C
Air in tire at 40°C

Figure 9 You can consider the bicycle pump, the tire, and the air inside of both to be a system. The person does work on the system by pushing on the pump. Some of the work is converted into thermal energy, which heats the air in the pump and the tire.

First Law of Thermodynamics Recall that energy cannot be created or destroyed. But energy can be converted into different forms. **The first law of thermodynamics states that energy is conserved.** If energy is added to a system, it can either increase the thermal energy of the system or do work on the system. But no matter what happens, all of the energy added to the system can be accounted for. Energy is conserved.

Look at the bicycle pump in Figure 9. You can consider the tire, the pump, and the air inside to be a system. The force exerted on the pump does work on the system. Some of this work is useful; it compresses air into the tire. The rest of the work is converted into thermal energy. That is why a bicycle pump heats up as you inflate a tire.

Second Law of Thermodynamics If you take a cold drink from the refrigerator and leave it out in a warm room, will the drink become colder? Of course it won't. You know that the drink will warm up. Thermal energy flows spontaneously only from hotter to colder objects. **The second law of thermodynamics states that thermal energy can flow from colder objects to hotter objects only if work is done on the system.** A refrigerator, for example, must do work to transfer thermal energy from the cold food compartment to the warm room air. The thermal energy is released by coils at the bottom or in the back of the refrigerator.

Facts and Figures

The "Zeroth" Law of Thermodynamics

In order for a thermometer to give meaningful information, its temperature must be equal to that of the object whose temperature is unknown. This occurs when both objects are in a state of *thermal equilibrium*, or when the thermal energy transferred by heat from the object to the thermometer is equal to the heat from the thermometer to the object. This is the same as saying that there is no net heat transfer between the object and thermometer.

The definition of thermal equilibrium is the basis of what is called the "zeroth" law of thermodynamics—two systems in thermal equilibrium with a third system are in thermal equilibrium with each other. As the name implies, this concept is fundamental to thermodynamics, and the first three laws are dependent on it. The zeroth law was established after the first two laws of thermodynamics had been accepted.

A **heat engine** is any device that converts heat into work. One consequence of the second law of thermodynamics is that the efficiency of a heat engine is always less than 100 percent. The best an engine can do is to convert most of the input energy into useful work. Thermal energy that is not converted into work is called **waste heat.** Waste heat is lost to the surrounding environment. In fact, a heat engine can do work only if some waste heat flows to a colder environment outside the engine.

Spontaneous changes will always make a system less orderly, unless work is done on the system. For example, if you walk long enough, your shoelaces will become untied. But the opposite won't happen; shoelaces don't tie themselves. Disorder in the universe as a whole is always increasing. You can only increase order on a local level. For instance, you can stop and tie your shoelaces. But this requires work. Because work always produces waste heat, you contribute to the disorder of the universe when you stop to tie a shoelace!

Third Law of Thermodynamics The efficiency of a heat engine increases with a greater difference between the high temperature inside and the cold temperature outside the engine. In theory, a heat engine could be 100 percent efficient if the cold outside environment were at absolute zero (0 kelvins). But this would violate the third law of thermodynamics. **The third law of thermodynamics states that absolute zero cannot be reached.** Scientists have been able to cool matter almost all of the way to absolute zero. Figure 10 shows the equipment used to produce the record lowest temperature, just 3 billionths of a kelvin above absolute zero!

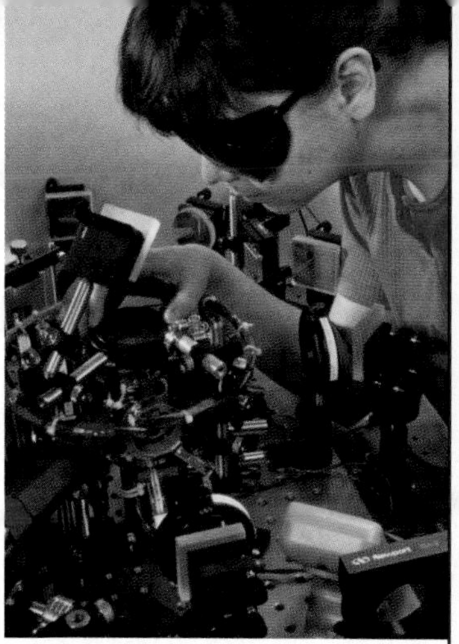

Figure 10 The third law of thermodynamics states that absolute zero cannot be reached. This physicist is adjusting a laser used to cool rubidium atoms to 3 billionths of a kelvin above absolute zero. This record low temperature was produced by a team of scientists at the National Institute of Standards and Technology.

Section 16.2 Assessment

Reviewing Concepts

1. Why is conduction in gases slower than conduction in liquids or solids?
2. Give three examples of convection currents that occur in natural cycles.
3. What happens to radiation from an object as its temperature increases?
4. State the first law of thermodynamics.
5. In your own words, what is the second law of thermodynamics?
6. State the third law of thermodynamics.
7. Why does a metal spoon feel colder than a wooden spoon at room temperature?
8. Why is solar energy transferred to Earth by radiation?

Critical Thinking

9. **Applying Concepts** If your bedroom is cold, you might feel warmer with several thin blankets than with one thick one. Explain why.
10. **Relating Cause and Effect** If every object is radiating constantly, why aren't all objects getting colder?

Connecting Concepts

Conservation of Energy Review energy conservation in Section 15.2. Describe how the first and the second laws of thermodynamics are consistent with the law of conservation of energy.

Integrate Space Science L2

As the universe has expanded, its overall temperature has decreased. Evidence of this is provided by background radiation that astronomers detect in the universe. This radiation is left over from the big bang, in which the universe was formed 13.7 billion years ago. The radiation fills the universe uniformly, and so has expanded with the universe. As a result, the radiation has undergone a Doppler shift toward low-energy radio waves called *microwaves.* These microwaves correspond to the radiation emitted by a blackbody with a temperature of 2.7 K, or just below three degrees above absolute zero. Were the universe to expand indefinitely, the background radiation would continue to decrease in energy, but it would always be greater than zero, so the temperature of the universe must always be above absolute zero.
Logical

3 ASSESS

Evaluate Understanding L2

Ask students to list three examples each of conduction, convection, and radiation. In each example, have them explain how thermal energy is transferred for that example and how energy is conserved in each case.

Reteach L1

Use Figures 5 through 8 to review heat transfer, emphasizing how thermal energy is changed in each case.

Connecting Concepts

Energy is conserved in both laws. In the first law of thermodynamics, thermal energy added to a system either increases the thermal energy of the system or is used to do work. In the second law of thermodynamics, when work is done to transfer thermal energy from a cold object to a hot object, some of the work is converted into thermal energy.

Interactive Textbook If your class subscribes to the Interactive Textbook, use it to review key concepts in Section 16.2.

Section 16.2 Assessment

1. Because particles in a gas collide less often than in a liquid or solid
2. Ocean currents, weather systems, the movement of molten rock in Earth's interior
3. Its rate of radiation increases.
4. The first law of thermodynamics states that energy is conserved.
5. Heat can flow from a colder place to a warmer place only if work is done on the system.
6. Absolute zero cannot be reached.
7. The metal feels colder because it is a better thermal conductor, and it transfers energy more rapidly from the warm hand to the cool room.
8. Radiation is the only type of energy transfer that can occur through a vacuum.
9. The thin blankets trap air between the layers, and air is a good insulator.
10. Objects both radiate and absorb thermal energy. If an object is cooler than its surroundings, it absorbs more energy than it radiates, and so it heats up.

CONCEPTS in Action

Solar Home L2

Background

Solar heating for the home can consist of either "passive" systems, which do not use any mechanical device to distribute the fluids heated by the sun, or "active" systems that use fans or pumps to transfer the heated fluids. Although it is not practical to use solar heating systems to completely meet heating needs year round, solar heating systems can reduce the amount of energy used in conventional heating systems, thus reducing heating costs.

Build Science Skills L2

Observing ACTIVITY

Purpose Students observe how passive solar heating can be used for heating.

Materials a box with black interior, a box with white interior, clear plastic wrap, 2 beakers, 2 thermometers

Class Time 50 minutes preparation, or one class period

Procedure Separate students into groups, each with its own set of materials. Members of each group place one beaker, half full of water, in each of their boxes and cover both boxes with plastic wrap. Both boxes are placed in sunlight for half an hour. Group members then remove the beakers from the boxes, placing a thermometer in each. Finally, all students record the temperature of the water.

Safety Have students wear lab aprons and safety goggles.

Expected Outcome Because the black box absorbs and remits radiation better than the white box, the thermal energy of its walls and interior will be greater. The water will be in thermal equilibrium with the interior of the box. Therefore, the water that had been in the black box will have a higher temperature than the water in the white box.
Kinesthetic, Group

CONCEPTS in Action

Solar Home

Huge amounts of radiant energy from the sun constantly fall on the surface of our planet. How can this energy be harnessed to help make a home that is warm and comfortable in all seasons?

Large area of glass to trap radiant energy from the sun
Automated louvers for cooling when needed
Trees on south and west sides for summer shade

Heating a home with solar energy means making the best use of available sunlight. To provide warmth, large windows are placed on the south side of the house to trap sunlight, while north-facing walls have good insulation and few windows. On the roof, solar collectors absorb energy from the sun's rays to heat water, while solar panels convert the sun's energy to electrical energy for use in household appliances. High-quality insulation is used in all outside walls to reduce heat lost through convection, conduction, and radiation. But because the sun does not shine continuously, solar-heated homes also use energy from conventional sources to keep the home heated day and night, year-round.

Positioning for sunlight
Windows should face south to trap as much light as possible from the winter sun, with few windows on the west side to reduce overheating in summer.

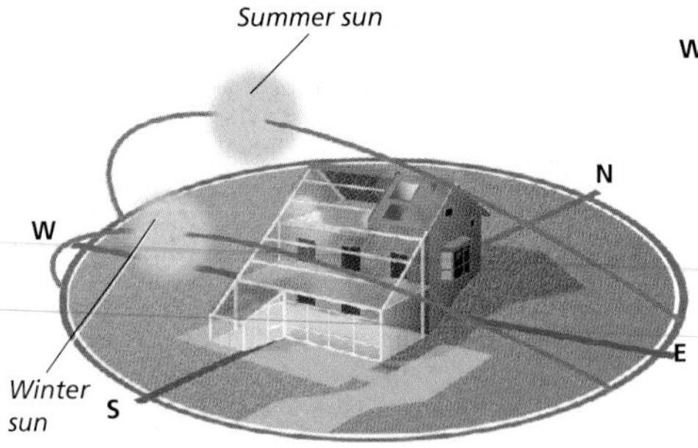

Summer sun
W
N
E
S
Winter sun

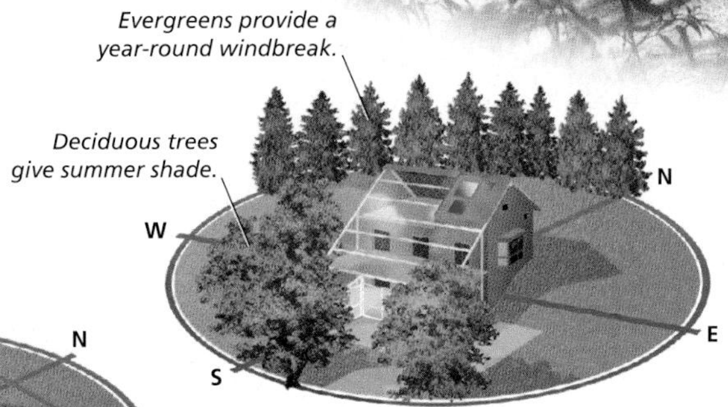

Evergreens provide a year-round windbreak.
Deciduous trees give summer shade.
W
N
E
S

Planting trees and shrubs
Trees placed away from the house act as a windbreak to reduce heat loss. Deciduous trees, planted closer, prevent overheating in summer, and allow sunlight to pass through in winter.

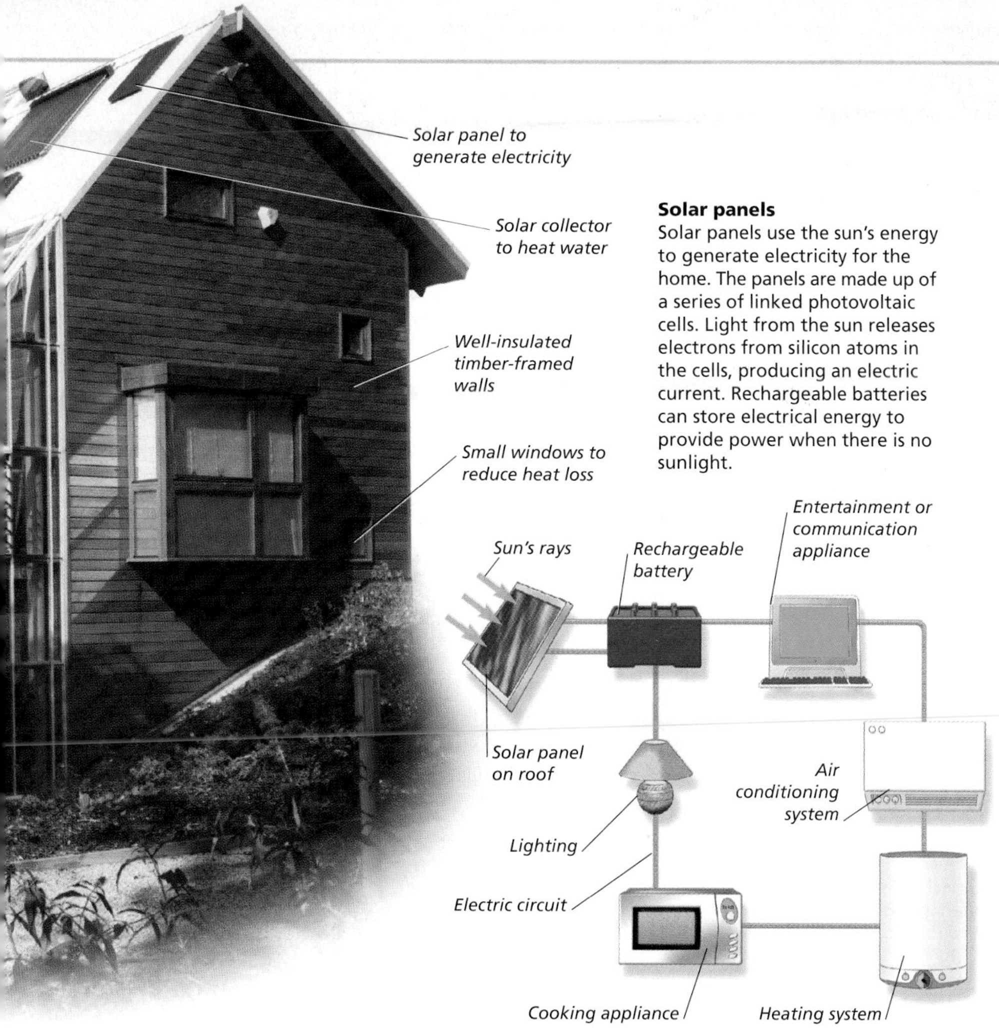
Solar panel to generate electricity
Solar collector to heat water
Well-insulated timber-framed walls
Small windows to reduce heat loss
Sun's rays
Rechargeable battery
Entertainment or communication appliance
Solar panel on roof
Air conditioning system
Lighting
Electric circuit
Cooking appliance
Heating system

Solar panels
Solar panels use the sun's energy to generate electricity for the home. The panels are made up of a series of linked photovoltaic cells. Light from the sun releases electrons from silicon atoms in the cells, producing an electric current. Rechargeable batteries can store electrical energy to provide power when there is no sunlight.

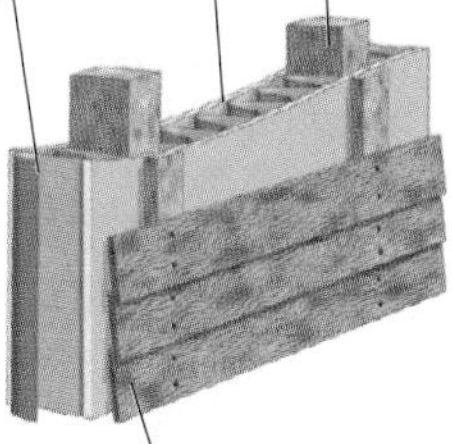
Stud frame
Plasterboard
Insulating material
Wood siding

Wall insulation
Wood is a natural insulator, so timber construction reduces heat flow through the walls. Filling the wall cavity with insulating material seals the walls against drafts, and greatly reduces heat loss.

Going Further

- Research solar-heated pools in the library or on the Internet. Make a poster display explaining how solar heating differs from a typical pool heating system. Include diagrams that explain how radiation, absorption, insulation, and convection are used in a solar-heated pool.
- Take a Discovery Channel Video Field Trip by watching "Powered by the Sun."

Discovery Channel School **Video Field Trip**

Going Further

Student posters should clearly show energy sources and energy transfers in solar-heated and conventionally heated pools. Diagrams should label places where radiation, absorption, and convection occur. For example, absorption occurs in the solar collector and convection occurs in the tubing that carries heated water to the pool. To reduce heat loss in a solar-heated pool, insulating plastic is placed on the water's surface when the pool is not in use. **Visual**

Discovery Channel School

Video Field Trip

Powered by the Sun

After students have viewed the Video Field Trip, ask them the following questions: **How long is energy from the sun expected to be available?** *(Billions of years)* **Why is it important to make effective use of solar energy?** *(Other sources of energy are being constantly used up.)* **How does the building at the Rocky Mountain Institute manage to produce crops throughout the year?** *(By using a greenhouse with glass walls that let in sunlight. Student answers may include that a greenhouse also stays warm inside partly by keeping out the colder air outside.)* **How does the heating system in the Rocky Mountain Institute building produce heat?** *(It converts sunlight into thermal energy.)* **How does this heating system work?** *(Solar panels absorb sunlight and heat a fluid. The fluid is pumped to a very large water tank. Heat from the stored hot fluid is transferred to the water that people use. Students may comment that the water can be heated to between 130°C and 140°C even in the coldest weather.)*

1 FOCUS

Objectives

16.3.1 **Describe** heat engines and **explain** how heat engines convert thermal energy into mechanical energy.

16.3.2 **Describe** how the different types of heating systems operate.

16.3.3 **Describe** how cooling systems, such as refrigerators and air conditioners, operate.

16.3.4 **Evaluate** benefits and drawbacks of different heating and cooling systems.

Reading Focus

Build Vocabulary L2

LINCS Have students: **L**ist the parts of the vocabulary that they know, such as *central, heating, system, heat,* and *pump.* **I**magine what a central heating system might look like and how the terms might fit together. **N**ote a reminding, sound-alike term, such as *central nervous system* or *sound system.* **C**onnect the terms, perhaps in a long sentence or a short story. **S**elf-test (quiz themselves).

Reading Strategy L2

a. Piston compresses the fuel-air mixture. **b.** Ignited mixture expands and pushes the piston. **c.** Exhaust gases leave the cylinder.

2 INSTRUCT

Heat Engines

Build Reading Literacy L1

Relate Cause and Effect Refer to page **260D** in **Chapter 9**, which provides the guidelines for relating cause and effect.

Have students read the paragraphs about the external combustion engine and study the illustration in Figure 11. Ask, **What causes the piston in the cylinder to do work?** *(The expanding steam pushes the piston, causing it to do work.)* **What is the effect of the movement of the slide valve?** *(It traps hot steam in the cylinder and allows cool steam to leave.)* **Logical**

16.3 Using Heat

Reading Focus

Key Concepts

- What are the two main types of heat engines?
- How do most heating systems distribute thermal energy?
- How does a heat pump reverse the normal flow of heat?

Vocabulary

- external combustion engine
- internal combustion engine
- central heating system
- heat pump
- refrigerant

Reading Strategy

Sequencing Copy the cycle diagram below and complete it as you read to show the sequence of events in a gasoline engine.

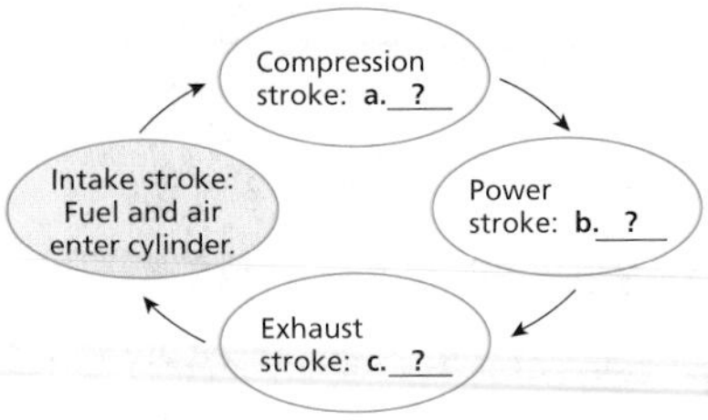

Compression stroke: a. ?
Power stroke: b. ?
Exhaust stroke: c. ?
Intake stroke: Fuel and air enter cylinder.

Steam locomotives were one of the most important early uses of the steam engine. Prior to the locomotive, steam engines provided power for coal mines and mills. But don't think that steam engines are only a thing of the past. In fact, most electric power plants today use steam turbines, a very efficient kind of steam engine.

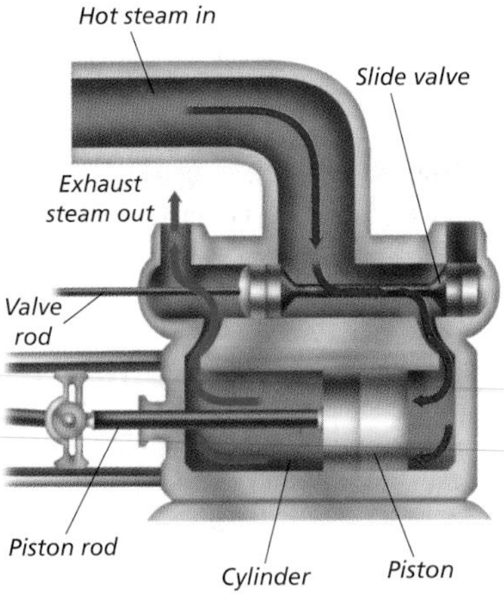

Hot steam in
Slide valve
Exhaust steam out
Valve rod
Piston rod
Cylinder
Piston

Figure 11 In an external combustion engine, combustion occurs outside of the engine.

Heat Engines

Heat engines played a key role in the development of the modern industrial world. **The two main types of heat engines are the external combustion engine and the internal combustion engine.**

External Combustion Engine A steam engine is an **external combustion engine**—an engine that burns fuel outside the engine. Thomas Newcomen developed the first practical steam engine in 1712. His engine was used to pump water out of coal mines. In 1765, James Watt designed an engine that was more efficient, in part because it operated at a higher temperature.

Figure 11 shows one type of steam engine. Hot steam enters the cylinder on the right side. When the valve slides to the left, hot steam is trapped in the cylinder. The steam expands and cools as it pushes the piston to the left. Thus heat is converted into work. The piston moves back and forth as hot steam enters first on one side and then on the other side.

Section Resources

Print

- ***Reading and Study Workbook With Math Support,*** Section 16.3
- ***Math Skills and Problem Solving Workbook,*** Section 16.3
- ***Transparencies,*** Section 16.3

Technology

- ***Interactive Textbook,*** Section 16.3
- ***Presentation Pro CD-ROM,*** Section 16.3
- ***Go Online,*** *Science News,* Heat

Internal Combustion Engine Most cars use internal combustion engines that burn gasoline. An **internal combustion engine** is a heat engine in which the fuel burns inside the engine. Most internal combustion engines use pistons that move up and down inside cylinders. Each upward or downward motion of a piston is called a stroke. The linear motion of each stroke is converted into rotary motion by the crankshaft. The crankshaft is connected to the transmission, which is linked to the vehicle's wheels through the drive shaft.

Figure 12 shows the sequence of events in one cylinder of a four-stroke engine. In the intake stroke, a mixture of air and gasoline vapor enters the cylinder. Next, in the compression stroke, the piston compresses the gas mixture. At the end of compression, the spark plug ignites the mixture, which heats the gas under pressure. In the power stroke, the hot gas expands and drives the piston down. During the exhaust stroke, gas leaves the cylinder, and the cycle repeats.

Recall that a heat engine must discharge some waste energy in order to do work. In an internal combustion engine, the cooling system and exhaust transfer heat from the engine to the environment. A coolant—usually water and antifreeze—absorbs some thermal energy from the engine and then passes through the radiator. A fan blows air through the radiator, transferring thermal energy to the atmosphere. Without a cooling system, an engine would be damaged by thermal expansion. If you are ever in a car that overheats, stop driving and allow the engine to cool. Otherwise, there is a risk of serious damage to the engine.

Gasoline engines are more efficient than old-fashioned steam engines, but they still are not very efficient. Only about one third of the fuel energy in a gasoline engine is converted to work. Auto makers have tried several ways to make engines more efficient. One design, called a hybrid design, uses a heat engine together with an electric motor. This design is explained in the How It Works box on the next page.

Figure 12 In an internal combustion engine, fuel is burned inside the engine. Most cars have a four-stroke internal combustion engine. This diagram shows only one of the cylinders during each stroke. **Classifying** ***In which of the strokes does the piston do work that can be used by the car?***

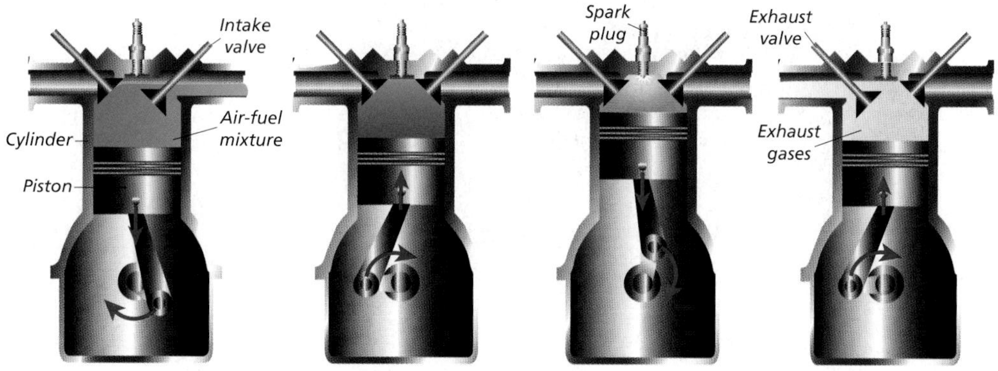

Intake valve
Air-fuel mixture
Cylinder
Piston
Spark plug
Exhaust valve
Exhaust gases
A Intake stroke
B Compression stroke
C Power stroke
D Exhaust stroke

Use Community Resources L2

Suggest that students learn more about internal combustion engines by visiting an auto repair shop and talking with a mechanic. Encourage students to construct a KWL chart, and to ask the mechanic questions based on what students want to learn about engines.
Interpersonal, Portfolio

Build Science Skills L2

Applying Concepts Have students write a short paragraph about how the increased temperature of the gasoline-air mixture allows it to do work during the power stroke in an internal combustion engine. Remind them to use what they know about forms of energy and the relationship between temperature, pressure, and average kinetic energy of particles that make up a substance. *(Answers should indicate that the energy released during ignition of the gasoline-air mixture increases the mixture's temperature, and thus the average kinetic energy of the gas particles. This greater energy produces an increase in gas pressure, which in turn does work.)*
Verbal, Logical

Customize for English Language Learners

Simplify the Presentation
The details in the operations of heat engines, heat systems, and cooling systems are rather complex. By simplifying your presentation, the English language learners in your class will have a better comprehension of the material. Speak directly, use simple words and short sentences, and make frequent use of the diagrams to clarify the workings of thermal systems.

Answer to . . .

Figure 12 *Work is done during the power stroke as the expanding gases push the piston out of the cylinder.*

DK HOW It Works

Hybrid Automobile L2

The hybrid automobile is a result of research that was begun initially to develop an efficient electric car. By combining a small gasoline engine with an electric motor, the hybrid automobile is able to travel longer distances, like a gasoline-powered vehicle, but with reduced fuel consumption and emissions. During regenerative braking, kinetic energy that is normally lost to friction is partially recovered for later use. This can be explained to students in simple terms: It takes work to turn a generator. When the spinning wheels do the work of turning the generator, the wheels lose kinetic energy. In other words, the wheels must slow down.

Interpreting Diagrams Fuel consumption is reduced by using lightweight materials, an aerodynamic design, and high-pressure tires that reduce friction. The use of two engines saves fuel because the small gasoline engine is more efficient than traditional larger engines, and the electric motor is more efficient than a gasoline engine for accelerating at low speeds.
Visual

For Enrichment L3

Interested students can make a multimedia presentation for the class explaining the hybrid automobile. Numerous articles on the subject can be found on the Internet and in science and engineering periodicals.
Verbal, Portfolio

DK HOW It Works

Hybrid Automobile

Internal combustion engines produce harmful emissions from the combustion of gasoline. Recently, cleaner electric cars have been developed, but these need frequent recharging. Hybrid cars solve these problems by using a combination of smaller gasoline engines and electric motors. **Interpreting Diagrams** ***Which features of the hybrid automobile help to reduce fuel consumption?***

A new breed of car
This hybrid car was first produced in 1999. It is light, aerodynamic, and has a small, efficient engine.

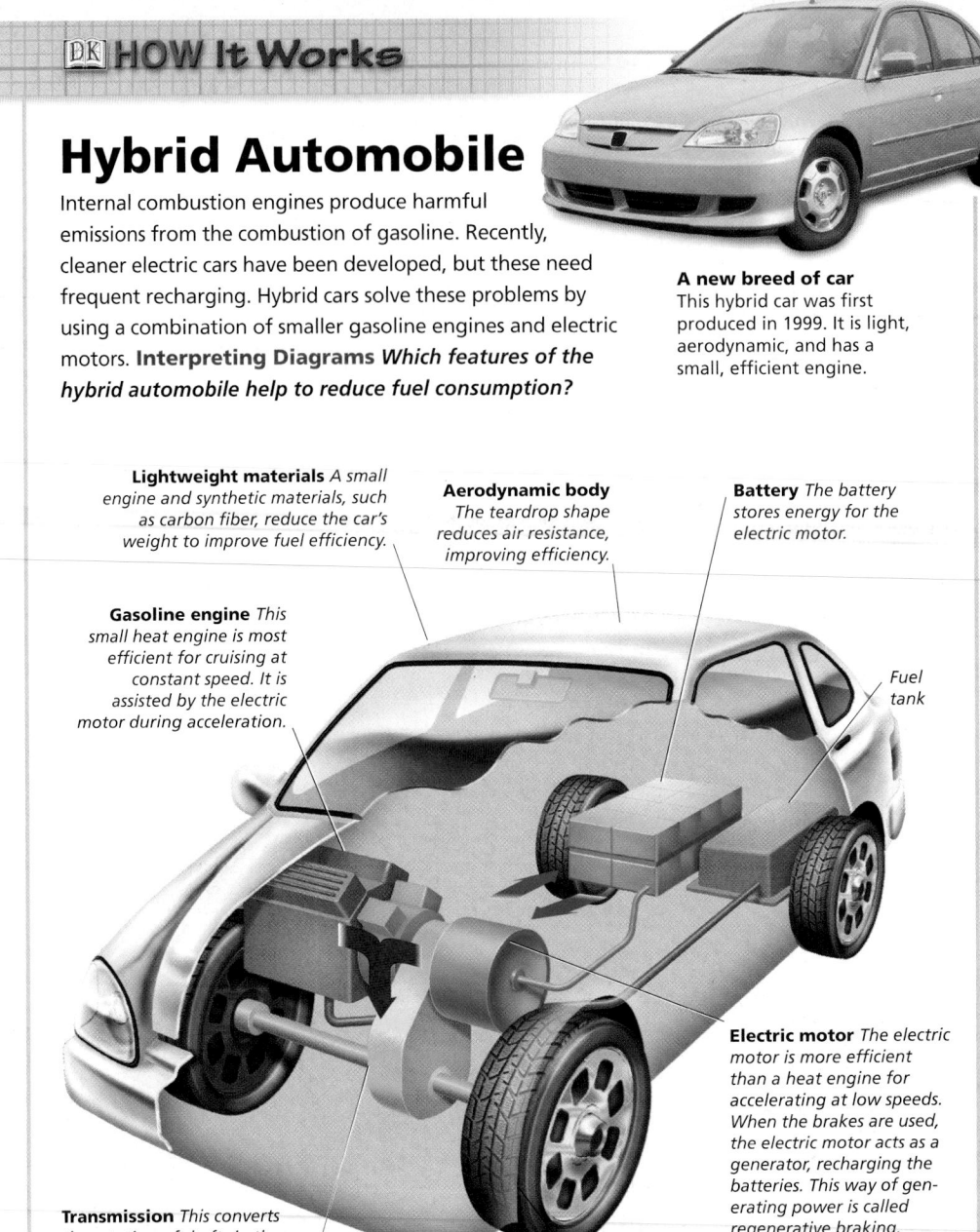

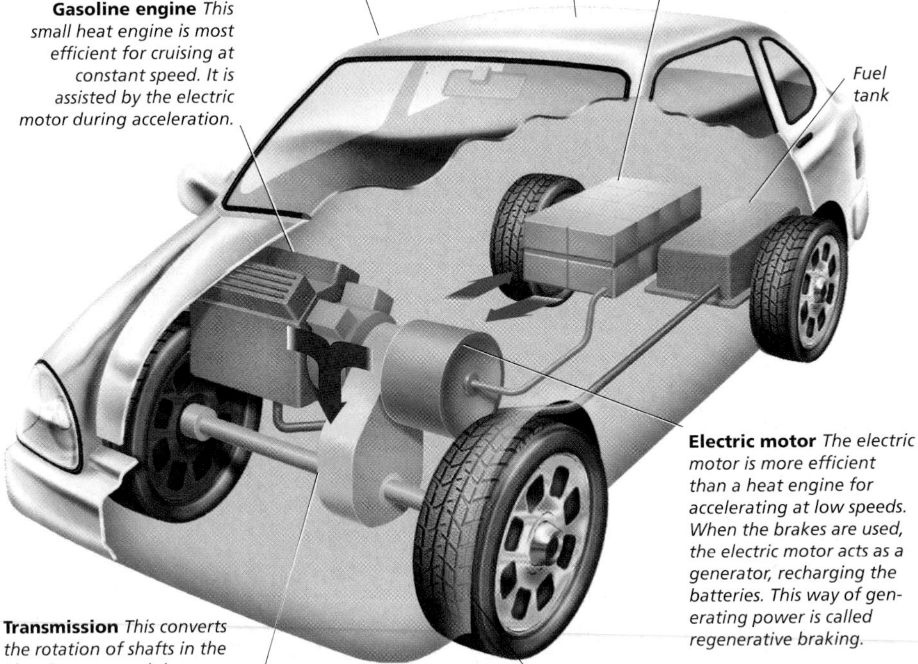
Lightweight materials *A small engine and synthetic materials, such as carbon fiber, reduce the car's weight to improve fuel efficiency.*
Aerodynamic body *The teardrop shape reduces air resistance, improving efficiency.*
Battery *The battery stores energy for the electric motor.*
Gasoline engine *This small heat engine is most efficient for cruising at constant speed. It is assisted by the electric motor during acceleration.*
Fuel tank
Electric motor *The electric motor is more efficient than a heat engine for accelerating at low speeds. When the brakes are used, the electric motor acts as a generator, recharging the batteries. This way of generating power is called regenerative braking.*
Transmission *This converts the rotation of shafts in the electric motor and the gas engine into wheel rotation. In this model, both the electric motor and the engine can directly drive the transmission.*
Tires *These tires are inflated to a higher pressure than conventional tires to reduce friction.*

Heating Systems

At the start of the industrial revolution, wood-burning fireplaces were the principal method of heating buildings. Rumford was keenly aware of the drawbacks of fireplaces. They were smoky and not very efficient. Too much heat went up the chimney. In 1796, Rumford designed a fireplace that now bears his name. His fireplace was not as deep as standard fireplaces, and it had slanted walls to reflect heat into the room. His improvements were quickly accepted and used throughout England.

Today, fireplaces are often used to supplement central heating systems. A **central heating system** heats many rooms from one central location. The central location of a heating system often is in the basement. The most commonly used energy sources for central heating systems are electrical energy, natural gas, oil, and coal. Heating systems differ in how they transfer thermal energy to the rest of the building. **Most heating systems use convection to distribute thermal energy.**

Hot-Water Heating Figure 13 shows the main components of a hot-water heating system. At the boiler, heating oil or natural gas burns and heats the water. The circulating pump carries the hot water to radiators in each room. The hot water transfers thermal energy to the radiator by conduction. As the pipes heat up, they heat the room air by conduction and radiation. Hot air rises and sets up a convection current in each room. After transferring much of its thermal energy to the room, the cooled water returns to the boiler and the cycle begins again.

Temperature is controlled by a thermostat. One kind of thermostat is like a thermometer, with a strip of brass and steel wound up in a coil. When the heating system is on, the coil heats up. The two metals in the coil expand at different rates, and the coil rotates. This trips a switch to turn off the heat. As the room cools, the coil rotates in the opposite direction, until it trips the switch to turn the heat back on.

Steam Heating Steam heating is very similar to hot-water heating except that steam is used instead of hot water. The transfer of heat from the steam-heated radiator to the room still occurs by conduction and radiation. Steam heating often is used in older buildings or when many buildings are heated from one central location.

Reading Checkpoint *How are fireplaces often used today?*

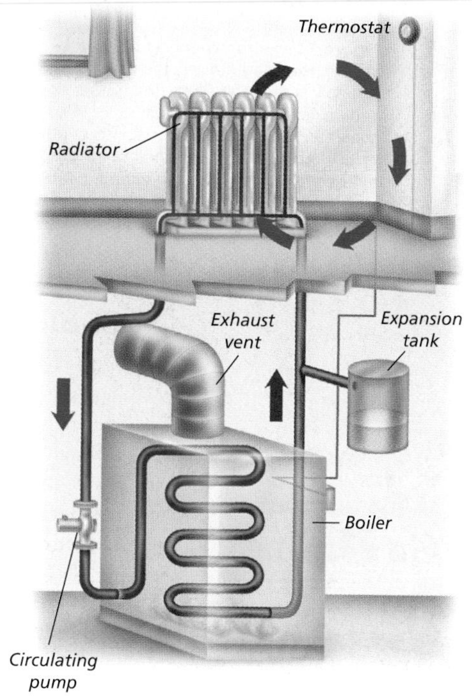

Thermostat
Radiator
Exhaust vent
Expansion tank
Boiler
Circulating pump

Figure 13 Within the pipes of this hot-water heating system, the water circulates in a convection current. In each room, the air moves in a convection current. **Relating Cause and Effect** ***Why has the water returning to the boiler cooled down?***

Heating Systems

Address Misconceptions **L2**

Students may think that heating systems are simply energy conversion devices because they can use a variety of energy sources to produce thermal energy. Remind students that the energy required to operate a heating system exceeds the amount of thermal energy distributed by the system, partly because there is always some energy that is lost through exhaust in the original central heating process. In addition, energy is lost through heat transfer processes from pipes and ducts that transfer heated fluids from the central heating system to the various rooms. Even in electric heating, some energy is lost in heating the wires used to transfer electrical energy to the heating coils.
Logical

Use Visuals **L1**

Figure 13 Point out that the system shown must be well insulated so as to prevent the loss of heat. Have students look at the various parts of the hot-water heating system. Ask, **Where can thermal energy be lost in this system, and by what manner of heat transfer?** *(Energy is lost through the water pipes leading from the boiler to the radiator. Most of this energy is lost by radiation, though some conduction to the air takes place. A good deal of energy is lost by convection from the exhaust vent. A smaller amount of heat is lost through the pipes leading from radiators to the boiler.)*
Visual

Facts and Figures

Heat of Vaporization Although hot-water heating and steam heating systems are similar in structure, steam systems convey more energy for each kilogram of water used. This difference occurs because the phase change that takes place during the boiling process, when liquid water is vaporized to steam, requires a much greater input of energy than is necessary to heat water in a hot-water system. The energy required for this phase change, called the *heat of vaporization,* is equal to 2.26×10^6 J/kg. This amount is more than 500 times as great as the energy required to raise the temperature of a kilogram of liquid water by 1°C (about 4180 J/kg). When steam completely condenses to liquid water, an amount of energy equal to the heat of vaporization is given up. This is why steam heating is effective, and also why steam is so hazardous.

Answer to . . .

Figure 13 *Water returning to the boiler has cooled because it has lost thermal energy in the radiator.*

Reading Checkpoint *Today, fireplaces are often used to supplement central heating systems.*

Cooling Systems

Teacher Demo

Cooling by Evaporation L2

Purpose Students observe how evaporation of a liquid can cool its surroundings.

Materials paper towels, water, tape, hand-held or electric fan, thermometer

Procedure Wrap a wet paper towel around the bulb of a thermometer and wait several minutes. Record the thermometer's temperature. Tape the wet paper towel to the thermometer's bulb. Blow air across the paper towel with the fan. Read the thermometer's temperature again.

Safety Clean up any spills immediately. Handle thermometers with care to avoid breakage. Be sure cords are untangled and cannot trip anyone. Do not handle electrical equipment with wet hands.

Expected Outcome Water absorbs energy as it evaporates. This removes energy from the thermometer bulb, so the temperature reading of the thermometer decreases.
Kinesthetic, Visual

Integrate Chemistry L2

Different compounds can be used as refrigerants, just as long as they can be made to evaporate at low temperatures. Among the refrigerants that have this property are certain *chlorofluorocarbons*, or CFCs, which have been used widely in refrigerators and air conditioners. In the 1970s, chlorine atoms released by CFCs were found to react with the layer of atmospheric ozone, which absorbs harmful ultraviolet radiation from the sun. The decomposition of the ozone layer prompted the establishment of the Montreal Accords in 1990 and the eventual replacement of CFCs with less harmful refrigerants.
Verbal, Logical

Go Online SCIENCE NEWS®

Science News provides students with current information on heat.

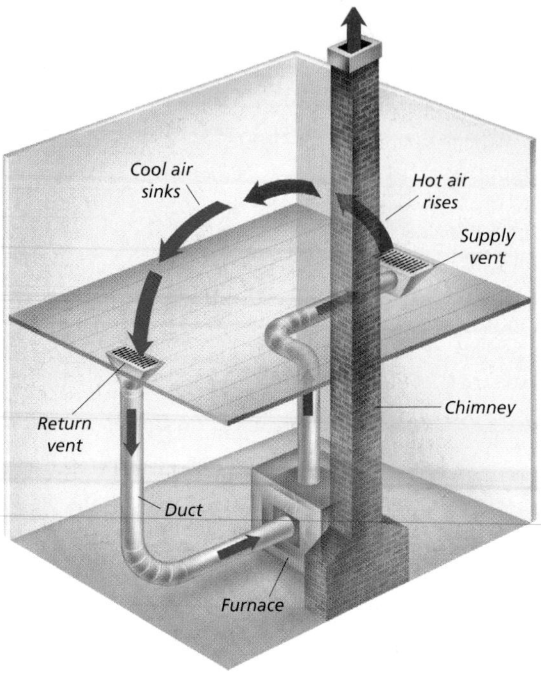

Cool air sinks
Hot air rises
Supply vent
Chimney
Return vent
Duct
Furnace

Figure 14 In a forced-air central heating system, the hot air enters the room through a supply vent in the floor. The hot air rises as cooler, denser air in the room sinks. The cooler air returns to the furnace through the return vent. **Inferring** ***If the hot air supply vent were located near the ceiling, what would be the warmest part of the room?***

Electric Baseboard Heating An electric baseboard heater uses electrical energy to heat a room. A conductor similar to the heating element in an electric stove is used to convert electrical energy to thermal energy. The hot coil heats the air near it by conduction and radiation. Then convection circulates the warm air to heat the room.

Radiant heaters are similar to electric baseboard heating. They are often sold as small portable units, and are used to supplement a central heating system. These "space heaters" are easy to turn on and off and to direct onto cold toes or other areas where heat is needed most. Sometimes these heaters have a fan that helps to circulate heat.

Forced-Air Heating To maintain even room temperatures, forced-air heating systems use fans to circulate warm air through ducts to the rooms of a building. In a forced-air heating system, shown in Figure 15, convection circulates air in each room. Because the warm air entering the room rises toward the ceiling, the warm-air vents are located near the floor. Cool room air returns to the furnace through floor vents on the other side of the room. One advantage of forced-air heating is that the air is cleaned as it passes through filters located near the furnace.

Reading Checkpoint *How do forced-air heating systems circulate air?*

Go Online SCIENCE NEWS®

For: Articles on heat
Visit: PHSchool.com
Web Code: cce-2163

Cooling Systems

Most cooling systems, such as refrigerators and air conditioners, are heat pumps. A **heat pump** is a device that reverses the normal flow of thermal energy. Heat pumps do this by circulating a refrigerant through tubing. A **refrigerant** is a fluid that vaporizes and condenses inside the tubing of a heat pump. When the refrigerant absorbs heat, it vaporizes, or turns into a gas. When the refrigerant gives off heat, it condenses, or turns back into a liquid.

Recall that thermal energy flows spontaneously from hot objects to cold objects. **Heat pumps must do work on a refrigerant in order to reverse the normal flow of thermal energy.** In this process, a cold area, such as the inside of a refrigerator, becomes even colder.

Data Analysis

What Is the Real Cost of a Washing Machine?

If you ever shop for a new washing machine, you'll notice the bright yellow Energy Guide sticker on each machine. The sticker gives the machine's operating cost per year as estimated by the U.S. Department of Energy. The largest part of the cost for cleaning clothes is heating the water that goes into the washing machine. So a machine that uses less water is more efficient.

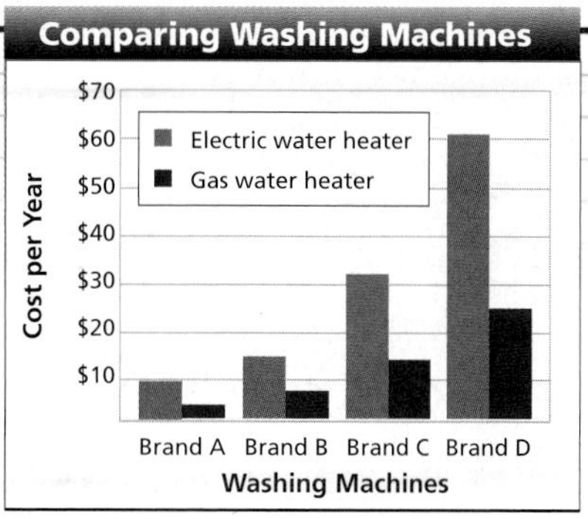

Comparing Washing Machines
$70
$60
$50
$40
$30
$20
$10
Cost per Year
Electric water heater
Gas water heater
Brand A
Brand B
Brand C
Brand D
Washing Machines

1. **Using Graphs** One family uses an electric water heater. What is their cost per year for machine A? For machine D?
2. **Calculating** How much money does this family save each year using machine A compared to using machine D?
3. **Calculating** The price of machine A is $300 more than the price of machine D. If the family uses a machine for 10 years, which one costs less overall? (*Hint:* Add the price to the operating cost for 10 years.)
4. **Calculating** Another family uses a gas water heater. Which machine should this family choose? Explain your thinking.
5. **Evaluating and Revising** A washing machine advertisement states that the annual cost assumes an electric water heater is used. Why would an advertisement include only this cost?

Refrigerators A refrigerator is a heat pump—it transfers thermal energy from the cold food compartment to the warm room. To move heat from a colder to a warmer location, a motor must do work to move refrigerant through tubing inside the refrigerator walls. Could you cool your kitchen on a hot day by leaving the refrigerator door open? It might seem so, but an open refrigerator would actually heat the kitchen! You may have noticed the hot coils underneath or behind the refrigerator. The coils not only release heat absorbed from the food compartment; they also release thermal energy produced by the work the motor does. That is why a refrigerator with an open door adds more heat to the room than it removes.

Reading Checkpoint *What is a heat pump?*

Temperature in room: 25°C
Temperature inside refrigerator: 3°C

Figure 15 When a refrigerator door is open, some thermal energy from the room enters the refrigerator. But more thermal energy leaves the refrigerator through the coils underneath the food compartment.
Interpreting Photos ***Why can't you cool a room by leaving the refrigerator door open?***

Data Analysis

What Is the Real Cost of a Washing Machine? L2

Answers

1. The annual cost of Brand A is about $10 per year. The annual cost of Brand D is $60 per year.
2. The family saves $50 each year using Brand A.
3. The operating cost of Brand A for 10 years is 10 × $10 = $100. The operating cost of Brand D for 10 years is 10 × $60 = $600. Brand A costs less overall because although the initial price is $300 higher, the machine saves $500 in operating costs.
4. Using a gas water heater, Brand A saves only $20 in operating costs each year. Based only on cost, the family should choose Brand D because it will cost $100 less to own and operate for 10 years.
5. The goal of the advertisement is to convince as many people as possible to buy the machine. Therefore, the advertisement emphasizes the money that could be saved under the best of circumstances (using an electric water heater).

For Extra Help L1

Discuss the basic features of a bar graph. Unlike line graphs, in which one quantity on the horizontal axis corresponds to a unique quantity on the vertical axis, more than one bar can be given for a particular item on the horizontal axis. For instance, in the above graph, each brand has two bars shown: one for electric heaters and one for gas heaters. Similarly, a comparison between results in different years can be shown using several bars. The placement of the bars allows easy comparison of changes on one graph. **Visual**

Answer to . . .

Figure 14 *The ceiling, because warm air entering the room tends to remain near the ceiling*

Figure 15 *The refrigerator gives off more thermal energy than it absorbs.*

Reading Checkpoint *In a forced-air heating system, fans circulate warm air through ducts to the rooms of a building.*

Reading Checkpoint *A heat pump is a device that reverses the normal flow of thermal energy.*

Facts and Figures

Water Cooling Although refrigerants are used to reach temperatures below the freezing point of water, water itself has been used for cooling for centuries. Because of its specific heat and heat of vaporization, water can greatly reduce the temperature of hot dry air. Fountains helped to cool the air in courtyards in places like Spain and Italy. In many desert cities, evaporative coolers, in which hot air is drawn through water-soaked pads into houses, are still widely used for air conditioning.

Use Visuals L1

Figure 16 Stress that evaporation is the key process for cooling in an air conditioner and refrigerator. Most of the work done by the air conditioner motor involves changing the pressure of the refrigerant so that it will evaporate (and so absorb thermal energy) and condense (to give up thermal energy) easily. Ask, **What is the direction of the net flow of thermal energy in an air conditioner?** *(Looking at the red arrows only, thermal energy is transferred from the air inside the room to the outdoor air.)*
Visual

3 ASSESS

Evaluate Understanding L2

Ask students to write two questions each about heating systems and cooling systems. Review the questions for accuracy, and then have students form groups and ask each other their approved questions.

Reteach L1

Use Figure 12 to review how an internal combustion engine operates during one cycle.

Writing in Science

Student flyers should clearly compare four heating systems. Students may choose to show the comparisons using a chart. Possible columns in the chart are efficiency, physical space used per room, environmental concerns, and local climate. Students may choose to compare systems in different climates. In southern states, a benefit of a forced-air heating system is that it combines easily with central air conditioning. Electric baseboard heating is advantageous in regions where electric power is inexpensive.

Interactive Textbook If your class subscribes to the Interactive Textbook, use it to review key concepts in Section 16.3.

Answer to . . .

Figure 16 *The compressor does work by pushing particles of vapor closer together to form a high-pressure vapor. It also does work as it pushes refrigerant through the tubing.*

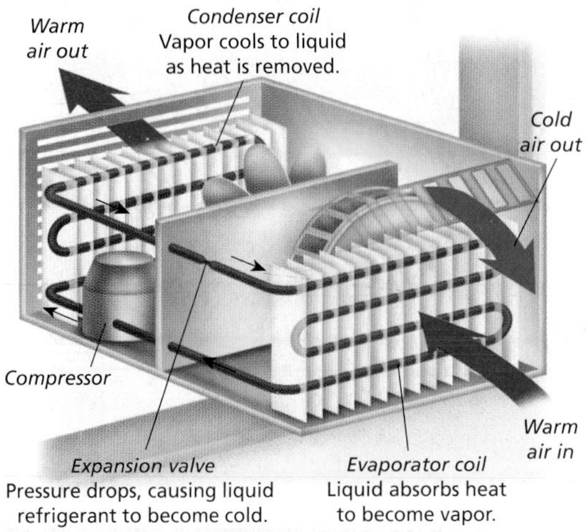
Warm air out
Condenser coil
Vapor cools to liquid as heat is removed.
Cold air out
Compressor
Warm air in
Expansion valve
Pressure drops, causing liquid refrigerant to become cold.
Evaporator coil
Liquid absorbs heat to become vapor.

Figure 16 In a window air conditioner, outside air is heated as a fan blows it through the condenser coil. Inside the room, a fan draws in warm air through the evaporator coil. The fan blows cooled air out into the room. **Interpreting Diagrams** ***What work is done by the compressor?***

Air Conditioners Have you ever been outside on a hot day and stood near a room air conditioner? The air conditioner is actually heating the outdoor air. Near the air conditioner is the last place you'd want to be on a hot day!

Where does the hot air come from? It must come from inside the house. But as you know from the second law of thermodynamics, heat only flows from a lower temperature (indoors) to a higher temperature (outdoors) if work is done on the system.

Figure 16 shows how a room air conditioner operates. The compressor raises the temperature and pressure of the refrigerant, turning it into a hot, high-pressure gas. The temperature of the condenser coil is higher than the outside air temperature, so heat flows spontaneously from the coil to the outside air. A fan increases the rate at which heat flows. As thermal energy is removed from the coil, the refrigerant cools and condenses into a liquid.

The liquid refrigerant then flows through the expansion valve and decreases in temperature. As the cold refrigerant flows through the evaporator coil, it absorbs thermal energy from the warm room air. The fan sends cold air back into the room. The refrigerant becomes a vapor, and the process starts all over again.

Section 16.3 Assessment

Reviewing Concepts

1. List the two main types of heat engines.
2. How is thermal energy distributed in most heating systems?
3. How does a heat pump move thermal energy from a cold area to a warm area?
4. If the efficiency of a gasoline engine is 25 percent, what happens to the missing 75 percent of the energy in the fuel?

Critical Thinking

5. **Predicting** A diesel engine runs at a higher temperature than a gasoline engine. Predict which engine would be more efficient. Explain your answer.
6. **Applying Concepts** Why would it be a mistake to locate a wood-burning stove on the second floor of a two-story house?

Writing in Science

Writing to Persuade Imagine that you are a marketing executive in a company that sells HVAC (heating, ventilation, and air conditioning) equipment. Write a one-page flyer comparing four kinds of heating systems. Organize the flyer so it is easy for customers to see the benefits of each system.

Section 16.3 Assessment

1. External combustion engine, internal combustion engine
2. Most heating systems distribute thermal energy by convection.
3. Heat pumps must do work on a refrigerant in order to reverse the normal flow of heat.
4. The energy that does not do useful work is converted into thermal energy.
5. The maximum efficiency of a heat engine increases with a greater difference between the temperature inside and the temperature outside the engine. A diesel engine is likely to be more efficient, assuming both engines discharge thermal energy into an environment at the same temperature.
6. Convection will carry cool air to the lower level so the lower level will be cooler than the upper level. This is inefficient because if the lower level is comfortable, the upper level will be warmer than necessary.

Design Your Own Lab

Using Specific Heat to Analyze Metals

In this lab, you will determine the specific heat of steel and aluminum. Then you will use specific heat to analyze the composition of a metal can.

Problem How can you use specific heat to determine the composition of a metal can?

Materials

- 10 steel bolts
- balance
- 50-cm length of string
- clamp
- ring stand
- boiling water bath (shared with class)
- thermometer
- 500-mL graduated cylinder
- ice water
- foam cup with lid
- aluminum nails
- crushed can

For the probeware version of this lab, see the Probeware Lab Manual, Lab 7.

Skills Calculating, Designing Experiments

Procedure

Part A: Determining Specific Heat

1. Copy the data table shown below.

Data Table

	Water	Steel Bolts
Mass (g)		
Initial temperature (°C)		
Final temperature (°C)		
Specific heat (J/g•°C)	4.18	

2. Measure and record the mass of 10 steel bolts.
3. Tie the bolts to the string. Use a clamp and ring stand to suspend the bolts in the boiling water bath. **CAUTION** *Be careful not to splash boiling water.* After a few minutes, record the water temperature as the initial temperature of the bolts.
4. Use a graduated cylinder to pour 200 mL of ice water (without ice) into the foam cup. Record the mass and temperature of the ice water. (*Hint:* The density of water is 1 g/mL.)

5. Use the clamp to move the bolts into the cup of ice water. Cover the cup and insert the thermometer through the hole in the cover.
6. Gently swirl the water in the cup. Record the highest temperature as the final temperature for both the water and the steel bolts.
7. Calculate and record the specific heat of steel. (*Hint:* Use the equation $Q = m \times c \times \Delta T$ to calculate the energy the water absorbs.)
8. Repeat Steps 3 through 7 with aluminum nails to determine the specific heat of aluminum. Start by making a new data table. Use a mass of aluminum that is close to the mass you used for the steel bolts.

Part B: Design Your Own Experiment

9. **Designing Experiments** Design an experiment that uses specific heat to identify the metals a can might be made of.
10. Construct a data table in which to record your observations. After your teacher approves your plan, perform your experiment.

Analyze and Conclude

1. **Comparing and Contrasting** Which metal has a higher specific heat, aluminum or steel?
2. **Drawing Conclusions** Was the specific heat of the can closer to the specific heat of steel or of aluminum? What can you conclude about the material in the can?
3. **Evaluating** Did your observations prove what the can was made of? If not, what other information would you need to be sure?
4. **Inferring** The can you used is often called a tin can. The specific heat of tin is 0.23 J/g•°C. Did your data support the idea that the can was made mostly of tin? Explain your answer.

Design Your Own Lab

Using Specific Heat to Analyze Metals L2

Objective
After completing this lab, students will be able to
- describe how specific heat is determined.

Address Misconceptions

Students may have the misconception that the temperatures of the metal and water are the only factors that will affect the final temperature of the mixture. To help dispel this misconception, ask them to compare the effects of dropping an ice cube into a lake and into a glass of water.

Skills Focus Calculating, Measuring, Designing Experiments

Prep Time 20 minutes

Advance Prep Crush a steel can for each lab group. Smooth any rough or sharp edges with a file while wearing heavy leather gloves and safety goggles. Puncture the lids of the foam cups to enable students to insert the thermometers. Provide a large beaker of boiling water (with a thermometer in it) on a hot plate for the entire class to use. Provide ring stands, clamps, and 50-cm lengths of string for suspending the bolts in the boiling water bath.

Class Time 45 minutes

Safety Provide only nonmercury thermometers. Students should use tongs or heat-resistant gloves when handling hot objects and liquids. Students should wear safety goggles and lab aprons and should not stir with the thermometers.

Teaching Tips
- Students may need some guidance in using the specific-heat equation.

Questioning Strategies Ask students the following questions. **Why is it important to quickly transfer the bolts into the beaker?** *(Because the bolts are very hot, they will lose thermal energy very quickly as soon as they leave the hot water.)* **Why is it important to swirl the water after adding the hot bolts?** *(This ensures an even temperature and more accurate results.)*

Expected Outcome Students should measure a specific heat for the steel can that is close to that of the steel bolts.

Sample Data Ten bolts with a mass of 100 g will raise the temperature of 200 mL of water by about 5°C. The same mass of aluminum nails will raise the temperature by about 9°C.

Analyze and Conclude
1. The specific heat of aluminum (about 0.90 J/g•°C) is higher than the specific heat of steel (about 0.45 J/g•°C).
2. The specific heat of the can was very close to the specific heat of steel. This is evidence that the can is made mostly of steel.
3. The observations support the idea that the can is made of steel, but do not prove it; other metals may have similar specific heats. A list of the specific heats of various metals for comparison would be helpful, as would other kinds of evidence, such as the densities and chemical properties of the metals.
4. The specific heat of the can is close to that of steel, suggesting that the can is primarily steel.
Logical

Probeware Lab Manual Versions of this lab for use with probeware available from Pasco, Texas Instruments, and Vernier are in the Probeware Lab Manual.

Study Guide

Study Tip

Organize New Information
Tell students to organize the information they learn each day. Remind them that doing this helps them to understand better how all of the information is connected.

Thinking Visually

a. Energy is conserved: Thermal energy added to a system can do work or increase the thermal energy of the system.
b. Heat can flow from an object at lower temperature to an object at higher temperature only if work is done on the system.
c. Third law

Assessment

Interactive Textbook If your class subscribes to the Interactive Textbook, your students can go online to access an interactive version of the Student Edition and a self-test.

Reviewing Content

1. d **2.** b **3.** a
4. b **5.** b **6.** c
7. a **8.** d **9.** b
10. a

Understanding Concepts

11. Heat flows spontaneously from hot to cold objects. In many collisions, more energetic particles tend to transfer thermal energy to less energetic particles.
12. The object that is a better conductor of heat feels cooler to the touch because it conducts heat away from the hand faster.
13. As the temperature of the air in the balloon increases, the particles' average kinetic energy increases. The more energetic particles hit the inside of the balloon with greater force, causing the balloon to expand.

CHAPTER 16

Study Guide

16.1 Thermal Energy and Matter

Key Concepts

- Heat flows spontaneously from hot objects to cold objects.
- Temperature is related to the average kinetic energy of an object's particles due to their random motion through space.
- Thermal energy depends on the mass, temperature, and phase (solid, liquid, or gas) of an object.
- Thermal expansion occurs because particles of matter tend to move farther apart as temperature increases.
- The lower a material's specific heat is, the more its temperature rises when a given amount of energy is absorbed by a given mass.
- A calorimeter uses the principle that heat flows from a hotter object to a colder object until both reach the same temperature.

Vocabulary

heat, *p. 474*
temperature, *p. 475*
absolute zero, *p. 475*
thermal expansion, *p. 476*
specific heat, *p. 476*
calorimeter, *p. 478*

16.2 Heat and Thermodynamics

Key Concepts

- Conduction in gases is slower than in liquids and solids because the particles in a gas collide less often.
- Convection currents are important in many natural cycles, such as ocean currents, weather systems, and movements of hot rock in Earth's interior.
- All objects radiate energy. As an object's temperature increases, the rate at which it radiates energy increases.
- The first law of thermodynamics states that energy is conserved.
- The second law of thermodynamics states that thermal energy can flow from colder objects to hotter objects only if work is done on the system.
- The third law of thermodynamics states that absolute zero cannot be reached.

Vocabulary

conduction, *p. 479*
thermal conductor, *p. 480*
thermal insulator, *p. 480*
convection, *p. 480*
convection current, *p. 481*
radiation, *p. 481*
thermodynamics, *p. 482*
heat engine, *p. 483*
waste heat, *p. 483*

16.3 Using Heat

Key Concepts

- The two main types of heat engines are the external combustion engine and the internal combustion engine.
- Most heating systems use convection to distribute thermal energy.
- Heat pumps must do work on a refrigerant in order to reverse the normal flow of thermal energy.

Vocabulary

external combustion engine, *p. 486*
internal combustion engine, *p. 487*
central heating system, *p. 489*
heat pump, *p. 490*
refrigerant, *p. 490*

Thinking Visually

Concept Map Copy the concept map below onto a sheet of paper. Use the information from the chapter to complete the diagram.

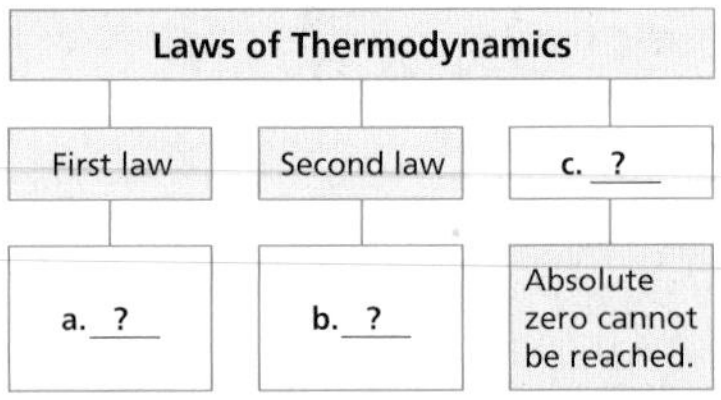
Laws of Thermodynamics
First law
Second law
c. ?
a. ?
b. ?
Absolute zero cannot be reached.

Chapter Resources

Print
- ***Chapter and Unit Tests,*** Chapter 16 Test A and Test B
- ***Test Prep Resources,*** Chapter 16

Technology
- ***Computer Test Bank,*** Chapter Test 16
- ***Interactive Textbook,*** Chapter 16
- ***Go Online,*** PHSchool.com, Chapter 16

Assessment

Interactive textbook with assessment at PHSchool.com iText

Reviewing Content

Choose the letter that best answers the question or completes the statement.

1. When a drill is used to bore a hole in an object,
   a. no useful work is done.
   b. no energy is lost due to friction.
   c. the drill is 100 percent efficient.
   d. friction causes the object to heat up.
2. Why does liquid rise in a thermometer?
   a. convection b. thermal expansion
   c. condensation d. radiation
3. To heat 1 g of water by 1°C requires
   a. 1 calorie. b. 1 Calorie.
   c. 1 joule. d. 1 watt.
4. The best thermal insulators
   a. conduct heat well. b. are gases.
   c. are metals. d. have free electrons.
5. A blow dryer transfers thermal energy mainly by
   a. conduction. b. convection.
   c. radiation. d. specific heat.
6. Which statement is NOT true about radiation?
   a. All objects radiate.
   b. Hot objects radiate faster than cold objects.
   c. Radiation only transfers energy in matter.
   d. The sun's energy reaches Earth by radiation.
7. Energy added to a system
   a. does work or increases thermal energy.
   b. cannot heat the environment.
   c. is converted to radiation.
   d. reduces the kinetic energy of the system.
8. All engines operate at less than 100 percent efficiency because they
   a. absorb heat. b. conduct heat.
   c. burn gasoline. d. emit heat.
9. Which occurs just before ignition?
   a. intake stroke b. compression stroke
   c. exhaust stroke d. power stroke
10. Which of the following is a FALSE statement about a heat pump?
    a. It requires no work.
    b. It moves heat from a cold to a hot area.
    c. It uses a refrigerant.
    d. Air conditioners are heat pumps.

Understanding Concepts

11. In what direction does heat flow? Why do particles of matter transfer thermal energy in this direction?
12. How can one object feel warmer than another object if the two objects are at the same temperature?
13. Why does a balloon filled with air expand when it is heated?
14. Power lines sag more between telephone poles in summer than in winter. Explain why this is so.

15. Why does a piece of steel heat up more than an equal mass of plastic when both absorb the same energy?
16. In a calorimeter, what determines how much energy is absorbed by the water?
17. Why are metals generally good thermal conductors?
18. How does sunlight reach an astronaut on the International Space Station?
19. How can the efficiency of a heat engine be improved?
20. What is waste heat?
21. What is the most important difference between an internal combustion engine and an external combustion engine?
22. Why does a heat pump need an external source of energy (such as electrical energy)?
23. Describe convection in a room heated by a radiator.

Assessment (continued)

14. The power lines are warmer in summer and the metal in the wire expands. Because the wires are longer, they sag more.
15. The metal has a lower specific heat than the plastic, so its temperature increases more as thermal energy is absorbed.
16. The energy given off by the test sample determines the energy absorbed by the water, assuming no energy is lost to the surroundings.
17. Metals are good thermal conductors because some of the electrons in the metal are free to move about.
18. Radiation from the sun can travel through space to reach the astronaut.
19. Efficiency can improve if the engine runs at a higher temperature or if the engine discharges heat into a colder environment.
20. Waste heat is thermal energy that is not converted into work.
21. In an internal combustion engine, fuel is burned inside the engine. Combustion occurs outside the engine in an external combustion engine.
22. A heat pump transfers thermal energy from a cool area to a warm area. To do this, work must be done, which requires a source of energy.
23. Warm air rises from the radiator to the ceiling, cools, and then sinks. The radiator heats the cool air, and the cycle repeats.

Homework Guide

Section	Questions
16.1	1–3, 11–16, 24, 28–30, 32, 36
16.2	4–7, 17–18, 25, 31, 33
16.3	8–10, 19–23, 26–27, 34–35

Critical Thinking

24. You cannot because your hand and forehead are probably at the same temperature, so there is no heat flow to your hand.

25. All three methods tend to transfer thermal energy from hot to cold objects. In conduction, the motion of particles within a material transfers thermal energy. In convection, thermal energy is transferred by motion of a fluid. In radiation, thermal energy is transferred by electromagnetic waves. Radiation is the only way to transfer thermal energy through a vacuum.

26. The engine is less efficient on Venus because it would discharge thermal energy into an environment at a higher temperature.

27. In the first few minutes after the heat comes on, the temperature is highest near the radiators. When the heat shuts off, convection currents have made the room temperature more uniform, but the highest temperature will be near the ceiling.

Math Skills

28. Aluminum has the highest specific heat. The temperature of aluminum rises the least for a given amount of energy added. In the equation $Q = m \times c \times \Delta T$, if Q and m are constant, then c is proportional to $1/\Delta T$. A smaller value for ΔT therefore means a larger value for c.

29. For aluminum, $Q = m \times c \times \Delta T$
$= (1\ g)(0.90\ J/g{\bullet}°C)(5.6°C) = 5.0\ J$
For iron, $Q = m \times c \times \Delta T$
$= (1\ g)(0.45\ J/g{\bullet}°C)(11.1°C) = 5.0\ J$

30. She should ask how mass and the rise in temperature are related. According to the equation $Q = m \times c \times \Delta T$, if Q and c are constant, an increase in m by a factor of 10 will reduce rather than increase the rise in temperature by a factor of 10.

Concepts in Action

31. Blood flowing toward your heart is colder because the cold environment removes thermal energy from your body's extremities. Blood flowing toward your fingers is warmer because it comes from the body's interior and is more insulated from the cold.

32. A casserole cover keeps thermal energy from escaping and from being lost by evaporation. A calorimeter's insulation keeps thermal energy inside the container. Therefore, most of the thermal energy heats the water, and the temperature change accurately measures the thermal energy released.

33. Accept all reasonable responses. Students may suggest that the foil reflects radiation that would be absorbed by the crust. The foil may also keep convection currents away from the crust. And because the foil is a good conductor, it may conduct heat away from the crust.

34. The fan would be helpful. It could be used to move warm air toward the rest of the apartment, heating the apartment by convection.

35. At night, the flow of thermal energy out of the home would be greater than during the day because it is colder outside. But this is also when passive solar heating is at a minimum, so it is important to reduce heat loss with insulation.

36. The best way to manage the building temperature is to prevent thermal energy from entering through the windows. The shades keep radiation from entering. Keeping the windows closed prevents convection currents that would bring thermal energy into the classroom.

CHAPTER 16 Assessment *(continued)*

Critical Thinking

24. **Controlling Variables** You can tell if your sister has a low fever by feeling her forehead with your hand. Can you detect your own fever with your hand? Explain why or why not.

25. **Comparing and Contrasting** How are conduction, convection, and radiation similar to one another? How are they different?

26. **Applying Concepts** Why would an engine be less efficient on Venus than on Earth? (*Hint:* On Venus, the surface temperature is 460°C.)

27. **Predicting** Just after a heating system turns on, what part of a room will be warmest? When the heat turns off and the radiators are cold, what part of the room will be warmest? Explain.

Math Skills

Use the following graph to answer Questions 28–30.

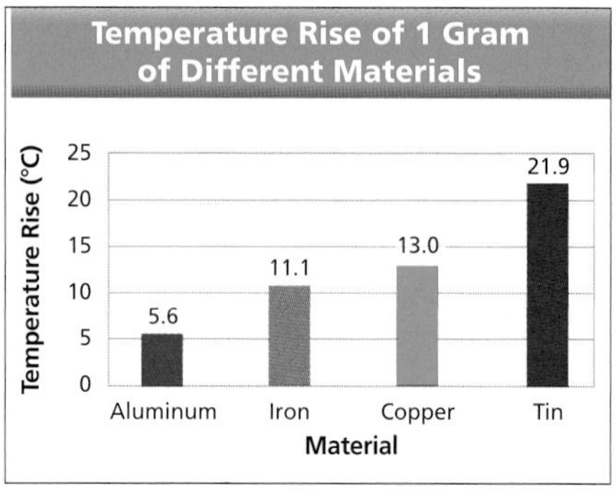

Temperature Rise of 1 Gram of Different Materials
Temperature Rise (°C)
25
20
15
10
5
0
5.6
11.1
13.0
21.9
Aluminum
Iron
Copper
Tin
Material

28. **Using Graphs** The same energy was added to each sample. Which material has the highest specific heat? Explain your answer.

29. **Calculating** The specific heat of aluminum is 0.90 J/g•°C and of iron is 0.45 J/g•°C. How much energy was absorbed by each 1-gram sample?

30. **Posing Questions** A friend infers from the graph that the temperature of a 10.0-g sample of iron would rise 110°C. What should she ask before using the graph this way?

Concepts in Action

31. **Applying Concepts** When you are outside on a cold winter day, which would you expect to be warmer, blood flowing toward your heart or blood flowing toward your fingers? Explain.

32. **Using Analogies** If you put a cover on a casserole at dinner, it will stay warm longer. In what way can this help you to explain why a calorimeter is more accurate if it is well insulated?

33. **Formulating Hypotheses** Some recipes say that while a pie is baking, aluminum foil should be put on the edges to keep the crust from burning. Hypothesize how the aluminum foil helps keep the crust from burning.

34. **Making Judgments** Suppose you try to heat an apartment using a portable heater in one of the rooms. Would a fan be helpful? Explain why or why not.

35. **Inferring** In a home heated only by solar energy, why is it especially important to have very good insulation?

36. **Writing in Science** Explain why a school might ask teachers to keep windows closed and the shades down during a heat wave.

Performance-Based Assessment

Making a Computer Presentation Make a computer slideshow presentation about conductors and insulators. Start by identifying various materials around your home as either good conductors or good insulators. Plan the organization of the slideshow. Finish the show with a summary table that classifies all of the materials in your presentation. Present your show to your class.

Go Online
PHSchool.com

For: Self-grading assessment
Visit: PHSchool.com
Web Code: cca-2160

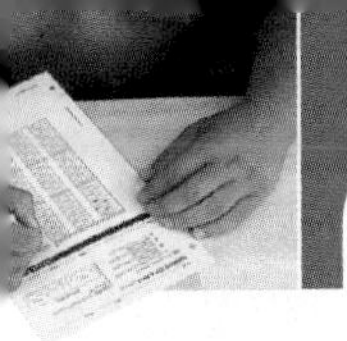

Standardized Test Prep

Test-Taking Tip

Sometimes all the response choices to a test question look similar. For example, they might have the same prefix or suffix. When all of the answer choices are similar, try answering the question BEFORE looking at the answers. Once you have answered the test item yourself, then look for the answer choice that agrees with your answer. Look for words that are correct words, but do not belong with the others.

The transfer of energy by collision of particles in a material occurs through

(A) convection.
(B) conduction.
(C) radiation.
(D) ionization.
(E) insulation.

(Answer: B)

Choose the letter that best answers the question or completes the statement.

1. Which statement describes the direction of spontaneous heat flow?
   (A) Heat flows between two objects at the same temperature.
   (B) Heat flows in a vacuum by conduction.
   (C) Heat flows from an object at high temperature to one at low temperature.
   (D) Heat flows from an object at low temperature to one at high temperature.
   (E) Thermal energy can only be absorbed by cool objects.

2. How are refrigerants used to remove heat in a refrigerator?
   (A) The refrigerant vaporizes as it absorbs heat from the food.
   (B) The refrigerant vaporizes as it supplies heat to the food.
   (C) The refrigerant condenses as it absorbs heat from the food.
   (D) The refrigerant condenses and turns into a liquid, giving off heat to the food.
   (E) The refrigerant condenses and turns into a gas, giving off heat to the food.

3. The table below shows the average high and low temperatures in January and July for two cities at the same latitude. Both cities receive about the same amount of sunlight. Which city is on an island in the ocean and which city is in a desert?
   (A) City A is on an island; City B is in the desert.
   (B) Both cities are in the desert.
   (C) Both cities are on an island.
   (D) City B is on an island; City A is in the desert.
   (E) Not enough information is given.

City Temperatures

	January High	January Low	July High	July Low
City A	26°C	18°C	28°C	20°C
City B	32°C	10°C	44°C	27°C

4. Which of the following best explains why gases expand more readily than liquids or solids?
   (A) Gases have less density than solids or liquids.
   (B) Gases are lighter than solids or liquids.
   (C) Gases have a higher average kinetic energy than solids or liquids.
   (D) Gas particles have weaker attractive forces than solids or liquids.
   (E) Gases are more compressible than solids or liquids.

5. Which substance will have the greatest increase in temperature when equal masses absorb equal amounts of thermal energy? (Specific heats are given in parentheses.)
   (A) water (4.18 J/g•°C)
   (B) ammonia gas (2.1 J/g•°C)
   (C) ethyl alcohol (2.43 J/g•°C)
   (D) aluminum (0.90 J/g•°C)
   (E) lead (0.46 J/g•°C)

6. Which of the following illustrates the first law of thermodynamics?
   (A) Refrigerators make objects colder.
   (B) A bicycle pump gets warm when used.
   (C) Stoves radiate energy.
   (D) Soft drinks served with ice melt the ice.
   (E) Absolute zero cannot be reached.

Standardized Test Prep

1. C 2. A 3. A
4. D 5. E 6. B

Performance-Based Assessment

Students' presentations should integrate research from sources outside the textbook. Presentations should be clearly organized and the list of materials should be correctly classified. The summary table could rank the conductors and insulators and provide additional information such as applications in the home, at school, or in the community. Extra credit should be given for creative visual display of information.

Go Online
PHSchool.com

Your students can independently test their knowledge of the chapter and print out their test results for your files.

Thermal Energy and Heat 497

CHAPTER 17

Planning Guide

Use these planning tools
Easy Planner
Teacher Express

SECTION OBJECTIVES	STANDARDS NATIONAL (See p. T18.)	STANDARDS STATE	ACTIVITIES and LABS
17.1 Mechanical Waves, pp. 500–503 1 block or 2 periods **17.1.1** **Define** mechanical waves and **relate** waves to energy. **17.1.2** **Describe** transverse, longitudinal, and surface waves and **discuss** how they are produced. **17.1.3** **Identify** examples of transverse and longitudinal waves. **17.1.4** **Analyze** the motion of a medium as each kind of mechanical wave passes through it.	A-1, A-2, B-6		**SE** Inquiry Activity: How Does a Disturbance Produce Waves? p. 499 L2 **SE** Quick Lab: Observing Waves in a Medium, p. 502 L2 **TE** Teacher Demo: Wave Dance, p. 501 L2
17.2 Properties of Mechanical Waves, pp. 504–507 1 block or 2 periods **17.2.1** **Define** frequency, period, wavelength, and wave speed and **describe** these properties for different kinds of waves. **17.2.2** **Solve equations** relating wave speed to wavelength and frequency or period. **17.2.3** **Describe** how to measure amplitude and **relate** amplitude to the energy of a wave.	A-1, A-2, B-6		**SE** Quick Lab: Comparing Frequency and Wave Speed, p. 505 L2
17.3 Behavior of Waves, pp. 508–512 1 block or 2 periods **17.3.1** **Describe** how reflection, refraction, diffraction, and interference affect waves. **17.3.2** **State a rule** that explains refraction of a wave as it passes from one medium to another. **17.3.3** **Identify** factors that affect the amount of refraction, diffraction, or interference. **17.3.4** **Distinguish** between constructive and destructive interference and **explain** how standing waves form.	B-6		**TE** Teacher Demo: Water-Wave Reflections, p. 508 L2 **TE** Teacher Demo: Standing Waves, p. 512 L2
17.4 Sound and Hearing, pp. 514–521 1 block or 2 periods **17.4.1** **Describe** the properties of sound waves and **explain** how sound is produced and reproduced. **17.4.2** **Describe** how sound waves behave in applications such as ultrasound and music. **17.4.3** **Explain** how relative motion determines the frequency of sound an observer hears. **17.4.4** **Analyze** the functions of the main regions of the human ear.	A-1, A-2, B-6, C-6, E-2, F-1, F-2 F-5, G-1		**SE** Exploration Lab: Investigating Sound Waves, pp. 524–525 L2 **TE** Build Science Skills: Observing, p. 515 L2 **LM** Investigation 17A: Comparing the Speed of Sound L2 **LM** Investigation 17B: Comparing Sound Conduction L1

Ability Levels	
L1	For students who need additional help
L2	For all students
L3	For students who need to be challenged

Components

SE	Student Edition	**RSW**	Reading & Study Workbook	**CUT**	Chapter & Unit Tests	**T**	Transparencies
TE	Teacher's Edition	**MSPS**	Math Skills & Problem Solving Workbook	**CTB**	Computer Test Bank	**iT**	Interactive Textbook
LM	Laboratory Manual			**TP**	Test Prep Resources	**P**	Presentation Pro CD-ROM
PLM	Probeware Lab Manual			**DC**	Discovery Channel Videotapes & DVDs	**GO**	Internet Resources

RESOURCES PRINT and TECHNOLOGY		SECTION ASSESSMENT
RSW Section 17.1	L1	**SE** Section 17.1 Assessment, p. 503
T Chapter 17 Pretest	L2	**iT** Section 17.1
Section 17.1	L2	
P Chapter 17 Pretest	L2	
Section 17.1	L2	
SCILINKS **GO** Vibrations and waves	L2	
RSW Section 17.2	L1	**SE** Section 17.2 Assessment, p. 507
RSW Math Skill	L2	**iT** Section 17.2
MSPS Section 17.2	L2	
T Section 17.2	L2	
P Section 17.2	L2	
SCILINKS **GO** Wave properties	L2	
RSW Section 17.3	L1	**SE** Section 17.3 Assessment, p. 512
T Section 17.3	L2	**iT** Section 17.3
P Section 17.3	L2	
SCILINKS **GO** Diffraction and interference	L2	
RSW Section 17.4	L1	**SE** Section 17.4 Assessment, p. 521
Discovery Channel School **DC** Noise!	L2	**iT** Section 17.4
T Section 17.4	L2	
P Section 17.4	L2	
SCIENCE NEWS **GO** Sound	L2	

Go Online

Go online for these Internet resources.

PHSchool.com
Web Code: cch-2173
Web Code: cca-2170

SCIENCE NEWS®
Web Code: cce-2174

NSTA SCILINKS
Web Code: ccn-2171
Web Code: ccn-2172
Web Code: ccn-2173

Materials for Activities and Labs

Quantities for each group

STUDENT EDITION

Inquiry Activity, p. 499
dropper pipet; wide, flat-bottomed container; meter stick

Quick Lab, p. 502
large, clear container; food coloring; ruler; droppers (optional)

Quick Lab, p. 505
3-m rope, tape measure, stopwatch

Exploration Lab, pp. 524–525
meter stick, 2 cardboard tubes, scissors or scalpel, 2 rubber bands, wax paper, balloon, small mirror, transparent tape, flashlight

TEACHER'S EDITION

Teacher Demo, p. 501
10 chairs, 10 students, space to move around

Teacher Demo, p. 508
clear bowl, water, overhead projector

Teacher Demo, p. 512
long, soft, heavy rope, such as a jump rope

Build Science Skills, p. 515
set of tuning forks of similar construction

Build Science Skills, p. 522
tuning fork hammer, 2 tuning forks with the same frequency (about 400 Hz), stethoscope

Chapter Assessment

CHAPTER ASSESSMENT

SE Chapter Assessment, pp. 527–528
CUT Chapter 17 Test A, B
CTB Chapter 17
iT Chapter 17
PHSchool.com GO
Web Code: cca-2170

STANDARDIZED TEST PREP

SE Chapter 17, p. 529
TP Diagnose and Prescribe

Interactive Textbook

Interactive Textbook with assessment at PHSchool.com

CHAPTER 17

Before you teach

From the Author

Sophia Yancopoulos
Manhattan College

Big Ideas

Later chapters will build on the basics of mechanical waves, so it's important that students get the wave types, properties, and behaviors under their belts. For waves traveling at a given speed, it can be shown that wavelength is inversely proportional to frequency. This is easily derived from the equation distance equals velocity times time because "distance" is equal to wavelength, and "time" for the passage of one wave is its period, which is inversely proportional to frequency. The most important idea is that when an object moves, the object itself moves from point A to point B. A wave, however, is different. A wave is the disturbance in a medium. Although the medium moves somewhat as the wave travels, what moves from point A to point B in this case is the disturbance.

Matter and Energy A mechanical wave is defined as a disturbance in matter that carries energy from one place to another. It takes energy to create any kind of wave, but a mechanical wave, unlike an electromagnetic wave, cannot travel without a medium.

Forces and Motion The behavior of a wave—whether this behavior is refraction, reflection, diffraction, or interference—depends on the medium through which it travels, as well as on the wave type. Sound waves, for example, can be manipulated in various ways, or even cancelled. Discussing technological applications that students are probably familiar with may be a good way to generate interest. Be as concrete and visual as possible, since the subject of electromagnetic waves builds on this information, and is far less easily grasped.

Physics Refresher

Mechanical Waves 17.1

Electromagnetic waves are not mechanical waves. For many years, physicists tried to develop a mechanical understanding of electromagnetic waves, searching without success for proof of the "ether," a medium for these waves. Physicists now know that electromagnetic waves do not require a medium.

For a medium to transmit a mechanical wave, the medium must be elastic. For example, when a gas is compressed in a cylinder with a piston, the piston springs back when released. Gases are elastic under compression, so they will transmit compression waves. Gases have almost no tensile strength, so a gas will not transmit a transverse wave. A steel bar will transmit both longitudinal and transverse waves.

Address Misconceptions

Students may mistakenly think that waves are part of the medium that travel with the waves. However, waves carry energy through a medium, but the medium usually has no net movement. For a strategy to overcome this misconception, see **Address Misconceptions** on **page 502.**

Properties of Mechanical Waves 17.2

The period of a wave, measured in seconds, equals $\frac{1}{\text{Frequency}}$. In symbols, the wave equation can be written as $v = \lambda \times f$, where v is the wave speed, λ is the wavelength, and f is the frequency. Amplitude, the maximum distance the medium is displaced from its rest position, is a measure of wave energy. As amplitude increases, the wave energy increases. The relationship is not linear. For most waves, energy is proportional to $(\text{amplitude})^2$.

Behavior of Waves 17.3

Reflection and refraction occur at the boundary between two mediums. Part or all of the wave is reflected. Part of the wave may pass through, but its speed and direction may change. The reflected wave always has the same speed and frequency as the original wave. The refracted wave will have the same frequency but different speed and wavelength. Refraction is a behavior of all waves. Earthquake waves are refracted as they pass through different layers inside of Earth. By studying the patterns and kinds of earthquake waves received around the world, geologists are able to infer the interior structure of Earth.

Go Online PDLINKS NSTA

For: Teaching methods for mechanical waves and sounds
Visit: www.SciLinks.org/PDLinks
Web Code: ccn-1799

When a wave moves past an obstacle or passes through a narrow opening, it diffracts, or bends in such a way as to recreate the form (in frequency and amplitude) that the wave had before encountering the obstacle or opening. Diffraction, as shown below, depends on how the size of the opening compares to the wavelength. The larger the opening, the greater the amount of signal that can pass through it unimpeded. The smaller the opening, the more the wave has to bend to reconstruct its original form.

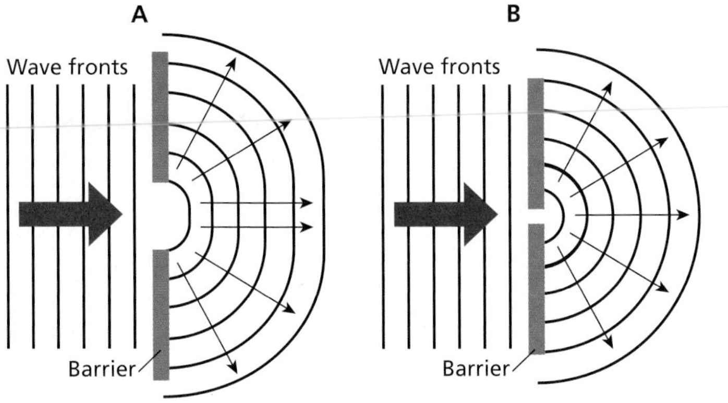
A
B
Wave fronts
Wave fronts
Barrier
Barrier

Diffraction at a large opening **Diffraction at a small opening**

Sound and Hearing 17.4

Address Misconceptions

Some students think that sound waves can push a dust particle away from a speaker or blow out a candle flame. Generally, there is no net transport of matter by a wave. For a strategy to overcome this misconception, see **Address Misconceptions** on **page 518.**

The three aspects of any sound are its source, the transference of energy from this source, and the detection of the sound. The transference of sound energy takes the form of longitudinal waves. Sound waves are longitudinal waves in matter. Fluids, such as air and water, can only transmit longitudinal waves. If the frequency of a sound wave is above the range of human hearing, it is called ultrasound. If the frequency of a sound wave is below the range of human hearing, it is called infrasound.

The unit of intensity level, the decibel or dB, was named after Alexander Graham Bell. Intensity can also be expressed in units of watts per square meter. Here are some intensities of sounds expressed in W/m^2.

Sound	Intensity Level (dB)	Intensity (W/m^2)
Threshold of hearing	0	1×10^{-12}
Whisper	20	1×10^{-10}
Normal conversation	65	3×10^{-6}
Street noise	70	1×10^{-5}
Rock concert	120	1
Threshold of pain	120	1

Build Reading Literacy

Active Comprehension

Engaging Interest in a Topic

Strategy Stimulate students' interest in a topic prior to reading. As with the KWL strategy, students generate questions based on their curiosity. Interest is thus translated into a purpose for reading. Looking for answers to the questions during reading helps keep students engaged in what they are reading. Before students begin reading, choose an opening paragraph from one of the sections in Chapter 17, for example, the first paragraph on p. 500.

Example

1. Have a student read the opening paragraph.
2. Ask the group, "What more would you like to know about _______?" (for example, mechanical waves). Make a list of student responses.
3. Tell students to read the remainder of the section, keeping the questions in mind as they read.
4. After reading, you may discuss the extent to which each question was answered by the text. Ask students also to comment on any new information they learned that was surprising.
5. Have students work in small groups, applying the active comprehension strategy to the reading of each section of the chapter.

See p. 509 for a script on how to use the active comprehension strategy with students. For additional Build Reading Literacy strategies, see pp. 503, 507, and 516.

ASSESS PRIOR KNOWLEDGE

Use the Chapter Pretest below to assess students' prior knowledge. As needed, review these Science Concepts and Math Skills with students.

Review Science Concepts

Section 17.1 Waves carry energy, so review the concept of energy and energy conversions with students.

Section 17.2 Remind students of the unit of time (seconds, s). Review what it means to say something is moving. Remind students how to measure and calculate speed (distance/time).

Section 17.3 Review velocity and displacement, which help with understanding interference and refraction. Remind students that energy is the ability to do work and that waves carry energy.

Section 17.4 Since the speed of sound depends on temperature and density, review how density and temperature are related to solids, liquids, and gases.

Review Math Skills

Formulas and Equations, Percents and Decimals Students will need to manipulate equations to solve for the unknown. They also may need practice working with decimal fractions. Review what is meant by powers of ten.

Direct students to **Math Skills** in the **Skills and Reference Handbook** at the end of the student text.

CHAPTER 17 Mechanical Waves and Sound

CONCEPTS in Action

How do science concepts apply to your world? Here are some questions you'll be able to answer after you read this chapter.

- Why does a wave topple over on itself when it approaches the shore? *(Section 17.1)*
- How does a surfer know when the next wave is coming? *(Section 17.2)*
- Why does a gymnast on a trampoline time her jumps to match the movement of the trampoline surface? *(Section 17.3)*
- How much faster is a sound wave than a car traveling on the highway? *(Section 17.4)*

Discovery Channel School **Video Field Trip**

Noise!

- How can headphones reduce noise without interfering with sounds you want to hear? *(page 522)*

Ocean waves, like all mechanical waves, ▶ carry energy through a medium.

Chapter Pretest

1. What is energy? *(Ability to do work)*
2. What is mechanical energy? *(Energy due to the motion or position of an object)*
3. True or False: Displacements in opposite directions add together. *(False. Displacements in opposite directions subtract.)*
4. How is speed calculated? *(Distance/time)*
5. What are the standard units of distance and time? *(Meters and seconds)*
6. Which is longer, 0.25 m or 25 m? *(25 m)*
7. What happens to the spacing of the particles within a solid or liquid as the temperature increases? *(The particles move farther apart.)*
8. What happens to the speed of the particles in a solid, liquid, or gas as the temperature is increased? *(The particles move faster.)*
9. If a car takes 2 hrs to travel 100 km, what is its average speed? *(b)*
   a. 25 km/h
   b. 50 km/h
   c. 75 km/h
   d. 100 km/h

Chapter Preview

Inquiry Activity

How Does a Disturbance Produce Waves?

Procedure

1. Fill a clear plastic container and a dropper pipet with water.
2. Observe the surface of the water by looking down at an angle into the container. Use the dropper pipet to release a drop of water from a height of about 3 cm above the surface of the water.
3. Repeat Step 2 with a drop released from each of these heights: 10, 20, 50, and 70 cm.

Think About It

1. **Observing** Which drop produced the highest waves?
2. **Making Generalizations** In general, how would you expect the distance a drop falls to affect the wave it produces? Explain your answer.
3. **Formulating Hypotheses** Why does the distance a drop falls affect the height of the waves it produces? Explain your answer.

Discovery Channel School

Video Field Trip

Noise!

Encourage students to view the Video Field Trip "Noise!"

ENGAGE/EXPLORE

Inquiry Activity

How Does a Disturbance Produce Waves? L2

Purpose In this activity, students begin to understand that the height or amplitude of a wave depends on the wave's energy.

Skills Focus Observing, Comparing and Contrasting

Prep Time 15 Minutes

Materials dropper pipet; wide, flat-bottomed container; meter stick

Advance Prep Distribute empty containers and fill them from a gallon jug once they are in place at the lab stations.

Class Time 10 minutes

Teaching Tips

- Instruct students to look at the surface of the water diagonally, rather than horizontally or vertically.

Expected Outcome The height (amplitude) of the wave will increase as the height from which the water is dropped increases.

Think About It

1. The drop that fell from 70 cm produced the highest waves.
2. The greater the distance a drop falls, the more kinetic energy it will have, and the larger the wave it will produce.
3. The greater the height from which a drop falls, the more energy it has because it accelerated to a greater speed than a drop that fell a shorter distance. Therefore, it transfers more energy to the surface of the water, producing higher waves.
Visual, Logical

Section 17.1

1 FOCUS

Objectives

17.1.1 **Define** mechanical waves and **relate** waves to energy.
17.1.2 **Describe** transverse, longitudinal, and surface waves and **discuss** how they are produced.
17.1.3 **Identify** examples of transverse and longitudinal waves.
17.1.4 **Analyze** the motion of a medium as each kind of mechanical wave passes through it.

Reading Focus

Build Vocabulary L2

Paraphrase This section contains several words that may not be familiar to students: *medium*, *crest*, *trough*, *transverse*, *longitudinal*, *compression*, and *rarefaction*. Have students paraphrase these words using words they know. For example, they might construct a sentence such as, "In other words, a *medium* is the stuff carrying the wave."

Reading Strategy L2

a. Troughs **b.** Rest position; Longitudinal Wave: Compressions, Rarefactions, Rest position, Direction; Surface Wave: Circular motion that returns to same position, Direction of wave

2 INSTRUCT

What Are Mechanical Waves?

Build Science Skills L2

Inferring Have students look at Figure 1. Ask, **What happens to the swimmers in the pool as a wave passes?** *(The swimmers move up and down and back and forth.)* **What kind of energy do the swimmers have as they bob up and down?** *(Kinetic)* **From where do they get this energy?** *(From the wave)*
Logical, Visual

17.1 Mechanical Waves

Reading Focus

Key Concepts

- What causes mechanical waves?
- What are the three main types of mechanical waves?

Vocabulary

- mechanical wave
- medium
- crest
- trough
- transverse wave
- compression
- rarefaction
- longitudinal wave
- surface wave

Reading Strategy

Previewing Copy the web diagram below. Use Figure 2 to complete the diagram. Then use Figures 3 and 4 to make similar diagrams for longitudinal waves and surface waves.

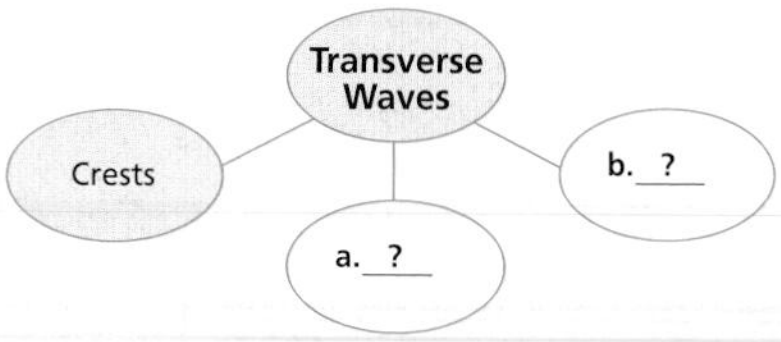
Transverse Waves
Crests
a. ?
b. ?

Have you ever gone to a wave pool at an amusement park? You can hear the laughter and screams as wave after wave passes by, giving the people a wild ride. It's obvious that waves are moving through the water, but you may not realize that the screams and laughter are also carried by waves. In this chapter, you will learn about the different kinds of mechanical waves, including sound waves.

What Are Mechanical Waves?

A **mechanical wave** is a disturbance in matter that carries energy from one place to another. Recall that energy is the ability to do work. In a wave pool, each wave carries energy across the pool. You can see the effects of a wave's energy when the wave lifts people in the water.

Figure 1 In a wave pool, the waves carry energy across the pool.

Mechanical waves require matter to travel through. The material through which a wave travels is called a **medium.** Solids, liquids, and gases all can act as mediums. In a wave pool, waves travel along the surface of the water. Water is the medium. Waves travel through a rope when you shake one end of it. In that case, the medium is the rope.

A mechanical wave is created when a source of energy causes a vibration to travel through a medium. A vibration is a repeating back-and-forth motion. When you shake a rope, you add energy at one end. The wave that results is a vibration that carries energy along the rope.

Section Resources

Print

- ***Reading and Study Workbook With Math Support,*** Section 17.1
- ***Transparencies,*** Chapter Pretest and Section 17.1

Technology

- ***Interactive Textbook,*** Section 17.1
- ***Presentation Pro CD-ROM,*** Chapter Pretest and Section 17.1
- ***Go Online,*** NSTA SciLinks, Vibrations and waves

Types of Mechanical Waves

Mechanical waves are classified by the way they move through a medium. **The three main types of mechanical waves are transverse waves, longitudinal waves, and surface waves.**

Transverse Waves When you shake one end of a rope up and down, the vibration causes a wave. Figure 2 shows a wave in a rope at three points in time. Before the wave starts, every point on the rope is in its rest position, represented by the dashed line. The highest point of the wave above the rest position is the **crest.** The lowest point below the rest position is the **trough** (TRAWF). You can see from the ribbon attached to the rope that crests and troughs are not fixed points on a wave. In Figure 2A, the ribbon is at a crest. In Figure 2C, the ribbon is at a trough. The motion of a single point on the rope is like the motion of a yo-yo. The point vibrates up and down between a maximum and minimum height.

Notice that the wave carries energy from left to right, in a direction perpendicular to the up-and-down motion of the rope. This is a transverse wave. A **transverse wave** is a wave that causes the medium to vibrate at right angles to the direction in which the wave travels.

Have you ever shaken crumbs off a picnic blanket? This is another example of a transverse wave. Shaking one end of the blanket up and down sends a transverse wave through the blanket. The up and down motion of the blanket helps to shake off the crumbs.

Go Online — NSTA SciLinks

For: Links on vibrations and waves
Visit: www.SciLinks.org
Web Code: ccn-2171

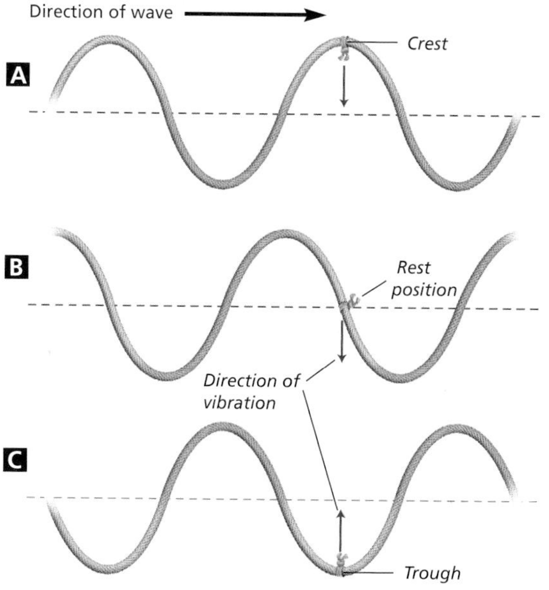

Direction of wave
A
Crest
B
Rest position
Direction of vibration
C
Trough

Figure 2 A transverse wave causes the medium to vibrate in a direction perpendicular to the direction in which the wave travels. In the wave shown here, each point on the rope vibrates up and down between a maximum and minimum height. **A** The ribbon is at a crest. **B** The ribbon is at the rest position. **C** The ribbon is at a trough. **Comparing and Contrasting** ***How does the direction of the wave compare with the direction in which the ribbon moves?***

Teacher Demo

Wave Dance **L2**

Purpose Students will simulate transverse and longitudinal waves.

Materials 10 chairs, 10 students, space to move around

Class Time 20 minutes

Procedure Prepare students for the demonstration ahead of time. To simulate a transverse wave, students will do a wave like the one fans do at a football or baseball game. Place the chairs in a line and have each student sit in a chair. Each student rises when the student in front of him or her is fully standing. To simulate a longitudinal wave, have students stand in a line, arm-length apart. The first student steps forward and back, then taps the next student. When each student feels a tap, he or she takes a step forward and then a step back. These steps can be repeated as a dance.

Expected Outcome Students will recognize that waves occur when a disturbance moves through a medium, and students will distinguish between two different kinds of disturbance.
Kinesthetic, Visual

Types of Mechanical Waves

Use Visuals **L1**

Figure 2 Have students examine the position of the ribbon in Figure 2A and Figure 2B. Ask, **How has the ribbon moved?** *(It has moved down. There is no left-to-right motion.)* **How does this compare to the direction of the wave?** *(Perpendicular)*
Visual

Go Online — NSTA SciLinks

Download a worksheet on vibrations and waves for students to complete, and find additional teacher support from NSTA SciLinks.

Customize for English Language Learners

Simplify the Presentation
In English, one word may have several different meanings. For that reason, students who are learning English may have additional difficulty grasping the scientific meanings of such words. Identify the multiple-meaning words in this section, such as *wave, matter,* and *medium.* Discuss with students the different meanings of each word and then explain which meaning is used in this section.

Answer to . . .

Figure 2 *The movement of the ribbon is up and down, which is perpendicular to the direction of the wave.*

Quick Lab

Observing Waves in a Medium **L2**

Objective
After completing this activity, students will be able to
- describe a mechanical wave as a passage of energy through a medium, with no net movement of the medium.

Address Misconceptions

This lab can dispel the misconception that waves are parts of the medium that travel with the wave.

Skills Focus **Inferring**

Prep Time 15 minutes

Materials large, clear container; food coloring; ruler; droppers (optional)

Advance Prep Dilute food coloring with water. Use droppers to drop colored water into the container.

Class Time 15 minutes

Safety Students should wear a laboratory apron to avoid stains.

Teaching Tips
- Instruct students to observe the wave and the drop from the side.

Expected Outcome The drop of food coloring sits on the bottom of the container as the water wave moves back and forth. Some small currents disturb the food coloring.

Analyze and Conclude
1. The wave moved. The food coloring stayed in place on the bottom.
2. Students may hypothesize that water at the bottom is not disturbed by a surface wave, or that the disturbance depends on the depth of the water.
Visual, Logical

For Enrichment **L3**

Float bits of cork on the water. Generate waves and observe the motion of the cork bits. Students should observe up-and-down motion and also side-to-side motion of the cork bits. Students should vary the depths of the water to see if this affects the results.
Visual

Quick Lab

Observing Waves in a Medium

Procedure

1. Fill a large, clear, square or rectangular container halfway with water. Add a drop of food coloring in the center of the container.
2. At the side of the container, submerge a ruler lengthwise. Move the ruler up and down to make waves.
3. Observe and record how the waves and the food coloring move.

Analyze and Conclude

1. **Comparing and Contrasting** Compare the movement of the waves with the movement of the food coloring.
2. **Formulating Hypotheses** Generate one or more hypotheses to explain the observed motion of the food coloring.

Longitudinal Waves Figure 3 shows a wave in a spring toy at two points in time. To start the wave, add energy to the spring by pushing and pulling the end of the spring. The wave carries energy along the spring from left to right. You can see in Figure 3A that when the wave starts, some of the coils are closer together than they would be in the rest position. An area where the particles in a medium are spaced close together is called a **compression** (kum PRESH un). As the compression moves to the right in Figure 3B, coils behind it are spread out more than they were in the rest position. An area where the particles in a medium are spread out is called a **rarefaction** (rehr uh FAK shun).

Look at the ribbon tied to one of the coils. The ribbon is first in a compression and then in a rarefaction. However, the ribbon and the coil it is tied to do not move along the spring. As compressions and rarefactions travel along the spring toward the right, each coil vibrates back and forth around its rest position. In this wave, the vibration is a back-and-forth motion of the coil that is parallel to, or in the same direction as, the direction in which the wave moves. This is a longitudinal wave. A **longitudinal wave** (lawn juh TOO duh nul) is a wave in which the vibration of the medium is parallel to the direction the wave travels.

Waves in springs are not the only kind of longitudinal waves. P waves (originally called primary waves) are longitudinal waves produced by earthquakes. Because P waves can travel through Earth, scientists can use these waves to map Earth's unseen interior.

Reading Checkpoint *What are compressions and rarefactions?*

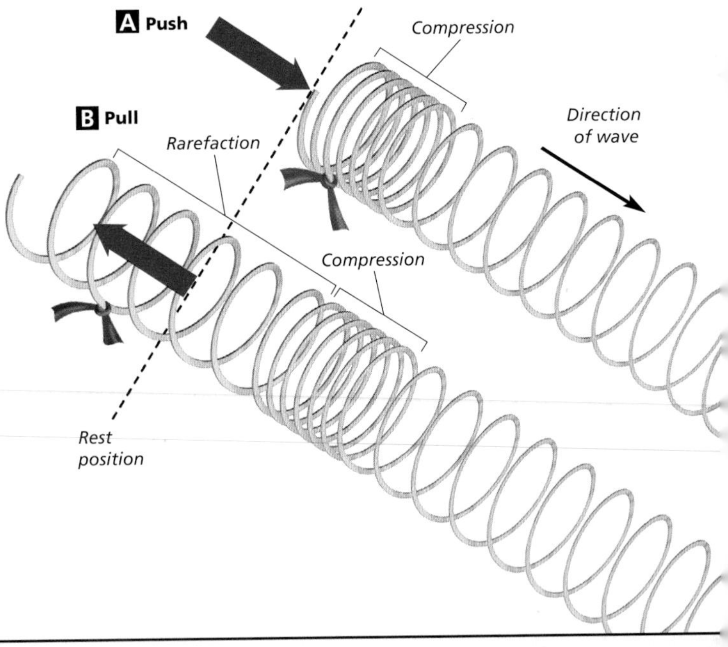

A Push
B Pull
Compression
Rarefaction
Compression
Direction of wave
Rest position

Figure 3 A longitudinal wave causes the medium to vibrate in a direction parallel to the direction in which the wave travels. Each point on the spring vibrates back and forth about its rest position. **A** When the end of the spring is pushed, a compression starts to move along the spring. **B** When the end of the spring is pulled, a rarefaction follows the compression along the spring.

Facts and Figures

Surfing Surfing originated in Polynesia and was developed in Hawaii. Native Hawaiians rode long, heavy, carved wooden surfboards. Surfing is possible because of the properties of waves as they enter shallower water. The speed of a wave in shallow water depends on the depth of the water. As a wave approaches the shore, it slows down. In shallow water with a sloping bottom, the front portion of the wave is in shallower water and moving slower than the rear portion, so the back of the wave catches up with the front. This causes the wave to "break." Surfers ride the breaking wave as the surfboard slides down the steep front of the wave. Modern surfboards are made from a foam core covered with plastic resin. These lighter and smaller surfboards are much easier to handle than the heavy wooden boards used by early Hawaiians.

Surface Waves If you ask people to describe waves, most likely they will describe ocean waves before they think of the waves that travel in a rope or a spring. Ocean waves are the most familiar kind of surface waves. A **surface wave** is a wave that travels along a surface separating two media.

The ocean wave in Figure 4 travels at the surface between water and air. The floating fishing bobber helps to visualize the motion of the medium as the wave carries energy from left to right. When a crest passes the bobber, the bobber moves up. When a trough passes, the bobber moves down. This up-and-down motion, like the motion of a transverse wave, is perpendicular to the direction in which the wave travels. But the bobber also is pushed back and forth by the surface wave. This back-and-forth motion, like the motion of a longitudinal wave, is parallel to the direction in which the wave travels. When these two motions combine in deep water, the bobber moves in a circle.

If you watched the bobber for ten minutes, it would not move closer to shore. Most waves do not transport matter from one place to another. But when ocean waves approach the shore, they behave differently. Perhaps you have seen seaweed washed ashore by breaking waves. As a wave enters shallow water, it topples over on itself because friction with the shore slows down the bottom of the wave. The top of the wave continues forward at its original speed. As a result, the wave carries the medium, along with anything floating in it, toward the shore.

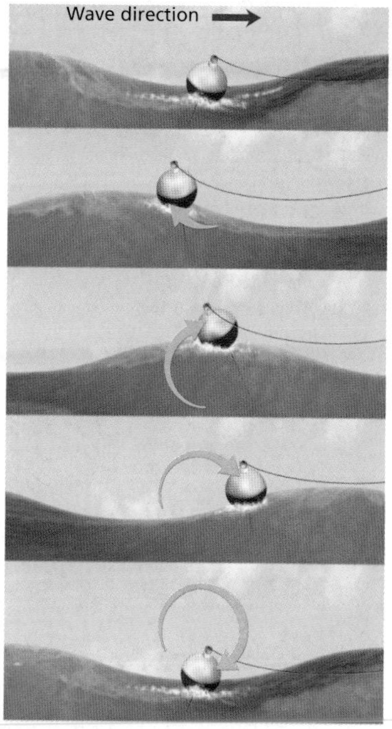
Wave direction

Figure 4 As the ocean wave moves to the right, the bobber moves in a circle, returning to its original position.
Making Generalizations ***If these were breaking waves near the shore, what would happen to the bobber over time?***

Section 17.1 Assessment

Reviewing Concepts

1. Describe how mechanical waves are produced.
2. List the three main types of mechanical waves.
3. For each type of wave, compare the vibration of the medium to the direction of the wave.
4. Name one example of each type of wave.

Critical Thinking

5. **Comparing and Contrasting** How are transverse and longitudinal waves similar? How are they different?
6. **Applying Concepts** A spring hangs from the ceiling. Describe how a single coil moves as a longitudal wave passes through the spring.
7. **Interpreting Diagrams** In Figure 4, why is the first position of the bobber the same as the fifth position of the bobber?

Connecting Concepts

Energy Review potential and kinetic energy in Section 15.1. Then, describe the energy changes in a single coil of a spring as longitudinal waves pass through it.

Build Reading Literacy L1

Summarize Refer to page **598D** in **Chapter 20**, which provides the guidelines for summarizing.

Have students construct a table to summarize what they have learned about mechanical waves. The rows could be labeled with the kind of wave and the columns could be labeled with the wave properties.
Logical

3 ASSESS

Evaluate Understanding L2

Have students write a paragraph summarizing the content of this section.

Reteach L1

Use Figures 2 and 3 to summarize the similarities and differences between transverse and longitudinal waves.

Connecting Concepts

The coil gains elastic potential energy and has the least kinetic energy when it is in a compression. In a rarefaction, the coil is moving fastest, has its greatest kinetic energy, and its elastic potential energy is at a minimum.

Interactive Textbook If your class subscribes to the Interactive Textbook, use it to review key concepts in Section 17.1.

Answer to . . .

Figure 4 *The bobber would be pushed to shore by breaking waves.*

Reading Checkpoint *Compressions are areas where particles in a medium are spaced close together. Rarefactions are areas where particles in a medium are spread out.*

Section 17.1 Assessment

1. Mechanical waves are formed when a source of energy causes a vibration to travel through a medium.
2. Transverse, longitudinal, and surface waves
3. Transverse wave: medium vibrates perpendicular to the direction the wave travels; Longitudinal wave: medium vibrates parallel to the direction the wave travels; Surface wave: medium vibrates both perpendicular and parallel to wave direction (circular motion)
4. Transverse wave: shaking the end of a rope up and down; Longitudinal wave: compressions and rarefactions moving through a spring; Surface wave: deep water wave in an ocean
5. Both kinds of waves carry energy through a medium without transferring matter. In transverse waves, the medium vibrates perpendicular to the direction in which the wave travels, while in longitudinal waves, the medium vibrates parallel to the direction in which the wave travels.
6. The coil will move up and down about its rest position as compressions and rarefactions pass through.
7. The bobber has moved in a full circle that returns it back to its starting position (because one complete surface wave has passed through the bobber's position).

1 FOCUS

Objectives

17.2.1 **Define** frequency, period, wavelength, and wave speed and **describe** these properties for different kinds of waves.

17.2.2 **Solve equations** relating wave speed to wavelength and frequency or period.

17.2.3 **Describe** how to measure amplitude and **relate** amplitude to the energy of a wave.

Reading Focus

Build Vocabulary L2

Word Forms The term amplitude contains the root *ampl-*, which comes from the Latin *amplus.* Have students think of other English words that contain *ampl- (amplify, ample).* What do these words have in common? *(All have to do with largeness or fullness.)*

Reading Strategy L2

a. The time required for one cycle **b.** The number of complete cycles in a given time **c.** The distance between a point on a wave and the same point on the next cycle of the wave **d.** The maximum displacement of a medium from its rest position

2 INSTRUCT

Frequency and Period

Use Visuals L1

Figure 5 Have students compare the number of complete cycles per second in Figures 5A and 5B. Ask, **What happens to the frequency when the number of cycles per second increases?** *(It increases.)* **If a wave has a frequency of 0.5 Hz, how many cycles per second is it vibrating?** *(It is vibrating at one-half cycle per second.)* **What is the period of a 0.5-Hz wave?** *(2 seconds)*
Logical

17.2 Properties of Mechanical Waves

Reading Focus

Key Concepts

- What determines the frequency of a wave?
- How are frequency, wavelength, and speed related?
- How is the amplitude of a wave related to the wave's energy?

Vocabulary

- periodic motion
- period
- frequency
- hertz
- wavelength
- amplitude

Reading Strategy

Building Vocabulary Copy and expand the table below. As you read, write a definition in your own words for each term.

Vocabulary Term	Definition
Period	a. ___?___
Frequency	b. ___?___
Wavelength	c. ___?___
Amplitude	d. ___?___

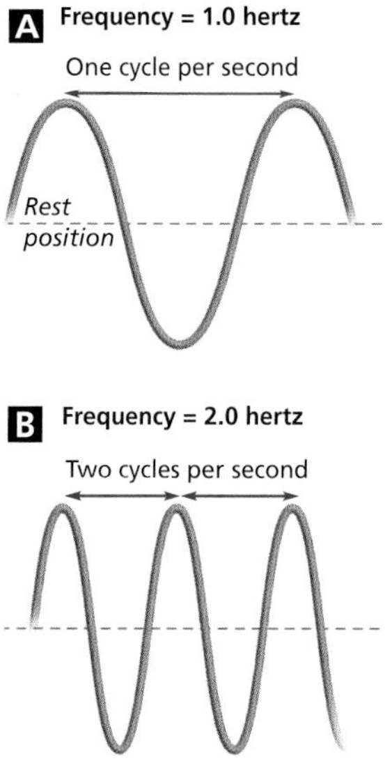

A
Frequency = 1.0 hertz
One cycle per second
Rest position
B
Frequency = 2.0 hertz
Two cycles per second

Figure 5 Frequency is the number of complete cycles in a given time. **A** A wave vibrating at one cycle per second has a frequency of 1.0 Hz. **B** A wave vibrating at two cycles per second has a frequency of 2.0 Hz.

Will it be a good day for surfing? You might not think that a surfer would check the Internet to find out. But some Web sites now update ocean wave data every hour. Of course, fishing boats and naval vessels also need this information. Usually, the properties used to describe waves are period, frequency, wavelength, speed, and amplitude.

Frequency and Period

How do surfers know when the next wave is coming? If they count the time between two successive crests, the next crest usually will come after this same time interval. Any motion that repeats at regular time intervals is called **periodic motion.** The time required for one cycle, a complete motion that returns to its starting point, is called the **period.** For an ocean wave, the period is the time between two successive crests.

Any periodic motion has a **frequency,** which is the number of complete cycles in a given time. For a wave, the frequency is the number of wave cycles that pass a point in a given time. Frequency is measured in cycles per second, or **hertz** (Hz).

A wave's frequency equals the frequency of the vibrating source producing the wave. The rope in Figure 5A is shaken with a frequency of one vibration per second, so the wave frequency is one cycle per second, or 1 hertz. In Figure 5B, the vibration is twice as fast, so the frequency is two cycles per second, or 2 hertz.

Section Resources

Print

- ***Reading and Study Workbook With Math Support,*** Section 17.2 and **Math Skill:** Calculating Wave Properties
- ***Math Skills and Problem Solving Workbook,*** Section 17.2
- ***Transparencies,*** Section 17.2

Technology

- ***Interactive Textbook,*** Section 17.2
- ***Presentation Pro CD-ROM,*** Section 17.2
- ***Go Online,*** NSTA SciLinks, Wave properties

Quick Lab

Comparing Frequency and Wave Speed

Materials

3-m rope, tape measure, stopwatch

Procedure

1. Tie one end of the rope to a chair. Shake the other end to send waves down the rope.
2. With a partner, measure the time it takes your hand to move back and forth ten times. Then, measure and record the distance from your hand to the chair and the time it takes a wave crest to travel this distance.
3. Repeat Step 2, but this time shake the rope more rapidly. Record your data.

Analyze and Conclude

1. **Calculating** What was the frequency of the waves in Steps 2 and 3? (*Hint:* Divide 10 waves by the time it took to make them.)
2. **Calculating** What was the wave speed in Steps 2 and 3? (*Hint:* Divide distance by time.)
3. **Drawing Conclusions** How was wave speed affected by increasing the frequency?

Wavelength

Wavelength is the distance between a point on one wave and the same point on the next cycle of the wave. For a transverse wave, wavelength is measured between adjacent crests or between adjacent troughs. For a longitudinal wave, wavelength is the distance between adjacent compressions or rarefactions. Notice in Figure 6 that when wavelength is shorter, crests are closer together. They must occur more frequently. **Increasing the frequency of a wave decreases its wavelength.**

Reading Checkpoint *What is wavelength?*

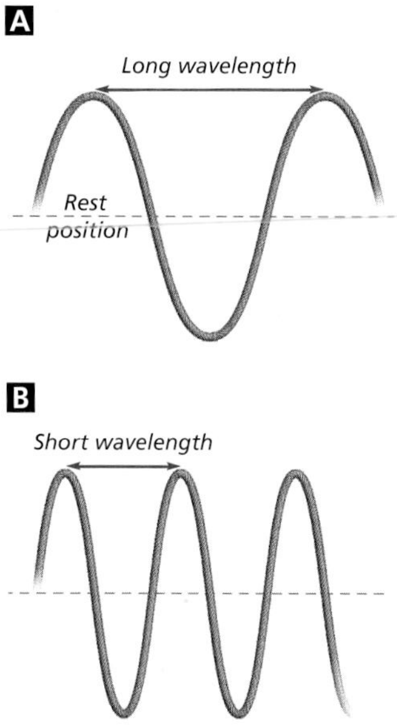

A
Long wavelength
Rest position
B
Short wavelength

Figure 6 Wavelength can be measured from any point on a wave to the same point on the next cycle of the wave. **A** The wavelength of a transverse wave equals the distance from crest to crest or from trough to trough. **B.** The wavelength of this wave is half the wavelength of the wave in A. **Inferring** *Which wave has a greater frequency?*

Wave Speed

Recall that the speed of an object equals distance divided by time. To calculate a swimmer's speed, for example, you can measure the length of one lap in a pool and the time it takes to swim one lap. This is like measuring the wavelength (one lap) and period (time to swim one lap) of the swimmer's motion. In much the same way, you can calculate the speed of a wave by dividing its wavelength by its period. You can also calculate wave speed by multiplying wavelength by frequency.

Speed of Waves

$$\text{Speed} = \text{Wavelength} \times \text{Frequency}$$

When the wavelength is in meters and the frequency is in hertz, the units for speed are meters per second. If you know any two of the values in this formula, you can solve for the third value.

Wavelength

Build Science Skills L2

Measuring Have students use a small ruler to measure the wavelength of each wave in Figure 6 and verify that the wavelength measured does not depend on which two corresponding points are used. **Visual, Logical**

Wave Speed

Quick Lab

Comparing Frequency and Wave Speed L2

Objective

After completing this activity, students will be able to
- distinguish between wave frequency and wave speed.

Skills Focus **Measuring, Comparing and Contrasting**

Prep Time 10 minutes

Class Time 20 minutes

Teaching Tips
- Have students practice before doing timed trials.
- Using a longer rope gives more clear-cut results.

Expected Outcome Neither the amplitude nor the frequency affects the speed of propagation of a wave.

Analyze and Conclude

1. Answers will depend on student data. Answers of one to five waves per second are reasonable.
2. Answers will depend on student data but should be expressed in units of m/s.
3. The wave frequency had no effect on the wave speed. **Logical**

For Enrichment L3

Students can time the speed of waves in various other solid media, such as wires and monofilament fishing line, and attempt to determine the properties of materials that affect the speed of wave transmission. **Kinesthetic**

Customize for Inclusion Students

Visually Impaired

Tie a weight (such as a washer or fishing weight) to a string, and attach the string to a pendulum clamp on a ring stand so that it hangs vertically and is free to swing. Allow students to touch the pendulum and make it swing. By holding their hand in the right place, they can feel the weight touch their hand as it completes each cycle. Students can compare the periods and frequencies of pendulums with different lengths (lengths of 1 m, 25 cm, and 6.25 cm should produce frequencies of about 0.5 Hz, 1 Hz, and 2 Hz, respectively).

Answer to . . .

Figure 6 *The frequency of B is greater than the frequency of A.*

Reading Checkpoint *Wavelength is the distance between one point on a wave and the same point on the next cycle of the wave.*

Math Practice

Solutions L2

1. The speed is 2.0 m × 2.0 Hz = 4.0 m/s.
2. The speed is 0.1 m × 4 Hz = 0.4 m/s.
3. The speed is 10 cm/0.2 s = 50 cm/s.
4. The wavelength is (5 km/s)/10 Hz = 0.5 km.

Logical

For Extra Help L1

Have students write the equation required to solve each problem first. Then, check that they recognize what they know and don't know in the equation. **Logical**

Direct students to the **Math Skills** in the **Skills and Reference Handbook** at the end of the student text for additional help.

Additional Problems

1. The waves in a pool have a wavelength of 0.20 m and a frequency of 2.8 Hz. What is the speed of these waves? *(0.56 m/s)*
2. A student moves the end of a soft spring back and forth to make waves. The waves travel at 1.8 m/s and have a wavelength of 1.2 m. What is the frequency of these waves? *(1.5 Hz)*

Logical, Portfolio

Build Science Skills L2

Inferring Physics includes many relationships similar to the wave equation. Students need to develop a sense of how each variable relates to the others. Ask, **If the speed of a wave decreases, but the frequency stays the same, what happens to the wavelength?** *(The wavelength must decrease.)*
Logical

Address Misconceptions L2

Students are sometimes unable to distinguish between the transverse motion of the medium and motion of the wave and think that waves with a higher frequency will move faster. In many mediums, mechanical waves move at approximately the same speed for a wide range of frequencies. To reinforce this idea, have students shake the end of the rope at several frequencies. They can confirm that this doesn't affect the wave speed. **Logical**

Math Practice

1. A wave on a rope has a wavelength of 2.0 m and a frequency of 2.0 Hz. What is the speed of the wave?
2. A motorboat is tied to a dock with its motor running. The spinning propeller makes a surface wave in the water with a frequency of 4 Hz and a wavelength of 0.1 m. What is the speed of the wave?
3. What is the speed of a wave in a spring if it has a wavelength of 10 cm and a period of 0.2 s? (*Hint:* Use the equation $\text{Speed} = \frac{\text{Wavelength}}{\text{Period}}$.)
4. What is the wavelength of an earthquake wave if it has a speed of 5 km/s and a frequency of 10 Hz?

Math Skills

Speed of Mechanical Waves

One end of a rope is vibrated to produce a wave with a wavelength of 0.25 meters. The frequency of the wave is 3.0 hertz. What is the speed of the wave?

1 Read and Understand

What information are you given?

Wavelength = 0.25 m

Frequency = 3.0 Hz

2 Plan and Solve

What unknown are you trying to calculate?

Speed = ?

What formula contains the given quantities and the unknown?

$$\text{Speed} = \text{Wavelength} \times \text{Frequency}$$

Replace each variable with its known value.

(Hint: *1Hz* = $\frac{1}{s}$)

$$\text{Speed} = 0.25\ \text{m} \times 3.0\ \text{Hz}$$

$$= 0.25\ \text{m} \times 3.0\ \frac{1}{\text{s}}$$

$$\text{Speed} = 0.75\ \text{m/s}$$

3 Look Back and Check

Is your answer reasonable?

Because the frequency is 3.0 hertz, the wave should travel a distance of 3 wavelengths in 1 second. This distance is 0.75 meters, which agrees with the calculated speed of 0.75 m/s.

The speed of a wave can change if it enters a new medium or if variables such as pressure and temperature change. However, for many kinds of waves, the speed of the waves is roughly constant for a range of different frequencies. **If you assume that waves are traveling at a constant speed, then wavelength is inversely proportional to frequency.** What does this mean for two waves with different frequencies? The wave with the lower frequency has a longer wavelength.

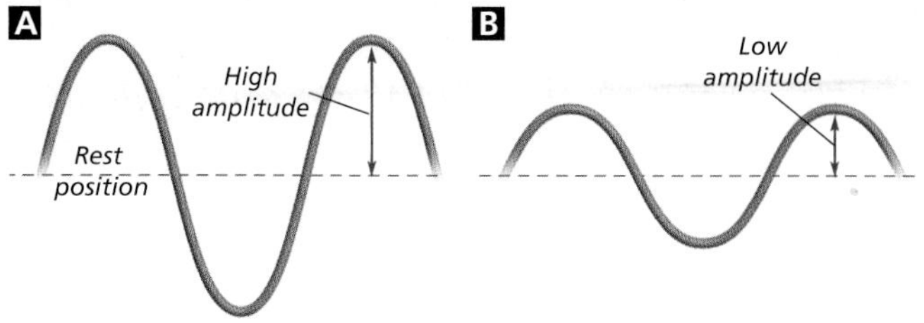
A
High amplitude
Rest position
B
Low amplitude

Figure 7 The more energy a wave has, the greater is its amplitude. **A** The amplitude of a transverse wave equals the distance to the highest point above the rest position. **B** This wave's amplitude is one half the amplitude of the wave in A. **Applying Concepts** *Which wave has more energy?*

Amplitude

If you drop a pebble into a pond, the wave is not very high. If you do a "cannonball" jump into the water, you know the wave will be much higher. These two waves have different amplitudes. The **amplitude** (AM pluh tood) of a wave is the maximum displacement of the medium from its rest position.

Figure 7 shows the amplitudes of two transverse waves in a rope. The amplitude of a transverse wave is the distance from the rest position to a crest or a trough. It takes more energy to produce a wave with higher crests and deeper troughs. **The more energy a wave has, the greater is its amplitude.**

How do you measure the amplitude of a longitudinal wave? In this case, the amplitude is the maximum displacement of a point from its rest position. The more energy the wave has, the more the medium will be compressed or displaced.

Go Online NSTA SCiLINKS

For: Links on wave properties
Visit: www.SciLinks.org
Web Code: ccn-2172

Section 17.2 Assessment

Reviewing Concepts

1. How is the vibration of the source related to a wave's frequency?
2. How is wavelength related to frequency for waves moving at a constant speed?
3. How is the energy of a wave related to its amplitude?
4. Describe two ways you could measure the wavelength of a longitudinal wave.
5. Describe how you measure the amplitude of a transverse wave.

Critical Thinking

6. **Applying Concepts** If a wave's period doubles, how does the wave's frequency change? (*Hint:* Period $= \frac{1}{\text{Frequency}}$)
7. **Designing Experiments** Describe an experiment to measure the frequency of a longitudinal wave in a spring.
8. **Predicting** If you double the frequency of a wave, what is the effect on its wavelength (assuming speed does not change)?

Math Practice

9. A wave on a rope has a frequency of 3.3 Hz and a wavelength of 1.2 m. What is the speed of the wave?
10. A spring toy vibrates at 2 Hz to produce a wave. What is the period of the wave?

Amplitude

Use Visuals L1

Figure 7 The two waves shown have different amplitudes, but the same wavelength and frequency. Ask, **If you were shaking the ropes, how would what you would feel in Figure 7A differ from what you feel in Figure 7B?** *("My hand would shake harder in A than B.")* Explain that wave A delivers more energy than wave B. **Visual, Logical**

Build Reading Literacy L1

Outline Refer to page **156D** in **Chapter 6**, which provides the guidelines for an outline.

Have students outline the section, leaving room for notes. Then, they should scan through each heading and try to find the main idea. **Logical**

3 ASSESS

Evaluate Understanding L2

Have students create cards of vocabulary terms and definitions, and then work in pairs to match them.

Reteach L1

Use Figure 7 to review the section's key concepts. Ask students to describe the frequency and wavelength of the waves.

Math Practice

Solutions

9. The speed is 1.2 m × 3.3 Hz = 4.0 m/s.
10. The period is 1/2 Hz = 0.5 s.

Interactive Textbook If your class subscribes to the Interactive Textbook, use it to review key concepts in Section 17.2.

Section 17.2 Assessment

1. A wave's frequency equals the frequency of the vibrating source.
2. Wavelength is inversely proportional to frequency for waves moving at a given speed.
3. The more energy a wave has, the greater is its amplitude.
4. The wavelength could be found by measuring the distance between adjacent compressions or adjacent rarefactions. The wavelength also could be calculated by measuring the wave speed and frequency.
5. The amplitude equals the distance from the rest position to a crest or trough.
6. The frequency is one half as great.
7. Put a ribbon on the spring. Set up a mechanical device to vibrate the spring back and forth in periodic motion. Measure the time it takes for the ribbon to vibrate back and forth 20 times. Divide the measured time into 20 cycles to calculate the frequency in Hz. Repeat the procedure for several trials and average the results.
8. Doubling the frequency will halve the wavelength.

Go Online NSTA SCiLINKS

Download a worksheet on wave properties for students to complete, and find additional teacher support from NSTA SciLinks.

Answer to . . .

Figure 7 *The wave in A*

17.3 Behavior of Waves

Reading Focus

Key Concepts

- How does reflection change a wave?
- What causes the refraction of a wave when it enters a new medium?
- What factors affect the amount of diffraction of a wave?
- What are two types of interference?
- What wavelengths will produce a standing wave?

Vocabulary

- reflection
- refraction
- diffraction
- interference
- constructive interference
- destructive interference
- standing wave
- node
- antinode

Reading Strategy

Identifying Main Ideas Copy and expand the table below. As you read, write the main idea of each topic.

Topic	Main Idea
Reflection	a. ___?___
Refraction	b. ___?___
Diffraction	c. ___?___
Interference	d. ___?___
Standing waves	e. ___?___

Have you ever noticed bright lines like those shown in Figure 8 dancing on the bottom of a pool? These lines are produced when light shines through waves on the surface of the water. The lines don't seem to have a pattern because there are so many waves interacting. Imagine following just one of these waves. What will happen when it strikes the side of the pool? When it encounters another wave or an obstacle like a person? As the waves crisscross back and forth, many interactions can occur, including reflection, refraction, diffraction, and interference.

Figure 8 The ripples visible on the bottom of the pool are caused by light shining through surface waves.

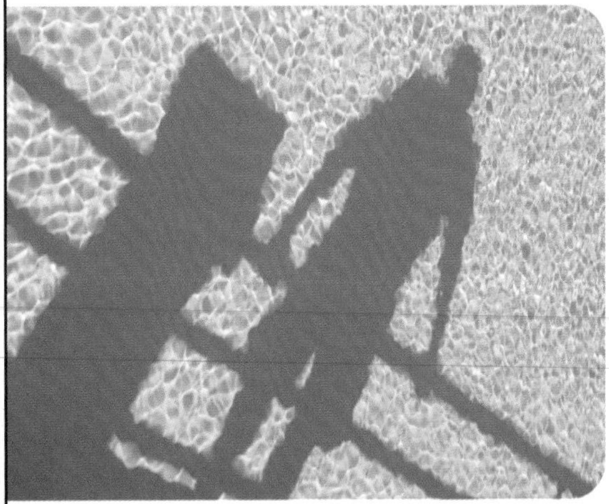

Reflection

The next time you are in a pool, try to observe ripples as they hit the side of the pool. **Reflection** occurs when a wave bounces off a surface that it cannot pass through. The reflection of a wave is like the reflection of a ball thrown at a wall. The ball cannot go through the wall, so it bounces back.

If you send a transverse wave down a rope attached to a wall, the wave reflects when it hits the wall. **Reflection does not change the speed or frequency of a wave, but the wave can be flipped upside down.** If reflection occurs at a fixed boundary, then the reflected wave will be upside down compared to the original wave.

1 FOCUS

Objectives

17.3.1 **Describe** how reflection, refraction, diffraction, and interference affect waves.

17.3.2 **State a rule** that explains refraction of a wave as it passes from one medium to another.

17.3.3 **Identify** factors that affect the amount of refraction, diffraction, or interference.

17.3.4 **Distinguish** between constructive and destructive interference and **explain** how standing waves form.

Reading Focus

Build Vocabulary L2

Concept Map Have students build a concept map using the terms in this section. Students should write Behavior of Waves in an oval at the top and connect it with linking words to ovals containing vocabulary terms.

Reading Strategy L2

a. A wave reflected at a fixed boundary is inverted but has the same speed and frequency. **b.** Refraction occurs because one side of a wave front moves more slowly than the other side. **c.** The larger the wavelength, the more a wave diffracts. **d.** It can be constructive or destructive. **e.** It forms only for multiples of one-half wavelength.

2 INSTRUCT

Reflection

Teacher Demo

Water-Wave Reflections L2

Purpose Students will observe surface wave reflections.

Materials clear bowl, water, overhead projector

Procedure Fill the bowl with water and place it on the overhead projector. Make gentle waves with a finger.

Expected Outcome Surface waves can be observed reflecting off the side of the bowl. **Visual**

Section Resources

Print

- ***Reading and Study Workbook With Math Support,*** Section 17.3
- ***Transparencies,*** Section 17.3

Technology

- ***Interactive Textbook,*** Section 17.3
- ***Presentation Pro CD-ROM,*** Section 17.3
- ***Go Online,*** NSTA SciLinks, Diffraction and interference

Refraction

Refraction is the bending of a wave as it enters a new medium at an angle. Imagine pushing a lawnmower from grass onto gravel, as shown in Figure 9. The direction of the lawnmower changes because one wheel enters the gravel before the other one does. The wheel on the gravel slows down, but the other wheel is still moving at a faster speed on the grass. The speed difference between the two wheels causes the lawnmower to change direction. Refraction changes the direction of a wave in much the same way. **When a wave enters a medium at an angle, refraction occurs because one side of the wave moves more slowly than the other side.**

Figure 10 shows the refraction of an ocean wave as it flows into a shallow area. The shallower water can be considered a new medium. The lines on the photograph show the changing direction of the wave. These lines, called wave fronts, are parallel to the crests of the wave.

Notice that the wave fronts approach the shore at an angle. The left side of each wave enters shallower water before the right side does. As the left side of the wave slows down, the wave bends toward the left.

If a wave front is parallel to the shoreline, the wave enters the shallower water all at once. The wave will slow down but it will not change direction. Refraction of the wave occurs only when the two sides of a wave travel at different speeds.

Reading Checkpoint *What is refraction?*

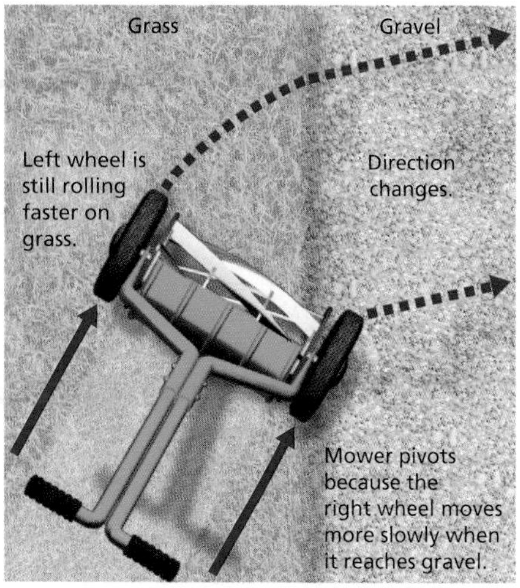

Grass
Gravel
Left wheel is still rolling faster on grass.
Direction changes.
Mower pivots because the right wheel moves more slowly when it reaches gravel.

Figure 9 A lawnmower turns when it is pushed at an angle from the grass onto the gravel. **Relating Cause and Effect** ***Explain why the lawnmower straightens out after both wheels are on the gravel.***

Figure 10 As an ocean wave approaches the shore at an angle, the wave bends, or refracts, because one side of each wave front slows down before the other side does.

Build Reading Literacy **L1**

Active Comprehension Refer to page **498D** in this chapter, which provides the guidelines for active comprehension.

Read the introductory paragraph on p. 508. Ask, **What more would you like to know about how waves interact?** or **What about wave behavior interests you?** You will need to make connections for the students between waves and their lives. For example, students may have observed ripples in a drink sitting on top of a loudspeaker. Write down several of the students' responses. Have students read the section. While reading, have them consider the questions that they had about the material. Have students discuss the section content, making sure that each question raised at the beginning is answered or that students know where to look for the answer.
Verbal

Refraction

Address Misconceptions **L2**

Some students may think that a wave always changes direction as it passes through a boundary. Refraction is always accompanied by a change in wavelength and speed. However, the direction of a wave does not always change. For example, although water waves approaching a beach perpendicular to the beach do not change direction, they do slow down as the wave fronts get closer together.
Verbal, Visual

Build Science Skills **L2**

Posing Questions Have students look at Figure 10. Ask, **How could you test the assertion that water waves move more slowly in more shallow water?** *(Possible answer: Set up a wave tank and measure wave speed at different depths, making sure to hold all other variables constant.)*
Logical

Customize for English Language Learners

Increase Word Exposure
This section contains several new and potentially confusing vocabulary word pairs, such as *reflection* and *refraction* or *constructive* and *destructive.* While students read the section in class, post the vocabulary terms on the board or wall. Carefully define each word when it first appears. Then, ask for student help in distinguishing between the similar-sounding words.

Answer to . . .

Figure 9 *Once both wheels are on the gravel, they move at the same speed, so the lawnmower no longer changes direction.*

Reading Checkpoint *Refraction is the bending of a wave as it enters a new medium at an angle.*

Diffraction

Use Visuals

L1

Figure 11 Emphasize to students that both pictures are showing the same phenomena, diffraction. Point out the similarities between the two images. Ask, **What would the diffraction pattern look like if one of the barriers were removed in Figure 11A?** *(The waves would still spread out behind the other barrier. This would look like half of the diffraction pattern in Figure 11B.)*
Visual, Logical

Interference

Address Misconceptions

L2

Students sometimes make an analogy between pulses and particles traveling toward each other and assume that when two pulses meet in the center of a long spring, they bounce or reflect as if they were solid objects. Use a long, soft spring and a jump rope to demonstrate two differently sized and shaped pulses approaching each other so that students can see that they pass through each other.
Verbal

Go Online NSTA SciLINKS

Download a worksheet on diffraction and interference for students to complete, and find additional teacher support from NSTA SciLinks.

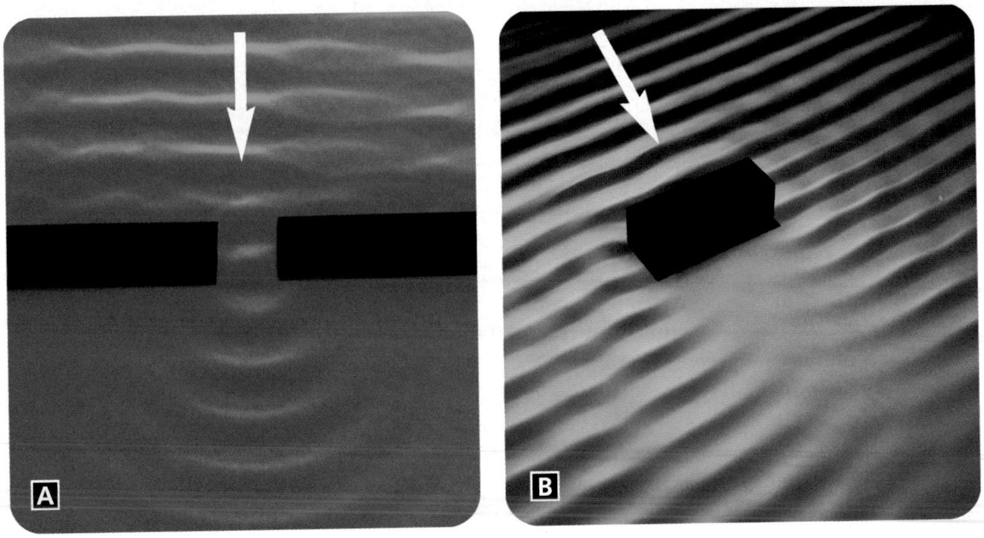

Figure 11 **A** Mechanical waves, like the water waves shown here, diffract as they move past an obstacle or through an opening. **A** This wave diffracts, or spreads out, after it passes through a narrow opening. **B** Diffraction also occurs when a wave encounters an obstacle.

Diffraction

Diffraction (dih FRAK shun) is the bending of a wave as it moves around an obstacle or passes through a narrow opening. Figure 11A shows how water waves spread out as they pass through a narrow opening. The pattern produced is very similar to the circular ripples you see when a pebble is tossed into a pond. Diffraction also occurs when waves bend around an obstacle, as shown in Figure 11B.

A wave diffracts more if its wavelength is large compared to the size of an opening or obstacle. If the wavelength is small compared to the opening or obstacle, the wave bends very little. The larger the wavelength is compared to the size to the opening or obstacle, the more the wave diffracts.

Reading Checkpoint *What is diffraction?*

Go Online NSTA SciLINKS

For: Links on diffraction and interference
Visit: www.SciLinks.org
Web Code: ccn-2173

Interference

If two balls collide, they cannot continue on their original paths as if they had never met. But waves can occupy the same region of space and then continue on. **Interference** occurs when two or more waves overlap and combine together. **Two types of interference are constructive interference and destructive interference.** The displacements of waves combine to increase amplitude in constructive interference and to decrease amplitude in destructive interference.

Facts and Figures

The First Known Seismometer Earthquakes travel through Earth as longitudinal waves, transverse waves, and surface waves. Surface waves are the most destructive and are the waves that people feel during an earthquake. The world's first earthquake wave detector was invented in 132 A.D. by Zhang Heng, a scientist in the Han Dynasty in China. It was sensitive enough to detect small surface waves. The device had eight dragons arranged in a circle. Each dragon's mouth held a brass ball. When an earthquake wave passed, a brass ball would fall, indicating the direction of the wave. One day a ball fell, indicating that an earthquake had occurred, although no one had felt an earthquake. A few days later, couriers arrived, reporting an earthquake in Lung-Hsi, about 640 km away.

Constructive Interference Imagine a child being pushed on a swing by her mother. If the mother times her pushes correctly, she will push on the swing just as the child starts to move forward. Then the mother's effort is maximized and the child gets a boost to go higher. In the same way, the amplitudes of two waves can add together. **Constructive interference** occurs when two or more waves combine to produce a wave with a larger displacement.

What happens if you and a friend send waves with equal frequencies toward each other on a jump rope? Figure 12A shows how constructive interference produces a wave with an increased amplitude. The crests of waves 1 and 2 combine to make a higher crest in wave 3. At the point where two troughs meet, wave 3 has a lower trough.

Destructive Interference What happens if the mother has bad timing while pushing on the swing? Instead of working to boost her daughter upward, some of her effort is wasted, and the girl will not swing as high. In much the same way, destructive interference can reduce the amplitude of a wave. **Destructive interference** occurs when two or more waves combine to produce a wave with a smaller displacements.

In Figure 12B, two waves with the same frequency meet, but this time the crest of wave 1 meets the trough of wave 2. The resulting wave 3 has a crest at this point, but it is lower than the crest of wave 1. Destructive interference produces a wave with a reduced amplitude.

Figure 12 Two waves with equal frequencies travel in opposite directions. The motions are graphed here to make it easier to see how the waves combine. **A** When a crest meets a crest, the result is a wave with an increased amplitude. **B** When a crest meets a trough, the result is a wave with a reduced amplitude. **Making Generalizations** ***How is the amplitude of wave 3 related to the amplitudes of waves 1 and 2?***

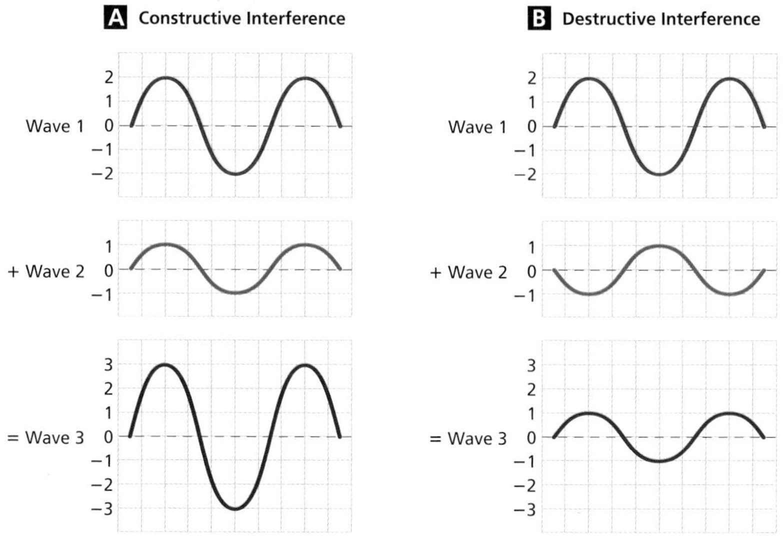

A Constructive Interference
Wave 1
2
1
0
−1
−2
+ Wave 2
1
0
−1
= Wave 3
3
2
1
0
−1
−2
−3
B Destructive Interference
Wave 1
2
1
0
−1
−2
+ Wave 2
1
0
−1
= Wave 3
3
2
1
0
−1
−2
−3

Use Visuals **L1**

Figure 12 Have students examine the figure carefully. Note that the two waves are moving in opposite directions. In Figure 12A, the crests line up with crests and the troughs line up with troughs. In Figure 12B, the crests line up with troughs and the troughs with crests. Ask, **In Figure 12A, what would wave 3 look like if wave 1 and wave 2 had the same amplitude?** *(The amplitude of wave 3 would be twice that of wave 1 or 2.)* **In Figure 12B, what would wave 3 look like if wave 1 and wave 2 had the same amplitude?** *(Wave 3 would have zero amplitude.)* Point out to students that even in the case of two waves with the same amplitude, the waves do not entirely cancel. After they pass through each other, they continue on in their original form.
Visual, Logical

Build Science Skills **L2**

Using Tables and Graphs Give students dimensions for the horizontal axis of the grid in Figure 12, such as each increment equals 10 cm. Ask students to determine the wavelength of waves 1 and 2 in Figures 12A and 12B. *(The wavelength of each of the waves equals 60 cm.)* Ask, **Do waves 1 and 2 in Figure 12B have the same wavelength?** *(Yes)* **If each graph grid represents a time period of 10 seconds, what is the period and frequency of wave 1 in Figure 12A?** *(Period = 6 s; frequency = 1/6 Hz)*
Logical

Answer to . . .

Figure 12 *The amplitude of wave 3 equals the sum of the amplitudes of waves 1 and 2 for constructive interference. For destructive interference, it's the difference of the amplitudes.*

Reading Checkpoint *Diffraction is the bending of a wave when it encounters an obstacle or a narrow opening.*

Standing Waves

Teacher Demo

Standing Waves L2

Purpose Students will observe different standing waves.

Materials long, soft, heavy rope, such as a jump rope

Class Time 10 minutes

Procedure Tie one end of the rope to a chair or other firm support. Hold the other end of the rope so that it is suspended in air. Start with the rope hanging in an arc. Make standing waves by shaking the rope at different frequencies. Ask students to estimate the wavelength as you increase the frequency and produce more nodes. *(As the frequency increases, the wavelength decreases.)*

Expected Outcome The length of the rope must be an integral number of half wavelengths for a standing wave to occur.
Kinesthetic, Visual

3 ASSESS

Evaluate Understanding L2

Have students write three review questions for this section.

Reteach L1

Use Figures 9–13 as examples that illustrate the key concepts of the section.

Writing in Science

Students will need to first decide how the time between photographs compares with the period of the wave. If the five photographs occur during one half period of the wave, the sequence will show the person starting at a maximum crest and moving downward to a minimum trough. No circular motion should result because the lateral motions caused by the two waves should cancel.

Interactive Textbook If your class subscribes to the Interactive Textbook, use it to review key concepts in Section 17.3.

Answer to . . .

Figure 13 *The upper photograph has waves with a longer wavelength.*

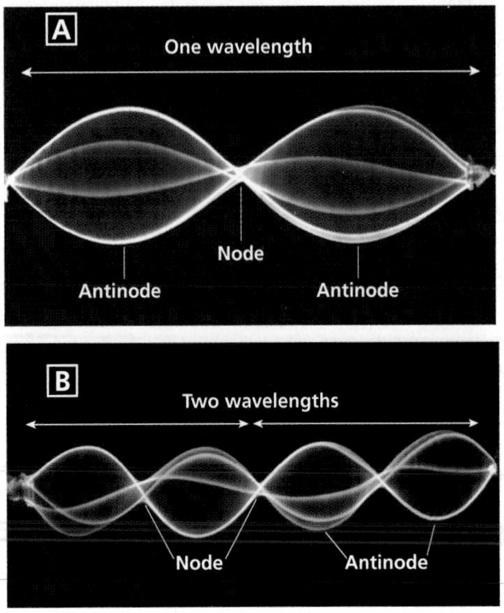

A
One wavelength
Node
Antinode
Antinode
B
Two wavelengths
Node
Antinode

Figure 13 These photos show standing waves for two different frequencies. **A** One wavelength equals the length of the cord. **B** Two wavelengths equal the length of the cord.
Interpreting Photos In which photo do the waves have a longer wavelength?

Standing Waves

If you tie one end of a rope to a chair and shake the other end, waves travel up the rope, reflect off the chair, and travel back down the rope. Interference occurs as the incoming waves pass through the reflected waves. At certain frequencies, interference between a wave and its reflection can produce a standing wave. A **standing wave** is a wave that appears to stay in one place—it does not seem to move through the medium.

You can observe a standing wave if you pluck a guitar string or any elastic cord. Only certain points on the wave, called nodes, are stationary. A **node** is a point on a standing wave that has no displacement from the rest position. At the nodes, there is complete destructive interference between the incoming and reflected waves. An **antinode** is a point where a crest or trough occurs midway between two nodes.

Why does a standing wave happen only at particular frequencies? **A standing wave forms only if half a wavelength or a multiple of half a wavelength fits exactly into the length of a vibrating cord.** In Figure 13A, the wavelength equals the length of the cord. In Figure 13B, the wavelength is halved. You can adjust the wavelength by changing the frequency of the waves. Once you find a frequency that produces a standing wave, doubling or tripling the frequency will also produce a standing wave.

Section 17.3 Assessment

Reviewing Concepts

1. How is a wave changed by reflection?
2. What causes refraction when a wave enters a medium at an angle?
3. What determines how much a wave diffracts when it encounters an opening or an obstacle?
4. List the types of interference.
5. At what wavelengths can a standing wave form in an elastic cord?

Critical Thinking

6. **Comparing and Contrasting** How does the frequency of a reflected wave compare to the frequency of the incoming wave?
7. **Comparing and Contrasting** How are diffraction and refraction similar? How are they different?
8. **Applying Concepts** What is the amplitude of the wave that results when two identical waves interfere constructively?

Writing in Science

Explain a Sequence Imagine you are floating in a wave pool. The crest of one wave hits you from the left just as the crest of another hits you from the right. The two waves are otherwise identical. A friend takes a series of five photos starting when the crests hit you. Write a paragraph describing the photos.

Section 17.3 Assessment

1. The reflected wave is upside down compared to the original wave.
2. Refraction occurs because the entire wave does not enter the new medium at the same time. One side of a wave front entering the new medium undergoes a speed change before the rest of the wave front does, resulting in the change in direction.
3. The larger the wavelength of a wave compared to the size of the obstacle or opening, the more the wave diffracts.
4. Destructive, constructive
5. A standing wave forms only if half a wavelength or a multiple of half a wavelength fits exactly into the length of the vibrating object.
6. The frequencies are equal. Reflection does not change the frequency of a wave.
7. Diffraction and refraction both involve the bending of waves. Refraction occurs when a wave enters a new medium at an angle, while diffraction occurs when a wave encounters an obstacle or a narrow opening.
8. The amplitude of the resulting wave is double the amplitude of the two interfering waves.

issues in SCIENCE

Are Regulations Needed to Protect Whales from Noise Pollution?

Researchers have known for decades that humpback whales sing complicated songs. Their songs can be as long as 30 minutes, and a whale may repeat the song for two or more hours. Songs can be heard at distances of hundreds of kilometers. There is evidence that whales use variations in the songs to tell other whales about the location of food and predators. Only the male humpbacks sing, which has led some researchers to think that songs are also used to attract a mate.

The whale songs may be threatened by noise pollution. In the past 50 years, ocean noise has increased due to human activity. Goods are transported across the ocean in larger ships than ever before. Large ships use bigger engines. They produce low-frequency noise by stirring up air bubbles with their propellers. Unfortunately, whales also use low-frequency sound in their songs, perhaps because these sounds carry farther than high-frequency sounds in the ocean. Propeller noise from large ships is loud enough to interfere with whale songs at a distance of 20 kilometers.

The Viewpoints

Regulations Are Needed to Reduce Noise Pollution From Large Ships

Whales use their songs in ways that affect their survival—eating, mating, and avoiding predators. Studies often focus on the effects of noise from a single ship, but in routes taken by ocean freighters, noise from many ships combines to produce a higher volume. Ocean freighters often travel near whale migration routes, so even noise that affects whales at a distance of 20 kilometers may have an impact on whale survival. If regulations are delayed until research can prove that noise pollution affects whales, it may be too late to help the whales. Many kinds of whales are on the endangered species list, so it is important to err on the side of safety.

Regulations Are Not Needed to Reduce Noise Pollution From Large Ships

Whale songs can be lengthy and are often repeated, so the effect of noise from ships is limited because ships quickly move out of an area. One study showed that whales changed the rhythm and tempo of their songs in response to noise from large ships, but there was no evidence that the communication was less effective. Also, it is expensive to modify ship propellers to reduce low-frequency noise. If less-developed countries cannot afford to modify ships, regulations will not be effective in reducing ocean noise levels.

Research and Decide

1. **Defining the Issue** In your own words, describe the major issue that needs to be resolved about ocean noise pollution.
2. **Analyzing the Viewpoints** List three arguments for those who think regulations should require large ships to reduce noise pollution. List three arguments for those who think regulations are not necessary.
3. **Forming Your Opinion** Explain which argument you find most convincing.

Go Online
PHSchool.com

For: More on this issue
Visit: PHSchool.com
Web Code: cch-2173

issues in SCIENCE

Are Regulations Needed to Protect Whales from Noise Pollution? L2

Background

In the United States, whales fall under the Marine Mammal Protection Act of 1972 (MMPA). This act makes it illegal for any person residing in the United States to kill, hunt, injure, or harass any species of marine mammal. The act includes noise pollution. Ocean noise may result from military testing, sonar, assembling and dismantling of drilling rigs, seismic testing, marine commerce, and proposed experiments using 195-dB pulses to measure the temperature in the North Atlantic. Low-frequency sonar produces 235-dB pulses. Oil tankers continuously produce low-frequency sounds of 177 dB at 500 Hz in all the shipping lanes of the world. Seismic oil-exploration pulses are 210 dB. For comparison, the call of a gray whale is 185 dB.

Since light does not penetrate very far in ocean water, whales use sound to find their way around, locate food, and understand their environment. Sound travels five times faster in water than in air and is transmitted more efficiently. Some sounds can travel for hundreds of kilometers.

Whales are thought to hear in the range of 40 Hz to 150 kHz, depending on the species. However, the upper and lower limits are inferred for many whales. Research into large whale hearing is limited by the large size and behaviors of these animals.

Answers

1. The issue is: Should regulations be passed to limit noise from large ships?
2. For Regulation: Whales depend on communication for breeding and locating food resources. Noise that affects whales at a short distance may still have an impact on behavior. Because many species are endangered, it is wise to err on the safe side of the issue. Against Regulation: Whale songs can be lengthy and are often repeated, so there are several opportunities for a message to get through. Whales may modify songs in response to noise pollution, but there's no evidence it makes communication less effective. Reducing noise of large ships may not be feasible in less developed countries, which makes regulations ineffective.
3. Students should support their decision by referring to the arguments in Question 2.

Go Online
PHSchool.com

Have students further research the issues related to this topic.

1 FOCUS

Objectives

17.4.1 **Describe** the properties of sound waves and **explain** how sound is produced and reproduced.
17.4.2 **Describe** how sound waves behave in applications such as ultrasound and music.
17.4.3 **Explain** how relative motion determines the frequency of sound an observer hears.
17.4.4 **Analyze** the functions of the main regions of the human ear.

Reading Focus

Build Vocabulary L2

Paraphrase Some terms in this section, such as *intensity, decibel,* and *resonance,* may be unfamiliar to students. Have students create a definition in their own words for these or other difficult words.

Reading Strategy L2

a. Intensity and loudness **b.** Frequency and pitch

2 INSTRUCT

Properties of Sound Waves

Use Community Resources L2

Invite members of the school band or orchestra or a community band or orchestra to demonstrate musical instruments for the class. Allow students to pose questions to the musicians, such as "How is the pitch of your instrument changed?" or "How do you increase the volume of sound coming from your instrument?"
Musical, Visual

17.4 Sound and Hearing

Reading Focus

Key Concepts

- What properties explain the behavior of sound?
- How is ultrasound used?
- How does frequency of sound change for a moving source?
- What are the functions of the three main regions of the ear?
- How is sound recorded?
- How do musical instruments vary pitch?

Vocabulary

- sound waves
- intensity
- decibel
- loudness
- pitch
- sonar
- Doppler effect
- resonance

Reading Strategy

Using Prior Knowledge Copy the web diagram below. Before you read, add properties you already know about. Then add details about each property as you read.

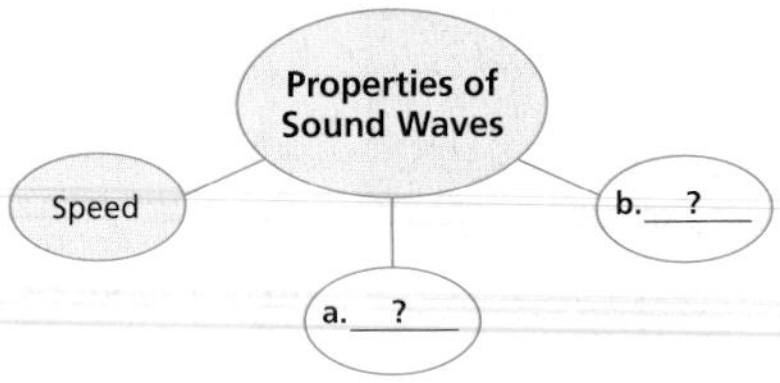
Properties of Sound Waves
Speed
a. ?
b. ?

Take a moment to listen. Even in a quiet room you can usually hear many different sounds. You might hear someone opening a book, people talking in the hall, cars and trucks driving outside, and maybe even an airplane flying overhead. You can identify sounds without seeing them because sound waves carry information to your ears.

Figure 14 The speed of sound is shown here for a variety of materials. **Making Generalizations** ***How does temperature affect the speed of sound?***

Speed of Sound

Medium (at 1 atm)	Speed (m/s)
Dry air, 0°C	331
Dry air, 20°C	342
Fresh water, 0°C	1401
Fresh water, 30°C	1509
Salt water, 0°C	1449
Salt water, 30°C	1546
Lead, 25°C	1210
Cast iron, 25°C	4480
Aluminum, 25°C	5000
Borosilicate glass, 25°C	5170

Properties of Sound Waves

Sound waves are longitudinal waves—compressions and rarefactions that travel through a medium. Have you ever stopped to question why sounds can hurt your ears? Why there is a delay before you hear an echo down a long, empty hallway at school? **Many behaviors of sound can be explained using a few properties—speed, intensity and loudness, and frequency and pitch.**

Speed Why is there a delay when you hear an echo? It takes time for sound to travel from place to place. In dry air at 20°C, the speed of sound is 342 meters per second. That's more than ten times faster than your speed in a car on a highway!

Figure 14 shows how the speed of sound varies in different media. In general, sound waves travel fastest in solids, slower in liquids, and slowest in gases. This is partly due to the fact that particles in a solid tend to be closer together than particles in a liquid or a gas. The speed of sound depends on many factors, including the density of the medium and how elastic the medium is.

Section Resources

Print
- ***Laboratory Manual,*** Investigations 17A and 17B
- ***Reading and Study Workbook With Math Support,*** Section 17.4
- ***Transparencies,*** Section 17.4

Technology
- ***Interactive Textbook,*** Section 17.4
- ***Presentation Pro CD-ROM,*** Section 17.4
- ***Go Online,*** *Science News,* Sound

Intensity and Loudness

Intensity is the rate at which a wave's energy flows through a given area. Sound intensity depends on both the wave's amplitude and the distance from the sound source. If someone whispers in your ear, the sound intensity may be greater than when someone shouts at you from the other end of a field.

Sound intensity levels are measured in units called decibels. The **decibel** (dB) is a unit that compares the intensity of different sounds. The decibel scale is based on powers of ten. For every 10-decibel increase, the sound intensity increases tenfold. Figure 15 shows the intensity levels of some common sounds. A 0-decibel sound can just barely be heard. A 20-decibel sound has 100 times more energy per second than a 0-decibel sound. A 30-decibel sound delivers 1000 times more energy per second than a 0-decibel sound.

Unlike intensity, loudness is subjective—it is subject to a person's interpretation. **Loudness** is a physical response to the intensity of sound, modified by physical factors. The loudness you hear depends, of course, on sound intensity. As intensity increases, loudness increases. But loudness also depends on factors such as the health of your ears and how your brain interprets the information in sound waves.

Sound Intensity Level

Sound	Intensity Level (decibels)
Threshold of human hearing	0
Whisper	15–20
Normal conversation	40–50
Street noise	60–70
Inside a bus	90–100
Operating heavy machinery	80–120
Rock concert (in audience)	110–120
Threshold of pain	120
Jet plane (taking off)	120–160

Figure 15 Lengthy exposure to sounds more intense than 90 decibels can cause hearing damage. **Analyzing Data** ***Which sounds are potentially dangerous?***

Frequency and Pitch

Try plucking a stretched rubber band. Then, stretch the rubber band farther and pluck again. You should be able to see the vibration become faster as you hear the sound frequency become higher. The frequency of a sound wave depends on how fast the source of the sound is vibrating.

The size of a musical instrument tells you something about the frequencies it can produce. The trumpet in Figure 16 can produce higher frequencies than the French horn. Both instruments produce different frequencies by changing the length of tubing through which air moves. The air in the tubing forms a standing wave. The longer the tubing, the longer is the wavelength of the standing wave, and the lower is the frequency of the note produced.

Pitch is the frequency of a sound as you perceive it. Pitch does depend upon a wave's frequency. High-frequency sounds have a high pitch, and low-frequency sounds have a low pitch. But pitch, like loudness, also depends on other factors such as your age and the health of your ears.

Reading Checkpoint *What is loudness?*

Figure 16 The French horn can produce lower notes than the trumpet because it can make a longer tube for a standing wave.

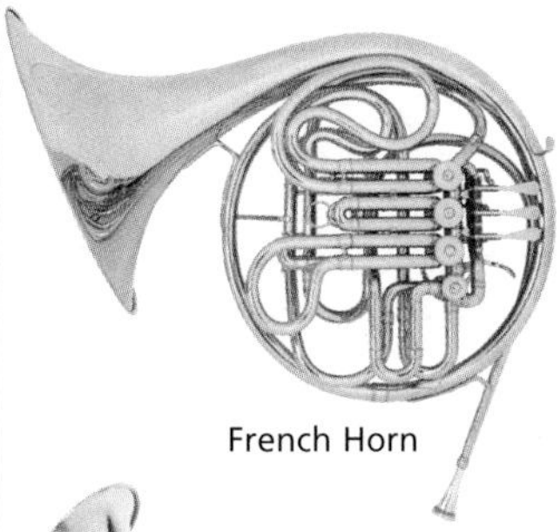

French Horn

Trumpet

Build Science Skills **L2**

Observing ACTIVITY

Purpose Students use tuning forks to model vibrations and sound waves.

Materials set of tuning forks of similar construction

Class Time 10 minutes

Procedure Instruct students in the proper way to strike the tuning forks. Emphasize that hitting the forks on a desk or other hard surface can damage them and also make it harder to hear the tone. Have students strike several different tuning forks and compare their pitches. Ask, **What is the relationship between the length of the tuning fork and its pitch?** *(The longer tuning forks produce lower pitches.)* Have students place the base of a vibrating tuning fork against a surface that can act as a soundboard, such as a window pane, desk, or thin board. Ask, **What happened when the vibrating tuning fork was placed against the soundboard?** *(The sound got louder.)*

Expected Outcome Students will observe that tuning forks of different lengths produce different pitches and that soundboards amplify sound.
Visual, Kinesthetic

Customize for Inclusion Students

Hearing Impaired
Depending on their degree of hearing loss, hearing-impaired students may have some difficulty with many of the concepts in this section. Since sound originates from vibrating objects, touch can substitute for hearing in some cases. Allow students to feel the vibrations of musical instruments as they are being played. Encourage them to describe differences in what they feel as high and low pitches are played. Students can also "see" vibrations if you strike a tuning fork, then quickly place the end of it in a pan of water. The ripples in the water show the vibrations.

Answer to . . .

Figure 14 *From the data given, the speed of sound increases with increasing temperature.*

Figure 15 *Riding in a bus, operating heavy machinery, attending a rock concert, and listening to a jet taking off are sounds that may damage hearing.*

Reading Checkpoint *Loudness is a physical response to the intensity of sound, modified by physical factors.*

Ultrasound

Build Reading Literacy L1

SQ3R Refer to page **530D** in **Chapter 18**, which provides the guidelines for SQ3R (Study, Question, Read, Recite, Review).

Teach this independent study skill as a whole-class exercise. Direct students to survey Section 17.4 and list the headings: Speed, Intensity and Loudness, Frequency, Pitch, and so on. As they survey, have students write one question for each heading, such as "What is one common application for ultrasound?" Then, have students write answers to the questions as they read the section. After reading, have students recite the questions and answers, explaining that vocalizing in your own words helps you retain what you learned.
Auditory, Group

The Doppler Effect

Use Visuals L1

Figure 18 Point out that the ambulance was in a different place when each circular wave was emitted. Reproduce this diagram on the board and number the waves 1 through 6, starting with the largest wave. Ask, **In the figure, where was the ambulance when wave 1 was emitted?** *(At the center of that wave)* **Where was the ambulance when the other waves were emitted?** *(At the center of each wave, moving to the right)*
Visual, Logical

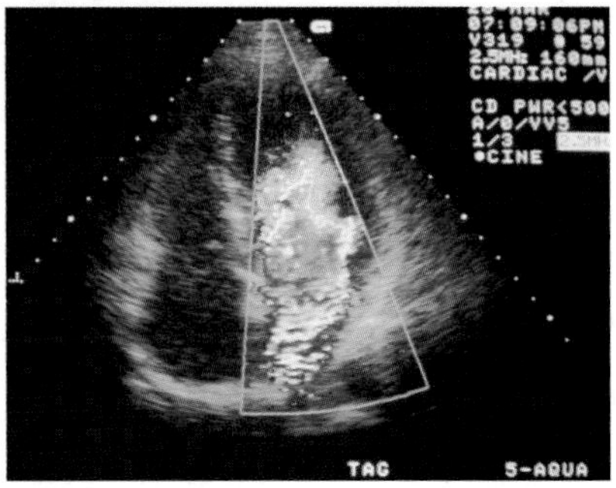

Figure 17 Ultrasound can be used to make images of the heart, which help doctors diagnose disease.

Ultrasound

Most people hear sounds between 20 hertz and 20,000 hertz. Infrasound is sound at frequencies lower than most people can hear, and ultrasound is sound at frequencies higher than most people hear. **Ultrasound is used in a variety of applications, including sonar and ultrasound imaging.**

Sonar is a technique for determining the distance to an object under water. Sonar stands for *so*und *na*vigation and *r*anging. The distance to the object is calculated using the speed of sound in water and the time that the sound wave takes to reach an object and the echo takes to return.

Ultrasound imaging is an important medical technique. Figure 17 shows an image of the heart made by sending ultrasound pulses into a patient. A pulse is a very short burst of a wave. Each ultrasound pulse is short—about $\frac{1}{8000}$ of a second—so that it doesn't interfere with the reflected pulse. Computer software uses the reflected pulses to make a detailed map of structures and organs inside the body.

The Doppler Effect

Perhaps you have heard the pitch of a siren change as it passed you. This is the **Doppler effect**—a change in sound frequency caused by motion of the sound source, motion of the listener, or both. The Doppler effect was discovered by the Austrian scientist Christian Doppler (1803–1853).

As a source of sound approaches, an observer hears a higher frequency. When the sound source moves away, the observer hears a lower frequency. Figure 18 shows a single frequency emitted by the ambulance siren. As the ambulance moves toward observer B, the wave fronts bunch together. Observer B hears a higher frequency than the frequency of the source. For observer A, however, the wave fronts are spread out, and the frequency is lower than the source frequency.

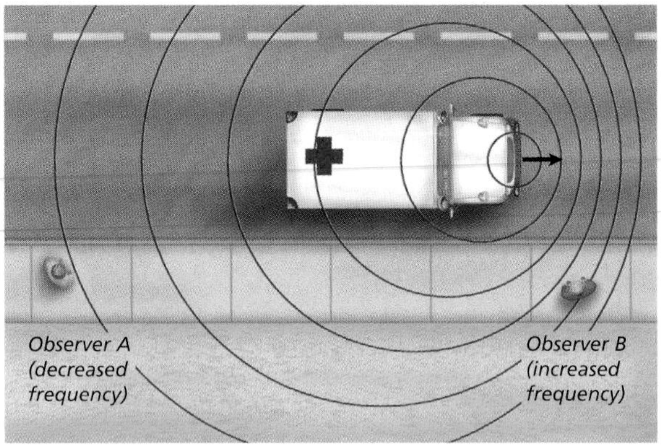

Observer A (decreased frequency)
Observer B (increased frequency)

Figure 18 Observer A hears a lower-pitch sound than observer B because the wave fronts are farther apart for observer A. ***Inferring** What can you infer about the pitch the ambulance driver hears?*

Facts and Figures

Diffraction of Sound All sound waves are diffracted when they pass by an obstacle or through an opening. The human voice has a range of approximately 70 to 400 Hz. This corresponds to wavelengths between 4.9 m and 0.86 m. Recall that the amount of diffraction depends on the wavelength of the wave compared to the size of the opening or obstacle. Because sound waves have wavelengths approximately the same size as the width of a doorway or a window opening, the sound of a person's voice easily diffracts from room to room.

Hearing and the Ear

Can you feel sound waves with your hand at this very moment? Probably you can't. But suppose you hold a balloon. Then your hand can feel sounds because the balloon membrane vibrates. Just like the balloon, your ear has a membrane that vibrates when sound waves strike it.

Your ear is a complex system that consists of three main regions—the outer ear, the middle ear, and the inner ear—as shown in Figure 19. **The outer ear gathers and focuses sound into the middle ear, which receives and amplifies the vibrations. The inner ear uses nerve endings to sense vibrations and send signals to the brain.**

Go Online SCIENCE NEWS®

For: Articles on sound
Visit: PHSchool.com
Web Code: cce-2174

Figure 19

The Anatomy of the Ear

Outer Ear The part of the ear you can see funnels sound waves down the ear canal, a tunnel about 2.5 cm long. There, sound waves strike the eardrum, a tightly stretched membrane between the outer and middle ear. The eardrum vibrates at the same frequency as the sound waves striking it.

Middle Ear The middle ear contains three tiny bones—the hammer, the anvil, and the stirrup. When the eardrum vibrates, the hammer vibrates at the same frequency. The hammer strikes the anvil, which in turn moves the stirrup back and forth. The three bones act as a lever system to amplify the motion of the eardrum.

Inner Ear Vibrations from the stirrup travel into the cochlea, a spiral-shaped canal filled with fluid. The inside of the cochlea is lined with thousands of nerve cells with tiny hair-like projections. As the fluid in the cochlea vibrates, the projections sway back and forth and send electrical impulses to the brain.

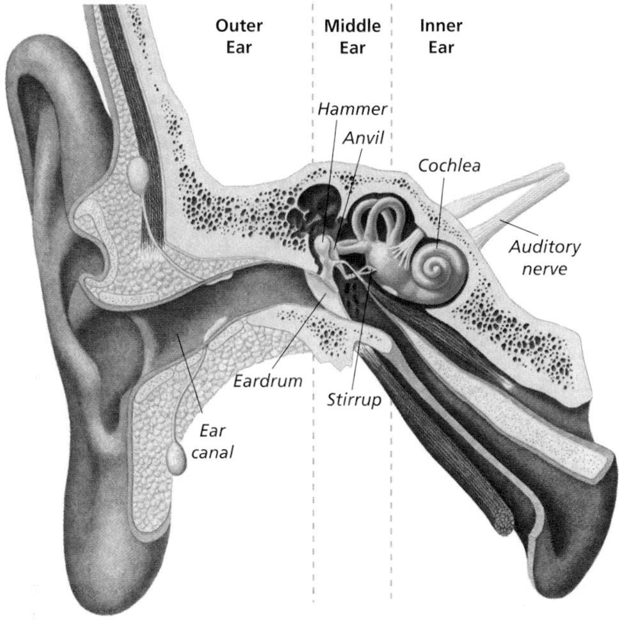
Outer Ear
Middle Ear
Inner Ear
Hammer
Anvil
Cochlea
Auditory nerve
Eardrum
Stirrup
Ear canal

Hearing and the Ear

Use Visuals L1

Figure 19 This figure contains a lot of information and is worth some extra time. Point out important features of the diagram for students. The outer ear is made up of the visible, sound-collecting part (the pinna) and the ear canal. The pinna gathers and reflects sound waves down the canal. Ask, **How do sounds get to the eardrum?** *(Through the air in the ear canal)* **What is the stirrup?** *(One of the small bones in the middle ear)* **What does the stirrup do?** *(It transfers vibrations into the cochlea.)* **What is the function of the auditory nerves?** *(To transmit nerve impulses to the brain)*
Visual, Logical

Go Online SCIENCE NEWS®

Science News provides students with current information on sound.

Answer to . . .

Figure 18 *The frequency for the driver is unchanged because the driver has no motion relative to the siren.*

How Sound Is Reproduced

Address Misconceptions L2

Students sometimes think that sound waves can push a dust particle away from a speaker or blow out a candle flame placed in front of a speaker. However, sound waves would actually make the dust particle or candle flame vibrate back and forth in a direction parallel to the direction in which the wave is moving.
Verbal

DK SCIENCE and History

Sound Recording L2

Edison, who was slightly deaf, discovered he could feel the vibrations in a telephone speaker with his finger. If a loudspeaker is available, have students gently touch the surface of the speaker grille as music is being played. They should easily be able to detect the vibrations. Ask, **What is causing the vibrations?** *(Sound waves striking the grille)* Students can also hold a book in front of their face, sing a note or speak loudly, and feel the vibrations in the book. Ask, **What is causing the vibrations of the book?** *(Sound waves in air striking the book)* Edison also noticed that a paper telegraph tape, when pulled through a telegraph machine at high speed, made sounds that resembled a human voice. He put these two ideas together and designed the first phonograph.

Over the years since, inventors have constructed many other types of recording devices. Today, there are several different digital audio compression technologies available in addition to MP3. Only time will tell if one becomes the preferred standard.
Logical, Kinesthetic

Writing in Science

Students should compare and contrast the new technology with a previous technology. To be persuasive, their writing must use facts to support benefits claimed for the new technology.
Logical

How Sound Is Reproduced

Sound has been reproduced in many ways, from old-fashioned records to modern digital technologies. But no matter how sound is recorded or stored, in the end it must be converted back into sound waves by loudspeakers. **Sound is recorded by converting sound waves into electronic signals that can be processed and stored. Sound is reproduced by converting electronic signals back into sound waves.**

A modern speaker produces sound waves in much the same way that a drum does. A drum skin vibrates up and down like a trampoline. As the drum vibrates, it sends a series of compressions and rarefactions through the air across the room. They carry energy to your ears in the form of sound waves.

DK SCIENCE and History

Sound Recording

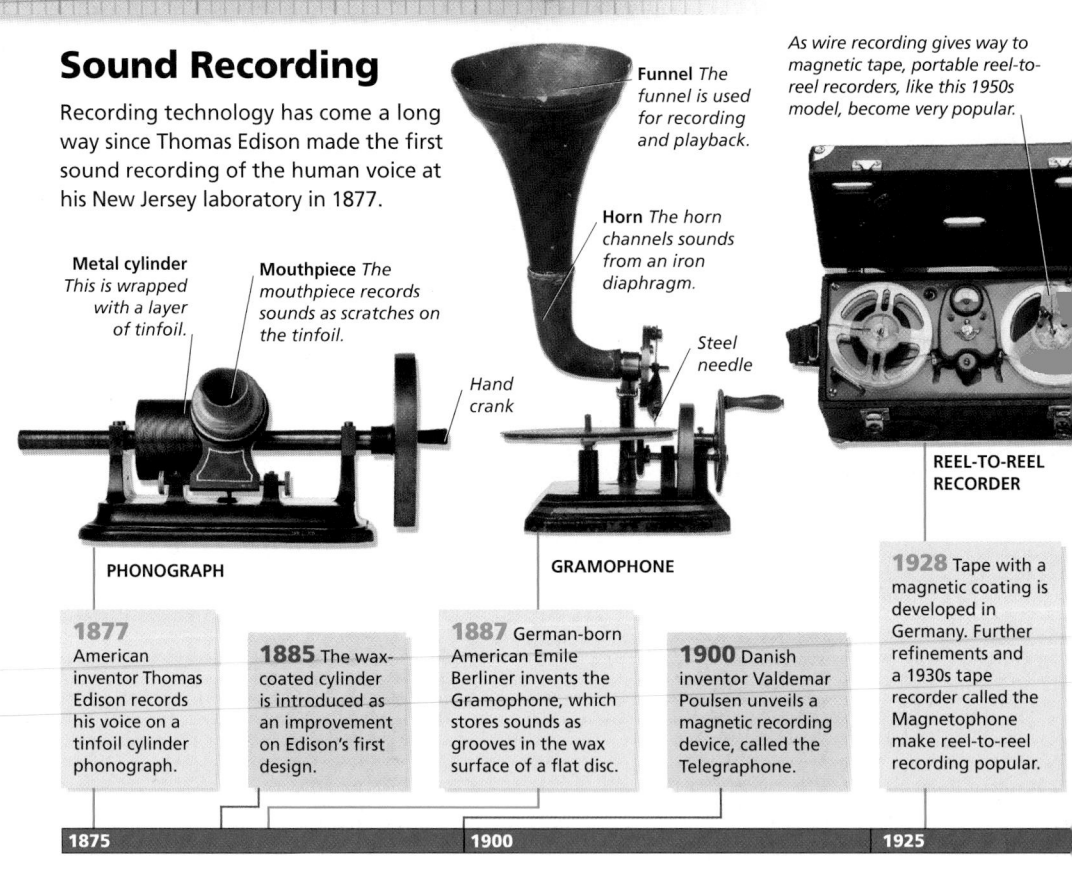

Recording technology has come a long way since Thomas Edison made the first sound recording of the human voice at his New Jersey laboratory in 1877.

Metal cylinder *This is wrapped with a layer of tinfoil.*
Mouthpiece *The mouthpiece records sounds as scratches on the tinfoil.*
Hand crank

PHONOGRAPH

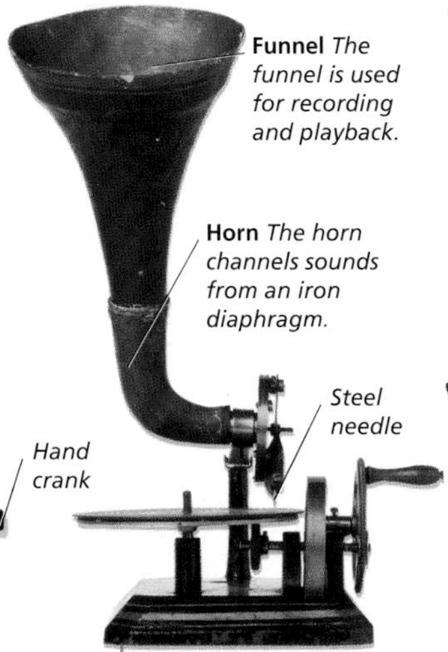
Funnel *The funnel is used for recording and playback.*
Horn *The horn channels sounds from an iron diaphragm.*
Steel needle

GRAMOPHONE

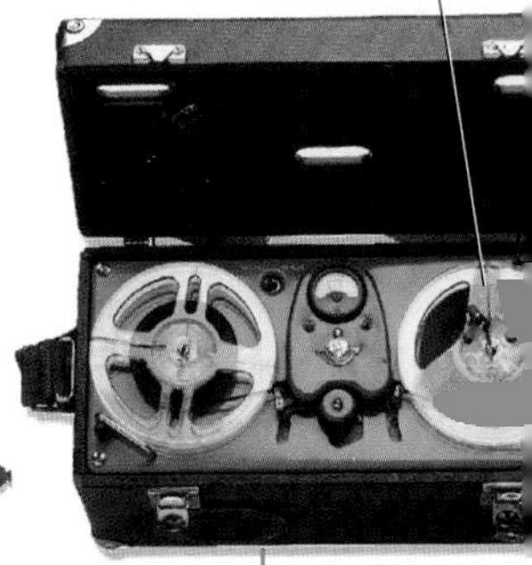
As wire recording gives way to magnetic tape, portable reel-to-reel recorders, like this 1950s model, become very popular.

REEL-TO-REEL RECORDER

1877 American inventor Thomas Edison records his voice on a tinfoil cylinder phonograph.

1885 The wax-coated cylinder is introduced as an improvement on Edison's first design.

1887 German-born American Emile Berliner invents the Gramophone, which stores sounds as grooves in the wax surface of a flat disc.

1900 Danish inventor Valdemar Poulsen unveils a magnetic recording device, called the Telegraphone.

1928 Tape with a magnetic coating is developed in Germany. Further refinements and a 1930s tape recorder called the Magnetophone make reel-to-reel recording popular.

1875 — 1900 — 1925

Facts and Figures

Sound Reproduction The first audio recordings were made by purely mechanical action. The singer or instrumentalist sang or played into a funnel-shaped tube that led directly to a cork diaphragm. The diaphragm was attached through a series of levers to a needle that would carve a groove into a wax cylinder or disk. Since there was no way to duplicate a recording, the orchestra or performer would be required to play the composition over and over for hours as up to 10 individual recordings were made at a time. Ensembles of musicians made recordings in a small room. One wall of the room was the opening of the huge recording tube. In an interesting historical twist, several contemporary musicians have started to use this old technology to record their compositions.

In a speaker, an electronic signal causes a magnet to vibrate. The magnet is attached to a membrane. The vibrating membrane sends sound waves through the air. Larger-diameter speakers, like a large bass drum, are better at reproducing lower frequencies of sound. Smaller-diameter speakers, like a small bongo drum, are better for reproducing higher frequencies of sound.

When a singer sings into a microphone, the reverse process happens. Sound waves from the singer's voice vibrate a membrane inside the microphone. The membrane causes a magnet to vibrate, which produces an electronic signal in the microphone wires. The energy of sound waves has been converted into an electronic signal that can be processed and stored.

Writing in Science

Writing to Persuade
Research one type of recording technology. Write a product review as if you lived at the time it was invented. Persuade people that this technology is much better than previously available technologies.

VINYL LONG PLAYING

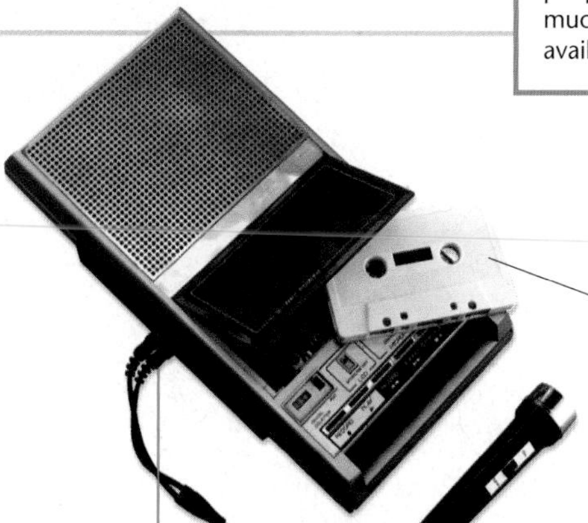

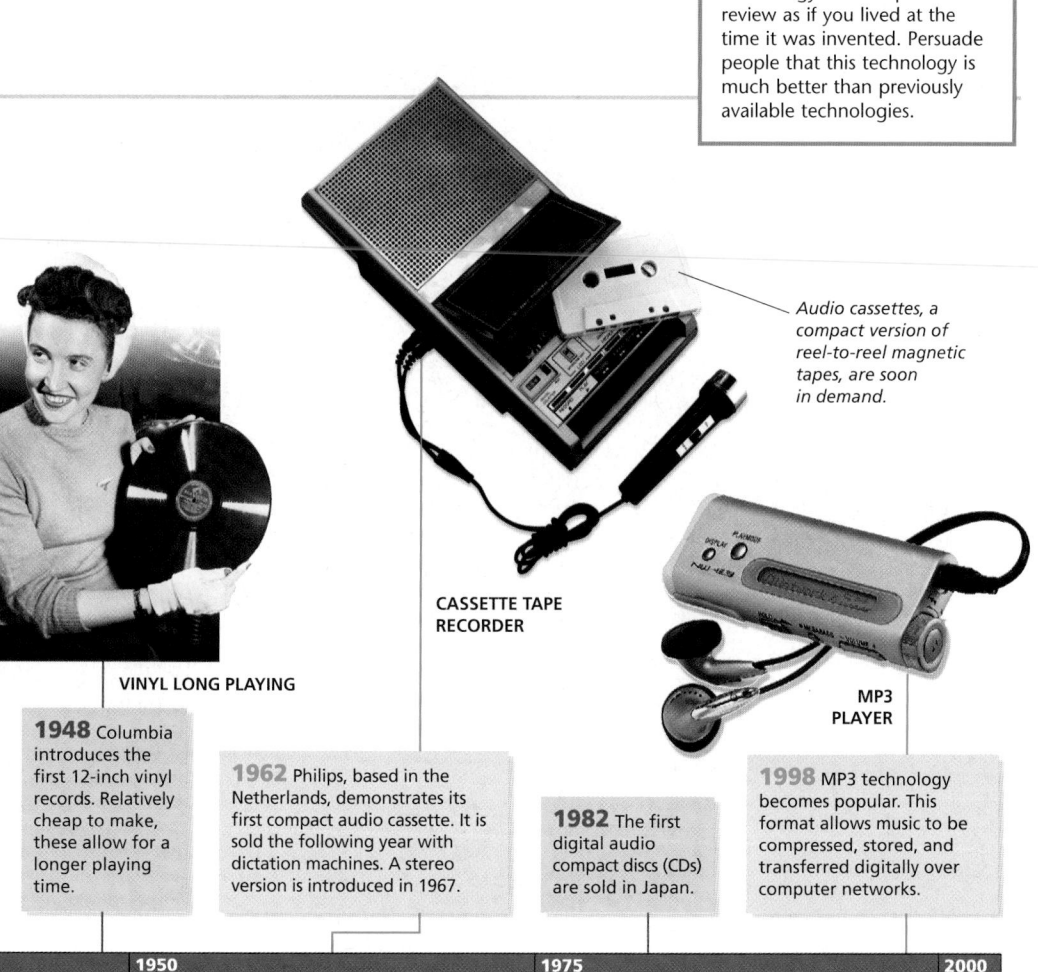

Audio cassettes, a compact version of reel-to-reel magnetic tapes, are soon in demand.

CASSETTE TAPE RECORDER

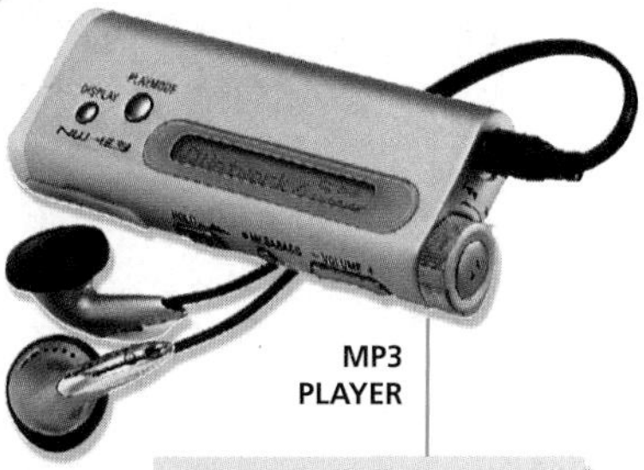

MP3 PLAYER

1948 Columbia introduces the first 12-inch vinyl records. Relatively cheap to make, these allow for a longer playing time.

1962 Philips, based in the Netherlands, demonstrates its first compact audio cassette. It is sold the following year with dictation machines. A stereo version is introduced in 1967.

1982 The first digital audio compact discs (CDs) are sold in Japan.

1998 MP3 technology becomes popular. This format allows music to be compressed, stored, and transferred digitally over computer networks.

1950 | 1975 | 2000

Integrate Social Studies L2

Thomas Edison is generally credited as the inventor of the phonograph, which he publicly demonstrated in 1877. He did not pursue the invention at first. Alexander Graham Bell, his cousin Chester Bell, and C. S. Tainter made improvements to Edison's design to improve the sound quality. They called their device the graphophone. The Bells and Tainter offered to combine their patents and designs with Edison's work, but Edison rejected the offer. Instead, he developed an improved machine similar to the graphophone. Edison's new system used thicker, reusable wax cylinders and a jewel-tipped recording stylus that did not need to be replaced after every recording. Emile Berliner further improved the phonograph by using a flat disk and a system for duplicating records from a steel master. These various phonographs were very popular, and after 1895, hundreds of companies appeared, yet quickly failed. Only a few companies survived into the twentieth century. Have students research later technological developments that affected phonographs and record players. **Logical**

HOW It Works

The Piano L2

Several keyboard instruments predated the piano. The most popular was the harpsichord. When a key is pressed on a harpsichord, a corresponding string is plucked. Consequently, it is difficult to control the loudness of the instrument. In a piano, however, the string is struck by a felt-covered hammer. Pressing the key with more force causes the string to be struck harder, producing a louder sound. Because of this, these instruments were called fortepianos (literally "loud-soft") for their ability to change dynamics. As the instrument evolved, the name was shortened to piano.

When a piano key is pressed, two things happen. The hammer strikes the string and rebounds, while the damper pad moves away. Therefore, the string will continue to vibrate as long as the key is held down.

The use of cast-iron frames allows heavier strings to be strung with greater tension. Greater tension in the string produces a better, cleaner sound and allows the string to vibrate much longer.

Interpreting Photos When a piano key is struck, a series of levers causes the hammer to strike a string. The vibration of the string is amplified by the soundboard.
Visual, Musical

For Enrichment L3

The piano and its family of instruments probably originated with the hammered dulcimer, which is played by striking the strings with small "hammers." Interested students can research the origin of plucked and struck stringed instruments such as dulcimers and harps.
Verbal, Portfolio

HOW It Works

The Piano

The piano is a highly versatile musical instrument. Usually there are 88 separate keys, which produce a range of notes and volume. The sounds are made by wire strings that vibrate against a soundboard inside the piano.
Interpreting Photos ***What causes the strings in a piano to vibrate?***

Grand piano
Pianos can be upright or, like this grand, horizontal. A grand piano makes a rich and powerful sound.

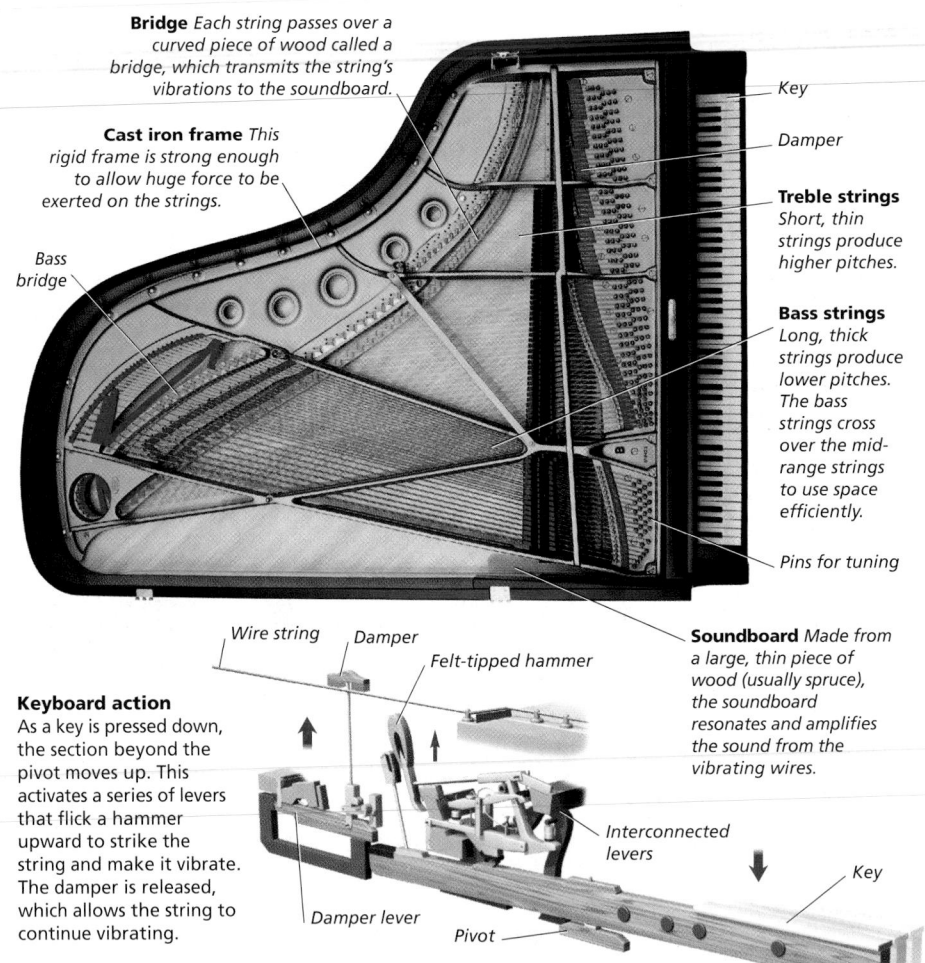

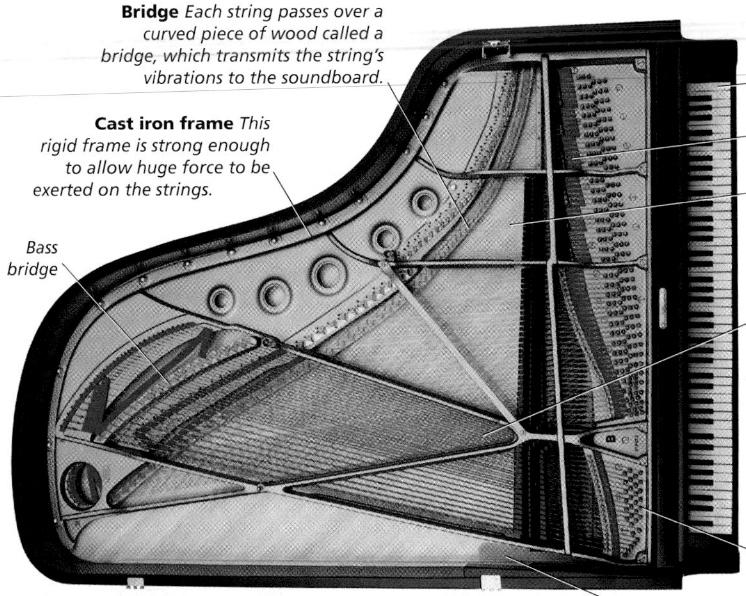
Bridge *Each string passes over a curved piece of wood called a bridge, which transmits the string's vibrations to the soundboard.*
Cast iron frame *This rigid frame is strong enough to allow huge force to be exerted on the strings.*
Bass bridge
Key
Damper
Treble strings *Short, thin strings produce higher pitches.*
Bass strings *Long, thick strings produce lower pitches. The bass strings cross over the mid-range strings to use space efficiently.*
Pins for tuning
Soundboard *Made from a large, thin piece of wood (usually spruce), the soundboard resonates and amplifies the sound from the vibrating wires.*

Keyboard action
As a key is pressed down, the section beyond the pivot moves up. This activates a series of levers that flick a hammer upward to strike the string and make it vibrate. The damper is released, which allows the string to continue vibrating.

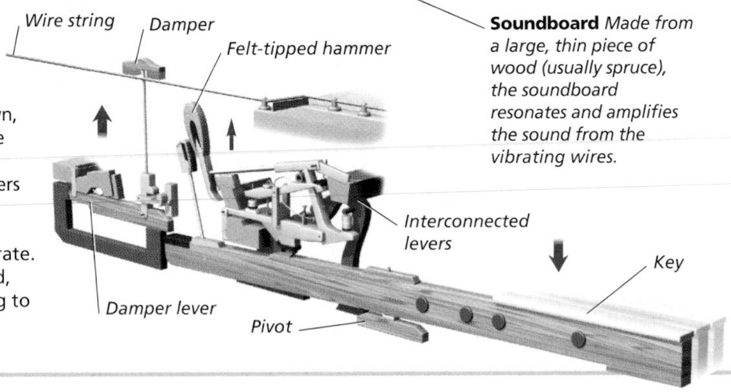
Wire string
Damper
Felt-tipped hammer
Interconnected levers
Key
Damper lever
Pivot

Music

Musical instruments can produce a wide variety of sounds. In a wind instrument, such as a flute or trumpet, holes are closed using fingers or valves. This changes the length of the column of air in which a standing sound wave is produced. For some stringed instruments, such as a violin, musicians change the length of the strings by pressing down with their fingers. For other instruments, such as a piano, they use a fixed set of strings of different lengths. **Most musical instruments vary pitch by changing the frequency of standing waves.**

Musical instruments often use resonance to amplify sound. **Resonance** (REZ uh nuhns) is the response of a standing wave to another wave of the same frequency. Think of a child being pushed on a swing. If the pushes are timed at the right frequency, the child can swing higher and higher. In the same way, one wave can "push" another wave to a higher amplitude. Resonance can produce a dramatic increase in amplitude. A piano, for example, amplifies sound with a soundboard. The soundboard resonates in response to the vibrating strings.

Once sound waves leave an instrument, they can take several routes to a listener. In a large concert hall, interference with reflected sound waves can be a problem. Theaters such as the one in Figure 20 are designed with reflecting panels and sound-absorbing tiles. These are located with great care to prevent "dead spots" where the volume is reduced by destructive interference of reflected sound waves.

Figure 20 The Central Michigan University Music Building, like many concert halls, was designed by acoustic engineers. Sound-absorbing tiles (on the sides and rear) reduce unwanted reflections. The curved reflecting panels above the stage help gather and direct sound waves toward the audience.

Section 17.4 Assessment

Reviewing Concepts

1. List five properties used to explain the behavior of sound waves.
2. Name two uses for ultrasound.
3. What is the Doppler effect?
4. What are the ear's three main regions? Describe the function of each region.
5. How is sound recorded?
6. How does a musical instrument produce notes at different pitches?

Critical Thinking

7. **Applying Concepts** If workers in a distant stone quarry are blasting, why can you feel the explosion in your feet before you hear it?
8. **Comparing and Contrasting** How does the intensity of a 40-decibel sound compare to the intensity of a 20-decibel sound?
9. **Applying Concepts** How could a bat use reflections of sound waves to determine distance to an insect?

Connecting Concepts

Frames of Reference Review what you learned about combining velocities in Section 11.2. Then explain why the Doppler effect depends on the velocity of the sound source in the observer's frame of reference.

Section 17.4 Assessment

1. Speed, intensity, loudness, frequency, pitch
2. Medical imaging, sonar
3. The Doppler effect occurs when an observer hears a higher frequency as a sound source approaches. When a sound source moves away, the observer hears a lower frequency.
4. The outer ear gathers and focuses sound into the middle ear, which amplifies the vibrations. The inner ear has nerve endings that sense vibrations and transmit signals to the brain.
5. Sound is recorded by converting sound waves into other forms of energy.
6. By changing the frequency of standing waves
7. The speed of sound in solids is generally faster than the speed of sound in air, so the sound wave reaches your feet first through the ground.
8. The intensity of a 40-dB sound is 100 times greater than the intensity of a 20-dB sound.
9. A bat can determine distance based on the amount of time it takes for ultrasound waves the bat emits to reach the insect and bounce back to the bat's ears.

Music

Integrate Language Arts **L2**

The folk musician Greg Brown has set several of William Blake's poems to music. Many other performers have found musical inspiration in poetry. Choose a recording, such as Greg Brown's setting of Blake's poem "The Chimney Sweeper," and allow students to listen. Ask, **How did the performer use rhythm or pitch to enhance the meaning of the poem?** *(Possible answers: A simple melody can heighten the drama of powerful images, such as those in "The Chimney Sweeper." The rhythm of the music can enhance the sense of rhythm in the poem.)*
Verbal, Musical

3 ASSESS

Evaluate Understanding **L2**

Have students outline and summarize the section. Then, divide the class into groups and have students exchange papers and edit each other's outlines. Exchange the papers again, and have students edit the edits. Then, return the papers to the original owners to rewrite.

Reteach **L1**

Write the vocabulary words for this section. Have students review the section and create definitions for the vocabulary words in their own words.

Connecting Concepts

Choosing a particular frame of reference does not change the sound heard by the observer. In physics, one often chooses a frame of reference that makes it easier to understand or solve a problem. With the Doppler effect, one simple choice is to use the observer's frame of reference. The shift in frequency can then be determined from the speed of the sound source in this frame of reference.

Interactive Textbook If your class subscribes to the Interactive Textbook, use it to review key concepts in Section 17.4.

CONCEPTS
in Action

Now Hear This **L2**

Background

There are many ways to reduce noise. Barriers are the most common. The idea of creating "anti-noise" was first developed in the 1970s. Because noise is chaotic and unpredictable, the only way to cancel a noise is by continuously monitoring the noise and generating an appropriate anti-noise signal. Only recently has technology become available that allows real-time, active noise cancellation. An active noise-cancellation system uses a high-speed digital signal processor to sample the noise thousands of times a second. It then is able to create the anti-noise wave. Applications for noise-cancellation technology include active mufflers that reduce exhaust noise; quiet zones in automobiles, airplanes, trucks, and locomotives; and active headsets that provide better hearing protection while still allowing communication.

Build Science Skills **L2**

Using Models ACTIVITY

Purpose Students observe destructive interference of sound waves.

Materials tuning fork hammer, 2 tuning forks with the same frequency (about 400 Hz), stethoscope

Safety Make sure that students handle the tuning forks carefully.

Procedure One student carefully strikes the tuning forks with the tuning fork hammer and holds the tuning forks about 10 cm apart. A second student listens with the stethoscope's listening end placed about 20 cm from the tuning forks. The listener moves the stethoscope's end to find a node where the volume is greatly reduced. This may require several trials. Ask, **What is causing the sound to become inaudible in certain places?** *(Destructive interference between the two sound waves)* Ask, **How is this different from noise-cancellation technology?** *(In noise-cancellation technology, the signal is much more complicated.)*

Expected Outcome Students will find regions where the sound is not audible. **Musical, Logical**

CONCEPTS in Action

Now Hear This

Imagine eliminating all unwanted noise and only hearing the sounds you need to hear. That is the goal of noise-cancellation technology.

Noise-cancelling headset *This headset removes noise but allows communication with co-workers.*

In the modern world, there is plenty of unwanted noise from jet aircraft engines, construction equipment, and factory machinery. Traditionally, the way to deal with noise has been to put a barrier, such as an ear plug or ear muffler, between the source of the noise and your ears. This type of ear protection has the drawback, however, that it blocks out most sound, not just unwanted noise. That makes communication with co-workers difficult. Now, new technology is available that selectively removes unwanted noise, but transmits the sounds you need to hear.

Sound Control
Airport workers, jet pilots, rock musicians, and some factory workers all have a need for noise reduction.

Noise-cancellation technology

In noise-cancellation technology, a headset is fitted with a tiny microphone. This microphone is linked to an electronic device that can analyze the amplitude and frequency of sounds. When an undesirable noise is picked up by the microphone, a tiny speaker generates an anti-noise wave. The two waves cancel each other in destructive interference.

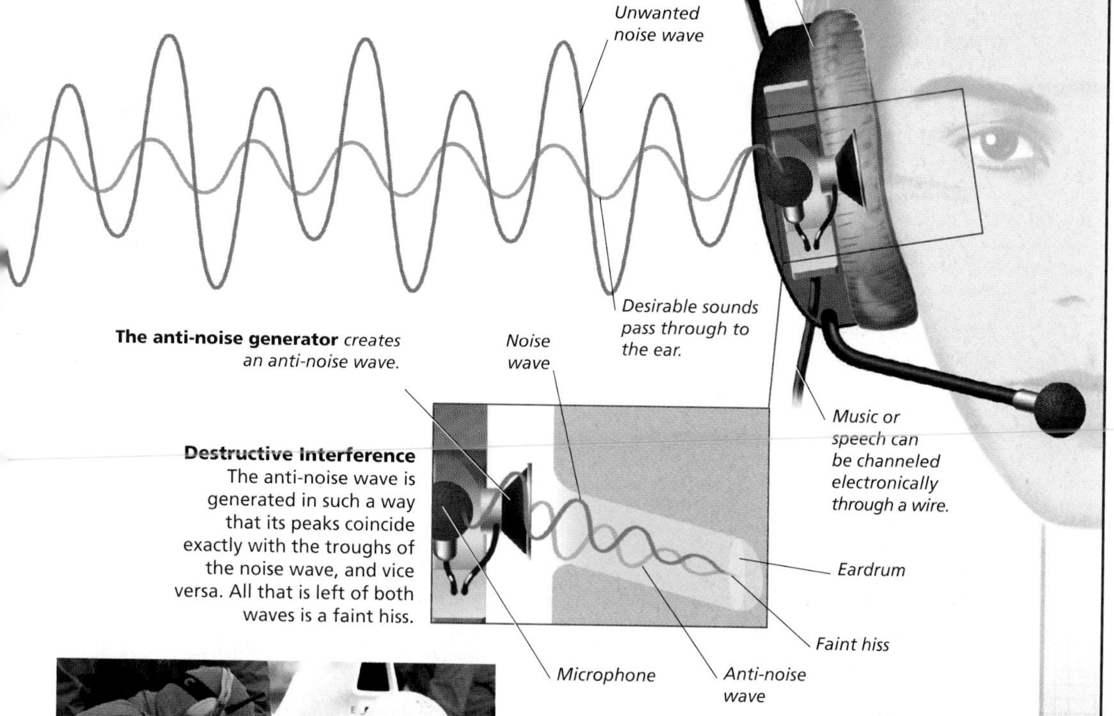

Wall of ear cup cuts out some noise.
Unwanted noise wave
Desirable sounds pass through to the ear.
The anti-noise generator *creates an anti-noise wave.*
Noise wave
Music or speech can be channeled electronically through a wire.
Destructive interference
The anti-noise wave is generated in such a way that its peaks coincide exactly with the troughs of the noise wave, and vice versa. All that is left of both waves is a faint hiss.
Eardrum
Faint hiss
Microphone
Anti-noise wave

Car racing
Noise-cancellation technology has numerous applications. It is used in the army, on building sites, and in noisy sports like car racing.

Going Further

- Research in the library or on the Internet products that use noise cancellation, such as car stereos that reduce road noise, mobile phones, stereo headphones, or headsets for customer service operators. Write a paragraph explaining how one of these products works.
- Take a Discovery Channel Video Field Trip by watching "Noise!"

Discovery Channel School **Video Field Trip**

Going Further

Students should write about how a particular product uses noise-cancellation technology. Brief explanations for two devices follow.

- **Car stereos** A microphone in the car picks up sound in the car. The noise-cancellation system subtracts music from the stereo and uses the remaining sound to create an anti-noise wave. The stereo system speakers then combine the anti-noise waves with the music.
- **Customer service headsets** Often, many operators answer phones in a large, noisy room. To avoid confusing cross-conversations, special headsets help both the operator and the customer. The headsets use noise-cancellation technology that separates speech, which varies rapidly, from background noise, which has slower variations. The headsets have to be light because operators wear them for hours at a time.

Logical

Discovery Channel School

Video Field Trip

Noise!

After students have viewed the Video Field Trip, ask them the following questions: **How can loud sounds be harmful?** *(Over time, loud sounds can damage the ability to hear.)* **What units are used to compare the intensity levels of sound?** *(Decibels)* **How are sounds transferred through air?** *(Student answers may include waves, mechanical waves, or vibrations of the air.)*

Exploration Lab

Investigating Sound Waves L2

Objective
After completing this activity, students will be able to
- define sound as a mechanical vibration whose frequency depends on the length of the vibrating object.
- state that pitch depends on the frequency and that loudness depends on the amplitude of the sound wave.

Address Misconceptions

This lab can help dispel the misconception that high-pitched sounds are louder than low-pitched sounds.

Skills Focus **Observing, Inferring, Drawing Conclusions**

Prep Time 15–30 minutes

Advance Preparation To save class time, cut the wax paper into 10-cm square sheets and cut 1-cm holes in the cardboard tubes. Use a thumbtack as a template for the 1-cm holes and use a sharp scalpel, razor blade, or electric drill to cut the holes. If small plastic mirrors are unavailable, you can substitute sequins or small pieces of aluminum foil.

Class Time 40 minutes

Teaching Tips
- Remind students that they must hum, and not sing, into the kazoo.
- Have half the class start Part A while the other half starts Part B. This will require fewer flashlights and meter sticks. It will also allow the students to hear the differences in pitch because fewer students are humming at the same time.

Questioning Strategies
Ask students: **What is the source of energy that caused the meter stick to vibrate?** *(The mechanical energy or muscle power used to pluck the meter stick)* **What happened to the sound waves when you changed the length of the vibrating object?** *(The pitch changed.)* **How does the pitch affect the frequency of the reflected light's vibration?** *(The higher the pitch, the greater the frequency is.)* **How does loudness affect the amplitude of the reflected light's vibration?** *(The greater the loudness, the greater the amplitude is.)*

Exploration Lab

Investigating Sound Waves

Sound is produced when a vibrating source causes a medium to vibrate. In this lab, you will investigate how the vibrating source affects characteristics of the sound produced.

Problem What determines the frequency and amplitude of the sound produced by a vibrating object?

Materials
- meter stick
- two cardboard tubes
- scissors or scalpel
- two rubber bands
- wax paper
- balloon
- small mirror
- transparent tape
- flashlight

Skills Observing, Inferring, Drawing Conclusions, Controlling Variables

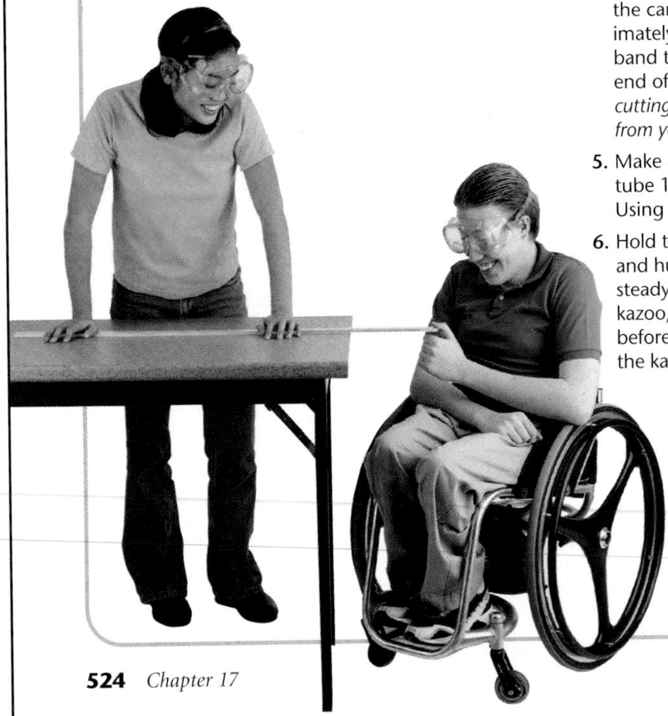

Procedure

Part A: Investigating How Length Affects Pitch

1. Hold one end of a meter stick down firmly on a table so that 20 centimeters of the meter stick extends past the edge of the table. Pluck the end of the meter stick that extends past the table to produce a vibration and a sound as shown. Observe the vibration and sound of the meter stick.
2. Repeat Step 1, but this time allow 40 centimeters of the meter stick to extend past the edge of the table. Observe and record how the length of the vibrating part of the meter stick affects the pitch.
3. Repeat Step 1, but this time allow 60 centimeters of the meter stick to extend past the edge of the table. Record your observations.
4. Investigate the relationship between length and frequency for a vibrating column of air, as you did with the vibrating meter stick. Make a kazoo by cutting a hole in the middle of one of the cardboard tubes. Make the hole approximately 1 centimeter in diameter. Use a rubber band to fasten the piece of wax paper over one end of the tube. **CAUTION** *Be careful when cutting with sharp instruments; always cut away from yourself and away from nearby people.*
5. Make a second kazoo by cutting the second tube 10 centimeters shorter than the first tube. Using the short tube, repeat Step 4.
6. Hold the shorter kazoo in front of your mouth and hum into the open end, keeping your pitch steady. Repeat this action with the longer kazoo, making sure to hum exactly as you did before. Observe and record how the length of the kazoo affects the pitch of the sound.

Part B: Investigating How Frequency Affects Pitch and How Amplitude Affects Loudness

7. Cut the neck off of the balloon. Replace the wax paper on the longer kazoo with the cut-open balloon. Wrap the rubber band several times around the end of the cardboard tube. The rubber band should hold the balloon tightly stretched over the end of the tube. Use tape to attach the small mirror onto the balloon on the end of the tube.
8. Have a classmate shine a flashlight on the mirror as shown while you hum into the kazoo. Your classmate should position the flashlight so that a spot of light is reflected on the wall. It may be necessary to darken the room. Observe how the spot of light moves when you hum into the kazoo. Make a note of your position and the position and angle of the kazoo and the flashlight.
9. Without changing how loudly you hum, use your voice to raise the pitch of your humming. Observe and record how the movement of the spot of light differs from your observations in Step 8. Make sure you do not change your distance from the wall or the angle at which the light from the flashlight strikes the mirror attached to the kazoo.
10. Repeat Step 9, but this time hum at a lower pitch than you did in Step 8.
11. Repeat Steps 9 and 10, but this time vary the loudness of your humming while keeping the pitch constant.

Analyze and Conclude

1. **Observing** What happened to the frequency of the meter stick's vibration when you made the overhanging part longer?
2. **Inferring** How did the frequency of the meter stick's vibration affect the pitch of its sound?
3. **Inferring** How did the kazoo's length affect its pitch?
4. **Analyzing Data** When you changed the pitch of your humming, how did it affect the frequency of vibration of the mirror?
5. **Analyzing Data** How is the amplitude of the kazoo's vibration related to its loudness?
6. **Controlling Variables** Explain why it was important to keep loudness constant when you changed the pitch of your humming in Step 9.

Go Further Design an experiment to investigate what variables affect the pitch and loudness of vibrating strings. Use an instrument such as a guitar or violin. After your teacher approves your plan, carry out your experiment.

Expected Outcome The pitch becomes lower as the length of the vibrating part of the meter stick and the air column inside the kazoo are lengthened. An increase in the sound's loudness increases the amplitude of the vibration of the reflected light. An increase of the sound's pitch increases the frequency of the vibration of the reflected light.

Go Further

The frequency and amplitude of a vibrating string are easily varied by adjusting the length of the vibrating portion of the string, or the force with which it is plucked, respectively. **Kinesthetic, Logical**

Analyze and Conclude

1. The frequency was reduced.
2. The pitch became lower as the frequency was reduced.
3. The longer kazoo had the lower pitch.
4. Humming at a higher pitch increased the frequency of the mirror's vibration.
5. Increasing the loudness increased the amplitude of the kazoo's vibration.
6. Keeping the loudness constant ensured that any change in the frequency of the mirror's vibration was due to the change in pitch. **Logical**

Study Guide

Study Tip

Organize New Information
This chapter contains many new words and much new information. Tell students to create outlines, charts, flashcards, time lines, and concept maps to help them visualize relationships. Have them create a vocabulary list with definitions for all of the vocabulary terms in their own words.

Thinking Visually

a. Reflection
b. Refraction
c. Diffraction

Assessment

Interactive Textbook If your class subscribes to the Interactive Textbook, your students can go online to access an interactive version of the Student Edition and a self-test.

Reviewing Content

1. b 2. a 3. c
4. b 5. d 6. c
7. b 8. a 9. c
10. b

Understanding Concepts

11. A wave in a spring and a P wave are longitudinal waves. Both waves have compressions and rarefactions.
12. A surface wave combines the motion of a transverse wave, (perpendicular to the direction of travel) and the motion of a longitudinal wave (back-and-forth parallel to the direction of travel).
13. See Wave B on the diagram below.
14. See Wave C on the diagram below.

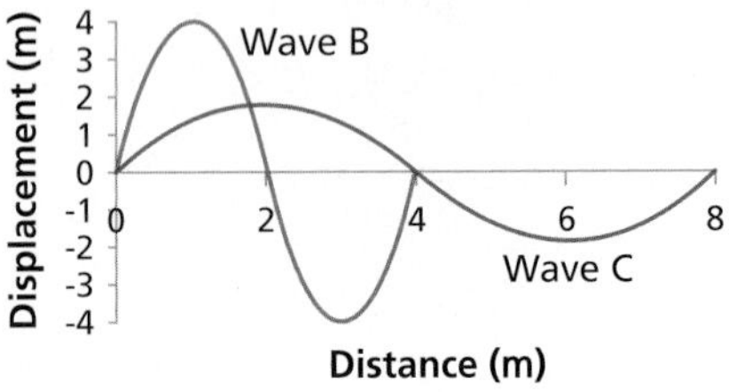

Wave B
Wave C
Displacement (m)
4
3
2
1
0
-1
-2
-3
-4
0
2
4
6
8
Distance (m)

CHAPTER 17

Study Guide

17.1 Mechanical Waves

Key Concepts

- A wave is created when a source of energy causes a vibration to move through a medium.
- The three main types of mechanical waves are transverse, longitudinal, and surface waves.

Vocabulary

mechanical wave, *p. 500;* medium, *p. 500;* crest, *p. 501;* trough, *p. 501;* transverse wave, *p. 501;* compression, *p. 502;* rarefaction, *p. 502;* longitudinal wave, *p. 502;* surface wave, *p. 503*

17.2 Properties of Mechanical Waves

Key Concepts

- A wave's frequency equals the frequency of the vibrating source producing the wave.
- For waves traveling at a constant speed, wavelength is inversely proportional to frequency.
- As energy of a wave increases, amplitude increases.

Vocabulary

periodic motion, *p. 504;* period, *p. 504;* frequency, *p. 504;* hertz, *p. 504;* wavelength, *p. 505;* amplitude, *p. 507*

17.3 Behavior of Waves

Key Concepts

- Reflection does not change the speed or frequency of a wave, but the wave can be flipped upside down.
- Refraction occurs because one side of a wave moves more slowly than the other side.
- A wave diffracts more if its wavelength is large compared to the size of an opening or obstacle.
- Interference can be constructive or destructive.
- A standing wave forms only if the length of a vibrating cord is a multiple of one half wavelength.

Vocabulary

reflection, *p. 508;* refraction, *p. 509;* diffraction, *p. 510;* interference, *p. 510;* constructive interference, *p. 511;* destructive interference, *p. 511;* standing wave, *p. 512;* node, *p. 512;* antinode, *p. 512*

17.4 Sound and Hearing

Key Concepts

- Many behaviors of sound can be explained using a few properties—speed, intensity and loudness, and frequency and pitch.
- Ultrasound is used in a variety of applications, including sonar and ultrasound imaging.
- As a source of sound approaches, an observer hears a higher frequency. When the sound source moves away, the observer hears a lower frequency.
- The outer ear gathers and focuses sound into the middle ear, which receives and amplifies the vibrations. The inner ear uses nerve endings to sense vibrations and send signals to the brain.
- Sound is recorded by converting sound waves into electronic signals that can be processed and stored. Sound is reproduced by converting electronic signals back into sound waves.
- Most instruments vary pitch by changing the frequency of standing waves.

Vocabulary

sound waves, *p. 514;* intensity, *p. 515;* decibel, *p. 515;* loudness, *p. 515;* pitch, *p. 515;* sonar, *p. 516;* Doppler effect, *p. 516;* resonance, *p. 521*

Thinking Visually

Web Diagram Copy the web diagram below onto a sheet of paper. Use information from the chapter to complete the diagram.

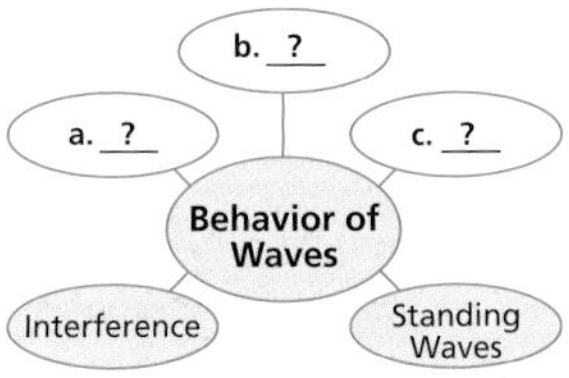

b. ?
a. ?
c. ?
Behavior of Waves
Interference
Standing Waves

Chapter Resources

Print

- ***Chapter and Unit Tests,*** Chapter 17 Test A and Test B
- ***Test Prep Resources,*** Chapter 17

Technology

- ***Computer Test Bank,*** Chapter Test 17
- ***Interactive Textbook,*** Chapter 17
- **Go Online,** PHSchool.com, Chapter 17

CHAPTER 17

Assessment

Interactive textbook with assessment at PHSchool.com iText

Reviewing Content

Choose the letter that best answers the question or completes the statement.

1. Which of the following is NOT true about mechanical waves?
   - a. They carry energy.
   - b. They transfer matter.
   - c. They can be longitudinal.
   - d. They require a medium.
2. In a transverse wave, the medium vibrates
   - a. at right angles to the wave direction.
   - b. in the same direction as the wave.
   - c. in a direction opposite that of the wave.
   - d. at a 45° angle to the wave direction.
3. The height of a wave crest is called
   - a. wavelength. b. frequency.
   - c. amplitude. d. energy.
4. For waves moving at a constant speed, if wavelength is doubled, then frequency is
   - a. doubled. b. halved.
   - c. unchanged. d. quadrupled.
5. When a wave is reflected, its speed
   - a. increases. b. increases or decreases.
   - c. decreases. d. is unchanged.
6. When a wave bends around an obstacle, it is called
   - a. reflection. b. refraction.
   - c. diffraction. d. interference.
7. When two waves interfere, the displacement where two troughs meet is
   - a. positive. b. negative.
   - c. zero. d. a crest.
8. A large speaker is better than a small speaker for producing sounds with
   - a. low frequency. b. high frequency.
   - c. low intensity. d. high intensity.
9. The highest-frequency sound human ears can usually hear is about
   - a. 20 Hz. b. 10,000 Hz.
   - c. 20,000 Hz. d. 30,000 Hz.
10. Sonar can make use of
    - a. the Doppler effect. b. ultrasound.
    - c. infrasound. d. resonance.

Understanding Concepts

11. Name two kinds of longitudinal waves and explain how you know they are longitudinal.
12. How are some surface waves similar to both transverse and longitudinal waves?

Copy the diagram below on a separate piece of paper and use it to answer Questions 13–15.

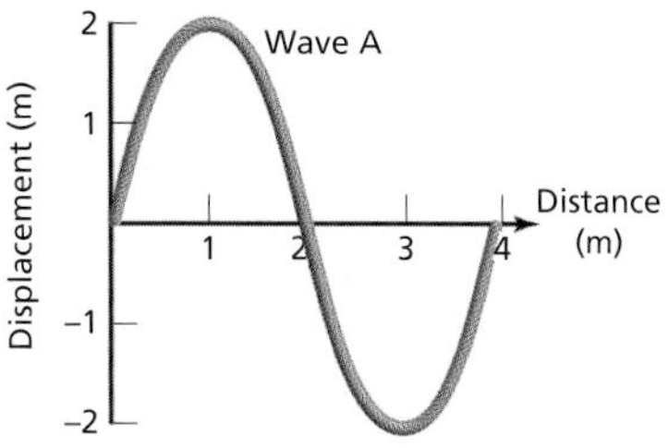

Wave A
Displacement (m)
2
1
−1
−2
Distance (m)
1
2
3
4

13. On your diagram, draw wave B with the same wavelength as wave A, but twice the amplitude.
14. On your diagram, draw wave C with the same amplitude as wave A, but twice the wavelength.
15. How does the frequency of wave C compare with the frequency of wave A, assuming they travel at the same speed?
16. What causes refraction of a wave as it enters a new medium at an angle?
17. Regardless of the direction of waves far from an island, waves close to the island move toward the shore on all sides. Explain.
18. Why does a node in a standing wave have zero displacement?
19. How is intensity different from loudness?
20. Explain why a fire engine's siren sounds lower in pitch after the fire engine passes you.
21. What is the function of the eardrum?
22. What are the names of the three small bones in the middle ear, and what is their purpose?
23. Why are the materials used in construction of a concert hall important?

Homework Guide

Section	Questions
17.1	1–2, 11–15, 24, 36
17.2	3–4, 16–17, 25, 30–33
17.3	5–8, 18, 26
17.4	9–10, 19–23, 27–29, 34–35

Assessment (continued)

15. The frequency of Wave C is half the frequency of Wave A.
16. A wave refracts because one side of the wave front moves faster than the other side.
17. As waves move into shallower water surrounding the island, they refract or bend toward the land because the shallower water acts as a new medium.
18. At a node, there is complete destructive interference at all times, so the displacement is zero.
19. Intensity is the rate at which a wave's energy flows through a given area. Loudness is a physical response to the intensity of sound.
20. As the siren moves away, each wave front produced by the siren is farther from the previous wave front than if the siren were standing still. The actual frequency does not change but the frequency or pitch heard by the observer is lower.
21. The eardrum is located between the middle ear and outer ear. Sound waves cause it to vibrate and convert the energy of the sound waves into mechanical energy.
22. The bones of the inner ear are the hammer, the anvil, and the stirrup. The vibration of the eardrum causes the hammer to vibrate. It strikes the anvil, which causes the stirrup to move back and forth. Together the three bones amplify the motion of the eardrum.
23. Reflection and interference can affect sound quality. Materials should be used that absorb sound to minimize reflection. The overall design of the interior of the concert hall can minimize the dead spots where destructive interference can occur.

Critical Thinking

24. The energy of a mechanical wave causes the medium to vibrate. As vibrating particles in the medium collide, most of the energy can be passed on to the next particle, but fluid friction will cause some energy to be converted into thermal energy.

25. The speed of a wave in a medium is measured under a particular set of conditions. The speed can change if the conditions change or if the density of the medium changes. Otherwise, the speed in the medium is a constant.

26. To form a standing wave, two waves must pass through each other and interfere in a regular way. This cannot happen if the waves are traveling in the same direction.

27. The mosquito's wings must be vibrating faster than the bee's. The higher-frequency vibration produces a higher-frequency sound.

28. Intensity depends upon the distance from the source. If the kitten is close and the thunder far away, the kitten's purr could have a greater intensity.

29. The intensity of the 25-dB sound is 10 times greater. A sound 100 times louder than a 25-dB sound has an intensity of 45 dB.

Math Skills

30. The wavelength is 0.69 m.

31. The frequency is 3 cycles/2 s = 1.5 Hz.

32. Speed = frequency × wavelength = 1.5 Hz × 0.69 m = 1.0 m/s

33. Period = wavelength/speed = (10.0 m)/(3.9 m/s) = 2.6 s

Concepts in Action

34. The device uses ultrasound frequencies that are above the range of human hearing, but are in a frequency range that animals can hear.

35. As a machine operates at higher speed, the vibrational frequency increases. The pitch of the noise should increase as well.

36. Students should describe the periodic circular motion of the lily pad. If the waves are not breaking waves, then the lily pad should have no net motion toward shore, regardless of whether the roots are attached to the pond floor.

CHAPTER 17

Assessment *(continued)*

Critical Thinking

24. **Making Generalizations** A friend says that all mechanical waves must lose energy as they move through a medium because some energy is lost due to friction. Explain why this is true.

25. **Forming Operational Definitions** Two sound waves with different frequencies travel through a steel rod at the same speed. Explain by giving an operational definition of wave speed.

26. **Relating Cause and Effect** Can two waves traveling in the same direction form a standing wave? Explain why or why not.

27. **Inferring** The buzzing sound of a mosquito flying around your head has a higher pitch than the buzz of a bumblebee. What can you infer about the mosquito's wings compared to the bee's wings?

28. **Relating Cause and Effect** At the same time, you hear a kitten's purr and a clap of thunder. The kitten's purr is louder. Explain how this is possible.

29. **Applying Concepts** How much greater is the intensity of a 25-dB sound than a 15-dB sound? What would be the intensity in dB for a sound that is 100 times louder than the 25-dB sound?

Math Skills

Use the illustration below to answer Questions 30–32.

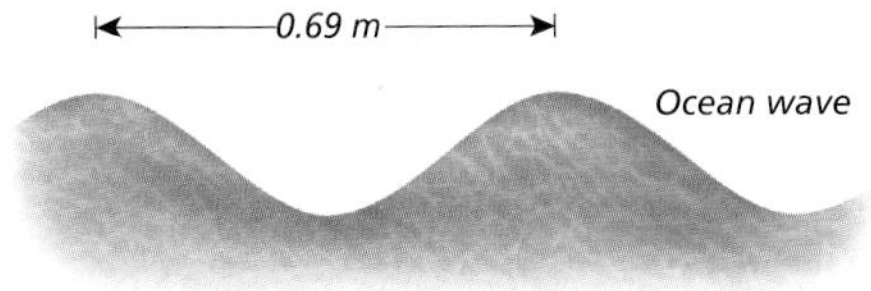

0.69 m
Ocean wave

30. **Interpreting Diagrams** What is the wavelength of the ocean wave shown in the figure?

31. **Evaluating Expressions** Three complete wavelengths pass a fixed point once every 2 seconds. What is the frequency of the wave?

32. **Calculating** What is the speed of the ocean wave in Question 31?

33. **Calculating** A deep-water wave has a wavelength of 10.0 meters. If it travels at 3.9 m/s, what is the wave's period?

Concepts in Action

34. **Applying Concepts** Some gardeners protect their gardens from animals by using sound that animals find irritating. Explain how the gardeners can tolerate the sound, while the animals cannot.

35. **Formulating Hypotheses** Generate a hypothesis about how the frequency of noise made by a machine changes as the machine operates at higher speeds.

36. **Writing in Science** Write a paragraph describing the motion of a lily pad as several waves from a boat pass by. Explain why the motion would be the same or different if the lily pad were floating free instead of attached by roots to the pond floor. (*Hint:* Before you write, draw a series of diagrams to show the motion.)

Performance-Based Assessment

Using Models Try blowing across the top of a bottle to produce a tone. Experiment to see how adding water of different heights affects the pitch. See if you can arrange a series of eight bottles to produce a musical scale. Learn to play a simple tune on your musical bottles. Summarize your results in a computer presentation that explains the relationship between the height of the air column and the pitch produced.

Go Online
PHSchool.com

For: Self-grading assessment
Visit: PHSchool.com
Web Code: cca-2170

528 *Chapter 17*

Performance-Based Assessment

Encourage students to critique presentations in small groups before making whole-class presentations. The frequency of the tone increases as the water level (depth) in a bottle increases. Students may be curious to try different bottle shapes to see if this affects the tone produced most easily. Students will discover that to play a scale, the series of bottles needs to be arranged in order of lowest water depth to greatest water depth.

Go Online
PHSchool.com

Your students can independently test their knowledge of the chapter and print out their test results for your files.

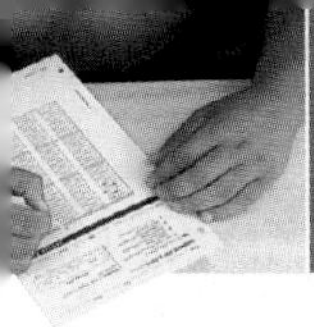

Standardized Test Prep

Test-Taking Tip

Controlling Variables
Some test questions ask which variables must be controlled in an experiment. It helps to start by writing an equation for the variables you are given. For the question below, write an equation that includes wavelength and frequency.

Speed = Wavelength × Frequency

This equation gives you one variable to control: the wave speed. Next, think of any conditions that might affect this variable. You know that wave speed changes in a different medium, so the medium must be controlled. Other conditions that are often controlled include conditions in the lab, such as temperature and pressure, or quantities of matter, such as mass or volume.

Which variables must be held constant in an experiment to determine how the frequency of a sound wave affects wavelength?
I. time
II. wave speed
III. temperature

(A) I only
(B) II only
(C) I and II only
(D) II and III only
(E) I, II, and III

(Answer: D)

Choose the letter that best answers the question or completes the statement.

1. Which of the following is required to transmit energy using mechanical waves?
   (A) medium
   (B) crest
   (C) trough
   (D) reflection
   (E) period

2. How are wavelength and frequency related for a wave moving at constant speed?
   (A) Wavelength equals frequency.
   (B) Wavelength is greater than frequency.
   (C) Frequency is greater than wavelength.
   (D) Wavelength is proportional to frequency.
   (E) Wavelength is inversely proportional to frequency.

3. Which of the following statements is generally true for the musical instrument (panpipes) below?

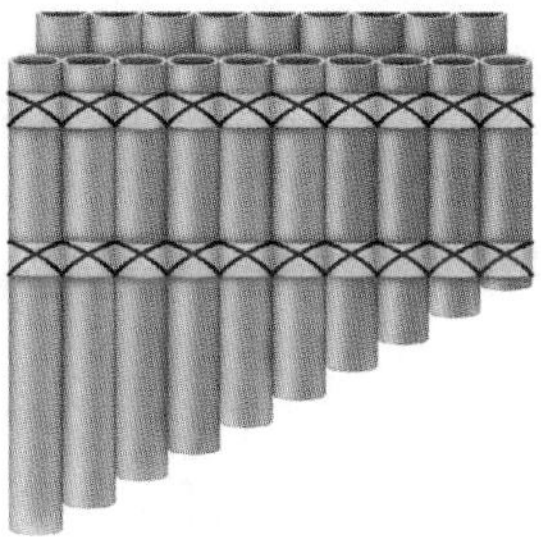

   (A) The longest pipe has the highest pitch.
   (B) The shortest pipe has the highest pitch.
   (C) The pipe in the middle has the highest pitch.
   (D) The pitch cannot be changed.
   (E) Any of the pipes could produce the highest pitch.

4. Which conditions best describe what happens when a transverse wave is reflected?
   (A) Some of a wave does not pass through a boundary or surface.
   (B) A wave enters a new medium at an angle.
   (C) A wave becomes longitudinal.
   (D) A wave combines with another wave.
   (E) A wave interferes with another wave.

5. Which of the following variables can affect the wavelength of a sound wave?
   I. the medium
   II. the frequency of the wave
   III. the amplitude of the wave

   (A) I only
   (B) II only
   (C) I and II only
   (D) II and III only
   (E) I, II, and III

6. Ocean waves flow past a concrete support for a bridge. The support is 30 meters wide and it sits in very deep water. Which of the following is LEAST likely to occur?
   (A) The waves will reflect.
   (B) The waves will diffract.
   (C) The waves will lose some energy.
   (D) The waves will continue past the support.
   (E) The waves will refract.

Standardized Test Prep

1. A	**2.** E	**3.** B
4. A	**5.** A	**6.** E

CHAPTER 18

Planning Guide

Use these planning tools
Easy Planner
Teacher Express

SECTION OBJECTIVES	STANDARDS NATIONAL (See p. T18.)	STANDARDS STATE	ACTIVITIES and LABS
18.1 Electromagnetic Waves, pp. 532–538 1 block or 2 periods **18.1.1 Describe** the characteristics of electromagnetic waves in a vacuum and how Michelson measured the speed of light. **18.1.2 Calculate** the wavelength and frequency of an electromagnetic wave given its speed. **18.1.3 Describe** the evidence for the dual nature of electromagnetic radiation. **18.1.4 Describe** how the intensity of light changes with distance from a light source.	A-1, B-5, B-6, G-1, G-2, G-3		**SE** Inquiry Activity: How Do Color Filters Work? p. 531 **L2** **TE** Teacher Demo: The Photoelectric Effect, p. 537 **L2** **TE** Build Science Skills: Observing, p. 538 **L2**
18.2 The Electromagnetic Spectrum, pp. 539–545 1 block or 2 periods **18.2.1 Rank** and **classify** electromagnetic waves based on their frequencies and wavelengths. **18.2.2 Describe** the uses for different waves of the electromagnetic spectrum.	A-1, A-2, B-5, B-6, E-1, E-2, F-1, F-5, G-1, G-2, G-3		**SE** Quick Lab: Evaluating Sunscreen, p. 544 **L2** **TE** Teacher Demo: Radio Reception, p. 541 **L2**
18.3 Behavior of Light, pp. 546–549 1 block or 2 periods **18.3.1 Classify** materials as transparent, translucent, or opaque to visible light. **18.3.2 Describe** what happens when light is reflected, refracted, polarized, or scattered.	A-1, A-2, B-5, B-6		**TE** Teacher Demo: Reflected Light and Vision, p. 547 **L2** **TE** Build Science Skills: Observing, p. 548 **L2** **LM** Investigation 18B: Using Polarized Light to Measure Sugar Concentration **L1**
18.4 Color, pp. 550–557 1 block or 2 periods **18.4.1 Explain** how a prism disperses white light into different colors. **18.4.2 Analyze** factors that determine the color of an object. **18.4.3 Distinguish** among primary, secondary, and complementary colors of light and of pigments.	A-1, B-5, B-6, E-1, E-2, G-1, G-2, G-3		**SE** Exploration Lab: Mixing Colored Lights, p. 563 **L2** **TE** Teacher Demo: Overlapping Filters, p. 553 **L2** **LM** Investigation 18A: Predicting Spectra **L2**
18.5 Sources of Light, pp. 558–562 1 block or 2 periods **18.5.1 Explain** how light is produced by common sources of light. **18.5.2 Describe** the uses of different light sources. **18.5.3 Distinguish** lasers from other light sources.	A-1, A-2, B-5, B-6, C-6, E-1, E-2, F-1, F-5, F-6, G-1, G-2, G-3		**SE** Quick Lab: Comparing Fluorescent and Incandescent Light, p. 559 **L2** **TE** Build Science Skills: Inferring, p. 561 **L2**

Ability Levels	
L1	For students who need additional help
L2	For all students
L3	For students who need to be challenged

Components

SE	Student Edition	**RSW**	Reading & Study Workbook	**CUT**	Chapter & Unit Tests	**T**	Transparencies
TE	Teacher's Edition	**MSPS**	Math Skills & Problem Solving Workbook	**CTB**	Computer Test Bank	**iT**	Interactive Textbook
LM	Laboratory Manual			**TP**	Test Prep Resources	**P**	Presentation Pro CD-ROM
PLM	Probeware Lab Manual			**DC**	Discovery Channel Videotapes & DVDs	**GO**	Internet Resources

RESOURCES PRINT and TECHNOLOGY		SECTION ASSESSMENT
RSW Section 18.1	L1	**SE** Section 18.1 Assessment, p. 538
RSW Math Skill	L2	**iT** Section 18.1
MSPS Section 18.1	L2	
T Chapter 18 Pretest	L2	
Section 18.1	L2	
P Chapter 18 Pretest	L2	
Section 18.1	L2	
SciLinks **GO** Waves	L2	
RSW Section 18.2	L1	**SE** Section 18.2 Assessment, p. 545
MSPS Section 18.2	L2	**iT** Section 18.2
T Section 18.2	L2	
P Section 18.2	L2	
SciLinks **GO** Electromagnetic spectrum	L2	
RSW Section 18.3	L1	**SE** Section 18.3 Assessment, p. 549
T Section 18.3	L2	**iT** Section 18.3
P Section 18.3	L2	
RSW Section 18.4	L1	**SE** Section 18.4 Assessment, p. 553
Discovery School **DC** Finding the Fakes	L2	**iT** Section 18.4
T Section 18.4	L2	
P Section 18.4	L2	
SciLinks **GO** Color	L2	
RSW Section 18.5	L1	**SE** Section 18.5 Assessment, p. 562
T Section 18.5	L2	**iT** Section 18.5
P Section 18.5	L2	
Science News **GO** Light and optics	L2	

Go Online

Go online for these Internet resources.

PHSchool.com
Web Code: cca-2180

SCIENCE NEWS
Web Code: cce-2185

NSTA SciLinks
Web Code: ccn-2181
Web Code: ccn-2182
Web Code: ccn-2184

Materials for Activities and Labs

Quantities for each group

STUDENT EDITION

Inquiry Activity, p. 531
cardboard with slit, light source, prism, white paper, filters (red, green, blue), colored markers

Quick Lab, p. 544
2 black paper strips, 2 petri dishes, 12 ultraviolet-detecting beads, sunscreen, clock/watch with second hand

Quick Lab, p. 559
spectroscope, clear incandescent bulb, fluorescent bulb, colored pencils

Exploration Lab, p. 563
light source (red, blue, green), tape, large sheet of white paper

TEACHER'S EDITION

Teacher Demo, p. 537
electroscope, zinc strip, rubber rod, wool, incandescent and UV light sources

Build Science Skills, p. 538
low-wattage bulb, light source

Teacher Demo, p. 541
portable radio with antenna, cardboard or wooden box, chicken wire

Teacher Demo, p. 547
wooden or cardboard box with removable top, white paper

Build Science Skills, p. 548
2 polarizing filters, light source

Teacher Demo, p. 553
2 overhead projectors; red, green, and blue acetate filters

Build Science Skills, p. 556
paints (acrylic, watercolor, oil), artist brushes, watercolor paper, hand lens, flat, wooden sticks

Build Science Skills, p. 561
spectroscope, neon lights

Chapter Assessment

CHAPTER ASSESSMENT

SE Chapter Assessment, pp. 565–566
CUT Chapter 18 Test A, B
CTB Chapter 18
iT Chapter 18
PHSchool.com GO
Web Code: cca-2180

STANDARDIZED TEST PREP

SE Chapter 18, p. 567
TP Diagnose and Prescribe

Interactive Textbook

Interactive Textbook with assessment at PHSchool.com

CHAPTER 18

Before you teach

From the Author

Sophia Yancopoulos
Manhattan College

Big Ideas

In studying light and electromagnetic waves, students must first understand that the electromagnetic spectrum extends far beyond the visible light seen by the unaided eye.

Space and Time Because it travels so fast, light is used as a "yardstick" to measure distances to the stars. We map our universe using light, probing the beginnings of time by using the entire electromagnetic spectrum. The afterglow of the big bang can be detected as background radiation of microwaves.

The challenge in measuring the speed of light is that it travels large distances in times too short to be easily measured. Using lanterns, Galileo tried to measure the speed of light from one mountaintop to another, and failed because light traveled back and forth in less time than it took to cover and uncover his lantern.

Forces and Motion Light in the form of electromagnetic waves behaves in many different ways: It can be reflected, refracted, polarized, scattered, and even interfere with itself. For the most part, however, light moves in a straight line at a constant speed, believed to be the ultimate speed in our universe. Uninterrupted, light can travel billions of years through space. However, as Einstein proved in his theory of general relativity, gravity affects light. The sun, neutron stars, and other concentrated matter can bend light from its straight path.

Matter and Energy Some students think of the world as entirely made up of matter. The world is made of both matter and energy, however, and the two interact. Photons can either be absorbed or emitted when interacting with matter. Light's interaction with matter in the photoelectric effect helped Einstein understand the particle nature of light.

Due to its dual particle-wave nature, we all experience difficulty in understanding the nature of light. Reassure students that this discomfort is part of the process of learning science.

Physics Refresher

Electromagnetic Waves 18.1

Isaac Newton analyzed light in terms of mechanical particles, not photons. Einstein showed that the photoelectric effect could be explained if light consisted of photons, each with energy

$$E = hf$$

where h is Planck's constant (6.61×10^{-34} J•s) and f is frequency. Higher-frequency photons have more energy. In the photoelectric effect, there is a threshold frequency below which photons do not have enough energy to eject electrons. But the rate at which electrons are emitted also depends on intensity.

Electromagnetic Spectrum 18.2

All electromagnetic waves travel at the same speed, c, in empty space. However, their speed through a medium depends on the medium and on the frequency of the wave.

An accelerating charge produces time-varying electric and magnetic fields. For radio waves, the accelerating charge can be a current oscillating back and forth in an antenna. The vibrations of atoms and molecules in heated matter result in the emission of infrared waves. Visible light and ultraviolet light generally result from transitions between different excited states of atoms and molecules. The energy of the photon emitted from an atomic or molecular electronic transition equals the difference in the energy levels.

> **Address Misconceptions**
>
> *All electromagnetic waves travel at the same speed in all media.* If true, then light would not refract when passed through a prism. For a strategy to overcome this misconception, see **Address Misconceptions** on **page 543.**

Behavior of Light 18.3

Reflection is a complex process that depends on the frequency of light and on the surface characteristics of a material.

The ratio of the speed of light in a vacuum to the speed of light in a medium is the medium's index of refraction, $n = c/v$.

Go Online PD LINKS NSTA

For: Teaching methods for the electromagnetic spectrum and light
Visit: www.SciLinks.org/PDLinks
Web Code: ccn-1899

Address Misconceptions

Students may think that only mirrors or shiny surfaces reflect light and that the eye somehow sees without light entering the eye. To be seen, an object must reflect or emit light toward the eyes. For a strategy to overcome this misconception, see **Address Misconceptions** on **page 547.**

The index of refraction is used in Snell's law to relate the angle of incidence, θ_1, to the angle of refraction, θ_2.

$$n_1 \sin \theta_1 = n_2 \sin \theta_2$$

In this equation, n_1 is the first medium's index of refraction and n_2 is the second medium's index of refraction. If $n_1 < n_2$, the light beam refracts toward the normal, as shown in the figure below.

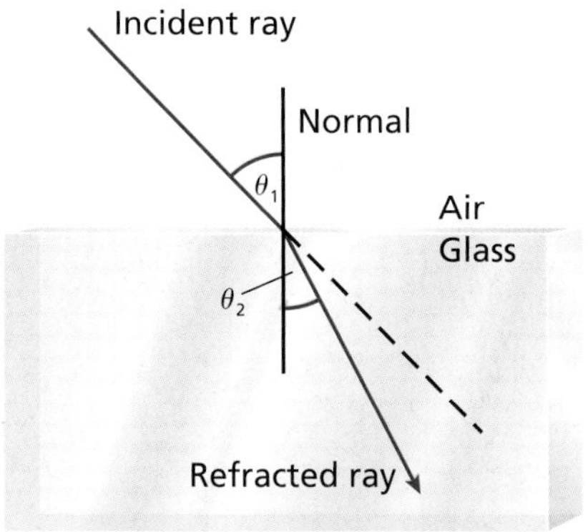

Incident ray
Normal
θ_1
Air
Glass
θ_2
Refracted ray

Students may wonder how an electromagnetic wave can be polarized in one plane if the electric and magnetic fields are at right angles to each other. The answer is that physicists determine the polarization of an electromagnetic wave by looking only at its electric field, as shown in the figure below.

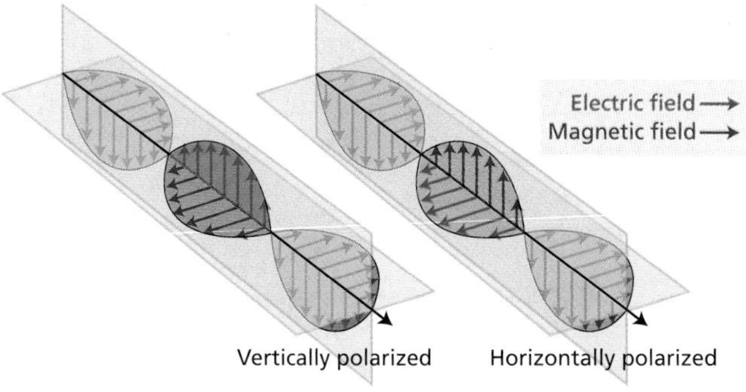

Electric field
Magnetic field
Vertically polarized
Horizontally polarized

Color 18.4 and 18.5

Each frequency of light is perceived by the human eye as a particular color, but what the human eye perceives as a color may consist of many different combinations of frequencies. An example is the light from a fluorescent light bulb, which consists of a mixture of distinct emission lines. Different sources of light differ in the mixture of frequencies they produce. A tungsten filament, the sun, and a heated object all emit electromagnetic radiation. The peak emission frequency increases as the temperature increases. For hot objects on Earth, the emitted radiation is mostly red and infrared. A tungsten filament at 2800 K also emits light from the entire visible spectrum, and so the light appears white.

Build Reading Literacy

SQ3R

Survey, Question, Read, Recite, and Review

Strategy Help students read material that contains technical information, diagrams, and figures. This strategy helps students focus on the main points in a section, making it easier for them to remember what they have read. Before students begin, assign a section in the textbook for them to read such as The Waves of the Spectrum, pp. 539–540.

Example

1. S Have students **survey** the entire assignment and look at the headings, material in boldface and italics, and chapter summary. Have them write a short explanation of what they see in each diagram, photo, graph, or chart.
2. Q Have students write **questions** they will answer when they complete their survey. They should turn each heading into a question and leave room below it for the answer.
3. R Have students **read** the section and look for the answers to their questions.
4. R When students finish reading, tell them to think about what they read. They should **recite** the questions they wrote and—using their own words—give the answers they found. If students can't answer a question, have them reread the material for the related heading, looking more carefully to find the answer.
5. R Have students **review** the section by writing the answers they recited. Finally, refer students to the key concepts questions on the first page of the section. Have students answer each of these questions.

See p. 560 for a script on how to use the SQ3R strategy with students. For additional Build Reading Literacy strategies, see pp. 534, 539, 546, and 552.

ASSESS PRIOR KNOWLEDGE

Use the Chapter Pretest below to assess students' prior knowledge. As needed, review these Science Concepts and Math Skills with students.

Review Science Concepts

Section 18.1 Review electric and magnetic forces. Remind students that mechanical waves require a medium. Review wavelength, frequency, and the wave equation. Remind students how the intensity of sound waves varies with distance from the source.

Section 18.2 Encourage students to recall what they have learned about radiation, thermal energy, and infrared rays. Ask students to think of other electromagnetic waves they have encountered in earlier chapters.

Section 18.3 Encourage students to review behaviors of mechanical waves.

Sections 18.4 and 18.5 Review atomic models if chemistry has been taught. Review conservation of energy and remind students that the colors produced in emission spectra are related to energy transitions in atoms.

Review Math Skills

Scientific Notation, Exponents, Formulas and Equations
Students will need to multiply and divide exponents to solve equations with wavelength and frequency.

Direct students to the **Math Skills** in the **Skills and Reference Handbook** at the end of the student text.

CHAPTER 18 The Electromagnetic Spectrum and Light

CONCEPTS — in Action —

How do science concepts apply to your world? Here are some questions you'll be able to answer after you read this chapter.

- Why does a lamp seem brighter the closer you are to it? *(Section 18.1)*
- How does a microwave oven cook food? *(Section 18.2)*
- How is a mirage formed? *(Section 18.3)*
- How can you make millions of colors from only three? *(Section 18.4)*
- Why are fluorescent lights commonly used in large buildings? *(Section 18.5)*

Discovery Channel School **Video Field Trip**
Finding the Fakes

- How can you tell if a painting is a forgery? *(Page 554)*

Colorful neon lights brighten up a walkway in Chicago's O'Hare Airport. ▶

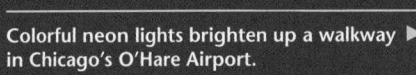

530 *Chapter 18*

Chapter Pretest

1. How are electric and magnetic forces related? *(They are two aspects of the same force.)*
2. Can a mechanical wave move through a vacuum? Explain. *(No, a mechanical wave is transmitted by matter.)*
3. What is the equation that relates wave speed, wavelength, and frequency? *(Wave speed = Wavelength × Frequency)*
4. If 3.0×10^7 people share a tax refund of 2.0×10^6 dollars, how much money does each person get? *($0.07 per person)*
5. True or False: An object radiates more energy at higher temperatures. *(True)*
6. If intensity equals *x* at 10 meters from an ambulance siren, what is the intensity at 20 meters from an ambulance siren? *(b)*
   a. 4*x* b. 0.25*x*
   c. 2*x* d. 0.5*x*
7. A refracted wave can do which of the following? *(d)*
   a. Slow down b. Speed up
   c. Bend d. All of the above
8. Electromagnetic energy can be converted into which of the following? *(d)*
   a. Chemical energy
   b. Mechanical energy
   c. Thermal energy
   d. All of the above

Chapter Preview

Inquiry Activity

How Do Color Filters Work?

Procedure

1. Place a piece of cardboard that has a slit cut into it in sunlight so that a beam of light passes through the slit. **CAUTION** *Never look directly at the sun.*
2. Create a rainbow by positioning a prism in the beam of light that has passed through the slit. Project the rainbow onto white paper.
3. Use colored markers to draw the colors in the order in which they appear on the paper.
4. Replace the paper. Place a red filter between the slit and the prism and draw the colors you see projected onto the paper.
5. Repeat Step 4 with a blue filter and then with a green filter.

Think About It

1. **Inferring** What happens to sunlight when it passes through a prism?
2. **Observing** Which colors did you see projected onto the paper while using each filter? Which colors didn't you see while using each filter?
3. **Drawing Conclusions** What can you conclude about what happens to sunlight as it passes through a filter?

Video Field Trip

Finding the Fakes

Encourage students to view the Video Field Trip "Finding the Fakes."

ENGAGE/EXPLORE

Inquiry Activity

How Do Color Filters Work?

Purpose In this activity, students begin to determine that white light contains other colors of light.

Address Misconceptions

Students may think that colored filters change white light into colored light or that white light is a single color. Challenge these misconceptions by asking students to explain their observations in this activity.

Skills Focus **Observing, Inferring**

Prep Time 10 minutes

Materials cardboard with slit, light source, prism, white paper, filters (red, green, blue), colored markers

Advance Prep Cut narrow slits (about 0.5 × 7.0 cm) in sheets of cardboard (one per group).

Class Time 10 minutes

Safety Students should never look at the sun through a prism. Do not use prisms that have sharp or chipped edges. Advise students to handle prisms carefully and review safety procedures for broken glass.

Teaching Tips

- If sunlight is not available, use an overhead or slide projector.
- Each group can use one filter at a time and then trade filters.
- For best results, fold colored cellophane several times.

Expected Outcome Primary-color filters will block all other colors in the rainbow. Non-primary color filters allow two or more colors to pass through.

Think About It

1. Students may infer that sunlight contains other colors. A prism makes the colors visible by separating them.
2. Red filters subtract all colors except red. Blue filters block all colors except blue. Only green light passes through a green filter. Secondary-color filters allow more than one color to pass through.
3. A filter allows some colors to pass through and blocks all other colors.
Visual, Group

1 FOCUS

Objectives

18.1.1 **Describe** the characteristics of electromagnetic waves in a vacuum and how Michelson measured the speed of light.

18.1.2 **Calculate** the wavelength and frequency of an electromagnetic wave given its speed.

18.1.3 **Describe** the evidence for the dual nature of electromagnetic radiation.

18.1.4 **Describe** how the intensity of light changes with distance from a light source.

Reading Focus

Build Vocabulary L2

Word-Part Analysis Ask students what words they know that have the key word parts *electro, magnet,* and *photo.* *(electricity, magnet,* and *photograph)* Give a definition of each word part. *(Electro* means *"shining," magnet* means *"attracting like material,"* and *photo* means *"light.")* Give additional examples that share the word parts in question *(electron, magnetism, photocopy).*

Reading Strategy L2

a. B **b.** E **c.** B **d.** M

18.1 Electromagnetic Waves

Reading Focus

Key Concepts

- How are electromagnetic waves different from mechanical waves?
- What is the maximum speed of light?
- How do electromagnetic waves differ from one another?
- What is the dual nature of electromagnetic radiation?
- What happens as light travels farther from its source?

Vocabulary

- electromagnetic waves
- electric field
- magnetic field
- electromagnetic radiation
- photoelectric effect
- photons
- intensity

Reading Strategy

Comparing and Contrasting Copy the table below. As you read about electromagnetic waves, fill in the table to compare them with mechanical waves. Use E for properties of electromagnetic waves, M for mechanical waves, and B for both.

Travels through vacuum	E
Travels through medium	a. ?
Fits wave model	B
Fits particle model	b. ?
Transverse wave	c. ?
Longitudinal wave	d. ?

What do X-ray machines, microwave ovens, and heat lamps have in common with police radar, television, and radiation therapy? They all use waves. You are surrounded by such waves all the time. But you may not realize it, because most waves are invisible.

With X-rays, you can take pictures of your bones. Your dentist uses X-rays to examine the inner structure of your teeth. Microwaves cook or reheat your meals and carry cell phone conversations between you and your friends. Radio waves bring your favorite music to your radio from the radio station. Ultraviolet rays can give you a sunburn. Without waves, the girl in Figure 1 wouldn't be able to talk with her friends on a cell phone. Without waves, you wouldn't be able to watch your favorite TV show. You wouldn't be able to see colors. In fact, without waves you wouldn't be able to see anything at all.

Figure 1 The waves that carry this girl's cell phone conversation are not visible. The girl may not even know they exist. But their existence is what makes cell phone technology possible.

Section Resources

Print
- ***Reading and Study Workbook With Math Support,*** Section 18.1 and **Math Skill:** Calculating Wavelength and Frequency
- ***Math Skills and Problem Solving Workbook,*** Section 18.1
- ***Transparencies,*** Chapter Pretest and Section 18.1

Technology
- ***Interactive Textbook,*** Section 18.1
- ***Presentation Pro CD-ROM,*** Chapter Pretest and Section 18.1
- ***Go Online,*** NSTA SciLinks, Waves

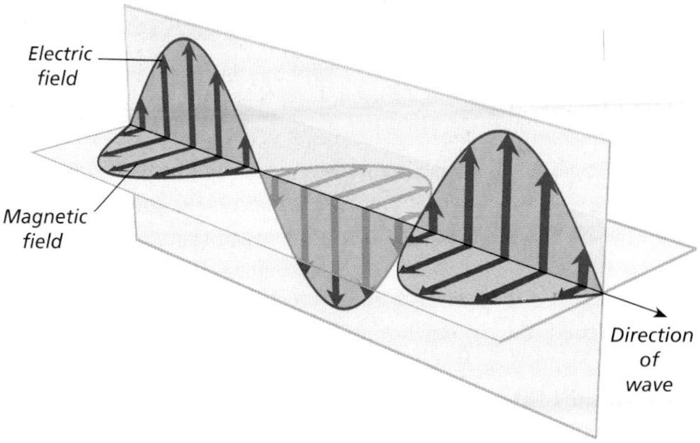
Electric field
Magnetic field
Direction of wave

Figure 2 Electromagnetic waves consist of changing electric fields and magnetic fields. The fields are at right angles to each other and to the direction of the wave. ***Interpreting Diagrams*** ***How can you tell that electromagnetic waves are transverse waves?***

What Are Electromagnetic Waves?

The visible and invisible waves you will learn about in this chapter exhibit some of the same behaviors as mechanical waves. Other behaviors are unique to electromagnetic waves. **Electromagnetic waves** are transverse waves consisting of changing electric fields and changing magnetic fields. Like mechanical waves, electromagnetic waves carry energy from place to place. Electromagnetic waves differ from mechanical waves in how they are produced and how they travel.

How They Are Produced Electromagnetic waves are produced by constantly changing fields. An **electric field** in a region of space exerts electric forces on charged particles. Electric fields are produced by electrically charged particles and by changing magnetic fields. A **magnetic field** in a region of space produces magnetic forces. Magnetic fields are produced by magnets, by changing electric fields, and by vibrating charges. **Electromagnetic waves are produced when an electric charge vibrates or accelerates.** Figure 2 shows that the fields are at right angles to each other. You can tell this is a transverse wave because the fields are also at right angles to the direction in which the wave travels.

How They Travel Because changing electric fields produce changing magnetic fields, and changing magnetic fields produce changing electric fields, the fields regenerate each other. As the fields regenerate, their energy travels in the form of a wave. Unlike mechanical waves, electromagnetic waves do not need a medium. **Electromagnetic waves can travel through a vacuum, or empty space, as well as through matter.** The transfer of energy by electromagnetic waves traveling through matter or across space is called **electromagnetic radiation.**

Reading Checkpoint *What are electromagnetic waves?*

Go Online NSTA SCILINKS

For: Links on waves
Visit: www.SciLinks.org
Web Code: ccn-2181

2 INSTRUCT

What Are Electromagnetic Waves?

Use Visuals L1

Figure 2 Emphasize that an electromagnetic (EM) wave consists of both an electric field and a magnetic field. Have students note that the electric field and magnetic field vibrate in planes that are perpendicular to each other (shown by the yellow areas). Ask, **In which direction is the EM wave in the figure traveling?** *(To the right)* **In which direction are the disturbances in the electric and magnetic fields traveling?** *(Perpendicular to the direction of the EM wave)* **Why can't the electric field wave exist without the magnetic field wave?** *(Each field produces the other—if one is present so must be the other.)* **How is the EM wave different from a wave traveling along a rope? How are they the same?** *(The EM wave does not need a medium to travel through, whereas the wave in the rope could not exist if the rope were not present. Also, the EM wave is made up of electric and magnetic waves, whereas the wave in the rope has a single component. Both waves are transverse waves.)*
Visual

Go Online NSTA SCILINKS

Download a worksheet on waves for students to complete, and find additional teacher support from NSTA SciLinks.

Customize for English Language Learners

Simplify the Presentation
The large number of vocabulary words in this section is a challenge to an English language learner. Help ease the challenge by tailoring your teaching presentation of the section content to the less-proficient English skills of your students. Do this by speaking directly and simplifying the words and sentence structures used to explain the material. Use body language when appropriate to emphasize important words. Restate complicated sentences into shorter phrases that make use of more common words.

Answer to . . .

Figure 2 *They are transverse because their fields are at right angles to the direction in which they are traveling.*

Reading Checkpoint *Electromagnetic waves are transverse waves consisting of changing electric fields and changing magnetic fields.*

The Speed of Electromagnetic Waves

Build Reading Literacy L1

Sequence Refer to page **290D** in **Chapter 10,** which provides the guidelines for a sequence.

Have students read the text on page 534 related to Michelson's experiment. Then, have students do the following:

1. Create a sketch of Michelson's experimental setup as shown in Figure 3. The sketch should include all labels shown in Figure 3.
2. Number and describe the steps the light follows on its path through the experimental setup. Students should start with the light emitted by the light source as Step 1.
3. Student sketches should include as much detail as they can find in the text, Figure 3, and its caption.

Visual, Portfolio

FYI

Michelson's work earned him a Nobel Prize in Physics, the first ever awarded to an American.

The Speed of Electromagnetic Waves

A thunderstorm is approaching. The sky is dark, and lightning flashes in the distance. Within a few seconds, you hear thunder's low rumble. As the storm approaches, the lightning gets brighter and the thunder louder. The lightning flashes and the sound of thunder come closer in time. Still, you see the lightning before you hear the thunder, because light travels faster than sound. But how much faster is light?

Michelson's Experiment In ancient times, people tried to measure the speed of light but no instrument was accurate enough. Light moves so fast that people thought its speed was infinite. Several experiments in the 1800s proved it was not infinite and gave approximate values. Then, in 1926, the American physicist Albert Michelson (1852–1931) measured the speed of light more accurately than ever before.

Figure 3 shows an experimental setup similar to Michelson's. On top of Mount Wilson in California, Michelson placed an eight-sided rotating mirror. He placed another mirror, this one stationary, on Mount San Antonio, 35.4 kilometers away. Michelson shined a bright light at one face of the rotating mirror. The light reflected to the stationary mirror on the other mountain and then back to Mount Wilson, where it struck another face of the rotating mirror. Michelson knew how fast the eight-sided mirror was rotating and how far the light traveled from mountain to mountain and back again. With those values he was able to calculate the speed of light quite accurately. His findings were similar to modern measurements.

The Speed of Light Since Michelson, many other scientists have measured the speed of light. Their experiments have confirmed that light and all electromagnetic waves travel at the same speed when in a vacuum, regardless of the observer's motion. **The speed of light in a vacuum, *c*, is 3.00×10^8 meters per second.**

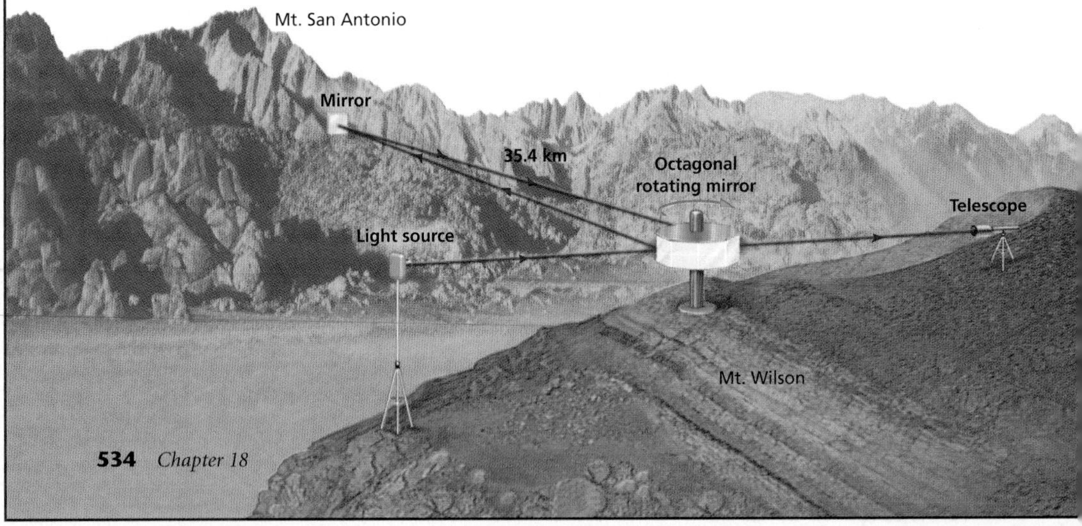
Mt. San Antonio
Mirror
35.4 km
Octagonal rotating mirror
Telescope
Light source
Mt. Wilson

Figure 3 Michelson timed a light beam as it traveled from one mountain to another and back again. His experiment measured the speed of light more accurately than it had been measured before. **Inferring** ***Why must the light beam travel so far for its speed to be measurable?***

534 *Chapter 18*

Facts and Figures

Speed of Light Due to the definition of the meter, the speed of light has an exact value. The meter is defined as the distance light travels in a vacuum in $\frac{1}{299,752,458}$ of a second. Thus, the speed of light has an exact value of 299,792,458 m/s.

To imagine the speed of light, consider driving non-stop at 60 miles per hour from New York City to San Francisco. This trip would take you about 50 hours (a little more than two days). Light travels this distance in less than two-hundredths of a second (0.02 second).

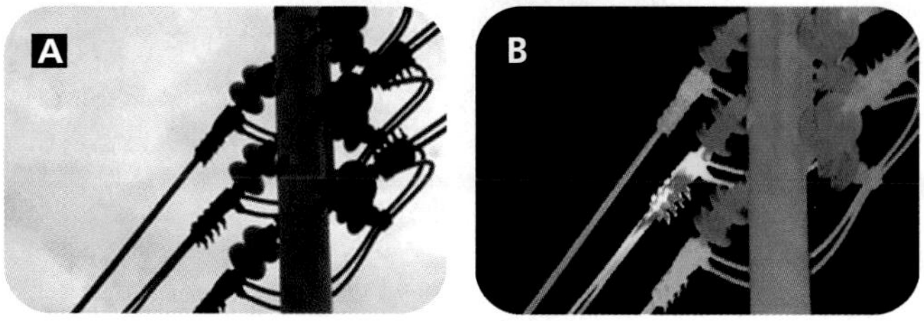
A
B

Figure 12 A thermogram can be used to diagnose problems in a utility line. **A** When viewed in visible light the wires all look the same. **B** The colors in the thermogram image show that the electric current in the center wire is not flowing as it should.

Infrared Rays

Infrared rays have higher frequencies than radio waves and lower frequencies than red light. Infrared wavelengths vary from about 1 millimeter to about 750 nanometers. (A nanometer is 10^{-9} meters, or one millionth of a millimeter.) **Infrared rays are used as a source of heat and to discover areas of heat differences.**

You cannot see infrared radiation, but your skin senses it as warmth. Reptile habitats at zoos are often kept warm with infrared lamps. Restaurants use infrared lamps to keep foods served buffet-style at a safe temperature for consumption.

Warmer objects give off more infrared radiation than cooler objects. A device called a thermograph uses infrared sensors to create thermograms. **Thermograms** (THUR moh gramz) are color-coded pictures that show variations in temperature. They are used to find places where a building loses heat to the environment. Thermograms can also locate problems in the path of electric current, as shown in Figure 12.

The human body is usually warmer than its surroundings. After a natural disaster such as an earthquake, search-and-rescue teams use infrared cameras to locate victims quickly—even underground.

Visible Light

The visible part of the electromagnetic spectrum is light that the human eye can see. Each wavelength in the visible spectrum corresponds to a specific frequency and has a particular color. Figure 13 shows the wavelength and frequency ranges of different colors of light in a vacuum.

People use visible light to see, to help keep them safe, and to communicate with one another. Light enables people to read. It is what makes flowers, boxes, signs, and all other objects visible. Automobiles have headlights and taillights that make night driving safer. Traffic lights communicate information to drivers about what is expected of them—to stop, for example, when the light is red.

Reading Checkpoint *What is the visible part of the electromagnetic spectrum?*

Figure 13 Each color of light corresponds to a different range of wavelengths. The wavelengths of visible light are quite small. Wavelengths of red light, for example, are about one hundredth the thickness of a human hair. **Using Tables** ***As the wavelength decreases from the red end of the spectrum to the violet end, what happens to the frequency?***

The Visible Spectrum

Color	Wavelength (nm)	Frequency ($\times 10^{14}$ Hz)
Red	610–750	4.9–4.0
Orange	590–610	5.1–4.9
Yellow	570–590	5.3–5.1
Green	500–570	6.0–5.3
Blue	450–500	6.7–6.0
Violet	400–450	7.5–6.7

Infrared Rays

Use Visuals

L1

Figure 12 Reinforce the idea that infrared rays are associated with heat and that they are not part of the visible spectrum. Tell students that electric charge dissipates energy in the form of heat as it flows through a conductor such as a wire. Tell students that electrical power transmission lines in good condition do not dissipate a lot of heat. Ask, **What can you infer from the colors of the pole and the top and bottom wires shown in the thermogram in Figure 12B?** *(The wires and the pole are at about the same temperature, and they are not dissipating a lot of heat.)* **What are some possible reasons why the middle wire and its insulating resistor are hot?** *(Student answers may include that excessive current is flowing through the wire, or that there is damage to the wire causing it to have a much higher resistance than the other wires.)*
Visual, Logical

FYI

A thermogram usually has a key to indicate what temperature each color corresponds to.

Visible Light

Address Misconceptions

L2

Because the speed of light in a vacuum is usually given early in any discussion of light, many students fail to realize that light has different speeds in different materials. Furthermore, students often don't understand that different colors of light have different speeds in materials such as glass. Explain that EM waves, which include many other types of waves besides visible light, travel at the speed of light only when in a vacuum. When EM waves travel through any medium other than a vacuum, they travel at speeds less than the speed of light. You may want to use this information to preview Section 18.3, which covers how light interacts with matter.
Verbal

Answer to . . .

Figure 13 *As wavelength decreases, frequency increases.*

Reading Checkpoint *The visible part of the electromagnetic spectrum is light that people can see.*

Ultraviolet Rays

Quick Lab

Evaluating Sunscreen L2

Objective
After completing this activity, students will be able to
- use the SPF of a sunscreen to predict its effectiveness in blocking ultraviolet radiation.

Skills Focus **Observing, Measuring**

Prep Time 10 minutes

Materials 2 black paper strips, 2 petri dishes, 12 ultraviolet-detecting beads, sunscreen, clock or watch with second hand

Advance Prep Provide each lab group with a small vial of the sunscreen labeled with its SPF.

Class Time 15 minutes

Safety Make sure that students wear plastic gloves and safety goggles when applying sunscreen and clean up when they are finished.

Teaching Tips
- Make sure that students spread the sunscreens uniformly.

Expected Outcome The unprotected beads change color within five seconds in the presence of sunlight. Depending on the SPF, sunscreen will delay this change by as much as two minutes.

Analyze and Conclude
1. The beads in the sunscreen-covered petri dish took longer to change color.
2. The color change represents absorption of ultraviolet light, which causes tanning or burning of skin. Sunscreen absorbs most ultraviolet light before it can affect skin or the beads.
3. A sunscreen with a higher SPF would delay the color change for a longer time.
Visual, Group

For Enrichment L3

Have students use the beads to compare the ultraviolet-protection value of different types of plexiglass, sunglasses, and window glass. Students will discover that plexiglass transmits the most ultraviolet light. High-quality sunglasses transmit the least.
Kinesthetic, Visual

Quick Lab

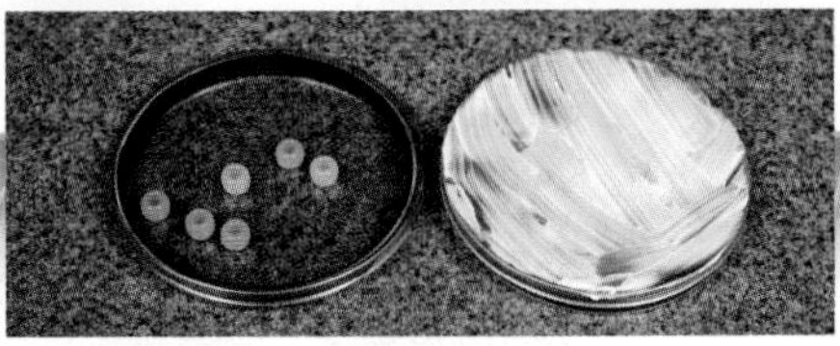

Evaluating Sunscreen

Procedure

1. Insert a black paper strip inside each of two plastic petri dishes to cover the sides. Place six ultraviolet-detecting beads in each dish. Cover each dish with its lid.
2. On one of the lids, spread a thin layer of sunscreen.
3. Place the dishes in direct sunlight. Record the time it takes for the beads in each dish to change color.

Analyze and Conclude

1. **Comparing and Contrasting** Compare the times the beads in the two dishes took to change color.
2. **Using Models** Explain how this lab models the use of sunscreen. What does the color change of the beads represent?
3. **Predicting** How might a sunscreen with a higher SPF (sun protection factor) affect the time needed for the beads to change color?

Ultraviolet Rays

The wavelengths of ultraviolet rays vary from about 400 nanometers to about 4 nanometers. Ultraviolet radiation has higher frequencies than violet light. **Ultraviolet rays have applications in health and medicine, and in agriculture.**

In moderation, exposure to ultraviolet rays helps your skin produce vitamin D. Vitamin D helps the body absorb calcium from foods to produce healthy bones and teeth. Excessive exposure can cause sunburn, wrinkles, and eventually skin cancer. It can also damage your eyes.

Ultraviolet rays are used to kill microorganisms. In heating and cooling systems of large buildings, ultraviolet rays disinfect the air that flows through the systems. In winter, plant nurseries use ultraviolet lights to help plants grow.

Figure 14 Airport security screeners use X-rays to search baggage for potentially dangerous objects.
Inferring *Why are there dark areas in this X-ray image?*

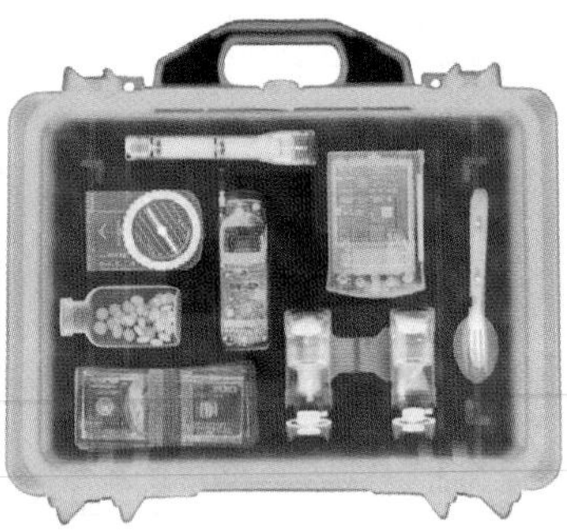

X-Rays

X-rays have very short wavelengths, from about 12 nanometers to about 0.005 nanometers. They have higher frequencies than ultraviolet rays. X-rays have high energy and can penetrate matter that light cannot. **X-rays are used in medicine, industry, and transportation to make pictures of the inside of solid objects.**

Your teeth and bones absorb X-rays. X-ray photographs show softer tissue as dark, highly exposed areas. Bones and teeth appear white. Too much exposure to X-rays can kill or damage living tissue.

The lids on aluminum cans are sometimes inspected with X-rays to make sure they are sealed properly. X-rays can be used to identify the contents of entire truck trailers. Packages and suitcases, such as the one in Figure 14, are X-rayed in search of dangerous contents.

Reading Checkpoint *What are X-rays used for?*

Section 18.2 Assessment

1. Radio waves, infrared rays, visible light, ultraviolet rays, X-rays, gamma rays
2. Radio waves: radio and television, microwave ovens, radar; Infrared rays: source of heat, indicator of heat differences, rescue missions; Visible light: sight, safety, and communication; Ultraviolet rays: health, medicine, and agriculture; X-rays: imaging interiors of solid objects in medicine, industry, and transportation; Gamma rays: cancer treatment, imaging the brain, industrial inspection tool
3. Radar sends out radio waves and uses the change in frequency of the reflected waves to calculate the speed of an object, as determined by the Doppler effect.
4. Soft materials show up as dark, highly exposed areas, while white areas are where X-rays are absorbed.

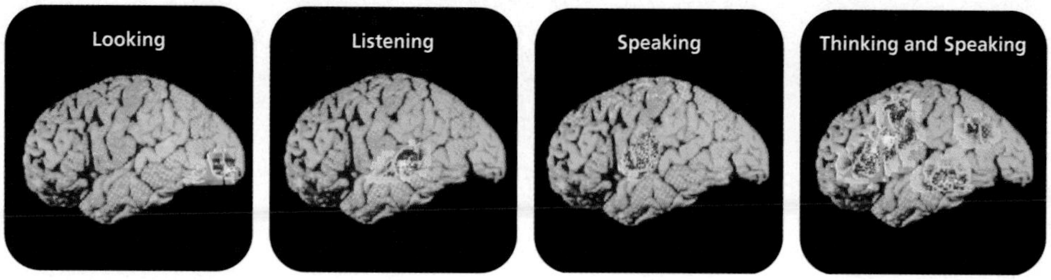
Looking
Listening
Speaking
Thinking and Speaking

Figure 15 Gamma rays emitted by radioactive tracers in the brain are used to produce color-coded images. Areas of high activity show up in red. These images show where the brain is active when the patient is (from left to right) looking at something, listening, speaking, and thinking and speaking. The more involved the task, the more parts of the brain are activated.

Gamma Rays

Gamma rays have the shortest wavelengths in the electromagnetic spectrum, about 0.005 nanometer or less. They have the highest frequencies and therefore the most energy and the greatest penetrating ability of all the electromagnetic waves. Exposure to tiny amounts of gamma rays are tolerable, but overexposure can be deadly. **Gamma rays are used in the medical field to kill cancer cells and make pictures of the brain, and in industrial situations as an inspection tool.**

Gamma rays are used in radiation therapy to kill cancer cells without harming nearby healthy cells. Gamma rays are also used to make pictures of the human brain, with different levels of brain activity represented by different colors. Four brain scans are shown in Figure 15.

Pipelines are checked with machines that travel on the inside of a pipe, taking gamma ray pictures along the entire length. Technicians examine the pictures for rusting, cracks, or other signs of damage.

Section 18.2 Assessment

Reviewing Concepts

1. List the kinds of waves included in the electromagnetic spectrum, from longest to shortest wavelength.
2. Name three uses for each type of wave.
3. How is radar used to determine the speed of a car?
4. How can X-rays make pictures of the inside of solid objects?

Critical Thinking

5. **Comparing and Contrasting** How are AM radio waves similar to FM radio waves? How are they different?
6. **Classifying** What type of electromagnetic wave are microwaves and radar?
7. **Predicting** Which do you think will penetrate farther into a block of lead, X-rays or gamma rays? Explain your reasoning.

Writing in Science

Explanatory Writing Write one paragraph each about three different kinds of electromagnetic waves that you will encounter today. Use a single characteristic, such as wavelength or frequency, to describe each wave. Explain how life might be different without each kind of wave.

5. AM and FM are similar in that they are a means of coding and transmitting information on radio waves. They are different because AM signals modulate amplitude while FM signals modulate frequency. AM signals travel farther because they reflect off particles in the upper atmosphere.
6. Radio waves
7. Gamma rays should penetrate farther into lead because they have higher-energy photons.

Writing in Science

Sample answer: Today I will encounter microwaves when I cook, infrared rays when I use a TV remote control, and ultraviolet light from the sun. These vary in wavelength, with microwaves the longest wavelength and ultraviolet rays the shortest. If these waves did not exist, I would have to cook differently, use a different kind of remote control, and perhaps need to use sunscreen less often.

X-Rays

Integrate Biology L2

To determine the structures of proteins, biologists at the Argonne National Laboratory Structural Biology Center are shining X-rays onto frozen crystals of proteins. The X-ray images are captured by a quick, electronic camera. With the help of advanced software this information is converted into three-dimensional images that biologists can study to determine how the proteins work. Have students find out the role that proteins play in living cells and have them write a short report.
Verbal, Portfolio

Gamma Rays

Integrate Space Science L2

Some deep-space objects emit bursts of gamma rays. These rays travel through the empty vacuum of space for millions of years before reaching Earth. However, Earth's atmosphere blocks the gamma rays and keeps them from reaching the surface. Because the rays are blocked, astronomers who want to detect and monitor gamma ray emissions use instruments that orbit above Earth's atmosphere. Ask students to research the cause of deep space gamma emissions and to summarize their findings in a short paragraph.
Logical, Portfolio

3 ASSESS

Evaluate Understanding L2

Ask students chosen at random to list the general properties of and one application for each electromagnetic wave type discussed in the section.

Reteach L1

Use Figure 9 to review the section's key concepts, emphasizing the relationship between the frequency and the wavelength of all electromagnetic waves.

Interactive Textbook — If your class subscribes to the Interactive Textbook, use it to review key concepts in Section 18.2.

Answer to . . .

Figure 14 *Dark areas are regions through which X-rays easily pass.*

Reading Checkpoint *In medicine, industry, and transportation to image the inside of solid objects*

Section 18.3

1 FOCUS

Objectives

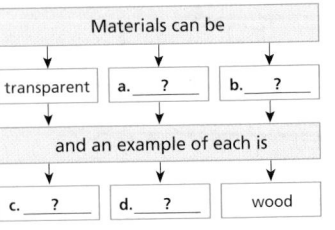

18.3.1 **Classify** materials as transparent, translucent, or opaque to visible light.

18.3.2 **Describe** what happens when light is reflected, refracted, polarized, or scattered.

Reading Focus

Build Vocabulary L2

Concept Map Have students construct a concept map of the vocabulary terms used in this section. Instruct students to place the vocabulary terms in ovals and connect the ovals with lines on which linking words are placed. Students should place the main concept (Behavior of Light) at the top or the center. As they move away from the main concept, the topics should become more specific.

Reading Strategy L2

a. translucent **b.** opaque **c.** glass or water **d.** frosted glass

2 INSTRUCT

Light and Materials

Build Reading Literacy L2

Anticipation Guide Refer to page **388D** in **Chapter 13,** which provides the guidelines for an anticipation guide.

Ask students which statements are true: **1.** All of the light striking an object is absorbed by that object. *(False)* **2.** It is possible to see an object in a room that is completely dark using only your eyes. *(False)* **3.** The cover of your book does not reflect light. *(False)*

Have students read the text on pp. 546 and 547, then revisit the three questions. **Verbal**

FYI

A material need not be transparent or opaque to all forms of electromagnetic radiation. For example, wood is opaque to visible light, but not to all electromagnetic waves. Microwaves and radio waves can pass through wood.

18.3 Behavior of Light

Reading Focus

Key Concepts

- What three types of materials affect the behavior of light?
- How does light behave when it enters a new medium?

Vocabulary

- transparent
- translucent
- opaque
- image
- regular reflection
- diffuse reflection
- mirage
- polarized light
- scattering

Reading Strategy

Monitoring Your Understanding Copy the flowchart below. As you read, complete it to show how different materials affect light.

Materials can be

transparent | a. ? | b. ?

and an example of each is

c. ? | d. ? | wood

Figure 16 Water is transparent. You can see through it. That characteristic makes it possible to photograph these fish and other animals living in the ocean.

What would you see if you were snorkeling in warm ocean waters over a coral reef? You might see fish of bright colors, clown fish, sea stars, sponges, and clams. You might see sharks or turtles, and of course, coral. But why can you see these animals so clearly? Why can you see the reef through the water but not, for example, through the bottom of the boat that brought you to the reef?

Light and Materials

Without light, nothing is visible. When you look at the reef animals, what you are really seeing is light. You can see the reef through the water, because light passes through the water between the reef and your eyes. But you can't see the reef through the bottom of the boat because light doesn't pass through the boat.

How light behaves when it strikes an object depends on many factors, including the material the object is made of. **Materials can be transparent, translucent, or opaque.** Each type of material affects the behavior of light in different ways.

A material through which you can see clearly is transparent. A **transparent** material transmits light, which means it allows most of the light that strikes it to pass through it. For example, the water where the fish and coral in Figure 16 live is transparent. While riding on a bus, you can see buildings and trees outside because the bus windows are transparent.

Section Resources

Print
- ***Laboratory Manual,*** Investigation 18B
- ***Reading and Study Workbook With Math Support,*** Section 18.3
- ***Transparencies,*** Section 18.3

Technology
- ***Interactive Textbook,*** Section 18.3
- ***Presentation Pro CD-ROM,*** Section 18.3

If you can see through a material, but the objects you see through it do not look clear or distinct, then the material is translucent (trans LOO sunt). A **translucent** material scatters light. The soaps in Figure 17A are translucent. When you look into a room through a frosted glass door, you can make out shapes of people and objects, but the shapes are fuzzy and lack detail.

Most materials are opaque (oh PAYK). An **opaque** material either absorbs or reflects all of the light that strikes it. The fruit in Figure 17B is opaque. An opaque object does not allow any light to pass through it. You can't see through a wooden table or a metal desk. Wood and metal are examples of opaque materials.

Interactions of Light

When light encounters matter, some or all of the energy in the light can be transferred to the matter. And just as light can affect matter, matter can affect light. **When light strikes a new medium, the light can be reflected, absorbed, or transmitted. When light is transmitted, it can be refracted, polarized, or scattered.**

Reflection When you look in a mirror, you see a clear image of yourself. An **image** is a copy of an object formed by reflected (or refracted) waves of light. Similarly, when you look at a still lake, you can see a sharp reflected image of the far shore. But what happens to the reflected image in the lake if the wind suddenly gusts, causing ripples in the surface of the water? The image is blurred, or fuzzy-looking. When light reflects from a smooth surface, you see a clear, sharp image. When light reflects from a rough surface, you see a blurred reflected image or no image at all.

Regular reflection occurs when parallel light waves strike a surface and reflect all in the same direction. Regular reflection happens when light hits a smooth, polished surface, like a mirror or the surface of a still body of water such as in Figure 18.

Diffuse reflection occurs when parallel light waves strike a rough, uneven surface, and reflect in many different directions. If you could look at this page of your book through a microscope, you would see that the paper has a rough surface. The rough surface causes diffuse reflection of the light that shines on it.

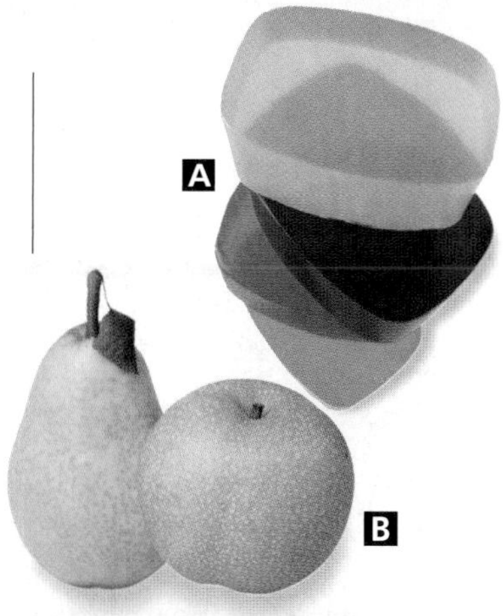

A
B

Figure 17 When light strikes a new medium, it can be reflected, absorbed, refracted, polarized, or scattered. **A** The translucent bars of soap scatter light, making the soaps and what you can see through them appear fuzzy. **B** You cannot see through the fruit because opaque materials do not transmit any light.

Figure 18 Almost all objects reflect light. **A** In regular reflection, a smooth surface reflects a clear image because parallel light waves reflect all in the same direction. **B** In diffuse reflection, parallel light waves reflect in many directions.

A Regular reflection
B Diffuse reflection

Interactions of Light

Address Misconceptions L2

Although most students accept that mirrors reflect light, some students reject the idea that ordinary objects also reflect light. This misconception is related to another one that many students have, namely that their eyes do not receive light when observing an object. Probe student misconceptions about vision by asking them to explain what makes it possible for people to see. You may discover a range of misconceptions, including the idea that light fills space (as expressed by saying, "the room is full of light") and the idea that it is the action of people's eyes that makes objects observable. Counter misconceptions using a careful explanation of the connections among reflected light, emitted light, and vision.
Verbal

Teacher Demo

Reflected Light and Vision L2

Purpose Students observe the role of reflected light in vision perception.

Materials medium-sized wooden or cardboard box with its interior lined with white paper or painted bright white. Box top must be removable or hinged, and have a small hole in its center.

Procedure Show students the box with its top on under normal room lighting conditions. Have students use their observations of the box (and the hole) to predict the box's interior color.

Expected Outcome Most students will not predict that the box's interior is white. Show students the white interior of the box. Explain that whatever amount of light enters the box, it is eventually absorbed after numerous reflections off the white interior surfaces. Because no light escapes the box and travels to the students' eyes, it is not possible to discern the interior color of the box.
Visual, Logical

Customize for English Language Learners

Increase Word Exposure
As students read through the section in class, post the section's nine vocabulary terms on a "word wall." Carefully define each word when it first appears. Then, ask for student help in organizing the words into groups based on their science meanings. Use the word wall as an interactive tool to help students become familiar with the terms. Make frequent references to the words and assign them in homework or an activity to validate their importance.

Build Science Skills L2

Observing

ACTIVITY

Purpose Students observe the effect of polarizing filters.

Materials 2 polarizing filters, light source

Class Time 10 minutes

Procedure Have students work in a group. One group member should hold one filter up to light coming through a window and observe the result. Ask, **Why is the light dimmer after passing through one of the filters?** *(The filter has absorbed some of the light.)* Have another group member align both filters in the same direction and then view the light from the window. Ask, **How does the brightness compare with what you saw when the light passed through a single filter?** *(The light is dimmer after passing through both filters.)* Have a third group member try to arrange the filters in such a way that no light is transmitted through the filters.

Safety Caution students to not look directly at the sun.

Expected Outcome Students will observe how the orientation of the two filters determines the amount of light that passes through. They will see that when the two filters are oriented at 90° to one another, no light is transmitted. **Kinesthetic, Group**

Use Visuals L1

Figure 20 Point out to students that Figure 20 represents how a vertical polarizing filter blocks light that is horizontally polarized. Tell students that the glare from horizontal surfaces such as roads and automobile hoods tends to be horizontally polarized. Then ask, **In what direction should the polarizing lenses in a pair of polarizing sunglasses be aligned?** *(To block the horizontally polarized glare, the lenses should be positioned with their polarizing slits aligned vertically.)*

FYI

An actual Polaroid polarizing filter consists of long chain molecules that are stretched preferentially in one direction. Light with an electric field parallel to the chain molecules is absorbed.

Figure 19 Light refracts, or bends, when it moves from one medium to another. Because the light bends, the image you see appears to be bent as well. **Relating Cause and Effect** ***Why do the underwater parts of the skewers appear to be closer to you than the parts above water?***

Refraction A light wave can refract, or bend, when it passes at an angle from one medium into another. You can easily observe two common effects of refraction when light travels from air into water. Refraction makes underwater objects appear closer and larger than they really are. Refraction can also make an object, such as a skewer, appear to break at the surface of the water, as shown in Figure 19.

Refraction can also sometimes cause a mirage. A **mirage** is a false or distorted image. Mirages occur because light travels faster in hot air than in cooler, denser air. On a sunny day, air tends to be hotter just above the surface of a road than higher up. Normally, light travels from the sun all the way to the ground before being reflected. But on a hot day, light is gradually refracted as it moves into layers of hotter and hotter air. This gradual refraction causes some of the light to follow a curved path, rather than a straight path to the ground. Light that reaches your eyes after traveling in this manner can look as if it was reflected from a layer of water. Mirages also form this way above the hot sand in deserts.

Reading Checkpoint *What is a mirage?*

Polarization Light with waves that vibrate in only one plane is **polarized light.** Polarizing filters transmit light waves that vibrate in this way. Look at Figure 20. Unpolarized light vibrates in all directions. A vertical polarizing filter stops waves vibrating on a horizontal plane. Waves vibrating on a vertical plane pass through. A horizontal polarizing filter then blocks the waves vibrating on a vertical plane. To understand how a polarizing filter works, think of a light wave as being like a postcard that you push through a mail slot in a door. If you hold the postcard so that it lines up with the mail slot, then you can easily push it through. But if the postcard is at an angle to the mail slot, it has trouble passing through. In the same way, a polarizing filter blocks waves with electric fields vibrating in one direction.

Figure 20 This simplified model shows how polarizing filters behave. A vertical polarizing filter blocks light that is horizontally polarized. **Applying Concepts** ***What would happen if you looked at light through a horizontally polarizing filter and a vertically polarizing filter at the same time?***

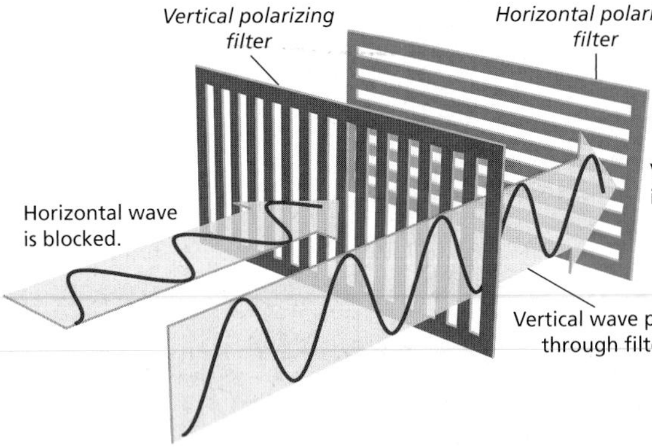
Vertical polarizing filter
Horizontal polarizing filter
Vertical wave is blocked.
Horizontal wave is blocked.
Vertical wave passes through filter.

Facts and Figures

Rainbows A rainbow is a series of concentric colored arcs that form when light from the sun passes through air containing water drops, usually from rain or fog. The rainbow is visible in the direction opposite to that of the sun. The different colors are caused by the refraction and internal reflection of light rays that enter the water drop. Because sunlight is made of light of varying frequencies, these different frequencies refract at different angles in the water drop. The different frequencies (and colors) emerge from the drop and form bands of color in the sky. One edge of the rainbow is red (the wavelength that refracts the least in the water drop) and the other edge is violet (the wavelength that refracts the most in the water drop). The other colors of the visible spectrum fill in the region between red and violet.

Light reflecting from a nonmetallic flat surface, such as a window or the surface of a lake, can become polarized. When sunlight reflects from a horizontal surface, horizontally polarized light reflects more strongly than the rest of the sunlight. This reflection produces glare. To block the glare, polarized sunglasses have vertically polarized filters, which block the horizontally polarized light.

Scattering Earth's atmosphere contains many molecules and other tiny particles. These particles can scatter sunlight. **Scattering** means that light is redirected as it passes through a medium. Look at Figure 21. A scattering effect reddens the sun at sunset and sunrise. Most of the particles in the atmosphere are very small. Small particles scatter shorter-wavelength blue light more than light of longer wavelengths. The sunlight encounters more of the molecules and tiny particles that scatter the shorter-wavelength colors. By the time the sunlight reaches your eyes, most of the blue and even some of the green and yellow have been scattered. Most of what remains for your eyes to detect are the longer wavelengths of light, orange and red.

When the sun is high in the sky, its light travels a shorter distance through Earth's atmosphere. It scatters blue light in all directions much more than other colors of light. Scattering explains why the sky appears blue on a sunny day, even though air itself is colorless.

Figure 21 The lower the sun is on the horizon, the more of the atmosphere the light travels through before it reaches Earth's surface. In certain weather conditions, the blue, green, and yellow wavelengths of sunlight are heavily scattered. What's left to enjoy are the beautiful reds and oranges of sunrise and sunset.

Section 18.3 Assessment

Reviewing Concepts

1. Explain the differences among opaque, transparent, and translucent materials. Name two objects made from each type of material.
2. List and explain three things that can happen to a light wave when it enters a new medium.
3. What is the difference between diffuse reflection and regular reflection?
4. What happens to light that passes through a horizontal polarizing filter?

Critical Thinking

5. **Predicting** A black car reflects much less light than a white car. Which car's surface will be warmer after 1 hour of sunshine? Explain.
6. **Formulating Hypotheses** A mountain climber finds that her sunglasses are not blocking glare from a vertical rock wall. What can you hypothesize about the polarizing filters in her sunglasses?
7. **Applying Concepts** On a foggy night, you can see a car's headlight beams but you may not be able to see the car itself. Explain why.

Connecting Concepts

Mechanical Waves Review the behaviors of mechanical waves discussed in Section 17.2, such as reflection and refraction. Compare them with the behaviors of light.

3 ASSESS

Evaluate Understanding L2

Ask students to identify objects or locations in the classroom that are examples of transparency, translucency, opaqueness, regular reflection, and diffuse reflection. Have students explain why their example is correct.

Reteach L1

Use Figures 16 to 21 as examples that illustrate the key concepts of the section.

Connecting Concepts

Reflection: In mechanical waves, the energy of the reflected wave is less than the energy of the original wave. The same is true of light waves because some light will be absorbed or transmitted. Refraction: In mechanical waves, refraction occurs because one side of a wave front moves more slowly than the other side when the wave enters a medium at an angle. Light waves also are refracted because they change speed as they move from one medium into another.

Interactive Textbook If your class subscribes to the Interactive Textbook, use it to review key concepts in Section 18.3.

Answer to . . .

Figure 19 *Refraction of light from the skewers makes them appear larger than they really are.*

Figure 20 *The two filters would block all of the light.*

Reading Checkpoint *A mirage is a false or distorted image.*

Section 18.3 Assessment

1. Transparent materials (glass window, water) transmit light. Translucent materials (soaps, frosted glass) scatter light that passes through. Opaque materials (wood table, metal desk) absorb or reflect all incident light.
2. The light can be reflected (bounce off), be absorbed (enter but not exit), or be transmitted (pass through).
3. Diffuse reflection: parallel light waves are reflected in many directions; Regular reflection: reflected parallel light waves are still parallel.
4. Only horizontally polarized light comes out the other side of the filter; all of the rest of the light is blocked by the filter.
5. The black car absorbs much more of the light striking it, so it will be warmer than the white car.
6. The sunglasses have vertically polarized filters that transmit vertically polarized glare reflected from the vertical rock wall.
7. Particles of water in the fog scatter the light from the car's headlights, creating an illuminated "beam" of light that is visible in front of a car. If the car is coming around a corner, the headlight beam is visible before the car is seen.

1 FOCUS

Objectives

18.4.1 **Explain** how a prism disperses white light into different colors.
18.4.2 **Analyze** factors that determine the color of an object.
18.4.3 **Distinguish** among primary, secondary, and complementary colors of light and of pigments.

Reading Focus

Build Vocabulary L2

Vocabulary Knowledge Rating Chart Have students construct a chart with four columns labeled Term, Can Define or Use It, Have Heard or Seen It, and Don't Know. Have students copy the six terms into the first column and rate their term knowledge by putting a check in one of the other columns. Ask how many students actually know each term. Have them share their knowledge. Ask focused questions to help students predict text content based on the term, thus giving students a purpose for reading. After students have read the section, have them re-rate themselves.

Reading Strategy L2

a. Blue **b.** Magenta **c.** Cyan **d.** Yellow
For primary colors of pigments:

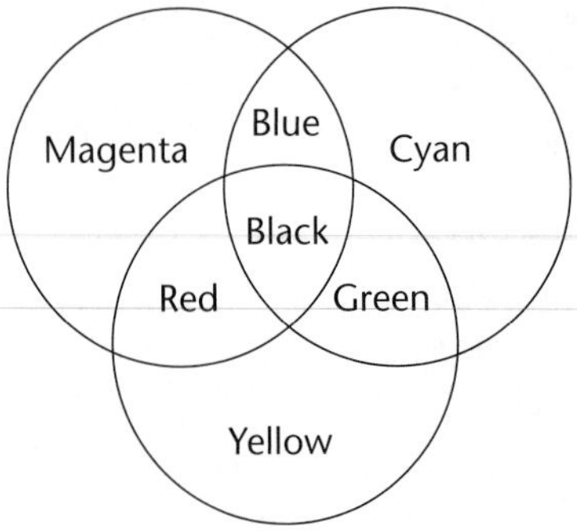
Magenta
Blue
Cyan
Black
Red
Green
Yellow

18.4 Color

Reading Focus

Key Concepts

- How does a prism separate white light?
- What determines the color of an object?
- What are the primary colors of light?
- What are the primary colors of pigments?

Vocabulary

- dispersion
- primary colors
- secondary color
- complementary colors of light
- pigment
- complementary colors of pigments

Reading Strategy

Venn Diagram Copy the Venn diagram below. After you read, label the diagram for mixing primary colors of light. Make a similar diagram for mixing primary colors of pigments.

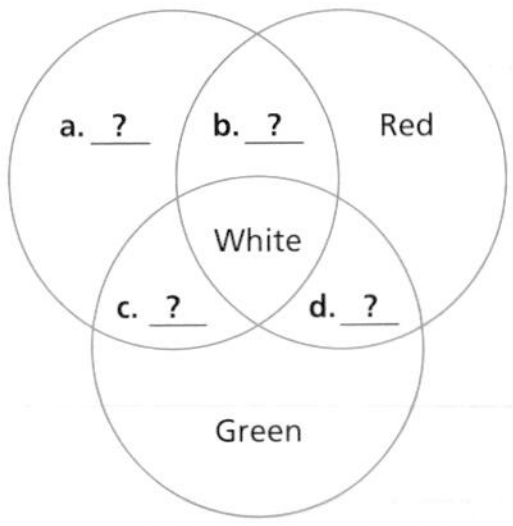
a. ?
b. ?
Red
White
c. ?
d. ?
Green

Have you ever zoomed in on a color photograph displayed on a computer screen? If you have, you've seen that the photograph is made up of many tiny squares, called *pixels,* as shown in Figure 22. Your computer screen might be set to display 256 colors, thousands of colors, or even millions of colors. All of these colors are generated using various combinations of only three colors of light. If you were to print the same photograph, your printer would also use only three colors, plus black, to create the image out of tiny dots of ink. The three colors the computer uses are different from the three the printer uses. How can that be?

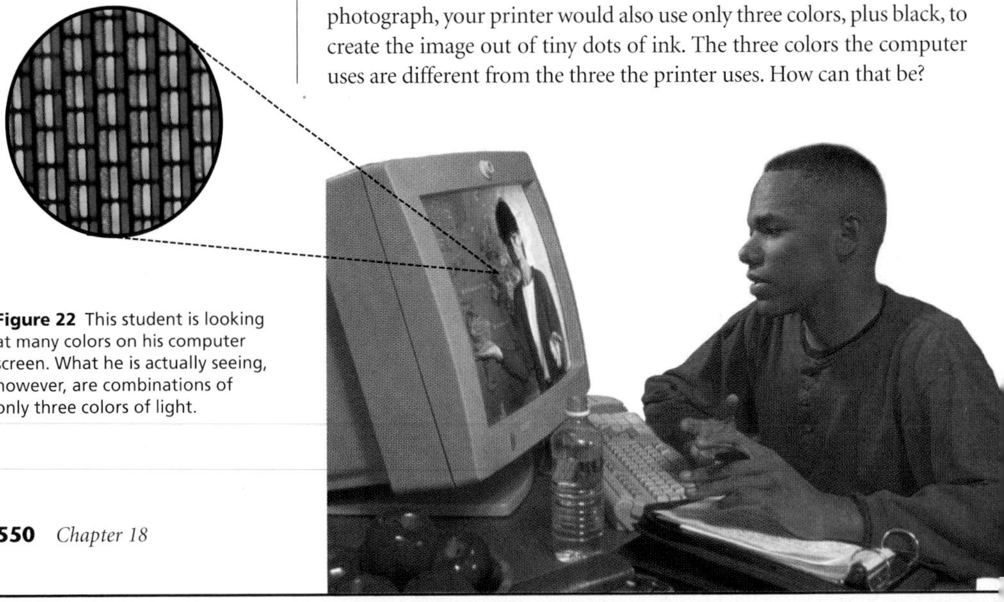

Figure 22 This student is looking at many colors on his computer screen. What he is actually seeing, however, are combinations of only three colors of light.

Section Resources

Print
- ***Laboratory Manual,*** Investigation 18A
- ***Reading and Study Workbook With Math Support,*** Section 18.4
- ***Transparencies,*** Section 18.4

Technology
- ***Interactive Textbook,*** Section 18.4
- ***Presentation Pro CD-ROM,*** Section 18.4
- ***Go Online,*** NSTA SciLinks, Color

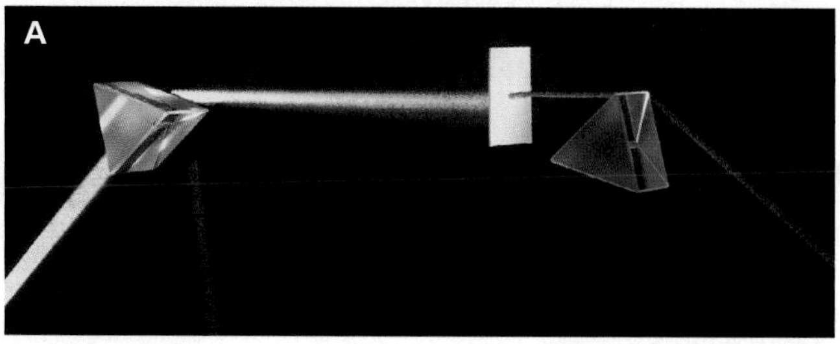
A

Figure 23 White light is dispersed by prisms and water droplets. **A** When white light passes through a prism, the shorter wavelengths are bent more than the longer wavelengths. The colors are separated. When red light enters the second prism, it is refracted but the color does not change. **B** Water droplets separate the colors of sunlight, producing a rainbow.

B

Separating White Light Into Colors

In 1666, the English physicist Isaac Newton investigated the visible spectrum. First, he used a glass prism to produce a visible spectrum from sunlight. With screens, he then blocked all colors of light except blue. Next, he placed a second prism where the blue light was visible. The second prism refracted the blue light but had no further effect on the color. Newton's experiments showed that white sunlight is made up of all the colors of the visible spectrum.

How does a prism separate white light into a visible spectrum? **As white light passes through a prism, shorter wavelengths refract more than longer wavelengths, and the colors separate.** Look at Figure 23A. When red light, with its longer wavelength, enters a glass prism, it slows down the least of all the colors, and so is bent the least. Violet light is bent the most. The process in which white light separates into colors is called **dispersion.**

A rainbow gives a beautiful example of dispersion. Droplets of water in the air act like prisms. They separate sunlight into the spectrum. When light enters a raindrop, it slows down and refracts. Then it reflects off the far inner surface of the raindrop. It refracts again as it exits the raindrop, speeds up, and travels back toward the source of the light.

Reading Checkpoint *What process causes a rainbow?*

The Colors of Objects

Would it surprise you to learn that an object of any color does not have a definite color? An object's color is the color of light that reaches your eye when you look at the object. **The color of any object depends on what the object is made of and on the color of light that strikes the object.** Sunlight contains all the colors of the visible spectrum. But when you look, for example, at a red car in sunlight, the red paint reflects mostly red light. Most of the other colors in white light are absorbed at the surface of the paint.

Go Online NSTA SCI LINKS

For: Links on color
Visit: www.SciLinks.org
Web Code: ccn-2184

Customize for English Language Learners

Think-Pair-Share
Have students work in pairs to think of situations in which the color of an object changes because of the light shining on it. Examples include a building at sunset or a shirt viewed under colored lights at a dance. Strengthen discussion skills by having students share their examples with the class. Encourage students to refer to Figure 24 for help in explaining the colors seen under different lighting conditions.

2 INSTRUCT

Separating White Light Into Colors

Use Visuals L1

Figure 23 Review refraction with students. Ask, **After leaving the prism, how does the path of red light compare to the path of blue light?** *(Both colors travel in a straight line. The red light travels at a different angle because it refracts less when passing through the prism.)* **If red and blue light refracted the same amount, would they be separated by the prism?** *(No)* **What is the purpose of the white card with the hole?** *(It blocks all of the colors except red.)* **What happens to the red light at the second prism?** *(The red light changes direction but is not separated into new colors).* **What can you conclude about the nature of red light and white light?** *(Red light is more fundamental than white light because it cannot be separated into other colors.)*
Visual, Logical

The Colors of Objects

Build Science Skills L2

Controlling Variables Help students see the importance of changing one variable at a time. If you look at a red object in white light and then look at a blue object in green light, two variables change, so you cannot draw valid conclusions. By comparing an object (with one color) under two different colors of light, only one variable changes, so valid conclusions can be drawn.
Logical, Visual

Go Online NSTA SCI LINKS

Download a worksheet on color for students to complete, and find additional teacher support from NSTA SciLinks.

Answer to . . .

Reading Checkpoint *A rainbow is caused by dispersion.*

Mixing Colors of Light

Address Misconceptions L2

Many students do not understand the difference between mixing colored lights and mixing pigments. Point out that when two beams of differently colored light overlap, colors are added. This result is in contrast to the more familiar experience of subtracting colors of light by mixing paints or inks that contain different light-absorbing pigments.
Visual

Build Reading Literacy L1

Compare and Contrast Refer to page **226D** in **Chapter 8**, which provides the guidelines for comparing and contrasting.

Students can avoid confusing light and pigments by studying similarities and differences in Figure 25 and Figure 26. Have students complete a compare-contrast table. Ask, **How are the figures similar?** *(Both have primary colors, secondary colors, and include red, green, blue, cyan, yellow, and magenta.)* **How are the figures different?** *(The three primary colors form white in one figure and black in the other. Red, blue, and green are primary colors of light but secondary colors of pigment. Cyan, yellow, and magenta are secondary colors of light but primary colors of pigment.)*
Visual

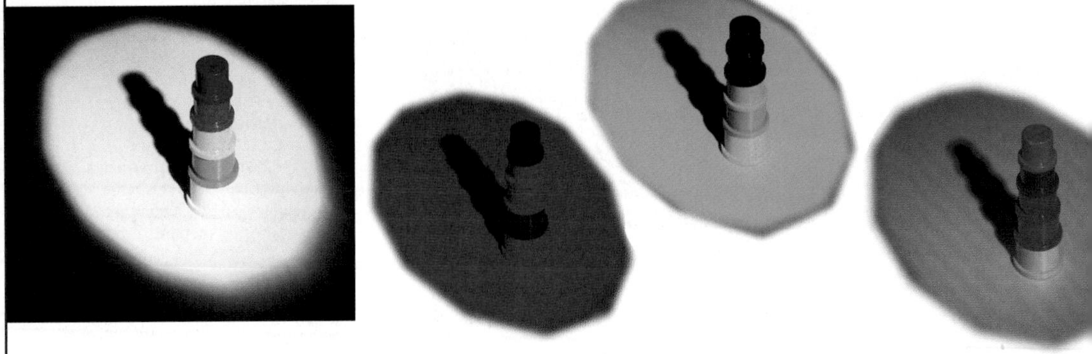

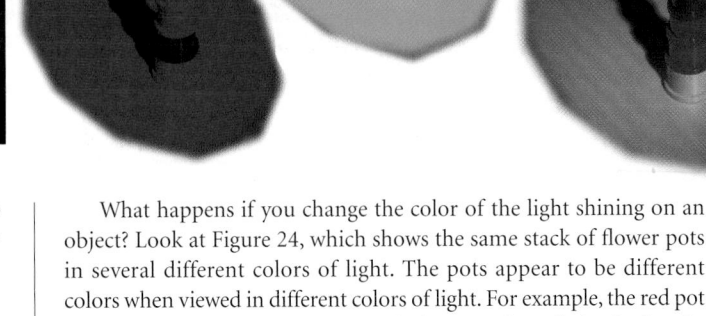

Figure 24 Under white light, the pots appear white, green, yellow, red, and blue. **Observing** ***How does the red pot appear under red, green, and blue light?***

What happens if you change the color of the light shining on an object? Look at Figure 24, which shows the same stack of flower pots in several different colors of light. The pots appear to be different colors when viewed in different colors of light. For example, the red pot looks black when viewed in blue light because the red plastic absorbs all of the light striking it. No red light reaches the object, so none can be reflected from it.

Mixing Colors of Light

Figure 25 shows how equal amounts of three colors of light—red, green, and blue—combine to produce white light. **Primary colors** are three specific colors that can be combined in varying amounts to create all possible colors. **The primary colors of light are red, green, and blue.**

When red light strikes a white surface, red light is reflected. Similarly, when blue light strikes a white surface, blue light is reflected. What happens if both red light and blue light strike a white surface? Both colors are reflected and the two colors add together to make a third color, magenta. When colors of light are mixed together, the colors add together to form a new color.

The secondary colors of light are cyan, yellow, and magenta. Each **secondary color** of light is a combination of two primary colors. Therefore, if you add a primary color to the proper secondary color, you will get white light. Any two colors of light that combine to form white light are **complementary colors of light.** A complementary color pair is a combination of one primary color and one secondary color. Blue and yellow are complementary colors of light, as are red and cyan, and green and magenta.

Figure 25 The three primary colors of light are red, green, and blue. When any two primary colors combine, a secondary color is formed. **Observing** ***What color of light is produced when all three primary colors combine in equal amounts?***

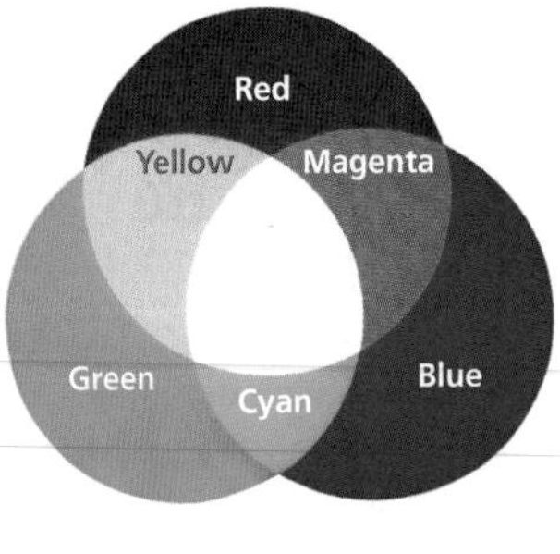
Red
Yellow
Magenta
Green
Cyan
Blue

Reading Checkpoint *How is a secondary color of light formed?*

Facts and Figures

Wavelength, Frequency, and Color It is better to think of color in terms of frequency than in terms of wavelength. The frequency of a wave is determined by the frequency of the source of the wave. When a light wave enters a new medium, the wavelength and speed of the wave change, but the frequency stays the same.

From an energy standpoint, a photon has a specific energy equal to Planck's constant multiplied by the frequency of the wave. Thus, a photon is defined by frequency, not by wavelength. When a photon enters a new medium, it slows down and its wavelength changes, but its energy (and therefore its frequency) remains unchanged.

Mixing Pigments

Paints, inks, photographs, and dyes get their colors from pigments. A **pigment** is a material that absorbs some colors of light and reflects other colors. Stone Age cave paintings were made with natural pigments from colored earth and clay. Over the centuries, natural pigments have been obtained from many sources, including metal oxide compounds, minerals, plants, and animals. Today's artists use paints made from natural pigments as well as from synthetic, or manufactured, pigments.

The primary colors of pigments are cyan, yellow, and magenta. Perhaps you have noticed that color printers and photocopiers use these three colors, plus black. You can mix varying amounts of these primary pigment colors to make almost any other color. Each pigment reflects one or more colors. As pigments are mixed together, more colors are absorbed and fewer colors are reflected. When two or more pigments are mixed together, the colors absorbed by each pigment are subtracted out of the light that strikes the mixture.

Look at Figure 26. The light filters absorb light in much the same way pigments do. When cyan and magenta are combined, blue is formed. Cyan and yellow combine to form green. Yellow and magenta combine to form red. The secondary colors of pigments are red, green, and blue. Any two colors of pigments that combine to make black pigment are **complementary colors of pigments.**

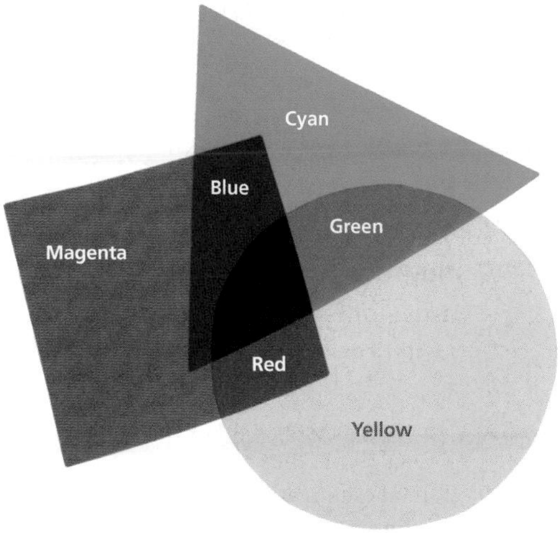

Cyan
Blue
Green
Magenta
Red
Yellow

Figure 26 The three primary colors of pigments are cyan, yellow, and magenta. When the three primary colors of pigments are combined, the secondary colors of pigments are formed. **Interpreting Diagrams** ***Which colors of pigments combine to make black?***

Section 18.4 Assessment

Reviewing Concepts

1. Explain how a prism separates white light into the colors of the spectrum.
2. What determines the color of an object?
3. What three colors of light can combine to form any other color?
4. What three colors of pigments can combine to form any other color?
5. Explain how the process of dispersion of light forms a rainbow.
6. What are pigments? Explain how different pigments affect light.

Critical Thinking

7. **Predicting** What color would a blue wall appear under green light?
8. **Applying Concepts** Why does combining equal amounts of cyan, yellow, and magenta paints form black?

Writing in Science

Explain a Concept Write a letter to a friend who is not in class with you. Explain how an object gets its color. Give evidence and use examples to support your explanation.

Mixing Pigments

Teacher Demo

Overlapping Filters L2

Purpose Students investigate how colors combine by addition and subtraction.

Materials 2 overhead projectors; red, green, and blue acetate filters

Procedure On the surface of an overhead projector, overlap red and green filters. Have students describe what they see projected on the screen. Ask them to predict what will happen when red and blue or green and blue filters overlap.

Expected Outcome Each filter subtracts all colors except one, so two overlapping filters subtract all colors to produce black. **Visual, Group**

3 ASSESS

Evaluate Understanding L2

Have students invent stage-lighting scenarios in which they describe clothing seen under a particular color of light. Encourage students to brainstorm what the clothing colors might be when viewed in white light.

Reteach L1

Compare Figures 25 and 26 to review how colors of light are different from colors of pigments.

Writing in Science

Student letters should discuss how color is reflected by an object and how the color depends on the color(s) of light shining on the object.

Interactive Textbook If your class subscribes to the Interactive Textbook, use it to review key concepts in Section 18.4.

Section 18.4 Assessment

1. Each wavelength refracts a different amount, separating the colors in white light.
2. The color depends on what the object is made of and the color(s) shining on the object.
3. Red, green, and blue
4. Cyan, yellow, magenta
5. Light refracts as it passes in and out of water droplets, separating the colors of the rainbow.
6. A pigment is a material that absorbs some colors and reflects others; each pigment reflects different colors.
7. A blue wall reflects blue light, so under green light the blue wall will appear black.
8. Cyan, yellow, and magenta paints combine in equal amounts to form black paint because these are the three primary colors of pigments.

Answer to . . .

Figure 24 *In red light, the red pot is red; in blue light or green light, the red pot looks black.*

Figure 25 *White light*

Figure 26 *Cyan + magenta + yellow; cyan + red; yellow + blue; magenta + green*

Reading Checkpoint *It is formed when two primary colors combine.*

CONCEPTS in Action

New Light on Old Art **L2**

Background

When a painting is suspected of being a forgery, scientists analyze it using a variety of noninvasive techniques such as optical microscopy, scanning electron microscopy (SEM), X-ray radiography, X-ray fluorescence (XRF), and infrared photography. In optical microscopy, light from the painting passes through a series of lenses in a microscope to produce a magnified image of the painting's surface. In X-ray radiography, the painting is bombarded with X-ray radiation. Areas that contain high-atomic-weight pigments such as white lead and lead-tin yellow appear light in the resulting image. Cracks and areas of low-atomic-weight pigments absorb fewer X-rays and appear dark.

X-ray fluorescence (XRF) is able to determine the types of elements present by bombarding the painting with X-rays. Instead of being scattered, the X-rays are absorbed. The energy that is absorbed results in the emission of X-rays from the paint. The frequency of the emitted X-ray identifies the elements in the paint.

Infrared photography is used to reveal the presence of charcoal or graphite drawings beneath the paint layers. The drawings are revealed because the infrared radiation is absorbed by carbon in the drawing, but not by other substances in the paint.

CONCEPTS in Action

New Light on Old Art

How does an expert know if a painting is by a famous artist, or is a fake? Scientific methods use electromagnetic radiation—visible light, ultraviolet, infrared, and X-rays.

Scientific methods cannot prove that a painting is genuine, but they can prove that it is a forgery. Careful examination may reveal aspects of the painting—the artist's methods or the materials used—that come from a time period later than the supposed date of the painting.

The simplest techniques used to examine paintings are those involving visible light. Looking at a cross section of a paint sample with a microscope or hand lens shows how the artist built up the layers of paint.

Scientists are able to examine the structure of the paint pigment in detail using high-powered microscopes. The structure can reveal whether the pigment is natural or has been made synthetically. Because synthetic paint pigments were not developed until the 1800s, the presence of synthetic pigment indicates the earliest date for the painting.

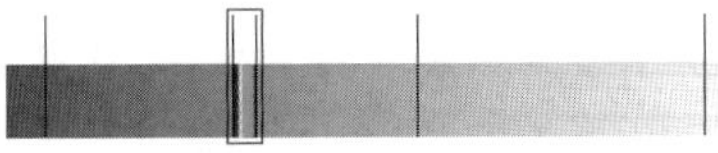

VISIBLE LIGHT

Interpreting visible light
This is the part of the electromagnetic spectrum to which human eyes are sensitive. Paint pigments reflect some parts of the visible spectrum and absorb others, so the eye perceives them as colored.

Examining samples
Using scalpels and tweezers, experts take tiny samples from a painting to examine the painted surface.

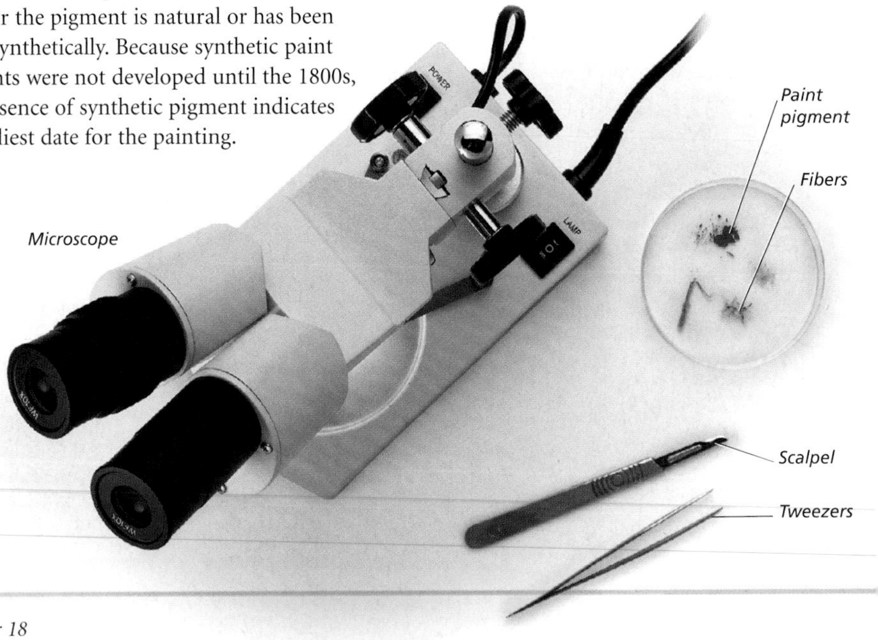

Microscope
Paint pigment
Fibers
Scalpel
Tweezers

Examining the Paint Surface

Identifying the pigments used in a painting usually requires taking one or more tiny samples from the painting. This sampling must be done with extreme care.

Carmine pigment
COCHINEAL BEETLES

Yellow lake pigment
BUCKTHORN BERRIES

Powdered pigment

Natural materials
Before the 1800s, most pigments used by artists were from natural sources. Many, including yellow lake, were obtained from plants. Some, such as carmine or cochineal, were of animal origin. Others, like ultramarine, came from minerals.

Lapis lazuli *was ground to a powder to make ultramarine pigment.*

Ultramarine pigment

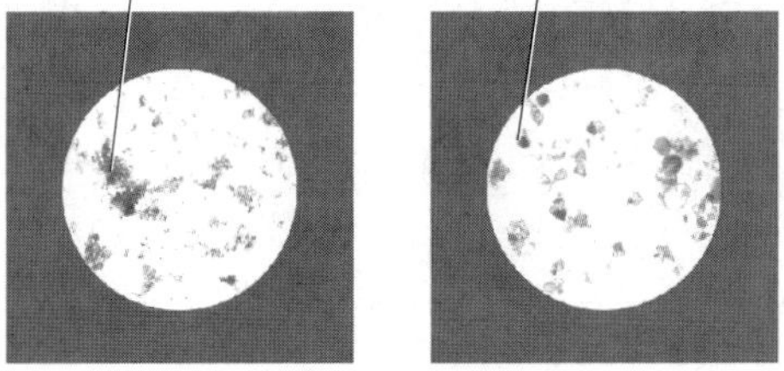
Synthetic pigment has round, fine particles
Natural pigment has rough, crystalline particles

Under the microscope
High magnifications (100 to 500 times) show the physical structure of pigment particles. Here, the particles in the sample of synthetic ultramarine are different from those in the natural sample. Synthetic ultramarine was introduced in 1828, so paintings using this pigment could not have been made earlier than that year.

Build Science Skills **L2**

Observing
Have students find out about some famous art forgeries by using the Internet or the library. Have them print or photocopy the forgeries. Then, have students look for a photograph of the original painting in art books or an encyclopedia. Have the class compare the two paintings. Ask, **Can you see any differences between the forgery and the real painting?** *(The differences will depend upon the paintings chosen.)* **What tests could be done to determine if the painting is a forgery?** *(Possible answers may include, examine a cross section of a paint sample under a microscope or hand lens; or examine an intact painting with ultraviolet light, infrared, and X-rays.)*
Visual, Portfolio

Build Science Skills L2

Comparing and Contrasting ACTIVITY

Purpose Students compare and contrast the properties of paints.

Materials acrylic, watercolor, and oil paints of the same or similar color; several small artist paint brushes; watercolor paper; hand lens; several flat, wooden sticks

Class Time 10 minutes, then 10 minutes after one week

Procedure Have students paint a strip of each type of paint on both the watercolor paper and the flat, wooden stick. Make sure that students label each strip with the type of paint used. Place the strips in an area where they will remain undisturbed. After one week, have students observe all of the paint strips and record their observations.

Safety Have students wear lab aprons and disposable gloves.

Expected Outcome Students will be able to observe the characteristics of each paint type.
Kinesthetic, Group

Looking Beneath the Paint Surface

Rather than removing samples of the paint layer, non-invasive methods examine an intact painting by using the nonvisible regions of the electromagnetic spectrum. Ultraviolet, infrared, and X-rays can reveal many secrets that are invisible to the human eye.

Ultraviolet rays are best at showing surface features. The varnish that is the top layer of most paintings will fluoresce when exposed to ultraviolet. This fluorescence shows whether the original varnish has been disturbed.

Infrared rays can penetrate the layers of paint, so infrared imaging can be used to detect charcoal sketches and other images that are often hidden beneath the painted surface.

X-rays are used to look through a painting. X-rays are absorbed by dense materials and pass through others. Pigments that include metal atoms, such as white lead, show up clearly, as do metal objects used in the painting's construction. One forger was caught when X-rays revealed a machine-made nail in the wooden panel under a painting that was supposedly painted in the 1500s! Machine-made nails were not manufactured until the 1800s.

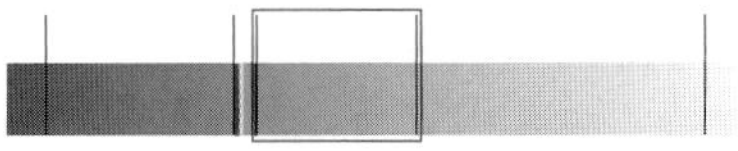
ULTRAVIOLET RAYS

Interpreting ultraviolet radiation
Although transparent to visible light, the varnish layer on the surface of most paintings can be seen using ultraviolet rays. In this copy of Cranach's painting, the ultraviolet makes the varnish layer fluoresce. Dark regions show areas that have been retouched or painted over.

Darker areas have been retouched or painted over.

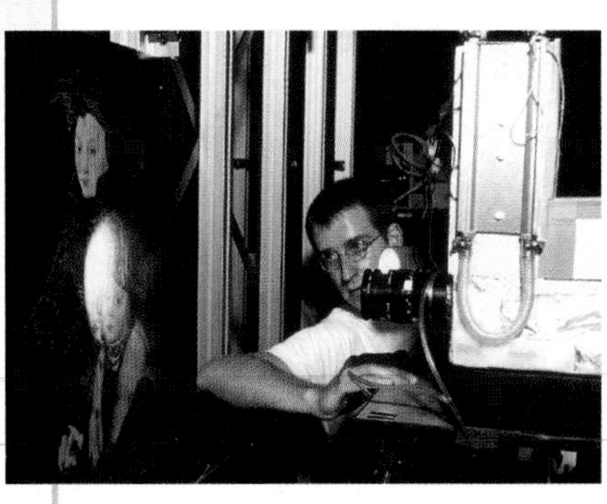

Art forgery detection
A technician operates an infrared scanner. He is examining a copy of a painting by the German painter Lucas Cranach the Elder (1472–1553).

INFRARED RAYS

Interpreting infrared imaging
The penetrating power of infrared most often uncovers preliminary sketches. But infrared imaging can also reveal surprising changes in the development of a work of art. In this self-portrait by Judith Leyster about 1630, the infrared image reveals that the artist originally included a portrait of herself on the easel. But later she changed the portrait to a musician.

Merry musician in the final painting

Infrared rays penetrate layers of paint, revealing an underlying self-portrait.

Part of the overpainted pattern of crossed keys

Horizontal wooden battens used to strengthen the panel

X-RAYS

Interpreting X-rays
X-rays can reveal the creative process at work. In this portrait of Pope Julius II, painted by Raphael in 1511–1512, the X-ray image shows a pattern of crossed keys on the wall behind the seated figure. The keys do not appear in visible light. Because oil paints are opaque to visible light, the artist probably simply painted over the keys.

Going Further

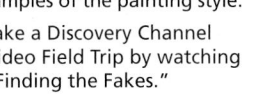

- Choose one of these painting styles to research: impressionism, surrealism, pointillism, or op art. Prepare an oral report to share with the class, including an explanation of the painting style, how light and color are used in the style, and three samples of the painting style.
- Take a Discovery Channel Video Field Trip by watching "Finding the Fakes."

Discovery Channel School Video Field Trip

Going Further

Student reports should contain relevant examples of the selected style. Brief explanations of each style follow.

- **Perspective** The art of picturing objects or a scene in such a way as to show them as they appear to the eye with reference to relative distance or depth.
- **Impressionism** A theory and school of painting exemplified by Claude Monet, Camille Pissarro, and Alfred Sisley, whose aim was to capture a momentary glimpse of a subject, especially by reproducing the changing effects of light. They applied paint to a canvas in short strokes of pure color.
- **Surrealism** A movement in art and literature in which an attempt is made to portray or interrupt the workings of the unconscious mind as manifested in dreams.
- **Pointillism** The method of painting of certain French impressionists in which a white background is systematically covered with tiny points of pure color that blend together when seen from a distance, producing a luminous effect.
- **Op Art** A style of abstract painting utilizing geometric patterns or figures to create various optical effects, such as the illusion of movement.
  Visual, Verbal

Discovery Channel School

Video Field Trip

Finding the Fakes

After students have viewed the Video Field Trip, ask them the following questions: **Why are pigment particles in older paintings different from the pigment particles in modern paintings?** *(Pigments ground by hand contained larger particles that varied in size. Today, machines use rollers that produce smaller, more uniform particles.)* **What sources were used for pigments in old paintings?** *(Rocks, minerals, and plants)* **How can forensic scientists tell if an old painting is a forgery?** *(Student answers may include, pigments found in the painting were not used in the artist's lifetime; brush strokes were not typical of the artist; or the canvas was not made of material used in that time period.)* **Why is it easier to prove that a painting is a forgery than to prove it is authentic?** *(Even if the pigments, style of brush strokes, and canvas material all match, the painting could still be the work of someone of the artist's own time or the work of a skilled forger.)*

1 FOCUS

Objectives

18.5.1 **Explain** how light is produced by common sources of light.
18.5.2 **Describe** the uses of different light sources.
18.5.3 **Distinguish** lasers from other light sources.

Reading Focus

Build Vocabulary L2

Word-Part Analysis Ask students what words they know other than those in the vocabulary list that have the key word parts *lum-*, *in-*, *fluor-*, and *co-*. *(illuminate, inactive, fluoride,* and *cooperate)* Give a definition of each word part. *(Lum- means "light," in- means "not," fluor- means "to flow,"* and *co- means "together.")* Give additional examples that share these word parts. *(Lumen, inactive, fluorine,* and *co-author)*

Reading Strategy L2

a. Filament gets hot. Sample answer: Fluorescent—electric current heats electrodes, which emit electrons; electrons strike mercury vapor atoms; mercury atoms emit ultraviolet rays; ultraviolet rays strike phosphor coating; phosphors emit visible light.

2 INSTRUCT

Incandescent Light

Use Visuals L1

Figure 27 Have students carefully examine the photograph. Ask, **How many filaments can you see in this bulb?** *(Possible answer: It looks like there are two filaments on top and one more filament lower down that is not glowing as brightly.)* **How could a bulb use more than one filament?** *(Several filaments could be used to vary the brightness of the bulb, as in a three-way bulb.)*
Logical, Visual

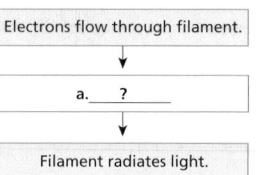

18.5 Sources of Light

Reading Focus

Key Concepts

- What are the six common sources of light?
- How does each type of light source generate light?

Vocabulary

- luminous
- incandescent
- fluorescence
- phosphor
- laser
- coherent light

Reading Strategy

Sequencing Copy and complete the flowchart below. As you read, pick two other light sources and complete a similar flowchart showing how each source generates light.

Incandescent Bulb

Electrons flow through filament.
↓
a. ___?___
↓
Filament radiates light.

Figure 27 An incandescent bulb contains a filament. As electrons flow through the filament, the filament gets hot and emits light. **Formulating Hypotheses** ***Why is a 100-watt bulb generally brighter than a 75-watt bulb?***

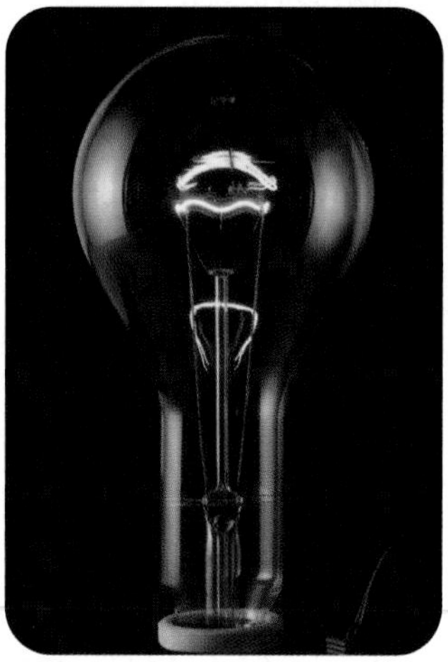

As sunlight fades toward the end of the day, objects around you become less and less visible. When the sun has completely set, you can no longer see your surroundings. Objects are invisible in the dark because no light is available to reflect off them. But some things, such as flashlights and fireflies, produce their own light. Objects that give off their own light are **luminous.** The sun is luminous, as are all light sources.

Common light sources include incandescent, fluorescent, laser, neon, tungsten-halogen, and sodium-vapor bulbs. Each type of bulb produces light in a different way.

Incandescent Light

The light produced when an object gets hot enough to glow is **incandescent.** Figure 27 shows an incandescent light bulb. Inside, you can see the filament, a thin coil of wire stretched between two thicker wires. **When electrons flow through the filament of an incandescent bulb, the filament gets hot and emits light.**

The filaments in incandescent light bulbs are made of a substance called tungsten. Incandescent light bulbs are filled with a mixture of nitrogen gas and argon gas at very low pressure. These gases do not react with the filament as oxygen would, and so the filament lasts longer. Incandescent bulbs give off most of their energy as heat, not light.

Section Resources

Print
- ***Reading and Study Workbook With Math Support,*** Section 18.5
- ***Transparencies,*** Section 18.5

Technology
- ***Interactive Textbook,*** Section 18.5
- ***Presentation Pro CD-ROM,*** Section 18.4
- ***Go Online,*** *Science News,* Light and optics

Fluorescent Light

In a process called **fluorescence** (floo uh RES uns), a material absorbs light at one wavelength and then emits light at a longer wavelength. A **phosphor** is a solid material that can emit light by fluorescence. **Fluorescent light bulbs emit light by causing a phosphor to steadily emit photons.** A fluorescent bulb, such as the one in Figure 28, is a glass tube that contains mercury vapor. Inside, the glass is coated with phosphors.

When electric current flows through a fluorescent bulb, small pieces of metal called electrodes heat up and emit electrons. The electrons hit atoms of the mercury vapor, causing the mercury atoms to emit ultraviolet rays. The ultraviolet rays strike the phosphor coating on the inside of the tube and the atoms emit visible light.

You may have noticed that office buildings and schools use mostly fluorescent lights. Fluorescent tubes do not get as hot as incandescent bulbs because they emit most of their energy as light. This means that they use energy very efficiently. One 18-watt fluorescent tube provides the same amount of light as a 75-watt incandescent bulb, and the fluorescent tube lasts ten times longer.

Reading Checkpoint *What happens during fluorescence?*

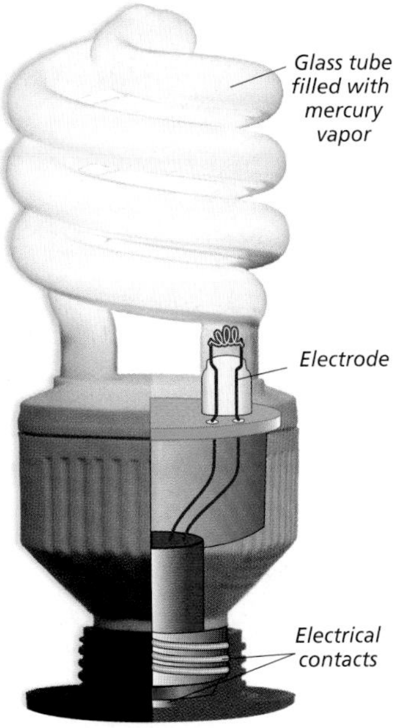
Glass tube filled with mercury vapor
Electrode
Electrical contacts

Figure 28 The electrodes in a fluorescent bulb emit electrons that cause the mercury atoms to emit ultraviolet rays. These rays cause the phosphor coating to emit light.

Quick Lab

Comparing Fluorescent and Incandescent Light

Materials

spectroscope, clear incandescent bulb, fluorescent bulb, colored pencils

Procedure

1. Turn on a clear, incandescent bulb. **CAUTION** *Incandescent bulbs get quite hot after they have been on for some time.* Observe the spectrum of the light coming from the incandescent bulb through a spectroscope.
2. Use colored pencils to draw this spectrum. Label the source of the spectrum.
3. Repeat Steps 1 and 2 with a fluorescent bulb.

Analyze and Conclude

1. **Comparing and Contrasting** How do the spectra produced by incandescent and fluorescent lights compare?
2. **Drawing Conclusions** During fluorescence, electrons absorb energy and move to specific higher energy levels. As they move back to a lower energy level, they release energy in the form of light. How does this fact help explain the appearance of the spectrum of fluorescent light?

Fluorescent Light

FYI

In fluorescent light, the phosphors are usually zinc sulfide with traces of copper.

Quick Lab

Comparing Fluorescent and Incandescent Light L2

Objective

After completing this activity, students will be able to

- explain the difference in spectra of incandescent and fluorescent lights.

Address Misconceptions

Students may think that all white light is similar and consists of a continuous distribution of frequencies that includes the entire visible spectrum. Use the observations in this activity to help students overcome this misconception.

Skills Focus Observing, Inferring

Prep Time 15 minutes

Class Time 20 minutes

Safety Caution students that they should never directly observe the spectrum of the sun or any other intense light source because it can cause immediate, permanent eye damage. Caution students to avoid touching bulbs, which may become hot.

Expected Outcome Students will observe that incandescent bulbs produce continuous spectra, while the spectra of fluorescent light sources include narrow lines of various colors.

Analyze and Conclude

1. Incandescent light has a continuous spectrum. The spectrum of fluorescent light consists of a number of colored lines.

2. The lines are produced by photons with specific energies emitted by electrons returning from higher energy levels to the ground state.

Visual, Group

Customize for Inclusion Students

Behaviorally Disordered

Divide the class into six groups. Each group will be assigned a light source. Explain that the goal of each group is to find out details about each kind of light source. Foster self-esteem by encouraging groups to give individuals ownership of particular research topics such as historical details or specialized uses. Give groups choices for presenting their results to minimize pressure related to this project. Options include written reports, posters, multimedia presentations, a Web site, or a mock science museum exhibit.

Answer to . . .

Figure 27 *Hypothesis: A 100-watt bulb is generally brighter because it emits more energy per second.*

Reading Checkpoint *A material converts UV rays into visible light.*

Laser Light

Build Reading Literacy L2

SQ3R Refer to page **530D** in this chapter, which provides guidelines for SQ3R (Study, Question, Read, Recite, Review).

Teach this independent-study skill as a whole-class exercise. Direct students to survey the section and write headings such as Laser Light. As they survey, ask students to write one question for each heading, such as "How does a laser emit light?" Then, have students write answers to the questions as they read the section. After students finish reading, demonstrate how to recite the questions and answers, explaining that vocalizing in your own words helps you retain what you learned. Finally, have students review their notes the next day.
Auditory, Group

DK HOW It Works

Gas Laser L2

Material excited in a laser is called lasing material. Lasing material can be a gas (CO_2), a gas mixture (helium-neon), a liquid (liquid crystals or organic dyes in a liquid solution or suspension), or a solid crystal (ruby). The lasing material determines the frequency of the light produced. Lasers do not have to produce visible light—there are infrared, ultraviolet, and X-ray lasers.

Interpreting Photographs The waves in the laser beam all have the same wavelength and direction of travel, and their peaks coincide.
Visual

For Enrichment L3

Interested students can make a multimedia presentation for the class explaining an application such as CD players, fiber optic networks, and laser eye surgery.
Verbal, Portfolio

Laser Light

A **laser** is a device that generates a beam of coherent light. The word *laser* stands for *l*ight *a*mplification by *s*timulated *e*mission of *r*adiation. **Laser light is emitted when excited atoms of a solid, liquid, or gas emit photons.** Light in which waves have the same wavelength, and the crests and troughs are lined up, is **coherent light.** A beam of coherent light doesn't spread out significantly from its source, so the light has a relatively constant intensity. The energy it carries may be focused on a small area.

Lasers can cut through metals and make computer chips. Surgeons use lasers to cut or repair damaged tissue. Lasers carry information through optical fibers. Laser light is used to measure distances precisely.

DK HOW It Works

Gas Laser

Laser light is produced by exciting the atoms of a solid, liquid, or gas so that they emit photons. Some of these photons collide with other excited atoms and stimulate the emission of more photons. Eventually some photons are released as an intense beam of light. The gas laser shown here uses a mixture of helium and neon gases. **Interpreting Photographs** ***How does a laser produce coherent light?***

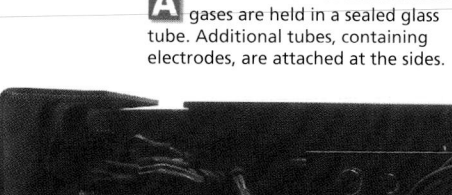

A Gas mixture Helium and neon gases are held in a sealed glass tube. Additional tubes, containing electrodes, are attached at the sides.

Fully reflective mirror *Photons bounce between this and a second, semi-reflective mirror.*

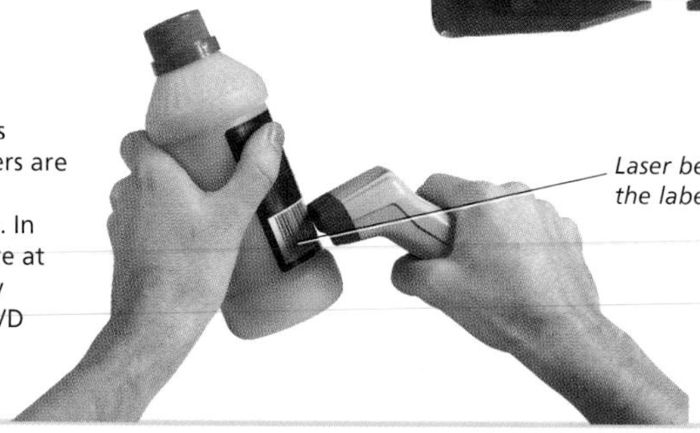

Using lasers Hand-held devices incorporating lasers are used in stores for reading bar codes. In the home, they are at the heart of many devices such as DVD and CD players.

Laser beam scans the label.

Facts and Figures

Diverging Laser Beams Lasers do not necessarily produce parallel rays of light. A typical pocket diode laser produces red light that would diverge like a point source. A lens inside the laser collimates the beam (makes the rays nearly parallel).

The Lunar Laser Ranging Experiment began in 1969 when Apollo 11 astronauts left reflectors on the moon. Scientists send a laser beam from Earth and measure the time it takes to detect a return signal. The time delay gives the distance to the moon to an accuracy of about 3 cm. The experiment has been used to precisely measure the moon's orbit and movement of tectonic plates on Earth. To hit the reflectors, a laser beam is fired in the reverse direction through a telescope pointing toward the moon. The beam starts out with the same width as the telescope mirror (a few meters). When the beam reaches the moon, it has diverged to a width of more than 6 km.

Neon Light

A big city at night is likely aglow in neon lights. **Neon lights emit light when electrons move through a gas or a mixture of gases inside glass tubing.** Many lights called neon lights contain gases other than neon. Often, other gases including helium, argon, and krypton are used in neon lights. Helium gas gives off a pink light. A mixture of argon gas and mercury vapor produces greenish-blue light. Krypton gas produces a pale violet light. Pure neon emits red light when electrons flow through the gas. Each kind of gas emits photons of different energies, and therefore different colors. The different photons emitted combine to give each glowing gas a distinctive color. The color of glass used to make the tube can also affect the color of the light.

Go Online SCIENCE NEWS®
For: Articles on light and optics
Visit: PHSchool.com
Web Code: cce-2185

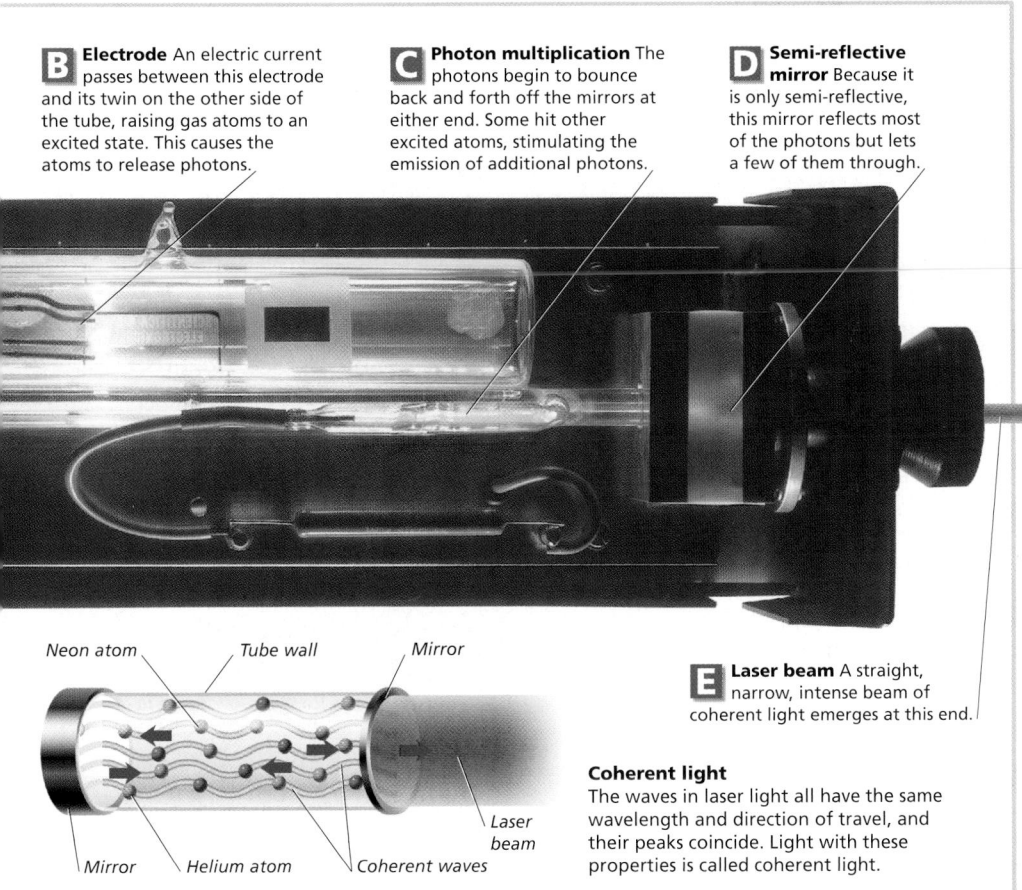

B Electrode An electric current passes between this electrode and its twin on the other side of the tube, raising gas atoms to an excited state. This causes the atoms to release photons.

C Photon multiplication The photons begin to bounce back and forth off the mirrors at either end. Some hit other excited atoms, stimulating the emission of additional photons.

D Semi-reflective mirror Because it is only semi-reflective, this mirror reflects most of the photons but lets a few of them through.

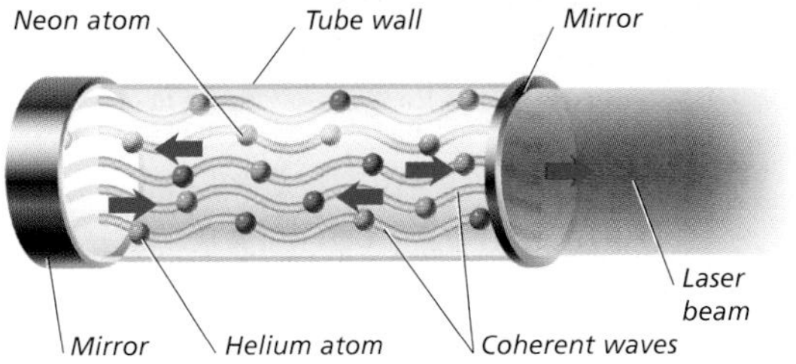
Neon atom
Tube wall
Mirror
Laser beam
Mirror
Helium atom
Coherent waves

E Laser beam A straight, narrow, intense beam of coherent light emerges at this end.

Coherent light
The waves in laser light all have the same wavelength and direction of travel, and their peaks coincide. Light with these properties is called coherent light.

Neon Light

Build Science Skills

L3

Inferring

ACTIVITY

Purpose Students observe and compare the spectra of different neon lights.

Materials spectroscope, neon lights

Safety Caution students never to view the sun or other intense light sources with a spectroscope because irreversible eye damage could result. Advise students to avoid touching neon lights, which can get quite hot.

Advance Prep To construct an inexpensive spectroscope, tape a 1-cm square of diffraction grating over a hole punched in an index card. Attach the card to cover one end of a small cardboard or plastic tube. Cover the other end of the tube with a card containing a narrow slit. Students will view spectra through the end of the tube with the diffraction grating.

Procedure Have students take home spectroscopes to observe spectra of neon signs near their homes. The lights of neon signs have fairly simple line spectra. Ask students to compare these spectra to determine which signs contain mixtures of gases or are made of colored glass that filters out certain colors.

Expected Outcome If the spectrum of a neon light appears to be a combination of two simpler spectra that students have observed, it probably contains a mixture of the gases responsible for the simpler spectra. If two spectra appear identical except for a specific region of one spectrum that is absent in the other, one of the signs may be made of colored glass that filters out a range of light frequencies.
Visual, Kinesthetic

Go Online SCIENCE NEWS®

Science News provides students with current information on light and optics.

Sodium-Vapor Light

Build Science Skills L2

Inferring Ask, **Why do sodium-vapor lights have less glare than incandescent lights?** *(In sodium-vapor lights, light comes from vapor filling the entire tube, rather than from a small filament. The light is emitted from a larger area and is easier to look at directly.)* **Logical, Visual**

Tungsten-Halogen Light

Integrate Health L2

Free, protective metal mesh covers have been offered to owners of tungsten-halogen lights because the bulbs get so hot. Have students find out how these covers can prevent fires. **Verbal**

3 ASSESS

Evaluate Understanding L2

Invite students to write quiz questions with answers. Announce that good questions will be used on the next test.

Reteach L1

Make a flowchart showing how each light source emits light. Cut each chart into pieces and shuffle and distribute them to students. Ask students to put the pieces back in the correct order.

Connecting Concepts

Sample answer: Incandescent—Electrons flow in wire (electrical energy); moving electrons heat the filament (thermal energy); filament glows (electromagnetic energy).

Interactive Textbook If your class subscribes to the Interactive Textbook, use it to review key concepts in Section 18.5.

Figure 29 The yellow color of sodium-vapor light makes objects look different than they look in sunlight.

Sodium-Vapor Light

Sodium-vapor lights contain a small amount of solid sodium, as well as a mixture of neon and argon gases. **As electric current passes through a sodium-vapor bulb, it ionizes the gas mixture. The mixture warms up and the heat causes the sodium to change from a solid into a gas.** The current of electrons knocks electrons in sodium to higher energy levels. When the electrons move back to lower energy levels, the sodium atoms emit light. Sodium-vapor lights are energy efficient and give off very bright light. Many streets and parking lots are illuminated with sodium-vapor lights. Figure 29 shows how sodium-vapor light produced with neon and argon can alter the color of the objects it illuminates.

Tungsten-Halogen Light

Tungsten-halogen light is produced in much the same way as incandescent light. But unlike incandescent lights, a tungsten-halogen's bulb has a small amount of a halogen gas, such as iodine, bromine, or fluorine. **Inside a tungsten-halogen bulb, electrons flow through a tungsten filament. The filament gets hot and emits light.** The halogen gas reduces wear on the filament, so tungsten-halogen bulbs last longer than incandescent bulbs. The bulb of a tungsten-halogen light is made of quartz, because quartz has a high melting point. If glass were used, it would start to melt when the bulb got hot.

Section 18.5 Assessment

Reviewing Concepts

1. Name six common sources of light.
2. Describe how each type of bulb produces visible light.
3. Why are fluorescent light bulbs often used in office buildings and schools?
4. List three uses for lasers.
5. How are tungsten-halogen bulbs different from incandescent bulbs?

Critical Thinking

6. **Comparing and Contrasting** How are the six main types of lights similar? How are they different?
7. **Applying Concepts** Why do some bulbs heat up more than others?
8. **Formulating Hypotheses** A friend rubs a compact fluorescent bulb on her shirt on a dry day, and the bulb lights up for a moment. Propose a hypothesis to explain why.

Connecting Concepts

Energy Review the types of energy in Section 15.1: mechanical, chemical, thermal, electrical, electromagnetic, and nuclear. Then pick two light sources and describe the energy changes in each after you turn on the light.

Section 18.5 Assessment

1. Incandescent, fluorescent, lasers, neon lights, sodium-vapor, tungsten-halogen
2. Incandescent: filament gets hot and emits light; Fluorescent: UV rays cause phosphors to emit visible light; Laser: excited atoms of a solid, liquid, or gas emit photons of coherent light; Neon: excited gas atoms emit light when they drop back down to a lower energy level; Sodium-vapor: a gas mixture ionizes, vaporizing sodium and producing excited atoms that emit light when they drop back down to a lower energy level; Tungsten-halogen: filament gets hot and emits light.
3. Fluorescent bulbs are very efficient.
4. Cut through metals; make computer chips; cut or repair tissue in surgery; transmit signals in fiber-optic cables
5. Tungsten-halogen bulbs are hotter and use a mixture of inert and halogen gases.
6. Incandescent and tungsten-halogen lights use a glowing filament. Fluorescent lights cause phosphors to fluoresce. Lasers emit coherent light. Neon lights and sodium vapor lights emit light when excited atoms return to a lower energy level. Refer to pp. 558–562 for differences.
7. Bulbs that heat a gas or a filament will heat up more than other light sources.
8. Hypothesis: The shirt acquires a net charge. The shirt's electric field excites mercury atoms in the bulb.

Exploration Lab

Mixing Colored Lights

What is color? How many different colors can be formed from a combination of only three colors? In this exploration, you will examine what happens when lights of three different colors are mixed.

Problem

How can you produce a range of colors from three lights of different colors?

Materials

- sources of red, blue, and green light
- tape
- large sheet of white paper

Skills

Observing

Procedure

1. On a separate sheet of paper, make a copy of the data table shown.

Data Table

Light Sources	Colors of Lights	Colors of Shadows
Red only		
Blue only		
Green only		
Red and blue		
Red and green		
Blue and green		
Red, blue, and green		

2. Dim the room lights. Turn on the red light source and shine it on a large sheet of white paper. In your data table, record the colors you observe on the paper. **CAUTION** *Do not touch lamps when they are on. They may be hot.*
3. Place your hand between the light source and the paper as shown. Record the color of your hand's shadow.
4. Repeat Steps 2 and 3 with the blue and then with the green light source.
5. Now turn on the red and blue light sources and allow their beams to partially overlap. Record your observations in your data table.

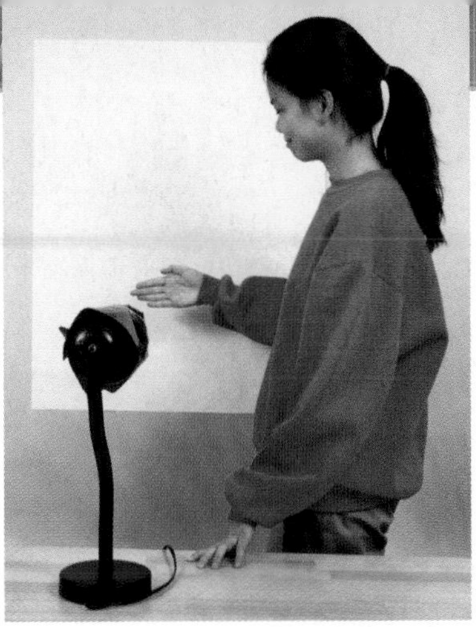

6. Place your hand in the overlapping beams of light. Note the colors of any shadows that your hand makes. Record your observations.
7. Repeat Steps 5 and 6 with the red and green light sources. Then repeat Steps 5 and 6 with the blue and green light sources.
8. Turn on all three light sources and allow their beams to overlap. Record your observations.
9. Place your hand in the overlapping red, green, and blue beams. Note the colors of any shadows that your hand makes on the white paper. Record your observations.

Analyze and Conclude

1. **Observing** What happened when two colored lights overlapped?
2. **Analyzing Data** How did the combination of two colored lights produce the shadows you observed?
3. **Applying Concepts** Explain how combining three colored lights produced the colors you observed.
4. **Drawing Conclusions** From the shadows you observed when using three colored lights, what can you conclude about how colors of light combine? Explain your answer.

Go Further Examine the effects of red, green, and blue lights on the appearance of familiar objects, such as red apples and green grass. Prepare a report explaining your observations and present the report to the class.

Exploration Lab

Mixing Colored Lights L2

Objective
After completing this activity, students will be able to
- describe how colors of light combine by addition.

Skills Focus **Observing, Formulating Hypotheses**

Prep Time 10 minutes

Advance Preparation The red, blue, and green light sources can be flood-lights, slide projectors, overhead projectors, or flashlights with filters. The light sources should provide a distinct colored spot of light whose position on the paper can be adjusted.

Class Time 40 minutes

Safety Take care that all electrical equipment is handled properly and plugged only into GFCI-protected receptacles. Do not allow students to handle the light sources because they will be extremely hot. Warn students not to look directly at the light sources or into the sun. Make sure there are no objects that create stumbling hazards, as students work in dim light.

Expected Outcome Overlapping two beams of primary colors of light produces secondary colors and two shadows, one of each primary color of light. Overlapping equal intensities of all three primary colors produces white light and three shadows that are secondary colors.

Sample Data

Red light only: Red light, dark shadow; Blue light only: Blue light, dark shadow; Green light only: Green light, dark shadow; Red and blue light: Magenta light, red and blue shadows; Red and green light: Yellow light, red and blue shadows; Blue and green light: Cyan light, red and blue shadows; Red, blue, and green light: White light, green, red, and blue shadows

Go Further

A colored object will reflect light of its own color and absorb light of other colors. For example, a red apple lit only by green light looks black.
Verbal, Visual

Analyze and Conclude
1. Two colors combined to make a new color.
2. Because there were two light sources, there were two overlapping shadows. In areas on the paper where the hand blocked only one beam of light, the other areas were lit by the other beam of light. Therefore, each shadow was the color of one beam of light.
3. Overlapping two beams produced secondary colors. Combining all three primary colors in equal intensity produced white light.
4. The colors of the shadows show how colors of light combine. In areas where the hand blocked one beam, the shadow was lit by the two other lights. Therefore, these areas were secondary colors of light. For example, where the hand blocked only the blue beam, the shadow was lit by red and green light, producing a yellow shadow. Similarly, red and blue light combined to produce a magenta shadow, and blue and green light combined to produce a cyan shadow.

Study Guide

Study Tip

Review Regularly
Tell students to make reviewing their notes part of their homework plan. They shouldn't just review homework that is assigned every night. Tell students that by reviewing their work for a few minutes each day they will spend less time studying for tests.

Thinking Visually

a. Infrared rays
b. Visible light
c. Ultraviolet rays
d. X-rays

Assessment

Interactive Textbook If your class subscribes to the Interactive Textbook, your students can go online to access an interactive version of the Student Edition and a self-test.

Reviewing Content

1. c **2.** a **3.** b
4. c **5.** d **6.** b
7. d **8.** b **9.** a
10. d

Understanding Concepts

11. The electric and magnetic fields regenerate each other.
12. Constructive and destructive interference
13. Infrared cameras are used to find victims because the human body is usually warmer than its surroundings.
14. Excessive exposure to ultraviolet rays can cause sunburn, wrinkles, skin cancer, and damage to eyes. In moderation, ultraviolet rays help the skin to produce vitamin D; they are also used to kill microorganisms in ventilation systems and to help plants grow in nurseries.

CHAPTER 18

Study Guide

18.1 Electromagnetic Waves

Key Concepts

- Electromagnetic waves are produced when an electric charge vibrates or accelerates.
- Electromagnetic waves can travel through a vacuum as well as through matter. The speed of light in a vacuum, *c*, is 3.00×10^8 m/s.
- Electromagnetic waves vary in wavelength and frequency.
- Electromagnetic radiation behaves sometimes like a wave and sometimes like a stream of particles.
- Light spreads out as it moves away from its source.

Vocabulary

electromagnetic waves, *p. 533;* electric field, *p. 533;* magnetic field, *p. 533;* electromagnetic radiation, *p. 533;* photoelectric effect, *p. 537;* photons, *p. 537;* intensity, *p. 538*

18.2 The Electromagnetic Spectrum

Key Concepts

- The electromagnetic spectrum includes radio waves, infrared waves, visible light, ultraviolet rays, X-rays, and gamma rays.
- Electromagnetic waves are used in communications, medicine, and industry.

Vocabulary

electromagnetic spectrum, *p. 540;* amplitude modulation, *p. 541;* frequency modulation, *p. 541;* thermograms, *p. 543*

18.3 Behavior of Light

Key Concepts

- Materials can be transparent, translucent, or opaque.
- When light strikes a new medium, it can be reflected, absorbed, or transmitted.

Vocabulary

transparent, *p. 546;* translucent, *p. 547;* opaque, *p. 547;* image, *p. 547;* regular reflection, *p. 547;* diffuse reflection, *p. 547;* mirage, *p. 548;* polarized light, *p. 548;* scattering, *p. 549*

18.4 Color

Key Concepts

- As white light passes through a prism, shorter wavelengths refract more than longer wavelengths, and the colors separate.
- The color of any object depends on what the object is made of and on the color of light that strikes the object.
- The primary colors of light are red, green, and blue.
- The primary colors of pigments are cyan, yellow, and magenta.

Vocabulary

dispersion, *p. 551;* primary colors, *p. 552;* secondary color, *p. 552;* complementary colors of light, *p. 552;* pigment, *p. 553;* complementary colors of pigments, *p. 553*

18.5 Sources of Light

Key Concepts

- Common light sources include incandescent, fluorescent, laser, neon, tungsten-halogen, and sodium-vapor bulbs.
- Each light source produces light in a different way.

Vocabulary

luminous, *p. 558;* incandescent, *p. 558;* fluorescence, *p. 559;* phosphor, *p. 559;* laser, *p. 560;* coherent light, *p. 560*

Thinking Visually

Web Diagram Copy the web diagram below onto a sheet of paper. Use information from the chapter to complete the diagram.

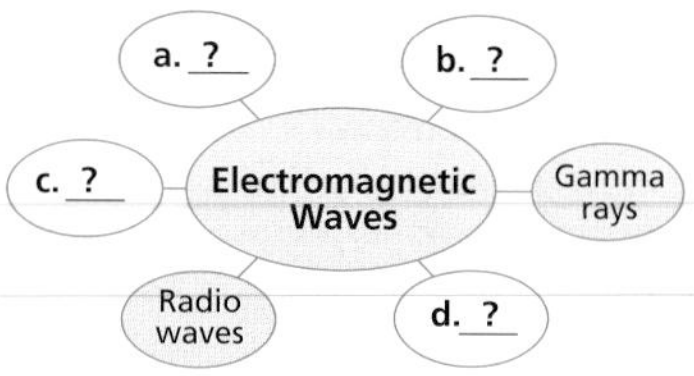

a. ?
b. ?
c. ?
Electromagnetic Waves
Gamma rays
Radio waves
d. ?

Chapter Resources

Print
- ***Chapter and Unit Tests,*** Chapter 18 Test A and Test B
- ***Test Prep Resources,*** Chapter 18

Technology
- ***Computer Test Bank,*** Chapter Test 18
- ***Interactive Textbook,*** Chapter 18
- ***Go Online,*** PHSchool.com, Chapter 18

CHAPTER 18

Assessment

Interactive textbook with assessment at PHSchool.com iText

Reviewing Content

Choose the letter that best answers the question or completes the statement.

1. Electromagnetic waves
   a. all have the same wavelength.
   b. do not carry energy.
   c. can travel through empty space.
   d. all have the same frequency.

2. The particle model describes light as
   a. a stream of photons.
   b. an interference pattern.
   c. a wave.
   d. an electric field.

3. The electromagnetic waves with the highest frequency are
   a. infrared rays. **b.** gamma rays.
   c. ultraviolet rays. **d.** radio waves.

4. Microwaves and radar are
   a. infrared rays. **b.** X-rays.
   c. radio waves. **d.** ultraviolet rays.

5. Light that vibrates in only one direction is
   a. scattered. **b.** reflected.
   c. refracted. **d.** polarized.

6. Objects appear fuzzy through a material that is
   a. polarized. **b.** translucent.
   c. transparent. **d.** opaque.

7. Combining equal intensities of red light, green light, and blue light makes
   a. a secondary color.
   b. a complementary color.
   c. black light.
   d. white light.

8. A green object
   a. absorbs green light.
   b. reflects green light.
   c. absorbs yellow and blue light.
   d. reflects red and blue light.

9. An object that produces its own light is
   a. luminous. **b.** coherent.
   c. opaque. **d.** translucent.

10. Which type of light bulb uses phosphors?
   a. neon **b.** incandescent
   c. tungsten-halogen **d.** fluorescent

Understanding Concepts

11. How do electric and magnetic fields interact in an electromagnetic wave?

12. What behavior of light is evidence for a wave model of light?

13. Why are infrared rays useful in search-and-rescue operations?

14. How are ultraviolet rays harmful? How can they be helpful?

15. X-rays can take pictures of your bones but visible light cannot. Explain why.

16. Explain why you can see through the glass walls of the terrarium below.

17. How do polarized sunglasses work?

18. What does a prism do to white light?

19. How are the secondary colors of light related to the primary colors?

20. What are complementary colors of pigments?

21. When mixing colors of light, why does combining a secondary color with its complementary color give white light?

22. Explain why fluorescent lights are more efficient than incandescent lights.

23. Explain how laser light is different from ordinary visible light.

24. What is the purpose of halogen gas in a tungsten-halogen lamp?

Assessment (continued)

15. X-rays have high energy and can penetrate matter, such as muscle, that light cannot. But X-rays are absorbed by teeth and bones, so these areas appear as white on an X-ray photograph.
16. The glass is transparent.
17. Polarized sunglasses block glare with vertically polarized filters, which block the horizontally polarized light reflected from horizontal surfaces.
18. A prism spreads out the colors in white light, separating the colors into a spectrum.
19. Each secondary color of light is produced by the combination of two primary colors.
20. Complementary colors of pigments are two colors that combine to make black pigment, such as blue and yellow, green and magenta, or red and cyan.
21. A secondary color is a combination of two primary colors; when added to its complementary color (the third primary color), white light results.
22. Fluorescent lights do not get as hot as incandescent lights. They are more efficient because they emit most of their energy as visible light.
23. Laser light is coherent light, which means all of the waves have the same wavelength and the crests and troughs are lined up. Laser light can form a beam that can be focused on a small area.
24. The halogen gas reduces wear on the filament, so the bulb lasts longer than an incandescent bulb.

Homework Guide

Section	Questions
18.1	1–2, 11–12, 33–35
18.2	3–4, 13–15, 25–26, 36, 39
18.3	5–6, 16–18, 27, 37
18.4	7–8, 19–21, 28–31, 38
18.5	9–10, 22–24, 32

Chapter 18

Critical Thinking

25. Similarities: Microwaves and infrared photons have less energy than invisible light photons. They both travel in a vacuum at the speed of light. Both have applications in communications. Differences: Microwaves are used for cooking and reheating food. Infrared photons have more energy than microwaves.
26. The frequency of the reflected radio waves is reduced because the car is moving away from a stationary radar source.
27. The sunset would be yellow because there would be no scattering if there is no atmosphere.
28. Light: The primary colors red, green, and blue mix to form white light. Pigment: The primary colors cyan, yellow, and magenta mix to form black pigment.
29. In all three cases, two primary colors of pigments combine to form a secondary color of pigment.
30. Only one color, magenta, is needed to produce black.
31. Students might predict that black will result because all three primary colors are being mixed. But the colors are not mixed in equal amounts. Two parts yellow plus two parts magenta plus one part cyan should result in black plus yellow and magenta, which is the same as black plus red. The result should be a dark red.
32. Laser light is very high intensity light that does not spread out, so it can damage tissue in the eye.

Math Skills

33. 3.3 m
34. 6.0×10^9 Hz
35. 40,260,000,000 mi/s; 670,000,000 mi/h

Concepts in Action

36. Rotating the food in a microwave oven will help the food to heat evenly. It works because areas of destructive interference, where little heating occurs, do not stay in one position within the food.
37. Mirages occur when light is gradually refracted through layers of hot air. At 32°C, a mirage is more likely because refraction will be greater than at 23°C.
38. The stage lights shining on the main character must be red. The green pants look black because there is no green light to reflect from them. Using white stage light will allow both the jacket and the pants to look their true colors.

39. Student answers should mention that lengthy exposure to the sun's ultraviolet rays causes both short-term and long-term damage to the skin. Sunscreens absorb ultraviolet rays before they reach the skin. If students have done the Quick Lab Evaluating Sunscreen, they may use their results to support the claims in the advertisement.

CHAPTER 18

Assessment *(continued)*

Critical Thinking

25. **Comparing and Contrasting** How are microwaves and infrared rays similar? How are they different?

26. **Applying Concepts** How does the frequency of a car's returning radar signal change if the car moves away from the radar source?

27. **Applying Concepts** What color would the sunset be if you observed it on the moon? (*Hint:* the moon has no atmosphere.)

28. **Comparing and Contrasting** List the three primary colors of light and the three primary colors of pigments. What is the result if the three primary colors of light are mixed? What is the result if the three primary colors of pigments are mixed?

Use the illustration below to answer Questions 29–31.

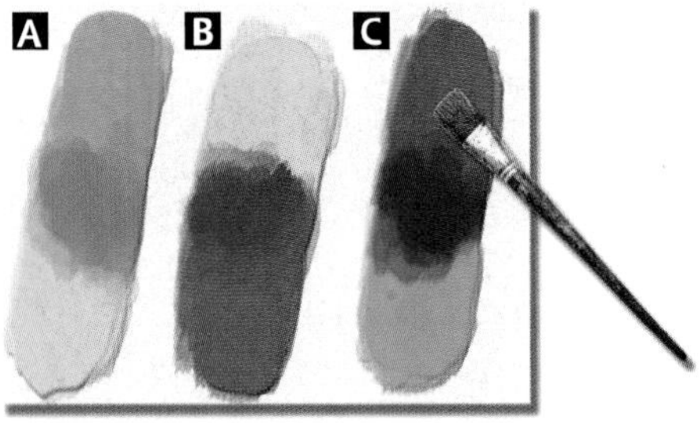
A
B
C

29. **Interpreting Photos** Describe each combination of colors in A, B, and C.

30. **Applying Concepts** If you had green paint, such as produced in mixture A in the illustration, what is the fewest number of colors you could mix with it to get black? What would the color or colors be?

31. **Predicting** What color would you expect to make if you combined cyan and yellow from A, magenta and yellow from B, and only the magenta from C? Explain why.

32. **Inferring** Why might it be unsafe to look directly at laser light?

Math Skills

33. **Calculating** An FM radio station broadcasts on a frequency of 91 MHz. What is the wavelength of the wave that carries the coded information?

34. **Calculating** What is the frequency of a microwave that has a wavelength of 0.050 m?

35. **Converting Units** Convert the speed of light to miles per second and miles per hour. (*Hint:* 1 mile = 1610 meters)

Concepts in Action

36. **Problem Solving** What can you do to ensure even heating of microwaved food? Why does that work?

37. **Predicting** Are you more likely to see a mirage in the desert when the temperature is 32°C or 23°C? Explain why.

38. **Relating Cause and Effect** You are working the lights for a school play. The red jacket on the main character looks red, but her green pants look black. What is happening? How can you make both her jacket and her pants look their true color?

39. **Writing in Science** Write an advertisement for a sunscreen product. Make sure to explain to consumers why ultraviolet rays are dangerous.

Performance-Based Assessment

Comparing and Contrasting Visit a store that sells a variety of light bulbs including incandescent bulbs, tungsten-halogen bulbs, and fluorescent bulbs. Gather information from the packages on price and expected hours of service and display the data in a table. Conclude from your data which kind of bulb provides the most economical lighting for a particular purpose. Write your conclusions in a paragraph and share it with your family and classmates.

Go Online
PHSchool.com

For: Self-grading assessment
Visit: PHSchool.com
Web Code: cca-2180

Standardized Test Prep

Test-Taking Tip

Analyzing Data
Some test questions are based on graphs. Take about 20 seconds to scan the graph. Read the labels. Describe the graph to yourself. *The graph gives information on wavelength, from shorter to longer, and frequency, from lower to higher.* Use the information to select which choice best answers the question.

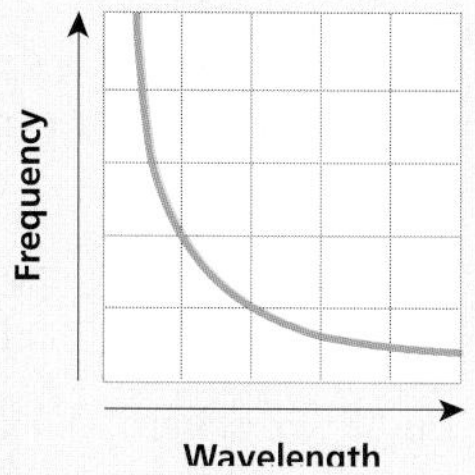

Frequency
Wavelength

What relationship is represented by the graph?

(A) Frequency is directly proportional to wavelength.
(B) Frequency is inversely proportional to wavelength.
(C) Comparing wavelength and frequency shows photon energy.
(D) Waves with lower frequencies and longer wavelengths exhibit the photoelectric effect.
(E) Wavelength is greater than frequency.

(Answer: B)

Choose the letter that best answers the question or completes the statement.

1. In order of increasing frequency, the electromagnetic waves are radio waves, infrared rays,
(A) microwaves, visible light, X-rays, and gamma rays.
(B) visible light, ultraviolet rays, X-rays, and gamma rays.
(C) ultraviolet rays, X-rays, visible light, and radar.
(D) gamma rays, X-rays, ultraviolet rays, and visible light.
(E) gamma rays, X-rays, visible light, and ultraviolet rays.

2. A light source that emits light partly because of its phosphor coating is
(A) an incandescent bulb.
(B) a tungsten-halogen lamp.
(C) a neon tube.
(D) a fluorescent tube.
(E) a laser.

3. A material that reflects or absorbs all of the light that strikes it is
(A) translucent. (B) opaque.
(C) black. (D) transparent.
(E) incandescent.

4. An electromagnetic wave in space has a frequency of 0.5×10^8 Hz. Its wavelength is
(A) 0.6 m. (B) 6 m.
(C) 60 m. (D) 600 m.
(E) 6000 m.

Both a source of red light and a source of blue light shine on a metal, as shown in the diagram below.

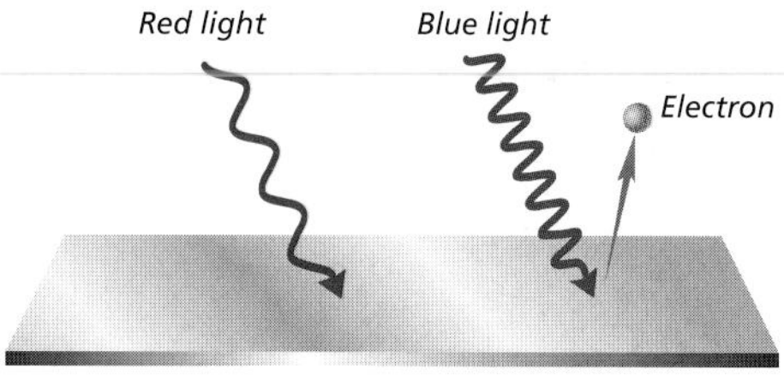

Red light
Blue light
Electron

5. What scientific concept does the diagram represent?
(A) interference
(B) the photoelectric effect
(C) polarization
(D) diffuse reflection
(E) refraction

6. Why was no electron emitted when the red light hit the metal?
(A) Photons of red light have too little energy.
(B) There were not enough photons available.
(C) All electrons had already been emitted when the blue light hit the metal.
(D) Red light is absorbed by metal.
(E) Red light is reflected by metal.

Standardized Test Prep

1. B **2.** D **3.** B
4. B **5.** B **6.** A

Performance-Based Assessment

Student answers must include a data table, and their conclusions need to take into consideration a particular lighting purpose. The data table should be organized with types of bulbs versus cost, lifespan, and other criteria such as brightness in lumens. Sample data for comparable bulbs that can be used in a tabletop desk lamp:

Sample Data Table

Type	Cost	Lumens	Lifespan
100-W long-life incandescent	$0.60	1710	5000 h
100-W tungsten-halogen	$4.50	1800	2000 h
26-W compact fluorescent	$7.50	1900	10,000 h

Go Online
PHSchool.com

Your students can independently test their knowledge of the chapter and print out their test results for your files.

CHAPTER 19

Planning Guide

Use these planning tools
Easy Planner
Teacher Express

SECTION OBJECTIVES	STANDARDS NATIONAL (See p. T18.)	STANDARDS STATE	ACTIVITIES and LABS
19.1 Mirrors, pp. 570–573 1 block or 2 periods **19.1.1 Describe** the law of reflection. **19.1.2 Describe** how a plane mirror produces an image. **19.1.3 Describe** real and virtual images and relate them to converging and diverging light rays. **19.1.4 Describe** the physical characteristics of plane, concave, and convex mirrors and **distinguish** between the types of images they form.	A-1, A-2, C-6		**SE** Inquiry Activity: How Can You Make Glass Disappear? p. 569 **L2** **SE** Quick Lab: Measuring the Height of Your Mirror Image, p. 571 **L2** **SE** Consumer Lab: Selecting Mirrors, p. 593 **L2** **TE** Build Science Skills: Observing, p. 570 **L2** **TE** Teacher Demo: Flashlight Mirrors, p. 572 **L2**
19.2 Lenses, pp. 574–578 1 block or 2 periods **19.2.1 Explain** what causes light to refract. **19.2.2 Define** index of refraction. **19.2.3 Describe** the physical characteristics of concave and convex lenses and **distinguish** between the types of images they form. **19.2.4 Describe** total internal reflection and **explain** its relationship to the critical angle.	A-1, B-6		**TE** Teacher Demo: Combining Lenses, p. 576 **L2** **TE** Build Science Skills: Observing, p. 577 **L2** **LM** Investigation 19A: Investigating Reflection and Refraction **L2**
19.3 Optical Instruments, pp. 580–585 1 block or 2 periods **19.3.1 Distinguish** between how reflecting and refracting telescopes form images. **19.3.2 Explain** how cameras regulate and focus light to form images. **19.3.3 Describe** how light travels in a compound microscope to produce an enlarged image.	A-1, A-2, B-6, C-6, E-2, F-1, G-1, G-2, G-3		**SE** Quick Lab: Building a Pinhole Viewer, p. 585 **L2** **TE** Teacher Demo: Making a Telescope, p. 581 **L2** **TE** Teacher Demo: Two Types of Microscopes, p. 584 **L2** **LM** Investigation 19B: Testing a Solar Furnace **L1**
19.4 The Eye and Vision, pp. 588–592 1 block or 2 periods **19.4.1 Name** the main parts of the eye and **describe** their functions. **19.4.2 Name** common vision problems, **identify** their causes, and **explain** how they can be corrected.	B-6, C-6, E-2, F-1, G-3		

Ability Levels

L1 For students who need additional help
L2 For all students
L3 For students who need to be challenged

Components

SE	Student Edition	**RSW**	Reading & Study Workbook	**CUT**	Chapter & Unit Tests	**T**	Transparencies
TE	Teacher's Edition	**MSPS**	Math Skills & Problem Solving Workbook	**CTB**	Computer Test Bank	**iT**	Interactive Textbook
LM	Laboratory Manual			**TP**	Test Prep Resources	**P**	Presentation Pro CD-ROM
PLM	Probeware Lab Manual			**DC**	Discovery Channel Videotapes & DVDs	**GO**	Internet Resources

RESOURCES PRINT and TECHNOLOGY	SECTION ASSESSMENT
RSW Section 19.1 L1 **T** Chapter 19 Pretest L2 Section 19.1 L2 **P** Chapter 19 Pretest L2 Section 19.1 L2 NSTA SciLinks **GO** Mirrors L2	**SE** Section 19.1 Assessment, p. 573 Interactive Textbook **iT** Section 19.1
RSW Section 19.2 L1 **RSW Math Skill** L2 **MSPS** Section 19.2 L2 **T** Section 19.2 L2 **P** Section 19.2 L2	**SE** Section 19.2 Assessment, p. 578 Interactive Textbook **iT** Section 19.2
RSW Section 19.3 L1 Discovery Channel School **DC** Traveling Light L2 **T** Section 19.3 L2 **P** Section 19.3 L2 Science News **GO** Light and optics L2	**SE** Section 19.3 Assessment, p. 585 Interactive Textbook **iT** Section 19.3
RSW Section 19.4 L1 **T** Section 19.4 L2 **P** Section 19.4 L2	**SE** Section 19.4 Assessment, p. 592 Interactive Textbook **iT** Section 19.4

Go Online

Go online for these Internet resources.

PHSchool.com
Web Code: cch-2193
Web Code: cca-2190

NSTA SciLinks
Web Code: ccn-2191

SCIENCE NEWS®
Web Code: cce-2193

Materials for Activities and Labs

Quantities for each group

STUDENT EDITION

Inquiry Activity, p. 569
vegetable oil, water, 2 clear plastic or glass containers, 2 equal lengths of borosilicate glass tubing

Quick Lab, p. 571
plane mirror, meter stick, newspaper, masking tape

Quick Lab, p. 585
aluminum foil, black construction paper, cardboard tube, pin, wax paper, 4 rubber bands

Consumer Lab, p. 593
plane, convex, and concave mirrors; 2 metric rulers; roll of string; protractor

TEACHER'S EDITION

Build Science Skills, p. 570
graph paper, metric ruler, pencil, plane mirror

Teacher Demo, p. 572
flashlight with a beam that can be focused

Teacher Demo, p. 576
modeling clay, 2 convex lenses, 2 concave lenses, 2 index cards

Build Science Skills, p. 577
5-cm diameter double-convex lens, pencil

Teacher Demo, p. 581
2 convex lenses (one with a focal length of 10 cm and the other with a focal length of 30 cm), 1 stick of modeling clay

Teacher Demo, p. 584
compound microscope, stereo microscope

Build Science Skills, p. 587
flashlight, fiber optic bundle

Chapter Assessment

CHAPTER ASSESSMENT

SE Chapter Assessment, pp. 595–596
CUT Chapter 19 Test A, B
CTB Chapter 19
iT Chapter 19
PHSchool.com GO
Web Code: cca-2190

STANDARDIZED TEST PREP

SE Chapter 19, p. 597
TP Diagnose and Prescribe

Interactive Textbook

Interactive Textbook with assessment at PHSchool.com

CHAPTER 19

Before you teach

From the Author

Sophia Yancopoulos
Manhattan College

Big Ideas

Optics is the science of how mirrors and lenses form images. Light travels in a straight line— except when it doesn't. The laws of optics at this level are straightforward and their applications to telescopes, cameras, fiber optics, and corrective eye gear have an immediate interest.

Forces and Motion Whether reflection or refraction, the bending of light rays depends on the substance the ray is traveling through. It can be tricky to distinguish the different kinds of images formed by concave and convex mirrors and lenses; it will help students if they actually reproduce the ray diagrams themselves, instead of simply looking at them. For a real image, the rays of light actually converge. For a virtual image, the eye and mind assume that light rays are coming in straight lines from the extrapolated point of origin. Students may understand the concept of a virtual image better if they remember that a plane mirror's virtual image is a copy of an object, formed as though the light rays came from behind the mirror. Obviously the rays do not really come from behind the mirror, however, and a virtual image cannot be projected.

The eye is like a self-focusing camera, but the eye's ability to see depends on its shape. Thanks to optics, if a person's cornea or eyeball is the wrong shape for perfect vision, corrective lenses can be used to change the path of the light rays and focus them into a clear image on the retina.

Physics Refresher

Mirrors 19.1

When a light ray reflects from any mirror, the angle of incidence equals the angle of reflection. To see this for a concave mirror, draw a tangent to the surface at the point where the ray is reflected. Then draw a normal line perpendicular to the tangent where the tangent line touches the surface. The angles of incidence and reflection can then be measured from the normal line.

Ray diagrams are useful for determining the locations of images formed by concave mirrors. To draw a diagram, first sketch the object, the mirror, the center of curvature *C*, the focal point *F*, and the principal axis. Next, draw three rays, each starting at the topmost point of the object: (1) parallel to the principal axis, reflected through *F*, (2) through *F*, reflected parallel to the principal axis, and (3) through *C*, reflected back along the same line. The point of intersection of the lines is the location of the tip of the image.

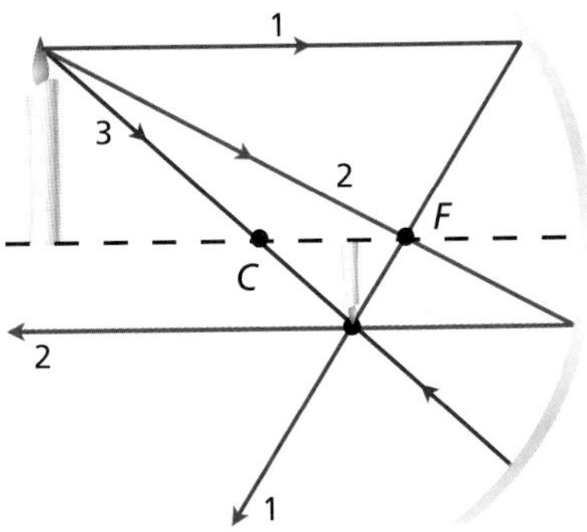
1
3
2
F
C
2
1

Lenses 19.2

A lens is a curved piece of transparent material used to focus light. A diverging lens is curved inward at the center and is thicker at the outer edges. A converging lens is curved outward at the center and is thinner at the outer edges. The focal length of a lens depends on the refractive index n of the lens as well as the shape of the lens (its radius of curvature). The refractive index depends on the material of which the lens is made. A higher refractive index causes a light ray to be bent more. For simplicity, the text refers to converging lenses as convex, and diverging lenses as concave.

Address Misconceptions

Students may mistakenly think that blocking part of a convex lens would block part of the image it forms. However, light rays reflect off an object through all parts of the lens. Blocking part of the lens produces a dimmer, but complete, image. For a strategy to overcome this misconception, see **Address Misconceptions** on **page 576.**

Go Online
NSTA
PD LINKS
For: Teaching methods for optics
Visit: www.SciLinks.org/PDLinks
Web Code: ccn-1999

The fraction of a lens is described by the distance from the object to the lens *(p)*, the distance from the image to the lens *(q)*, and the focal length *(f)*. These distances are related by the lens equation:

$$\frac{1}{p} + \frac{1}{q} = \frac{1}{f}$$

The image distance q is always negative for a virtual image because the image is on the same side of the lens as the object. A real image is on the side opposite that of the object, and it has positive q. For a concave lens, the focal length f is negative because the image is virtual. The image distance q is always negative for a concave lens.

As with concave mirrors, ray diagrams are useful for determining the image formed by convex lenses. The rules used to draw the diagrams are similar to those used for concave mirrors. However, a lens has two focal points equidistant on either side of the lens. The primary focal point is on the side of the object, and the secondary focal point is on the other side of the lens. To sketch the image, first draw the object, the lens, the axis of the lens, the two focal points F_1 and F_2, and the principal axis. Next, draw three rays, each starting at the topmost point of the object: (1) parallel to the principal axis and refracting through F_2, (2) through the center point of the lens, passing undisturbed through to the other side, (3) through F_1 and refracting parallel to the principal axis.

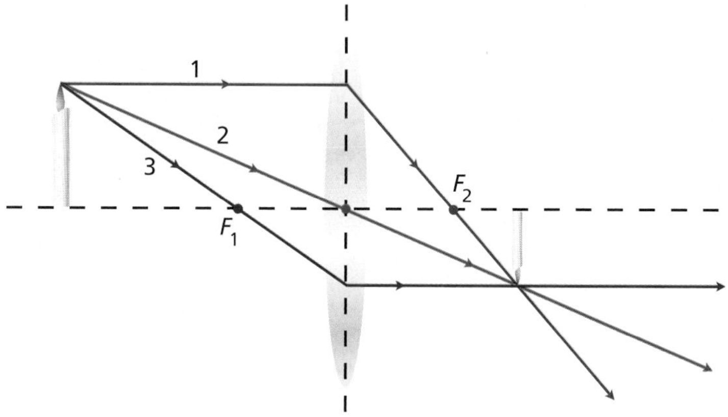
1
2
3
F_1
F_2

The Eye and Vision 19.4

Eyes are optical instruments that gather and focus light reflected and emitted from objects. Light enters the eye through the cornea. It then passes through the pupil and the lens and (ideally) is focused onto the retina. The cornea and the lens are responsible for focusing the light. The eyes' focus can be changed by tightening or relaxing the muscles around the lens. This slightly changes the shape of the lens so that the amount of refraction changes.

The image that is projected onto the retina is inverted and reversed. The brain translates signals from the retina so that it seems upright. However, there is no way that the brain can adapt to an image that is out of focus. The problems of nearsightedness and farsightedness must be corrected before the light enters the eye.

Build Reading Literacy

Using Context Clues

Understanding the Meanings of Words

Strategy Help students determine the meaning of unfamiliar words. This strategy helps students use clues from the surrounding text to help them infer an unfamiliar word's meaning. Before students begin, assign a section in Chapter 19 for them to read, such as The Law of Reflection, pp. 570–571.

Example

- When students encounter a word they are unfamiliar with have them read the rest of the sentence to determine clues other words in the sentence may give as to the meaning of the unfamiliar word.
- Have students read the surrounding sentences looking for hints to the word's meaning.
- Have students synthesize the meaning from a reading of the whole passage.
- Have students scan the text for a possible definition of the word highlighted in bold or an illustration of it in a diagram.
- Once students think they have determined the word's meaning they should verify it by checking in a dictionary.

See p. 580 for a script on how to use the using context clues strategy with students. For additional Build Reading Literacy strategies, see pp. 573, 574, and 590.

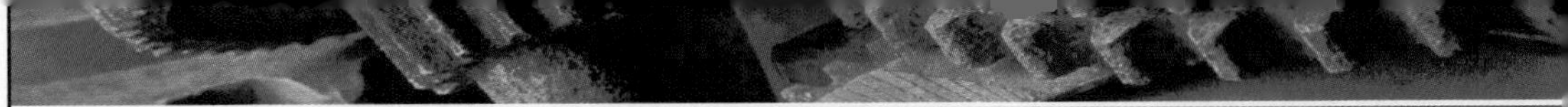

ASSESS PRIOR KNOWLEDGE

Use the Chapter Pretest below to assess students' prior knowledge. As needed, review these Science Concepts with students.

Review Science Concepts

Section 19.1 Review the behavior of light from Chapter 18. Remind students that light waves can be reflected when they strike a new medium. Review the definition of *image*.

Section 19.2 Students should recall that a transparent material transmits light. Review how light rays change as they pass from one medium to another. Remind students that when light passes at an angle from one medium to another, the speed and direction of travel can change.

Section 19.3 Encourage students to review the behaviors of light waves known as reflection and refraction.

Section 19.4 Ask students to recall what they know about the human eye. They should understand that they can see because light reflects from objects into their eyes.

CHAPTER

19 Optics

CONCEPTS — in Action —

How do science concepts apply to your world? Here are some questions you'll be able to answer after you read this chapter.

- Why do some large trucks have a sign that reads, "If you can't see my mirrors, then I can't see you"? *(Section 19.1)*
- Why do automobile manufacturers place warnings on some side-view mirrors saying that objects seen in the mirror are closer than they appear? *(Section 19.1)*
- Why is movie film placed upside down in a movie projector? *(Section 19.2)*
- How is it possible to see something that no longer exists? *(Section 19.3)*
- How can you relax your eyes? *(Section 19.4)*

Discovery Channel School **Video Field Trip**
Traveling Light

- How can a television signal be transmitted using light? *(Page 587)*

Each of these small water droplets acts like a lens and forms an image of the flowers in the background. ▶

Chapter Pretest

1. What five things can happen to light that strikes a new medium? *(It can be reflected, absorbed, refracted, polarized, scattered)*
2. Define *image*. *(An image is a copy of an object formed by reflected or refracted waves of light.)*
3. True or False: Parallel light rays reflect in many different directions off a smooth surface. *(False)*
4. Which of the following makes an underwater object appear closer and larger than it really is? *(c)*
 a. Reflection **b.** Absorption
 c. Refraction **d.** Transmission
5. Which of the following types of material transmits almost all of the light that strikes it? *(c)*
 a. Translucent **b.** Opaque
 c. Transparent **d.** Mirror
6. Which of the following occurs to a light ray when it passes from one transparent medium into another at an angle other than 90°? *(d)*
 a. Bent
 b. Changed speed
 c. Refracted
 d. All of these
7. True or False: It is impossible to see unless light enters the eye. *(True)*

Chapter Preview

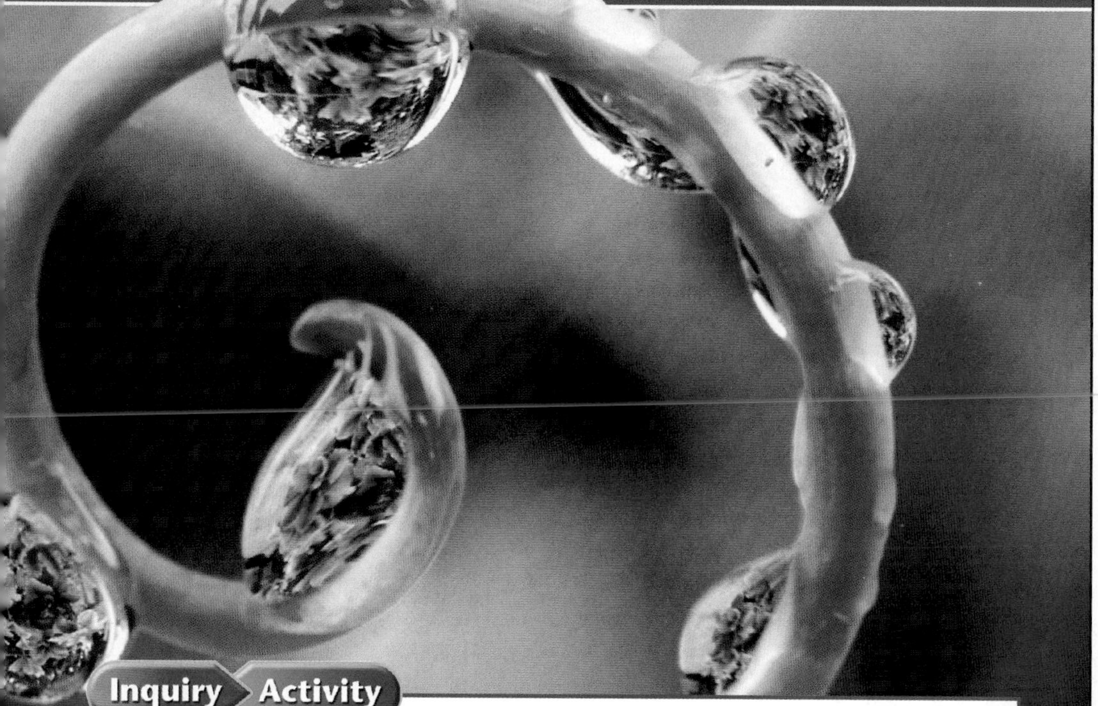

Inquiry Activity

How Can You Make Glass Disappear?

Procedure

1. Pour vegetable oil into a container until it is half full. Repeat this procedure using a second container and water.
2. Insert a section of glass tubing into each container.
3. Look at the glass tubing through the side of the container with vegetable oil. Then look at the glass tubing through the side of the container with water.

Think About It

1. **Observing** What did you see when you looked at the glass tubing through the container with the vegetable oil? Through the container with the water?
2. **Inferring** Based on your observations, what can you infer about how light travels through the vegetable oil and the glass tubing? Through the water and the glass tubing?

Discovery Channel School **Video Field Trip**
Traveling Light

Encourage students to view the Video Field Trip "Traveling Light."

ENGAGE/EXPLORE

Inquiry Activity

How Can You Make Glass Disappear? L2

Purpose In this activity, students begin to recognize that the change in the path of light as it passes from one material to another depends on differences between the two materials.

Skills Focus Observing

Prep Time 10 minutes

Materials 2 clear plastic or glass containers, vegetable oil, water, 2 equal lengths of borosilicate glass tubing

Advance Prep Use borosilicate glass tubing, which is sold as heat-resistant glass under various brand names. If necessary, you can substitute rods for tubing.

Class Time 15 minutes

Safety Students should use care with breakable glass and wear safety goggles. Quickly wipe up any spilled liquid to avoid slips and falls.

Expected Outcome The glass tubing will seem to disappear when it is placed in the vegetable oil, but the tubing will be visible in the water.

Think About It

1. When the tubing is placed in the vegetable oil, the tubing appears almost invisible. When the tubing is placed in the water, the tubing can be seen clearly.
2. Students may infer that the glass tubing appears invisible in vegetable oil because the light is bent at the water–glass interface, but not at the oil–glass interface.

Visual

Section 19.1

1 FOCUS

Objectives

19.1.1 **Describe** the law of reflection.

19.1.2 **Describe** how a plane mirror produces an image.

19.1.3 **Define** real and virtual images and relate them to converging and diverging light rays.

19.1.4 **Describe** the physical characteristics of plane, concave, and convex mirrors and **distinguish** between the types of images they form.

Reading Focus

Build Vocabulary L2

Vocabulary Knowledge Rating Chart Have students construct a chart with four columns: Term, Can Define or Use It, Have Heard or Seen It, Don't Know. Students should copy the vocabulary terms for this section under column 1. They should then place a checkmark under one of the other columns for each term.

Reading Strategy L2

a. Inside curved surface **b.** Both
c. Outside curved surface **d.** Virtual

2 INSTRUCT

The Law of Reflection

Build Science Skills L2

Observing

Purpose Students compare object and image distance in a plane mirror.

Materials graph paper, metric ruler, pencil, plane mirror

Class Time 15 minutes

Procedure Use lumps of clay to mount a mirror vertically on a sheet of graph paper. Hold a pencil in front of the mirror and observe its image. Place the pencil point down on one of the squares. Look into the mirror to observe the image of the pencil point. Count the number of squares from the object to the mirror and from the image to the mirror.

Expected Outcome The image distance behind the mirror appears to be the same as the distance from the mirror to the object.
Visual, Kinesthetic

19.1 Mirrors

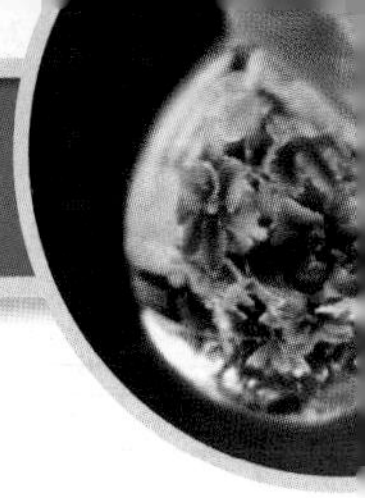

Reading Focus

Key Concepts

- What is the law of reflection?
- What type of image is produced by each of the three types of mirrors?

Vocabulary

- ray diagram
- angle of incidence
- angle of reflection
- plane mirror
- virtual image
- concave mirror
- focal point
- real image
- convex mirror

Reading Strategy

Comparing and Contrasting After reading this section, compare mirror types by copying and completing the table.

Mirror	Shape of Surface	Image (virtual, real, or both)
Plane	Flat	Virtual
Concave	a. ___?___	b. ___?___
Convex	c. ___?___	d. ___?___

It is a bright, sunny day and you are enjoying a peaceful afternoon by a lake. The air is still and the surface of the lake looks just like a sheet of glass. In fact, it is so smooth that you can see your reflection in it.

Figure 1 The flat (plane) mirror and the mirror-like lake surface both obey the law of reflection. According to the law of reflection, the angle of an incident ray equals the angle of the reflected ray.

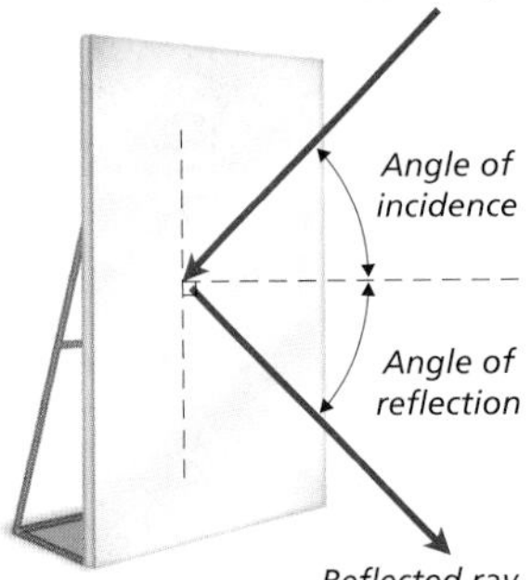
Incident ray
Angle of incidence
Angle of reflection
Reflected ray

The Law of Reflection

Optics includes the study of how mirrors and lenses form images. In your study of optics, assume that light is made up of rays that travel in straight lines. A **ray diagram** shows how rays change direction when they strike mirrors and pass through lenses.

Figure 1 shows a simple ray diagram of the law of reflection. The incoming ray, called the incident ray, approaches the mirror. The **angle of incidence** is the angle the incident ray makes with a line drawn perpendicular to the surface of the mirror. The mirror reflects the incident ray. The **angle of reflection** is the angle the reflected ray makes with the perpendicular line. **The law of reflection states that the angle of reflection is equal to the angle of incidence.**

Section Resources

Print

- ***Reading and Study Workbook With Math Support,*** Section 19.1
- ***Transparencies,*** Chapter Pretest and Section 19.1

Technology

- ***Interactive Textbook,*** Section 19.1
- ***Presentation Pro CD-ROM,*** Section 19.1
- ***Go Online,*** NSTA SciLinks, Mirrors

Next time you are in a car behind a large truck, look for a sign that reads, "If you can't see my mirror, then I can't see you." Light travels from you to the mirror to the driver's eyes and also from the driver to the mirror to your eyes. If you do not have a line of vision to the truck's side-view mirror, then the truck driver does not have a line of vision to you. It can be dangerous to drive too close to large trucks!

Plane Mirrors

Mirrors are usually made of a sheet of glass that is coated with a thin layer of shiny metal on one surface. A mirror with a flat surface is a **plane mirror.** The large mirror in your bathroom is a plane mirror. When you look into a plane mirror, you see your reversed reflection—a right-left reversed image of yourself. An image is a copy of an object formed by rays of light.

Figure 2 shows how a plane mirror forms an image. To produce your image in a mirror, rays of light strike you and reflect. These reflected rays then strike the mirror and are reflected into your eyes. The dashed lines show how your brain interprets where the rays are coming from. The rays appear to come from behind the mirror. Your image appears the same distance behind the mirror as you are in front, and the image is right side up. If you walk toward the mirror, you'll see your image also move toward the mirror. **A plane mirror always produces a virtual image.** Although you can see a virtual image, this type of image cannot be projected onto any surface. A **virtual image** is a copy of an object formed at the location from which the light rays appear to come. It is important, however, to realize that the rays do not really come from behind the mirror.

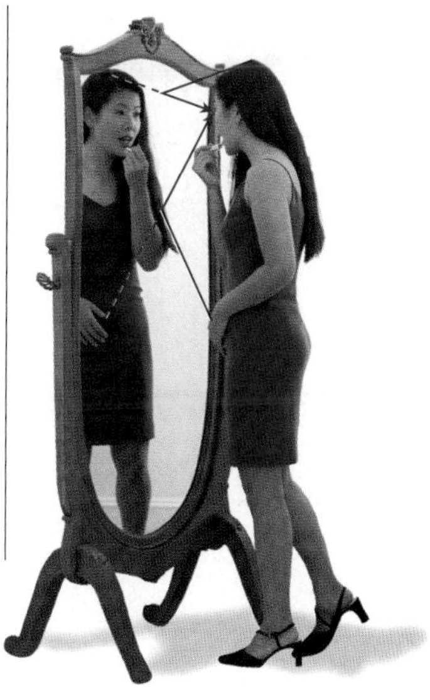

Figure 2 The girl sees a virtual image of herself in the plane mirror. Virtual images such as this cannot be projected onto a screen. Note also how light rays from the object (the girl) reflect from the mirror's surface and obey the law of reflection. **Interpreting Photos** ***What do the dashed lines represent?***

Quick Lab

Measuring the Height of Your Mirror Image

Materials

plane mirror, meter stick, newspaper, masking tape

Procedure

1. Have a classmate measure and record your height in centimeters.
2. Stand directly in front of the mirror, 1 m away from it.
3. Look at your image in the mirror. Have a classmate tape newspaper over those parts of the mirror (above and below your image) where you do not see any part of yourself.
4. Measure and record the height of your image by measuring the uncovered part of the mirror.
5. Repeat Steps 3 and 4 for distances of 2 m, 3 m, and 4 m.

Analyze and Conclude

1. **Analyzing Data** How did the height of your image change as you moved farther away from the mirror?
2. **Drawing Conclusions** What is the relationship between your height and the height of your image in the plane mirror?

Plane Mirrors

Quick Lab

Measuring the Height of Your Mirror Image **L2**

Objective

After completing this lab, students will be able to

- describe how the size of a mirror limits the size of the area that it reflects.

Address Misconceptions

Completing this lab can help students overcome the misconception that it is possible to see an image of one's full height in a mirror of any size, if the mirror is sufficiently far away.

Skills Focus **Drawing Conclusions**

Prep Time 10 minutes

Advance Prep Full length mirrors can be framed with black construction paper to provide mirror surfaces of different heights. One mirror should be longer than one-half the average height of the students. Another should be shorter than most of the students. The mirrors should be mounted on the wall and perpendicular to the floor. You can mark off distances of 1 to 4 m from each mirror on the floor with masking tape.

Class Time 20 minutes

Safety Framed mirrors should be used. If the mirrors aren't framed, cover the edges with duct tape to reduce the risk of breakage and injury. Students should use caution and wear safety goggles when working with breakable glass mirrors.

Expected Outcome A mirror must be at least half the height of a student to produce a full-length image of the student.

Analyze and Conclude

1. The image became smaller.
2. The image is never more than half the student's height.
Logical

Customize for English Language Learners

Cause/Effect Chart

Using a cause/effect chart can ensure that students understand the concepts, as well as the word meanings, in this section. Have students work independently or as a group and make a two-column chart. The left column should be labeled Cause and the right column Effect. Next, have students read the paragraphs about plane mirrors on this page. Encourage them to write on their charts different cause/effect relationships about plane mirrors described in the paragraphs. For example, one cause is light reflecting off an object, and the effect is the light striking the mirror. Another cause is walking toward the mirror, and the effect is seeing the image also move toward the mirror.

Answer to . . .

Figure 2 *The dashed lines show the point of origin of the virtual image that is formed behind the mirror.*

Concave and Convex Mirrors

Address Misconceptions L2

Students may incorrectly think that concave mirrors form only real images. Challenge this misconception by having students look carefully at Figure 3C. Point out that when the object is very close to the mirror, the curvature of the mirror has less effect. The object's image is similar to the virtual image produced by a plane mirror. Also point out that the reflected rays in Figure 3C don't converge. The rays must converge to form a real image. Finally, explain that a real image produced by a mirror is always inverted. Have students hold a convex mirror very close to their eyes (closer than focal point) and then farther away. **Visual**

Teacher Demo

Flashlight Mirrors L2

Purpose Students observe how a small flashlight can focus a beam.

Materials flashlight with a beam that can be focused

Procedure Unscrew the head of the flashlight to show students the small bulb. Draw a diagram on the board showing the placement of the bulb at the focal point of the parabolic lens. Replace the head and show how the beam changes size as the head moves back and forth. Have students draw ray diagrams showing the pattern of reflection at different positions.

Expected Outcome The concave mirror in the flashlight focuses the light into a narrow bright beam when the bulb is placed at the focal point of the concave mirror. When the bulb is in front of or behind the focal point, the rays diverge. **Visual, Logical**

Go Online NSTA SCILINKS

Download a worksheet on mirrors for students to complete, and find additional teacher support from NSTA SciLinks.

Go Online NSTA SCILINKS

For: Links on mirrors
Visit: www.SciLinks.org
Web Code: ccn-2191

Concave and Convex Mirrors

Sometimes you see images that are very distorted. Look into both sides of a polished metal spoon. The images you see are quite different from the image formed by a plane mirror. Each side of the spoon produces a different image because each side is curved differently. The curved surface of the spoon changes the way light is reflected.

Concave Mirrors When the inside surface of a curved mirror is the reflecting surface, the mirror is a **concave mirror.** Figure 3A shows how a concave mirror reflects light rays that are parallel to the optical axis. The curvature of the reflecting surface causes the rays to come together. The point at which the light rays meet is called the **focal point.**

Look again at your reflection in the bowl of a spoon. The upside-down image you see is a real image. A **real image** is a copy of an object formed at the point where light rays actually meet. Unlike a virtual image, a real image can be viewed on a surface such as a screen.

Concave mirrors can form either real or virtual images. The type of image formed depends upon where the object is in relation to the mirror. Figure 3B shows how a concave mirror forms a real image. When the object is farther from the mirror than the focal point, the reflected rays meet in front of the mirror. Figure 3C shows how a concave mirror forms a virtual image. When the object is closer to the mirror than the focal point is the reflected rays spread out and appear to come from behind the mirror.

Concave mirrors are often used in automobile headlights and flashlights to direct the illumination from a single light bulb into a beam. If the bulb is placed at the focal point of a concave mirror, the reflected light rays will be parallel to one another. This results in a brighter beam of light.

Reading Checkpoint *At what location does a real image form?*

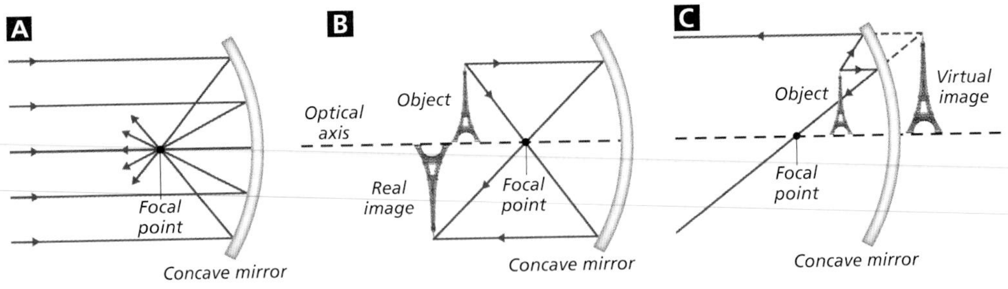
A
Focal point
Concave mirror
B
Optical axis
Object
Real image
Focal point
Concave mirror
C
Object
Virtual image
Focal point
Concave mirror

Figure 3 Concave mirrors can form either real or virtual images. **A** When parallel incoming rays strike a concave mirror, they are reflected through the focal point. **B** Concave mirrors form real images when the reflected light rays converge. **C** Concave mirrors form virtual images when the reflected rays appear to come from a point behind the mirror.
Interpreting Diagrams ***What determines the type of the image formed by a concave mirror?***

Facts and Figures

Concave Mirror Images There are five general types of images formed by a concave mirror. Consider the distance from the focal point to the mirror as f. The image types are: (1) If the object is between the focal point and the mirror, the image is virtual, upright, and enlarged. (2) If the object is located exactly at the focal point, no image is produced. (3) If the object is located between a distance f and a distance $2f$ from the mirror, the image is real, inverted, and enlarged. (4) If the object is located at exactly a distance $2f$ from the mirror, the image is real, inverted, and the same size as the object. (5) If the object is located at a distance greater than $2f$, the image is real, inverted, and smaller than the object.

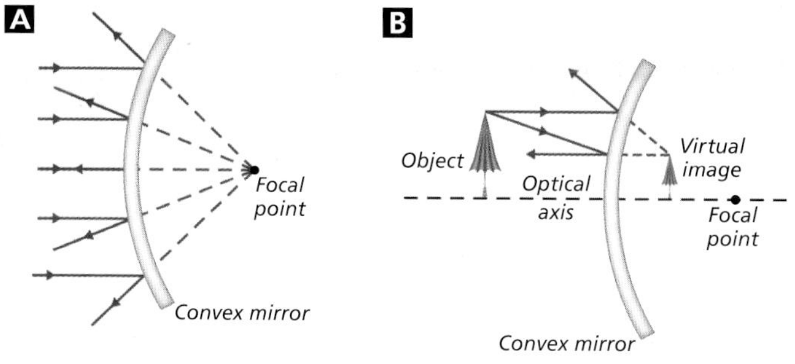
A
Focal point
Convex mirror
B
Object
Optical axis
Virtual image
Focal point
Convex mirror

Figure 4 Convex mirrors can only form virtual images. **A** When parallel incoming rays strike a convex mirror, they are reflected away from one another. **B** Convex mirrors always form virtual images that are upright and smaller than the object. Because of their reduced image size, convex mirrors on automobiles warn that "Objects are closer than they appear."

Convex Mirrors When the outside surface of a curved mirror is the reflecting surface, the mirror is a **convex mirror.** Figure 4A shows how a convex mirror reflects parallel light rays. Note how the curvature of the convex mirror causes the reflected rays to spread out.

Convex mirrors always cause light rays to spread out and can only form virtual images. Figure 4B shows how a convex mirror forms a virtual image. As the rays from the object reflect from the mirror, the rays spread out. Because they appear to be coming from a point behind the mirror, that is where the image appears. The image formed by a convex mirror is always upright and smaller than the object. This allows the mirror to show a wide angle of view. Because of their wide angle of view, round, convex mirrors are often used in store aisles, at hazardous traffic intersections, and for side mirrors on automobiles.

Section 19.1 Assessment

Reviewing Concepts

1. How is the angle of incidence of a light ray related to the angle of reflection?
2. What type of image does a plane mirror form?
3. What types of image can be produced by a concave mirror? A convex mirror?
4. How are real images different from virtual images?
5. Why can convex mirrors form only one type of image?

Critical Thinking

6. **Applying Concepts** Explain why a plane mirror cannot form a real image.
7. **Inferring** If you place an object 10 cm from a particular concave mirror, a virtual image forms behind the mirror. What can you infer about the focal point of the mirror?
8. **Applying Concepts** If you look inside the bowl of a shiny metal spoon, your image is upside down. If you look at the outside of the bowl, your image is right side up. Explain.

Writing in Science

Compare-Contrast Paragraph Write a paragraph comparing convex mirrors and concave mirrors. (*Hint:* Use the information from your completed Reading Strategy on page 570.)

Section 19.1 Assessment

1. The law of reflection states that the angle of reflection is equal to the angle of incidence.
2. A plane mirror always produces a virtual image.
3. Concave mirror: virtual and real; convex mirror: virtual
4. Real images can be projected onto a screen and form at the point where light rays actually converge, whereas virtual images cannot be projected and are formed at the point from which the light rays appear to be coming.
5. Convex lenses always cause light rays to diverge, therefore, they can form only virtual images.
6. For a real image to form, light rays must converge. Because a plane mirror cannot cause light rays to converge, it cannot form a real image.
7. The focal point of the mirror must be farther than 10 cm from the mirror.
8. Light rays from the convex side diverge forming an upright image. Light rays from the concave side converge forming an inverted image.

Use Visuals L1

Figure 4 Have students look carefully at the incident and reflected rays in Figures 4A and 4B. Ask, **How can you apply the law of reflection to a convex mirror?** *(Draw a tangent to the mirror at the point where the incident ray strikes and through this point draw a normal line, perpendicular to the tangent. The angles from the normal line to the incident and reflected rays are equal.)* **Visual**

Build Reading Literacy L1

Use Prior Knowledge Refer to page **2D** in **Chapter 1**, which provides the guidelines for using prior knowledge.

Ask students to think about times they have looked in a store's convex mirror. Have them explain the advantages and disadvantages a convex mirror has over a plane mirror. *(The convex mirror allows store workers to monitor a greater area of the store. The disadvantage is that the images are smaller and more difficult to see.)* **Verbal**

Interactive Textbook If your class subscribes to the Interactive Textbook, use it to review key concepts in Section 19.1

3 ASSESS

Evaluate Understanding L2

Have students model the law of reflection by rolling a ball at an angle toward a wall. Encourage them to explain the angle of incidence and the angle of reflection of the ball's path.

Reteach L1

Have students make a chart summarizing how different types of images can be made with each mirror. They can use their charts to review the section.

Writing in Science

Student paragraphs should include several similarities and differences. Similarities include each mirror having a curved reflecting surface and the ability to form images. Differences include shape of the reflecting surface and the ability to make light rays converge or diverge.

Answer to . . .

Figure 3 *The location of the object*

Reading Checkpoint *At the point where the light rays meet*

1 FOCUS

Objectives

19.2.1 **Explain** what causes light to refract.
19.2.2 **Define** index of refraction.
19.2.3 **Describe** the physical characteristics of concave and convex lenses and **distinguish** between the types of images they form.
19.2.4 **Describe** total internal reflection and **explain** its relationship to the critical angle.

Reading Focus

Build Vocabulary L2

Concept Maps Creating concept maps can help students understand the convex and concave lenses studied in this section. Have students include the following topics: lens shape, images formed, applications, diverging rays, and converging rays. Advanced students could incorporate sketches showing how the images are formed.

Reading Strategy L2

a. Ratio of the speed of light in a vacuum to the speed of light in the material.
b. Angle of incidence that produces an angle of refraction of 90 degrees.
c. The complete reflection of a light ray back into its original medium.

2 INSTRUCT

Index of Refraction of Light

Build Reading Literacy L1

Outline Refer to page **156D** in **Chapter 6**, which provides the guidelines for using an outline.

Have students create an outline of the section (pp. 574–578). Ask, **Based on your outline, what is an index of refraction, and what is total internal reflection?** *(An index of refraction is a measure of how much light changes speed as it enters a new medium. Total internal reflection is the complete reflection of a light ray back into its original medium. The angle depends on the index of refraction.)*
Verbal, Logical

19.2 Lenses

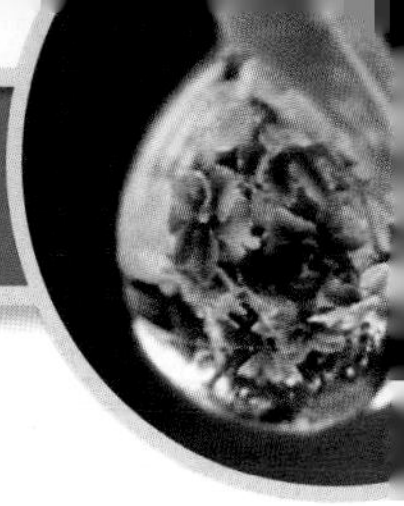

Reading Focus

Key Concepts

- What causes light to refract?
- What type of images do concave and convex lenses form?
- In what types of materials is total internal reflection likely to occur?

Vocabulary

- index of refraction
- lens
- concave lens
- convex lens
- critical angle
- total internal reflection

Reading Strategy

Building Vocabulary Copy the table below. As you read the section, define in your own words each vocabulary word listed in the table.

Vocabulary Term	Definition
Index of refraction	a. ___?___
Critical angle of refraction	b. ___?___
Total internal reflection	c. ___?___

You may wear eyeglasses or contact lenses and you have probably used a hand lens like the one shown in Figure 5. If so, you have seen how the bending, or refracting, of light can change the way you see something. The enlarged image seen through the lens in Figure 5 is due to refraction. The lens material changes the path of the light rays passing through it. The amount the light rays change direction determines the appearance of the image you see.

Index of Refraction of Light

Light usually travels in straight lines. In a vacuum, light travels at a speed of 3.00×10^8 meters per second. Once light passes from a vacuum into any other medium, it slows down. The speed of light in the new medium depends on the material of the new medium.

Some media, such as air, allow light to pass through almost as fast as it would through a vacuum. In fact, air slows the speed of light only by about three ten-thousandths of one percent (0.0003%). Other media cause light to slow down much more. For instance, the speed of light in water and in glass slows to 2.25×10^8 meters per second and 2.00×10^8 meters per second respectively.

574 Chapter 19

Figure 5 Light rays slow and bend as they pass through the curved glass lens. In this case, the result is a magnified image.

Section Resources

Print
- ***Laboratory Manual,*** Investigation 19A
- ***Reading and Study Workbook With Math Support,*** Section 19.2 and **Math Skill:** Calculating Index of Refraction
- ***Math Skills and Problem Solving Workbook,*** Section 19.2
- ***Transparencies,*** Section 19.2

Technology
- ***Interactive Textbook,*** Section 19.2
- ***Presentation Pro CD-ROM,*** Section 19.2

When light enters a new medium at an angle, the change in speed causes the light to bend, or refract. For example, when light passes from air into glass or water, it slows down. When light passes from glass or water into air, it speeds up. The amount by which the light refracts as it passes from one medium to another depends upon the difference between the speeds of light in the two media.

Figure 6 shows how the path of a light ray changes as it passes from one medium into another. The incident ray of light, traveling through air, first strikes the boundary between the air and the water. As the light ray enters the water, it is refracted. You can see in Figure 6 that the light ray is now traveling in a new direction. As the ray enters the glass, it is refracted even more. Finally, when the ray reenters air, its path is bent again, but back to its original direction. Note that regardless of the refraction that occurs in the water and glass layers, the ray again travels in its original direction when it reenters the air.

How much the speed of a light ray slows as it enters a new material depends on the material's index of refraction. The **index of refraction** for a material is the ratio of the speed of light in a vacuum to the speed of the light in the material. A material with a low index of refraction (near 1) causes light to slow and refract very little. Air, with an index of refraction of 1.0003, is such a material. Diamond, however, with an index of refraction of 2.42, causes light to slow and refract significantly.

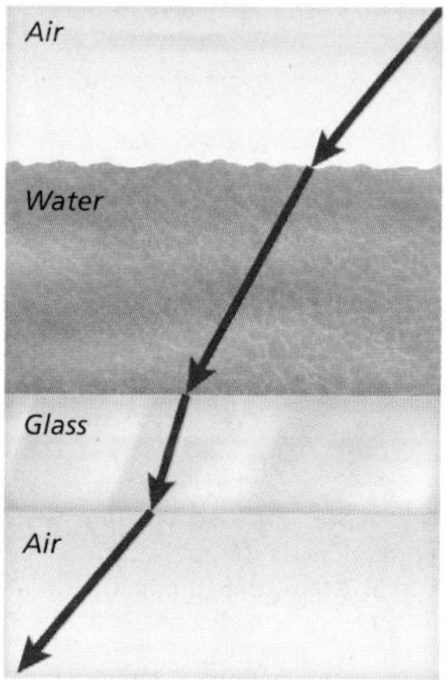

Air
Water
Glass
Air

Figure 6 A light ray bends (refracts) as it passes through media with different indices of refraction. **Inferring** ***Based on the path of the light ray, which medium has the greatest index of refraction?***

Data Analysis

Properties of Gemstones

Gemstones used in jewelry are known for several of their physical properties—primarily luster and optical brilliance. Luster is a measure of the amount of light that strikes a gemstone's surface and is reflected. Flat and smooth surfaces increase a gemstone's luster.

Like luster, the brilliance of a gemstone involves reflected light. Light that is not reflected by a gem's lustrous surface passes into the stone. The brilliance of a gemstone is a measure of the amount of light entering the gem that is reflected back to the viewer. Precise techniques are used to cut gemstones into shapes that produce maximum brilliance. The combination of a specialized shape and the gemstone's inherent high index of refraction gives gems their brilliance.

The table summarizes the index of refraction and luster of several common gemstones. Note that moissanite is a manufactured material used to simulate diamond.

Properties of Natural and Synthetic Gemstones

Material	Index of Refraction	Luster
Diamond	2.42	17.2%
Moissanite	2.65	20.4%
Ruby	1.77	7.4%
Sapphire	1.77	7.4%
Emerald	1.58	4.8%

1. **Interpreting Tables** Which material is the most lustrous? The least lustrous?
2. **Calculating** What percentage of light striking a sapphire gemstone enters it?
3. **Applying Concepts** If a light ray strikes each material at an angle, in which material would the light ray bend the most?
4. **Applying Concepts** The speed of light through an unknown gemstone is 1.69×10^8 m/s. Identify the gemstone.

Use Visuals L1

Figure 6 Have students use a small ruler to compare the directions of the incoming light ray and the outgoing light ray. Point out that the ray bends toward the normal, or a line perpendicular to the edge of the medium, when traveling from a less dense material to a more dense material. It bends away from the normal when traveling from a more dense material to a less dense material. In this figure, the light ray changes direction three times. Ask, **Which change of direction is the largest?** *(From glass into air)* **Compare the change from air into water with glass into air. What does this tell you about the index of refraction of glass?** *(The index of refraction of glass is higher than the index of refraction of air.)*
Visual, Logical

Data Analysis

Properties of Gemstones L2

Answers

1. Moissanite is the most lustrous (20.4%); emerald is the least lustrous (4.8%)
2. 92.6% of the light striking the sapphire enters the gemstone.
3. Light bends the most in moissanite because it has the greatest index of refraction.
4. Index of refraction = speed of light in vacuum/speed of light in unknown gemstone; Index of refraction = $(3.00 \times 10^8\ \text{m/s})/(1.69 \times 10^8\ \text{m/s}) = 1.77$; the gemstone could be either a ruby or a sapphire.

For Extra Help L1

Help students understand luster by showing them samples of obsidian and galena.
Visual

Customize for Inclusion Students

Visually Impaired
Optics may be especially difficult for visually impaired students. Help them understand the behavior of light rays passing through different mediums by creating a kinesthetic version of Figure 6. First, glue a length of string on construction paper to represent the trajectory of the original light ray if it continued through air. Then, glue toothpicks to the side of the string in the same design shown by the arrows in Figure 6. Explain that the direction of the toothpicks shows how much the light is bent toward or away from the normal as it passes from air through water, then glass, then air. Students will be able to feel how the direction of the light changes as it moves from one medium to another.

Answer to . . .

Figure 6 *Glass must have the greatest index of refraction because the light ray is bent farthest away from its initial path in the glass layer.*

Concave and Convex Lenses

Use Community Resources L2

Invite a person who repairs cameras to come to your class and demonstrate how a camera operates and forms images. Encourage students to prepare and ask questions related to optical design. Check the phone book to find camera shops that are authorized repair centers.
Interpersonal, Visual

Address Misconceptions L2

A common misconception is that blocking part of the surface of a convex lens will block the corresponding part of the image. Address this misconception by holding a convex lens between a lamp and a flat surface (such as a wall or book). Adjust the distances so students see an inverted image of the lamp on the surface. Next, cover part of the lens with your hand. Students will see that the lamp's image on the flat surface is dimmer, but because the light rays bend, the image is complete. Draw a ray diagram on the board to explain this effect.
Visual

Teacher Demo

Combining Lenses L2

Purpose Students see the effects of combining lenses.

Materials modeling clay, 2 convex lenses, 2 concave lenses, 2 index cards

Procedure Prior to class, use balls of modeling clay to support each lens vertically. Sketch an object, such as a tree, on the index cards and use clay to support them vertically also. Set up a display with an index card about 10 cm behind a convex lens, and a concave lens about 1 cm in front of a concave lens. Set up a similar display, but now have the concave lens about 10 cm in front of the concave lens. Allow students to look through both setups.

Expected Outcome Students will observe that the effect of a concave lens cancels the effect of a convex lens, as long as the lenses are close together.
Visual

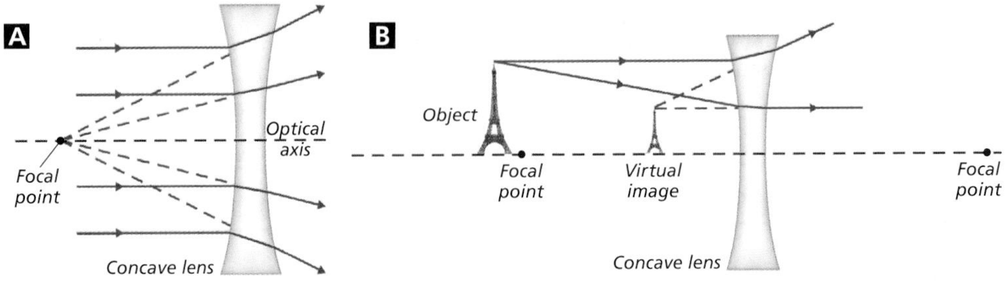
A
Optical axis
Focal point
Concave lens
B
Object
Focal point
Virtual image
Focal point
Concave lens

Figure 7 Concave lenses can only form virtual images. **A** When parallel incoming rays strike a concave lens, they are refracted away from one another. **B** As the light rays diverge after passing through the concave lens, they form a virtual image of the object.

Concave and Convex Lenses

Lenses are used to change the path of light rays before they enter your eyes. A **lens** is an object made of transparent material that has one or two curved surfaces that can refract light. The curvature and thickness of a lens affect the way it refracts light.

Concave Lenses A **concave lens** is curved inward at the center and is thickest at the outside edges. Figure 7A shows how a concave lens refracts light rays. As the rays pass through the lens, each one is refracted due to the change of medium. The rays enter the lens at different angles and so they emerge from the lens at different angles. Concave lenses cause incoming parallel rays to spread out, or diverge. (Concave lenses are a type of diverging lens.) The diverging rays appear to come from a single point, the focal point, on the same side of the lens as the object.

Concave lenses always cause light rays to spread out and can only form virtual images. Figure 7B shows how a concave lens forms a virtual image. The image is formed at the point from which the refracted rays appear to come. The image formed by a concave lens is always smaller than the object.

Concave lenses are often used in the viewfinders of cameras. The small virtual image you see through the viewfinder lens is similar to what the photograph will show. Concave lenses are also combined with mirrors or other lenses to form images in optical instruments such as telescopes.

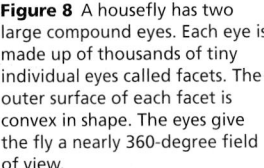

Figure 8 A housefly has two large compound eyes. Each eye is made up of thousands of tiny individual eyes called facets. The outer surface of each facet is convex in shape. The eyes give the fly a nearly 360-degree field of view.

Convex Lenses Note how the shape of each of the fly's eyes in Figure 8 resembles the exterior surface of a sphere. A shape like this is known as convex. Figure 9A shows that a **convex lens** is curved outward at the center and is thinnest at the outer edges. Figure 9A also shows how light is refracted by a convex lens. As the rays pass through the lens, each one is refracted, and they emerge at different angles. Convex lenses cause incoming parallel rays to come together, or converge. (Convex lenses are also called converging lens.) The converging rays meet at a single point, the focal point, on the side of the lens opposite to the object.

Facts and Figures

Eyeglass Scientists at Lawrence Livermore National Laboratory in California are working on a new type of space telescope known as "Eyeglass." An Eyeglass is different from other space telescopes because it does not use mirrors or traditional glass lenses, but diffractive optics (or Fresnel lenses). The advantages of using an Eyeglass telescope would include its flexibility, lightness, and ability to be folded. The Livermore team has currently constructed the world's largest such lens. It has a diameter of 5 meters and is made of 72 glass panels that can be folded. Although the lens is larger than the Hubble Space telescope, it weighs ten times less.

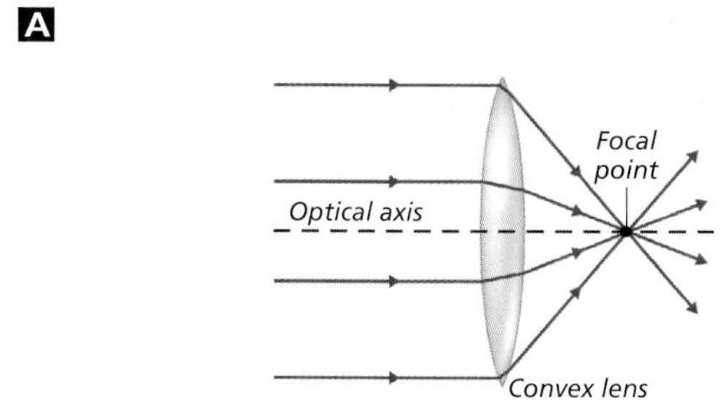
A
Focal point
Optical axis
Convex lens

Figure 9 Convex lenses can form either real or virtual images. A When parallel incoming rays strike a convex lens, they are refracted toward each other and pass through the focal point. B When an object is located beyond the focal point of a convex lens, a real image is formed. C A magnified, virtual image is formed when the object is located between the focal point and the lens.

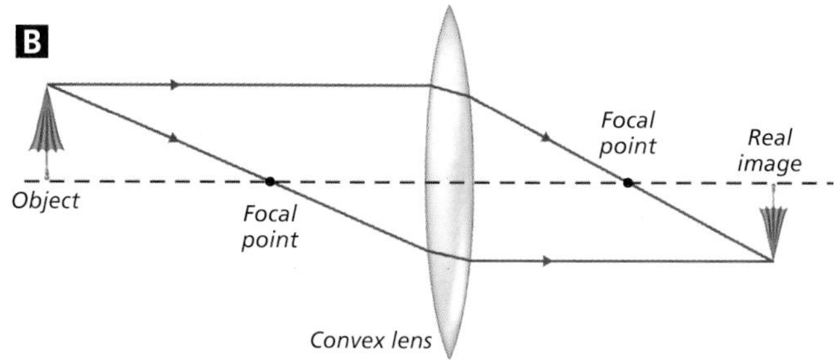
B
Focal point
Real image
Object
Focal point
Convex lens

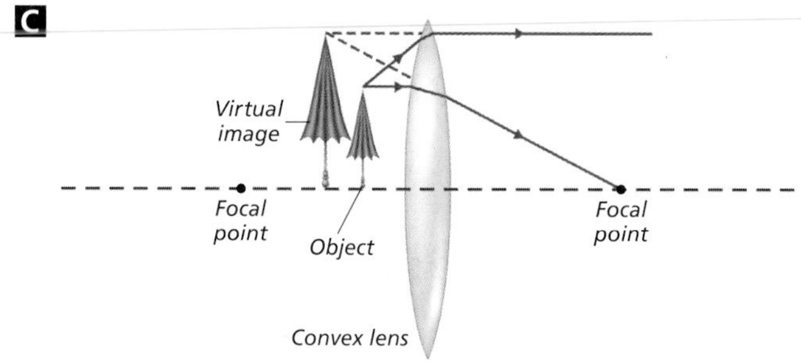
C
Virtual image
Focal point
Object
Focal point
Convex lens

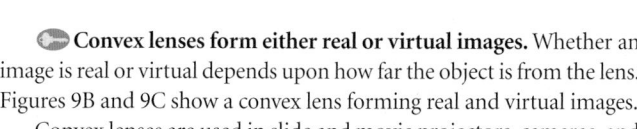

Figure 10 In the past, lighthouses used a light source placed at the focal point of a convex lens or series of convex lenses to form a beam of parallel light rays. **Comparing and Contrasting** ***How does the setup shown in Figure 9A compare with that used in old lighthouses?***

Convex lenses form either real or virtual images. Whether an image is real or virtual depends upon how far the object is from the lens. Figures 9B and 9C show a convex lens forming real and virtual images.

Convex lenses are used in slide and movie projectors, cameras, and lighthouses like the one in Figure 10. Of course, you don't see an upside-down real image at the movie theatre because the film is placed upside down in the projector. When the rays of light from the upside-down film pass through the projector's convex lens, the real image is projected onto the screen right side up.

Reading Checkpoint *How is a convex lens shaped?*

FYI

The distance from a lens or a mirror to its focal point is known as the focal length, *f*. Notice that Figures 6 and 7 show double concave and double convex lenses, insofar as both surfaces are concave, or convex, respectively. Note that the text uses convex for any converging lens, and concave for any diverging lens. Converging lenses have a positive focal length, and diverging lenses have a negative focal length.

Build Science Skills L2

Observing ACTIVITY

Purpose Students use parallax to find the position of the real image formed by a convex lens.

Materials 5-cm diameter double-convex lens, pencil

Class Time 15 minutes

Procedure Have students hold the lens vertically at arm's length and observe a light source about 4 meters away. Ask, **How would you describe the image of the light source?** *(Smaller and inverted)* Have students hold the pencil vertically between the lens and their eyes so that the image of the light source can't be seen. If they move their heads slowly left and right with one eye closed, they will observe parallax. Explain that if an object and an image are the same distance away, they will appear to move the same distance as you move your head. Have students try to locate the image position (of the light) by eliminating the parallax between the image and the pencil. With students still moving their heads, have them lower the pencil slightly and move it closer to their face (about 10 cm away) until the pencil appears to move with the light source. Ask, **Where is the image?** *(At the same position as the pencil)* **Is this a real image?** *(Yes)*

Expected Outcome Students will observe the real image formed by a lens and locate its position.
Kinesthetic, Group

Build Math Skills L1

Formulas and Equations Students can relate the distances from a lens to the focal point *(f)*, from the lens to the object *(p)*, and from the lens to the image *(q)* using the lens equation:

$$\frac{1}{f} = \frac{1}{p} + \frac{1}{q}$$

Have students practice solving this equation for each of the three unknowns.
Logical

Direct students to the **Math Skills** in the **Skills and Reference Handbook** at the end of the student text for additional help.

Answer to . . .

Figure 10 *The source of light in the lighthouse is located at the focal point shown in Figure 9A.*

Reading Checkpoint *A convex lens is curved outward at its center and is thinnest at the outer edges.*

Total Internal Reflection

Integrate Social Studies L2

Alhazen, an eleventh-century Arabian scientist, was an early pioneer in the field of optics. He challenged a common belief that rays emanating from the eyes enabled vision. Alhazen's theory was that light originated from the sun and other luminous objects. The eye saw the light that was reflected from objects. Alhazen also studied the refraction of light and the focusing of light by lenses. He constructed a pinhole camera, magnifying lenses, and parabolic mirrors. Have students research other early scientists who studied optics, such as Archimedes, Galileo, and Kepler. **Verbal, Logical**

FYI

Note in Figures 11A and 11B that there are two rays emanating from the glass-air boundary where the incident ray strikes. The size of these rays are approximately representative of the amount of light from the incident ray that is reflected and refracted.

3 ASSESS

Evaluate Understanding L2

Randomly ask students to list the general properties of a convex or concave lens. Also, have them name at least one application for the lens.

Reteach L1

Have students draw sketches of the different types of image formation by lenses. They may need to refer to Figures 7 and 9.

Connecting Concepts

Student answers should demonstrate an understanding that, because the frequency does not change, the only way for the speed to decrease is if the wavelength decreases.

Interactive Textbook If your class subscribes to the Interactive Textbook, use it to review key concepts in Section 19.2

Total Internal Reflection

A relatively new and very important application of refraction is fiber optics. Light rays are generally unable to exit through the sides of the curving fiber optic strands. Because of this, fiber optics are very useful for carrying information in the form of light. Figures 11A through 11C explain how fiber optics work.

As shown in Figure 11A, a light ray exiting from glass into air is refracted. Figure 11B shows that as the angle of incidence of the exiting ray increases, an angle known as the critical angle of refraction is reached. The **critical angle** is the angle of incidence that produces an angle of refraction of 90 degrees. At the critical angle the light ray bends so much that it takes a path along the glass-air boundary. Figure 11C shows that at angles larger than the critical angle, the light ray bends so much that it is reflected back into the glass. This situation is known as total internal reflection. **Total internal reflection** is the complete reflection of a light ray back into its original medium.

Materials that have small critical angles are likely to cause most of the light entering them to be totally internally reflected. Such materials include diamond and the type of glass used in fiber optic strands. By making use of total internal reflection, fiber optics are able to transmit data in the form of light pulses over large distances with little loss in signal strength. To learn more about fiber optics, see page 586.

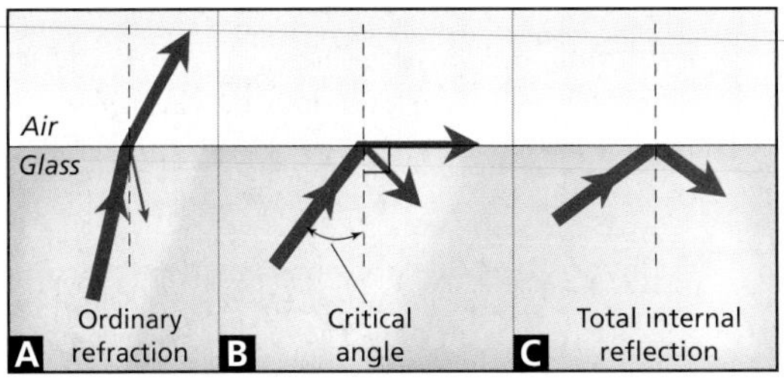

Air
Glass
A
Ordinary refraction
B
Critical angle
C
Total internal reflection

Figure 11 Fiber optics make use of total internal reflection. **A** When a ray hits the glass-air boundary at an angle less than the critical angle, it is partly refracted and partly reflected. **B** At the critical angle, the angle of refraction is 90 degrees. **C** When the critical angle is exceeded, all of the light is reflected—total internal reflection occurs.

Section 19.2 Assessment

Reviewing Concepts

1. What causes light rays to bend?
2. Why can concave lenses form only one type of image?
3. What type of images are formed by concave lenses? By convex lenses?
4. Most of the light entering what type of material is likely to be totally internally reflected?

Critical Thinking

5. **Comparing and Contrasting** How is a convex lens different from a concave lens? How are they the same?
6. **Applying Concepts** Explain how a convex lens is similar to a concave mirror.

Connecting Concepts

Speed of Light In Chapter 18, you learned that light travels at 3.00×10^8 m/s through the air. This speed is the product of frequency and wavelength (Speed = Frequency × Wavelength). Use this equation to show that the wavelength of the light changes when it passes from air to water. (*Hint:* The speed decreases and the frequency does not change.)

Section 19.2 Assessment

1. When light enters a new medium at an angle, the change in speed causes the light to bend, or refract. The part of the wavefront in the new medium moves at a different speed, causing the wave's direction to change (bend).
2. Because concave lenses always cause light rays to spread out, they can form only virtual images.
3. Concave lenses form only virtual images, whereas convex lenses can form either real or virtual images.
4. Materials that have small critical angles of refraction cause most of the light entering them to be totally internally reflected.
5. Similarities: Both lenses have curved surfaces, refract light rays, and can form images. Differences: Concave lenses make light rays diverge and can only form virtual images, whereas convex lens can make light rays converge or diverge and can form both real and virtual images.
6. Both cause light rays to diverge and can form virtual images.

issues in SCIENCE

Is Video Surveillance an Invasion of Privacy?

Not long ago, video cameras were cumbersome pieces of equipment. They required long cables and stored images on bulky magnetic tape cassettes. Recent advances in optics, digital imaging, and electronic technology have revolutionized video equipment. High-quality digital video cameras that are able to store their images in a variety of convenient formats are now very affordable. Extremely small, battery-powered video cameras are also available to the public.

However, not everyone is excited about the spread of affordable video technology. The explosion in the number of cameras being used for surveillance purposes is a huge concern to many Americans. Is your right to privacy being violated?

The Viewpoints

Video Surveillance Is Not an Invasion of Privacy

Video surveillance is an existing and proven technology that is very effective for many purposes. Traffic cameras on highways help motorists avoid accidents and traffic jams. Video cameras in stores have been used for years to deter and help capture shoplifters. Many major cities have installed cameras at large intersections, to photograph drivers who run red lights. Citations from such systems have cut down on traffic violations and on pedestrian accidents. Sophisticated video systems at some airports can identify known criminals before they board an airplane. The common thing in all of these examples is that the general public is safer because of the use of video surveillance cameras. Having some of our actions recorded on video is a small price to pay for our greatly increased safety.

Video Surveillance Violates a Person's Right to Privacy

Video surveillance comes at a very high price—the loss of personal privacy. Our society is quickly heading toward the day when any individual can be tracked throughout an entire day. Do you want the government and private companies to know every aspect of your life? The United States Supreme Court has stated that some acts that violate a person's reasonable expectation of privacy constitute an illegal search. Yet these actions are going on every day! Video surveillance, which is currently out of control, is just one of many threats to a person's right to a private life. Strict laws designed to protect a person's right to privacy need to be enacted as soon as possible.

Research and Decide

1. **Defining the Issue** Use your own words to describe at least two of the major issues involved in the use of video surveillance cameras.
2. **Analyzing the Viewpoints** List the arguments for and against the use of video surveillance cameras. What are the advantages? What are the disadvantages or risks?
3. **Forming Your Opinion** Is video surveillance an invasion of your right to privacy? If so, in what situations, if any, is it acceptable?
4. **Going Further** Research a recent court case involving video surveillance and privacy. Write a short report summarizing the case. Explain why you agree or disagree with the decision.

Go Online PHSchool.com

For: More on this issue
Visit: PHSchool.com
Web Code: cch-2193

issues in SCIENCE

Is Video Surveillance an Invasion of Privacy? L2

Background

An important issue of video surveillance is whether it is legal. The courts, including the United States Supreme Court, have repeatedly ruled that video surveillance is legal under certain circumstances. A primary requirement is that the surveillance must be done with high regard for a person's right to privacy. It should only be done if other methods for restricting crime are impossible or ineffective. Surveillance cannot be performed in areas such as restrooms or locker rooms, where a person can reasonably expect privacy.

Answers

1. Student answers will vary but should include the issues of safety and privacy.
2. Arguments "for" center around increased safety and the general idea of freedom, whereas "against" arguments center around the right to live your life in privacy. Advantages and disadvantages are closely related to these arguments.
3. Student answers will vary but should clearly state a position and detail situations when video surveillance is acceptable and when it is not.
4. Reports will vary, but should contain a concise summary of the key points in the case and an explanation as to why the student agrees or disagrees with the decision.

Go Online PHSchool.com

Have students further research the issues related to this topic.

Section 19.3

1 FOCUS

Objectives

19.3.1 **Distinguish** between how reflecting and refracting telescopes form images.

19.3.2 **Explain** how cameras regulate and focus light to form images.

19.3.3 **Describe** how light travels in a compound microscope to produce an enlarged image.

Reading Focus

Build Vocabulary L2

Flowchart As students read about reflecting telescopes, have them make a flowchart showing the steps in the image formation process. Ask students to provide definitions for any scientific words used in their flowcharts.

Reading Strategy L2

Acceptable answers for **a.** and **b.** include any optical instruments, such as microscopes and cameras. After completing the section, revised diagrams should include refracting and reflecting telescopes, cameras (pinhole, and modern or SLR), and microscopes.

2 INSTRUCT

Telescopes

Build Reading Literacy L1

Using Context Clues Refer to page **568D** in this chapter, which provides guidelines for using context clues.

As students read Section 19.3 (pp. 580–585), have them look for unfamiliar words. For example, students may not know definitions for the words *specimen, elements,* and *platform.* Encourage them to use surrounding sentences and figures to help them understand the word. Demonstrate this procedure with the word *shutter* on p. 584. **Verbal**

Use Community Resources L2

Invite a member of the local astronomical society to discuss how different types of telescopes form images and demonstrate their use. **Interpersonal, Visual**

19.3 Optical Instruments

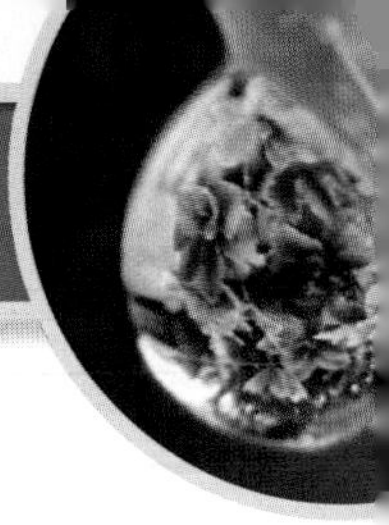

Reading Focus

Key Concepts

- What are the two main types of telescopes?
- How does a camera form an image on film?
- What type of lenses does a compound microscope use to form an image?

Vocabulary

- telescope
- reflecting telescope
- refracting telescope
- camera
- microscope

Reading Strategy

Using Prior Knowledge Copy the diagram below and add to it the names and descriptions of other optical instruments you know. Revise the diagram after reading the section.

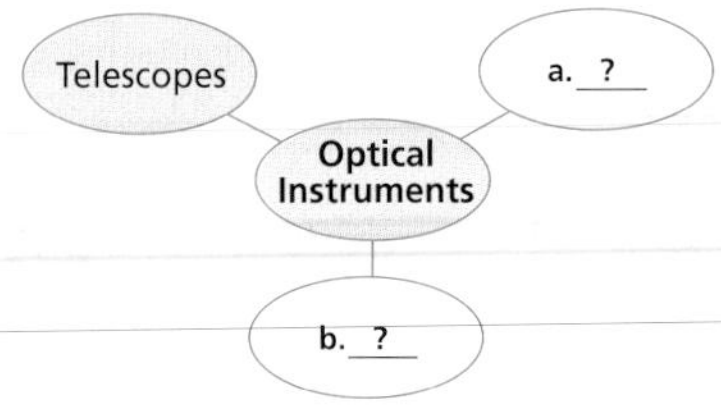

Telescopes
a. ?
Optical Instruments
b. ?

Figure 12 Shown below is one of the two Keck telescopes located on the summit of Hawaii's dormant Mauna Kea volcano. The telescopes, one optical and one infrared, are the largest in the United States. **Inferring** ***What might be a reason for the telescopes being located on a mountain top?***

Your view of the world is not shaped solely by what you can see with the unaided eye. From the most distant star in the galaxy to the tiniest cell of your skin, optical instruments improve your ability to see objects. With telescopes, you can see images of astronomical, far-away objects—some of which may no longer exist. With microscopes, you can see detailed images of objects too tiny to otherwise be seen. With cameras, you can fill your photo album with images of your family and friends, or places you have visited.

Telescopes, microscopes, and cameras are all examples of optical instruments that enhance your ability to see. All of these optical instruments have something in common—they all use lenses or mirrors, or a combination of the two, to reflect and refract light.

Telescopes

The universe is so vast that the light coming from the farthest stars has traveled billions of years before it reaches Earth. Some of the light takes so long to reach Earth that by the time it gets here, the source of the light—the star—has long since burned out. With a telescope you can see images of the star even though it no longer exists. A **telescope** is an instrument that uses lenses or mirrors to collect and focus light from distant objects. In Greek, the word *teleskopos* means "seeing from a distance."

Section Resources

Print
- ***Laboratory Manual,*** Investigation 19B
- ***Reading and Study Workbook With Math Support,*** Section 19.3
- ***Transparencies,*** Section 19.3

Technology
- ***Interactive Textbook,*** Section 19.3
- ***Presentation Pro CD-ROM,*** Section 19.3
- ***Go Online,*** *Science News,* Light and optics

Most historians credit Dutch eyeglass maker Hans Lippershey with inventing the first telescope in 1608. In 1671, Isaac Newton invented a telescope that formed images by reflecting light with a curved mirror. By the end of the 1800s, scientists were looking farther and farther into the universe. Today's telescopes map the universe past and present, helping astronomers figure out its history and its future. **There are two main types of telescopes, reflecting telescopes and refracting telescopes.**

Reflecting Telescopes The **reflecting telescope** uses mirrors and convex lenses to collect and focus light. Figure 13A shows the path of light through a reflecting telescope. Light from a distant object strikes a large concave mirror and is brought to a focus. This focused light is reflected by an angled mirror and forms a real image. The convex lens of the eyepiece then enlarges the image.

Refracting Telescopes The **refracting telescope** uses convex lenses to collect and focus light. Light from a distant object enters the telescope by passing through a convex lens called the objective lens. The convex lens forms a real image at its focal point inside the telescope. A convex lens in the eyepiece then magnifies this real image. As you look through the eyepiece, you see an enlarged, upside-down, virtual image of the real image. Figure 13B shows the path of light through a refracting telescope.

Go Online SCIENCE NEWS

For: Articles on light and optics
Visit: PHSchool.com
Web Code: cce-2193

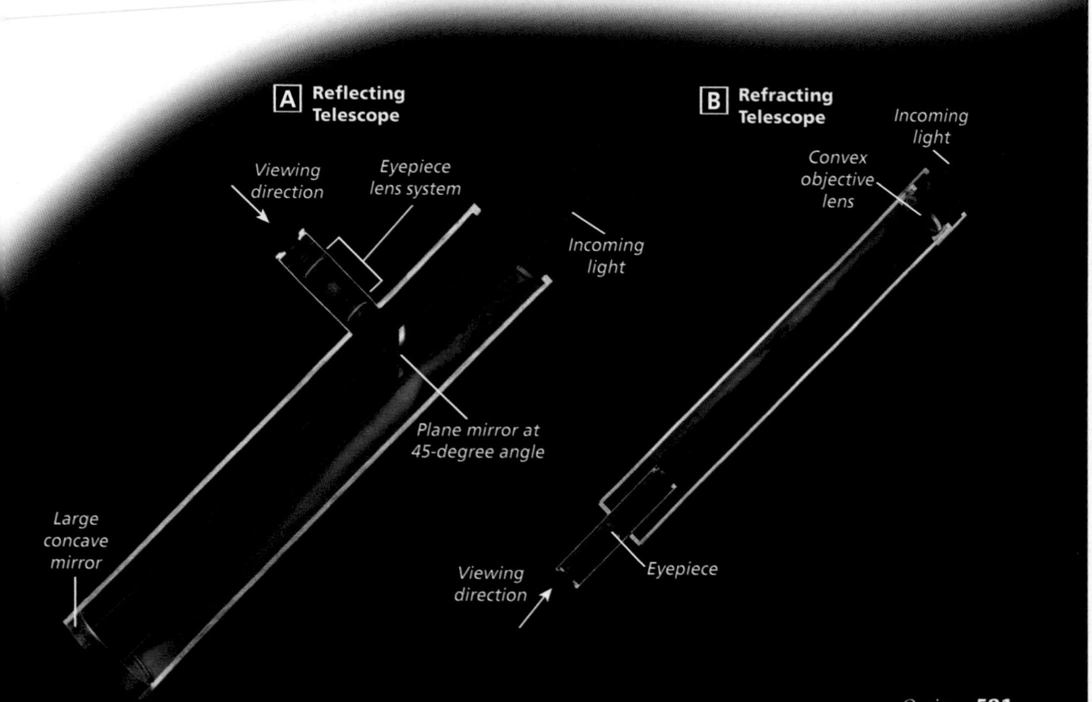

A Reflecting Telescope
Viewing direction
Eyepiece lens system
Incoming light
Plane mirror at 45-degree angle
Large concave mirror
B Refracting Telescope
Incoming light
Convex objective lens
Eyepiece
Viewing direction

Figure 13 The two main types of telescopes use combinations of mirrors and lenses to magnify images of distant objects. **A** The reflecting telescope uses a large concave mirror to focus the incoming light rays. **B** The refracting telescope uses a series of lenses to focus light from distant objects.

Use Visuals L1

Figure 13 Have students trace the path of the incoming light ray in each kind of telescope. Ask, **What is the purpose of the objective lens or mirror?** *(To gather and focus the light rays)* **What is the purpose of the convex eyepiece lens?** *(To magnify the image produced by the mirror or objective lens)* **Visual, Logical**

Teacher Demo L2

Making a Telescope

Purpose Students observe the basic requirements for a telescope.

Materials 2 convex lenses (one with a focal length of 10 cm and the other with a focal length of 30 cm), 1 stick of modeling clay

Procedure Use a lump of clay on a desk to hold the 10-cm focal length lens vertically. Place the other lens vertically in clay a few centimeters away. Align the lenses so that you can look through both, with your eyes a few centimeters from the 10-cm focal length lens. Move the 30-cm focal length lens until you see a sharp image in the lens. This image will be upside down and enlarged. Allow students to look through the lenses.

Expected Outcome Students will recognize that one lens gathers light and the other forms a magnified image. **Visual, Logical**

Go Online SCIENCE NEWS

Science News provides students with current information on light and optics.

Customize for English Language Learners

Building a Science Glossary
Allow students to work in pairs. Post the section's vocabulary terms on the board. Model how to divide each word into parts, determine the meaning of the word, pronounce the word, and use the word in a sentence. Point out that four of the five vocabulary terms contain the word part *-scope*. Tell students that *-scope* means "an instrument for seeing or observing." Ask students how knowing this word part might help them learn the meaning of the vocabulary words. Students can add the words and definitions to their science glossaries. Make frequent references to the words and assign them in homework or another activity to emphasize their importance.

Answer to . . .

Figure 12 *The high elevation means the telescope looks through less of Earth's atmosphere, resulting in better images.*

Cameras

Build Science Skills L2

Comparing and Contrasting Have students carefully examine the first camera (1826) and the modern digital camera (2000). Ask, **What features are common to both cameras?** *(Both cameras are dark containers that gather light through a small hole.)* **What are some improvements that the modern digital camera has over the first camera?** *(The digital camera is smaller, lighter, easier to use, has a low-light indicator, automatic flash, auto-focus zoom lens, and camera dock for image transfer to a computer.)*
Visual

SCIENCE and History

Photography L2

Divide the class into groups of two or three students, and assign each group a date from the time line on p. 583. Have each group discuss how the events they're investigating helped spread the use of photography. *(Each advancement made taking photographs easier for the average person.)* Ask them also to relate the advancements in materials to changes in camera design. *(Lightweight plastics replaced metal bodies and glass lenses.)*
Interpersonal, Verbal

Writing in Science

Light enters each camera by passing through a lens that focuses the light into an image at the back of the camera. The Kine-Exakta forms an image on film that must be removed from the camera and developed. The Land camera records the image on film that develops itself in just a minute or two. The digital camera records the image as an electronic file that is later output to a computer or a printer.

Cameras

A **camera** is an optical instrument that records an image of an object. No matter the type of camera, it uses the same basic principle of focusing light rays to form real images. **Light rays enter a camera through an opening, are focused by the opening or lens, and form an image that is recorded on film or by a sensor.**

Pinhole Camera Did you know that the word *camera* is Latin for "room?" The earliest cameras were in fact the size of an entire room, and were known as *camera obscura*, or "dark room." One of the earliest uses of a camera obscura is credited to Leonardo da Vinci.

SCIENCE and History

Photography

Photography has come a long way since the 1800s, although the basic apparatus is still the same—a box with a hole to let in light.

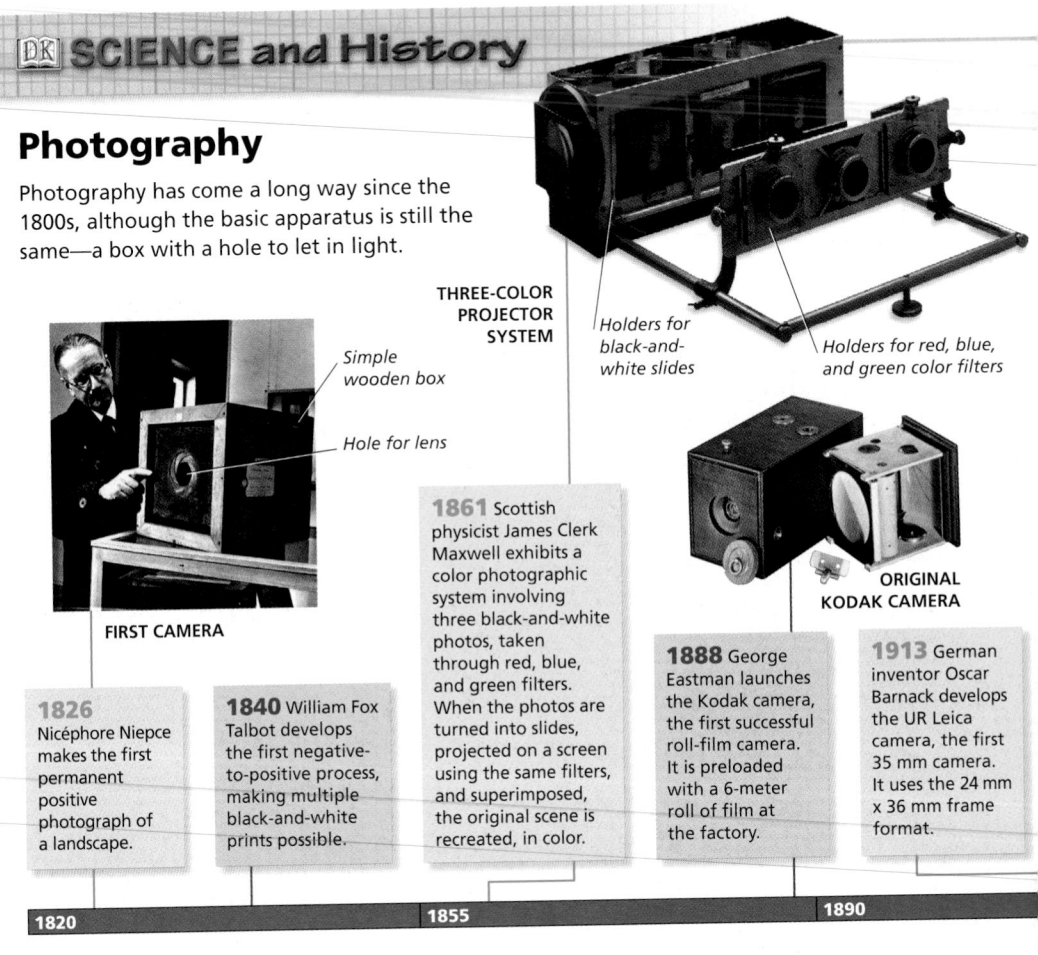

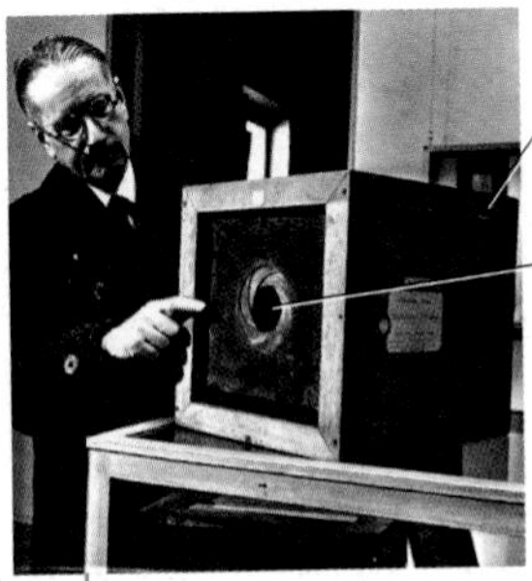
Simple wooden box
Hole for lens

FIRST CAMERA

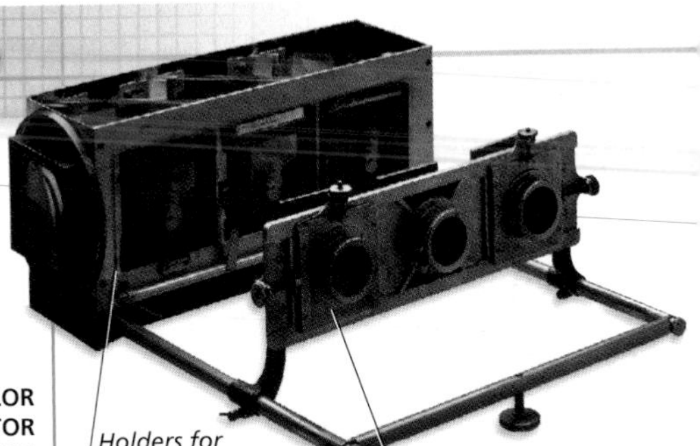
Holders for black-and-white slides
Holders for red, blue, and green color filters

THREE-COLOR PROJECTOR SYSTEM

ORIGINAL KODAK CAMERA

1826 Nicéphore Niepce makes the first permanent positive photograph of a landscape.

1840 William Fox Talbot develops the first negative-to-positive process, making multiple black-and-white prints possible.

1861 Scottish physicist James Clerk Maxwell exhibits a color photographic system involving three black-and-white photos, taken through red, blue, and green filters. When the photos are turned into slides, projected on a screen using the same filters, and superimposed, the original scene is recreated, in color.

1888 George Eastman launches the Kodak camera, the first successful roll-film camera. It is preloaded with a 6-meter roll of film at the factory.

1913 German inventor Oscar Barnack develops the UR Leica camera, the first 35 mm camera. It uses the 24 mm x 36 mm frame format.

1820 — 1855 — 1890

Facts and Figures

Lenses A variety of lenses can be used with cameras. The standard lens used on cameras is a fixed focal length lens. The magnification of images taken with this lens cannot be changed. In general, this type of lens is the lightest, most compact, and most useful for everyday photography. A variable zoom lens permits the photographer to choose the magnification of the image. These lenses are useful for taking up-close pictures of faraway objects. A wide-angle lens captures a wider field of view. You can take photographs of large objects, such as buildings, with this type of lens. Modern cameras may have retractable zoom lenses. These lenses slide back into the camera when not in use. Cameras may also have interchangeable lenses. The entire lens may be removed from the camera and replaced with another type of lens. Point out to students that, although there are many types of camera lenses, they are all converging lenses that focus light to form an image at the back of the camera.

Da Vinci, an Italian scientist, constructed his camera by making a pinhole opening in the shutter of a window of a darkened room. Images of the outside scenery were projected onto the wall opposite the window. Pinhole cameras do not have to be the size of a room. A simple pinhole camera can consist of a cardboard box with a small hole in one side. Light rays from the top and bottom of an object pass through the pinhole and cross paths. The rays form an upside-down, real image on the back wall of the box. For firsthand experience with a pinhole optical device, build and use the pinhole viewer in the QuickLab later in this section.

Reading Checkpoint *What type of image does a pinhole camera form?*

Writing in Science

Compare-Contrast Paragraph Write a paragraph summarizing how all of the cameras shown are similar. Also describe how the Kine-Exakta camera (1936), the Land camera (1947), and the digital camera (2000) differ in the way in which they record images.

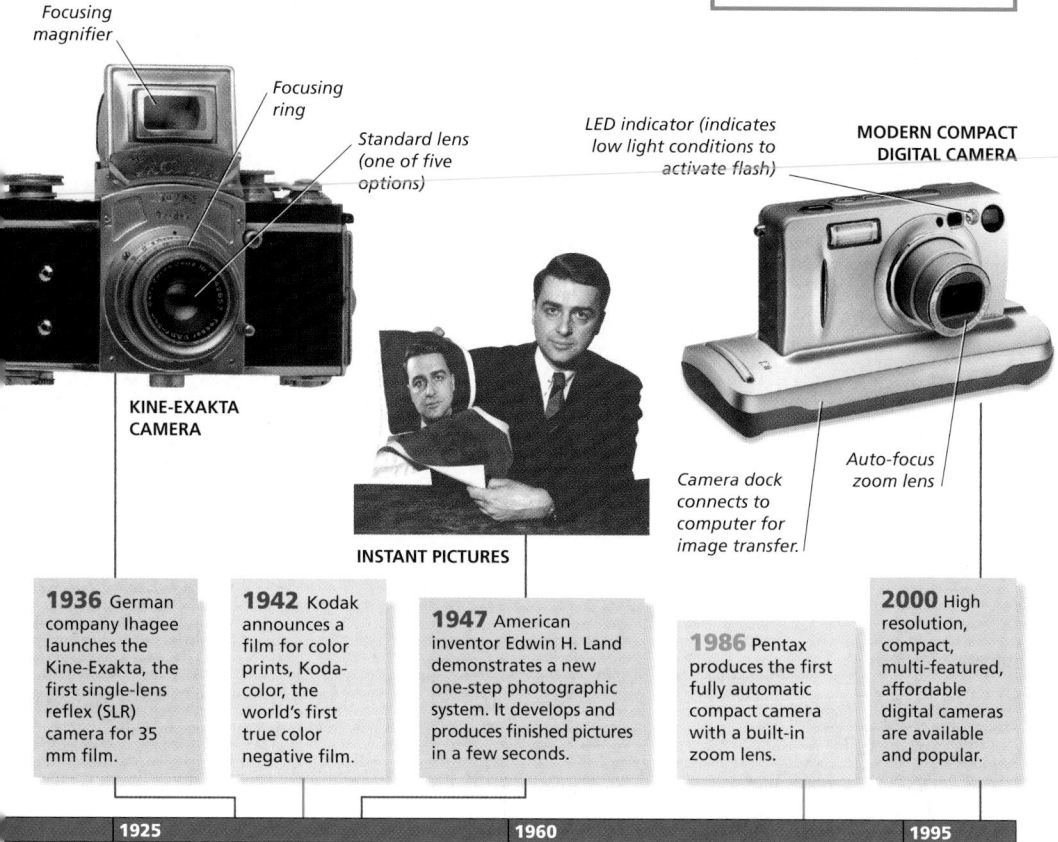

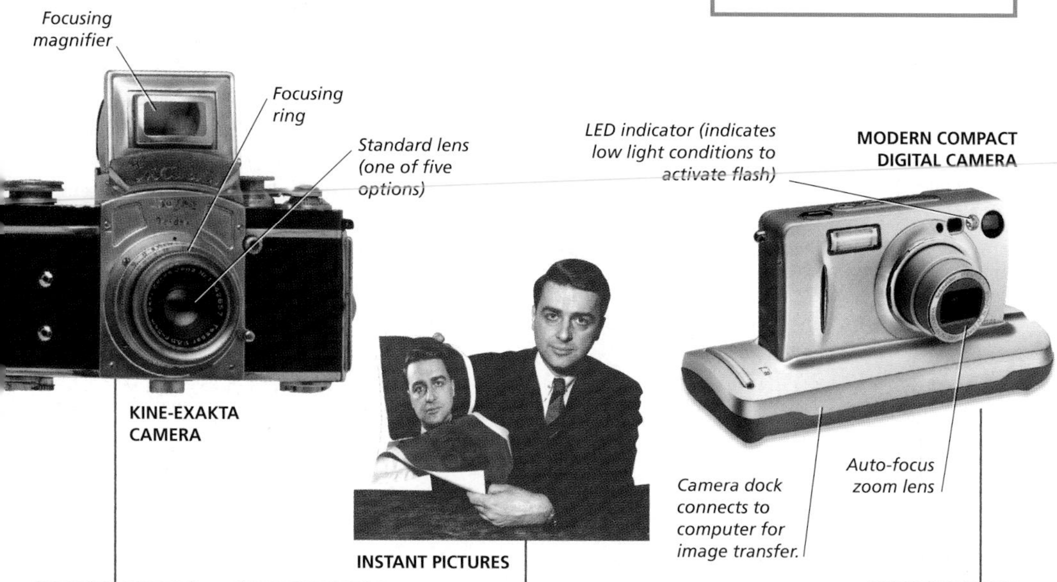
Focusing magnifier
Focusing ring
Standard lens (one of five options)
KINE-EXAKTA CAMERA
INSTANT PICTURES
LED indicator (indicates low light conditions to activate flash)
MODERN COMPACT DIGITAL CAMERA
Camera dock connects to computer for image transfer.
Auto-focus zoom lens

1936 German company Ihagee launches the Kine-Exakta, the first single-lens reflex (SLR) camera for 35 mm film.

1942 Kodak announces a film for color prints, Koda-color, the world's first true color negative film.

1947 American inventor Edwin H. Land demonstrates a new one-step photographic system. It develops and produces finished pictures in a few seconds.

1986 Pentax produces the first fully automatic compact camera with a built-in zoom lens.

2000 High resolution, compact, multi-featured, affordable digital cameras are available and popular.

1925 | 1960 | 1995

Build Science Skills L2

Applying Concepts Point out to students that the first camera shown on the time line had no lens. This is also true for the pinhole camera described in the text. Instead, light enters through a small hole, and the image is formed on the back wall of the camera. Ask, **Why is it sufficient to have light enter through a hole rather than a lens?** *(Light rays entering the camera travel in a straight line through the pinhole and therefore form an image at the back of the camera.)* **Why is the image inverted, even without a lens?** *(Light entering near the top of the hole goes downward through the pinhole, and light entering near the bottom of the hole goes upward through the pinhole.)* **What advantage does a lens offer over a pinhole?** *(More light can be collected, while still providing a focused image)*
Verbal, Logical

Facts and Figures

Autofocus Most cameras today contain an electronic system for autofocusing the image. The camera may do this by emitting an infrared signal that reflects off the object that is being photographed. By measuring the intensity of the reflected light, the camera can determine the object's distance. It then adjusts the lens to optimize the focus. Autofocusing may also be done using electronics that examine the amount of contrast in an image. A blurry image has less contrast than a well-focused image. The camera's electronics adjust the lens placement to maximize the image contrast.

Answer to . . .

Reading Checkpoint *A pinhole camera forms an upside-down, real image.*

Use Visuals L1

Figure 14 Encourage students to discuss how the camera in the figure works. Point out the lenses located both before and after the diaphragm. Explain that together these form the lens elements. Tell students that adjusting the size of the diaphragm's opening (the aperture) controls the amount of light. Ask, **What is the purpose of the prism in the camera?** *(The prism redirects the light from the mirror to the viewfinder.)* **What is the purpose of the shutter?** *(The shutter is usually closed to protect the film. It briefly opens to expose the film to light.)*
Visual, Logical

Microscopes

Teacher Demo L2

Two Types of Microscopes

Purpose Students will learn about compound and stereo microscopes.

Materials compound microscope, stereo microscope

Procedure Show students the two types of microscopes. Draw simple sketches on the chalkboard of their optical paths. Explain that the compound and stereo microscopes are the two basic types of microscopes. Point out that a compound microscope has high magnification (often 10X, 100X, and 400X) and gives an inverted image of the object. A stereo microscope has low magnification and an erect, three-dimensional image.

Expected Outcome Students will learn about compound and stereo microscopes.
Visual, Logical

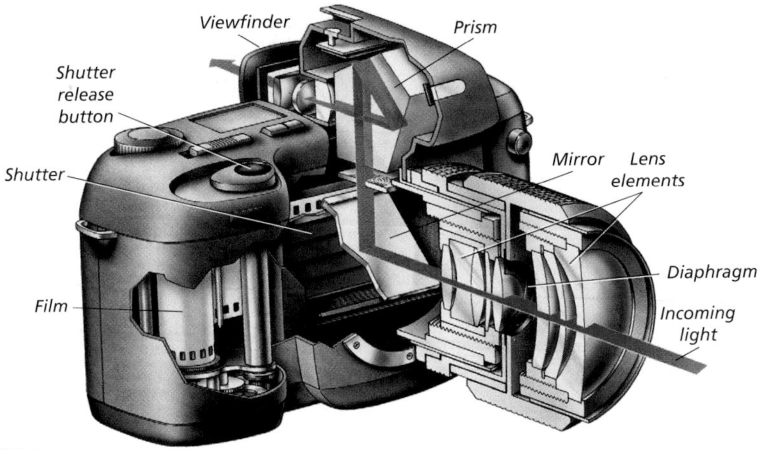
Viewfinder
Prism
Shutter release button
Shutter
Mirror
Lens elements
Diaphragm
Incoming light
Film

Figure 14 Shown here is a typical single lens reflex (SLR) camera. The mirror reflects the image through the viewfinder so the photographer can bring it into focus. When the shutter release button is pushed, the mirror flips up. This allows the focused light rays to pass straight through the lens system and onto the film.

Modern Film Camera Figure 14 shows a typical modern film camera. The lens elements focus the incoming light rays. The focused rays then pass through the diaphragm, a device that controls the amount of light passing through the lens. When the shutter release button is pressed, the mirror flips up and the shutter briefly opens to let the focused light rays strike the film.

To bring an object into focus, the lens must be moved toward or away from the film. This focusing, which can be done manually or automatically, is needed to form a sharp image. The focused light reacts with a light-sensitive chemical coating on the film that records the real image. The image is upside down and smaller than the object. After the film is developed and printed, you have photographs for your album.

Figure 15 This compound microscope uses a mirror to reflect light up and into the microscope.
***Comparing and Contrasting** How is the way in which a focused image is formed the same in both a camera and a microscope?*

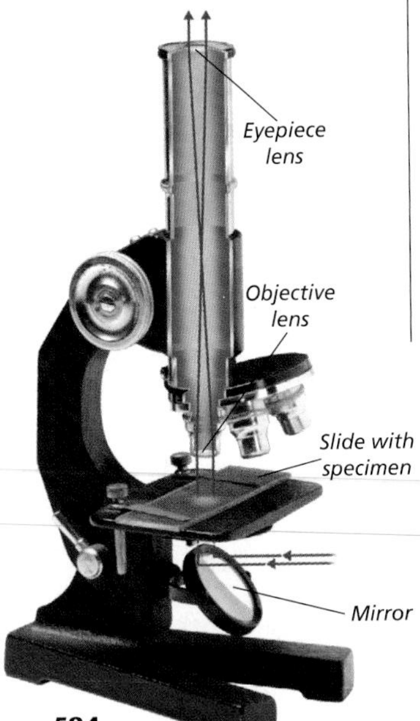
Eyepiece lens
Objective lens
Slide with specimen
Mirror

Microscopes

A **microscope** is an optical instrument that uses lenses to provide enlarged images of very small, near objects. One common type of microscope is called a compound microscope. **The compound microscope uses two convex lenses to magnify small objects.**

Figure 15 shows the structure of a compound microscope. To view an enlarged image of an object, you place the object on a glass slide. You then place the slide on a platform located above a light source. Light rays from below pass up through the object and then pass through a convex lens called the objective. The lens produces an enlarged, upside-down, real image. This image then becomes the "object" for a second convex lens called the eyepiece. The eyepiece enlarges the image. When you look through the eyepiece, you see an enlarged, virtual image of the object. Under the best conditions, modern light microscopes can magnify images more than 1000 times.

Facts and Figures

Microscope Objectives A typical school microscope has three objectives. The shortest objective is low power, with a magnification of 10X. The intermediate objective may have a multiplication of 40X. The longest objective may have a magnification of 100X. The convex lens in the eyepiece, however, typically provides an additional multiplication of 10X. This means the total magnification of the three objectives is 100X, 400X, and 1000X. To obtain enough light with the 1000X magnification, you must place a drop of immersion oil on the lens. When the objective is lowered, the oil eliminates the space between the lens and the coverslip over the specimen. The oil has the same index of refraction as glass. Light, therefore, is not refracted, and you obtain sufficient light to view the object.

Quick Lab

Building a Pinhole Viewer

Materials

- cardboard tube
- black construction paper
- aluminum foil
- wax paper
- 4 rubber bands
- pin

Procedure

1. Place aluminum foil over one end of the cardboard tube and use a rubber band to hold the foil in place.
2. Place wax paper over the other end of the tube and hold the paper in place with a rubber band. There should be no wrinkles in the wax paper covering the opening of the tube.
3. Roll a piece of black construction paper lengthwise around the tube. The foil end should be flush with one end of the construction paper as shown. Use two more rubber bands to hold the construction paper in place.
4. Verify that the wax paper end is now in the middle of the black construction paper tube.

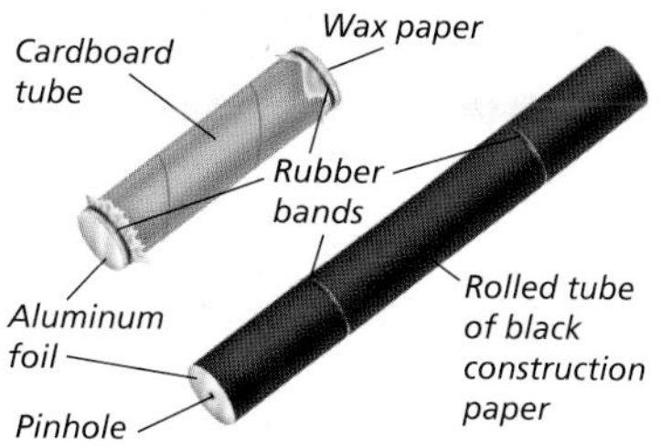

Cardboard tube
Wax paper
Rubber bands
Aluminum foil
Rolled tube of black construction paper
Pinhole

5. Use a pin to make a hole in the center of the aluminum foil. You may have to enlarge the hole slightly to see an image clearly.
6. Point the pinhole toward a light source and look through the other end of the viewer. Observe several objects inside your classroom (chairs, tables, and books) and outside of your classroom (houses, trees, and cars). **CAUTION** *Do not use the viewer to look at the sun, as you may injure your eyes.*

Analyze and Conclude

1. **Observing** Describe the images that appeared on the wax paper.
2. **Relating Cause and Effect** What caused the images to appear on the wax paper the way they did?

Section 19.3 Assessment

Reviewing Concepts

1. Name the two main types of telescopes.
2. How does a film camera work?
3. Describe the system of lenses in a compound microscope.
4. What is the purpose of the lens in a camera?

Critical Thinking

5. **Inferring** High-speed film is very sensitive to light. Explain how this could be useful for dim-light photography.
6. **Applying Concepts** Can the image seen in the eyepiece of a compound microscope be projected on a screen?

Connecting Concepts

Speed of Light From Chapter 18 you know that light travels at an extremely high speed. Explain how the images of deep-space objects you see through telescopes are images of the past.

Quick Lab

Building a Pinhole Viewer **L2**

Objective
After completing this activity, students will be able to
- describe the formation of an inverted image by a pinhole camera.

Skills Focus Observing

Prep Time 20 minutes

Class Time 25 minutes

Safety Caution students not to look directly into the sun.

Expected Outcome Students will observe an inverted image on the wax paper.

Analyze and Conclude
1. The images produced on the wax paper are reversed left to right, and top to bottom.
2. The rays are reversed left-right and top-bottom as they pass through the opening. **Logical**

3 ASSESS

Evaluate Understanding **L2**

Ask students to name some optical instruments they use. Have students describe what kind of lens or mirror they think is used in the device.

Reteach **L1**

Have students write several sentences that briefly explain how telescopes, cameras, and microscopes form images.

Connecting Concepts

Because deep-space objects are so far away, it takes thousands of years or more for light emanating from them to reach Earth. Thus, images we currently see in telescopes are actually images of how those deep-space objects appeared thousands or more years ago.

Interactive Textbook If your class subscribes to the Interactive Textbook, use it to review key concepts in Section 19.3

Answer to . . .

Figure 15 *Both use a movable lens or series of lenses to focus the image.*

Section 19.3 Assessment

1. The refracting telescope and the reflecting telescope
2. Light rays enter the camera through an opening, are focused by the lens, and form an image on the film.
3. A compound microscope uses two convex lenses to magnify small objects.
4. Camera lenses focus the incoming light rays to form a sharp image.
5. High-speed film is useful in situations where there are very low light levels because it requires less time to form an image.
6. Yes, the light could be projected onto a screen, but it would not form an image. The enlarged virtual image formed by a microscope cannot be projected onto a screen.

CONCEPTS in Action

Fiber Optics L2

Background

Optical fibers are usually made of a highly transparent glass. The glass must be extremely pure. Even small amounts of impurities would absorb too much of the light.

To enable light transmission, the refractive index of the core must be greater than the refractive index of the cladding, or layer just outside the core. Ideally, the difference in the refractive indices should be as great as possible. However, consideration must also be given to whether or not the cladding material is able to adhere to the core fiber.

Light propagates through a fiber by total internal reflection. When light inside the fiber optic reaches the interface of the core and the outer layer, it reflects off the outer layer back into the core provided that the angle of incidence is greater than or equal to the critical angle. The light continues to totally internally reflect down the length of the fiber.

CONCEPTS in Action

Fiber Optics

Optical fibers have caused a revolution in information technology by making it possible to transmit huge amounts of information along slender strands of glass.

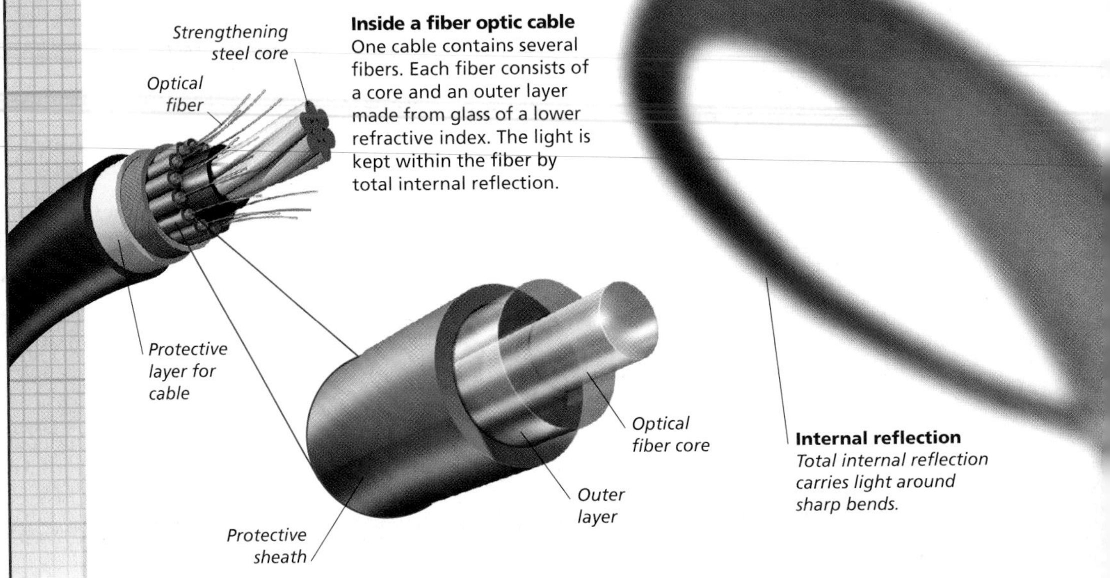
Strengthening steel core
Optical fiber
Inside a fiber optic cable
One cable contains several fibers. Each fiber consists of a core and an outer layer made from glass of a lower refractive index. The light is kept within the fiber by total internal reflection.
Protective layer for cable
Optical fiber core
Outer layer
Protective sheath
Internal reflection
Total internal reflection carries light around sharp bends.

Transmitting a TV signal
TV signals can be sent along optical cables in the form of light. The electrical signal produced by the camera is turned into a digital code by the transmitter, and sent along the cable as rapid pulses of light. The receiver then converts this signal back into an electrical signal, which in turn forms a picture on the TV screen.

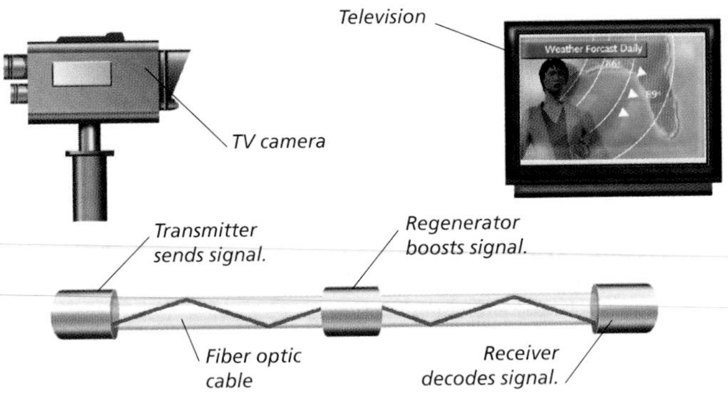
Television
Weather Forcast Daily
TV camera
Transmitter sends signal.
Regenerator boosts signal.
Fiber optic cable
Receiver decodes signal.

Optical fibers in medicine

As well as carrying digital information, optical fibers are useful in medicine. This is because they can bend around corners, allowing otherwise inaccessible parts of the body to be viewed.

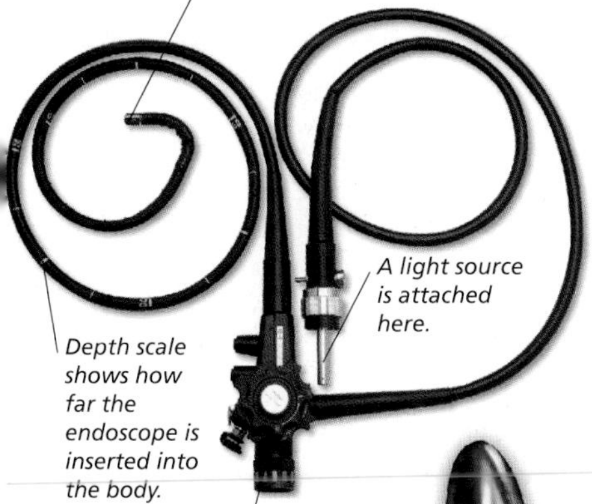

Tip of the endoscope is inserted first into the body.
A light source is attached here.
Depth scale shows how far the endoscope is inserted into the body.
Eyepiece

ENDOSCOPE

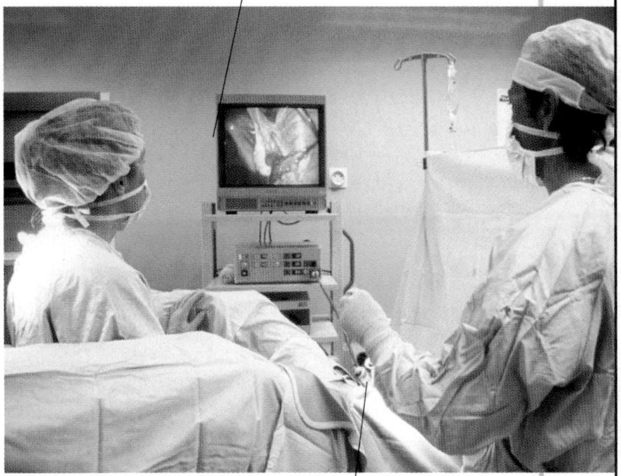

Internal organ is viewed on a computer screen.
Surgeons use an endoscope to look at internal organs.

Endoscope
Endoscopes are used to view the interior of the body. They are often used for investigations—such as checking for a stomach ulcer—and during surgery, to guide the surgeon.

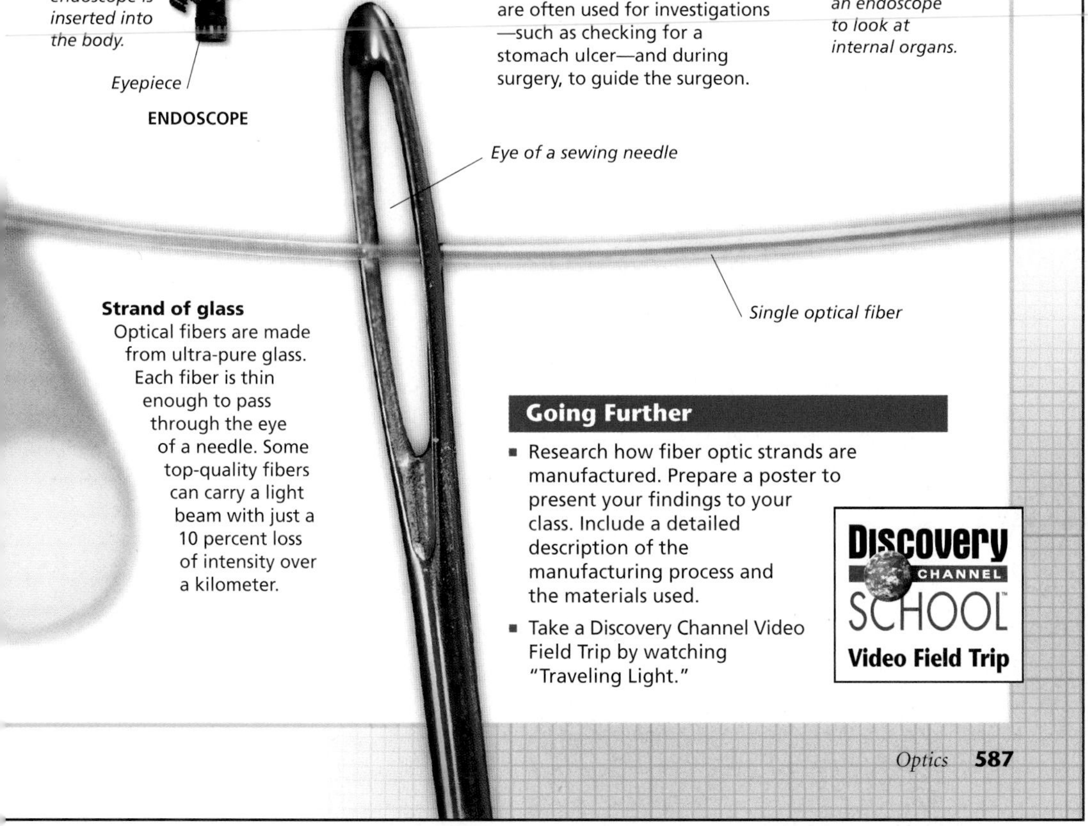

Eye of a sewing needle
Single optical fiber

Strand of glass
Optical fibers are made from ultra-pure glass. Each fiber is thin enough to pass through the eye of a needle. Some top-quality fibers can carry a light beam with just a 10 percent loss of intensity over a kilometer.

Going Further

- Research how fiber optic strands are manufactured. Prepare a poster to present your findings to your class. Include a detailed description of the manufacturing process and the materials used.
- Take a Discovery Channel Video Field Trip by watching "Traveling Light."

Discovery Channel School **Video Field Trip**

Build Science Skills **L2**

Observing ACTIVITY

Purpose Students observe properties of optical fibers.

Materials flashlight, fiber optic bundle

Class Time 10 minutes

Procedure In a darkened room, shine a bright light at the end of a straight bundle of optical fibers. Students will notice that the light exits the fibers only at the ends. Now bend the bundle of fibers while continuing to shine the light on the ends of the fibers. Students will observe that the light still only exits the fibers at the ends. Ask, **Why does the light travel through the length of the fibers, even though the fibers are bent?** *(Internal reflection causes the light to bounce off the outer layer of the fibers.)*

Expected Outcome Light enters one end of the fiber bundle and exits the other end, even if the fibers are bent.
Visual, Logical

Going Further

Student posters and research findings will vary but should include a description of the materials used and the manufacturing process. Optical fiber manufacturing is basically a two-step process involving the fabrication of a specially constructed glass rod called a preform, followed by the melting of the preform, which is then drawn into a thin fiber. Commercial producers use a variety of processes to fabricate the preform, all of which are based on a thermal chemical vapor reaction that forms mixed oxides which are deposited as layers of glass soot onto a rotating high-purity glass rod or tube.
Visual

Discovery Channel School

Video Field Trip

Traveling Light

After students have viewed the Video Field Trip, ask them the following questions: **Name one advantage of using light signals through glass fibers to transmit information.** *(The information is transmitted at very high speeds through the fiber.)* **Who was the first person to use light to transmit telephone conversations?** *(Alexander Graham Bell)* **Describe the process of making a glass fiber for sending signals using light.** *(Pure silica is used to make a fine glass rod. The rod is heated. Molten glass from the end of the rod drips down to form a long thin fiber.)* **Name a practical advantage that glass fibers have over copper wire.** *(The glass is less expensive than copper.)*

1 FOCUS

Objectives

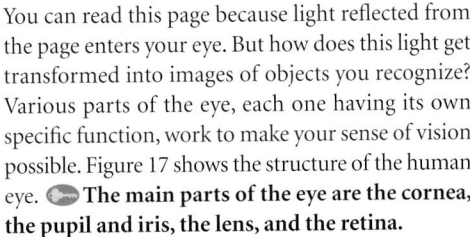

19.4.1 **Name** the main parts of the eye and **describe** their functions.

19.4.2 **Name** common vision problems, **identify** their causes, and **explain** how they can be corrected.

Reading Focus

Build Vocabulary L2

Word-Part Analysis Tell students that the vocabulary terms *nearsightedness* and *farsightedness* are compound words with a suffix. Explain that the suffix *-ness* means "the state of being." Have students tell each word's word parts and tell what the words mean based on their word parts. *(The word parts of nearsightedness are* near, sighted, *and* -ness. *The word parts of farsightedness are* far, sighted, *and* -ness. *Nearsightedness means the state of being able to see near. Farsightedness means the state of being able to see far.)*

Reading Strategy L2

I. The Eye and Vision
- A. Structure of the Eye
  1. Cornea
  2. Pupil and Iris
  3. Lens
  4. Retina
  5. Rods and Cones
- B. Correcting Vision Problems
  1. Nearsightedness
  2. Farsightedness
  3. Astigmatism

2 INSTRUCT

Structure of the Eye

Address Misconceptions L2

Many people incorrectly assume that the lens of the eye is the primary focusing element. Explain to students that light entering the eye encounters the greatest difference in optical density (indices of refraction) when it passes from the air to the cornea. Therefore, light is focused most by the cornea.
Visual, Logical

19.4 The Eye and Vision

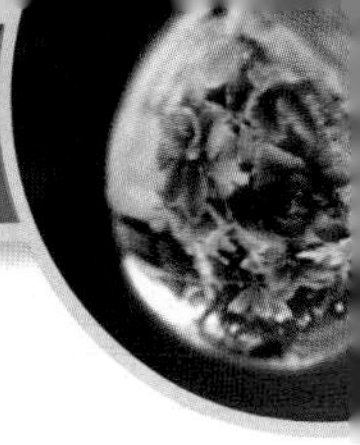

Reading Focus

Key Concepts
- What are the main parts of the eye?
- What are some common vision problems?

Vocabulary
- cornea
- pupil
- iris
- retina
- rods
- cones
- nearsightedness
- farsightedness
- astigmatism

Reading Strategy

Outlining As you read, make an outline of the important ideas in this section. Use the green headings as the main topics and the blue headings as subtopics.

I. The Eye and Vision
A. Structure of the Eye
1. ______
2. ______
and so on . . .
B. ______
and so on . . .

Have you ever stopped to appreciate how remarkable your eyes are? They play a very important role in your perception of the world around you. Your eyes, like the one shown in Figure 16, are optical instruments that perform the same tasks of bending and focusing light as telescopes, cameras, and microscopes.

Your eyes form images every moment they are exposed to light. They receive and focus visible light from objects near and far. Your brain then interprets the images of the objects formed by your eyes.

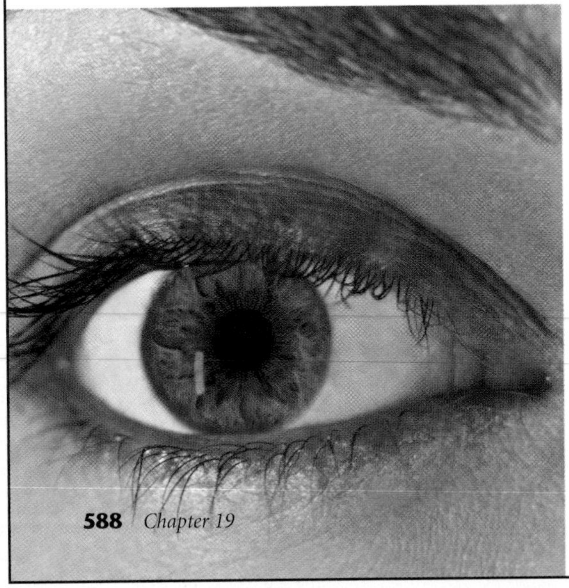

Figure 16 The lens of the eye focuses incoming light rays onto light-sensitive nerve endings located inside and at the back of your eye.

Structure of the Eye

You can read this page because light reflected from the page enters your eye. But how does this light get transformed into images of objects you recognize? Various parts of the eye, each one having its own specific function, work to make your sense of vision possible. Figure 17 shows the structure of the human eye. **The main parts of the eye are the cornea, the pupil and iris, the lens, and the retina.**

Cornea Light rays enter your eyes through the transparent outer coating of the eye, called the **cornea.** The cornea's curved surface helps to focus light entering your eye.

Section Resources

Print
- ***Reading and Study Workbook With Math Support,*** Section 19.4
- ***Transparencies,*** Section 19.4

Technology
- ***Interactive Textbook,*** Section 19.4
- ***Presentation Pro CD-ROM,*** Section 19.4

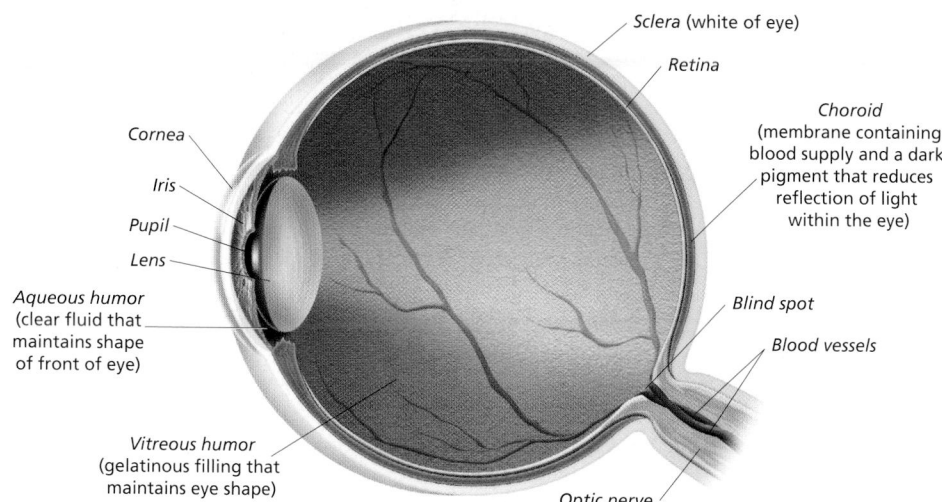

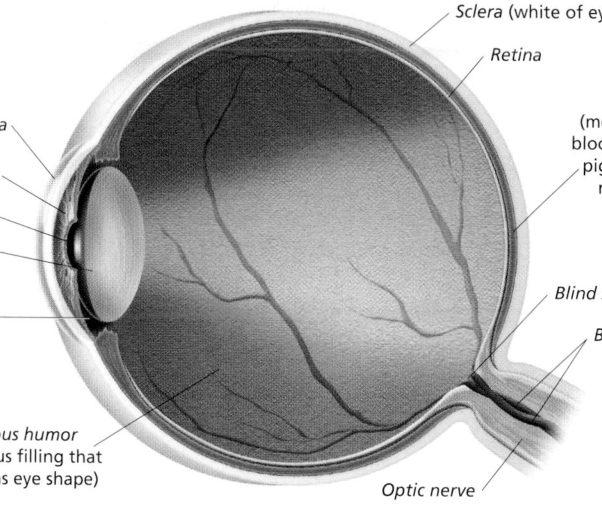
Sclera (white of eye)
Retina
Choroid (membrane containing blood supply and a dark pigment that reduces reflection of light within the eye)
Cornea
Iris
Pupil
Lens
Aqueous humor (clear fluid that maintains shape of front of eye)
Blind spot
Blood vessels
Vitreous humor (gelatinous filling that maintains eye shape)
Optic nerve

Figure 17 The eye is the organ that provides you with sight. Light passes through the cornea, pupil, and lens before striking the retina. Signals from light-sensitive nerves on the retina are sent through the optic nerve to the brain. **Predicting** ***What may result if the eyeball has an elongated (too long) shape?***

Pupil and Iris After the cornea, light rays pass through the pupil, the part of your eye that looks black. The **pupil** is the opening that allows light rays to enter your eye. The colored part of your eye, the **iris,** contracts and expands to control the amount of light that enters your eye. The controlled movement of the iris is regulated by signals from your brain.

Lens After passing through the pupil, light enters the convex lens in your eye. The lens is a sealed capsule containing a clear fluid. This lens focuses the light onto the light sensor cells at the back of the eye. As you change your focus from near to distant objects, muscles inside the eye change the shape of the flexible lens. The muscles relax and the lens becomes thinner and flatter. If you read for a long time, you'll notice that your eyes become tired and feel strained. This is because the muscles have been contracting for a long time. The best way to relax your eyes is to look far away.

Retina The focused, refracted light is collected at the retina. The **retina** is the inner surface of the eye. Its surface is covered by light-sensitive nerve endings called **rods** and **cones.** The rods and cones convert the light into electrical signals that are sent to the brain through the optic nerve. The area of the retina where the nerve endings come together to form the optic nerve creates a blind spot. This blind spot has no rods or cones and cannot sense light.

Reading Checkpoint *Which part of the eye controls how much light enters?*

Use Visuals L1

Figure 17 Have students look at the figure and describe the refraction of light as it passes through each part. Ask, **Are the light rays that enter the eye always parallel?** *(No, they enter at all angles.)* **Describe the mediums that light encounters as it passes through the eye.** *(Light passes through air, the cornea, aqueous humor, the lens, and vitreous humor before striking the retina at the back of the eye.)* **What prevents most of the light that enters the eye from being reflected?** *(The choroid is filled with blood, which absorbs most of the incoming light.)*
Visual

Build Science Skills L2

Observing It is easy for most students to detect their "blind spot." Pass out some white index cards. Have students turn the cards so the long dimension is horizontal and make an *X* on the card about 3 or 4 cm from the right hand edge and a dot 5 or 6 cm further to the left. Then have students cover their right eyes with one hand and stare at the *X* with their left eye while slowly bringing the card closer to the eye. At some distance (around 18 cm) the dot will disappear. Ask students to explain what happened. *(The image of the dot fell on the eye's blind spot.)*
Logical, Visual

Customize for Inclusion Students

Gifted
The process by which a lens changes to alter its depth of focus is called accommodation. In humans, this is done by muscles that increase or decrease the roundness of the lens. In animals, accommodation is done in other ways, such as moving the lens toward or away from the retina. Some animal eyes are not capable of accommodating. Have students research the method of accommodation in various animals. Have students present their research findings to the class.

Answer to . . .

Figure 17 *The image formed by the lens may not be in focus at the location of the retina.*

Reading Checkpoint *The iris controls the amount of light that enters the eye.*

Build Reading Literacy L1

Relate Cause and Effect Refer to page **260D** in **Chapter 9**, which provides the guidelines for relating cause and effect.

Cause-and-effect relationships are the basis of scientific discovery. However, some students may not fully understand the nature of the cause-and-effect relationship. Ask, **When you enter a dark theatre from bright sunlight, the pupil opens very quickly. However it may be a few minutes before your eye fully adjusts to the low light conditions. Why?** *(Although the iris opens quickly, a few minutes are required for the rods and cones to adjust to the low light conditions.)*
Visual

Correcting Vision Problems

Integrate Health L2

Explain that both optometrists and ophthalmologists are trained to diagnose vision defects and prescribe corrective lenses. Tell students that ophthalmologists also treat diseases of the eye. Encourage students to research eye diseases such as glaucoma, cataracts, and conjunctivitis. Have students describe methods of treatment used by ophthalmologists for these diseases, and any means of preventing the diseases.
Visual

Rods and Cones Low-intensity light is sensed by rods. The brain uses signals from rods to distinguish among white, black, and different shades of gray. Cones are sensitive to color, but are less sensitive than rods; that is, they need more light than rods in order to function. The decreased light sensitivity of cones explains why you can't make out the colors of objects in very dim light. There are three different types of cones. Each type of cone is able to sense only a single color—red light, green light, or blue light. People who are colorblind have missing or defective cones of one or more of the three kinds.

Correcting Vision Problems

You have probably heard the expression "20/20 vision." Having 20/20 vision means that you can clearly see things of a certain size from 20 feet. 20/20 vision is considered normal. Not everybody, however, has 20/20 vision. **Several common vision problems are nearsightedness, farsightedness, and astigmatism.** They result in people having vision that is worse than 20/20. In many cases, less-than-perfect vision can be corrected with eyeglasses or contact lenses. Corrective eyeware is not new—eyeglasses were used in China and Italy as early as the 1200s.

Reading Checkpoint *What does it mean to have 20/20 vision?*

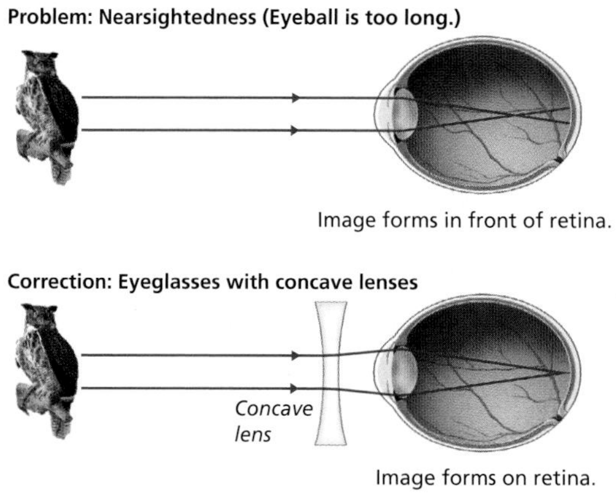
Problem: Nearsightedness (Eyeball is too long.)
Image forms in front of retina.
Correction: Eyeglasses with concave lenses
Concave lens
Image forms on retina.

Figure 18 When the eyeball is too long, the focused image forms in front of the retina. By the time the image reaches the retina, it is no longer in focus. This common condition, called nearsightedness, can be corrected with a diverging (concave) lens.

Nearsightedness If you have normal vision, the images you see are clear and undistorted. The light rays that enter your eyes are focused on your retinas. However, for approximately one out of four people, the rays focus before they reach the retina. This condition, called **nearsightedness,** causes distant objects to appear blurry. Nearsightedness occurs either because the cornea is too curved or the eyeball is too long. In either case, the rays of light focus too close to the lens. A nearsighted person can see nearby objects clearly, but distant objects seem blurred. Nearsightedness can be corrected by placing a diverging (concave) lens in front of the eye. The lens spreads the rays out a little before they enter the eye. This causes the image to form farther back, at the retina, instead of in front of it. Some cases of nearsightedness can now be treated with surgery. Figure 18 shows a diagram of a nearsighted eye and how it can be corrected with a diverging (concave) lens.

Facts and Figures

Interfaces in the Eye Light entering the eye encounters four interfaces: (1) air to cornea, (2) cornea to aqueous humor, (3) aqueous humor to lens, and (4) lens to vitreous humor. The indices of refraction are 1.00 for air, approximately 1.376 for the cornea, 1.336 for aqueous humor, and 1.337 for vitreous humor. The index of refraction for the lens ranges from 1.386 to 1.406. Light that enters the eye is bent most when it passes from air into the cornea, because this is where the largest change in index of refraction occurs.

DK HOW It Works

Laser Eye Surgery

The laser has become a sight-saving tool. In laser eye surgery, a laser beam makes small incisions, half the thickness of a human hair, in the eye. Surgeons correct and control different types of vision problems by careful positioning of the laser incisions. As shown below, a laser can be used to destroy abnormal blood vessels that cause failing vision in patients with diabetes. **Interpreting Diagrams** ***On what part of the eye do the abnormal blood vessels form?***

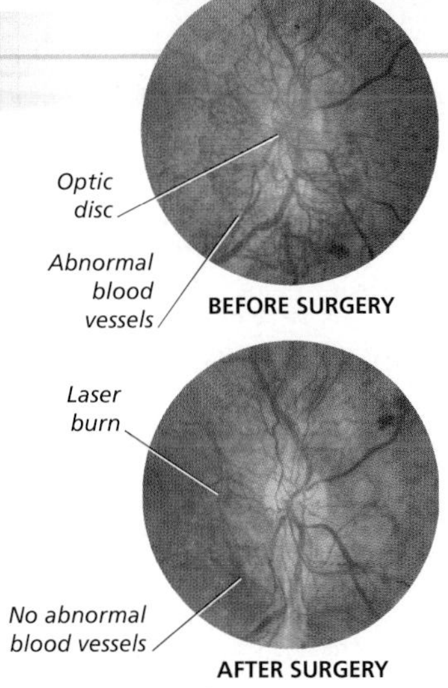

Optic disc
Abnormal blood vessels
BEFORE SURGERY
Laser burn
No abnormal blood vessels
AFTER SURGERY

Results of surgery
Taken through the pupil of the eye, these pictures show how abnormal blood vessels on the retina are burned away by laser treatment. After surgery, the retina appears paler.

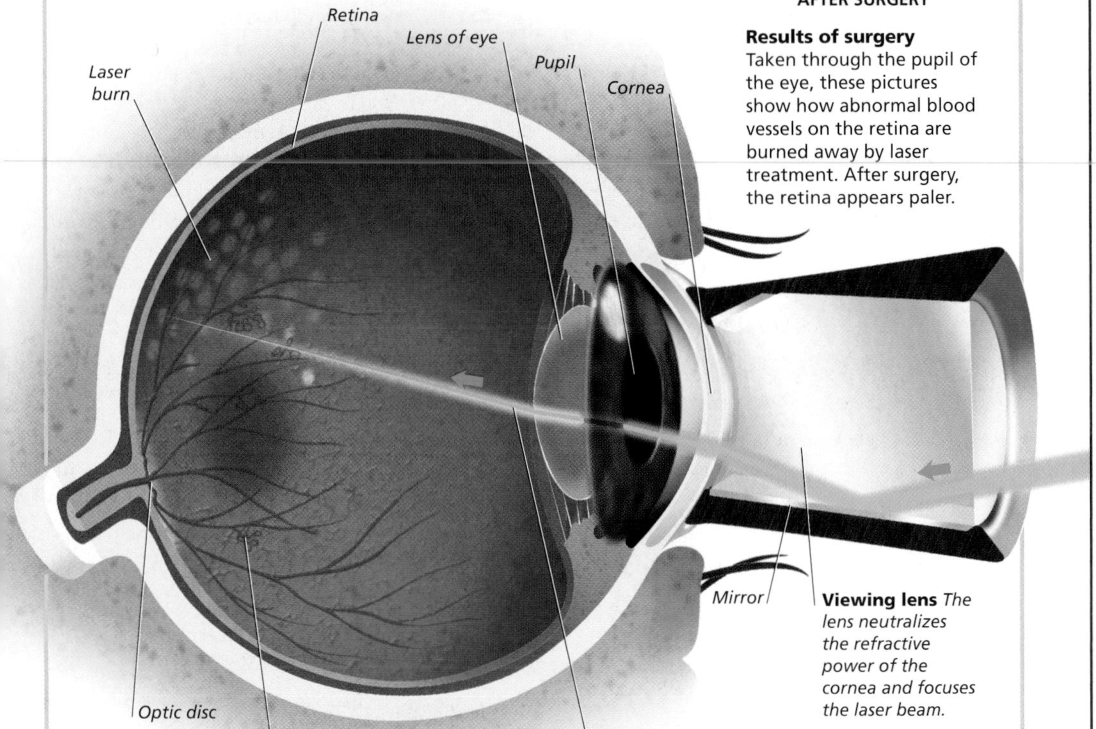

Retina
Lens of eye
Pupil
Cornea
Laser burn
Mirror
Optic disc

Viewing lens *The lens neutralizes the refractive power of the cornea and focuses the laser beam.*

Abnormal blood vessels *Due to diabetes, abnormal blood vessels form on the retina, impairing vision.*

Laser beam *By destroying parts of the outer layer of the retina and the abnormal blood vessels, it is possible to prevent further deterioration of the patient's vision.*

DK HOW It Works

Laser Eye Surgery L2

Most people who undergo laser eye surgery have a significant improvement in their vision. This is especially true for those who previously had moderate vision problems. However, not everyone with vision problems is eligible for the surgery. Patients must be over 18 years old with stable vision for at least two years. Their corneas must be sufficiently thick to allow the physician to safely perform the incision. People with severe eye problems should not have the surgery. In addition, certain eye disorders, such as cataracts and glaucoma, as well as eye injuries may prevent a person from having laser eye surgery. Patients should realize that the surgery does not guarantee 20/20 vision, and, as with all surgery, there are risks involved.

Interpreting Diagrams The abnormal blood vessels form on the retina.
Visual

For Enrichment L3

Have interested students interview a physician who performs laser eye surgery or a person who has undergone the procedure. Students might ask about the requirements, risks, and benefits of the surgery, as well as any drawbacks. Afterwards, students can report to the class about what they learn.
Interpersonal

Answer to . . .

Reading Checkpoint *20/20 vision means that you can recognize objects of a certain size at a distance of 20 feet.*

3 ASSESS

Evaluate Understanding L2

Randomly quiz students about the parts of the eye and their function. Have students draw diagrams showing vision correction for nearsightedness and farsightedness using convex and concave lenses.

Reteach L1

Review the structure of the eye using Figure 17. Have students review Figures 18 and 19 and discuss how the shape of the eyeball affects the eye's ability to focus.

Writing in Science

Student paragraphs will vary but must include all of the parts of the eye (at least the cornea, iris, pupil, lens, and retina) and their functions. More detailed descriptions may include the aqueous humor, vitreous humor, rods, cones, and optic nerve.

Interactive Textbook If your class subscribes to the Interactive Textbook, use it to review key concepts in Section 19.4.

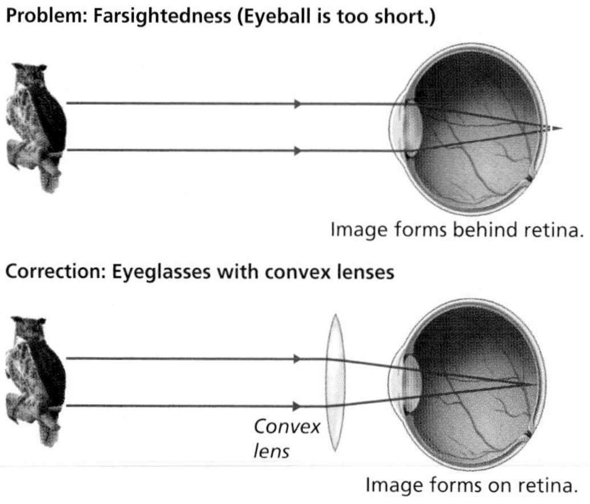
Problem: Farsightedness (Eyeball is too short.)
Image forms behind retina.
Correction: Eyeglasses with convex lenses
Convex lens
Image forms on retina.

Figure 19 Farsightedness occurs when an image is not focused before it reaches the retina. Farsightedness can be corrected by using a converging (convex) lens in front of the eye. **Comparing and Contrasting** ***In what ways are farsightedness and nearsightedness similar?***

Farsightedness Blurred images can also be a result of farsightedness. **Farsightedness** is a condition that causes nearby objects to appear blurry. Common causes of farsightedness are either a cornea that is not curved enough or an eyeball that is too short. In either case, the rays of light focus too far from the lens. As a result, the image focuses beyond the retina. A farsighted person can see distant objects clearly, but nearby objects seem blurred. Farsightedness is usually corrected by placing a converging (convex) lens in front of the eye. The lens bends the light rays toward each other before they enter the eye. Because the rays entering the eye are converging, the image is formed on the retina instead of behind the retina. Figure 19 shows a diagram of a farsighted eye and how it can be corrected.

Astigmatism For clear vision, the lens of the eye and the cornea must be properly shaped. When the cornea or lens is misshapen, a defect in vision called astigmatism results. **Astigmatism** is a condition in which objects at any distance appear blurry because the cornea or lens is misshapen. Just as with an eyeball that is too long or too short, this irregularity can prevent light from focusing properly on the retina. The result is that the lens has two different focal points, causing distortion or blurring of the image. Specialized eyeglass lens shapes are used to correct astigmatism.

Section 19.4 Assessment

Reviewing Concepts

1. List, in order, the parts of the eye that light encounters.
2. What are three common problems that affect vision?
3. What is the eye's blind spot?
4. Which kind of lens can correct nearsightedness? Farsightedness?

Critical Thinking

5. **Inferring** Why is the cornea transparent?
6. **Comparing and Contrasting** How is the structure of the eye similar to that of a simple camera?
7. **Making Judgments** Suppose that when you sit at the back of the room, you can't read the chalkboard. What vision problem might you have?
8. **Connecting Concepts** The index of refraction of the cornea is about the same as that of water. Use this fact to explain why you cannot see as well in water as in air.

Writing in Science

Steps in a Process Write a paragraph describing how a light ray passes through the eye and results in vision.

Section 19.4 Assessment

1. Cornea, aqueous humor, iris, lens, vitreous humor
2. Nearsightedness, farsightedness, astigmatism
3. The eye's blind spot is the area of the retina where nerve endings come together to form the optic nerve.
4. Nearsightedness: concave lens; farsightedness: convex lens
5. The cornea must be transparent in order for light to pass through it into the rest of the eye.
6. Light enters through an opening and is focused by a lens onto a surface where an image is formed.
7. You are probably nearsighted, that is, unable to see objects far away.
8. Light passing from water into your eye is not bent as much as it passes through the cornea as it is when light passes from air into your eye. This difference in the bending of the light results in the image not being in focus when it strikes the retina.

Answer to . . .

Figure 19 *Both conditions result from length of the eyeball or the curvature of the lens.*

Consumer Lab

Selecting Mirrors

In this lab, you will compare several mirrors and select the type that is best for a specific use.

Problem What mirror shape is best for magnifying images? For providing a wide view?

Materials
plane, convex, and concave mirrors; 2 metric rulers; roll of string; protractor

Skills Observing, Measuring

Procedure

Part A: Comparing Magnification

1. Construct a data table with three rows and four columns. Label the columns Mirror, Size of Image, Magnification, and Field of View. In the column labeled Mirror, label the three rows Plane, Concave, and Convex.
2. Place the plane mirror on a tabletop with its mirror side facing up. Position a metric ruler horizontally across the center of the mirror.
3. Hold the other metric ruler horizontally against your nose, just below your eyes, as shown below. Make sure the ruler's markings face away from you. Look down at the mirror.
4. Use the ruler resting on the mirror to measure the actual length of the image of a 3-cm-long portion of the ruler you are holding. Record the size of the image in your data table.
5. Repeat Steps 2 through 4 using concave and convex mirrors. Observe each image from the same distance.
6. Divide each image size you measured by 3 cm to determine its magnification. Record the magnification in your data table.

Part B: Comparing Fields of View

7. Tie a string to a ruler. Hold the protractor, mirror, and free end of the string. Have a classmate hold the ruler vertically off to one side of the mirror. Position a third classmate (the observer) directly in front of and about 2 meters away from the mirror as shown.
8. Have the classmate holding the ruler slowly move toward the observer while keeping the string tight. The observer should look directly into the mirror and say "Stop!" as soon as the reflection of the ruler can be seen.
9. Measure the angle the string makes with the protractor. Multiply this angle by 2 and record it as the field of view in your data table.
10. Repeat Steps 7 through 9 using concave and convex mirrors. Observe each mirror from the same distance.

Analyze and Conclude

1. **Observing** Which mirror provided the greatest magnification? The widest view?
2. **Applying Concepts** Which mirror shape would work best for a dentist who needs to see a slightly magnified image of a tooth? Explain your answer.
3. **Drawing Conclusions** Could one of the mirrors be used both to view a wide area and to magnify? Explain your answer.

Consumer Lab

Selecting Mirrors L2

Objective
After completing this activity, students will be able to describe differences between the images formed by plane, concave, and convex mirrors.

Address Misconceptions

This lab may help to correct the misconception that the field of view and magnification are independent of one another.

Skills Focus **Observing, Measuring**

Prep Time 10 minutes

Class Time 40 minutes

Safety Caution students to be careful with breakable glass mirrors.

Teaching Tips
- Do not provide transparent rulers for this lab. They are difficult to see in the mirror.
- Students who wear glasses or contact lenses will need to experiment to find a comfortable viewing distance in Step 4.
- You may need to show students how to hold the protractor in Step 7. It should be positioned so that the 0° mark is pointing directly toward the observer and the 90° mark is parallel to the surface of the mirror.

Expected Outcome The plane mirror produces an image that is slightly smaller than the actual ruler. The concave mirror magnifies the image and reduces the field of view, and the convex mirror produces the smallest image and the widest field of view.

Sample Data A typical concave hand mirror magnifies by a factor of 2 to 3, and a plane mirror produces an image that is reduced by approximately one-third. Typical fields of view for concave, plane, and convex mirrors are 70°, 80°, and 140°, respectively.

Analyze and Conclude
1. The concave mirror provided the greatest magnification, and the convex mirror produced the widest field of view.
2. A concave mirror is best for a dentist because it magnifies the most.
3. None of these mirrors could be used to observe both a wide area and a magnified view of small details because increasing the magnification reduces the width of the field of view, and increasing the width of the field of view reduces the magnification. **Logical**

Study Guide

Study Tip

Flashcards
Making flashcards is a good way to organize new or hard-to-learn information. Encourage students to review their notes every evening and make flash cards for the material covered that day. Students can review the flash cards alone or with a study partner.

Thinking Visually

a. real
b. virtual
c. converge

CHAPTER 19

Study Guide

19.1 Mirrors

Key Concepts
- The law of reflection states that the angle of reflection is equal to the angle of incidence.
- A plane mirror always produces a virtual image.
- Concave mirrors can form either real or virtual images.
- Convex mirrors always cause light rays to spread out and can only form virtual images.

Vocabulary

ray diagram, *p. 570*
angle of incidence, *p. 570*
angle of reflection, *p. 570*
plane mirror, *p. 571*
virtual image, *p. 571*
concave mirror, *p. 572*
focal point, *p. 572*
real image, *p. 572*
convex mirror, *p. 573*

19.2 Lenses

Key Concepts
- When light enters a new medium at an angle, the change in speed causes the light to bend, or refract.
- Concave lenses always cause light rays to spread out and can only form virtual images.
- Convex lenses can form either real or virtual images.
- Materials that have small critical angles of refraction are likely to cause most of the light entering them to be totally internally reflected.

Vocabulary

index of refraction, *p. 575*
lens, *p. 576*
concave lens, *p. 576*
convex lens, *p. 576*
critical angle, *p. 578*
total internal reflection, *p. 578*

19.3 Optical Instruments

Key Concepts
- There are two main types of telescopes, reflecting telescopes and refracting telescopes.
- Light rays enter a camera through an opening, are focused by the opening or lens, and form an image that is recorded on film or by a sensor.
- The compound microscope uses two convex lenses to magnify small objects.

Vocabulary

telescope, *p. 580*
reflecting telescope, *p. 581*
refracting telescope, *p. 581*
camera, *p. 582*
microscope, *p. 584*

19.4 The Eye and Vision

Key Concepts
- The main parts of the eye are the cornea, the pupil and iris, the lens, and the retina.
- Some common vision problems are nearsightedness, farsightedness, and astigmatism.

Vocabulary

cornea, *p. 588*
pupil, *p. 589*
iris, *p. 589*
retina, *p. 589*
rods, *p. 589*
cones, *p. 589*
nearsightedness, *p. 590*
farsightedness, *p. 592*
astigmatism, *p. 592*

Thinking Visually

Concept Map Use the information from the chapter to complete the concept map below.

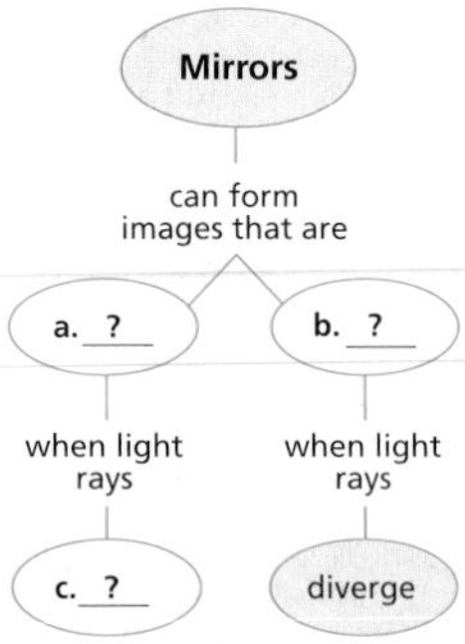
Mirrors
can form images that are
a. ?
b. ?
when light rays
when light rays
c. ?
diverge

Chapter Resources

Print
- ***Chapter and Unit Tests,*** Chapter 19 Test A and Test B
- ***Test Prep Resources,*** Chapter 19

Technology
- ***Computer Test Bank,*** Chapter Test 19
- ***Interactive Textbook,*** Chapter 19
- ***Go Online,*** PHSchool.com, Chapter 19

CHAPTER 19

Assessment

Interactive textbook with assessment at PHSchool.com iText

Reviewing Content

Choose the letter that best answers the question or completes the statement.

1. A reflected ray of light is one that
- **a.** bends as it enters a new medium.
- **b.** bounces off a surface.
- **c.** always forms an image.
- **d.** travels faster after it is reflected.

2. Which law states that the angle of incidence equals the angle of reflection?
- **a.** law of refraction **b.** law of diffraction
- **c.** law of reflection **d.** law of images

3. A plane mirror is
- **a.** curved outward. **b.** flat.
- **c.** curved inward. **d.** always round.

4. A virtual image
- **a.** can never be seen.
- **b.** cannot be projected.
- **c.** is always enlarged.
- **d.** is formed in front of a plane mirror.

5. Concave lenses cause rays to
- **a.** come together. **b.** spread apart.
- **c.** reflect. **d.** form real images.

6. Which forms where light rays converge?
- **a.** imaginary image **b.** real image
- **c.** virtual image **d.** blind image

7. A ray is incident on a material at the material's critical angle. At what angle does the ray refract?
- **a.** 0 degrees **b.** 45 degrees
- **c.** 90 degrees **d.** 180 degrees

8. Which optical device uses mirrors and lenses to magnify images of distant objects?
- **a.** reflecting telescope **b.** pinhole camera
- **c.** microscope **d.** refracting telescope

9. The two areas in the eye in which light rays are refracted are
- **a.** the cornea and the lens.
- **b.** the pupil and the lens.
- **c.** the retina and the lens.
- **d.** the rods and the cones.

10. Which corrects nearsightedness?
- **a.** concave lens **b.** converging lens
- **c.** diverging mirror **d.** astigmatism

Understanding Concepts

11. According to the law of reflection, the angle of incidence is equal to what other angle?

12. Describe the image formed by a plane mirror.

13. Why can convex mirrors produce only virtual images?

14. Under what conditions does light bend when it enters a new medium?

15. How is the index of refraction of a medium related to the speed of light in the medium?

16. Explain why a concave lens cannot form a real image.

17. What occurs when the critical angle is exceeded?

18. A student-drawn ray diagram for a lens is shown below. Identify the errors the student made in the diagram.

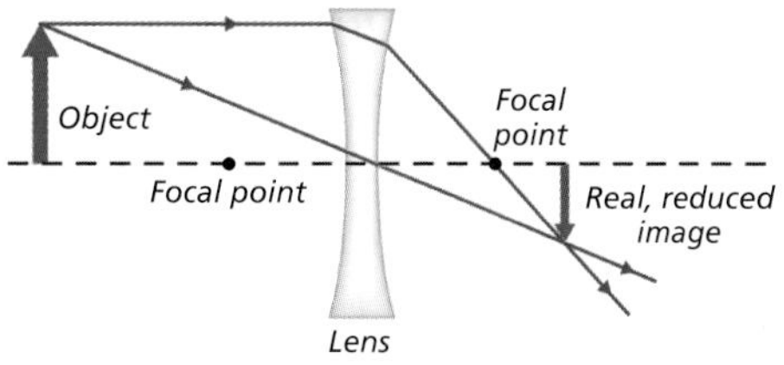

Object
Focal point
Focal point
Real, reduced image
Lens

19. Which part of the camera shown in Figure 14 controls the amount of light that strikes the film?

20. Explain how the human eye changes focus from near objects to faraway objects.

21. Explain why rods are more effective than cones for seeing objects at night.

22. Explain how diverging and converging lenses are effective for treating nearsightedness and farsightedness.

Homework Guide

Section	Questions
19.1	1–4, 11–13, 23, 30
19.2	5–7, 14–18, 24–25, 27–28, 31, 33
19.3	8, 19, 26, 29,
19.4	9–10, 20–22, 32

Assessment

Interactive Textbook If your class subscribes to the Interactive Textbook, your students can go online to access an interactive version of the Student Edition and a self-test.

Reviewing Content

1. b **2.** c **3.** b
4. b **5.** b **6.** b
7. c **8.** a **9.** a
10. a

Understanding Concepts

11. The angle of reflection
12. The image formed by a plane mirror is virtual, upright, and is located the same distance behind the mirror as the object is in front of the mirror.
13. Convex mirrors always cause light rays to diverge, therefore they can form only virtual images.
14. Light bends when it enters a new medium (with a different index of refraction) at an angle.
15. The greater the index of refraction, the slower the speed of light in the medium.
16. Concave lenses always cause light rays to diverge, therefore they are not able to form real images.
17. Total internal reflection
18. The concave lens produces a reduced, virtual image in front of the lens, not a reduced, real image in back of the lens. The rays should diverge as they exit the lens.
19. The diaphragm and the shutter
20. Ciliary muscles inside the eye change the shape of the flexible lens.
21. Rods are more sensitive to low-intensity light, thus they are more effective at seeing objects at night.
22. Each lens adjusts the path of the incoming light rays before they enter the eye, thus compensating for the vision problems caused by the curvature of the cornea, curvature of the lens, or the length of the eyeball.

Critical Thinking

23. A concave mirror
24. No; Student-designed experiments should somehow allow for the determination of the position of a submerged object based upon its apparent position when viewed above the water. This position should then be compared with the actual position of the submerged object.
25. Placing light-sensitive film at the image plane of the pinhole viewer would convert it into a camera.
26. Refracting telescopes use only lenses to form an image, whereas reflecting telescopes use both mirrors and lenses.
27. Student diagrams should show a ray striking the water at a very low angle and being reflected, a ray striking the water at a larger angle and bending toward the normal as it is refracted, and a ray striking the water at a right angle and not being reflected or refracted.
28. The ray bends toward the normal as it is refracted when it enters the water. The ray reflects off of the mirror such that the angle of incidence equals the angle of reflection. The ray then bends away from the normal as it is refracted when exiting the water.
29. Most telescopes produce inverted images.

Concepts in Action

30. Billiard balls often behave the same as light rays that are reflected from flat surfaces, that is, their angle of incidence equals their angle of reflection. Knowing this allows you to plan how a struck billiard ball will travel after it bounces off of a bumper.
31. A convex lens
32. Virtual image; applications will vary but may include use as a magnifying lens.
33. The examples used in student paragraphs will vary but should include the following classifications.

Plane mirror: virtual image; same size image
Convex mirror: virtual image; reduced size image
Concave mirror: virtual or real; reduced, equal, or enlarged size images

Assessment *(continued)*

Critical Thinking

23. Applying Concepts Which type of mirror would you use to view an enlarged image of an object?

24. Designing Experiments Can the position of an object on the bottom of a swimming pool be accurately determined when viewed from above and at an angle to the water? Design an experiment to find out if refraction affects the apparent position of a submerged object.

25. Applying Concepts How could you convert the pinhole viewer used in the Quick Lab on page 585 into a device that could take a permanent picture?

26. Comparing and Contrasting What are the differences between a reflecting telescope and a refracting telescope?

27. Using Models Draw a ray diagram showing three rays of light traveling in air and striking the surface of water. Show one ray being reflected, one being refracted, and one entering the water without bending.

28. Predicting The illustration below shows a flashlight aimed down into a tub of water with a flat mirror lying on the bottom. Copy and complete the illustration by predicting the path of the light beam. (*Hint:* Remember to consider the effects of refraction and reflection.)

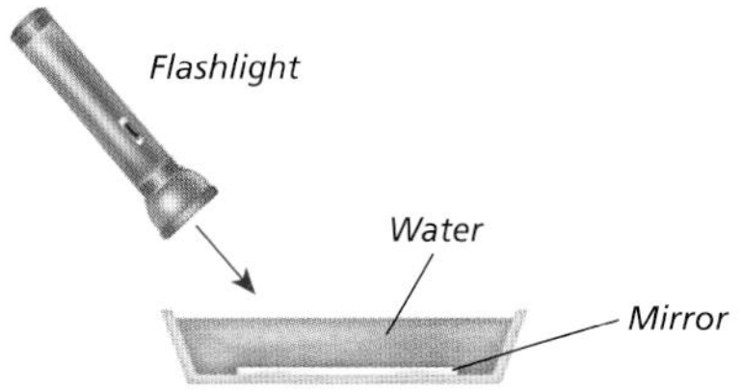
Flashlight
Water
Mirror

29. Inferring Many maps of the moon are printed showing the moon flipped upside down. What can you infer about the optical instruments used to view the moon?

Concepts in Action

30. Using Models How can you use the law of reflection to model a game of billiards?

31. Applying Concepts What kind of lens would you use to help you see a splinter in your finger?

32. Interpreting Diagrams The ray diagram below shows the formation of an image using a lens. Is the image a real or virtual image? What kind of lens is producing the image? Give a possible application for this type of lens.

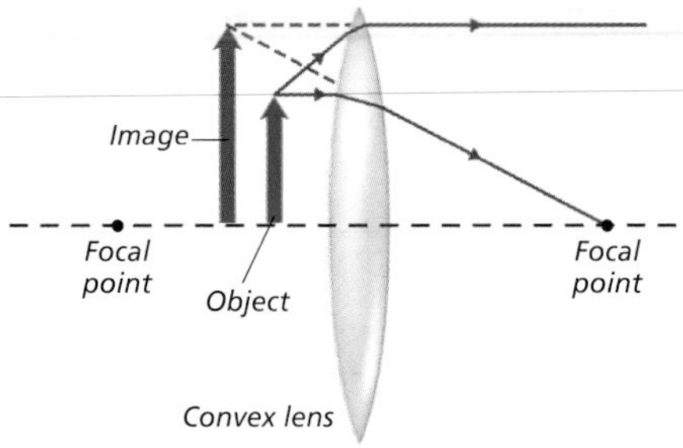
Image
Focal point
Object
Focal point
Convex lens

33. Writing in Science Classify plane, convex, and concave mirrors in terms of image type or image size. Write a paragraph citing examples for each classification.

Performance-Based Assessment

Make a telescope using two convex lenses and a cardboard tube from a finished roll of paper towels. Attach the lenses using tape. If possible, get two tubes of slightly different diameters so that one can fit inside the other. Wrap the smaller tube with tape or cardboard to make the smaller tube fit snugly inside the larger tube. How can you focus your telescope?

Go Online PHSchool.com
For: Self-grading assessment
Visit: PHSchool.com
Web Code: cca-2190

Performance-Based Assessment

By sliding the two tubes, you can change the overall length of the telescope and bring the object into focus.

Go Online PHSchool.com

Your students can independently test their knowledge of the chapter and print out their test results for your files.

Standardized Test Prep

Test-Taking Tip

Anticipate the Answer
When answering multiple choice questions, a useful strategy is to cover up the given answers and supply your own answer. Then compare your answer with those listed and select the one that most closely matches.

Practice anticipating the answer in this question.

When the incident angle of a light ray exceeds the critical angle, the ray undergoes
(A) total refraction.
(B) systemic diffraction.
(C) astigmatism.
(D) total internal reflection.
(E) mirror imaging.

(Answer: D)

Choose the letter that best answers the question or completes the statement.

1. Which statement correctly describes a property of mirrors?
(A) Plane mirrors always form real images.
(B) Concave mirrors can form real and virtual images.
(C) The law of reflection only applies to convex mirrors.
(D) Real images formed by concave mirrors are right side up.
(E) All mirrors refract light rays to form images.

2. If a light ray slows down as it enters a medium at an angle, the ray is
(A) totally reflected.
(B) refracted.
(C) diffracted.
(D) evenly dispersed in the new medium.
(E) travelling faster than 3.0×10^8 m/s.

3. When a ray strikes a plane mirror at an angle,
(A) the light ray slows down and bends.
(B) an inverted virtual image is formed.
(C) the light ray is refracted.
(D) the angle of incidence of the ray equals the angle of reflection of the ray.
(E) the image formed is real.

4. Which of the following statements about convex lenses is FALSE?
(A) They cause light rays to refract.
(B) They can form real and virtual images.
(C) They cause incoming parallel rays to converge.
(D) They are thickest at the outside edges.
(E) They are used in lighthouses.

5. Which description correctly matches the type of optical instrument?
(A) Microscope—forms enlarged images of distant objects.
(B) Camera—focuses incoming light using a series of mirrors.
(C) Refracting telescope—is made up of two convex lenses.
(D) Reflecting telescope—is made up of one convex lens and one concave lens.
(E) Pinhole camera—focuses incoming light using a series of lenses.

Question 6 refers to the ray diagram shown below.

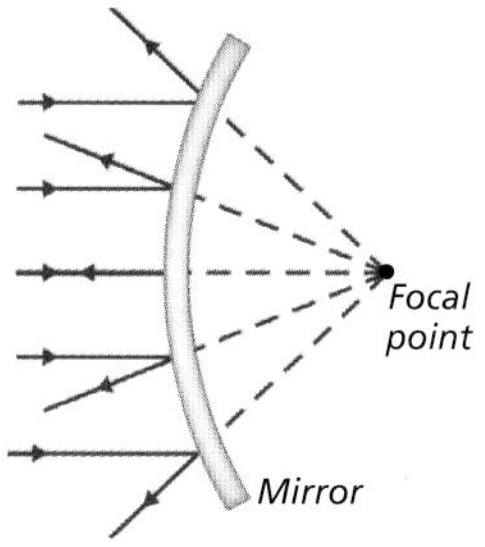
Focal point
Mirror

6. Which of the following statements is TRUE?
(A) The mirror shown is concave.
(B) The converging light rays form a real image.
(C) The diverging rays form a real image.
(D) The diverging rays form a virtual image.
(E) The reflected light rays are parallel.

Standardized Test Prep

1. B **2.** B **3.** D
4. D **5.** C **6.** D

CHAPTER 20

Planning Guide

Use these planning tools
Easy Planner
Teacher Express

SECTION OBJECTIVES	STANDARDS NATIONAL (See p. T18.)	STANDARDS STATE	ACTIVITIES and LABS
20.1 Electric Charge and Static Electricity, pp. 600–603 1 block or 2 periods **20.1.1** **Analyze** factors that affect the strength and direction of electric forces and fields. **20.1.2** **Describe** how electric forces and fields affect electric charges. **20.1.3** **Describe** how electric charges are transferred and **explain** why electric discharges occur.	A-1, B-4, B-6, G-1, G-3		**SE** Inquiry Activity: How Can You Reverse the Battery Direction in a Flashlight? p. 599 **L2** **TE** Teacher Demo: Electric Attraction and Repulsion, p. 601 **L2** **LM** Investigation 20B: Investigating Static Charge **L1**
20.2 Electric Current and Ohm's Law, pp. 604–607 1 block or 2 periods **20.2.1** **Describe** electric current and **identify** the two types of current. **20.2.2** **Describe** conduction and **classify** materials as good electrical conductors or good electrical insulators. **20.2.3** **Describe** the factors that affect resistance. **20.2.4** **Explain** how voltage produces electric current. **20.2.5** **Calculate** voltage, current, and resistance using Ohm's law.	A-1, A-2, B-4, B-5, B-6, F-6, G-3		**SE** Quick Lab: Modeling Resistance in a Wire, p. 606 **L2** **LM** Investigation 20A: Investigating the Telephone **L2**
20.3 Electric Circuits, pp. 609–613 1 block or 2 periods **20.3.1** **Analyze** circuit diagrams for series circuits and parallel circuits. **20.3.2** **Solve equations** that relate electric power to current, voltage, and electrical energy. **20.3.3** **Describe** devices and procedures for maintaining electrical safety.	A-1, A-2, B-4, E-2, F-1, G-3		**SE** Quick Lab: Modeling a Fuse, p. 612 **L2** **SE** Forensics Lab: Evaluating Electrical Safety, p. 623 **L2** **TE** Teacher Demo: Series and Parallel Circuits, p. 610 **L2**
20.4 Electronic Devices, pp. 618–622 1 block or 2 periods **20.4.1** **Explain** how electronics conveys information with analog or digital signals. **20.4.2** **Describe** electronic devices used to control electron flow. **20.4.3** **Illustrate** how semiconductors are used to make three kinds of solid-state components. **20.4.4** **Describe** how solid-state components are used in electronic devices.	A-1, A-2, B-4, B-6, E-2, F-1, G-3		**TE** Teacher Demo: Semiconductors and Current, p. 621 **L2**

Ability Levels	
L1	For students who need additional help
L2	For all students
L3	For students who need to be challenged

Components

SE	Student Edition	RSW	Reading & Study Workbook	CUT	Chapter & Unit Tests	T	Transparencies
TE	Teacher's Edition	MSPS	Math Skills & Problem Solving Workbook	CTB	Computer Test Bank	iT	Interactive Textbook
LM	Laboratory Manual			TP	Test Prep Resources	P	Presentation Pro CD-ROM
PLM	Probeware Lab Manual			DC	Discovery Channel Videotapes & DVDs	GO	Internet Resources

RESOURCES PRINT and TECHNOLOGY	SECTION ASSESSMENT
RSW Section 20.1 L1 T Chapter 20 Pretest L2 Section 20.1 L2 P Chapter 20 Pretest L2 Section 20.1 L2	SE Section 20.1 Assessment, p. 603 iT Section 20.1
RSW Section 20.2 L1 MSPS Section 20.2 L2 T Section 20.2 L2 P Section 20.2 L2 SciLinks GO Conductors and insulators L2	SE Section 20.2 Assessment, p. 607 iT Section 20.2
PLM Lab 8: Evaluating Electrical Safety L2 RSW Section 20.3 L1 RSW Math Skill L2 MSPS Section 20.3 L2 DC Current Computers L2 T Section 20.3 L2 P Section 20.3 L2 SciLinks GO Electric circuits L2	SE Section 20.3 Assessment, p. 613 iT Section 20.3
RSW Section 20.4 L1 T Section 20.4 L2 P Section 20.4 L2	SE Section 20.4 Assessment, p. 622 iT Section 20.4

Go Online

Go online for these Internet resources.

PHSchool.com
Web Code: cca-2200
Web Code: cch-2203

NSTA SciLinks
Web Code: ccn-2202
Web Code: ccn-2203

Materials for Activities and Labs

Quantities for each group

STUDENT EDITION

Inquiry Activity, p. 599
flashlight (uses 2 D batteries), 2 D batteries

Quick Lab, p. 606
white paper, metric ruler, number 2 pencil, multimeter

Quick Lab, p. 612
6-volt battery, 2 wires with stripped ends, strip of aluminum foil, scissors, wooden block, unpainted thumbtacks

Forensics Lab, p. 623
9-volt battery, battery clip, multimeter, 3 alligator clips, 4 resistors: 1-ohm, 10-ohm, 100-ohm, 1000-ohm

TEACHER'S EDITION

Teacher Demo, p. 601
pith ball, thread, rubber or ebonite rod, fur

Teacher Demo, p. 610
a 6-volt battery, 3 small light bulbs with sockets, 2 long strands of wire (12 cm), 4 short strands of wire (6 cm)

Build Science Skills, p. 616
several discarded computers, each having its top removed

Teacher Demo, p. 621
a light-emitting diode (LED), an ohmmeter, a DC power source, wires, alligator clips

Chapter Assessment

CHAPTER ASSESSMENT

SE Chapter Assessment, pp. 625–626
CUT Chapter 20 Test A, B
CTB Chapter 20
iT Chapter 20
PHSchool.com GO
Web Code: cca-2200

STANDARDIZED TEST PREP

SE Chapter 20, p. 627
TP Diagnose and Prescribe

Interactive Textbook

Interactive Textbook with assessment at PHSchool.com

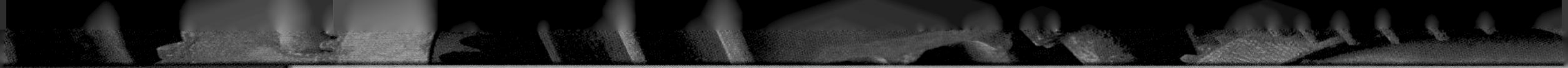

CHAPTER 20

Before you teach

From the Author

Sophia Yancopoulos
Manhattan College

Big Ideas

Electricity is one of the four known universal forces of nature. Electric fields are everywhere. They can produce heat, light, chemical changes, and magnetic fields. They even permeate our bodies.

Matter and Energy Charge is a fundamental property of matter, just as mass is. A net electric charge, positive or negative, usually results from the loss or gain of electrons. Like charges repel, and unlike charges attract, according to the amount of each charge and the distance between them.

Forces and Motion The attraction or repulsion between electrically charged objects is called electric force. Charge can be transferred by friction or by direct contact. The transfer of charge by induction can occur with no contact between objects. Many students will have difficulty with the concept of an electric field. An electric field surrounds any charged particle, whether or not the charge is moving. Because the electric field is defined as the electric force per unit charge, the strength of the field does not depend on the amount of charge acted upon, although field strength does depend on position within the field.

Electric current, the flow of electric charge, is caused by an electrical potential difference, called voltage. Electrical resistance is exactly as it sounds, an opposition to the flow of charge.

Encourage students to create their own mnemonics. For example, in studying electric circuits, students can distinguish between series and parallel more easily if they remember that a series circuit is a single path and serious trouble for the whole circuit if any element in the circuit stops functioning.

Physics Refresher

Electric Charges, Forces, and Fields

20.1 and 20.2

The force between electric charges is described by Coulomb's law: $F = k_C q_1 q_2 / r^2$. This force increases as the charge (q_1 or q_2) increases, and decreases as the square of the distance between the charges (r) increases. Because like charges repel and opposite charges attract, the sign of F indicates a repulsive force (F positive) or an attractive force (F negative). The Coulomb constant, k_C, is 8.99×10^9 N•m^2/C^2.

Like gravitational force, the electric force is a field force: $E = F/q_1 = k_C q_2 / r^2$. The direction of the field lines depends on the charge that produces the field. Positive charges produce a field that points away from the charge. Negative charges produce a field that points toward the charge. The field is stronger where the field lines are closer together. The diagrams below show the electric fields around two unlike charges and around two like charges.

Address Misconceptions

Students may think that most atoms in a charged object contribute to the net charge. In fact, only a small fraction of the atoms or molecules give up or gain electrons. For a strategy to overcome this misconception, see **Address Misconceptions** on **page 602**.

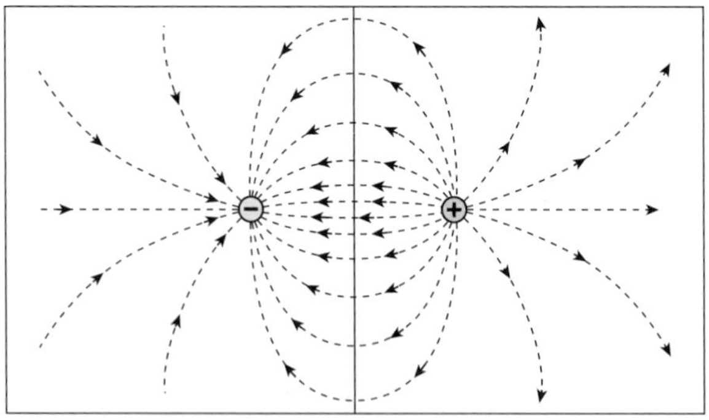

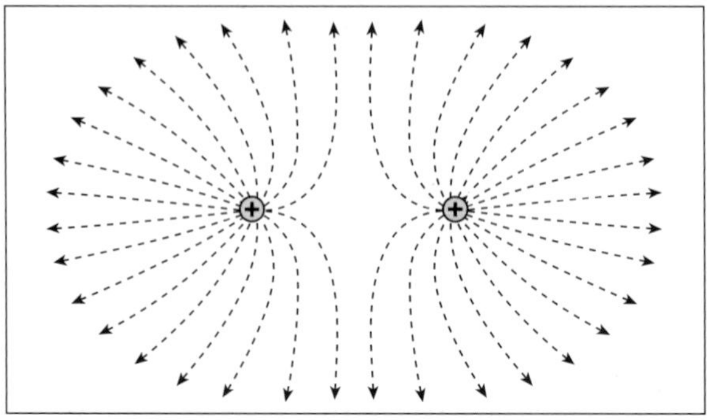

Go Online PD LINKS NSTA

For: Teaching methods for electricity
Visit: www.SciLinks.org/PDLinks
Web Code: ccn-2099

Voltage, Current, and Resistance in Circuits 20.2 and 20.3

Address Misconceptions

Students may think that only metals make good conductors. In fact, solutions containing ions and ionized gases are also good conductors. For a strategy to overcome this misconception, see **Address Misconceptions** on **page 605.**

An electrical circuit contains either direct current (flowing in one direction) or alternating current (constantly changing direction). For many materials, the voltage (V), current (I), and resistance (R) in a circuit are related by Ohm's Law: $V = IR$.

In an ideal series circuit, the total current is constant, as it has only one path to follow. The voltage, current, and resistance for each circuit element are:

$$I = I_1 = I_2 = I_3 = \ldots$$
$$V = V_1 + V_2 + V_3 + \ldots$$
$$R = R_1 + R_2 + R_3 + \ldots$$

In an ideal parallel circuit, the voltage across each parallel branch in the circuit is equal in magnitude to the voltage across the power supply (V), but the currents through each element, when added, equal the current through the entire circuit:

$$V = V_1 = V_2 = V_3 = \ldots$$
$$I = I_1 + I_2 + I_3 + \ldots$$
$$1/R = 1/R_1 + 1/R_2 + 1/R_3 + \ldots$$

Electronic Devices 20.4

Both vacuum tubes and diodes can be used to change alternating current to direct current. In a vacuum tube, this is done by a heated filament, which emits electrons, and a metal plate that changes from positive to negative charge with the alternating input current. The emitted electrons are attracted to the plate when it is positively charged, and an output current is produced. The electrons are repelled when the plate is negatively charged, and then there is no output current. In this way, charges in the output current move only in one direction.

The pn junction in a diode works in a similar way, except that the increased resistance in one direction results from the properties of n-type and p-type semiconductors. For charge in the form of positively charged holes and negatively charged electrons to flow through the diode, the p side is connected to the positive battery terminal and the n side is connected to the negative battery terminal. Connected this way, the diode offers very little resistance to current.

Charge Flow in pn Junctions

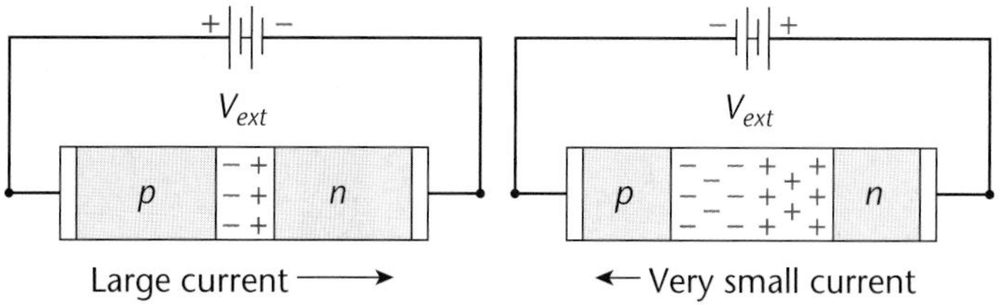

V_{ext}
p
n
Large current →
V_{ext}
p
n
← Very small current

Suppose the battery connections were reversed as shown on the right. Then holes are pulled from the p side toward the negative terminal. Similarly, electrons are pulled from the n side toward the positive terminal. Charges build up quickly in the junction. These charges repel current-carrying charges being pushed through the circuit, and the diode's resistance becomes very large. Almost immediately, the current stops.

Build Reading Literacy

Summarize

Briefly Restating the Main Ideas

Strategy Help students understand a topic by restating the main ideas. Students read a section of the text and then identify main ideas and supporting details. They summarize what they have read by briefly restating the main concepts in a sentence or two. Summarizing can be employed to review brief subsections as well as entire sections and chapters. Have students read the beginning of Section 20.1, pp. 600–601.

Example

1. Ask students to carefully read the selected passage. Then, have them review the passage and identify the main ideas. Demonstrate this process by using the bold headings, Key Concept statements, and vocabulary as aids in determining what the passage is mostly about. List the main ideas on the board.
2. Direct students to write brief summaries of the passage by restating each of the main ideas in one or two sentences, using their own words. Remind students to focus on the most important concepts, omitting details and examples. Students should check to be sure that their summary covers the terms mentioned in the bold headings.
3. Assign the next passage for students to read and summarize. You may want to have students work in small groups to compare their summaries.
4. Have students read and summarize the rest of Section 20.1.

See p. 609 for a script on how to use the summarize strategy with students. For additional Build Reading Literacy strategies, see pp. 600, 606, and 619.

ASSESS PRIOR KNOWLEDGE

Use the Chapter Pretest below to assess students' prior knowledge. As needed, review these Science Concepts and Math Skills with students.

Review Science Concepts

Section 20.1 Review universal forces, magnitude and direction of force, universal gravitation (analogous to $F = kqq/r^2$), electric force, and actions between charged particles.

Section 20.2 Review potential energy and electrical energy as an introduction to voltage. Review work, energy conversions, and conservation of energy.

Section 20.3 Remind students of the definition and units for power. Review thermal energy to prepare for discussion of heating in resistors.

Section 20.4 Review the definition of a vacuum. Review speed, time, and distance (to relate why smaller circuits are faster).

Review Math Skills

Calculating with Significant Figures, Formulas and Equations Students will need to calculate with significant figures and use formulas and equations to solve problems dealing with power, voltage, and current.

Direct students to the **Math Skills** in the **Skills and Reference Handbook** at the end of the student text.

CHAPTER

20 Electricity

CONCEPTS in Action

How do science concepts apply to your world? Here are some questions you'll be able to answer after you read this chapter.

- Why do you sometimes feel a shock if you walk across carpet on a winter day and then touch a metal door handle? *(Section 20.1)*
- What causes lightning? *(Section 20.1)*
- How does a battery enable a flashlight to light? *(Section 20.2)*
- Why do some appliances use three-prong plugs? *(Section 20.3)*
- How is information stored on a DVD? *(Section 20.4)*

Discovery Channel School **Video Field Trip**

Current Computers

- How do computers process data? *(page 614)*

Lightning provides a powerful display ▶ of electrical energy in Manitoba, Canada.

598 *Chapter 20*

Chapter Pretest

1. Which particles move freely through metals, speeding the transfer of thermal energy? *(b)*
   a. Atoms b. Electrons
   c. Protons d. Molecules
2. Electric forces act between ________. *(charged objects or particles)*
3. True or False: Objects with opposite charges repel one another. *(False)*
4. How will doubling the distance between two masses affect the strength of the gravitational force between them? *(The force of gravity will be only one fourth as strong.)*
5. Energy that is stored and can later be used to move an object is called ________. *(potential energy)*
6. What happens to the kinetic energy of the particles in an object when the thermal energy of the object is increased? *(The kinetic energy of the particles increases.)*
7. True or False: Power is measured in units of joules. *(False)*
8. If 2.0×10^4 J of energy are produced in 5 s, how much power is generated? *(a)*
   a. 4×10^3 W b. 1×10^5 W
   c. 1×10^4 W d. 4×10^4 W

PHYSICS

Chapter Preview

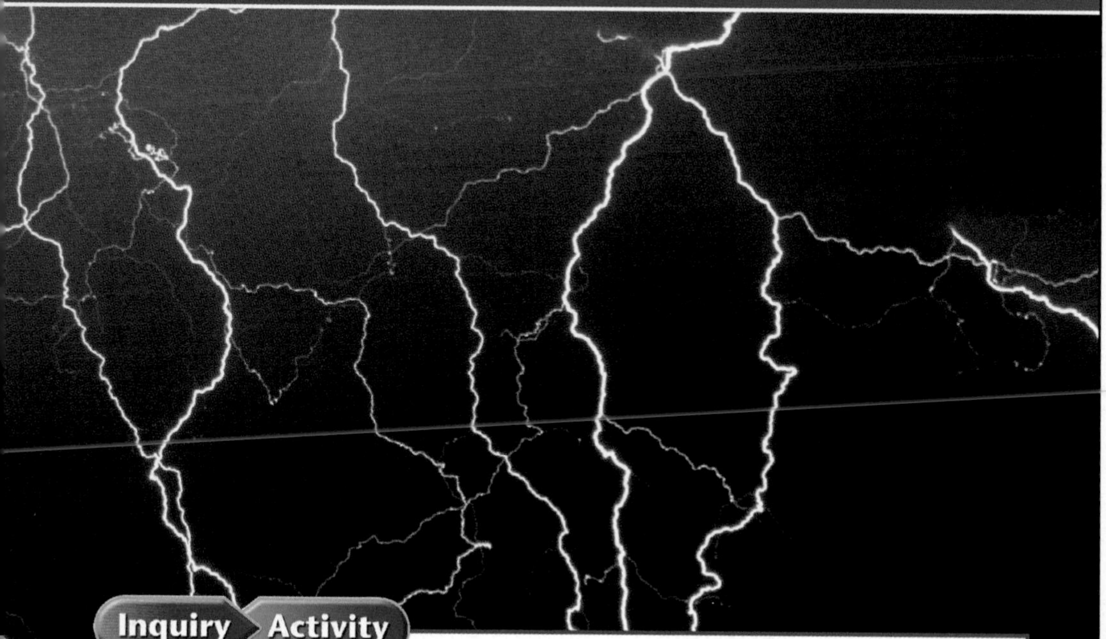

Inquiry Activity

How Can You Reverse the Battery Direction in a Flashlight?

Procedure

1. Remove a battery from a two-battery flashlight. Notice that one end of the battery is labeled + (positive).
2. Return the battery to the flashlight in the same position it was in before. Turn the flashlight on and then off. Observe what happens.
3. Remove the battery and replace it so that it faces the opposite direction. Predict what will happen if you turn the flashlight on. Test your prediction.

Think About It

1. **Comparing and Contrasting** Describe your results when the batteries faced the same direction and when they faced opposite directions. How are these results the same or different?
2. **Inferring** What do your results indicate about how batteries might work?
3. **Predicting** Do you think that the flashlight will work if you reverse the direction of both batteries? Explain your answer.

Discovery Channel School **Video Field Trip**

Current Computers

Encourage students to view the Video Field Trip "Current Computers."

ENGAGE/EXPLORE

Inquiry Activity

How Can You Reverse the Battery Direction in a Flashlight? L2

Purpose In this activity, students are introduced to the idea that current consists of moving charged particles.

Address Misconceptions

Some students may mistakenly think that electric current does not move in a specific direction. Therefore, they may be unaware of the significance of having the batteries both pointing in the same direction in a flashlight.

Challenge this misconception by showing students how the needle of an ammeter or galvanometer changes direction when the electrodes connected to a battery's terminals are reversed.

Skills Focus **Observing, Inferring**

Prep Time 10 minutes

Materials flashlight (uses 2 D-sized batteries), 2 D-sized batteries

Class Time 10 minutes

Safety Students should avoid flashlight breakage, which can produce sharp edges.

Expected Outcome Students will learn that, for a flashlight to work, the batteries in it must be placed so positive and negative ends touch.

Think About It

1. When the batteries faced the same direction, the flashlight worked. When they faced different directions, the flashlight did not work.
2. Students may infer that whatever goes in one end of a battery and out the other end can travel in only one direction.
3. Yes, because the batteries are positioned in the same direction, the flashlight will work, provided good contact exists between the batteries and flashlight terminals. Many flashlights are designed so that the batteries can only make good contact when they point in one direction.

Logical, Group

1 FOCUS

Objectives

20.1.1 **Analyze** factors that affect the strength and direction of electric forces and fields.

20.1.2 **Describe** how electric forces and fields affect electric charges.

20.1.3 **Describe** how electric charges are transferred and **explain** why electric discharges occur.

Reading Focus

Build Vocabulary — L2

Word-Part Analysis Ask students, **What word appears in most of the definitions?** *(Electric, electrical, electricity)* Explain that the root word for *electricity* comes from the Greek word for "amber," a substance that is easily charged. Ask, **What can be inferred from this?** *(Electricity deals with charges.)* Explain that the word *static* comes most recently from the Greek word *statikos,* which means "causing to stand." Point out to students that in static electricity, or static discharge, charges jump from one location to another. Thus, charges do move, so the term *static* is unfortunate.

Reading Strategy — L2

a. The attraction or repulsion between electrically charged objects

b. Field strength depends on the net charge and distance from the charge.

c. Charge can be transferred by friction, contact, or induction.

2 INSTRUCT

Electric Charge

Build Reading Literacy — L1

Outline Refer to page **156D** in **Chapter 6**, which provides the guidelines for an outline.

Have students create an outline of the section (pp. 600–603). Outlines should follow the head structure used in the section. Major headings are shown in green, and subheadings are shown in blue. Ask, **Based on your outline, what are the three ways static electric charges are transferred?** *(Friction, contact, and induction)*

Verbal, Logical

20.1 Electric Charge and Static Electricity

Reading Focus

Key Concepts

- What produces a net electric charge?
- What determines whether an electric force is attractive or repulsive?
- What determines the strength of an electric field?
- What are three ways in which charge is transferred?
- How does a static discharge occur?

Vocabulary

- electric charge
- electric force
- electric field
- static electricity
- law of conservation of charge
- induction

Reading Strategy

Identifying Main Ideas Copy the table below. As you read, write the main idea for each topic.

Topic	Main Idea
Electric Charge	An excess or shortage of electrons produces a net electric charge.
Electric Forces	a.__________
Electric Fields	b.__________
Static Electricity	c.__________

Think back to the last time a thunderstorm swept through your area. A bolt of lightning streaked across the sky, followed moments later by the crash of thunder. Have you ever wondered what causes lightning? Perhaps you've observed something similar on a smaller scale closer to home. When you take clothes out of a dryer, some of them can stick together, like the socks and towel in Figure 1. If you pull the clothes apart in a darkened room, you can see sparks that are like tiny bolts of lightning. This shouldn't be surprising once you realize that lightning and "static cling" have a similar cause—the movement of electric charges.

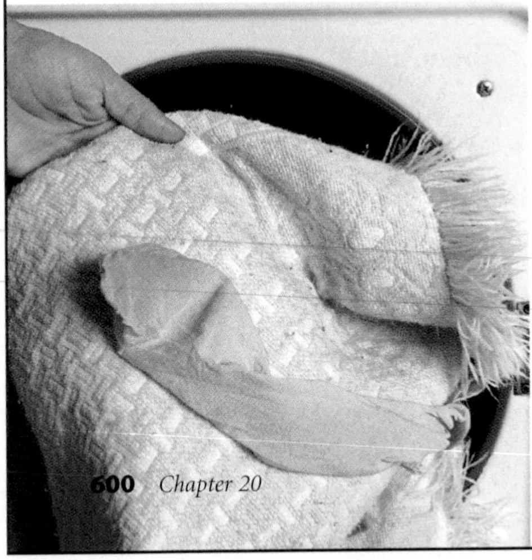

Figure 1 Electric charge is responsible for clothes that stick together when they are removed from a dryer.

Electric Charge

Recall that electrical energy is the energy associated with electric charges. But what exactly is electric charge? **Electric charge** is a property that causes subatomic particles such as protons and electrons to attract or repel each other. There are two types of electric charge, positive and negative. Protons have a positive charge and electrons have a negative charge. Electric charges move in a flash through a lightning bolt. Electric charges attract one another in clothes taken from the dryer. Although charged particles are too small to see, just about everything in your daily life is affected by charge in one way or another.

Section Resources

Print

- ***Laboratory Manual,*** Investigation 20B
- ***Reading and Study Workbook With Math Support,*** Section 20.1
- ***Transparencies,*** Chapter Pretest and Section 20.1

Technology

- ***Interactive Textbook,*** Section 20.1
- ***Presentation Pro CD-ROM,*** Chapter Pretest and Section 20.1

Figure 2 shows how charges are arranged in an atom. A cloud of negatively charged electrons surrounds the positively charged nucleus. The atom is neutral because it has an equal number of positive and negative charges. If an atom gains one or more electrons, it becomes a negatively charged ion. If an atom loses electrons, it becomes a positively charged ion. **An excess or shortage of electrons produces a net electric charge.**

The SI unit of electric charge is the coulomb (C). It takes about 6.24×10^{18} electrons to produce a single coulomb. A lightning bolt is about 10 to 20 coulombs of charge. In comparison, a flash camera uses the energy from 0.025 coulombs of charge to produce each flash.

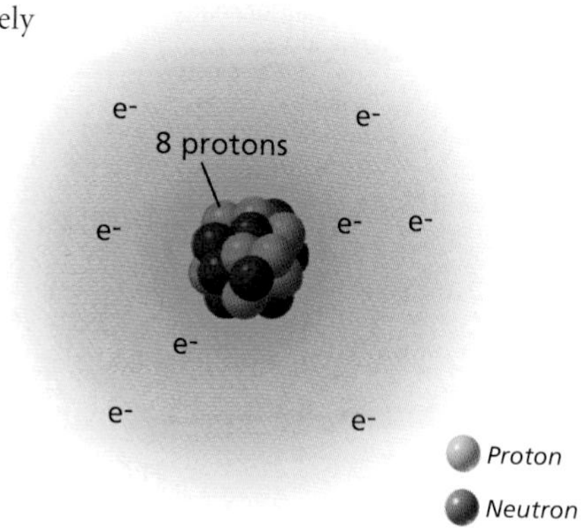
e-
e-
8 protons
e-
e-
e-
e-
e-
e-
Proton
Neutron

Figure 2 A neutral atom has equal numbers of protons and electrons.
***Drawing Conclusions** What is the overall charge if the atom loses an electron?*

Electric Forces

Rub an inflated rubber balloon on your clean, dry hair. If it's a dry day, you can use the balloon to pick up bits of paper. The balloon attracts the paper because the balloon is negatively charged and the paper is positively charged. Now rub a second balloon on your hair and bring the two balloons close together. You can feel the balloons repel. The two balloons repel because they are negatively charged. **Like charges repel, and opposite charges attract.** The force of attraction or repulsion between electrically charged objects is **electric force.**

The French scientist Charles-Augustin de Coulomb (1736–1806) discovered that electric forces obey a law similar to the law of universal gravitation. The electric force between two objects is directly proportional to the net charge on each object and inversely proportional to the square of the distance between them. As you can see in Figure 3, doubling the net charge on one object doubles the electric force. If instead you double the distance between the objects, the electric force is one fourth as strong.

Inside an atom, electric forces are much stronger than gravitational forces. Electric forces form chemical bonds, which must be overcome in chemical changes. Electric forces also cause friction and other contact forces. But on a large scale, matter is mostly neutral and in that case, electric forces are close to zero.

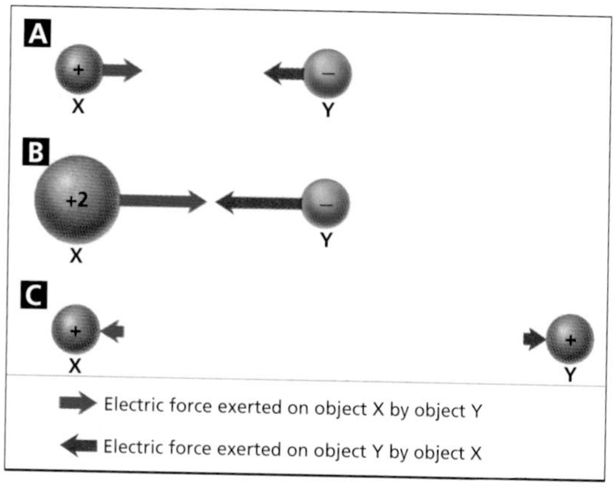
A
+
X
−
Y
B
+2
X
−
Y
C
+
X
+
Y
Electric force exerted on object X by object Y
Electric force exerted on object Y by object X

Figure 3 Electric force depends on charge and distance. **A** Opposite charges attract each other. **B** Doubling one charge doubles the force on both charges. **C** Like charges repel. Doubling the distance makes the force one fourth as great.

Reading Checkpoint *What is electric force?*

Customize for English Language Learners

Reinforce Vocabulary
Reinforce the vocabulary for this section by having English language learners construct a concept map. This will not only increase their familiarity with the terms, but will also help them understand how the various words, especially those that include the word *electric* or *electrical,* are related to each other.

Build Science Skills **L2**

Using Models Have students apply what they know about force and mass to explain why negative charges are more mobile than positive charges. *(Positive charges are provided by protons, which are much more massive than electrons. Electrons, which carry negative charge, are less massive and therefore more easily moved.)*
Logical

Electric Forces

Teacher Demo

Electric Attraction and Repulsion **L2**

Purpose To show that attractive forces exist between unlike charges, and repelling forces exist between like charges.

Materials pith ball, thread, rubber or ebonite rod, fur

Procedure Attach the thread to the pith ball. Rub the fur against the rubber rod, and then touch this rod briefly to the pith ball. Bring the rod close to the pith ball. Next, move the fur near the pith ball.

Expected Outcome Friction causes the fur to become positively charged and the rod to become negatively charged. The rod then transfers negative charge to the pith ball. When the rod is brought close to the pith ball, the like charges exert a repelling force on each other, and the ball moves away from the rod. When the fur, which has an opposite charge to the rod, is brought close to the ball, the ball is attracted to the fur.
Visual

Answer to . . .

Figure 2 *Net charge would be +1.*

Reading Checkpoint *An electric force is a force of repulsion or attraction between electrically charged objects.*

Section 20.1 (continued)

Electric Fields

Use Visuals L1

Figure 4 Stress that the directions of the electric fields for positive and negative charges are a matter of convention, much in the same way that the proton has charge that is called "positive." Emphasize that the field lines show the direction of the force on a positive "test" charge placed in the field. Ask, **In what direction is the force on a proton that is placed in each of these fields?** *(The force is outward [repulsive] in A and inward [attractive] in B.)*
Visual

Static Electricity and Charging

Address Misconceptions L2

Students may think that most or all of the atoms in an object charged by friction contribute to the object's net charge. Emphasize that only a small fraction of the atoms or molecules in a substance give up electrons. For instance, an acrylic rod that has been rubbed with fur may only have a net charge of 10^{-9} C. Explain that, while such a charge is produced by 10 billion electrons, there are about 10^{22} to 10^{24} atoms from which charges could be taken. In other words, only about one in a trillion atoms or molecules donate charges during charging by friction.
Logical

Use Visuals L1

Figure 5 Stress that friction usually separates charges on a pair of electrically neutral objects, whereas charging by contact moves some of the net charge on a charged object to another object. Ask, **What would happen if electrons were conveyed by contact to an object with a positive charge?** *(The electrons would reduce the overall positive charge of the object.)* Ask, **What would happen if the positive and negative charges were equal?** *(The object would become electrically neutral.)*
Visual

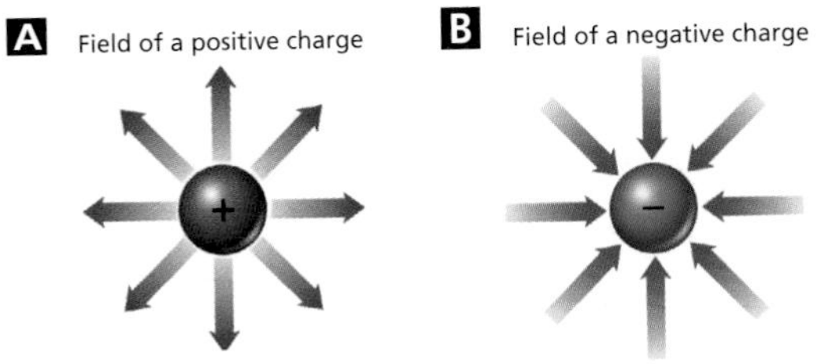

A Field of a positive charge
+
B Field of a negative charge
−

Figure 4 The strength of an electric field depends on the amount of charge that produces the field and on the distance from the charge. **A** The electric field around a positive charge points outward. **B** The electric field around a negative charge points inward.

Electric Fields

The effect an electric charge has on other charges in the space around it is the charge's **electric field.** Figure 4 shows the fields of positive and negative charges. **The strength of an electric field depends on the amount of charge that produces the field and on the distance from the charge.** The lines representing the field are closer together near the charge, where the field is stronger.

An electric field exerts forces on any charged object placed in the field. The force depends on the net charge in the object and on the strength and direction of the field at the object's position. The more net charge an object has, the greater is the force on it. The direction of each field line shows the direction of the force on a positive charge.

Figure 5 Charge can be transferred by friction and by contact. **A** Friction transferred electrons from the hair to the balloon. The balloon then attracts the hair because opposite charges attract. **B** A Van de Graaff generator has charged the metal sphere. Touching the sphere transfers charge. The hairs repel each other because like charges repel.

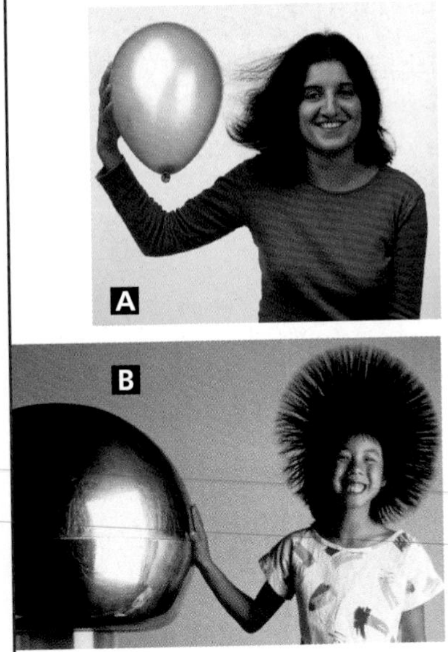

A
B

Static Electricity and Charging

Static electricity is the study of the behavior of electric charges, including how charge is transferred between objects. There are several ways that a net charge can build up on an object or move from one object to another. **Charge can be transferred by friction, by contact, and by induction.** Keep in mind that whenever there is a charge transfer, the total charge is the same before and after the transfer occurs. This is the **law of conservation of charge**—the total charge in an isolated system is constant.

Charging by Friction The balloon in Figure 5A attracts hair because opposite charges attract. But how do balloons and hair pick up a net charge? Rubbing a balloon on your hair is an example of charging by friction. Electrons move from your hair to the balloon because atoms in rubber have a greater attraction for electrons than atoms in hair. The balloon picks up a net negative charge. Because your hair loses electrons, it becomes positively charged. Even simple everyday activities like walking across a carpet can build up charge this way.

Charging by Contact Why do the girl's hairs repel each other in Figure 5B? In this case, charge is transferred by contact. A Van de Graaff generator has charged the metal sphere. When the girl touches the sphere, she acquires a charge large enough to make her hairs stand on end. The sphere is still charged, but its net charge is reduced.

Facts and Figures

Electrical Force and Gravitational Force
Electrical forces are much stronger than the gravitational forces that operate among particles in an atom. For instance, an electron and a proton in a hydrogen atom are 5.3×10^{-11} m apart, on average. The mass of the electron is 9.11×10^{-31} kg and the mass of the proton is 1.67×10^{-27} kg, while both have a charge with magnitude 1.60×10^{-19} C. The gravitational force of attraction between the two particles is 3.6×10^{-47} N, while the electrical force of attraction is 8.2×10^{-8} N, or about 2×10^{39} times greater than the gravitational attraction between them.

Charging by Induction Suppose you reach for a doorknob after walking across a carpet. You have picked up extra electrons from the carpet, so your hand is negatively charged. The net negative charge in your hand repels electrons in the metal doorknob. Figure 6 shows that electrons move to the base of the doorknob, leaving a net positive charge in the part of the doorknob closest to the hand. Overall, the doorknob is still neutral, but charge has moved within it. This is **induction,** a transfer of charge without contact between materials.

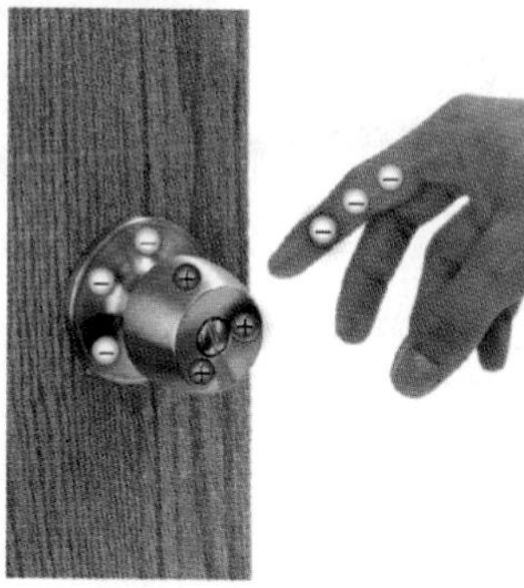

Figure 6 Induction occurs when charge is transferred without contact between materials. Negative charges in the hand induce charges to move within the metal doorknob. ***Predicting** What would happen if the hand had a net positive charge?*

Static Discharge

Why do you get a shock from a doorknob? The spark you feel is a static discharge. **Static discharge occurs when a pathway through which charges can move forms suddenly.** Charges will not travel through air from your hand to the doorknob. But air becomes charged suddenly when the gap between your finger and the doorknob is small. This air provides a path for electrons to flow from your hand to the doorknob. If the room is dark, you can even see this spark.

Lightning is a more dramatic discharge. Charge can build up in a storm cloud from friction between moving air masses. Negative charge in the lower part of the cloud induces a positive charge in the ground below the cloud. As the amount of charge in the cloud increases, the force of attraction between charges in the cloud and charges in the ground increases. Eventually the air becomes charged, forming a pathway for electrons to travel from the cloud to the ground.

Section 20.1 Assessment

Reviewing Concepts

1. How is a net electric charge produced?
2. What determines whether charges attract or repel?
3. Name two factors that affect the strength of an electric field.
4. List three methods of charge transfer.
5. Explain how static discharge occurs.
6. How does electric force depend on the amount of charge and the distance between charges?
7. What is the law of conservation of charge?

Critical Thinking

8. **Forming Hypotheses** Why does plastic food wrap cling better to some materials than to others?
9. **Inferring** When a glass rod is rubbed with neutral silk, the glass becomes positively charged. What charge does the silk now have? Explain.
10. **Relating Cause and Effect** Many lightning strikes occur within a cloud, rather than between clouds and the ground. Explain why. (*Hint:* Assume a cloud has no net charge.)

Writing in Science

Explanatory Paragraph Write a paragraph explaining the series of events that may cause you to receive a shock from a metal doorknob on a dry winter day. (*Hint:* Use a flowchart to organize your ideas before writing your paragraph.)

Static Discharge

Build Science Skills L2

Relating Cause and Effect Have students write a short paragraph describing lightning. Be sure students suggest a reason why excess electrons in a cloud induce a positive charge in the ground. Have students discuss the electric forces in static discharge. *(Friction between water droplets separates charges. Tell students that convection currents within a cloud move positive charges to the top of the cloud and negative charges to the bottom. Through induction, the electric force from the negatively charged region of the cloud repels nearby negative charges on Earth's surface. This leaves a positive charge on the ground. Lightning is the discharge between the oppositely charged regions—either cloud-to-ground or cloud-to-cloud.)* **Logical**

3 ASSESS

Evaluate Understanding L2

Ask students to write a paragraph describing interactions between charges. The paragraph should indicate the two kinds of charges, the forces between the charges, and the ways (friction, contact, and induction) that charges are transferred to and from surfaces.

Reteach L1

Have students use Figure 3 to summarize the way electric forces act between charges.

Writing in Science

Paragraphs should start by describing a buildup of charge on the person, for example by friction with the carpet. When the hand nears the doorknob, charge moves within the metal doorknob by induction. When the hand gets very close, the air suddenly becomes charged. Electrons then flow rapidly either to or from the doorknob, depending on whether the hand has a net negative or positive charge.

Interactive Textbook If your class subscribes to the Interactive Textbook, use it to review key concepts in Section 20.1.

Section 20.1 Assessment

1. An excess or shortage of electrons produces a net electric charge.
2. If charges are alike, they will repel. Opposite charges will attract.
3. Net charge and distance from the charge
4. Friction, contact, induction
5. A pathway through which charges can move forms suddenly.
6. Electric force increases proportionally with charge, while the force is inversely proportional to the square of the distance.
7. The total charge in a system is constant, so that the total charge before charges are transferred is the same as after.
8. The plastic attracts electrons more strongly than some materials and less strongly than others.
9. The charge on the silk must be negative because charge is conserved.
10. If the cloud is neutral, some areas will have a net positive charge, and others a net negative charge. Within the clouds, an area with negative charge buildup discharges to an area with positive charge buildup.

Answer to . . .

Figure 6 *Electrons in the doorknob would move close to the hand. The base of the doorknob would be positively charged.*

Section 20.2

1 FOCUS

Objectives

20.2.1 **Describe** electric current and **identify** the two types of current.

20.2.2 **Describe** conduction and **classify** materials as good electrical conductors or good electrical insulators.

20.2.3 **Describe** the factors that affect resistance.

20.2.4 **Explain** how voltage produces electric current.

20.2.5 **Calculate** voltage, current, and resistance using Ohm's law.

Reading Focus

Build Vocabulary L2

LINCS Have students: **L**ist the parts of the vocabulary that they know, such as *potential* and *difference.* **I**magine what a *potential difference* might look like and how the terms might fit together. **N**ote a reminding sound-alike word, such as *potential energy.* **C**onnect the terms, perhaps in a long sentence or a short story. **S**elf-test (quiz themselves).

Reading Strategy L2

a. Electric current is the flow of electric charge.
b. Electric current is the continuous flow of electric charge.

2 INSTRUCT

Electric Current

Use Visuals L1

Figure 7 Emphasize that electric current needs a continuous path through the flashlight. Ask, **How is the direction of current related to the direction of the flow of electrons?** *(Electrons flow from the negative terminal of one battery to the positive terminal of the other; the direction of current is in the opposite direction.)* Then ask, **What is the function of the switch?** *(Flipping the switch to the "on" position completes the path for the flow of charge)*
Visual, Logical

20.2 Electric Current and Ohm's Law

Reading Focus

Key Concepts

- What are the two types of current?
- What are some examples of conductors and insulators?
- What factors affect electrical resistance?
- What causes an electric current?
- How are voltage, current, and resistance related?

Vocabulary

- electric current
- direct current
- alternating current
- electrical conductor
- electrical insulator
- resistance
- superconductor
- potential difference
- voltage
- battery
- Ohm's law

Reading Strategy

Predicting Copy the table below and write a prediction of what electric current is. After you read the section, if your prediction was incorrect or incomplete, write what electric current actually is.

Electric Current Probably Means	Electric Current Actually Means
a. ?	b. ?

If you've ever tried to fix a flashlight, you know there are several parts to check. The batteries may be dead, or the bulb may have burned out. The switch could be broken, or the spring might be corroded. If even one part isn't functioning, the flashlight won't light.

Electric Current

As you can see in Figure 7, the parts of a flashlight form a continuous path through which charge can flow. This continuous flow of electric charge is an **electric current.** The SI unit of electric current is the ampere (A), or amp, which equals 1 coulomb per second.

The two types of current are direct current and alternating current. Charge flows only in one direction in **direct current** (DC). A flashlight and most other battery-operated devices use direct current. Electric current in your home and school is mostly alternating current. **Alternating current** (AC) is a flow of electric charge that regularly reverses its direction.

In a flashlight, electrons flow from the negative terminal of one battery to the positive terminal of the other battery. But notice that the current is in the opposite direction. This is because scientists define current as the direction in which positive charges would flow.

Figure 7 A complete path is required for charge to flow in a flashlight. Batteries must be placed so that charge can flow from negative to positive, passing through the bulb. **Interpreting Diagrams** ***What purpose does the spring at the base of a flashlight have?***

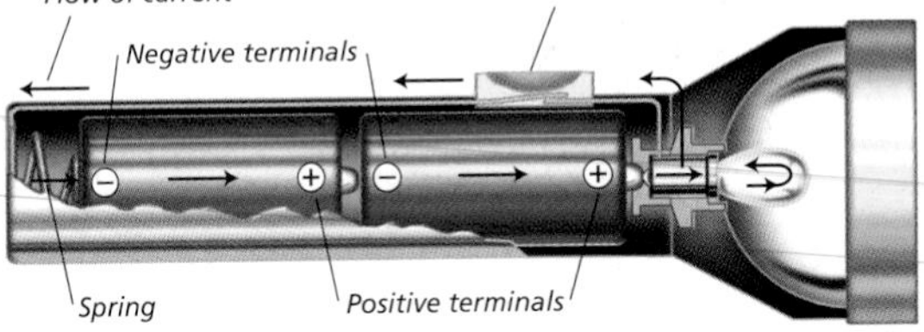

Flow of current
Switch
Negative terminals
Spring
Positive terminals

Section Resources

Print
- ***Laboratory Manual,*** Investigation 20A
- ***Reading and Study Workbook With Math Support,*** Section 20.2
- ***Math Skills and Problem Solving Workbook,*** Section 20.2
- ***Transparencies,*** Section 20.2

Technology
- ***Interactive Textbook,*** Section 20.2
- ***Presentation Pro CD-ROM,*** Section 20.2
- ***Go Online,*** NSTA SciLinks, Conductors and insulators

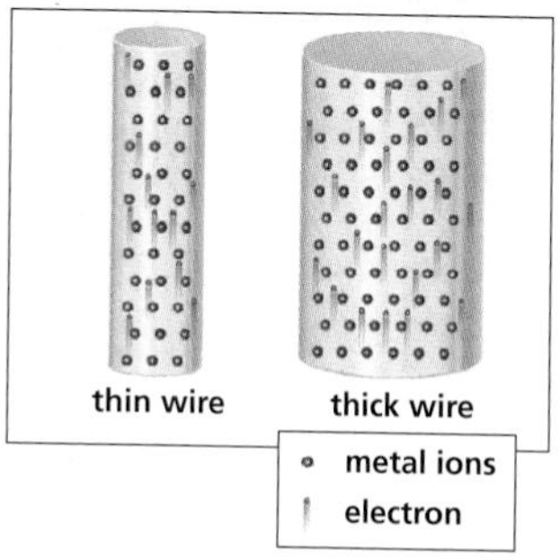
thin wire
thick wire
metal ions
electron

Conductors and Insulators

Why is a metal wire usually coated with plastic or rubber? The metal wire is an electrical conductor. The rubber and plastic are electrical insulators. An **electrical conductor** is a material through which charge can flow easily. A material through which charge cannot flow easily is called an **electrical insulator.** The coating around a wire helps to control the current and keep it where it is needed.

A metal is made up of ions in a lattice. The ions are not free to move. But each ion has one or more electrons that are not tightly bound to it. These free electrons can conduct charge. Most materials do not easily conduct charge because they don't have free electrons. **Metals such as copper and silver are good electrical conductors. Wood, plastic, rubber, and air are good electrical insulators.**

Resistance

As electrons move through a conducting wire, they collide with electrons and ions. These collisions convert some kinetic energy into thermal energy. Because less energy is available to move electrons through the wire, the current is reduced. **Resistance** is opposition to the flow of charges in a material. The SI unit of resistance is the ohm.

When you drink a milkshake as shown in Figure 8, it is easier if you use a thicker straw. In the same way, resistance is lowered if you make a wire thicker because more electrons can flow through a thicker wire. **A material's thickness, length, and temperature affect its resistance.** Resistance is greater in a longer wire because the charges travel farther. As temperature increases, a metal's resistance increases because electrons collide more often.

If resistance increases as temperature increases, what happens as you cool a conductor? Could you reduce the resistance to zero? This is the idea behind superconductors. A **superconductor** is a material that has almost zero resistance when it is cooled to low temperatures. The best superconductor found thus far must be cooled to about 138 K.

Figure 8 Using a thick straw to drink a milkshake is easier than using a thin straw. Similarly, electrons flow more easily through a thick wire than they flow through a thin wire, assuming the wires are made of the same material.
Applying Concepts ***Why should the wire in light bulb filaments be very thin?***

Go Online NSTA SCILINKS

For: Links on conductors and insulators
Visit: www.SciLinks.org
Web Code: ccn-2202

Conductors and Insulators

Address Misconceptions L2

Students may think that only metals make good conductors. Point out that many solutions containing ions are good conductors. The acid inside a battery is one example. Charges also flow freely in ionized gases, such as the gases inside a fluorescent light or a neon light. In contrast to metals, where electrons are the only moving charges, both positive and negative charges move freely in ionized gases and in solutions containing ions.
Logical

Resistance

Integrate Earth Science L2

Although early research in superconductivity concentrated on metals, the best superconducting materials known to date belong to the broad class of minerals called perovskites. Perovskites are composed of barium, lanthanum, copper, and oxygen. Certain ceramics made from clays containing perovskites were found in 1986 to become superconducting at the relatively high temperature of 35 K. This was 12 K higher than the highest temperature at which any metal alloy was superconducting. By altering some of the components in perovskites, higher superconducting temperatures have been reached. At present, the highest temperature for a superconducting material is 138 K. Have students research the history of superconducting ceramics and report on their findings.
Verbal

Go Online NSTA SCILINKS

Download a worksheet on conductors and insulators for students to complete, and find additional teacher support from NSTA SciLinks.

Customize for Inclusion Students

Visually Impaired
Analogies, such as drinking a milkshake through a straw, are useful tools for improving the comprehension of visually impaired students. Develop similar analogies for other electrical processes. For instance, have students consider the insulating qualities of a winter ski jacket. Just as an electrical insulator coating a wire helps to control electric current, the jacket contains thermal insulation that reduces the flow of thermal energy to help a person stay warm. Be sure that students understand that such analogies are not exactly the same as the processes that they help to illustrate, but have enough similarities in certain physical properties to make them useful.

Answer to . . .

Figure 7 *It provides firm contact to the negative terminal of one battery and pushes the other battery into contact with the light bulb.*

Figure 8 *Thin wire will heat up and become hot enough to glow.*

Quick Lab

Modeling Resistance in a Wire **L2**

Objective
After completing this activity, students will be able to
- describe how the thickness of a conductor affects its resistance.

Skills Focus **Observing, Measuring, Controlling Variables, Using Models**

Prep Time 15 minutes

Materials white paper, metric ruler, number 2 pencil, multimeter

Class Time 25 minutes

Safety Students should wear safety goggles and aprons during the lab. Be sure students wash their hands after completing the lab.

Expected Outcome Students will learn that electrical resistance decreases as the width of the resisting material is increased or the length of the resisting material is decreased.

Analyze and Conclude
1. Resistance is greater in the narrower rectangle; it decreases.
2. There are more available electrons for current within the cross-sectional area of a thick wire than of a thin wire. As wire length decreases, the distance electrons travel decreases, so the number of collisions that cause resistance decreases.
Logical, Group

For Enrichment **L3**

Have students repeat the experiment with different metal strips of identical dimensions and make a table listing the resistances. **Kinesthetic**

Voltage

Build Reading Literacy **L1**

Relate Text and Visuals Refer to page **190D** in **Chapter 7**, which provides the guidelines for relating text and visuals.

Have students read the paragraphs about potential difference while referring to Figure 9. Emphasize that the figure provides an analogy, so that the difficult concept in the text will be easier to visualize. Ask, **How are gravity and an attractive electric field similar?** *(Work must be done against each to increase the potential energy of an object.)*
Logical

Quick Lab

Modeling Resistance in a Wire

Materials
white paper, metric ruler, number 2 pencil, multimeter

Procedure
1. Draw a narrow rectangle 1 cm wide by 5 cm long on the paper. Draw a wide rectangle, 3 cm by 5 cm. Use the pencil to completely fill in both rectangles with graphite.
2. Place the multimeter electrodes at opposite ends of the narrow rectangle. Record the resistance. Keep one electrode in place and slowly drag the other one toward it. Record your observations.
3. Repeat Step 2 using the wide rectangle.

Analyze and Conclude
1. **Observing** In which rectangle is the resistance greater? How does resistance change as the electrodes move together?
2. **Using Models** Explain why a thick wire has lower resistance than a thin wire if all else is equal. Why does resistance decrease as a wire's length decreases?

Voltage

If you remove the batteries from a flashlight, the light will not shine. Why? Because there is resistance in the wires and the bulb, charges do not flow on their own without a source of energy. **In order for charge to flow in a conducting wire, the wire must be connected in a complete loop that includes a source of electrical energy.**

Potential Difference Recall that potential energy is related to position. In Figure 9, water at the top of the fountain has more gravitational potential energy than water at the bottom. That is why water falls spontaneously from a higher to a lower height. In the same way, charges flow spontaneously from a higher to a lower potential energy.

The potential energy of a charge depends on its position in an electric field. **Potential difference** is the difference in electrical potential energy between two places in an electric field. Potential difference is measured in joules per coulomb, or volts. Because it is measured in volts, potential difference is also called **voltage.**

Figure 9 A water fountain has a pump inside that lifts water to the top, increasing the gravitational potential energy of the water. In the same way, a voltage source increases the electrical potential energy of electric charges.

Voltage Sources How does water get to the top of the fountain? A pump inside the fountain does work on the water to increase its potential energy. In the same way, a source of voltage such as a battery does work to increase the potential energy of electric charges.

Three common voltage sources are batteries, solar cells, and generators. A **battery** is a device that converts chemical energy to electrical energy. Batteries, like other voltage sources, have terminals that can connect to wires in a circuit. One terminal is positive and the other is negative. A voltage drop, or potential difference, is maintained across the terminals. In a 9-volt battery, for example, the voltage drop is about 9 volts.

Facts and Figures

Diamond As a rule, good conductors of heat are also good conductors of electricity. This is because most conductors are metals, and the electrons in metals can move with ease, transferring energy through the metal, regardless of whether the energy is thermal or electrical. However, one substance that is a good thermal conductor (in fact, the best thermal conductor) is an electrical insulator: diamond. Diamond is a form of carbon in which all carbon atoms are bound to other carbon atoms in a tetrahedral crystal. These strong bonds give diamond its great hardness, and make it possible for kinetic energy to pass easily through the crystal by heat. However, because there are no free electrons to move throughout the crystal, diamond cannot conduct electricity.

Ohm's Law

The unit of resistance, the ohm, is named after the German scientist Georg Ohm (1789–1854). It was Ohm who first determined how resistance and current affect voltage. He discovered that voltage is not the same everywhere in a circuit. Ohm hypothesized that resistance reduces the voltage. He published his research in 1826, but his findings were so controversial that he lost his job. Eventually his work became widely accepted.

Ohm found a mathematical relationship between voltage, current, and resistance. This relationship became known as Ohm's law. According to **Ohm's law,** the voltage (V) in a circuit equals the product of the current (I) and the resistance (R).

Ohm's Law

$$V = I \times R \text{ or } I = \frac{V}{R}$$

When the current is in amperes and the resistance is in ohms, the voltage is in volts. What is the voltage if the resistance is 3 ohms and the current is 3 amps?

$$V = I \times R = 3 \text{ amps} \times 3 \text{ ohms} = 9 \text{ volts}$$

Increasing the voltage increases the current. Keeping the same voltage and increasing the resistance decreases the current. A multimeter, shown in Figure 10, is a device used to measure current, voltage, and resistance.

9.08

Figure 10 A multimeter can be used to measure current, voltage, or resistance. Here the voltage of a 9-volt battery is measured.

Section 20.2 Assessment

Reviewing Concepts

1. List the two types current.
2. Name two good electrical conductors and two good electrical insulators.
3. What variables affect the resistance of a material?
4. What causes charge to flow?
5. According to Ohm's law, how is voltage related to resistance and current?
6. What is a superconductor?

Critical Thinking

7. **Problem Solving** Suppose you have two wires of equal length made from the same material. How is it possible for the wires to have different resistances?
8. **Applying Concepts** Use Ohm's law to explain how two circuits could have the same current but different resistances.

Writing in Science

Compare-Contrast Paragraph Write a paragraph comparing and contrasting conductors and insulators and the ways in which they might be used. (*Hint:* Identify materials that are good conductors and materials that are good insulators.)

Ohm's Law

Build Science Skills L2

Calculating Help students use Ohm's law to calculate the voltage when the current is 4.0 amps and the resistance is 3.0 ohms.

$V = I \times R =$

4.0 amps $\times$ 3.0 ohms = 12 volts

Then, help students understand that current is indirectly proportional to resistance by doubling the resistance and calculating the new current while the voltage remains constant:

$I = V/R$ = 12 volts/6.0 ohms = 2.0 amps

Point out that when the resistance is doubled, the current decreases by one half.

Logical

3 ASSESS

Evaluate Understanding L2

Ask students to write two questions each about current, resistance, and voltage. Review the questions for accuracy. Then, have students form groups and ask each other their approved questions.

Reteach L1

Have students use Figure 9 to explain how voltage increases the electrical potential of a charge.

Writing in Science

Paragraphs should describe conductors as materials, such as copper and silver, through which charges move easily. Insulators should be described as materials, such as wood, plastic, or rubber, through which charges do not move easily. Conductors are used in electrical wiring for buildings, and in electrical appliances, while insulators are used to isolate conductors from unwanted contact.

Interactive Textbook: If your class subscribes to the Interactive Textbook, use it to review key concepts in Section 20.2.

Section 20.2 Assessment

1. Direct current, alternating current
2. Good conductors: silver, copper; good insulators: air, plastic
3. Length, thickness, temperature
4. A source of electrical energy causes charge to flow.
5. Voltage equals the product of current and resistance. An increase in voltage increases current. Keeping the same voltage and increasing resistance decreases current.
6. A superconductor is a material that has almost zero resistance when cooled to low temperatures.
7. The two wires may have different thicknesses or different temperatures, which would give them different resistances.
8. If the voltages in the two circuits were such that the ratio of voltage to resistance was the same, both circuits would have the same amount of current.

issues in SCIENCE

Should Car Companies Be Required to Make Electric Cars? L2

Background

In the 1990s, attempts were made by a number of auto manufacturers to develop an electric automobile. Difficulties with the early models include the long amount of time needed to recharge the batteries and the limited distance that such vehicles can travel before they need to be recharged. Such problems may be overcome in the future. Nevertheless, electric vehicles work well enough for driving within a city, and they can be recharged overnight. For this reason, the United States Postal Service is planning to acquire fleets of electric vehicles for local mail delivery. Additionally, the research on the electric vehicle has led to the development of another new type of car: the hybrid automobile (see p. 488).

Answers

1. Answers may include the costs of production regardless of demand, legal questions about how much government can or should be involved with business, and the disadvantage of having to manufacture electric cars even if the technology of the cars does not improve.
2. Answers for regulation may include: Auto companies are not likely to develop or market the cars on their own; electric cars are efficient and quiet with low upkeep costs. Answers against regulation may include: Technology should progress as people need and want it; electric cars are expensive and unpopular, and they need frequent recharging.
3. Students should state their opinions and provide reasons based on facts.
4. Students' letters should be written in a persuasive style.

Go Online PHSchool.com

Have students further research the issues related to this topic.

issues in SCIENCE — Should Car Companies Be Required to Make Electric Cars?

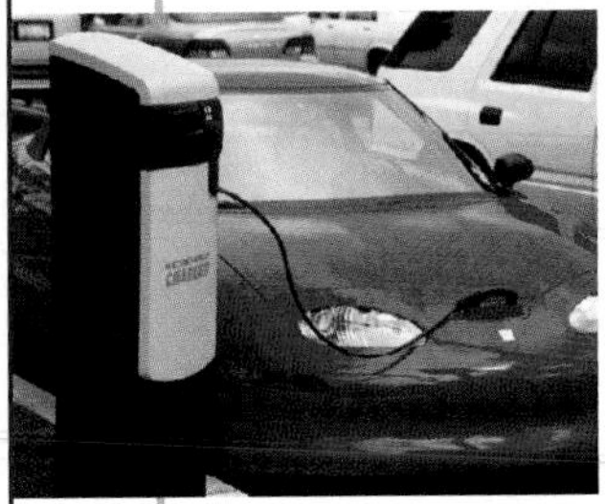

Battery-powered electric cars were first introduced in the late 1880s. They could only be used for short distances at low speeds, but they were quiet and had low maintenance costs. By the 1920s, electric cars were mostly replaced by gasoline-powered cars. Since the 1970s, growing concerns about fuel shortages and pollution from car exhaust has renewed interest in electric cars.

When an electric car is turned on, current flows from the battery to a controller. The controller converts the battery's direct current into alternating current that can be used by the motor. The controller also determines how much power the motor needs.

Electric cars rely indirectly on fossil fuels used at electric power plants. However, these cars don't have engines that burn fossil fuels, so they have no harmful emissions. For this reason, the U.S. government has begun requiring vehicle manufacturers to meet development requirements for electric cars. Should car manufacturers be required to make electric cars?

The Viewpoints

Car Companies Should Be Required to Make Electric Cars

The issue seems clear to those in favor of electric cars. If everyone agrees that electric cars have the lowest emissions of any automobile, shouldn't everyone use them? These people feel that the best way to encourage drivers to use electric cars is to require car manufacturers to produce them. It may take people time to get used to driving electric cars, but now is the time to start changing attitudes.

Electric cars are efficient and quiet, and they have low upkeep costs. Today's electric cars are expensive because they are a relatively new technology and aren't widely used. When the cars can be mass produced, prices will drop.

Car Companies Should Not Be Required to Make Electric Cars

Other people argue that production of electric cars should not be encouraged by government regulations. This type of technology should progress as people need and want it.

At present electric cars are expensive and unpopular. Recent sales of these cars have been low, so manufacturers don't want to keep making them.

Opponents of required production also point out that electric cars have some drawbacks. With gasoline-powered cars, you can fill the tank and drive hundreds of miles before refueling. Electric cars run on batteries that need frequent recharging.

Research and Decide

1. **Defining the Issue** Describe the major issues involved in requiring car companies to produce electric cars.
2. **Analyzing the Viewpoints** What are some reasons people think the government should or should not regulate production of electric cars?
3. **Forming Your Opinion** Should car companies be required to produce electric cars? Explain why or why not.
4. **Writing in Science** Write a letter to the editor of a local newspaper stating your opinion.

Go Online PHSchool.com

For: More on this issue
Visit: PHSchool.com
Web Code: cch-2203

608 Chapter 20

20.3 Electric Circuits

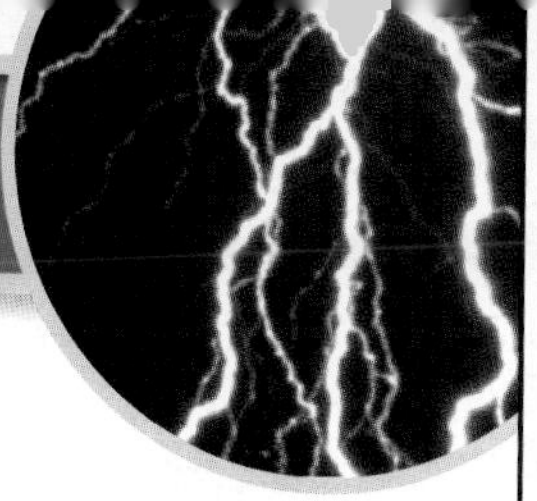

Reading Focus

Key Concepts

- What is included in a circuit diagram?
- How do series and parallel circuits differ?
- How do you calculate electric power and electrical energy use?
- What devices make electricity safe to use?

Vocabulary

- electric circuit
- series circuit
- parallel circuit
- electric power
- fuse
- circuit breaker
- grounding

Reading Strategy

Relating Text and Visuals Copy the table below. As you read, look at Figure 13 on page 610. List three things that the diagram helps you understand about circuits.

What Can Be Seen in the Circuit Diagram?
Wire bringing current from outside
a. ?
b. ?
c. ?

If you've ever seen a house being built, you know that wires hidden inside the walls connect to every electrical outlet and to every light switch. If you were responsible for wiring a house, like the electrician in Figure 11, how would you do it? A good place to start would be the circuit diagrams supplied by the builder or contractor.

Figure 11 To bring electric current into a building, an electrician installs wiring. In a house, all of the wires usually come from one main box.

Circuit Diagrams

An **electric circuit** is a complete path through which charge can flow. Wires in a house form a complex network of circuits. It may look like a maze of wires, but each connection has a purpose. An electrician uses circuit diagrams to keep track of how elements in a circuit are connected. **Circuit diagrams use symbols to represent parts of a circuit, including a source of electrical energy and devices that are run by the electrical energy.** In a simple circuit, for example, a battery provides the energy to operate a device such as a bell or a light bulb.

A circuit diagram shows one or more complete paths in which charge can flow. Switches show places where the circuit can be opened. If a switch is open, the circuit is not a complete loop, and current stops. This is called an open circuit. When the switch is closed, the circuit is complete and charge can flow. This is called a closed circuit.

Reading Checkpoint *What is an open circuit?*

Section Resources

Print

- ***Reading and Study Workbook With Math Support,*** Section 20.3 and **Math Skill:** Power, Voltage, and Current
- ***Math Skills and Problem Solving Workbook,*** Section 20.3
- ***Transparencies,*** Section 20.3

Technology

- ***Probeware Lab Manual,*** Lab 8
- ***Interactive Textbook,*** Section 20.3
- ***Presentation Pro CD-ROM,*** Section 20.3
- ***Go Online,*** NSTA SciLinks, Electric circuits

Section 20.3

1 FOCUS

Objectives

20.3.1 **Analyze** circuit diagrams for series circuits and parallel circuits.

20.3.2 **Solve equations** that relate electric power to current, voltage, and electrical energy.

20.3.3 **Describe** devices and procedures for maintaining electrical safety.

Reading Focus

Build Vocabulary L2

Vocabulary Knowledge Rating Chart Have students construct a chart with four columns labeled Term, Can Define or Use It, Have Heard or Seen It, and Don't Know to rate their knowledge of each term. Ask students to share what they know about *electric circuit* and the other terms for this section. Help students establish a purpose for reading by using the terms to predict the text content. After students have read the section, have them re-rate themselves.

Reading Strategy L2

a. Circuits are wired in parallel so devices can operate independently. **b.** The fuse box or circuit breaker is located where electrical energy enters the house. **c.** All of the circuits connect to the ground wire.

2 INSTRUCT

Circuit Diagrams

Build Reading Literacy L1

Summarize Refer to page **598D** in this chapter, which provides the guidelines for summarizing.

Summarizing the information presented in the text will help students to focus on main ideas and remember what they read. Have students read the paragraphs about circuit diagrams and summarize them by restating the main idea in their own words.
Verbal

Answer to . . .

Reading Checkpoint *An open circuit is not a complete loop, so charge cannot flow through it.*

Series Circuits

Teacher Demo

Series and Parallel Circuits

L2

Purpose To show how current moves in each kind of circuit.

Materials a 6-volt battery, 3 small light bulbs with sockets, 2 long strands of wire (12 cm), 4 short strands of wire (6 cm)

Procedure Strip the insulation from the ends of the wires and connect the battery and light bulbs in series, similar to the setup shown in Figure 12A. Unscrew one bulb and have students note the results. Rewire the circuit in parallel, similar to Figure 12B. Unscrew one bulb, and have students note the results.

Expected Outcome When one bulb in series is unscrewed, the circuit is broken and all bulbs go out. When the bulb in the parallel circuit is unscrewed, the other lamps are still lit up.
Visual

Parallel Circuits

Use Visuals

L1

Figure 12 Have students trace the possible paths for current to move through each circuit, starting at the positive terminal of the battery and ending at the negative terminal. Ask, **If there is a break in the part of the circuit containing the outer light bulb in Figure 12B, will there still be a complete circuit?** *(Yes)* **Where will there be a current?** *(In the part of the circuit with the inner bulb)* **Why will the current in the inner bulb be the same as before the outer circuit was broken, but the current in the battery will be less than before?** *(The voltage across and resistance in the inner bulb are unchanged, so the current in the bulb is unchanged. There are fewer bulbs that need current, so the overall current in the battery is less.)*
Visual

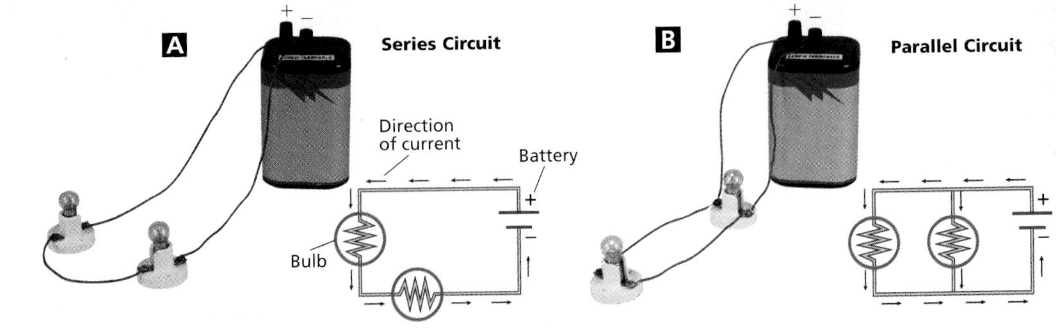

A
Series Circuit
Direction of current
Battery
Bulb
B
Parallel Circuit

Figure 12 Circuits can be represented with circuit diagrams. Symbols correspond to each element. **A** A series circuit has one path that each charge can follow. **B** A parallel circuit has more than one path each charge can follow.
Interpreting Diagrams *Which symbol represents a light bulb?*

Figure 12 shows two circuit diagrams. The + and − on the battery symbol indicate the positive and negative terminals. Arrows show the direction of current, from positive to negative. Recall that the direction of current is defined as the direction in which positive charges would flow. Electrons in a wire flow in the opposite direction.

Reading Checkpoint *How is the direction of current defined?*

Series Circuits

In a **series circuit,** charge has only one path through which it can flow. Look at the series circuit in Figure 12A. If one light bulb burns out in a series circuit, it becomes an open circuit. **If one element stops functioning in a series circuit, none of the elements can operate.** The bulbs in a circuit are a source of resistance. Adding bulbs to a series circuit increases the resistance. As a result, the current decreases, and each bulb shines less brightly.

Parallel Circuits

Imagine what would happen if circuits in your home were wired in series. If a light bulb burned out, the television would turn off. To avoid this problem, circuits in the home are mostly wired in parallel. A **parallel circuit** is an electric circuit with two or more paths through which charges can flow. If one bulb in Figure 12B burns out, charge still flows along the other path, and the other bulb stays lit. **If one element stops functioning in a parallel circuit, the rest of the elements still can operate.**

Figure 13 shows a network of circuits connecting electrical devices in a home. These circuits are wired in parallel so they can operate independently.

Figure 13 Most circuits in a house are parallel. This way, even if one device stops working, the others will still work.

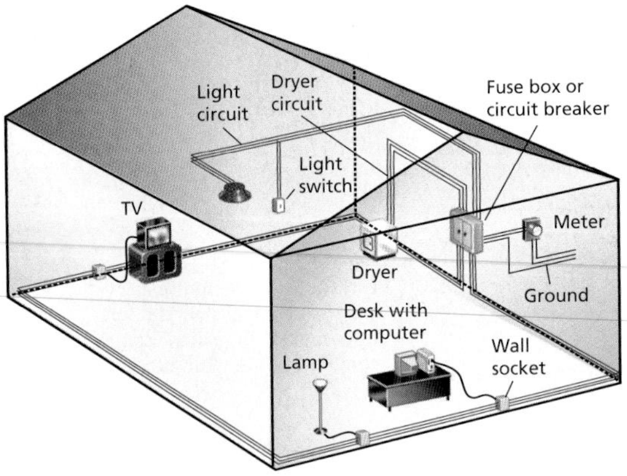

Light circuit
Dryer circuit
Fuse box or circuit breaker
Light switch
TV
Meter
Dryer
Ground
Desk with computer
Wall socket
Lamp

Customize for English Language Learners

Clarifying Key Concepts
The details of electrical circuits may be confusing to English language learners. To be sure that these students understand circuits, have them keep a Reading/Learning Log. Encourage students to write what they understand in the left column, and what they still have questions about in the right column. Check student logs to determine which, if any, concepts remain unclear.

Power and Energy Calculations

Recall that power is the rate of doing work. The rate at which electrical energy is converted to another form of energy is **electric power.** The unit of electric power is the joule per second, or watt (W). Power often is measured in thousands of watts, or kilowatts (kW). **Electric power can be calculated by multiplying voltage by current.**

Electric Power

$$P \text{ (watts)} = I \text{ (amps)} \times V \text{ (volts)}$$

Every time you use a 1875-watt hair dryer or turn on a 75-watt light bulb you use electric power. Appliances vary in the amount of power they use.

Go Online NSTA SciLinks

For: Links on electric circuits
Visit: www.SciLinks.org
Web Code: ccn-2203

Math Skills

Calculating Electric Power

An electric oven is connected to a 240-volt line, and it uses 34 amps of current. What is the power used by the oven?

1 Read and Understand

What information are you given?

Current = I = 34 amps

Voltage = V = 240 volts

2 Plan and Solve

What unknown are you trying to calculate?

Power = P = ?

What formula contains the given quantities and the unknown?

$P = I \times V$

Replace each variable with its known value.

P = 34 amps × 240 volts

= 8200 watts

3 Look Back and Check

Is your answer reasonable?

The answer is reasonable because an electric oven should use much more power than a 1875-watt hair dryer.

Math Practice

1. A clothes dryer uses about 27 amps of current from a 240-volt line. How much power does it use?
2. A camcorder has a power rating of 2.3 watts. If the output voltage from its battery is 7.2 volts, what current does it use?
3. A power tool uses about 12 amps of current and has a power rating of 1440 watts. What voltage does the tool require?

Power and Energy Calculations

Address Misconceptions **L2**

Students may think that electrical energy is produced or consumed, rather than converted. Stress that electrical energy is conserved in electric circuits. Power is the rate at which electrical energy is used or converted to other forms of energy. Examples include electromagnetic energy emitted by a light bulb, thermal energy provided by the heating element on a stove, and mechanical energy provided by an electric motor. **Logical**

Math Practice

Solutions **L2**

1. $P = I \times V$ = (240 V)(27 A) = 6500 W
2. $I = P/V$ = (2.3 W)/(7.2 V) = 0.32 A
3. $V = P/I$ = (1440 W)/(12 A) = 120 V
Logical

For Extra Help **L1**

Students can write and solve forms of the equation for electric power. **Logical**

Direct students to the **Math Skills** in the **Skills and Reference Handbook** at the end of the student text for additional help.

Additional Problems

1. A lamp has a voltage of 120 V across it and uses a current of 0.5 A. What is the power used by the lamp? *(60 W)*
2. A 1.5 V battery provides 0.067 A of current for a calculator. What is the calculator's power rating? *(0.10 W)*
Logical, Portfolio

Go Online NSTA SciLinks

Download a worksheet on electric circuits for students to complete, and find additional teacher support from NSTA SciLinks.

Answer to . . .

Figure 12 *A zigzag line in a circle*

Reading Checkpoint *The direction in which positive charges would flow*

Electrical Safety

Quick Lab

Modeling a Fuse L2

Objective
After completing this activity, students will be able to
- describe the principle of an electric fuse.

Skills Focus **Observing, Inferring, Using Models**

Prep Time 20 minutes

Materials 6-volt battery, 2 wires with stripped ends, strip of aluminum foil, scissors, wooden block, unpainted thumbtacks

Advance Prep Strip the insulation from the ends of the two pieces of wire and the battery leads.

Class Time 20 minutes

Safety Students should wear safety goggles. Caution students to be careful to avoid injury from splinters in the wood or from the thumbtacks. The wire can become very hot. Caution them to avoid touching it when the ends are connected to the battery.

Expected Outcome The foil fuse will melt, interrupting the circuit. Students will learn that a fuse works by conducting a small amount of electric current and by blocking the flow of a large amount of electric current.

Analyze and Conclude
1. The current caused the aluminum foil to become heated until it melted.
2. The foil, like the metal wire in a fuse, is a conductor that, when too much current passes through it, becomes so hot that it melts.
Logical, Group

For Enrichment L3

Have students repeat the experiment using a multimeter to measure the current and voltage across the foil strip before and after it melts. Ask them to explain their observations. When the foil melts, the current will stop and the voltage will increase to the voltage of the battery.
Kinesthetic, Logical

Quick Lab

Modeling a Fuse

Materials

6-volt battery, two wires with stripped ends, aluminum foil, scissors, wooden block, unpainted metal thumbtacks

Procedure

1. Connect the two wires to the two battery terminals.
2. Cut a strip of aluminum foil about 0.5 cm by 3 cm. In the center, cut the width down to 1 mm. Attach the ends of the foil strip to the wooden block with the thumbtacks.
3. Touch one of the wires to each end of the foil strip to form a circuit.
4. Observe what happens to the foil strip. **CAUTION** *If the wire and the battery become very hot, remove the wires from the foil.*

Analyze and Conclude

1. **Observing** What happened to the foil strip when the wires were attached to it?
2. **Using Models** How is the foil like a fuse? Explain.

An appliance's power rating lets you know how much power it uses under normal conditions. An electric stove uses about 6000 watts, and a microwave oven uses about 1000 watts. To find the electrical energy used by an appliance, multiply power by time.

Electrical Energy

$$E = P \times t$$

For example, the power rating of a typical clothes dryer is 5400 watts, or 5.4 kilowatts. If you use the clothes dryer for 2 hours, the energy use is 5.4 kilowatts multiplied by 2 hours, or 10.8 kilowatt-hours. Electric power companies usually determine charges on your electric bill using kilowatt-hours as a unit of energy. A kilowatt-hour equals 3,600,000 joules.

Electrical Safety

Inspectors check all new houses to make sure electrical wiring is installed safely. All wires must be able to carry the maximum expected current. But correct wiring is not enough to prevent electrical accidents. **Correct wiring, fuses, circuit breakers, insulation, and grounded plugs help make electrical energy safe to use.**

In the United States, most household circuits usually have an average voltage of 120 volts. The amount of current in a circuit can vary, depending on the number of devices that are in the circuit. Each device that is turned on increases the current. If the current exceeds the circuit's safety limit, the wire may overheat and start a fire.

Home Safety A **fuse** prevents current overload in a circuit. A wire in the center of the fuse melts if too much current passes through it. This melting is known as "blowing a fuse." After a fuse like one of those shown in Figure 14 blows, it must be replaced with a new fuse before the circuit can carry a current again.

Most houses today use circuit breakers instead of fuses to prevent overloads. A **circuit breaker** is a switch that opens when current in a circuit is too high. The circuit breaker must be reset before the circuit can be used again.

Personal Safety Imagine what could happen if your body became part of an electric circuit. Figure 15 shows some effects that current may have on a person. You might not notice a current of 1 milliamp, but higher currents can be quite dangerous.

Electrical wiring in a home is insulated to protect people. If the insulation is damaged, you may accidentally touch the bare wire and get a shock. Avoid touching electrical devices with wet hands because your hands conduct current more readily when they are wet.

Figure 14 Fuses have an internal wire that burns out if a current is too great.

Facts and Figures

Early Fuses Electrical fuses date back almost to the time when electricity itself was first used. Thomas Edison is credited with inventing the first fuse. It is said that platinum wires were used as fuses to protect the submarine telegraph cables that established electrical communication between Europe and North America.

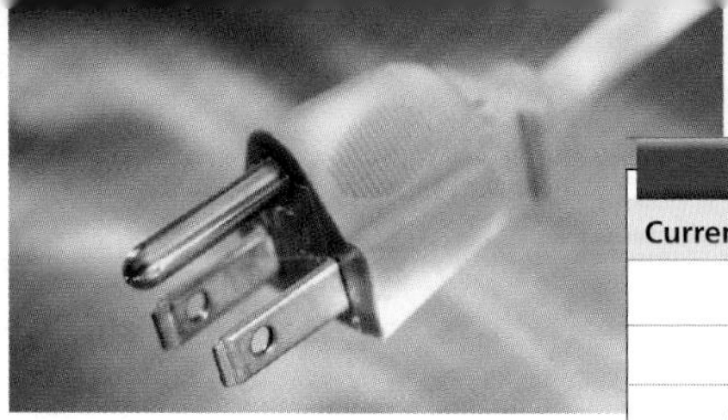

Figure 15 Even a small current in your body can cause a painful shock or injury. **Analyzing Data** ***What is the lowest level of current that causes serious injury?***

Effect of Current on Human Body	
Current Level	**Effect**
1 mA	Slight tingling sensation
5 mA	Slight shock
6–30 mA	Painful shock; loss of muscular control
50–150 mA	Extreme pain; severe muscular contractions. Breathing stops; death is possible.
1000–4300 mA	Nerve damage; heart stops, death is likely.
10,000 mA	Severe burns; heart stops, death is probable.

Ground-fault circuit interrupter (GFCI)

Insulation also prevents short circuits. In a short circuit, current finds a short path through the circuit with less resistance than the full path through the circuit. A three-prong plug can prevent shocks caused by short circuits. In Figure 15 you can see the circular third prong, which connects to ground. These plugs are used on devices with metal exteriors, such as an electric drill. If a short circuit develops, you might get a shock by holding the drill. But instead of entering your body, the current takes an easier path to ground through the grounding wire. The transfer of excess charge through a conductor to Earth is called **grounding.**

A ground-fault circuit interrupter (GFCI) like the one shown in Figure 15 is an electrical safety outlet. It monitors current flowing to and from an outlet or appliance. If these two currents are not equal, it means current is escaping. The GFCI opens the circuit to prevent serious electric shocks.

Section 20.3 Assessment

Reviewing Concepts

1. Name two elements included in a circuit diagram.
2. What is the difference between a series circuit and a parallel circuit?
3. Write the equations for calculating electric power and electrical energy.
4. Name five safety devices used with electric current.

Critical Thinking

5. **Problem Solving** Two bulbs connected in parallel shine more brightly than when they are connected to the same voltage source in series. Explain why this doesn't violate the law of conservation of energy.
6. **Applying Concepts** You plug in a string of holiday lights and notice that the entire string turns off when you remove one bulb. Explain why this happens.

Math Practice

7. A stereo receiver uses a current of 2.2 amps from a 120-volt line. What is its power?
8. A television connected to a 120-volt line uses 102 watts of power. How much current flows through it?

Section 20.3 Assessment

1. Sample answers: a source of electrical energy; one or more devices that use electrical energy; conducting wires.
2. A series circuit has only one path for the current. A parallel circuit has two or more paths for the current.
3. The equation for electric power is $P = I \times V$. The equation for electrical energy is $E = P \times t$.
4. Fuses, circuit breakers, insulation, grounded (three-prong) plugs, and ground-fault circuit interrupters (GFCIs)
5. In the parallel circuit, the overall resistance is lower and the voltage across each bulb is the same as the voltage across the power source. Therefore, the current through the bulbs is greater in the parallel circuit than in the series circuit. Energy is still conserved, but it is used at a faster rate by the battery when the bulbs are in a parallel circuit.
6. The bulbs are connected in a series circuit. When one of the holiday lights burns out, current in the entire string is stopped.

Build Science Skills **L2**

Analyzing Data Have students look at the information given in the table in Figure 15 after they have read the paragraph about the ground-fault circuit interrupter. Suggest students imagine that they are designing a GFCI device and have to determine how great a current difference must exist between the two currents before the circuit is interrupted. Tell students to decide what this maximum current difference is based on the information in the table. *(Answers should be no greater than 5 mA of current.)*
Logical

3 ASSESS

Evaluate Understanding **L2**

Have students write three math problems (with solutions) based on the electric power equation used in this section. Each problem should require solving for a different variable: power, voltage, and current. Have students take turns analyzing and solving the problems in class. Note that even incorrectly worded problems are useful, as students can be asked to identify and correct the errors.

Reteach **L1**

On six different cards, draw a circuit diagram of a series or parallel circuit. Include several components in each circuit, making each diagram more challenging than the previous one, but be sure that components are only in series or only in parallel with each other. Hold up one card at a time and ask students to identify the type of circuit shown.

Math Practice

Solutions
7. $P = V \times I = 120\text{ V} \times 2.2\text{ A} = 260\text{ W}$
8. $I = P/V = (102\text{ W})/(120\text{ V}) = 0.85\text{ A}$

Interactive Textbook If your class subscribes to the Interactive Textbook, use it to review key concepts in Section 20.3.

Answer to . . .

Figure 15 *The lowest level of current that causes serious injury is 6–30 mA.*

CONCEPTS in Action

Getting Personal with Computers L2

Background

Throughout the 1960s and early 1970s a number of steps were taken toward creating smaller computers. The Altair 8800 came on the market in April, 1975. It was the first affordable microcomputer that was widely available for use. The Altair had 256 bytes of memory, no keyboard or video monitor, and sold for $375. The Alto, which was developed in 1973, more closely resembled modern personal computers. Although the Alto was not marketed commercially, it anticipated some standard features that all personal computers have today, such as a video monitor and a mouse.

In 1969, the first computer network, ARPANET, established a connection among four university computer systems. This network ultimately led to the creation of the Internet. While the early networks did not reach the general public or involve personal computers, the 1970s saw the development of the capability of sending information between computers. This paved the way for e-mail and other features which are now so popular on personal computers.

The personal computer began taking its familiar form in the early 1980s as it became faster, more versatile, and easier to use. These changes were largely due to the higher density of components on microprocessors. As personal computers with increased capability were created, their commercial appeal increased. The World Wide Web was established in 1991. The Internet made it possible to transmit text, pictures, and sound instantly across great distances. Within five years, the Internet was being used commercially by over 50 million people.

CONCEPTS in Action

Getting Personal with Computers

Millions of people use personal computers every day for activities such as writing letters, browsing the Internet, or playing games.

Disk drive

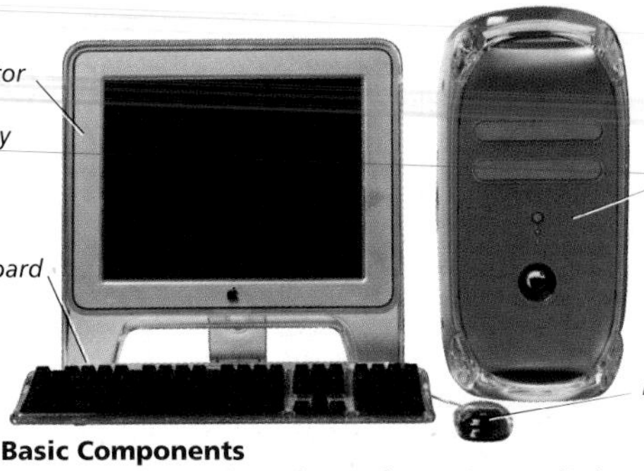

Monitor or display
Computer
Keyboard
Mouse

Basic Components
A computer system is made up of a monitor or display, a keyboard, a mouse, and a computer. Input devices, such as the mouse and keyboard, feed information into the computer. Output devices, such as the monitor, display information that has been taken in by the input devices and processed by the central processing unit (CPU). The computer contains the CPU, memory chips, hard disk, and motherboard.

Inside a Computer
The CPU and other chips in a computer contain integrated circuits. The circuits consist of millions of miniaturized electronic components deposited onto a thin slice of silicon. Computers use the electric signals and circuits within these chips to represent and process data. A binary number system is used, in which data are stored digitally as strings of 1's and 0's. The digits of a binary number are transmitted as electrical pulses. Each digit is called a bit, with 8 bits making up a byte.

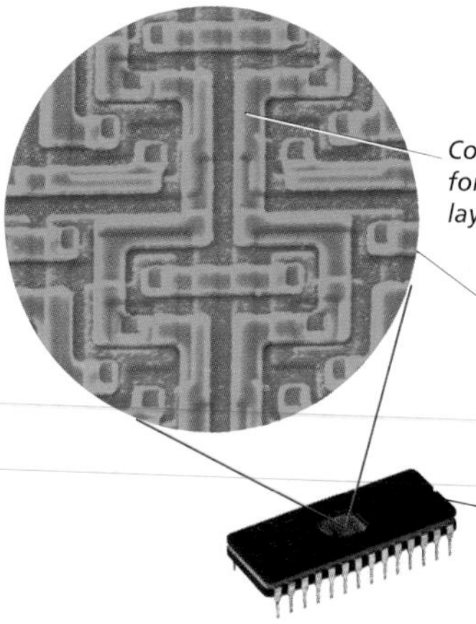

Components formed from layers of silicon
Magnified section of part of the surface of a silicon chip through which data are transmitted
Microprocessor chip

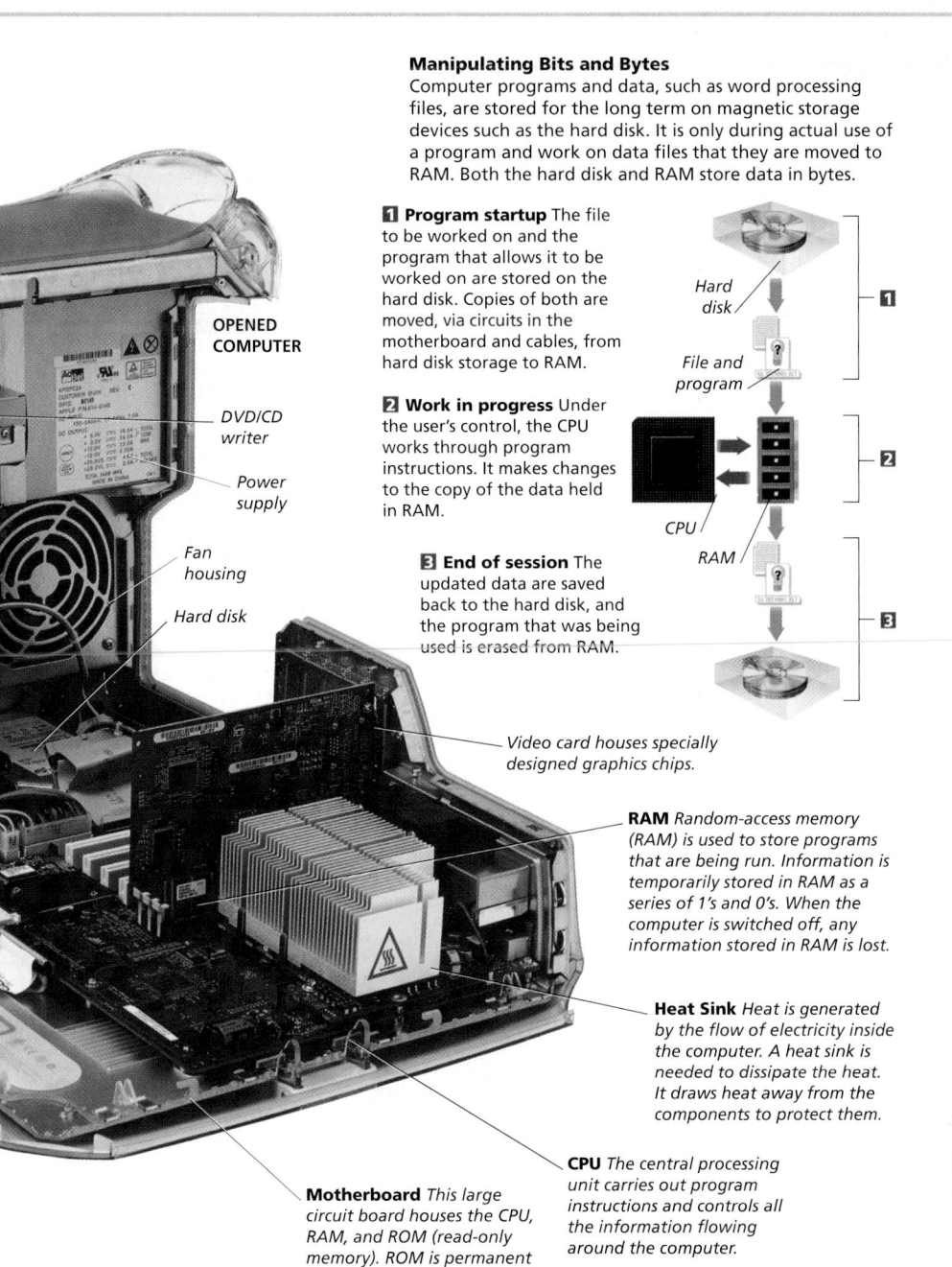

Manipulating Bits and Bytes
Computer programs and data, such as word processing files, are stored for the long term on magnetic storage devices such as the hard disk. It is only during actual use of a program and work on data files that they are moved to RAM. Both the hard disk and RAM store data in bytes.

1 Program startup The file to be worked on and the program that allows it to be worked on are stored on the hard disk. Copies of both are moved, via circuits in the motherboard and cables, from hard disk storage to RAM.

2 Work in progress Under the user's control, the CPU works through program instructions. It makes changes to the copy of the data held in RAM.

3 End of session The updated data are saved back to the hard disk, and the program that was being used is erased from RAM.

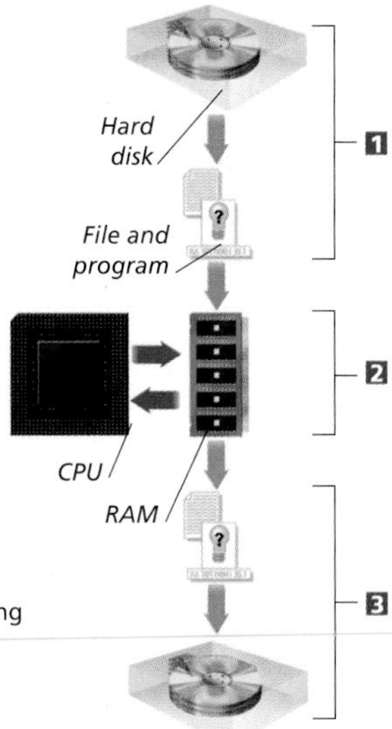

Hard disk
File and program
CPU
RAM
1
2
3

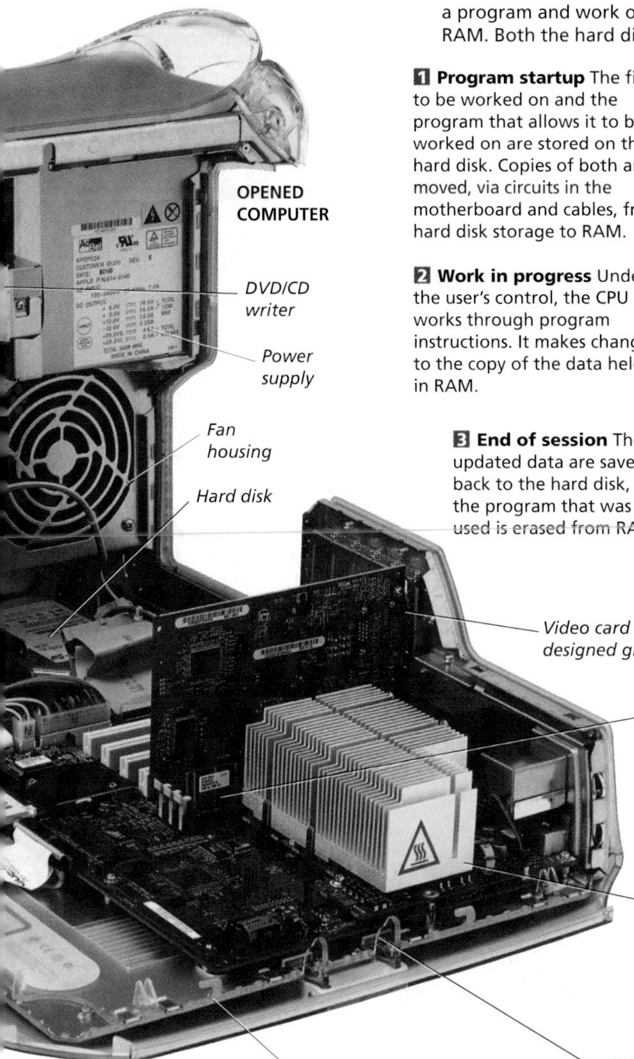

OPENED COMPUTER

DVD/CD writer

Power supply

Fan housing

Hard disk

Video card houses specially designed graphics chips.

RAM *Random-access memory (RAM) is used to store programs that are being run. Information is temporarily stored in RAM as a series of 1's and 0's. When the computer is switched off, any information stored in RAM is lost.*

Heat Sink *Heat is generated by the flow of electricity inside the computer. A heat sink is needed to dissipate the heat. It draws heat away from the components to protect them.*

CPU *The central processing unit carries out program instructions and controls all the information flowing around the computer.*

Motherboard *This large circuit board houses the CPU, RAM, and ROM (read-only memory). ROM is permanent memory that includes startup instructions.*

Build Science Skills L2

Communicating Results Have students research the origins of the various components of the personal computer. Allow time for them to present their findings. Encourage them to include in their presentations some form of visual aid (for example, pictures of the components at various stages of their development, or a time line showing advances). You may want to have two or three students work together to research and create presentations for more complex components, such as the CPU.

Ask, **Was the personal computer invented at one time?** *(No. It was the result of several different inventions being developed independently at about the same time.)* **What feature of the personal computer has contributed to its becoming smaller, more efficient, and easier to use?** *(Although there may be several valid opinions, such as the video monitor, which has made computers more accessible to many nontechnical users, the most important development has been smaller, higher-capacity CPUs.)* **Do new inventions become widely used immediately?** *(Not as a rule. Many of the features of the personal computer, like the mouse, did not become widely used until many years after their invention.)*
Verbal, Portfolio

CONCEPTS in Action

(continued)

Build Science Skills L2

Applying Concepts ACTIVITY

Purpose Students become familiar with the inside parts of a personal computer.

Materials several discarded computers, each having its top removed

Class Time 30 minutes

Procedure Have students separate into groups to observe the inside parts of a computer. They should try to locate the computer parts shown on p. 615 of their textbooks.

Expected Outcome Students will be able to point out the different parts of a computer and gain a better understanding of how the parts work together.
Kinesthetic, Visual, Group

CONCEPTS in Action

Using Computers

Even before there were personal computers, digital computing was put to use in a variety of different ways. Today, computer technology has been miniaturized to create mobile phones, and expanded to allow supercomputers to work at high speed. Virtual reality, a relatively recent development, now allows for realistic simulations in a three-dimensional, computer-generated world.

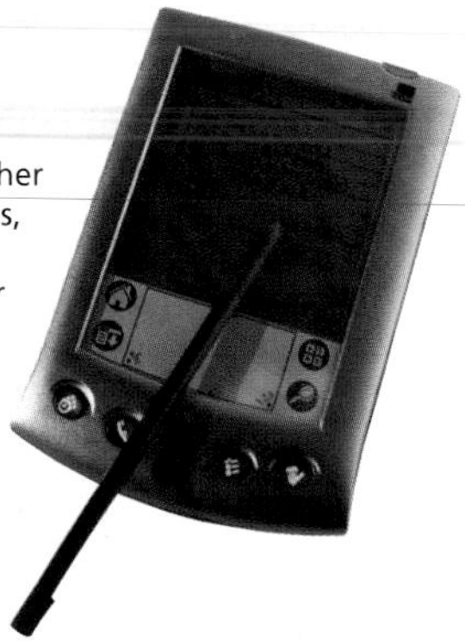

Mini Computers
Mobile phones and other small electronic devices, such as hand-held computers, use smaller and smaller chips to allow for portability and convenience.

Supercomputers
By cooling the components so that they conduct electricity more efficiently, supercomputers are able to process information at a very fast rate. These computers gain speed by multi-tasking, performing several processes at once. The computer shown here is used in the study of particle physics.

3-D image projector
Instruments and controls

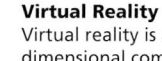

Virtual Reality
Virtual reality is a three-dimensional computer-generated world. Programs such as the NASA flight simulator shown here train students through interactive simulations.

616 Chapter 20

Illuminated markers

Computer Games
In human-movement tracking technology, computers simulate human movement for realistic computer games. As shown here, markers are placed on a person and used to track his movements. A computer analyzes the path shown by each marker. The computer then recreates the paths for the simulated figures in a computer game, as shown above.

Going Further

- Use the library or the Internet to research how making computer circuits smaller allows a computer to operate at a faster speed. Write a paragraph describing one technology that has increased processing speed.
- Take a Discovery Channel Video Field Trip by watching "Current Computers."

Discovery Channel School **Video Field Trip**

Going Further

Student research should indicate that smaller computer circuits increase computer speed by shortening the circuit size, and thus the distance electricity must travel. Smaller circuits also allow for more components to be placed in a CPU. The CPU can perform more tasks at once, so less time is required to carry out a series of operations. Also, smaller components provide more space for components to store data. This allows more information to be processed in a given time, and so shortens the overall processing time of a given task. Students' paragraphs on technologies affecting computer speed may include the means of etching smaller circuits on chips, bus design to provide quicker access between the processor and memory, and faster hard drives for reading input faster.
Verbal

Discovery Channel School

Video Field Trip

Current Computers

After students have viewed the Video Field Trip, ask them the following questions: **Name a device that connects the computer to the outside world in ways that allow information to flow in.** *(Student answers may include keyboard, mouse, modem, high-speed broadband connection, or a connection to a digital camera or scanner.)* **Describe how pressing the key for the letter *p* on the keyboard gets translated into information the computer can use.** *(Pressing the key sends a signal to the BIOS, or basic input/output system, chip. There it is converted into a number in binary notation using an internally stored table, and the binary number is transferred to the central processing unit.)* **Name one device that connects to the computer and allows useful information to flow out from it.** *(Student answers may include computer screen, printer, modem, broadband connection, and a set of speakers.)* **Which part of the computer controls its operation?** *(The central processing unit, or CPU.)*

Section 20.4

1 FOCUS

Objectives

20.4.1 **Explain** how electronics conveys information with analog or digital signals.

20.4.2 **Describe** electronic devices used to control electron flow.

20.4.3 **Illustrate** how semiconductors are used to make three kinds of solid-state components.

20.4.4 **Describe** how solid-state components are used in electronic devices.

Build Vocabulary L2

Concept Map Have students construct a concept map of the vocabulary terms used in this section. Instruct students to write the vocabulary terms in ovals and connect the ovals with lines on which linking words are placed. Students should place the main concept (Electronics) at the top or the center. Moving away from the main concept, the content should become more specific.

Reading Strategy L2

a. Two semiconductors combined so that current moves in one direction but not the other. **b.** Maintains proper voltage level in circuits, controls direction of current **c.** Three semiconductors combined so that current can be switched on or off, or voltage can be amplified. **d.** Amplifies telephone signals **e.** A thin slice of silicon with many tiny solid-state components built up on it **f.** Processes and stores information in computers

2 INSTRUCT

Electronic Signals

Use Community Resources L2

Arrange for your class to visit a local telephone company. Have students observe the type of equipment used to transmit telephone calls to anywhere in the world. Encourage students to ask about the relative importance of analog and digital signals in present telephone communication, and have them explain it in their own words in a brief written report. **Interpersonal, Portfolio**

20.4 Electronic Devices

Reading Focus

Key Concepts

- How do electronic signals convey information?
- How do vacuum tubes control electron flow?
- What are two types of semiconductors?
- How are semiconductors used?
- What are the benefits of using microchips in communication devices?

Vocabulary

- electronics
- electronic signal
- analog signal
- digital signal
- semiconductor
- diode
- transistor
- integrated circuit
- computer

Reading Strategy

Summarizing Copy the table below. As you read, complete the table to summarize what you learn about solid-state components.

Solid-State Component	Description	Uses
Diode	a. ?	b. ?
Transistor	c. ?	d. ?
Integrated circuit	e. ?	f. ?

How do a toaster and a lamp use electric current differently than a computer or a mobile phone? The toaster and lamp are *electrical* devices. They change electrical energy into heat or light. The computer and mobile phone are *electronic* devices, which use electric current to process or send information.

Figure 16 A computer uses electric current to process information. A toaster uses electric current to change electrical energy into thermal energy.

Electronic Signals

The science of using electric current to process or transmit information is **electronics.** The information is carried by an electronic signal. An **electronic signal** is information sent as patterns in the controlled flow of electrons through a circuit.

To understand how this works, think about circuits. If a voltage source is connected to a circuit by a wire, electrons will flow through the wire. Controlling the electron flow—by either altering the voltage or turning the current on and off—produces a coded signal. **Electronics conveys information with electrical patterns called analog and digital signals.**

Section Resources

Print
- ***Reading and Study Workbook With Math Support,*** Section 20.4
- ***Transparencies,*** Section 20.4

Technology
- ***Interactive Textbook,*** Section 20.4
- ***Presentation Pro CD-ROM,*** Section 20.4

Analog Signals An **analog signal** is a smoothly varying signal produced by continuously changing the voltage or current in a circuit. Information is encoded in the strength or frequency of the analog signal. Figure 17A shows one familiar example—a signal used by an AM radio station. The music is encoded as a smoothly changing pattern of the voltage.

Digital Signals A **digital signal** encodes information as a string of 1's and 0's. Figure 17B shows how pulsing a current on and off can produce a digital signal. When the current is off, it represents a "0." When the current is on, it represents a "1." You may be familiar with Morse code, which in a similar way uses two signals. A dot and a dash are all you need to represent the 26 letters of the alphabet and the digits 0 through 9.

Digital signals are more reliable than analog signals. For example, a DVD, or digital video disc, encodes digital signals as a series of pits in the DVD surface. If a pit is damaged, it is often still readable as a 0 or a 1. The quality of video is not affected unless the damage is severe. In comparison, damage to an analog videotape adds noise to the signal.

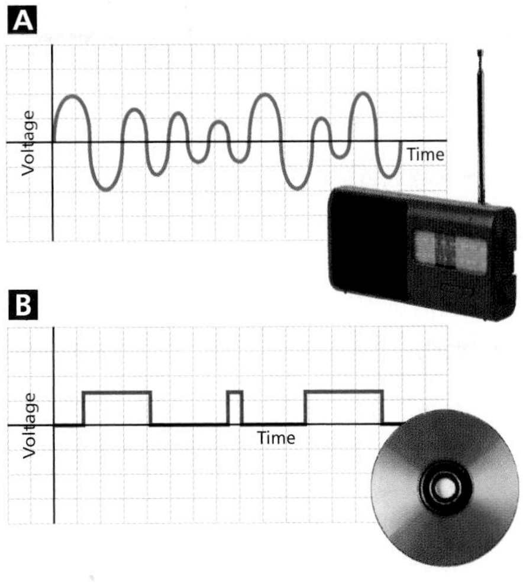

A
Voltage
Time
B
Voltage
Time

Figure 17 Electronic signals convey information by changing voltage or current in a circuit. **A** An analog signal can be produced by smoothly changing voltage. **B** A digital signal can be produced by pulsing a current on and off. **Applying Concepts** ***Could a portable radio, in theory, receive and process a digital signal?***

Vacuum Tubes

To create an electronic signal, you must be able to control the flow of electrons. A vacuum tube was used to control electron flow in early electronic devices. **Vacuum tubes can change alternating current into direct current, increase the strength of a signal, or turn a current on or off.**

One useful type of vacuum tube is a cathode-ray tube (CRT) shown in Figure 18. Many computer monitors and televisions contain CRTs. One side of the CRT has three metal plates that emit electron beams. The electrons are emitted at one end of an airless tube and strike a glass surface on the other end. The glass is coated with phosphors that glow red, green, or blue in response to the electron beams. An electronic signal controls the strength and position of the beams to produce images with the light from the phosphors.

Although vacuum tubes have many useful features, some types burn out frequently and need to be replaced. They are also much too large for use in small electronic devices.

Reading Checkpoint *What is a CRT?*

Figure 18 A cathode-ray tube is used in many computer monitors and television sets.

Use Visuals L1

Figure 17 Emphasize that, because a digital signal requires a computer to encode and decode the signal, its appearance differs greatly from the source signal. Ask, **How can you tell that the signal in Figure 17A is analog?** *(There is a wide and continuous range of voltages in the signal.)* Ask, **How can you tell that the signal in Figure 17B is digital?** *(There are only two values of voltage in the signal, corresponding to a "1" or a "0.")*
Visual

Build Science Skills L2

Comparing and Contrasting Have students list in columns under the headings Analog and Digital the ways in which the two signals contrast. Then, have them write below the table a list of the similarities of the signals. *(Analog changes continuously, has many voltage values, resembles the pattern of the original signal, and is easily distorted. Digital changes abruptly, has only two voltage values, does not resemble the original signal, and is not easily distorted. Both signals accurately reproduce the original signal.)*
Verbal, Logical

Vacuum Tubes

Build Reading Literacy L1

Anticipation Guide Refer to page **388D** in **Chapter 13**, which provides the guidelines for an anticipation guide.

Ask students if they have ever seen an old radio or television set with vacuum tubes. Emphasize that these tubes performed the same functions as modern diodes and transistors, but were larger and less efficient. Ask students to think of problems that might arise from using vacuum tubes. *(Possible answers include heat produced by tubes, tended to burn out easily, required a long time to warm up, and made appliances very large.)*
Verbal, Interpersonal

Customize for Inclusion Students

Learning Disabled
Strengthen students' understanding of electronic components by bringing in samples of the various components for them to examine. Examining a vacuum tube and having the parts explained to them will increase their understanding of these devices. An old transistor that has been opened so that the junction inside is visible can be compared to a vacuum tube. By visually experiencing what these devices look like and how they are put together, students can better understand how they work.

Answer to . . .

Figure 17 *Yes, if it contained the electronics necessary to decode the digital signal.*

Reading Checkpoint *A CRT is a cathode-ray tube, in which electrons emitted at one end strike a glass surface at the other end.*

HOW It Works

Digital Camera

L2

Digital photography was initially developed by NASA to transmit images from spacecraft back to Earth. Early cameras on space vehicles were originally television camera units called vidicons, but in the 1970s, charged-coupled devices (CCDs) were developed. Unlike photographic film or vidicon tubes, CCDs have the advantage of detecting most of the light that falls on them. As the technology improved and became more affordable, the number of photosites on a CCD became larger, and the photosites themselves became smaller. This improved the resolution, or sharpness, of the image. The first digital camera for the general public was marketed in 1994.

Interpreting Diagrams The number of photosites on a CCD controls the image sharpness.
Visual

For Enrichment

L3

Interested students or students familiar with digital camera and image technology can make a presentation showing a digital camera and how its images are electronically stored and manipulated. They can obtain additional information on the Internet and in science and engineering periodicals.
Verbal, Portfolio

HOW It Works

Digital Camera

When light enters an analog camera, it strikes a strip of light-sensitive film behind the lens. In a digital camera, the pattern of light is sensed electronically and turned into digital code.

Interpreting Diagrams ***What controls the sharpness of a digital image?***

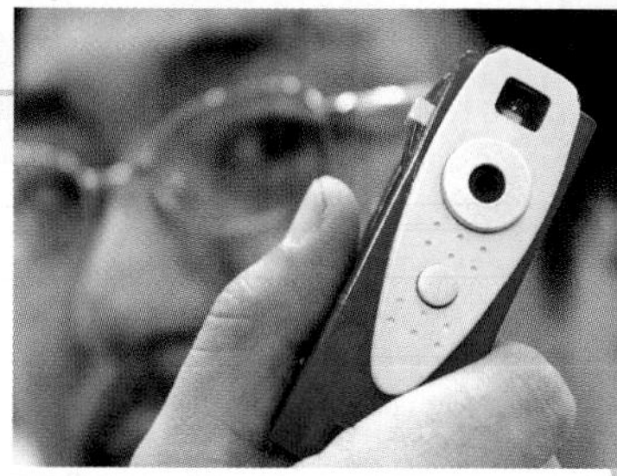

Miniature digital camera
Digital cameras can be much smaller than traditional cameras because high resolution CCDs do not need to use large lenses.

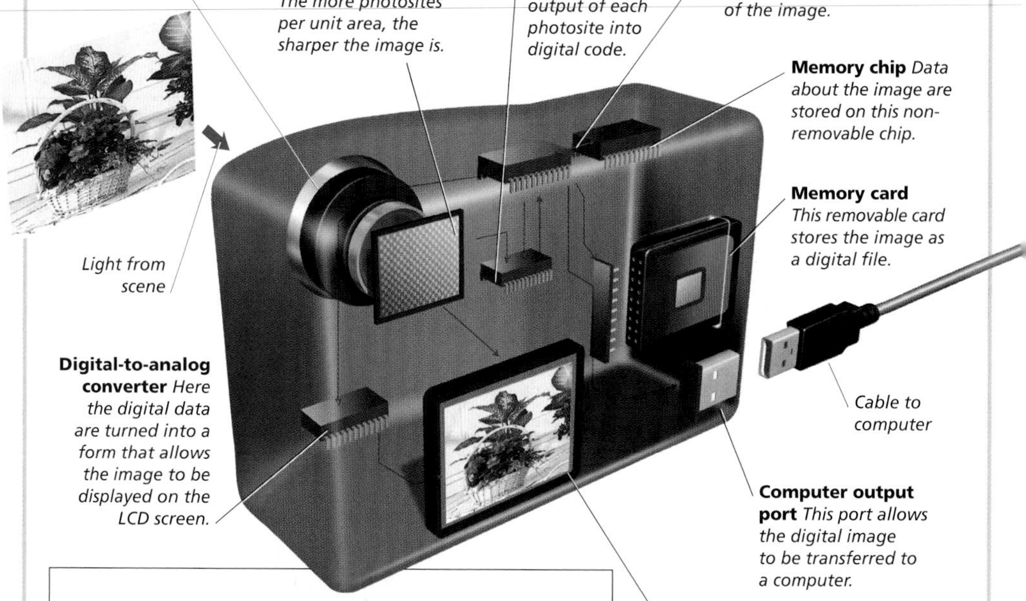
Lens *The lens focuses light from the scene onto the CCD.*
CCD (charged-coupled device) *The CCD has millions of light-sensitive cells, called photosites. The more photosites per unit area, the sharper the image is.*
Analog-to-digital converter *The analog-to-digital converter turns the output of each photosite into digital code.*
Microprocessor *The microprocessor calculates color values for each part of the image.*
Memory chip *Data about the image are stored on this non-removable chip.*
Memory card *This removable card stores the image as a digital file.*
Light from scene
Digital-to-analog converter *Here the digital data are turned into a form that allows the image to be displayed on the LCD screen.*
Cable to computer
Computer output port *This port allows the digital image to be transferred to a computer.*
LCD (liquid crystal display) screen *The LCD screen displays an image of the scene that the camera is aimed at. Images that have been previously saved can also be displayed on the screen.*

How the CCD works
In a CCD, a lens focuses light onto a photosite, which converts the light intensity into an electric current. To create a full color image, the CCD contains a color filter. The filter separates incoming light into one of the three primary colors at each photosite. The microprocessor creates a color image by evaluating the color data for groups of photosites.

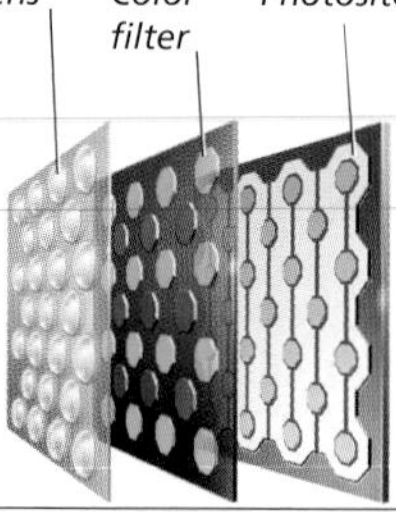
Lens
Color filter
Photosite

Semiconductors

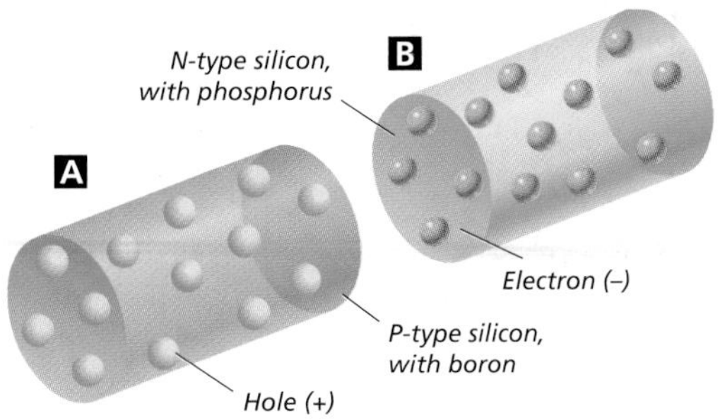

A
B
N-type silicon, with phosphorus
Electron (–)
P-type silicon, with boron
Hole (+)

Figure 19 A semiconductor becomes a good conductor of charge if trace amounts of elements are added to it.

A **semiconductor** is a crystalline solid that conducts current only under certain conditions. Most semiconductors are made with silicon or germanium. In pure form, these elements are poor conductors. But when trace amounts of other elements are added, it becomes possible to control the current inside of the crystals. Figure 19 shows two types of semiconductors. **In n-type semiconductors, the current is a flow of electrons. In p-type semiconductors, it appears as though positive charge flows.**

A p-type semiconductor can be made by adding a trace amount of boron to silicon. In Figure 19A, you can see spaces, called holes, at each boron atom. The holes are positively charged. Figure 19B shows an n-type semiconductor made by adding phosphorus to silicon. Phosphorus atoms provide weakly bound electrons that can flow.

By themselves, n-type and p-type semiconductors cannot do much. But when joined together, electrons in the n-type semiconductor are attracted toward the positively charged holes in the p-type semiconductor. As electrons jump from hole to hole, it looks like a flow of positive charge because the locations of the holes change.

Solid-State Components

Semiconductor devices were first used in the late 1940s. These devices were named solid-state components because they used solids rather than vacuum tubes to control current. **Most modern electronic devices are controlled by solid-state components.** Three of the most useful solid-state components are diodes, transistors, and integrated circuits.

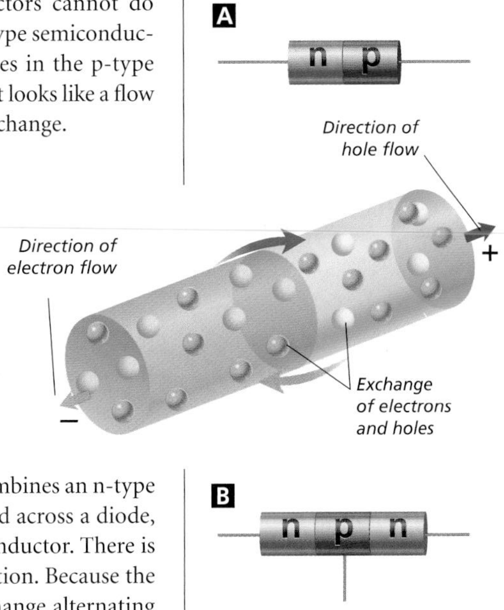

A
n
p
Direction of hole flow
Direction of electron flow
+
–
Exchange of electrons and holes
B
n
p
n

Figure 20 A A diode is two different semiconductors joined in one component. **B** A transistor is three semiconductors with the middle one different from the outer ones. **Applying Concepts** ***In addition to the arrangement of the transistor in B, how else might you arrange the transistor?***

Diodes A **diode** is a solid-state component that combines an n-type and p-type semiconductor. When a voltage is applied across a diode, electrons flow from the n-type to the p-type semiconductor. There is no current if voltage is applied in the opposite direction. Because the current can be in only one direction, a diode can change alternating current to direct current.

Transistors Figure 20B shows a **transistor,** a solid-state component with three layers of semiconductors. A small current flowing through its center layer changes its resistance. A transistor can be used as a switch because the small current can turn another current on or off. It can also be used as an amplifier. A small voltage applied to one side of the transistor produces a large voltage on the other side.

Semiconductors

Teacher Demo

Semiconductors and Current

L2

Purpose Students observe how a semiconductor allows and limits current depending on how a voltage is applied across it.

Materials a light-emitting diode (LED), an ohmmeter, a DC power source, wires, alligator clips

Procedure Attach the terminals of the ohmmeter to the LED and have students note the resistance reading. Reverse the positions of the terminals and show students the new resistance. Repeat the test, attaching the wires to the ends of the LED and the DC power source, so that the LED offers minimum resistance. Slowly increase the voltage until the LED glows. Turn off the power supply, reverse the connections, and increase the voltage slowly to the same level as before. Have students note the LED's appearance.

Expected Outcome When the voltage across the LED is positioned one way, the resistance in the LED is high, with little current. When the voltage is reversed, the resistance is low and the current is larger. **Visual**

Solid-State Components

Address Misconceptions

L2

Students may think that the positive charges in p-type semiconductors are the result of positive charges moving. While this is the effective result, this is not what is literally happening. The only charges that are actually moving are electrons. The term "holes" suggests the absence of something (in this case, negative charges). Have students think of other ways to consider the motion of an object as the opposite motion of what is left behind. For instance, moving checkers across a board is like moving empty spaces in the opposite direction. Electrons, like checkers, can only move into an empty space. **Logical**

Answer to . . .

Figure 20 *Place two p-type semiconductors on either side of an n-type semiconductor*

Facts and Figures

Smaller Components Over the last 40 years, electronic components have become smaller and more efficient, allowing more computing power to be placed in a smaller space. In 1965, the engineer Gordon Moore stated that the number of transistors on an integrated circuit would double about every two years. This observation is called Moore's law. Over the years, the rate of technological development has met or surpassed Moore's prediction. In 1972, the leading processing chip held 2500 transistors. By 1974, the number had increased to 5000. In 2003, the largest chip had 410 million transistors, nearly 10 times the number in 2000. There is considerable question as to how small electronic devices can become. Moore himself said that "No physical quantity can continue to change exponentially forever."

Communications Technology

Integrate Language Arts L2

The development of solid-state technology has introduced many new terms into the world's languages. Some are borrowed from other languages. For instance, the term *cybernetics* refers to the study of communication and control in machines. The term comes from the Greek for the steersman of a boat, that is, the one who navigates or controls. Another term, *robot,* comes from the Czech word meaning "worker." Other terms, like *Internet,* are abbreviations, while some terms are initials (such as WWW or Y2K). Have students research and report on several expressions that have appeared because of developments in communications technology.
Verbal

3 ASSESS

Evaluate Understanding L2

Randomly ask students to list the general properties of one electronic device, either a solid-state or vacuum-tube component. Then, have them give examples of applications for these devices.

Reteach L1

Have students use Figure 20 to explain how semiconductors allow electrons to flow in a preferred direction.

Connecting Concepts

All electronic components have some resistance. Their temperature increases when electrons moving through them collide with the atoms in the component. Thus, electrical energy is converted to thermal energy. Heat sinks withdraw this thermal energy from the circuits in various ways. In each energy conversion, energy is conserved, but its form is different.

Interactive Textbook If your class subscribes to the Interactive Textbook, use it to review key concepts in Section 20.4.

Answer to . . .

Figure 21 *No, the vacuum tubes would be too large.*

Figure 21 A mobile phone uses many solid-state components. **Drawing Conclusions** ***Would it be possible to make a mobile phone using vacuum tubes rather than solid-state components?***

Integrated Circuits An **integrated circuit** is a thin slice of silicon that contains many solid-state components. The components are carefully built layer by layer on the silicon base. Integrated circuits are sometimes called chips or microchips. They perform as well as a network of vacuum tubes, but they need only a tiny fraction of the space. Mobile phones, pagers, and computers all use microchips.

Electronic devices today are so small because hundreds of millions of components fit on a microchip smaller than your fingertip. Integrated circuits are also blindingly fast compared to vacuum tubes. One reason is that current does not have to travel far to get from point to point in the circuit. So it shouldn't be surprising that as technology improves, and chips get smaller, the chips operate at higher speeds.

Communications Technology

A **computer** is a programmable device that can store and process information. Today you find microchips in all sorts of devices that you wouldn't call computers. **Communication devices use microchips to make them more portable, reliable, and affordable.**

Figure 21 shows the inside a mobile phone, which contains many solid-state components. Transistors amplify the phone's incoming signal. Electronic devices called capacitors store electric charge. They allow a mobile phone to store data such as phone numbers, even if the battery is removed for a short time. Diodes maintain proper voltage levels in the circuits. Without solid-state components, none of this would be possible.

Section 20.4 Assessment

Reviewing Concepts

1. How are electronic devices used to process information?
2. Describe how electron flow is controlled in vacuum tubes.
3. What are two types of semiconductors?
4. How are solid-state components used?
5. How are microchips beneficial for communication devices?

Critical Thinking

6. **Comparing and Contrasting** How are solid-state components like vacuum tubes? How are they different?
7. **Applying Concepts** Explain how a diode can be used to change alternating current into direct current.
8. **Using Analogies** Explain how a diode is like a one-way street.

Connecting Concepts

Conservation of Energy Review Section 15.2. How is energy conserved when a heat sink is used to protect electronic components in a computer?

Section 20.4 Assessment

1. Electronic devices process information by using electric current to form patterns called analog and digital signals.
2. Vacuum tubes can control electron flow by changing alternating current into direct current or by turning a current on or off.
3. N-type and p-type
4. Solid-state components are used to control modern electronic devices.
5. Microchips make communications devices more portable, reliable, and affordable.
6. Both control electron flow in electronic devices. Both can convert alternating current to direct current, or amplify a signal. Solid-state components use semiconducting materials to achieve these results instead of the hot wires and charged plates in vacuums.
7. When alternating current enters a diode, only current moving in one direction can pass through. Current moving in the reverse direction is blocked.
8. Charges can only move in one direction through the diode, just as an automobile can only go in one direction on a one-way street.

Forensics Lab

Evaluating Electrical Safety

Electrical appliances must be safely insulated to protect users from injury. In this lab, you will play the role of a safety engineer determining whether an electric power supply is safely insulated.

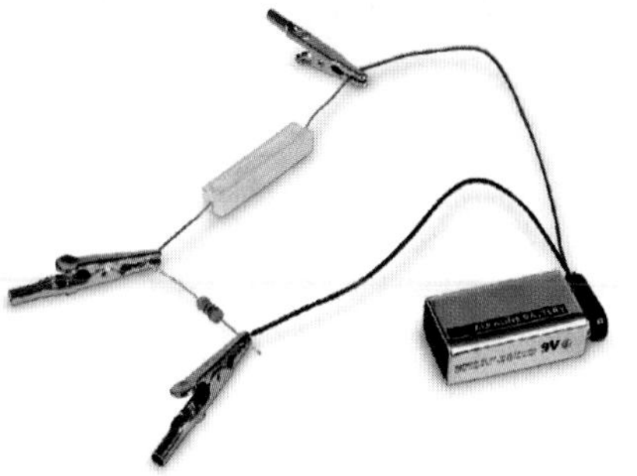

Problem How much resistance is needed in series with a known resistance to reduce the voltage by 99 percent?

Materials

- 9-volt battery
- battery clip
- multimeter
- 3 alligator clips
- 4 resistors: 1-ohm, 10-ohm, 100-ohm, 1000-ohm

For the probeware version of this lab, see Probeware Lab Manual, Lab 8.

Skills Calculating, Using Tables

Procedure

1. On a separate sheet of paper, make a copy of the data table shown below.

Data Table

Resistance (ohms)		Voltage difference (volts)	
Current-Carrying	Insulating	Current-Carrying	Insulating
1	1000		
1	100		
10	1000		
10	100		

2. Attach the battery clip to the battery. **CAUTION** *The circuit may become hot.*
3. Use an alligator clip to attach one wire of the 1-ohm resistor to one of the battery clip's wires as shown.
4. Clip one wire of the 1000-ohm resistor to the free end of the 1-ohm resistor. Clip the other wire of the 1000-ohm resistor to the free wire of the battery clip.
5. The 1-ohm resistor represents the current-carrying part of the appliance. The 1000-ohm resistor represents the insulation for the current-carrying part. Place one of the multimeter's electrodes on each wire of the 1-ohm resistor. Record the voltage difference.
6. Place the multimeter's electrodes on the wires of the 1000-ohm resistor. Record the voltage difference.
7. To model a reduction in the resistance of the insulation, repeat Steps 5 and 6, replacing the 1000-ohm resistor with a 100-ohm resistor. Disconnect the resistors from the battery clip.
8. **Predicting** Record your prediction of how increasing the resistance of the current-carrying part of the appliance will affect the voltage difference across the insulating part.
9. To test your prediction, repeat Steps 3 through 7, using a 10-ohm resistor to represent the current-carrying part of the appliance.

Analyze and Conclude

1. **Calculating** When the resistance of the current-carrying part was 1 ohm and the resistance of the insulating part was 100 ohms, what was the ratio of the voltage differences across the current-carrying part and the insulating part?
2. **Drawing Conclusions** In the circuit you built, what is the voltage difference across each resistor proportional to?
3. **Applying Concepts** You know the resistance of the current-carrying part of an appliance. What should the resistance of the insulation be to reduce the voltage by 99 percent?

Sample Data Table

Resistance (ohms)		Voltage difference (volts)	
Current-Carrying	Insulating	Current-Carrying	Insulating
1	1000	< 0.01	8.6
1	100	0.09	8.5
10	1000	0.09	8.5
10	100	0.9	7.7 >

Forensics Lab

Evaluating Electrical Safety

L2

Objective
After completing this lab, students will be able to
- determine the voltage differences across resistances in series.

Skills Focus **Measuring, Calculating, Using Data Tables**

Prep Time 20 minutes

Advance Preparation Strip 1–2 cm of insulation from the ends of the wires attached to the battery clips. Label the resistors with their resistances. Each resistor has four colored bands at one end. From the end of the resistor inward, the first three bands for the resistors used in this lab are: 1 ohm brown, black, gold; 10 ohms brown, black, black; 100 ohms brown, black, brown; 1000 ohms brown, black, red. The fourth band indicates the accuracy of the labeled resistance.

Class Time 45 minutes

Safety Caution students to be careful with the sharp tips of the wires when assembling the circuit. Also caution them about handling the circuits when they are carrying current because the circuit parts may become hot.

Teaching Tips
- You may need to show students how to use the multimeters.

Expected Outcome The voltage difference across each resistor in the circuit is proportional to its resistance. The total voltage difference across both resistors is equal to the voltage of the battery, which may decline after the battery has been used for a while.

Analyze and Conclude
1. The ratio of the voltage differences was 0.01 (1/100).
2. The voltage difference across each resistor was proportional to its resistance.
3. The resistance of the insulation should be about 100 times the resistance of the current-carrying part.

Logical, Group

Probeware Lab Manual
Versions of this lab for use with probeware available from Pasco Scientific, Texas Instruments, and Vernier are in the Probeware Manual.

Study Guide

Study Tip

Switch Subjects and Take Breaks
When you feel yourself losing focus, switch the type of task you are working on, the subject you are studying, or the environment that you are in. Tell students to organize all of the subjects that they need to study in a night into manageable blocks, based on a single portion of a chapter section. When they have finished one block, suggest that they switch to another block in another part of the subject they are studying, or even another subject altogether. Suggest they take five minute breaks every 30 to 40 minutes to refresh themselves. Taking a 20 minute walk also helps to renew energy and enthusiasm.

Thinking Visually

a. Current
b. Potential difference, or voltage
c. Alternating current

Assessment

Interactive Textbook If your class subscribes to the Interactive Textbook, your students can go online to access an interactive version of the Student Edition and a self-test.

Reviewing Content

1. c	**2.** d	**3.** c
4. d	**5.** c	**6.** d
7. d	**8.** c	**9.** a
10. a		

Understanding Concepts

11. The electric force becomes one-fourth as large.
12. The electric field direction depends on whether a positive or negative charge produces the field.
13. If the uncharged object is a conductor, the charged object can attract opposite charges in the uncharged object, causing these charges to move closer to the charged object. The charged object can also transfer charges to the conductor through friction or by contact, and then the charges will move to redistribute charge evenly throughout the conductor.

CHAPTER 20

Study Guide

20.1 Electric Charge and Static Electricity

Key Concepts

- An excess or shortage of electrons produces a net electric charge.
- Like charges repel and opposite charges attract.
- Electric field strength depends on the net charge and distance from the charge.
- Charge can be transferred by friction, by contact, and by induction.
- Static discharge occurs when electric charge is transferred suddenly.

Vocabulary

electric charge, *p. 600;* electric force, *p. 601;* electric field, *p. 602;* static electricity, *p. 602;* law of conservation of charge, *p. 602;* induction, *p. 603*

20.2 Electric Current and Ohm's Law

Key Concepts

- The two types of current are direct current and alternating current.
- Metals such as copper and silver are good conductors. Wood, plastic, rubber, and air are good insulators.
- A material's thickness, length, and temperature affect its resistance.
- In order for charge to flow in a conducting wire, the wire must be connected in a complete loop that includes a source of electrical energy.
- Increasing the voltage increases the current. Keeping the same voltage and increasing the resistance decreases the current.

Vocabulary

electric current, *p. 604;* direct current, *p. 604;* alternating current, *p. 604;* electrical conductor, *p. 605;* electrical insulator, *p. 605;* resistance, *p. 605;* superconductor, *p. 605;* potential difference, *p. 606;* voltage, *p. 606;* battery, *p. 606;* Ohm's law, *p. 607*

20.3 Electric Circuits

Key Concepts

- An electric circuit has a source of electrical energy and devices run by electrical energy.
- If one element stops functioning in a series circuit, none of the elements can operate, but in a parallel circuit, the rest of the elements still can operate.
- Electric power is voltage multiplied by current. Electrical energy is power multiplied by time.
- A variety of devices make electrical energy safe.

Vocabulary

electric circuit, *p. 609;* series circuit, *p. 610;* parallel circuit, *p. 610;* electric power, *p. 611;* fuse, *p. 612;* circuit breaker, *p. 612;* grounding, *p. 613*

20.4 Electronic Devices

Key Concepts

- Electronics convey information with electrical patterns called analog and digital signals.
- Vacuum tubes and solid-state components are two kinds of devices that can control electron flow.
- Solid-state components use semiconductors.

Vocabulary

electronics, *p. 618;* electronic signal, *p. 618;* analog signal, *p. 619;* digital signal, *p. 619;* semiconductor, *p. 621;* diode, *p. 621;* transistor, *p. 621;* integrated circuit, *p. 622;* computer, *p. 622*

Thinking Visually

Web Diagram Copy the web diagram below and use information from the chapter to complete it.

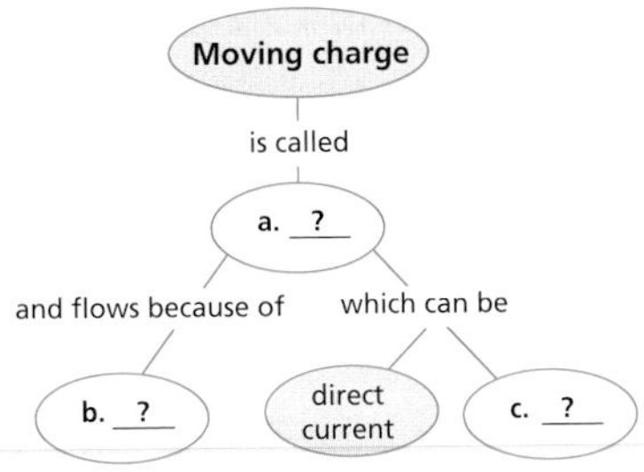
Moving charge
is called
a. ?
and flows because of
which can be
b. ?
direct current
c. ?

624 Chapter 20

Chapter Resources

Print
- ***Chapter and Unit Tests,*** Chapter 20 Test A and Test B
- ***Test Prep Resources,*** Chapter 20

Technology
- ***Computer Test Bank,*** Chapter Test 20
- ***Interactive Textbook,*** Chapter 20
- ***Go Online,*** PHSchool.com, Chapter 20

CHAPTER 20

Assessment

Interactive textbook with assessment at PHSchool.com

Reviewing Content

Choose the letter that best answers the question or completes the statement.

1. A material has a net electric charge because it
   a. discharges.
   b. has an alternating current.
   c. has an excess or shortage of electrons.
   d. has a direct current.
2. Static electricity is the study of
   a. buildup of charge.
   b. electric discharges.
   c. electric fields.
   d. all of the above.
3. A strong electric field is
   a. directed toward a charge.
   b. directed away from a charge.
   c. caused by a large quantity of charge.
   d. caused by a small quantity of charge.
4. What is a material called that easily carries a current?
   a. insulator b. semiconductor
   c. electric potential d. conductor
5. A superconducting material
   a. requires very high current.
   b. has no resistance at room temperature.
   c. has no resistance at low temperatures.
   d. has high resistance at low temperatures.
6. What does Ohm's law state?
   a. Current equals voltage times resistance.
   b. Voltage equals resistance divided by current.
   c. Voltage equals current divided by resistance.
   d. Voltage equals current times resistance.
7. Which melts to protect a circuit?
   a. three-prong plug
   b. wiring
   c. diode
   d. fuse
8. What does " I " represent in the equation $P = I \times V$?
   a. voltage b. resistance
   c. current d. kilowatts
9. The output of a diode can be
   a. direct current. b. a superconductor.
   c. resistance. d. alternating current.
10. Three layers of semiconductor material can form
    a. a transistor only.
    b. a diode only.
    c. either a transistor or a diode.
    d. neither a transistor nor a diode.

Understanding Concepts

11. How does the electric force between two charged objects change if you double the distance between the objects?
12. What determines the direction of the electric field near a charge?
13. How can a charged object cause charges to move within an uncharged object?
14. If the current in a circuit is clockwise, what is the direction of electron flow?
15. Explain why a wire becomes warmer when charges flow through it.
16. Does voltage flow in a circuit? Explain.

Use the following diagram to answer Questions 17 and 18. The three bulbs are identical.

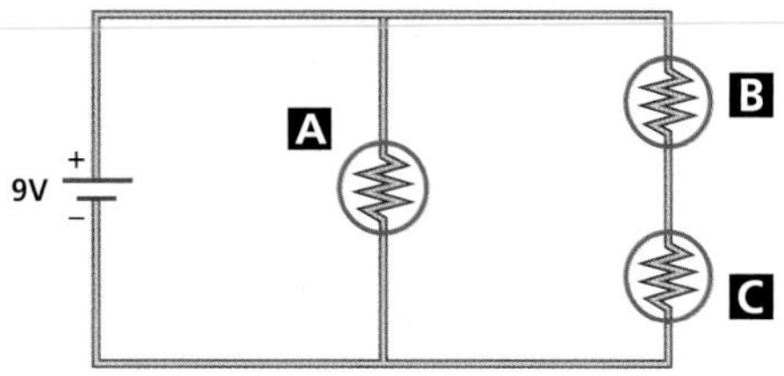

9V
+
−
A
B
C

17. Does the same current pass through each bulb? Explain why or why not.
18. What happens to the other bulbs if bulb A burns out? If bulb B burns out?
19. A battery and a light bulb are connected in a simple circuit. What is the source of electrons that flow through the wire?
20. Explain why a light bulb does not change its brightness when another bulb is added in parallel.
21. What are digital and analog signals?

Assessment (continued)

14. Counterclockwise
15. Because of the wire's resistance, some electrical energy is transformed into thermal energy.
16. No. Voltage is applied across a circuit. Only the current is a flow (of charge).
17. No. Together bulbs B and C have twice the resistance that bulb A does, so the current is half as much in bulb B and bulb C as it is in bulb A.
18. If bulb A burns out, bulb B and bulb C stay lit; if bulb B burns out, bulb A stays lit but bulb C doesn't.
19. The electrons come mostly from the atoms in the wire.
20. The current to each bulb is independent of current through other paths in a parallel circuit, so brightness doesn't change when a bulb is added.
21. Digital and analog signals are electronic signals. A digital signal is based on the high and low voltage pattern in a circuit. An analog signal depends only on the varying level of the signal.

Homework Guide

Section	Questions
20.1	1–3, 11–13, 22, 31, 35
20.2	4–6, 14–16, 23, 27–28, 32–33
20.3	7–8, 17–20, 24–25, 29–30, 34
20.4	9–10, 21, 26

Critical Thinking

22. Each hair receives the same type of charge as that on the sphere, so they repel each other.
23. Current will only pass between oppositely charged terminals. The negative terminal is a source of electrons, and the positive terminal accepts electrons.
24. The person has probably overloaded the circuit. He or she should unplug one or two appliances on the circuit and then reset the circuit breaker.
25. Voltage is the same for both settings, but the high-heat setting uses more power. According to $P = IV$, the current must be greater for the high-heat setting. By Ohm's law, then, the resistance for the high-heat setting must be lower.
26. Both n-type and p-type semiconductors are crystalline materials that conduct current only under certain conditions. They differ in that electrons flow in n-type semiconductors, whereas positively charged "holes" flow in p-type semiconductors.

Math Skills

27. On a wet day: $V = I \times R$; $I = V/R =$ (9 V)/(1000 ohms) = 0.009 A
On a dry day: $I = V/R =$ (9 V)/(100,000 ohms) = 0.00009 A
28. The voltage of the battery equals the sum of the potential differences across the bulbs. Each bulb has the same resistance, so the voltage drop across each is the same. Therefore, $V_{bulb} = V_{battery}/6$ = (9.0 V)/6 = 1.5 V
29. $P = V \times I$; $I = P/V =$ (105 W)/(120 V) = 0.88 A
30. $P = V \times I$; $I = P/V =$ (9300 W)/(240 V) = 39 A
$V = I \times R$; $R = V/I$ = (240 V)/(39 A) = 6.2 ohms

CHAPTER 20

Assessment *(continued)*

Critical Thinking

22. **Applying Concepts** In a science museum demonstration, a person on an insulated stand touches a metal sphere. The sphere has a large charge. Explain why the person's hair stands on end.

23. **Applying Concepts** Explain why a battery is always connected so that one wire goes to the battery's positive terminal and one to the negative terminal.

24. **Relating Cause and Effect** A person plugs a fan into a wall socket and turns it on. Suddenly, the lights go out in several rooms of the house. Explain what has probably happened and what can be done to fix it.

25. **Applying Concepts** Explain why a hair dryer has a high-heat setting with a lower resistance than the low-heat setting. (*Hint:* Use the equation $P = IV$.)

26. **Comparing and Contrasting** How are n-type semiconductors and p-type semiconductors alike. How are they different?

Math Skills

27. **Calculating** On a wet day, your skin's resistance may be as low as 1000 ohms. On a dry day, it may be as high as 100,000 ohms. How much current moves through your fingers if you touch the terminals of a 9-volt battery on a wet day? On a dry day?

28. **Calculating** Six light bulbs are connected in series with a 9.0-volt battery. What is the voltage across each bulb?

29. **Calculating** A freezer has a power rating of 105 watts. How much current does it use if it is plugged into a 120-volt line?

30. **Calculating** The power rating on an electric oven is 9300 watts. If the oven is plugged into a 240-volt line, how much current does it use? What is the resistance of the oven?

Concepts in Action

31. **Relating Cause and Effect** You turn a television on and notice a faint crackling sound. If you touch the screen, you get a small shock. What is the source of this electric charge?

32. **Inferring** Plugs used for connecting an electrical appliance such as a toaster to a wall socket have two prongs. Explain why plugs have two prongs instead of one prong.

33. **Inferring** The photograph below shows ceramic insulators holding the power lines at each pole. What is the purpose of the insulators?

34. **Making Judgments** Explain why you think builders should or should not be required to install GFCI (ground-fault circuit interrupter) outlets in all new homes.

35. **Writing in Science** Write a paragraph explaining in detail why you could be struck by lightning if you stand outside during a thunderstorm. Include a sketch that illustrates the ideas in your paragraph.

Performance-Based Assessment

Designing an Experiment Design and conduct an experiment that uses a light-emitting diode in a simple circuit to demonstrate that current flows only one way through a diode. Before beginning, research the properties and limitations of your diode .

Go Online
PHSchool.com
For: Self-grading assessment
Visit: PHschool.com
Web Code: cca-2200

Concepts in Action

31. Electrons build up a static charge on the screen of the CRT.
32. You need a complete circuit. Current moves into the smaller prong of a plug and back through the larger prong. If there is only one prong, the circuit is not complete.
33. The insulators prevent current in the power lines from traveling down the poles to the ground.
34. Students in favor of GFCIs may stress the need for safety. Those opposed may discuss the costs involved.
35. Students should discuss charge buildup on both the person and in the clouds. They should also mention discharge and the attraction between opposite charges.

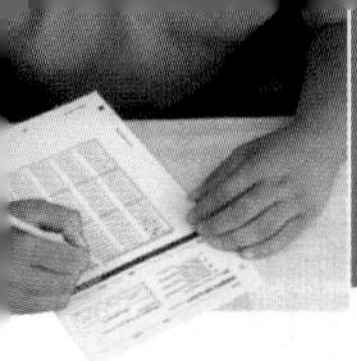

Standardized Test Prep

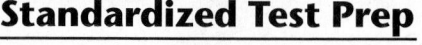

Test-Taking Tip

When a question refers to a diagram, start by scanning the whole diagram. See if you can remember what each symbol means.

In a circuit diagram, determine if the circuit is series or parallel. Check to make sure that each part of the circuit is complete. In the question below, a wire goes to device #2, but no wire leaves it, so no current enters the device.

The direction of current is from the positive terminal to the negative terminal of the voltage source. Note that the direction of current is opposite the direction of electron flow. In the circuit below, current is in a clockwise direction.

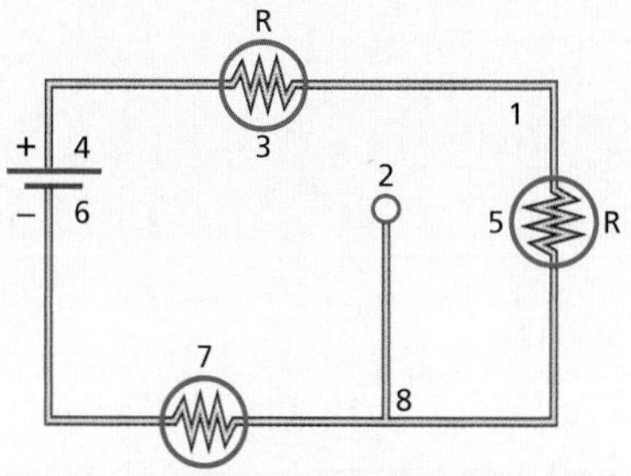

R
1
+
4
3
2
–
6
5
R
7
8

In what order does current flow in the circuit above?

(A) 5 – 6 – 7 – 1 – 5 – 3 – 4
(B) 6 – 7 – 8 – 2 – 5 – 1 – 3 – 4
(C) 4 – 3 – 5 – 7 – 6
(D) 3 – 2 – 5 – 6 – 4 – 7
(E) 4 – 3 – 1 – 5 – 8 – 7 – 6

(Answer: E)

1. In the diagram above, the battery is replaced by an AC voltage source. Which of the following is now true?
(A) The current enters and leaves device #2.
(B) The current is always clockwise.
(C) There is not net movement of charge in the circuit.
(D) The current is always counterclockwise.
(E) There is no current in the circuit.

2. If you rub a neutral glass rod with silk, the silk acquires a negative charge. If you rub a neutral glass rod with a rubber rod, the rubber acquires a negative charge. If you rub a neutral rubber rod with silk, the rubber rod acquires a negative charge. Which of the three materials has the strongest attraction for electrons?
(A) glass
(B) silk
(C) rubber
(D) not enough data to answer
(E) none, because they have equal attractions for electrons

3. A 1.5-m wire carries a 5.0-A current when a potential difference of 3.7 V is applied. What is the resistance of the wire?
(A) 0.49 ohms
(B) 0.74 ohms
(C) 1.1 ohms
(D) 1.4 ohms
(E) 2.0 ohms

4. A space heater is connected to a standard 120-V line. If the resistance of the operating heater is 15 ohms, what power does the heater use? (*Hint*: First calculate the current.)
(A) 8.0 W
(B) 64 W
(C) 960 W
(D) 1800 W
(E) 220 kW

5. A 1700-W machine operates at 120 V. What is the resistance in the machine?
(A) 7.1 x 10^{22} ohms
(B) 1.2 x 10^{21} ohms
(C) 1.4 ohms
(D) 8.5 ohms
(E) 14 ohms

6. A lamp with three 40-W bulbs connected in parallel is plugged into a 120-V outlet. What is the current in the lamp?
(A) 1 A
(B) 3 A
(C) 9 A
(D) 40 A
(E) 120 A

Standardized Test Prep

1. C **2.** C **3.** B
4. C **5.** D **6.** A

Performance-Based Assessment

The experiment designs should show that reversing the current through a diode prevents the diode from lighting. The voltage and current limits for an LED should be noted.

Go Online
PHSchool.com

Your students can independently test their knowledge of the chapter and print out their test results for your files.

CHAPTER 21

Planning Guide

Use these planning tools
Easy Planner
Teacher Express

SECTION OBJECTIVES	STANDARDS NATIONAL (See p. T18.)	STANDARDS STATE	ACTIVITIES and LABS
21.1 Magnets and Magnetic Fields, pp. 630–633 1 block or 2 periods **21.1.1** **Describe** the effects of magnetic forces and magnetic fields and **explain** how magnetic poles determine the direction of magnetic force. **21.1.2** **Interpret diagrams** of magnetic field lines around one or more bar magnets. **21.1.3** **Describe** Earth's magnetic field and its effect on compasses. **21.1.4** **Explain** the behavior of ferromagnetic materials in terms of magnetic domains.	A-1, A-2, B-1, B-4		**SE** Inquiry Activity: How Do Magnets Interact With One Another? p. 629 **L2** **SE** Quick Lab: Observing Magnetic Field Lines, p. 632 **L2** **TE** Build Science Skills: Inferring, p. 631 **L2** **LM** Investigation 21B: Investigating a Compass **L1**
21.2 Electromagnetism, pp. 635–639 1 block or 2 periods **21.2.1** **Describe** how a moving electric charge creates a magnetic field and **determine** the direction of the magnetic field based on the type of charge and the direction of its motion. **21.2.2** **Relate** the force a magnetic field exerts on a moving electric charge to the type of charge and the direction of its motion. **21.2.3** **Explain** how solenoids and electromagnets are constructed and **describe** factors that affect the field strength of both. **21.2.4** **Describe** how electromagnetic devices use the interaction between electric currents and magnetic fields.	A-1, A-2, B-4, B-6, E-2, F-1, G-1, G-2, G-3		**SE** Quick Lab: Making an Electromagnet, p. 637 **L2** **TE** Teacher Demo: Magnetic Field from Electric Current, p. 636 **L2** **TE** Teacher Demo: Electromagnetic Force, p. 638 **L2**
21.3 Electrical Energy Generation and Transmission, pp. 642–647 1 block or 2 periods **21.3.1** **Describe** how electric current is generated by electromagnetic induction. **21.3.2** **Compare** AC and DC generators and **explain** how they work. **21.3.3** **Analyze** factors that determine the output voltage and current produced by a transformer. **21.3.4** **Summarize** how electrical energy is produced, transmitted, and converted for use in the home.	A-1, A-2, B-4, E-1, F-1, F-3, G-1, G-2, G-3		**SE** Application Lab: Investigating an Electric Generator, pp. 648–649 **L2** **TE** Teacher Demo: Generating Alternating Current, p. 643 **L2** **LM** Investigation 21A: Modeling a Computer **L2**

Ability Levels	
L1	For students who need additional help
L2	For all students
L3	For students who need to be challenged

Components

SE	Student Edition	RSW	Reading & Study Workbook	CUT	Chapter & Unit Tests	T	Transparencies
TE	Teacher's Edition	MSPS	Math Skills & Problem Solving Workbook	CTB	Computer Test Bank	iT	Interactive Textbook
LM	Laboratory Manual			TP	Test Prep Resources	P	Presentation Pro CD-ROM
PLM	Probeware Lab Manual			DC	Discovery Channel Videotapes & DVDs	GO	Internet Resources

RESOURCES PRINT and TECHNOLOGY		SECTION ASSESSMENT
RSW Section 21.1	L1	**SE** Section 21.1 Assessment, p. 633
T Chapter 21 Pretest	L2	**iT** Section 21.1
Section 21.1	L2	
P Chapter 21 Pretest	L2	
Section 21.1	L2	
RSW Section 21.2	L1	**SE** Section 21.2 Assessment, p. 639
DC Magnetic Viewpoints	L2	**iT** Section 21.2
T Section 21.2	L2	
P Section 21.2	L2	
SciLinks **GO** Electromagnets	L2	
PLM Lab 9: Investigating an Electric Generator	L2	**SE** Section 21.3 Assessment, p. 647
RSW Section 21.3	L1	**iT** Section 21.3
RSW Math Skill	L2	
T Section 21.3	L2	
P Section 21.3	L2	
SciLinks **GO** Transformers	L2	
PHSchool.com Data sharing	L2	

Go Online

Go online for these Internet resources.

PHSchool.com
Web Code: ccd-2210
Web Code: cca-2210

NSTA SciLinks
Web Code: ccn-2212
Web Code: ccn-2213

Materials for Activities and Labs

Quantities for each group

STUDENT EDITION

Inquiry Activity, p. 629
2 bar magnets

Quick Lab, p. 632
small container of iron filings, 2 bar magnets, paper, 2 textbooks, masking tape

Quick Lab, p. 637
iron nail, 20 small metal paper clips, 20-cm length and 1-m length of insulated wire with stripped ends, 6-volt battery, switch

Application Lab, pp. 648–649
cardboard tube, 5-m length of insulated wire, metric ruler, multimeter, bar magnet, graph paper

TEACHER'S EDITION

Build Science Skills, p. 631
2 bar magnets, a small magnetic compass

Teacher Demo, p. 636
insulated wire, cardboard (10 cm × 10 cm), a burner tripod, a variable DC power supply, 4–6 compasses

Teacher Demo, p. 638
insulated wire, a large horseshoe magnet, a variable DC power supply, 2 ring stands with clamps

Build Science Skills, p. 640
a short pencil (about 5 cm long), a cardboard disk (7 cm wide), a steel thumbtack, a bar magnet, paper

Teacher Demo, p. 643
a hand-operated generator, a galvanometer, insulated wire (2 strands)

Chapter Assessment

CHAPTER ASSESSMENT

SE Chapter Assessment, pp. 651–652
CUT Chapter 21 Test A, B
CTB Chapter 21
iT Chapter 21
PHSchool.com GO
Web Code: cca-2210

STANDARDIZED TEST PREP

SE Chapter 21, p. 653
TP Diagnose and Prescribe

Interactive Textbook

Interactive Textbook with assessment at PHSchool.com

CHAPTER 21

Before you teach

From the Author

Sophia Yancopoulos
Manhattan College

Big Ideas

Like electric fields, magnetic fields are everywhere. Earth has a magnetic field that can be sensed by some migrating birds and fish, bees, and some butterflies. Even humans have vestigial amounts of magnetic material in their noses, which is thought to contribute to a sense of direction. Remind students that electricity and magnetism are different aspects of a single force called electromagnetism.

Forces and Motion Magnetism, like electricity (but unlike gravity), can be either an attractive or repulsive force. A magnet has two poles, labeled north and south. Like poles repel and unlike poles attract, even without touching. This action at a distance is nonintuitive. Once a magnet has been defined by its behavior, however, some surprisingly logical deductions follow. William Gilbert, the seventeenth-century English physician who first recorded and named magnetic polar behavior, did not set out to prove that Earth is a magnet. It was simply the only logical explanation for Earth's behavior. Scattering iron filings around a magnet reveals the magnetic field lines. It is these lines that suggested to English physicist Michael Faraday the concept of the magnetic field. Because it is so easily visualized, the concept of a magnetic field seems deceptively simple. It is in fact extremely subtle. It is important for students to understand that a magnetic field is not a region but a measurement of direction and strength *within* a region.

Matter and Energy Magnetism is caused by moving charged particles. To understand magnetism inside a substance, look at the motion of the electrons inside its atoms. Single electrons act like tiny magnets. Most electrons cancel each other's magnetic effect, but in a ferromagnetic material the fields combine to give the atoms a net magnetic field, and the cluster of atoms behaving like a tiny magnet is called a magnetic domain.

Physics Refresher

Magnetic Materials 21.1

In many substances, the magnetic fields produced by the various electron motions cancel each other out, and the atoms have a net magnetic dipole moment of zero. However, these substances will become strongly magnetic while in an external magnetic field. Such substances are called *paramagnetic.* Substances where the induced atomic magnetic fields align so as to oppose an applied magnetic field are called *diamagnetic.*

In certain substances, such as iron, nickel, and cobalt, the magnetic fields of the atoms align in an externally applied magnetic field and remain aligned after the field is removed. Such substances are called *ferromagnetic.*

Address Misconceptions

Students may visualize electrons as spinning particles. The electron property known as "spin" doesn't refer to a spinning motion. It's a model used to help explain the characteristics of electron behavior. For a strategy to overcome this misconception, see **Address Misconceptions** on **page 633.**

Electromagnetism 21.2

Magnetic fields are produced whenever an electric charge is in motion. Magnetic field lines always form closed loops, never cross each other, and by convention are directed from the "north" magnetic pole to the "south" magnetic pole. The closer the lines are together, the greater the magnetic field strength.

For a current in a wire, the magnetic field strength (B) decreases with radial distance (r) from the wire and increases with current (I).

$$B \propto \frac{I}{r}$$

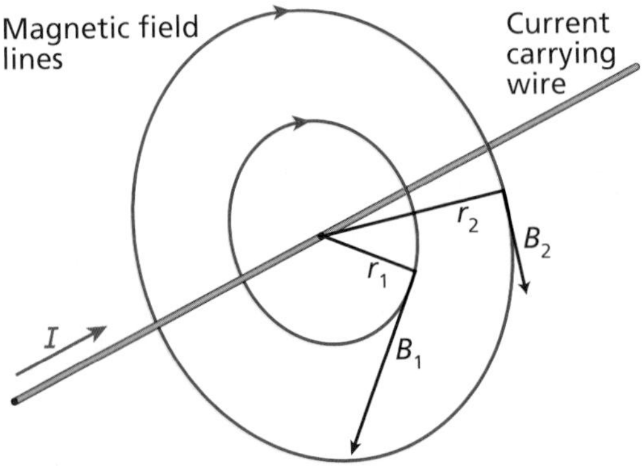
Magnetic field lines
Current carrying wire
I
r1
r2
B1
B2

Go Online PD LINKS NSTA

For: Teaching methods for magnetism
Visit: www.SciLinks.org/PDLinks
Web Code: ccn-2199

An applied magnetic field interacts with the magnetic field produced by a moving charge or current. The result of this interaction is a force that is exerted on the charge or current. This force is largest when the direction of the charge motion or current is perpendicular to the magnetic field ($\theta = 90°$), and is zero when the two are parallel ($\theta = 0°$). The equation describing the force on a charge moving with a velocity v or a current moving along a distance L is as follows:

$$F = qvB \sin \theta = ILB \sin \theta$$

Electrical Energy Generation 21.3

When a magnetic field moves through a closed loop of wire, or the loop of wire moves through a magnetic field, a potential difference is induced in the wire, and thus a current is produced. This process is called electromagnetic induction. The induced potential difference and current depend on the rate at which the magnetic field strength changes, or, alternatively, the rate at which the cross-sectional area of the loop changes. This change in the loop's area can take the form of rotating the loop in the magnetic field, which is the basic process for inducing a current in an electrical generator.

Address Misconceptions

Students may think that the changes in voltage and current produced by a transformer violate the principle of energy conservation. For an ideal transformer, the amount of energy that goes into the transformer each second (the input power) is equal to the energy leaving the transformer each second (the output power). For a strategy to overcome this misconception, see **Address Misconceptions** on **page 644.**

A Loop perpendicular to field

N
S

B Loop at an angle to field

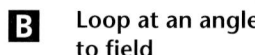

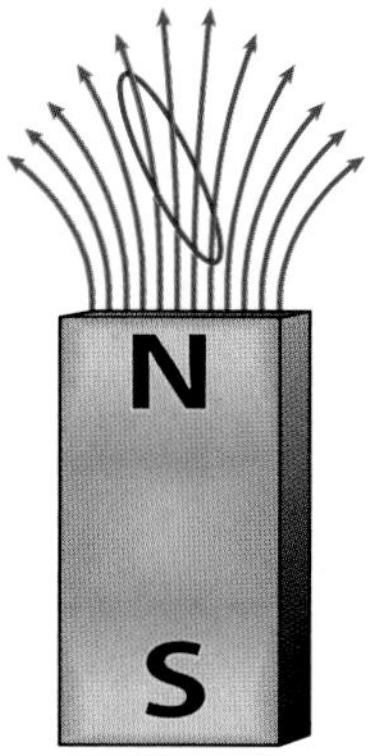
N
S

Because the sides of a rotating coil in a generator move through a magnetic field in an opposite direction after one half turn, the current produced by the generator alternates direction. Another aspect of induction—using a changing current to induce a changing magnetic field—provides the basis for the operation of a transformer.

Build Reading Literacy

Reciprocal Teaching

Modeling Strategies in Combination

Strategy Help students learn to apply the strategies of predict, question, clarify, and summarize. Teaching this strategy should take place over several days, beginning with the teacher modeling and leading students in discussion. The teacher gradually turns leadership over to students and becomes a facilitator, intervening only as needed. Prepare for the reading by choosing a passage of several paragraphs from Chapter 21. Make a copy of the paragraphs and note appropriate places to model the strategies for students.

Example

1. Read a few paragraphs aloud or have one student read aloud as other students follow along silently.
2. Discuss appropriate strategies for clarifying meaning and getting past trouble spots in the passage. Engage the group in discussing ways to apply each of the following strategies:
• Predicting what will come next in the text. Remind students to use what they already know about a topic to make connections that will help them understand what comes next.
• Asking "teacher-like questions" to check understanding and to think about what they need to find out.
• Clarifying the meaning of unfamiliar words or concepts.
• Summarizing what has been read.
3. Reread the paragraphs, modeling all four strategies.
4. Continue reading a few paragraphs at a time, discussing and modeling the strategies.
5. Repeat the process with different passages over a few days, gradually turning over the leadership role to students by having them lead the discussion of portions of the text.
6. When students are comfortable with the strategies, they can lead the entire discussion. Intervene only to get students back on track or to jump-start a discussion.

See p. 645 for a script on how to use the reciprocal teaching strategy with students. For additional Build Reading Literacy strategies, see pp. 630 and 635.

ASSESS PRIOR KNOWLEDGE

Use the Chapter Pretest below to assess students' prior knowledge. As needed, review these Science Concepts and Math Skills with students.

Review Science Concepts

Section 21.1 Review fundamental forces. Review electric charge, repulsive and attractive electric forces between charges, and electric fields. Review electric fields. Remind students of the atomic and molecular structure of solids as a preview to magnetic materials.

Section 21.2 Review direct current. Remind students that current is defined by the direction in which positive charges would flow.

Section 21.3 Review energy conservation and how work or heat can transfer energy. Remind students of how voltage and current determine electric power. Review alternating current, Ohm's law, and electrical safety.

Review Math Skills

Ratios and Proportions Students will use ratios and proportions to calculate voltage changes.

Direct students to the **Math Skills** in the **Skills and Reference Handbook** at the end of the student text.

CHAPTER 21 Magnetism

CONCEPTS in Action

How do science concepts apply to your world? Here are some questions you'll be able to answer after you read this chapter.

- What causes two magnets to push and pull each other, even when they aren't touching? *(Section 21.1)*
- How do electric motors work? *(Section 21.2)*
- How do loudspeakers use magnets to change electrical signals into sound? *(Section 21.2)*
- How is electric current generated? *(Section 21.3)*
- How does electric current get to your home? *(Section 21.3)*

Discovery Channel School **Video Field Trip**
Magnetic Viewpoints

- How do doctors use magnetic fields to see inside the human body? *(page 640)*

When charged particles from the sun are ▶ pulled toward the North or South Pole, they may cause colorful lights in the night sky.

628 *Chapter 21*

Chapter Pretest

1. True or False: Like charges exert an attractive force on each other. *(False)*
2. True or False: Electric force and magnetic force are two aspects of the same force. *(True)*
3. An electric field tells you *(d)*
   a. force on a charge in the field.
   b. how force varies with position.
   c. direction of force on a positive charge.
   d. All of the above
4. What is the difference between a series circuit and a parallel circuit? *(A series circuit has only one path for current. A parallel circuit has more than one path.)*
5. What is an insulator? *(A material through which charge cannot easily flow)*
6. True or False: The particle in an atom that moves around the nucleus is the electron. *(True)*
7. If current in a circuit increases and power stays the same, what happens to the voltage? *(It decreases.)*
8. True or False: An alternating current is one in which the charges repeatedly change direction. *(True)*

Chapter Preview

Inquiry Activity

How Do Magnets Interact With One Another?

Procedure

1. Bring the north pole of one bar magnet close to the south pole of another bar magnet. Observe and record what happens.
2. Bring the north pole of one bar magnet close to the north pole of another bar magnet. Observe and record what happens.
3. **Predicting** Predict what will happen if you bring the north pole of one bar magnet close to the center of another bar magnet. Test your prediction.

Think About It

1. **Observing** Describe the similarities and differences between the interactions of the north and south poles and the two north poles.
2. **Inferring** How do you think distance affects the way magnets interact?
3. **Posing Questions** Write a question about how magnets interact with other materials, such as glass, plastic, paper, and cloth.

Discovery Channel School **Video Field Trip**

Magnetic Viewpoints

Encourage students to view the Video Field Trip "Magnetic Viewpoints."

ENGAGE/EXPLORE

Inquiry Activity

How Do Magnets Interact With One Another? L2

Purpose In this activity, students will learn how magnetic fields attract or repel each other, and learn about the direction of magnetic fields.

Address Misconceptions

Some students may think that magnetic poles are like charges, which can exist in isolation. Challenge this misconception by having students think of magnets as behaving like a pair of opposite charges on opposite ends of a short stick. Ask, **What would the direction of the electric field be between these charges?** *(The electric field lines would spread out from the positive charge and extend toward the negative charge.)* Have students compare their observations of magnetic fields with their conclusions about the fields from pairs of opposite charges. Emphasize that magnetic poles never exist on their own; they always come in pairs.

Skills Focus **Observing, Inferring**

Prep Time 5 minutes

Materials 2 bar magnets

Class Time 15 minutes

Teaching Tips

- Advise students not to drop or bang the magnets, as this causes the magnets to lose their strength.

Expected Outcome Students will realize that magnets interact differently when like and unlike poles are brought near each other. When a pole of one bar magnet is brought near the middle of another bar magnet, there is a weak attraction, similar to the attraction for nonmagnetized iron.

Think About It

1. The north pole and south pole attracted each other. The north poles repelled each other.
2. Students will probably infer that the magnets will attract or repel each other more strongly the closer they are.
3. Students may ask which materials are attracted to magnets and which are not.

Kinesthetic, Group

Section 21.1

1 FOCUS

Objectives

21.1.1 **Describe** the effects of magnetic forces and magnetic fields and **explain** how magnetic poles determine the direction of magnetic force.

21.1.2 **Interpret diagrams** of magnetic field lines around one or more bar magnets.

21.1.3 **Describe** Earth's magnetic field and its effect on compasses.

21.1.4 **Explain** the behavior of ferromagnetic materials in terms of magnetic domains.

Reading Focus

Build Vocabulary L2

Word-Part Analysis Have students research the origin of the word *magnet* and write a short paragraph explaining how the word originated. *(The word* magnet *is derived from the name* Magnesia, *a region that was once part of ancient Greece. This area was known for its magnetite ore mines.)*

Reading Strategy L2

a. Can be temporary or permanent **b.** Have north and south poles; like poles repel, unlike poles attract **c.** Only a few materials can be magnets. **d.** Magnets affect objects with iron but don't affect most materials, such as paper, cotton, and so on.

2 INSTRUCT

Magnetic Forces

Build Reading Literacy L1

KWL (Know/Want to Know/Learned) Refer to page **124D** in **Chapter 5,** which provides the guidelines for a KWL strategy.

Have students label three columns on a sheet of paper K, W, and L. Have them write in the K column what they know about magnetic forces, and in the W column questions they would like answered about the forces exerted by magnets. Then, have students read the paragraphs on this page and record in the L column the answers to as many of their questions as possible.
Verbal, Interpersonal

21.1 Magnets and Magnetic Fields

Reading Focus

Key Concepts

- How do magnetic poles interact?
- How can a magnetic field affect a magnet that enters the field?
- Why are some materials magnetic while others are not?

Vocabulary

- magnetic force
- magnetic pole
- magnetic field
- magnetosphere
- magnetic domain
- ferromagnetic material

Reading Strategy

Using Prior Knowledge Copy the diagram below and add what you already know about magnets. After you read, revise the diagram based on what you learned.

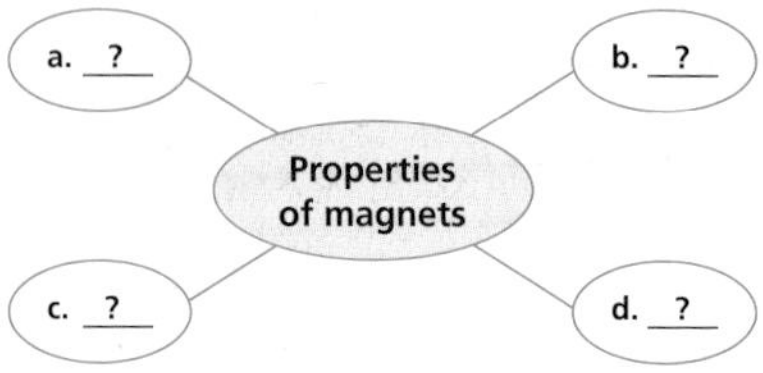
a. ?
b. ?
Properties of magnets
c. ?
d. ?

Ancient Greeks observed that magnetite, or lodestone, attracts iron. Some time before 200 A.D., the Chinese sculpted magnetite into spoon-shaped compasses. They called these stones "south pointers." By 1150 A.D., Chinese navigators used compasses with magnetized iron needles. But properties of magnets were not well explained until 1600. In that year, the English physician William Gilbert published *De Magnete.*

Magnetic Forces

You can explore properties of magnets on your own. Either side of a magnet sticks to a refrigerator. Yet if you push two magnets together, they may attract or repel. **Magnetic force** is the force a magnet exerts on another magnet, on iron or a similar metal, or on moving charges. Recall that magnetic force is one aspect of electromagnetic force.

Magnetic forces, like electric forces, act over a distance. Look at the suspended magnets in Figure 1. If you push down on the top two magnets, you can feel the magnets repel. Push harder, and the force increases. Magnetic force, like electric force, varies with distance.

Gilbert used a compass to map forces around a magnetite sphere. He discovered that the force is strongest at the poles. All magnets have two **magnetic poles,** regions where the magnet's force is strongest. One end of a magnet is its north pole; the other end is its south pole. The direction of magnetic force between two magnets depends on how the poles face. **Like magnetic poles repel one another, and opposite magnetic poles attract one another.**

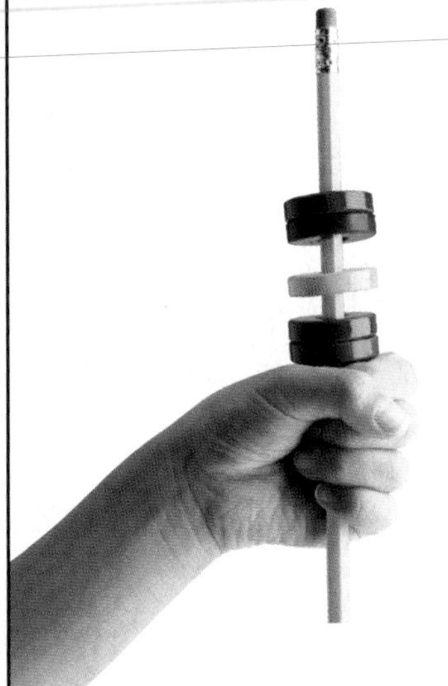

Figure 1 The green magnet and lower red magnet attract each other. The lower red magnet and the yellow magnet repel each other. **Predicting** ***What would happen if the upper red magnet on the pencil were flipped over?***

Section Resources

Print

- ***Laboratory Manual,*** Investigation 21B
- ***Reading and Study Workbook With Math Support,*** Section 21.1
- ***Transparencies,*** Chapter Pretest and Section 21.1

Technology

- ***Interactive Textbook,*** Section 21.1
- ***Presentation Pro CD-ROM,*** Chapter Pretest and Section 21.1

Magnetic Fields

A **magnetic field** surrounds a magnet and can exert magnetic forces. In Figure 2, iron filings are used to show the shape of the magnetic field around a bar magnet. **A magnetic field, which is strongest near a magnet's poles, will either attract or repel another magnet that enters the field.** The field lines begin near the magnet's north pole and extend toward its south pole. The arrows on the field lines indicate what direction a compass needle would point at each point in space. Where lines are close together, the field is strong. Where lines are more spread out, the field is weak.

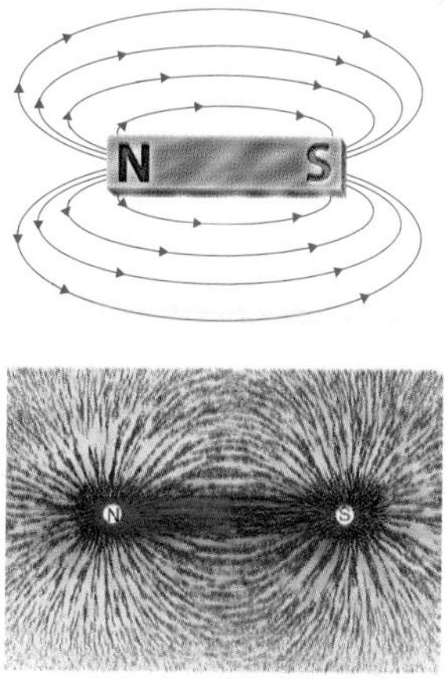

N
S

Figure 2 A magnetic field surrounds every magnet. Iron filings reveal the field lines, which start near the north pole and extend toward the south pole. **Interpreting Diagrams** ***In which two areas of a bar magnet is the field strongest?***

Magnetic Fields Around Magnets

You can use iron filings to visualize how magnetic fields of two magnets interact. Figure 3A shows the north pole of one magnet facing the north pole of another magnet. Notice that there are no iron filings in the gap between the magnets. Iron filings are not attracted to this area because the combined magnetic field is very weak. Figure 3B shows the combined field of two magnets with opposite poles facing each other. The field lines start at the north pole of one magnet and extend to the south pole of the other magnet. The field in the gap between the magnets is very strong, as you can see from the dense crowding of iron filings in this area.

Figure 3 Iron filings reveal the combined magnetic field of two interacting magnets. **A** When like poles of two magnets come together, the magnets repel each other. **B** When opposite poles of magnets come together, the magnets attract each other.

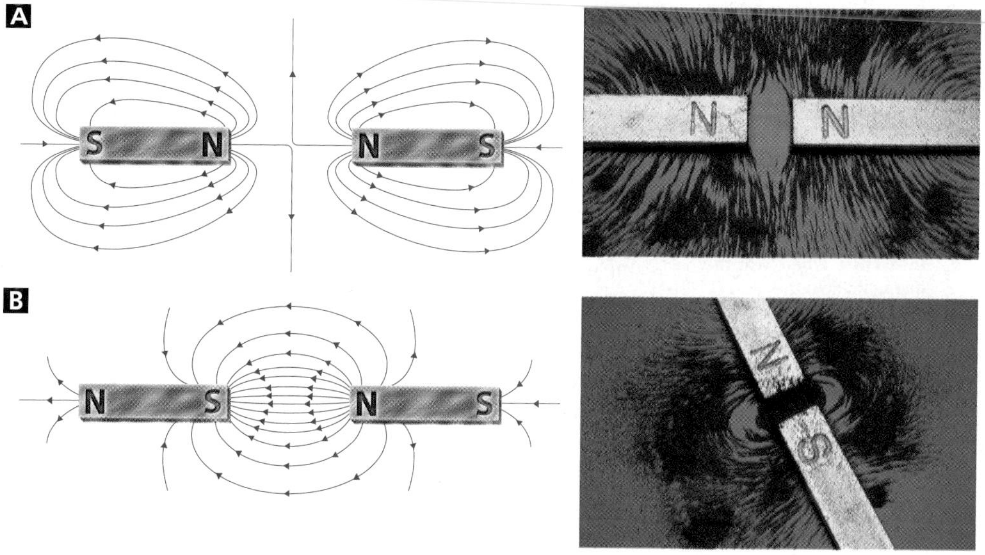

A
S
N
N
S
N
N
B
N
S
N
S
N
S

Magnetic Fields

Integrate Earth Science L2

Earth's magnetic field is produced by the motions of hot, liquefied iron within its core. Induced electric currents in the iron give rise to magnetic fields, which affect the flow of the iron and cause the resulting magnetic fields to become stronger.

Earth's magnetic field undergoes sudden reversals every few hundred thousand years, although the change does not happen at regular intervals. Currently the North Magnetic Pole is a south pole, which explains why "North" on a compass points to the north. Evidence for reversals is found in cooled magma, where iron atoms have aligned with Earth's magnetic field at the time of cooling. Cooled magma in ridges along the ocean floor provides a continuous record of magnetic field reversals over time. **Logical**

Build Science Skills L2

Inferring

ACTIVITY

Purpose Students are helped to an understanding of the shape of the magnetic field around two bar magnets.

Materials 2 bar magnets, a small magnetic compass

Class Time 20 minutes

Procedure Arrange two magnets as shown in either part of Figure 3. Have students place the compass at different positions about 1–2 cm away from the magnets and sketch the direction in which the compass needle points for each position. Ask them how the direction of the needle corresponds to the direction of the field lines in each location. Have them identify any patterns they notice.

Expected Outcome The compass needle will be parallel to the field lines at any location. The needle's south pole points along the field lines toward the north pole of a nearby magnet. **Logical, Visual**

Customize for English Language Learners

Reinforce Science Concepts
The various concepts, such as magnetic field, magnetic forces, and magnetic domains, each use the word *magnetic,* but mean and refer to different things. To help English language learners develop a clear understanding of these concepts, have them construct a Word Analysis Chart. Instruct students to write each of the vocabulary words on a separate chart and give a definition of each word. Suggest that they compare and contrast the vocabulary words. Finally, have them draw a picture or diagram to illustrate each concept.

Answer to . . .

Figure 1 *The red magnet would float above the blue magnet.*

Figure 2 *The field is strongest at the poles.*

Quick Lab

Observing Magnetic Field Lines L2

Objective
After completing this activity, students will be able to
- recognize how the magnetic fields of two magnets combine.

Skill Focus Observing

Prep Time 10 minutes

Class Time 20 minutes

Safety Students should wear safety goggles, not inhale the iron filings, and wash their hands when finished.

Teaching Tips
- Dropping or banging magnets causes them to lose their strength.
- Suggest that students tape the paper in place, so that the pattern is not accidentally disturbed.

Expected Outcome Students will realize that the interaction of the field lines of two magnets depends on how the magnets are positioned.

Analyze and Conclude
1. The field was strongest in the gap between opposite poles and weakest in the gap between like poles.
2. The field lines of two like poles spread apart and had a gap between the poles with very few field lines. The field lines of two unlike poles extended in lines connecting the north and south pole.
3. No pattern would appear, because sawdust is not magnetic. **Visual, Group**

For Enrichment L3

Have students repeat the experiment using different separations between the magnets. Ask, **What happens to the iron filings and to the field strength when two opposite poles are moved apart?** *(The filings are less crowded, indicating the field is weaker.)*
Visual, Logical

Magnetic Materials

FYI

Magnetic domains are quite small and can only be imaged using microscopes. A variety of instruments are used, such as scanning tunneling microscopes, magnetic force microscopes, and light microscopes with polarizing filters.

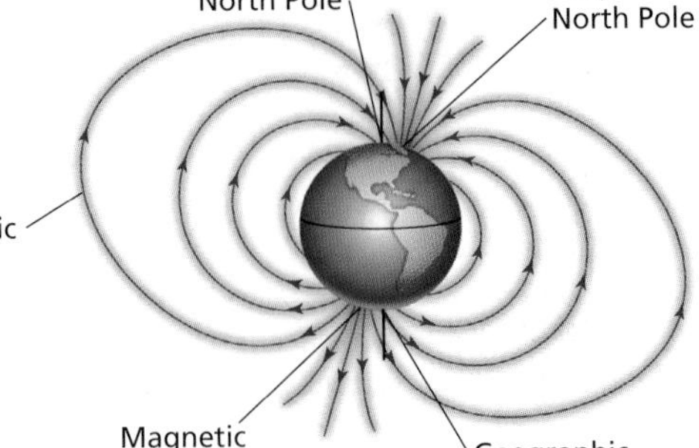
Geographic North Pole
Magnetic North Pole
Magnetic field
Magnetic South Pole
Geographic South Pole

Figure 4 Earth is surrounded by magnetic field lines. These lines are densest at the poles.

Quick Lab

Observing Magnetic Field Lines

Materials
small container of iron filings, 2 bar magnets, paper, 2 textbooks, masking tape

Procedure
1. Place two textbooks side by side, about 7 cm apart.
2. Place the magnets between the books, with north poles facing, about 2 cm apart. Tape the magnets in place.
3. Place the paper over the magnets to form a bridge.
4. Sprinkle iron filings on the paper until you can see the magnetic field lines. Sketch your observations.
5. Carefully return the filings to their container.
6. Repeat Steps 2 through 5 with opposite poles facing.

Analyze and Conclude
1. **Inferring** Where was the magnetic field the strongest? The weakest?
2. **Analyzing Data** How did the fields of like poles facing differ from those of unlike poles facing?
3. **Predicting** What result would you expect if you used sawdust instead of iron filings?

Magnetic Field Around Earth Earth is like a giant magnet surrounded by a magnetic field. The area surrounding Earth that is influenced by this field is the **magnetosphere** (mag NET oh sfeer).

A compass points north because it aligns with Earth's magnetic field. However, as Figure 4 shows, Earth's magnetic poles are not at the geographic poles. The geographic North Pole is at 90° N latitude, but the magnetic North Pole is at about 81° N latitude. Because of this, a compass may point east or west of north. The angle between the direction to true north and to magnetic north is called magnetic declination. Magnetic declination varies with your location on Earth.

Reading Checkpoint *Why does a compass point toward north?*

Magnetic Materials

Within an atom, electrons move around the nucleus. This movement, along with a property of electrons called "spin," causes electrons to act like tiny magnets. In many materials, each electron is paired with another having an opposite spin. Magnetic effects mostly cancel each other. As a result, these materials have extremely weak magnetic fields.

Many other materials have one or more unpaired electrons. The unpaired electrons produce magnetic fields. But the fields usually don't combine because the arrangement of the atoms isn't quite right. These materials have weak magnetic fields. In a few materials, such as iron, nickel, and cobalt, the unpaired electrons make a strong magnetic field. Then the fields combine to form magnetic domains. A **magnetic domain** is a region that has a very large number of atoms with aligned magnetic fields. A **ferromagnetic material** (fehr oh mag NET ik), such as iron, can be magnetized because it contains magnetic domains. **When a material is magnetized, most of its magnetic domains are aligned.**

Facts and Figures

Strong and Weak Magnetic Fields Earth has the strongest magnetic field of the rocky inner planets. Earth has an average field strength at its surface of between 30 μT and 60 μT. (A tesla, T, is the unit by which magnetic fields are measured.) This is some 100 times stronger than the magnetic field of Mercury, roughly 1000 to 5000 times stronger than the field of Mars, and about 100,000 times stronger than the field of Venus.

Nonmagnetized Materials The fact that a material is ferromagnetic does not mean it is a magnet. If the domains of a ferromagnetic material are aligned randomly, the magnetization of the domains is cancelled, and it is not a magnet. An iron nail is an example of a nonmagnetized material. It is ferromagnetic, so the domains have the potential to be aligned, but normally they are not. Figure 5A shows the random orientation of domains in nonmagnetized iron.

Magnetized Materials You can easily magnetize a nonmagnetized ferromagnetic material by placing it in a magnetic field. For example, if you put a nonmagnetized iron nail near a magnet, you will turn the nail into a magnet. Figure 5B shows the alignment of magnetic domains in magnetized iron. The applied magnetic field causes magnetic domains aligned with the field to grow larger. This magnetization can be temporary. If the magnet is moved away from the nail, the motion of the atoms in the nail causes the magnetic domains to become randomly oriented again. In some ferromagnetic materials, the domains stay aligned for a long time. These materials are called permanent magnets. They are not truly permanant, because heat or a jarring impact can realign the domains.

If you cut a magnet in half, each half will have its own north pole and south pole because the domains will still be aligned. If you cut the pieces in half again, each half will again have a north pole and a south pole. No matter how many times you cut the magnets, each piece will have two different poles. A magnet can never have just a north pole or just a south pole.

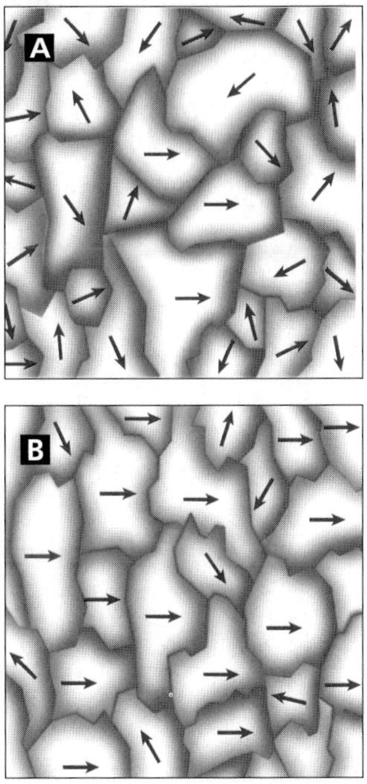
A
B

Figure 5 A magnetic field can magnetize ferromagnetic materials. **A** Before magnetization, domains are random. **B** Domains aligned with the field grow during magnetization. Unaligned domains can shrink.

Section 21.1 Assessment

Reviewing Concepts

1. Describe the interaction of magnetic poles.
2. What two things can happen to a magnet entering a magnetic field?
3. What makes a material magnetic?
4. Describe what happens to the fields of two bar magnets when you bring their north poles together.

Critical Thinking

5. **Predicting** What happens if you suspend a bar magnet so that it can swing freely?
6. **Relating Cause and Effect** How are electrons responsible for magnetism?
7. **Predicting** What will happen if you hit a magnet with a hammer? Explain.
8. **Designing Experiments** How could you test the effects of heating and cooling on the magnetization of a bar magnet?

Connecting Concepts

Electric Charge Review electric charge in Section 20.1. Compare the attraction and repulsion of positive and negative charges with the behavior of two bar magnets placed near one another.

Address Misconceptions L2

Students may be visualizing the motion of the electron as if it were a planet rotating on its axis. Emphasize that the "spin" of an electron is not like the spin of a ball, any more than the orbital motion of an electron around an atom's nucleus is like the motion of a planet around the sun. The term *spin* is applied to electron behavior that mathematically resembles that of a spinning object. Remind students of how electrons in atoms are modeled as "clouds" where they are most likely to be located.
Logical

3 ASSESS

Evaluate Understanding L2

Ask students why a refrigerator magnet sticks to the door of a refrigerator. Be sure they explain which material is a permanent magnet, and what happens at the atomic level in the magnetized material. *(The atoms in the refrigerator magnet, which is made of ferromagnetic material, are aligned in the various magnetic domains, and so give the magnet a permanent field. When the magnet is attached to the unmagnetized door of the refrigerator, the atoms of the door are aligned, and so become magnetized temporarily.)*

Reteach L1

Use Figure 3 to explain the shape and direction of a magnetic field around a bar magnet.

Connecting Concepts

Like charges and like poles repel, while opposite charges and opposite poles attract. In contrast to electric charges, magnetic poles can't be separated.

Interactive Textbook If your class subscribes to the Interactive Textbook, use it to review key concepts in Section 21.1.

Section 21.1 Assessment

1. Magnetic poles that are alike repel one another, and magnetic poles that are different attract one another.
2. A magnetic field will either attract or repel another magnet that enters the field.
3. For a material to be magnetized, most of its magnetic domains must be aligned.
4. The fields interact, and the field between the magnets becomes very weak.
5. The north end of the magnet will swing toward north, aligning with Earth's magnetic field just as a compass does.
6. The spin and orbital motion of electrons in an atom give the atom a magnetic field.
7. The motion of the atoms can cause the magnetic domains to become randomly aligned. The material loses its magnetization.
8. Students' suggestions for experiments should include some method for testing the magnetization of a bar magnet before and after it is heated and before and after it is cooled.

Answer to . . .

Reading Checkpoint *The north end of a compass points north because a freely suspended bar magnet aligns with Earth's magnetic field.*

HOW It Works

Anti-Theft Security Devices L2

Electromagnetic tag systems were first developed in the 1960s, along with other similar RFID (Radio Frequency Identification) technology. This type of system uses electromagnetic waves to identify objects that have been tagged with magnetic material.

Electromagnetic waves consist of changing electric fields and changing magnetic fields that are at right angles to each other and to the direction of the wave. The EM tag system uses the magnetic component of an electromagnetic wave to temporarily magnetize an activated tag as it passes between the pedestals. This change in the tag's magnetic domains produces a small electromagnetic wave with a particular frequency. The wave is detected by a receiver, causing an alarm to sound.

A deactivated tag, however, is fully magnetized, so no change occurs in the magnetic domains when the tag passes between the pedestals. Thus, no electromagnetic wave is produced, and the tag passes through the electromagnetic field undetected.

The magnetic properties of the tag cause it to become temporarily magnetized more easily than ordinary steel objects. This is why a screwdriver or box of paper clips can pass through the system without setting off the alarm.

Other systems make use of thin wire coils in the tags that act as antennas, as well as small circuit elements. Electromagnetic waves emitted from the pedestal at a particular frequency induce a current in the tag's antenna, and this induced current produces an electromagnetic wave with a characteristic frequency. This wave is then detected by the receiver pedestal.

Applying Concepts The deactivated tag is more highly magnetized than the activated tag.
Logical

For Enrichment L3

Students can make a multimedia presentation about the EM tag system, as well as other RFID systems. Articles on the subject can be found on the Internet and in science and engineering periodicals.
Verbal, Portfolio

HOW It Works

Anti-Theft Security Devices

Anti-theft security devices are found in stores across the world. One of the best of these devices is the electromagnetic (EM) tag system. This system is based on the interaction between a small piece of magnetic material (a tag) and an EM field created between two pedestals at the store exit. **Applying concepts** ***Which is more highly magnetized, an activated or a deactivated tag?***

Library security
Powerful magnets are used to deactivate tags in library books before borrowing. If the tag is not deactivated, the alarm will go off at the library exit.

A Activated tag An activated tag is slightly demagnetized. When it passes through the pedestal's EM field, the tag's magnetic domains line up with the field. This change in magnetic domain emits a signal that is picked up by the receiver, which sets off the alarm.

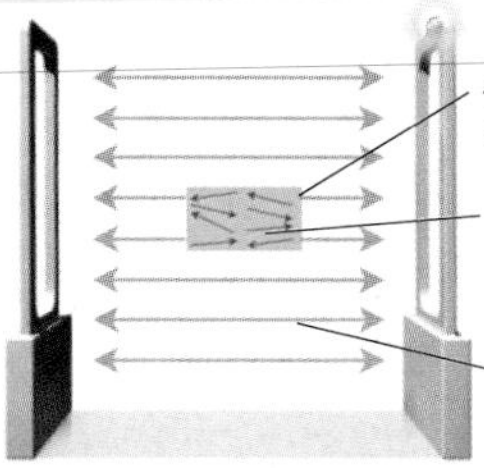
Activated tag (demagnetized)
Magnetic domain
Changing electromagnetic field

B Deactivated tag
A deactivated tag is fully magnetized. When it passes through the exit, the tag's domains do not change. Because no signal is emitted, the alarm is not set off.

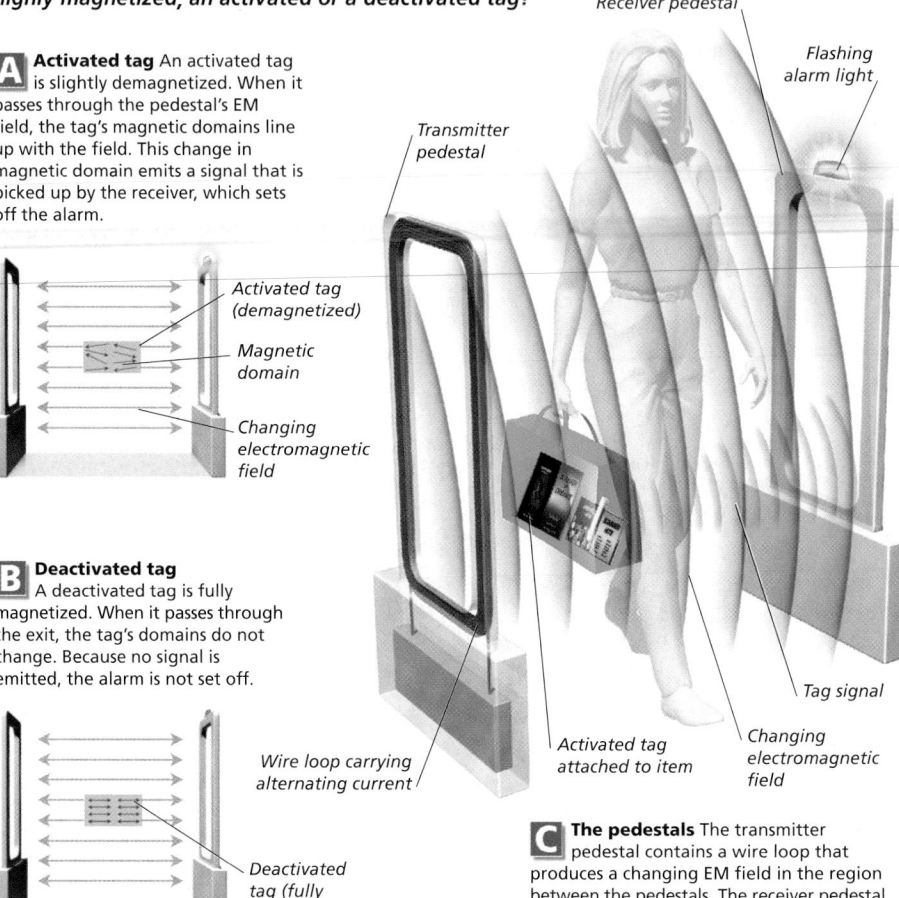

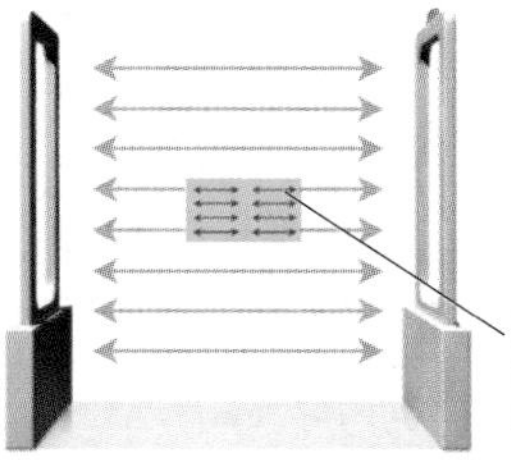
Deactivated tag (fully magnetized)

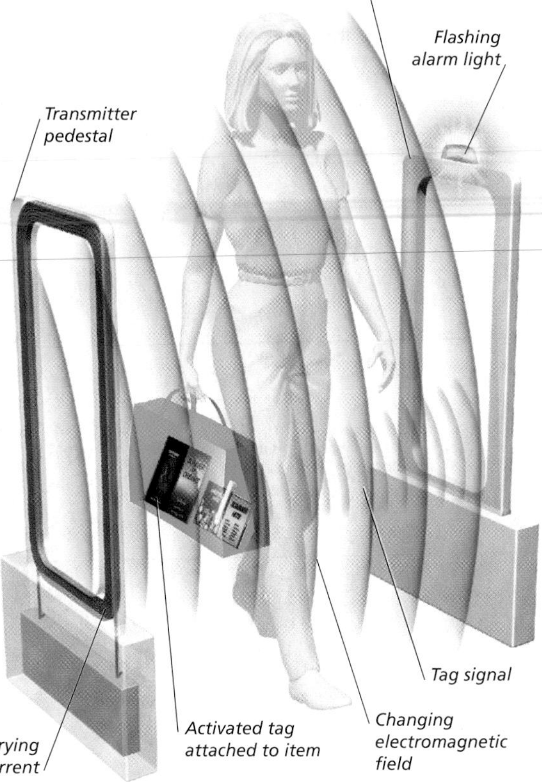
Receiver pedestal
Flashing alarm light
Transmitter pedestal
Tag signal
Wire loop carrying alternating current
Activated tag attached to item
Changing electromagnetic field

C The pedestals The transmitter pedestal contains a wire loop that produces a changing EM field in the region between the pedestals. The receiver pedestal picks up any signal produced by the tag.

21.2 Electromagnetism

Reading Focus

Key Concepts

- How can an electric charge create a magnetic field?
- How is an electromagnet controlled?
- How do galvanometers, electric motors, and loudspeakers work?

Vocabulary

- electromagnetic force
- solenoid
- electromagnet
- galvanometer
- electric motor

Reading Strategy

Identifying Main Idea Copy the table below. As you read, write the main idea of the text that follows each topic.

Topic	Main Idea
Electricity and magnetism	a. ?
Direction of magnetic fields	b. ?
Direction of electric currents	c. ?
Solenoids and electromagnets	d. ?
Electromagnetic devices	e. ?

You know that unlike electric charges attract one another and that like electric charges repel one another. It is easy to discover a similar effect with the north and south poles of two magnets. However, it's much more difficult to figure out the relationship between electricity and magnetism. In fact, the connection was discovered accidentally by the Danish scientist Hans Christian Oersted in 1820.

One evening Oersted, pictured in Figure 6, was conducting scientific demonstrations for his friends and students in his home. One demonstration used electric current in a wire, and another used a compass needle attached to a wooden stand. As Oersted turned on the current for the electricity demonstration, he saw the compass needle move. When he turned off the current, the needle moved back to its original position. Further investigation showed that the current in the wire produced a magnetic field. Oersted had discovered a relationship between electricity and magnetism.

Figure 6 In 1820 Hans Oersted discovered how magnetism and electricity are connected. A unit of measure of magnetic field strength, the oersted, is named after him.

Electricity and Magnetism

Electricity and magnetism are different aspects of a single force known as the **electromagnetic force.** The electric force results from charged particles. The magnetic force usually results from the movement of electrons in an atom. Both aspects of the electromagnetic force are caused by electric charges.

Section Resources

Print
- ***Reading and Study Workbook With Math Support,*** Section 21.2
- ***Transparencies,*** Section 21.2

Technology
- ***Interactive Textbook,*** Section 21.2
- ***Presentation Pro CD-ROM,*** Section 21.2
- ***Go Online,*** NSTA SciLinks, Electromagnets

Section 21.2

1 FOCUS

Objectives

21.2.1 **Describe** how a moving electric charge creates a magnetic field and **determine** the direction of the magnetic field based on the type of charge and the direction of its motion.

21.2.2 **Relate** the force a magnetic field exerts on a moving electric charge to the type of charge and the direction of its motion.

21.2.3 **Explain** how solenoids and electromagnets are constructed and **describe** factors that affect the field strength of both.

21.2.4 **Describe** how electromagnetic devices use the interaction between electric currents and magnetic fields.

Reading Focus

Build Vocabulary L2

Concept Map Have students make a concept map comparing the devices in the vocabulary list.

Reading Strategy L2

a. Electricity and magnetism are different aspects of electromagnetic force. **b.** Magnetic fields are produced at right angles to an electric current. **c.** Electric currents are deflected perpendicular to a magnetic field. **d.** Changing the current in an electromagnet controls the strength and direction of its magnetic field. **e.** Electromagnetic devices change electrical energy into mechanical energy.

2 INSTRUCT

Electricity and Magnetism

Build Reading Literacy L1

Predict Refer to page **66D** in **Chapter 3,** which provides the guidelines for predicting.

Have students read the first two paragraphs on p. 635. Ask them to predict what Oersted discovered about the relationship between electricity and magnetism. *(Predictions should indicate that an electric current produces a magnetic field.)* **Logical**

Teacher Demo

Magnetic Field from Electric Current L2

Purpose Students observe how an electric current produces a magnetic field.

Materials insulated wire, cardboard (10 cm × 10 cm), a burner tripod, a variable DC power supply, 4–6 compasses

Procedure Punch a small hole in the center of the cardboard and thread the wire through the hole. Lay the cardboard flat on the burner tripod's ring support so that the wire passes through the tripod center, perpendicular to the cardboard and extending in a straight line 10 cm on either side. (A ring stand and clamp may be needed to support the upper end of the wire.) Connect both ends of the wire to the terminals of the power supply. Place the compasses on the cardboard at a distance of 3–4 cm from the wire. Turn on the power supply and increase the current until the compass needles begin to deflect. Have students notice how the needles deflect with respect to the wire. Remove the compasses, turn off the power supply, reverse the wire connections, and repeat the demonstration.

Safety Use insulated wire. Follow procedures for electrical safety.

Expected Outcome When the top end of the wire is connected to the positive terminal of the power supply, the magnetic field will be in a counter-clockwise pattern around the wire, according to the right-hand rule. This will cause the poles of the compasses to align themselves along the edge of a circle around the wire. The south poles will form a clockwise pattern. When the connections are reversed, the direction in which the compasses point will reverse.
Visual, Group

Use Visuals L1

Figure 8 Explain that the right-hand rule also applies to Figure 8. Ask, **How could you use your hand to determine the deflection of an electron moving through the magnetic poles?** *(Use your right hand with your thumb in the direction of the current, which will be opposite the direction of the electron's travel.)*
Visual

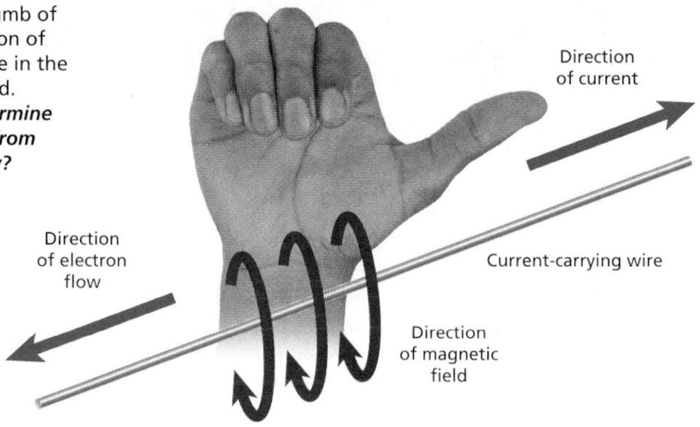

Direction of current
Current-carrying wire
Direction of electron flow
Direction of magnetic field

Figure 7 If you point the thumb of your right hand in the direction of the current, your fingers curve in the direction of the magnetic field. **Inferring** ***How can you determine the magnetic field direction from the direction of electron flow?***

Magnetic Fields Around Moving Charges Oersted's discovery about the relationship between a current-carrying wire and a magnet established an important physics principle. **Moving electric charges create a magnetic field.** These moving charges may be the vibrating charges that produce an electromagnetic wave. They may also be, as in Oersted's experiment, the moving charges in a wire. Figure 7 shows how to remember the direction of the magnetic field that is produced. The magnetic field lines form circles around a straight wire carrying a current.

Forces Acting on Moving Charges Recall that an electric field exerts a force on an electric charge. The force is either in the same direction as the electric field or in the opposite direction, depending on whether it is a positive or negative charge.

The effect of a magnetic field on a moving charge is different, as shown in Figure 8. A charge moving in a magnetic field will be deflected in a direction perpendicular to both the magnetic field and to the velocity of the charge. If a current-carrying wire is in a magnetic field, the wire will be pushed in a direction perpendicular to both the field and the direction of the current. Reversing the direction of the current will still cause the wire to be deflected, but in the opposite direction. If the current is parallel to the magnetic field, the force is zero and there is no deflection.

Reading Checkpoint *What are two kinds of moving charges that can create a magnetic field?*

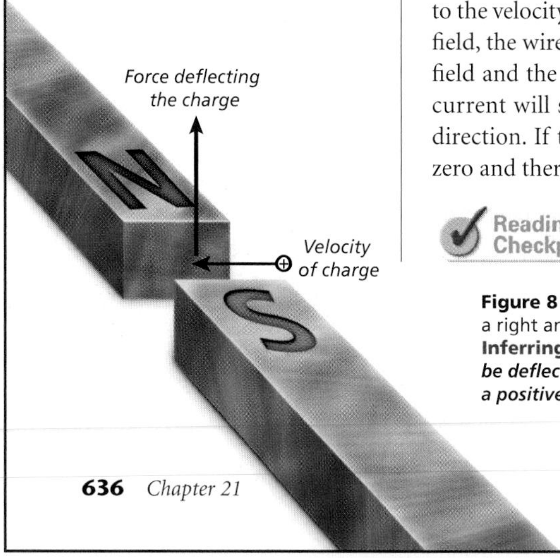

Force deflecting the charge
N
S
Velocity of charge

Figure 8 A moving positive charge is deflected at a right angle to its motion by a magnetic field. **Inferring** ***In what direction would the particle be deflected if it had a negative charge instead of a positive charge?***

Customize for Inclusion Students

Visually Impaired
The right-hand rule can be used by students with visual impairments to understand magnetic fields and forces. Explain how students can use their right hand to predict the directions of magnetic fields for an electric current in a straight wire and a solenoid. As students may have difficulty using Figure 7, instruct them using a wire, so that they can understand how the right-hand thumb and fingers are oriented for a positive current and its magnetic field. Then, have students adapt the rule for positive charges moving in a magnetic field, as shown in Figure 8 (that is, the thumb points in the direction of the moving charge, the fingers extend in the direction of the magnetic field, and the force on the charge points outward from the palm). Encourage those students who successfully master the rule to explain it to the class.

Quick Lab

Making an Electromagnet

Materials

iron nail, 20 small metal paper clips, 20-cm length and 1-m length of insulated wire with stripped ends, 6-volt battery, switch

Procedure

1. Make a circuit using the nail, wire, battery, and switch. Use the shorter wire to connect one terminal of the battery to the switch. Connect the longer wire to the other terminal of the battery. Wrap this wire around the nail 10 times. Then connect the longer wire to the switch.
2. Hold the head of the nail over the pile of paper clips. Close the switch. Record how many paper clips the nail can pick up.
3. Open the switch. **CAUTION** *If the switch is left closed, the wire will become very warm.* Wrap the longer wire 40 more times around the nail in the same direction as before.
4. Close the switch. Record how many paper clips the nail can pick up now.
5. Open the switch and disconnect the circuit.

Analyze and Conclude

1. **Observing** How did your ability to pick up paper clips with the nail change when you increased the number of turns in the coil?
2. **Drawing Conclusions** Why did the nail become a magnet when a current-carrying wire was wrapped around it?

Solenoids and Electromagnets

Before you can use electromagnetic force, you need to be able to control it. Using electromagnetic force requires some simple tools. Figure 9A shows a current-carrying wire with a loop in it. The magnetic field in the center of the loop points right to left through the loop, as shown in Figure 9A.

Suppose you loop the wire many times to make a coil, as shown in Figure 9B. Then the magnetic fields of the loops combine so that the coiled wire acts like a bar magnet. The field through the center of the coil is the sum of the fields from each turn of the wire. A coil of current-carrying wire that produces a magnetic field is called a **solenoid.**

If you place a ferromagnetic material, such as an iron rod, inside the coil of a solenoid, the strength of the magnetic field increases. The magnetic field produced by the current causes the iron rod inside the coil of the solenoid to become a magnet. An **electromagnet** is a solenoid with a ferromagnetic core. **Changing the current in an electromagnet controls the strength and direction of its magnetic field.** You can also use the current to turn the magnetic field on and off. People use many devices every day, such as hair dryers, telephones, and doorbells, that utilize electromagnets.

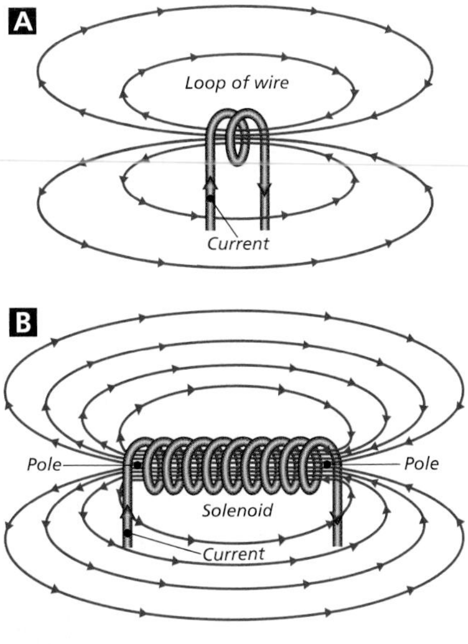
A
Loop of wire
Current
B
Pole
Pole
Solenoid
Current

Figure 9 The magnetic field lines around a solenoid are like those of a bar magnet. **Applying Concepts** *Which of the poles is north?*

Facts and Figures

Big Magnets Because the magnetic fields produced by electromagnets can be made stronger by properly designing the electromagnet, it is not surprising that the strongest magnetic fields on Earth are produced by specially designed electromagnets. At the National High Magnetic Field Laboratory (NHMFL) at Florida State University in Tallahassee, electromagnets have been designed that produce continuous magnetic fields with strengths up to 50 teslas. These fields are about a million times stronger than Earth's magnetic field at Earth's surface.

Solenoids and Electromagnets

Quick Lab

Making an Electromagnet L2

Objective
After completing this activity, students will be able to
- predict how the number of turns of wire affects the strength of the electromagnet.

Skill Focus Observing, Drawing Conclusions

Prep Time 20 minutes

Advance Prep Cut the wires in advance and use a wire stripper or wire-cutting pliers to remove 2 cm of insulation from each end of the wires.

Class Time 25 minutes

Safety Students should wear safety goggles and be careful handling the coil of wire, as the wire may become hot. Students should open the switch when the electromagnet is not in use.

Expected Outcome Students will learn that the strength of an electromagnet, as indicated by the number of paper clips picked up, is directly related to the number of turns in the coil of wire. More turns make the magnet stronger.

Analyze and Conclude
1. The electromagnet became stronger with more turns in the coil.
2. The current in the coil produced a magnetic field around and through the nail. This caused the magnetic domains in the nail to align, temporarily strengthening the magnetic field of the nail.
Logical, Group

Answer to . . .

Figure 7 *Use the right-hand rule, but point your thumb in the opposite direction of the electron flow (which will be the direction of the current).*

Figure 8 *It would be deflected down.*

Figure 9 *The one on the left because magnetic field lines start at the north pole and end at the south pole.*

Reading Checkpoint *Vibrating charges, flowing charges in a current*

Address Misconceptions L2

Students may wonder how the magnetic field of a solenoid can be fairly simple when there are magnetic fields around each segment of wire in the coil. Explain that such fields are present, but that they combine in such a way that the field outside the solenoid is much weaker than inside. The fields combine to effectively form a magnetic field that is similar to that of a bar magnet.
Logical

Electromagnetic Devices

Teacher Demo

Electromagnetic Force L2

Purpose Students observe the magnetic force exerted on a wire carrying an electric current.

Materials insulated wire, a large horseshoe magnet, a variable DC power supply, 2 ring stands with clamps

Procedure Pass the wire through the rings of the ring stands, so that it extends horizontally about 5–10 cm above the table surface. Position the magnet on its side, so that the wire passes between the magnet's poles. Connect the wires to the power supply and turn it on, increasing the current until the wire is deflected. Turn off the power, reverse the connections, and repeat the demonstration.

Safety Use insulated wire. Follow procedures for electrical safety.

Expected Outcome Depending on the orientation of the magnet, the wire will be deflected either in toward the magnet's center or away from it. The deflecting force is proportional to the current in the wire and the strength of the magnetic field.
Visual, Group

Go Online NSTA SciLinks

Download a worksheet on electromagnets for students to complete, and find additional teacher support from NSTA SciLinks.

Go Online NSTA SciLinks

For: Links on electromagnets
Visit: www.SciLinks.org
Web Code: ccn-2212

The strength of an electromagnet depends on the current in the solenoid, the number of loops in the coil in the solenoid, and the type of ferromagnetic core. To increase the strength of an electromagnet, increase the current flowing through the solenoid. A greater current produces a stronger magnetic field. Increasing the number of turns, while keeping the same current, will also increase the field strength. Cores that are easily magnetized, such as "soft" iron, make stronger electromagnets.

Reading Checkpoint *What does the strength of an electromagnet depend on?*

Electromagnetic Devices

Electromagnets can convert electrical energy into motion that can do work. **Electromagnetic devices such as galvanometers, electric motors, and loudspeakers change electrical energy into mechanical energy.** A galvanometer measures current in a wire through the deflection of a solenoid in an external magnetic field. An electric motor uses a rotating electromagnet to turn an axle. A loudspeaker uses a solenoid to convert electrical signals into sound waves you can hear.

Galvanometers Figure 10 shows a **galvanometer,** a device that uses a solenoid to measure small amounts of current. A solenoid is attached to a spring and is free to rotate about an iron core. The solenoid is placed between the poles of two permanent magnets. When there is a current in the solenoid's coils, the resulting magnetic field attempts to align with the field of the permanent magnets. The greater the current, the more the solenoid rotates, as shown by the pointer on the scale. In an automobile fuel gauge, for example, a sensor in the gas tank reduces the current as the gas level decreases. This causes the needle to rotate towards the "empty" mark.

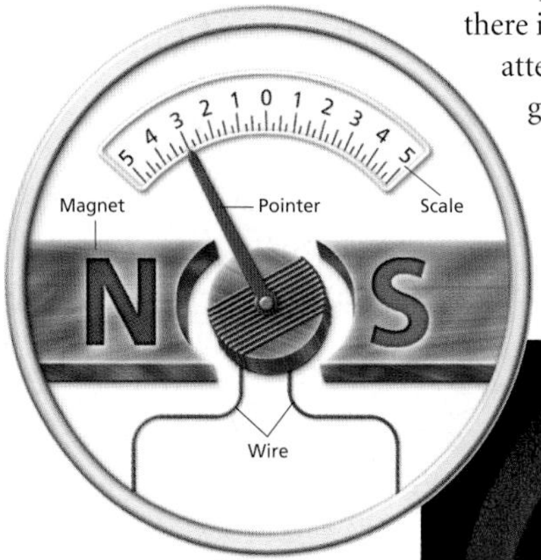
5 4 3 2 1 0 1 2 3 4 5
Magnet
Pointer
Scale
N
S
Wire

½
0
1
GASOLINE
ONLY
20

Figure 10 A galvanometer uses an electromagnet to move a pointer. One common application is in an automobile gas gauge. The pointer indicates the amount of current in the wire. The wire is connected to a sensor in the gas tank.

Electric Motors An **electric motor** is a device that uses an electromagnet to turn an axle. Figure 11 shows how an electric motor works. In this figure, the wire is connected to a battery. An actual motor has many loops of wire around a central iron core to make the motor stronger. In the motor of an electric appliance, the wire would be connected to an electrical circuit in a building.

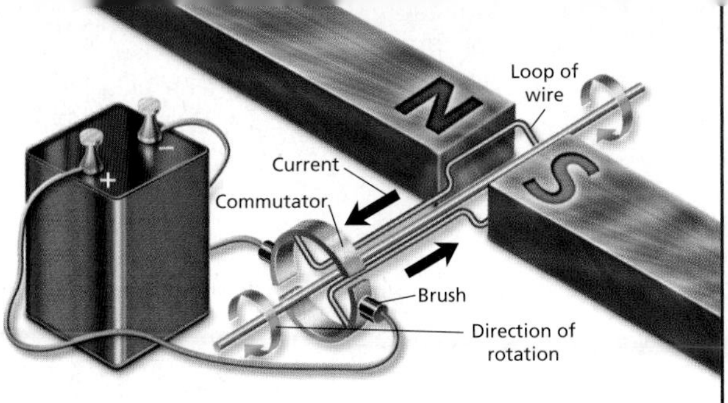

Loop of wire
N
S
Current
Commutator
Brush
Direction of rotation
+
−

Figure 11 A battery supplies current to a loop of wire through the commutator. As the commutator turns, the direction of current switches back and forth. As a result, the coil's magnetic field keeps switching direction, and this turns the coil about an axle.
Predicting ***What would happen if you reversed the positive and negative connections on the battery?***

What makes a motor turn? When current flows through a loop of wire, one side of the loop is pushed by the field of the permanent magnet. The other side of the loop is pulled. These forces rotate the loop. If there were no commutator ring, the coil would come to rest. But as the loop turns, each C-shaped half of the commutator connects with a different brush, reversing the current. The forces now change direction, so the coil continues to rotate. As long as current flows, rotation continues.

Loudspeakers A loudspeaker contains a solenoid placed around one pole of a permanent magnet. The current in the wires entering the loudspeaker changes direction and increases or decreases to reproduce music, voices, or other sounds. The changing current produces a changing magnetic field in the solenoid coil. The magnetic force exerted by the permanent magnet moves the coil back and forth. As the coil moves, it causes a thin membrane to vibrate, producing sound waves that match the original sound.

Section 21.2 Assessment

Reviewing Concepts

1. Besides a magnet, what can create a magnetic field?
2. How is the magnetic field of an electromagnet controlled?
3. How are solenoids and electromagnets used in galvanometers, electric motors, and loudspeakers?
4. How does a ferromagnetic rod inside a solenoid affect the strength of an electromagnet?

Critical Thinking

5. **Comparing and Contrasting** What is the effect of a magnetic field on a stationary electric charge? On a moving electric charge?
6. **Applying Concepts** Why is it a good idea to have the coil of a solenoid wound closely with many turns of wire?
7. **Inferring** What is the purpose of the commutator in an electric motor?
8. **Relating Cause and Effect** What causes the membrane in a loudspeaker to vibrate?

Connecting Concepts

Insulators In Section 20.2 you learned that electric charge doesn't flow easily through electrical insulators. Use this to explain why a solenoid has insulated wires.

Build Science Skills L2

Applying Concepts Have students read the paragraphs on electric motors and help them apply what they already know about work, different forms of energy, and energy conservation. Ask, **What forms of energy are shown for the electric motor in Figure 11?** *(Chemical energy, electrical energy, and mechanical energy)* Ask, **What energy transformations take place when operating the motor?** *(Chemical energy in the battery is converted to electrical energy. Electrical energy interacts with the magnetic field to do work, and so is transformed into the kinetic energy of the rotating wire loop and into any work the motor does.)*
Logical

3 ASSESS

Evaluate Understanding L2

Ask students to list three examples of devices that use electromagnetic forces (at least one of which is not given in the section). Have students explain what each device does and how electricity and magnetism interact in the device. *(Could be an electric bell, relay switch, or microphone)*

Reteach L1

Use Figures 7 and 9 to review the direction of magnetic fields produced by electric currents.

Connecting Concepts

The strength of the electromagnet depends upon the current in the solenoid. Insulated wires make it possible to direct the current through several tightly wound loops, enhancing the strength of the magnetic field. The insulated wire prevents a short circuit between adjacent coils.

Interactive Textbook If your class subscribes to the Interactive Textbook, use it to review key concepts in Section 21.2.

Section 21.2 Assessment

1. A moving electric charge can create a magnetic field.
2. It can be turned on and off. Its strength and direction can be controlled by controlling the current.
3. They change electrical energy into mechanical energy.
4. It makes the magnetic field much stronger. When current flows through the coil, it creates a magnetic field that magnetizes the ferromagnetic rod.
5. A magnetic field doesn't affect a stationary charge. A magnetic field deflects a moving charge in a direction perpendicular to both the field and the velocity.
6. It produces a more uniform field and increases its strength.
7. The commutator reverses the current in the electromagnet, reversing the magnetic field of the electromagnet, and enabling the axle to turn continuously in one direction.
8. The interaction of the magnetic field of the permanent magnet with the changing field of the electromagnet

Answer to . . .

Figure 11 *The motor's axle would spin in the opposite direction.*

Reading Checkpoint *It depends on the strength of the current, the number of coils of wire, and the type of ferromagnetic core.*

CONCEPTS in Action

Peeking Inside the Human Body **L2**

Background

MRI is an example of a procedure called tomography, where many images of the body are combined to give a composite view. MRI uses nuclear magnetic resonance, or NMR, to obtain information from hydrogen atoms in the body. NMR was discovered in 1946, and was originally used to identify hydrocarbon molecules. In the 1970s, the technique was combined with computers to produce images of tissues in the body.

Build Science Skills **L2**

Using Analogies ACTIVITY

Purpose Students will simulate how applied magnetic fields can disrupt the magnetic fields of atoms.

Materials a short pencil (about 5 cm long), a cardboard disk (7 cm wide), a steel thumbtack, a bar magnet, paper

Class Time 15 minutes

Procedure Insert the thumbtack into the eraser end of the pencil, and punch the pencil through the center of the cardboard disk to make a "top" that can spin. Make sure the cardboard does not slip along the surface of the pencil. Place the top on a piece of paper to prevent marking the table. Spin the top with the thumbtack side upward, making sure that the top is neither too stable or unstable while spinning. Spin the top again, and place one end of the magnet about 2 cm to the side of the thumbtack. Repeat the test, placing the magnet slightly closer, until the spinning top is deflected by the magnet. Make sure that the top is not simply pulled into contact with the magnet. Remove the magnet while the top is still spinning and note its behavior.

Expected Outcome Because the top is fairly stable while spinning, it is analogous to the spinning hydrogen atoms in the body. The alignment and deflection of these atoms by the magnetic fields is analogous to the deflection of the top by the magnet. By observing a large-scale model of an atomic process, students can visualize the atomic process more clearly. **Visual**

CONCEPTS in Action

Peeking Inside the Human Body

Magnetic Resonance Imaging (MRI) is used by doctors to create more detailed images of the human body than are possible with X-rays.

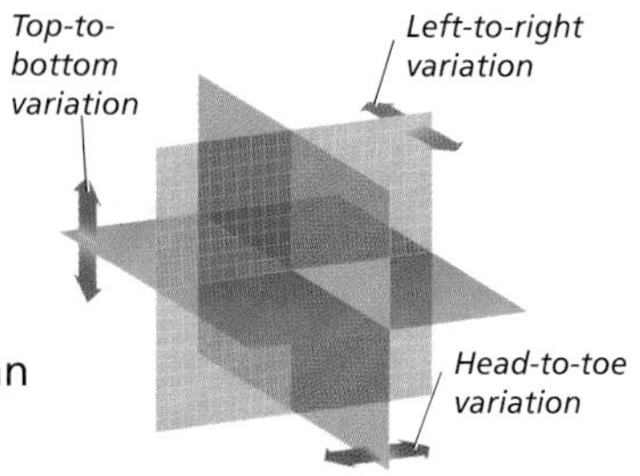

Top-to-bottom variation
Left-to-right variation
Head-to-toe variation

Creating an MRI image The scanner uses three magnetic fields to read data up and down and along slices of the body. This produces an image that is viewed and interpreted by doctors and radiographers.

Body tissues vary in their concentration of hydrogen atoms. Fat has a high concentration, as do tissues containing water, because of the hydrogen in H_2O. The concentration of hydrogen atoms in bone is very low. MRI reveals these differences in great detail, with fat and fluids (including blood) showing up as bright areas and bone as dark areas. MRI scans can even depict the brain. It produces images of such detail that they are used by researchers studying how the brain works, as well as by doctors investigating diseases.

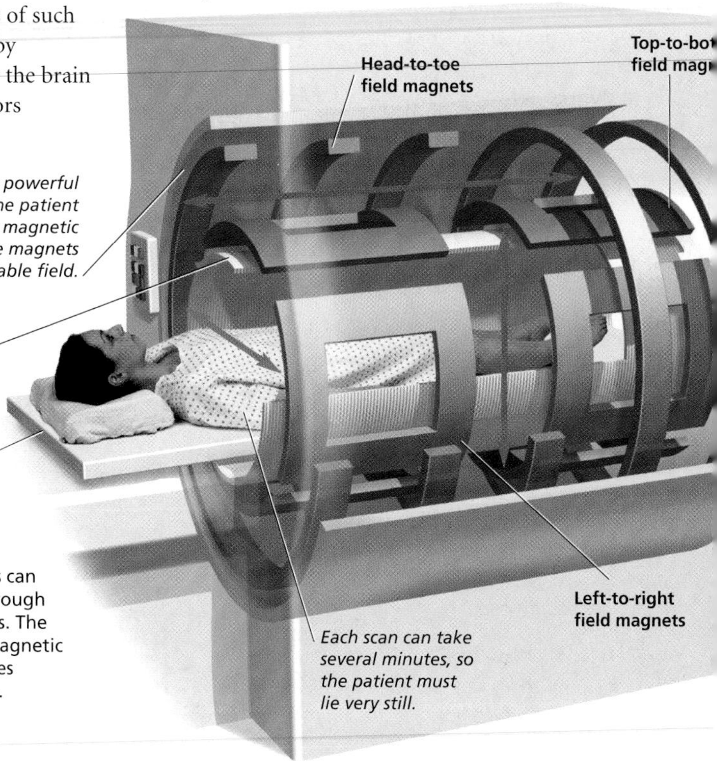

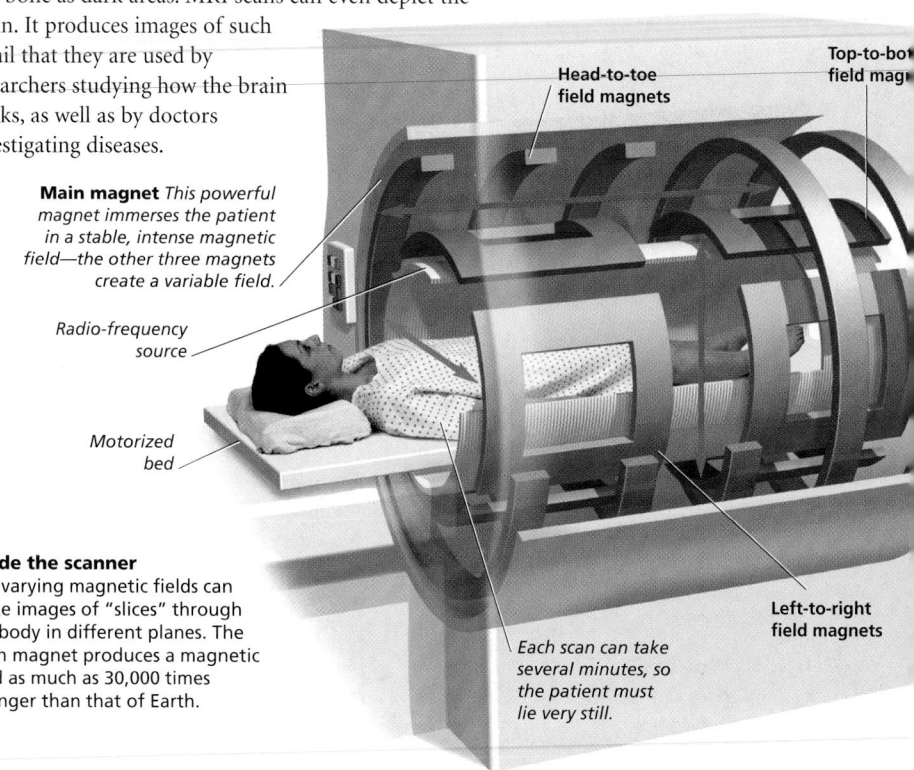

Head-to-toe field magnets
Top-to-bo field mag
Main magnet *This powerful magnet immerses the patient in a stable, intense magnetic field—the other three magnets create a variable field.*
Radio-frequency source
Motorized bed
Each scan can take several minutes, so the patient must lie very still.
Left-to-right field magnets

Inside the scanner The varying magnetic fields can make images of "slices" through the body in different planes. The main magnet produces a magnetic field as much as 30,000 times stronger than that of Earth.

How MRI works

MRI affects the nuclei of hydrogen atoms in the body. The nuclei are made to absorb and then re-emit energy by a combination of strong magnetic fields and radio wave pulses. The emitted signals are then used to map concentrations of hydrogen in the body.

1. Random axes
The spins of hydrogen nuclei point in random directions. Like tiny magnets, each nucleus has a north pole and a south pole.

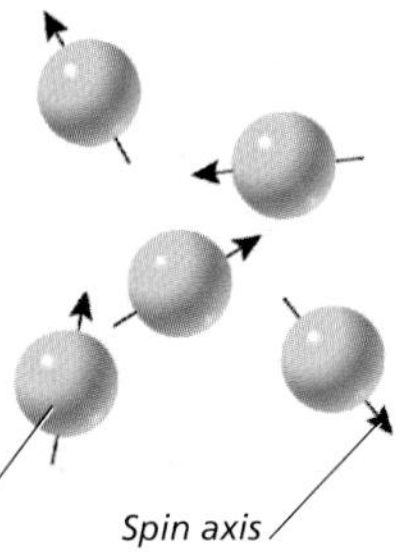
Hydrogen nucleus
Spin axis

2. Aligning axes
When the main MRI magnet is switched on, the magnetic field makes the spins of hydrogen nuclei mostly point in the same direction.

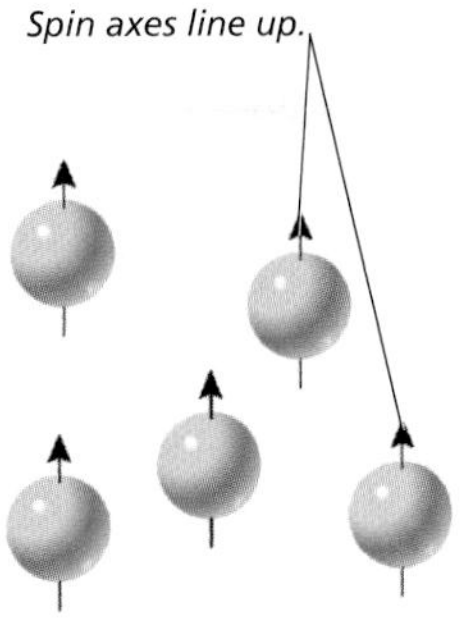
Spin axes line up.

3. Wobbling axes
A pulse of radio waves from the MRI scanner knocks the hydrogen nuclei out of alignment.

Pulse of radio waves from scanner
Spin axes change direction.

4. Realigning axes
When the pulse stops, hydrogen nuclei emit radio waves as they return to alignment with the main magnetic field. With the lesser magnets switched on as necessary to alter the magnetic field at a local level, these waves are picked up by the scanner, which builds up an image of different tissues.

Spin axes realign with magnetic field.
Radio waves emitted by nuclei.

MRI spinal cord scan
The bright red patch here indicates a tumor on the dark green spinal cord. While bone tissue itself is not visible, the vertebrae can be seen because of the marrow they contain.

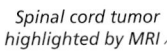

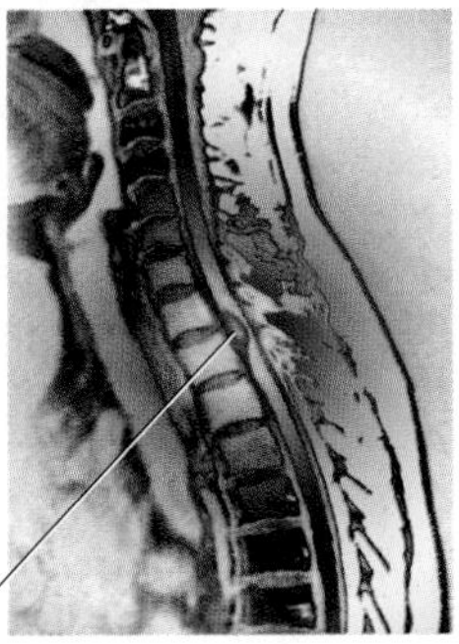
Spinal cord tumor highlighted by MRI

Going Further

- Items such as jewelry, watches, coins, keys, and credit cards must be removed before beginning an MRI. Research in the library or on the Internet why these items interfere with the procedure or pose a risk to the patient.
- Take a Discovery Channel Video Field Trip by watching "Magnetic Viewpoints."

Discovery Channel School **Video Field Trip**

Going Further

Student research should indicate that most of these items can be attracted by the powerful magnets in the MRI scanner, and this attraction could result in injury to the patient or damage to the machine. Credit cards and other identification with magnetic strips are in danger of being erased by the magnetic field. Watches with mechanical works can become permanently magnetized, and so cease to keep correct time. The electronics in digital watches may also be temporarily or permanently affected by strong magnetic fields.
Verbal, Logical

Discovery Channel School — Video Field Trip

Magnetic Viewpoints

After students have viewed the Video Field Trip, ask them the following questions: **What is the purpose of magnetic resonance imaging (MRI)?** *(Student answers may include recording images of internal body organs, detecting tumors, and observing how the brain works.)* **How does MRI work?** *(The patient is bathed in a strong magnetic field that causes some nuclei in the body's atoms to line up like spinning tops. A radio pulse knocks the nuclei out of alignment, and when the pulse stops the nuclei emit a signal as they line up again. A computer analyzes the signal to form an image.)* **What advantage does MRI have over X-rays in the detection of cancers?** *(It can detect some kinds of cancer earlier than X-rays can, and MRI is safer to use than X-rays.)* **Give an example of how MRI is used to study how the brain works.** *(Student answers may include that MRI images show the area of the brain that responds to a sensation such as pain in a particular part of the body. The images can be used to study medical disorders such as epilepsy and schizophrenia.)*

1 FOCUS

Objectives

21.3.1 **Describe** how electric current is generated by electromagnetic induction.

21.3.2 **Compare** AC and DC generators and **explain** how they work.

21.3.3 **Analyze** factors that determine the output voltage and current produced by a transformer.

21.3.4 **Summarize** how electrical energy is produced, transmitted, and converted for use in the home.

Reading Focus

Build Vocabulary — L2

Paraphrase Have students explain what the vocabulary terms mean by paraphrasing their definitions. Have them write a sentence in which the word is used, then have the word followed by the phrase *in other words*. This exercise allows students to be certain that they understand the meaning of a given term.

Reading Strategy — L2

a. Produces changing magnetic field
b. Induces current in larger coil

2 INSTRUCT

Generating Electric Current

Build Science Skills — L2

Classifying Have students recall the process of charge induction from Chapter 20. Ask, **How is electromagnetic induction similar to electric charge induction?** *(Both types of induction involve manipulating charges by using fields, either electric or magnetic, without any other contact with the charges.)* By grouping the processes of using fields to manipulate charges in conductors, the general idea of induction will become more concrete for students.
Verbal, Logical

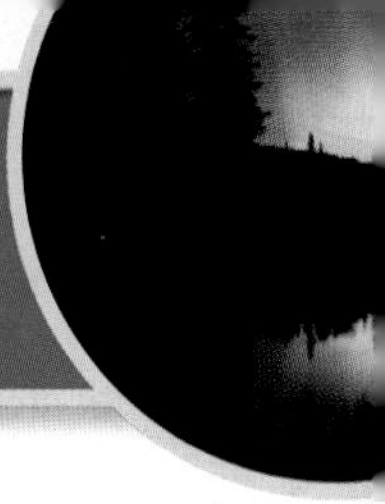

21.3 Electrical Energy Generation and Transmission

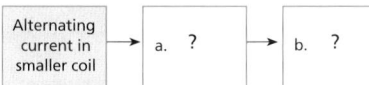

Reading Focus

Key Concepts
- How is voltage induced in a conductor?
- Name two types of generators.
- How can a transformer change voltage and current?
- What are some sources of electrical energy in the United States?

Vocabulary
- electromagnetic induction
- generator
- transformer
- turbine

Reading Strategy

Sequencing Copy the flowchart below. As you read, complete it to show how a step-up transformer works. Then make a similar flowchart for a step-down transformer.

Alternating current in smaller coil → a. ? → b. ?

Think about how electrical energy affects a city. Traffic lights change colors to control the flow of cars. Flashing neon lights advertise businesses. Subways use electrical energy to move from place to place. People use electrical energy to warm their homes, cook their suppers, and wash their clothes. At night, lights shine from the windows of tall buildings as shown in Figure 12. Where does all the electrical energy come from?

Generating Electric Current

All of the electrical energy that moves subway trains, lights buildings, and powers factories comes from the two aspects of the electromagnetic force. You already know that an electric current produces a magnetic field. However, you may not know that a magnetic field can be used to produce an electric current. **Electromagnetic induction** is the process of generating a current by moving an electrical conductor relative to a magnetic field. Recall that electrical conductors are materials through which charge can easily flow.

Figure 12 Photographs of large cities, such as Seattle, Washington, are visible reminders of how much people rely on electrical energy.

642

Section Resources

Print
- ***Laboratory Manual,*** Investigation 21A
- ***Reading and Study Workbook With Math Support,*** Section 21.3 and **Math Skill:** Calculating Voltage
- ***Transparencies,*** Section 21.3

Technology
- ***Probeware Lab Manual,*** Lab 9
- ***Interactive Textbook,*** Section 21.3
- ***Presentation Pro CD-ROM,*** Section 21.3
- ***Go Online,*** NSTA SciLinks, Transformers; PHSchool.com, Data sharing

The English scientist Michael Faraday (1791–1867) discovered electromagnetic induction in 1831, opening the way for many practical uses of electromagnetism. **According to Faraday's law, a voltage is induced in a conductor by a changing magnetic field.** For example, changing the magnetic field through a coil of wire induces a voltage in the coil. But a current results only if the coil is part of a complete circuit.

You can see this process at work by placing a magnet inside a coil of wire attached to a galvanometer, as shown in Figure 13. If you hold the magnet still, the galvanometer will detect no current in the wire. However, if you quickly move the magnet out of the coil, the current flows briefly, and then immediately drops back to zero. Moving the magnet in and out of the coil causes an electric current first in one direction and then in the other. The same alternating current occurs if you move the coil and keep the magnet still. As long as the magnet and coil are moving relative to one another, the galvanometer will record a current.

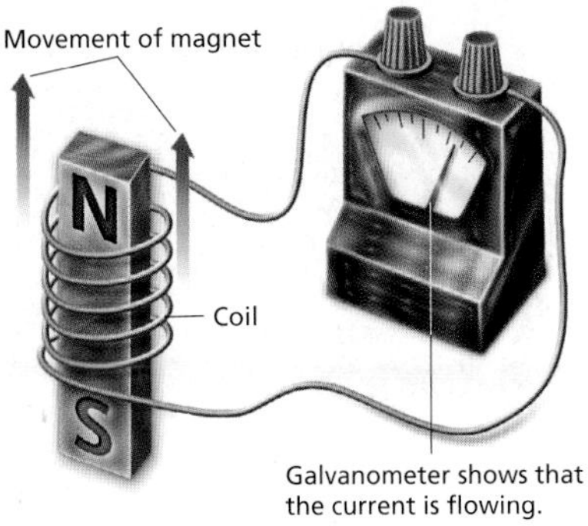

Movement of magnet
N
S
Coil
Galvanometer shows that the current is flowing.

Figure 13 According to Faraday's law, the moving magnetic field induces a current in the coil. ***Predicting*** ***If you increase the number of turns in the coil, and move the magnet at the same speed, will the current increase or decrease?***

Generators

Moving the magnet in the coil shown in Figure 13 produces only a small amount of electric current. Most of the electrical energy used in homes and businesses is produced at large power plants using generators. A **generator** is a device that converts mechanical energy into electrical energy by rotating a coil of wire in a magnetic field. Electric current is generated by the relative motion of a conducting coil in a magnetic field. **The two types of generators are AC generators and DC generators.** Although both types have been used, most power plants today use AC generators.

AC Generators Figure 14 shows a simplified AC generator. An actual generator has many loops of wire. The generator produces alternating current, in which charges flow first in one direction and then in the other direction. As you can see, the generator looks very similar to the electric motor you previously studied. While a motor converts electrical energy into mechanical energy, a generator does the opposite.

A wire coil in the generator is attached to metal bands called slip rings. The slip rings are in contact with metal brushes that are in turn attached to a circuit. As the loop of wire is rotated, perhaps by someone turning it, the magnetic field induces a current in the wire. This current is in one direction, and then when the loop turns halfway around, the current reverses direction.

Figure 14 In a simple AC generator, an external force rotates the loop of wire in the magnetic field. This induces a current in the wire. ***Forming Hypotheses*** ***Could you also induce a current if you rotated the magnets instead of the wire loop?***

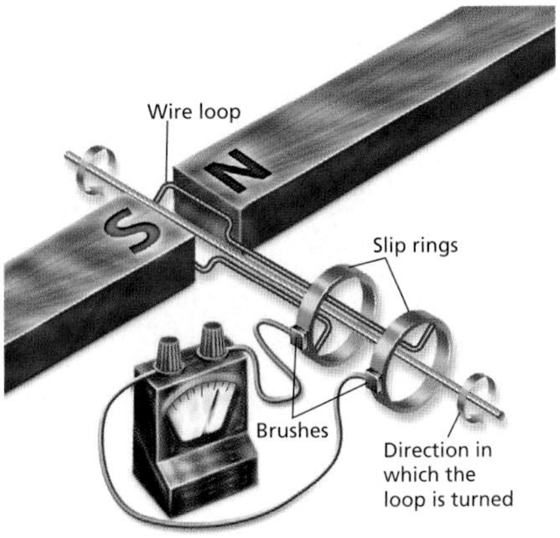

Wire loop
N
S
Slip rings
Brushes
Direction in which the loop is turned

Use Visuals

L1

Figure 13 Stress that the upward movement of the magnet produces the same results as moving the coil downward over the magnet. In both situations, the relative change of the magnetic field with respect to the coil is identical. Have students examine the figure carefully. Ask, **In which direction would the galvanometer needle deflect if the magnet were moved downward?** *(To the left side of the gauge)* Ask, **Would the result be the same if the coil were moved upward over the magnet?** *(Yes)*
Logical, Visual

Generators

Teacher Demo

Generating Alternating Current

L2

Purpose Students will observe how a generator produces an alternating current that varies with the speed of rotation of the generator coils.

Materials a hand-operated generator, a galvanometer, insulated wire (2 strands)

Procedure Connect the output terminals of a hand-cranked generator (preferably the demonstration type found in school labs) to the wires, and the other ends of the wires to the terminals of the galvanometer. Point out the various parts of the generator that are shown in Figure 14 (loop or coil, slip rings, and brushes). Turn the generator crank slowly and smoothly, and allow students to observe the changes in the galvanometer needle. Increase the speed of cranking to demonstrate how this increases the current.

Safety Be sure to use insulated wire. Follow lab safety for use of electrical devices.

Expected Outcome The galvanometer needle should move back and forth, indicating the changing direction of the electric current produced by the generator.
Visual, Group

Customize for English Language Learners

Reading/Learning Log
The concept of electromagnetic induction is subtle, and is the basis for understanding generators, transformers, and electric power transmission. Be sure that English language learners have a clear understanding of this concept by having them construct a Reading/Learning Log. Have students write what they understand in the left column, and what they still have questions about in the right column. Allow time for groups of students of mixed language abilities to share their logs.

Answer to . . .

Figure 13 *Increase*

Figure 14 *Yes, induction takes place regardless of whether the loop or magnets are moved.*

Transformers

Integrate Social Studies L2

During the early 1880s, electric power in the United States was distributed as direct current. This system was successful at first because electric energy did not have to be transmitted very long distances. However, as demand and the distances between production and consumption increased, direct-current production could only succeed by transmitting electric energy with greater currents. At the same time, the Europeans were developing alternating-current systems for electric power. In 1885, George Westinghouse imported an AC generator and transformers, and installed an electric power system in Pittsburgh, Pennsylvania. Over the next seven years, alternating-current generation became more widespread, despite strong resistance from Thomas Edison and other supporters and producers of direct current.
Verbal

Address Misconceptions L2

Students may be confused in thinking that a transformer violates the principle of energy conservation. Explain to students that, for an ideal transformer, the amount of energy that goes into the transformer each second (the input power) is equal to the energy leaving the transformer each second (the output power). Remind students that electrical power equals voltage times current. Because a great deal of electrical energy is lost by heating, which is dependent upon the resistance of the conductor and current, less energy is lost when the voltage is high and the current is low. Thus, while transformers do not create electrical energy, they do help to reduce the loss of electrical energy.
Logical

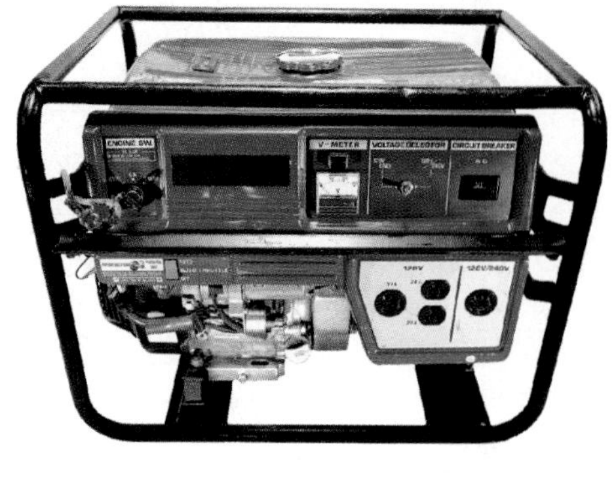

Figure 15 Small generators provide power in areas that are not served by power companies. These generators may also be used to provide electrical energy during a power outage.

You can buy a small AC generator to power electrical devices during a power outage or to use in areas not served by a power company. Figure 15 shows an AC generator that can produce 3300 watts of power. This is enough for a household or small business to use. Power plants use AC generators that are huge compared to the generator shown here.

DC Generators A DC generator produces a direct current. Its design is very much like the design of an AC generator except that a commutator replaces the slip rings. As the loop rotates, an alternating current is induced in the wire. First, one side of the commutator contacts a brush. When the loop rotates, current is induced in the other direction, but now the other side of the commutator contacts that brush. For this reason, the current that leaves the generator flows in only one direction.

Reading Checkpoint *What kind of current does a DC generator produce?*

Transformers

The electrical energy produced by power plants is transmitted through power lines at very high voltages. These voltages are too high to be used safely in homes. The voltage must first be changed, or transformed. A **transformer** is a device that increases or decreases the voltage and current of two linked AC circuits. A series of transformers changes high-voltage current in power lines into 240-volt current that can be used safely in your home.

A transformer works only with alternating current because only alternating current induces a constantly changing magnetic field. **A transformer changes voltage and current by inducing a changing magnetic field in one coil. This changing field then induces an alternating current in a nearby coil with a different number of turns.**

Why Transformers Are Needed Early power plants used DC generators because the power plants were close to the customers. As the demand for electric power increased, power plants had to transmit power much farther. Remember that an electric charge moving through a wire heats the wire. Over long distances, the resistance of the wire causes large losses of power. Power losses can be reduced by using lower current transmitted at a higher voltage. However, voltage and current can be transformed only with alternating current.

Go Online NSTA SCiLINKS
For: Links on transformers
Visit: www.SciLinks.org
Web Code: ccn-2213

Go Online NSTA SCiLINKS

Download a worksheet on transformers for students to complete, and find additional teacher support from NSTA SciLinks.

Facts and Figures

Uniform Direct Current The direct current produced by a generator with a commutator moves in one direction, but it is not a steady current. As with AC, the induced current from the generator ranges from a maximum value to 0 amps, then increases to the maximum value again. To remedy this, many DC generators use several coils that are mounted on the rotating axle. The commutator consists of many segments, with each coil attached to two oppositely positioned segments. The coils rotate in the magnetic field, and at any given moment they are at different places in their rotation—one may be at a maximum output while another is at a minimum. The different amounts of current are combined and transferred to the output circuit. The coils are oriented in a uniform way to the magnets, so the total output current is nearly the same at all times. In this way, a nearly constant direct current is produced.

Changing Voltage and Current Figure 16 shows two types of transformers. Notice that each transformer has two sets of coils wrapped around a ring-shaped iron core. When there is an alternating current in the primary coil, the current creates a changing magnetic field in the iron core. Because the iron core is also inside the secondary coil, the changing field induces an alternating current in the secondary coil.

The number of turns in the primary and secondary coils determines the voltage and current. To calculate the voltage, divide the number of turns in the secondary coil by the number of turns in the primary coil. The result is the ratio of the output voltage to the input voltage.

Transformers are very efficient because very little energy is lost as heat. Assuming 100% efficiency, the power ($I \times V$) must be the same in the primary and secondary coils. Therefore, if voltage increases in the secondary coil, the current must decrease in the same ratio.

Types of Transformers A step-down transformer decreases voltage and increases current. Notice in Figure 16A that the primary coil has 400 turns, and the secondary coil has 100 turns. If the input voltage in the primary coil is 120 volts, then the output voltage is reduced to 30 volts.

A step-up transformer increases voltage and decreases current. In Figure 16B, the primary coil has 100 turns, and the secondary coil has 400 turns. If the input voltage is 20 volts, the output voltage is 80 volts.

Figure 16 Transformers, such as those at substations of power plants, change voltage. **A** A step-down transformer decreases voltage and increases current. **B** A step-up transformer increases voltage and decreases current.

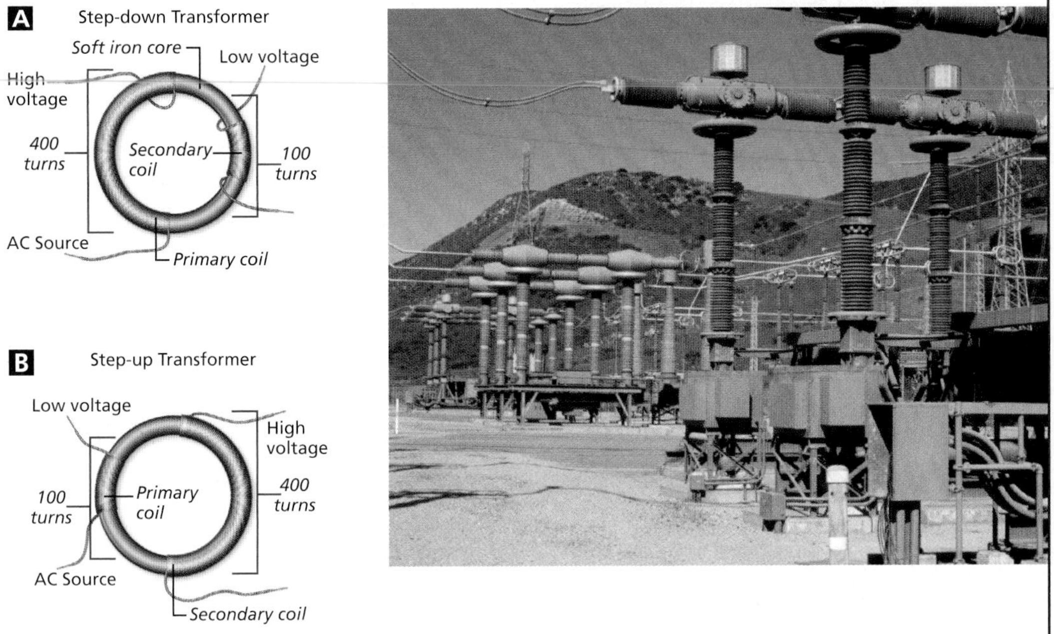
A
Step-down Transformer
Soft iron core
Low voltage
High voltage
400 turns
Secondary coil
100 turns
AC Source
Primary coil
B
Step-up Transformer
Low voltage
High voltage
100 turns
Primary coil
400 turns
AC Source
Secondary coil

Build Reading Literacy L1

Reciprocal Teaching Refer to page **628D** in this chapter, which provides the guidelines for reciprocal teaching.

To help students understand science concepts, have them apply the strategies of summarize, question, clarify, and predict as they read the section under the heading Transformers. For instance, before students begin to read, ask, **What do you think a transformer is used for?** *(Students may respond that transformers are used to transform, or change, electric current in some way.)* Have students read to verify their predictions. To help students determine what information is important and to check understanding, ask questions such as **Why must voltage from power lines be reduced before entering homes?** *(Voltage is stepped up at power plants so that electric current can be transmitted more efficiently over long distances. Overheating, and therefore loss of power, can be avoided by transmitting lower current at higher voltage. A step-down transformer reduces voltage and increases current to levels that can safely be used to operate appliances in a home.)* Clarify the meanings of unfamiliar words and concepts. Ask students to summarize what has been read. Encourage students to assume the role of leader in these discussions as they become familiar with the use of these strategies.
Verbal, Group

Use Community Resources L2

Suggest that students learn more about different transformers by contacting the Public Information Office of the local electric utility. Have students find out where step-up and step-down transformers are used in your city, how many types of each kind are used, and the number of turns of wire used for the primary and secondary coils of each. Encourage them also to gather information on the efficiency of the transformers. Have them write a short report of their findings.
Intrapersonal, Portfolio

Answer to . . .

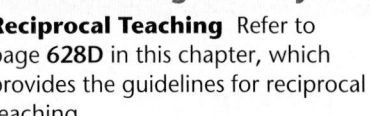

Reading Checkpoint: *Direct current*

Electrical Energy for Your Home

Problem-Solving Activity

Transmitting Electricity to a New School L2

Defining the Problem As an engineer, I must first find out what voltage and current are needed for the school, and how this compares with the voltage and current generated at the power plant. If the power plant is very far away from the school, the voltage needs to be stepped up and down more than if the school is close.

Organizing Information Students can find out from the local electric company what the voltage use for schools is, and how far they are from substations. Transformer conversion factors must also be obtained.

Creating a Solution Once a nearby substation has been located and the distance to a power plant determined, connection of power lines can be planned. The voltage changes along the path should ensure that power can travel the necessary distances, and that the final voltage at the school is correct.

Presenting Your Plan Students' posters should include values for the different voltages along the transmission path, and should resemble Figure 18 in layout and content. The school should have some devices with input voltages of 120 V and some that operate at 220–240 V. The generated voltages will depend on how far the power is transmitted. Locally produced electricity may need to be stepped up or down only once, and then only by a factor of about 10. If the school is far from a substation, student designs may include a power substation specifically for the school's use.
Logical, Interpersonal

For Extra Help L1

Be sure that the need for transformers is clear to students. Emphasize that stepped-up voltages are necessary to reduce heat loss for long-distance transmissions. Encourage students to examine and understand Figure 18, as the information and presentation given there is similar to what they are to prepare.
Verbal, Visual

Problem-Solving Activity

Transmitting Electricity to a New School

You have been hired as an electrical engineer at your local power plant. Your first task is to plan how electrical energy can be transmitted from the power plant to a school that will soon be built. There are many things you need to investigate. What is the voltage generated at the power plant? How should it be stepped up for transmission? How can it be stepped down for use in the new school?

Defining the Problem Write a few sentences that describe your task and the steps you can take to complete it.

Organizing Information Research the steps that are taken to transmit electrical energy from the power plant to other schools in your area.

Creating a Solution Decide what steps you would take to transmit electrical energy to the new school.

Presenting Your Plan Create a poster showing how electrical energy can be transmitted to the new school. Include descriptions of the types of transformers you could use.

Figure 17 A turbine turns the magnet inside the coil of a generator. **Predicting** *What would happen if a turbine turned faster?*

Electrical Energy for Your Home

A single electric light uses relatively little electrical energy by itself. A massive amount of electrical energy, however, is needed for the lights and other electrical devices that are used by people in an entire city. Consumption on that scale requires equally huge production of electrical energy to meet the demand.

Most of the electrical energy generated in the United States is produced using coal as an energy source. Some other sources are water (hydroelectric), nuclear energy, wind, natural gas, and petroleum. Below each of the generators that are shown in Figure 17 is a large turbine, which can convert energy from one of these sources into electrical energy. A **turbine** is a device with fanlike blades that turn when pushed, for example, by water or steam. Burning fossil fuels or nuclear reactions can heat water to produce steam that spins a turbine. Water pouring over a dam can also turn a turbine. To produce electrical energy, the turbine may turn the coils of a generator or it may spin magnets around the coils of wire.

Reading Checkpoint *What can push the blades of a turbine?*

Facts and Figures

Appliance Power Usage Most appliances in the United States are designed to operate between 110 V and 120 V with an alternating-current frequency of 60 Hz. However, some larger appliances, such as electric ranges, clothes dryers, and air conditioners operate at 240 V. Special wiring is needed in the parts of a house where these appliances are used.

Many countries, particularly in Europe, have a household voltage between 220 V and 240 V with a frequency of 50 Hz. Appliances used in these countries are manufactured to operate at these higher voltages. International travelers often carry converters, devices that use a transformer to change voltage and current so that an appliance designed for one system can be used in another system.

646 Chapter 21

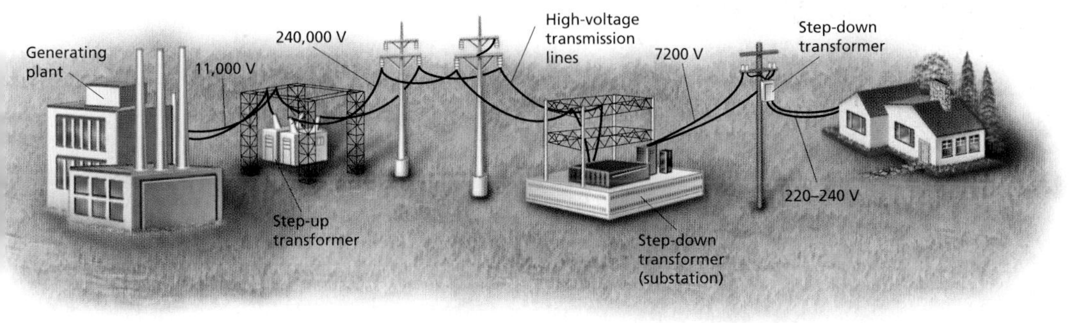
Generating plant
11,000 V
240,000 V
Step-up transformer
High-voltage transmission lines
Step-down transformer (substation)
7200 V
Step-down transformer
220–240 V

Follow the steps shown in Figure 18 from the point where electrical energy is generated. The power plant on the left generates electrical energy that is stepped up to hundreds of thousands of volts. Transformers, which are shown in the middle of the diagram, make it possible to bring electrical energy efficiently from the power plant to users. After traveling along the high-voltage transmission lines, the voltage is stepped down at a substation, to a few thousand volts. The electrical energy is then distributed to neighborhoods. Just before the electrical energy reaches people's homes, the voltage is stepped down to between 220 and 240 volts. Heavy duty appliances, like an electric stove, use 240-volt circuits. Most other appliances in the home use 120 volts.

Figure 18 Voltage is increased for long-distance transmission, and then decreased near homes, schools, and businesses. **Interpreting Diagrams** ***How many step-down transformers are shown in the figure?***

Section 21.3 Assessment

Reviewing Concepts

1. How is voltage induced in a conductor?
2. Name two types of generators.
3. How does a transformer work?
4. Name six sources of electrical energy in the United States.

Critical Thinking

5. **Relating Cause and Effect** Explain how water can be used to create electrical energy.
6. **Applying Concepts** What is the connection between Faraday's law and the generation of electrical energy?
7. **Comparing and Contrasting** Describe how AC generators and DC generators are alike and how they are different.
8. **Drawing Conclusions** Why can't you use electrical energy directly from a high-voltage line?
9. **Calculating** An electronic device contains a transformer. Its primary coil has 200 turns, and its secondary coil has 20 turns. If the device is plugged into a 120-volt line, what is the output voltage of the device?

Writing in Science

Compare-Contrast Paragraph Write a paragraph comparing and contrasting what step-up and step-down transformers do. (*Hint:* Use the terms *voltage, primary coil, secondary coil, input,* and *output.*)

Use Visuals — L1

Figure 18 Have students look carefully at the various changes in voltage that occur during power transmission between the generating plant and a home. Ask, **What is the stepped-up voltage for transmission?** *(The voltage is stepped up from 11,000 V to 240,000 V.)* Ask, **By how much is the voltage stepped down at the substation?** *(The voltage is stepped down from 240,000 V to 7200 V.)*
Visual

3 ASSESS

Evaluate Understanding — L2

Ask each student to write two questions about generating and transmitting electric power. Review the questions for accuracy, and then have students form groups and quiz each other, using their approved questions.

Reteach — L1

Use Figure 14 to review how a generator uses electromagnetic induction to produce an alternating current.

Writing in Science

Student paragraphs should include the following comparisons: both transformers have iron cores to channel the magnetic field; both have primary and secondary coils of wire for the input and output of electricity; neither has any moving parts. Contrasts should include: a step-up transformer increases voltage and decreases current, while a step-down transformer decreases voltage and increases current; a step-up transformer has more wire turns in the secondary (output) coil than in the primary (input) coil, while a step-down transformer has more wire turns in the primary coil.

Interactive Textbook If your class subscribes to the Interactive Textbook, use it to review key concepts in Section 21.3.

Section 21.3 Assessment

1. Voltage is induced in a conductor by a changing magnetic field.
2. AC, which produces alternating current, and DC, which produces direct current
3. A transformer changes voltage and current by generating a changing magnetic field in one coil. This field then induces a current in a nearby coil with a different number of turns.
4. Coal, nuclear power, water (hydroelectric), wind, natural gas, and petroleum
5. Water can turn a turbine that turns the axle of a generator and produces electricity.
6. The relative motion of a magnet and a coil of wire will cause charges to flow in the wire, thus generating an electric current and electrical energy.
7. Both produce an electric current by the rotation of a wire coil in a magnetic field. In a DC generator, current flows in only one direction.
8. High voltages are dangerous. Household devices are designed to use much lower voltages.
9. 12 V

Answer to . . .

Figure 17 *A faster-turning turbine would turn the generator faster, generating a higher current.*

Figure 18 *Two*

Reading Checkpoint *Steam or water*

Application Lab

Investigating an Electric Generator L2

Objective
After completing this activity, students will be able to
- describe how an electric generator works.

Skill Focus **Observing, Using Data Tables, Using Graphs**

Prep Time 20 minutes

Advance Prep Cut a 5-m length of wire for each lab group and strip 3 cm of the insulation from the ends of the wires. Provide cardboard tubes from empty paper towel rolls.

Class Time 45 minutes

Safety Students should wear safety goggles and lab aprons.

Teaching Tips
- You may need to show students how to use the multimeters if they have not used them earlier.
- In Step 12 and subsequent steps, make sure that students read the sign or direction of the current correctly; it will be the reverse of the direction observed in the previous steps. If the multimeter does not permit a reading of current flowing in either direction, it may be necessary to reverse the connections of the multimeter wires.

Expected Outcome The induced current is directly proportional to the number of turns. Reversing the poles of the magnet or the direction of the turns reverses the direction of the current.

Application Lab

Investigating an Electric Generator

All generators have two main parts—a magnet and a wire that is wrapped into a coil. The arrangement of these parts varies, depending on the size and power of the generator and whether it produces direct or alternating current. In this lab, you will determine how several variables affect the current produced by a simple generator.

Problem
How do the direction in which the magnet moves and the number and direction of the turns in the coil affect the current that a generator produces?

Materials
- cardboard tube
- 5-m length of insulated wire
- metric ruler
- multimeter
- bar magnet
- graph paper

For the probeware version of this lab, see the Probeware Lab Manual, Lab 9.

Skills
Observing, Using Graphs

Procedure

Part A: Changing the Number of Turns

1. On a separate sheet of paper, make a copy of the data table shown below.

Data Table

Number of Turns	Direction of Turns	Pole Inserted	Current (mA)
10	Clockwise	North	
20	Clockwise	North	
30	Clockwise	North	
30	Clockwise	South	
30	Counterclockwise	North	

2. Slip the wire between your hand and the cardboard tube so that 15 cm of wire extends from the tube. Use your other hand to wrap the long end of the wire around the tube 10 times in a clockwise direction. Make sure all the turns are within 10 cm of the end of the tube. **CAUTION** *Be careful not to cut yourself on the sharp ends of the wire.*
3. Connect both ends of the wire to the multimeter. Set the multimeter to measure current.
4. Hold the bar magnet by its south pole. Observe the multimeter as you quickly insert the bar magnet into the open end of the cardboard tube that is wrapped with the wire coil. Repeat this step if necessary as you adjust the scale of the multimeter. Record the maximum current in your data table.
5. Disconnect the multimeter from the end of the wire that is farther from the turns.
6. **Predicting** Record your prediction of how increasing the number of turns in the coil will affect the current.
7. To test your prediction, wrap the wire around the end of the tube 10 more times in the same direction as you did previously—clockwise. You should now have a total of 20 turns. Reconnect the wire to the multimeter.
8. Repeat Step 4.
9. Again, disconnect the multimeter from the same end of the wire. Wrap the wire clockwise around the tube 10 more times for a total of 30 turns. Reconnect the wire to the multimeter.
10. Repeat Step 4 and then disconnect the multimeter from the same end of the wire.

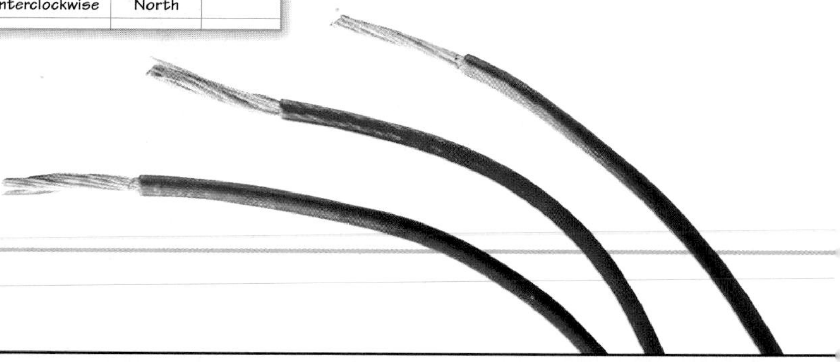

Sample Data Table

Number of Turns	Direction of Turns	Pole Inserted	Current (mA)
10	Clockwise	North	0.4
20	Clockwise	North	1.0
30	Clockwise	North	2.5
30	Clockwise	South	−2.4
30	Counterclockwise	North	−2.4

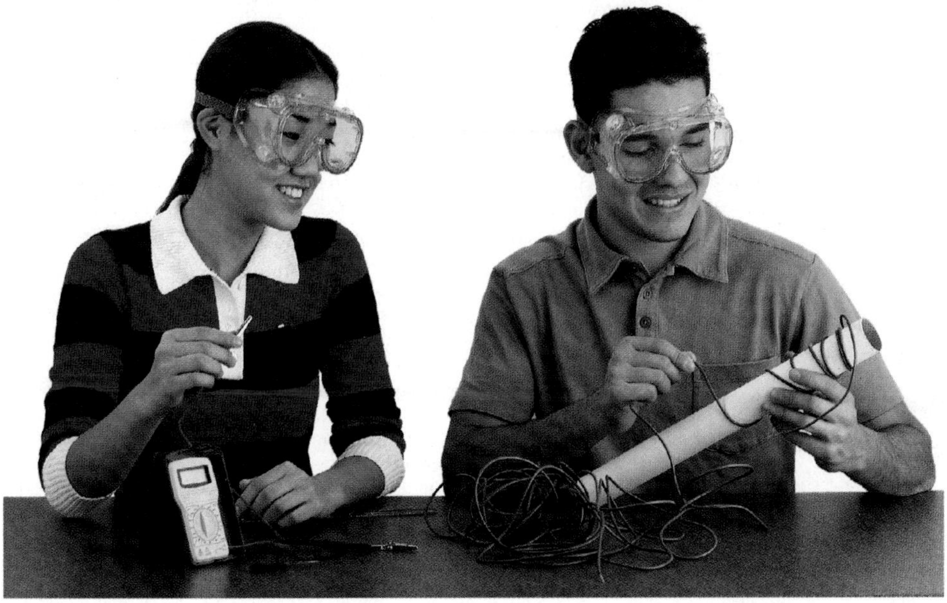

Part B: Changing Other Properties of the Generator

11. **Predicting** Record your prediction of how reversing the direction of the magnet will affect the current.
12. To test your prediction, reconnect the wire to the multimeter exactly as you did before. Repeat Step 4, but this time, hold the magnet by its north pole.
13. **Predicting** Record your prediction of how reversing the direction of the turns in the coil will affect the current if you hold the magnet by its south pole.
14. To test your prediction, remove the wire from the tube. Now wrap 30 turns of wire in the opposite direction—counterclockwise.
15. Repeat Step 4, holding the magnet by its south pole.
16. Construct a graph using the data from the first three rows of your data table. Plot the number of turns on the horizontal axis and the current on the vertical axis.

Analyze and Conclude

1. **Inferring** What caused a current in the wire?
2. **Using Graphs** Based on your graph, what is the relationship between the number of turns and the amount of current?
3. **Analyzing Data** Explain the effect that reversing the direction of the magnet or the direction of the turns had on the direction of the current.
4. **Predicting** Explain whether a generator could be built with a stationary magnet and a coil that moved.
5. **Evaluating and Revising** Did your observations support your predictions? If not, evaluate any flaws in the reasoning you used to make the predictions.

Go Online PHSchool.com

For: Data sharing
Visit: PHSchool.com
Web Code: ccd-2210

Probeware Lab Manual Versions of this lab for use with probeware available from Pasco, Texas Instruments, and Vernier are in the Probeware Lab Manual.

Analyze and Conclude

1. A current flowed in the wire because the moving magnetic field exerted a force on the electrons in the wire, causing them to move.
2. The graph indicates that the number of turns are in direct proportion to the amount of current.
3. Reversing the direction of the magnet or the turns reversed the direction of the force of the magnetic field on the electrons in the wire. This change in direction caused the charges to move in the opposite direction.
4. Yes, it is possible for such a generator to be built. It is only necessary that the magnetic field in the wire coils change. It does not matter which part moves to accomplish this task.
5. Correct predictions should state that an increase in the number of turns in the coil increases the strength of the current, and that reversing the direction of the turns or the magnet will reverse the direction of the current. Errors in reasoning may involve assuming that the direction of the coil or magnet motion does not affect current direction. If a current is too weak to observe, students may fail to realize that the speed of the magnet's motion may account for a weak induced current, and that increasing the number of turns may not provide the right results if the change in the magnetic field is not kept fairly constant throughout the experiment.
Logical

Go Further

Students should easily identify the wire coils and magnets in an actual generator. Generators and motors vary in the placement of the magnets, whether they are permanent or electromagnets, and whether the magnets or the coils rotate.
Logical, Group

Go Online PHSchool.com

Students should see that the current increases in proportion to the number of turns and that it reverses direction when the direction of the magnet or the turns are reversed, but their results will depend on their own data and the data on the site.

Study Guide

Study Tip

Occasionally, Study With a Friend
Tell students to occasionally work together by quizzing each other, comparing notes, and discussing discrepancies in each other's ideas about a subject. This process allows for each student to critically assess accumulated knowledge. Stress that the work should be shared equally between the two students.

Thinking Visually

a. A magnetic field
b. An electric current

CHAPTER 21 Study Guide

21.1 Magnets and Magnetic Fields

Key Concepts

- Like magnetic poles repel one another, and opposite magnetic poles attract one another.
- A magnetic field, which is strongest near a magnet's poles, will either attract or repel another magnet that enters the field.
- When a material is magnetized, most of its magnetic domains are aligned.

Vocabulary

magnetic force, *p. 630*
magnetic pole, *p. 630*
magnetic field, *p. 631*
magnetosphere, *p. 632*
magnetic domain, *p. 632*
ferromagnetic material, *p. 632*

21.2 Electromagnetism

Key Concepts

- Moving electric charges create a magnetic field.
- Changing the current in an electromagnet controls the strength and direction of its magnetic field.
- Electromagnetic devices such as galvanometers, electric motors, and loudspeakers change electrical energy into mechanical energy.

Vocabulary

electromagnetic force, *p. 635*
solenoid, *p. 637*
electromagnet, *p. 637*
galvanometer, *p. 638*
electric motor, *p. 639*

21.3 Electrical Energy Generation and Transmission

Key Concepts

- According to Faraday's law, a voltage is induced in a conductor by a changing magnetic field.
- The two types of generators are AC generators and DC generators.
- A transformer changes voltage and current by inducing a changing magnetic field in one coil. This changing field then induces an alternating current in a nearby coil with a different number of turns.
- Most of the electrical energy generated in the United States is produced using coal as an energy source. Some other sources are water (hydroelectric), nuclear energy, wind, natural gas, and petroleum.

Vocabulary

electromagnetic induction, *p. 642*
generator, *p. 643*
transformer, *p. 644*
turbine, *p. 646*

Thinking Visually

Concept Map Copy the concept map below onto a sheet of paper. Use information from the chapter to complete the chart.

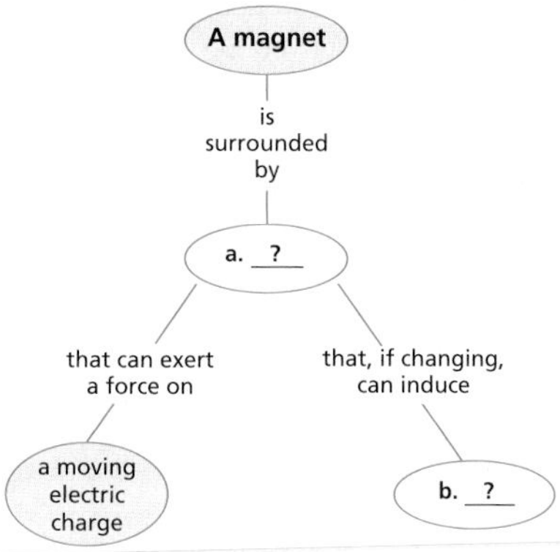
A magnet
is surrounded by
a. ?
that can exert a force on
that, if changing, can induce
a moving electric charge
b. ?

Chapter Resources

Print
- ***Chapter and Unit Tests,*** Chapter 21 Test A and Test B
- ***Test Prep Resources,*** Chapter 21

Technology
- ***Computer Test Bank,*** Chapter Test 21
- ***Interactive Textbook,*** Chapter 21
- ***Go Online,*** PHSchool.com, Chapter 21

CHAPTER 21

Assessment

Interactive textbook with assessment at PHSchool.com iText

Reviewing Content

Choose the letter that best answers the question or completes the statement.

1. Where is the field of a magnet strongest?
   a. near the north pole
   b. near the south pole
   c. near both poles
   d. near the middle
2. If you cut a magnet in half, you have
   a. no magnets.
   b. two half magnets.
   c. one magnet.
   d. two magnets.
3. A magnet's field lines always start near the magnet's
   a. middle. b. south pole.
   c. north pole. d. side.
4. A ferromagnetic material is
   a. always a magnet.
   b. a magnet if its domains are aligned.
   c. a magnet if its domains are not aligned.
   d. never a magnet.
5. An iron bar is placed in a solenoid to
   a. decrease the voltage.
   b. increase the voltage.
   c. increase the magnetic field strength.
   d. decrease the magnetic field strength.
6. Which of these cannot increase the strength of an electromagnet?
   a. making the loops smaller in the coil
   b. placing an iron bar in the coil
   c. winding more loops in the coil
   d. increasing the current in the coil
7. An electric generator converts
   a. electrical energy into mechanical energy.
   b. power into energy.
   c. mechanical energy into electrical energy.
   d. energy into power.
8. What effect does a magnetic field have on a charge moving perpendicular to the field?
   a. It has no effect.
   b. It pulls the charge forward.
   c. It pushes the charge backward.
   d. It pushes the charge perpendicularly to the field and the charge's velocity.
9. A galvanometer is a device used to measure
   a. current.
   b. resistance.
   c. voltage.
   d. magnetic field strength.
10. A transformer increases or decreases
    a. energy.
    b. resistance.
    c. voltage.
    d. direct current.

Understanding Concepts

11. What part of an atom is responsible for producing magnetic fields?
12. Why is iron easy to magnetize when used in an electromagnet?
13. How are magnetic domains in nonmagnetized materials different from the magnetic domains in magnetized materials?
14. Explain how you can determine the direction of a magnetic field produced by a wire if you know the direction of current through the wire.
15. The figure below shows a current-carrying wire between the poles of two magnets. In which direction is charge deflected by the magnetic field?

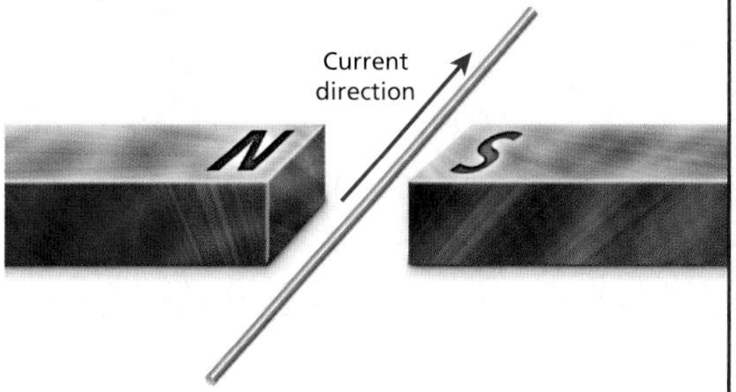
Current direction
N
S

16. How can a change in the voltage of a transformer's primary coil create a change in the secondary coil's voltage, without the coils touching?
17. A transformer is connected to a 9-volt battery. A student tries to use this setup to double the voltage for an experiment. However, the output voltage is zero. Explain why.

Homework Guide

Section	Questions
21.1	1–4, 11–13, 18, 28
21.2	5–6, 8–9, 14–15, 19–21
21.3	7, 10, 16–17, 22–27, 29–31

Assessment

Interactive Textbook If your class subscribes to the Interactive Textbook, your students can go online to access an interactive version of the Student Edition and a self-test.

Reviewing Content

1. c 2. d 3. c
4. b 5. c 6. a
7. c 8. d 9. a
10. c

Understanding Concepts

11. Moving electrons
12. It is ferromagnetic and can be easily magnetized to become a temporary magnet.
13. The domains in a nonmagnetized material are not aligned. The domains in a magnetized material are aligned.
14. Point your thumb in the direction of the current. Your fingers curl in the direction of the magnetic field.
15. Down
16. The changing voltage in the primary coil creates a changing magnetic field. The secondary coil's voltage is induced by the changing magnetic field that passes through both coils.
17. Transformers only operate with alternating current. The battery provides direct current.

Critical Thinking

18. The magnetic domains of the iron nail will align under the influence of the magnet, and so will act temporarily as a magnet. The nail is thus attracted to the magnet. There is no such alignment of the atoms in the button into magnetic domains, and so there is no attraction.
19. The force an electric field exerts is in the direction of the electric field. The force exerted by a magnetic field is perpendicular to both the velocity and the direction of the magnetic field.
20. The left hand could be used for negative charge flow. By pointing the left thumb in the direction of electron flow, the curl of the fingers would indicate the direction of the magnetic field.
21. If you observe the beam traveling horizontally from your left to your right, the beam would be deflected toward you.
22. No. Transformers need a changing magnetic field. The magnetic field of a permanent magnet doesn't change easily.

Math Skills

23. Ratio of secondary turns to primary turns = ratio of output voltage to input voltage
60 turns/20 turns = 3
3 = output voltage/25 V
output voltage = 3 × 25 V = 75 V
24. Ratio of secondary turns to primary turns = ratio of output voltage to input voltage
60 turns/10 turns = 6
6 = output voltage/15 V
output voltage = 6 × 15 V = 90 V
25. Ratio of secondary turns to primary turns = ratio of output voltage to input voltage
50 turns/500 turns = 1/10
1/10 = output voltage/120 V
output voltage = 120 V/10 = 12 V
26. Ratio of secondary turns to primary turns = ratio of input current to output current
60 turns/12 turns = 5
5 = 5 A/output current
output current = 5 A/5 = 1 A

CHAPTER 21 Assessment *(continued)*

Critical Thinking

18. **Inferring** Using the concept of magnetic domains, explain why a magnet will attract an iron nail but not a plastic button.

19. **Comparing and Contrasting** How does the force that an electric field exerts on a moving charged particle differ from the force exerted by a magnetic field? Assume both fields point in the same direction.

20. **Inferring** You know that if you point the thumb of your right hand in the direction of the current, your fingers curve in the direction of the magnetic field. Could you use your left hand to demonstrate this rule correctly? Explain your answer. (*Hint:* See Figure 7 on page 636.)

21. **Applying Concepts** A beam of electrons travels from left to right between the poles of a horseshoe magnet. The north pole is on the top, and the south pole is on the bottom. In which direction will the beam be deflected when it passes through the poles of the magnet?

22. **Predicting** Would a permanent magnet be a good core for a transformer? Explain.

Math Skills

23. **Calculating** A transformer has 20 turns in its primary coil and 60 turns in its secondary coil. The input voltage for the transformer is 25 volts. What is the output voltage?

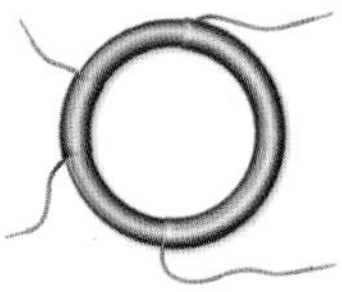

24. **Calculating** A transformer has an input voltage of 10 volts and an output voltage of 60 volts. If the input voltage is changed to 15 volts, what will the output voltage be?

25. **Calculating** A toy train uses a step-down transformer with 500 turns on its primary coil and 50 turns on its secondary coil. If it is connected to a 120-volt line, what voltage does the toy train use?

26. **Calculating** A transformer has 12 turns on its primary coil and 60 turns on its secondary coil. If the current in the primary coil is 5 amps, what is the current in the secondary coil?

Concepts in Action

27. **Applying Concepts** In a tape recorder, the tape is coated with iron oxide that has been magnetized in patterns corresponding to sounds. To play recorded sounds, the tape moves past a tiny coil of wire. Explain how this produces an electrical signal.

28. **Problem Solving** A child's toy has a magnet hidden inside. How can you determine where the north and south poles of the magnet are, without damaging the toy?

29. **Applying Concepts** A power plant generates electricity at 1200 volts. The electricity is transmitted at 180,000 volts and then reduced to 2400 volts at a substation. Finally, it is reduced to 120 volts for use in a home. For each transformer, describe the ratio of the number of turns in the primary and secondary coils.

30. **Inferring** Credit cards have a magnetic strip on them that contains information in a pattern. When a cashier runs the card through a card reader, the magnetic strip passes by a small wire coil. Why is motion necessary for the coil to read the card?

31. **Writing in Science** Write a paragraph explaining why alternating current is used for power generation and distribution instead of direct current.

Performance-Based Assessment

Creating an Educational Booklet Write a booklet for elementary students describing how electricity is brought from the power plant to their homes. Include simple illustrations and caution statements that young children can understand.

Go Online
PHSchool.com

For: Self-grading assessment
Visit: PHschool.com
Web Code: cca-2210

Concepts in Action

27. As the tape moves past the coil, the changing magnetization produces a changing current in the coil, which produces an electrical signal.
28. Move a compass around the toy. The north pole of the compass needle will be attracted to the south pole of the toy's magnet.
29. (1) step-up, ratio 150:1; (2) step-down, ratio 1:75; (3) step-down, ratio 1:20
30. The magnetic field must change to induce a current. The magnetization on the moving card induces a variable current in the coil that corresponds to a pattern of information imprinted on the card.
31. Students' paragraphs should indicate that transformers require alternating current that can be stepped up for long-range transmission. At higher voltages, there is not as much heat loss because the current is low. To make the electrical energy safe to use, it must be stepped down, which again can only be done with transformers and alternating current.

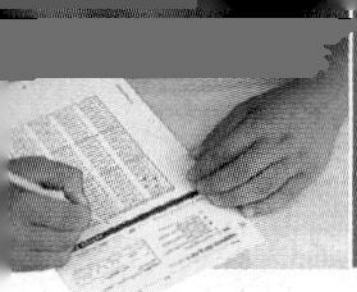

Standardized Test Prep

Test-Taking Tip

Forming Operational Definitions
Some test questions ask you to apply an operational definition. Start by using details in the question as clues to help you recall the definition. The question below describes current direction and asks for the magnetic field direction. Then write what you recall about the definition. How is current defined? *(flow of positive charge)* Which hand do you use? *(right hand)* What points in the direction of the current? *(thumb)* What determines the magnetic field direction? *(curl of fingers)* Lastly, rule out choices that must be wrong. Responses A and B cannot be correct because the magnetic field is at right angles to the current.

Suppose a vertical wire is pushed through a hole in a horizontal tabletop. Current in the wire is directed into the plane of the tabletop from above. What is the magnetic field direction caused by this current, as seen from above?

(A) into the plane of the tabletop
(B) out of the plane of the tabletop
(C) clockwise
(D) counter-clockwise
(E) left to right

(Answer: C)

1. Two solenoids are nested one inside the other. The inner solenoid is connected to a 12-V AC voltage source. The outer solenoid is part of a complete circuit. Will the setup function as a transformer?
(A) No, there is no core.
(B) No, there needs to be a ring.
(C) No, both sides need a voltage source.
(D) It is unclear, because current is not given.
(E) Yes, AC induces a current in the outer coil.

2. What causes a ferromagnetic material to become magnetic?
(A) unpaired electrons
(B) paired electrons
(C) unpaired protons
(D) paired protons
(E) none of the above

3. A transformer has 22 coils in its primary coil and 132 coils in its secondary coil. If the input voltage is 112 V, what is the secondary voltage?
(A) 6.00 V (B) 18.7 V
(C) 222 V (D) 266 V
(E) 672 V

4. The figure below is a transformer used in lighting dimmer switches. It has one coil wrapped around an iron core. Three moveable taps (T_1, T_2, and T_3) are connected to the wire. When a tap is moved, the number of coils between that tap and the next tap changes. The coils between T_1 and T_2 form the primary coil. The coils between T_2 and T_3 form the secondary coil. To lower the output voltage for this transformer (to dim a light), how should one tap be moved?

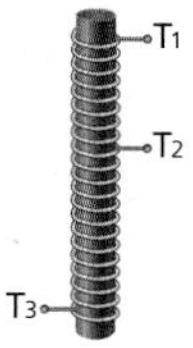

T1
T2
T3

(A) Move T_1 closer to T_2.
(B) Move T_2 closer to T_3.
(C) Move T_2 farther from T_3.
(D) Move T_3 farther from T_2.
(E) Move T_1 closer to T_3.

5. Particle accelerators use electromagnets to change the direction in which charged particles travel. How does a charged particle move within a magnetic field?
(A) It moves in the same direction as the magnetic field lines.
(B) It moves in the direction opposite to the magnetic field lines.
(C) It comes to a stop.
(D) It moves in a direction perpendicular to the magnetic field lines.
(E) none of the above

6. Is it possible for a magnetic field to slow down a charged particle moving through the field?
(A) Yes, if the charge is moving perpendicular to the field at all times.
(B) Yes, if the charge is moving in the direction of the magnetic field lines.
(C) Yes, if the charge is moving in the direction opposite to the magnetic field lines.
(D) Yes, if the charge is moving very slowly.
(E) No, a magnetic field can only deflect a charged particle.

Standardized Test Prep

1. E **2.** A **3.** E
4. B **5.** D **6.** E

Performance-Based Assessment

Students' booklets should begin with the process by which some form of energy (falling water, nuclear power, or burning coal, petroleum, or natural gas) is used to drive a turbine. Work used to generate electrical energy, the simple components of a generator, and the use of transformers to increase voltages (to increase transmission distance) and decrease voltages (to make electricity safer to use) must all be included. The text should be simple, with information provided visually through the illustrations.

Go Online
PHSchool.com

Your students can independently test their knowledge of the chapter and print out their test results for your files.

EARTH AND SPACE

Interactive Textbook

The Interactive Textbook, found both online and on CD-ROM, includes the following materials.

Activities and Labs

Worksheets for each activity and lab are available as PDF files with clickable safety symbols.

Colorful Visuals

All art and relevant photographs from the Student Edition can be accessed in the Interactive Textbook.

Self Assessment

Provides additional assessment opportunities and questions:

- Interactive Reading Checkpoint questions
- Interactive Figure caption questions
- Chapter Pretests with hints
- Printable Chapter Assessments
- Standardized Test Prep

My Notes

Students can enter answers for questions or make notes about what they are learning.

References

Provides a drop-down menu of resources:

- Skills and Reference Handbook
- Glossary

Careers

Information on science careers is available through the Career page on www.PHSchool.com.

EARTH AND SPACE SCIENCE UNIT PREVIEW

Earth and Space Science

Stars Over Arches National Park, Utah ▶ Both Earth science and space science are represented in this time exposure photo, taken at night. Stars appear as long curved trails of light circling the north celestial pole. The apparent motion of the stars is due to Earth's rotation on its axis.

654

Go Online PHSchool.com

For students, the PHSchool.com Web site contains interactive data-sharing labs, interactive self-assessments, and science-related links. The PHSchool.com Web site also provides teachers with curriculum support, reference links, a way to create state-specific lesson plans, and instructions on how to create a Web page.

Go Online NSTA SciLinks

NSTA SciLinks provides student worksheets for specific topics with additional teacher support.

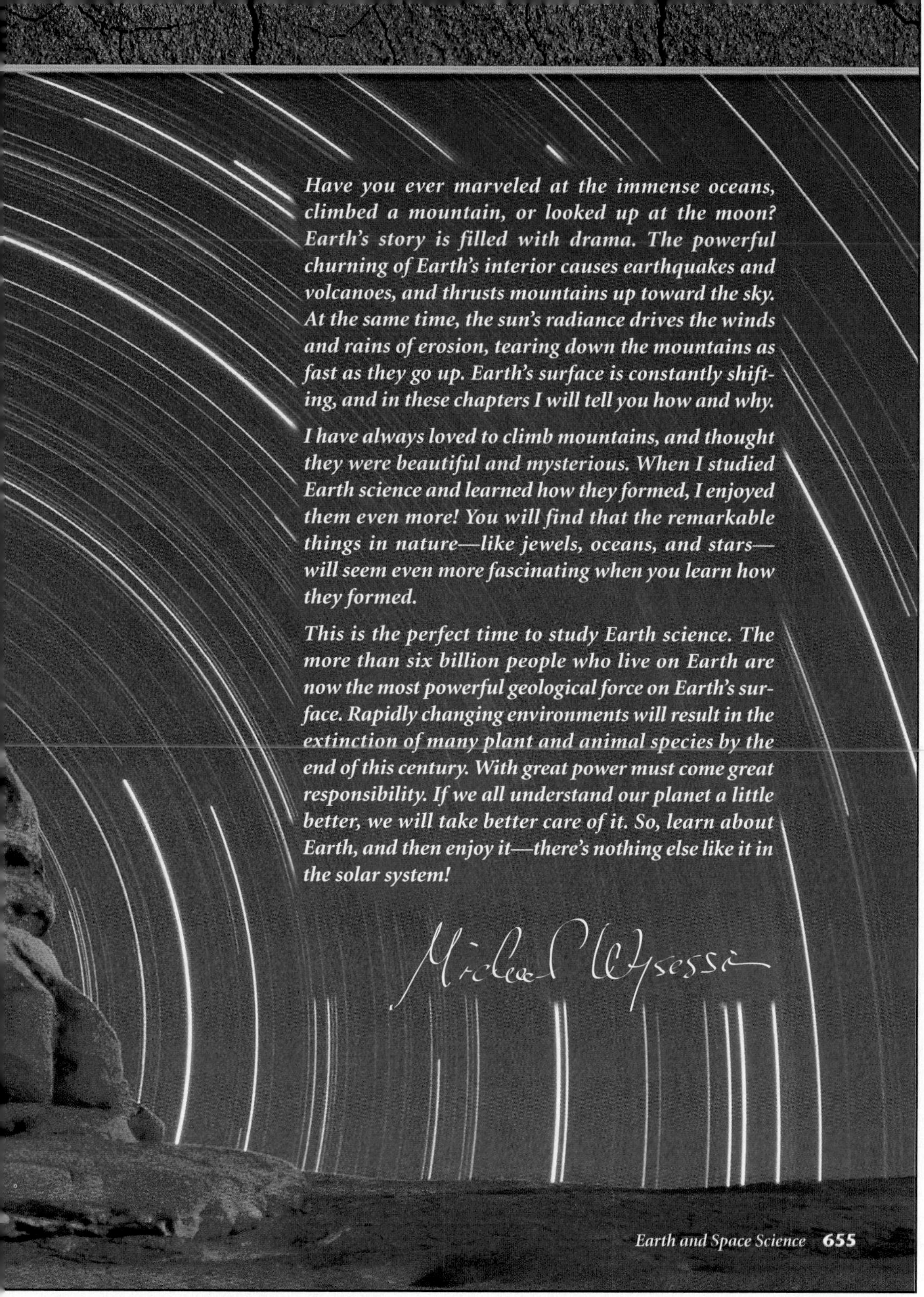

Have you ever marveled at the immense oceans, climbed a mountain, or looked up at the moon? Earth's story is filled with drama. The powerful churning of Earth's interior causes earthquakes and volcanoes, and thrusts mountains up toward the sky. At the same time, the sun's radiance drives the winds and rains of erosion, tearing down the mountains as fast as they go up. Earth's surface is constantly shifting, and in these chapters I will tell you how and why.

I have always loved to climb mountains, and thought they were beautiful and mysterious. When I studied Earth science and learned how they formed, I enjoyed them even more! You will find that the remarkable things in nature—like jewels, oceans, and stars—will seem even more fascinating when you learn how they formed.

This is the perfect time to study Earth science. The more than six billion people who live on Earth are now the most powerful geological force on Earth's surface. Rapidly changing environments will result in the extinction of many plant and animal species by the end of this century. With great power must come great responsibility. If we all understand our planet a little better, we will take better care of it. So, learn about Earth, and then enjoy it—there's nothing else like it in the solar system!

Michael Wysession

Discovery Channel School **Video Field Trip**

Use the following videos to help students understand the concepts in each chapter.

Chapter 22 Earth's Interior
Mountains of Fire
Introduces three major types of volcanoes: cinder cones, shield volcanoes, and composite volcanoes. Includes spectacular footage of various eruptions.

Chapter 23 Earth's Surface
Under the Sea
Examines how sonar and remotely operated underwater vehicles help scientists map the ocean floor, find objects lost at sea, and explore this last frontier.

Chapter 24 Weather and Climate
Wild Weather
Features hurricanes, tornadoes, and other types of severe weather.

Chapter 25 The Solar System
Lighting Up the Sky
Discusses how comets, asteroids, and meteoroids move through the solar system. Also explains the difference between meteors, meteoroids, and meteorites and how impact craters are formed.

Chapter 26 Exploring the Universe
Measuring Up To Space
Features astronomer Sheldon Schaefer and the scale model of the solar system that he created in the city of Peoria, Illinois, to help people understand the enormity of space.

Go Online SCIENCE NEWS®

Students can find current information about specific discoveries in science from *Science News.*

Go Online PLANETDIARY

Planet Diary contains current geological, astronomical, meteorological, and environmental news from around the world. Additional information and activities are included in the Phenomena Backgrounders.

Careers in Earth and Space Science

These careers constitute only a few of the many careers in the fields of Earth and space science. Whether you want to be a seismologist or an astronomer, you can put the ideas you learn in this book to work toward a future career.

Meteorologist

Connection to Chapter 24
Characteristics Good oral and written communication skills, analytical
Preparation Courses in chemistry, physics, statistics, computer science, physical climatology
Employers Federal government, research and testing services, radio and television broadcasting, airlines

Seismologist

Connection to Chapter 22
Characteristics Works well in a team environment, computer literate, good oral and written communication skills, curious, meticulous
Preparation Courses in computer science, physics, electronics, geology
Employers Federal and state governments, universities, engineering firms

Surveying Technician

Connection to Chapter 22
Characteristics Computer literate, works well in a team environment
Preparation Courses in mathematics, computer science, training in GPS (Global Positioning System) and GIS (Geographic Information System), must also pass a written exam in surveying
Employers Engineering, architectural, and surveying services firms

Careers in Earth and Space Science

The career opportunities available in Earth and space science are far reaching—from exploring distant galaxies to investigating deep inside Earth. Here are a few of these exciting careers.

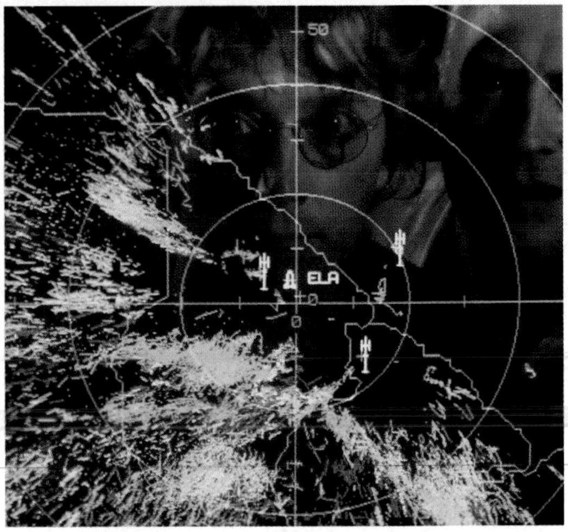

Meteorologist
Meteorologists study how the physical characteristics, processes, and movements of the atmosphere affect the environment. They use this information to forecast the weather and study the patterns of weather change, such as droughts and global warming.
Educational requirements Four-year college degree, majoring in meteorology or atmospheric science

Seismologist
Seismologists are Earth scientists who investigate earthquakes and tremors. They determine the source, the nature, and the size of earthquakes and try to predict where earthquakes will occur. They also search for ways to help the building industry construct earthquake-proof structures.
Educational requirements Four-year college degree, majoring in geology, geophysics, or mathematics

Surveying Technician
Helping to measure and map Earth's surface are the responsibilities of surveying technicians. They assist land surveyors who measure distances, directions, and contours on, above, or below Earth's surface. Surveying technicians use surveying instruments to collect data and then enter the data into computers.
Educational requirements Two-year junior or community college program, one to three years of technical school

656

Go Online PHSchool.com

For: Career links
Visit: PHSchool.com
Web Code: ccb-3000

Commercial Diver
Just about anywhere there is water, there is a need for commercial divers. Their work ranges from operating submersibles to helping map the ocean floor. They may perform underwater surveys or carry out underwater rescue and salvage operations.
Educational requirements High-school diploma, diving-school certification or naval training

Archaeologist
Archaeologists excavate, preserve, study, and classify objects and structures from past cultures. In order to interpret what they see at a particular site, archaeologists must be able to identify different types of soil and notice the smallest of changes in soil characteristics.
Educational requirements Master's degree in anthropology or archeology

Astronomer
Astronomers use the laws of physics and mathematics to study the universe. They may specialize to investigate the moon, sun, planets, stars, or galaxies, such as the Andromeda Galaxy shown in the photo at the left. They also may use what they know about astronomy to help develop satellites and spacecraft.
Educational requirements Doctoral degree in physics, astrophysics, or space physics

Commercial Diver

Connection to Chapter 23
Characteristics Athletic, technical (welding, engineering, and inspection skills), healthy, be able to swim well
Preparation Courses in physics, mechanical engineering, diving certification
Employers Federal and state governments, diving companies, search and recovery companies, oil industry, environmental companies

Archaeologist

Connection to Chapter 23
Characteristics Curious, creative, thinks logically, objective, open-minded, systematic, perseverant, excellent written and oral communication skills, computer literate, works well in a team situation
Preparation Courses in geology, paleontology, botany, zoology, geography, statistics, mathematics, political science, physics, chemistry, history, art history
Employers Museums, engineering and environmental companies, universities and colleges, local, state, and federal governments, historical societies

Astronomer

Connection to Chapter 26
Characteristics Analytical, good oral and written communication skills, computer literate, works well independently
Preparation Courses in physics, mathematics, chemistry, geology
Employers Universities, museums

Go Online PHSchool.com

Career Teaching Strategy
Students can use the Internet to research careers related to Earth and space science. Ask students to summarize their findings in a poster. The poster should provide information on educational requirements, working conditions, job responsibilities, salary, and long-term career prospects.

CHAPTER 22

Planning Guide

Use these planning tools
Easy Planner
Teacher Express

SECTION OBJECTIVES	STANDARDS NATIONAL (See p. T18.)	STANDARDS STATE	ACTIVITIES and LABS
22.1 Earth's Structure, pp. 660–663 1 block or 2 periods **22.1.1 Describe** the science of geology. **22.1.2 Describe** the main layers of Earth's interior.	A-1, B-6, D-1, D-3, G-1, G-2, G-3		**SE** Inquiry Activity: How Are Rocks and Minerals Different? p. 659 L2 **TE** Teacher Demo: Density, p. 662 L2 **LM** Investigation 22B: Modeling Petroleum Recovery L1
22.2 Minerals, pp. 664–669 1 block or 2 periods **22.2.1 Distinguish** between rocks and minerals and **explain** several properties used to identify minerals.	A-1, A-2, B-2		**SE** Quick Lab: Mineral Hardness, p. 668 L2 **TE** Build Science Skills: Design an Experiment, p. 666 L2
22.3 Rocks and the Rock Cycle, pp. 670–675 1 block or 2 periods **22.3.1 Classify** rocks as igneous, sedimentary, or metamorphic and **explain** how different types of rocks form. **22.3.2 Describe** the processes by which rocks continually change from one type to another in the rock cycle.	A-1, A-2, B-2, B-3, D-2		**SE** Quick Lab: Observing the Size of Crystals, p. 671 L2 **TE** Build Science Skills: Classifying, p. 672 L2 **LM** Investigation 22A: Identifying Rocks L2
22.4 Plate Tectonics, pp. 676–683 1 block or 2 periods **22.4.1 Explain** the hypothesis of continental drift. **22.4.2 Relate** how the theory of plate tectonics explains sea-floor spreading, subduction, and the formation of mountains. **22.4.3 Explain** the mechanisms of plate movement.	D-1, D-3, G-1, G-2, G-3		**TE** Teacher Demo: Convection and Plate Motion, p. 680 L2
22.5 Earthquakes, pp. 684–689 1 block or 2 periods **22.5.1 Describe** the causes and effects of stress in Earth's crust. **22.5.2 Explain** why earthquakes occur and how their energy is propagated as seismic waves. **22.5.3 Explain** how earthquakes are measured and how earthquake data is used to learn about Earth's interior.	A-1, A-2, B-6, D-1, D-3, F-5		**SE** Quick Lab: Modeling a Seismograph, p. 687 L2 **SE** Exploration Lab: Using Earthquakes to Map Plate Boundaries, p. 697 L2 **TE** Teacher Demo: Faults and Folds, p. 685 L2 **TE** Build Science Skills: Using Models, p. 686 L2
22.6 Volcanoes, pp. 690–696 1 block or 2 periods **22.6.1 Describe** the internal structure of a volcano and how volcanoes form. **22.6.2 Relate** the type of volcanic eruption to the characteristics of magma. **22.6.3 Describe** the different types of volcanoes and where they are typically located. **22.6.4 Describe** several types of igneous features and how they are formed.	B-2, D-1, D-2, D-3, F-5		

Ability Levels
L1 For students who need additional help
L2 For all students
L3 For students who need to be challenged

Components							
SE	Student Edition	**RSW**	Reading & Study Workbook	**CUT**	Chapter & Unit Tests	**T**	Transparencies
TE	Teacher's Edition	**MSPS**	Math Skills & Problem Solving Workbook	**CTB**	Computer Test Bank	**iT**	Interactive Textbook
LM	Laboratory Manual			**TP**	Test Prep Resources	**P**	Presentation Pro CD-ROM
PLM	Probeware Lab Manual			**DC**	Discovery Channel Videotapes & DVDs	**GO**	Internet Resources

RESOURCES PRINT and TECHNOLOGY	SECTION ASSESSMENT
RSW Section 22.1 L1 **T** Chapter 22 Pretest L2 **P** and Section 22.1 L2 NSTA SCiLINKS **GO** Earth's layers L2	**SE** Section 22.1 Assessment, p. 663 Interactive Textbook **iT** Section 22.1
RSW Section 22.2 L1 **MSPS** Section 22.2 L2 **T P** Section 22.2 L2 NSTA SCiLINKS **GO** Minerals L2	**SE** Section 22.2 Assessment, p. 669 Interactive Textbook **iT** Section 22.2
RSW Section 22.3 L1 **T P** Section 22.3 L2 NSTA SCiLINKS **GO** Rocks L2	**SE** Section 22.3 Assessment, p. 675 Interactive Textbook **iT** Section 22.3
RSW Section 22.4 L1 **T P** Section 22.4 L2 SCIENCE NEWS **GO** Earthquakes, volcanoes, and plate tectonics L2	**SE** Section 22.4 Assessment, p. 683 Interactive Textbook **iT** Section 22.4
RSW Section 22.5 L1 **RSW Math Skill** L2 **T P** Section 22.5 L2 PLANETDIARY **GO** Earthquake activity L2	**SE** Section 22.5 Assessment, p. 689 Interactive Textbook **iT** Section 22.5
RSW Section 22.6 L1 Discovery Channel School **DC** Mountains of Fire L2 **T P** Section 22.6 L2 PLANETDIARY **GO** Volcano activity L2	**SE** Section 22.6 Assessment, p. 696 Interactive Textbook **iT** Section 22.6

Go Online

Go online for these Internet resources.

PHSchool.com
Web Code: cca-3220

SCIENCE NEWS
Web Code: cce-3224

NSTA SCiLINKS
Web Code: ccn-3221
Web Code: ccn-3222
Web Code: ccn-3223

PLANETDIARY
Web Code: ccc-3225
Web Code: ccc-3226

Materials for Activities and Labs

STUDENT EDITION

Inquiry Activity, p. 659
4 mineral samples labeled as minerals A to D, 4 rock samples labeled as rocks A to D, newspaper, plastic bag, small hammer, hand lens

Quick Lab, p. 668
labeled samples of graphite, galena or halite, hornblende, feldspar, pyrite, and olivine; penny; iron nail; steel file

Quick Lab, p. 671
salol, plastic spoon, 2 watch glasses, tongs, hot plate, hand lens, Petri dish, ice cube, watch with second hand

Quick Lab, p. 687
pencil, roll of cash-register paper, felt-tip pen

Exploration Lab, p. 697
graph paper

TEACHER'S EDITION

Teacher Demo, p. 662
2 glass jars with lids, $\frac{1}{2}$ cup of salt, sand, and metal filings; 100 mL of water, vegetable oil, and corn syrup

Build Science Skills, p. 666
mineral samples, beakers, graduated cylinders, balances

Build Science Skills, p. 672
10 numbered rock samples for each group of students

Teacher Demo, p. 680
Bunsen burner or hot plate, deep and wide glass container, thin tomato soup, large sponges, scissors, tongs

Teacher Demo, p. 685
several different shades of potter's clay, 6 wood blocks, hammer, large garbage bags

Build Science Skills, p. 686
1 spring toy per group

Build Science Skills, p. 694
several samples of pumice, obsidian, ropy basalt, and angular rhyolite

Chapter Assessment

CHAPTER ASSESSMENT

SE Chapter Assessment, pp. 699–700
CUT Chapter 22 Test A, B
CTB Chapter 22
iT Chapter 22

PHSCHOOL.COM GO
Web Code: cca-3220

STANDARDIZED TEST PREP

SE Chapter 22, p. 701
TP Diagnose and Prescribe

Interactive Textbook

Interactive Textbook with assessment at PHSchool.com

CHAPTER 22

Before you teach

From the Author

Michael Wysession
Washington University

Big Ideas

The study of Earth science is multidisciplinary, combining geology, chemistry, physics, and biology. Earth is a complicated system of interrelated processes involving the interchange of matter and energy between layers, from the atmosphere to the core. People are part of this system, made of atoms borrowed from rocks and previous organisms. Plate tectonics is the unifying theory of Earth science, providing a framework within which geological observations can be interpreted and understood.

Space and Time Earth is layered according to the density of materials, with an iron core, rocky mantle and crust, liquid hydrosphere, and gaseous atmosphere. Earth is continuously changing. Internally, the rock and metal of the core and mantle is cyclically churning because of convection. At the surface, matter moves through the rock cycle, which includes multiple pathways amongst magma, igneous rock, sediment, sedimentary rock, and metamorphic rock.

Forces and Motion The top hundred kilometers of Earth is separated into distinct lithospheric plates. The oceanic regions of plates are the surface expression of mantle convection. They cool and harden at mid-ocean ridges, and sink back into the mantle at subduction zones within 200 million years. Continents are too buoyant to subduct, so they have been dragged about the surface by plate motions for more than four billion years. Most active geology, including most earthquakes, volcanoes, and mountain building, occurs at the boundaries between plates.

Matter and Energy Rocks are made of minerals. Nearly all minerals are silicates, made of SiO_4 tetrahedra bonded to small amounts of other elements. Plate tectonics is driven by the flow of heat from the hot interior (>5000°C) to the surface. Heat moves by convection in the core and mantle, conduction across the core-mantle boundary and crust, and radiation out into space. The radioactive decay of long-lived isotopes is responsible for Earth staying so hot after more than 4.5 billion years.

Earth Science Refresher

Accretion and Differentiation 22.1

Approximately 4.6 billion years ago, Earth was forming from the accretion of planetesimals, solid chunks in the disc of matter revolving around the young sun. As this accretion phase progressed, the energy of colliding planetesimals, the compression of Earth's mass due to its increasing gravity, and the radioactive decay of heavy elements all acted to heat the planet. Eventually, the temperature rose to the melting point of iron, an abundant element accounting for about one-third of the planet's mass. This great quantity of iron began sinking toward the planet's center, resulting in an enormous amount of potential energy being converted into heat. The amount of heat released was enough to cause most of Earth to become molten. In the process, Earth's interior differentiated into density-based layers, as can be seen below.

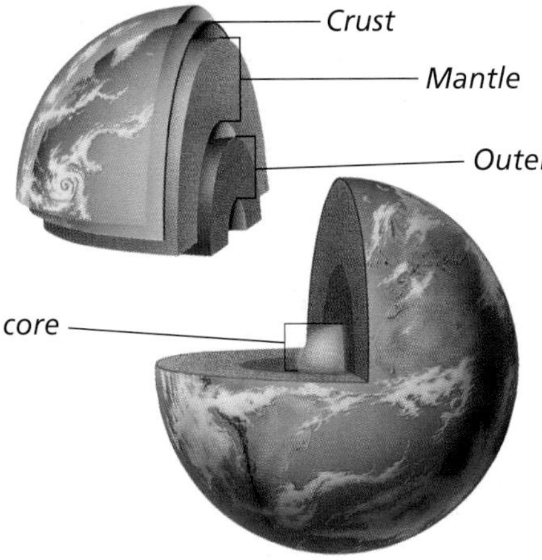
Crust
Mantle
Outer core
Inner core

Rock and Mineral Formation 22.2 and 22.3

The careful study of a rock or mineral reveals information about the conditions under which it was formed. The grains from a sedimentary rock can tell you from what, and often where, the source rock was formed, as well as the conditions under which erosion and deposition occurred. Silt, for example, is usually deposited in calm waters, while conglomerates are associated

Address Misconceptions

Gravity pulls matter toward the bottom of a planet. Gravity pulls matter toward the center of mass. For a strategy to overcome this misconception, see **Address Misconceptions** on **page 662.**

Go Online PD LINKS

NSTA

For: Teaching methods for Earth's interior
Visit: www.SciLinks.org/PDLinks
Web Code: ccn-2299

with landslides and glacial deposition. Metamorphic rocks reveal information about the temperature and pressure conditions during the metamorphic event, when existing minerals were changed by high temperature or pressure or chemical reaction.

Plate Motion 22.4

Address Misconceptions

Continents are permanent features that do not move or change. For a strategy to overcome this misconception, see **Address Misconceptions** on **page 676.**

Plate motion is the surface expression of convection currents inside Earth. Recall that heat is transferred by radiation, conduction, and convection. Radiation primarily occurs at Earth's surface, which emits infrared radiation into the atmosphere. Conduction through rock is slow and inefficient, and is an important mechanism only at layer boundaries. Most of the heat flow in Earth is accomplished through convection, the physical movement of matter.

Earthquakes and Volcanoes 22.5 and 22.6

A plot of the location of earthquakes and volcanoes around the globe reveals the close association of these phenomena. Plate boundaries and hot spots are typical sites for both earthquakes (seen in blue below) and volcanoes (seen in red).

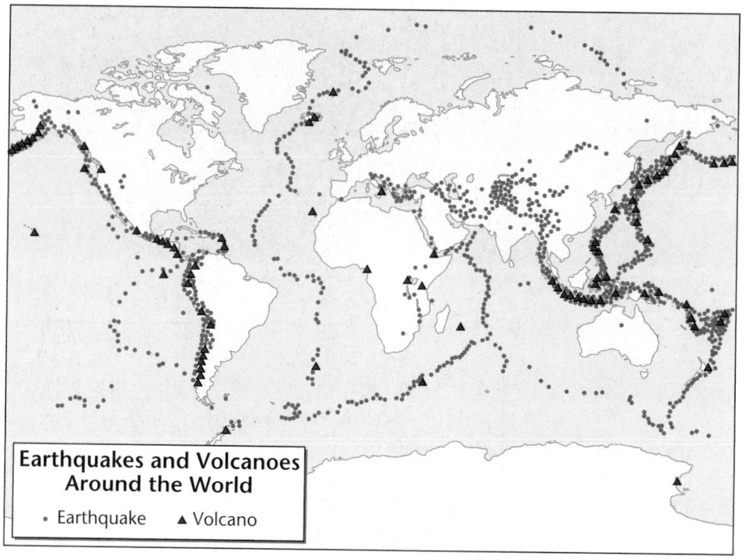
Earthquakes and Volcanoes Around the World
• Earthquake
▲ Volcano

At convergent boundaries, volcanism is produced from magma rising from the melting slab of subducting oceanic crust. Earthquakes occur at the boundaries of the subducting plate. By mapping the location of these deep earthquakes, scientists can determine the position of the subduction plate as it re-enters the mantle. At divergent boundaries, magma flows to the surface at mid-ocean ridges, and earthquakes occur along the crest of the ridge, and along transform faults between offset ridge segments.

Occasionally, parts of the mid-ocean ridge rise above sea level, and volcanism can be observed, such as in Iceland. While most earthquakes and volcanoes occur at or near plate boundaries, they are also associated with intraplate hotspots. Low-magnitude earthquakes abound when magma rises to the surface. These earthquakes can be used to predict impending volcanism. A series of such earthquakes occurred under Mt. St. Helens nearly two months before its catastrophic eruption in 1980. Because of these earthquakes, the USGS was able to issue a formal earthquake hazard alert, informing local residents of imminent danger.

Build Reading Literacy

Preview

Activating Comprehension Before Reading

Strategy Help students activate prior knowledge, set a purpose for reading, and gain an advance idea of how the text is organized. Previewing is like checking a road map before beginning a trip; the process enables readers to see what lies ahead. After students preview opening material, headings, visuals, and boldfaced materials in the text, they can use further prereading strategies such as predicting (see page 66D), KWL (see page 124D), or active comprehension (see page 498D). Before students begin using the preview strategy, assign them a section in the textbook, such as Section 22.1, pp. 660–663.

Example

1. Have students skim the title, headings, and section opening material. Tell them to ask themselves questions such as, "How is this section organized?"

2. Next, have students look over the visuals and boldfaced portions of the text. Tell them to look for connections to what they already know.

- Familiar images: What do the images call to mind?
- Key ideas or concepts: Are the ideas already familiar?
- Key words: Boldfaced words are frequently important.

3. If the key concepts are somewhat familiar, students may wish to prepare a KWL chart to guide them as they read.

See pp. 661 and 670 for scripts on how to use the preview strategy with students. For additional Build Reading Literacy strategies, see pp. 665, 674, 678, 681, 683, 689, and 692.

ASSESS PRIOR KNOWLEDGE

Use the Chapter Pretest below to assess students' prior knowledge. As needed, review these Science Concepts with students.

Review Science Concepts

Section 22.1 Review density and remind students how gravity can cause mixtures to separate into layers based on the density of the constituent materials.

Section 22.2 Review atoms, elements, compounds, and chemical bonds. Remind students that a crystal is a solid in which atoms are arranged in a regular repeating pattern.

Section 22.3 Review precipitation reactions.

Sections 22.4 and 22.6 Help students recall the dynamics of convection cells, including the tendency of heated fluids to expand and rise, and cooling fluids to contract and move down.

Section 24.5 Review the transfer of energy from one form to another and the principles that govern how mechanical waves propagate through different media.

CHAPTER

22 Earth's Interior

CONCEPTS in Action

How do science concepts apply to your world? Here are some questions you'll be able to answer after you read this chapter.

- How is Earth's interior like a hard-boiled egg? *(Section 22.1)*
- What does a precious gem have in common with table salt? *(Section 22.2)*
- How can one kind of rock change into another kind of rock? *(Section 22.3)*
- Where is the longest mountain range in the world? *(Section 22.4)*
- Where was the largest earthquake ever recorded? *(Section 22.5)*
- Is there really a "Ring of Fire" around the Pacific Ocean? *(Section 22.6)*

DISCOVERY CHANNEL SCHOOL **Video Field Trip**

Mountains of Fire

- How were the Hawaiian islands formed? *(page 694)*

In this photo, the fishing port of ▶ Vestmannaeyjar, Iceland, is threatened by volcanic ash and lava from the nearby Eldfell volcano.

Chapter Pretest

1. True or False: Covalent bonds can be stronger or weaker depending on the type of atoms sharing the bond. *(True)*

2. Which of these statements best describes what happens when a solution of salt water is left in the sun? *(c)*
  a. The solution will change phases.
  b. Water will condense from the solution.
  c. Salt crystals will precipitate from the solution as water evaporates.

3. Which of these statements best describes mechanical waves? *(a)*
  a. They travel at different speeds through different substances.
  b. They travel at the speed of sound in a vacuum.
  c. They are produced by vibrations in an electric field.
  d. They have properties of both particles and waves.

4. Which of these statements best describes what happens when a guitar string is plucked? *(d)*
  a. Kinetic energy is created.
  b. Potential energy is created.
  c. Matter is converted into kinetic energy.
  d. Potential energy is converted into kinetic energy.

Chapter Preview

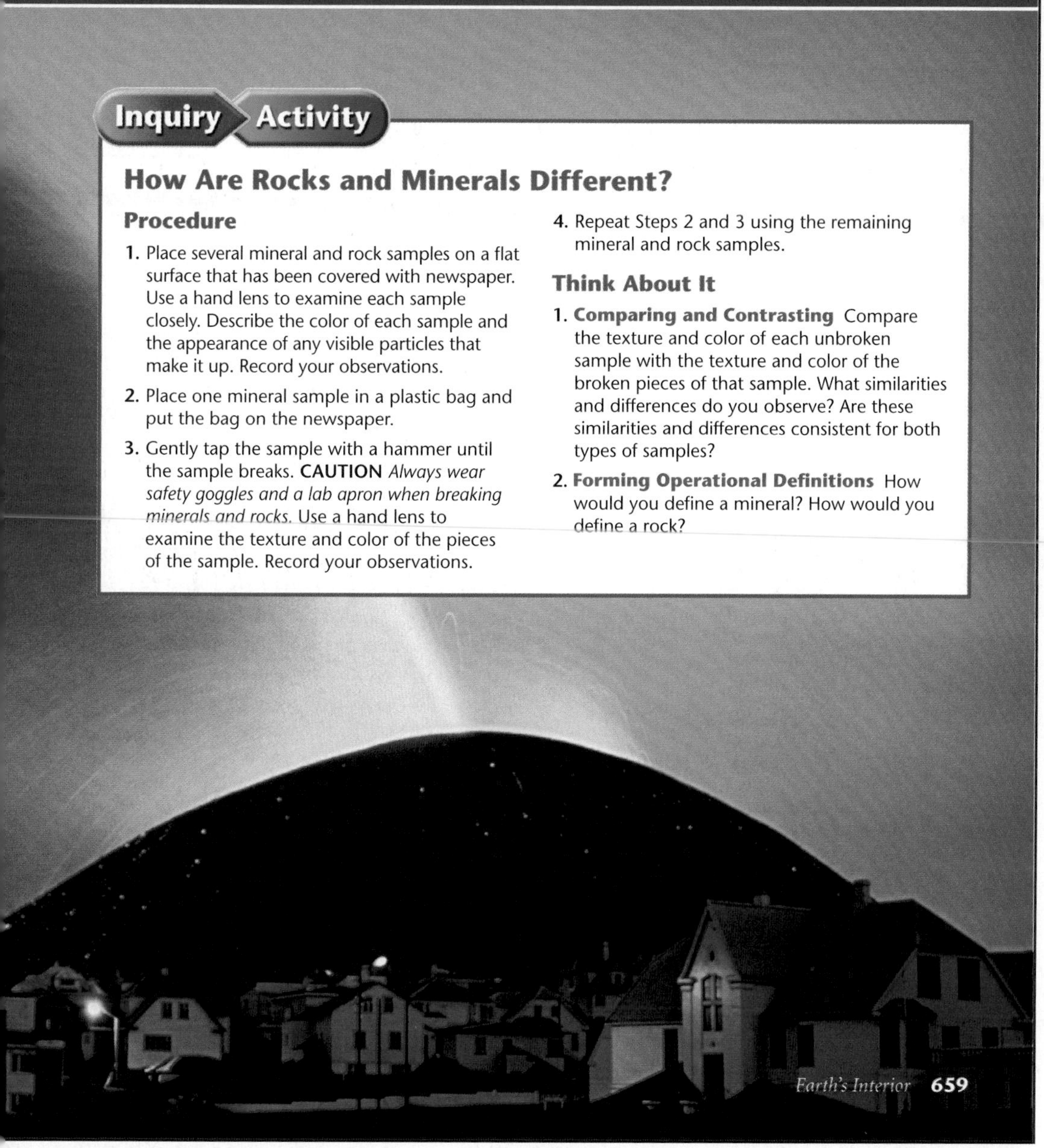

Inquiry Activity

How Are Rocks and Minerals Different?

Procedure

1. Place several mineral and rock samples on a flat surface that has been covered with newspaper. Use a hand lens to examine each sample closely. Describe the color of each sample and the appearance of any visible particles that make it up. Record your observations.
2. Place one mineral sample in a plastic bag and put the bag on the newspaper.
3. Gently tap the sample with a hammer until the sample breaks. **CAUTION** *Always wear safety goggles and a lab apron when breaking minerals and rocks.* Use a hand lens to examine the texture and color of the pieces of the sample. Record your observations.
4. Repeat Steps 2 and 3 using the remaining mineral and rock samples.

Think About It

1. **Comparing and Contrasting** Compare the texture and color of each unbroken sample with the texture and color of the broken pieces of that sample. What similarities and differences do you observe? Are these similarities and differences consistent for both types of samples?
2. **Forming Operational Definitions** How would you define a mineral? How would you define a rock?

DISCOVERY CHANNEL SCHOOL **Video Field Trip**
Mountains of Fire

Encourage students to view the Video Field Trip "Mountains of Fire."

ENGAGE/EXPLORE

Inquiry Activity

How Are Rocks and Minerals Different? L2

Purpose In this activity, students begin to recognize the differences and similarities between rocks and minerals.

Address Misconceptions

Students may think of "mineral" only as a nutritional term. You may need to explain that a mineral is a broad category of inorganic substances found in the earth.

Skills Focus **Observing**

Prep Time 20 minutes

Materials 4 mineral samples labeled as minerals A to D, 4 rock samples labeled as rocks A to D, newspaper, plastic bag, small hammer, hand lens

Advance Prep Provide students with mineral samples such as biotite, halite, galena, calcite, fluorite, or feldspar. Provide rock samples such as basalt, limestone, granite, sandstone, slate, or conglomerate.

Class Time 15 minutes

Safety Caution students to wear safety goggles and lab aprons at all times.

Teaching Tips

- Explain that cleavage is more typical of minerals than of rocks, but the presence of cleavage planes is not a hard and fast rule for distinguishing minerals from rocks. You can cite slate as an example of a rock with definite cleavage planes.

Expected Outcome Most minerals will exhibit cleavage and appear homogeneous and crystalline. Most rocks will break irregularly and appear heterogeneous or amorphous.

Think About It

1. The unbroken rocks are composed of several materials that differ in texture and color. These materials separate when rocks are broken. Minerals do not change or separate into parts that differ in texture or color when broken.
2. Acceptable answers must be consistent with observations of the samples provided. An example of an acceptable answer at this stage is that minerals are Earth materials composed of a single, usually crystalline substance, and rocks are Earth materials composed of two or more substances. **Kinesthetic, Visual**

Section 22.1

1 FOCUS

Objectives

22.1.1 **Describe** the science of geology.

22.1.2 **Describe** the main layers of Earth's interior.

Reading Focus

Build Vocabulary L2

Word-Part Analysis Ask students to define the word *sphere* and to think of any words they know that include *sphere* as a word part *(spherical, atmosphere)*. Have students use a dictionary to look up the prefixes *litho- (stone), astheno- (weak),* and *meso- (middle)*.

Reading Strategy L2

a. A scientist who studies Earth and the processes that have shaped Earth over time **b.** The concept that geologic processes that are occurring today also occurred in the past **c.** Earth's rocky outer layer

2 INSTRUCT

The Science of Geology

Use Community Resources L2

The U.S. Geological Survey (USGS) has a network of regional offices where geologists study local, regional, and global Earth phenomena. USGS activities include monitoring earthquake activity, mapping the rock formations beneath the surface, and providing people with information about geologic events such as floods and landslides. Ask a USGS geologist to talk to your class about all of the different types of studies and activities that a professional geologist undertakes.
Interpersonal

22.1 Earth's Structure

Reading Focus

Key Concepts

- What is the science of geology?
- What are the characteristics of Earth's principal layers?

Vocabulary

- geologists
- uniformitarianism
- crust
- silicates
- mantle
- lithosphere
- asthenosphere
- mesosphere
- core

Reading Strategy

Building Vocabulary Draw a table similar to the one below that includes all the vocabulary terms listed for the section. As you read the section, define each vocabulary term in your own words.

Vocabulary Term	Definition
Geologist	a. ?
Uniformitarianism	b. ?
Crust	c. ?

In many ways, scientists know more about the structure of the universe and the workings of microscopic cells than they do about the ground beneath their feet. With a telescope, an astronomer can see stars at the farthest edges of the universe. With a microscope, a biologist can see the inner structure of cells. But there is no instrument that allows geologists to look deep inside Earth. The reason is both simple and profound: light does not travel through most rocks.

Though scientists cannot see into Earth, in a sense they can listen to it. The waves from earthquakes travel through Earth in a manner similar to the way that sound waves travel to our ears. These waves vibrate within Earth and are recorded at Earth's surface. Scientists are able to interpret these waves to learn about the structure and composition of Earth's interior. Scientists have also drilled holes to a depth of about 12 kilometers to collect data on the uppermost portion of Earth's interior. Figure 1 shows one such drilling effort.

Figure 1 These workers are drilling a hole that will be more than two kilometers deep. Later they will lower instruments into the hole to record data at that depth.

660 Chapter 22

The Science of Geology

Geology is the study of planet Earth, including its composition and structure. Scientists who study Earth and the processes that have shaped Earth over time are called **geologists.** Geologists such as the one shown in Figure 2 divide the forces that change Earth's surface into two groups: constructive forces and destructive forces. Constructive forces shape the surface by building up mountains and other land areas. Destructive forces slowly wear away mountains and, eventually, every other feature on Earth's surface.

Section Resources

Print
- ***Laboratory Manual,*** Investigation 22B
- ***Reading and Study Workbook With Math Support,*** Section 22.1
- ***Transparencies,*** Chapter Pretest and Section 22.1

Technology
- ***Interactive Textbook,*** Section 22.1
- ***Presentation Pro CD-ROM,*** Chapter Pretest and Section 22.1
- ***Go Online,*** NSTA SciLinks, Earth's layers

The modern science of geology began in the late 1700s. James Hutton, a Scottish physician and farmer, made observations of rocks that he could explain only if Earth were far older than most people had imagined. He observed that some rocks were made of particles that came from older rocks. Hutton realized that Earth's surface had changed gradually over time.

From his observations, Hutton developed the principle of uniformitarianism. **Uniformitarianism** is the idea that the geologic processes that operate today also operated in the past. Thus, ancient rocks can be understood by observing present-day geologic processes. According to the principle of uniformitarianism, dramatic features such as mountains and canyons are the result of geologic processes that work very slowly over long periods of time.

Reading Checkpoint *What do geologists study?*

Figure 2 This geologist is examining the rocks that make up the side of a canyon.

A Cross Section of Earth

Since Hutton's time, geologists have learned a great deal about Earth's structure. Earth's surface and interior can be compared to a hard-boiled egg, such as the one shown in Figure 3. Beneath an egg's hard outer shell is a layer of egg white that surrounds the yolk at the center. Earth has a similar layered structure. **Earth can be divided into three main layers—the crust, mantle, and core—based on the materials that make up each layer.** This layering is largely due to differences in density.

Physical conditions in Earth's interior vary from layer to layer. Temperature and pressure in Earth's interior increase with depth. As the temperature and pressure increase, the properties of the materials inside Earth also change.

The Crust The rocky outer layer of Earth is the **crust.** Like the shell of an egg, Earth's crust is thin compared to its other layers. Much of the crust is made up of **silicates,** rocks made of compounds of silicon and oxygen. Silicates often contain metals such as aluminum, iron, or calcium.

There are two different types of crust: continental crust and oceanic crust. Continental crust, the rock that makes up the continents, consists mainly of less-dense rocks such as granite. Continental crust averages about 40 kilometers in thickness, although it ranges in thickness from about 8 to 75 kilometers. It is thickest under mountain chains such as the Himalayas. The rock that makes up the ocean floor is oceanic crust. Oceanic crust is composed mostly of dense rocks like basalt. Oceanic crust is about 7 kilometers thick on average, and so is much thinner than continental crust.

Figure 3 Earth's structure is similar to that of a hard-boiled egg. **Using Analogies** *Which of Earth's layers corresponds to the shell of the egg?*

A Cross Section of Earth

Build Reading Literacy L1

Preview Refer to page **36D** in **Chapter 2**, which provides the guidelines for a preview.

Before students read A Cross Section of Earth, have them preview the words in bold, including subheadings and vocabulary. Then, ask students to write down what they already know before even reading the selection. *(Earth has three major layers: crust, mantle, and core. The core is divided into a liquid outer core and a solid inner core.)*
Intrapersonal

Build Science Skills L2

Inferring Because they cannot observe it directly, scientists must rely on inferences to learn about Earth's interior. Have students work in groups to make an inference about the layering of Earth's interior. Say, **Based upon the knowledge that pressure increases with depth in Earth's interior, make a logical argument to explain which layers will have the greatest density and why.** Have students create a visual aid to explain their deductions.
Logical, Group

Integrate Math L2

Earth is close to being a sphere, but it is actually an oblate ellipsoid. The centrifugal force resulting from spinning on its axis causes Earth to bulge outward at the equator. This bulge is big enough to be measured. The radius of Earth at the poles is 6357 km, and the radius of Earth at the equator is 6378 km. Ask, **What is the difference between Earth's diameter at the equator and at the poles?** *(Earth's diameter is 42 km longer at the equator.)*
Logical

Customize for English Language Learners

Use a Concept Map
Have students create a concept map to organize information about Earth's layers. Use Earth's Layers as the main concept, and *crust, mantle,* and *core* as subordinate concepts. Have students connect additional concepts pertaining to Earth's layers as they read each subsection. Students could also create their own visual of Earth's layers to accompany the concept map.

Answer to . . .

Figure 3 *The crust*

Reading Checkpoint *Geologists study Earth and the processes that have shaped it over time.*

Teacher Demo

Density

L2

Purpose Students see how liquids separate into layers based on density and composition.

Materials 2 large glass jars with lids, $\frac{1}{2}$ cup salt, $\frac{1}{2}$ cup sand, $\frac{1}{2}$ cup metal filings, 100 mL water, 100 mL vegetable oil, 100 mL corn syrup

Procedure At the beginning of class, place all of the liquids in one jar, and all of the solids in the other jar. Tighten the lids on both jars and shake the contents. Let the jars settle during the class period. Then, have students examine the jars.

Expected Outcome The liquids will separate into layers based on their densities; the solids will remain mixed. Ask, **Why did the liquids separate into layers?** *(The composition of the liquids makes them separate rather than blend together, and gravity causes the layers to increase in density towards the center of Earth.)* **What can you infer about the state of Earth when it separated into layers?** *(The materials that comprised Earth must have been liquid or molten when Earth separated into layers.)* **Visual, Logical**

Address Misconceptions

L2

Students may think that gravity should pull denser layers to the "bottom" of the planet, rather than to the center. Point out that, while we perceive gravity as a "downward" force, it is more properly described as a force acting toward the center of the planet. **Logical**

Use Visuals

L1

Figure 4 Point out that the numbers refer to the thickness, not the depth, of each layer. Ask, **How does the thickness of the crust compare with that of the other layers?** *(It is much thinner.)* **Visual**

Go Online NSTA SCILINKS

Download a worksheet on Earth's layers for students to complete, and find additional teacher support from NSTA SciLinks.

Go Online NSTA SCILINKS

For: Links on Earth's layers
Visit: www.SciLinks.org
Web Code: ccn-3221

The Mantle Beneath the crust is the **mantle,** a thick layer of hot but solid rock. As Figure 4 shows, the mantle extends about 2850 kilometers, from beneath the crust to the top of the core. Both pressure and temperature increase tremendously the deeper you go into the mantle. Like the crust, the mantle is composed mainly of silicates. The mantle is rich in iron and magnesium, and so is denser throughout than the crust.

Geologists divide the mantle into three layers based on the physical properties of the rock. The **lithosphere** (LITH uh sfeer) is a layer of relatively cool, rigid rock that includes the uppermost part of the mantle as well as Earth's crust. On average, the lithosphere measures about 100 kilometers thick, although it is thicker below the continents and thinner beneath the oceans. Beneath the lithosphere in the mantle is the **asthenosphere** (as THEN uh sfeer), a layer of softer, weaker rock that can flow slowly, the way taffy does. Beneath the asthenosphere is the stronger lower part of the mantle called the **mesosphere.** The stiffer rock of the mesosphere extends all the way down to the upper surface of Earth's core.

Reading Checkpoint *What is the asthenosphere?*

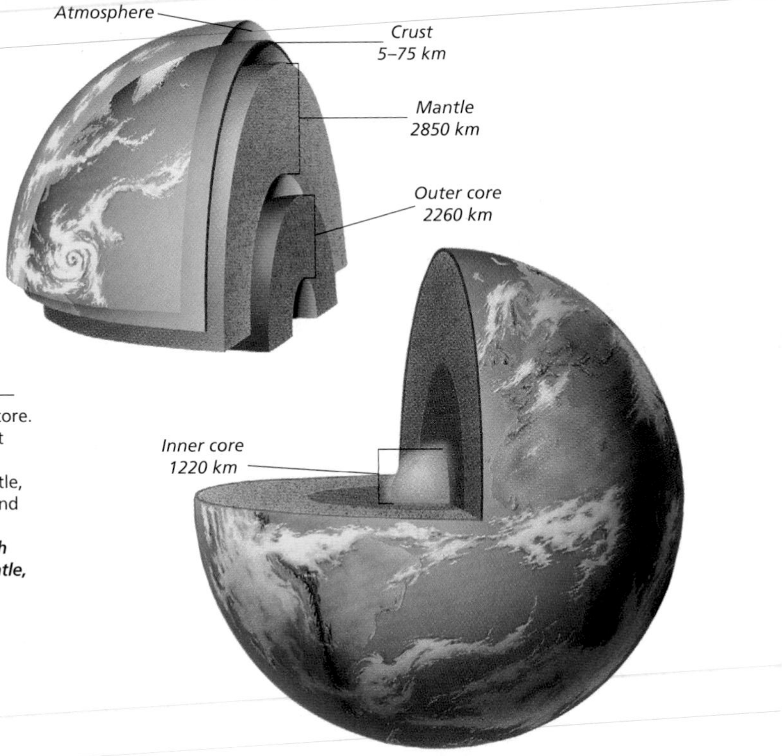

Atmosphere
Crust
5–75 km
Mantle
2850 km
Outer core
2260 km
Inner core
1220 km

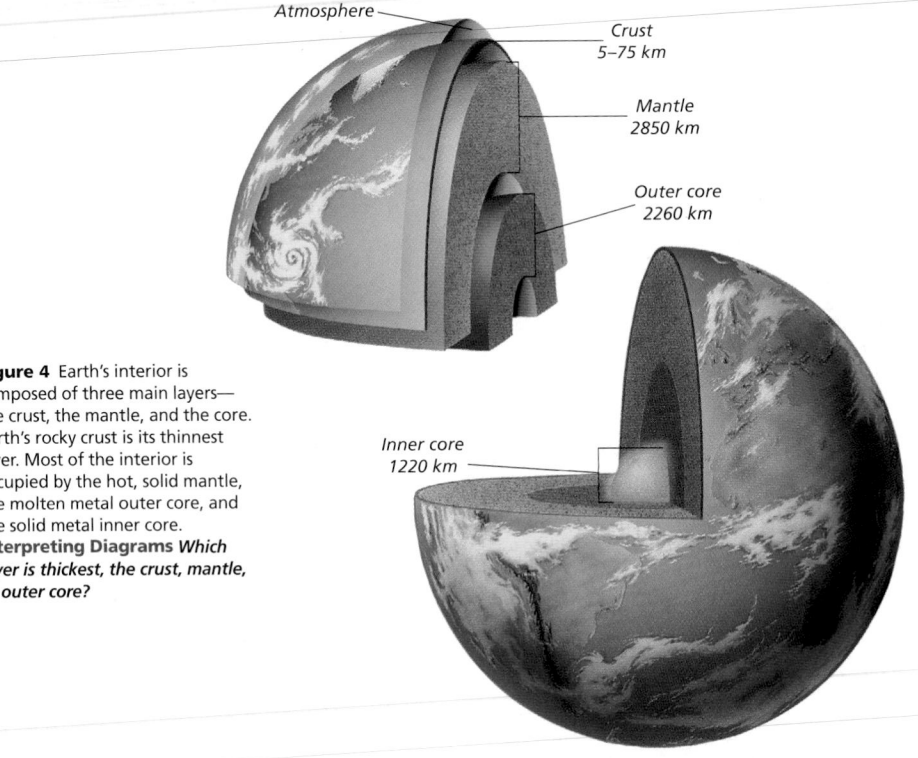

Figure 4 Earth's interior is composed of three main layers—the crust, the mantle, and the core. Earth's rocky crust is its thinnest layer. Most of the interior is occupied by the hot, solid mantle, the molten metal outer core, and the solid metal inner core. ***Interpreting Diagrams** Which layer is thickest, the crust, mantle, or outer core?*

Facts and Figures

Andrija Mohorovičić
Croatian scientist Andrija Mohorovičić first discovered the mantle in 1909. The change in composition from the crust to the mantle causes some seismic waves from earthquakes to be reflected and refracted. Mohorovičić observed these refracted waves on a seismometer that recorded a local earthquake, and inferred that there must be a different layer under the crust. This boundary between the crust and mantle, the Moho, is named after Mohorovičić.

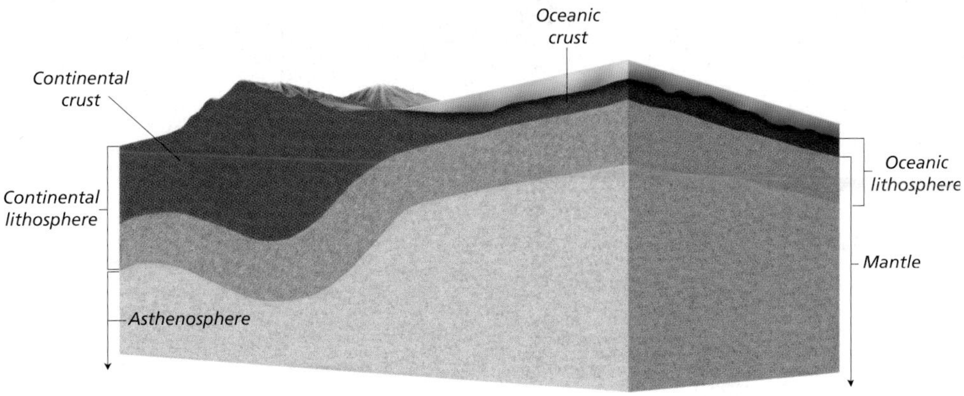
Oceanic crust
Continental crust
Continental lithosphere
Oceanic lithosphere
Mantle
Asthenosphere

Figure 5 The structure of Earth's upper layers is complex. The lithosphere includes the crust and the rigid, uppermost layer of Earth's mantle. Notice that the continental crust is thicker beneath mountain ranges. **Applying Concepts** ***What is the relationship between the lithosphere and the mantle?***

The Core Beneath the mantle is the **core,** a large sphere of metal that occupies Earth's center. Scientists think that the core is composed mostly of iron, with lesser amounts of nickel and some lighter elements. Within the core, pressure increases greatly with depth. At Earth's center, the pressure is estimated to be 3.6 million times the pressure at Earth's surface! The temperature at the center of Earth is estimated to be about 5500°C, nearly equal to the temperature of the sun's surface.

The core is divided into two parts—the outer core and the inner core. In the outer core, high temperatures keep the metal liquid. Because of Earth's rotation, the flowing iron of the outer core produces an electric current and creates Earth's magnetic field. In the inner core, very high pressure is a more important factor than temperature. As a result, the inner core is solid.

Section 22.1 Assessment

Reviewing Concepts

1. What are the two types of forces studied by geologists? How does each process affect Earth's surface?
2. What are the three main layers of Earth? What are the characteristics of each layer?
3. What is the principle of uniformitarianism?
4. Describe the mesosphere.

Critical Thinking

5. **Comparing and Contrasting** What are the two types of crust, and how are they different?
6. **Relating Cause and Effect** Why is Earth's outer core liquid while its inner core is solid? Explain your answer.

Writing in Science

Creative Writing Suppose that you have a vehicle in which you travel to the center of Earth. Write 3 or 4 logbook entries for your trip, describing each of Earth's layers.

3 ASSESS

Evaluate Understanding L2

Ask students to create a compare-contrast table with the headings Lithosphere and Asthenosphere. Students should understand that the lithosphere includes both the uppermost part of the mantle and the crust, and is relatively cool and brittle. The asthenosphere, by contrast, is deeper within the mantle, where tremendous heat and pressure cause the rock to be soft and ductile.

Reteach L1

Use Figure 4 to review the layers of Earth. Review the main characteristics of each layer while discussing the diagram.

Writing in Science

Students should write an imaginative description of their journey. They should describe each of Earth's layers in order, noting such characteristics as thickness, composition, and temperature.

Interactive Textbook If your class subscribes to the Interactive Textbook, use it to review key concepts in Section 22.1.

Answer to . . .

Figure 4 *The mantle*

Figure 5 *The lithosphere includes the crust and the uppermost portion of the mantle.*

Reading Checkpoint *The asthenosphere is a layer of relatively soft, weak rock that lies between the lithosphere and the mesosphere.*

Section 22.1 Assessment

1. The two types of forces studied by geologists are constructive and destructive forces. Constructive forces build up areas on the surfaces of Earth, such as mountains. Destructive forces wear away those features.
2. The crust, mantle, and core. The crust is thin and rocky. The mantle is a thick layer of hot but solid rock. The core is a large sphere of metal. The outer core is liquid. The inner core is solid.
3. The principle of uniformitarianism states that the same geologic processes that can be observed working at present were also at work in the past. Thus, ancient rock features are the result of geologic processes working slowly over long periods of time.
4. The mesosphere is the relatively strong, stiff, lower part of the mantle that lies between the asthenosphere and the outer core.
5. The two types of crust are oceanic and continental. Oceanic crust is typically thinner and denser than continental crust.
6. The outer core is a liquid because the temperature is great enough to melt metal. The inner core is a solid because, although the temperature is very high, the pressure is so intense that it keeps the metal solid.

Section 22.2

1 FOCUS

Objectives

22.2.1 **Distinguish** between rocks and minerals and **explain** several properties used to identify minerals.

Reading Focus

Build Vocabulary L2

Paraphrase Most of the vocabulary words in this section are properties of minerals. Use mineral samples to demonstrate each of the properties, and have students describe the property in their own words. For example, make a streak with a mineral and say, **This is what geologists call a *streak*. How would you describe this property in your own words?**

Reading Strategy L2

B. Color **C.** Streak **D.** Luster

22.2 Minerals

Reading Focus

Key Concepts

- What is a mineral?
- What are some important properties of minerals?

Vocabulary

- rock
- inorganic
- streak
- luster
- hardness
- fracture
- cleavage

Reading Strategy

Outlining Before you read, make an outline of this section. Use the green headings as the main topics and the blue headings as subtopics. As you read, add supporting details.

Minerals
I. Minerals and Rocks
II. The Properties of Minerals
A. Crystal Structure
B. ________
C. ________
D. ________

Have you ever imagined finding a sunken treasure? In September 2002, a diver in Florida did just that. His job was to dive for objects from the *Santa Margarita*, a Spanish galleon, or treasure ship, that sank off the Florida Keys nearly 400 years ago. While rinsing sand off a conch shell found near the shipwreck, the diver spotted a shiny green stone. The stone proved to be a large and valuable emerald, like the ones in Figure 6.

Of course, the conch did not produce the emerald. The precious gem was almost certainly from the *Santa Margarita*. Scientists who have studied the emerald think that it originally came from mountains in South America where substances produced deep inside Earth have been brought toward the surface. Emeralds are a variety of the mineral beryl. The magnificent green color that makes emeralds so highly valued as gemstones is probably due to the presence of small amounts of chromium.

Figure 6 Emeralds are a form of the mineral beryl. These gems form deep beneath Earth's surface and are found in relatively few locations.

Section Resources

Print

- ***Reading and Study Workbook With Math Support***, Section 22.2
- ***Math Skills and Problem Solving Workbook***, Section 22.2
- ***Transparencies***, Section 22.2

Technology

- ***Interactive Textbook***, Section 22.2
- ***Presentation Pro CD-ROM***, Section 22.2
- ***Go Online***, NSTA SciLinks, Minerals

Figure 7 This portrait of Abraham Lincoln on Mt. Rushmore in South Dakota was sculpted in a granite cliff.

Minerals and Rocks

Plants and soil cover much of Earth's land surface. Beneath the plants and soil, however, is a layer of solid rock. You can see this rock where it is exposed on mountains and canyons, or where a highway cuts through a hillside. What is this material? A **rock** is a solid combination of minerals or mineral materials. **A mineral is a naturally occurring, inorganic solid with a crystal structure and a characteristic chemical composition.**

Minerals are **inorganic,** meaning that living things did not produce them. Geologists don't classify coal as a mineral because coal was created from plant remains over the course of millions of years. Materials like brick and concrete, which humans manufacture from a combination of natural materials, are not considered minerals either.

Each mineral is a unique substance with its own chemical composition and crystal structure. For most minerals, the proportion of elements can vary slightly while the mineral still retains a similar set of characteristics. Within each mineral crystal, the chemical composition is nearly constant.

Minerals are the building blocks of rocks. Only a fraction of the nearly 4000 known minerals are common. These common minerals are called the rock-forming minerals because they make up most of Earth's rocks. For example, granite is made up of the rock-forming minerals quartz, feldspar, mica, and hornblende. If you were to look closely at a piece of granite like that in Figure 8, you would see that it is made up of different-colored particles. Each particle is a separate mineral crystal. As you learned in chemistry, a crystal is a solid in which atoms are arranged in a regular repeating pattern.

Reading Checkpoint *What does it mean to say that a mineral is inorganic?*

Go Online NSTA SCILINKS

For: Links on minerals
Visit: www.SciLinks.org
Web Code: ccn-3222

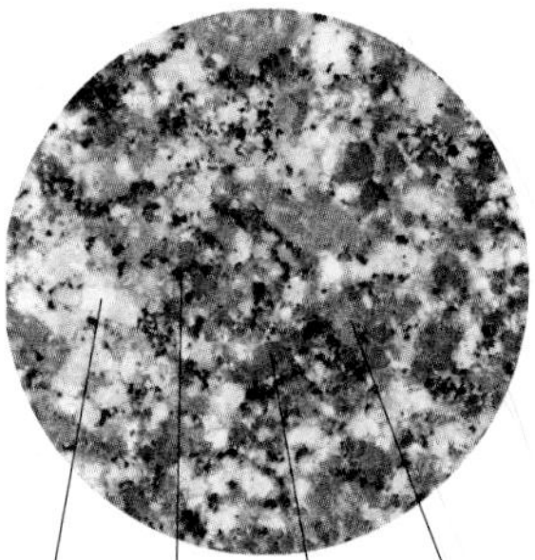

Quartz
Mica
Feldspar
Hornblende

Figure 8 A magnified view reveals the individual crystals of the minerals that make up granite.

2 INSTRUCT

Minerals and Rocks

Build Reading Literacy L2

Monitor Your Understanding Refer to page **326D** in **Chapter 11,** which provides the guidelines for monitoring your understanding.

Before students read Minerals and Rocks, ask them to stop and monitor their understanding after each paragraph. Explain that if they have not fully understood the paragraph, they should apply one of the reading techniques that has worked for them in the past. In this case, outlining, summarizing, and/or identifying main ideas may be helpful strategies. **Intrapersonal**

FYI

Some minerals can be produced by animals. Examples include the minerals in bones and shells. However, for these materials to be considered minerals, they must also form in nature through inorganic processes.

Use Visuals L1

Figure 8 Point out that each particle (grain) of granite is a separate solid crystal compound with a single composition. Different grains have different colors because they have different chemical compositions. The dark grains tend to have more atoms of iron and magnesium. The light grains tend to have more atoms of silicon and oxygen. Within each grain, the chemical composition is constant. A rock is therefore a solid aggregate of minerals bound tightly together. Ask, **What is the most common mineral in this piece of granite?** *(Quartz)* **What properties can you use to identify the minerals in a piece of granite?** *(Color, crystal shape or structure)* **Visual**

Go Online NSTA SCILINKS

Download a worksheet on minerals for students to complete, and find additional teacher support from NSTA SciLinks.

Customize for Inclusion Students

Behaviorally Disordered
For students who have difficulty concentrating during lectures or reading, have them explore mineral samples to learn about the main concepts in this section. Place students in small, mixed groups to explore 3–5 minerals and rocks. Have them verbally describe each mineral's color, streak, luster, hardness, crystal structure, fracture, and cleavage.

Answer to . . .

Reading Checkpoint *It means that the mineral was not produced by living things.*

The Properties of Minerals

Build Science Skills L2

Design an Experiment ACTIVITY

Purpose Students will design an experiment to test the density of solid crystals.

Materials mineral samples (preferably samples that have similar appearances but can be distinguished by density, such as galena and pyrite, amethyst and fluorite, hematite and magnetite); general laboratory materials such as beakers, graduated cylinders, mass balances, etc.

Class Time 30–45 minutes

Procedure Have students work in groups. Ask them to design an experiment to test the density of solid crystals using the materials provided. Students should hand in a written experimental design.

Expected Outcome Students will discuss the problem, and experiment with various laboratory materials to devise a way to measure the density of solids. Students may have varying approaches, but the most common method is to use water displacement to determine the volume of the solid and a balance to measure the mass. Students should measure the volume of water without the solid, then with the solid, and then subtract to obtain the volume of the solid. They should use a balance to measure the mass of the solid. Density is then calculated.
Logical, Portfolio, Group

Figure 9 Quartz that is pure silicon dioxide is clear or white. Slight impurities produce a range of colors, including the violet quartz (amethyst) specimen shown here.

The Properties of Minerals

Each mineral has a characteristic set of properties that results from its chemical composition and crystal structure. **The properties by which minerals can be identified include their crystal structure, color, streak, luster, density, hardness, fracture, and cleavage.** The properties of many common minerals are summarized in Appendix D.

Crystal Structure In each type of mineral, the atoms are arranged in a particular geometric shape, or crystal structure. Each mineral always has the same crystal structure. However, the size of a mineral's crystals can vary. Some crystals are too small to be seen without a microscope. Others can be the size of telephone poles! Many crystals form long prisms with a specific number of sides. For example, quartz crystals, shown in Figure 9, have six sides. Other minerals have crystals shaped like cubes, sheets, needles, or threads. Halite, the mineral form of table salt, forms cubic crystals. Garnet, a red, semiprecious gem, often forms 12-sided crystals.

Color Some minerals can be identified by a characteristic color. Pyrite, also known as fool's gold, is always golden in color. Crystals of pure sulfur are always yellow. But a mineral's color can often be deceptive, because slight changes in composition can cause significant changes in a mineral's color. For example, Figure 9 shows crystals of different colors, but they are all quartz.

Streak The color of a mineral's powder is known as its **streak.** A mineral's streak can be found by scraping the mineral on a piece of unglazed porcelain called a streak plate. The color of a mineral's streak is not always the same as the color of the mineral itself. For example, the hematite shown in Figure 10 looks black or silvery, but has a red-brown streak.

Reading Checkpoint *What is a mineral's streak?*

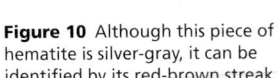

Figure 10 Although this piece of hematite is silver-gray, it can be identified by its red-brown streak.

Facts and Figures

Colors of Quartz Pure quartz, containing only SiO_2, is clear and colorless. However, natural quartz comes in many color varieties that form when different elements are contained in the crystal structure. If small amounts of titanium and iron are included, the result is rose quartz. The inclusion of manganese produces amethyst, the purple form of quartz shown in Figure 9. Smoky quartz is produced by inclusion of aluminum.

Galena
Pyrite
Sulfur

Figure 11 Galena has a metallic luster and a density of about 7.5 g/cm^3. Pyrite, also known as "fool's gold," has a metallic luster and a density of 5.0 g/cm^3. Sulfur has a resinous-to-greasy luster and a density of 2.0–2.1 g/cm^3. **Designing Experiments** ***How could you distinguish a sample of galena from a sample of pyrite?***

Luster The **luster** of a mineral is the way in which its surface reflects light. Luster refers to the general appearance of a mineral, or how shiny it is. As seen in Figure 11, galena and pyrite have a metallic luster, and sulfur has a resinous-to-greasy luster. Geologists use a variety of terms to describe a mineral's luster. For example, a mineral with a rough, crumbly surface is said to have an earthy luster. Other terms used to describe luster include silky, pearly, and vitreous (glassy.)

Density The density of a mineral depends on its chemical composition. In general, minerals made up of elements with higher atomic masses have higher densities than minerals made up of atoms with lower atomic masses. For example, galena contains much lead, which has a relatively high atomic mass of 207. Galena's density is about 7.5 grams per cubic centimeter. In contrast, quartz is made up of silicon and oxygen, which have relatively low atomic masses of 28 and 16 respectively. Quartz's density is only about 2.6 grams per cubic centimeter.

Data Analysis

Density of Minerals

The density of minerals varies, depending on what elements the minerals contain. Samples of the minerals in the data table were analyzed for density, silicon and oxygen content, and the presence of metals. Study the data table, and then answer the questions.

Mineral Properties

Mineral	Density (g/cm^3)	Percent Si and O	Metals Present
Olivine	3.3	65	Mg, Fe
Augite	3.2	65	Mg, Fe, Ca
Hornblende	3.0	67	Mg, Fe, Ca, Al
Muscovite	2.8	71	K, Al, Mg, Fe
Quartz	2.6	100	None

1. **Using Tables** Which mineral has the lowest density? The highest density?
2. **Using Tables** Which minerals have the lowest percentage of silicon and oxygen? Which has the highest?
3. **Formulating Hypotheses** Olivine and augite are abundant in oceanic crust and in the mantle. Quartz, muscovite, and hornblende are abundant in continental crust. Formulate a hypothesis to explain why continental crust floats higher on the mantle than oceanic crust.
4. **Drawing Conclusions** How is a mineral's density related to its silicon and oxygen content?

Data Analysis

Density of Minerals L2

Answers

1. Quartz; olivine
2. Olivine and augite; quartz
3. Continental crust is composed of less dense minerals than oceanic crust. Therefore, continental crust is more buoyant and floats higher on the mantle.
4. In general, the higher the silicon and oxygen content of a mineral, the lower its density.

For Extra Help L1

Explain that a table is set up to help the reader see patterns in the data. Instruct students to look down the columns to see the patterns of density and percent Si and O for each mineral. Look across the rows to find the data for each specific mineral. Have students practice reading the table by asking them to name the metals found in specific minerals. Then, have them practice finding patterns by asking them to describe the pattern in the density column.
Verbal

Facts and Figures

Formation of Diamonds Why can diamond and graphite be made of the same material but form different minerals? You could make a diamond out of your pencil if you could squeeze it hard enough. The pressure would compress the carbon atoms of the graphite together until they eventually formed the strong covalent bonds of diamond. In fact, this is roughly how synthetic diamonds are made: by squeezing carbon very tightly. Natural diamonds are thought to form more than 150 km beneath the surface, where the pressures are very high. The diamonds that we find at the surface have been brought up from deep within Earth by geologic processes.

Answer to . . .

Figure 11 *One way would be to calculate the density of each sample. The denser sample would be galena. Color could also be used to distinguish the samples.*

Reading Checkpoint *The color of the mineral's powder, which can be found by scraping the mineral on a streak plate.*

Address Misconceptions L2

Many people have the misconception that any clear crystal that scratches glass is diamond. Since glass has a hardness of 5.5, any mineral that is 6 or higher on the hardness scale will scratch glass. Provide students with mineral samples of clear quartz to perform a scratch test with the glass in order to debunk this common misconception. **Kinesthetic**

Quick Lab

Mineral Hardness L2

Objective
After completing this activity, students will be able to
- determine the hardness of minerals.

Skills Focus **Observing**

Prep Time 10 minutes

Materials labeled samples of graphite, galena or halite, hornblende, feldspar, pyrite, and olivine; penny; iron nail; steel file

Class Time 15 minutes

Safety Caution students to wear safety goggles and lab aprons when performing hardness tests.

Expected Outcome Students will be able to estimate the hardness of the minerals relative to the known standards provided (copper, steel, fingernail, and iron) and then rank them by hardness.

Analyze and Conclude
1. The hardnesses of the minerals provided are: graphite 1–2, galena and halite 2.5, hornblende 5–6, feldspar 6, pyrite 6–6.5, and olivine 6.5–7.
2. Students should list four of the minerals provided in the order graphite, galena or halite, hornblende, feldspar, pyrite, and olivine.
3. Precise determination of hardness is not possible without more known standards. Other helpful information includes structure, streak, color, density, and cleavage. **Kinesthetic, Logical**

For Enrichment L3

For hardness standards, provide some minerals (labeled) shown in Figure 12. Then, provide some unlabeled minerals and ask students to identify them by determining their hardness. **Logical**

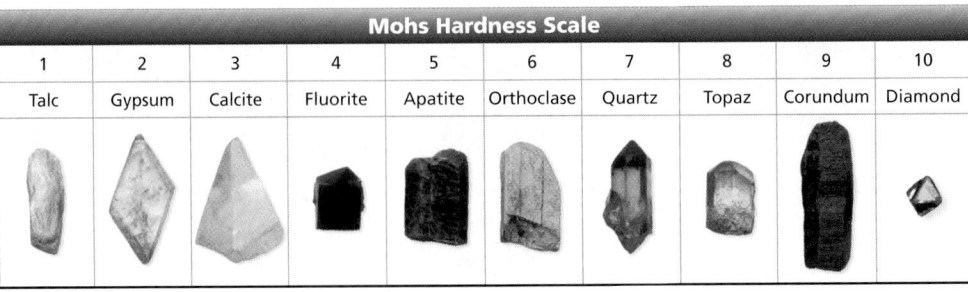

Mohs Hardness Scale

1	2	3	4	5	6	7	8	9	10
Talc	Gypsum	Calcite	Fluorite	Apatite	Orthoclase	Quartz	Topaz	Corundum	Diamond

Figure 12 Mohs hardness scale ranks minerals according to hardness on a scale from 1 to 10.
Inferring *Which of the minerals in the table would scratch a glass plate, which has a hardness of 5.5?*

Quick Lab

Mineral Hardness

Procedure

1. Select four minerals.
2. Try scratching each mineral's surface with your fingernail (hardness: 2.5), the edge of a penny (hardness: 3.5), the tip of an iron nail (hardness: 4.5), and the face of a steel file (hardness: 6.5). Then, scratch each mineral with every other mineral. Record your observations.

Analyze and Conclude

1. **Observing** Based on your observations and Mohs hardness scale provided above, estimate the hardness of each mineral.
2. **Classifying** Make a list of the minerals, going from the softest to the hardest.
3. **Posing Questions** What other information would you need in order to identify each mineral?

Hardness The atoms of minerals are held together by chemical bonds of different kinds and strengths. As a result, minerals have different hardnesses. **Hardness** is the resistance of a mineral to scratching. A hard mineral can scratch a softer mineral, but not the other way around. The hardness of minerals is ranked on a scale from 1 to 10, called Mohs hardness scale. Diamond is the hardest mineral, with a hardness of 10. Talc is one of the softest minerals, with a hardness of 1. Figure 12 shows the hardness of some minerals according to Mohs scale.

Geologists use scratch tests systematically to determine the hardness of mineral specimens. First, a geologist may try to scratch a glass plate, which has a hardness of 5.5, with the mineral. Having determined that the mineral is either harder or softer than 5.5, the geologist can continue to perform scratch tests. Everyday materials can also be used to compare the hardness of minerals. For example, a copper penny, which has a hardness of about 3.5, can scratch talc but it cannot scratch quartz. A fingernail, with a hardness of 2.5, and a streak plate, with a hardness of 6.5, can also be used to test hardness.

Fracture and Cleavage The **fracture** of a mineral is how the mineral breaks. When a piece of quartz is broken, it has a curved, shell-shaped fracture. Other minerals fracture unevenly along curved or jagged surfaces. Fracture is determined by the crystalline structure of the mineral and the bonds between the atoms in the crystals.

Some minerals split evenly when they break apart. **Cleavage** is a type of fracture in which the mineral tends to split along regular, well-defined planes (flat surfaces) where the bonds are weakest. For example, mica and graphite form sheets. Each sheet of mica contains chemical bonds that are very strong. However, the sheets are held together with weak bonds, so they can easily be peeled apart from each other. In contrast, halite, shown in Figure 13, can be split into block-like pieces that reflect the cubic structure of halite crystals.

Facts and Figures

Asbestos Like mica, asbestos is a sheet-forming mineral. However, unlike flat sheets of mica, sheets of asbestos roll up in a tight needle-like formation. These needles can cause serious damage to lungs if inhaled. Before people realized that asbestos caused a health risk, it was a popular insulation material. Now, many older buildings must undergo expensive asbestos removal in order to be safe for people.

Other Properties Some minerals have unusual properties. For example, acids dissolve calcite easily. If you put a few drops of dilute hydrochloric acid on calcite, the calcite will bubble vigorously. In this way, calcite can be distinguished from the similar-looking mineral quartz. Another mineral with an unusual property is magnetite, which is strongly attracted by a magnet. Fluorescent minerals like fluorite give off visible light when they are held under an ultraviolet light. Certain minerals produce small flashes of light when rubbed with a metal point. For example, a form of quartz called rock crystal emits these flashes when it is sawed.

Some minerals have unusual electrical properties. Quartz and tourmaline, for example, become electrically charged when heated and cooled or subjected to pressure. Quartz's electrical properties have applications in electronics equipment.

Iceland spar is a transparent form of the mineral calcite that has the property of refracting light into two separate rays. If you looked at these words through a piece of Iceland spar, you would see a double image of the words. This property is useful in certain optical instruments.

Figure 13 Mica (left) forms in thin, flat sheets that can be easily peeled apart. When halite (right) is broken apart, it forms small cubes that show its crystal structure. **Interpreting Photos** ***Which mineral property do these photos illustrate?***

Section 22.2 Assessment

Reviewing Concepts

1. What is a mineral?
2. Describe three properties of minerals that can be used to identify them.
3. What determines the crystal shape of a mineral?
4. What determines how a mineral fractures? Explain.

Critical Thinking

5. **Designing Experiments** Suppose you are given two mineral samples that have the same color and luster. What tests could you conduct to determine whether the two samples are the same mineral?
6. **Formulating Hypotheses** Like diamond, graphite is a mineral composed of pure carbon. But its hardness is only between 1 and 2 on the Mohs scale. Formulate a hypothesis to explain the difference in hardness of these minerals.

Connecting Concepts

Covalent Bonds Recall what you learned in Chapter 6 about the characteristics of molecules held together by covalent bonds. Predict a characteristic of quartz (SiO_2), which is covalently bonded.

3 ASSESS

Evaluate Understanding **L2**

Provide students with 5–10 common mineral samples to identify based on the properties covered in this section.

Reteach **L1**

In order to help students understand the concept that minerals are the building blocks of rocks, show them samples of pure quartz, feldspar, mica, and hornblende, and samples of granite. Have students use a magnifying lens to identify the mineral constituents of the granite samples.

Connecting Concepts

The covalent bonds in quartz are very strong. As a result, quartz is relatively hard and does not fracture into a predictable geometric shape.

Interactive Textbook If your class subscribes to the Interactive Textbook, use it to review key concepts in Section 22.2.

Section 22.2 Assessment

1. A mineral is a naturally occurring, inorganic solid with a regular crystal structure and a definite chemical composition.
2. Answers will vary. Students may choose to describe any three of the mineral characteristics included in the section, including crystal structure, color, streak, luster, density, hardness, fracture, and cleavage.
3. The atomic structure of a mineral determines its crystal shape.
4. The crystal structure of a mineral and the nature of the bonds between the atoms in the crystals determine how a mineral fractures.
5. There a variety of tests available. These include checking each mineral's streak using a streak plate, determining the density of each sample by measuring its mass and volume, using a scratch test to determine the hardness of each sample, and breaking the samples apart to see how they fracture.
6. The atoms in diamond are held together by much stronger bonds than those in graphite, resulting in a much harder mineral.

Answer to . . .

Figure 12 *All of the minerals with a hardness greater than 5.5, which are orthoclase, quartz, topaz, corundum, and diamond*

Figure 13 *Cleavage*

Section 22.3

1 FOCUS

Objectives

22.3.1 **Classify** rocks as igneous, sedimentary, or metamorphic and **explain** how different types of rocks form.

22.3.2 **Describe** the processes by which rocks continually change from one type to another in the rock cycle.

Reading Focus

Build Vocabulary L2

Concept Map Have students build a concept map to organize the vocabulary words pertaining to the classification of rocks. Include the concepts *igneous rocks, sedimentary rocks,* and *metamorphic rocks* under the main concept, Types of Rocks. As they read the section, have students add descriptive concepts for each type of rock. The vocabulary terms *intrusive, extrusive, clastic,* and *foliated* should be included in the map.

Reading Strategy L2

a. Cooling of magma or lava **b.** Possible answers include granite, basalt, and gabbro. **c.** Sedimentary **d.** Compression and cementing together of sediment **e.** Metamorphic **f.** Possible answers include slate, schist, and gneiss.

2 INSTRUCT

Classifying Rocks

Build Reading Literacy L1

Preview Refer to page **658D** in this chapter, which provides the guidelines for a preview.

Before reading Section 22.3, have students read the bold subheads and examine Figure 21. Then, ask students to list the important concepts they will learn in the section. *(How rocks are classified into the major groups—igneous, sedimentary, and metamorphic—and how rocks continually change from one type to another in the rock cycle)*
Intrapersonal

22.3 Rocks and the Rock Cycle

Reading Focus

Key Concepts

- What are the three major groups of rocks?
- How do igneous rocks form?
- How are sedimentary rocks classified?
- How do metamorphic rocks form?
- How can one type of rock change into another?

Vocabulary

- igneous rock
- magma
- lava
- intrusive rock
- extrusive rock
- sediment
- sedimentary rock
- clastic rocks
- metamorphic rock
- foliated rocks
- rock cycle

Reading Strategy

Comparing and Contrasting Copy the table below. After you read, compare groups of rocks by completing the table.

Rock Group	Formed by	Example
Igneous	a. ?	b. ?
c. ?	d. ?	Sandstone
e. ?	Heat and pressure	f. ?

Towering more than 1000 meters above Yosemite Valley, California, the steep rock face of El Capitan attracts rock climbers from around the world. In 1993, climber Lynn Hill accomplished the first "free climb" of El Capitan. That is, she climbed without the aid of a rope, except to provide safety in case of a fall. Over four days, Hill ascended El Capitan's steep "nose route," with its sheer cliffs and many overhangs. For an encore, she climbed the same route in 1994 in less than 24 hours!

El Capitan is one of the largest and most impressive chunks of granite on Earth. Yet each of the much smaller rocks that we pass every day also has a fascinating story to tell. Was it formed deep inside a volcano, or crushed by tremendous forces deep within Earth? A few easy-to-observe properties can reveal much about a rock's history.

Figure 14 Lynn Hill climbing the granite face of El Capitan.

Classifying Rocks

The properties that geologists use to identify rocks include color and crystal size. The color of a rock indicates the minerals it contains. However, because the colors of most minerals can vary, a rock's color is not always a reliable way to identify it. A better way to identify rocks is by the size of the crystals or other particles they contain.

The size, shape, and arrangement of the crystals and other particles that make up a rock give the rock its texture. A rock's texture reveals what the rock is made from and how and where it formed. **Rocks are classified into three major groups—igneous, sedimentary, and metamorphic—based on how they form.**

Section Resources

Print
- ***Laboratory Manual,*** Investigation 22A
- ***Reading and Study Workbook With Math Support,*** Section 22.3
- ***Transparencies,*** Section 22.3

Technology
- ***Interactive Textbook,*** Section 22.3
- ***Presentation Pro CD-ROM,*** Section 22.3
- ***Go Online,*** NSTA SciLinks, Rocks

Igneous Rock

An **igneous rock** is a rock that forms from magma. **Magma** is a mixture of molten rock and gases, including water vapor, which forms underground. Magma that flows out of volcanoes is called **lava.** **Igneous rock forms when molten material cools and solidifies either inside Earth or at the surface.** An igneous rock that forms underground from hardened magma is called an **intrusive rock.** An igneous rock that forms at Earth's surface is called an **extrusive rock.**

Extrusive rocks and intrusive rocks have differences in texture caused by differences in how the rocks formed. Intrusive rocks cool slowly underground, allowing their crystals to grow large. Large crystals give intrusive rocks a coarse-grained texture. Extrusive igneous rocks cool very quickly at the surface. Their crystals do not grow much before the rock cools. This gives extrusive rocks a fine-grained texture.

An igneous rock's color gives a clue to its mineral composition. The rock's composition depends on the composition of the magma from which it was formed. Magma that is rich in iron and magnesium produces rocks that are dark and dense, such as gabbro, an intrusive rock, and basalt, an extrusive rock. Some igneous rocks are less dense and lighter in color than basalt and gabbro. These rocks have a high silica content. One such rock is granite, a coarse-grained, intrusive rock.

Figure 15 Basalt is a fine-grained, extrusive rock. As this basalt cooled, the rock formed into hexagonal columns.

Quick Lab

Observing the Size of Crystals

Materials

salol, plastic spoon, 2 watch glasses, tongs, hot plate, hand lens, Petri dish, ice cube, watch with second hand

Procedure

1. Use the spoon to place just enough salol on two watch glasses to cover an area 0.5 cm in width. **CAUTION** *Handle the watch glasses with care to avoid breakage. Salol is poisonous. Don't get it on your skin or breathe its vapor.*
2. Turn the hot plate on to medium heat. Use tongs to place one watch glass on the hot plate.
3. When the salol is almost fully melted, use tongs to place the watch glass on the table. Use the spoon to gently sprinkle a few crystals of salol on the melted salol. Record the time.
4. Use a hand lens to observe the salol as it cools. Record the time when salol crystals begin to reform and how large they are.
5. Place the ice cube on the Petri dish. Repeat Steps 2 to 4 with the second watch glass, but this time, place the watch glass of melted salol on the ice cube instead of the table. Wash your hands with soap and warm water.

Analyze and Conclude

1. **Analyzing Data** How did the rate of cooling affect the size of the crystals that formed?
2. **Using Models** What characteristic of igneous rocks did this lab model? Explain.
3. **Predicting** Pegmatite is an igneous rock that forms when magma cools deep beneath Earth's surface. In contrast, rhyolite is an igneous rock that forms when magma escapes onto the surface. In which rock would you expect to find larger crystals? Explain your answer.

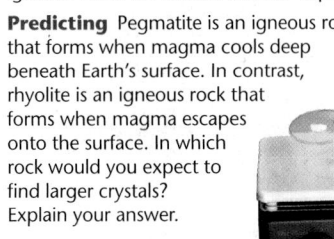

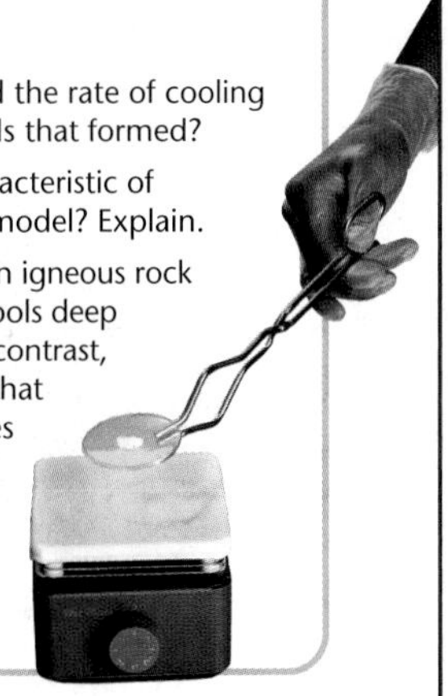

Igneous Rock

Quick Lab

Observing the Size of Crystals **L2**

Objective

After completing this activity, students will be able to
- describe the effect of cooling rate on the size of crystals in igneous rocks.

Address Misconceptions

Students may not have observed the formation of crystals before and may think that the process is always very slow and results in the formation of perfectly shaped crystals. This lab gives students the opportunity to observe rapid crystallization and the size and shape of the resulting crystals.

Skills Focus **Observing, Using Models**

Prep Time 10 minutes

Advance Prep Salol (phenyl salicylate) can be obtained from a drugstore or chemical supply house. There should be two borosilicate watch glasses for each lab group.

Class Time 20 minutes

Safety Share the safety information in the Material Safety Data Sheet for salol with students. Provide only heat-resistant borosilicate watch glasses. Students must wear goggles, lab aprons, and plastic gloves. Caution students not to touch the salol or their faces, not to inhale the vapor of the salol, and to wash their hands with soap or detergent and warm water after working with salol. Caution students not to overheat the watch glasses because they might break.

Teaching Tips
- Students should try to notice where the dusted crystals of salol fall and focus on those sites to observe crystal growth.
- Keep the watch glasses on which the salol has hardened for remelting by other classes. You can use alcohol or acetone with adequate ventilation, or vegetable oil to remove salol.

Expected Outcome The crystals on the watch glass that cooled slowly at room temperature will be larger than the crystals on the watch glass that cooled quickly on ice.

Customize for English Language Learners

Make a Flowchart

Have students create a flowchart describing the processes of the rock cycle. Students may use Figure 21 as a guide, but ask them to expand the descriptions of both the processes and the rock types using their own words.

Analyze and Conclude

1. The faster the salol cooled, the smaller the crystals were.
2. The formation of igneous rocks from the cooling and hardening of magma, which is one of the ways in which mineral crystals can form
3. Students should predict that pegmatite is made up of larger crystals because it cools more slowly, and that rhyolite is made up of smaller crystals because it cools more rapidly.

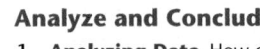

Kinesthetic, Visual

Sedimentary Rock

Build Science Skills **L2**

Classifying

ACTIVITY

Purpose Students will classify rocks into the three major groups.

Materials 10 numbered rock samples for each group of students

Class Time 20–25 minutes

Procedure Have students work in groups to classify the rocks into the three main groups: igneous, sedimentary, or metamorphic.

Expected Outcome Each group will classify the rocks appropriately.
Kinesthetic, Group

Integrate Language Arts **L2**

Clastic means "made of clasts." It is taken from the Greek word for broken, *klastos*. Ask, **What is a *clast* in a clastic rock?** *(A broken fragment of another rock)* **Describe the subgroups of clastic rocks based on the types of clasts they contain.** *(Conglomerate rocks have large, rounded clasts. Breccia have sharp-edged clasts. In sandstone the clasts are grains of sand. In mudstone the clasts are fine grains of clay or silt.)*
Verbal

FYI

Sand is primarily made of quartz grains. This occurs for two reasons. The mineral quartz is not easily dissolved in water, so it survives the trip down rivers. Quartz is also a hard mineral. Even though beach sands get repeatedly pounded by ocean waves, the quartz grains are still hard to pulverize.

Figure 16 Colorful layers of sandstone, like those in this Utah canyon, formed over millions of years as water and wind laid down sediment.

Sedimentary Rock

The process of weathering breaks down rock at Earth's surface, turning it into smaller pieces. Some rocks are dissolved by rainwater. Other rocks are broken apart by water, wind, or ice. (Weathering will be covered in detail in Chapter 23.)

Sediment is small, solid pieces of material that comes from rocks or living organisms. Minerals dissolved in water are also sediment. As in Figure 16, sediment is often carried away by running water or wind to a new location, where it is deposited in layers. This process occurs mainly in the oceans, but it also occurs on river beds, on the bottoms of lakes, and in deserts. Rivers carry sand, mud, and dissolved minerals into the oceans, where these materials are deposited as layers of sediment on the ocean floor.

As more and more sediment piles up, the pressure causes the deeper sediment to be compressed. Dissolved minerals in the water seep into the space between particles of sediment and form a kind of cement. A **sedimentary rock** is a rock that forms over time as sediment is squeezed and cemented together. **Geologists classify sedimentary rocks into three main groups according to how they form: clastic rocks, chemical rocks, and organic rocks.**

Clastic Rock Sedimentary rocks that form from the broken fragments of other rocks are called **clastic rocks.** The fragments that make up clastic rocks are usually held together by cement. Otherwise, the fragments would fall apart, like a handful of sand. Clastic rocks are classified mainly based upon the average size of the fragments that they contain. If the rock fragments consist of gravel and pebbles, then the rock is called conglomerate. Like the example in Figure 17, conglomerate usually contains rounded pieces that have been worn smooth in a river or stream. In contrast, breccia is a clastic rock made up of sharp-edged fragments, such as those produced in a volcanic explosion.

Other clastic rocks are made of smaller particles. Sandstone is formed from grains of sand. (Sand itself is made up mostly of small particles of quartz.) If the sediment is primarily mud or silt, the clastic rock is called mudstone. The clay minerals that form mudstone are flat minerals, similar to mica. If these clay minerals are aligned so that the rock can split into sheets, the rock is called shale.

Figure 17 Conglomerate is a sedimentary rock in which rounded pieces of other rocks are cemented together. **Classifying** ***What type of sedimentary rock is conglomerate?***

Facts and Figures

Sedimentary Rocks While most of the rock of the continents and ocean sea floor had an igneous origin, much of the rock at the surface of the continents is sedimentary. The reason for this is that at various times in Earth's history, the continents have been flooded by the ocean. During these times, ocean sediments were deposited on the continents and were compressed to form new sedimentary rock.

Figure 18 The strangely shaped rocks in Mono Lake, California, are made of tufa, a chemical rock composed of calcium carbonate.

Chemical Rock Chemical sedimentary rocks form when minerals precipitate out of solution. Rainwater dissolves many minerals on the land. These dissolved minerals are then carried down rivers and into the ocean. These minerals remain in solution in ocean water as water evaporates from the ocean surface. The process of evaporation increases the concentration until the minerals precipitate out and sink to the ocean floor. A common type of limestone forms from the precipitation of calcium carbonate in the oceans.

Chemical rocks can also form on land. Many dry basins in the western United States, such as the great salt flats of Utah, are covered with thick layers of precipitated salt. Figure 18 shows chemical rocks that formed in Mono Lake, California.

Go Online NSTA SciLinks

For: Links on rocks
Visit: www.SciLinks.org
Web Code: ccn-3223

Organic Rock Some rocks form as the result of organic processes. Marine animals such as coral, clams, and mussels extract calcium carbonate from ocean water to form their shells and skeletons. After these organisms die, their shells and skeletons sink to the ocean floor. Over time, the fragments compact and cement together, forming limestone. Organic limestone is one of the most common sedimentary rocks. Chalk, shown in Figure 19, is a fine-grained, white limestone that formed on the bottom of ancient seas.

Reading Checkpoint *How does organic limestone form?*

Figure 19 The cliffs of Dover on the southern coast of England are composed of chalk, a type of fine-grained organic limestone.

673

Build Science Skills L2

Inferring Ask, **What could be the origin of the great salt flats of Utah?** *(A body of water evaporated, leaving behind the salt deposits.)* Have students work in groups to discuss ways in which rock formations such as those shown in Figure 18 could have formed. Have each group produce a flowchart showing the steps that they think contributed to these formations.
Logical, Group

FYI

Fossils are mainly found in sedimentary rocks. Most fossils form from organisms that once lived in or near quiet bodies of water such as lakes, swamps, or shallow seas. Fossils form when such organisms die and are buried by sediments. The sediments are gradually compressed and harden into sedimentary rock. The heat and/or pressure of forming an igneous or metamorphic rock generally destroys any preexisting fossils. The types of fossils found in a rock help scientists to determine the origins of the rock.

Go Online NSTA SciLinks

Download a worksheet on rocks for students to complete, and find additional teacher support from NSTA SciLinks.

Facts and Figures

Evaporites Chemical rocks produced by evaporation are called evaporites. The evaporites in the Bonneville Salt Flats and Great Salt Lake in Utah were mostly formed from the residue of a giant lake that existed there during the Pleistocene ice ages.

Answer to . . .

Figure 17 *Conglomerate is a clastic sedimentary rock.*

Reading Checkpoint *Organic limestone forms when the shells and skeletons of marine organisms sink to the ocean floor and are compacted and cemented together over time.*

Metamorphic Rock

Build Reading Literacy L1

Anticipation Guide Refer to page **388D** in **Chapter 8**, which provides the guidelines for an anticipation guide.

Show students samples of a sedimentary rock and its metamorphic counterpart (e.g., shale and gneiss, limestone and marble). Tell students that tremendous heat and pressure caused the sedimentary rock to change into the metamorphic rock. Have students work in groups to discuss the change of sedimentary rock to metamorphic rock. Ask them to note the differences in the rocks. Also ask them for their ideas about the processes involved in changing the rock. Then, have students read Metamorphic Rock and regroup to discuss what they have learned.
Verbal, Interpersonal

The Rock Cycle

Address Misconceptions L2

Students commonly think that rocks are permanent Earth features that do not change. Explain that, although the process often takes millions of years (with the exception of volcanism, which can often take minutes, or sediments, which can form quickly from mass movement and other types of erosion), rocks are continually changing from one type to another in the rock cycle. Provide students with different types of rocks and have them work in groups to tell a story about how each rock was formed and the ways in which it may change in the future.
Logical, Interpersonal

Use Visuals L1

Figure 21 Point out that the rock cycle is a dynamic process in which there are many paths a rock can take. Ask, **What is the process by which metamorphic rock can become sedimentary rock?** *(Weathering, deposition, compaction, and cementation)* **What type of rock is produced by melting and cooling?** *(Igneous)* **What conditions are necessary for the formation of metamorphic rock?** *(Heat pressure or chemical reactions)*
Visual

Shale
Slate
Schist
Gneiss

Figure 20 Heat, pressure, and chemical reactions change the form of rocks. In this sequence, shale changes to slate. Additional heat and pressure may change slate into schist or gneiss.
Comparing and Contrasting ***How does gneiss appear to be similar to schist? How is it different?***

Metamorphic Rock

The word *metamorphic* comes from the Greek for "changing form." **Metamorphic rock** is rock that has been changed by temperature, pressure, or reactions with hot water. Geologists call this process of change metamorphism. **Metamorphic rock forms when a rock is transformed by heat, pressure, or chemical reactions. Most metamorphic rocks form under high temperatures and pressures deep underground.** The original rock could have been any kind of rock: igneous, sedimentary, or even another metamorphic rock. The result is a new kind of rock.

Metamorphism can result in a rock with a mineral content that is different from that of the original rock. The process begins when heat deep inside Earth allows the minerals to recrystallize, and small crystals to enlarge. As chemical changes occur, new minerals may replace the original minerals. For example, shale is a fine-grained clastic rock that contains clay. During metamorphism, some of the clay changes to the mineral mica, forming the metamorphic rock slate, as you can see in Figure 20.

Metamorphism also changes the texture of rocks. The particles that make up sedimentary and igneous rocks tend to be distributed randomly through the rock. But when pressure is applied from one direction, the particles may line up and lock together in layers or bands. Metamorphic rocks with crystals arranged in parallel layers or bands are **foliated rocks.** Some foliated rocks have a striped appearance. For example, when schist is subjected to heat and pressure, the result is gneiss (nys). Other metamorphic rocks have a nonfoliated texture. Nonfoliated rocks don't have bands. Their crystals are arranged randomly.

The Rock Cycle

Earth is a dynamic planet. Constructive forces form new igneous rock. Destructive forces break down rock, forming sediment. Other forces push rock deep beneath the surface, where heat and pressure form metamorphic rock.

These changes form a cycle—a set of events that repeats again and again. The **rock cycle** is a series of processes in which rocks continuously change from one type to another. **In the rock cycle, forces within Earth and at the surface cause rocks to change form.**

To follow the rock cycle in Figure 21, imagine a newly formed igneous rock such as granite. In one path through the rock cycle, the granite is pushed to the surface where it is broken into sand. A river then carries the sand to the ocean floor. There, the sand becomes part of the sedimentary rock sandstone.

The rock cycle doesn't necessarily end with the formation of sandstone. Over millions of years, the sandstone could be pushed deep underground and form the metamorphic rock quartzite. The quartzite could be heated past its melting point and then cool to form a new igneous rock.

Facts and Figures

Metamorphism Most metamorphism occurs over a broad volume of rock. This is called regional metamorphism. Some metamorphism occurs when magma rises up through cold rock. This is called contact metamorphism. Contact metamorphism usually involves low pressures and high temperatures. Different geologic settings can involve various degrees of increased temperature and pressure. For instance, the rock within a subduction zone can be subjected to high-pressure, low-temperature metamorphism.

Igneous rock
Weathering & erosion
Sediment
Compacting & cementation
Sedimentary rock
Weathering & erosion
Heat & pressure
Melting
Heat & pressure
Cooling
Magma
Melting
Metamorphic rock

Figure 21 There are many different paths in the rock cycle. Depending on their pathway through the cycle, rocks can wear away, undergo metamorphism, or melt and form new igneous rock.

Section 22.3 Assessment

Reviewing Concepts

1. What are the three groups into which geologists classify rocks?
2. What are the two ways in which igneous rocks can form?
3. What are the three main groups of sedimentary rocks, and how does each group form?
4. How are metamorphic rocks formed?
5. Describe a path through the rock cycle that begins with magma and ends with a sedimentary rock.

Critical Thinking

6. **Comparing and Contrasting** How is conglomerate different from sandstone?
7. **Applying Concepts** What do the crystal sizes of granite and basalt tell you about where they formed?
8. **Predicting** Forces inside Earth may push granite, a coarse-grained igneous rock, deep below the surface. Predict how the granite could be changed by heat and pressure.

Writing in Science

Steps in a Process Write a paragraph describing the steps in the rock cycle by which an igneous rock could become a sedimentary rock and then a metamorphic rock.

3 ASSESS

Evaluate Understanding L2

Ask students to classify the rocks in Figure 20 using the categories covered in the section. *(Shale: clastic sedimentary; slate, schist, and gneiss: foliated metamorphic)*

Reteach L1

Use Figure 21 to review the processes by which each of the three major groups of rocks are formed.

Writing in Science

Students' paragraphs should describe how an igneous rock could be broken down into sediment by weathering and how this sediment could be transformed into a clastic sedimentary rock as layers of sediment build up over time and are compressed and cemented together. They should further describe how a sedimentary rock could be thrust deep underground and transformed into a metamorphic rock by heat, pressure, or chemical reactions.

Interactive Textbook If your class subscribes to the Interactive Textbook, use it to review key concepts in Section 22.3.

Answer to . . .

Figure 20 *Both gneiss and schist are foliated metamorphic rocks with a similar composition of light- and dark-colored minerals. Gneiss, however, shows obvious banding, while schist does not.*

Section 22.3 Assessment

1. Igneous, sedimentary, and metamorphic
2. Igneous rocks are formed from the cooling of either magma or lava.
3. Clastic, chemical, and organic. Clastic sedimentary rocks form from the broken pieces of other rocks that are cemented together. Chemical sedimentary rocks form when minerals precipitate out of a solution. Organic sedimentary rocks are the result of organic processes.
4. Metamorphic rocks generally form deep underground when an existing rock is transformed by heat, pressure, or chemical reactions.
5. The magma cools to form igneous rock. The igneous rock is weathered to form sediment. The sediment is deposited and compacted to form sedimentary rock.
6. Both are clastic sedimentary rocks, but the fragments of rock that make up conglomerate are much larger than those that compose sandstone.
7. Granite has relatively large crystals, so it must be an intrusive rock that cooled slowly underground. In contrast, basalt has small crystals, so it is an extrusive rock that cooled quickly above ground.
8. Granite could be transformed by the intense heat and pressure within Earth into a metamorphic rock.

Section 22.4

1 FOCUS

Objectives

22.4.1 **Explain** the hypothesis of continental drift.

22.4.2 **Relate** how the theory of plate tectonics explains sea-floor spreading, subduction, and the formation of mountains.

22.4.3 **Explain** the mechanisms of plate movement.

Reading Focus

Build Vocabulary L2

Word Forms Have students look up the meanings of *convergent* and *divergent* and find other related word forms (e.g., *converge, convergence*). Be sure students can define all of the word forms.

Reading Strategy L2

Students' questions may include: **a.** What is the process of sea-floor spreading? **b.** What is the mid-ocean ridge? **c.** How does oceanic crust form?

2 INSTRUCT

Address Misconceptions L2

A commonly held misconception among students is that major Earth features, such as continents and mountain chains, do not change. It is easy to see why this misconception is so pervasive, as major landmasses do not appear to be moving when observed from the scale of human life. Explain that plate movement occurs on the order of 0.1–10 cm/yr. During the course of millions of years, continents can move great distances. Have students calculate how long it would take for a continent to move 10,000 km if it was on a plate that was moving at 2 cm/yr. *(500 million years)*
Logical

22.4 Plate Tectonics

Reading Focus

Key Concepts

- What are plate tectonics and continental drift?
- What are the roles of sea-floor spreading and subduction in plate tectonics?
- Why do tectonic plates move?
- What are the types of plate boundaries and what are their characteristics?
- Where do most mountains form?

Vocabulary

- plate tectonics
- Pangaea
- continental drift
- mid-ocean ridge
- sea-floor spreading
- subduction
- trench
- divergent boundary
- convergent boundary
- transform boundary

Reading Strategy

Previewing Copy the table below. Before you read this section, rewrite the headings as how, why, and what questions about plate tectonics. As you read, write answers to the questions.

Questions on Plate Tectonics
What is the hypothesis of continental drift?
a. ?
b. ?
c. ?

Sometimes a single idea can revolutionize an entire field of study. Many observations that previously made little sense will suddenly fit together. Plate tectonics is such an idea. The discovery of plate tectonics revolutionized the field of geology. **Plate tectonics** (tek TAHN iks) is the theory that pieces of Earth's lithosphere, called plates, move about slowly on top of the asthenosphere. **The theory of plate tectonics explains the formation and movement of Earth's plates.**

As recently as the 1960s, many aspects of geology were not well understood. Geologists could not explain why there were mountains in some places and oceans in others. Nor could they explain how fossils of ocean creatures could be found on top of some of the highest mountains. Plate tectonics helps geologists to answer these questions. As you will learn later in this chapter, plate tectonics also does much to explain patterns in the locations of earthquakes and volcanoes.

Africa
Asia
Red Sea

Figure 22 The Red Sea between Africa and the Arabian peninsula in Asia marks a region where two pieces of the lithosphere are slowly moving apart. Over the next 100 million years, the Red Sea could become an ocean.

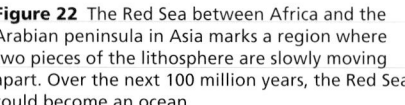

Section Resources

Print
- ***Reading and Study Workbook With Math Support,*** Section 22.4
- ***Transparencies,*** Section 22.4

Technology
- ***Interactive Textbook,*** Section 22.4
- ***Presentation Pro CD-ROM,*** Section 22.4
- ***Go Online,*** *Science News,* Earthquakes, volcanoes, and plate tectonics

Figure 23 Fossils of *Glossopteris* and other plants and animals on widely separated land masses led Alfred Wegener to hypothesize that the continents had once been joined.

Continental Drift

Although the process of plate tectonics was not fully understood until the 1960s, many clues were observed earlier. For instance, when the early explorers began to discover the shapes of the continents, mapmakers noticed how well the shapes of North and South America fit together with Europe and Africa. It seemed almost as if the continents were pieces of a giant jigsaw puzzle that had been broken apart.

Later on, geologists discovered fossils of species of land-based plants and animals on continents separated by large oceans. For example, fossils of the same species of *Glossopteris* (glaw SAHP tuh ris) plant, shown in Figure 23, were found in South America, Africa, Antarctica, India, and Australia. These fossils puzzled geologists because their locations are widely separated.

In 1912, a German scientist named Alfred Wegener (1880–1930) proposed a hypothesis to explain these puzzling observations. **Wegener hypothesized that the continents were once joined in a single supercontinent, which then broke into pieces that moved apart.** Wegener called this ancient supercontinent **Pangaea** (pan JEE uh), which means "all land." According to Wegener's hypothesis, the continents move slowly across Earth's surface in a process called **continental drift,** as shown in Figure 24. Continental drift explains why the continents seem to fit together. It also explains why the fossils of plants and animals that once lived in a single region are now scattered across the globe.

However, there were many problems with Wegener's hypothesis. Wegener was unable to explain how the continents could plow through the solid rock of the sea floor. Also, he was unable to give a convincing explanation of what force could move entire continents. As a result, most geologists rejected continental drift.

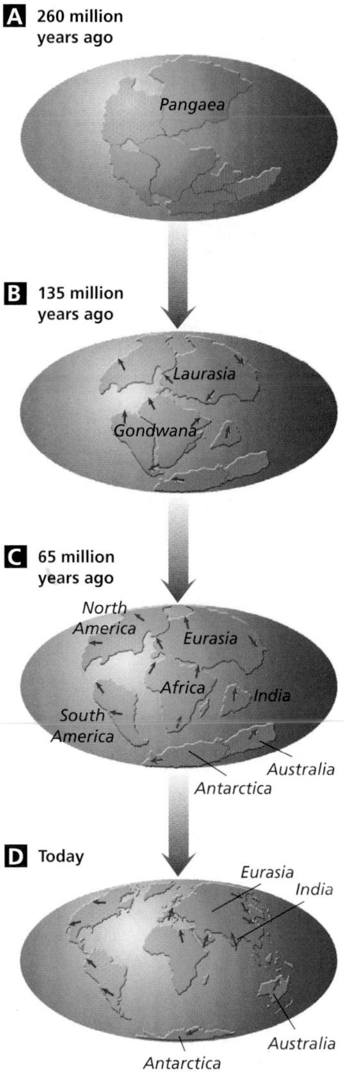
A 260 million years ago
Pangaea
B 135 million years ago
Laurasia
Gondwana
C 65 million years ago
North America
Eurasia
Africa
India
South America
Australia
Antarctica
D Today
Eurasia
India
Australia
Antarctica

Figure 24 The continents move slowly across Earth's surface over time. **A** Earth's continents had joined to form the supercontinent Pangaea by 260 million years ago. **B** Pangaea gradually split into two separate land masses, Laurasia and Gondwana. **C** Laurasia split into North America and Eurasia, and South America moved away from Africa. **D** India has now combined with Eurasia, and Australia has broken off from Antarctica.

Continental Drift

Use Visuals L1

Figure 24 Relate other evidence supporting continental drift, such as landforms (mountain ranges and coal beds) that match up across widely separated continents. Ask, **By what time did Gondwana separate from other land masses of Pangaea?** *(135 million years ago)* **How was the arrangement of land masses 65 million years ago different from that of today?** *(India was a separate mass, North and South America were separate, and Australia and Antarctica were joined.)* **In what direction is North America currently moving?** *(West/away from Eurasia)*
Visual

FYI

Wegener accumulated a great deal of evidence in support of his hypothesis of continental drift. His evidence included fossils of the reptiles *Mesosaurus* and *Lystrosaurus*, which are found in regions now separated by oceans. Wegener also noted that the climates of Spitsbergen, an island in the Arctic Ocean, and South Africa were very different in the past. He hypothesized that the locations of these places on Earth's surface had changed over time.

Customize for Inclusion Students

Learning Disabled
For students with difficulty reading and writing, customize the Writing in Science feature on p. 681 to allow students to make a multimedia presentation in lieu of a written report.

Sea-floor Spreading

Build Science Skills L2

Using Models Have students use a geologic globe to learn about sea-floor spreading and plate tectonics. Have students work in a group to find the mid-ocean ridges and trace them with their fingers around the globe. Have students describe the motion of the plates based on the direction of sea-floor spreading. Ask, **Which spreading center is causing North America to move?** *(The Mid-Atlantic Ridge)* **In what direction is North America moving?** *(To the west, away from the Mid-Atlantic Ridge)*
Kinesthetic, Group

Use Visuals L1

Figure 26 Explain that as the ocean lithosphere moves horizontally away from a mid-ocean ridge, it is continually cooling and becoming denser and heavier. Eventually, it becomes denser than the rock that is underneath it. The densities of two colliding plates determine what happens when the two plates ram together. Oceanic plates are denser than continental plates. When an oceanic plate meets a continental plate, the oceanic plate, being denser, subducts or slides under the less dense plate and down into the mantle. Ask, **Why are there volcanoes over the subducting plate?** *(Pressure and heat build up and melt rock, causing magma to rise.)* **What is the source of the sediment on the beach side of the volcanoes?** *(The erosion of coastal mountains, including volcanoes)*
Visual

Build Reading Literacy L2

Sequence Refer to page **290D** in **Chapter 10**, which provides the guidelines for a sequence.

Have students create a flowchart describing the process of ocean floor subduction.
Logical, Verbal

Sea-floor Spreading

Several decades after Wegener proposed his hypothesis, new evidence led geologists to reconsider his ideas. Some of this evidence came from mapping the sea floor and studying the characteristics of oceanic crust. This evidence helped scientists propose the theory of plate tectonics.

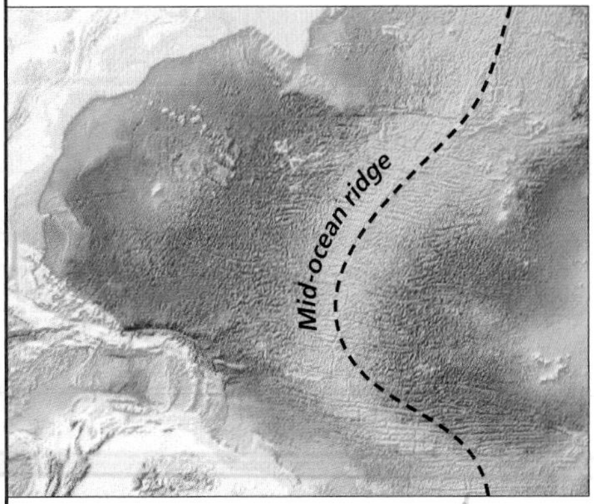
Mid-ocean ridge

Figure 25 This false-color satellite image shows the mid-ocean ridge in the Atlantic Ocean. This ridge is part of a larger ridge system that winds through all of Earth's oceans.

The Mid-Ocean Ridge If you go swimming in a lake, you expect the water in the middle to be deeper than near the shore. Surprisingly, this is often not the case in oceans. When scientists mapped the ocean floor during the mid-1900s, they found a chain of underwater mountains which they called the **mid-ocean ridge.** Like the seams on a baseball, the mid-ocean ridge extends into all of Earth's oceans. It forms the world's longest mountain chain. A segment is shown in Figure 25.

As scientists mapped the Atlantic mid-ocean ridge, they found that it had a remarkable feature: a deep valley running the length of its crest. Scientists also discovered that the rocks of the ocean floor were youngest near the mid-ocean ridge. At first, scientists were puzzled by this new information.

Formation of Oceanic Crust In 1960, the American geologist Harry Hess proposed the theory of sea-floor spreading to explain these discoveries about the ocean floor. **Sea-floor spreading** is the process by which new oceanic crust is created at mid-ocean ridges as older crust moves away. The mid-ocean ridge is a huge crack in the crust where magma pushes upward. As shown in Figure 26, the pieces of ocean floor on each side of the central valley are slowly moving apart. As they move, magma from the mantle wells up and solidifies to form new oceanic crust.

Reading Checkpoint *What is sea-floor spreading?*

Figure 26 During sea-floor spreading, oceanic crust forms at the mid-ocean ridge. This crust gradually moves toward a subduction zone, where old crust sinks beneath a trench. **Inferring** ***Where is the oldest oceanic crust found?***

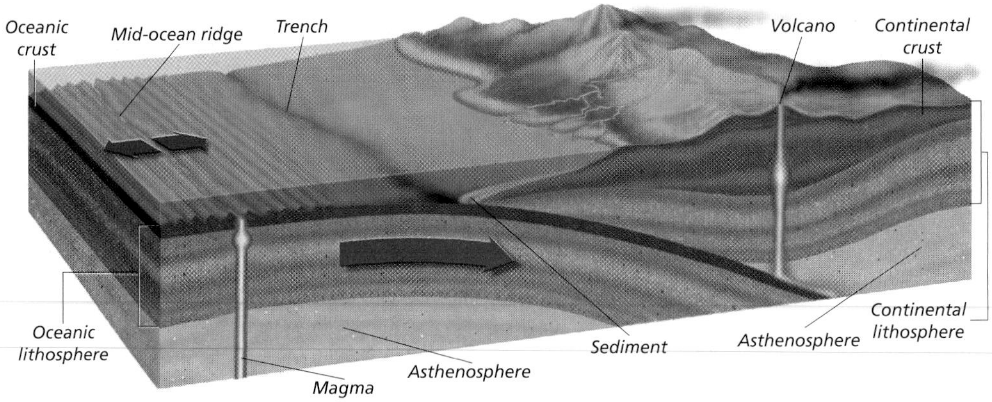
Oceanic crust
Mid-ocean ridge
Trench
Volcano
Continental crust
Oceanic lithosphere
Magma
Asthenosphere
Sediment
Asthenosphere
Continental lithosphere

Facts and Figures

Early Supercontinents Earth's continents have moved over Earth's surface for at least 4 billion years. During this time, oceans have repeatedly opened and closed. Supercontinents have been formed and then disassembled. The earliest known supercontinent was called Rodinia, and it is thought to have existed between 1100 and 750 million years ago. During this time, Antarctica was off of the west coast of North America, Australia was adjacent to Alaska, and what would become South America was off the east coast of North America! It is probable that there were supercontinents before Rodinia, but they have not yet been identified.

Subduction of Oceanic Plates As sea-floor spreading occurs, old oceanic plates sink into the mantle in the process of **subduction.** Subduction occurs near the edges of oceanic plates in regions called subduction zones. As a plate sinks through a subduction zone, it bends, forming a depression in the ocean floor called a **trench.** Subduction occurs because, as an oceanic plate moves away from the mid-ocean ridge, it gradually cools and becomes more dense. During subduction, the force of gravity slowly pulls the dense edges of oceanic plates into the mantle, destroying old ocean floor. Sea-floor spreading and subduction together act like a giant conveyor belt. **Sea-floor spreading creates new oceanic crust at mid-ocean ridges. Subduction destroys old oceanic crust at subduction zones.** As a result, the ocean floor is renewed about every 200 million years. Over time, these processes change the size and shape of the oceans.

Go Online SCIENCE NEWS

For: Articles on earthquakes, volcanoes, and plate tectonics
Visit: PHSchool.com
Web Code: cce-3224

Evidence for Sea-floor Spreading Other scientists soon provided convincing evidence for Hess's theory. They sampled rocks on both sides of the mid-ocean ridge. They found patterns of parallel magnetic "stripes" that were identical on the two sides. The stripes exist because Earth's magnetic field has reversed itself many times in the past. The stripes formed when Earth's magnetic field caused rock crystals to line up in a certain way before the rock solidified. The stripes showed that new ocean floor was being added to both sides of the mid-ocean ridge at roughly the same rate. This pattern of stripes is shown in Figure 27.

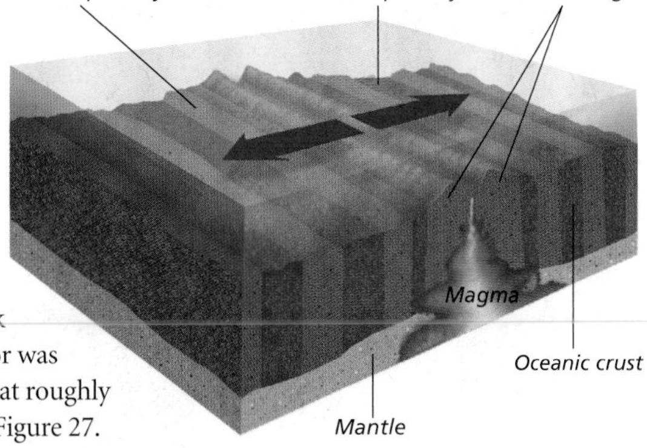
Normal polarity
Reversed polarity
Mid-ocean ridge
Magma
Oceanic crust
Mantle

Figure 27 The pattern of magnetic stripes in the rock of the ocean floor is the same on both sides of the mid-ocean ridge. **Relating Cause and Effect** ***Why is the pattern of stripes the same on both sides of the ridge?***

Geologists used radioactive dating to determine the ages of rock samples from the ocean floor. They found that rocks nearer the mid-ocean ridge were younger, and the rocks farther from the ridge were older.

The Theory of Plate Tectonics

The evidence of sea-floor spreading provided what was missing from Wegener's hypothesis—a way for pieces of the crust to move. With this knowledge, geologists developed the theory of plate tectonics during the 1960s. According to the theory, Earth's plates are constantly moving, each with a different rate and direction.

What force is powerful enough to move the heavy continents? Look at Figure 28 on page 680. Convection currents form in the mantle as hot rock rises at mid-ocean ridges, cools and spreads out horizontally as ocean lithosphere, and then sinks back into the mantle at subduction zones. These sinking slabs of dense lithosphere and heat from within Earth drive the circulation of convection currents in the mantle. **Plate motions are the visible part of the process of mantle convection.**

The Theory of Plate Tectonics

Integrate Social Studies L2

The Cold War between the United States and the Soviet Union inadvertently led to great advances in the theory of plate tectonics. The U.S. Navy wanted to be able to move submarines around the world's oceans without using sonar, which would give away their locations because it requires producing sound waves. Instead, the Navy decided to produce a detailed map of the ocean floor. In order to do this, they mapped the bathymetry, gravity, and magnetic fields of the ocean floor. Eventually, this data was used to develop and support the theory of plate tectonics.

During this period, Harry Hess was a submarine captain who was mapping the ocean floor when he noticed the existence of guyots, flat-topped ocean seamounts. Harry guessed correctly that these guyots had their tops eroded at the surface but had since sunk below the sea surface as the sea floor sank. Ask, **How did the collection of data on the magnetic field of the ocean floor help advance the theory of plate tectonics?** *(It provided evidence in support of sea-floor spreading.)* **How do guyots relate to the theory of plate tectonics?** *(Their formation depends on the sea floor sinking as it cools.)*
Logical, Verbal

Go Online SCIENCE NEWS

Science News provides students with current information on earthquakes, volcanoes, and plate tectonics.

Facts and Figures

Pole Reversals Earth's magnetic field reverses itself frequently (in geologic time), but not regularly. As measured on the ocean floor, consecutive pole reversals are between 5 thousand and 50 million years apart. The most recent reversal happened 740,000 years ago. You will know if a reversal happens because compasses will point south instead of north.

Answer to . . .

Figure 26 *Near subduction zones*

Figure 27 *Because new ocean floor is being added to both sides of the mid-ocean ridge at about the same rate*

Reading Checkpoint *Sea-floor spreading is the process in which magma wells up at the mid-ocean ridge, forming new oceanic crust that slowly spreads apart on each side of the ridge.*

Teacher Demo

Convection and Plate Motion L2

Purpose Students observe how convection cells can move crustal masses.

Materials Bunsen burner or hot plate, deep and wide glass container, thin tomato soup, large sponges, scissors, tongs

Procedure Cut out rough plate shapes from the sponges. Fill the glass container about halfway with tomato soup, and place on heat source. Slowly heat the soup until convection cells form. Carefully place the sponges on top of the soup surface. Have students observe the demo in small groups.

Expected Outcome The convection cells in the soup will cause the floating plates to move around and bump each other. Be sure to explain that the mantle is not a thin liquid like the soup, and that convection cells in ductile rock take hundreds of millions of years to move plates in a way comparable to this demo.
Visual

DK SCIENCE and History

Milestones in Geology L2

Have students work in groups to discuss how each milestone improved our understanding of Earth's geology. Have each group make a presentation to the class on one of the milestones, detailing how the event contributed to modern scientific understanding of Earth processes.
Interpersonal, Verbal

Writing in Science

Students should use library or Internet resources to research the geologist that they have chosen. Consider expanding the list of geologists and having students prepare posters on the life and work of their scientist and present the results to the class.
Interpersonal, Verbal

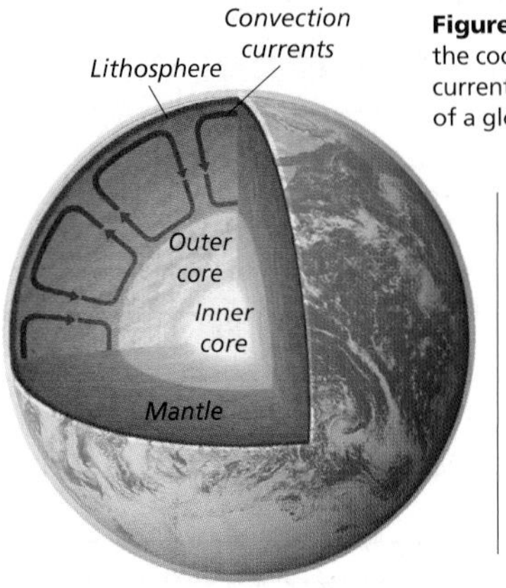

Convection currents
Lithosphere
Outer core
Inner core
Mantle

Figure 28 Heat flows from Earth's hot interior toward the cooler surface mainly through large convection currents in the mantle. Plates are the uppermost part of a global convection system.

The process that drives plate movement on Earth's surface is similar to convection in a pot of boiling soup. The soup is heated from below and rises to the top of the pot, moves across the top and cools, and then sinks back down.

The heat that drives convection in the mantle comes from two sources. Earth was very hot when it first formed, and some of the heat moving upward in convection currents is due to the gradual cooling of its interior. A second source of heat is the result of the decay of radioactive isotopes that are distributed throughout the mantle and crust.

DK SCIENCE and History

Milestones in Geology

Scientific knowledge about Earth's age and geological history has mostly been gathered since the late 1700s. Some of the major advances are described here.

JAMES HUTTON

Ammonites *come in many forms, each specific to a particular rock layer and time in the past. They are used as index fossils for the Jurassic period.*

AMMONITE FOSSIL

CHARLES DARWIN

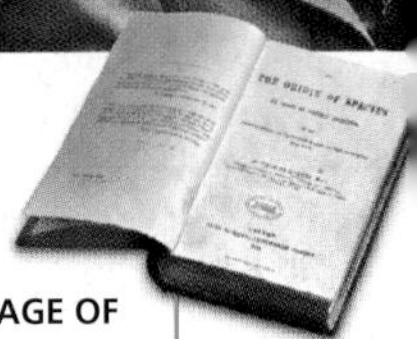

TITLE PAGE OF *ON THE ORIGIN OF SPECIES*

1795 James Hutton publishes his *Theory of the Earth*, which proposes that our planet is much older than previously thought.

1815 William Smith completes the first geological map of England and Wales. He observes that each layer in a column of sedimentary rock contains index fossils.

1830 British geologist Charles Lyell publishes the first of three volumes of his *Principles of Geology*. The book proposes that Earth has gradually changed over time and that processes still acting today have shaped its surface.

1859 Charles Darwin publishes his ground-breaking work *On the Origin of Species*. The book encourages geologists to begin interpreting their fossil collections in terms of the evolution of life.

1790 | 1820 | 1850 | 1880

Facts and Figures

Tectonics The examination of seismic waves that travel through the mantle has provided a picture of what happens to the sheets of oceanic lithosphere when they sink into Earth. The cold, sinking slabs heat up in the hot mantle by conduction. However, because this conduction is a slow process, the slabs are able to sink all the way to the base of the mantle. After some time, aided by the heat from the core, this rock will become buoyant enough to rise back up toward the surface. The entire cycle of mid-ocean ridge to core-mantle boundary and back again may take as long as a half billion years.

Plate Boundaries

There are about a dozen major tectonic plates, shown in Figure 29 on page 682. Most major plates contain both continental and oceanic crust. The edges of plates meet at plate boundaries. **There are three types of plate boundaries: divergent boundaries, convergent boundaries, and transform boundaries.** At each type of boundary, plates move in a different way. As the plates move apart, collide, or slide past each other, they cause changes in Earth's surface.

The motions of Earth's plates have been measured directly using global positioning system (GPS) sensors. The plates move very slowly, about 0.1 to 10 centimeters per year. This speed is similar to the rate at which your fingernails grow—about 4 centimeters per year.

Writing in Science

Summary Research the life and career of one of the geologists in the time line. Write two or three paragraphs that sum up the geologist's major contribution to geology.

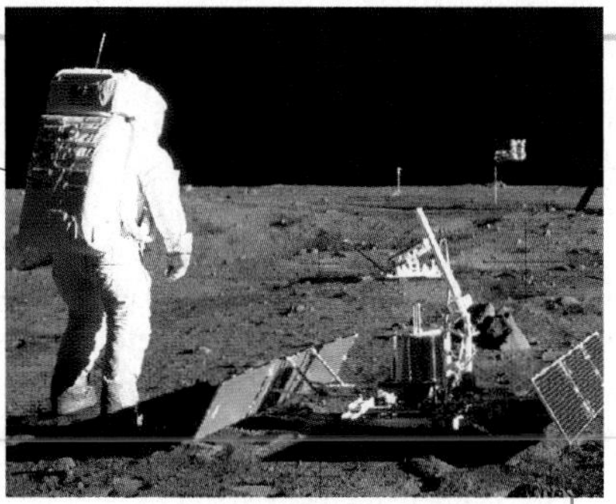

Astronauts conduct experiments on the surface of the moon

EDWIN "BUZZ" ALDRIN, JR. WALKING ON THE MOON DURING THE *APOLLO 11* MISSION

TYRANNOSAURUS REX

URANIUM ORE

1907 Bertram Boltwood uses recent discoveries about radioactivity to date uranium-containing rocks. He shows that some are at least 2 billion years old.

1912 Alfred Wegener proposes that the continents were once joined in a supercontinent called Pangaea and have since drifted apart.

1969 Apollo mission astronauts bring rocks back from the moon, a giant leap for lunar geology.

1979 Walter Alvarez discovers a mineral layer containing the element iridium in 65-million-year-old rocks worldwide. He proposes that the iridium came from a huge comet or asteroid that hit Earth. It caused many plant and animal species, including the dinosaurs, to become extinct.

1910 | 1940 | 1970

Facts and Figures

Early Theories Although Alfred Wegener made in 1912 the first formal proposal that the continents had once been joined, other people had previously made note of the fact that the continents seemed like pieces of a jigsaw puzzle. One of the first references to the continents seeming to fit together is from the Dutch cartographer Abraham Ortelius in 1596.

Plate Boundaries

Build Reading Literacy L1

Relate Text and Visuals Refer to page **190D** in **Chapter 7**, which provides the guidelines for relating text and visuals.

Direct students' attention to the reference to Figure 29 in the first sentence of Plate Boundaries. Ask students to refer to this visual as they read the first paragraph. Instruct students to find the plate boundaries; note the location of divergent, convergent, and transform boundaries; and visualize the movement of the plates.
Visual

Use Visuals

L1

Figure 29 Have students examine the directions in which plates are moving. Ask, **What type of boundary exists between the Arabian plate and the Eurasian plate?** *(Convergent)* **Describe how you know it is a convergent boundary without consulting the key.** *(The arrows indicate that these plates are moving toward each other.)*
Visual

Build Science Skills

L2

Interpreting Diagrams Refer students to Figures 26, 27, and 30, and explain that block diagrams such as these are frequently used to describe geological processes. Ask, **Why are block diagrams useful tools to help visualize geological processes?** *(Because you can see the land surface as well as two perpendicular cross sections revealing the features beneath the surface)* Have students work in groups of three. First, ask each student in the group to verbalize what one of the diagrams in Figures 26, 27, and 30 is depicting. Then, have students work together to draw their own series of block diagrams modeling different tectonic movements. Possible examples that they might draw include sedimentary rocks forming in a depositional environment, igneous rocks forming in a volcano, or a thick crust extending into the asthenosphere under a mountain chain.
Visual, Group

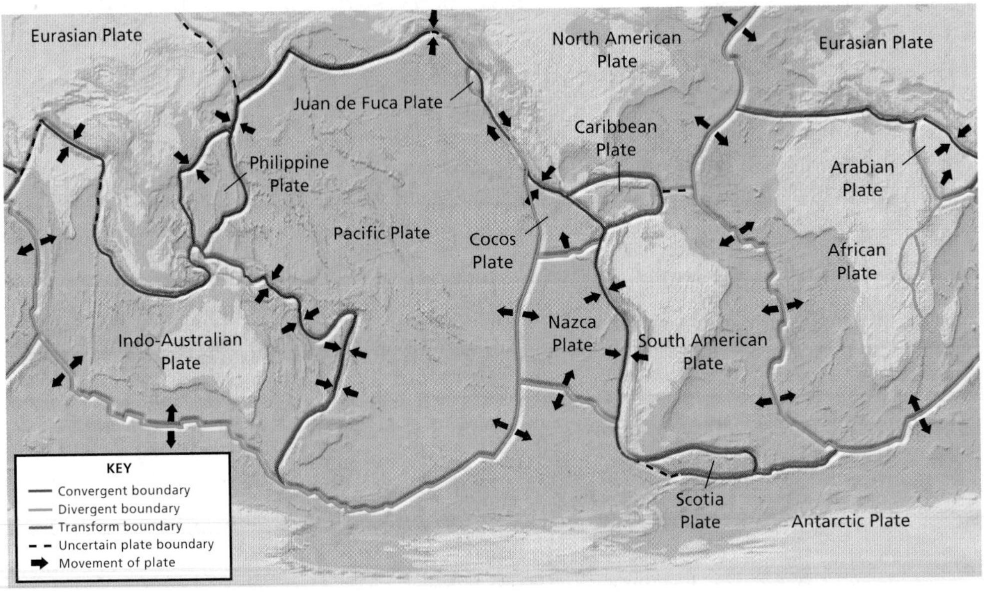

Eurasian Plate
North American Plate
Eurasian Plate
Juan de Fuca Plate
Caribbean Plate
Philippine Plate
Arabian Plate
Pacific Plate
Cocos Plate
African Plate
Nazca Plate
Indo-Australian Plate
South American Plate
Scotia Plate
Antarctic Plate
KEY
Convergent boundary
Divergent boundary
Transform boundary
Uncertain plate boundary
Movement of plate

Figure 29 The lithosphere is broken into about a dozen large plates, which move slowly over Earth's surface.
Interpreting Maps ***What type of boundary exists between the Pacific plate and the Cocos plate?***

Plates move away from each other along a **divergent boundary,** shown in Figure 30. The mid-ocean ridge forms a divergent boundary. Divergent boundaries can also be found on land, for instance, in Africa. When plates move apart, magma rises from the mantle to fill the gap. The magma cools to form new rock at the edge of each plate.

Plates come together, or collide, at a **convergent boundary.** The most common convergent boundary is one where an oceanic plate is subducted beneath a trench. When oceanic crust collides with continental crust, the denser oceanic crust slides under the less dense continental crust. At a **transform boundary,** plates slide past each other, moving in opposite directions. Rock is neither created nor destroyed at a transform boundary.

Figure 30 Plates meet at three types of boundaries: divergent boundaries, convergent boundaries, and transform boundaries.

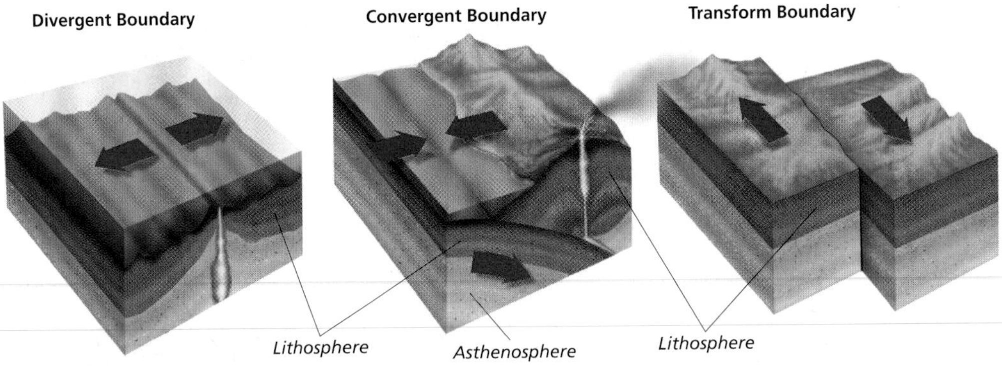

Divergent Boundary
Convergent Boundary
Transform Boundary
Lithosphere
Asthenosphere
Lithosphere

Facts and Figures

The Formation of the Himalayas The most dramatic example of mountain building occurring today is the creation of the Himalayan Mountains from the collision of India with the rest of Asia. India used to be attached to Antarctica, but has moved rapidly northward over the past 100 million years. Its collision with Asia has created a huge plateau of rock that has been thrust upward. Some of this rock was ancient ocean crust that was caught between India and Asia.

All of the 10 highest mountains in the world are found in the Himalayas, with Mount Everest (8848 m) the highest. In addition, the mountains are underlain by a deep crustal root that extends about 75 km beneath the surface.

Mountain Building

The theory of plate tectonics helped geologists understand why mountains form in some regions but not in others. **Geologists found that most mountains form along plate boundaries.**

Some mountains form when two plates with continental crust at their edges collide along a convergent boundary. Neither plate is subducted during such collisions. Instead, the crust buckles, folds, and thickens, pushing up tall mountains. The collision of the Indo-Australian and Eurasian plates produced Earth's highest mountain range, the Himalayas. Mountains may also form when an oceanic plate collides with a continental plate. The collision of the Nazca and South American plates produced the Andes, shown in Figure 31.

Mountains can also form along diverging plate boundaries. The mid-ocean ridge system forms one long chain of mountains on the ocean floor. In places, the mountains of the mid-ocean ridge rise above sea level. One example is the island of Iceland in the North Atlantic Ocean. As you will read in the next two sections, plate tectonics explains not only mountain building, but many other changes on Earth's surface as well.

Figure 31 The Andes, which extend along the western side of the South American plate, have risen as a result of a collision between that plate and the Nazca Plate. **Inferring** ***What type of plate boundary exists between the South American and Nazca plates?***

Section 22.4 Assessment

Reviewing Concepts

1. What is the theory of plate tectonics and what evidence supports it?
2. How is the rock of the ocean floor formed?
3. What force powers the movement of the continents?
4. Describe three main ways in which plates move along plate boundaries.
5. Where do most mountains form and how do they form?
6. What was Pangaea and when did it form?
7. How and where is old oceanic crust destroyed?

Critical Thinking

8. **Applying Concepts** Why are trenches usually located at the edges of oceans?
9. **Predicting** The African plate is slowly moving north toward the Eurasian plate. What could eventually happen if the two plates continue to converge?

Connecting Concepts

Convection Currents Recall what you learned about convection currents in Chapter 16. Explain how differences in density and temperature could drive convection currents in Earth's mantle.

Mountain Building

Build Reading Literacy L1

Outline Refer to page **156D** in **Chapter 6**, which provides the guidelines for an outline.

Have students outline the main points of Mountain Building, focusing on the types of plate boundaries where mountains form, and the process of mountain formation at each type. **Verbal**

3 ASSESS

Evaluate Understanding L2

Refer to Figure 29 and ask students to create index cards for each type of boundary. On one side of the card, write the name of the boundary type, and on the reverse side describe the types of geologic features found nearby.

Reteach L1

Use Figure 26 to discuss how oceanic crust is created and destroyed.

Connecting Concepts

Rock within the mantle is heated by the decay of radioactive elements and leftover heat from Earth's formation. The heated particles move faster and spread apart, becoming less dense. Hot rock rises toward the surface of Earth as cooler, denser rock sinks back down toward the mantle, like a conveyor belt transporting heat upward toward the surface.

Interactive Textbook If your class subscribes to the Interactive Textbook, use it to review key concepts in Section 22.4.

Answer to . . .

Figure 29 *Divergent boundary*

Figure 31 *Convergent boundary*

Section 22.4 Assessment

1. The theory of tectonics explains the formation and movement of Earth's plates. Today, the actual movement of plates can be measured using GPS sensors. Other evidence includes sea-floor magnetic stripes, which show that the sea floor has spread over time.
2. The rock of the ocean floor forms at mid-ocean ridges, where magma rises from the mantle to fill the gap created as two plates pull apart and then cools to form rock.
3. Convection within the mantle powers the movement of the continents.
4. Plates move away from one another at a divergent boundary. Plates collide at a convergent boundary. Plates slide past one another at a transform boundary.
5. Most mountains form along plate boundaries. They can form at a convergent boundary where two continental plates collide or a continental plate and an oceanic plate collide. They can also form at a divergent boundary where magma rises and cools to form new crust.
6. Pangaea was an ancient supercontinent that formed by about 260 million years ago as the continents came together.
7. Old oceanic crust is destroyed at subduction zones.
8. Trenches occur where an ocean plate meets a continental plate and the ocean plate is sinking into the mantle. This usually occurs off the coast of a continent.
9. A mountain range may form along the boundary where the two plates converge.

Section 22.5

1 FOCUS

Objectives

22.5.1 **Describe** the causes and effects of stress in Earth's crust.

22.5.2 **Explain** why earthquakes occur and how their energy is propagated as seismic waves.

22.5.3 **Explain** how earthquakes are measured and how earthquake data is used to learn about Earth's interior.

Reading Focus

Build Vocabulary L2

Concept Map Have students build a concept map using all of the terms in the vocabulary list. Instruct students to begin with the main concept, Earthquakes, and add the remaining concepts as they read the section.

Reading Strategy L2

a. A movement of the lithosphere that occurs when rocks in the lithosphere suddenly shift, releasing energy
b. Vibrations caused by an earthquake that carry the earthquake's energy away
c. A force within Earth that either squeezes rocks together, pulls them apart, or pushes them in different directions

2 INSTRUCT

Address Misconceptions L2

There are many incorrect popular notions about the types of damage an earthquake can cause, such as swallowing cities or causing California to fall into the ocean. Inform students that these myths have some basis in reality, but are completely exaggerated. In some rare cases, crevasses may open up during a quake, but they would be too small to swallow buildings, much less entire cities. Ask students to use what they have learned about continental crust and plate tectonics to refute the myth of California falling into the ocean. *(California is a transform fault where two plates are moving in different directions, so it will never fall into the ocean.)*
Logical

22.5 Earthquakes

Reading Focus

Key Concepts

- What causes faults and folds?
- What causes earthquakes?
- How are earthquakes measured?
- Where do most earthquakes occur?

Vocabulary

- earthquake
- seismic waves
- stress
- fault
- fold
- focus
- epicenter
- P waves
- S waves
- surface waves
- seismograph

Reading Strategy

Building Vocabulary Make a table like the one below that includes all the vocabulary terms for this section. As you read, define each term in your own words.

Vocabulary Term	Definition
Earthquake	a. ___?___
Seismic waves	b. ___?___
Stress	c. ___?___

The time was 5:04 P.M. on October 17, 1989. It was the third game of the World Series, and the Oakland A's were about to play the San Francisco Giants. More than 60,000 people were crowded into San Francisco's Candlestick Park to watch the game. Suddenly, near Loma Prieta, a mountain 90 kilometers south of San Francisco, a powerful earthquake struck.

An **earthquake** is a movement of Earth's lithosphere that occurs when rocks in the lithosphere suddenly shift, releasing stored energy. The energy released during an earthquake is carried by vibrations called **seismic waves.** During the Loma Prieta earthquake, seismic waves began spreading away from Loma Prieta at about 6 kilometers per second. After 3 seconds, roads were crumbling in Santa Cruz. After 5 seconds, buildings were cracking in San Jose. After 15 seconds, the seismic waves reached Candlestick Park. The stadium shook and cracked, but fortunately no one there was hurt.

Harbor
Terminals
SECOND RIGHT

Figure 32 The Loma Prieta earthquake destroyed the Cypress Freeway in Oakland, California.

Section Resources

Print
- ***Reading and Study Workbook With Math Support,*** Section 22.5 and **Math Skill:** Seismic Wave Travel Time
- ***Transparencies,*** Section 22.5

Technology
- ***Interactive Textbook,*** Section 22.5
- ***Presentation Pro CD-ROM,*** Section 22.5
- ***Go Online,*** *Planet Diary,* Earthquake activity

As a result of the earthquake, 62 people died and $6 billion in damage was done. One of the earthquake's most serious effects was the collapse of the freeway shown in Figure 32. But the earthquake could have been much more severe. Worldwide, on average more than 10,000 people die each year from earthquakes. A single large earthquake can cause more than $100 billion in damage.

Stress in Earth's Crust

Earthquakes happen because of the ways that plate movements affect the lithosphere. The forces of plate movement cause deformation, or changes in the shape or volume of a mass of rock. Deformation acting on the rocks of the crust is an example of stress. **Stress** is a force that squeezes rocks together, stretches or pulls them apart, or pushes them in different directions.

One way of applying stress to a material is to try to bend it. If you try to bend a brittle material, such as chalk, it will break. Other sorts of materials, such as copper wire, can bend without breaking. **As tectonic plates move, they cause stress in the crust, which in turn produces faults and folds.**

A **fault** is a break in a mass of rock along which movement occurs. The two slabs of rock on either side of a fault move in relation to each other. Many faults occur along plate boundaries. The Loma Prieta earthquake occurred along the San Andreas fault, a crack in the lithosphere that extends for several hundred kilometers through California. The San Andreas fault, shown in Figure 33, is part of a transform boundary between the Pacific and North American plates. Along this fault, the crust slides in opposite horizontal directions.

A **fold** is a bend in layers of rock. Folds form where rocks are squeezed together, but do not break. Rocks tend to fold rather than break when they are under high temperature or pressure. The folds in rock can vary greatly in size. For example, the wavy patterns in some metamorphic rocks that you can hold in your hand are folds. Folds can also be seen in the rock layers that make up a mountain range, as in Figure 34.

Reading Checkpoint *What is a fault?*

Figure 33 This portion of the San Andreas fault runs through the Carrizo Plain in south-central California. **Classifying** ***What type of plate boundary forms the San Andreas fault?***

Figure 34 Stress can squeeze rock together, producing folds in layers of rock.

Stress in Earth's Crust

Teacher Demo

Faults and Folds — L2

Purpose Students observe a model of the creation of faults and folds in Earth's crust.

Materials several different shades of potter's clay, 6 wood blocks, hammer, large garbage bags

Procedure Make two demonstration "crusts" for folding and faulting by pounding or rolling out different shades of clay, and then layering the shades. Each crust should be approximately 30 cm^2 by 15 cm deep. Lay the crusts on top of garbage bags on a large table. Cover one crust in plastic (or prepare this crust the day of the demo) and leave the other crust out to dry for a few weeks. Place two wooden blocks together on one side of the crust, and the other block on the parallel side. Have a student hold the single block firmly. Explain that you will model the compressional force of a continental collision by applying horizontal force to the model crust with a hammer. Be sure that students understand that the clay in this model represents rock: The dried clay represents cool, brittle rock, and the soft clay represents ductile rock at high temperature or pressure. Ask, **What do you predict will happen when I apply horizontal compressional force by hitting this side with the hammer (point to the two blocks)?** Then, hit the outer of the two blocks (on the side that is not being held by the student) firmly and horizontally so that compressional force is applied in the plane of the model. Depending on the size of your model, you may want to hit the block a couple of times to achieve the desired effect.

Expected Outcome Students may predict that folding or faulting will occur in the demonstration crusts. The crust that is still soft will fold under the force, while faulting will be produced in the brittle crust.

Visual, Logical

Customize for English Language Learners

Create a Cause/Effect Table

Have students create a cause/effect table after viewing the Teacher Demo and reading Stress in Earth's Crust. The effect side of the table should have two entries: *folds* and *faults*. Students should fill in the table with an explanation of the causes of folds and faults.

Answer to . . .

Figure 33 *A transform boundary*

Reading Checkpoint *A fault is a break in a mass of rock along which movement occurs.*

Earthquakes and Seismic Waves

Use Visuals **L1**

Figure 35 Explain that most earthquakes occur along the boundaries between plates, and that these boundaries consist of many faults, not just a single, clean fault between adjacent plates. Deep beneath the surface the rock behaves in a ductile manner and the plates move continuously. The plates continue to move down below, but near the surface the fault remains locked up. This causes stress across the fault to build up. At some point the strength of the fault is exceeded, and an earthquake occurs. In a matter of a few seconds, the two sides of the fault catch up with the motion that has been occurring below. The focus is the point at which the fault gives way. Ask, **What would happen to a road or fence that extended across the fault shown in Figure 35?** *(It would be split and displaced to the right.)* **Why is the epicenter not on the fault?** *(The fault plane extends beneath the ground at an angle.)*
Visual

Build Science Skills **L2**

Using Models ACTIVITY

Purpose Students will work in groups and use a spring toy to model P waves and S waves.

Materials 1 spring toy per group

Class Time 10–15 minutes

Procedure Have students work in groups to model P waves and S waves using the spring toy. Use Figure 36 as a guide.

Expected Outcome Students will hold the spring toy at both ends so it is horizontal to the floor. They can model P waves by pushing forward or pulling back on one end, and S waves by moving one end from side to side.
Kinesthetic, Group

Figure 35 When an earthquake occurs on a fault, seismic waves move out from the focus. The epicenter lies on the surface, directly above the focus.

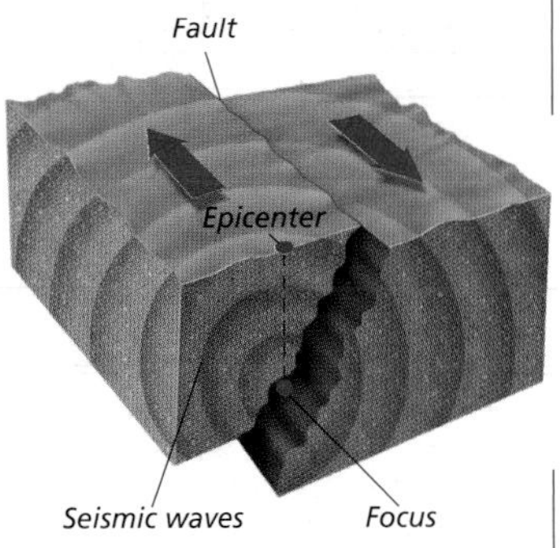
Fault
Epicenter
Seismic waves
Focus

Earthquakes and Seismic Waves

The buildup of stress along a fault provides the energy that powers an earthquake. **Earthquakes occur because stress forces have exceeded the strength of rock.**

As you can see in Figure 35, the location beneath Earth's surface where an earthquake begins is called the **focus.** The location on Earth's surface directly above the focus is called the **epicenter** (EHP uh sen tur). As an earthquake occurs, seismic waves move out in all directions from the focus.

The Physics of Earthquakes Within Earth's crust, forces are at work along faults. They cause the two sides of a fault to move past each other. Sometimes the rocks along the two sides of a fault may snag and remain locked because of friction between the two fault surfaces. As a result, tremendous stress builds up in these areas.

Any material has a limit to how much stress it can absorb. When rocks are strained beyond their limit, they break and grind past each other, releasing huge amounts of energy in the form of an earthquake. As the rocks break and move, potential energy is transformed into kinetic energy in the form of seismic waves.

Types of Seismic Waves Earthquakes produce three main types of seismic waves: P waves, S waves, and surface waves. Each type of seismic wave has different characteristics.

P waves (originally called primary waves) are longitudinal waves similar to sound waves. Recall that, as longitudinal waves move through a material, they cause particles in the material to vibrate in the direction of the waves' motion. Thus, P waves compress and expand the ground like an accordion, as you can see in Figure 36. Because P waves are the fastest seismic waves, they are the first to be detected at a distance. P waves can travel through both solids and liquids.

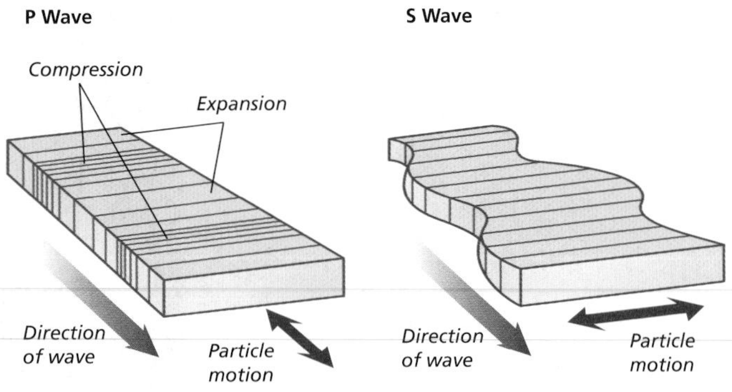
P Wave
Compression
Expansion
Direction of wave
Particle motion
S Wave
Direction of wave
Particle motion

Figure 36 P waves and S waves are seismic waves that travel through Earth's interior. P waves are longitudinal waves that compress and expand the ground. S waves are transverse waves in which particles vibrate at right angles to the waves' direction of movement.

Facts and Figures

The History of "P" and "S" The "P" and "S" labels come from the earliest days of seismology. These waves were labeled Primary and Secondary before seismologists knew what they were. The P wave is always the first wave to arrive, and on many seismograms, the S wave is the second significant reading.

S waves (originally called secondary waves) are transverse waves, like light and other electromagnetic radiation. S waves cause the particles in the materials they pass through to vibrate at right angles to the direction the waves move. You can see how S waves move in Figure 36. Unlike P waves, S waves cannot travel through liquids.

Surface waves are waves that develop when seismic waves reach Earth's surface. Surface waves move more slowly than P waves and S waves, but usually produce larger ground movements and greater damage. Some surface waves are transverse waves, and others have a rolling motion at Earth's surface that is similar to ocean waves.

Go Online PLANETDIARY

For: Earthquake activity
Visit: PHSchool.com
Web Code: ccc-3225

Measuring Earthquakes

When an earthquake occurs, the first things people want to know are how big it was and where it was centered. **To measure earthquakes and pinpoint their epicenters, geologists record seismic waves using seismographs.** A device that can detect and record seismic waves is called a **seismograph.** The How It Works box on page 688 illustrates a seismograph. The record of an earthquake on a seismograph is called a seismogram. Earthquakes can be located using the seismic waves recorded by many different seismographs.

The range in recorded earthquake sizes is enormous. Most earthquakes are too small to be felt by humans. The largest earthquakes release more energy than the United States consumes in a year.

Richter Scale The most well-known scale is the Richter scale. The Richter scale rates earthquakes based on measurements of the times and amplitudes of seismic waves by certain seismographs. However, the Richter scale is no longer used by geologists.

Moment Magnitude Scale The most useful scale for geologists is the moment magnitude scale (M_W). This scale gives a measure of the amount of energy released by an earthquake. Each unit increase on this scale represents about a 32-times increase in the energy released. The largest earthquake ever recorded was a M_W 9.5 earthquake that occurred in southern Chile in 1960.

Modified Mercalli Scale The effects of earthquakes can also be rated using the modified Mercalli scale. This scale, which ranges from 1 to 12, is based on observations of the intensity of ground shaking and damage in the areas affected by an earthquake. For example, an earthquake rated 7 on the Mercalli scale would knock over some chimneys. A rating of 12 applies to earthquakes that cause total destruction of nearby towns or cities.

Reading Checkpoint *What is the moment magnitude scale?*

Quick Lab

Modeling a Seismograph

Procedure

1. Obtain cash register paper from your teacher. Roll it up and place a pencil through the center of the roll so the roll turns freely around the pencil.
2. Hold the pencil and paper roll horizontally on a flat surface so that a classmate can slowly pull the free end of the paper across the surface. Have a second classmate hold a felt-tip pen so that it marks a line on the paper as it is pulled across the surface.
3. While the paper is being pulled and marked, have a third classmate do each of the following for 5 seconds: shake the desk gently, shake the desk more vigorously, and hold the desk still.

Analyze and Conclude

1. **Observing** How did shaking affect the ink line?
2. **Using Models** What did the shaking represent?

Facts and Figures

Past Earthquakes The largest earthquake recorded within the United States was a magnitude 9.1 earthquake that occurred on March 27, 1964, near Anchorage, Alaska. This earthquake occurred when a large piece of the subducting Pacific plate rapidly slid seven meters beneath Alaska in a matter of seconds. This earthquake was about 1000 times larger than the 1989 Loma Prieta earthquake near San Francisco, which had a magnitude of 7.1. The great San Francisco earthquake of 1906 had a magnitude of 8.2.

Measuring Earthquakes

Quick Lab

Modeling a Seismograph L2

Objective
After completing this activity, students will be able to
- interpret a seismogram.

Skills Focus **Using Models**

Prep Time 5 minutes

Materials pencil, roll of cash-register paper, felt-tip pen

Class Time 10 minutes

Safety Make sure that students do not shake the desks so vigorously that they knock the desks over.

Expected Outcome The size of the waves created by the pen on the paper will increase as the shaking becomes more vigorous.

Analyze and Conclude
1. The shaking caused the ink line to become wavy.
2. The shaking represented the movement of Earth's crust during an earthquake.
Visual, Logical, Kinesthetic

For Enrichment L3

Repeat the lab, but this time use two paper-strip seismographs that are moving at right angles to each other simultaneously. Have students compare the two ink lines to determine the direction of the shaking. Students will discover that each ink line records the magnitude of the shaking in one dimension.
Visual, Logical, Kinesthetic

Go Online PLANETDIARY

Find links to additional activities and have students monitor phenomena that affect Earth and its residents.

Answer to . . .

Reading Checkpoint *A scale used to measure the amount of energy released by an earthquake*

HOW It Works

Measuring Earthquakes L2

At least three seismometers are needed to locate an earthquake using triangulation, similar to how a GPS sensor can determine its location from satellites. Seismometers where the P and S waves arrive sooner than other seismometers are closer to the focus of the earthquake. In practice, the records from hundreds to thousands of seismometers are incorporated into an earthquake location.

Interpreting Diagrams The base of a seismometer must be cemented to bedrock so that it moves precisely as Earth moves in response to seismic waves. **Logical**

For Enrichment L3

Have interested students research the locations of recent earthquakes in their region, or in the United States. Ask the students to present their findings in class. **Verbal**

Use Community Resources L2

Scientists from the U.S. Geological Survey monitor earthquakes at many stations throughout the country. Many USGS offices have educational outreach staff and programs. Contact your regional office and ask a USGS scientist to demonstrate a seismograph to the class. **Visual, Interpersonal**

HOW It Works

Measuring Earthquakes

Modern seismometers have been placed all around the world. Some are permanently installed hundreds of feet below ground to avoid noise. Others can be temporarily placed anywhere on land. Many seismometers transmit seismograms via satellite, allowing geologists to analyze earthquakes as they are occurring.

Interpreting Diagrams ***Why must the base of a seismometer be cemented to bedrock?***

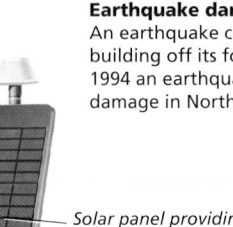

Earthquake damage
An earthquake can shake a building off its foundation. In 1994 an earthquake caused this damage in Northridge, California.

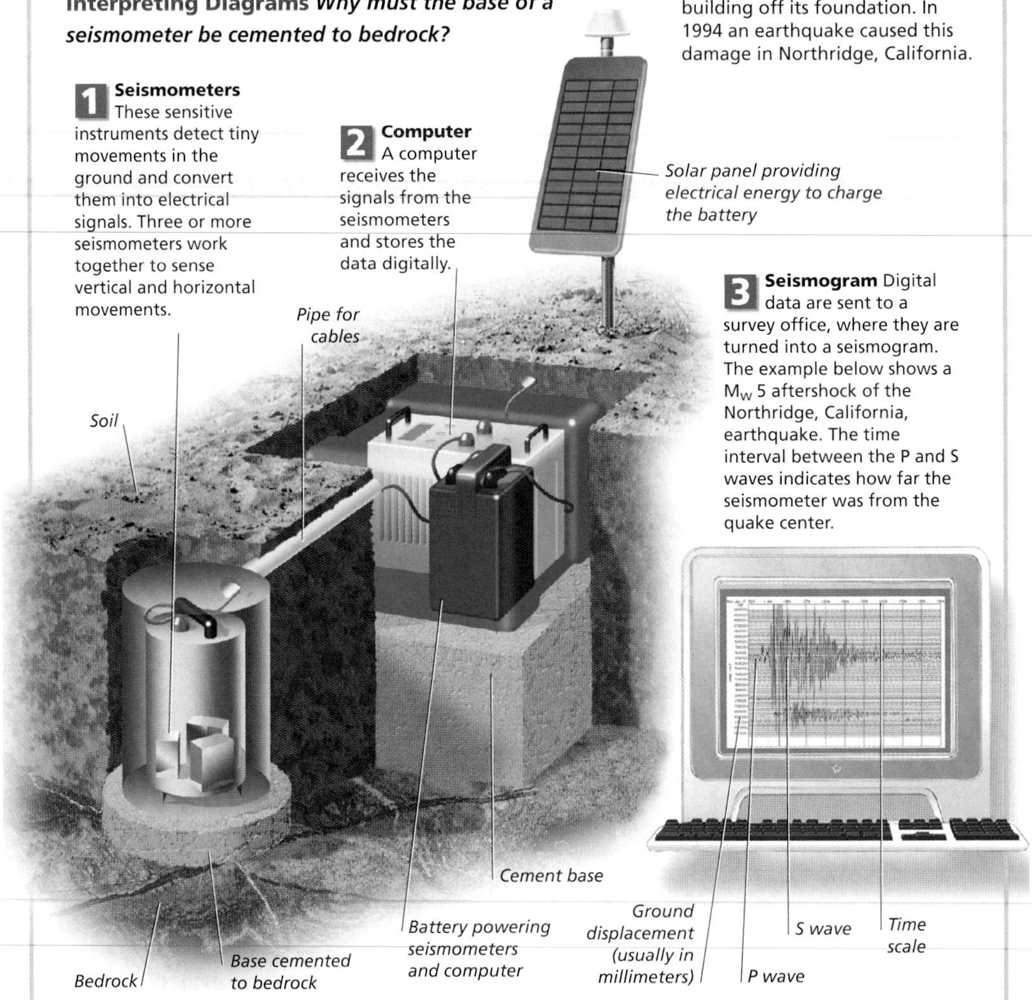
Solar panel providing electrical energy to charge the battery
Pipe for cables
Soil
Cement base
Battery powering seismometers and computer
Ground displacement (usually in millimeters)
S wave
Time scale
P wave
Bedrock
Base cemented to bedrock

1 Seismometers These sensitive instruments detect tiny movements in the ground and convert them into electrical signals. Three or more seismometers work together to sense vertical and horizontal movements.

2 Computer A computer receives the signals from the seismometers and stores the data digitally.

3 Seismogram Digital data are sent to a survey office, where they are turned into a seismogram. The example below shows a M_W 5 aftershock of the Northridge, California, earthquake. The time interval between the P and S waves indicates how far the seismometer was from the quake center.

Facts and Figures

Earthquake Magnitudes On average, each year around the world there are about one magnitude 8 earthquakes, 12 magnitude 7 earthquakes, 110 magnitude 6 earthquakes, and so on. Smaller earthquakes occur more often than larger ones. However, the large earthquakes release much more energy. A single magnitude 8 earthquake usually releases much more energy than all the rest of the earthquakes for the year combined.

Seismographic Data

A worldwide network of seismographs has provided scientists with a wealth of data on earthquakes. These data have enabled geologists to map the distribution of earthquakes. In addition, seismographic data have been used to probe the structure of Earth's interior. Unfortunately, so far these data have not resulted in a method that can be used to predict when earthquakes will occur.

Every day, earthquakes occur all around the world. **Most earthquakes are concentrated along plate boundaries, where many faults are found.** Some earthquakes occur in the interior of plates, far away from plate boundaries. As a plate moves, it undergoes deformation. The resulting stresses are released as earthquakes.

Scientists have mapped Earth's interior, analyzing how seismic waves move through its layers. The speeds of seismic waves and the paths they take are affected by the temperature, composition, and density of the rocks they pass through. Seismic waves are much like other kinds of waves. When they interact with boundaries between different kinds of rock within Earth, they can be reflected, refracted, or diffracted. Look at Figure 37. Geologists infer that Earth's outer core is liquid because S waves cannot pass through it. They can also tell that the core is mostly iron because P waves travel through it at a speed that matches laboratory experiments on iron.

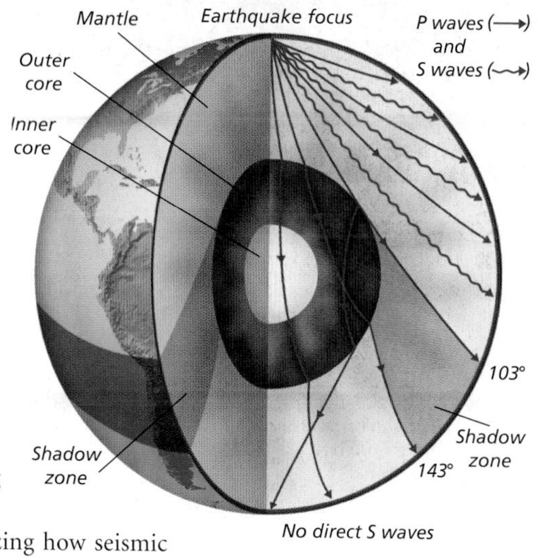

Mantle
Earthquake focus
P waves and S waves
Outer core
Inner core
103°
Shadow zone
143°
Shadow zone
No direct S waves

Figure 37 Earth's liquid outer core blocks S waves and bends P waves. The result is a shadow zone on the surface where no direct seismic waves from an earthquake are detected. **Comparing and Contrasting** ***Compare where P waves and S waves can be detected on Earth's surface. What does this reveal about Earth's layers?***

Section 22.5 Assessment

Reviewing Concepts

1. Describe how faults and folds form in Earth's crust.
2. What happens along a fault before and during an earthquake?
3. How can the magnitude and location of earthquakes be measured?
4. Where do earthquakes occur most often?

Critical Thinking

5. **Comparing and Contrasting** Compare and contrast P waves, S waves, and surface waves.
6. **Relating Cause and Effect** How can layers within Earth be identified by means of seismic waves?

Math Practice

7. How much more energy is released by a M_W 8 earthquake than a M_W 6 earthquake?
8. P waves move through the crust at a speed of about 6.5 km/s. How far will a P wave move in 5 seconds?

Seismographic Data

Build Reading Literacy L1

Use Prior Knowledge Refer to page **2D** in **Chapter 1**, which provides the guidelines for using prior knowledge.

Have students read the key concept (in bold) on p. 689. Ask, **Why are faults and earthquakes concentrated along plate boundaries?** *(Because the plates are moving with respect to one another)* **Logical**

3 ASSESS

Evaluate Understanding L2

Ask students to create a visual showing each of the three kinds of seismic waves.

Reteach L1

Use Figure 35 to review the focus, epicenter, and propagation of seismic waves.

Math Practice

Solutions

7. Each unit of magnitude increase represents about a 32 times increase in energy released, so a 2-unit increase in magnitude is an increase of about 1000 (32×32) in energy released.

8. 6.5 km/s $\times$ 5.0 s = 32.5 km

Interactive Textbook — If your class subscribes to the Interactive Textbook, use it to review key concepts in Section 22.5.

Section 22.5 Assessment

1. The movement of the plates creates a great deal of stress within the crust, which in turn creates faults and folds.
2. Stress builds up along a fault before an earthquake. When stress forces exceed the strength of rocks, an earthquake occurs. The rocks break and grind past one another during an earthquake, releasing large amounts of energy in the form of seismic waves.
3. By analyzing arriving seismic waves on a seismogram
4. Most earthquakes occur along plate boundaries.
5. P waves are longitudinal waves that can travel through solids and liquids. They are the fastest-moving seismic waves, and so are the first to be detected at a distance. S waves are transverse waves that can only travel though solids. Surface waves are seismic waves that travel along Earth's surface.
6. Earth's layers can be identified because seismic waves interact with the boundaries between layers, where they can be reflected, refracted, or diffracted.

Answer to . . .

Figure 37 *No direct P waves or S waves can be detected in an earthquake's shadow zone, and no direct S waves can be detected on the far side of Earth's outer core from the earthquake. This shows that Earth's outer core is liquid.*

Section 22.6

1 FOCUS

Objectives

22.6.1 **Describe** the internal structure of a volcano and how volcanoes form.

22.6.2 **Relate** the type of volcanic eruption to the characteristics of magma.

22.6.3 **Describe** the different types of volcanoes and where they are typically located.

22.6.4 **Describe** several types of igneous features and how they are formed.

Reading Focus

Build Vocabulary L2

Venn Diagram Have students build a Venn diagram to compare the similarities and differences between *composite volcanoes, shield volcanoes,* and *cinder cones.* Ask students to incorporate terms from the vocabulary list.

Reading Strategy L2

a. Gases in magma expand rapidly and, depending on the characteristics of the magma, there is a quiet or explosive eruption. **b.** Lava and other types of volcanic material cool and solidify, building up layers of a volcano over time.

22.6 Volcanoes

Reading Focus

Key Concepts

- How do volcanoes form?
- Why are some volcanic eruptions quiet and others explosive?
- Where are volcanoes found?
- What landforms are formed from lava and magma?

Vocabulary

- volcano
- magma chamber
- pipe
- vent
- crater
- caldera
- hot spot
- shield volcano
- cinder cone
- composite volcano
- batholith
- sill
- dike
- volcanic neck

Reading Strategy

Sequencing Copy the flowchart. As you read, complete it to show how a volcano forms.

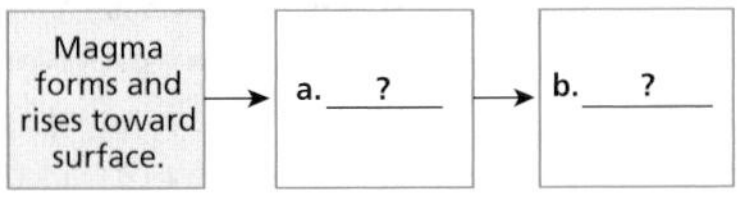

Magma forms and rises toward surface.
a. ?
b. ?

From northern California through the state of Washington, a chain of snow-capped, cone-shaped mountains rises majestically above the surrounding evergreen forests. These peaks form the backbone of the Cascade Range, which is made up of volcanoes. A **volcano** is a mountain that forms when magma reaches the surface.

Most of the time, the volcanoes of the Cascade Range are inactive. Occasionally, however, one of these volcanoes erupts with great violence. That's what happened in May 1980, when Mount St. Helens in Washington exploded. This eruption blew away the top of the mountain. It flattened trees as far as 17 kilometers away, and spewed a cloud of ash more than 20 kilometers into the sky, as shown in Figure 38.

Halfway across the Pacific Ocean, on the island of Hawaii, is another volcano called Kilauea. Unlike Mount St. Helens, Kilauea is often active. Lava bubbles out of the ground and quietly flows down gentle slopes. Although Mount St. Helens and Kilauea are both volcanoes, they are quite different from each other. Volcanoes can result from several different geological processes, and can take a variety of forms.

Figure 38 When Mount St. Helens erupted, trapped gases caused the north side of the mountain to explode. Volcanic ash was ejected high into the atmosphere.

Section Resources

Print
- ***Reading and Study Workbook With Math Support,*** Section 22.6
- ***Transparencies,*** Section 22.6

Technology
- ***Interactive Textbook,*** Section 22.6
- ***Presentation Pro CD-ROM,*** Section 22.6
- ***Go Online,*** *Planet Diary,* Volcano activity

Formation of a Volcano

The process that leads to a volcanic eruption begins deep inside Earth. **Under certain conditions, small amounts of mantle rock can melt, forming liquid magma. The magma rises upward through the crust, erupting at the surface as a volcano.** Magma rises because it is less dense than the solid rock around and above it.

How a Volcano Erupts What causes a volcanic eruption? The process is similar to what happens when you quickly open a bottle of soda that has been shaken. Like the soda in the bottle, magma is under pressure and contains dissolved gases. In the case of magma, the gases include carbon dioxide and water vapor. As magma approaches the surface, lower pressure allows the gases in magma to expand rapidly. An eruption occurs when the gases bubble out through a crack in the crust, propelling magma to the surface.

Structure of a Volcano Before an eruption, magma often collects in a pocket called a **magma chamber,** shown in Figure 39. Magma slowly accumulates in the magma chamber until enough pressure builds up to start an eruption. Then, magma rises to the surface in a narrow, vertical channel called a **pipe.**

An opening in the ground where magma escapes to the surface is called a **vent.** Often there is one central vent at the top of a volcano. Sometimes there are other vents that open along a volcano's side. At the top of the central vent in most volcanoes is a bowl-shaped pit called a **crater.**

After an eruption, a volcano's magma chamber and main vent may empty of magma, creating a hollow shell. If this shell collapses inward, it creates a huge depression, called a **caldera,** at the top of the volcano.

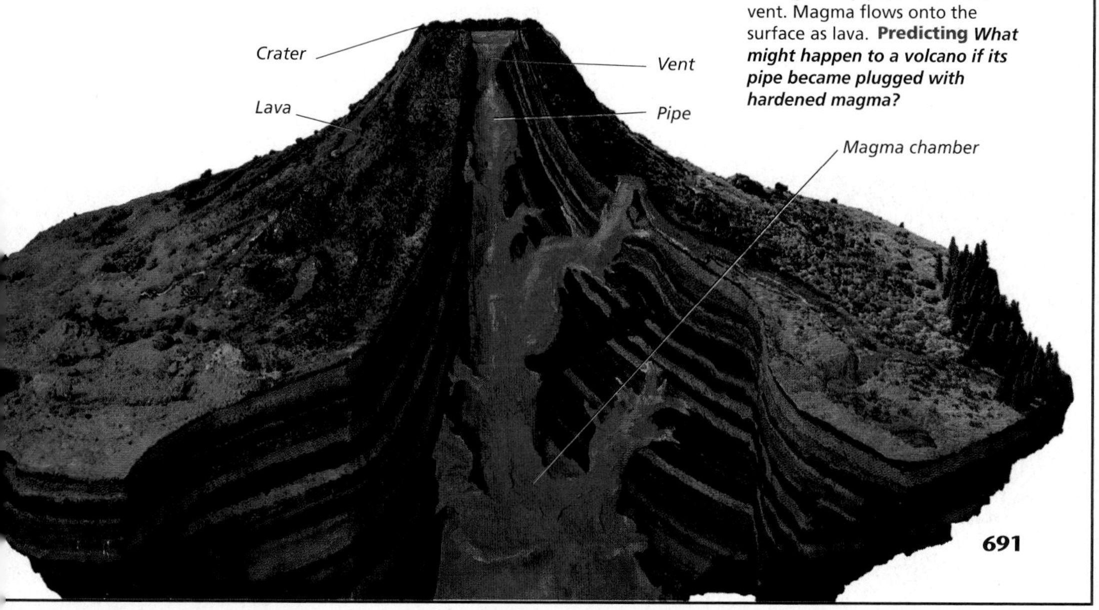

Crater
Vent
Lava
Pipe
Magma chamber

Figure 39 When a volcanic mountain erupts, magma under pressure is forced upward from the magma chamber. It passes through the pipe, and out the vent. Magma flows onto the surface as lava. ***Predicting What might happen to a volcano if its pipe became plugged with hardened magma?***

691

Customize for Inclusion Students

Learning Disabled
For students with difficulty absorbing concepts by reading, use Figure 39 as a visual aid as you describe the path of magma through a volcano. Be sure students understand which part is which and the order in which magma travels through each part.

2 INSTRUCT

Formation of a Volcano

Build Science Skills L2

Using an Analogy Have students expand upon the soda bottle analogy presented in How a Volcano Erupts. Review the analogy to be sure students understand that the water in the magma is being compared to the carbon dioxide in the soda. The presence of water in magma can cause explosive, steam-filled eruptions. As magma erupts, the pressure drops. This drop in pressure allows the hot water to expand into steam. This expansion can cause very explosive eruptions. Ask, **How does opening the bottle relate to magma rising to the surface?** *(The pressure drops in both cases.)* **Why does the gas expand when the pressure drops?** *($\frac{P_1V_1}{T_1} = \frac{P_2V_2}{T_2}$, with temperature constant, as pressure decreases, volume increases)* **What volcanic rock is similar to the frothy part of the soda outburst?** *(Pumice)*
Logical

FYI

There is another similarity between a steam-filled, explosive volcanic eruption and a shaken bottle of soda. In both cases, what comes out is often frothy and filled with bubbles. When this molten volcanic froth is ejected, it cools and solidifies in the air before it lands on the ground. These bits of solidified froth are called pyroclastic deposits, and they have a large range in size and appearance. The most common pyroclastic deposit is ash, which has very small grains. Because ash is so small, it can be thrown high into the atmosphere, where it can be carried all around Earth.

In some pyroclastic deposits, like pumice, the bubbles of the molten froth are retained as pockets of air called vesicles. Pumice has so much air trapped in vesicles that it will float on top of water. Some pyroclastic deposits contain a black glass called obsidian. This occurs when the magma cools so fast that crystals do not have time to form, and the atoms solidify in a random, amorphous structure.

Answer to . . .

Figure 39 *Pressure will build up until the volcano erupts explosively.*

Quiet and Explosive Eruptions

Build Reading Literacy **L1**

Identify Main Idea/Details Refer to page **98D** in **Chapter 4**, which provides the guidelines for identifying main ideas and details.

Have students read Quiet and Explosive Eruptions. Ask them to read the key concept aloud. Then, have students find the details that support this key concept. Ask, **Which characteristics of the magma determine how the volcano erupts?** *(Temperature, water content, and silica content)*
Verbal

pahoehoe
aa

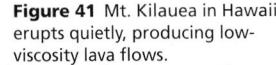

Figure 40 Lava may flow in the form of rough chunks called aa, or smooth coils called pahoehoe. **Formulating Hypotheses** ***Develop a hypothesis to account for the difference in texture between pahoehoe and aa.***

Quiet and Explosive Eruptions

A volcanic eruption like that of Mount St. Helens has the force of a powerful explosion. But in other volcanic eruptions, lava flows gently over the surface. **Volcanoes erupt explosively or quietly, depending on the characteristics of the magma.**

Magma can vary in viscosity, the resistance to flow. Magma with high viscosity is thick and resists flowing. Magma with low viscosity is thin and flows easily.

There are three main factors that determine the viscosity of magma: temperature, water content, and silica content. Higher temperatures lower the viscosity of magma, so it flows more easily. The presence of water in magma also helps it flow more easily. Magma that is high in silica has high viscosity. The silicon and oxygen atoms in silica are held together with strong bonds. The silica in magma acts like glue, preventing the magma from flowing easily.

Quiet Eruptions Volcanoes that have very hot, low-silica magma generally erupt quietly. In a quiet eruption, lava erupts in a stream of low-viscosity lava, called a lava flow. Lava flows from a quiet eruption can travel for great distances. Quiet eruptions produce two different kinds of lava, as shown in Figure 40. Hot, fast-moving lava with a ropelike surface is called pahoehoe (pah HOH ee hoh ee). Cooler, slow-moving lava with a chunky, crumbly appearance is called aa (AH ah).

Explosive Eruptions High-silica magma produces explosive eruptions. Thick magma can clog a volcanic pipe, causing enormous pressure to build up. Trapped steam inside the volcano adds to the pressure, as was the case in the eruption of Mount St. Helens. When the volcano finally explodes, lava and hot gases are hurled outward. The lava solidifies very quickly and shatters into pieces of different sizes. These particles range in size from fine dust and ash, to pebble-sized cinders, to bombs—chunks of lava that can be the size of a small car.

Figure 41 Mt. Kilauea in Hawaii erupts quietly, producing low-viscosity lava flows.

Facts and Figures

Pyroclastic Flows Under certain conditions, volcanic eruptions can be very dangerous. One of the most deadly volcanic hazards is a pyroclastic flow, which is a hot cloud of gas and dust that rushes down the sides of a volcano at speeds of up to 150 kilometers per hour. With temperatures of up to 700°C, a pyroclastic flow can burn everything in its path. One of the most famous pyroclastic flows destroyed the town of Herculaneum during the eruption of Mt. Vesuvius in A.D. 79.

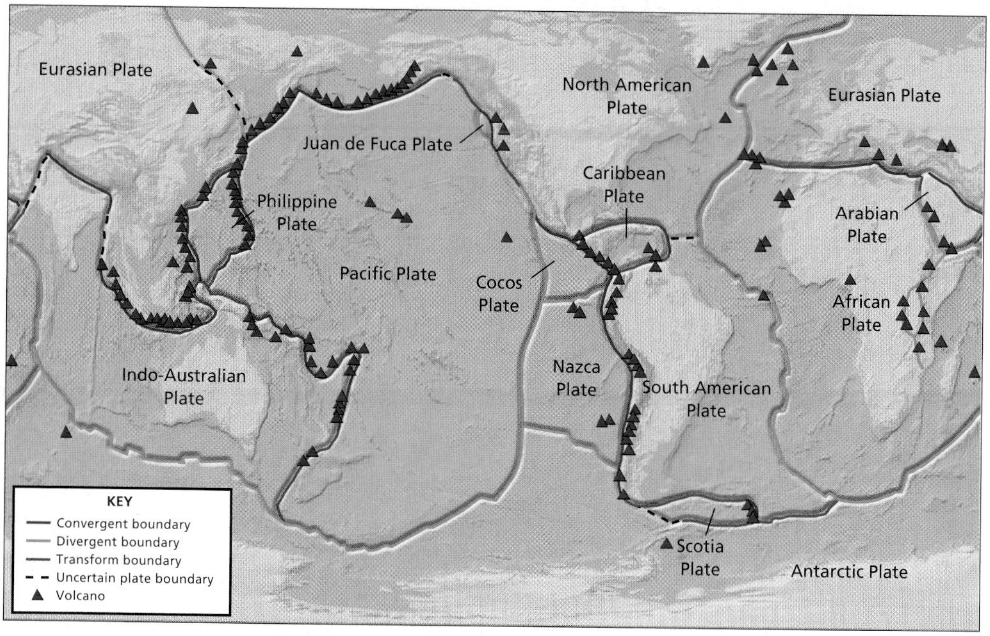
Eurasian Plate
North American Plate
Eurasian Plate
Juan de Fuca Plate
Caribbean Plate
Philippine Plate
Arabian Plate
Pacific Plate
Cocos Plate
African Plate
Indo-Australian Plate
Nazca Plate
South American Plate
Scotia Plate
Antarctic Plate
KEY
Convergent boundary
Divergent boundary
Transform boundary
Uncertain plate boundary
Volcano

Figure 42 Except for hot-spot volcanoes, most of the world's volcanoes form near plate boundaries.
Relating Cause and Effect ***Why are there volcanoes in the middle of the Atlantic Ocean?***

Location and Types of Volcanoes

Most volcanoes occur along plate boundaries or at hot spots in the crust. Volcanoes often form along a converging plate boundary where an oceanic plate is subducted into the mantle. As it sinks through the mantle, the plate causes melting. Magma forms and rises to the surface. As Figure 42 shows, many volcanoes have formed along the trenches that rim the Pacific Ocean. This region is called the "Ring of Fire." Volcanoes also form along a diverging plate boundary where magma rises to fill the gap between two separating plates.

Some volcanoes occur at hot spots, as shown in the Concepts in Action pages. A **hot spot** is a region where hot rock extends from deep within the mantle to the surface.

Different types of volcanic eruptions produce different types of volcanoes. Each type is named for its shape or interior structure. **The three major types of volcano are shield volcanoes, cinder cones, and composite volcanoes.** A quiet eruption of low-viscosity lava produces a wide, flat volcano called a **shield volcano.** If an eruption is entirely ash and cinders, the result will be a small, steep-sided volcano called a **cinder cone.** A volcano that forms from explosive eruptions that produce a combination of lava and ash is called a **composite volcano.**

Reading Checkpoint *What is a shield volcano?*

Go Online PLANETDIARY

For: Volcano activity
Visit: PHSchool.com
Web Code: ccc-3226

Location and Types of Volcanoes

Use Visuals **L1**

Figure 42 Point out that most volcanoes occur at the boundaries between plates. Mid-ocean ridges are not marked by individual volcano symbols on this diagram, but are places where magma erupts at Earth's surface, forming oceanic crust. Ask, **Which volcanoes are formed from melting slabs of subducting oceanic crust?** *(Students should point to volcano symbols at convergent boundaries.)* **Where are volcanoes located in the United States?** *(Alaska, Hawaii, the west coast)*
Visual

Go Online PLANETDIARY

Find links to additional activities and have students monitor phenomena that affect Earth and its residents.

Answer to . . .

Figure 40 *The difference in texture between pahoehoe and aa is mainly due to the different temperatures of the two lavas and the speed at which they flow. Pahoehoe is hotter and faster moving than aa. Also, escaping gas within aa helps to produce a rough surface.*

Figure 42 *Many of these volcanoes are located along the Mid-Atlantic ridge, a divergent boundary where magma is rising from the mantle to form new oceanic crust.*

Reading Checkpoint *A wide, flat volcano produced by quiet eruptions of low-viscosity lava*

CONCEPTS in Action

Types of Volcanoes L2

Background

Composite and cinder cone volcanoes form when magma is rich in silicates, the primary source of which is melting continental crust. These types of volcanoes are often found above subduction zones, where magma from the melting slab of oceanic crust must travel through a thick wedge of continental crust to reach the surface, contact melting occurs, and silica-rich magma becomes incorporated in the volcanic arc. Similarly, when hot spots are located beneath continental crust, cinder cones and composite volcanoes again result. However, hot spots in the ocean melt only silica-poor oceanic crust. In these cases, therefore, shield volcanoes are produced.

Build Science Skills L2

Inferring ACTIVITY

Purpose Students will infer the type of volcano based on the characteristics of the rock it produced.

Materials several samples of pumice, obsidian, ropy basalt, and angular rhyolite per group

Class Time 15–20 minutes

Procedure After reading the Concepts in Action feature, have students work in groups to study volcanic rock samples. For each rock, ask, **What type of volcano do you think this rock most likely came from?** *(Basalt is most associated with shield volcanoes, rhyolite with cinder cones or composite volcanoes.)*

Expected Outcome Using the information about pumice and obsidian on p. 695, students can deduce that these samples came from near the surface of a lava flow. The contact with air caused quick cooling in both cases. Students can infer that the ropy basalt came from the type of runny basaltic flow associated with shield volcanoes. Rhyolite has a higher silica content than the basalt, and is much lighter in color and "ashier" in appearance. Many rhyolite samples also contain vesicles. The gases trapped in viscous, silica-rich magma produce the explosive eruptions associated with composite volcanoes and cinder cones.
Kinesthetic, Logical

CONCEPTS in Action

Types of Volcanoes

Volcanoes have different types of magma. The viscosity of the magma plays a large part in determining a volcano's ultimate shape and appearance.

Volcanoes most commonly occur at three major locations on Earth—mid-ocean ridges, subduction zones, and hot spots. Each type of volcanic region produces a different kind of volcano because of the type of magma that exists there. The three main types of volcano are shield volcanoes, composite volcanoes, and cinder cones. Most volcanoes that form above subduction zones, for example, are composite volcanoes. In contrast, many volcanoes that form above hot spots are shield volcanoes.

Shapes of Volcanoes

Each type of volcano has a different shape. The shape is determined by the kind of lava, ash, and cinders that erupt from the volcano's vent, and especially the viscosity of the lava.

Shield volcano
Shield volcanoes are broad, gently sloping volcanic mountains. Their eruptions consist of hot, flowing basaltic lava that travels a long way before it solidifies.

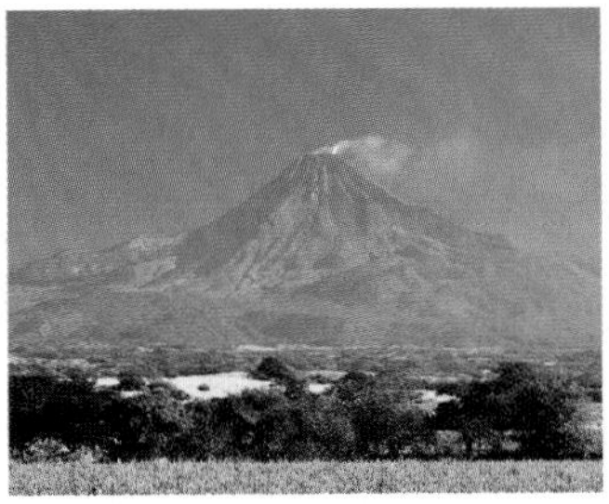

Composite volcano
Composite volcanoes are tall with steep sides that are built up from layers of viscous lava, ash, and volcanic bombs. They often have secondary vents.

Cinder cone
Cinder cones are small with steep sides. They form from ash and cinders that are ejected into the air and fall back onto the volcano.

Facts and Figures

Yellowstone Hot Spot A special case of hot spot volcanism occurs when the hot spot is beneath a continent. One such hot spot is located in Yellowstone National Park. The continent acts like a thick lid, and it is hard for the hot spot to break through. When this does happen, a lot of continental rock gets melted as well, giving the magma a composition rich in silica. The result can be very explosive eruptions. Gigantic eruptions at Yellowstone 2.1 million and 640,000 years ago blanketed the western half of North America with ash. Fortunately, these giant explosions are very rare, and most hot spot activity at Yellowstone consists of hot springs of water. However, Yellowstone is still geologically active, and could have another large explosion in the future.

Volcanic Rocks

The silica and water content of magma help to determine whether an eruption is quiet or explosive and how viscous the lava is when hot. When the lava cools, different types of rock are formed.

Obsidian
Obsidian is a dense, volcanic glass formed from lava that has cooled too quickly for minerals to crystallize.

Pumice
Pumice is a light, sponge-like rock usually found at the surface of a lava flow. It consists of a mass of gas bubbles frozen in fragile volcanic glass and minerals.

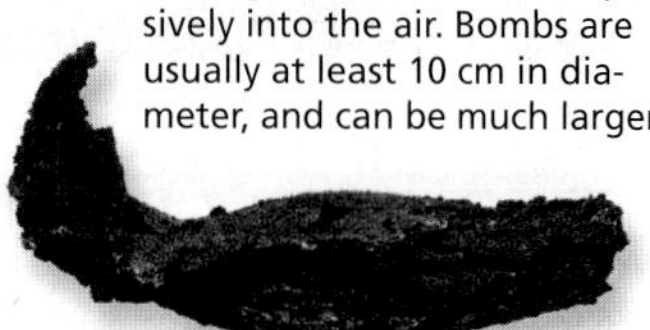

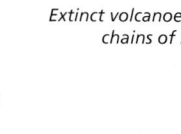

Lava bombs
Lava bombs form from a glob of magma that is blown explosively into the air. Bombs are usually at least 10 cm in diameter, and can be much larger.

Hot-spot Volcanoes

A hot spot is a rising column of hot rock that extends from deep within the mantle to the surface. Hot spots often exist in the middle of plates. Because the hot spot stays in one place while the plate moves over it, a chain of volcanoes is formed over time.

A very ancient hot spot under the Pacific plate has, over millions of years, produced the Hawaiian Islands.

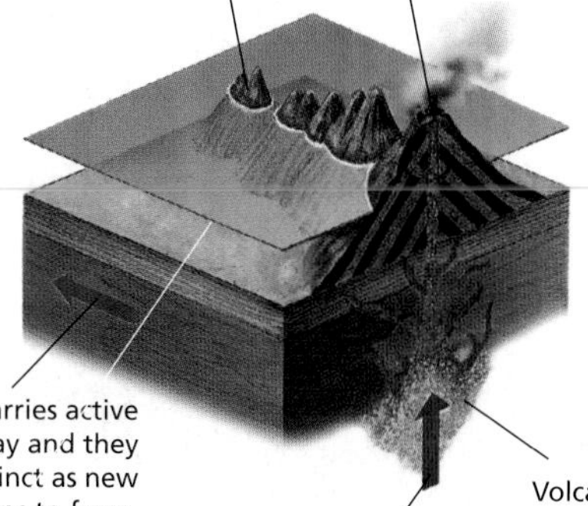

Extinct volcanoes form chains of islands
Vent
Plate carries active volcanoes away and they become extinct as new island begins to form.
Rising magma
Volcano erupts over stationary hot spot and creates an island.

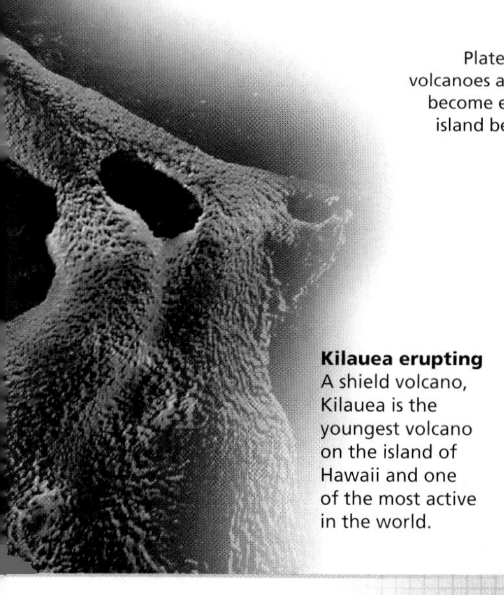

Kilauea erupting
A shield volcano, Kilauea is the youngest volcano on the island of Hawaii and one of the most active in the world.

Going Further

- Use library or Internet resources to research a volcano located on another planet or moon. Write a one-page report describing the volcano that you select. Include an explanation of how this volcano compares with volcanoes on Earth.
- Take a Discovery Channel Video Field Trip by watching "Mountains of Fire."

Discovery Channel School
Video Field Trip

Going Further **L3**

Volcanoes occur on several planets and moons in the solar system besides Earth, including Venus, Mars, Io, and possibly Triton. In addition, there is evidence of ancient volcanic activity on Mercury and Earth's moon. Some of the most well-known volcanoes include Olympus Mons, Arsia Mons, Pavonis Mons, Ascraeus Mons, and Elysium Mons on Mars; Theia Mons, Sif Mons, and Maat Mons on Venus; and Pele, Ra, Loki, and Prometheus on Io. Have interested students research volcanoes on other planets or moons and present photos to the class.
Visual

Discovery Channel School

Video Field Trip

Mountains of Fire

After students have viewed the Video Field Trip, ask the following questions: **Where do the most violent volcanic eruptions typically occur?** *(Near subduction zones, where Earth's tectonic plates are pushed together and one plate slips under another.)* **What is a composite volcano?** *(A volcano with alternating layers of different materials.)* **What is a shield volcano?** *(A wide, flat volcano that produces quiet eruptions of low-viscosity lava.)* **Name a third major kind of volcano.** *(Cinder cone volcanoes.)*

Other Igneous Features

Address Misconceptions **L2**

Many students have the misconception that the only way igneous rocks are formed is when molten lava flows onto Earth's surface. After students read Other Igneous Features, have them work in groups to create a visual describing five ways igneous rocks can form. *(In lava flows at the surface, dikes, sills, batholiths, and volcanic necks)*
Visual, Group

3 ASSESS

Evaluate Understanding **L2**

Using Figure 41, ask students what type of volcano most likely produced this type of lava. *(Shield volcano)*

Reteach **L1**

Use Figure 39 to explain the main features of a volcano.

Writing in Science

Students have many eruptions to choose from, including Mt. Mazama (Crater Lake), Oregon, around 5000 B.C.; Mt. Vesuvius, Italy, in A.D. 79; Mt. Fuji, Japan, in 1707; Tambora, Indonesia, in 1815; Krakatoa, Indonesia, in 1883; Mt. Pelée, Martinique, in 1902; Mt. Katmai, Alaska, in 1912; Mt. St. Helens in 1980; Mt. Pinatubo, Philippines, in 1991; and Montserrat in 1995.

Interactive Textbook If your class subscribes to the Interactive textbook, use it to review key concepts in Section 22.6.

Figure 43 Ship Rock in New Mexico is a volcanic neck. It formed when the soft rock around a volcano's pipe wore away, revealing hard, igneous rock. The long ridge extending from the volcanic neck is a dike.

Other Igneous Features

Sometimes magma does not reach the surface, but cools and hardens in the crust. This magma forms intrusive igneous rock that may eventually be forced upward and exposed at Earth's surface. **Igneous features formed by magma include batholiths, sills, dikes, and volcanic necks.** Lava plateaus are features formed of extrusive igneous rock.

A **batholith** is the largest type of intrusive igneous rock mass. Batholiths often form the core of a mountain range, such as the Sierra Nevada range in California. Magma sometimes squeezes into a crack between layers of rock and then hardens. If the crack is parallel to existing rock layers, the magma hardens into a structure called a **sill.** If the crack cuts across rock layers, the hardened magma forms a **dike.** When magma hardens in a volcano's pipe, a structure called a **volcanic neck** may form, as shown in Figure 43.

The largest lava flows don't come from individual volcanoes. Rather, large amounts of easily-flowing lava sometimes erupt from a cluster of long, thin cracks in the crust. This lava may spread out over an enormous area before solidifying. After many years, layers of hardened lava may form a high, level area called a lava plateau. An example is the Columbia Plateau, which has an average thickness of more than 1 kilometer and covers an area of nearly 200,000 square kilometers in the Pacific Northwest.

Section 22.6 Assessment

Reviewing Concepts

1. Describe the process that leads up to the eruption of a volcano.
2. How does the silica content of magma affect how explosive an eruption is?
3. Explain why volcanoes form in certain regions of Earth's surface.
4. Describe four types of intrusive igneous rock features.

Critical Thinking

5. **Relating Cause and Effect** What condition must exist in a volcano for a caldera to form?
6. **Predicting** What would eventually happen, as a result of plate movement, to a volcano that formed over a hot spot?
7. **Comparing and Contrasting** What is the difference between a dike and a sill?

Writing in Science

Descriptive Paragraph Use library or Internet resources to research a major volcanic eruption. Write a paragraph about the eruption including when and where it took place and the type of volcano involved.

696 *Chapter 22*

Section 22.6 Assessment

1. Magma is formed from melted rock within the mantle. The magma is under pressure and less dense than the solid rock around it. The magma is forced upward through the crust, erupting at the surface.
2. Magma with a low silica content results in gentle eruptions. Magma with a high silica content can lead to explosive eruptions.
3. Volcanoes form above converging plate boundaries (where a plate is subducted into the mantle) and at diverging boundaries (where magma rises to fill the gap left by two separating plates). Hot spot volcanoes form from columns of hot rock that have risen up through the mantle to the surface.
4. Batholiths are large rock masses that form the core of many mountain ranges. A sill is hardened lava squeezed into a crack that is parallel to existing rock layers. A dike is hardened lava in a crack that cuts across existing rock layers. A volcanic neck is an igneous structure formed from lava that hardened in a volcano's pipe.
5. The magma chamber and main vent must be empty after an eruption, creating an empty shell that can collapse inward.
6. As the plate moves, the volcano would be carried away from the hot spot, and the volcano would no longer be active.
7. Both are structures formed from magma that hardens in cracks in layers of rock. If the crack is parallel to existing rock layers, the structure is called a sill. If the crack cuts across rock layers, the structure is called a dike.

Exploration Lab

Using Earthquakes to Map Plate Boundaries

In this lab, you will analyze data from several earthquakes to determine how the plates in the northwestern United States are moving.

Problem How can you use earthquake data to infer the movement of tectonic plates?

Materials
- graph paper

Skills Inferring, Analyzing Data

Procedure

1. Examine the map of Oregon and Washington states. Earthquakes occur in the western parts of these states as a result of the movements of two plates—the Juan de Fuca Plate, which lies under the Pacific Ocean, and the North American plate.
2. Examine the table of earthquake data. Record any patterns that you observe.
3. Draw a diagram showing how the edges of the Juan de Fuca and North American plates would move if they formed a convergent boundary. Use Figure 30 on page 682 to help you draw this diagram.
4. Draw a diagram showing how the edges of the two plates would move if they formed a transform boundary. Use Figure 30 again to help you draw this diagram.
5. Use the information in the data table to construct a graph showing the location and depth of earthquakes. Plot the distance from the coast on the horizontal axis and the depth of the focus on the vertical axis. Label the vertical axis with zero at the top and maximum depth at the bottom.
6. Draw a curve as close as possible to all the points you plotted on your graph. The curve shows the shape and position of the boundary between the Juan de Fuca and North American plates. Compare your graph to the two diagrams you drew in Steps 3 and 4.

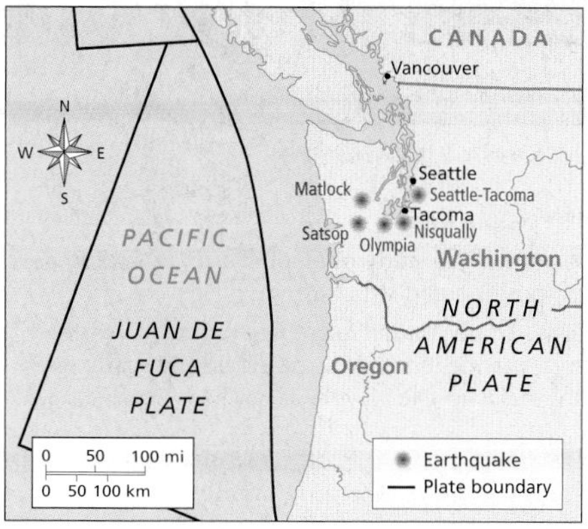

CANADA
Vancouver
N
W
E
S
Seattle
Seattle-Tacoma
Matlock
Tacoma
Nisqually
Satsop
Olympia
Washington
PACIFIC OCEAN
JUAN DE FUCA PLATE
NORTH AMERICAN PLATE
Oregon
0 50 100 mi
0 50 100 km
Earthquake
Plate boundary

Data Table

Year	Location of Epicenter	Distance From Coast (km)	Depth of Focus (km)
1949	Olympia	116	53
1965	Seattle-Tacoma	141	63
1999	Satsop	58	41
2001	Nisqually	108	52
2001	Matlock	60	41

Analyze and Conclude

1. **Using Graphs** What kind of boundary do the Juan de Fuca and North American plates form? Explain how your graph supports your answer.
2. **Inferring** What does your graph suggest about the direction in which the Juan de Fuca and North American plates are moving?
3. **Predicting** In California, the Pacific plate and the North American plate meet along a transform boundary called the San Andreas fault. Would you expect to observe a similar curve in a graph of the earthquake data from the San Andreas fault? Explain.
4. **Drawing Conclusions** Based on your data, how is earthquake depth related to distance from a convergent plate boundary? Explain.

Go Further Use resources in the library or on the Internet to learn how geologists estimate the depth of an earthquake's focus. Report your findings to the class.

Exploration Lab

Using Earthquakes to Map Plate Boundaries L2

Objective
After completing this activity, students will be able to
- use earthquake data to determine the type and direction of plate boundaries.

Skills Focus **Using Tables and Graphs**

Prep Time 5 minutes

Class Time 35 minutes

Teaching Tips
- You may need to show students how to set up the axes of their graphs in Step 5.

Expected Outcome
The graph will produce a curve that slopes down to the right, indicating that the Juan de Fuca Plate is subducting under the North American Plate at a convergent boundary.

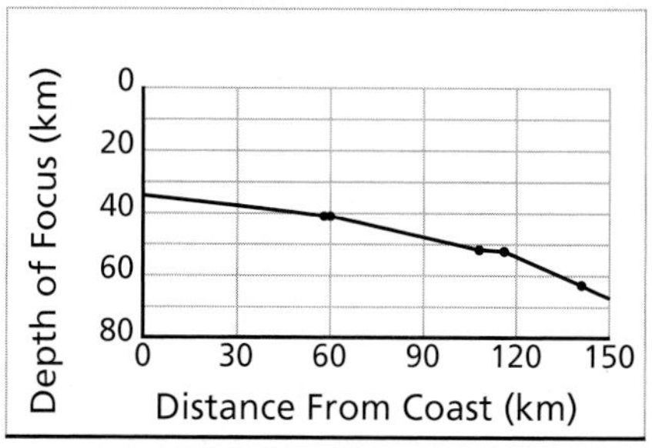

Depth of Focus (km)
0
20
40
60
80
0
30
60
90
120
150
Distance From Coast (km)

Analyze and Conclude

1. The curve slopes down to the right, indicating that the border between the two plates slopes down to the east under the North American Plate as a convergent boundary.
2. The graph suggests that the North American Plate is moving west, over the Juan de Fuca Plate.
3. No, in a transform boundary, the plates form a vertical boundary that would appear as a vertical line on the graph.
4. The depth of the earthquakes increases with distance from the boundary because the earthquake foci are located along the upper surface of the subducting plate.
Visual, Logical, Portfolio

Go Further

Students should find that the depth of an earthquake focus is determined in a manner similar to how an epicenter is located, that is, by comparing the arrival times of vibrations at geographically separated observing stations. By extending this method to three dimensions, the depth of the focus can be estimated as well. **Verbal, Interpersonal**

Study Guide

Study Tip

Write Questions
Encourage students to prepare for a chapter test by writing and answering their own test questions. Tell students to write at least one essay question for each key concept or fill-in-the-blank questions using all of the vocabulary terms. Encourage students to quiz each other with their test questions.

Assessment

Interactive Textbook If your class subscribes to the Interactive Textbook, your students can go online to access an interactive version of the Student Edition and a self-test.

Reviewing Content

1. a **2.** d **3.** a
4. c **5.** d **6.** b
7. a **8.** c **9.** c
10. a

Understanding Concepts

11. Earth's inner core is solid and its outer core is liquid.
12. Based on the information provided in the table, students should describe how they would perform two of the following tests: calculating density by measuring each sample's mass and volume; measuring each mineral's hardness using a series of scratch tests; and using a streak plate to find the color of each mineral's streak. Note that color is not a good way to distinguish these minerals.
13. Talc is the only mineral in the list. Coal is made of organic material. Brick is man-made. Granite is a rock.
14. An intrusive igneous rock such as granite or gabbro forms inside Earth. An extrusive igneous rock forms on Earth's surface.
15. A metamorphic rock forms when a rock is subjected to heat, pressure, or chemical reactions and changes into a new rock.

CHAPTER 22

Study Guide

22.1 Earth's Structure

Key Concepts
- Geology is the study of planet Earth, including its composition and structure.
- Earth can be divided into three main layers—the crust, mantle, and core—based on the materials that make up each layer.

Vocabulary
geologists, uniformitarianism, silicates, crust, mantle, lithosphere, asthenosphere, mesosphere, core

22.2 Minerals

Key Concepts
- A mineral is a naturally ocurring, inorganic solid with a crystal structure and a characteristic composition.
- The properties by which minerals can be identified include their crystal structure, color, streak, luster, density, hardness, fracture, and cleavage.

Vocabulary
rock, inorganic, streak, luster, hardness, fracture, cleavage

22.3 Rocks and the Rock Cycle

Key Concepts
- Rocks are classified into three major groups—igneous, sedimentary, and metamorphic.
- In the rock cycle, forces within Earth and at the surface cause rocks to change form.

Vocabulary
igneous rock, magma, lava, intrusive rock, extrusive rock, sediment, sedimentary rock, clastic rocks, metamorphic rock, foliated rocks, rock cycle

22.4 Plate Tectonics

Key Concepts
- The theory of plate tectonics explains the formation and movement of Earth's plates.
- Sea-floor spreading creates new oceanic crust at mid-ocean ridges. Subduction destroys old oceanic crust at subduction zones.
- Plate motions are the visible part of the process of mantle convection.
- There are three types of plate boundaries: divergent, convergent, and transform.
- Most mountains form along plate boundaries.

Vocabulary
plate tectonics, Pangaea, continental drift, mid-ocean ridge, sea-floor spreading, subduction, trench, divergent boundary, convergent boundary, transform boundary

22.5 Earthquakes

Key Concepts
- As tectonic plates move, they cause stress in the crust, which in turn produces faults and folds.
- Earthquakes occur because stress forces have exceeded the strength of rock.
- To measure earthquakes and pinpoint their epicenters, geologists record seismic waves using seismographs.
- Most earthquakes occur along plate boundaries.

Vocabulary
earthquake, seismic waves, stress, fault, fold, focus, epicenter, P waves, S waves, surface waves, seismograph

22.6 Volcanoes

Key Concepts
- Under certain conditions, small amounts of mantle rock can melt, forming liquid magma. The magma rises upward through the crust, erupting at the surface as a volcano.
- Volcanoes erupt explosively or quietly, depending on the characteristics of the magma.
- Most volcanoes occur along plate boundaries, or at hot spots in the crust.
- The three major types of volcano are shield volcanoes, cinder cones, and composite volcanoes.
- Igneous features formed by magma include batholiths, sills, dikes, and volcanic necks.

Vocabulary
volcano, magma chamber, pipe, vent, crater, caldera, hot spot, shield volcanoes, cinder cone, composite volcano, batholith, sill, dike, volcanic neck

698 *Chapter 22*

Chapter Resources

Print
- ***Chapter and Unit Tests,*** Chapter 22 Test A and Test B
- ***Test Prep Resources,*** Chapter 22

Technology
- ***Computer Test Bank,*** Chapter Test 22
- ***Interactive Textbook,*** Chapter 22
- ***Go Online,*** PHSchool.com, Chapter 22

CHAPTER 22

Assessment

Interactive textbook with assessment at PHSchool.com iText

Reviewing Content

Choose the letter that best answers the question or completes the statement.

1. The lithosphere includes the crust and portions of the
   a. mantle. b. asthenosphere.
   c. mesosphere. d. outer core.

2. The layer of Earth consisting of weak, soft rock that can flow easily is called the
   a. crust. b. core.
   c. lithosphere. d. asthenosphere.

3. Which of the following properties is NOT useful in identifying a mineral?
   a. size b. cleavage
   c. density d. hardness

4. The way that the surface of a mineral reflects light is called
   a. density. b. hardness.
   c. luster. d. streak.

5. Sedimentary rocks that form from the broken fragments of other rocks are called
   a. chemical rocks. b. organic rocks.
   c. intrusive rocks. d. clastic rocks.

6. A long, deep depression in the ocean floor is called a
   a. mid-ocean ridge. b. trench.
   c. caldera. d. batholith.

7. What type of plate boundary occurs when two plates move away from each other?
   a. divergent b. convergent
   c. transform d. subduction

8. Which type of earthquake wave moves the fastest?
   a. surface wave b. S wave
   c. P wave d. transverse wave

9. The location inside Earth where an earthquake begins is called the
   a. fold. b. epicenter.
   c. focus. d. hot spot.

10. Magma that hardens in a pipe of a volcano may form a
   a. volcanic neck. b. sill.
   c. batholith. d. dike.

Understanding Concepts

11. What is the major difference between Earth's inner and outer cores?

12. Use the table below to choose two tests that you would perform to distinguish gold from pyrite and chalcopyrite. Describe how you would perform each test.

Mineral Characteristics

Mineral	Gold	Pyrite	Chalcopyrite
Color	Rich yellow	Light yellow	Rich yellow
Density (g/cm^3)	19.3	5.0	4.3
Hardness	2.5–3.0	6.0–6.5	3.5–4.0
Streak	Yellow	Greenish black	Greenish black

13. Which of the following is a mineral: coal, brick, talc, and granite?

14. What is the difference between an intrusive rock and an extrusive rock?

15. How do metamorphic rocks form?

16. What is continental drift?

17. What evidence is there for sea-floor spreading?

18. What is the importance of convection currents in the theory of plate tectonics?

19. What determines the viscosity of magma?

20. How do hot-spot volcanoes form?

21. Sometimes water is considered a mineral and sometimes it is not. Explain.

22. Coquina is a rock made of fragments of small shells cemented together. What type of rock is coquina?

23. What is the major difference between Wegener's original hypothesis of continental drift and the theory of plate tectonics? How are they similar?

Assessment (continued)

16. Continental drift is the theory proposed by Alfred Wegener that the continents move slowly across Earth's surface. At one time, all the continents were joined in a single supercontinent. This explains why the continents look like they fit together like a puzzle, and why some fossils and surface features seem to continue on to other continents.
17. The evidence for sea-floor spreading includes a series of parallel magnetic stripes in rocks on either side of the mid-ocean ridge. Geologists have also found that the age of rocks increases with distance from the mid-ocean ridge.
18. Convection currents transfer heat from Earth's interior toward the surface. Hot rock rises and spreads out beneath the lithosphere, causing tectonic plates to move in a horizontal direction.
19. The viscosity of magma is determined by the magma's temperature, water content, and silica content.
20. A hot spot volcano forms where a column of hot rock extends from deep within the mantle all the way to the surface.
21. Water is considered a mineral when it is frozen, since all minerals are solids. Water in the form of a liquid or gas is not considered to be a mineral.
22. An organic sedimentary rock
23. Plate tectonics and continental drift each offer explanations for phenomena that occur on Earth's surface. Continental drift attempts to explain why the continents seem to fit together like a puzzle, and why some fossils are found on different continents. Continental drift's major downfall was that it did not offer a mechanism for the movement of Earth's plates. Plate tectonics explains that mechanism of movement as well as the relationship between the location of most earthquakes and volcanoes and the movement of the plates.

Homework Guide

Section	Questions
22.1	1–2, 11, 25
22.2	3–4, 12–13, 21
22.3	5, 14–15, 22, 30
22.4	6–7, 16–18, 23–24, 31, 33
22.5	8–9, 27–29
22.6	10, 19–20, 26, 32

Critical Thinking

24. The Pacific Ocean is getting smaller because of subduction that is occurring on its western edge. The Pacific Ocean plate is slowly sinking beneath Asia.
25. They are able to interpret seismic waves to learn about the composition and thickness of the different layers of Earth's interior.
26. Magma is a mixture of molten rock and gases found beneath the surface of Earth. When magma reaches the surface, it is called lava.

Analyzing Data

27. 4 minutes; 7.5 minutes
28. 3.5 minutes
29. 1000 km

Concepts in Action

30. No. The rock is now considered to be igneous.
31. Antarctica must have been much closer to the equator at the time these organisms were alive.
32. Krakatoa was a high-silica volcano. High silica volcanoes tend to be explosive and generate a lot of dust and ash that is ejected into the atmosphere. Such dust can partially block the sun's rays, impacting the overall temperature of the planet.
33. Student answers will vary but should include evidence for plate tectonics such as sea-floor spreading, the fact the continents fit together like puzzles, fossil evidence, and modern satellite tracking of continental movement.

Go Online PHSchool.com

Your students can independently test their knowledge of the chapter and print out their test results for your files.

CHAPTER 22

Assessment *(continued)*

Critical Thinking

24. **Applying Concepts** New oceanic crust is being produced in the Pacific Ocean due to a mid-ocean ridge that runs along the ocean floor. But the Pacific Ocean is not getting bigger. What must be happening in the Pacific Ocean?

25. **Inferring** How do scientists know about the structure and composition of Earth's interior?

26. **Comparing and Contrasting** What is the difference between magma and lava?

Analyzing Data

Use the graph below to answer Questions 27–29.

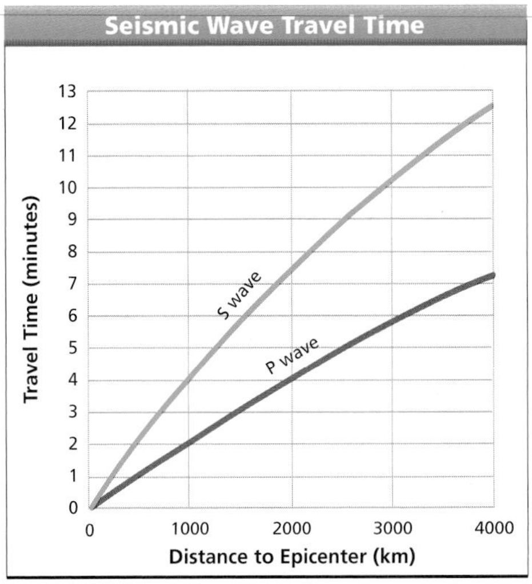
Seismic Wave Travel Time
Travel Time (minutes)
0
1
2
3
4
5
6
7
8
9
10
11
12
13
S wave
P wave
0
1000
2000
3000
4000
Distance to Epicenter (km)

27. **Using Graphs** An earthquake occurs 2000 km from seismograph station A. How much later does the first P wave arrive at the station? How much later does the first S wave arrive?

28. **Calculating** What is the difference in time between the arrivals of the first P wave and the first S wave at station A?

29. **Drawing Conclusions** The first P waves of the earthquake arrived at seismograph station B about 2 minutes before the first S waves arrived. How far is seismograph station B from the epicenter of the earthquake?

Concepts in Action

30. **Classifying** A piece of the metamorphic rock gneiss is formed when a chain of mountains is created. The pressure and temperature surrounding the rock increase so that the gneiss melts completely and then hardens again. Is the new rock still considered a metamorphic rock? Explain.

31. **Hypothesizing** The fossils of tropical plants and animals have been found in Antarctica. Using your knowledge of plate tectonics, provide a possible explanation for this observation.

32. **Applying Concepts** When the volcano Krakatoa erupted in the 1880s, the eruption released so much volcanic ash into the atmosphere that temperatures temporarily cooled worldwide. Do you think that Krakatoa's eruption involved low-silica magma or high-silica magma? Explain.

33. **Writing In Science** Imagine you had to give a presentation on plate tectonics to a group of scientists who were still skeptical about the theory. Organize your talk into sections with the main points and evidence to support them. Be convincing.

Performance-Based Assessment

Classifying Gather about a dozen different local rock and mineral samples. Classify and identify each sample. Present your findings about your collection of rocks and minerals to the class. Indicate how you identified some of the more difficult samples.

Go Online PHSchool.com

For: Self-grading assessment
Visit: PHSchool.com
Web Code: cca-3220

Performance-Based Assessment

Students should be able to identify common rocks and minerals such as granite, sandstone, quartz, mica, slate, and gneiss. They should use a rock and mineral guide to aid in their identification of various samples, and discuss how they were able to identify some less common samples.

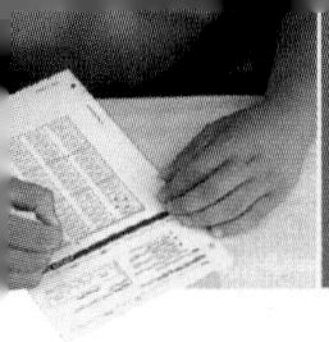

Standardized Test Prep

Test-Taking Tip

Multiple-Part Answer Choice
Some test questions list a series of possible answers labeled with Roman numerals. From the list, you must choose the combination of Roman numerals that make up a correct response. For example, the sample question lists three characteristics of one type of volcano. Before you answer, evaluate each Roman numeral separately in relation to the question. Then, determine which answer choice corresponds to the numerals you have selected.

Which of the following are characteristics of a composite volcano?
I. erupts explosively
II. made up of layers of lava and ash
III. produces only low-silica lava

(A) I only
(B) III only
(C) I and II only
(D) II and III only
(E) I, II, and III

(Answer: C)

Choose the letter that best answers the question or completes the statement.

1. In which part of the mantle would you expect temperature and pressure to be greatest?
(A) asthenosphere (B) lithosphere
(C) lower crust (D) mesosphere
(E) outer core

2. Which are examples of how a sedimentary rock can form?
I. Heat and pressure form banded layers inside a rock.
II. Magma cools and hardens beneath the surface.
III. Sediment hardens through compaction and cementation.

(A) I only (B) III only
(C) I and II only (D) II and III only
(E) I, II, and III

3. Which is NOT evidence for the theory of plate tectonics?
(A) the buildup of sedimentary rock layers
(B) the way the shapes of some continents fit together
(C) the location of Earth's volcanoes
(D) the distribution of certain fossils
(E) magnetic stripes in ocean-floor rock

4. A subduction zone, where oceanic crust sinks into the mantle, is an example of a
(A) diverging boundary.
(B) fold.
(C) transform boundary.
(D) mid-ocean ridge.
(E) converging boundary.

5. Which of these statements is (are) true of P waves?
I. They travel only across the surface.
II. The liquid iron of the outer core blocks them.
III. They are longitudinal waves.

(A) I only (B) III only
(C) I and II only (D) I and III only
(E) I, II, and III

6. Which intrusive igneous rock feature is formed when magma cuts across rock layers?
(A) batholith (B) dike
(C) caldera (D) sill
(E) shield volcano

Hardness

Mineral	Hardness
Gypsum	2
Fluorite	4
Quartz	7

7. Which test would be most helpful in identifying the three minerals in the table above?
(A) Try to scratch each one with a penny.
(B) Try to scratch each one with a diamond.
(C) Try to scratch quartz with gypsum.
(D) Try to scratch gypsum and quartz with fluorite.
(E) Try to scratch each one with a streak plate.

Standardized Test Prep

1. D **2.** B **3.** A
4. E **5.** B **6.** B
7. D

CHAPTER 23

Planning Guide

Use these planning tools
Easy Planner
Teacher Express

SECTION OBJECTIVES	STANDARDS NATIONAL (See p. T18.)	STANDARDS STATE	ACTIVITIES and LABS
23.1 Fresh Water, pp. 704–708 1 block or 2 periods **23.1.1** **Describe** the processes that make up the water cycle. **23.1.2** **Identify** the sources of fresh water on Earth.	A-1, A-2, D-1, D-2		**SE** Inquiry Activity: How Do Freezing and Thawing Affect Rocks? p. 703 L2 **SE** Quick Lab: Modeling the Water Cycle, p. 705 L2 **TE** Build Science Skills: Using Models, p. 706 L2
23.2 Weathering and Mass Movement, pp. 709–712 1 block or 2 periods **23.2.1** **Describe** the processes by which erosion wears down and carries away rock. **23.2.2** **Distinguish** between chemical and mechanical weathering and **describe** the factors that affect the rate of weathering. **23.2.3** **Explain** how the force of gravity contributes to erosion by mass movement.	B-3, D-2, D-3, F-5		**TE** Teacher Demo: Chemical Weathering, p. 710 L2
23.3 Water Shapes the Land, pp. 713–717 1 block or 2 periods **23.3.1** **Explain** how running water erodes the land. **23.3.2** **Identify** features formed by erosion and deposition due to running water. **23.3.3** **Describe** how caves and sinkholes are formed by groundwater erosion.	A-1, A-2, D-2, D-3		**SE** Quick Lab: Forming Sedimentary Layers, p. 714 L2 **SE** Exploration Lab: Modeling Erosion, p. 739 L2 **LM** Investigation 23B: Modeling Beach Erosion L1
23.4 Glaciers and Wind, pp. 719–724 1 block or 2 periods **23.4.1** **Describe** the formation and movement of glaciers and **identify** features formed by glacial erosion and deposition. **23.4.2** **Explain** the mechanisms and effects of wind erosion and deposition.	D-2, D-3		**TE** Teacher Demo: Glacial Erosion and Deposition, p. 720 L2 **LM** Investigation 23A: Constructing a Relief Map L2
23.5 The Restless Oceans, pp. 725–729 1 block or 2 periods **23.5.1** **Explain** how the properties of ocean water change with depth. **23.5.2** **Distinguish** between surface currents, deep currents, and upwelling. **23.5.3** **Explain** the processes by which waves and currents cause erosion and deposition.	D-1, D-2, D-3, E-2, F-1		**TE** Teacher Demo: Salinity of Ocean Water, p. 726 L2
23.6 Earth's History, pp. 732–738 1 block or 2 periods **23.6.1** **Distinguish** between the relative and absolute dating of rocks. **23.6.2** **Describe** the geologic time scale and what happened during the major divisions of geologic time.	A-1, A-2, B-1, C-3, D-3		

Ability Levels

- **L1** For students who need additional help
- **L2** For all students
- **L3** For students who need to be challenged

Components

SE Student Edition	**RSW** Reading & Study Workbook	**CUT** Chapter & Unit Tests	**T** Transparencies
TE Teacher's Edition	**MSPS** Math Skills & Problem Solving Workbook	**CTB** Computer Test Bank	**iT** Interactive Textbook
LM Laboratory Manual		**TP** Test Prep Resources	**P** Presentation Pro CD-ROM
PLM Probeware Lab Manual		**DC** Discovery Channel Videotapes & DVDs	**GO** Internet Resources

RESOURCES PRINT and TECHNOLOGY	SECTION ASSESSMENT
RSW Section 23.1 L1 **T** Chapter 23 Pretest L2 **P** and Section 23.1 SCIENCE NEWS GO Earth's waters L2	**SE** Section 23.1 Assessment, p. 708 **iT** Section 23.1
RSW Section 23.2 L1 **T** Section 23.2 L2 **P** Section 23.2 L2 NSTA SCiLINKS GO Weathering L2	**SE** Section 23.2 Assessment, p. 712 **iT** Section 23.2
RSW Section 23.3 L1 **T** Section 23.3 L2 **P** Section 23.3 L2 SCIENCE NEWS GO Earth's surface L2	**SE** Section 23.3 Assessment, p. 717 **iT** Section 23.3
RSW Section 23.4 L1 **T** Section 23.4 L2 **P** Section 23.4 L2 NSTA SCiLINKS GO Glaciers and landforms L2	**SE** Section 23.4 Assessment, p. 724 **iT** Section 23.4
RSW Section 23.5 L1 Discovery Channel School **DC** Under the Sea L2 **T** Section 23.5 L2 **P** Section 23.5 L2	**SE** Section 23.5 Assessment, p. 729 **iT** Section 23.5
RSW Section 23.6 L1 **RSW Math Skill** L2 **T** Section 23.6 L2 **P** Section 23.6 L2 SCIENCE NEWS GO Earth's history L2	**SE** Section 23.6 Assessment, p. 738 **iT** Section 23.6

Go Online

Go online for these Internet resources.

PHSchool.com
Web Code: cca-3230
Web Code: cch-3233

SCIENCE NEWS
Web Code: cce-3231
Web Code: cce-3233
Web Code: cce-3236

NSTA SCiLINKS
Web Code: ccn-3232
Web Code: ccn-3234

Materials for Activities and Labs

Quantities for each group

STUDENT EDITION

Inquiry Activity, p. 703
5 pieces of pumice, waterproof marker, 5 plastic freezer bags

Quick Lab, p. 705
100-mL graduated cylinder, 250-mL beaker, evaporating dish or large watch glass, hot plate, ice

Quick Lab, p. 714
clay; gravel; sand; small dish; tall, narrow jar with cover; tablespoon; clock or watch

Exploration Lab, p. 739
metric ruler, large sheet of cardboard, plastic wrap, newspaper, soil, blocks, pencil, paper cup, scissors, drinking straw, modeling clay, paper towels, small rocks

TEACHER'S EDITION

Build Science Skills, p. 706
USGS Topographic Quadrangle for your area, state and/or U.S. topographic map (if your watershed extends beyond your quadrangle), tracing paper, markers

Teacher Demo, p. 710
calcite, 1M HCl, dropper

Teacher Demo, p. 720
a block of ice, approximately 15×25×12 cm; clay, sand, gravel, and pebbles to fill a 25×30-cm baking pan 3–5 cm deep; flat metal or plastic surface such as an old cutting board or cookie sheet; freezer; sink

Teacher Demo, p. 726
1-L beaker, 100-mL beaker, mass balance, salt, water

Build Science Skills, p. 730
large sheets of paper connected to make a 1.5-m square, metric ruler, markers

Chapter Assessment

CHAPTER ASSESSMENT

SE Chapter Assessment, pp. 741–742
CUT Chapter 23 Test A, B
CTB Chapter 23
iT Chapter 23
PHSchool.com GO
Web Code: cca-3230

STANDARDIZED TEST PREP

SE Chapter 23, p. 743
TP Diagnose and Prescribe

Interactive Textbook

Interactive Textbook with assessment at PHSchool.com

CHAPTER

23 Before you teach

From the Author

Michael Wysession
Washington University

Big Ideas

The sun drives the water cycle at Earth's surface through evaporation and atmospheric circulation. When water falls to land as rain, it becomes the primary agent of the erosion and deposition of sediment, and of the surface part of the rock cycle. Water is not only responsible for the existence of life, but also for shaping Earth's surface. These two sciences are not unrelated: Much of geochemistry is actually biogeochemistry, involving single-cell organisms.

Space and Time Geologic processes occur throughout the spectrum of continuous and catastrophic events. For instance, streams run continuously, but 100-year floods may cause most of the erosion experienced by land. Similarly, Earth is constantly bombarded by meteoroids, but large catastrophic impacts have shaped the evolution of life by causing mass extinctions. The fossil record shows that single-cell life began nearly 4 billion years ago, though complex multi-cellular life began to flourish little more than a half-billion years ago.

Forces and Motion More than 1000 km^3 of water—equivalent to a cube measuring 10 km on each side—evaporate every day! The gravitational potential energy does an enormous amount of work on land surfaces when it falls as rain and flows back to the ocean. Water is the primary agent of both mechanical and chemical weathering, with streams being the dominant mechanism by which sediment is transported to oceans. Sediment settles and lithifies to form new (sedimentary) rock. Sediment is also transported by glaciers, by wind, and along shorelines. Temperature and salinity variations drive a complex system of connected ocean currents.

Matter and Energy Scientists believe that Earth formed from a pre-solar nebula at the same time as the rest of the solar system. From the analysis of meteorites, it is estimated that this occurred about 4.56 billion years ago. It is estimated that Earth heated to a nearly molten state at the time of formation, but has continuously cooled since. Earth's oceans and atmosphere formed from volcanic degassing and bombardment by comets.

Earth Science Refresher

Erosion, Weathering, and the Creation of Landscapes 23.1–23.4

Teaching students to become readers of the landscape will impart to them a visceral sense of living amongst active geologic processes. It will help change students' view of the physical world from an inert surrounding to a dynamic, living planet on whose surface humans occupy but a brief moment in geologic history.

People's surroundings are affected by erosion. While plate tectonics is the engine that drives the building up of landscapes, erosion is the process that breaks them down.

Address Misconceptions

Earth's surface features, such as mountains and valleys, have always existed in the same form as they do now. Earth features do not change over time. This misconception impedes students' ability to understand the mechanisms and effects of geologic processes on Earth. For strategies to overcome this misconception, see **Address Misconceptions** on **pages 711, 716, and 720.**

Mountains are worn down over hundreds of millions of years. The action of wind, water, and ice turns jagged peaks into rolling highlands. As the landscape changes, different rock formations erode at different rates. For example, feldspar-rich granite is weathered to clay relatively quickly in humid conditions, while quartz and basalt are more resistant to wind and water. As erosion proceeds, easily weathered rock formations can often become valleys and basins, while adjacent formations of more resistant rock become ridges and peaks.

Flatlands exist in depositional environments, where eroded sediment is deposited. The vast flatlands of the central United States were formed when large amounts of sediment were deposited in a shallow sea that filled the center of the continent in the Mesozoic Era. The limestone layers from this ancient seabed, along with even older limestone deposits in the Appalachian Mountain region, are constantly subjected to chemical weathering by the acids in groundwater. A map of caves and caverns in the United States (seen on the opposite page) reveals the location of limestone-rich formations.

Go Online PD LINKS NSTA

For: Teaching methods for Earth's surface
Visit: www.SciLinks.org/PDLinks
Web Code: ccn-2399

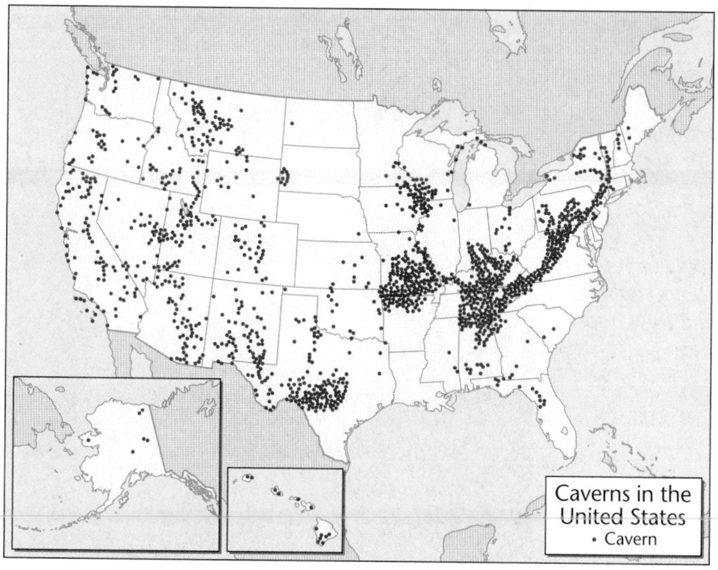
Caverns in the United States
• Cavern

The northern United States is filled with prominent examples of glacial features, such as Long Island, Cape Cod, the Great Lakes, and many of the hills and valleys from the mid-Atlantic to northern Plains states. These features were formed during the Pleistocene by glacial activity, the maximum extent of which is shown below.

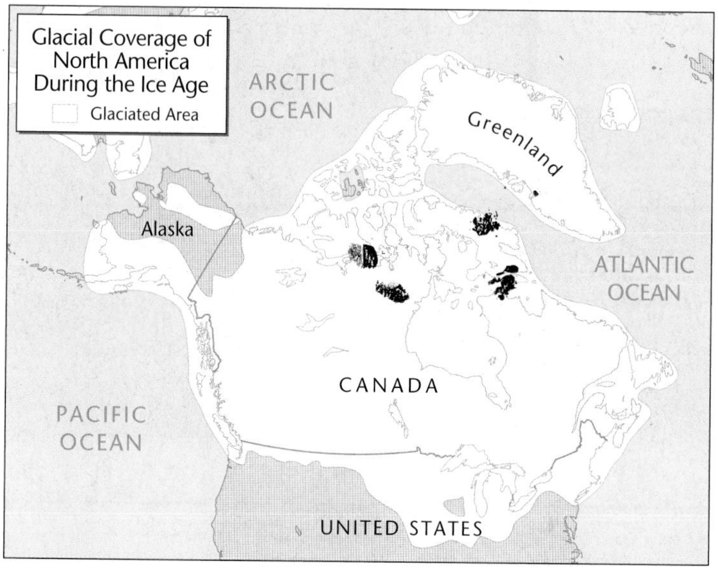
Glacial Coverage of North America During the Ice Age
Glaciated Area
ARCTIC OCEAN
Greenland
Alaska
ATLANTIC OCEAN
CANADA
PACIFIC OCEAN
UNITED STATES

Hydrothermal Vent Communities 23.5

For a long time, scientists did not think communities of organisms could exist in the extreme physical conditions of the deep sea. However, in 1977, using a remote-controlled submersible, scientists discovered a whole community of organisms, including tubeworms and giant clams, existing around a deep-sea hydrothermal vent (a volcanic feature that forms around mid-ocean ridges). These deep-sea animals exist in symbiosis with chemosynthetic bacteria that use hydrogen sulfide as raw material for synthesizing carbohydrates in a process that mimics photosynthesis.

The Geologic Time Scale 23.6

Since radioactive decay occurs at a constant rate, it can be used to record the age of rocks that are millions and even billions of years old. During radioactive decay, a "parent" isotope spontaneously loses atomic particles to form a "daughter" isotope. When a rock forms, it starts off with a known ratio of daughter and parent isotopes. As the rock ages, this ratio changes as the parent isotope is continually decaying into the daughter isotope. If you can be certain that these isotopes have not escaped from the rock since its formation (due to partial melting and recrystallization, for example), this ratio reveals the age of the rock.

Build Reading Literacy

Identify Main Ideas/Details

Paragraph and Subheading Organization

Strategy Help students become aware of text organization and help students identify key information. By identifying the main idea and supporting details under each subhead, students will be able to distinguish important and unimportant information. Before you begin, assign students the two paragraphs under the heading Erosion on p. 709 to read.

Example

1. Main Idea of a Paragraph Review with students the fact that most paragraphs have a topic sentence expressing the paragraph's main idea, while the other sentences provide supporting details.
2. Main Idea of a Subheading Guide students to make the connection that just as a paragraph has a main idea and supporting details, the text under each subheading has a main idea with supporting details carried within the paragraphs.
3. Inferring or Synthesizing a Main Idea State that it may be necessary to infer an unstated main idea by combining information carried in several paragraphs.
4. Practice Have students read through a section noting each of the subheads as they read.

See pp. 711 and 735 for scripts on how to use the identify main ideas/details strategy with students. For additional Build Reading Literacy strategies, see pp. 706, 709, 716, 719, 721, 726, and 732.

ASSESS PRIOR KNOWLEDGE

Use the Chapter Pretest below to assess students' prior knowledge. As needed, review these Science Concepts with students.

Review Science Concepts

Section 23.1 Help students recall the conditions under which water changes phases.

Section 23.2 Review acid-base and oxidation reactions. Recall the mechanisms of dissolution and precipitation.

Sections 23.3 and 23.4 Remind students that the amount of energy it takes to move an object increases with the object's mass.

Section 23.5 Review the characteristics of aqueous solutions.

Section 23.6 Review concepts related to radioactive decay, including isotopes and half-life.

CHAPTER

23 Earth's Surface

CONCEPTS in Action

How do science concepts apply to your world? Here are some questions you'll be able to answer after you read this chapter.

- Where is most of Earth's fresh water found? *(Section 23.1)*
- What are hoodoos, and how are they formed? *(Section 23.2)*
- How is a river like a dump truck? *(Section 23.3)*
- When was the Chicago region covered by a sheet of ice more than a kilometer thick? *(Section 23.4)*
- How would Earth's surface look if the oceans were drained? *(Section 23.5)*
- How can scientists determine the age of a fossil or a rock? *(Section 23.6)*

Discovery CHANNEL SCHOOL **Video Field Trip**

Under the Sea

- How do scientists explore the ocean floor? *(page 730)*

At Gooseneck State Park in Utah, the San Juan River winds through deep canyons it has cut into layers of sedimentary rocks. ▶

702 *Chapter 23*

Chapter Pretest

1. What type of phase change is described by the word *sublimation*? *(The phase change that is described by this word is from a solid to a gas.)*

2. An acid is a substance that has *(a)*
   a. more H^+ than OH^-.
   b. more OH^- than H^+.
   c. the same amount of H^+ and OH^-.
   d. no H^+ or OH^-.

3. Which of these processes causes iron to rust? *(b)*
   a. Radiation b. Oxidation
   c. Dissolution d. Evaporation

4. What is the equation that describes the relationship between kinetic energy, mass, and velocity? *($KE = \frac{1}{2}mv^2$)*

5. In a solution of seawater, is salt or water the solvent? *(Water)*

6. Which of the following best describes isotopes? *(c)*
   a. Atoms with the same number of protons, but different numbers of electrons
   b. Atoms with the same number of electrons, but different numbers of protons
   c. Atoms with the same number of protons, but different numbers of neutrons
   d. Atoms with the same number of neutrons, but different numbers of protons

Chapter Preview

Inquiry Activity

How Do Freezing and Thawing Affect Rocks?

Procedure

1. Your group will receive 5 similar rocks to examine for signs of damage. First, look closely at rock A, which was not treated. It is the control. Record your observations.
2. Examine rocks B through E. (Rock B was soaked, frozen, and thawed once; rock C was soaked, frozen, and thawed twice; rock D was soaked, frozen, and thawed three times; and rock E was soaked, frozen, and thawed four times.) Record your observations.

Think About It

1. **Observing** What effect did one freezing and thawing cycle have on rock B? How did repeated freezing and thawing cycles affect rocks C through E?
2. **Inferring** What property of water do you think causes the changes you observed?
3. **Predicting** How would frequent freezing and thawing be likely to affect rocks exposed on the tops of mountains?

Discovery Channel School **Video Field Trip**

Under the Sea

Encourage students to view the Video Field Trip "Under the Sea."

ENGAGE/EXPLORE

Inquiry Activity

How Do Freezing and Thawing Affect Rocks? L2

Purpose In this activity, students begin to describe the physical weathering of rocks by the freezing and thawing of water.

Address Misconceptions

Students may think that rocks are too hard to be damaged by the expansion of ice. To help overcome this misconception, ask students why potholes tend to appear in roads as ice melts in the spring.

Skills Focus **Observing**

Prep Time 10 minutes per day for five days

Materials 5 pieces of pumice, waterproof marker, 5 plastic freezer bags

Advance Prep Use a waterproof marker to label five rocks A through E. Soak rocks B through E in water for one hour and then seal them in plastic bags and freeze them overnight. After the rocks thaw, repeat the soaking and freezing until rock C has been frozen twice, rock D three times, and rock E four times. Pumice stones are sold in pharmacies as callus removers.

Class Time 10 minutes

Safety Students should wear only closed-toe shoes during this activity. To avoid students dropping rocks on their hands or feet, tell students to keep the rocks on the table.

Expected Outcome As rocks are repeatedly frozen and thawed, they become slightly more rough, cracked, and worn.

Think About It
1. Freezing and thawing once had little effect on rock B. Repeated freezing and thawing caused the surfaces of rocks C through E to become rough and cracked. **2.** Water expands as it freezes and melts, causing the rocks to crack. The cracks widen as more water fills the cracks and freezes. At this stage, students may not be able to describe this process precisely. **3.** The rocks would slowly break up into smaller fragments.
Visual, Group

1 FOCUS

Objectives

23.1.1 **Describe** the processes that make up the water cycle.

23.1.2 **Identify** the sources of fresh water on Earth.

Reading Focus

Build Vocabulary L2

Word-Part Analysis Direct students to consider the words *permeable* and *impermeable.* Ask, **What does the prefix *im-* mean?** *(Not)* If students have difficulty answering, have them think of word pairs they know that use *im-* (for example, *possible-impossible* or *practical-impractical*). After students have read the definitions for *permeable* and *impermeable*, ask them to define *permeate* and *permeability.*

Reading Strategy L2

a. Fresh water found underground among particles of rock and soil **b.** The continuous movement of water among the oceans, atmosphere, and land **c.** The process by which water evaporates from the leaves of plants and enters the atmosphere

2 INSTRUCT

Use Visuals L1

Figure 2 Point out that the order of the processes in the water cycle is one way (evaporation-condensation-precipitation-evaporation, and so on), but within this framework of cyclical processes, there are many different paths that water can take. For example, water can evaporate from the ocean, condense into clouds, and then precipitate right back into the ocean. Or, water evaporated from the ocean can take a more complicated route, through precipitation onto land, uptake by plants, transpiration back into the atmosphere, and so on. Ask, **Which process removes water vapor from the atmosphere?** *(Condensation)* **What paths can liquid water take to move from the hills to the ocean?** *(It can move over land in streams or as runoff or underground as groundwater.)* **Visual**

23.1 Fresh Water

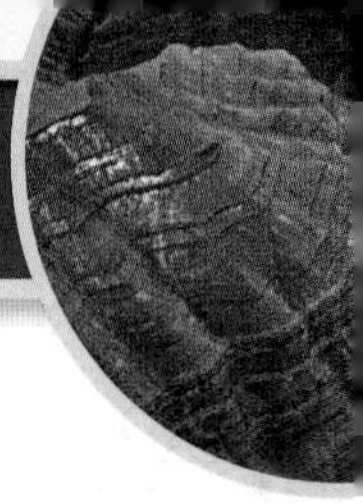

Reading Focus

Key Concepts

- What processes are involved in the water cycle?
- Where is Earth's fresh water found?

Vocabulary

- groundwater
- water cycle
- transpiration
- glacier
- runoff
- tributaries
- watershed
- saturated zone
- water table
- permeable
- aquifer
- impermeable

Reading Strategy

Building Vocabulary Make a table like the one below that includes all the vocabulary terms for the section. As you read, add definitions.

Vocabulary Term	Definition
Groundwater	a. ___?___
Water cycle	b. ___?___
Transpiration	c. ___?___

How would you describe Earth's surface? Would you mention mountains and valleys, or cities and farms? Most people would describe the landscape. But if you could look at Earth from space, you would see that most of its surface—about 71 percent— is covered with water. For this reason, Earth is sometimes called the "water planet." For billions of years, the presence of water has shaped the geology and biology of Earth's surface.

The temperature range on Earth allows water to occur in three states: liquid, solid, and gas. As shown in Figure 1, most of Earth's water is the salt water found in the oceans. Only about three percent of Earth's water is fresh. Most of this fresh water occurs as ice and snow in Earth's high mountains and polar regions. Most of Earth's liquid fresh water is in the form of **groundwater,** the water found underground within cracks and between particles of rock and soil. Smaller amounts of fresh water are found in lakes and streams and as water vapor or clouds in the atmosphere.

Earth's Water

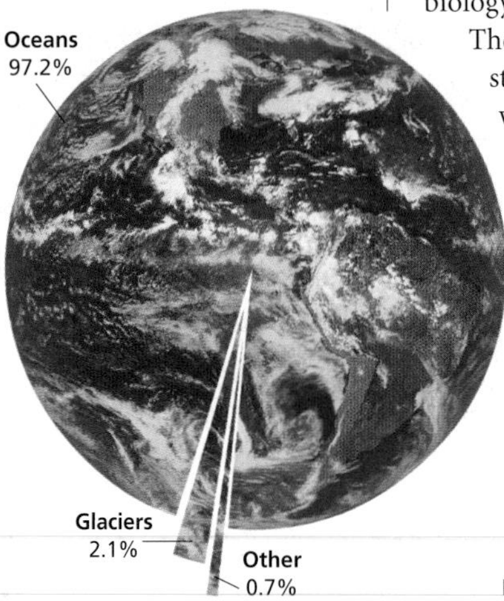

Oceans
97.2%
Glaciers
2.1%
Other
0.7%
(including water vapor, groundwater, lakes, and rivers)

Figure 1 Earth is the only planet with liquid water at its surface. **Using Graphs** ***What percentage of Earth's water can be found in glaciers?***

Section Resources

Print
- ***Reading and Study Workbook With Math Support,*** Section 23.1
- ***Transparencies,*** Chapter Pretest and Section 23.1

Technology
- ***Interactive Textbook,*** Section 23.1
- ***Presentation Pro CD-ROM,*** Chapter Pretest and Section 23.1
- ***Go Online,*** *Science News,* Earth's waters

The Water Cycle

Water moves among the oceans, atmosphere, and land in a cycle that covers the entire surface of Earth and even extends below the ground. This continuous movement of water, called the **water cycle,** is shown in Figure 2. **The water cycle is made up of several processes, including evaporation, transpiration, condensation, precipitation, and the eventual return of flowing water to the ocean.** The energy of sunlight and the force of gravity power the water cycle.

Evaporation Solar energy causes water on Earth's surface to evaporate. Recall that evaporation is the process that changes a liquid into a gas. Sunlight heats water and causes it to change into water vapor in the air. This warm, moist air expands and rises, carrying the water vapor higher into the atmosphere. Most evaporation occurs over the ocean and large lakes. Smaller amounts of water evaporate from streams, ponds, and other sources. Some water vapor also enters the atmosphere when it is released from the leaves of trees and other plants in a process called **transpiration.**

Condensation Water vapor does not stay in the atmosphere for long. As warm air rises, it expands and cools. Because colder air can hold less water vapor than warm air, condensation occurs. In condensation, water vapor forms droplets on small particles in the air. At lower temperatures, ice crystals form. Billions of these droplets or ice crystals make up clouds.

Precipitation When the water droplets or ice crystals in clouds get too heavy, gravity causes them to fall to the ground as precipitation—rain, snow, sleet, hail, or freezing rain. Worldwide, the rates of evaporation and precipitation are balanced.

The Water Cycle

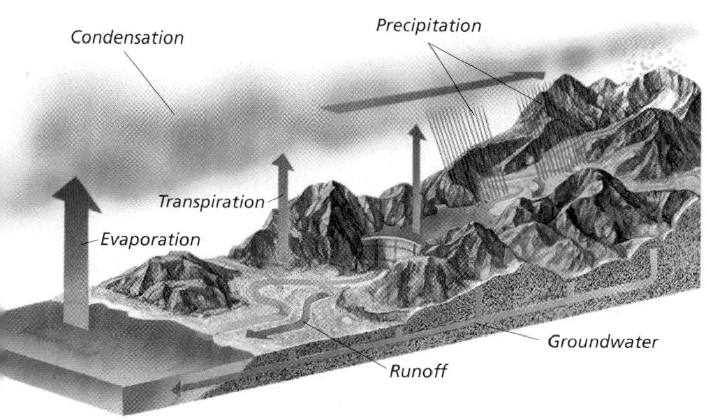

Condensation
Precipitation
Transpiration
Evaporation
Groundwater
Runoff

Figure 2 Water is constantly moving through the water cycle. **Interpreting Diagrams** ***In which step of the water cycle is liquid water converted to water vapor?***

Quick Lab

Modeling the Water Cycle

Procedure

1. Place 100 mL of water in a 250-mL beaker. Cover the beaker with an evaporating dish or a large watch glass.
2. Put the beaker on a hot plate. **CAUTION** *Be careful not to spill the water.* Fill the evaporating dish with ice.
3. Turn the hot plate on to medium. Observe the contents of the beaker for 10 minutes. Record your observations. Be sure to turn off the hot plate.

Analyze and Conclude

1. **Using Models** What source of energy drives the water cycle in your model? What energy source does this correspond to in Earth's water cycle?
2. **Using Models** What is the effect of the ice in your model? What part of the water cycle does the ice help to model?
3. **Predicting** As water evaporates, what will happen to the concentration of any substances dissolved in the water? How does evaporation affect the concentration of salts in the ocean?

The Water Cycle

Quick Lab

Modeling the Water Cycle **L2**

Objective
After completing this activity, students will be able to
- use a model water cycle to test ideas about Earth's water cycle.

Skills Focus **Using Models**

Prep Time 10 minutes

Materials 100-mL graduated cylinder, 250-mL beaker, evaporating dish or large watch glass, hot plate, ice

Class Time 15 minutes

Safety Students should wipe up any spilled water immediately to avoid slips and falls and use tongs to remove the hot equipment from the hot plate.

Expected Outcome Water will evaporate in the beaker, condense on the underside of the evaporating dish, and drip back into the bottom of the beaker.

Analyze and Conclude
1. The hot plate is the source of energy in the model. The hot plate corresponds to solar heating in Earth's water cycle.
2. The ice cools the system, causing water to condense. The ice helps to model the cooling of humid air as it rises in the atmosphere. Eventually, the water vapor cools enough to condense, forming clouds that produce precipitation.
3. As water evaporates, the concentration of any dissolved substances will increase. Evaporation alone would cause an increase in the concentration of salts in the ocean. However, the ocean also loses salt via deposition as sediment, salt spray, and removal by animals and plants. Thus, in reality, the ocean is not getting any saltier.

Visual, Group

Customize for English Language Learners

Use a Flowchart
After they have read The Water Cycle, have students work in small, heterogeneous language-level groups to complete a flowchart showing the processes of the water cycle. To help them develop their English skills, students should use their own words in the flowchart to explain the key concepts of the water cycle. Check the charts for comprehension before students continue reading the section.

Answer to . . .

Figure 1 *2.1%*

Figure 2 *Evaporation and transpiration*

Build Science Skills L2

Using Models ACTIVITY

Purpose Students will model their own watershed by creating a map of the creeks, streams, and land area that contributes runoff to their watershed.

Materials USGS Topographic Quadrangle for your area, state and/or U.S. topographic map (if your watershed extends beyond your quadrangle), tracing paper, markers

Class Time 30 minutes

Procedure Provide students with a copy of the topographic map for your quadrangle, and for your state or the United States if your watershed extends beyond your quadrangle. Have students locate the creek nearest the school on the quadrangle map. Follow the creek to the river for which it is a tributary (the creek may empty into streams before it reaches a major river). Once students find the major river to which local creeks and streams connect, have them lay the tracing paper over the applicable maps and trace all connecting streams and creeks in your watershed, and then outline the land area that contributes runoff to the river system. Students can mark the location of the school, their homes, and other major landmarks on their watershed map.

Expected Outcome Students will complete a map of their watershed.
Visual, Group

Fresh Water

Build Reading Literacy L1

Preview Refer to page **36D** in **Chapter 2**, which provides the guidelines for previewing.

Before reading Fresh Water, have students preview all of the bold subheads under the Fresh Water head. Then, ask them to list the major sources of fresh water on Earth. *(The atmosphere, streams, rivers, ponds, lakes, groundwater, glaciers, and icebergs)* **Verbal**

Go Online SCIENCE NEWS

Science News provides students with current information on Earth's waters.

Go Online SCIENCE NEWS

For: Articles on Earth's waters
Visit: PHSchool.com
Web Code: cce-3231

Completing the Cycle A single molecule of water moves between the surface and atmosphere many times. About 90 percent of the water that evaporates from the oceans falls back into the oceans. Most precipitation that falls on land quickly returns to the atmosphere through evaporation and transpiration. Much of the remaining water seeps into the soil as groundwater or becomes frozen in glaciers. A **glacier** is a large mass of moving ice and snow on land. Some water that falls on land flows into streams before it returns to the ocean.

Fresh Water

Only a small portion of the water on Earth exists as fresh water. Fresh water is relatively free of minerals and salts. **A small portion of Earth's fresh water is located in the atmosphere, streams, and lakes. Most is located in groundwater and glaciers.**

The Atmosphere A tiny percentage of Earth's fresh water is found in the atmosphere in the form of water vapor or clouds. Water enters the atmosphere by evaporation, mostly from the oceans. Water vapor stays in the atmosphere for just a short time—a few hours or a few days—before it falls to the surface as precipitation.

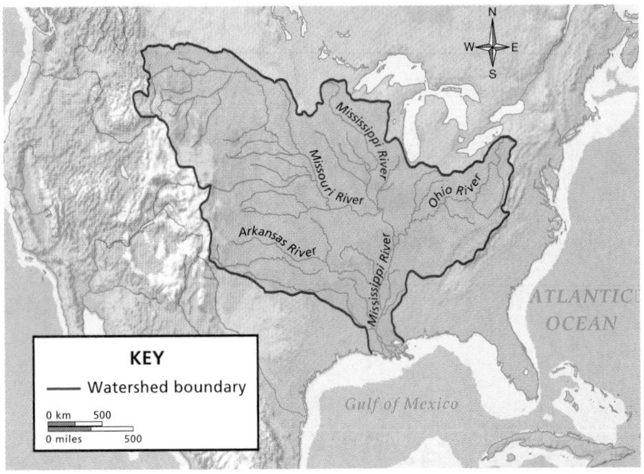

N
W
E
S
Mississippi River
Missouri River
Ohio River
Arkansas River
Mississippi River
ATLANTIC OCEAN
Gulf of Mexico
KEY
Watershed boundary
0 km 500
0 miles 500

Figure 3 The Mississippi River watershed covers most of the central United States. **Interpreting Maps** *Name two tributary rivers that flow into the Mississippi River.*

Streams and Rivers Streams and rivers contain even less fresh water than the atmosphere. However, a great deal of water passes through streams, making them very important in shaping the surface of the land.

When rain falls on land, much of it enters the ground, but some becomes runoff. **Runoff** is water that flows over Earth's surface. Runoff and some groundwater flows into streams. A stream is any natural channel of flowing water. Streams flow together to form a network, called a river system, that resembles a tree. There is no clear distinction between a large stream and a river. A major river has many smaller streams, called **tributaries,** that flow into it. Tributaries collect runoff from the surrounding land and channel it into rivers.

The area of land that contributes water to a river system is called a **watershed.** Watersheds, also called drainage basins, can be small or large. For example, the Mississippi River watershed drains most of the central United States. As you can see in Figure 3, this watershed extends from the Rocky Mountains in the west to the Appalachian Mountains in the east.

Facts and Figures

Relative Sources of Fresh Water Because water is the dominant feature on Earth, it is sometimes difficult to imagine why some areas experience water shortages. However, consider that only 2.8% of Earth's water is fresh water. Furthermore, scientists estimate that 70–75% of this fresh water is frozen in glaciers and ice caps, 20–25% is groundwater, and only 1–2% is found in lakes and rivers.

Ponds and Lakes Ponds and lakes form in depressions in the land. Lakes form in large, deep depressions. Ponds, like the one in Figure 4, form in smaller depressions and tend to be smaller and shallower than lakes. Both lakes and ponds usually drain into streams.

Reading Checkpoint *What is the difference between a pond and a lake?*

Water Beneath the Surface About a quarter of all fresh water is groundwater. Close to the surface, the pore spaces in rock and soil are filled with air. Deeper below the surface is the **saturated zone,** a region where the pore spaces are entirely filled with groundwater. The top of the saturated zone is called the **water table.** Look at Figure 5 to see the saturated zone and the water table. The shape of the water table is usually similar to the ground surface above it. Water flows slowly from high elevations of the water table to low elevations. Lakes and streams are usually found where the ground is below the water table. The level of the water table rises and falls, depending in part on the amount of rainfall. During droughts, the water table can drop significantly.

Water flows more easily through some rocks than others. A rock is **permeable** if water can easily pass through it. Rocks like sandstone and limestone are permeable. A permeable rock layer that is saturated with water is called an **aquifer.** In many parts of the world, people rely on aquifers as a source of water for drinking and for agriculture. They can withdraw water from an aquifer by drilling a well below the water table. Aquifers are refilled, or recharged, as rainwater seeps into them.

Rocks are **impermeable** if water cannot easily pass through them. Shale and unbroken granite are examples of impermeable rock. In places where an impermeable rock layer is exposed on a hillside, water may seep to the surface. Groundwater in loose rock or soil above the impermeable layer flows out of the hillside as a spring.

Figure 4 Ponds like this one form when water collects in small, shallow depressions. Many ponds support lush plant growth and animal life.

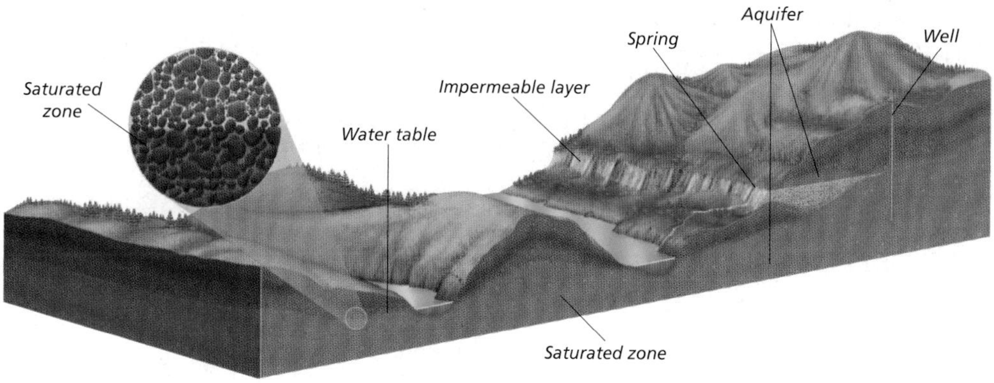
Saturated zone
Water table
Impermeable layer
Spring
Aquifer
Well
Saturated zone

Figure 5 Groundwater makes up about one quarter of all fresh water. In the saturated zone, groundwater flows in the pore spaces in underground rock. **Interpreting Diagrams** ***What is the source of the water in a spring?***

Address Misconceptions **L2**

Students may think that groundwater exists below the surface in reservoirs, similar to reservoirs above the surface where surface water is found, such as underground ponds, lakes, streams, and rivers. Explain that actually groundwater often exists in the pore spaces of rock, like water in a sponge. Have students create a Venn diagram comparing and contrasting the attributes of ground and surface water.
Verbal

Use Visuals **L1**

Figure 5 Point out that the water table extends across the entire length of the diagram. Make sure that students understand that groundwater simply refers to water underground. Where the water table intersects with the land surface, the same water can be found in lakes, ponds, swamps, and so on, and is no longer referred to as "groundwater." Ask, **What is the source of well water?** *(Groundwater)* **Why is there a spring?** *(Water in the aquifer above the impermeable layer flows onto the surface where the aquifer meets the surface.)* **Why are the ponds shown in these locations?** *(The surface elevation is below the water table, which causes the depressions to fill with water.)*
Visual

Facts and Figures

Lake Formation Some lakes are formed from tectonic processes like rifting or faulting. Most current lakes formed from the glaciers of the Ice Age. The large ice sheets that covered much of North America and Europe more than 10,000 years ago pushed down the crust, creating depressions that now form the Great Lakes and the Baltic Sea (in northern Europe). Glaciers also scoured out rock and left depressions where glacial sediment piled around giant pieces of ice. The state of Minnesota, which was covered with ice 10,000 years ago, is sometimes called the "land of ten thousand lakes."

Answer to . . .

Figure 3 *The tributaries shown on the map are the Missouri River, Ohio River, and Arkansas River.*

Figure 5 *An aquifer above an impermeable layer*

Reading Checkpoint *Ponds form in small, shallow depressions. Lakes form in larger, deeper depressions.*

Section 23.1 (continued)

3 ASSESS

Evaluate Understanding L2

Have students create a mnemonic device to remember all of the sources of fresh water on Earth, such as "Look! Seven Red Pandas Go Grandly Walking!" for lakes, streams, rivers, ponds, glaciers, groundwater, and water vapor.

Reteach L1

Use Figure 2 to review the processes by which water moves from one reservoir to another in the water cycle.

Connecting Concepts

According to Archimedes' principle, the buoyant force on an object equals the weight of the fluid displaced by the object. An iceberg is composed of frozen fresh water, which is slightly less dense than the liquid salt water of the ocean. Because the densities of ice and salt water are so close, an iceberg is pushed up only a small amount by the buoyant force of the ocean. Nearly 90% of the iceberg remains submerged.

Interactive Textbook If your class subscribes to the Interactive Textbook, use it to review key concepts in Section 23.1.

Figure 6 Icebergs such as this one are formed when a piece of a glacier breaks off into the ocean. Although this iceberg may drift thousands of kilometers in the salty ocean, it is made of fresh water.

Glaciers and Icebergs Glaciers form in areas where more snow falls than melts each year. As snows build up, the weight of the snow presses on the layers below, changing them to ice. When the weight of the snow is great enough, glaciers begin to flow slowly downhill. Ice is added at the top of the glacier through snowfall. Ice is removed from the glacier by melting, sublimation, and the formation of icebergs. Recall that sublimation is the process of converting a solid directly into a gas.

Icebergs are large pieces of ice that break off when a glacier reaches the ocean. Many icebergs drift great distances from glaciers each year, creating a hazard to ships and ocean drilling platforms. Icebergs eventually melt as they drift into warmer water.

Section 23.1 Assessment

Reviewing Concepts

1. What are five major processes that move water through Earth's environment?
2. Identify five places where fresh water can be found on Earth. In what two places is most of it located?
3. What energy source powers the water cycle?
4. Starting with runoff, describe the flow of water through a watershed.
5. What is the water table?
6. How do permeable and impermeable rock layers contribute to the formation of a spring?
7. How do icebergs form?

Critical Thinking

8. **Applying Concepts** What might cause a well that draws water from an aquifer to run dry? In your answer, refer to the parts of the groundwater system.
9. **Predicting** How would the path of a water molecule moving through the water cycle be different in Antarctica than in Brazil?

Connecting Concepts

Buoyancy Use what you learned about buoyancy in Section 13.3 to explain why icebergs float very low in ocean water.

Section 23.1 Assessment

1. Evaporation, condensation, precipitation, transpiration, and return of flowing water to the ocean
2. Glaciers, groundwater, water vapor, lakes, ponds, rivers, streams. Most fresh water is found as glacier ice or as groundwater.
3. Energy from sunlight
4. Runoff flows over Earth's surface into streams. Streams flow together into a river system (a river and its tributaries).
5. The top of the saturated zone
6. When an impermeable rock layer is exposed on a hillside, groundwater in permeable rock or soil above it may flow out of the ground as a spring.
7. A glacier flows into the ocean, and pieces of the glacier break off and float away.
8. A well would run dry if the water table dropped below the bottom of the well. This could occur if there was a drought or if people withdrew too much water from an aquifer.
9. In Antarctica, precipitation would likely fall in the form of snow, much of which would turn into ice on top of glaciers. The glaciers flow slowly to the ocean, where they break off as icebergs, eventually melting to become part of the ocean. In Brazil, precipitation would likely fall as rain, evaporate or flow through rivers or groundwater, and then flow into the ocean. Because it is typically much warmer in Brazil than Antarctica, the rate of evaporation would be much higher in Brazil.

23.2 Weathering and Mass Movement

Reading Focus

Key Concepts
- What are the agents of erosion?
- What causes mechanical and chemical weathering?
- What factors affect the rate at which rocks weather?
- What force causes mass movement?

Vocabulary
- erosion
- weathering
- mechanical weathering
- abrasion
- chemical weathering
- mass movement

Reading Strategy
Concept Map As you read, draw a concept map showing the key factors that affect the rate of weathering.

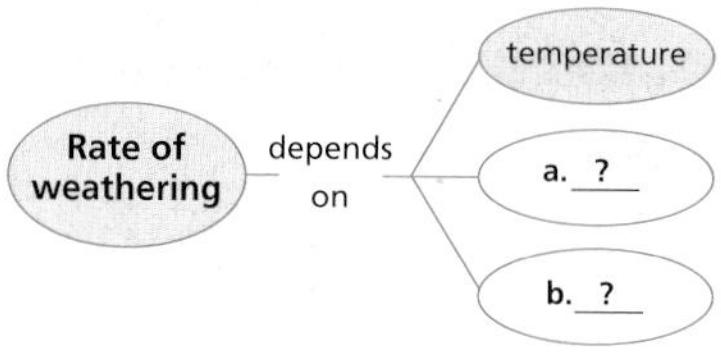

Rate of weathering
depends on
temperature
a. ?
b. ?

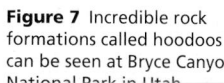

Imagine walking through a pine forest in southern Utah. Suddenly your trail twists, leading you to the edge of a canyon. The curved end of the canyon is shaped like a huge football stadium. But instead of cheering sports fans, this stadium is full of strange columns of rock in yellow, brilliant orange, and rusty red. You are looking at Bryce Canyon, which is famous for its fantastic rock formations, called "hoodoos." The hoodoos are made of different types of sedimentary rock.

Millions of years ago, what is now Bryce Canyon was solid layers of rock. Very slowly, much of this rock was broken down and worn away until only the hoodoos were left standing.

Erosion

Bryce Canyon formed by **erosion,** the process that wears down and carries away rock and soil. Erosion cuts canyons through solid rock and wears away the cliffs above beaches.

Erosion is the destructive process that has shaped Earth's surface over hundreds of millions of years. **Erosion acts through weathering, the force of gravity, and through the movement of streams, groundwater, glaciers, wind, and waves.** Over time, erosion breaks down even the tallest mountains. The end product of erosion is sediment. Recall that sediment is composed of particles of rock and soil and the remains of living things.

Figure 7 Incredible rock formations called hoodoos can be seen at Bryce Canyon National Park in Utah.

Section Resources

Print
- ***Reading and Study Workbook With Math Support,*** Section 23.2
- ***Transparencies,*** Section 23.2

Technology
- ***Interactive Textbook,*** Section 23.2
- ***Presentation Pro CD-ROM,*** Section 23.2
- ***Go Online,*** NSTA SciLinks, Weathering

Section 23.2

1 FOCUS

Objectives
23.2.1 **Describe** the processes by which erosion wears down and carries away rock.
23.2.2 **Distinguish** between chemical and mechanical weathering and **describe** the factors that affect the rate of weathering.
23.2.3 **Explain** how the force of gravity contributes to erosion by mass movement.

Reading Focus

Build Vocabulary L2

Venn Diagram Have students use a Venn diagram to compare chemical and mechanical weathering. Instruct students to create the diagram while they read Mechanical Weathering and Chemical Weathering, pp. 710–711. After they have completed the diagrams, have students work in groups to derive concise definitions of *mechanical weathering* and *chemical weathering.*

Reading Strategy L2

a. Availability of water **b.** Type of rock

2 INSTRUCT

Erosion

FYI

Although erosion is often narrowly defined as the transportation of weathered rock to distant areas, this text defines erosion more broadly as the process that wears down and carries away rock and soil. This conforms with the definition of erosion in the *Dictionary of the American Geological Institute.*

Build Reading Literacy L1

Predict Refer to page **66D** in **Chapter 3**, which provides the guidelines for predicting.

Before students begin reading Erosion, tell them to examine the picture of Bryce Canyon in Figure 7. Ask students to make a written prediction about how this landscape was formed. After they read Erosion, have students write a response to their prediction, correcting any misconceptions and adding details.
Visual, Verbal

Weathering

Teacher Demo

Chemical Weathering L2

Purpose Students observe how rock can be broken down by a chemical reaction.

Materials calcite, 1M HCl, dropper

Procedure Tell students that calcite is particularly susceptible to chemical weathering by acidic solutions such as rain. Explain that rain contains sulfuric and nitric acids, and can be strongly acidic in areas of heavy pollution. Buildings and other structures made of marble and other calcite-containing stone exhibit severe chemical weathering over a period of years in regions where acid rain is a common problem. Ask, **What do you think will happen when I drip acid on the rock?** *(The calcite crystals will react with the acid.)* Drip a few drops on the rock, being sure to hit calcite crystals.

Expected Outcome The calcite crystals will fizz and bubble.
Visual

Go Online NSTA SCILINKS

Download a worksheet on weathering for students to complete, and find additional teacher support from NSTA SciLinks.

Weathering

Erosion starts with weathering. **Weathering** is the process by which rocks are chemically altered or physically broken down into fragments at or near Earth's surface. **There are two forms of weathering: mechanical and chemical. They cause rocks to disintegrate or decompose.**

Mechanical Weathering Under the right conditions, even the hardest rock can be broken into smaller pieces. **Mechanical weathering** is the process of physically breaking rock into smaller fragments. Mechanical weathering occurs through frost wedging, abrasion, growth of plant roots, and other processes.

The most common form of mechanical weathering is frost wedging, shown in Figure 8. When water freezes to form ice, the water expands. This expansion pries open any cracks that the water has seeped into. Frost wedging is an important cause of weathering in mountains, where water often freezes at night and melts during the day. Frost wedging pries rocks apart a little bit every night. If you live in a region that has cold winters, you may see how frost wedging damages roads. Many of the potholes that form in roads during winter are the result in part of frost wedging.

Another form of mechanical weathering, called **abrasion,** occurs when rocks scrape or grind against one another. For example, abrasion occurs when sand carried by water or wind causes bits of rock to break off as if they were being sandblasted.

Mechanical weathering also occurs in other ways. Plant roots can grow into cracks in a rock. Roots exert a powerful force that can slowly pry the rock apart. In another form of weathering, erosion removes material from the surface of a mass of rock, reducing pressure on the rock that remains. This release of pressure allows the rock to expand, causing the outside of the rock to crack and flake off like layers of pastry.

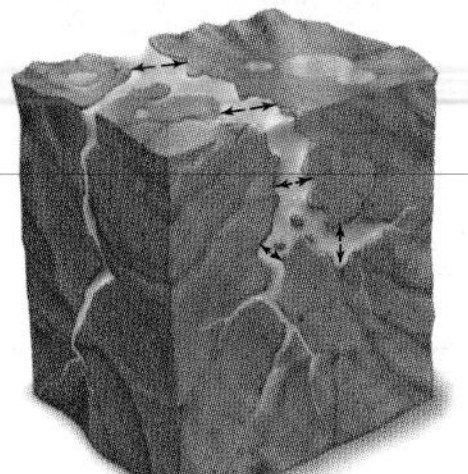

Figure 8 When water expands to form ice, it can pry open cracks in rock. This is called frost wedging. **Classifying** ***Is frost wedging a form of mechanical weathering or chemical weathering?***

Go Online NSTA SCILINKS

For: Links on weathering
Visit: www.SciLinks.org
Web Code: ccn-3232

Chemical Weathering **Chemical weathering** is a process in which rock is broken down by chemical reactions. Chemical weathering involves chemical reactions that dissolve the minerals making up rock or change them into new minerals. Over time, the effects of chemical weathering can be dramatic. Pits or holes may form in the rock surface. Eventually, the rock crumbles and disintegrates.

Water is the main agent of chemical weathering. Water is an effective solvent. All minerals dissolve in water, though most do so very slowly.

Customize for Inclusion Students

Gifted
Have students collect rain samples from around their homes or the school, and use litmus paper or a pH meter to measure the pH of the rain in your area. Tell students to make sure they place their collection containers away from buildings, trees, or other structures that the rain might run off of before entering the container. While you are covering chemical weathering, have students report to the class on the pH of the rain in your area.

Chemical weathering also occurs because rain is slightly acidic. Water and carbon dioxide naturally combine to form carbonic acid. The carbonic acid in rainwater dissolves many minerals, such as calcite. The statue of the lion in Figure 9 has been weathered by carbonic acid in rain. Carbonic acid and water react with other minerals, such as the feldspar in granite, to produce clay minerals.

Another type of chemical weathering, the rusting of minerals that are rich in iron, involves oxidation. This results in the formation of new minerals that often have a red or brown color, such as the rusted bicycle in Figure 9.

Reading Checkpoint *What is the main agent of chemical weathering?*

A
B

Figure 9 In chemical weathering, rock is broken down by chemical reactions. **A** One form of chemical weathering occurs through oxidation. Iron-rich minerals become rusted like this old bicycle. **B** Chemical weathering also occurs when rainwater dissolves or reacts with the minerals in rocks, as with this statue of a lion.

Rates of Weathering

The rate at which mechanical and chemical weathering take place depends on three main factors: temperature, the availability of water, and the type of rock. Chemical weathering occurs more rapidly in places with high temperatures and abundant rainfall. These conditions generally speed up chemical reactions. For example, granite weathers slowly in cool regions, but more rapidly in regions that are hot and wet. Mechanical weathering occurs faster in places where temperature conditions frequently alternate between freezing and thawing.

The rate of weathering also depends upon the kind of rock that is exposed at the surface. Some rocks, such as limestone and marble, undergo rapid chemical weathering. These rocks are composed primarily of calcite, a mineral that reacts readily with carbonic acid. One of the tombstones in Figure 10 shows the effects of chemical weathering on marble. In contrast, the other tombstone is made of slate, which is composed of minerals, such as quartz and mica, that are much more resistant to chemical weathering than calcite.

Figure 10 Different rocks weather at different rates. Even though the slate tombstone (right) is older, it is much less weathered than the marble one (left). **Inferring** ***What type of weathering was likely responsible for wearing away the lettering on the marble tombstone?***

Rates of Weathering

Address Misconceptions **L2**

A common misconception is that soil has always existed in its present form, rather than being a product of weathering rocks and decaying organic matter. The weathering of rocks produces sediment, one of the main components of soil. Soil-producing sediment is often created right underneath people's feet as rain percolates down into the ground and bedrock undergoes chemical weathering. In addition to sediment, soil also contains both living and decomposing organisms. Encourage students to look for examples of weathering rock and soil formation in their outdoor activities, or bring a heavily weathered rock to class for students to examine. Ask, **Why does soil often contain tiny stone fragments and quartz crystals (sand)?** *(As rocks undergo weathering, more reactive minerals break down first, and the more stable minerals, such as quartz, are left behind.)* **Why is soil different in different regions?** *(Both the bedrock and organic material that produce soil are different in different regions.)*
Logical

Build Reading Literacy **L1**

Identify Main Ideas/Details Refer to page **702D** in this chapter, which provides the guidelines for identifying main ideas and details.

Have students read the main topic sentence (in bold) of Rates of Weathering. Then, ask, **Given this topic sentence, what are the main ideas that you should look for in this selection?** *(How temperature, availability of water, and the type of rock affect the rate of chemical and mechanical weathering)* After reading Rates of Weathering, have students work in groups to create index cards with brief explanations of how these factors affect the rate of weathering.
Verbal, Group

Facts and Figures

Humans as Agents of Erosion Many human activities cause or accelerate weathering. Industrial activity may cause highly acidic rain that results in more rapid chemical weathering. Humans also carry out mechanical weathering by leveling ground for roads and cities, and by strip mining for mineral resources. The paving of large tracts of land causes more severe erosion of adjacent unpaved areas due to the sheeting action of water. Soil erosion is a major problem in agricultural areas. It was agricultural practices that led to the great Dust Bowl of the 1920s. Deforestation also contributes to erosion, including devastating mass movements such as landslides.

Answer to . . .

Figure 8 *Mechanical weathering*

Figure 10 *Chemical weathering from acidic precipitation*

Reading Checkpoint *Water*

Section 23.2 (continued)

Mass Movement

Build Science Skills L2

Relating Cause and Effect Have students work in groups to create a poster showing the cause and effect of each type of mass movement described on p. 712. Posters should include a flowchart that describes the conditions during which the events occur. **Portfolio**

Use Visuals L1

Figure 11 Ask, **In the top diagram, what evidence can you see that creep is occurring?** *(Displacement of a fence, road, and electric lines)* **Visual**

3 ASSESS

Evaluate Understanding L2

Have students create flowcharts describing the processes that produced the formations in Figure 7.

Reteach L2

Use Figures 8 and 9 to review the differences between chemical and mechanical weathering.

Connecting Concepts

Cracked sidewalk: physical change; rusty nail: chemical change; hard-to-read marble tombstone: chemical change

Interactive Textbook If your class subscribes to the Interactive Textbook, use it to review key concepts in Section 23.2.

Answer to . . .

Figure 11 *The greater the slope of the hillside, the greater the amount of creep or slumping is.*

Figure 11 Creep can be caused by the alternate freezing and thawing of water in soil. Slumping often occurs when soil that is rich in clay is soaked by water. ***Predicting How would the steepness of the slope of the hillside affect the amount of creep or slumping?***

Creep

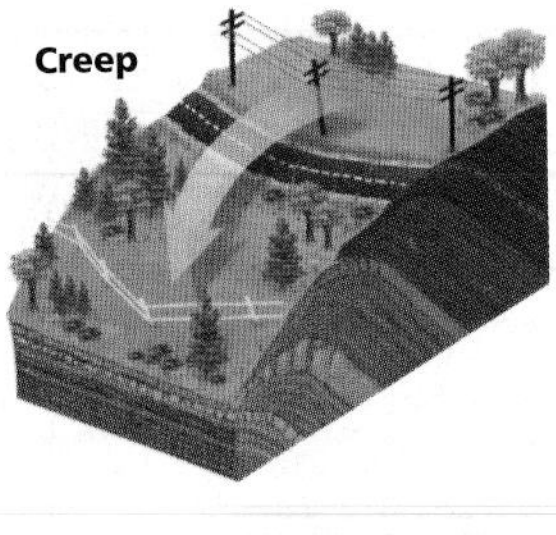

Slumping

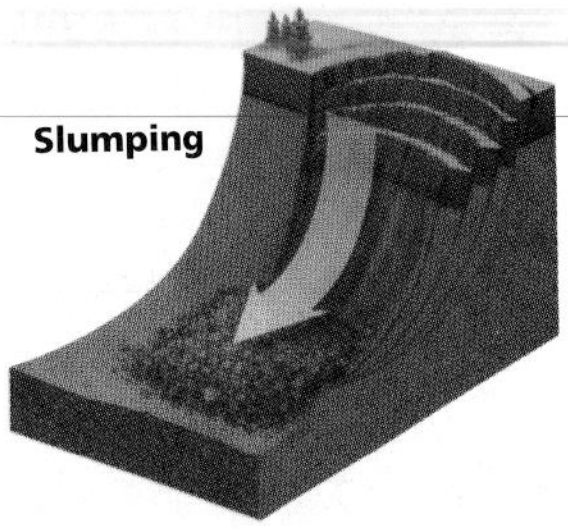

Mass Movement

Once weathering loosens particles of rock, the particles, or sediment, do not stay in the same place. **Mass movement** is the downward movement of rock and soil due to gravity. **Through the process of mass movement, gravity moves loose material down a slope.** There are several types of mass movement.

Landslides The rapid movement of large amounts of rock and soil is a landslide. Landslides often occur after heavy rains or after earthquakes loosen materials on a steep slope. Landslides that occur on the sides of mountains can destroy entire towns.

Mudflows Rapid mass movements of soil and other sediment mixed with water are called mudflows. Mudflows tend to occur in areas where fine sediment has collected in thick layers. When it rains, water loosens the sediment and increases its weight. After a heavy rainfall, the sediment mixed with water washes down the slope.

Creep Creep occurs when soil gradually moves down a slope. Creep often occurs because of the formation of ice. Each time the ground freezes, the soil expands outward. When the ground thaws, the soil moves a small distance downhill. Creep, shown in Figure 11, happens so slowly that it's hard to notice. But over time the results of creep become evident.

Slumping Slumping occurs when weak layers of soil or rock suddenly move downslope as a single unit. Gravity acting on water-saturated soil and rock causes slumping. Slumping often leaves a curved scar.

Section 23.2 Assessment

Reviewing Concepts

1. What is erosion? List five agents of erosion.
2. How are mechanical weathering and chemical weathering similar? How do they differ?
3. What three factors are most significant in determining the rate at which rocks weather?
4. How does gravity cause erosion?
5. Identify three processes that cause mechanical weathering.
6. What is the role of rainwater in chemical weathering?

Critical Thinking

7. **Predicting** Would you expect chemical weathering to occur more rapidly in a desert or in a rainforest? Explain.
8. **Relating Cause and Effect** What conditions can cause landslides and mudflows?

Connecting Concepts

Chemical and Physical Changes Use what you learned in Chapter 2 to classify each of the following as a chemical or physical change: a cracked sidewalk, a rusty nail, a hard-to-read marble tombstone.

Section 23.2 Assessment

1. Erosion is the process that wears away rock and soil. Agents of erosion include weathering, the force of gravity, and the movement of streams, groundwater, glaciers, wind, and waves.
2. Both mechanical and chemical weathering are forms of erosion that cause rocks to disintegrate. Mechanical weathering breaks rocks into smaller pieces through physical processes like frost wedging and abrasion. Chemical weathering occurs through chemical reactions that dissolve rock or convert existing minerals into new minerals.
3. Temperature, the availability of water, and the type of rock involved
4. Gravity causes erosion through mass movement, which is the movement of rock and soil down a slope.
5. Examples include frost wedging, abrasion, plant roots that pry a rock apart, and release of pressure from erosion of surface material.
6. Rainwater is acidic and dissolves many minerals. Rainwater also reacts with some minerals to change them into different minerals.
7. In a rainforest. The greater availability of water in a rainforest would cause higher rates of chemical weathering.
8. Heavy rains can loosen sediment and increase its weight, increasing the likelihood of a landslide or mudflow. An earthquake can also cause these types of mass movement.

23.3 Water Shapes the Land

Reading Focus

Key Concepts

- What is the most important factor influencing the ability of a stream to cause erosion?
- What features are formed by surface water erosion?
- What features are deposited by running water?
- What causes groundwater erosion?

Vocabulary

- deposition
- saltation
- flood plain
- meander
- oxbow lake
- alluvial fan
- delta
- stalactite
- stalagmite
- sinkhole

Reading Strategy

Concept Map As you read, draw a concept map showing how moving water shapes the land. Begin with the map below.

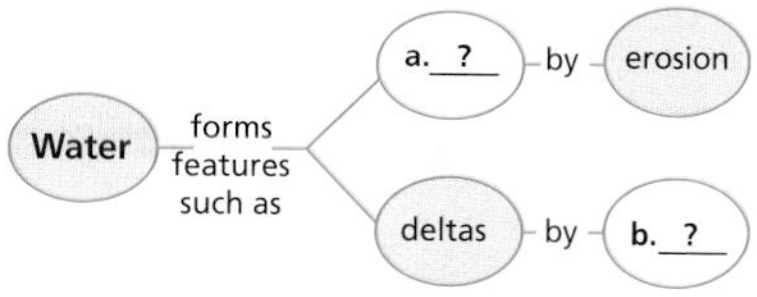

Water
forms features such as
a. ?
by
erosion
deltas
by
b. ?

The Mississippi River is like an enormous convoy of dump trucks. Every year it carries more than 300 million tons of sediment to the ocean. This amount of sediment would fill a line of dump trucks wrapped nearly three times around Earth! This sediment has been washed away from the surface of the land. As mountains are made by volcanoes or the motions of tectonic plates, erosion begins to wear them away.

The primary force of erosion is gravity. Gravity pulls sediment and water downhill. The end result of erosion is the deposition of sediment. **Deposition** is the process in which sediment is laid down in new locations.

Most sediment is moved and deposited by flowing water. Flowing water is the major agent of erosion responsible for shaping Earth's surface. Everywhere you look on land, there are features formed by water erosion and deposition.

Figure 12 Streams play an important role in the process of erosion. This stream has cut a deep channel in the soil. The stream banks collapse in mass movement. The soil is then carried away by the stream as sediment.

Section Resources

Print
- ***Laboratory Manual,*** Investigation 23B
- ***Reading and Study Workbook With Math Support,*** Section 23.3
- ***Transparencies,*** Section 23.3

Technology
- ***Interactive Textbook,*** Section 23.3
- ***Presentation Pro CD-ROM,*** Section 23.3
- ***Go Online,*** *Science News,* Earth's surface

Section 23.3

1 FOCUS

Objectives

23.3.1 **Explain** how running water erodes the land.

23.3.2 **Identify** features formed by erosion and deposition due to running water.

23.3.3 **Describe** how caves and sinkholes are formed by groundwater erosion.

Reading Focus

Build Vocabulary L2

Compare/Contrast Table Have students work in groups to make compare/contrast tables with the headings Features Formed by Erosion and Features Formed by Deposition. Ask them to sort the words from the vocabulary list into the appropriate columns.

Reading Strategy L2

a. Any of the following: V-shaped valleys, waterfalls, flood plains, meanders, oxbow lakes **b.** Deposition

2 INSTRUCT

Running Water Erodes the Land

Quick Lab

Forming Sedimentary Layers L2

Objective
After completing this activity, students will be able to
- describe the formation of sedimentary layers under water.

Skills Focus Using Models

Prep Time 15 minutes

Advance Prep Sand, clay, and gravel can be obtained from a landscaper, garden supply shop, or home repair store. Olive jars are ideal for this lab. Graduated cylinders with rubber stoppers can be used if the stoppers make a watertight seal.

Class Time 20 minutes

Expected Outcome Gravel settles first, then sand, and finally clay. Some clay remains suspended in the water, making the water cloudy.

Analyze and Conclude
1. Gravel, sand, and clay
2. Some clay remained suspended in the water, making the water cloudy.
3. Water in a lake. It was not moving quickly and it contained suspended particles.
4. The separation of sand and clay would have been less distinct. This would occur in a turbulent, fast-moving river such as one with rapids.
Kinesthetic

For Enrichment L3

Use a soil-sampling tube or a section of pipe to collect a core sample of sediment from a riverbed or the bottom of a lake. Students can use a hand lens or microscope to examine the particle sizes in each layer and determine their distribution. Variation in particle size in these layers may reflect seasonal or historical changes in the speed or volume of the water from which the sediment was deposited. Students should wear safety goggles, lab aprons, and plastic gloves during this activity.
Kinesthetic

Quick Lab

Forming Sedimentary Layers

Materials

clay; gravel; sand; small dish; tall, narrow jar with cover; tablespoon; clock or watch

Procedure

1. Crumble the clay into a fine powder over a small dish.
2. Fill the jar three quarters full of water. Add one spoonful each of gravel, sand, and clay.
3. Put the cover on the jar tightly and invert the jar several times. Then, place the jar on a flat surface and record the time.
4. For 5 minutes, observe the layers of sediment as they pile up on the bottom of the jar. Record what you observe.
5. Observe the appearance of the water in the jar. Record your observations.

Analyze and Conclude

1. **Observing** In what order did the sediment layers form?
2. **Inferring** Why did the water look the way it did after the sediment layers formed?
3. **Using Models** Was the water in the jar similar to the water in a lake or the water in a fast-moving river? Explain your answer.
4. **Predicting** Would the order of the sediment layers be different if you had stirred the water as the layers accumulated? Under what circumstances would this happen in nature?

Running Water Erodes the Land

Water from rain or melted snow may soak into the ground, evaporate, or flow over the surface as runoff. Erosion begins when runoff carries small particles of soil downhill. Runoff gradually forms small channels in the soil. These channels join together to form larger channels called gullies. As water flows down a hillside through gullies, the water can erode large quantities of soil. Gullies, in turn, flow together to form streams. Unlike gullies, streams flow year-round, except in dry areas or during droughts.

Streams continue the process of erosion by transporting sediment, as shown in Figure 13. Most of the sediment in streams is carried in suspension, in which tiny sediment grains move along with the water. Larger particles of sediment slide, roll, or bounce along the bottom of a stream. The process of particles bouncing along a stream bottom is called **saltation.** During floods, a fast-moving river can move boulders the size of a small car. A large amount of sediment is also carried in solution. Faster streams carry more sediment, which increases abrasion.

Figure 13 Small grains of sediment are carried in suspension by a stream. Large grains move by sliding or rolling, and medium-sized grains move by saltation. Material is also carried in dissolved form. **Predicting** ***How might the speed of the stream affect the amount and size of particles it can carry?***

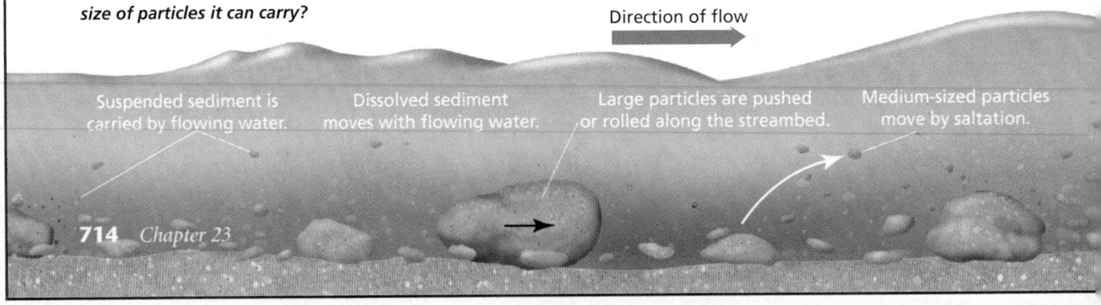
Direction of flow
Suspended sediment is carried by flowing water.
Dissolved sediment moves with flowing water.
Large particles are pushed or rolled along the streambed.
Medium-sized particles move by saltation.

Customize for English Language Learners

Use Flowcharts
Have students work in groups to create flowcharts describing the formation of alluvial fans and deltas. As an extension, students could also create flowcharts for some or all of the features formed by water erosion, wind erosion, and wind deposition. Students should use their own words and/or drawings in the flowcharts.

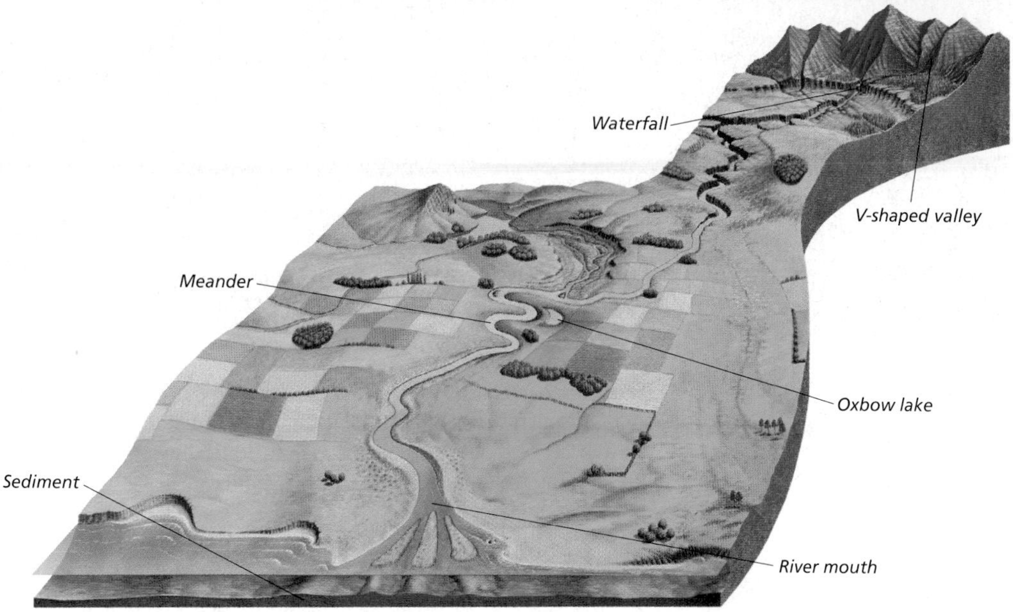
Waterfall
V-shaped valley
Meander
Oxbow lake
Sediment
River mouth

Figure 14 As a river winds its way from the mountains to the ocean, it changes the surrounding landscape through erosion and deposition.
Comparing and Contrasting ***Which features formed by river erosion typically form near a river's source?***

A stream's ability to erode depends mainly on its speed. The water in a mountain stream moves quickly because it is flowing down a steep slope. Fast streams carry more sediment than slow streams of equal size. Fast streams can also carry large sediment grains. As a stream flows toward the sea, its slope decreases. Because the stream is moving slower, larger sediments settle on the stream bottom.

Features Formed by Water Erosion

Erosion by flowing water reshapes entire watersheds—all the land along and between streams and rivers. **Water erosion forms V-shaped valleys, waterfalls, meanders, and oxbow lakes.** Figure 14 shows the features formed along the course of a river.

V-Shaped Valleys Near a stream's source, the stream flows fast as it plunges down steep slopes. As a stream erodes the rock of its streambed, it causes the valley's sides to become steeper. Mass movement on the stream slopes causes a V-shaped valley with sharply angled sides to form.

V-shaped valleys often contain rapids and waterfalls. A waterfall may develop where a stream crosses rock layers that differ in hardness. The harder layers resist erosion, forming the top of the waterfall. The softer rock layers downstream are worn away, leaving the cliff over which the waterfall tumbles.

Reading Checkpoint *How do waterfalls form?*

Go Online SCIENCE NEWS

For: Articles on Earth's surface: weathering, erosion, and deposition
Visit: PHSchool.com
Web Code: cce-3233

Features Formed by Water Erosion

Use Visuals **L1**

Figure 14 Explain that, as the streams cut down into the rock, the V-shaped valley slopes become steeper. When the valleys become very steep, waterfalls form or mass movement can occur, and rock and soil falls into the stream in the form of landslides or slumps. Once the rock and soil falls into the water, it is quickly washed downstream. When a river flows across a flat area, the V-shaped valley may be very broad and hard to recognize. The floor of the valley is called the floodplain. **At what location is the river most able to carry large rocks?** *(In the mountains)* **What is the source of much of the sediment being deposited on the flood plain?** *(The mountains shown in the background)* **What feature will result from the buildup of sediment where the river flows into the ocean?** *(A delta)*
Visual

Go Online SCIENCE NEWS

Science News provides students with current information on Earth's surface: weathering, erosion, and deposition.

Facts and Figures

Great Waterfalls The world's tallest waterfall is Angel Falls, Venezuela, at an amazing height of 979 m, almost a kilometer! Yosemite Falls is the tallest waterfall in the United States, falling an impressive 739 m.

Answer to . . .

Figure 13 *The greater the speed of a stream, the more kinetic energy it possesses and the larger the amount and size of particles it can carry.*

Figure 14 *V-shaped valleys and waterfalls*

Reading Checkpoint *Waterfalls may form where a river crosses rock layers of different hardnesses. The harder layers of rock resist erosion, forming the top of the waterfall. The softer layers of rock downstream are eroded, creating a cliff over which the waterfall tumbles.*

Build Reading Literacy **L1**

Visualize Refer to page **354D** in **Chapter 12**, which provides the guidelines for visualizing.

Instruct students to close their eyes and form mental pictures as you read Flood Plains. Read aloud to the students, going slowly so that they have time to form mental images of the processes you are describing. Then, tell the students to read the passage again by themselves and recreate the mental images as they read. Explain that visualizing the text as they read will be particularly useful throughout the next few pages, which detail the processes by which landforms are created by erosion and deposition.
Intrapersonal, Visual

Address Misconceptions **L2**

A common misconception among students is that Earth's features, such as mountains, do not change. A related misconception is that any changes that occur are sudden and catastrophic, resulting in the complete destruction of an old feature or the sudden creation of a new feature. The erosion of mountain valleys by running water is an ideal context in which to address this misconception. Explain that erosion is a slow, constant process that wears down old landforms. New landforms are created through erosion and deposition, often over thousands of years.
Verbal

Features Formed by Water Deposition

Build Science Skills **L2**

Inferring Bring a variety of river rocks into class. Have students work in groups to make inferences about the geologic history of the rocks. Explain that they should use what they have learned about the formation of rocks and the rock cycle to describe the history of each rock from its formation to its erosion and deposition. Have students create a flowchart for each rock's history.
Logical, Kinesthetic

Figure 15 Rivers often form winding meanders across their flood plain. An oxbow lake formed by the Big Sioux River near Westfield, Iowa, is shown.

Flood Plains Where a river or stream crosses gently sloping land, a flood plain forms. A **flood plain** is the flat area along a stream that is entirely covered only during times of flood. As a river flows across its flood plain, it deposits sediment, making the flood plain flat. Over time, this sediment builds up into long, low ridges called natural levees. These natural levees help prevent a river from spilling over its banks. During very large floods, however, a river may overflow its levees and erosion may further widen the valley.

Where a river curves slightly, the water on the outside of the curve moves more rapidly than the water on the inside. Fast-moving water causes more erosion. Therefore, the river tends to remove soil from the outside of the curve. Sediment is deposited on the inside of the curve, where water moves more slowly. Over time, this process forms a loop-like bend in the river called a **meander.**

Sometimes during a flood, the river erodes through a narrow neck of land at the base of a meander and forms a new path. Sediments build up along the new channel, cutting the old meander off from the rest of the river. The result is a separate, curved lake, called an **oxbow lake.** Figure 15 shows an oxbow lake formed by the Big Sioux River.

Features Formed by Water Deposition

As a stream or river slows down, it begins to deposit sediment. The slower water cannot carry larger particles of sediment, so these particles fall to the bottom first. As the water slows down even more, smaller particles of sediment are deposited. **Features deposited by flowing water include alluvial fans and deltas.**

As a stream flows out of the mountains and onto the plains, it slows down and sediment settles out. The result is a fan-shaped deposit of sediment on land called an **alluvial fan.** As shown in Figure 16, alluvial fans often grow into thick deposits of sediment.

When a stream flows into a lake or an ocean, the water slows down. The sediment that the stream was carrying is deposited in the form of a delta. A **delta** is a mass of sediment deposited where a river enters a large body of water. Some deltas have a roughly triangular shape.

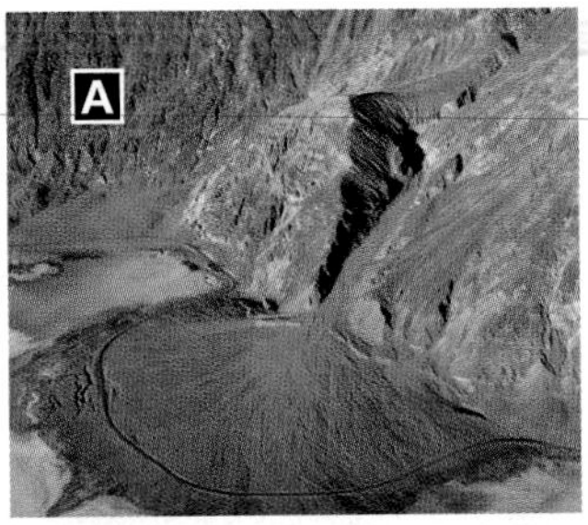
A

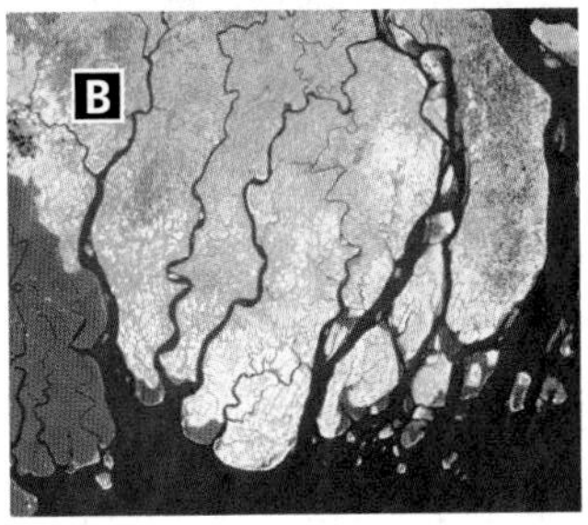
B

Figure 16 Alluvial fans and deltas form from sediment deposited by moving water. **A** This alluvial fan in Death Valley, California, formed from sediment deposited when a mountain stream reached flat land. **B** When a large river empties into the ocean, the deposited sediment often forms a delta.

Facts and Figures

Deltas The word *delta* comes from the Greek letter delta (Δ). The river feature received this name from the Greek historian Herodotus, who noticed that the Nile River delta had a shape similar to that of the triangular symbol for the Greek letter.

However, not all deltas have a triangular shape. The Mississippi River, for example, has a birdfoot-shaped delta that extends far out into the Gulf of Mexico.

Groundwater Erosion

Erosion and deposition occur below ground as well as at the surface. **The processes of chemical weathering causes much groundwater erosion, including the formation of caves and sinkholes.** Recall that carbon dioxide in the air combines with rainwater to form carbonic acid. As the acidic rainwater moves down through the ground, it reacts with some rocks and may become more acidic.

Limestone easily erodes away through this process, forming caves, or caverns. Most caves are small, narrow passages, but some are hundreds of feet high and wide. Caves usually form when they are in the saturated zone, below the water table. When the water table drops, the water flows downward, leaving dry caves like the one in Figure 17.

Sometimes water drips into the cavern from the rock layers above, carrying dissolved minerals. When this mineral-laden water reaches the air of the cave, some of the dissolved carbon dioxide escapes and the minerals are left behind. If the water drips from the cavern ceiling, an icicle-like formation called a **stalactite** (stuh LAK tyt) grows. If the water drips down to the floor, a pillar of minerals called a **stalagmite** (stuh LAG myt) forms.

If erosion weakens a layer of limestone, entire portions of the ground can suddenly collapse. The resulting hole is called a **sinkhole.** Areas of the southern and central United States have many sinkholes. Sinkholes can appear suddenly, swallowing buildings and roads.

Figure 17 Carlsbad Caverns in New Mexico contain spectacular formations, such as the stalactites and stalagmites shown here.

Section 23.3 Assessment

Reviewing Concepts

1. What is the major factor that affects the ability of a stream to erode land?
2. As a stream erodes the land, what features are likely to form in steep areas? What features form in more level areas?
3. Compare and contrast deltas and alluvial fans.
4. What process forms caves and sinkholes?
5. What force provides the energy for the erosion caused by running water?

Critical Thinking

6. **Applying Concepts** What determines how much sediment flowing water can carry?
7. **Relating Cause and Effect** How does an oxbow lake form?
8. **Comparing and Contrasting** What is the difference between a stalactite and a stalagmite?

Writing in Science

Describing a Process Imagine that you are a particle of sediment on a mountaintop. Write a paragraph describing your journey to the ocean. (*Hint:* Be sure to mention at least three steps in the transportation of sediment.)

Groundwater Erosion

Use Community Resources L2

Most states have caves. Contact your regional USGS office or State Park Service to find out about caves in your area. Ask a park ranger or geologist to present a slide show to your class that includes pictures of caves in your region. If possible, arrange a field trip to a nearby cave.

Visual, Kinesthetic

3 ASSESS

Evaluate Understanding L2

Have students create a flowchart that explains how an oxbow lake like the one in Figure 15 formed.

Reteach L1

Use Figure 14 to explain the features formed by water erosion.

Writing in Science

Students' paragraphs should describe how a particle could be transported downhill by runoff from a storm. They should describe how the particle continues to be carried downhill through small channels of water into a gully, then into a small stream, a large stream, or a river. Depending on the size of the particle, they should further describe how it is carried in suspension, by saltation, or is rolled along the bottom of the riverbed until it reaches the ocean, where it may be deposited in a delta or carried out to the deep ocean floor.

Interactive Textbook If your class subscribes to the Interactive Textbook, use it to review key concepts in Section 23.3.

Section 23.3 Assessment

1. The stream's speed
2. V-shaped valleys and waterfalls; a flood plain, oxbow lakes, and meanders
3. Deltas and alluvial fans both form when a river slows down or ends, depositing sediment. However, deltas form in water and alluvial fans form on land.
4. Caves and sinkholes form by the chemical dissolution of underground rock by the flow of acidic water. If erosion weakens a layer of limestone below the ground, it may collapse and form a sinkhole.
5. Gravity provides the energy for erosion caused by the downward flow of rivers and streams to the ocean.
6. The speed that the water flows. Water can carry more sediment when it flows faster.
7. An oxbow lake forms when a river erodes through a narrow neck of land and a meander gets cut off.
8. A stalactite hangs from the ceiling of a cave, while a stalagmite sticks up from the floor of a cave.

issues in SCIENCE

Should Cave Access Be Restricted? L2

Background
While investigating a small cave in the side of a limestone sinkhole, Randy Tufts and Gary Tenen noticed a breeze coming out of a crack in the rock. This indicated the presence of a larger cave.

Answers
1. Students should explain the major issues outlined in the text. These issues include: Should living caves be developed at all? What is the scientific value of preserving such caves? What are the risks and rewards of developing living caves? If such caves are developed, how can this best be done?
2. Those in favor of opening living caves to the public argue that development will educate the public, create new jobs in the region, and protect the caves from potential damage by vandals. They assert that with proper equipment and safeguards, the risk of visitor damage to the caves is small. Those opposed to opening such caves to the public argue that each is a unique geological and biological laboratory. They believe that opening such caves would be too risky. Even under the best circumstances, they argue, the living caves would be damaged and will "die."
3. Students should clearly express their opinion about the possible development of living caves and provide supporting arguments for their opinion.
4. Students should prepare a letter to their governor containing a series of specific recommendations. Sample recommendations might include: "Limit the number of people that can visit the cave, and use the proceeds from admissions to establish a scientific research program for the cave." or "The cave should not be developed. It should be preserved for scientific research."

Go Online
PHSchool.com

Have students further research the issues related to this topic.

issues in SCIENCE

Should Cave Access Be Restricted?

In a limestone cavern, it can take 300 years to add one centimeter of rock to a stalactite! These and other formations build up drop by drop. In a "living" cave, deposits form under conditions of constant temperature and high humidity. If these conditions change, the formation of new deposits stops, and the cave "dies."

In 1974, two explorers discovered a cavern outside Tucson, Arizona. The two cavers had to wriggle through a narrow, hidden tunnel to reach a network of magnificent caverns that stretched for several kilometers. Eventually, the state of Arizona decided to develop the caverns as Kartchner Caverns State Park. Cave experts designed special systems that allow access to the cave, but minimize the impact of visitors on the caverns' fragile environment. Some scientists, however, are concerned that even these special systems will not be enough to maintain Kartchner Caverns as a "living" cave. Should all caverns be opened to the public?

The Viewpoints

Let the Caverns Be

A living cave undisturbed by public access provides scientists with a unique laboratory. Because of caverns' isolation from the surface world, organisms found nowhere else sometimes evolve. Caverns also hold evidence of climate change and fossils of extinct animals.

Proponents of cave preservation argue that even under the best circumstances, human visitors change a cave's environment for the worse. They cite Carlsbad Caverns as a case in point. Each year, about 600,000 people visit Carlsbad Caverns. The visitors have taken bits and pieces of rock as souvenirs. They have disrupted the narrow range of temperature and humidity needed for limestone deposits to form.

Let the People See

Proponents of opening living caves to the public maintain that the beauty of such caverns simply demands to be seen. Caverns provide an important recreational and educational resource. They bring jobs to the region where they are located. In addition, development may help protect caves that would otherwise be vulnerable to vandals.

At Kartchner Caverns, an air lock at the entrance maintains the caverns' environmental conditions. Blowers remove lint and dust from the visitors' clothing. Walkways are designed to keep visitors hands away from cavern walls—skin oils disrupt the process by which limestone is deposited. With these safeguards, human impact on the cave should be minimal.

Research and Decide

1. **Defining the Issue** In your own words, explain the major issues involved in preservation versus development of limestone caverns.
2. **Analyzing the Viewpoints** What are the risks and benefits of opening caverns to the public? What is the value of preserving them solely for scientific research?
3. **Forming Your Opinion** Should caverns like Kartchner Caverns be open to the public? Give reasons for your opinion.
4. **Persuasive Writing** Suppose that you have discovered a cavern. Write a letter to your governor presenting your position regarding whether the cavern should be opened to the public or preserved for research.

Go Online
PHSchool.com

For: More on this issue
Visit: PHSchool.com
Web code: cch-3233

Facts and Figures

Cave Life Lechuguilla Cave, inside Carlsbad Caverns National Park in New Mexico, has been kept closed to all but scientific researchers since its discovery in 1986. Even scientific access has been limited. Only six expeditions are allowed per year with no more than 12 researchers on each expedition. Scientists have been studying microorganisms in Lechuguilla Cave to get an idea of what life on Mars might be like. Opening the cave to tourists would probably destroy these microorganisms.

23.4 Glaciers and Wind

Reading Focus

Key Concepts

- How do glaciers form?
- What landscape features are created by glacial erosion and deposition?
- What are the effects of wind erosion and deposition?

Vocabulary

- continental glacier
- valley glacier
- plucking
- cirques
- till
- moraines
- deflation
- dunes
- loess

Reading Strategy

Sequencing Copy the flowchart below. As you read, complete it to show how a glacier forms and moves, and how it erodes and deposits sediment. Add more steps to the chart if necessary.

Snow is compacted to form glacial ice. → a. ___?___ → b. ___?___

Today, the city of Chicago, Illinois, is one of America's largest and busiest cities. But about 15,000 years ago, the land that is now Chicago was buried under a huge glacier more than one kilometer thick! At that time, an enormous ice sheet covered much of the midwestern and northeastern United States and almost all of Canada. That ice sheet changed the landscape of a large portion of North America.

Figure 18 This valley glacier in Alaska has bands that look like ripples. The dark bands, which include rock debris, show the glacier's slower growth in summer. The light bands form in the winter.
Interpreting Photos *Which part of the glacier moves faster, its center or its sides?*

How Glaciers Form and Move

Glaciers form in places where more snow falls than melts or sublimates. As the layers of snow pile up, the weight on the underlying snow increases. Eventually, this weight packs the snow so tightly that glacial ice is formed.

Even though glaciers may appear to be stationary, they are constantly moving. The force of gravity pulls the ice downhill. The ice flows slowly, like honey dripping down a spoon. Sometimes the pressure is great enough to melt the ice at the base of the glacier. This melting can aid the motion of the glacier, with the ice sliding along the bottom. Like a river, a glacier flows fastest in the middle and slowest along the sides.

There are two types of glaciers: continental glaciers and valley glaciers. A **continental glacier** is a thick sheet of ice that covers a huge area, such as a continent or large island. Most of Earth's fresh water is frozen in the continental glaciers that cover Antarctica and Greenland. A glacier that occurs in a high mountain valley is called a **valley glacier.** Like the glacier in Figure 18, a valley glacier usually begins near a mountain peak and winds down through a valley formed originally by a stream.

Section Resources

Print
- ***Laboratory Manual,*** Investigation 23A
- ***Reading and Study Workbook With Math Support,*** Section 23.4
- ***Transparencies,*** Section 23.4

Technology
- ***Interactive Textbook,*** Section 23.4
- ***Presentation Pro CD-ROM,*** Section 23.4
- ***Go Online,*** NSTA SciLinks, Glaciers and landforms

Section 23.4

1 FOCUS

Objectives

23.4.1 **Describe** the formation and movement of glaciers and **identify** features formed by glacial erosion and deposition.

23.4.2 **Explain** the mechanisms and effects of wind erosion and deposition.

Reading Focus

Build Vocabulary L2

Compare/Contrast Table Have students make a two-column table with the headings Features Formed by Glacial Erosion and Features Formed by Glacial Deposition. Instruct students to fill in the table using words from the vocabulary list as they read the section.

Reading Strategy L2

a. Gravity pulls the glacier slowly downhill. **b.** The glacier erodes underlying rock by plucking and abrasion and deposits till at its front and sides as it melts.

2 INSTRUCT

How Glaciers Form and Move

Build Reading Literacy L1

Using Context Clues Refer to page **530D** in **Chapter 18,** which provides the guidelines for using context clues.

Ask students if they can define the word *sublimate.* If they have difficulty, have them read the first paragraph of How Glaciers Form and Move. Then, ask them to use clues from the selection to infer the meaning of the term *(A phase change from a solid directly to a gas).* Students should be able to infer that it is a process by which snow is removed.
Logical

Answer to . . .

Figure 18 *A center of a glacier moves faster than its sides.*

Glacial Erosion and Deposition

Teacher Demo

Glacial Erosion and Deposition

L2

Purpose Students will see a demonstration of how glaciers can move boulders and create depositional features.

Materials a block of ice, approximately 15 × 25 × 12 cm; clay, sand, gravel, and pebbles to fill a 25 × 30-cm baking pan 3–5 cm deep; flat metal or plastic surface such as an old cutting board or cookie sheet; freezer; sink

Procedure Fill the baking pan with clay, sand, gravel, and a few pebbles. Place the ice block on top, and explain that this is a model of a glacier forming on land. Ask, **What do you think will happen as the glacier melts and refreezes?** *(It will pick up some of the clay, sand, gravel, and pebbles.)* Allow the glacier to sit in the pan for 30 minutes, or until it is approximately $\frac{1}{4}$ melted. Pick up the glacier to show students the underside. Replace the ice in the pan and place it in the freezer overnight. Remove it from the pan and show students the results. Explain that this is similar to how a glacier picks up sediment and rocks as the bottom melts and refreezes. Place the flat sheet at a very shallow angle so that it will slowly drain into the sink. Place the glacier on the sheet and allow it to melt overnight. Have students examine the sheet and identify depositional features, such as moraines and erratics.

Expected Outcome The glacier will contain a significant amount of the clay, sand, gravel, and pebbles after refreezing. As it melts, many of the typical glacial features will be produced.
Visual

Address Misconceptions L2

There is a common misconception that glaciers are formed by one sudden action, rather than being features that form and change over long periods of time. Ask students to examine Figure 18 and work in groups to discuss how glaciers move and grow.
Logical, Visual

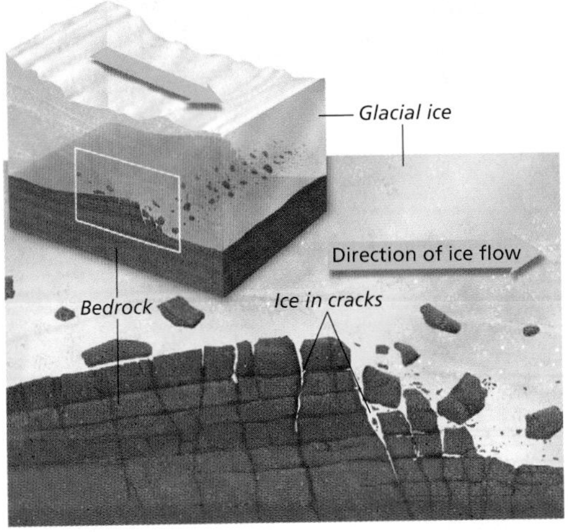
Glacial ice
Direction of ice flow
Bedrock
Ice in cracks

Figure 19 As a glacier moves downhill, it loosens and lifts pieces of rock from the ground underneath in a process known as plucking. **Predicting** ***What evidence of plucking would you expect to find after a glacier has melted?***

Glacial Erosion and Deposition

Though glaciers move much more slowly than rivers, they are very effective at eroding and depositing sediment. This is because glaciers tear away the underlying rock as they move. Glaciers erode rock through abrasion and plucking. In **plucking,** shown in Figure 19, glacial ice widens cracks in bedrock beneath the glacier. Pieces of loosened rock are then frozen to the bottom of the glacier, which carries them away. The pieces of rock that are stuck to the bottom and sides of the glacier act like sandpaper. As the glacier moves, it scrapes the bedrock and soil under it and along its sides.

Features Formed by Glacial Erosion **Glaciers cause many distinctive features in the landscape, including cirques, horns, U-shaped valleys, and glacial lakes.** Valley glaciers cause erosion high in the mountains where such glaciers begin. For example, a glacier can carve large bowl-shaped valleys out of a mountainside. These valleys, called **cirques,** look as if they were made by a giant ice cream scoop. If several cirques form close together, a ridge may be left between them. If several ridges connect to form a pyramid-shaped peak, the peak is called a horn. The peaks in the Swiss Alps, including the famous Matterhorn, were sculpted by glaciers. Figure 20 shows several of these features.

Cirque
Horn
Ridge
Glacial lake

Figure 20 The distinctive landscape near Mount Robson in British Columbia, Canada, was formed by glaciers.

Customize for Inclusion Students

Learning Disabled
Help students who have difficulty absorbing information from written text by using Figure 20 to discuss the processes of glacial erosion. Point out each feature in the photograph, and ask students to verbalize how glaciers produced the feature. Fill in any gaps in students' understanding.

Figure 21 Glaciers can carve out large U-shaped valleys, such as this one in Glacier National Park, Montana.

Glaciers also widen and deepen the valleys through which they flow. When glaciers flow through V-shaped valleys cut by running water, they widen them into U-shaped valleys. Glacial valleys are U-shaped because the moving ice scours the entire valley, eroding rock from the valley's bottom and sides. Glacier National Park, shown in Figure 21, contains many U-shaped valleys that were carved by glaciers.

Unlike valley glaciers, continental glaciers tend to level large surface areas through the scraping and grinding of thick ice. Continental glaciers can enlarge and deepen natural depressions in the surface. These depressions then fill with water when the glaciers retreat. The Great Lakes and the Finger Lakes in New York are examples of glacial lakes that formed by this process.

Features Formed by Glacial Deposition A glacier gathers and transports a huge amount of rock and soil as it moves. **When a glacier melts, it deposits its load of sediment, creating a variety of landforms.** Glacial sediment is called **till.** Till is an unsorted mixture of sediment containing fragments of many sizes. Giant boulders, gravel, sand, and pulverized rock dust are all found in till. Glaciers deposit till as they melt. The till forms **moraines,** mounds of sediment at the downhill end of the glacier and along its sides. As the How It Works box on page 722 explains, glacial deposits leave many traces in the landscape.

Reading Checkpoint *What are moraines?*

Go Online NSTA SCILINKS

For: Links on glaciers and landforms
Visit: SciLinks.org
Web Code: ccn-3234

Build Science Skills L2

Inferring Geologists can learn a lot about the geological history of a region by examining its landscape and making inferences about the processes that contributed to its formation. Tell students that they will practice making inferences about the processes that created landscapes by examining photographs and making deductions about which landscapes were formed by glacial activity. Direct students to examine Figures 20 and 21. Then, have them look through nature magazines or other sources to find photographs of landscapes that were formed by glaciers. Students should cut out pictures if possible. Otherwise, have students photocopy or trace photographs. Have students label the features that were formed by glacial erosion or deposition, and create a poster display of the labeled photographs to hang in the classroom.
Logical, Portfolio

Build Reading Literacy L1

Visualize Refer to page **354D** in **Chapter 12**, which provides the guidelines for visualizing.

Ask students to read the first paragraph on p. 721. After the first reading, instruct students to close their eyes and imagine a V-shaped valley with a river flowing through it. Then, imagine a glacier forming in the valley, and how the moving ice would carve out the sides and floor of the valley. Have them refer to Figure 21 to help them visualize the resulting U-shaped valley.
Intrapersonal

Go Online NSTA SCILINKS

Download a worksheet on glaciers and landforms for students to complete, and find additional teacher support from NSTA SciLinks.

Facts and Figures

Pleistocene Glacial Activity During the Pleistocene Epoch (1.6 million–10,000 years ago) glaciers advanced and retreated across North America. The four major glacial advances during that time are referred to as the Nebraskan, Kansan, Illinoian, and Wisconsonian glacial stages, each named for the southernmost point to which the glaciers advanced.

Answer to . . .

Figure 19 *Rock fragments and boulders would be found along the path where a glacier has retreated.*

Reading Checkpoint *Moraines are mounds of sediment that can be found at the downhill end of a glacier and along its sides.*

HOW It Works

Glacial Deposition L2

Though glaciers move much more slowly than rivers, they are very efficient at eroding, transporting, and depositing sediment. This is because the ice of glaciers tears away the underlying rock as the ice flows. Glaciers erode rock all along their paths, and deposit the rock mostly at the front of the glacier. Glaciers are always flowing, even if the front position of the glacier is not changing. This means that a glacier continuously erodes rock and transports it to the front of the glacier.

After a glacier has been active for a long time, a great deal of till becomes deposited at the glacier's front and forms an end moraine. During ice ages, when glaciers cover large parts of continents, a great deal of eroded rock is carried southward by glaciers. Many of the northern states of the United States are covered with till that was scraped off of the surface of Canada by glaciers. Sometimes the resulting end moraines can be enormous. Long Island, in New York, and Cape Cod, in Massachusetts, are both examples of end moraines from continental glaciers that once covered parts of North America.

Interpreting Diagrams The composition of an erratic reflects the bedrock of the region where it was formed. Glaciers may carry erratics to a region where the bedrock is composed of a different type of rock.
Visual

For Enrichment L3

Glaciers covered large parts of the United States in recent geologic history (10,000–1.6 million years ago) and created many prominent features of the northern U.S. landscape. Have students research the extent of the glacial advances during the most recent ice age, and create a map showing the location of the glacial activity and prominent glacial features. Display the maps in class.
Visual

HOW It Works

Glacial Deposition

Melting glaciers leave behind a landscape full of glacial deposits. The material from which most of these deposits are created is called till, which is a mixture of different-sized rock particles. In parts of the northern United States, the deposits provide clues to the land's glacial history. **Inferring** ***Explain why erratics are often composed of a different type of rock than the surrounding bedrock.***

Kettle lake
As a glacier retreats, large blocks of glacial ice become buried in till and other deposits, where they slowly melt, forming pits in the outwash plain. Water often fills these bowl-shaped depressions, creating kettle lakes.

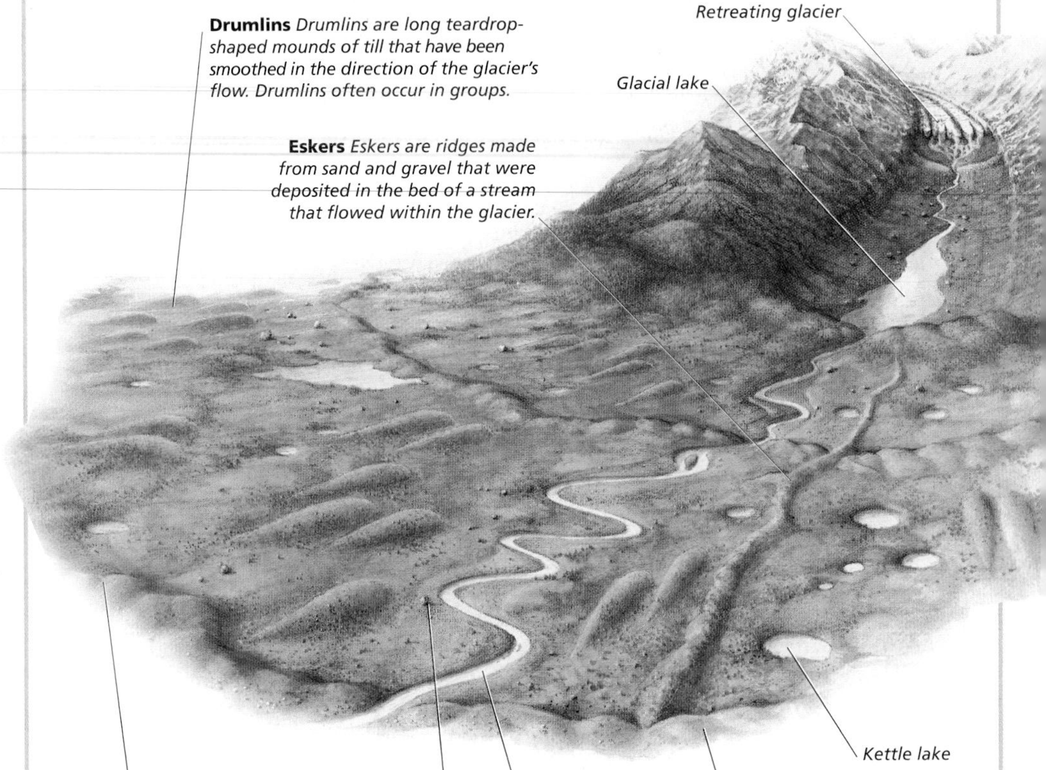
Retreating glacier
Glacial lake
Glacial stream
Kettle lake

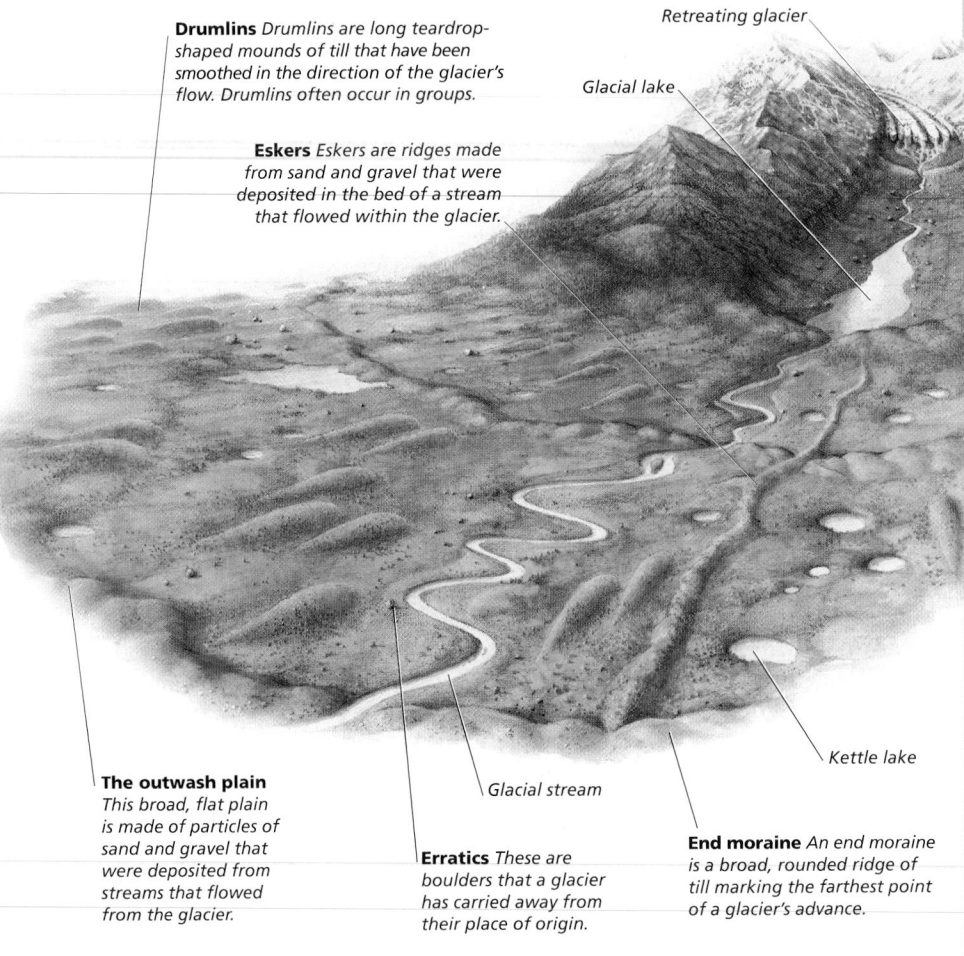

Drumlins *Drumlins are long teardrop-shaped mounds of till that have been smoothed in the direction of the glacier's flow. Drumlins often occur in groups.*

Eskers *Eskers are ridges made from sand and gravel that were deposited in the bed of a stream that flowed within the glacier.*

The outwash plain *This broad, flat plain is made of particles of sand and gravel that were deposited from streams that flowed from the glacier.*

Erratics *These are boulders that a glacier has carried away from their place of origin.*

End moraine *An end moraine is a broad, rounded ridge of till marking the farthest point of a glacier's advance.*

Facts and Figures

Medial Moraines Glaciers often have multiple tributaries, similar to rivers. The tributaries of glaciers each start in a different mountain valley. When tributaries of glaciers come together, the rock that has been torn off the sides of valleys comes together to form streaks of crushed rock within the glacier. The streaks of crushed rock found within glaciers are called medial moraines.

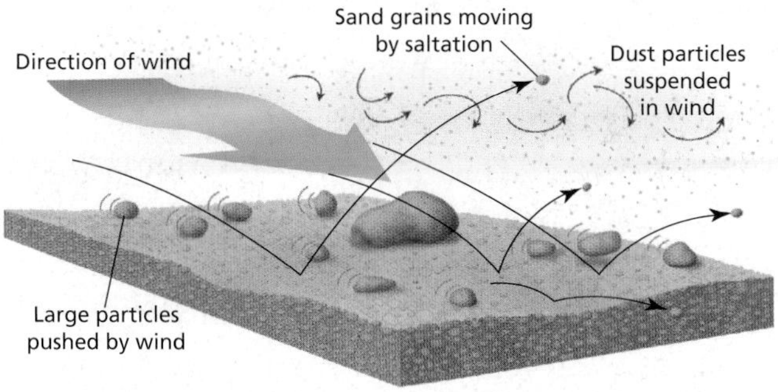
Direction of wind
Sand grains moving by saltation
Dust particles suspended in wind
Large particles pushed by wind

Figure 22 Wind erosion moves particles of different sizes. Small dust particles suspended in the air are blown about by the wind. Heavier sand grains move by saltation. Large particles slide or roll along the surface.

Wind Erosion and Deposition

Wind can also cause erosion and deposition. As with running water, the speed of the wind determines the size of the materials it carries. Slower winds carry only small particles, like dust. Faster winds have more energy and can lift larger particles, such as sand grains. A constant, strong wind can produce a large cloud of dust or sand.

Most wind erosion occurs in the dry areas of the world, such as deserts. Wind erosion also occurs in areas where drought has caused the ground to dry out and the soil is not held in place by plants.

How Wind Causes Erosion As you can see in Figure 22, the wind moves small particles such as sand grains in a series of leaps called saltation. In saltation, wind lifts sand grains a short distance into the air. Gravity pulls the grains back down to the ground, where they collide with and loosen other grains. The result is that the sand grains leap-frog along.

Wind erodes the land by deflation and abrasion. The process of **deflation** occurs when wind picks up and carries away loose surface material. In dry regions where winds are strong, sand and dust are lifted from the surface and carried away. Over time, the surface of the ground is lowered. Larger rocks are left behind, forming a rocky surface that covers much of the land in dry regions.

Recall that abrasion is a type of mechanical weathering. Abrasion by wind occurs in much the same way as abrasion by flowing water. Wind blows sand against other rocks, slowly sandblasting them away and removing the weathered particles.

Reading Checkpoint *What is deflation?*

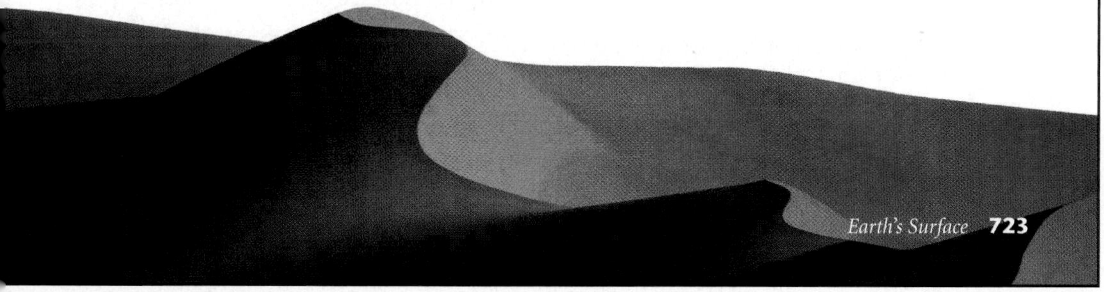
Earth's Surface 723

Figure 23 Wind deposits sand in the form of dunes. These large sand dunes are found in the Namib Desert in Africa.

Facts and Figures

Menacing Dunes Approximately one-third of Earth's land surface is desert. The constant movement of sand dunes threatens to envelop villages and towns in China, Africa, and the Middle East. Scientists are trying to learn more about how sand moves in order to develop more effective means of protecting populated areas from encroaching dunes.

Wind Erosion and Deposition

Use Visuals L1

Figure 22 Point out the similarities between the processes described by this visual and the processes described in Figure 13. Remind students that saltation is the process by which particles bounce or skip along the ground. Ask, **How do the largest particles move?** *(They are pushed along the ground by the wind.)* **Which particles would you expect to move the farthest in a windstorm?** *(Dust)* **Which particles move by saltation?** *(Sand)*
Visual

Build Science Skills L2

Comparing and Contrasting Have students work in groups to make a presentation comparing the processes of wind and water erosion. Instruct students to include the way in which the two forces of erosion move particles and how both types of erosion change the landscape. The presentations can include pictures, diagrams, video, and/or demonstrations.
Interpersonal, Portfolio

Answer to . . .

Reading Checkpoint *Deflation is a form of wind erosion in which the wind lifts and carries away loose surface material.*

3 ASSESS

Evaluate Understanding L2

Have students make flashcards of features caused by erosion and deposition from glaciers and wind. Write and draw the feature on one side, and write a description of how it is formed on the other. Students can use these flashcards to quiz each other in class.

Reteach L1

Use the How It Works feature on p. 722 to discuss the ways that a continental glacier affects the landscape by erosion and deposition.

Writing in Science

Students should explain that a V-shaped valley is formed by a stream eroding the rock of its streambed near its source in the mountains. They should note that, in contrast, the movement of a valley glacier forms a U-shaped valley. When a valley glacier flows through a valley formed by a stream, it transforms the valley from V-shaped to U-shaped.

Interactive Textbook If your class subscribes to the Interactive Textbook, use it to review key concepts in Section 23.4.

Figure 24 This large dust storm blew through downtown Phoenix, Arizona, in 1999.

Effects of Wind Deposition When wind slows down, it drops the sediment it is carrying. **Features deposited by wind include sand dunes and loess deposits.** Deposits formed from windblown sand are called **dunes.** Over time, sand dunes can move great distances. A dune moves as the wind picks up sand from the back of the dune and blows it to the front. Sand dunes can take many different forms, depending on wind direction and how much sand is available.

Deposits formed from windblown dust are called **loess** (LES). Loess consists mainly of finely ground particles. The two major sources of loess are deserts and glacial deposits. A dust storm like the one in Figure 24 can transport tons of dust for long distances. Dust from the Sahara Desert in Africa regularly blows across the Atlantic Ocean.

Section 23.4 Assessment

Reviewing Concepts

1. What conditions are necessary for a glacier to form?
2. Identify three features caused by glacial erosion.
3. Describe three features caused by glacial deposition.
4. What are the two ways that wind erodes particles of rock?
5. What features can form as wind deposits sediment?
6. What is plucking?
7. How does deflation affect the land surface in dry regions?
8. How do sand dunes form and move?

Critical Thinking

9. **Relating Cause and Effect** How are both glaciers and wind involved in the formation of loess deposits?
10. **Comparing and Contrasting** How is the way wind carries sediment similar to the way a stream carries sediment? How are these processes different? Explain.

Writing in Science

Compare and Contrast Paragraph Write a paragraph comparing how V-shaped valleys and U-shaped valleys are formed. Include an explanation of how a V-shaped valley could turn into a U-shaped valley.

Section 23.4 Assessment

1. For a glacier to form, more snow must fall on a region over a sustained period than melts or sublimates.
2. Correct answers include: cirques, horns, U-shaped valleys, ridges, and glacial lakes.
3. Students should describe three of the following features: moraines, drumlins, eskers, and kettle lakes.
4. Deflation and abrasion
5. Sand dunes and loess deposits
6. Plucking is the process in which a glacier loosens and carries away pieces of the bedrock that it passes over.
7. Deflation removes sand and dust from the ground and leaves a hard surface of larger rocks behind.
8. Sand dunes form from windblown sand. They can move great distances over time as the wind picks up sand from the back of the dune and blows it to the front.
9. The movement of glaciers creates ground-up rock dust, which is one source of loess deposits.
10. Both water and wind move some sediment by saltation, in which small particles move in a series of small bounces. Both also move smaller particles that are suspended in the water or air. Larger particles may be pushed along a river bottom or land surface by running water and wind, respectively. Unlike wind, some of the sediment carried by streams is in solution.

23.5 The Restless Oceans

Reading Focus

Key Concepts

- How do conditions in the ocean change with depth?
- What causes surface currents, density currents, and upwelling?
- How do waves erode rock and deposit sediment?

Vocabulary:

- salinity
- continental shelf
- surface current
- density currents
- upwelling
- hydraulic action
- longshore drift

Reading Strategy

Relating Cause and Effect Copy the table below. After you read, complete the table to compare ways that ocean water can move.

Movement Type	Causes	Effects
Surface current	a. ___?___	b. ___?___
Density current	c. ___?___	d. ___?___
Upwelling	e. ___?___	f. ___?___
Longshore drift	g. ___?___	h. ___?___

Oceans surround all of the continents. Earth's ocean waters are divided into four major oceans: the Pacific Ocean, Atlantic Ocean, Indian Ocean, and Arctic Ocean. These oceans also include smaller bodies of water, such as the Gulf of Mexico and the Mediterranean Sea.

Exploring the Ocean

Most of Earth's water exists as salt water in the oceans. Ocean water is a mixture that includes dissolved salts and gases. **Salinity** is the proportion of dissolved salts in water. On average, there are about 35 grams of dissolved salts in each kilogram of ocean water. The most abundant salt in ocean water is table salt, sodium chloride (NaCl).

Salt is added to the oceans by rivers and volcanoes. Rain slowly dissolves salts out of surface rocks. These salts are washed into rivers which then carry them to the ocean. In addition, volcanic eruptions send elements such as sulfur and chlorine into the atmosphere and the oceans. At the same time, salt is removed from seawater by animals and plants as they build hard parts and also by deposition as sediment.

Figure 25 Wave action is the primary means of erosion along coastlines. Here, waves are breaking onto rocks at Cape Kiwanda State Park along the Oregon coast.

725

Section Resources

Print

- ***Reading and Study Workbook With Math Support,*** Section 23.5
- ***Transparencies,*** Section 23.5

Technology

- ***Interactive Textbook,*** Section 23.5
- ***Presentation Pro CD-ROM,*** Section 23.5

Section 23.5

1 FOCUS

Objectives

23.5.1 **Explain** how the properties of ocean water change with depth.

23.5.2 **Distinguish** between surface currents, deep currents, and upwelling.

23.5.3 **Explain** the processes by which waves and currents cause erosion and deposition.

Reading Focus

Build Vocabulary L2

Paraphrase Have students come up with a definition of each vocabulary term in their own words, and create an index card for each term with the definition.

Reading Strategy L2

a. Winds **b.** Warm water generally flows away from the equator along the east side of continents; cold water generally flows away from polar regions along the west side of continents. **c.** Differences in ocean water density **d.** Responsible for slow mixing of water between the surface and deep ocean **e.** Warm water is blown aside by winds and currents, allowing colder water to rise from the deep ocean. **f.** Nutrients are brought up from the deep ocean, providing a food source for algae, which serve in turn as food for fish. **g.** Waves carrying sediment approach a beach at an angle. **h.** Sand can be moved great distances along a beach.

2 INSTRUCT

Exploring the Ocean

Integrate Biology L2

Organisms that live in the deepest parts of the ocean have extraordinary adaptations to help them survive these extreme conditions. Ask, **What physical factors would be most challenging for organisms that live in the deep sea?** *(Lack of sunlight, low temperatures, extremely high pressure)* Have students create a photo display of deep-sea life that highlights such organisms' adaptations to their physical environment. **Visual**

Address Misconceptions L2

Students may have misconceptions about the relative sizes of the oceans. Because it is commonly known that Earth's oceans are divided into four major oceans, many people think that the four ocean basins are roughly the same size. This misconception is reinforced by map projections commonly used for wall maps that exaggerate the area of the high latitudes, and therefore of the Arctic Ocean. Also, the Pacific Ocean is usually cut so that it is shown in two parts, one on the left side of the map and one on the right. Show students a globe and ask them to compare the sizes of the oceans. Point out that the Pacific Ocean is nearly twice the size of the Atlantic Ocean and is larger than all of Earth's land masses combined.
Visual

Teacher Demo

Salinity of Ocean Water L2

Purpose Students observe the ratio of salt to water in the ocean.

Materials 1-L beaker, 100-mL beaker, mass balance, salt, water

Procedure Fill the 1-L beaker with one liter of water. Ask, **How much salt would I have to add to this to equal the salinity of ocean water?** *(35 g)* Then, place the 100-mL beaker on the balance and reset the balance to zero or note the mass of the beaker. Add 35 g of salt into the beaker.

Expected Outcome This demonstration will help students visualize the difference in salinity between fresh and ocean water.
Visual

Ocean Currents

Build Reading Literacy L1

Summarize Refer to page **598D** in **Chapter 20**, which provides the guidelines for summarizing.

Have students work in groups to summarize the information in Ocean Currents. Ask them to discuss the material, identify the key information, and create a single-page summary using the same bold heads as the selection.
Verbal, Group

Figure 26 Kelp forests such as this one off the coast of California occur in coastal waters swept by cold ocean currents. Light can penetrate to the floor of the continental shelf in this region, allowing the long strands of kelp to grow in nutrient-rich waters.

Changes With Depth Conditions in the ocean, such as the amount of sunlight, temperature, and pressure, change as you move from the surface to the ocean floor. **Light and temperature decrease with depth, whereas pressure increases.**

Sunlight decreases with depth in the ocean. The deep ocean is totally dark. Light cannot penetrate deeper than about 200 meters.

Water temperature decreases with depth. The top 100 to 500 meters of the ocean are well mixed and relatively warm in the temperate and equatorial zones. Deeper water is much colder and denser. Deep water moves very slowly, and does not interact much with the surface layer.

Pressure increases continuously with depth in the ocean. At a depth of 500 meters, the pressure is about 50 times greater than atmospheric pressure at sea level. Few forms of life can tolerate such great pressures.

The Ocean Floor What would the ocean floor look like if all the water were drained from the oceans? First you would see the **continental shelf.** This gently sloping plain forms an apron of shallow water along the edges of most continents. Beyond the continental shelf, the continental slope descends more steeply to the floor of the deep ocean. In places, you would see deep canyons cutting through the continental shelf and slope.

The ocean floor itself is a vast, flat plain dotted with volcanic peaks. You would also see the mid-ocean ridges winding through the ocean basins, and deep trenches along the edges of some oceanic plates. The deepest point in the ocean is in the Mariana Trench, more than 11 kilometers below sea level. Overall, the oceans have an average depth of 3.8 kilometers!

Ocean Currents

Ocean currents, shown in Figure 27, are the patterns of flow in Earth's oceans. Because of these currents, water flows from one ocean to another. Ocean currents are affected by winds, Earth's rotation, and the positions and shapes of the continents.

Surface Currents Have you ever tried to cool a cup of hot chocolate by blowing across it? If you have, then you have imitated the way that winds move currents near the ocean's surface. A **surface current** is a large stream of ocean water that moves continuously in about the same path. **Winds blowing across the surface of the ocean cause the continuous flow of surface currents.**

Customize for English Language Learners

Use a Cloze Strategy
Help beginning language learners by using a Cloze strategy to extract from the text key information about physical properties of the ocean. After reading Exploring the Ocean, have students fill in the blanks in the following sentences: **Ocean water is a mixture that includes dissolved ________ and ________. The proportion of dissolved salts to water is called the ________. In the ocean, ________ and ________ decrease with depth. Pressure ________ with depth.** Then, ask students to explain *salinity*, *pressure*, and *depth* in their own words.

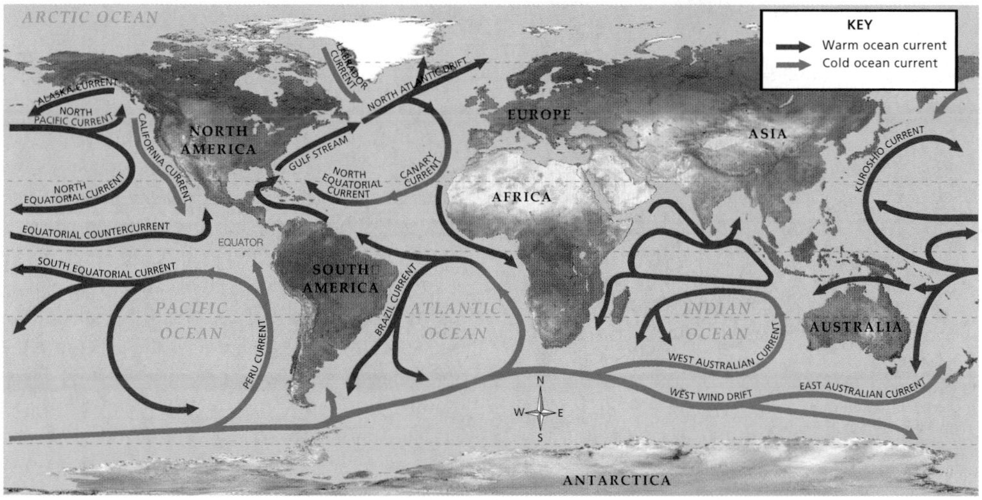
ARCTIC OCEAN
KEY
Warm ocean current
Cold ocean current
ALASKA CURRENT
NORTH PACIFIC CURRENT
LABRADOR CURRENT
NORTH ATLANTIC DRIFT
CALIFORNIA CURRENT
NORTH AMERICA
EUROPE
ASIA
GULF STREAM
NORTH EQUATORIAL CURRENT
CANARY CURRENT
KUROSHIO CURRENT
NORTH EQUATORIAL CURRENT
AFRICA
EQUATORIAL COUNTERCURRENT
EQUATOR
SOUTH EQUATORIAL CURRENT
SOUTH AMERICA
BRAZIL CURRENT
PACIFIC OCEAN
ATLANTIC OCEAN
INDIAN OCEAN
AUSTRALIA
PERU CURRENT
WEST AUSTRALIAN CURRENT
WEST WIND DRIFT
EAST AUSTRALIAN CURRENT
N
W
E
S
ANTARCTICA

Figure 27 Prevailing wind patterns drive the ocean's surface currents.
Interpreting Maps ***What current flows south along the west coast of North America? Is it warm or cold?***

Global surface currents reflect the effects of wind patterns in the atmosphere. In general, currents of warm water flow away from the equator along the east side of continents. Currents of cold water flow away from the polar regions along the west side of continents. One major current is the Gulf Stream, which carries warm water from the Gulf of Mexico to the North Atlantic Ocean. Figure 28 shows a satellite image of the Gulf Stream. Another is the California current, which carries cool water from the Gulf of Alaska south along the west coast of the United States.

Deep Currents Unlike surface currents, deep currents are not caused by winds. **Deep ocean currents are caused by differences in the density of ocean water.** Denser water results from colder temperatures or higher salinity. Because deep ocean currents are affected by density, they are called **density currents.** Density currents are responsible for a slow mixing of water between the surface and deeper ocean. For example, a density current flows south through the Atlantic Ocean. This density current forms near Greenland in an area where very cold, salty water sinks into the deep ocean. Another density current in the Atlantic forms near Antarctica and flows north.

Reading Checkpoint *What are density currents?*

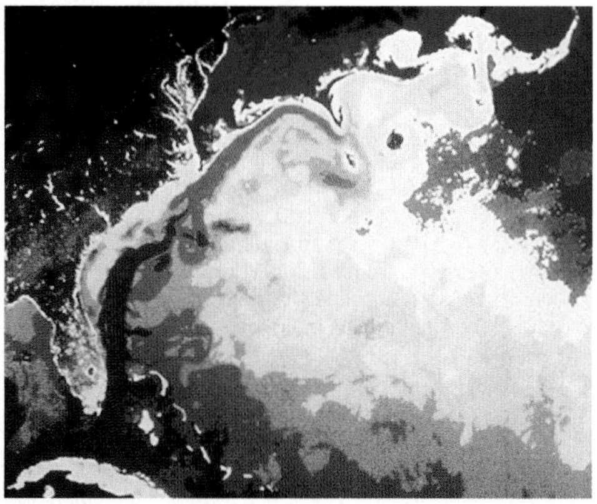

Figure 28 This satellite image of the Atlantic Ocean shows the Gulf Stream, which carries warm water northward from the Gulf of Mexico toward the British Isles. The image has been enhanced so that the colors indicate water temperature (Red indicates warmer water and blue indicates cooler water.)

Use Visuals L1

Figure 27 Be sure students understand that the map represents surface currents only. Ask, **Why is the east-flowing current in the Pacific Ocean at the equator called a countercurrent?** *(Because it is running in the reverse direction of currents directly to the north and south)* **Compare the direction of the currents in the North and South Atlantic.** *(Clockwise in the North Atlantic and counterclockwise in the South Atlantic)* **Compare the temperature of the ocean water in the mid-coast regions of the eastern and western United States.** *(Ocean water would be warmer off the East Coast as compared to the West Coast because the Gulf Stream carries warm water from the equator, while the California current carries cold water from the North Pacific.)*
Visual

FYI

The Coriolis effect also affects the direction in which currents move. The Coriolis effect causes moving objects to veer to the right in the Northern Hemisphere and to the left in the Southern Hemisphere. As a result, ocean surface currents form clockwise-moving cycles in the Northern Hemisphere. These rotating cycles are called gyres. The gyres in the Southern Hemisphere move in a counterclockwise direction. See Chapter 24 for more information on the Coriolis effect.

Answer to . . .

Figure 27 *California current; cold*

Reading Checkpoint *Density currents are deep ocean currents caused by differences in the density of ocean water.*

Wave Erosion and Deposition

Build Science Skills L2

Interpreting Photographs Direct students to examine Figure 30. Have students work in groups to explain the processes of erosion or deposition that formed each feature. For each photograph, have students create a flowchart with diagrams depicting the formation of the feature.
Visual, Group

FYI

Waves can quickly erode rock and sand along the coast. For example, about 85% of California's coast is being eroded at a rate of 0.15 to 0.75 m per year. The result is that many houses built along the coast are falling into the ocean. Erosion is most active during large storms. In parts of North Carolina, the shoreline has receded as much as 25 m (82 ft) in just one year!

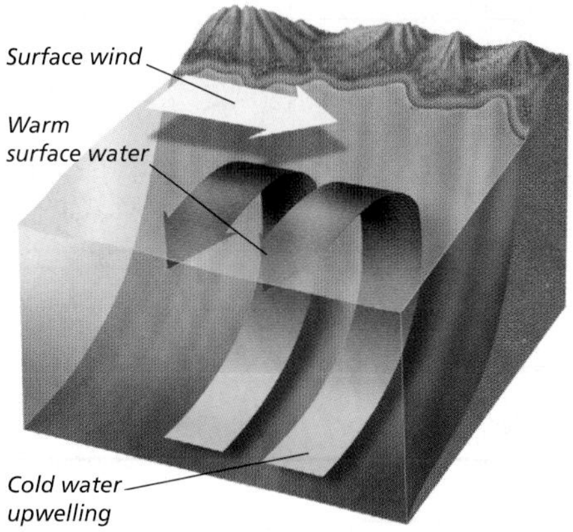
Surface wind
Warm surface water
Cold water upwelling

Figure 29 Upwelling of deeper ocean water occurs along some coastlines.
Relating Cause and Effect ***Why are areas of upwelling often excellent areas for commercial fishing?***

Upwelling At certain places in the oceans, water from the deep ocean moves upward toward the surface. The movement of water from the deep ocean to the surface is called **upwelling.** Much upwelling occurs along the western coasts of continents. **In upwelling, winds blow warm surface water aside. This allows cold water from the deep ocean to rise and take the place of the warmer water.** You can see how upwelling works in Figure 29. Another major area of upwelling lies along the equator. Here, currents and winds pull surface water on both sides of the equator toward the poles. Upwelling occurs in the strip of ocean where the surface currents move apart.

Upwelling brings nutrients from deep in the ocean to the surface. The nutrients support large populations of algae, which serve as food for tiny ocean animals. These animals, in turn, are eaten by fishes. Areas of upwelling often support large populations of fishes and whales.

Wave Erosion and Deposition

Waves can pound a coastline with a tremendous amount of energy. So it's not surprising that waves are the major cause of erosion along coastlines. On a rocky coast, wave erosion creates cliffs, arches, caves, and tall rock towers called sea stacks, as shown in Figure 30. **Two physical processes, hydraulic action and abrasion, are responsible for much wave erosion.** Over time, wave erosion and deposition work together to straighten a coastline.

How Waves Cause Erosion The process of **hydraulic action** occurs when waves pound on cracks in rocks. First, a wave fills a crack with water. Before the water drains from the crack, another wave forces more water into the crack. This pressure causes the crack to get bigger. Waves also compress air as they slam into a cracked rock. This compressed air contributes to wave erosion. Eventually, the rock breaks apart into smaller pieces that are further eroded by waves. Abrasion also breaks up rocks into smaller pieces. The sediment carried by waves acts like sandpaper, rubbing away at the rocks.

Figure 30 Waves produce distinctive geological features. **A** A sea cliff with a sea stack and arch in Etretat, France **B** A barrier beach in South Carolina **C** A sand spit along the Red Sea in Egypt

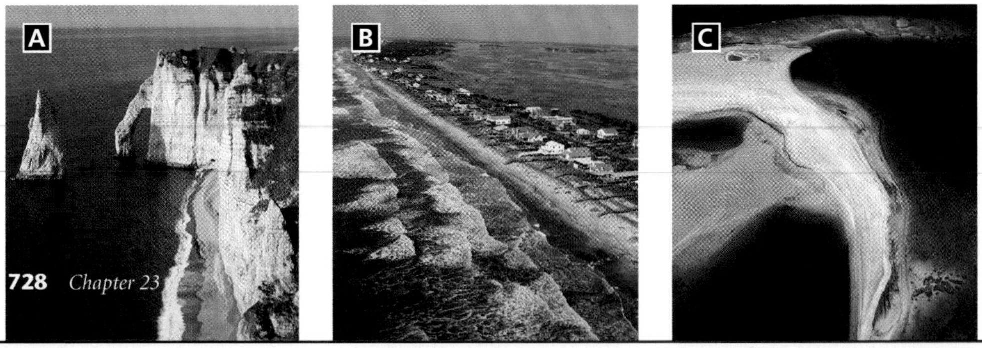
A
B
C
728 Chapter 23

Facts and Figures

Cape Cod Wave deposition can create dramatic land features. The long, curving arm of Cape Cod, Massachusetts is an example of longshore drift. Cape Cod was originally a moraine, a pile of till deposited at the far end of a glacier that was covering the Northeast during the last glacial advance 20,000 years ago. At that time, the sea level was low, and the moraine was deposited on dry land. Since the sea level rose and the moraine became subjected to wave erosion, sediment from the loose pile of till has been carried northward along the shore, continually extending the arm of land in that direction.

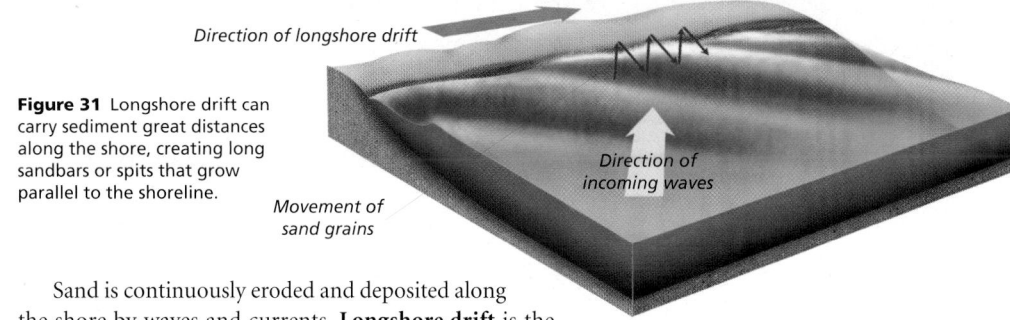

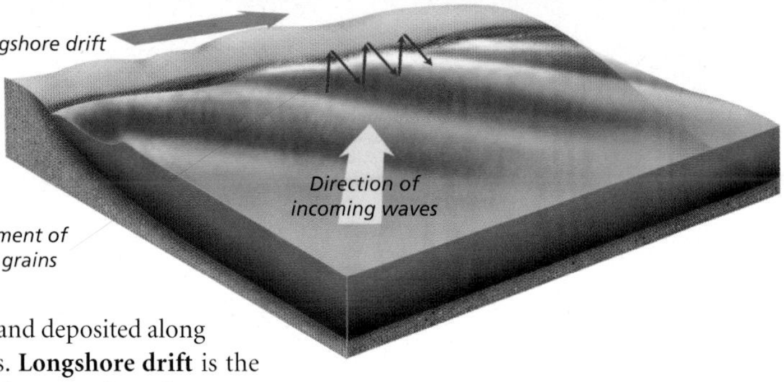
Direction of longshore drift
Direction of incoming waves
Movement of sand grains

Figure 31 Longshore drift can carry sediment great distances along the shore, creating long sandbars or spits that grow parallel to the shoreline.

Sand is continuously eroded and deposited along the shore by waves and currents. **Longshore drift** is the process that moves sand along a shore. Look at Figure 31 to see how longshore drift occurs. Waves carrying sediment approach the shore at an angle. As the waves break, they carry sand up the beach at that angle. The water and sand then flow directly back toward the water. In this way, longshore drift produces a zigzag motion that moves sand great distances along a shore.

Deposition by Currents and Waves The sediment that is eroded from a coastline or brought to the ocean by rivers is also deposited. Currents and waves deposit sediment in bays and inlets as the water slows down. Over time, sediment can collect along the shore. A shoreline covered with sand or other sediment is a beach. In many areas, rivers that discharge into the ocean are the main source of the sand on ocean beaches.

Currents move large amounts of sediment parallel to the shore. When these currents meet a bend in the shoreline, they slow down and deposit the sediment. This deposit is called a spit.

Section 23.5 Assessment

Reviewing Concepts

1. How do temperature and pressure change with depth within the ocean?
2. Compare and contrast how surface currents and density currents form.
3. What causes upwelling?
4. What happens to rock as waves hit the shore?
5. What process moves sand down a coastline?

Critical Thinking

6. **Predicting** El Niño is a weather event in the Pacific Ocean. It pushes warm water over the cold current that flows along the western coast of South America, where upwelling normally occurs. How might El Niño affect the fishing industry in this area?
7. **Developing Hypotheses** A dam is built on a major river that flows into the ocean. Several years later, people observe that nearby ocean beaches have less sand than before. Develop a hypothesis to explain this phenomenon.

Connecting Concepts

Energy Conversion Use what you learned about energy conversion in Section 15.2 to explain how surface currents are produced.

3 ASSESS

Evaluate Understanding L2

Have students create a simple cross-sectional diagram describing how physical factors change with depth in the ocean. Include temperature, depth, and light, and draw arrows showing whether they increase or decrease with depth.

Reteach L1

Use Figure 27 to review how surface currents are formed, and how they circulate water around the world's oceans.

Connecting Concepts

Wind has kinetic energy. As molecules of air moving primarily in a certain direction strike the ocean's surface, energy is transferred from the air to the ocean. Molecules of water gain kinetic energy and move primarily in the direction that the wind is blowing.

Interactive Textbook If your class subscribes to the Interactive Textbook, use it to review key concepts in Section 23.5.

Answer to . . .

Figure 29 *Because upwelling brings nutrients from the deep ocean, which supports large amounts of algae that provide food for fish*

Section 23.5 Assessment

1. Temperature decreases with depth in the ocean, and pressure increases with depth in the ocean.
2. Surface currents are caused by wind blowing across the ocean surface. Density currents are deep currents caused by differences in the density of ocean water.
3. Upwelling is caused as warm water is blown aside by winds and currents, allowing colder water to rise from the deep ocean.
4. Rock is eroded by processes such as hydraulic action and abrasion as waves hit the shore.
5. Longshore drift moves sand along a coastline.
6. El Niño may diminish or prevent the normal upwelling that takes place along the western coast of South America. This would reduce the supply of nutrients to this region and hurt the local fishing industry, as fish would starve or be driven elsewhere to find food.
7. A major river carries sediment, including sand, to the ocean, where it is deposited as the water slows down. A dam would likely reduce the movement of sediment to the ocean. Erosion will eventually wear away or move sand from the beach, and nearby beaches will have less sand as the existing supply of sand is not being replenished.

CONCEPTS in Action

Exploring the Ocean L2

Background

One of the first practical ways of finding the depth of the deepest parts of the ocean was the development of sonar in 1919. Sonar is still used today, although there have been many advances. Technologies such as rapid-scanning sonar, side-scan sonar, and WPESS (within-pulse electronic-sector-scanning) sonar enable scientists to map the relief of the ocean floor with great precision.

Build Science Skills L2

Using Models ACTIVITY

Purpose Students will make a vertical scale model of the ocean floor to compare the size of ocean features with those above land.

Materials large sheets of paper connected to make a 1.5-m square, metric ruler, markers

Class Time 20–30 minutes

Procedure Have students work in groups. Ask them to find the middle of their paper, and draw a line across the expanse. This represents sea level. Tell them that they will be making a vertical scale model (5 cm = 1000 m) of features on the ocean floor to compare them to features on land. Explain that it is not possible to do the model to scale horizontally because there is not enough room in the classroom! Ask them to include the continental shelf and slope; the abyssal plain at an average depth of 3800 m; Mauna Kea, Hawaii at 9698 m off the ocean floor (4260 m above sea level); and the Mariana Trench at a maximum depth of 11,034 m. Ask students also to mark two altitudes above sea level for comparison: Mount Everest at 8848 m and your own locality.

Expected Outcome Students will be able to compare the depth of ocean features to those on land, and come to a greater understanding of the relief of Earth's surface.
Visual, Logical

CONCEPTS in Action

Exploring the Ocean

About 71 percent of Earth's surface is covered by oceans and seas. Within the last century, deep-sea explorations have revealed amazing features of the ocean floor. These include continental slopes, undersea mountains, and the mid-ocean ridges that form between Earth's plates.

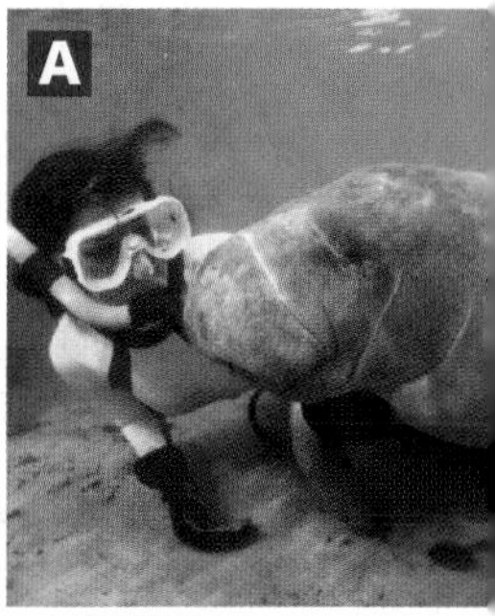
A

Snorkeling
Snorkeling allows great freedom of movement. However, a diver must constantly return to the surface to breathe.

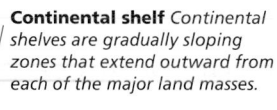

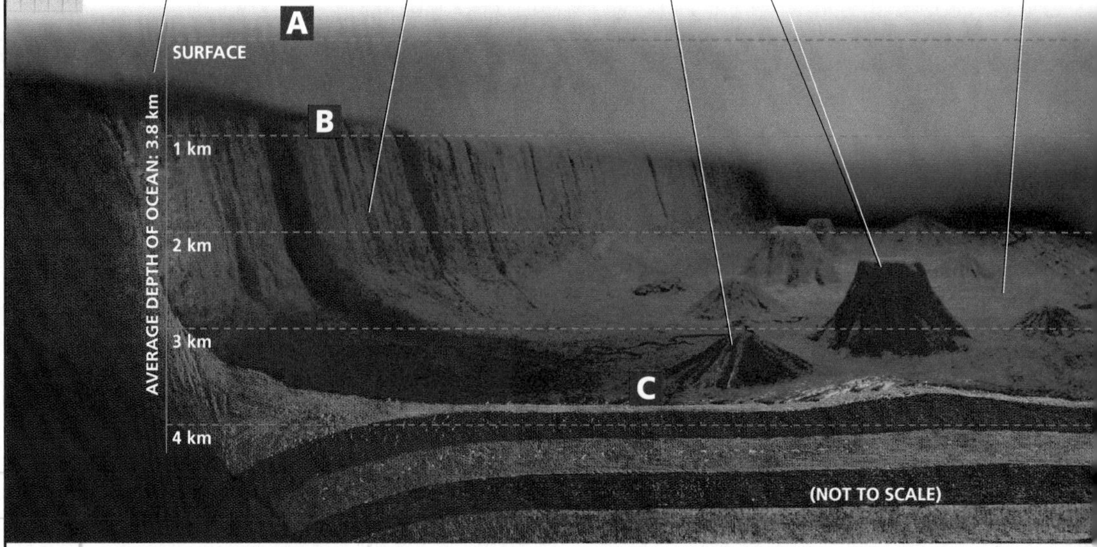
Continental shelf *Continental shelves are gradually sloping zones that extend outward from each of the major land masses.*
Guyot *Some seamounts are guyots—extinct volcanoes with flat tops. Guyots were once islands, but are now below water because the entire ocean floor sinks as it gets older.*
Continental slope *This steep incline extends downward from the edge of a continental shelf.*
Seamount *Seamounts are submarine mountains whose peaks do not break the ocean's surface.*
Abyssal plain *Thick layers of sediment, formed by dust and the remains of microscopic organisms, cover these broad, flat expanses of sea floor.*
A
SURFACE
B
AVERAGE DEPTH OF OCEAN: 3.8 km
1 km
2 km
3 km
4 km
C
(NOT TO SCALE)

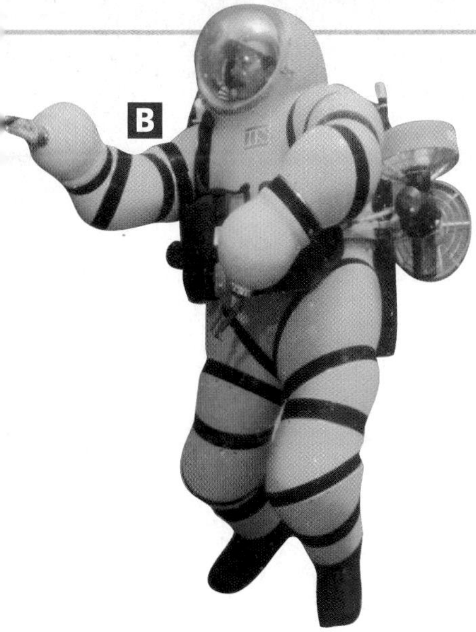
B

Deep-sea diver
Surface areas of the ocean (50 m or less in depth) can be explored by scuba divers, who breathe from tanks of compressed air. However, advanced deep sea diving suits allow divers to operate at depths as great as 700 m. The type shown here includes propellors that are operated by the diver's feet.

C

Mid-ocean ridge *This line of mountains marks a boundary between diverging tectonic plates. New oceanic crust forms at the mid-ocean ridge.*

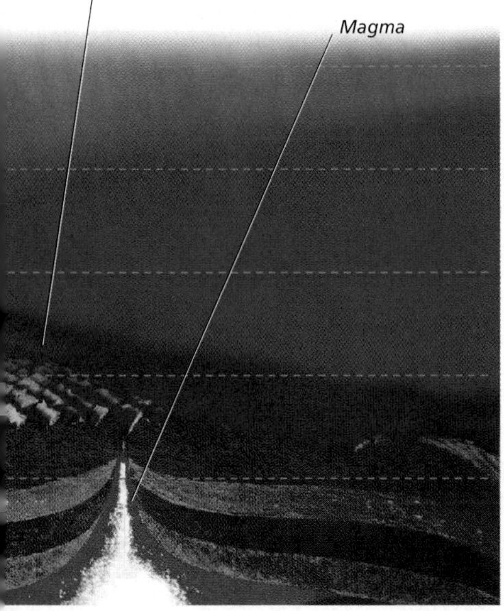
Magma

Deep-sea exploration
Submersibles—small, maneuverable submarines with data-collecting equipment—enable researchers to explore the ocean depths. *Alvin* (shown above) can dive to a maximum depth of about 4 km. Scientists aboard *Alvin* discovered the first hydrothermal vents in the Pacific Ocean in 1977. These vents are underwater hot springs located along ocean ridges, where new oceanic crust is forming. The vents spew dark, heated, mineral-rich fluids which support a unique group of organisms.

Going Further

- New technologies allow scientists to discover and explore many sunken ships, including the *Titanic,* Roman trading ships, and pirate vessels. Research how scientists are able to locate and explore such ships. Write a short essay summarizing what you have learned.
- Take a Discovery Channel Video Field Trip by watching "Under the Sea."

Discovery Channel School
Video Field Trip

Going Further

Robert Ballard and others have made a series of exciting underwater discoveries in recent years, including discoveries of ancient shipwrecks and partially sunken ancient cities. They have also made discoveries of more recent historical significance, such as the *Lusitania*, the *Bismarck*, and *PT-109*. Sonar, remotely controlled submersibles, and satellites are among the technologies that have made these discoveries possible. A new generation of submersibles is being planned, including *Deep Flight*, a so-called underwater airplane.
Verbal

Discovery Channel School

Video Field Trip

Under the Sea

After students have viewed the Video Field Trip, ask them the following questions: **How does sonar work?** *(It sends sound signals to the ocean floor and detects their return. This gives information about the object that reflected the sound and where it is located.)* **Describe how sonar was used to help locate the space landing vehicle Liberty Bell.** *(Using NASA's best estimates of where to search, sonar images were taken over the area to detect objects on the ocean floor. The most likely objects were investigated with an undersea vehicle.)* **Why is it impractical to map the mountains and valleys beneath the sea using sonar?** *(The process is too slow to scan over such a large area as the ocean.)* **How are satellites used to map the ocean floor?** *(The surface of the ocean has bumps and dips too small to be seen. These mimic the ocean floor. A satellite with a precise altimeter can measure these dips and bumps to give information about the depth of the ocean floor.)*

1 FOCUS

Objectives

23.6.1 **Distinguish** between the relative and absolute dating of rocks.

23.6.2 **Describe** the geologic time scale and what happened during the major divisions of geologic time.

Reading Focus

Build Vocabulary L2

Compare/Contrast Table Have students make a simple T-Chart with the column headings Relative Age and Absolute Age. Instruct students to fill in the chart as they read the section. They should include an explanation of how scientists would determine the relative and absolute age of rocks.

Reading Strategy L2

Students' questions may include: **a.** What events mark the beginning and end of each geologic era? **b.** When did the dinosaurs live?

2 INSTRUCT

Determining the Age of Rocks

Build Reading Literacy L1

Relate Text and Visuals Refer to page **190D** in **Chapter 7**, which provides the guidelines for relating text and visuals.

Have students read all of p. 732. Point to the photograph of the Grand Canyon in Figure 32 and help students notice the layers. Ask, **What type of rock are these layers composed of?** *(Sedimentary)* Direct students to examine Figure 33 and ask, **Would a fossil found in the Hermit shale be older or younger than a fossil in the Supai sandstone?** *(Younger)*
Visual

23.6 Earth's History

Reading Focus

Key Concepts

- How do geologists determine the relative and absolute ages of rock layers?
- What forms the basis for the geologic time scale?
- What are the major divisions of Earth's history?

Vocabulary

- fossils
- relative age
- law of superposition
- extinct
- index fossils
- absolute age
- era
- periods
- mass extinction

Reading Strategy

Previewing Copy the table below. Before you read, examine Figures 34 and 36 to help you understand about geologic time. Write at least two questions about them in the table. As you read, write answers to your questions.

Questions on Geologic Time
a. ____________ ?
b. ____________ ?

The Grand Canyon slices down nearly two kilometers through many horizontal layers of rock. Each layer formed millions of years ago, as a shallow sea repeatedly flooded this part of North America. The sea slowly filled up with a flat layer of sediment that had eroded from the nearby land. The next time the sea flooded the land, a new, flat sedimentary layer formed on top of the older layer beneath it. As the layers of sediment increased, they slowly changed to rock. At the same time, the remains of living things trapped in the sediment became fossils. **Fossils** are the preserved remains or traces of once living things.

Determining the Age of Rocks

Suppose that a geologist finds a fossil in a sedimentary rock near the rim of the Grand Canyon. Is this fossil older or younger than a fossil found near the canyon bottom? The geologist is trying to determine the relative age of the fossil as well as that of the rock containing it. The **relative age** of a rock is its age compared to the ages of other rocks above or below it in a sequence of rock layers. Figure 33 shows the sequence of rock layers in the Grand Canyon.

Figure 32 Layers of rock are deposited horizontally, like the layers of the Grand Canyon shown here.

732 *Chapter 23*

Section Resources

Print

- ***Reading and Study Workbook With Math Support,*** Section 23.6 and **Math Skill:** Exploring Radioactive Dating
- ***Transparencies,*** Section 23.6

Technology

- ***Interactive Textbook,*** Section 23.6
- ***Presentation Pro CD-ROM,*** Section 23.6
- ***Go Online,*** *Science News,* Earth's history

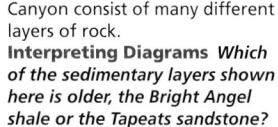

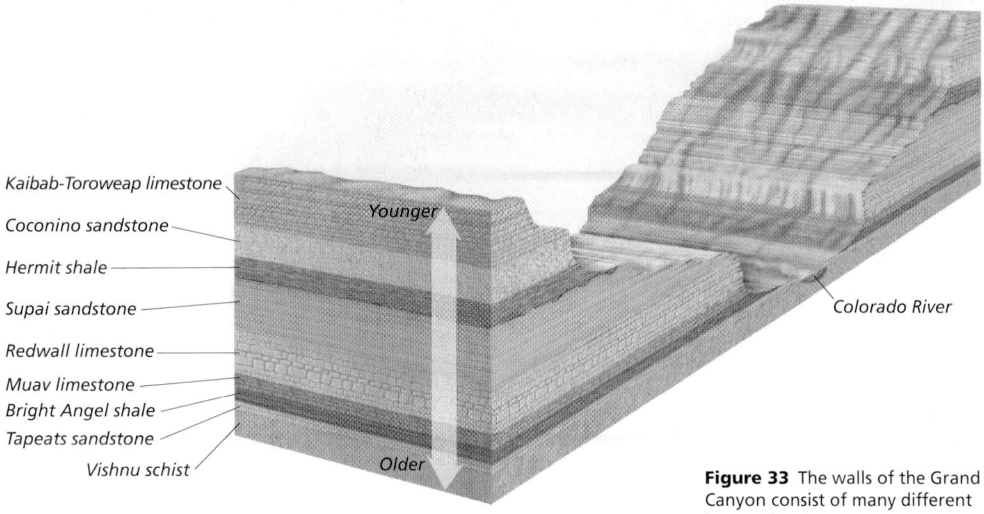
Kaibab-Toroweap limestone
Coconino sandstone
Hermit shale
Supai sandstone
Redwall limestone
Muav limestone
Bright Angel shale
Tapeats sandstone
Vishnu schist
Younger
Older
Colorado River

Figure 33 The walls of the Grand Canyon consist of many different layers of rock.
Interpreting Diagrams ***Which of the sedimentary layers shown here is older, the Bright Angel shale or the Tapeats sandstone? Explain your answer.***

The Law of Superposition Sedimentary rocks form as horizontal layers. Geologists have used this fact to establish a principle for determining the relative ages of rocks. The **law of superposition** states that if rock layers are undisturbed, younger rocks lie above older rocks, and the oldest rocks are at the bottom. **Geologists use the law of superposition to determine the relative ages of sedimentary rocks from the sequence of rock layers and the fossils within each layer.** Rock layers often extend over large regions. Geologists have examined sedimentary rocks from locations around the world to develop a relative time scale for many rock layers.

Index Fossils and Relative Dating Geologists can also determine the relative ages of sedimentary rocks by examining the fossils that are found in them. Most types of organisms preserved as fossils are now extinct. An **extinct** type of organism is one that no longer exists.

Fossils of organisms that are easily identified, occurred over a large area, and lived during a well-defined period of time are called **index fossils.** With index fossils, geologists can determine the relative ages of rocks. If a rock contains examples of an index fossil, then the rock must have formed during the time that that organism lived.

Earth's Surface 733

Build Science Skills L2

Inferring Tell students that they can learn a lot about the geologic history of a region just by looking at rocks and landforms. Instruct students to study Figures 32 and 33. Then, using what they know about how different types of rocks and geologic features are formed, have them work in groups to create a relative timeline describing the evolution of the Grand Canyon. *(Based on what they have learned in Chapters 22 and 23, students should be able to determine that the layers were deposited in a shallow sea environment. Limestone layers were created by the shells of marine organisms, while the shale and sandstone were deposited when sediment was eroded from nearby landscapes. Students should infer the order in which the rock layers were formed. Tectonic uplift or a lowering of the sea level caused the shallow sea to drain. Then, the Colorado River and its tributaries eroded the rock layers, exposing them to additional erosion by wind.)*
Logical, Portfolio

Customize for Inclusion Students

Gifted
The topic of geologic history offers ample opportunities for extended studies. Interested students can research any of the geologic eras or periods in more detail. Some students may have interest in fossils or prehistoric organisms. Have students contact the geology or paleontology department in your local community or state college, the regional USGS office, or a local science museum for information on fossils in your area. Ask students to present their research to the class.

Answer to . . .

Figure 33 *The Tapeats sandstone; according to the law of superposition, in a sequence of undisturbed sedimentary rock layers, older layers lie below younger layers.*

Problem-Solving Activity

Interpreting Rock Layers L2

Answers

1. B; J
2. Younger, since E and J are the same age and F lies atop E
3. Layer D must be more than 430 million years old.
4. From oldest to youngest, the order of the rock layers is: A, B, C, D and K, E and J, F and I, H, G

For Extra Help L1

If students are having difficulty getting started, have them sort out the processes that produced the formations in the diagram by constructing a simple cross-sectional drawing. Have them begin the flowchart with eight boxes representing the formation of the eight different horizontal sedimentary layers, in order, using the same colors as in the map. Then, have them cut apart one part of the rock mass and drop it down to simulate faulting.
Kinesthetic

A Brief History of Earth

Use Visuals L2

Figure 34 Point out that the break in the scale between Precambrian time and the Paleozoic Era is because the relative length of Precambrian time is too long to show in this figure. Ask, **How long was Precambrian time?** *(About 4.1 billion years, or about 88% of Earth's history)* **How long has the current period lasted?** *(About 18 million years)* **When was the Jurassic Period?** *(213–145 million years ago)*
Visual

Problem-Solving Activity

Interpreting Rock Layers

The law of superposition states that in undisturbed beds, younger sedimentary rocks lie on top of older sedimentary layers. But over time, layers of sedimentary rock can change. Deformation can produce faults and folds. Erosion can remove some layers of rock entirely. Igneous dikes may cut across the layers. As you determine the relative ages of rock layers, remember these rules:

- Sedimentary rock layers are horizontal before they deform.
- A fault or dike did not exist when the sedimentary layers formed, so it is younger than the layers it cuts across.

Study the rock layers in the diagram, and then answer the following questions.

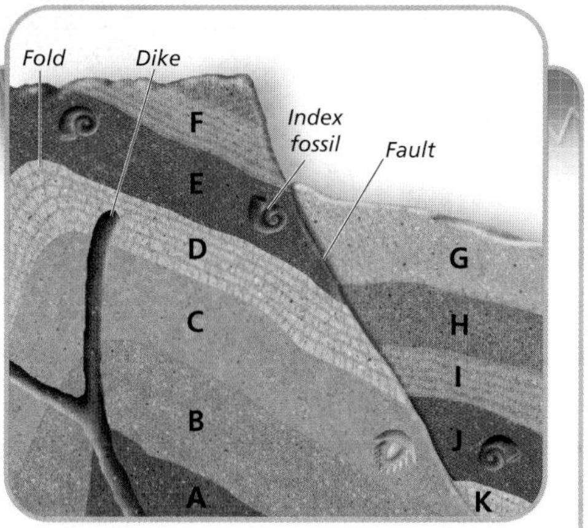
Fold
Dike
Index fossil
Fault
F
E
D
C
B
A
G
H
I
J
K

1. **Inferring** Which rock layer is older, B or E? J or G?
2. **Analyzing Data** Would a fossil in layer F be older or younger than fossils from layer J?
3. **Inferring** If the dike is 430 million years old, what can you say about the age of layer D?
4. **Drawing Conclusions** Make a table showing the relative ages of all the layers in the diagram, from oldest to youngest.

Radioactive Dating **Geologists use radioactive dating to determine the absolute ages of rocks.** A rock's **absolute age** is the time that has passed since the rock formed. When a rock forms, it has a known ratio of radioactive and stable isotopes. Because a radioisotope decays into a stable isotope at a steady rate as the rock ages, scientists can measure this ratio to find the rock's absolute age. Recall from chemistry that the time for half of a radioisotope to decay is called its half-life. Many igneous rocks are very old, so radioisotopes with a very long half-life are used to find their absolute age. A common radioisotope for dating older rocks is potassium-40, which has a half-life of 1.3 billion years.

A Brief History of Earth

Geologists have used information about the relative and absolute ages of rocks to develop a time line for the history of Earth. **The geologic time scale is based on the relative ages of rock layers and the use of radioactive dating to find the absolute ages of rocks.** The geologic time scale, shown in Figure 34, is a way of dividing Earth's history.

Figure 34 The geologic time scale shows the major intervals in Earth's history. **Interpreting Diagrams** *What three periods make up the Mesozoic Era?*

GEOLOGIC TIME SCALE
Millions of years ago

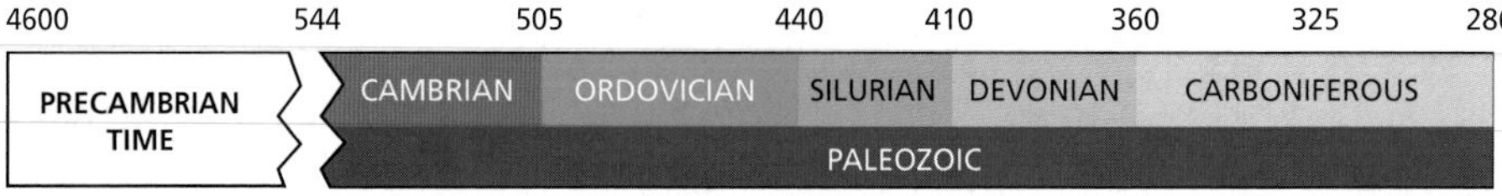
4600
544
505
440
410
360
325
286
PRECAMBRIAN TIME
CAMBRIAN
ORDOVICIAN
SILURIAN
DEVONIAN
CARBONIFEROUS
PALEOZOIC

Facts and Figures

Names on the Geologic Time Scale
The names of the periods are taken from the locations where some of the rocks from these periods were found. "Devonian" is from Devon, England. "Jurassic" is from the Jura Mountains in Switzerland. "Cambrian" comes from Cambria, an old name for the principality of Wales.

Earth's history is divided into several large units, called eras. Each **era** is one major stage in Earth's history. An era is further divided into smaller units called **periods.** Eras and periods help scientists locate changes and events in Earth's history.

Some boundaries between eras mark a time when many different kinds of organisms became extinct within a relatively short time. Such an event is called a **mass extinction.** Scientists have developed several theories to explain what caused mass extinctions. These theories include asteroid impacts, volcanic activity, disease, and climate change.

For nearly 4 billion years, changes in Earth's surface, atmosphere, and oceans have effected the development of living things. Living things, in turn, have changed Earth. **The major divisions of Earth's history are Precambrian time and the Paleozoic, Mesozoic, and Cenozoic Eras.**

Precambrian Time: 4.6 Billion–544 Million Years Ago

The earliest portion of Earth's history, known as Precambrian time, includes the formation of Earth and the early development of life. At first, Earth's surface was largely molten and was continually bombarded by meteorites. By 4 billion years ago, the forces that cause plate movement were already at work. Soon after, one-celled organisms appeared in the oceans. Tiny photosynthetic organisms took up carbon dioxide from the atmosphere and released oxygen. Later in the Precambrian, simple soft-bodied animals developed. Since soft bodies don't usually form fossils, there are few fossils from Precambrian time.

Paleozoic Era: 544–248 Million Years Ago Early in the Cambrian period (the first period of the Paleozoic Era), a variety of animals developed in the oceans. Scientists think that some of these animals were related to the clams and worms found in the oceans today. Many other types of early animals, such as those shown in Figure 35, became extinct. But more than 450 million years ago, fishes evolved in the oceans. Plants and animals, including early reptiles, began to live on land. Dense forests of mosses and cone-bearing plants covered much of the land.

At times during the Paleozoic, parts of many continents were flooded by seas. Thick layers of sediment deposited in these seas formed much of the sedimentary rock found on the continents today. During the last period of the Paleozoic Era, the Permian period, the supercontinent Pangaea formed.

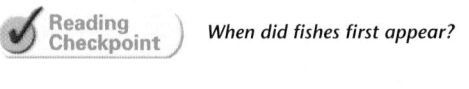

Reading Checkpoint *When did fishes first appear?*

Go Online SCIENCE NEWS

For: Articles on Earth's history
Visit: PHSchool.com
Web Code: cce-3236

Figure 35 During the early Paleozoic Era, life began to evolve into many different forms. This scene shows how life might have looked on the sea floor during the Cambrian Period.

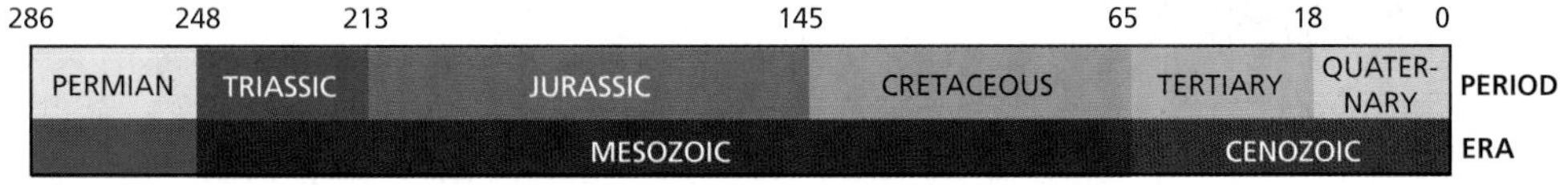

286
248
213
145
65
18
0
PERMIAN
TRIASSIC
JURASSIC
CRETACEOUS
TERTIARY
QUATER-NARY
PERIOD
MESOZOIC
CENOZOIC
ERA

Integrate Chemistry L2

Half of the remaining potassium-40 in a rock will decay to Ar^{40} every 1.3 billion years. This means that if a rock is 3.9 billion years old, or three half-lives of potassium-40, the rock will contain $\frac{1}{8}$ of its original potassium-40. For recent geologic events like volcanic eruptions, the isotope carbon-14 is often used to measure the age. Carbon-14 has a half-life of 5730 years, so it is useful for dating geologic and anthropological objects that are less than a hundred thousand years old. Ask, **If three-quarters of the carbon-14 in a piece of pottery had decayed into daughter isotopes, approximately how old is the pottery?** *(11,460 years)* **Why wouldn't carbon-14 be useful for dating rocks?** *(The ages of rocks are typically in the tens or hundreds of millions of years. With a half-life of only 5730 years, only a miniscule amount of carbon-14 would be left in a rock that old.)*
Logical

Build Reading Literacy L1

Identify Main Idea/Details Refer to page **702D** in this chapter, which provides the guidelines for identifying main idea and details.

Using four index cards, have students write the name of each geologic era on a card. While reading A Brief History of Earth, have students record the main details of each era on the appropriate index card. Encourage students to use bullet points, rather than copying whole sentences. Have the students share their cards in small groups and fill in any missing main details, then align them in geologic time.
Verbal, Group

Go Online SCIENCE NEWS

Science News provides students with current information on Earth's history.

Facts and Figures

Early History Earth, like the rest of the solar system, formed about 4.6 billion years ago out of a cloud of dust and gas. After 50 million years, Earth was close to its current size and was so hot it was possibly entirely molten. The following 4.5 billion years have been a period of continuous cooling.

The molten state of early Earth allowed the planet to separate into different layers. The surface was not stable, so the early crust would sink back into the molten interior. Eventually, Earth cooled enough to resemble the planet you see today. Water vapor in the atmosphere condensed to form rain and create the oceans. The mantle solidified, and the continental crust began to form at the surface. The core cooled enough so that the inner core began to solidify. The exact timing of these events is uncertain. However, radioactive dating shows that Earth had developed a system of plate tectonics approximately 4 billion years ago.

Answer to . . .

Figure 34 *The Triassic, Jurassic, and Cretaceous periods*

Reading Checkpoint *Fishes first appeared in the early Paleozoic Era, more than 450 million years ago.*

Use Visuals L1

Figure 36 Point out that a larger amount of space in the visual is allotted to more recent times, and that the bulk of Earth history is in the smallest spirals. This is because there is much more known about the Paleozoic, Mesozoic, and Cenozoic eras than Precambrian time, and also because many more species of life existed during the more recent periods. Ask, **When did the Colorado River begin eroding the rock layers that form the Grand Canyon?** *(In the Tertiary period)* **When did photosynthesis evolve?** *(In Precambrian time)* **In what period did the plants that would eventually become coal deposits live?** *(In the Carboniferous)* **What were some of the first multicellular animals?** *(Worms and jellyfish)*
Visual

Build Science Skills L2

Using Models Have students examine Figures 34 and 36. Both visuals represent the geologic time scale. Have students work in groups to create their own model to describe geologic time. One possible method would use a toilet paper roll, with each square representing a certain length of geologic time. Cash register tape can also be used. Have each group present its model to the class.
Kinesthetic, Group

Mesozoic Era: 248–65 Million Years Ago The Mesozoic Era was the time of the dinosaurs. The first dinosaurs appeared about 225 million years ago. About this same time, Pangaea began to break up. The first mammals, which evolved from warm-blooded reptiles, also appeared in the Mesozoic. Many areas had a warm, wet climate. Another major development was the appearance of flowering plants.

All the dinosaurs and many other types of organisms were killed at the end of the Mesozoic Era. What caused this mass extinction?

Figure 36 This spiral diagram provides an overview of Earth's history. Start at the bottom left, which begins with Earth's formation approximately 4.6 billion years ago. Then follow the spiral upward to see many of the major events in the history of life and geology on Earth. **Interpreting Diagrams** ***During what era did small mammals first appear?***

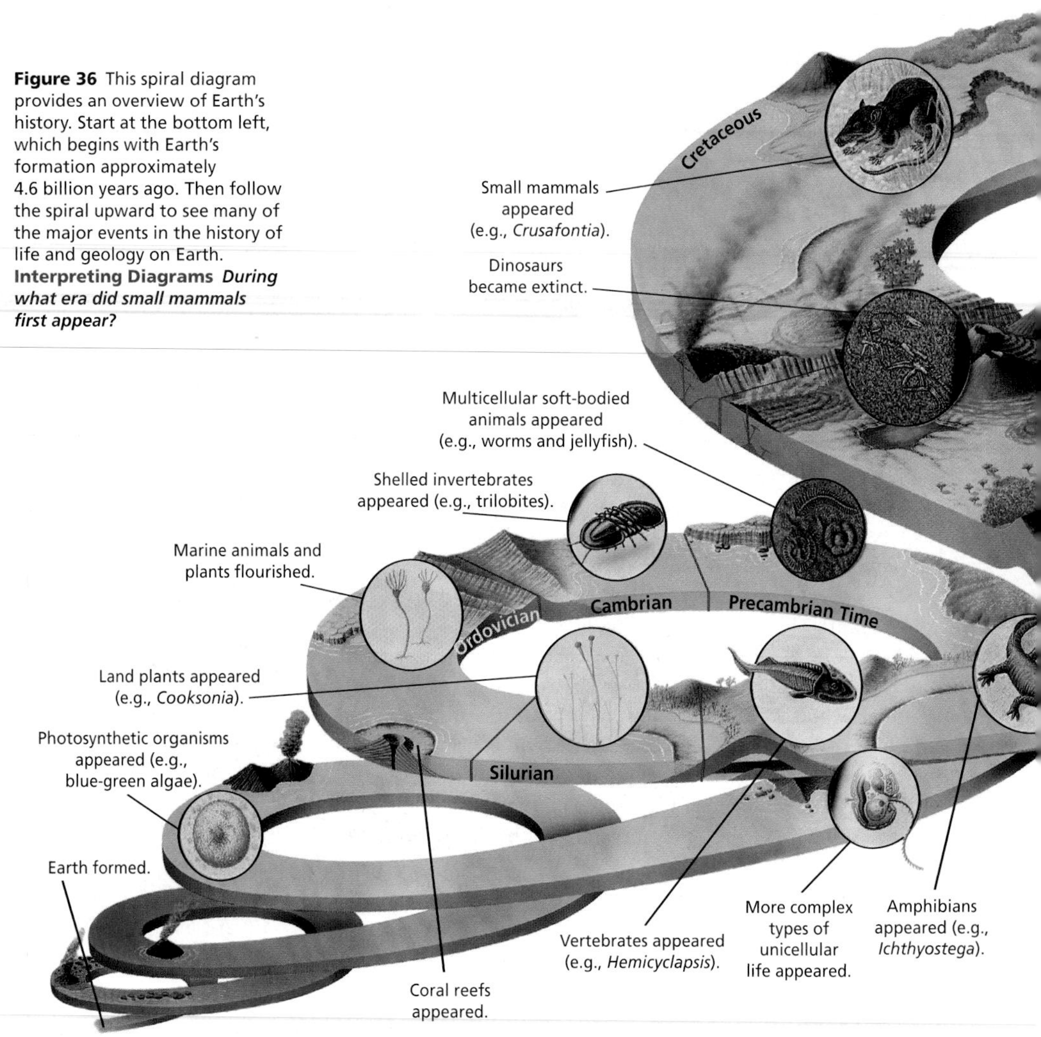

Cretaceous
Small mammals appeared (e.g., *Crusafontia*).
Dinosaurs became extinct.
Multicellular soft-bodied animals appeared (e.g., worms and jellyfish).
Shelled invertebrates appeared (e.g., trilobites).
Marine animals and plants flourished.
Ordovician
Cambrian
Precambrian Time
Land plants appeared (e.g., *Cooksonia*).
Photosynthetic organisms appeared (e.g., blue-green algae).
Silurian
Earth formed.
Vertebrates appeared (e.g., *Hemicyclapsis*).
More complex types of unicellular life appeared.
Amphibians appeared (e.g., *Ichthyostega*).
Coral reefs appeared.

Facts and Figures

Trilobites One of the earliest fossil groups is the trilobites. These distinctive three-segmented arthropods appeared in a fully developed form 540 million years ago in the Cambrian period, suggesting that they had evolved sometime during Precambrian time. Different groups of trilobites are often used as index fossils. Geologists use index fossils to get relative dates of rock layers. Because of their interesting form, natural beauty, and ancient origin, trilobites have been popular with fossil collectors throughout time, and are commonly used for jewelry.

The leading hypothesis is that the cause was the impact of one or more large asteroids. Such an impact would have filled the atmosphere with ejected rock and dust and the smoke from enormous fires, blocking out sunlight worldwide. It is possible that volcanic activity at this time had already cooled global climates, worsening the effects of the impact.

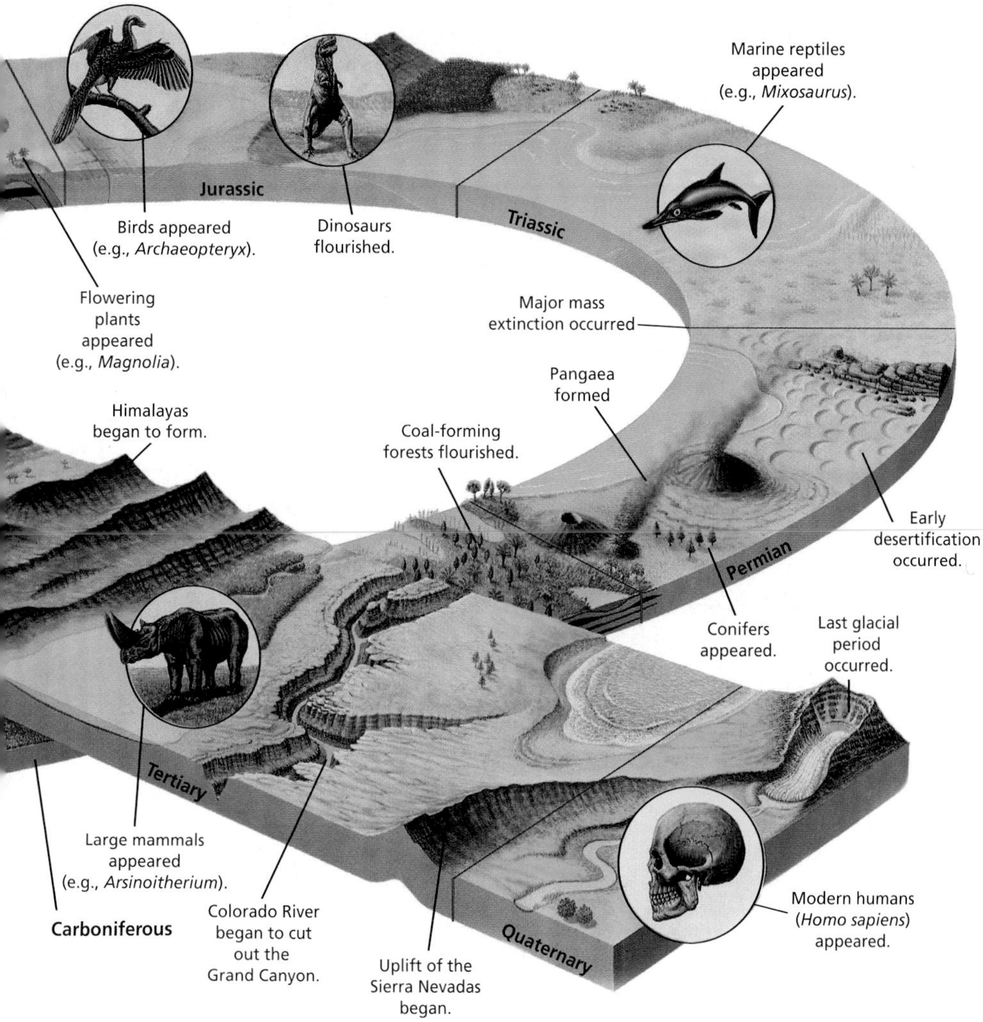

Marine reptiles appeared (e.g., *Mixosaurus*).
Jurassic
Triassic
Birds appeared (e.g., *Archaeopteryx*).
Dinosaurs flourished.
Flowering plants appeared (e.g., *Magnolia*).
Major mass extinction occurred
Pangaea formed
Himalayas began to form.
Coal-forming forests flourished.
Early desertification occurred.
Permian
Conifers appeared.
Last glacial period occurred.
Tertiary
Large mammals appeared (e.g., *Arsinoitherium*).
Carboniferous
Colorado River began to cut out the Grand Canyon.
Uplift of the Sierra Nevadas began.
Quaternary
Modern humans (*Homo sapiens*) appeared.

Address Misconceptions

L2

A common misconception, perhaps in part due to popular cartoons, is that dinosaurs coexisted with early humans. Point out that all remaining dinosaurs were killed in a mass extinction 65 million years ago, and that modern humans did not evolve until approximately 100,000 years ago. Have students mark the extinction of dinosaurs and the evolution of humans on their geologic time models in the Build Science Skills activity on p. 736. **Logical**

Facts and Figures

Mass Extinctions The boundaries between geologic eras are based upon observations of index fossils. These boundaries represent times that lifeforms changed suddenly. In many cases, they mark points of mass extinctions of many species around the globe. There are many possible causes for these mass extinctions, including meteorite impacts, high volcanic activity, rapid changes in climate, and even nearby supernova explosions.

The Permian period ended with the largest mass extinction in Earth's history. Scientists aren't certain what caused this mass extinction of about 90% of Earth's oceanic species.

The best known of the extinctions is the Mesozoic-Cenozoic boundary, 65 million years ago, when all remaining species of dinosaurs became extinct. Geologic evidence supports the hypothesis that one or more asteroid impacts played a major role in this mass extinction event.

Answer to . . .

Figure 36 *The Mesozoic Era*

Section 23.6 (continued)

3 ASSESS

Evaluate Understanding L2

Ask students to write a quiz question on the topic of geologic history. Have students work in groups to quiz each other.

Reteach L1

Use Figure 36 to discuss the main events that occurred in each era of geological time.

Math Practice

8. 10.0 milligrams $\times \frac{1}{2} \times \frac{1}{2} =$ 2.5 milligrams of carbon-14
9. 50 milligrams of potassium-40 will decay to 12.5 milligrams in two half-lives, a period of 2.6 billion years.

Interactive Textbook If your class subscribes to the Interactive Textbook, use it to review key concepts in Section 23.6.

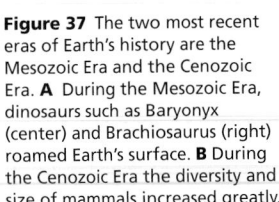

Figure 37 The two most recent eras of Earth's history are the Mesozoic Era and the Cenozoic Era. **A** During the Mesozoic Era, dinosaurs such as Baryonyx (center) and Brachiosaurus (right) roamed Earth's surface. **B** During the Cenozoic Era the diversity and size of mammals increased greatly.

Cenozoic Era: 65 Million Years Ago to the Present

Since the end of the Mesozoic Era, Earth has been in the Cenozoic Era. During this time, Earth's climate has generally become cooler and drier. Several ice ages have come and gone in the last 5 million years.

Although small mammals existed during the Mesozoic Era, mammals became very diverse and widespread during the Cenozoic Era. Some of these mammals, like those in Figure 37B, were much larger than modern land mammals. About 100,000 years ago, modern humans first appeared in Africa. Since then, humans have migrated to every continent. Today, humans are the dominant form of life on Earth. They have a significant influence on Earth's environments.

Section 23.6 Assessment

Reviewing Concepts

1. What evidence do geologists use to determine the relative age of rocks?
2. How can the absolute age of a rock be determined?
3. What types of information did geologists use to develop the geologic time scale?
4. How does the geologic time scale divide Earth's history?
5. What is one hypothesis about the cause of the dinosaurs' extinction?

Critical Thinking

6. **Inferring** Geologists in two widely separated locations find rocks that contain fossils of an extinct organism that lived for only a brief time. What can the geologists conclude about the ages of the rocks?
7. **Drawing Conclusions** Using radioactive dating, geologists determine that a layer of igneous rock from a lava flow is 60 million years old. What can you conclude about the age of a layer of sedimentary rock that lies just below the igneous rock? Explain.

Math Practice

8. A fossil contains 10.0 milligrams of radioactive carbon-14. How much carbon-14 will remain after two half-lives?
9. How long will it take for the amount of potassium-40, which has a half-life of 1.3 billion years, in a rock to decay from 50.0 milligrams to 12.5 milligrams?

Section 23.6 Assessment

1. Geologists use the law of superposition and index fossils to determine the relative age of rocks.
2. Geologists use radioactive dating to determine the absolute age of a rock.
3. Geologists used information on the relative and absolute dating of rocks to develop the geologic time scale.
4. The geologic time scale divides Earth's history into a series of eras and periods. The boundaries between geologic time periods are times that separate the kinds of fossils that are found, and represent times when life forms changed suddenly.
5. The dinosaurs likely became extinct through the impact of one or more large asteroids with Earth. This effect may have been increased by a large amount of volcanic activity at that time.
6. Since both rocks contain the same index fossil, the scientists can conclude that the rocks were formed at about the same time.
7. According to the law of superposition, a younger rock layer is found atop an older rock layer if the layers are undisturbed. The underlying layer of sedimentary rock must be somewhat more than 60 million years old.

Exploration Lab

Modeling Erosion

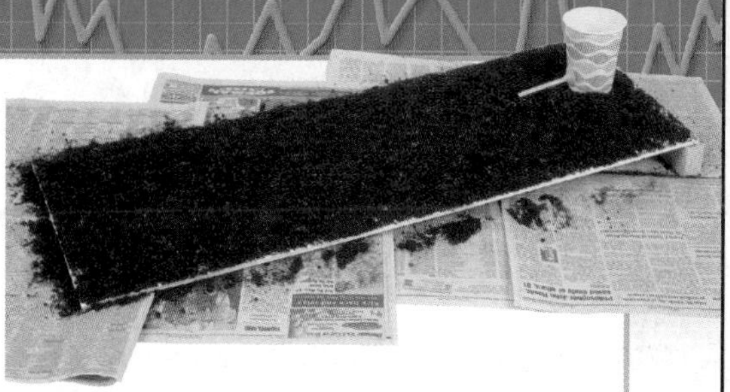

Moving water is the major cause of erosion on Earth. In this lab, you will investigate some factors that affect the rate of erosion by moving water.

Problem What are some of the factors that affect the rate of water erosion?

Materials

- metric ruler
- large sheet of cardboard
- plastic wrap
- newspaper
- soil
- blocks
- pencil
- paper cup
- scissors
- drinking straw
- modeling clay
- paper towels
- small rocks

Skills Using Models, Inferring

Procedure

1. On a separate sheet of paper, make a data table with 4 columns and 4 rows. Label the columns Elevation of Cardboard, Slope of Cardboard, Rocks, and Observations.
2. Measure and record the length of the cardboard in centimeters. Wrap the cardboard with plastic wrap to keep it dry.
3. Put several sheets of newspaper on a flat surface. Place cardboard on the newspaper and spread a thin layer of soil over the cardboard.
4. To model a hillside, raise one end of the cardboard about 5 cm from the flat surface by placing blocks under one end.
5. Using a pencil, make a hole in a paper cup 1 cm from the bottom.
6. Cut the straw in half with the scissors and insert the end of one of the halves 2 cm into the hole in the cup.
7. Use modeling clay to seal the hole around the straw. Make sure that the clay forms a tight seal around the straw.
8. Place the cup in the middle of the raised end of the cardboard, so that the straw is pointing downhill as shown.
9. Place your finger over the straw's opening as another student fills the cup with water.
10. Remove your finger. Record your observations in your data table.
11. Clean the cardboard with paper towels and cover it again with soil. Put used soil in the trash.
12. Now use blocks to raise the end of the cardboard 15 cm above the flat surface. Repeat Steps 8 through 11.
13. Lower the end of the cardboard to 5 cm above the flat surface. Repeat Steps 8 through 11 again, but this time place a small rock on the cardboard directly in front of the straw. In your data table, record your observations about how water moves around the rock.
14. Repeat Step 13, but this time place a pile of several small rocks on the cardboard directly in front of the straw. In your data table, record your observations about how water moves around the rocks.

Analyze and Conclude

1. **Observing** Does water erosion create smooth curves or sharp angles?
2. **Analyzing Data** How did increasing the elevation of the cardboard affect the speed of the water?
3. **Calculating** The slope of a hillside is equal to its height divided by the horizontal distance it covers. Using the length of the table under the cardboard and the height it was raised, calculate and record the slope of the model hillside in each row of your data table.
4. **Inferring** What is the relationship between the slope of a hillside and the rate of erosion?
5. **Analyzing Data** Compare the movement of the water with one rock and several rocks in front of the straw. Explain any differences you observed.

Exploration Lab

Modeling Erosion L2

Objective

After completing this activity, students will be able to
- describe the effects of slope and water speed on the water erosion of soil.

Skills Focus Using Models, Inferring

Prep Time 30 minutes

Advance Prep Purchase sterile garden soil and cut cardboard sheets measuring approximately 30 × 100 cm from large boxes.

Class Time 45 minutes

Safety Make sure that students wash their hands well after handling soil.

Teaching Tips
- This lab can be performed outdoors to avoid cleanup problems in the classroom.

Expected Outcome Increasing the slope or adding rocks increases the quantity of soil that will be washed away.

Analyze and Conclude

1. Water erosion produces smooth curves.
2. Increasing the elevation of the cardboard increased the speed of the water.
3. The slope depends on the length of the table under the cardboard. If the table under the cardboard was 100 cm long, the slope was 0.05 when the elevation was 5 cm, and 0.15 when the elevation was 15 cm.
4. The steeper the hillside, the greater the rate of erosion.
5. Increasing the number of rocks caused the stream of water to spread out more widely and to move more quickly.

Kinesthetic, Visual

Go Further L2

Students can make small changes to this basic setup to model many different erosion scenarios. Encourage students to add an additional step to the procedure that will allow them to compare another factor that affects erosion, such as the type of materials eroded, the amount of water flow, and so on. Have them write the procedure for the additional step before running the experiment, and have them record their observations.

Visual, Kinesthetic

Study Guide

Study Tip

Review Daily
Encourage students to set a time each day to review their science notes and text. This is an easier, more effective, and less stressful way to prepare for quizzes and tests, as compared to cramming all of the studying in a day or two before an exam. Even spending as little time as 15–20 minutes per day reviewing information recently covered in class can help students improve performance by monitoring their understanding before the class moves on to new concepts. Encourage students to write down any questions that come up during this daily study routine, and bring them to class so that you can address them.

Assessment

Interactive Textbook If your class subscribes to the Interactive Textbook, your students can go online to access an interactive version of the Student Edition and a self-test.

Reviewing Content

1. b	**2.** a	**3.** b
4. c	**5.** a	**6.** d
7. a	**8.** c	**9.** c
10. d		

CHAPTER 23

Study Guide

23.1 Fresh Water

Key Concepts
- The water cycle is made up of several processes, including evaporation, transpiration, condensation, precipitation, and the eventual return of flowing water to the ocean.
- A small portion of Earth's fresh water is located in the atmosphere, streams, and lakes. Most is located in groundwater and glaciers.

Vocabulary
groundwater, water cycle, transpiration, glacier, runoff, tributaries, watershed, saturated zone, water table, permeable, aquifer, impermeable

23.2 Weathering and Mass Movement

Key Concepts
- Erosion acts through weathering, the force of gravity, and through the movement of streams, groundwater, glaciers, wind, and waves.
- There are two forms of weathering: mechanical weathering and chemical weathering. Both cause rocks to disintegrate.
- The rate at which mechanical and chemical weathering take place depends on three main factors: temperature, the availability of water, and the type of rock.
- Through the process of mass movement, gravity moves loose material down a slope.

Vocabulary
erosion, weathering, mechanical weathering, abrasion, chemical weathering, mass movement

23.3 Water Shapes the Land

Key Concepts
- A stream's ability to erode depends mainly on its speed.
- Water erosion forms V-shaped valleys, waterfalls, flood plains, meanders, and oxbow lakes.
- Features deposited by flowing water include alluvial fans and deltas.
- The process of chemical weathering causes much groundwater erosion, including the formation of caves and sinkholes.

Vocabulary
deposition, saltation, flood plain, meander, oxbow lake, alluvial fan, delta, stalactite, stalagmite, sinkhole

23.4 Glaciers and Wind

Key Concepts
- Glaciers form in places where more snow falls than melts or sublimates.
- Glacial erosion causes many distinctive features in the landscape, such as cirques, horns, U-shaped valleys, and glacial lakes.
- Most till is deposited at the front of a glacier.
- Wind erodes the land by deflation and abrasion.
- Features deposited by wind include sand dunes and loess deposits.

Vocabulary
continental glacier, valley glacier, plucking, cirques, till, moraines, deflation, dunes, loess

23.5 The Restless Oceans

Key Concepts
- Light and temperature decrease with the depth of the ocean, whereas pressure increases.
- Winds blowing across the surface of the ocean cause the continuous flow of surface currents.
- Deep ocean currents are caused by differences in the density of ocean water.
- In upwelling, winds blow warm surface water aside. This allows cold water to rise.
- Two physical processes, hydraulic action and abrasion, are responsible for much wave erosion.

Vocabulary
salinity, continental shelf, surface current, density currents, upwelling, hydraulic action, longshore drift

23.6 Earth's History

Key Concepts
- Geologists use the law of superposition to determine the relative ages of rocks.
- Geologists use radioactive dating to determine the absolute ages of rocks.
- The geologic time scale is based on the relative ages of rock layers and the use of radioactive dating to find the absolute ages of rocks.
- The four major divisions of Earth's history are Precambrian time and the Paleozoic, Mesozoic, and Cenozoic Eras.

Vocabulary
fossils, relative age, law of superposition, extinct, index fossils, absolute age, era, periods, mass extinction

Chapter Resources

Print
- ***Chapter and Unit Tests,*** Chapter 23 Test A and Test B
- ***Test Prep Resources,*** Chapter 23

Technology
- ***Computer Test Bank,*** Chapter Test 23
- ***Interactive Textbook,*** Chapter 23
- ***Go Online,*** PHSchool.com, Chapter 23

CHAPTER 23

Assessment

Interactive textbook with assessment at PHSchool.com iText

Reviewing Content

Choose the letter that best answers the question or completes the statement.

1. The greatest supply of fresh water on Earth is found in
   a. the oceans. b. glaciers.
   c. the atmosphere. d. rivers and lakes.
2. The release of water into the atmosphere by plants is called
   a. transpiration. b. evaporation.
   c. precipitation. d. sublimation.
3. Which of the following is NOT an example of mechanical weathering?
   a. frost wedging b. oxidation
   c. plucking d. abrasion
4. The type of mass movement that occurs when soil gradually moves down a slope is called (a)
   a. landslide. b. mudflow.
   c. creep. d. slumping.
5. Which of the following is the most important factor influencing the ability of a stream to erode?
   a. salinity b. depth
   c. speed d. volume of flow
6. As rivers flow from mountains to the ocean, they tend to
   a. move more quickly. b. get narrower.
   c. get steeper. d. become less steep.
7. A feature formed by chemical weathering is
   a. a cave. b. a dune.
   c. loess. d. till.
8. The sediment deposited at the front of a glacier is called a
   a. stalagmite. b. slump.
   c. moraine. d. meander.
9. Which feature is the result of wind deposition?
   a. horn b. delta
   c. sand dune d. cirque
10. Absolute ages of rocks are found from
    a. the law of superposition.
    b. the relative order of rock layers.
    c. index fossils.
    d. radioactive dating.

Understanding Concepts

11. Why is less than 1 percent of Earth's water available for human use?
12. Describe the path that one rain drop would take through the water cycle.
13. What is the role of gravity in the water cycle?
14. A simplified diagram of the water cycle is shown below. Identify the process associated with the movement of water in each arrow.

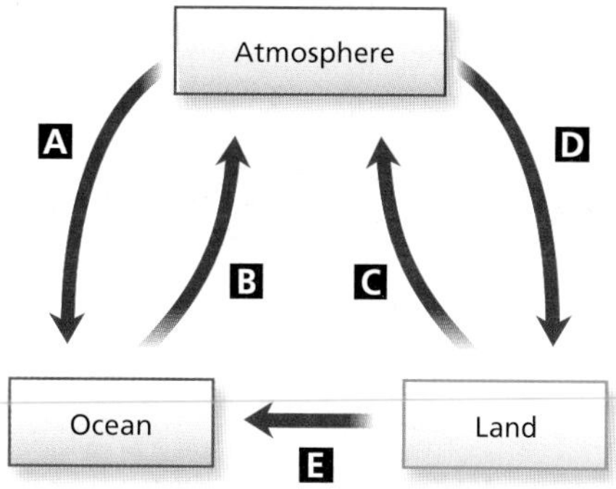

Atmosphere
A
B
C
D
Ocean
Land
E

15. Explain how the saturated zone is related to the water table. How might the water table change during a drought?
16. Give one example of mass movement that occurs quickly, and one example of mass movement that occurs slowly.
17. What is saltation?
18. Why are caves most often found in regions where the bedrock is composed of limestone?
19. How can you tell if a mountain valley was formed by a stream or by a glacier?
20. How does the wind-driven process of deflation alter the surface?
21. How are waves responsible for both erosion and deposition?
22. What is an index fossil?

Homework Guide

Section	Questions
23.1	1–2, 11–15
23.2	3–4, 16, 31–32
23.3	5–7, 17–18, 33–35
23.4	8–9, 19–20, 23–24
23.5	21, 25, 36
23.6	10, 22, 26–30, 37

Assessment (continued)

Understanding Concepts

11. Because most of Earth's water is either too salty, as in the oceans or salt lakes, or frozen in the form of glaciers

12. There are several different paths. Gravity will cause the raindrop to fall as precipitation from a cloud, either into the ocean or onto land. From there, sunlight may cause it to evaporate directly back into the atmosphere. If it falls on land, the raindrop may seep into the soil as groundwater, flow into a stream, evaporate, or become frozen in a glacier. Some groundwater is taken up by plant roots and transpires from plant leaves. Other groundwater and water in streams eventually flows downhill to the ocean, where it evaporates. Water vapor in the atmosphere rises and cools, condensing as water droplets or ice crystals on small particles in the air. Billions of these droplets or crystals form a cloud.

13. Gravity is responsible for precipitation falling to the ground, and for stream water and groundwater flowing downhill to the ocean.

14. A and D: precipitation; B: evaporation; C: evaporation and transpiration; E: runoff and other water flow into the oceans

15. The water table is the top of the saturated zone. During a drought, the water table will likely drop and the saturated zone will become smaller.

16. Fast: landslides, mudflows, and slumping; slow: creep

17. Saltation is the process wherein running water or wind causes particles of sediment to bounce or skip along the bottom of a stream or a land surface.

18. The limestone bedrock is easily eroded by flowing groundwater, leaving caves behind.

19. A stream would make a V-shaped valley, and a glacier would make a U-shaped valley.

20. By removing sand and dust from the ground, deflation leaves a hard surface of larger rocks behind.

21. Waves carry out erosion through hydraulic action and abrasion, which can widen cracks and break rocks down into smaller pieces. Waves can also deposit sand on beaches and in bays and inlets, where the water moves more slowly.

22. An index fossil is the remains of an organism that lived during a well-defined period of time and occurred over a large region.

Critical Thinking

23. Much of the rock of these mountains has been eroded away and washed by streams into the Atlantic Ocean.
24. A continental glacier is a thick sheet of ice that covers a huge region, such as Greenland. A valley glacier is a much smaller sheet of ice that occurs in high mountain valleys. Valley glaciers usually wind downhill through a valley originally formed by a stream. Both types of glaciers are similar in that they occur in cold climates where more snow falls than melts or sublimates, form in the same manner, are constantly moving downhill, and are composed of fresh water.
25. Answers will vary. One way would be to track the flow of currents using floating GPS sensors across the ocean. Another method would be to dump some sort of floating objects in the ocean, and track where they wash up. Another would be to anchor floating buoys that would record the direction of flow at many different locations.
26. Because most organisms at that time had soft bodies that didn't fossilize well

Analyzing Data

27. 50%; 75%
28. 17,100 years
29. Two half-lives
30. No. The half-life of carbon-14 is too short to determine the age of a bone from the Mesozoic Era. Carbon-14 is an effective tool for dating organisms that lived within the past 100,000 years or so.

Concepts in Action

31. To find water, you must locate an aquifer, a permeable layer of rock that is saturated with water. Since sandstone is a permeable rock, you may discover water in it. In contrast, shale is impermeable. It does not contain water.
32. In the northern states, there is more freezing and thawing during the winter, so frost wedging causes more severe weathering of roads.
33. It would be better to use granite, which is less susceptible to chemical weathering than marble.
34. Quartz is a very hard mineral, so it is more resistant than other common minerals to weathering caused by the pounding of waves and by streams as it is transported to the ocean.

CHAPTER 23

Assessment *(continued)*

Critical Thinking

23. **Hypothesizing** The Appalachian Mountains, which stretch from Alabama to Maine, were much higher in the past. Provide an explanation for how these mountains could have become lower.

24. **Comparing and Contrasting** What is the difference between a valley glacier and a continental glacier? How are they similar?

25. **Designing an Experiment** Design an experiment that could be used to track ocean currents.

26. **Inferring** Why are there few fossils from the Precambrian Era?

Analyzing Data

The chart below represents the radioactive decay of 100 milligrams of carbon-14. The colors show the percentage of carbon-14 that has decayed after each half-life. Carbon-14 has a half-life of 5700 years. Use this graph to answer Questions 27–30 below.

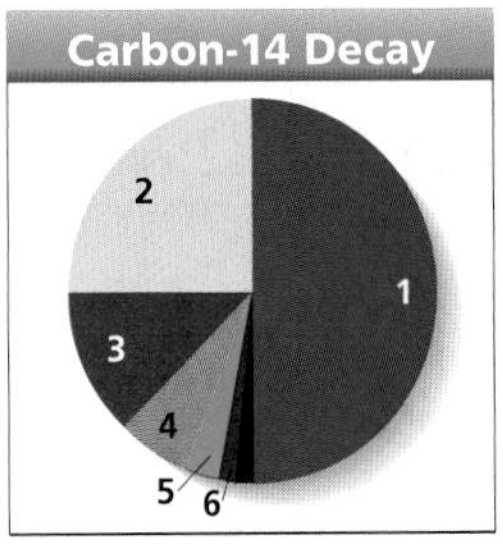
Carbon-14 Decay
1
2
3
4
5
6

27. **Using Graphs** What percent of the original carbon-14 has decayed after one half-life? After the second half-life?

28. **Calculating** How much time is needed for three half-lives to pass?

29. **Calculating** Your sample now has 25 milligrams of carbon-14. How many half-lives have passed?

30. **Making Judgments** Would carbon-14 dating be an effective tool to determine whether a dinosaur bone is from the Mesozoic Era? Explain.

Concepts in Action

31. **Drawing Conclusions** You are going to dig a well. You have the choice of digging it into sandstone or into shale. Which type of rock would probably be a better source of water? Explain your answer.

32. **Inferring** Why do roads in northern states such as Maine or Michigan need to be repaired more often than roads in southern states such as Florida or Louisiana?

33. **Predicting** Suppose you are building an outdoor sculpture in an area where it rains frequently. Explain whether it would be better to use marble or granite. (*Hint:* Granite is rich in the mineral quartz.)

34. **Inferring** Given your knowledge of minerals, why does it make sense that beach sand is mostly made of quartz grains?

35. **Observing** Sinkholes are familiar hazards in areas such as southwestern Virginia or Florida. They can sometimes damage highways, houses, and even farms. Explain how this happens.

36. **Comparing and Contrasting** The continental shelf and the abyssal plain are very different environments. Compare the conditions of these two regions with regard to light, pressure, and temperature.

37. **Writing in Science** Select one era or period of geologic time. Write a paragraph describing the environment and common organisms of that time.

Performance-Based Assessment

Classifying Take a walk around your neighborhood. List and describe as many examples of chemical and physical weathering as you can find. Present your findings with a map of the area to your class.

Go Online
PHSchool.com

For: Self-grading assessment
Visit: PHSchool.com
Web Code: cca-3230

35. Sinkholes form when erosion weakens an underground layer of limestone and portions of the ground suddenly collapse.
36. The shallow water over the continental shelf receives a great deal of sunlight, is relatively warm, and has relatively low pressures. No sunlight reaches the deep ocean above the abyssal plain. The water in the deep ocean is cold and pressures are very high.

37. Students should focus their paragraphs on one era or period depicted on the geologic time scale shown in Section 24.6. You may wish to consider allowing students to consult library or Internet resources to prepare a more detailed description of their selected time interval.

Standardized Test Prep

Test-Taking Tip

Multiple-Part Answer Choices
Multiple-choice questions may have answer choices that include two or more parts. In such cases, each part of the answer must be true for the entire answer choice to be correct. Even if you are uncertain of the correct answer, you can still improve your chances by eliminating any answer choices that you know are incorrect. For example, consider the following question:

Which of the following accurately describes how ocean conditions change with greater depth?

I. pressure decreases
II. density increases
III. temperature decreases

(A) I only (B) III only
(C) I and II (D) II and III
(E) I, II, and III

If you know that pressure increases with greater depth, you know that I is wrong. Therefore, you can eliminate choices A, C, and E, since each includes I as part of the answer. If you know that II is correct, you can also eliminate choice B.

(Answer: D)

Choose the letter that best answers the question or completes the statement.

1. In the water cycle, water is returned to the atmosphere through
I. condensation
II. evaporation
III. precipitation
(A) I only (B) III only
(C) I and II (D) II and III
(E) II only

2. Which of the following features is NOT formed by water erosion?
(A) meanders (B) oxbow lakes
(C) deltas (D) V-shaped valleys
(E) waterfalls

3. The rate at which rock is weathered depends on which of the following factors?
I. temperature
II. rate of deposition
III. availability of water
(A) I only (B) I and III
(C) I and II (D) II and III
(E) I, II, and III

The table below shows the yearly rates of erosion and deposition at four different stream locations. Use the table to answer questions 4 and 5.

Stream Erosion & Deposition

Location	Rate of Erosion (tons per year)	Rate of Deposition (tons per year)
A	3.00	3.25
B	4.75	4.00
C	4.50	4.65
D	5.60	5.20

4. At which locations is sediment building up?
(A) A and B (B) C and D
(C) A and C (D) B and D
(E) A and D

5. In total, how much sediment is gained or lost at Location D?
(A) 0.40 tons per year gained
(B) 0.40 tons per year lost
(C) 10.80 tons per year gained
(D) 10.80 tons per year lost
(E) 5.60 tons per year gained

6. The fact that younger rock layers lie above older rock layers if the rocks remain undisturbed is known as the law of
(A) superposition. (B) deflation.
(C) deposition. (D) absolute dating.
(E) relative dating.

7. Dinosaurs became extinct at the end of which division of geologic time?
(A) Precambrian time (B) Cambrian period
(C) Paleozoic Era (D) Mesozoic Era
(E) Cenozoic Era

Standardized Test Prep

1. E **2.** C **3.** B
4. C **5.** B **6.** A
7. D

Performance-Based Assessment

Students should be able to identify several examples of weathering in their neighborhoods. Common examples of physical weathering include cracked sidewalks or walls, potholes, and animal burrows. Common examples of chemical weathering include rusty objects such as cars or metallic tools, worn-away lettering on tombstones, and statues worn away by acidic precipitation.

Go Online
PHSchool.com

Your students can independently test their knowledge of the chapter and print out their test results for your files.

CHAPTER 24

Planning Guide

Use these planning tools
Easy Planner
Teacher Express

SECTION OBJECTIVES	STANDARDS NATIONAL (See p. T18.)	STANDARDS STATE	ACTIVITIES and LABS
1 block or 2 periods for each of the following sections. **24.1 The Atmosphere, pp. 746–751** **24.1.1** **Describe** Earth's atmosphere and **explain** how it is essential to life. **24.1.2** **Describe** the layers of the atmosphere and their properties.	A-1, A-2, C-1, C-5, D-1, F-1, F-5, G-1		**SE** Inquiry Activity: Why Do Cold Surfaces Become Wet? p. 745 L2 **SE** Quick Lab: Demonstrating the Effect of Air Pressure, p. 749 L2 **TE** Teacher Demo: Air Pressure, p. 748 L2
24.2 The Sun and the Seasons, pp. 752–754 **24.2.1** **Describe** how Earth moves through space and **explain** how seasons are caused by the tilt of Earth's axis. **24.2.2** **Explain** why different latitude zones have different average temperatures.	D-1		**TE** Teacher Demo: Solar Energy and the Seasons, p. 753 L2
24.3 Solar Energy and Winds, pp. 755–759 **24.3.1** **Describe** the processes by which solar energy heats the troposphere. **24.3.2** **Identify** local and global winds and **explain** how they are produced.	B-5, D-1		**TE** Teacher Demo: Wind Creation, p. 757 L2 **TE** Teacher Demo: Convection Cells, p. 758 L2
24.4 Water in the Atmosphere, pp. 760–764 **24.4.1** **Explain** condensation in the atmosphere and **describe** the formation and characteristics of basic cloud forms. **24.4.2** **Identify** the common types of precipitation and **explain** how they form.	D-1, D-2, G-1, G-2, G-3		**SE** Exploration Lab: Determining Relative Humidity, p. 783 L2 **LM** Investigation 24A: Modeling Cloud Formation L2
24.5 Weather Patterns, pp. 765–771 **24.5.1** **Explain** how air masses form and how they are classified. **24.5.2** **Describe** the four types of fronts, and the weather associated with each. **24.5.3** **Describe** cyclones and anticyclones. **24.5.4** **Describe** the major types of storms and how they are formed.	A-1, A-2, B-4, D-1, F-5		**SE** Quick Lab: Modeling Air Masses, p. 766 L2
24.6 Predicting the Weather, pp. 774–777 **24.6.1** **Interpret** weather map features and **describe** the technology used to forecast weather.	A-1, E-2		
24.7 Climate, pp. 778–782 **24.7.1** **Distinguish** between weather and climate and **describe** the main factors that affect a region's climate. **24.7.2** **Compare** climate variations due to natural and human causes.	A-1, A-2, D-1, F-1, F-2, F-4, F-5		**LM** Investigation 24B: Modeling Global Warming L1

Ability Levels	
L1	For students who need additional help
L2	For all students
L3	For students who need to be challenged

Components

SE	Student Edition	RSW	Reading & Study Workbook	CUT	Chapter & Unit Tests	T	Transparencies
TE	Teacher's Edition	MSPS	Math Skills & Problem Solving Workbook	CTB	Computer Test Bank	iT	Interactive Textbook
LM	Laboratory Manual			TP	Test Prep Resources	P	Presentation Pro CD-ROM
PLM	Probeware Lab Manual			DC	Discovery Channel Videotapes & DVDs	GO	Internet Resources

RESOURCES PRINT and TECHNOLOGY		SECTION ASSESSMENT
RSW Section 24.1	L1	**SE** Section 24.1 Assessment, p. 751 **iT** Section 24.1
RSW Math Skill	L2	
T P Chapter 24 Pretest	L2	
Section 24.1	L2	
PLANETDIARY **GO** Atmosphere	L2	
RSW Section 24.2	L1	**SE** Section 24.2 Assessment, p. 754 **iT** Section 24.2
T P Section 24.2	L2	
RSW Section 24.3	L1	**SE** Section 24.3 Assessment, p. 759 **iT** Section 24.3
T P Section 24.3	L2	
NSTA SCILINKS **GO** Winds	L2	
PLM Lab 10: Determining Relative Humidity	L2	**SE** Section 24.4 Assessment, p. 764 **iT** Section 24.4
RSW Section 24.4	L1	
T P Section 24.4	L2	
NSTA SCILINKS **GO** Clouds and fog	L2	
PHSchool.com **GO** Data sharing	L2	
RSW Section 24.5	L1	**SE** Section 24.5 Assessment, p. 771 **iT** Section 24.5
Discovery Channel School **DC** Wild Weather	L2	
T P Section 24.5	L2	
PLANETDIARY **GO** Storms	L2	
RSW, MSPS Section 24.6	L1	**SE** Section 24.6 Assessment, p. 777 **iT** Section 24.6
T P Section 24.6	L2	
SCIENCE NEWS **GO** Weather	L2	
RSW Section 24.7	L1	**SE** Section 24.7 Assessment, p. 782 **iT** Section 24.7
T P Section 24.7	L2	
PLANETDIARY **GO** Drought	L2	
PHSchool.com **GO** Data sharing	L2	

Go Online

Go online for these Internet resources.

PHSchool.com
Web Code: ccd-3240
Web Code: cca-3240

SCIENCE NEWS
Web Code: cce-3246

NSTA SCILINKS
Web Code: ccn-3243
Web Code: ccn-3244

PLANETDIARY
Web Code: ccc-3241
Web Code: ccc-3245
Web Code: ccc-3247

Materials for Activities and Labs

Quantities for each group

STUDENT EDITION

Inquiry Activity, p. 745
metal pitcher, thermometer, crushed ice, long-handled spoon, paper towels, 100-mL beaker

Quick Lab, p. 749
plastic cup, index card, plastic tub

Quick Lab, p. 766
shallow, clear 3–4-L tank; plastic or cardboard divider; 1-L beaker of cold sugar solution; 1-L beaker of warm, colored, sugar solution

Exploration Lab, p. 783
sling psychrometer, relative humidity chart from Appendix G, clock or watch with second hand

TEACHER'S EDITION

Teacher Demo, p. 748
2 large sheets of newspaper, ruler

Teacher Demo, p. 753
large-face flashlight, globe with stand

Teacher Demo, p. 757
clear plastic tank, plastic wrap, 2 1-L beakers, water, hot plate or Bunsen burner, ice, wood splint (smoker), matches

Teacher Demo, p. 758
1-L beaker, water, hot plate or Bunsen burner, 5–10 drops of food coloring

Build Science Skills, p. 772
colored pencils, hurricane-tracking map (This can be downloaded from the NOAA Web site or made by superimposing a map of North America on graph paper. Label 5° intervals of latitude and longitude.)

Chapter Assessment

CHAPTER ASSESSMENT

SE Chapter Assessment, pp. 785–786
CUT Chapter 24 Test A, B
CTB Chapter 24
iT Chapter 24
PHSchool.com GO
Web Code: cca-3240

STANDARDIZED TEST PREP

SE Chapter 24, p. 787
TP Diagnose and Prescribe

Interactive Textbook

Interactive Textbook with assessment at PHSchool.com

CHAPTER 24

Before you teach

From the Author

Michael Wysession
Washington University

Big Ideas

Earth's atmosphere has allowed for the evolution of life on land by burning up meteoroids, by having ozone absorb much of the sun's ultraviolet radiation, and through the availability of gases like oxygen and carbon dioxide. Climate is the result of many complex factors, including human activities such as the burning of fossil fuels and deforestation.

Space and Time Climate is largely a result of Earth's location with respect to the sun. Equatorial regions receive more sunlight than polar regions, so they are warmer. Seasonal climate changes occur because Earth's axis of rotation is tilted with respect to the ecliptic, and because the direction of the axis changes slowly with time. As Earth revolves around the sun, the Northern and Southern Hemispheres each spend six months facing the sun more directly.

Forces and Motion Wind is caused by differences in air pressure, in turn caused by the unequal heating of Earth's surface with latitude and by the locations of continents. Global wind patterns are largely affected by the Coriolis effect, a result of Earth's rotation.

Weather is measured and predicted using land and satellite observations. Changes in weather often result from interactions between different air masses. It is difficult to forecast weather due to rapid changes that result from complex land, air, and sea interactions.

Matter and Energy Air can hold more water vapor when it is warm. Therefore, if warm, moist air cools, the water vapor condenses to first form clouds and eventually falls to the ground in the form of precipitation.

The historical climate record, as read from glacial ice cores, shows that global temperatures have often changed dramatically over short time periods. It is not known why. The climate of the past 10,000 years has been both unusually warm and unusually stable. This has allowed for the establishment of agriculture and human civilization. It is not known what factors could kick global climates into an unstable mode of rapidly changing temperatures.

Earth Science Refresher

Gases in the Atmosphere 24.1 and 24.4

Earth's atmosphere is a reservoir for several important geochemical and biogeochemical cycles, including the water, carbon, and nitrogen cycles. The average amount of time any one molecule of a substance stays in the reservoir is described as the residence time. The estimated residence time of the two major atmospheric constituents, N_2 and O_2, is quite long (in the thousands of years for O_2 and billions of years for N_2). Water vapor, by contrast, has an estimated residence time of just 10 days. Since complete mixing of the troposphere takes several years, water vapor is unequally distributed. This is reflected in varying degrees of humidity around the globe. When the atmosphere is saturated with respect to water vapor, condensation occurs. The amount of water vapor that the atmosphere can hold before it is saturated is different at different temperatures. For this reason, relative humidity is a more useful measurement than absolute humidity, in that it expresses how close the air is to saturation, or the dew point of water.

Address Misconceptions

Condensation is when air turns to liquid. Water vapor is only one component of air. For a strategy to overcome this misconception, see **Address Misconceptions** on **page 760**.

Seasons 24.2

Because Earth is tilted on its axis, the Northern Hemisphere points toward the sun at the June solstice and away from the sun at the December solstice. This causes the Northern Hemisphere to receive more concentrated solar radiation, and therefore warmer weather, in the months around June.

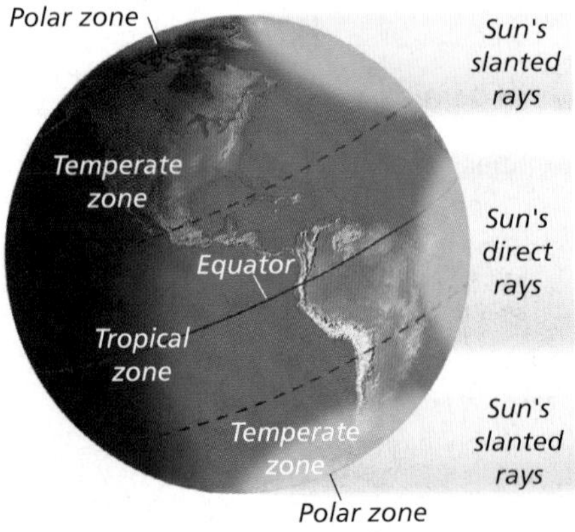
Polar zone
Sun's slanted rays
Temperate zone
Sun's direct rays
Equator
Tropical zone
Sun's slanted rays
Temperate zone
Polar zone

Go Online PD LINKS NSTA

For: Teaching methods for weather and climate
Visit: www.SciLinks.org/PDLinks
Web Code: ccn-2499

Convection Cells 24.3, 24.4, 24.5, and 24.7

Address Misconceptions

The seasons are caused by Earth moving closer to or farther from the sun on its elliptical orbit. Seasons are caused by Earth's tilt on its axis as it orbits the sun. For a strategy to overcome this misconception, see **Address Misconceptions** on **page 754.**

Convection cells in the atmosphere exist simultaneously on global, regional, and local scales. For example, global convection cells produce high pressure in the region of 30° N. Within that region, different surfaces, such as water and land, have different heat capacities. This sets up temperature and pressure differences, and smaller cells are formed, resulting in local winds. Within the local region, even smaller cells can form when surfaces such as asphalt absorb more heat than grass, resulting in winds that whirl leaves over parking lots even on still days.

Weather Maps 24.6

Weather maps provide visual models of the conditions in Earth's atmosphere. They reveal the interconnections between pressure, temperature, and humidity—the primary factors that drive weather phenomena.

Climate Change 24.7

The carbon cycle is one way Earth's climate is regulated.

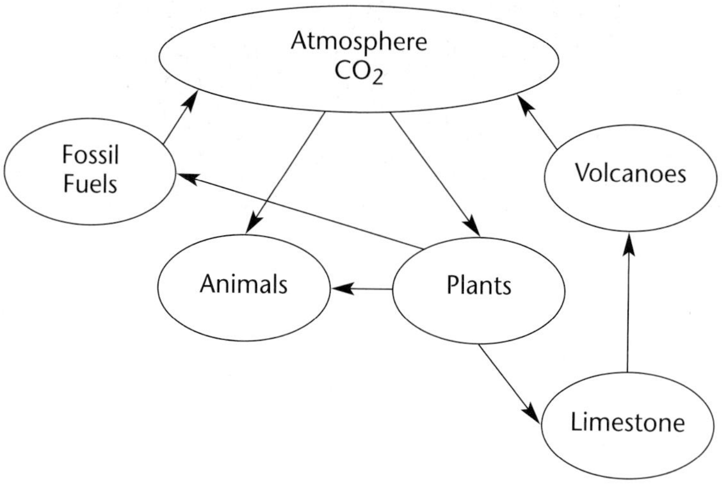

Atmosphere CO_2
Fossil Fuels
Volcanoes
Animals
Plants
Limestone

For example, during times of increased volcanic activity, more CO_2 enters the atmosphere, causing Earth's average temperature to increase. These conditions allow plants to flourish, which removes more atmospheric CO_2. Humans are increasing the CO_2 flow to the atmosphere by burning fossil fuels, while at the same time cutting down vast amounts of Earth's forests, which steadily increases CO_2 concentration in the atmosphere. Scientists are concerned that the increasing greenhouse effect could cause ice sheets to partially melt and more solar radiation to be absorbed (ice sheets are very reflective), thus further increasing global warming. Sea levels might rise and climate patterns and ecosystems might be seriously disrupted. This would, in turn, affect many human activities, including agriculture and the ability to carry on life in the many large coastal cities around the world.

Build Reading Literacy

Predict

Using Prior Knowledge/Correcting Misconceptions

Strategy Activate students' prior knowledge, provide a motivation for reading, and set the stage for confirming or correcting preconceptions. This strategy helps students develop and apply logic in predicting and analyzing what they read. Always avoid asking for predictions on topics about which students cannot be expected to have enough prior knowledge to make a valid prediction. Begin by assigning Section 24.1 and implementing the strategies below.

Example

1. Have students preview the section by skimming the headings, visuals, and boldfaced material. Ask students what they already know about this topic.
2. Then, ask students to predict what they might learn about the topic. List students' predictions on the board.
3. Tell students to read the section, taking notes as they come across information that supports or contradicts their predictions.
4. After they have read the section, discuss what they learned that proves or disproves their predictions. Point out that it is not unusual for people to have incorrect ideas about a topic before studying it, but that by making and then confirming or disproving predictions, they can replace their own misunderstandings with correct information.
5. Have students work with partners to repeat the process with other sections.

See pp. 764, 767, and 780 for a script on how to use the predict strategy with students. For additional Build Reading Literacy strategies, see pp. 747, 753, 755, 763, 769, 770, and 774.

EARTH SCIENCE

Chapter 24

ASSESS PRIOR KNOWLEDGE

Use the Chapter Pretest below to assess students' prior knowledge. As needed, review these Science Concepts with students.

Review Science Concepts

Section 24.1 Review the gas laws. Remind students that gases have weight and can be compressed. Review the definitions of pressure and density.

Section 24.2 Using a physical model of the sun-Earth system (or a tilted pencil), show students one full revolution around the sun and draw their attention to the way in which Earth's tilt on its axis causes a different part of the globe to face the sun during different times of the year.

Section 24.3 Review the three methods of energy transfer (convection, condensation, and radiation).

Section 24.4 Review how condensation is an exothermic process by which a substance changes from a gas to a liquid.

Sections 24.5 and 24.6 Review the principles of convection and how convection currents affect the movement of air masses. Help students recall the importance of air pressure in regards to weather from previous sections. Review the Doppler effect.

Section 24.7 Help students pull together what they have learned in previous sections about temperature, precipitation, and regional weather patterns.

CHAPTER

24 Weather and Climate

CONCEPTS in Action

How do science concepts apply to your world? Here are some questions you'll be able to answer after you read this chapter.

- What would Earth be like without an atmosphere? *(Section 24.1)*
- Why causes the seasons? *(Section 24.2)*
- Why is there often a cool breeze at the beach? *(Section 24.3)*
- How can the air cause a bad hair day? *(Section 24.4)*
- What causes thunder and lightning? *(Section 24.5)*
- How reliable are weather forecasts? *(Section 24.6)*
- How do human activities affect climate? *(Section 24.7)*

Discovery Channel School

Video Field Trip

Wild Weather

- What happens when a hurricane reaches land? *(page 772)*

The swirling clouds of Hurricane Pauline can be seen over Mexico and Central America in this satellite image. ▶

Chapter Pretest

1. What does density measure? *(The amount of matter in a given volume)*

2. Which of these changes is most likely to occur when the temperature of a gas increases? *(c)*
   - a. Density increases.
   - b. Energy decreases.
   - c. Volume increases.
   - d. Pressure decreases.

3. What is the gas law equation that relates temperature, pressure, and volume? $\left(\frac{P_1V_1}{T_1} = \frac{P_2V_2}{T_2}\right)$

4. Which type of heat transfer requires the physical movement of matter? *(b)*
   - a. Conduction
   - b. Convection
   - c. Radiation

5. Which of these phase changes is most likely to occur with a decrease in temperature? *(c)*
   - a. Evaporation
   - b. Sublimation
   - c. Condensation

6. Briefly explain the Doppler effect. *(The frequency of waves changes when the source of the waves or the observer of the waves is moving.)*

Chapter Preview

Inquiry Activity

Why Do Cold Surfaces Become Wet?

Procedure

1. Fill a metal pitcher halfway with warm water. Use paper towels to dry off the outside of the pitcher. With a thermometer, measure the temperature of the air in the classroom and the temperature of the water in the pitcher. Record these temperatures. **CAUTION** *Wipe up any spilled water right away to avoid slips and falls.*
2. Fill a 100-mL beaker with crushed ice. Then, pour the ice into the pitcher and stir the ice with a long-handled spoon.
3. Repeat Step 2 until water begins to appear on the outside of the pitcher. When this occurs, measure and record the temperature of the water in the pitcher.

Think About It

1. **Analyzing Data** Compare the temperature at which drops of water appeared on the outside of the pitcher to the temperature of the air in the classroom.
2. **Formulating Hypotheses** How do you think the water appeared on the outside surface of the pitcher?

Discovery Channel School **Video Field Trip**

Wild Weather

Encourage students to view the Video Field Trip "Wild Weather."

ENGAGE/EXPLORE

Inquiry Activity

Why Do Cold Surfaces Become Wet? L2

Purpose In this activity, students begin to understand how condensation occurs on a cold surface.

Address Misconceptions

Some students may think that cold water somehow moves out through the pitcher. Explain that water actually condenses on cold surfaces from the surrounding air.

Skills Focus **Observing, Comparing and Contrasting**

Prep Time 5 minutes

Materials metal pitcher, thermometer, crushed ice, long-handled spoon, paper towels, 100-mL beaker

Advance Prep If water from a sink is not sufficiently warm, you may need to heat the water to 30–40°C.

Class Time 10 minutes

Safety Students should wear safety goggles, plastic gloves, and lab aprons throughout this activity. Use a nonmercury-filled thermometer and do not use the thermometer to stir. Make sure that the temperature of the warm water is between 30°C and 40°C. Remind students to wipe up any spilled water to avoid slips and falls.

Expected Outcome As the crushed ice reduces the temperature of the warm water, the outside of the pitcher will become cooler than the air, and small droplets of water will begin to appear on the pitcher.

Think About It

1. Drops of water do not appear on the pitcher until the pitcher is cooler than the air in the room. The difference in temperature between the pitcher and the air at which condensation begins depends on the relative humidity of the air.
2. When warm air comes into contact with a cool surface, such as the pitcher containing the ice, water molecules in the air lose energy and slow down after colliding with the cold surface. Some of these molecules lose enough energy to condense on the cooler surface, where they join to form small drops of water. **Visual**

Section 24.1

1 FOCUS

Objectives

24.1.1 **Describe** Earth's atmosphere and **explain** how it is essential to life.

24.1.2 **Describe** the layers of the atmosphere and their properties.

Reading Focus

Build Vocabulary L2

Word-Part Analysis Ask students to define the word *sphere*. Make the connection between the word and its use as a root. *(Ancient astronomers thought that all of the heavenly bodies were set in transparent concentric spheres around Earth.)* Ask students to guess what some of the prefixes used with *sphere* might mean, based on other science words they have learned so far. They may think of *thermo-* and *iono-* from previous chapters. Have students use a dictionary to find the definitions of all of the prefixes used with *sphere* in the Section 24.1 vocabulary list. (*atmos-*, "vapor"; *tropo-*, "change"; *strato-*, "layer"; *meso-*, "middle"; *thermo-*, "heat"; *iono-*, "ions" or "charged particles")

Reading Strategy L2

a. 0–12 km **b.** Temperature decreases as altitude increases. **c.** Stratosphere **d.** Temperature remains nearly constant to 20 km, then increases with altitude. **e.** Mesosphere **f.** 50–80 km **g.** Above 80 km **h.** Temperature increases rapidly with altitude.

24.1 The Atmosphere

Reading Focus

Key Concepts

- How does the atmosphere affect conditions on Earth?
- What is Earth's atmosphere composed of?
- How do pressure and density vary with altitude?
- What are the characteristics of the major layers of the atmosphere?

Vocabulary

- atmosphere
- air pressure
- barometer
- troposphere
- weather
- stratosphere
- ozone layer
- mesosphere
- thermosphere
- ionosphere
- aurora

Reading Strategy

Relating Text and Diagrams As you read, refer to Figure 5 and the text to complete the table on the layers of the atmosphere below.

Layer	Altitude Range	Temperature Change
Troposphere	a. ?	b. ?
c. ?	12–50 km	d. ?
e. ?	f. ?	Decreases as altitude increases
Thermosphere	g. ?	h. ?

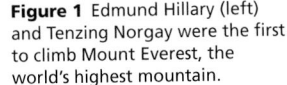

At 8848 meters (29,030 feet) above sea level, Mount Everest is the highest mountain in the world. In 1952 Edmund Hillary, a New Zealand mountaineer, and Tenzing Norgay, a mountain guide from Nepal, became the first humans to reach the top. The climb was very dangerous for several reasons, including the extremely low temperature and low level of oxygen at the summit. When they finally made it to the top, the two men cheered and embraced. Then Hillary did something to prove a point—he took off his oxygen mask. He wanted to show that a person could stay alive while breathing naturally at that high altitude. But after a few minutes, his vision began to fail. When Hillary replaced his mask, his vision improved. Then the two men started back down the mountain.

Why did Hillary and Tenzing need to carry oxygen to the top of Mount Everest? And why was it so cold there? The answers to these questions depend on how the air around Earth changes with altitude.

Figure 1 Edmund Hillary (left) and Tenzing Norgay were the first to climb Mount Everest, the world's highest mountain.

Section Resources

Print
- ***Reading and Study Workbook With Math Support***, Section 24.1 and **Math Skill:** Calculating Volume of Gases
- ***Transparencies***, Chapter Pretest and Section 24.1

Technology
- ***Interactive Textbook***, Section 24.1
- ***Presentation Pro CD-ROM***, Chapter Pretest and Section 24.1
- ***Go Online***, *Planet Diary*, Atmosphere activity

Earth's Protective Layer

What you commonly call air, scientists call the atmosphere. The **atmosphere** (AT muh sfeer) is the layer of gases that surrounds Earth. **The atmosphere forms a protective boundary between Earth and space and provides conditions that are suitable for life.** The atmosphere protects Earth's surface from continual pounding by meteoroids, chunks of rock and metal from space. The atmosphere also protects Earth from much of the high-energy radiation from space.

The atmosphere holds in heat and helps to moderate Earth's temperatures. Without the atmosphere, Earth's surface would be similar to the moon's, boiling hot during the day and freezing cold at night. Earth's relatively constant temperatures allow life to flourish.

The atmosphere also provides the gases that are essential for life. Carbon dioxide in the atmosphere is essential for plants and some other organisms to carry out photosynthesis. Photosynthesis is the process of capturing the sun's energy to make food. Oxygen is produced during photosynthesis and released into the atmosphere. Your body uses oxygen to carry out many life functions.

Composition of Earth's Atmosphere (Dry Air)

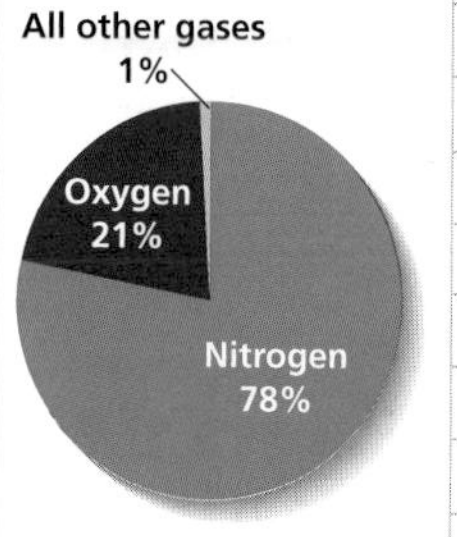

All other gases 1%
Oxygen 21%
Nitrogen 78%

Gas	Percentage by Volume
Nitrogen (N_2)	78.084
Oxygen (O_2)	20.946
Argon (Ar)	0.934
Carbon dioxide (CO_2)	0.037
Neon (Ne)	0.00182
Helium (He)	0.00052
Methane (CH_4)	0.00015
Krypton (Kr)	0.00011
Hydrogen (H_2)	0.00005

Figure 2 Dry air is a mixture of many gases. Air also contains water vapor, which makes up between 0.02 percent and 4.0 percent of air's volume. **Using Tables** ***What is the most abundant gas in dry air?***

Composition of the Atmosphere

The atmosphere is a mixture of different gases. The composition of the atmosphere is fairly uniform up to an altitude of about 80 kilometers. **Earth's atmosphere is a mixture of nitrogen, oxygen, water vapor, and many other gases, in which tiny solid and liquid particles are suspended.** As Figure 2 shows, two gases—nitrogen and oxygen—make up more than 99 percent of clean, dry air. The amount of water vapor in air varies from 0.02 percent in cold, dry air to more than 4.0 percent in warm, moist air.

Various amounts of water droplets and solid particles are suspended in the atmosphere. Some solid particles can be seen as floating dust, but most particles are microscopic. These solid particles come from various sources, including smoke from fires, ash and dust from volcanic eruptions, and salt from ocean spray.

Go Online PLANETDIARY

For: Atmosphere activity
Visit: PHSchool.com
Web Code: ccc-3241

2 INSTRUCT

Earth's Protective Layer

Build Reading Literacy L1

Active Comprehension Refer to page **498D** in **Chapter 17**, which provides the guidelines for active comprehension.

Have students read the first two sentences of Earth's Protective Layer. Then ask, **What would you like to know about how the atmosphere protects Earth?** *(Possible answers may include, "How can gases protect Earth?" and "What gases are in the atmosphere?")* Write student responses on the board, and have students read the remainder of the selection. After students are finished reading, ask them to respond to each question on the board.
Verbal

Composition of the Atmosphere

Address Misconceptions L2

Many students may think that water disappears or disintegrates into hydrogen and oxygen as it enters the gaseous phase. Furthermore, students sometimes have difficulty distinguishing between water vapor and liquid water in the atmosphere. Ask students to explain what happens when water evaporates. Be sure students understand that the water does not disappear or disintegrate into hydrogen and oxygen as it enters the gaseous phase. Explain that the variation in the amount of water vapor in the air causes the weather to feel humid or dry. Ask students for examples of liquid water in the atmosphere. *(Clouds, fog, mist, rain)*
Logical

Go Online PLANETDIARY

Find links to additional activities and have students monitor phenomena that affect Earth and its residents.

Answer to . . .

Figure 2 *Nitrogen is the most abundant gas.*

Customize for English Language Learners

Use a T-Chart
Have students work in small, heterogeneous language-level groups to complete T-Charts for the topic Atmosphere. Create a simple chart with two columns labeled What I Know and What I Have Learned. Give students time to complete the What I Know column before reading p. 747. After reading the page, students complete the What I Have Learned column. Check the charts for comprehension before students continue reading the section.

Air Pressure

Teacher > Demo

Air Pressure L2

Purpose Students observe the presence of air pressure.

Materials 2 large sheets of newspaper, ruler

Procedure Place the ruler on the edge of a table so that nearly half of the ruler is hanging off the edge. Ask, **What will happen if I hit the edge of the ruler that is hanging off of the table?** *(The ruler will flip off of the table.)* Hit the edge of the ruler with a small force applied straight down. Replace the ruler as before. Place the newspaper sheets on top of the half of the ruler that is on the table. Smooth out the paper so that no air is trapped underneath. (This must be done carefully, or the activity will not work.) Ask, **What will happen if I hit the edge of the ruler that is hanging off of the table?** *(Students will most likely guess that the ruler will flip the newspaper off the table.)* Hit the ruler to show students what will happen. **CAUTION** *Do not hit the ruler too hard, as it could shatter.*

Expected Outcome The part of the ruler on the table underneath the newspaper will not lift off of the table This may be difficult for students to predict because the weight of the newspaper is minimal, and students may believe it should be easy to lift off of the table by hitting the free end of the ruler. However, the force of air pressure being exerted over the large surface area of the newspaper is strong enough to hold the ruler down.
Logical, Kinesthetic

Use Visuals L1

Figure 3 Explain that altitude is measured as height above sea level, not above ground level at any given location. Ask, **What do the dots in the three circles represent?** *(The density of gas molecules)* **Why is the number of dots in each circle different?** *(The density of gas molecules changes with altitude.)* **What does the column labeled in km represent?** *(Altitude)* **True or False: Washington, D.C. is under a higher column of air than Denver, CO.** *(True)*
Visual

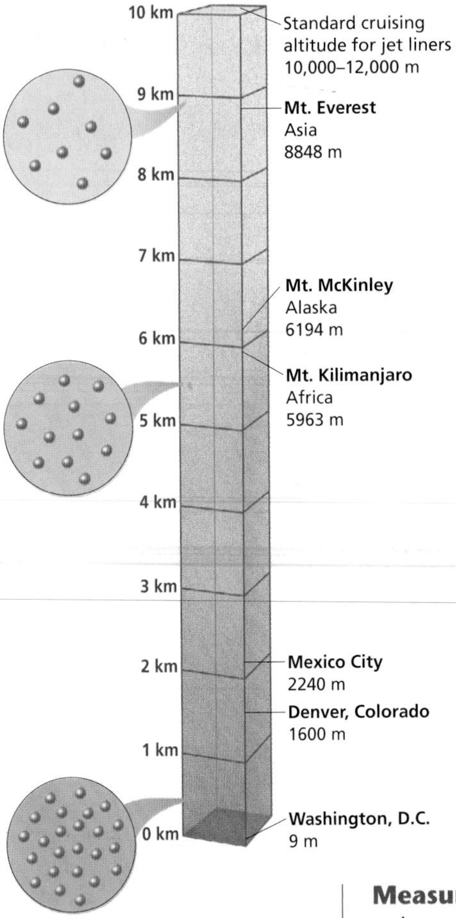

10 km
9 km
8 km
7 km
6 km
5 km
4 km
3 km
2 km
1 km
0 km
Standard cruising altitude for jet liners 10,000–12,000 m
Mt. Everest Asia 8848 m
Mt. McKinley Alaska 6194 m
Mt. Kilimanjaro Africa 5963 m
Mexico City 2240 m
Denver, Colorado 1600 m
Washington, D.C. 9 m

Figure 3 The atmosphere is densest close to Earth's surface. **Applying Concepts** ***How does air pressure change as altitude increases?***

Air Pressure

The atmosphere has weight because of Earth's gravity. As a result of this weight, the atmosphere exerts pressure. Recall that pressure is the force exerted on a surface divided by the area over which the force is exerted. **Air pressure** is the force exerted by the weight of a column of air on a surface. At sea level, air pressure is about 101,325 newtons per square meter, more commonly expressed as 1013.25 millibars. One millibar equals 100 newtons per square meter.

Effect of Altitude Air pressure changes with altitude. The atmosphere is densest near Earth's surface and becomes less dense as altitude increases, as shown in Figure 3. Why is this? Air can be compressed, as it is when you pump air into a tire or a basketball. Near Earth's surface, the column of air includes the entire depth of the atmosphere, so the pressure and density are high. As altitude increases, the depth of the column of air above decreases, so the pressure decreases. At high altitudes there is very little air in the column above, so air pressure is lower. **As altitude increases, air pressure and density decrease.**

About half of the total mass of the atmosphere is found below an altitude of 5.6 kilometers. When Hillary and Tenzing climbed Mount Everest, they went well above this halfway point. As they climbed, the air became less dense. Hillary had trouble breathing without an oxygen mask because there were many fewer oxygen molecules per cubic meter of air at the summit than at sea level.

Measuring Air Pressure Scientists measure air pressure with an instrument called a **barometer.** The first barometer was invented in 1643 by the Italian scientist Evangelista Torricelli. Torricelli invented a mercury barometer, similar to the one shown in Figure 4. As air pressure increases, the column of mercury in the barometer rises. As air pressure decreases, the column of mercury falls. Thus, a measurement of the height of a column of mercury is a measurement of air pressure. At sea level, the average air pressure is about 760 millimeters of mercury or, more commonly, 29.92 inches of mercury.

An aneroid (AN uh royd) barometer is a smaller, more portable type of barometer. The word *aneroid* means "not using liquid." Aneroid barometers use a metal chamber that expands and contracts with changes in air pressure.

Reading Checkpoint *What instrument is used to measure air pressure?*

Facts and Figures

Evolution of the Atmosphere When Earth formed about 4.6 billion years ago, it had an atmosphere that consisted of water vapor, hydrogen cyanide, and other gases. This earliest atmosphere did not last long because the gas molecules were swept away by the solar wind.

Earth's modern atmosphere developed gradually. About 3 billion years ago, oxygen was less than 1.0% of the atmosphere. By about 0.6 billion years ago, an oxygen-rich atmosphere like the one we have today had developed. Scientists have long held the theory that the abundant oxygen in the atmosphere was created by cyanobacteria in the process of photosynthesis. However, recent evidence suggests that oxygen may have already been present before the evolution of the cyanobacteria.

Layers of the Atmosphere

Temperature changes dramatically as you move up from Earth's surface high into the atmosphere. Scientists use variations in temperature to divide the atmosphere into four vertical layers. **The four layers of the atmosphere are the troposphere, the stratosphere, the mesosphere, and the thermosphere.**

The Troposphere You, along with many other living things, live in the layer of the atmosphere called the troposphere. The **troposphere** (TROH puh sfeer) is the lowest layer of Earth's atmosphere. This layer contains almost all of the atmosphere's water vapor and suspended particles, which are important in the formation of clouds and precipitation. Most weather takes place in the troposphere. **Weather** is the condition of the atmosphere in a particular place at a particular time.

The height of the troposphere ranges from about 9 kilometers above the poles to 16 kilometers above the tropics. The average height of the troposphere is about 12 kilometers.

In the troposphere, temperature generally decreases as altitude increases. Though it varies somewhat, the rate of decrease averages about 6.5 Celsius degrees per kilometer. For example, if it is 20°C where you are on Earth's surface, then it is probably about 7°C at an altitude of 2 kilometers above you. This characteristic of the troposphere accounts for the extremely low temperatures that Hillary and Tenzing had to withstand when they scaled Mount Everest.

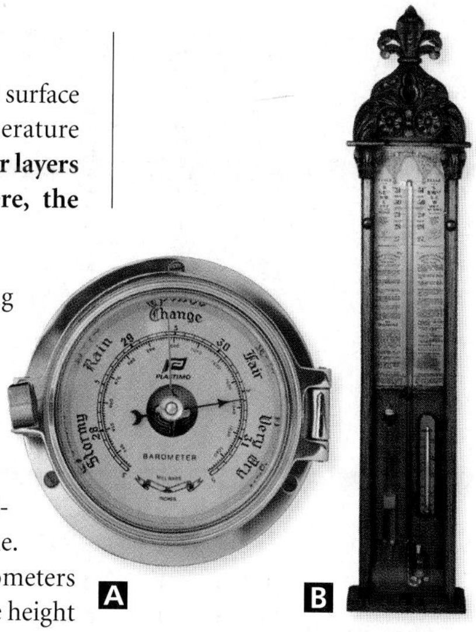
Change
Rain
Fair
Stormy
Very Dry
BAROMETER
A
B

Figure 4 Barometers measure air pressure. **A** Changes in air pressure cause the airtight chamber of this aneroid barometer to flex in and out. **B** Changes in air pressure cause the level of mercury in the open glass tube of this antique mercury barometer to move up or down.

Quick Lab

Demonstrating the Effect of Air Pressure

Materials

plastic cup, index card, plastic tub

Procedure

1. Completely fill the plastic cup with water. Then place the index card on the cup. Make sure that no air is trapped between the water and the card. **CAUTION** *Quickly wipe up any spilled water to avoid slips and falls.*
2. **Predicting** Record your prediction of what will happen when the cup is inverted.
3. To test your prediction, place the palm of one hand on the card. Then use your other hand to invert the cup so that the cup rests upside-down on the card in your hand.
4. Hold the cup and card over the plastic tub and slowly remove your hand from the card. Observe what happens.

Analyze and Conclude

1. **Applying Concepts** What two forces acted on the card after you inverted the cup?
2. **Inferring** After you inverted the cup, which surface of the card experienced a greater force due to air pressure?
3. **Drawing Conclusions** How can you explain what happened when you removed your hand from the card?

Facts and Figures

Torricelli's Barometer Torricelli was a pupil of the great scientist Galileo Galilei. In 1643, Torricelli was working on a practical problem having to do with pumping water out of a mine. Galileo suggested he try to measure the pressure exerted by air, and Torricelli invented a device to do so. He filled a tube (closed at one end) with mercury and then inverted the open end into a pan of mercury. The mercury flowed down and out of the tube until the flow was stopped by the pressure of air on the mercury in the pan, and then the level in the tube stabilized. Torricelli observed that as air pressure increased, the column of mercury in the tube rose, and as air pressure decreased, the column of mercury fell. Since that time, scientists have often measured air pressure in terms of a column of mercury.

Layers of the Atmosphere

Quick Lab

Demonstrating the Effect of Air Pressure L2

Objective

After completing this activity, students will be able to
- use the concept of air pressure to explain how water can be held inside an inverted container.

Address Misconceptions

Some students hold the misconception that air pressure only acts downward (like gravity). In reality, air pressure acts equally well in all directions. Discussion of student observations in this lab may help to overcome this misconception.

Skills Focus Observing

Prep Time 5 minutes

Advance Prep Provide students with small, rigid, plastic drinking cups. Do not use beakers or other containers that have pouring lips.

Class Time 20 minutes

Safety Students should wear safety goggles and aprons in the laboratory.

Teaching Tips
- Water *must* be filled to the brim so that all air bubbles are eliminated. Otherwise, the activity will not work.

Expected Outcome The cup will not release the water with the card in place.

Analyze and Conclude

1. The force of gravity, due to the weight of the card and the water above it, and the force of air pressure acted on the card.
2. The lower surface of the card experienced a greater force due to air pressure.
3. Because more area on the lower surface of the card was exposed to the atmosphere, the surrounding air pressure exerted an upward net force. This force opposed the weight of the water and card, keeping them from falling as the hand was removed. **Kinesthetic, Logical**

Answer to . . .

Figure 3 *Air pressure decreases as altitude increases.*

Reading Checkpoint *A barometer*

Build Science Skills

L2

Using Tables Have students create a table to organize the key information about each layer of the atmosphere. Instruct students to set up the table with the following headings: Layer, Altitude, Temperature Range, Main Characteristics. *(Troposphere, 0–12 km, variable temperatures falling to −57°C, weather takes place in this layer, contains almost all of the atmosphere's water vapor; Stratosphere, 12–50 km, −57° to 0°C, contains ozone layer; Mesosphere, 50–80 km, 0°C to nearly −90°C, most meteorites burn up in this layer; Thermosphere, above 80 km, from about −90°C to more than 1000°C, contains ionosphere, gradually dissipates into space)*
Visual, Portfolio

Address Misconceptions

L2

Many students think that heat and temperature are equivalent. A discussion of the thermosphere is an ideal context for addressing this misconception. Air molecules at this high altitude receive great amounts of energy from the sun. The kinetic energy of the air molecules in the thermosphere, measured as temperature, is extremely high. However, the density of air molecules in the thermosphere is extremely low. Therefore, the overall amount of heat in the thermosphere is low. An analogy to help students grasp this concept is to imagine two 100-L tanks, one with four drops of boiling water, the other filled to the brim with boiling water. The temperature of the water is the same in both tanks, but the second tank has far more heat energy. Have students make a chart comparing the heat and temperature in the mesosphere and thermosphere. *(The mesosphere has low temperature and low heat, while the thermosphere has high temperature and low heat.)*
Logical

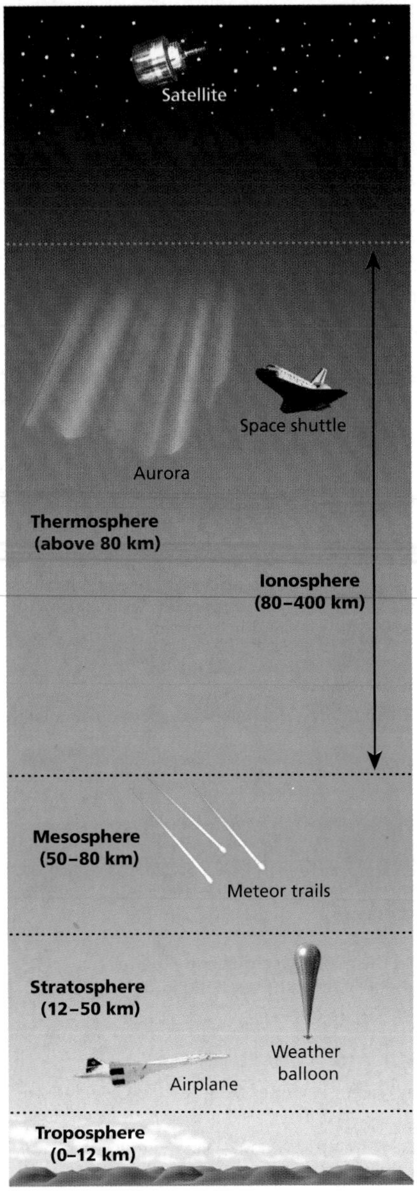
Satellite
Space shuttle
Aurora
Thermosphere (above 80 km)
Ionosphere (80–400 km)
Mesosphere (50–80 km)
Meteor trails
Stratosphere (12–50 km)
Weather balloon
Airplane
Troposphere (0–12 km)

Figure 5 The atmosphere has four principal layers—the troposphere, the stratosphere, the mesosphere, and the thermosphere. The ionosphere overlaps the lower thermosphere. **Interpreting Diagrams** *In which layer do auroras appear?*

The Stratosphere Above the troposphere, as shown in Figure 5, is the stratosphere. The **stratosphere** (STRAT uh sfeer) extends from an altitude of about 12 kilometers to about 50 kilometers. The temperature of the stratosphere remains nearly the same from the boundary with the troposphere to an altitude of about 20 kilometers. Above that height, temperature increases as altitude increases. The temperature in the lower stratosphere remains about −57°C. Above 20 kilometers, the temperature rises to about 0°C.

The upper stratosphere is warmer than the lower stratosphere because of the presence of the **ozone layer,** a region of high ozone concentration. Recall that ozone is a highly reactive gas whose molecules are composed of three oxygen atoms (O_3). Most of the oxygen molecules you breathe are composed of two oxygen atoms (O_2). In the stratosphere, the energy of sunlight is great enough to split O_2 molecules into single oxygen atoms (O). When an oxygen atom (O) collides with a molecule of oxygen (O_2), ozone (O_3) is formed.

Ozone absorbs ultraviolet (UV) radiation in sunlight and filters much of it out before such radiation can reach Earth's surface. The energy absorbed from UV radiation is converted into thermal energy, warming the upper stratosphere.

Because UV radiation can be harmful to living things, the presence of the ozone layer is extremely important to life on Earth. In humans, UV radiation can cause a deadly form of skin cancer. Certain chemical pollutants have been depleting ozone in the stratosphere, permitting more UV radiation to reach Earth's surface. However, the release of such chemicals was limited by international agreements and national policies adopted in the 1990s. As a result, ozone levels in the stratosphere appear to have stabilized.

The Mesosphere The layer above the stratosphere is the mesosphere. The **mesosphere** (MEZ oh sfeer) begins at an altitude of about 50 kilometers and extends to about 80 kilometers. In the mesosphere, temperature decreases as altitude increases. At the top of the mesosphere, the temperature approaches –90°C.

The air is very thin in the mesosphere. Studies in the 1990s discovered that air in this layer may move at speeds of more than 320 kilometers per hour. Most meteoroids that enter the atmosphere burn up in the mesosphere.

Reading Checkpoint *In which layer of the atmosphere do most meteoroids burn up?*

The Thermosphere The outermost layer of the atmosphere, the **thermosphere** (THUR moh sfeer), begins at an altitude of about 80 kilometers and extends outward into space. No boundary marks the end of the atmosphere. Instead, the thin air of the thermosphere gradually merges with space. In the thermosphere, temperature increases rapidly with altitude, from about –90°C to more than 1000°C. Recall from physics that temperature is a measure of the average kinetic energy of molecules. Because gas molecules in the thermosphere absorb solar radiation and move very fast, the temperature is quite high.

The Ionosphere The **ionosphere** (eye AHN uh sfeer) is not a distinct layer of the atmosphere. Rather, it is a region of charged particles, or ions, that overlaps the lower thermosphere. In the ionosphere, molecules of nitrogen and oxygen lose one or more electrons as they absorb high-energy wavelengths of solar radiation. The molecules become positively charged ions. These ions are most dense between the altitudes of 80 and 400 kilometers. At these high altitudes, certain radio waves sent from Earth's surface, such as AM radio waves, bounce off ions and travel back to Earth. You can often hear AM radio stations from very far away at night because the sun's radiation is blocked by Earth. The ions start to recombine at night, allowing AM radio waves to travel farther.

One of nature's most spectacular displays occurs in the ionosphere. An **aurora,** shown in Figure 6, is a colorful display of light in the sky, produced when charged particles from the sun are attracted to Earth's magnetic poles. There, these particles cause ions in the ionosphere to glow. In the Northern Hemisphere, these displays are called the aurora borealis, or Northern Lights.

Figure 6 Auroras provide spectacular displays of light in the polar regions. Auroras are produced by glowing ions in the ionosphere.

Section 24.1 Assessment

Reviewing Concepts

1. How does the atmosphere protect life on Earth?
2. What are the two major gases in Earth's atmosphere?
3. How does air pressure change with altitude?
4. List the major layers of the atmosphere in order, beginning with the layer closest to Earth's surface.

Critical Thinking

5. **Predicting** How might human health be affected if the ozone layer suddenly became thinner?
6. **Comparing and Contrasting** Compare the way temperature changes with altitude in the mesosphere and in the thermosphere.

Math Practice

7. If the temperature is 10°C at an altitude of 1000 meters, what would the temperature be on top of a nearby 5000-meter mountain? (*Hint:* Assume that temperature falls 6.5°C per kilometer.)
8. About how much oxygen would there be in a 1000-m^3 volume of dry air?

3 ASSESS

Evaluate Understanding **L2**

Ask students to create flashcards showing the ways in which the atmosphere protects Earth and provides conditions suitable for life.

Reteach **L1**

Use Figure 3 to review the relationship between air pressure, density of gas molecules, and altitude. Ask students why it is harder to breathe at higher altitudes. *(There is less oxygen per cubic meter of air.)*

Math Practice

Solutions

7. In the troposphere, the temperature decreases about 6.5 Celsius degrees per kilometer. $10^\circ C - (6.5^\circ C/km \times 4\ km) = (10^\circ C - 26^\circ C) = -16^\circ C$
8. Oxygen makes up about 20.9% of the volume of dry air. So, there would be about 209 m^3 of oxygen in 1000 m^3 of dry air.

Interactive Textbook If your class subscribes to the Interactive Textbook, use it to review key concepts in Section 24.1.

Section 24.1 Assessment

1. The atmosphere protects life on Earth from bombardment by meteors and high-energy radiation from space. Most meteoroids that enter the atmosphere burn up in the mesosphere. Ozone in the stratosphere filters out much ultraviolet radiation before it can reach the surface.
2. Nitrogen and oxygen
3. Air pressure decreases with altitude.
4. Troposphere, stratosphere, mesosphere, thermosphere
5. One effect might be that the incidence of melanoma, a skin cancer, might increase.
6. In the mesosphere, the temperature decreases as the altitude increases. In the thermosphere, the temperature increases rapidly as the altitude increases.

Answer to . . .

Figure 5 *Auroras usually appear in the thermosphere. (The ionosphere is also an acceptable answer.)*

Reading Checkpoint *Most meteoroids burn up in the mesosphere.*

Section 24.2

1 FOCUS

Objectives

24.2.1 **Describe** how Earth moves through space and **explain** how seasons are caused by the tilt of Earth's axis.

24.2.2 **Explain** why different latitude zones have different average temperatures.

Reading Focus

Build Vocabulary L2

LINCS There are several words in the vocabulary list that sound like other words students may be familiar with. Have students: **L**ist the parts that they know; **I**magine a picture; **N**ote a reminding sound-alike word; **C**onnect the terms; and **S**elf-test.

Reading Strategy L2

a. The spinning of Earth on its axis
b. The movement of one body in space around another

2 INSTRUCT

Earth's Latitude Zones

Build Science Skills L2

Using Models Draw a large circle, approximately 1 m in diameter, on the board. This circle represents Earth. Find and draw the axis at 23.5° off center tilting from left to right, as in Figure 7. Draw in the equator. To the right of Earth, draw a wide arc representing the sun. Color in a horizontal bar between the sun and Earth near 30° S. Make this bar 15 cm wide. This line represents a fixed amount of solar radiation. Now color in another horizontal bar (again with a width of 15 cm) connecting the sun and Earth near 60° N. Compare the lengths of the arcs on Earth's surface covered by the bars at 30° S and at 60° N. *(The arc covered by the bar at 60° N will be longer than the arc covered by the bar at 30° S.)* These arcs represent the areas of Earth's surface that the same amount of solar radiation falls on at 30° S and at 60° N in the Northern Hemisphere winter. Be sure students understand that a fixed amount of radiation falling over a larger area will cause the radiation to be more diffuse. **Visual**

24.2 The Sun and the Seasons

Reading Focus

Key Concepts

- What are two ways in which Earth moves?
- How is Earth's surface divided into zones based on latitude?
- What causes the seasons?

Vocabulary

- rotation
- revolution
- tropic zone
- temperate zones
- polar zones
- solstice
- equinox

Reading Strategy

Building Vocabulary Draw a table like the one below that includes all the vocabulary terms listed for the section. As you read, define each vocabulary term in your own words.

Vocabulary Term	Definition
Rotation	a. ___?___
Revolution	b. ___?___

Figure 7 Earth is constantly moving in two ways. **A** Earth rotates around its axis once a day. **B** Earth revolves around the sun once a year.

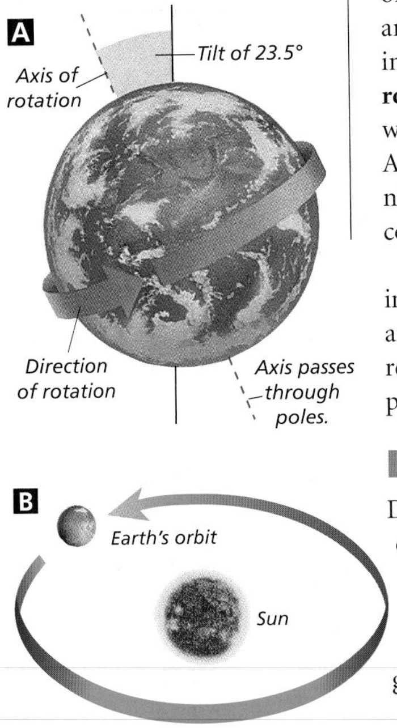
A
Axis of rotation
Tilt of 23.5°
Direction of rotation
Axis passes through poles.
B
Earth's orbit
Sun

No one can feel it, yet Earth is constantly moving in space. **Earth moves in two major ways: rotation and revolution.** As shown in Figure 7A, Earth spins like a top around an imaginary line, or axis, that connects the north and south geographic poles. The poles are the two points at opposite ends of Earth where Earth's axis intersects the surface. The spinning of Earth on its axis is called **rotation.** Earth's rotation causes day and night. As Earth rotates from west to east, the sun appears to move from east to west across the sky. As Earth continues to spin toward the east, the sun sets in the west and night falls. It takes one day, or just under 24 hours, for Earth to complete one rotation.

As Earth rotates on its axis, it also travels around the sun, as shown in Figure 7B. **Revolution** is the movement of one body in space around another. It takes Earth one year, about $365\frac{1}{4}$ days, to complete a full revolution around the sun. Earth revolves around the sun in a broad path, or orbit.

Earth's Latitude Zones

Different parts of Earth receive different amounts of sunlight depending on their latitude. Latitude measures distance in degrees north or south of the equator. For example, the equator is at 0° and the North Pole is at 90° north latitude. As you can see in Figure 8, regions near the equator receive more direct sunlight than the poles. As a result, Earth is generally warmer near the equator and colder toward the poles.

Section Resources

Print
- ***Reading and Study Workbook With Math Support,*** Section 24.2
- ***Transparencies,*** Section 24.2

Technology
- ***Interactive Textbook,*** Section 24.2
- ***Presentation Pro CD-ROM,*** Section 24.2

Scientists use lines of latitude to mark out three different types of regions within which temperatures are generally similar: the tropic, temperate, and polar zones. Between the latitudes of 23.5° south and 23.5° north is the **tropic zone,** where Earth is generally warm. From 23.5° north to 66.5° north and from 23.5° south to 66.5° south are the **temperate zones,** which are generally cooler than the tropics. From 66.5° north to the North Pole and from 66.5° south to the South Pole are the **polar zones,** which are generally cold.

Reading Checkpoint *Which is the coldest type of latitude zone?*

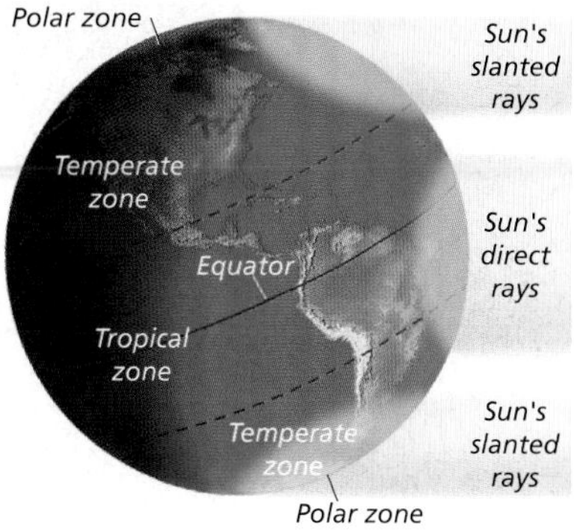
Polar zone
Sun's slanted rays
Temperate zone
Sun's direct rays
Equator
Tropical zone
Sun's slanted rays
Temperate zone
Polar zone

Figure 8 The angle that sunlight strikes Earth's surface varies with latitude. As a result, it is generally warmer near the equator than near the poles.
Interpreting Diagrams *Which latitude zone receives the most direct sunlight?*

The Seasons

Most of the United States is in the temperate zone. In much of the country, therefore, temperature and other weather conditions change over the year with the cycle of the seasons. What causes these seasonal changes? The answer is related to Earth's rotation and its revolution.

Earth's axis of rotation is not straight up and down. Instead, the axis tilts at an angle of about 23.5° relative to a line perpendicular to its orbital path. As Earth orbits the sun, the north end of Earth's axis points in the same direction—toward the North Star. But the orientation of Earth's axis changes relative to the sun over the course of a year. **The seasons are caused by the tilt of Earth's axis as it moves around the sun.**

Solstices Because Earth's axis is tilted, the latitude at which the noon sun appears directly overhead changes each day according to a yearly cycle. A **solstice** (SOHL stis) occurs on the two days each year when the sun is directly overhead at latitude 23.5° north or 23.5° south. In the Northern Hemisphere, the summer solstice, which marks the beginning of summer, occurs around June 21. At this time, the Northern Hemisphere is tilted toward the sun, so it receives more sunlight than the Southern Hemisphere. On this day, daylight hours are longest in the Northern Hemisphere and shortest in the Southern Hemisphere.

Six months later, on about December 21, the winter solstice, which marks the beginning of winter, occurs in the Northern Hemisphere. On the winter solstice, the Northern Hemisphere is tilted away from the sun. As a result, the Northern Hemisphere now receives less sunlight than the Southern Hemisphere. At this time, the daylight hours are shortest in the Northern Hemisphere, but longest in the Southern Hemisphere.

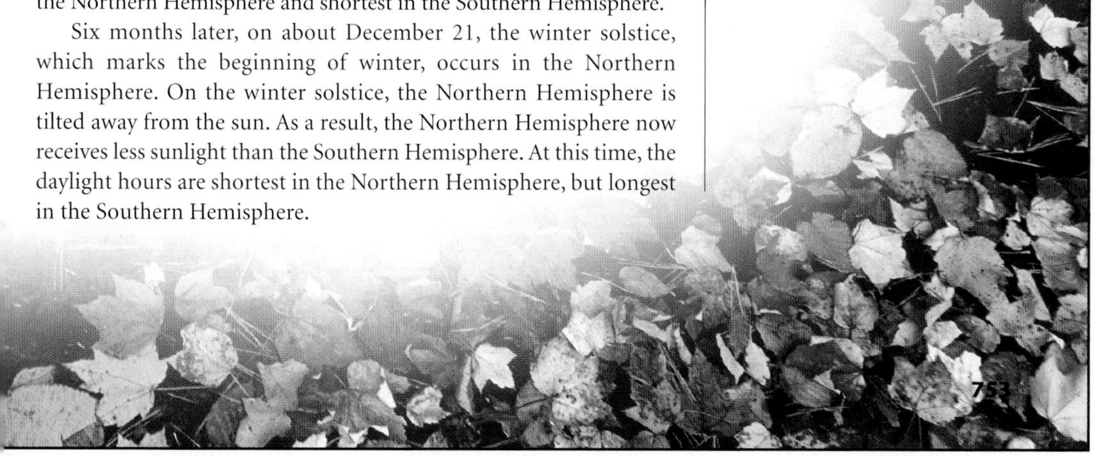

Figure 9 In the temperate zones, the beginning of autumn brings cooler weather and colorful leaves.

Customize for Inclusion Students

Gifted
Have students design a survey to find out whether people know the cause of the seasons. Ask them to survey a sample of students and teachers at your school and report the results to the class in preparation for doing Address Misconceptions on p. 754.

The Seasons

Build Reading Literacy

L1

Use Prior Knowledge Refer to page **2D** in **Chapter 1**, which provides the guidelines for using prior knowledge.

Before reading The Seasons, have students work in groups to brainstorm lists of things they know about the seasons and the cause of the seasons. After reading the selection, ask students to review their lists and determine how accurate their prior knowledge was. Have students identify any specific misconceptions on the list and replace these with their new understanding of the concepts. **Interpersonal, Group**

Teacher Demo

L2

Solar Energy and the Seasons

Purpose Students observe how the angle of incoming solar radiation affects how regions of Earth are heated.

Materials large-face flashlight, globe with stand

Procedure Dim the lights. Place the globe so that the top of its axis is tilted away from you. Hold the flashlight horizontally and close to the globe. Shine the light on the low latitudes of the Southern Hemisphere so that it produces a circular print. Explain that this model represents the Southern Hemisphere summer. Now, keeping the flashlight horizontal, move it slowly upward so that it is shining on the middle latitudes of the Northern Hemisphere. Ask students to describe how the area covered by the light changes, and what season the Northern Hemisphere is experiencing in this model.

Expected Outcome The area covered by the light will increase. Students should explain that this model represents the Northern Hemisphere winter. Be sure students understand that the light from the flashlight represents a fixed amount of solar radiation. When the light hits the globe directly, the fixed amount of radiation falls on a smaller area and therefore produces more heat than when it hits the globe at an angle.
Visual, Logical

Answer to . . .

Figure 8 *The tropic zone*

Reading Checkpoint *The polar zone*

Address Misconceptions **L2**

Many students think the seasons are caused by the changing distance from Earth to the sun throughout the year. Have students work in groups to create posters, multimedia presentations, songs or spoken word presentations, or TV interviews to teach others the true cause of the seasons. **Interpersonal, Portfolio**

Use Visuals **L1**

Figure 10 Explain that the figure shows Earth's orbit as seen from the side and slightly above the ecliptic (Earth is not closer to the sun at the equinoxes). Ask, **When is the summer solstice in Australia?** *(December)* **Visual, Logical**

3 ASSESS

Evaluate Understanding **L2**

Have students explain the cause of local (Northern Hemisphere) seasons.

Reteach **L1**

Use Figure 8 to reinforce the concept that parts of Earth experience summer when hit by more direct sunlight.

Writing in Science

Students' paragraphs should describe how life in their community might be different without seasons.

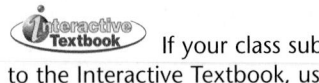

Interactive Textbook If your class subscribes to the Interactive Textbook, use it to review key concepts in Section 24.2

Answer to . . .

Figure 10 *Earth's axis is tilted most toward the sun during the December solstice.*

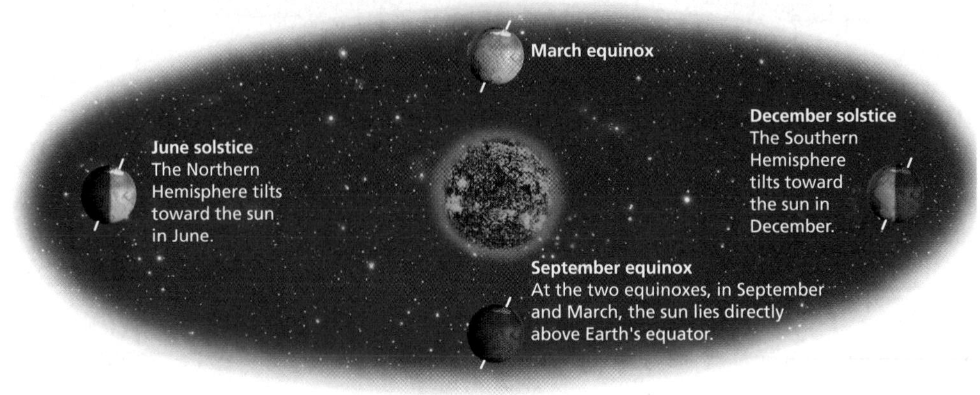
March equinox
June solstice
The Northern Hemisphere tilts toward the sun in June.
December solstice
The Southern Hemisphere tilts toward the sun in December.
September equinox
At the two equinoxes, in September and March, the sun lies directly above Earth's equator.

Figure 10 The seasons are caused by the tilt of Earth's axis as it revolves around the sun. **Interpreting Visuals** ***When is the south end of Earth's axis tilted most toward the sun?***

The seasons are not affected by Earth's changing distance from the sun. In fact, in the Northern Hemisphere, Earth is closer to the sun during winter than it is during summer.

Equinoxes Look at Figure 10. Notice that halfway between the solstices are two days, called equinoxes. The equinoxes mark the beginning of spring and autumn. At an **equinox,** neither hemisphere is tilted toward the sun, and the lengths of daylight and of darkness are approximately equal. The vernal equinox, which occurs about March 21 in the Northern Hemisphere, marks the start of spring. The autumnal equinox, which occurs about September 22 in the Northern Hemisphere, marks the start of autumn. On these two days, the noon sun is directly overhead at the equator. Sunlight reaches the Northern Hemisphere and Southern Hemisphere in equal amounts on the equinoxes.

Section 24.2 Assessment

Reviewing Concepts

1. Describe two ways in which Earth moves in space.
2. What are three zones on Earth's surface that are based on latitude? What are their characteristics?
3. What determines the change in seasons?
4. Describe one effect of Earth's rotation.

Critical Thinking

5. **Classifying** Classify each of the following latitudes as part of the tropic, temperate, or polar zones: 15° north, 29° south, and 70° north.
6. **Inferring** What is Earth's orientation at the time of the winter solstice in the Southern Hemisphere? Explain.
7. **Comparing and Contrasting** How are solstices and equinoxes similar? How are they different?

Writing in Science

Cause and Effect Write a paragraph describing how life in your community might be different if Earth's axis were not tilted. (*Hint:* Consider how the tilt of Earth's axis affects the seasons.)

Section 24.2 Assessment

1. Earth rotates around its axis and revolves around the sun.
2. The three types of zones are the tropic, temperate, and polar zones. The tropic zone is generally warm, and the polar zones are generally cold. The temperate zones are generally cooler than the tropics, but warmer than the polar zones.
3. The tilt of Earth's axis as it revolves around the sun
4. Earth's rotation causes a cycle of day and night to take place about once every 24 hours.
5. 15° N: tropic zone; 29° S: temperate zone; 70° N: polar zone
6. The winter solstice in the Southern Hemisphere occurs at the same time as the summer solstice in the Northern Hemisphere. The Northern Hemisphere is tilted to the greatest extent toward the sun, and the Southern Hemisphere is tilted to the greatest extent away from the sun, at this time.
7. Solstices and equinoxes are similar in that there are two of each every year and that they both mark the beginning of seasons on Earth. Solstices mark the times when the sun is directly overhead at either 23.5° north or south, and the Northern and Southern Hemispheres are tilted to the greatest extent relative to the sun. Equinoxes mark the times when the sun is directly over the equator and neither hemisphere is tilted relative to the sun.

24.3 Solar Energy and Winds

Reading Focus

Key Concepts

- What happens to the energy Earth receives from the sun?
- How is energy transferred within the troposphere?
- What causes winds?
- What are some examples of local winds and global winds?

Vocabulary

- greenhouse effect
- wind
- local wind
- sea breeze
- land breeze
- global winds
- Coriolis effect
- monsoon
- jet stream

Reading Strategy

Comparing and Contrasting Copy the table below. After you read, compare sea and land breezes by completing the table.

Type of Wind	Day or Night?	Direction of Air Movement
Sea breeze	a. ?	b. ?
Land breeze	c. ?	d. ?

The heat you feel when you're out in the sun is one effect of solar energy. You might think that sunlight heats the air directly, just as it heats you directly. But the process is more complicated than that.

Energy in the Atmosphere

Some solar energy that reaches Earth's atmosphere is reflected back, some is absorbed by the atmosphere, and some is absorbed by Earth's surface. About 30 percent of the incoming solar energy is reflected back into space by clouds, dust in the air, gases, and Earth's surface. About 20 percent of the sun's energy is absorbed by clouds and gases. But the greatest amount of solar energy—about half—passes through the atmosphere and is absorbed by the surface.

The atmosphere is heated primarily by energy that is reradiated by Earth's surface. Unlike incoming solar energy, which has much of its energy in the visible spectrum, the energy radiated back into the atmosphere is mostly infrared radiation. Certain gases in the atmosphere, including water vapor and carbon dioxide, allow visible light to pass through but absorb most infrared radiation. These gases radiate some of this absorbed energy back to Earth's surface, warming the lower atmosphere in a process called the **greenhouse effect.** Without the greenhouse effect, Earth's surface would be much cooler than it is.

Energy is transferred within the troposphere in three ways: radiation, convection, and conduction. As the How It Works box on page 756 explains, these processes work together to heat the troposphere.

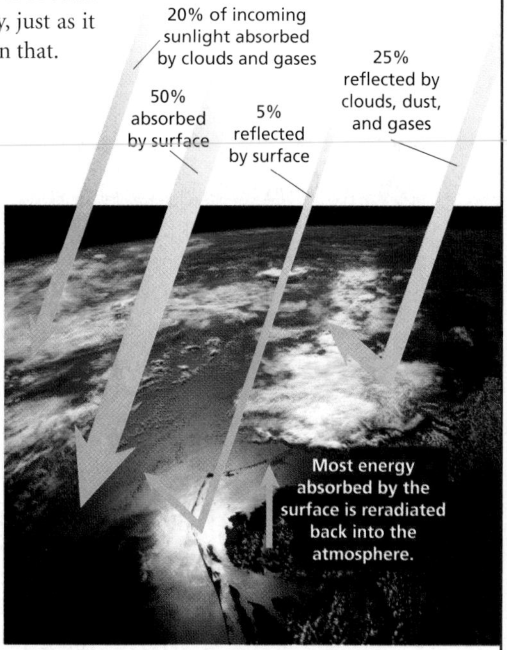

20% of incoming sunlight absorbed by clouds and gases
25% reflected by clouds, dust, and gases
50% absorbed by surface
5% reflected by surface
Most energy absorbed by the surface is reradiated back into the atmosphere.

Figure 11 About half of the sunlight that reaches Earth is absorbed by the surface. The rest is either reflected back into space or absorbed in the atmosphere.

Section Resources

Print
- ***Reading and Study Workbook With Math Support,*** Section 24.3
- ***Transparencies,*** Section 24.3

Technology
- ***Interactive Textbook,*** Section 24.3
- ***Presentation Pro CD-ROM,*** Section 24.3
- ***Go Online,*** NSTA SciLinks, Winds

Section 24.3

1 FOCUS

Objectives

24.3.1 **Describe** the processes by which solar energy heats the troposphere.

24.3.2 **Identify** local and global winds and **explain** how they are produced.

Reading Focus

Build Vocabulary L2

Concept Map Have students construct a concept map connecting the main topic of Wind to *local winds* and *global winds*. Have students expand the map as they read to include *sea breeze, land breeze, monsoon,* and *jet stream.*

Reading Strategy L2

a. Day **b.** Cool air moves toward land. **c.** Night **d.** Cool air moves toward the water.

2 INSTRUCT

Energy in the Atmosphere

Build Reading Literacy L1

Summarize Refer to page **598D** in **Chapter 20**, which provides the guidelines for summarizing.

Tell students that pp. 755–756 cover technical material, and that summarizing it will help them pull together the main ideas and avoid getting lost in the details. Allow students to choose whether they would like to present a verbal, written, or pictorial summary. Point out to students that the bolded key concepts on p. 755 and A, B, and C in How It Works on p. 756 contain important information that should be included in a summary. **Intrapersonal**

Address Misconceptions L2

Students may think that the greenhouse effect is always bad, possibly because it is often mentioned in conjunction with global warming. Have students write a paragraph describing what Earth would be like without the greenhouse effect. *(Earth's surface would be much colder, possibly inhospitable to life.)* **Logical**

HOW It Works

Energy Transfer in the Troposphere **L2**

Solar radiation heats Earth's surface, which, in turn, transfers energy to the troposphere. Energy is released by Earth's surface in the form of infrared radiation. Atmospheric gases—such as water vapor, carbon dioxide, and methane—absorb infrared radiation. These greenhouse gases also reradiate some of that energy back to Earth's surface. This transfer of energy by radiation is very efficient, and is the primary mechanism by which the troposphere is heated. Because in convection some heat energy is converted into kinetic energy, convection is a less efficient way of transferring heat to the troposphere. Because air is not a good heat conductor, conduction is the least significant way in which heat is transferred in the troposphere.

Interpreting Diagrams The sun **Visual**

For Enrichment **L3**

Students can research the specific wavelengths of infrared radiation that are absorbed by each of the major gases in the atmosphere. **Verbal, Portfolio**

Integrate Physics **L2**

The sun emits energy over a wide range of wavelengths, from radio waves through X-rays. Slightly more than half of the sun's radiation is in the visible and ultraviolet spectra (10–750 nm). Most of the radiation in this range passes through the atmosphere and is absorbed by Earth's surface, heating the land and water. These surfaces then radiate energy back into the atmosphere in the infrared spectrum (750–1000 nm). Certain gases in the atmosphere, including carbon dioxide and water vapor, efficiently absorb infrared radiation. This process is called the greenhouse effect, which is the accumulation of heat in the lower atmosphere through the radiation and reradiation of energy. Ask, **Why is only 20% of incoming solar energy absorbed by the atmosphere?** *(Most solar radiation is in the visible and ultraviolet range, which most atmospheric gases cannot absorb.)* **Which has more energy, infrared or ultraviolet radiation?** *(Ultraviolet)* **Logical**

HOW It Works

Energy Transfer in the Troposphere

Energy is transferred within the troposphere by radiation, conduction, and convection. Radiation from the sun heats Earth's surface, which then radiates heat skyward. The air in direct contact with Earth's surface is heated by conduction. Warm air near the surface expands and rises and cooler, denser air sinks, forming convection currents that move heat through the troposphere.

Interpreting Diagrams ***Where does most of the energy in the troposphere originally come from?***

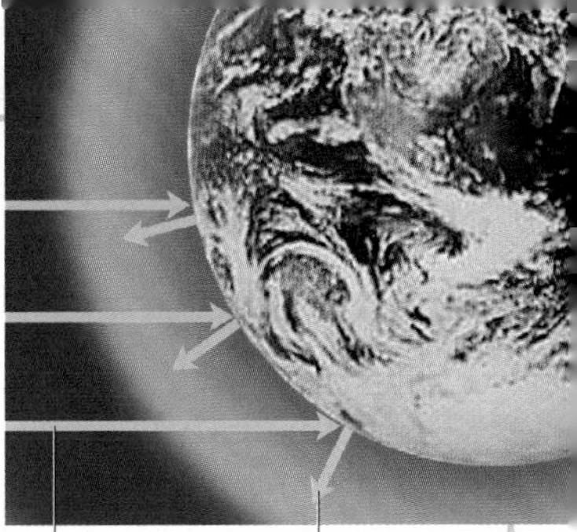
Solar radiation
Infrared radiation

Greenhouse effect When Earth's surface is heated, much of this energy is radiated back as infrared radiation. Some of this radiation is absorbed by gases in the atmosphere. The process by which gases hold heat in the air is called the greenhouse effect.

A Radiation Much of the sun's radiation reaches Earth's surface, where it heats the land and water. Land and water radiate heat back into the atmosphere.

B Conduction The conduction process transfers heat from land and water directly to the few meters of air nearest Earth's surface.

C Convection Convection moves heat through the troposphere. As surface air is heated by radiation and conduction, rising warm air is replaced by denser, downward-flowing cool air.

Customize for English Language Learners

Flowchart
Tailor your presentation to ELL students by using a flowchart to help students visualize the sequence of events with minimal use of language. Title the flowchart The Path of Energy. Use three boxes entitled Sun, Earth's Surface, and Troposphere. Have students fill in the boxes to explain the energy transfer in their own words.

Wind

What happens when you open a vacuum-packed can of chips? You hear a rush of air, which is the sound of air moving from the high-pressure area outside the can to the low-pressure area inside the can. A similar process occurs in the atmosphere.

Air naturally flows from areas of higher pressure to areas of lower pressure. This flow is **wind,** which is the mainly horizontal movement of air. **Winds are caused by differences in air pressure.** Larger pressure differences produce stronger winds.

Differences in air pressure are often caused by the unequal heating of Earth's surface. As you've learned, the atmosphere is warmed largely by reradiation from Earth's surface below it. As air is heated, it expands. As it becomes less dense, air rises. Cooler, denser air flows in to replace it. This process occurs on both local and global scales, producing local and global winds.

Go Online NSTA SCILINKS

For: Links on winds
Visit: www.SciLinks.org
Web Code: ccn-3243

Local Winds

On a hot summer day, there is often a cool breeze blowing in from the water to the beach. This breeze is an example of a **local wind,** a wind that blows over a short distance. Local winds are caused by the unequal heating of Earth's surface within a small region.

The breezes that occur where land meets a large body of water are examples of local winds. Water has a higher specific heat than land, and therefore takes longer to heat up and cool down. During the day, the sun heats the land more quickly than it heats the water. The air above the land becomes warmer than the air above the water. The warm air expands and rises, creating a lower-pressure area above the land. The cooler air over the water flows toward the land, creating a **sea breeze.**

At night, these temperature and pressure conditions are reversed, as Figure 12 shows. Land cools off more quickly than water. The cooler air over land has a higher density than the warmer air over water. The result is a **land breeze,** where cooler air over land moves toward water. Winds are named for the direction from which they originate—sea breezes begin over the ocean and land breezes begin over land.

Reading Checkpoint *In which direction does a land breeze blow?*

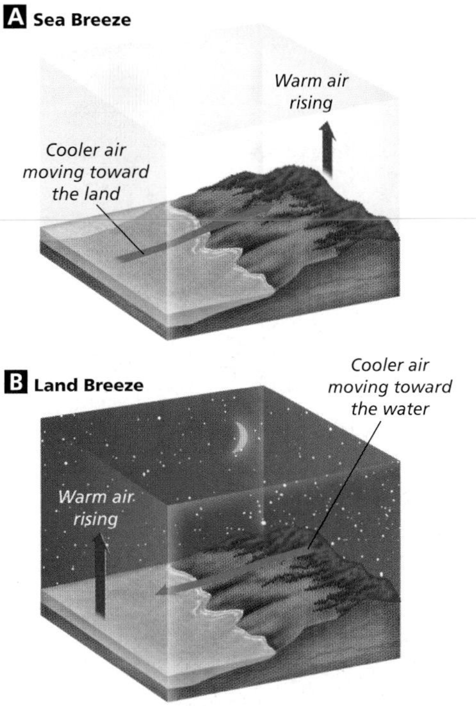

A Sea Breeze
Warm air rising
Cooler air moving toward the land
B Land Breeze
Cooler air moving toward the water
Warm air rising

Figure 12 Sea breezes and land breezes are local winds. **A** During the day, air pressure differences due to unequal heating cause a sea breeze. **B** At night, pressure differences are reversed, causing a land breeze. **Comparing and Contrasting** *How are land breezes and sea breezes different?*

Wind

Teacher Demo

Wind Creation L2

Purpose Students observe how winds are produced.

Materials clear plastic tank, plastic wrap, 2 1-L beakers, water, hot plate or Bunsen burner, ice, wood splint (smoker), matches

Procedure Fill one beaker about halfway with water and heat it to nearly boiling. Fill the other beaker with ice. Place the beakers inside the tank on opposite sides and cover the tank with plastic wrap. Cut a small hole in the wrap over the ice large enough to fit the splint through easily. Ask students which way they think the wind will blow. Light the splint, blow on it until it is smoking, and insert it deep into the tank over the ice.

Expected Outcome The smoke will sink over the ice, move across the tank, and rise over the hot water, making the movement of air in the convection current visible. **Visual, Logical**

Local Winds

Build Science Skills L2

Designing Experiments Have groups of students design an experiment to test whether a breeze over a lake is produced by the same process described on p. 757. Provide them with the following headings to fill in: Hypothesis, Materials, Procedure, and Observations. Students' experiments may include observations of air pressure, temperature, and/or wind direction. **Interpersonal, Portfolio**

Go Online NSTA SCILINKS

Download a worksheet on winds for students to complete, and find additional teacher support from NSTA SciLinks.

Answer to . . .

Figure 12 *They occur at different times and move in opposite directions.*

Reading Checkpoint *A land breeze blows from the land toward the water.*

Global Winds

Use Visuals L1

Figure 13 Identify 0°, 30° S, 60° S, 30° N, and 60° N. Explain that the global wind patterns shown in this figure remain fairly constant throughout the year, though the change of seasons does have some effect on the circulation of the atmosphere. Heating patterns change as the seasons change, and patterns of air pressure (and thus wind) change as a result. Point out that convection cells are vertical and reach to the top of the troposphere. Point to the convection cell between 0° and 30° S and ask, **Which direction is this wind pattern felt on the ground?** *(Northwest)* **In which regions of Earth are the global winds moving generally from the east in a westerly direction?** *(0°–30° N, 0°–30° S, 60° N–90° N, and 60° S–90° S)* **Why are the arrows in the 0°–30° S region (over South America) curving to the left?** *(The northerly winds curve westward as the result of Earth's rotation—or the Coriolis effect.)* This figure can be used to help explain the movements of fronts and storms in Section 24.5 and global climate patterns in Section 24.7. **Visual**

Teacher Demo

Convection Cells L2

Purpose Students observe a convection cell produced in water.

Materials 1-L beaker, water, hot plate or Bunsen burner, 5–10 drops of food coloring

Procedure Fill the beaker with approximately 750 mL water. Place the beaker on a hot plate or Bunsen burner and heat water until some steam is rising, but before boiling. Turn off the heat source. Explain that convection cells are common phenomena in both air and water on many scales, from global to local winds, and from ocean currents to coffee cups. Slowly add the drops of food coloring (they will spread quickly, so only add enough to make the convection cell visible). Ask students to explain what is causing the convection cell.

Expected Outcome The food coloring will reveal the circulation of water in a convection cell before dissipating. This cell is produced when warm water touches surface air, cools, and sinks again to the bottom. **Visual, Logical**

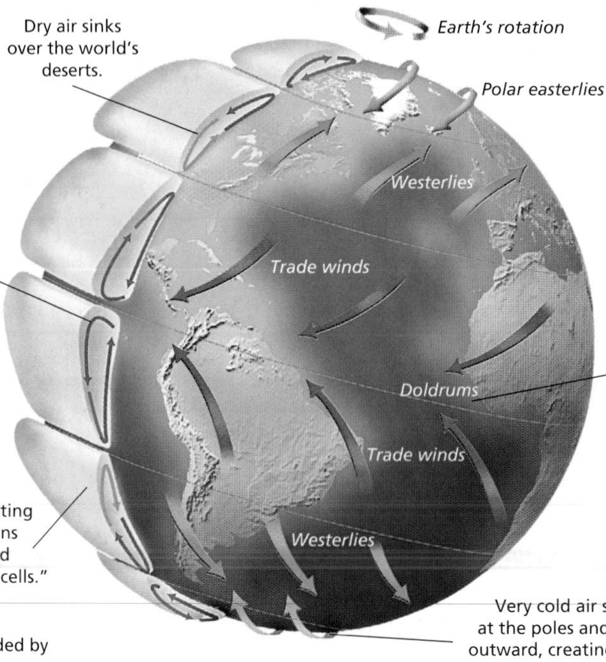

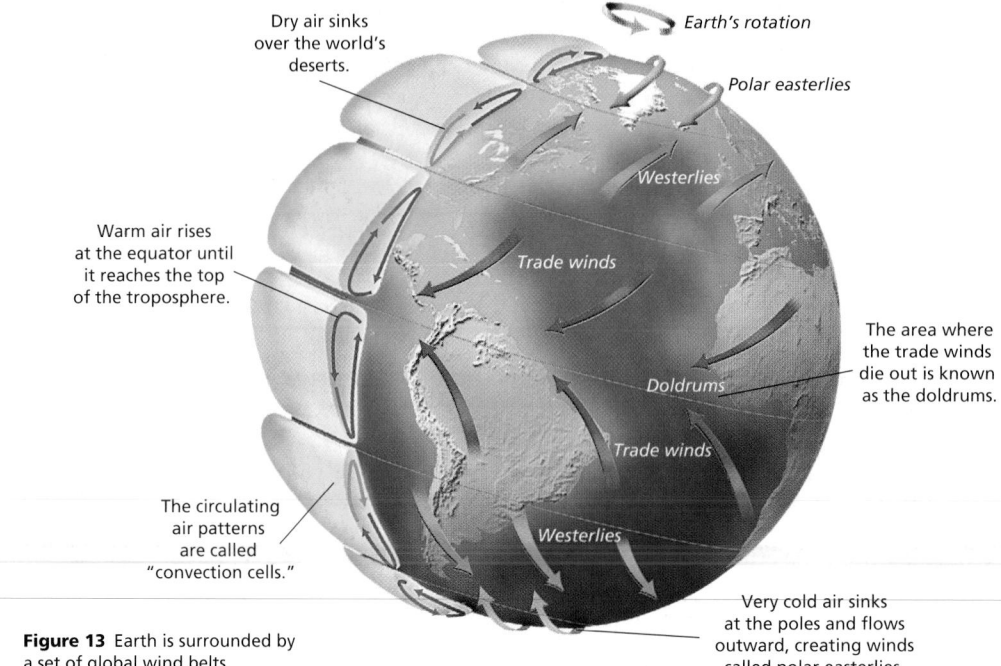

Dry air sinks over the world's deserts.
Earth's rotation
Polar easterlies
Westerlies
Warm air rises at the equator until it reaches the top of the troposphere.
Trade winds
The area where the trade winds die out is known as the doldrums.
Doldrums
Trade winds
The circulating air patterns are called "convection cells."
Westerlies
Very cold air sinks at the poles and flows outward, creating winds called polar easterlies.

Figure 13 Earth is surrounded by a set of global wind belts.

Figure 14 For hundreds of years, sailing ships have relied on global winds to transport cargo across the oceans.
Interpreting Visuals ***Which band of global winds would a sailing ship use to move cargo from Canada to Europe?***

758

Global Winds

Winds that blow over long distances from a specific direction are called **global winds.** These winds are part of a worldwide pattern of air circulation. Global winds are caused by the unequal heating of Earth's surface across a large region.

Convection Cells Global winds move in a series of huge bands called convection cells. As you can see in Figure 13, these bands look like loops from the side. These bands are caused by temperature variations across Earth's surface. At the equator, for example, temperatures tend to be warmer than at other latitudes. Warm air rises at the equator, creating a low-pressure region. This warm air is replaced by cooler air brought by global winds blowing near the surface. Higher in the atmosphere, air blows away from the equator toward the poles. Similar convection cells cover large bands of latitude across Earth.

The trade winds are wind belts just north and south of the equator. In the Northern Hemisphere, they blow from the northeast to the southwest. The prevailing westerlies occur between 30° and 60° latitude in both hemispheres. These winds generally blow from west to east over much of North America. The polar easterlies extend from 60° latitude to the poles in both hemispheres. **Trade winds, westerlies, and polar easterlies are examples of global winds.**

Facts and Figures

Where the Wind Dies While trade winds and westerlies occur where convection cells blow across the surface, there are also areas where the wind dies out. These occur where the convection cells produce areas of rising or sinking air, such as at the equator, at 30° north and south latitude, and at 60° north and south latitude. The area of low winds at the equator is referred to as the *doldrums,* and the low wind regions at 30° north and south latitude are called the *horse latitudes.* This name has a gruesome historical origin. Colonial sailors traversing the Atlantic would frequently get stuck around 30° N when the wind died. To survive at sea with a limited supply of fresh water on board (and to lighten the ship's weight) the sailors would throw a few horses overboard.

If Earth were not rotating on its axis, global winds would move in roughly straight paths from the poles to the equator. However, because Earth rotates, global winds move in a curved path between the poles and the equator. Notice in Figure 13 that global winds curve to the right in the Northern Hemisphere and to the left in the Southern Hemisphere. The curving effect that Earth's rotation has on all free-moving objects, including global winds, is called the **Coriolis effect.** If Earth were not rotating, a rocket launched from the North Pole toward the equator would move in a straight line, as shown in Figure 15. However, because Earth is rotating underneath the rocket, the rocket would appear to an observer on Earth to curve to the right. Similary, Earth's rotation causes global winds to curve.

Monsoons Seasonal changes in the heating of Earth's surface affect the circulation of the atmosphere. A **monsoon** is a wind system that is characterized by seasonal reversal of direction. Monsoons are similar to land and sea breezes except that they occur on a much wider scale and longer time frame. For example, the summer monsoon that occurs over much of South and Southeast Asia blows warm, humid air from the ocean onto land. As this air rises over land, it cools and brings heavy rainfall to parts of that region. In winter the monsoon reverses, blowing from land onto water and bringing drier weather.

Jet Stream Global wind patterns are also affected by fast-moving streams of air at high altitudes. A belt of high-speed wind in the upper troposphere is called a **jet stream.** Jet streams are caused by great differences in air pressure that develop at high altitudes.

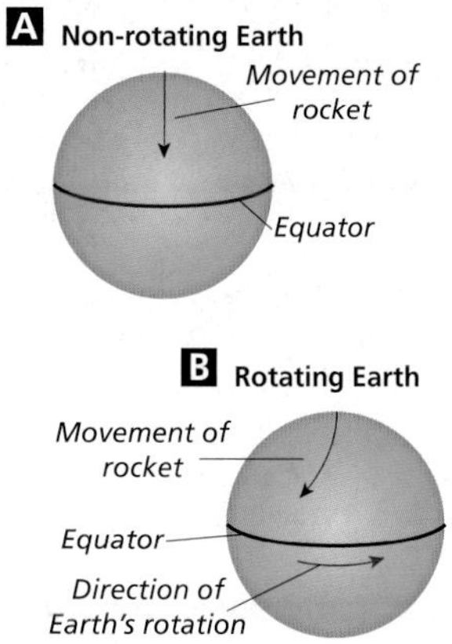
A Non-rotating Earth
Movement of rocket
Equator
B Rotating Earth
Movement of rocket
Equator
Direction of Earth's rotation

Figure 15 The Coriolis effect causes free-moving objects, such as rockets and global winds, to move in a curved path. **A** A rocket launched from the North Pole toward the equator would move in a straight line if Earth were not rotating. **B** The Coriolis effect causes such a rocket to appear to curve to the right. Similarly, the Coriolis effect causes global winds to curve to the right in the Northern Hemisphere.

3 ASSESS

Evaluate Understanding L2

Ask students to create a flowchart describing how local winds are created.

Reteach L1

Use Figure 13 to explain convection cells and the Coriolis effect.

Connecting Concepts

Water has a high specific heat, higher than that of land. As a result, water warms up slower during the day and cools down slower at night than land. This affects the temperature of the air above the water and land. Land and sea breezes are created by this daily cycle of unequal heating of air in coastal regions.

Interactive Textbook If your class subscribes to the Interactive Textbook, use it to review key concepts in Section 24.3.

Section 24.3 Assessment

Reviewing Concepts

1. What happens to solar energy when it reaches Earth's atmosphere?
2. Explain how energy is transferred within the troposphere.
3. What causes the wind to blow?
4. How are local winds and global winds similar? How are they different?
5. What are monsoons, and what causes them?

Critical Thinking

6. **Relating Cause and Effects** How does the Coriolis effect influence global wind patterns?
7. **Applying Concepts** You and your family vacation at a cabin on the shore of a large lake. At night, you notice that a breeze blows over your cabin toward the lake. Explain what causes the wind to blow in that direction.

Connecting Concepts

Thermal Energy Recall what you learned in Chapter 16 about the specific heat of water. Use this information to explain why land and sea breezes undergo daily reversals in direction.

Answer to . . .

Figure 14 *A sailing ship would use the westerlies to move cargo from Canada to Europe.*

Section 24.3 Assessment

1. Solar energy is distributed in three ways: some is reflected, some is absorbed by the atmosphere, and some is absorbed by Earth's surface.
2. Energy is transferred within the troposphere by radiation, convection, and conduction.
3. Wind is caused by differences in air pressure between different locations.
4. Both local and global winds are produced by differences in air pressure that result from the unequal heating of Earth's surface. For local winds, this unequal heating takes place within a small region, and the resulting wind blows over only a short distance. In contrast, global winds are caused by unequal heating across a large area, and blow over long distances for extended periods of time.
5. Monsoons are large wind systems that have seasonal reversals of direction. They are caused by air pressure differences that result from the unequal heating of air above the ocean and land.
6. The Coriolis effect causes global winds to turn to the right in the Northern Hemisphere and to the left in the Southern Hemisphere.
7. When night falls, the lake water remains warm as the land cools off quickly. The warmer air over the water has a lower pressure than the cooler air over the land. The result is a land breeze, which is when the cooler air over land moves toward water.

1 FOCUS

Objectives

24.4.1 **Explain** condensation in the atmosphere and **describe** the formation and characteristics of basic cloud forms.

24.4.2 **Identify** the common types of precipitation and **explain** how they form.

Reading Focus

Build Vocabulary L2

Concept Map Have students create a concept map with the topic Clouds. Connect *stratus clouds, cumulus clouds,* and *cirrus clouds.* Have students connect additional concepts related to the three types of clouds as they read the section.

Reading Strategy L2

a. Air pressure decreases, and air expands and cools to a temperature below its dew point. **b.** Water vapor condenses on small solid particles in the air.

2 INSTRUCT

Humidity

Address Misconceptions L2

Students may think that condensation occurs when air turns to liquid. Reiterate that condensation consists of water droplets, and that water vapor is only one component of air. Have students work in groups to create visuals showing the main types of molecules found in air in their approximate ratios. Include droplets of liquid water and an arrow indicating that gaseous water turns to liquid in the process of condensation. **Visual, Group**

24.4 Water in the Atmosphere

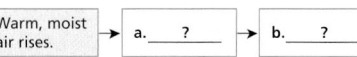

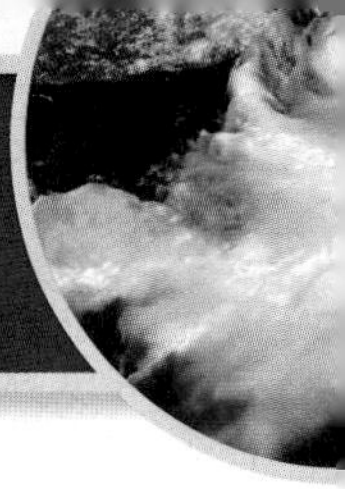

Reading Focus

Key Concepts

- What are some ways in which water condenses in the atmosphere?
- How do clouds form?
- What are the major types of clouds?
- What are the major forms of precipitation?

Vocabulary

- humidity
- relative humidity
- dew point
- cloud
- fog
- stratus clouds
- cumulus clouds
- cirrus clouds

Reading Strategy

Sequencing Copy the flowchart below. As you read, complete it to show how a cloud forms. Add more steps to the chart if necessary.

Cloud Formation

Warm, moist air rises. → a. ___?___ → b. ___?___

What do fogged-up windows on a cold winter morning and a bad hair day have in common? Both result from high levels of water vapor in the air. The atmosphere contains only about 0.001 percent of the total water in the world. Yet this relatively small amount of water has a great effect on the processes that occur in the atmosphere, including cloud formation and precipitation. It can also cause your windows to fog up and your hair to become limp or frizzy.

Figure 16 This antique "weather house" shows the humidity, or moisture content, of the air. If the air is humid, a hair inside the house expands and allows the man to come out of the door. When the air is dry, the hair contracts and the woman comes out.

Gruß aus Villach

Humidity

The amount of water in the atmosphere can vary greatly. Dry air contains much less water vapor than the air above a rainforest. The amount of water vapor in the air is called **humidity.** Warm, tropical air tends to contain more water vapor than cold, polar air does.

When you hear someone talking about the "humidity" of the air, that person is probably talking about relative humidity. **Relative humidity** is the ratio of the amount of water vapor in the air to the maximum amount of water vapor that can exist at that temperature.

Relative humidity is always expressed as a percentage. When the relative humidity is 60 percent, for example, air contains 60 percent of the maximum amount of water vapor that can exist at that temperature. When relative humidity reaches 100 percent, air is said to be saturated.

Section Resources

Print

- ***Laboratory Manual,*** Investigation 24A
- ***Reading and Study Workbook With Math Support,*** Section 24.4
- ***Transparencies,*** Section 24.4

Technology

- ***Probeware Lab Manual,*** Lab 10
- ***Interactive Textbook,*** Section 24.4
- ***Presentation Pro CD-ROM,*** Section 24.4
- ***Go Online,*** NSTA SciLinks, Clouds and fog; PHSchool.com, Data sharing

The maximum amount of water that can exist as a gas is greater at high temperatures than at low temperatures. Therefore, if the air temperature decreases, the atmosphere can hold less water vapor. After sunset, the temperature often decreases, and so the maximum amount of water vapor that the atmosphere can hold also decreases. The relative humidity rises, although the amount of water vapor in the air remains the same. Eventually, the air may become saturated with water vapor. The temperature at which air becomes saturated is called its **dew point.** If the temperature drops further, water vapor will condense.

Water vapor typically condenses as dew, frost, clouds, or fog. Dew, shown in Figure 17A, is water vapor that condenses on Earth's surface. Frost, shown in Figure 17B, forms when the dew point of air is below freezing. Frost isn't frozen dew. Rather, frost is formed when water vapor in air changes directly from a gas to solid ice crystals.

When the air warms, as can happen during the day, the amount of water vapor that air can contain increases. As a result, the relative humidity decreases.

Reading Checkpoint *What is the dew point of air?*

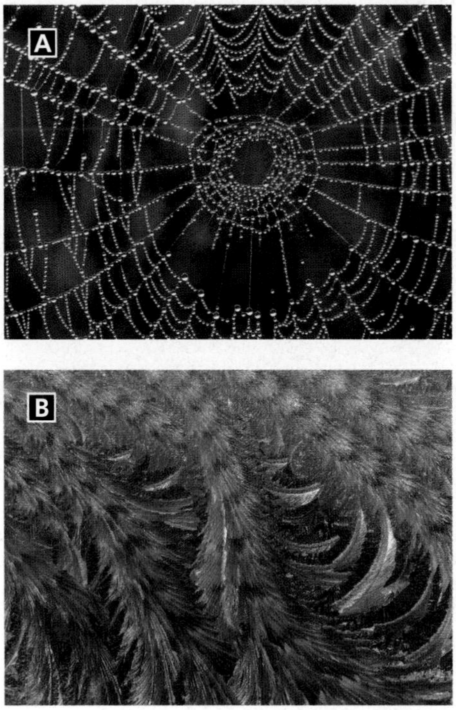

A
B

Figure 17 Dew and frost are two forms of condensation. **A** Dew can often be seen on spider webs early in the morning after a cool night. **B** Frost is visible on this pane of glass.
Comparing and Contrasting ***How are dew and frost similar? How are they different?***

Cloud Formation

The most noticeable features of the atmosphere are clouds. Some are high and wispy; others are thick and dark. A **cloud** is a dense, visible mass of tiny water droplets or ice crystals that are suspended in the atmosphere. The droplets or crystals that form a cloud are extremely small—one cloud might consist of billions of such droplets and crystals.

Clouds form as warm, moist air rises and water vapor condenses in the atmosphere. Water vapor condenses when air cools to a temperature below its dew point. Such cooling occurs naturally as warm air rises through the atmosphere. As air rises, air pressure decreases. As a result, the air expands and cools, and condensation occurs. Cloud formation, then, is the result of the expansion of air and the resulting drop in temperature.

For a cloud to form, solid particles such as dust and salt must be present for the water vapor to condense upon. When air is cooled below its dew point, water vapor changes into tiny water droplets or ice crystals on these solid particles. This process is similar to the way water vapor condenses onto the bathroom mirror when you take a hot shower.

Go Online NSTA SCiLINKS

For: Links on clouds and fog
Visit: www.SciLinks.org
Web Code: ccn-3244

Cloud Formation

Address Misconceptions **L2**

Students have many misconceptions about what clouds are and how they are formed. Some common misconceptions include: clouds are made of smoke, clouds come from above the sky, clouds are formed when bodies of water boil, clouds are made of water vapor, and clouds are refilled by the sea. Have students work in groups to construct a flowchart with graphics to explain the formation of clouds.
Interpersonal, Visual

Go Online NSTA SCiLINKS

Download a worksheet on clouds and fog for students to complete, and find additional teacher support from NSTA SciLinks.

Customize for Inclusion Students

Learning Disabled
Have students look through nature magazines for photographs of clouds. Ask them to cut out examples of each type of cloud and create a poster display for the classroom. With the help of this text and other resources, have students identify and label the clouds shown in the photographs.

Answer to . . .

Figure 17 *Dew is water vapor that condenses on Earth's surface. Frost is formed when water vapor in air changes directly from a gas to solid ice crystals.*

Reading Checkpoint *The dew point of air is the temperature at which air becomes saturated with water vapor.*

Classifying Clouds

Use Visuals L1

Cloud Photos Explain that these photos are representative examples, and that actual clouds of the types shown may vary in appearance. Ask, **What is the identifying feature of the two types of cumulus clouds shown?** *(They are puffy/tall/resemble cotton.)* **Which type of clouds are most likely to produce precipitation?** *(Cumulonimbus, nimbostratus, altostratus)* **Which clouds are at the highest altitude?** *(Cirrus, cirrostratus)* **Which type of cloud would you most likely associate with a thunderstorm?** *(Cumulonimbus)* **Visual**

Cirrostratus clouds

◀ Cirrus clouds

Cumulonimbus clouds

Classifying Clouds

Clouds seem to come in an endless variety of forms, constantly shifting shapes as they move through the sky. Yet, different clouds have some similarities. Scientists classify clouds on the basis of form and height.

The first cloud classification system was developed in 1803 by the British naturalist Luke Howard. His classification system and the terms he coined for different types of clouds are the basis for what scientists use today. **There are three basic cloud forms: stratus, cumulus, and cirrus.** Scientists use these three forms to name and describe a variety of common cloud types. Notice that clouds are generally grouped into families by the altitude at which they occur. Photos of common types of clouds are shown on this and the following page.

Fog is a cloud that is near or touching the ground. Fogs often form when warm, moist air passes over land. Other fogs form when the ground cools at night, cooling the humid air immediately above the ground to the dew point.

Stratus Clouds Flat layers of clouds that cover much or all of the sky are known as **stratus clouds** (STRAT us). The word *stratus* comes from the Latin word meaning "to spread out." Nimbostratus clouds are low stratus clouds that produce steady and widespread rain or snow. When *nimbo-* or *-nimbus* is added to a cloud's name, it means that the cloud produces precipitation.

Stratus clouds

Facts and Figures

Types of Fog There are three different types of fog. Radiation fog occurs when the land loses heat by radiation, usually after the sun sets. The air above the land cools rapidly past the dew point, causing water vapor to condense into fog. This type of fog tends to collect in valleys and is also known as ground fog or tule fog. Sea fog occurs when a body of water is warmer than the air above it, and is similar to the steam forming over a hot bath in a cool bathroom. Advection fog occurs when warm, moist air is suddenly cooled. This often happens when a warm air mass comes in contact with a cold body of water.

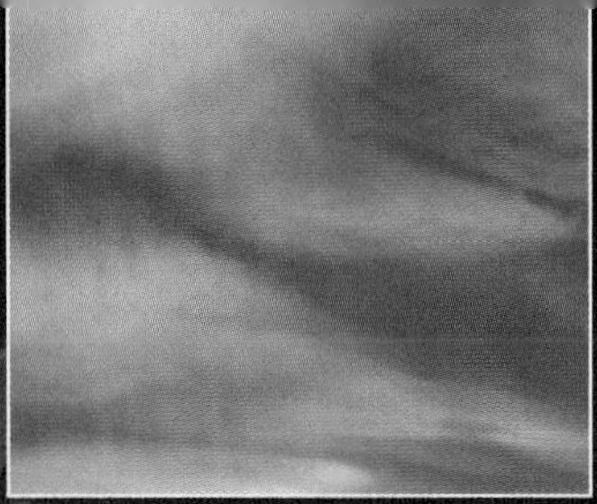

◀ Altostratus clouds

▼ Cumulus clouds

Altostratus clouds, which are middle-level clouds, often form a layer that covers most of the sky. These clouds can produce light rain or snow. Middle-level clouds, which occur at altitudes between 2000 and 6000 meters, are given the prefix *alto-*.

Cumulus Clouds Puffy white clouds that look like piles of cotton balls with flat bottoms are **cumulus clouds** (KYOO myuh lus). The word *cumulus* comes from the Latin for "heap." Cumulus clouds are the "fair-weather clouds" that you often see on sunny days. Cumulonimbus clouds are dark, towering clouds that produce heavy precipitation, often together with thunder and lightning. Cumulus clouds and cumulonimbus clouds develop vertically. They form less than 2 kilometers from the ground and grow upward. Cumulonimbus clouds usually have a flat base and a billowing tower rising above. They are sometimes called thunderheads.

Cirrus Clouds Thin, white, wispy clouds, often with a feathery or veil-like appearance, are **cirrus clouds** (SEER us). You can see cirrus clouds high in the sky on a clear, sunny day. The prefix *cirro-* is used to describe high-altitude clouds. Because temperatures at high altitudes are so low, cirrus clouds are mostly ice crystals. Cirrus and cirrostratus clouds generally produce no rain. But such high-altitude clouds often blow into an area just ahead of rain-producing clouds.

Reading Checkpoint *What are cirrus clouds made of?*

▼ Nimbostratus clouds

Build Reading Literacy L1

Compare and Contrast Refer to page **226D** in **Chapter 8**, which provides the guidelines for comparing and contrasting.

Before reading pp. 762–763, have students set up a table with three columns entitled Sky Coverage, Precipitation, and Altitude. Have students fill in the table with the prefixes and suffixes used in this selection (for example, *cirro/cirrus, strato/stratus, cumulo/cumulus, nimbo/nimbus*) and the definition of each term. Then, have students work in groups to produce as many combinations as they can, writing each one on an index card. Have each student select two cards from the stack and verbally compare and contrast the two cloud types. Tell students that all possible combinations may not be actual types of clouds, and have them remove from the stack names that are not.
Verbal, Group

Build Science Skills L2

Observing Ask students if they have ever wondered how some people can look out the window and predict the weather. Explain that learning to identify and observe clouds will help build the ability to predict weather. Have students keep a log of cloud and weather observations for at least one month. Encourage students to continue the activity for a whole year to develop a sense of seasonal changes. For each page of their logs, have students record the date and time of observation; a description and drawing of the cloud cover, including the general altitude (high, low), percent of sky coverage, and the thickness or relative height of clouds; a general description of any weather phenomena, such as wind or precipitation; and the temperature (either specific or general). After a period of time, have students reread observations and analyze patterns.
Visual, Portfolio

Answer to . . .

Reading Checkpoint *Cirrus clouds are made mostly of ice crystals.*

Forms of Precipitation

Build Reading Literacy L1

Predict Refer to page **744D** in this chapter, which provides the guidelines for predicting.

Before reading p. 764, ask students to recall what they just learned about cloud formation. Based on that information, have them make a written prediction of how precipitation is formed. Have students revise their ideas after reading the selection.
Logical, Portfolio

3 ASSESS

Evaluate Understanding L2

Ask students to create a table describing what type of weather they would expect to experience with each of the cloud types shown on pp. 762–763.

Reteach L1

Use the flowchart students completed for the Reading Strategy activity on p. 760 to review cloud formation. Have students extend the flowchart to include various forms of precipitation.

Connecting Concepts

When a gas loses enough thermal energy, it changes phase and becomes a liquid. Clouds form when water vapor in the air cools to a temperature below the dew point.

Interactive Textbook If your class subscribes to the Interactive Textbook, use it to review key concepts in Section 24.4

Figure 18 Freezing rain creates beautiful effects but can be dangerous.

Forms of Precipitation

Precipitation occurs when water droplets or ice crystals in clouds join together and become large enough to fall to the ground without evaporating. Clouds are the source of all precipitation. **The most common types of precipitation are rain, snow, hail, sleet, and freezing rain.**

Rain and Snow Rain is liquid precipitation that usually forms in either nimbostratus clouds or cumulonimbus clouds. Snow is precipitation in the form of ice crystals called snowflakes. The size and shape of snowflakes depend on the temperature at which they form.

Hail, Sleet, and Freezing Rain Hail is precipitation in the form of round, solid pieces of ice more than 5 millimeters in diameter. Hail forms within cumulonimbus clouds when small ice pellets are tossed up and down by rising and falling air. As the ice is tossed about, it collides and combines with water droplets that then freeze, creating more and more layers of ice. Eventually, the ice becomes heavy enough to fall to the ground as hail. Hail can sometimes cause tremendous damage to crops, vehicles, and buildings.

Sleet is precipitation in the form of ice particles that are usually smaller than 5 millimeters in diameter. Sleet is rain that freezes as it falls. Sleet rarely damages crops or vehicles directly, but it can make driving extremely hazardous.

Freezing rain is rain that freezes after hitting the surface. Freezing rain produces beautiful effects, as Figure 18 shows, but it can be dangerous. Roads become very slippery, and branches or power lines can fall from the weight of the ice.

Section 24.4 Assessment

Reviewing Concepts

1. List the ways in which water vapor condenses in the atmosphere
2. Explain how clouds form.
3. Describe each of the three main cloud forms.
4. What are the most common types of precipitation?

Critical Thinking

5. **Classifying** A winter storm produced precipitation in the form of ice particles that averaged about 4 millimeters in diameter. What kind of precipitation was it?
6. **Applying Concepts** Suppose the dew point of the air in your area is 20°C. The temperature outside is supposed to drop from 25°C to about 15°C by midnight. What weather condition will probably occur by morning? Explain why.

Connecting Concepts

Condensation Use what you learned about phase changes and condensation in Section 3.3 to explain how clouds form.

Section 24.4 Assessment

1. Water vapor condenses as dew, frost, clouds, or fog.
2. Clouds form when warm, moist air rises and water vapor condenses on tiny solid particles in the atmosphere.
3. Stratus clouds are flat layers of clouds that typically cover much or all of the sky. Cumulus clouds are puffy white clouds with flat bottoms that are often seen on sunny days. Cirrus clouds are thin, white, wispy clouds that occur at high altitudes.
4. Rain, snow, hail, sleet, and freezing rain
5. It was sleet because sleet is precipitation in the form of ice pellets that are typically less than 5 mm in diameter.
6. Fog. Many fogs occur when the ground cools at night and the air immediately above it cools to below the dew point as a result. The next morning, the temperature of the air will likely rise above the dew point. The fog will disappear as the condensed water evaporates.

24.5 Weather Patterns

Reading Focus

Key Concepts

- How do air masses form?
- What are the four types of fronts?
- What types of weather are associated with cyclones and anticyclones?
- How do thunderstorms and tornadoes form?

Vocabulary

- air mass
- front
- cold front
- warm front
- stationary front
- occluded front
- cyclone
- anticyclone
- thunderstorm
- lightning
- thunder
- tornado
- hurricane

Reading Strategy

Outlining Before you read, make an outline of this section. Use the green headings as the main topics and the blue headings as subtopics. As you read, add supporting details.

Weather Patterns

I. Air Masses
II. Fronts
  A. Cold Fronts
  B. ____________
  C. ____________
  D. ____________

"We've been basking in this high-pressure system for a week," says the weather reporter on a local TV station, pointing to a large weather map of the country. "But here comes trouble in the form of a cold front moving in from the northwest."

What does it mean to be "basking in a high-pressure system"? Why is a cold front "trouble"? What, in fact, is a "cold front"? In this section, you'll find out the answers to these questions, as well as the meanings of many terms you've heard weather reporters use.

Air Masses

The weather that you experience from day to day is the result of the movement and interactions of air masses in Earth's atmosphere. An **air mass** is a large body of air that has fairly uniform physical properties, such as temperature and moisture content, at any given altitude. Air masses can cover large portions of continents. **An air mass forms when a large body of air becomes fairly stationary over a region of Earth's surface or as air moves over a large, uniform region like an ocean.** The air is strongly influenced by the properties of the region.

Direction of front

Figure 19 A cold front moving in brings stormy weather. The arrow shows the direction that the front is moving.

Section Resources

Print
- ***Reading and Study Workbook With Math Support,*** Section 24.5
- ***Transparencies,*** Section 24.5

Technology
- ***Interactive Textbook,*** Section 24.5
- ***Presentation Pro CD-ROM,*** Section 24.5
- ***Go Online,*** *Planet Diary,* Storm activities

Section 24.5

1 FOCUS

Objectives

24.5.1 **Explain** how air masses form and how they are classified.
24.5.2 **Describe** the four types of fronts, and the weather associated with each.
24.5.3 **Describe** cyclones and anticyclones.
24.5.4 **Describe** the major types of storms and how they are formed.

Reading Focus

Build Vocabulary L2

Compare/Contrast Table Have students create a compare/contrast table with the headings Cyclone and Anticyclone. Students should fill in the table as they read the section.

Reading Strategy L2

B. Warm Fronts C. Stationary Fronts D. Occluded Fronts

2 INSTRUCT

Air Masses

Build Science Skills L2

Inferring Have students read the paragraph under the heading Air Masses. Based on this information and the concepts they have learned in previous chapters, ask students to infer the characteristics of an air mass that develops over the ocean at 20° N. *(Warm, humid)*
Logical

Quick Lab

Modeling Air Masses

L2

Objective
After completing this activity, students will be able to
- describe how the effect of temperature on the density of a fluid can cause water or air masses to move relative to one another.

Skills Focus **Using Models**

Prep Time 10 minutes

Materials shallow, clear 3–4-L tank; plastic or cardboard divider; 1-L beaker of cold sugar solution; 1-L beaker of warm, colored, sugar solution

Advance Prep Clear, plastic boxes such as sweater boxes can be used as tanks. Enclose cardboard dividers in plastic bags to make them waterproof. The warm and cold sugar solutions each contain 23 g of sucrose per liter of water. The warm, colored, sugar solution also contains a few drops of food coloring. Use hot tap water or heat this solution before use. However, do not make it too hot for students to handle safely.

Class Time 15 minutes

Safety Warm water should be between 30°C and 40°C. Make sure that students wipe up any spilled water immediately to avoid slips and falls.

Teaching Tips
- To help students understand the results, ask, **What makes hot air rise above cooler air?** *(Hot air expands, reducing its density. The less-dense hot air moves above the denser cool air.)*

Expected Outcome The warm, colored solution will spread out above the cooler, clear solution, and the cooler, clear solution will move beneath the warm, colored solution.

Analyze and Conclude
1. The warm solution was less dense than the cooler solution. Less dense materials float above denser materials.
2. The warm solution moved over the cooler solution, and the cooler solution moved under the warm solution. Similarly, when a warm air mass meets a cooler air mass, the warm air tends to move up above the cooler air, while the cooler air tends to flow under the warm air. **Logical, Kinesthetic**

Quick Lab

Modeling Air Masses

Materials: plastic or cardboard divider, clear plastic tank, warm colored sugar solution, cold sugar solution

Procedure
1. Use the divider to separate the clear plastic tank into two equal parts.
2. To model a front between warm and cool air masses, pour the warm, colored sugar solution into one part of the tank. At the same time, have a classmate pour an equal amount of the cold sugar solution into the other part.
3. Observe the two solutions through the side of the tank as you quickly lift the divider straight up and out of the tank.

Analyze and Conclude
1. **Applying Concepts** What caused the solutions to move as they did? Explain your answer.
2. **Using Models** How is this model similar to the behavior of air masses when they meet?

Air masses can vary greatly. Think of the differences in the air above the Gulf of Mexico and the air above northwestern Canada. The first property you might think of is temperature. It's usually a lot warmer near the Gulf of Mexico than it is in Canada. You might also think of humidity. The air above the Gulf of Mexico contains more water vapor than the air above northwestern Canada. Each type of air mass reflects the characteristics of the region where it formed. An air mass that forms over water, for example, contains more water vapor than one that forms over land. An air mass that forms over the Arctic is much colder than one that forms over the tropics.

Air masses are classified according to whether they form over water or land, and the latitude where they form. A maritime air mass forms over water. A continental air mass forms over land. An air mass that forms north of 50° north latitude or south of 50° south latitude, where it is often extremely cold, is called a polar air mass. An air mass that originates in the tropics, where it is warm, is called a tropical air mass.

The air masses that most affect weather in North America include maritime polar air masses, continental polar air masses, maritime tropical air masses, and continental tropical air masses. As shown in Figure 20, maritime polar air masses originate over the frigid North Pacific and North Atlantic oceans. They are cool and moist, and often bring heavy precipitation to coastal areas. Continental polar air masses form over northern Canada and bring cold, dry air to the central and eastern United States. Maritime tropical air masses originate over the Gulf of Mexico and warm oceans to the south. They bring warm, moist air and are often accompanied by fog or rain. Continental tropical air masses form over northern Mexico and dry areas of the Southwest. They bring hot, dry air to the southern Great Plains.

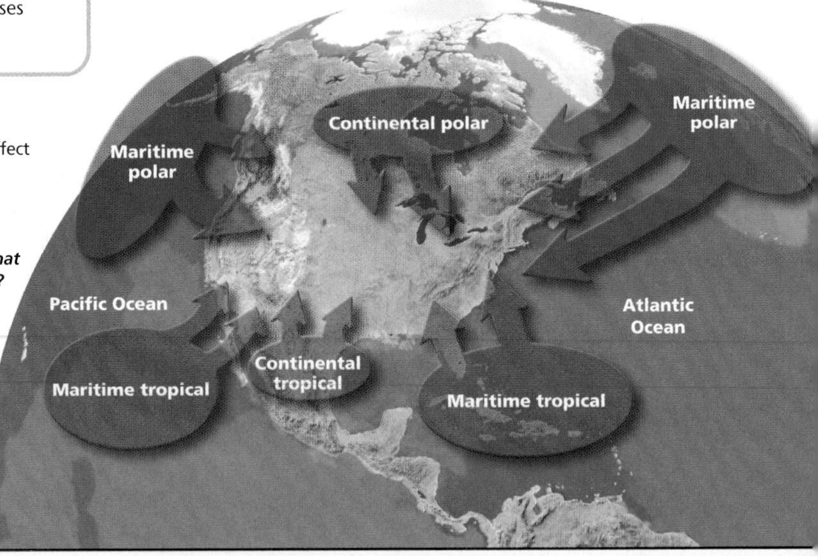

Continental polar
Maritime polar
Maritime polar
Pacific Ocean
Atlantic Ocean
Continental tropical
Maritime tropical
Maritime tropical

Figure 20 Air masses that form in different regions affect North American weather. **Interpreting Diagrams** ***What type of air mass is moving toward the northwestern United States? What type of air does it contain?***

Customize for English Language Learners

Make a Flowchart
Have students work in groups to construct flowcharts to explain the formation of the four types of fronts. Instruct students to begin with the formation of air masses and include the meeting of air masses, the formation of the front, and the development of weather associated with the front. Have members of each group present their flowcharts to the class.

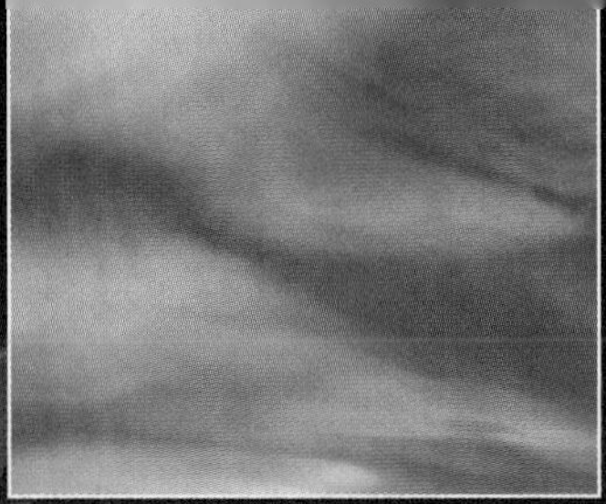

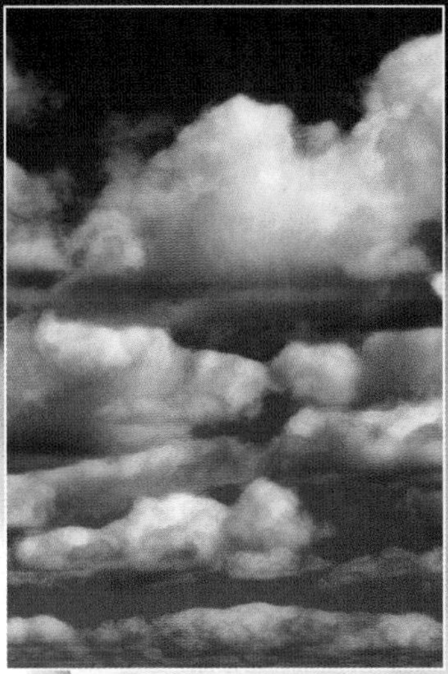

Weather and Climate 765

Fronts

Air masses don't stay where they form. They move with the circulation of air throughout the world. Recall that convection currents cause warm air near the equator to move toward the poles and cold air at the poles to move toward the equator. Polar air masses, therefore, tend to move toward the equator, and tropical air masses tend to move toward the poles. These air masses collide in the middle latitudes.

As an air mass moves, it tends to retain the properties of the region where it formed. So, a continental polar air mass retains the low temperatures and dryness of its source region as it moves south. Likewise, a maritime tropical air mass retains the high temperatures and moisture of its source region as it moves north. When such different air masses meet, they ordinarily don't mix. Instead, a boundary forms between them.

The sharply defined boundary that forms when two unlike air masses meet is called a **front.** For example, when a continental polar air mass moves southeast and collides with a maritime tropical air mass, a front forms between the two. Clouds and precipitation often accompany fronts. **There are four types of fronts: cold fronts, warm fronts, stationary fronts, and occluded fronts.**

Reading Checkpoint *What is a front?*

Cold Fronts In North America, a cold continental polar air mass often moves southeastward into the Midwest. There, it may collide with a maritime tropical air mass from the Gulf of Mexico. At the boundary between the two air masses, a cold front forms. A **cold front** occurs when a cold air mass overtakes a warm air mass.

Figure 21 shows what happens when a cold front forms. Because cold air is denser than warm air, the cold air mass remains close to the ground and moves underneath the warm air mass. The cold air mass forces the warm air mass to rise. Cold fronts usually move quickly and are relatively steep, so the warm air mass is often lifted rapidly.

The rapid rise of warm air often produces cumulus and cumulonimbus clouds. Strong winds, severe thunderstorms, and large amounts of precipitation are often associated with cold fronts. However, because the slope of a cold front is steep and such fronts travel quickly, the severe weather usually lasts for only a short time. Then, as the front passes, the cold air mass settles in, the skies clear, and temperatures drop.

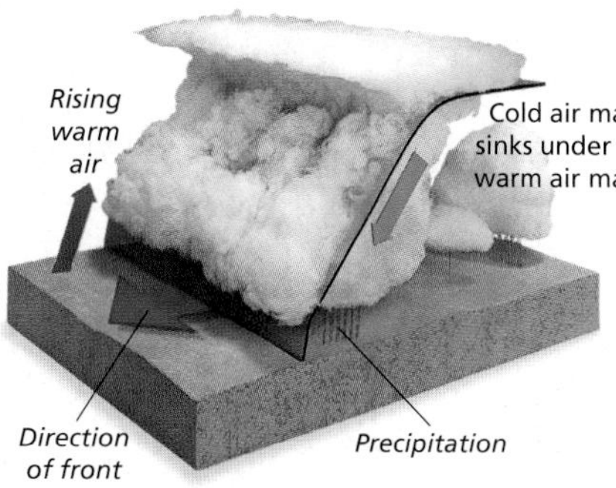
Rising warm air
Cold air mass sinks under the warm air mass.
Direction of front
Precipitation

Figure 21 A cold front forms when a cold air mass overtakes a warm air mass.

Use Visuals L1

Figure 20 Be sure students can identify the part of the globe they are looking at in the figure. Point out Alaska, Hawaii, the continental United States, Central America, and your own locality. Ask, **Which of the air masses would most likely bring precipitation?** *(The air masses that formed over oceans: the two maritime polar and two maritime tropical air masses)* **Which of the air masses would most likely bring hot, dry weather?** *(The continental tropical mass moving north over Mexico and the south-central United States.)* **Which parts of the United States would be experiencing cold, dry weather?** *(The northern Midwest states)*
Visual, Logical

Fronts

Build Reading Literacy L1

Predict Refer to page **744D** in this chapter, which provides the guidelines for predicting.

Before students read Fronts, have them look at Figure 20 and write a response to the question, **What do you think will happen when one of the warm air masses meets one of the cold air masses?** *(Warm air will rise over the cold air, and a front will be created.)* After reading the selection, have students revise their prediction based on what they have learned.
Logical, Portfolio

Answer to . . .

Figure 20 *A maritime polar air mass that contains cool, humid air.*

Reading Checkpoint *A front is the sharply defined boundary that forms when two unlike air masses meet.*

Use Visuals **L1**

Figure 22 Point out that the block part of the diagram represents a region of land. Ask, **Which direction is the precipitation moving?** *(The same direction as the front)* **Why does the rising, moist, warm air condense?** *(The temperatures are cooler higher in the troposphere. As the air cools past the dew point, water vapor condenses to liquid.)* **Imagine that you are living on the left edge of the block. Describe the weather that you would observe as the front passes over you.** *(First the weather is cold, then there is some precipitation, possibly a steady rain, and then the weather grows warmer.)*
Visual

Build Science Skills **L2**

Relating Cause and Effect Have students work in groups to design a graphic that explains why there is often precipitation at the edge of a front.
Visual, Group

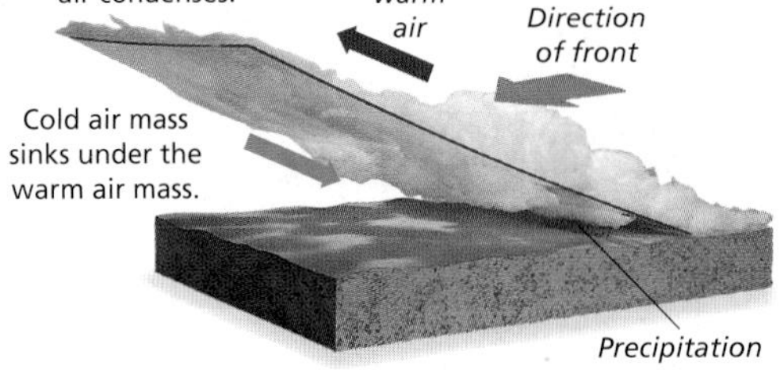

Clouds form as rising moist, warm air condenses.
Rising warm air
Direction of front
Cold air mass sinks under the warm air mass.
Precipitation

Figure 22 A warm front occurs when a warm air mass overtakes a cold air mass.
***Applying Concepts** What types of weather are associated with cold fronts and warm fronts?*

Warm Fronts Imagine that a continental polar air mass has settled in the Midwest and a maritime tropical air mass moves toward it from the southeast. As the air masses collide, a warm front results. A **warm front** occurs when a warm air mass overtakes a cold air mass.

Figure 22 shows what happens when a warm front forms. Because the cold air is denser, it remains close to the ground. The advancing warm air mass rises up over the cold air mass. The surface of a warm front is usually less steep than that of a cold front, as you can see by comparing Figures 21 and 22. A warm front has a gentle slope because the advancing warm air mass gradually moves up and over the cold air mass.

As the warm air rises, stratus clouds form. If the warm air mass contains a large amount of moisture, there will be a steady rain. Occasionally heavy showers or thunderstorms occur. Once the front has passed, the warm air mass settles in. The skies are mostly clear, often with some cumulus clouds present, and temperatures rise.

Stationary Fronts The clash of air masses is not always as simple as those that produce cold fronts and warm fronts. Sometimes when two air masses converge, neither air mass overruns the other. Rather, a front forms, and either stays where it formed or moves slowly. When two unlike air masses have formed a boundary but neither is moving, the front is called a **stationary front.** Stationary fronts often result in clouds and steady rain or snow for several days.

Occluded Fronts Another kind of front can occur because cold fronts generally move faster than warm fronts. An **occluded front** forms when a warm air mass is caught between two cooler air masses. The colder air masses force the warm air mass to rise, cutting it off from the ground and trapping it between the two cold air masses. As this warm air rises and cools, its water vapor typically condenses. As a result, occluded fronts are generally accompanied by cloudy skies and precipitation.

Figure 23 Winds and heavy rain are common in low pressure areas, also called cyclones.

Low- and High-Pressure Systems

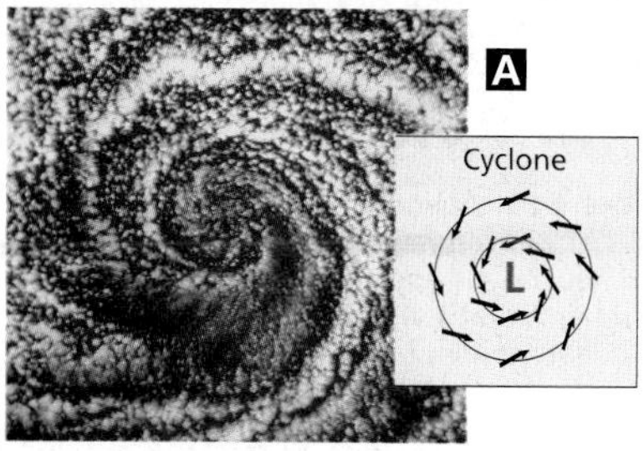
A
Cyclone
L

Air masses are part of larger weather systems. Weather systems are organized around either a center of high air pressure or a center of low air pressure, and may include more than one type of air mass. Weather systems can be huge. Centers of high air pressure may have diameters of 1500 kilometers and centers of low air pressure often have diameters of more than 1000 kilometers.

Cyclones A weather system with a center of low air pressure is called a **cyclone,** or sometimes simply a low. As Figure 24 shows, winds in a cyclone circulate counterclockwise in the Northern Hemisphere.

As the warm air at the center of a cyclone rises, pressure decreases. Because air moves from high-pressure areas to low-pressure areas, air spirals in toward the center of a cyclone. Clouds form and precipitation develops. **Cyclones are associated with clouds, precipitation, and stormy weather.** Because air is converging in a cyclone, air masses collide and fronts develop.

Cyclones don't stay in one place. A cyclone generally moves in the direction of global winds, and the weather of the cyclone moves along with it. In the middle latitudes of the Northern Hemisphere, the global winds are the westerlies. The westerly winds typically cause fronts and storms to move across the United States from west to east.

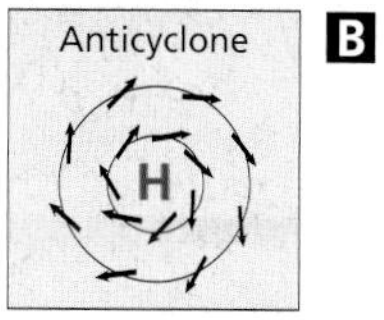
Anticyclone
B
H

Figure 24 Cyclones and anticyclones are large weather systems. **A** In the Northern Hemisphere, winds in a cyclone blow counterclockwise and converge. **B** In an anticyclone, winds blow clockwise and diverge.

Anticyclones A weather system with a swirling center of high air pressure is called an **anticyclone,** or sometimes simply a high. As Figure 24 shows, winds in an anticyclone circulate clockwise in the Northern Hemisphere. Because the center of an anticyclone has high pressure, air flows away from that center. As air flows away from the center, air from higher in the troposphere descends and replaces it. When air descends, it warms and its relative humidity decreases. **The weather associated with an anticyclone includes clear skies, very little precipitation, and generally calm conditions.**

Reading Checkpoint *How does air move in an anticyclone?*

Low- and High-Pressure Systems

Address Misconceptions **L2**

Students who are familiar with the use of the term *cyclone* to refer to hurricanes in the Pacific Ocean may confuse the discussion of cyclones as a low-pressure weather system with hurricanes. Be sure to point out that the term *cyclone* has two distinct meanings in weather. Have students create a 2-column table with the headings Cyclone: A Hurricane and Cyclone: A Low-Pressure System. Instruct them to fill in the hurricane column with their prior knowledge and fill in the weather system column after reading p. 769.
Logical

Build Reading Literacy **L1**

Relate Text and Visuals Refer to page 190D in Chapter 7, which provides the guidelines for relating text and visuals.

Instruct students to refer to Figure 24 after reading the first paragraph of Cyclones and note the counterclockwise rotation of cyclones in the Northern Hemisphere. Say, **Look at the arrows to see the direction of rotation, then study the satellite image, imagining how the system is rotating. Now, read the second paragraph and look again at the diagram. Make sure you can visualize how air masses converge in a cyclone.** Repeat the process for the reading of Anticyclones. Be sure students note the clockwise rotation in the diagram, and can visualize how air flows away from the center of an anticyclone.
Visual, Intrapersonal

Facts and Figures

Nor'Easters The National Oceanic and Atmospheric Administration (NOAA) defines a Northeast Storm, or Nor'Easter, as a cyclonic storm of the east coast of North America. Its name derives from the fact that the winds over the coastal area preceding the storm's passage are from the northeast. Nor'Easters may occur at any time of the year, but are most frequent and most violent between September and April. When a cyclone in the Atlantic Ocean meets a cold arctic air mass moving east from Canada, a Nor'Easter can bring ice storms and blizzard conditions to the region.

Answer to . . .

Figure 22 *Cold fronts are generally associated with strong winds, thunderstorms, and heavy precipitation. Warm fronts are typically associated with steady rain and occasionally heavy showers or thunderstorms.*

Reading Checkpoint *Air in a Northern Hemisphere anticyclone moves clockwise and away from the center.*

Storms

Build Reading Literacy L1

Active Comprehension Refer to page **498D** in **Chapter 17**, which provides the guidelines for active comprehension.

Before students read Thunderstorms, ask them what they would like to know about thunderstorms. Write a few of their questions on the board, such as "What causes thunder?" "What causes lightning?" "Why do you hear thunder after you see lightning?" and "Why do thunderstorms frequently happen on hot, humid days?" After students finish reading the selection, ask them to answer the questions.
Verbal

Integrate Physics L2

The speed of light in a vacuum is 3×10^8 meters per second, while sound travels at only 331.21 meters per second in air at 32°F. Have students work in groups to create a poster that shows light and sound moving away from a lightning strike. Ask students to show people at different distances away from the strike and, for each distance, an approximate time difference between seeing the lightning and hearing the thunder. Lightning can occur within a cloud, between nearby clouds, or between a cloud and the ground.
Visual, Group

Storms

You've probably read a mystery or seen a horror film in which the setting is an old house on a stormy night. The winds howl, lightning flashes, and rain pounds the roof. Storms feature strong winds and heavy precipitation. The major types of storms are thunderstorms, tornadoes, and tropical storms, including hurricanes.

Figure 25 Thunderstorms are associated with tall cumulonimbus clouds where there are strong updrafts of warm air. Thunderstorms produce thunder and lightning.

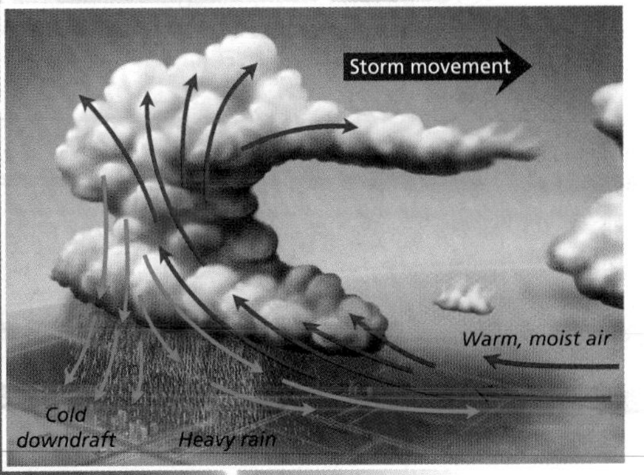

Storm movement
Warm, moist air
Cold downdraft
Heavy rain

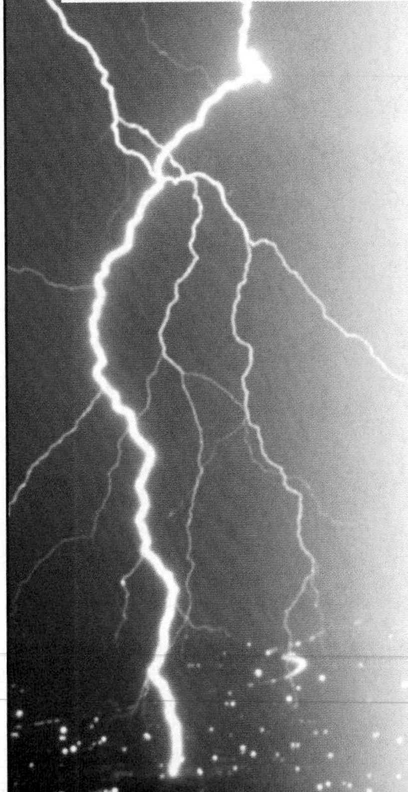

Thunderstorms A **thunderstorm** is a small weather system that includes thunder and lightning. It is usually accompanied by strong winds and heavy rain or hail. **Thunderstorms form when columns of air rise within a cumulonimbus cloud.** These rising columns are often the result of colliding air masses. When a cold front forms, the cold air mass quickly lifts the warm air mass up, and thunderstorms often result. Thunderstorms can also occur on hot summer days when buoyant air rises as part of a convection current within an air mass. If the rising air is cooled to the dew point and the convection is strong enough, a thunderstorm can result. Figure 25 shows how this process occurs.

One striking feature of a thunderstorm is **lightning,** which is a sudden electrical discharge in the atmosphere. Recall from physics that there must be separated positive and negative charges for an electrical discharge to occur. Positive charges tend to develop near the top of a cumulonimbus cloud, while negative charges tend to develop near the base of the cloud. When the potential difference between the positive and negative charges becomes great enough, a discharge occurs. You see the discharge as a lightning flash.

When you think of lightning, you probably also think of thunder. **Thunder** is the sound produced by rapidly expanding air along the path of a lightning discharge. When lightning occurs, the air around it is heated to as much as 33,000°C. The heated air expands explosively, producing sound waves that you hear as thunder. Although thunder and lightning occur at the same time, you hear thunder after you see lightning because light travels much faster than sound.

Tornadoes Twister—even the mere mention of one of these violent storms is enough to make most people shudder. Twister is a common name for a **tornado,** a small but intense windstorm that takes the form of a rotating column of air that touches the ground.

Tornadoes most often form at the leading edge of an advancing cold front or along a line of thunderstorms where winds are converging to a center of very low pressure. **A tornado forms when a vertical cylinder of rotating air develops in a thunderstorm.**

Facts and Figures

Storm Safety Tornadoes are terrifying storms that cause an average of 70 fatalities and 1500 injuries nationwide per year. However, flash floods are the primary cause of death associated with thunderstorms, with over 140 fatalities nationwide each year. Most of these deaths occur when vehicles are swept away by running water. Tell students to never walk or drive through running water during a flood. It only takes two feet of water to cause most vehicles to float, and a mere six inches of running water can knock over an adult.

Figure 26 A tornado crosses a farm field. **Applying Concepts** ***Why do most tornadoes occur in the spring?***

A tornado appears as a twisting funnel cloud descending from the bottom of a cumulonimbus cloud, as shown in Figure 26. A tornado's winds can sometimes be more than 500 kilometers per hour, although they are more typically about 150 kilometers per hour. A large tornado can cause death and tremendous destruction.

For a tornado to develop, there must be great differences between the properties of colliding air masses. Air masses in the spring tend to have the most contrasting properties, and therefore it is during this season that most tornadoes occur. In the United States, where most of the world's tornadoes develop, these storms occur mainly in the Midwest and the South.

Tropical Storms and Hurricanes Thunderstorms and tornadoes are often associated with cyclones of the middle latitudes. Cyclones also develop in the tropics, where they can develop into tropical storms or hurricanes. A **hurricane** is a large tropical cyclone with winds of at least 119 kilometers per hour (74 miles per hour).

Go Online PLANETDIARY

For: Storm activities
Visit: PHSchool.com
Web Code: ccc-3245

Section 24.5 Assessment

Reviewing Concepts

1. How does an air mass form?
2. What are the four types of fronts?
3. What types of weather do cyclones and anticyclones bring?
4. Compare and contrast how a typical thunderstorm forms with how a tornado forms.

Critical Thinking

5. **Applying Concepts** Why do continental polar air masses have different properties than maritime tropical air masses?
6. **Predicting** A weather reporter says that a warm air mass is caught between two cooler air masses in your area. What kind of weather can you expect in the near future, and why?

Connecting Concepts

Electricity Use what you learned about static electricity in Chapter 20 to explain what lightning is and how it is caused.

3 ASSESS

Evaluate Understanding L2

Ask students to create a study guide to help them remember what types of weather occur with each of the four types of fronts.

Reteach L1

Use Figure 21 and Figure 22 to help students distinguish between cold fronts and warm fronts.

Connecting Concepts

Lightning is an example of static discharge. During thunderstorms, the air swirls violently, and a potential difference develops between the base and the top of a cloud. When this potential difference becomes sufficiently large, lightning occurs.

Interactive Textbook If your class subscribes to the Interactive Textbook, use it to review key concepts in Section 24.5.

Go Online PLANETDIARY

Find links to additional activities and have students monitor phenomena that affect Earth and its residents.

Answer to . . .

Figure 26 *Because air masses tend to have the most contrasting properties in the spring, and collisions of such contrasting air masses can produce tornadoes*

Section 24.5 Assessment

1. An air mass forms when a body of air remains fairly stationary over a region for some time or as air moves over a large uniform region. The air is strongly influenced by the properties of that region.
2. The four types of fronts are warm fronts, cold fronts, stationary fronts, and occluded fronts.
3. Cyclones are associated with clouds, precipitation, and storms. Anticyclones are associated with clear skies, little precipitation, and calm conditions.
4. A typical thunderstorm forms when there are strong rising movements of air within a cumulonimbus cloud, often as the result of the collision of air masses. A tornado forms when a vertical cylinder of rotating air develops in the updraft of a thunderstorm.
5. Continental polar air masses form in cold, dry regions, whereas maritime tropical air masses form in warm, humid regions. The properties of these air masses are strongly influenced by the properties of the region in which they form.
6. When a warm air mass is caught between cooler air masses, an occluded front occurs. The weather may include cloudy skies and precipitation.

CONCEPTS in Action

Hurricanes L2

Background

Meteorologists use the Saffir-Simpson Hurricane Scale to categorize hurricanes based on wind speed. This scale also describes typical storm surges and property damage. A Category One hurricane has winds of 119–153 km/h (74–95 mph), with storm surges typically 4–5 ft above normal and minimal property damage. A Category Two hurricane has winds of 154–177 km/h (96–110 mph), with storm surges typically 6–8 ft above normal and damage to roofs, doors, and windows. A Category Three hurricane has winds of 178–209 km/h (111–130 mph), with storm surges typically 9–12 ft above normal. Some structural damage to permanent structures is typical, and mobile homes are often destroyed. A Category Four hurricane has winds of 210–249 km/h (131–155 mph), with storm surges typically 13–18 ft above normal. Roofs are blown off homes, and extensive flooding is caused by the storm surge. A Category Five hurricane has winds greater than 249 km/h (155 mph), with storm surges over 18 ft above normal. Property damage is extensive, with complete structural failure of some buildings.

Build Science Skills L2

Using Graphs ACTIVITY

Purpose Students create a hurricane-tracking map.

Materials colored pencils, hurricane-tracking map (This can be downloaded from the NOAA Web site or made by superimposing a map of North America on graph paper. Label 5° intervals of latitude and longitude.)

Class Time 20–30 minutes

Procedure Students may be familiar with hurricane-tracking maps from weather reports. Provide students with 10–15 sample coordinates that model the path of a hurricane in the Atlantic Ocean. Actual hurricane paths can be found on the NOAA Web site, or use coordinates that model a typical path. Have students mark each coordinate on their map, and connect the coordinates to form the track of the hurricane.

Expected Outcome Students' graphs will show the path of the hurricane.
Visual, Portfolio

CONCEPTS in Action

Hurricanes

A hurricane is a huge column of spiraling air with winds blowing at speeds of at least 119 kilometers per hour. Hurricanes are highly destructive if they reach land.

All hurricanes start as storms over warm tropical seas where the water temperature is at least 27°C. As the sun heats the ocean's surface, masses of moist, warm air accumulate and rise up, forming huge clouds. More air is sucked into the region from all directions and spirals toward the center. As the hurricane grows stronger, it moves westward, pushed by prevailing winds. Eventually, hurricanes in the Northern Hemisphere move northward, where the cooler temperatures reduce the supply of warm air and moisture needed to maintain the storm. If the hurricane hits land, it is no longer fed by heat and moisture from the ocean, so it loses energy and dissipates.

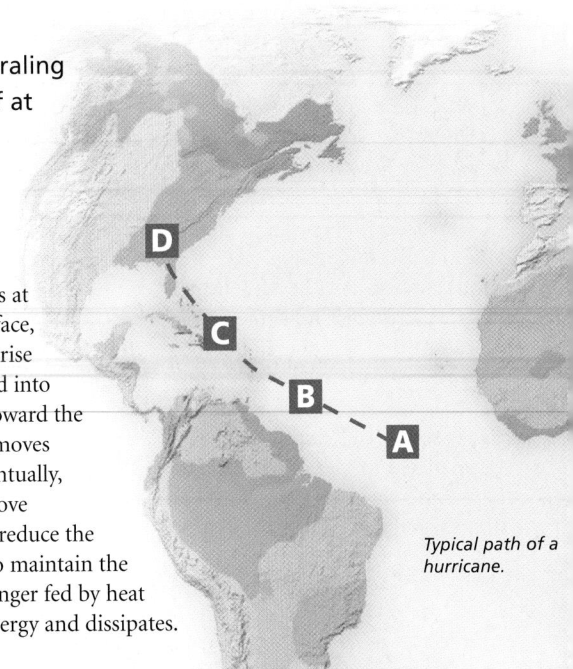
D
C
B
A

Typical path of a hurricane.

Life of a Hurricane

These satellite images show hurricanes at four stages of development.

1. The hurricane begins as a swirling cloud of rising air.
2. By day 3, the storm has developed an eye, which is a sign that the hurricane has strengthened.
3. Within 6 days the hurricane has reached its greatest intensity.
4. As the hurricane reaches land, it begins to weaken.

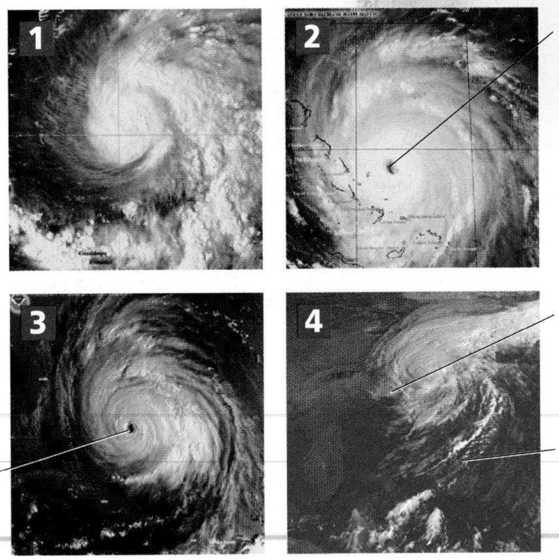
1
2
Eye starting to form
3
Sharply defined eye
4
Hurricane starting to weaken as it moves over land
Clouds dissipating

Facts and Figures

Storm Strength Wind speeds can exceed 250 km/h in the most violent hurricanes. This was the case in the Labor Day Hurricane that pummeled the Florida Keys in 1935. More recently, in 1998, Hurricane Mitch devastated Central America with gusts more than 320 km/h (>200 mph).

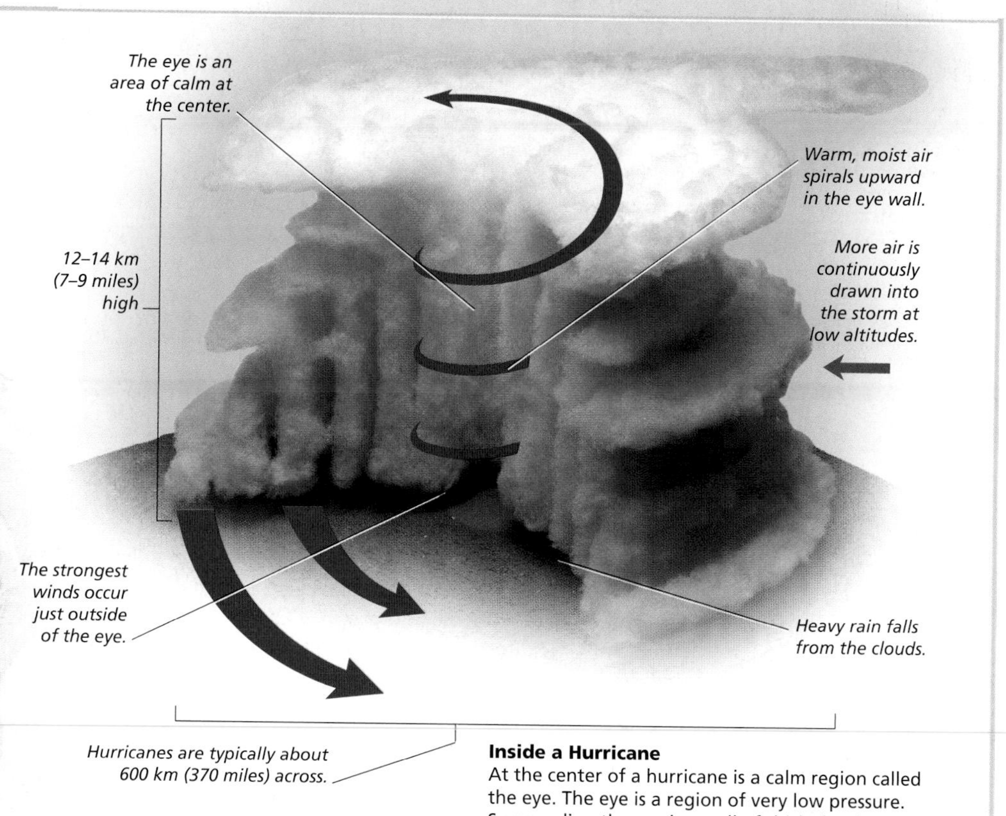
The eye is an area of calm at the center.
Warm, moist air spirals upward in the eye wall.
12–14 km (7–9 miles) high
More air is continuously drawn into the storm at low altitudes.
The strongest winds occur just outside of the eye.
Heavy rain falls from the clouds.
Hurricanes are typically about 600 km (370 miles) across.

Inside a Hurricane
At the center of a hurricane is a calm region called the eye. The eye is a region of very low pressure. Surrounding the eye is a wall of thick clouds, rain, and spiraling winds. Outside of this wall there are often additional bands of clouds and rain. Hurricanes spin in a counterclockwise direction in the Northern Hemisphere, and clockwise in the Southern Hemisphere.

Storm Surge
As it moves across the ocean, the low-pressure eye of the hurricane sucks water into a mound or swell, which can be as high as 8 m (26 ft). When the hurricane hits land, this water surges over coastal regions. The surge may destroy homes and wash boats inland, as in the Alabama photo above, following Hurricane Georges in 1998.

Going Further

- Hurricanes are often remembered for the damage they cause. Some hurricanes may even have changed the course of history. Use library or Internet resources to research a past hurricane. Prepare a poster summarizing what you have learned.
- Take a Discovery Channel Video Field Trip by watching "Wild Weather."

Discovery Channel School
Video Field Trip

Going Further

There are many historical and recent hurricanes of significance for students to choose from. Some options include: Agnes (1972), Andrew (1992), Audrey (1957), Camille (1969), and Hugo (1989). Some unnamed hurricanes of the past include those that struck Galveston, Texas in 1900; the Caribbean in 1780; and Japan in 1281. Students' posters should include photographs and charts, if available. They should also include such information as date, location, damage estimates, maximum wind speed, and so forth.
Visual, Verbal

Discovery Channel School

Video Field Trip

Wild Weather

After students have viewed the Video Field Trip, ask them the following questions: **Name two kinds of dangerous storms.** *(Student answers may include hurricanes, tornadoes, and lightning/thunderstorms.)* **Why is a tidal surge considered to be the greatest danger from a hurricane?** *(Drowning causes the great majority of the deaths in a hurricane.)* **Which states in the United States are most likely to have tornadoes?** *(Texas, Oklahoma, and Kansas. Furthermore, students may correctly note that tornadoes also occur in many other states.)* **How long do tornadoes usually last?** *(Most last several minutes.)*

1 FOCUS

Objectives

24.6.1 **Interpret** weather map features and **describe** the technology used to forecast weather.

Reading Focus

Build Vocabulary L2

Word-Part Analysis Have students look up the words *isotherm* and *isobar.* Ask them to infer the meaning of the prefix *iso- (equal).* Tell students that *iso-* is a prefix common in math and science, and ask if they know of any other words with this prefix (e.g., *isosceles, isomer, isometric).*

Reading Strategy L2

a. Meteorologists use a variety of technologies to help forecast the weather. **b.** Weather maps include a variety of symbols that help to illustrate the weather patterns across a certain region.

2 INSTRUCT

Weather Forecasting

Build Reading Literacy L1

Use Prior Knowledge Refer to page **2D** in **Chapter 1**, which provides the guidelines for using prior knowledge.

Before students read this section, have them work in groups to discuss what they already know (from television and newspapers) about weather forecasting. Previous knowledge could include information about weather chart symbols or how meteorologists work. Have students make lists of the information they already know, then read the section and add any new knowledge to their lists.
Interpersonal, Portfolio

24.6 Predicting the Weather

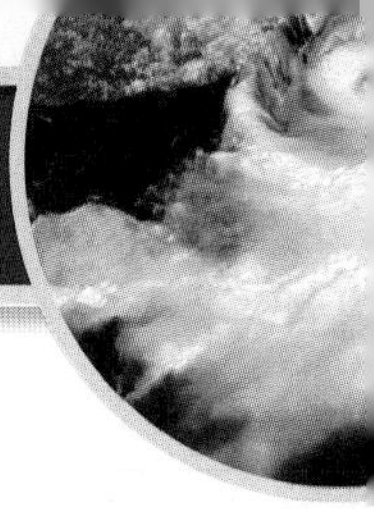

Reading Focus

Key Concepts

- What technologies help meteorologists predict the weather?
- How do meteorologists show information on weather maps?

Vocabulary

- meteorologists
- isotherm
- isobar

Reading Strategy

Identifying the Main Idea Copy the table below. As you read the text, write the main idea for each topic heading.

Heading	Main Idea
Weather forecasting	a. ____?____
Weather maps	b. ____?____

An old folk rhyme includes this line: "The moon in halos hid her head. . . ." The rhyme suggests that a halo around the moon is a sign that rain or snow should be expected. This bit of folk wisdom has some scientific validity. When you see a halo around the moon, what you're seeing is moonlight shining through cirrostratus clouds. Because cirrostratus clouds often move in before storm clouds, a halo around the moon might indeed indicate precipitation in the near future.

Now consider another bit of weather wisdom from long ago: If a cat scratches itself while sitting on a fence, expect rain before night. Would you look for rain if you saw a cat do that? Probably not. That's the trouble with folk wisdom. Some of it makes sense, and some of it doesn't. Luckily, there are now more reliable ways of forecasting the weather.

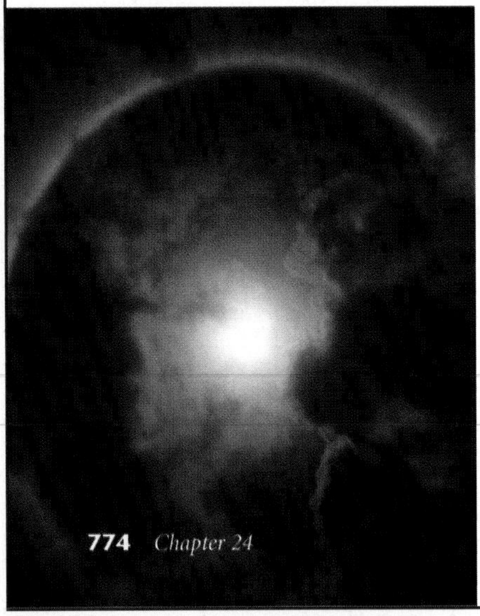
774 Chapter 24

Figure 27 Moonlight reflecting off ice crystals in cirrostratus clouds can cause a halo to appear around the moon. Such a halo often indicates that precipitation is on the way.

Weather Forecasting

The study of Earth's atmosphere is called meteorology. **Meteorologists** (mee tee uh RAWL uh jists) are scientists who study weather. **Meteorologists use many technologies to help predict the weather, including Doppler radar, automated weather stations, weather satellites, and high-speed computers.**

Doppler Radar Doppler radar is a technology based on use of the Doppler effect. Recall from physics that the Doppler effect is the apparent change in frequency of waves as either the source of the waves moves or the observer moves. Doppler radar works by bouncing radio waves off particles of precipitation in moving storms and then measuring the frequency of the waves that return.

Section Resources

Print

- ***Reading and Study Workbook With Math Support,*** Section 24.6
- ***Math Skills and Problem Solving Workbook,*** Section 24.6
- ***Transparencies,*** Section 24.6

Technology

- ***Interactive Textbook,*** Section 24.6
- ***Presentation Pro CD-ROM,*** Section 24.6
- ***Go Online,*** *Science News,* Weather and climate

The frequency changes as the storm moves, so the speed of the storm can be calculated from how much the frequency changes. With Doppler technology, meteorologists can now track the paths of thunderstorms and potential tornadoes with much greater accuracy than in the past.

Weather Stations and Satellites

Automated weather stations are important in gathering weather data. These stations gather information without a human observer being present. A typical weather station is shown in Figure 28. It includes sensors that measure weather data such as temperature, precipitation, and wind speed and direction. The information collected is transmitted as radio signals to a weather center, where it can be displayed on a computer monitor.

Since the early 1960s, weather satellites have been placed in orbit around Earth to collect information about weather, including cloud cover, humidity, temperature, and wind speed. Meteorologists combine data from various weather stations and satellites to form a comprehensive view of a region's weather.

Figure 28 These scientists are setting up an automatic weather station on an island in the Bigourdan Fjord, Antarctica.

Data Analysis

Tracking the Weather

Meteorologists track weather data closely to help produce accurate short-term forecasts and to understand longer-term variations in weather. The table at the right provides the actual daily average temperature and daily precipitation for Minneapolis and St. Paul, Minnesota, for a seven-day period. Use the table and your knowledge of weather to answer the questions below.

November Weather

Day	1	2	3	4	5	6	7
Average Daily Temp. (°C)	−7	−7	−4	−4	−6	−5	−13
Daily Precip. (cm)	0	0	11	1	3	16	3

1. **Using Tables** On which day was the average daily temperature highest? On which day was it lowest?
2. **Calculating** The average daily temperature on Day 7 was 11°C below normal. What is the normal temperature for that date?
3. **Using Tables** What were the maximum and minimum average daily temperatures over the week? What was the temperature range?
4. **Inferring** What was the total precipitation over the seven days? What was the likely form of this precipitation? (*Hint:* Recall that the freezing point of water is 0°C.)
5. **Predicting** What type of front most likely passed through the region on Day 6 or Day 7? Predict the weather conditions that followed.
6. **Making Generalizations** Suppose you were visiting Minneapolis during this period. Describe how the weather changed during your visit.

Customize for Inclusion Students

Behaviorally Disordered
Help students stay on task by focusing their attention on the personal relevance of weather forecasting. Ask students if they saw a recent weather report on the news, or if they have any weather-dependent plans in the near future. Encourage students to watch weather forecasts and periodically ask them to share their weather observations in class.

Use Community Resources **L2**

Many of the meteorologists who forecast weather in the United States work for the National Weather Service (NWS), which is the U.S. government agency responsible for gathering weather data and disseminating it to the public. The NWS has the responsibility for forecasting hazardous weather. It also makes short-term and long-term weather forecasts in all parts of the United States. The NWS daily collects a tremendous amount of information about the weather. It also uses data collected by the World Meteorological Organization, to which 130 countries around the world belong. Data from thousands of stations are transmitted to centers in the United States, Russia, and Australia, where the information is used to make forecasts and broadcast warnings. Ask a meteorologist from the NWS to talk to the class about advances in weather forecasting technology. **Interpersonal**

Data Analysis

Tracking the Weather **L2**

Answers
1. Day 3 and Day 4; Day 7
2. −2°C
3. Maximum was −4°C; minimum was −13°C; range was 9°C
4. 34 cm; snow
5. A cold front passed through, as seen from the heavy snow on Day 6 and the significant drop in temperature on Day 7. Cold temperatures and clear skies follow cold fronts.
6. Students should describe a week of chilly weather, with temperatures becoming even colder on Day 7. They should also mention two days of heavy snow and light snow on three other days.

For Extra Help **L1**

Explain that a table is set up to help the reader see patterns in the data. Instruct students to look across the rows to see patterns of temperature and precipitation over the course of seven days. Look down the columns to get the temperature and precipitation data for any specific day. Have students practice reading the table by asking them to describe the temperature and precipitation on specific days. **Verbal**

Weather Maps

Use Visuals L1

Figure 29 Have students spend a moment examining the Weather Map Key symbols. Also point out that the temperature key is found at the bottom of the map. Ask, **What areas are experiencing sunny conditions?** *(The Southwest and Northeast)* **What is the air pressure in the sunny areas?** *(1008–1024 millibars)* **What areas are experiencing rains related to a tropical storm or hurricane?** *(The Gulf coast and the Caribbean)* **What is the air pressure around these storm systems?** *(996–1008 millibars)* Students should draw the conclusion that low pressures are associated with stormy weather and high pressures are associated with sunny weather.
Visual

Address Misconceptions L2

Many people misunderstand symbols on a weather map. Students may think that the H stands for areas of high temperatures and the L for areas of low temperatures. Isobars may be misinterpreted as representing wind speed or temperature. Using Figure 29 or other weather maps, ask students for the meanings of these symbols. Have students construct their own model weather map and include a key describing all of the symbols.
Visual

Go Online SCIENCE NEWS

Science News provides students with current information on weather and climate.

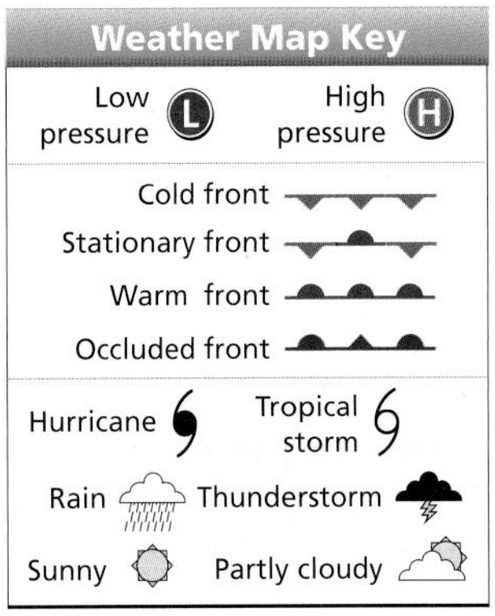

Weather Map Key
Low pressure
High pressure
Cold front
Stationary front
Warm front
Occluded front
Hurricane
Tropical storm
Rain
Thunderstorm
Sunny
Partly cloudy

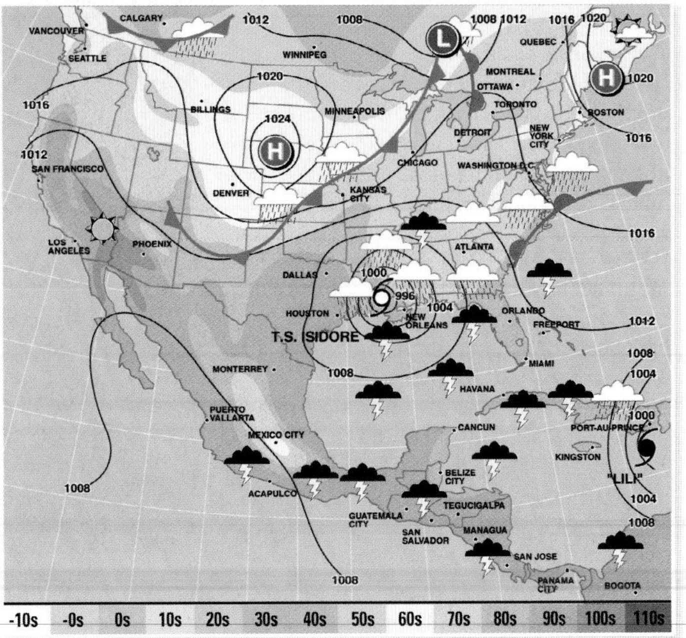

VANCOUVER
CALGARY
SEATTLE
WINNIPEG
QUEBEC
MONTREAL
OTTAWA
TORONTO
BOSTON
NEW YORK CITY
WASHINGTON D.C.
DETROIT
CHICAGO
MINNEAPOLIS
BILLINGS
DENVER
KANSAS CITY
SAN FRANCISCO
LOS ANGELES
PHOENIX
DALLAS
ATLANTA
HOUSTON
NEW ORLEANS
ORLANDO
FREEPORT
MIAMI
HAVANA
T.S. ISIDORE
MONTERREY
PUERTO VALLARTA
MEXICO CITY
ACAPULCO
CANCUN
BELIZE CITY
GUATEMALA CITY
SAN SALVADOR
TEGUCIGALPA
MANAGUA
SAN JOSE
PANAMA CITY
BOGOTA
KINGSTON
PORT-AU-PRINCE
"LILI"
1008
1012
1016
1020
1024
1000
1004
996
-10s
-0s
0s
10s
20s
30s
40s
50s
60s
70s
80s
90s
100s
110s

Figure 29 The isobars on this weather map encircle the centers of low-pressure and high-pressure systems. You can also see a cold front, a warm front, and a stationary front as well as a hurricane and a tropical storm. **Interpreting Visuals** ***According to the weather map, what are the weather conditions in New Orleans, Louisiana?***

High-Speed Computers High-speed computers help meteorologists compile and analyze the tremendous amount of weather data collected every day. With these data, scientists make both short-term and long-term forecasts. How accurate are these forecasts? Most forecasts can be quite accurate in the short term, from 12 hours to 3 days. Meteorologists can also accurately forecast the movement of large weather systems, such as cyclones, over a period of 3 to 7 days. Predicting beyond a week, however, remains extremely difficult, even with modern technology. The movement of weather systems depend on too many variables for meteorologists to forecast the weather reliably over longer periods.

Reading Checkpoint *How accurate are most weather forecasts?*

Go Online SCIENCE NEWS

For: Articles on weather and climate
Visit: PHSchool.com
Web Code: cce-3246

Weather Maps

To help analyze weather data, meteorologists make maps that show weather patterns of different regions. You've probably seen weather maps in newspapers or on TV weather reports. **Weather maps typically show predicted temperatures and include sun or cloud symbols to indicate cloud cover. They have drawings of rain or snow to show areas of precipitation.** They also usually include symbols for the different kinds of fronts and areas of high and low pressure.

Facts and Figures

Folk Rhymes and Weather Forecasting
There's an old rhyme that sailors once learned to help them remember the signs of weather and forecast what was to come: "Rainbow in the morning, / Sailors take warning; / Rainbow at night, / Sailors delight." This rhyme made good sense for sailors in the Northern Hemisphere, where most weather moves from west to east. A rainbow in the morning would be seen in the west, because the sun is then shining from the east. Rain, therefore, would be west of the sailors—and coming toward them. A rainbow in the evening, by contrast, would be seen in the east, because the sun is then shining from the west. Rain, therefore, would be east of the sailors—and moving away from them.

Although the weather maps you see in newspapers or on TV are useful to most people, meteorologists need additional information on maps. For example, temperatures might be plotted and analyzed on a map using isotherms. An **isotherm** is a line on a map that connects points of equal air temperature. With this kind of map, a meteorologist can quickly see temperature patterns.

A comprehensive weather map that meteorologists prepare and use is a summary of weather conditions at a given moment for a given region. This kind of weather map typically includes information about weather systems and fronts. It also includes specific locations where weather data have been collected. More information on this type of map is included in Appendix F.

Figure 29 shows a simplified weather map similar to what you might find in your local newspaper. Notice that temperature data are displayed using a series of colored bands that group regions in ten-degree temperature intervals. Also notice that there is a tropical storm near New Orleans and a hurricane near Cuba on the weather map. Both are low-pressure centers. To the left of the map is a key for weather symbols used on such maps.

The lines on this weather map are isobars. An **isobar** is a line that connects points of equal air pressure. Notice that the isobars on this map are plotted at intervals of 4 millibars. Isobars help meteorologists, such as the woman shown in Figure 30, to identify the centers of high- and low-pressure systems and the locations of fronts.

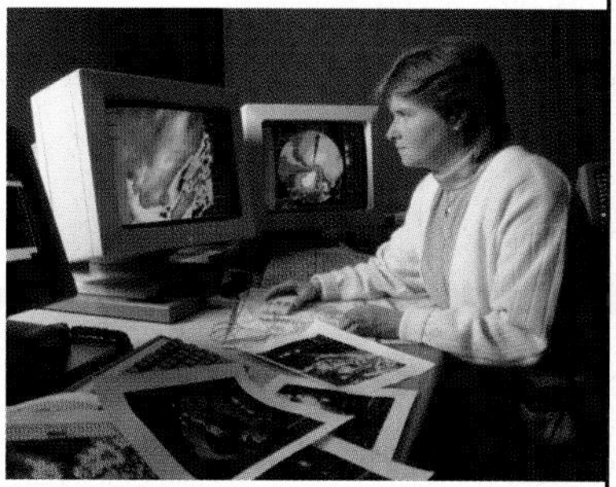

Figure 30 Meteorologists use computers to help forecast the weather.

Section 24.6 Assessment

Reviewing Concepts

1. What are some of the technologies meteorologists use to collect weather data?
2. How do meteorologists show differences in temperature and pressure on weather maps?
3. Explain how meteorologists use Doppler radar to track and predict the weather.
4. How do meteorologists use high-speed computers to help forecast the weather?
5. Describe the type of information that is typically shown on the weather maps prepared by meteorologists.

Critical Thinking

6. **Inferring** Why might a meteorologist want to compare today's weather map with yesterday's weather map?
7. **Applying Concepts** Why can't meteorologists accurately forecast the weather beyond a period of about a week?

Writing in Science

Solving a Problem Suppose you live in "Tornado Alley," a region in the central United States that is frequently hit by tornadoes. What technology discussed in the text would you recommend to warn residents of your area about an approaching tornado? Write a brief proposal describing the potential benefits of this technology.

Section 24.6 Assessment

1. Among the tools that meteorologists use to collect weather data are Doppler radar, weather satellites, and automated weather stations.
2. Weather maps show differences in temperature with isotherms, which are lines on a map that connect points of equal air temperature. They show differences in air pressure with isobars, which are lines on a map that connect points of equal air pressure.
3. Doppler radar bounces radio waves off particles of precipitation in storms. The change in frequency of the returning wave allows scientists to calculate a storm's speed and direction of movement.
4. High-speed supercomputers are used to process large amounts of weather data in order to produce accurate weather forecasts.
5. Daily high temperature, air pressure, cloud cover, precipitation, weather systems, and fronts
6. To determine the direction and speed that weather systems and fronts are moving
7. Because there are too many uncertain variables that can affect the weather

Build Science Skills **L2**

Using Models Have students practice plotting isotherms in order to help them understand the weather map as a model of weather over a large region. Provide them with a table of daily high temperatures in major U.S. cities (which can be found in most major U.S. newspapers) and a blank outline map of the United States. Instruct students to plot the temperatures on the map (students may need to refer to a political map to find the location of the cities) and draw isotherms in 10-degree intervals. Color in the isotherms and include a key, such as the one shown in Figure 29. **Visual, Portfolio**

3 ASSESS

Evaluate Understanding **L2**

Show students a weather map from the newspaper, and ask them to identify all of the fronts, isotherms, and high- and low-pressure regions. Ask them to make some simple predictions based on what they have learned about the movements and characteristics of fronts.

Reteach **L1**

Use Figure 29 to review all of the features of a weather map.

Writing in Science

Students will likely choose Doppler radar, which can be used to track with great accuracy tornadoes or weather systems that could develop into tornadoes. Students' proposals should note that Doppler radar could save lives by providing sufficient warning for residents to take cover.

Interactive Textbook If your class subscribes to the Interactive Textbook, use it to review key concepts in Section 24.6.

Answer to . . .

Figure 29 *According to the map, it is raining heavily and there are thunderstorms around New Orleans. The temperature is between 80°F and 89°F and air pressure is between 996 and 1000 mb. This weather is being caused by a tropical storm.*

Reading Checkpoint *Most weather forecasts are quite accurate over the short term, up to about three days. They are also accurate in forecasting the movement of large weather systems three to seven days in advance.*

Section 24.7

1 FOCUS

Objectives

24.7.1 **Distinguish** between weather and climate and **describe** the main factors that affect a region's climate.

24.7.2 **Compare** climate variations due to natural and human causes.

Reading Focus

Build Vocabulary L2

Paraphrase Have students work in groups of five. Ask each student to explain one of the section vocabulary terms in his or her own words.

Reading Strategy L2

a. Ice ages or El Niño **b.** Caused by humans **c.** Global warming

2 INSTRUCT

Classifying Climates

Address Misconceptions L2

People often use the terms "weather" and "climate" interchangeably. Be sure students understand that in science, the terms have different meanings. Have students work in groups to write definitions in their own words for "climate" and "weather." Discuss how these definitions are related to scientific ones.
Group, Verbal

24.7 Climate

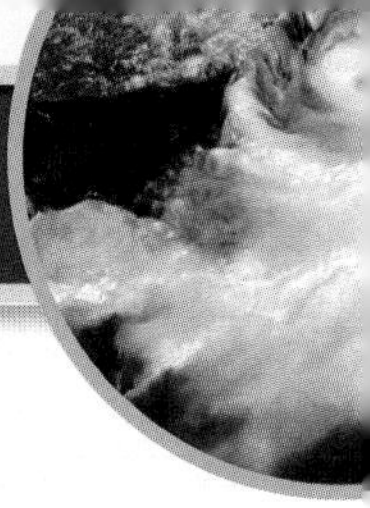

Reading Focus

Key Concepts

- How is climate different from weather?
- What factors determine the climate of a region?
- How has Earth's climate changed over time?
- How can human activities affect Earth's climate?

Vocabulary

- climate
- desert
- ice ages
- El Niño
- global warming

Reading Strategy

Building Vocabulary Copy the partially completed concept map below. Then, as you read, complete it with terms from this section.

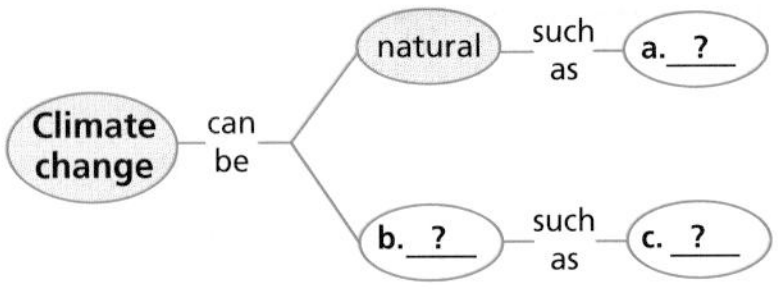

Climate change
can be
natural
such as
a. ?
b. ?
such as
c. ?

A friend from another state wants to visit you during school vacation. She's never been to your area, and wants to know what type of clothes to bring. Should she bring her heavy coat or her rain gear? How would you answer her? You could look outside to check the current weather, but that can change quickly. Weather maps can give you information about today's weather and what might be coming in the next few days. But what your friend really needs to know is the typical weather for your area at that time of year. She needs to know about the **climate,** that is the long-term weather conditions of a place or region. **Climate is a description of the pattern of weather over many years.** It includes average weather conditions as well as how weather varies over time, rather than day-to-day changes in the condition of the atmosphere.

Warm wishes from the tropics!

Figure 31 This postcard shows a warm coastal climate. **Classifying** *How might a postcard for your town illustrate its climate?*

Classifying Climates

Scientists divide the world's climates into several different types. What type of climate do you live in? Look at the world map in Figure 32 to find out. The map is divided into six major climate groups: tropical, temperate marine, temperate continental, polar, dry, and highlands. One of the six major groups, the dry climates, is determined mainly by precipitation. Another group, the highland climates, is determined mainly by elevation. The four remaining groups are determined mostly on the basis of temperature. Scientists further divide the major climate groups into many different specific climates.

Section Resources

Print

- ***Laboratory Manual,*** Investigation 24B
- ***Reading and Study Workbook With Math Support,*** Section 24.7
- ***Transparencies,*** Section 24.7

Technology

- ***Interactive Textbook,*** Section 24.7
- ***Presentation Pro CD-ROM,*** Section 24.7
- ***Go Online,*** *Planet Diary,* Drought activity

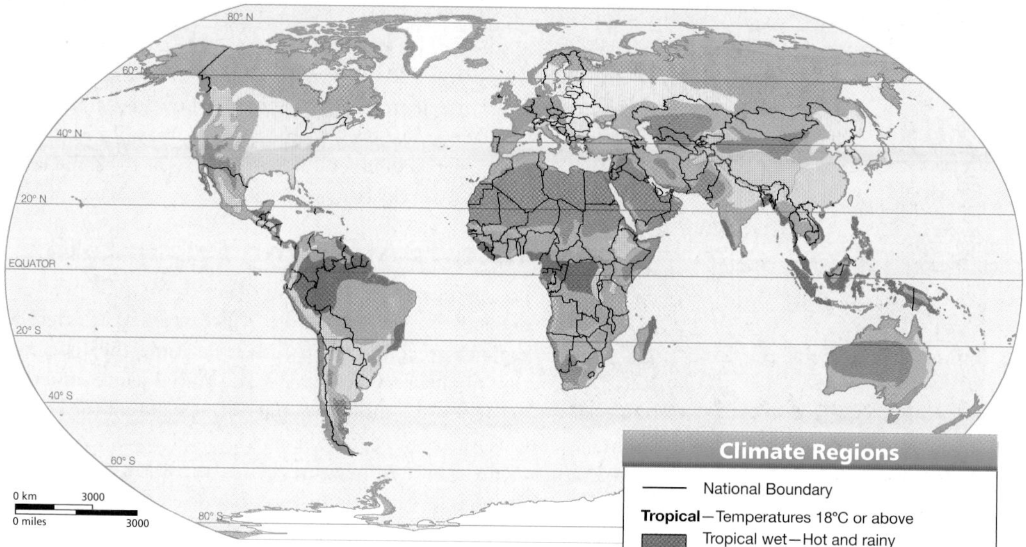
80° N
60° N
40° N
20° N
EQUATOR
20° S
40° S
60° S
80° S
0 km 3000
0 miles 3000
Climate Regions
National Boundary
Tropical—Temperatures 18°C or above
Tropical wet—Hot and rainy all year round
Tropical wet-and-dry—Hot with wet and dry seasons
Dry - Potential evaporation exceeds precipitation.
Semiarid—Dry but about 25–50 cm/yr of precipitation
Arid—Desert with little precipitation
Temperate Marine—Humid with mild winters
Mediterranean—Warm, dry summers and rainy winters
Humid subtropical—Hot summers and cool to mild winters
Marine west coast—Cool summers and mild winters
Temperate Continental—Cold, snowy winters
Humid continental—Hot summers and cold winters
Subarctic—Short summers and long, cold winters
Highlands
Mountains—Cool, wet, and mountainous
Polar—Averages below 10°C in warmest month
Tundra—Always cold and dry with short summer
Ice cap—Always cold, averaging below 0°C

Figure 32 This map illustrates the major climates of the world. **Interpreting Diagrams** ***What type of climate do you live in?***

In their study and classification of climates, scientists consider many factors, including soil, vegetation, and animal life. Two factors, however, are most important. **The two main factors that determine a region's climate are temperature and precipitation.** Scientists consider average temperature and precipitation over the year, as well as how these factors vary from day to day and season to season.

Factors Affecting Temperature

A region's pattern of temperature depends on several factors. **Factors that affect a region's temperature include its latitude, distance from large bodies of water, ocean currents, and altitude.** The latitude of a region is perhaps the most important factor affecting temperature. Places at the same latitude experience the same seasonal changes in solar radiation and therefore generally have similar temperatures throughout the year.

Another important factor affecting the temperature of a region is its distance from a large body of water. The air above large bodies of water has much less variation in temperature than the air over land. The moderating effects of water are felt in coastal regions. These regions typically have less variation in temperature over the course of a year than do regions located at the same latitude within continents. The temperature of coastal regions is also influenced by nearby ocean currents.

Factors Affecting Temperature

Use Visuals **L1**

Figure 32 Orient students to the map projection by pointing out the equator and lines of latitude. Tell students to study the key and note that the six major climate groups are represented by 12 subgroups in the map. Ask, **In which of the climate subtypes would you expect snowy winters?** *(Humid continental, subarctic, tundra, ice cap, mountains)* **At which latitudes do the dry regions mostly occur?** *(Around 30° N and 30° S)* **At which latitudes are polar climates found?** *(60–90° N and 60–90° S)* **Which areas of the United States typically have hot summers and cold winters?** *(Students should point out areas designated as humid continental or subarctic.)*
Visual

Customize for English Language Learners

Use a Cloze Strategy
Use a Cloze strategy for students with very limited English proficiency. Have students fill in the blanks in the following sentences while reading Classifying Climates. **The two main factors that determine a region's climate are __________ and __________. One of the main climate groups, the __________, is determined mainly by elevation. Most of the climate groups are determined mainly on the basis of __________.**

Answer to . . .

Figure 31 *Students' responses should show a clear understanding of the factors, such as temperature and precipitation, that affect the local climate.*

Figure 32 *The map shown in Figure 32 should be used to determine the type of local climate. Answers will vary depending on location.*

Factors Affecting Precipitation

Build Reading Literacy L1

Predict Refer to page **744D** in this chapter, which provides the guidelines for predicting.

Before students read Factors Affecting Precipitation, have them work in groups to brainstorm a list of factors that they think would affect the amount of precipitation a region gets. Ask, **Why do you think some areas of the world are very wet, and others very dry?** When students have a list of ideas, ask them to read the selection and evaluate whether their predictions were correct.
Logical, Group

Build Science Skills L2

Relating Cause and Effect Point out on Figure 32 that arid climates are typically found at 30° N and 30° S. Have students work in groups to discuss why this should occur, based upon their prior knowledge of global convection cells.
Interpersonal, Group

Figure 33 Giraffes inhabit the grasslands near Mount Kilimanjaro, Tanzania. Although Mount Kilimanjaro is near the equator, its top is covered by snow all year because of its high altitude.

Not all locations at the same latitude have similar temperatures. As you've learned, temperature decreases as altitude increases. As Figure 33 shows, areas that are high above sea level, such as parts of East Africa, have lower average temperatures than areas at the same latitude that are closer to sea level.

Factors Affecting Precipitation

Like temperature, a region's pattern of precipitation depends on several factors. **Factors that affect a region's precipitation include its latitude, the distribution of air pressure systems and global winds, and the existence of a mountain barrier.** Recall that the maximum amount of water vapor that the air can hold is greater at high temperatures than at low temperatures. Thus, the warm air over the equator usually contains more moisture than the cold air over the poles. As a result, precipitation is generally higher near the equator than near the poles.

A **desert** is an extremely dry region, receiving less than 25 centimeters of rain per year. Deserts may be hot or cold. Many deserts receive almost no rain because they are located within high-pressure belts. A series of deserts can be found around 30° north and south of the equator.

The direction of prevailing winds can play an important role in the amount of precipitation a region receives. For example, a coastal region where the wind generally blows from the ocean onto land will receive a large amount of precipitation. However, if prevailing winds blow from the land toward the ocean, the region will receive much less precipitation.

The very dry high plains of western North America are the result of a mountain barrier. The moist air from the Pacific Ocean loses its moisture as it rises over the mountains of the West, as shown in Figure 34. As the air rises, it cools and its water vapor condenses. Rain or snow falls on the ocean side of the mountains. The air that reaches the far side of the mountains is much drier.

Figure 34 A mountain range can form a barrier to the movement of humid air.
Applying Concepts ***Where does the heaviest rainfall occur?***

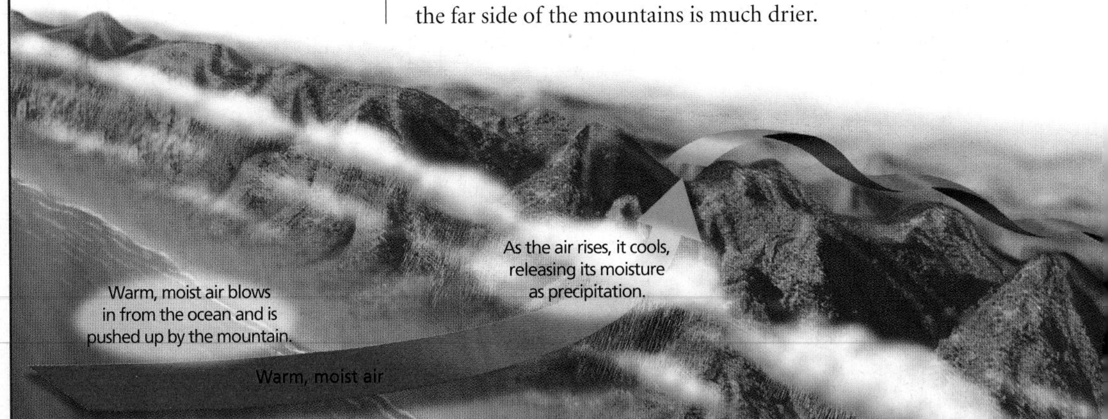
As the air rises, it cools, releasing its moisture as precipitation.
Warm, moist air blows in from the ocean and is pushed up by the mountain.
Warm, moist air

780 Chapter 24

Facts and Figures

The Wettest and Driest Lloro, Colombia, receives the world's highest average annual precipitation—an estimated 523.6 inches per year! Ironically, the lowest average annual precipitation is also found in South America, in Arica, Chile, which receives only 0.03 inches per year.

Natural Climate Change

You might expect that the climate of your own region always has been and always will be the same. This is not quite true, however. **Climates change over the long term, and they vary somewhat over the short term.** Natural forces cause climates to change. Scientists are also concerned that human activities may cause changes in the world's climates.

Ice Ages Climates change naturally over time. As Figure 35 shows, glaciers once covered much of North America. These huge ice sheets existed during **ice ages,** which were periods when climates were colder than usual and glaciers covered a large portion of Earth's surface. Ice ages have occurred many times in the past, the earliest known being more than 2 billion years ago. There have been four major ice ages in the last 2 million years. The most recent ice age didn't end until about 10,000 years ago. Possible causes of ice ages include variations in Earth's orbit around the sun, changes in the angle of Earth's axis, and global levels of volcanic activity.

El Niño In addition to long-term climate changes such as ice ages, there are short-term natural variations in climate patterns. One such variation that happens every three to eight years is **El Niño,** the periodic warming of water in the central and eastern Pacific Ocean. A deep cold-water current flows northward along the Pacific coast of South America. The water rises to the surface near Peru, and a strong current moves the water west across the Pacific. The temperature of these currents affects the atmosphere above the ocean and, therefore, the weather in that part of the world.

Every few years, for reasons that are not well understood, conditions change. Air pressure drops in the Pacific, and the normal direction of winds changes. Instead of blowing west across the Pacific, winds blow east toward South America, causing ocean surface currents to shift direction. During some El Niño years, these changes have caused abnormal weather patterns in many parts of the world.

Reading Checkpoint *How often does El Niño typically occur?*

Figure 35 Glaciers covered much of North America in the past. The rock in the front shows deep scratches made by glaciers.

Go Online PLANETDIARY

For: Drought activity
Visit: PHSchool.com
Web Code: ccc-3247

Dry, hot air

Natural Climate Change

Use Community Resources L2

Farmers and gardeners are affected by variations in local climate, especially changes due to El Niño, which can cause an area to receive significantly more or less rainfall than usual. Invite a local farmer, gardener, or landscaper to talk about the resources he or she uses to make seasonal climate predictions. **Interpersonal**

Go Online PLANETDIARY

Find links to additional activities and have students monitor phenomena that affect Earth and its residents.

Answer to . . .

Figure 34 *On the ocean side of the mountain range*

Reading Checkpoint *Once every 3–8 years*

Global Warming

Address Misconceptions L2

Students may think that global warming is caused by the ozone hole. In fact, CFCs (or other gases that cause stratospheric ozone depletion) are not related to global warming. The reason the depletion of the stratospheric ozone layer is a serious environmental problem is because having less of an ozone layer leads to a rise in ultraviolet radiation, which can hurt living things like people, animals, and plants. However, this is a different problem from global warming. Have students create a poster showing the actual causes of global warming, such as the release of carbon dioxide gas when coal, oil, and natural gas are burned. **Visual**

3 ASSESS

Evaluate Understanding L2

Ask students to discuss their local climate subtype, including naming factors that affect local temperature and precipitation.

Reteach L1

Use Figure 32 to review the major climate subtypes, some regions where they are located, and why they occur in those locations.

Connecting Concepts

Students should describe how their chosen resource could reduce the use of fossil fuels and therefore decrease emissions of carbon dioxide and other greenhouse gases.

Interactive Textbook If your class subscribes to the Interactive Textbook, use it to review key concepts in Section 24.7.

Figure 36 Carbon dioxide emissions from motor vehicles, power plants, and other sources may contribute to global warming.

Global Warming

Human activities may also change climate over time. **One possible climate change is caused by the addition of carbon dioxide and certain other gases into the atmosphere.** The burning of fossil fuels such as coal releases large quantities of carbon dioxide into the air.

Recall that carbon dioxide (CO_2) is one of the gases in the atmosphere that absorbs radiation from Earth's surface and then radiates energy back toward the surface. This process, known as the greenhouse effect, keeps the troposphere at normal temperatures. The amount of CO_2 in the atmosphere has increased from about 290 parts per million (ppm) in 1860 to more than 370 ppm currently. What will happen if the amount of CO_2 continues to increase? Evidence suggests that a greater amount of CO_2 will increase the greenhouse effect and cause the temperature of the atmosphere to rise, a process called **global warming.** In fact, average worldwide surface temperatures have increased by about 0.6 degree Celsius since the late 1800s. The 1990s were the warmest decade on record.

The effects of global warming may be widespread. For example, if the world's atmosphere warms, water in the oceans could expand, raising sea levels. Glaciers, including the continental glaciers that cover Antarctica and Greenland, could partially melt. A rise in sea level could flood low-lying regions and place many populated areas at risk of destruction. Other regions may be at greater risk of drought.

What could limit the effects of global warming? Energy conservation and a greater reliance on solar, nuclear, or geothermal power would reduce the amount of carbon dioxide released. This might reduce or delay global warming. The issue of global warming will be an important topic for science and public policy for decades to come.

Section 24.7 Assessment

Reviewing Concepts

1. What is climate, and how is climate different from weather?
2. What are the two main factors that determine a region's climate?
3. How do climates change over time?
4. How can the burning of fossil fuels affect world climates?
5. What is El Niño, and what causes it?

Critical Thinking

6. **Applying Concepts** Why do you think there is more precipitation in southern Florida than there is in northern Alaska?
7. **Inferring** Would a single unusually hot summer prove that global warming is occurring? Explain your answer.

Connecting Concepts

Energy Resources Recall what you learned about nuclear energy, renewable energy resources, and conservation in Chapters 10 and 15. Choose one of those resources and describe how its use might help to reduce global warming.

Section 24.7 Assessment

1. Weather is the state of the atmosphere at a given time and place. Climate is the typical weather patterns experienced over a period of years at a given location.
2. Temperature and precipitation
3. Climates change over the long term, and they vary somewhat over the short term. Natural forces cause climates to change. Human activities may also cause major changes in the world's climates.
4. Burning fossil fuels increases emissions of carbon dioxide into the atmosphere. These emissions may increase the greenhouse effect and cause global warming.
5. El Niño is the periodic warming of water in the central and eastern Pacific Ocean. It is caused by a shift in the normal direction of winds and ocean surface currents.
6. Florida is much closer to the equator than northern Alaska, and thus the air temperatures are generally warmer in Florida than in Alaska. Because warm air can hold more water vapor than cold air, precipitation is generally higher near the equator than near the poles.
7. No. One unusually warm summer would provide insufficient evidence. Scientists would have to track temperatures over much longer periods to establish that a trend such as global warming is occurring.

Exploration Lab

Determining Relative Humidity

To measure relative humidity, you can use a sling psychrometer. This device contains two thermometers. An absorbent wick keeps the bulb of one thermometer wet. As you spin the psychrometer, air flows over the wet bulb, increasing the rate of evaporation. In this lab, you will discover how a sling psychrometer measures the relative humidity of the air.

Problem How can you measure the relative humidity of the air?

Materials

- sling psychrometer
- relative humidity chart from Appendix G
- clock or watch with second hand

For the probeware version of this lab, see the Probeware Lab Manual, Lab 10.

Skills Using Tables, Formulating Hypotheses

Procedure

Data Table

Location	Dry Bulb Temp. (°C)	Wet Bulb Temp. (°C)	Relative Humidity (%)
Classroom			

1. On a separate sheet of paper, make a copy of the data table shown above.
2. Wet the cotton wick of the sling psychrometer with water.
3. Observe the temperature of the wet-bulb thermometer. Then, spin the psychrometer for 30 seconds. **CAUTION** *Take care not to spin the psychrometer near anyone or anything.*
4. Repeat Step 3 until the temperature of the wet-bulb thermometer remains constant. Then, record the temperatures of both thermometers in your data table.
5. Calculate the difference between your dry-bulb and wet-bulb temperatures.
6. In the relative humidity chart, find the row and column that list the dry-bulb temperature and the difference in temperature that you calculated. The number located where this row and column meet is the relative humidity of the classroom. Record the relative humidity in your data table.
7. Place the psychrometer on a flat surface. Observe the temperature of the wet-bulb thermometer every 30 seconds until it remains constant. Then, repeat Steps 2 through 5 at the location your teacher indicates.

Analyze and Conclude

1. **Analyzing Data** Why did the two thermometers have different temperatures?
2. **Formulating Hypotheses** Explain how the relative humidity of the air affected the difference between the temperatures of the two thermometers.
3. **Drawing Conclusions** What do you think caused the difference in relative humidity between the two locations?
4. **Predicting** How would the relative humidity change if you cooled the air in the classroom?

Go Further Measure and record the temperature and relative humidity outside your school or at home at various times of day for several days. Graph these data and explain any patterns that you observe.

Go Online PHSchool.com

For: Data sharing
Visit: PHSchool.com
Web Code: ccd-3240

Exploration Lab

Determining Relative Humidity L2

Objective

After completing this activity, students will be able to

- explain how a sling psychrometer works and how to determine relative humidity.

Skills Focus Using Tables, Applying Concepts

Prep Time 15 minutes

Advance Prep Make certain that the relative humidity charts that you supply to students express temperatures in degrees Celsius to match the laboratory thermometers that students will use.

Class Time 40 minutes

Safety Provide only nonmercury-filled thermometers. Care should be taken when swinging the psychrometer to avoid striking it against anything or anyone.

Teaching Tips

- Demonstrate beforehand the use of the sling psychrometer.

Expected Outcome The wet-bulb thermometer will have a lower temperature than the dry-bulb thermometer.

Sample Data

Typical data could consist of a dry-bulb reading of 21°C, a wet-bulb reading of 15°C, and a relative humidity of 51 percent. Data will depend on local conditions. In any case, the wet-bulb reading will be less than or equal to the dry-bulb reading.

Go Further

Relative humidity is typically highest in early morning due to evaporation of moisture condensed during the night. Students may observe additional patterns of change in relative humidity depending on location, current weather conditions, and the season.
Kinesthetic, Logical

Analyze and Conclude

1. The wet-bulb thermometer is usually cooler than the dry-bulb thermometer because evaporation of water from the wet bulb absorbed energy from the thermometer, which cooled it.
2. The difference in temperature between the two thermometers depends on the degree to which evaporation cools the wet bulb. The lower the relative humidity, the greater the rate at which water evaporates, cooling the wet bulb. Relative humidity does not affect the temperature of the dry-bulb thermometer. Therefore, the lower the relative humidity, the cooler the wet bulb will be, and the greater the difference in temperature between the two thermometers.
3. Factors could include sources of water, especially warm water, and variation in the effectiveness of heating and cooling throughout the school building.
4. Cooling the room would increase the relative humidity. The maximum concentration of water vapor in air is reduced at lower temperatures. Therefore, as the air in the room is cooled, the same concentration of water vapor becomes a higher percentage of the maximum concentration, or a higher relative humidity. **Logical, Portfolio**

Go Online PHSchool.com

Have students pool and compare their data with students nationwide by visiting the Prentice Hall Web site at www.PHSchool.com.

Study Guide

Study Tip

Form Study Groups
Encourage students to form study groups to help prepare for quizzes and tests. Students can work together to quiz each other using questions embedded in the reading as well as section and chapter assessments. They can work together to produce study aids such as flashcards, visuals, and rhymes or other mnemonic devices.

Assessment

Interactive Textbook If your class subscribes to the Interactive Textbook, your students can go online to access an interactive version of the Student Edition and a self-test.

Reviewing Content

1. b 2. c 3. a
4. c 5. a 6. d
7. c 8. c 9. b
10. d

Understanding Concepts

11. It protects the surface from bombardment by meteoroids, filters out much harmful radiation from space, moderates the temperature, and provides the gases necessary for life.
12. In the troposphere, temperature decreases as altitude increases.
13. Earth has seasons because its axis is tilted relative to a line perpendicular to its orbital path.
14. The troposphere is heated by radiation from Earth's surface and the sun, convection currents, and conduction from Earth's surface.
15. The illustration shows a cold front. Cold fronts typically bring strong winds, thunderstorms, and heavy precipitation.
16. Global winds are caused by the unequal heating of Earth's surface across a large region. Locations near the equator generally receive more direct sunlight than areas near the poles.

CHAPTER 24

Study Guide

24.1 The Atmosphere

Key Concepts

- Earth's atmosphere forms a protective boundary and provides conditions that are suitable for life.
- Earth's atmosphere is a mixture of many gases in which tiny solid and liquid particles are suspended.
- As altitude increases, pressure and density decrease.
- Scientists use variations in temperature to divide the atmosphere into four vertical layers.

Vocabulary

atmosphere, air pressure, barometer, troposphere, weather, stratosphere, ozone layer, mesosphere, thermosphere, ionosphere, aurora

24.2 The Sun and the Seasons

Key Concepts

- Earth moves by rotation and revolution.
- Scientists use lines of latitude to mark out regions within which temperatures are similar.
- The seasons are caused by the tilt of Earth's axis.

Vocabulary

rotation, revolution, tropic zone, temperate zones, polar zones, solstice, equinox

24.3 Solar Energy and Winds

Key Concepts

- Solar energy may be reflected, absorbed by the atmosphere, or absorbed by the surface.
- Energy is transferred within the troposphere in three ways: radiation, convection, and conduction.
- Winds are caused by differences in air pressure.
- Sea breezes and land breezes are local winds. Trade winds and westerlies are global winds.

Vocabulary

greenhouse effect, wind, local wind, sea breeze, land breeze, global winds, Coriolis effect, monsoon, jet stream

24.4 Water in the Atmosphere

Key Concepts

- Water vapor condenses as dew, frost, clouds, or fog.
- Clouds form as warm, moist air rises and water vapor condenses in the atmosphere. The basic cloud forms are stratus, cumulus, and cirrus.
- The most common types of precipitation are rain, snow, hail, sleet, and freezing rain.

Vocabulary

humidity, relative humidity, dew point, cloud, fog, stratus clouds, cumulus clouds, cirrus clouds

24.5 Weather Patterns

Key Concepts

- An air mass forms when a large body of air becomes fairly stationary over Earth's surface or as air moves over a large uniform area.
- There are four types of fronts: cold fronts, warm fronts, stationary fronts, and occluded fronts.
- Cyclones are associated with stormy weather. Anticyclones are associated with clear, calm weather.
- Thunderstorms form when columns of air rise within a cumulonimbus cloud. A tornado forms when an area of rotating air develops in a thunderstorm.

Vocabulary

air mass, front, cold front, warm front, stationary front, occluded front, cyclone, anticyclone, thunderstorm, lightning, thunder, tornado, hurricane

24.6 Predicting the Weather

Key Concepts

- Meteorologists use technologies such as Doppler radar to help predict the weather.
- Weather maps often show predicted temperatures, cloud cover, and precipitation.

Vocabulary

meteorologists, isotherm, isobar

24.7 Climate

Key Concepts

- Climate is a pattern of weather over many years.
- The two main factors that determine a region's climate are temperature and precipitation.
- Factors that affect a region's temperature include its latitude, distance from large bodies of water, ocean currents, and altitude.
- Factors that affect a region's precipitation include its latitude, the distribution of air pressure systems and global winds, and the existence of a mountain barrier.
- Climates change over the long term, and they vary somewhat over the short term.
- Human activities may contribute to global warming.

Vocabulary

climate, desert, ice ages, El Niño, global warming

Chapter Resources

Print
- ***Chapter and Unit Tests,*** Chapter 24 Test A and Test B
- ***Test Prep Resources,*** Chapter 24

Technology
- ***Computer Test Bank,*** Chapter Test 24
- ***Interactive Textbook,*** Chapter 24
- ***Go Online,*** PHSchool.com, Chapter 24

CHAPTER 24

Assessment

Interactive textbook with assessment at PHSchool.com iText

Reviewing Content

Choose the letter that best answers the question or completes the statement.

1. The most abundant gas in air is
   a. oxygen. b. nitrogen.
   c. carbon dioxide. d. hydrogen.

2. Earth's weather occurs primarily in the
   a. thermosphere. b. stratosphere.
   c. troposphere. d. mesosphere.

3. Wind is caused by differences in
   a. air pressure. b. altitude.
   c. humidity. d. condensation.

4. The amount of water vapor in the air is called
   a. dew. b. rain.
   c. humidity. d. precipitation.

5. A type of cloud that is commonly associated with fair weather is
   a. cumulus. b. cumulonimbus.
   c. altostratus. d. nimbostratus.

6. When the temperature equals the dew point, the relative humidity is
   a. zero. b. about 25%.
   c. about 50%. d. 100%.

7. When a warm air mass overtakes a cold air mass, the result is a (an)
   a. cold front. b. stationary front.
   c. warm front. d. occluded front.

8. Lines connecting areas of equal pressure on a weather map are called
   a. isotherms. b. barometers.
   c. isobars. d. weather symbols.

9. Generally, climates located farther from the equator have
   a. warmer ocean currents.
   b. lower temperatures.
   c. more rain.
   d. higher relative humidity.

10. A periodic warming of water in the central and eastern Pacific Ocean is called a (an)
    a. monsoon. b. jet stream.
    c. global warming. d. El Niño.

Understanding Concepts

11. Describe three functions of the atmosphere that make life on Earth possible.

12. How does temperature vary with altitude in the troposphere?

13. Why does Earth have seasons?

14. Describe three ways that the troposphere is heated.

15. Identify the type of front shown on the weather map below. What type of weather will this front likely bring?

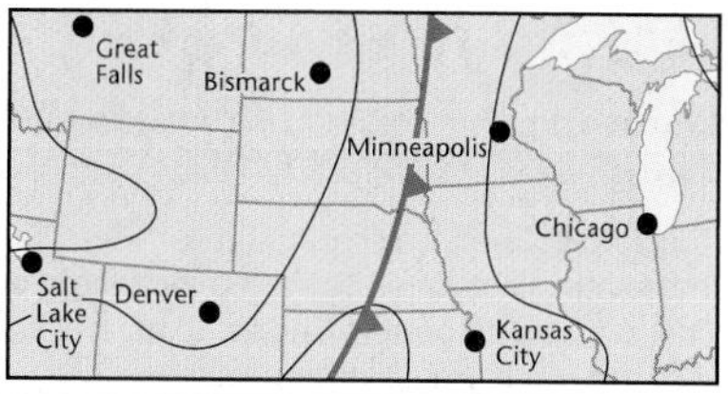

Great Falls
Bismarck
Minneapolis
Chicago
Salt Lake City
Denver
Kansas City

16. What causes global winds?

17. How does hail form?

18. What is the difference between sleet and freezing rain?

19. What is an air mass, and how do air masses form?

20. What are the major types of air masses that influence the weather in North America?

21. Explain how a warm front forms, and describe the weather that is usually associated with a warm front.

22. What is a stationary front, and how does one form?

23. Why do you hear thunder after you see a bolt of lightning?

24. Decribe two technologies that help meteorologists to forecast the weather.

25. Describe two ways in which oceans affect the climate of coastal areas.

26. What are ice ages, and why do they occur?

Homework Guide

Section	Questions
24.1	1–2, 11–12, 27–30
24.2	13, 31
24.3	3, 14, 16, 25, 32
24.4	4–6, 17–18, 39–40
24.5	7, 15, 19–23, 33–36, 41, 43
24.6	8, 24
24.7	9–10, 26, 37–38, 42

Assessment (continued)

17. Hail forms in cumulonimbus clouds when pieces of ice are tossed about in the moving air. These ice pellets combine with water droplets, which then freeze onto the pellets. Eventually the pellets become heavy enough to fall to the ground.
18. Sleet is rain that freezes as it falls. Freezing rain freezes only after it reaches the surface.
19. An air mass is a large body of air that has fairly uniform physical properties at a given altitude. Air masses form when a body of air remains fairly stationary over a region of Earth's surface or passes over a large uniform region like an ocean. Air masses are strongly influenced by the properties of that region.
20. Maritime polar, continental polar, maritime tropical, and continental tropical
21. A warm front forms when a warm air mass overtakes a cold air mass. Stratus clouds usually form as a warm front moves into an area, and steady rain often occurs. After the front passes, the skies become mostly clear and temperatures rise.
22. A stationary front is a front that occurs when two unlike air masses meet and the resulting front is stationary or moves very slowly.
23. Because thunder is produced by lightning, and the light from lightning travels much faster than the sound of thunder
24. Students should describe two of the following: Doppler radar, weather stations, weather satellites, and high-speed computers.
25. Coastal areas generally have less variation in temperature over the course of a year than other regions of similar latitude. Ocean currents also affect the temperature of the water in coastal areas and, therefore, affect the air temperature near a coast.
26. Ice ages are periods in Earth's history when climates are colder than normal and glaciers cover much of Earth's surface. Possible causes include variations in Earth's orbit, changes in the angle of Earth's axis, and the level of volcanic activity around the world.

Critical Thinking

27. The ozone in the ozone layer absorbs ultraviolet radiation in sunlight and filters it out before the sunlight reaches the surface of Earth. One likely effect of removing the layer would be an increase in skin cancer. Organisms that are sensitive to such radiation would be harmed.
28. The column of mercury would be shorter at the top of the mountain. The reason is that as air pressure decreases the column of mercury falls, and air pressure decreases as altitude increases.
29. The troposphere is sometimes called the "weather sphere" because almost all weather takes place in this layer.
30. Designs may vary. A typical design might describe using an airplane or weather balloons to measure air pressure at various altitudes.
31. If Earth were not tilted on its axis, there would be no seasons. The angle of the sun's rays and the number of hours of daylight each day would not vary at a given location over the year, although they would still vary with latitude. Temperatures would not vary as much at a given location.
32. Fogs form when moist air cools below the dew point during the night. The following day, the fog will dissipate when the air warms above the dew point.
33. A cold front has probably moved in. Cold fronts are typically accompanied by precipitation and a drop in temperature.
34. Because air is converging toward the center of a cyclone, air masses collide and fronts develop. In contrast, air is diverging in an anticyclone. As the air diverges, air from higher in the atmosphere descends to replace it. Calm conditions generally result.
35. The reading on a barometer will drop as a storm moves in because storms are cyclones, or centers of low pressure.
36. A hurricane loses strength as it moves over land. This occurs because it has lost its supply of moisture and heat from the ocean.
37. Little precipitation. The prevailing winds will bring dry, continental air masses that formed over land.
38. The difference in climate can be explained by the two cities' distances from a large body of water. Portland is close to the Pacific Ocean. Humid ocean air brings mild, rainy winters. St. Louis, which is located in the interior of North America, is far from any ocean or other large body of water.

CHAPTER 24

Assessment *(continued)*

Critical Thinking

27. **Inferring** How might Earth be different if there were no ozone layer?
28. **Applying Concepts** Imagine that you measured air pressure with a mercury barometer at the bottom of a mountain and at the top of that mountain. At which location would the column of mercury be shorter? Explain your answer.
29. **Inferring** Scientists sometimes refer to one of the layers of the atmosphere as the "weather sphere." Which layer do you think this is, and why?
30. **Designing an Experiment** Design an experiment that could be used to determine how air pressure changes with altitude.
31. **Predicting** How might Earth's weather be different if Earth were not tilted on its axis?
32. **Applying Concepts** Sometimes, when you rise in the morning, you'll see fog over a large area. The fog is often gone by noon. Explain why the fog forms and why it disappears.
33. **Classifying** In just a few minutes, the weather in your neighborhood changes from sunny and warm to cool and windy, and rain begins to fall. What type of front has probably moved in?
34. **Comparing and Contrasting** Air masses collide and fronts develop in a cyclone, while air masses don't collide in an anticyclone. What causes this difference?
35. **Inferring** How would you expect the reading on a barometer to change as a storm moves into your area?
36. **Applying Concepts** Describe what happens to a hurricane when it passes over land, and why.
37. **Inferring** Would you expect a land area where the prevailing winds blow from the land to the ocean to receive very much or very little precipitation? Explain your answer.
38. **Formulating Hypotheses** Portland, Oregon, which is located near the Pacific coast, has milder winters than St. Louis, Missouri, which is located deep in the interior of North America. Yet Portland is farther north than St. Louis. How can you explain this difference in climate?

Analyzing Data

Use the graph below to answer Questions 39 and 40.

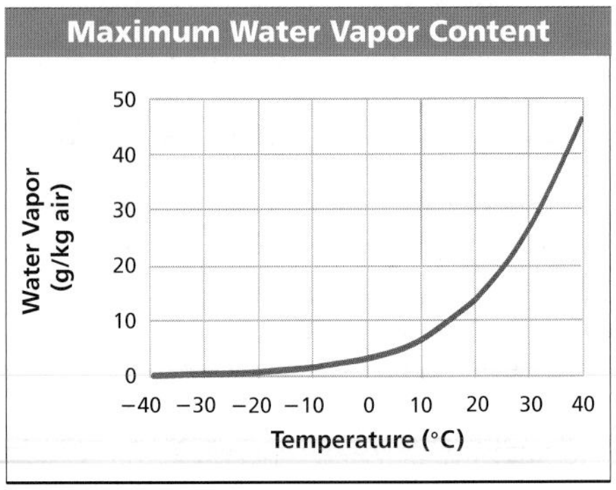
Maximum Water Vapor Content
Water Vapor (g/kg air)
50
40
30
20
10
0
−40 −30 −20 −10 0 10 20 30 40
Temperature (°C)

39. **Using Graphs** What is the maximum number of grams of water vapor that can exist in a kilogram of air at −20°C, 0°C, 20°C, and 40°C?
40. **Making Generalizations** Use the graph to make a general statement about temperature and water vapor in the atmosphere.

Concepts in Action

41. **Inferring** Why don't hurricanes form over the Arctic Ocean?
42. **Applying Concepts** What factors discussed in this chapter affect the climate where you live?
43. **Writing in Science** Write a descriptive paragraph about a storm that you have experienced. What kind of storm was it?

Performance-Based Assessment

Predicting Use weather maps to interpret weather data for a city of your choice for three consecutive days. Record these data in a table, and predict what the weather will be for the city on the fourth day.

Go Online
PHSchool.com
For: Self-grading assessment
Visit: PHSchool.com
Web Code: cca-3240

Analyzing Data

39. At −20°C, a kilogram of air can hold about 1 g of water vapor; at 0°C, about 4 g; at 20°C, about 15 g; and at 40°C, about 47 g.
40. Between −40°C and 40°C, the higher the temperature of air, the more water vapor it can contain.

Concepts in Action

41. Hurricanes form only over warm water (at least 27°C). The air temperature over the Arctic is much too cold to produce a hurricane.
42. Answers will vary depending on location. Students should mention such factors as latitude, altitude, proximity to a large body of water, ocean currents, global winds, and the existence of a mountain barrier.
43. Students should describe a storm they have experienced. They should also classify it according to the type of storm it was.

786 Chapter 24

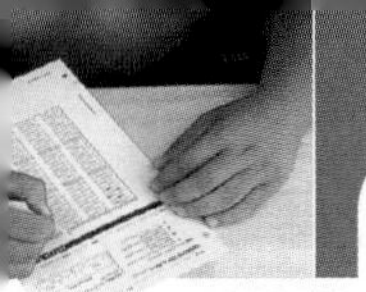

Standardized Test Prep

Test-Taking Tip

Avoiding Careless Mistakes
Students often make mistakes when they fail to examine a test question and possible answers thoroughly. Always read a question carefully and underline key words, such as *not, except, excluding,* and so forth. After choosing an answer, reread the question to check your selection.

Which of the following are NOT global winds?
(A) polar easterlies
(B) sea breezes
(C) monsoons
(D) westerlies
(E) trade winds

(Answer: B)

Choose the letter that best answers the question or completes the statement.

1. The stratosphere helps to protect Earth's surface from too much ultraviolet radiation because it contains a layer of
   (A) nitrogen.
   (B) carbon dioxide.
   (C) ozone.
   (D) ions.
   (E) water vapor.

2. Which of the following is NOT a type of precipitation?
   (A) dew
   (B) sleet
   (C) snow
   (D) hail
   (E) freezing rain

3. Which of the following is NOT generally associated with large amounts of precipitation?
   (A) anticyclone
   (B) hurricane
   (C) cold front
   (D) occluded front
   (E) thunderstorm

4. The two main factors that determine a region's climate are
   (A) air pressure and relative humidity.
   (B) temperature and precipitation.
   (C) air pressure and temperature.
   (D) precipitation and relative humidity.
   (E) temperature and relative humidity.

Use the graph below to answer questions 5 and 6.

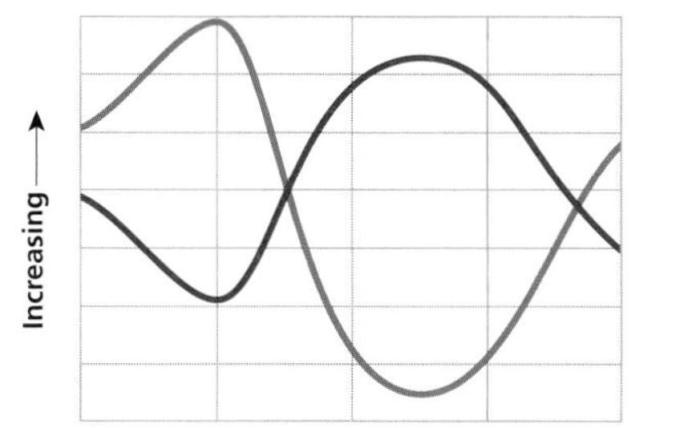

Increasing
Midnight
6 A.M.
Noon
6 P.M.
Midnight
Air temperature
Relative humidity

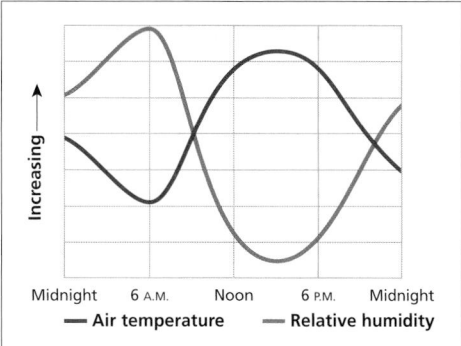

5. Relative humidity is at a minimum at about
   (A) midnight
   (B) 6 A.M.
   (C) 9 A.M.
   (D) 3 P.M.
   (E) 10 P.M.

6. At about what time is condensation most likely to occur?
   (A) 6 A.M.
   (B) 9 A.M.
   (C) noon
   (D) 3 P.M.
   (E) 6 P.M.

7. Isobars are lines on a weather map that connect points of equal
   (A) air temperature.
   (B) wind speed.
   (C) air pressure.
   (D) air density
   (E) precipitation.

Standardized Test Prep

1. C **2.** A **3.** A
4. B **5.** D **6.** A
7. C

Performance-Based Assessment

Students should collect weather data for a city of interest for three consecutive days and develop a weather prediction for the fourth day based on the movement of air masses and fronts. Students should explain their prediction.

Go Online PHSchool.com

Your students can independently test their knowledge of the chapter and print out their test results for your files.

CHAPTER 25

Planning Guide

Use these planning tools
Easy Planner
Teacher Express

SECTION OBJECTIVES	STANDARDS NATIONAL (See p. T18.)	STANDARDS STATE	ACTIVITIES and LABS
25.1 Exploring the Solar System, pp. 790–794 1 block or 2 periods **25.1.1** **Compare** and **contrast** the geocentric and heliocentric models of the solar system. **25.1.2** **Describe** the orbits of the planets around the sun and **explain** how gravity and inertia keep the planets in orbit. **25.1.3** **Name** the components of the solar system. **25.1.4** **Identify** different technologies used for exploring the solar system.	A-1, A-2, D-3, E-2, F-1, G-1, G-2, G-3		**SE** Inquiry Activity: Why Does the Sun Seem to Move? p. 789 L2 **SE** Quick Lab: Modeling Orbits, p. 793 L2 **TE** Teacher Demo: Ellipses, p. 792 L2 **LM** Investigation 25B: Investigating Eccentric Orbits L1
25.2 The Earth-Moon System, pp. 796–801 1 block or 2 periods **25.2.1** **Explain** why the moon lacks an atmosphere and the effect this has on the range of temperatures on the moon. **25.2.2** **Describe** the features of the moon's surface. **25.2.3** **State** a theory about the formation of the moon. **25.2.4** **Explain** why phases of the moon, eclipses, and tides occur and **interpret diagrams** of the relative positions of the sun, moon, and Earth during these events.	D-3, F-6, G-1		**TE** Build Science Skills: Using Models, p. 796 L2
25.3 The Inner Solar System, pp. 803–809 1 block or 2 periods **25.3.1** **Compare** the terrestrial planets and **describe** characteristics of each. **25.3.2** **Define** asteroids and **state** alternative hypotheses about how they formed.	D-1, D-3, G-1, G-2, G-3		**TE** Build Science Skills: Designing Experiments, p. 805 L2 **TE** Teacher Demo: Asteroids, p. 809 L2
25.4 The Outer Solar System, pp. 810–815 1 block or 2 periods **25.4.1** **Compare** the gas giants and **describe** characteristics of each. **25.4.2** **Distinguish** between comets and meteoroids and **describe** their characteristics. **25.4.3** **Locate** and **describe** the Kuiper belt and the Oort cloud.	D-1, D-3, G-1, G-2, G-3		**SE** Exploration Lab: Modeling the Solar System, p. 821 L2 **TE** Teacher Demo: Rings of Uranus, p. 813 L2 **LM** Investigation 25A: Modeling an Asteroid's Path L2
25.5 The Origin of the Solar System, pp. 818–820 1/2 block or 1 period **25.5.1** **State** the nebular theory. **25.5.2** **Relate** the nebular theory to the orbits of the planets and the composition and size of the planets.	A-1, A-2, D-3		**SE** Quick Lab: Forming Planets, p. 819 L2

Ability Levels

- **L1** For students who need additional help
- **L2** For all students
- **L3** For students who need to be challenged

Components

SE Student Edition	**RSW** Reading & Study Workbook	**CUT** Chapter & Unit Tests	**T** Transparencies
TE Teacher's Edition	**MSPS** Math Skills & Problem Solving Workbook	**CTB** Computer Test Bank	**iT** Interactive Textbook
LM Laboratory Manual		**TP** Test Prep Resources	**P** Presentation Pro CD-ROM
PLM Probeware Lab Manual		**DC** Discovery Channel Videotapes & DVDs	**GO** Internet Resources

RESOURCES PRINT and TECHNOLOGY	SECTION ASSESSMENT
RSW Section 25.1 L1 **RSW Math Skill** L2 **T** Chapter 25 Pretest L2 Section 25.1 L2 **P** Chapter 25 Pretest L2 Section 25.1 L2 SciLinks **GO** Early astronomers L2	**SE** Section 25.1 Assessment, p. 794 **iT** Section 25.1
RSW Section 25.2 L1 **T** Section 25.2 L2 **P** Section 25.2 L2	**SE** Section 25.2 Assessment, p. 801 **iT** Section 25.2
RSW Section 25.3 L1 **T** Section 25.3 L2 **P** Section 25.3 L2 SciLinks **GO** The solar system L2	**SE** Section 25.3 Assessment, p. 809 **iT** Section 25.3
RSW Section 25.4 L1 Discovery Channel School **DC** Lighting Up the Sky L2 **T** Section 25.4 L2 **P** Section 25.4 L2 Science News **GO** The solar system L2	**SE** Section 25.4 Assessment, p. 815 **iT** Section 25.4
RSW Section 25.5 L1 **T** Section 25.5 L2 **P** Section 25.5 L2	**SE** Section 25.5 Assessment, p. 820 **iT** Section 25.5

Go Online

Go online for these Internet resources.

PHSchool.com
Web Code: cca-3250
Web Code: cch-3252

SCIENCE NEWS
Web Code: cce-3254

NSTA SciLinks
Web Code: ccn-3251
Web Code: ccn-3253

Materials for Activities and Labs

Quantities for each group

STUDENT EDITION

Inquiry Activity, p. 789
pencil, tape, magnetic compass

Quick Lab, p. 793
string, scissors, ball, duct tape, meter stick

Quick Lab, p. 819
2 2.5-cm by 30-cm strips of paper, tape, pencil, metric ruler

Exploration Lab, p. 821
calculator, large sheet of unlined paper, meter stick, scale models of the sun and planets

TEACHER'S EDITION

Teacher Demo, p. 792
string, 2 thumbtacks, pencil, cardboard

Build Science Skills, p. 796
clay or pens and paper

Build Science Skills, p. 805
pencils and paper

Teacher Demo, p. 809
pile of pebbles (about 5 cm high), large rock, chunk of dried plaster or foam

Teacher Demo, p. 813
penlight, window blind

Build Science Skills, p. 816
4 small fans, foam ball, strips of newspaper, thumbtacks

Chapter Assessment

CHAPTER ASSESSMENT

SE Chapter Assessment, pp. 823–824
CUT Chapter 25 Test A, B
CTB Chapter 25
iT Chapter 25
PHSchool.com GO
Web Code: cca-3250

STANDARDIZED TEST PREP

SE Chapter 25, p. 825
TP Diagnose and Prescribe

Interactive Textbook

Interactive Textbook with assessment at PHSchool.com

Before you teach

From the Author

Michael Wysession
Washington University

Big Ideas

The solar system in which people on Earth live consists of a medium-sized star and a relatively small amount of additional matter in the form of planets, asteroids, meteoroids, comets, and other solid bodies. This solar system formed from a vast nebula of gas and dust that contracted under the force of gravity and began to rotate quickly due to the conservation of angular momentum.

Space and Time The solar system, though occupying a miniscule region within the Milky Way galaxy, is still huge. Pluto, generally considered the farthest planet, is on average 39.5 AU from the sun (1 AU is the mean Earth-sun distance). The Kuiper belt, containing rock/ice bodies like Pluto, extends to more than 100 AU from the sun. The Oort cloud, consisting of comets, extends to more than 50,000 AU from the sun!

Because elements with atomic masses higher than lithium are formed during the supernova stage of dying stars, the solar system incorporated the exploded remains of previous stars when it formed. The nebula condensed to form millions of planetesimals (baby planets), which collided to form the current planets. Earth's moon was formed from the remains of a Mars-sized planetesimal that collided with the early Earth.

Forces and Motion Gravity, a warping of space-time around massive objects, causes the planets and other objects of the solar system to follow elliptical orbits around the sun. Gravity acting between these objects changes their orbits, and Earth is occasionally hit by large meteoroids flung in its direction. Gravity also creates tidal forces between planetary objects.

Matter and Energy The solar system is hot near the sun and cold away from the sun. This temperature range deterred ices from condensing in the inner solar system, preventing the terrestrial planets from getting very large. This also caused the terrestrial planets to have metal/rock ratios that decrease from Mercury to Mars. Farther from the sun, ices condensed, making the gas giants (Jupiter, Saturn, Uranus, Neptune) massive enough to hold onto hydrogen and helium and become very big.

Space Science Refresher

Exploring the Solar System 25.1

From the vantage point of an observer on Earth, planets generally move in an eastward direction across the night sky. Sometimes, however, the path of a planet in relation to the stars appears to reverse. This is known as retrograde motion. For example, at times Mars appears to move backward, as shown below.

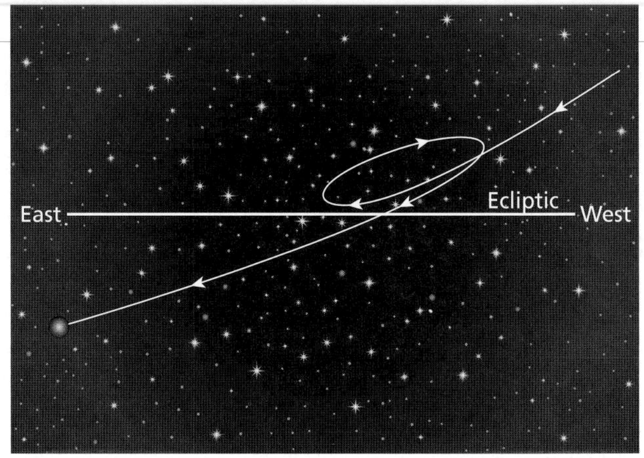
East
Ecliptic
West

To explain this motion, Ptolemy suggested that each planet in the solar system revolves in a small circle (or epicycle), the center of which revolves around Earth in a larger circle. Because part of each revolution of the small circle would cause the planet to move in the opposite direction of the larger orbit, the planet would appear to be moving backward when viewed from Earth.

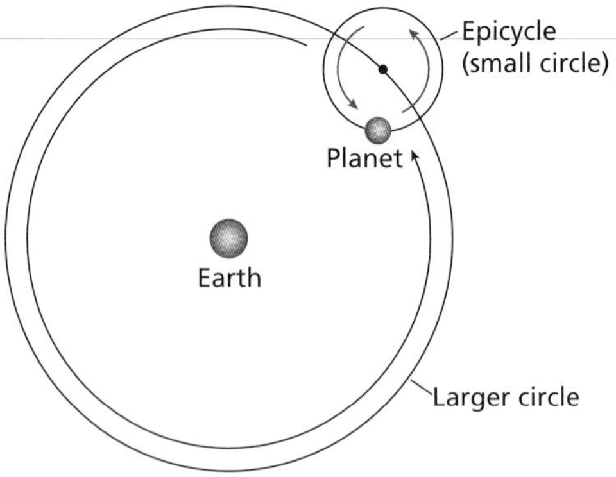
Epicycle
(small circle)
Planet
Earth
Larger circle

Ptolemy's Epicycle Model

This model was incorrect, and the geocentric system became increasingly complex to explain retrograde motion. Eventually, astronomers concluded that planets must orbit around the sun, not Earth, and that Mars appears to travel backward because Earth revolves more quickly and is closer to the sun than Mars is.

Go Online PD LINKS NSTA

For: Teaching methods for the solar system
Visit: www.SciLinks.org/PDLinks
Web Code: ccn-2599

The Earth-Moon System 25.2

Address Misconceptions

The phases of the moon are caused by the shadow of Earth. The moon's phases are caused by changes in the relative positions of the moon, sun, and Earth as the moon revolves around Earth. For a strategy to overcome this misconception, see **Address Misconceptions** on **page 798.**

The moon takes 27.32 days, or one sidereal month, to complete one revolution around Earth. At the end of a sidereal month, the moon returns to the same place as seen against the background stars. In the meantime, however, Earth has completed almost one-twelfth of its orbit around the sun. To an observer on Earth, the sun appears to have moved slightly eastward. This means that the moon has to travel a little bit farther to bring itself into the same position in the sky relative to the sun. The time it takes for the moon to return to that same position relative to the sun takes 29.53 days and is called a synodic month.

Inner and Outer Planets 25.3 and 25.4

Address Misconceptions

The solar system and outer space in general are very crowded. There are actually vast distances between the planets. For a strategy to overcome this misconception, see **Address Misconceptions** on **page 811.**

Scientists study and compare the atmospheres of the planets in the solar system. On Earth, most carbon dioxide (CO_2) is either dissolved in oceans or deposited as carbonate rocks formed in the oceans. Different situations, however, exist on other planets. Venus, for example, does not have oceans, which are vital for controlling a greenhouse effect. About 4.6 billion years ago, the solar output of the sun was 25% less bright than it is now. Scientists theorize that early in its history, Venus was cool enough to have water. As the sun's output slowly grew, however, Venus's surface may have begun to heat up and react with iron oxide in rocks or with carbon monoxide. Gases were released from the interior of the planet. During this process, called outgassing, hydrogen atoms escaped into space and highly reactive oxygen molecules bonded with other elements, including carbon. The loss of water allowed more CO_2 to accumulate in the atmosphere, which in turn accelerated the heating of the surface and led to a runaway greenhouse effect. The atmosphere of Venus is now 96.5% carbon dioxide.

The Origin of the Solar System 25.5

The age of the solar system, about 4.6 billion years, is determined from radiometric dating. Planetary rocks have been greatly altered over time, and thus cannot be used for dating purposes. Carbonaceous chondrites, however, are meteorites that contain certain compounds (including water in minerals) that would not be present had the meteorite been exposed to extreme heat or pressure. The meteorites presumably have been largely unaltered since the formation of the solar system. Carbonaceous chondrites are usually dated using potassium-40 (half-life of 1.28 billion years) and uranium-238 (half-life of 4.5 billion years).

Build Reading Literacy

Use Prior Knowledge

Building from the Familiar

Strategy Relate new material to something already known and address misconceptions. Learning is easier when new material can be linked to familiar concepts. Choose a section from Chapter 25, such as Exploring the Solar System (pp. 790–794), to use in modeling the strategy. Create a three-column chart with the chapter or section topic written at top, and columns labeled Heading (subtopic), Prior Knowledge, and New Knowledge.

Example

1. Record Chapter 25 and a section number in the title line of the chart. Choose a section heading and record it in the first column.
2. Have students turn to the assigned section and scan its bold headings. Ask students what they already know, or think they know, about the topic of each heading. List responses in the second column of the chart.
3. Use students' responses to determine whether they have any misconceptions about the topic. If so, begin to address those misconceptions directly in discussion.
4. Have students read the section and correct or revise information recorded in the column labeled Prior Knowledge. Direct them to add information that is new to them in column three.
5. After reading, discuss their findings and clarify any additional misconceptions.

See p. 805 for a script on how to use the use prior knowledge strategy with students. For additional Build Reading Literacy strategies, see pp. 794, 798, 807, 811, and 820.

ASSESS PRIOR KNOWLEDGE

Use the Chapter Pretest below to assess students' prior knowledge. As needed, review these Science Concepts with students.

Review Science Concepts

Section 25.1 Have students define gravity and inertia. Ask them to describe an example of Newton's first law of motion. Review the factors that determine the force of gravitational attraction between two objects. Review orbits and rotation.

Section 25.2 Discuss the role that Earth's atmosphere plays in regulating surface temperatures. Review tides. Remind students that light travels in straight lines and is refracted when entering a new medium at an angle.

Section 25.3 Remind students that Earth is the only planet in the solar system where water occurs in the atmosphere as a liquid, gas, and solid. Review Earth's structure. Review the greenhouse effect.

Sections 25.4 and 25.5 Review the periodic table of elements, comparing lighter elements, such as hydrogen and helium, to heavier elements, such as iron. Also review how matter changes state. Ask students to describe an erupting volcano. Have them explain why a hurricane eventually runs out of energy.

CHAPTER

25 The Solar System

CONCEPTS in Action

How do science concepts apply to your world? Here are some questions you'll be able to answer after you read this chapter.

- How does a spacesuit work? *(Section 25.1)*
- Why shouldn't you park a car too close to the ocean's edge? *(Section 25.2)*
- Why isn't Earth covered by craters? *(Section 25.3)*
- Did Mars once have liquid water? *(Section 25.3)*
- Where, besides Earth, is life most likely to occur in our solar system? *(Section 25.4)*
- What lies at the outer edges of the solar system? *(Section 25.4)*
- Are there planets around other stars? *(Section 25.5)*

DISCOVERY CHANNEL SCHOOL

Video Field Trip

Lighting Up the Sky

- Why do comets have tails? *(page 816)*

This composite photo shows Saturn and ▶ four of its moons. The image was created by combining several images taken by the Voyager 1 space probe during its flyby of the Saturn system in 1981.

788 *Chapter 25*

Chapter Pretest

1. What determines the strength of the gravitational attraction between two objects? *(c)*
   a. Mass and weight
   b. Weight and distance
   c. Mass and distance
   d. Distance and density
2. What are the two most abundant gases in Earth's atmosphere? *(Nitrogen and oxygen)*
3. True or False: Earth's atmosphere plays a role in regulating its surface temperature. *(True. Earth's atmosphere plays a major role in keeping surface temperatures in their present ranges.)*
4. What is Newton's first law of motion? *(The state of motion of an object does not change as long as there is no net force acting on it.)*
5. Describe Earth's structure. What are the three main layers? *(The three main layers are the crust, or rocky outer layer; the mantle, a thick layer of hot, solid rock; and the core, a large sphere found in Earth's center, mostly made of iron and nickel.)*
6. Explain the process of condensation. *(In condensation, a gas changes into a liquid as it cools.)*

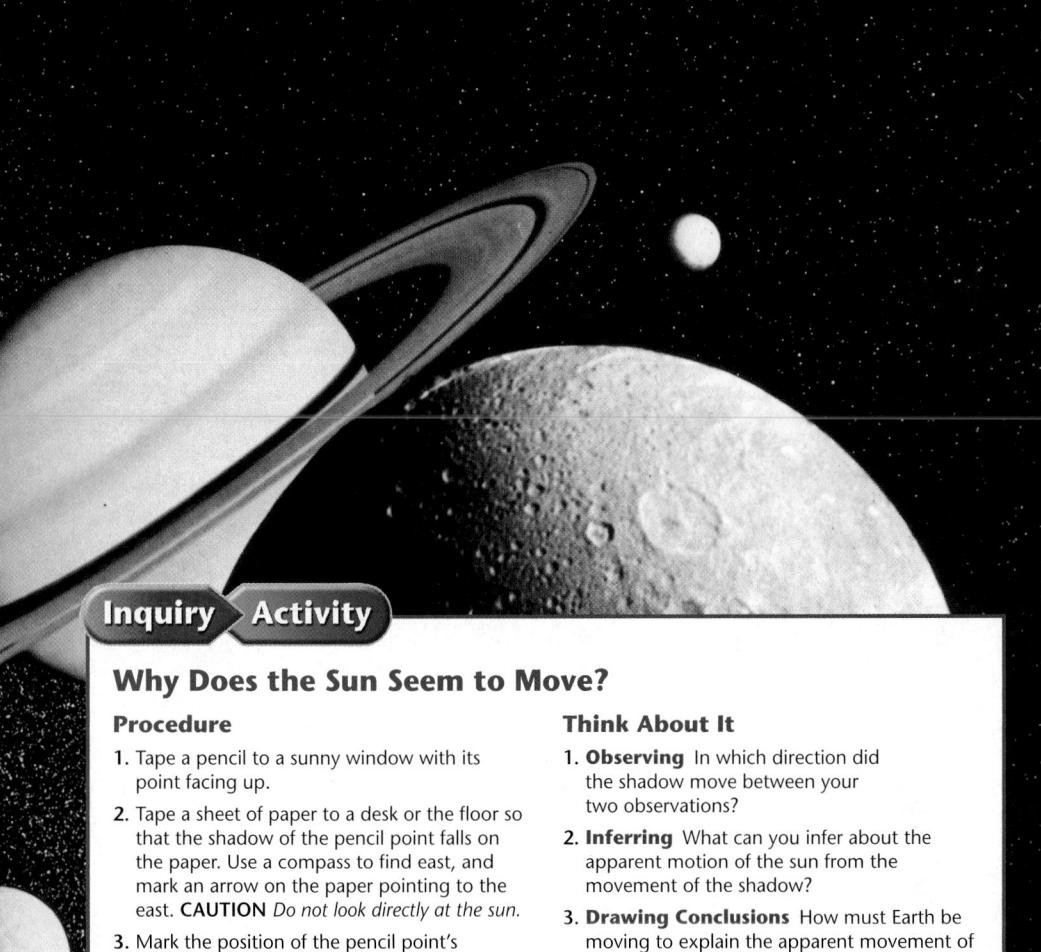

Chapter Preview

Inquiry Activity

Why Does the Sun Seem to Move?

Procedure

1. Tape a pencil to a sunny window with its point facing up.
2. Tape a sheet of paper to a desk or the floor so that the shadow of the pencil point falls on the paper. Use a compass to find east, and mark an arrow on the paper pointing to the east. **CAUTION** *Do not look directly at the sun.*
3. Mark the position of the pencil point's shadow on the paper. Record the time of day.
4. After 10 minutes, repeat Step 3.

Think About It

1. **Observing** In which direction did the shadow move between your two observations?
2. **Inferring** What can you infer about the apparent motion of the sun from the movement of the shadow?
3. **Drawing Conclusions** How must Earth be moving to explain the apparent movement of the sun?

ENGAGE/EXPLORE

Inquiry Activity

Why Does the Sun Seem to Move? L2

Purpose In this activity, students begin to understand the movement of shadows and the apparent movement of the sun due to the rotation of Earth.

Skills Focus **Observing, Inferring**

Prep Time 5 minutes

Materials pencil, tape, magnetic compass

Advance Prep Try this activity in advance to determine how quickly the shadow of the pencil will move and where students should place the paper.

Class Time 20 minutes

Safety Make sure that students do not look directly at the sun.

Teaching Tips

- If the classroom windows have only a northern exposure, you may need to do the activity outside.
- Help students model Earth's rotation. Have students slowly spin clockwise (to the right). They will see objects move left across their field of view.

Expected Outcome Students will notice that the shadow moves from west to east.

Think About It

1. The shadow moved from west to east.
2. The sun seems to move from east to west.
3. The sun seems to move from east to west because Earth rotates from west to east.
Visual, Logical

Discovery Channel School **Video Field Trip**
Lighting Up the Sky

Encourage students to view the Video Field Trip "Lighting Up the Sky."

1 FOCUS

Objectives

25.1.1 **Compare** and **contrast** the geocentric and heliocentric models of the solar system.

25.1.2 **Describe** the orbits of the planets around the sun and **explain** how gravity and inertia keep the planets in orbit.

25.1.3 **Name** the components of the solar system.

25.1.4 **Identify** different technologies used for exploring the solar system.

Reading Focus

Build Vocabulary L2

Word-Part Analysis From their Earth science studies, students may know that *geo* is the Greek word for "Earth." Have them use dictionaries to look up the Greek words *helio* and *centric.* (*Helio* is the Greek word for "sun." *Centric* is the Greek word for "center.") Tell students to review the list of key concepts for this section, and then infer the meaning of the phrases *geocentric model* and *heliocentric model.* (*Geocentric* means "Earth-centered." *Heliocentric* means "sun-centered.")

Reading Strategy L2

a. Revolves around Earth **b.** Ancient Greeks, Ptolemy **c.** Revolves around sun **d.** Center of solar system

2 INSTRUCT

Models of the Solar System

Use Visuals L1

Figure 2 Have students examine the two models. **In which model is Earth at the center?** *(Geocentric model)* **Where is the sun in the heliocentric model?** *(In the center)*
Visual

25.1 Exploring the Solar System

Reading Focus

Key Concepts

- How are the geocentric and heliocentric models of the solar system different?
- What keeps the planets in orbit around the sun?
- What bodies make up the solar system?
- How is the solar system being explored today?

Vocabulary

- geocentric
- heliocentric
- ecliptic plane
- moon
- astronomical unit
- space probe

Reading Strategy

Comparing and Contrasting After you read, compare the geocentric and heliocentric systems by completing the table below.

	Location of Earth	Location of Sun	Developer(s) of Theory
Geocentric System	Center of universe	a. ?	b. ?
Heliocentric System	c. ?	d. ?	Aristarchus, Copernicus

For thousands of years, people have used the sky to track the passage of time. Farmers in ancient Egypt watched for the first morning appearance of the bright star Sirius to know when to prepare for planting. Stonehenge, in England, consists of a group of large stones set in a circular pattern long ago. The locations of certain stones mark the spots where the sun rises or sets on the longest and shortest days of the year. About 1000 years ago in Central America, the Mayans built observatories such as the one shown in Figure 1. They used their observations to develop calendars and even predict astronomical events.

Figure 1 The Mayan ruin of El Caracol, also known as "The Observatory," is located on the Yucatan peninsula. It is thought that the Mayans used El Caracol for astronomical observations.

Models of the Solar System

Ancient observers noticed that most objects in the sky seem to be in a state of slow but steady motion. Every day the sun appears to rise in the east and set in the west. The moon, too, rises and sets every day. Similarly, the stars move across the sky in a fixed pattern.

Camp out for a few nights and you'll notice, as the ancients did, that the stars appear to circle around a fixed point in the sky. In the Northern Hemisphere, the stars circle around Polaris, the North Star. Most ancient people concluded that Earth was stationary and the sun, moon, and stars moved around Earth.

Ancient observers noticed that a few bright starlike objects seemed to wander slowly among the fixed patterns of stars. These objects were called planets, from the Greek word for "wanderers." Besides Earth itself, the ancients knew of the five planets that can be seen with the unaided eye: Mercury, Venus, Mars, Jupiter, and Saturn.

Section Resources

Print
- ***Laboratory Manual,*** Investigation 25B
- ***Reading and Study Workbook With Math Support,*** Section 25.1 and **Math Skill:** Calculating Distances Between Objects in Space
- ***Transparencies,*** Chapter Pretest and Section 25.1

Technology
- ***Interactive Textbook,*** Section 25.1
- ***Presentation Pro CD-ROM,*** Chapter Pretest and Section 25.1
- ***Go Online,*** NSTA SciLinks, Early astronomers

790 Chapter 25

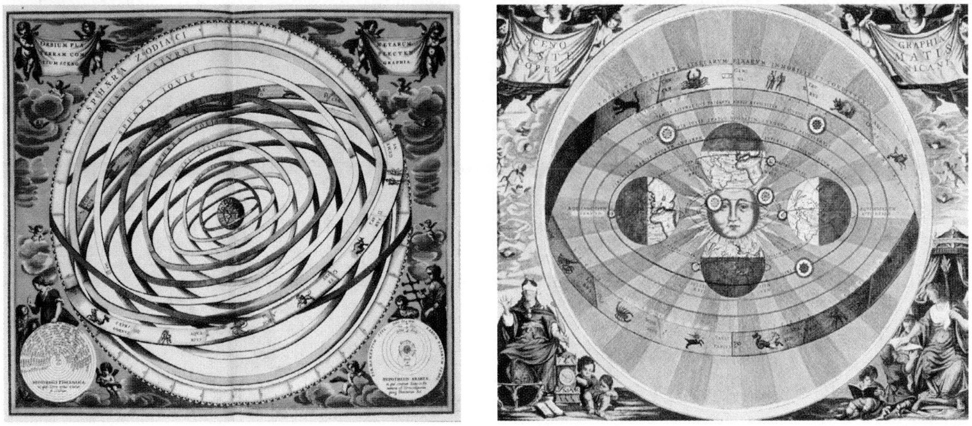

Figure 2 Andreas Cellarius drew these maps of the geocentric model (left) and heliocentric model (right) in the 1660s. **Comparing and Contrasting** ***Where does Earth appear in each diagram?***

Geocentric Model Most ancient Greeks thought that Earth was at the center of the universe. They believed that all the stars and planets lay on the inside of a giant sphere that revolved around Earth once a day. Since *geo* is the Greek word for "Earth," such a model is called a **geocentric** (jee oh SEN trik) model. **In a geocentric model, Earth is stationary while objects in the sky move around it.** The original geocentric model was modified about A.D. 140 by the Egyptian astronomer Ptolemy (TAHL uh mee) to more accurately predict positions of the planets. Ptolemy's geocentric model was widely accepted for nearly 1400 years.

Heliocentric Model Even in ancient times, not everyone thought that Earth was at the center of the universe. The Greek astronomer Aristarchus developed a **heliocentric** (hee lee oh SEN trik) model. **In a heliocentric model, Earth and the other planets revolve around the sun.** Figure 2 illustrates the geocentric and heliocentric models. Although today we know that Aristarchus was correct, his model was not accepted by most ancient Greeks. The geocentric model could explain all observations made at that time. Moreover, Earth's motions are not obvious to observers on Earth.

In the early 1500s, the heliocentric model was revived by the Polish scientist Nicolaus Copernicus. Copernicus realized that the motion of the planets could be more simply expained if they are revolving around the sun rather than around the Earth. The observations of Italian scientist Galileo Galilei and other scientists later proved that the heliocentric model was correct.

The apparent motions of the sun, moon, and stars result from Earth's daily rotation on its axis. As Earth rotates, it seems that we are stationary and all of the objects in the sky are spinning around us. The northern stars appear to circle around the North Star because Earth's axis points toward a spot in the sky close to that star.

Build Science Skills L2

Communicating Results Have students use reference materials and the Internet to research the evidence gathered by early astronomers in support of the heliocentric model. For example, students can focus on Galileo's observations of the phases of Venus and his discovery of the four large moons of Jupiter. The phases of Venus cannot be explained by the geocentric model. However, the heliocentric model fully accounts for all of Venus's phases, from new to full. The discovery of the four large moons of Jupiter proved that natural satellites orbited other planets, and provided evidence that all objects in the solar system did not move around Earth. Students may also choose to research the attempts to explain retrograde motion, the apparent reversal in the direction of movement of a planet. Have students present the results of their research in written reports, including diagrams and time lines.
Verbal, Portfolio

Customize for English Language Learners

Provide Reading Opportunities
Keep an updated library in the classroom of magazines, journals, and newspaper articles that relate to chapter content. Specifically choose reading materials that include the new vocabulary words covered in this section. (Be sure these sources have low reading levels.) This will allow English language learners to study how the words are used in different contexts.

Answer to . . .

Figure 2 *Earth appears at the center of the solar system in the geocentric model on the left and revolving around the sun in the heliocentric model on the right.*

Planetary Orbits

Teacher Demo

Ellipses

L2

Purpose Students observe the shape of planetary orbits.

Materials string, 2 thumbtacks, pencil, cardboard

Procedure Place 2 thumbtacks several centimeters apart on a rectangular piece of cardboard, approximately 8 × 11 cm. Put a loop of 18-cm string over the thumbtacks and trace around the tacks, keeping the string taut. Explain to students that the traced line represents a planetary orbit. Repeat the procedure several times, each time varying the distance between the thumbtacks. Emphasize that most of the planets' orbits are nearly circular.

Expected Outcome Students will note that the distance between the thumbtacks determines the shape of the orbit—the closer the thumbtacks, the more circular the orbit. Explain that each thumbtack represents a focus of an ellipse. In planetary orbits, the sun is located at one of the foci. **Visual**

Components of the Solar System

Address Misconceptions

L2

Many students think that the sun and moon are not influenced by Earth's gravitational force. Remind students that all objects exert gravitational forces on other objects. The force may be slight depending on the mass and the distance between the objects, but it exists nonetheless. Tell them that according to Newton's third law, if the moon exerts a gravitational force on Earth, then Earth must exert an equal and opposite gravitational force on the moon. **Logical**

Go Online NSTA SCILINKS

Download a worksheet on early astronomers for students to complete, and find additional teacher support from NSTA SciLinks.

Go Online NSTA SCILINKS

For: Links on early astronomers
Visit: www.SciLinks.org
Web Code: ccn-3251

Planetary Orbits

In the year 1600, Johannes Kepler, a German mathematician, began to analyze the paths of the planets around the sun. Kepler used data that had been collected for more than twenty years by the Danish astronomer Tycho Brahe.

Kepler discovered that the orbit of a planet around the sun is not a circle, but an ellipse. An ellipse looks like an oval, or a circle that has been stretched out along one axis. Most planets' orbits are nearly circular, and so are only slightly elliptical. Imagine that the path of Earth's orbit is traced on the top of a giant table. The plane of this imaginary tabletop containing Earth's orbit is called the **ecliptic plane.**

The force that holds the planets in orbit around the sun wasn't understood until Isaac Newton's discoveries about gravity. Recall that Newton's first law of motion states that an object in motion continues to move in a straight line at a constant speed unless acted upon by a force. This property of matter is known as inertia. Newton realized that the sun must be exerting a gravitational force on the planets that keeps them in orbit. Otherwise, the planets' inertia would cause them to fly off into space. **Gravity and inertia combine to keep the planets in orbit around the sun.**

Components of the Solar System

Our solar system consists of the sun, the planets, their moons, and a variety of smaller objects that mostly revolve in the same plane around the sun. Recall that the ancients knew of six planets. Since the invention of the telescope in the early 1600s, three more planets have been discovered: Uranus in 1781, Neptune in 1846, and Pluto in 1930. Except for Mercury and Venus, all of the planets have moons. A **moon** is a relatively small natural body in space that revolves around a planet.

Suppose you were surveying the solar system from a great distance. You might be tempted to say that it consists mainly of a single star, the sun, with a few small objects revolving around it all in the same plane. You would not be far wrong, since the sun's mass is about 750 times greater than the mass of the rest of the solar system combined.

Figure 3 The planets orbit mostly in the same plane, though they do not line up as shown here. This figure shows the average distance from the sun to each of the nine planets. The sizes of the sun and planets are not to scale. **Calculating** ***Which planet is closest to Earth?***

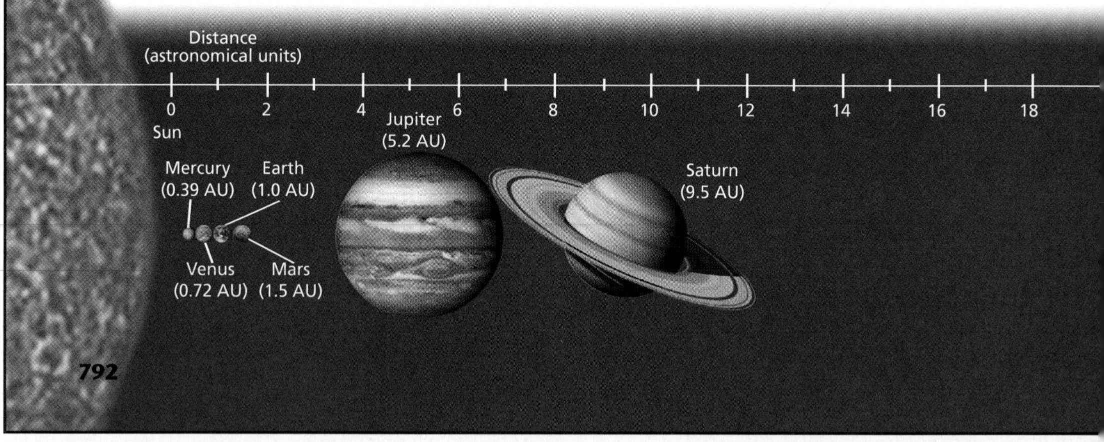

Distance (astronomical units)
0
2
4
6
8
10
12
14
16
18
Sun
Jupiter (5.2 AU)
Mercury (0.39 AU)
Earth (1.0 AU)
Saturn (9.5 AU)
Venus (0.72 AU)
Mars (1.5 AU)

Facts and Figures

Kepler's Laws Johannes Kepler and Tycho Brahe worked together for two years. Brahe died in 1601, leaving his extensive data to Kepler. Kepler spent much of the next 10 years attempting to match Brahe's observations of the retrograde motion of Mars to circular orbits. Finally, he concluded that the planets move in ellipses around the sun—a discovery known as Kepler's first law of planetary motion. Kepler eventually formulated two additional laws. His second law of planetary motion states that planets sweep out equal amounts of area in equal amounts of time. His third law relates the size of a planet's orbit to the time it takes for the planet to complete one orbit.

Unlike the sun, planets and moons don't produce their own light. The nearby planets and moons are visible because sunlight is reflected from their surfaces. In Figure 3 you can see that the orbits of the first four planets—Mercury, Venus, Earth, and Mars—are relatively close to the sun. The orbits of the outer planets, Jupiter, Saturn, Uranus, Neptune, and Pluto, are much farther from the sun.

Distances between objects in the solar system are much smaller than distances to the stars, but are much larger than distances on Earth. As a result, astronomers often use astronomical units to describe distances within the solar system. One **astronomical unit** (AU) equals the average distance from Earth to the sun—149,598,000 kilometers. In comparison, Pluto is an average of about 39.53 AU from the sun.

Reading Checkpoint *What is an astronomical unit?*

Exploring the Solar System

Modern technology, including complex telescopes, piloted spacecraft, and space probes, has allowed scientists to explore the solar system. The first rockets powerful enough to escape Earth's atmosphere and enter space were developed in the 1940s and 1950s. The Soviet Union launched the first artificial satellite, Sputnik 1, into orbit in 1957. Sputnik stirred the United States to start its own space program. The so-called space race was underway. On April 12, 1961, Soviet cosmonaut Yuri Gagarin became the first human to orbit Earth. Astronaut Alan Shepard became the first American in space on May 5, 1961.

Travel to the Moon Following Shepard's flight, President John F. Kennedy directed the National Aeronautics and Space Administration (NASA) to launch a major effort to place an astronaut on the moon. The quest to reach the moon progressed through a series of increasingly complex missions. The final step in this effort was a series of space flights called the Apollo program. On July 20, 1969, Neil Armstrong, commander of the *Apollo 11* spacecraft, became the first person to set foot on the moon.

Quick Lab

Modeling Orbits

Procedure

1. Cut a 200-cm piece of string. Tie one end of the string securely to a whiffle ball.
2. Wrap the string's other end around your hand, leaving 50 cm of string between your hand and the ball.
3. To model a planet's orbit, swing the ball above your head with just enough force to keep the ball moving parallel to the ground. **CAUTION** *Make sure the ball cannot hit anyone or anything.* Record the number of orbits the ball makes in 10 s.
4. Repeat Step 3, increasing the string's length to 150 cm from the ball.

Analyze and Conclude

1. **Calculating** How long did a single orbit take in Step 3? In Step 4?
2. **Analyzing Data** How did the radius of the ball's orbit affect the time to complete one orbit?
3. **Using Models** How does this lab model the orbits of the planets?

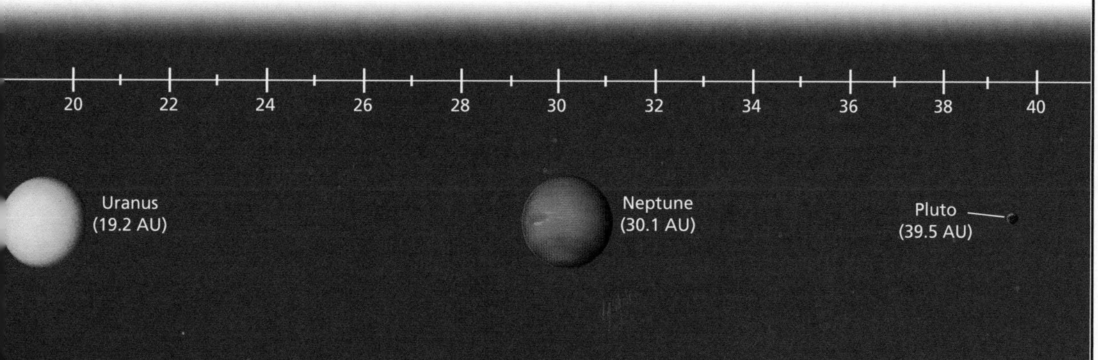

20
22
24
26
28
30
32
34
36
38
40
Uranus
(19.2 AU)
Neptune
(30.1 AU)
Pluto
(39.5 AU)

Facts and Figures

Space Telescopes NASA currently has four Great Observatories, or space telescopes. The Hubble Space Telescope is probably the best known—it captures images of nebulas and other space phenomena across a wide spectrum, including visible light and portions of the infrared and ultraviolet spectrums. The Compton Gamma-Ray Observatory creates images using gamma rays. The third telescope, launched in 1999, is the Chandra X-ray Observatory. This telescope makes X-ray images. X-rays are absorbed by Earth's atmosphere and thus cannot be studied from Earth's surface. Astronomers hope to use Chandra's images to learn more about black holes. The latest telescope, "SIRTF" (Space Infrared Telescope Facility), was launched in 2003. This telescope detects infrared radiation from celestial objects and will be used to search for extrasolar planets and to probe distant galaxies.

Exploring the Solar System

Quick Lab

Modeling Orbits L2

Objective
After completing this activity, students will be able to
- describe the relationship between the radius and speed of a planet's orbit.

Skills Focus Using Models, Analyzing Data

Prep Time 20 minutes

Materials string, scissors, ball, duct tape, meter stick

Advance Prep If whiffle balls are not available, provide punctured tennis balls. To prepare a ball, puncture or drill two holes through it. If puncturing a tennis ball is too difficult, you can substitute a one-hole cork stopper.

Class Time 20 minutes

Safety Students should wear safety goggles and stand at least 5 m apart when performing this lab.

Teaching Tips
- This lab should be performed outdoors or in a large room with a very high ceiling such as an auditorium or gymnasium.

Expected Outcome As the radius of the ball's orbit increases, it will make fewer revolutions in 10 seconds. Data will depend in part on the force with which students swing the ball. A typical result is that in an orbit with a radius = 50 cm, the ball makes 20 revolutions in 10 seconds. With a 150-cm radius, the ball makes 14 revolutions in 10 seconds.

Analyze and Conclude
1. Using the sample data above,
Step 3: Period = 10 s/20 rev = 0.5 s;
Step 4: 10 s/14 rev = 0.7 s
2. Increasing the radius of the ball's orbit increased the time it took to travel in a complete circle.
3. Like the ball, the planets that are farthest from the sun take the longest to go around the sun. **Kinesthetic, Logical**

Answer to . . .

Figure 3 *Venus*

Reading Checkpoint *The average distance from Earth to the sun, which is 149,598,000 km*

Section 25.1 (continued)

Build Reading Literacy L1

Identify Main Idea/Details Refer to page **98D** in **Chapter 4**, which provides the guidelines for identifying main idea and details.

Remind students that a topic sentence expresses the main idea of a paragraph. Have students read the text on p. 794 relating to recent space missions. Then, ask, **What is the topic sentence of the first paragraph?** *(Although humans have not yet traveled across the solar system, scientists have gathered much new information about various planets and moons.)* **What details support the main idea?** *(Information about space probes and space telescopes)*
Verbal

3 ASSESS

Evaluate Understanding L2

Refer students to the vocabulary list at the beginning of this section. Have them take turns describing a fact that they have learned about one of these vocabulary words.

Reteach L1

Have students create a time line showing the space missions discussed in this section in chronological order.

Math Practice

Solutions
7. 1.5 AU × 149,598,000 km/AU = 220 million km
8. 2.77 AU × 149,598,000 km/AU = 414 million km; between Mars and Jupiter

Interactive Textbook If your class subscribes to the Interactive Textbook, use it to review key concepts in Section 25.1.

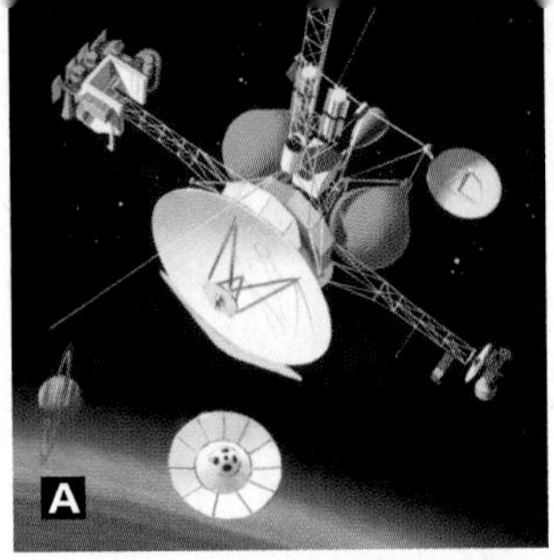
A

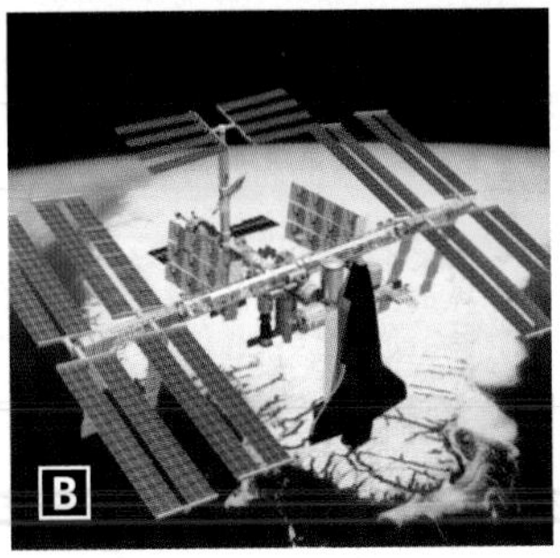
B

Figure 4 Modern technology is used to send spacecraft into orbit and to explore the planets. **A** The space probe Cassini launches a probe to explore Saturn's largest moon, Titan, in this illustration. **B** A space shuttle is docked to the International Space Station in this computer-generated illustration.

Over the next few years, five more moon landings took place. Astronauts performed many scientific experiments and brought back to Earth 382 kilograms of rock and soil samples. The last lunar mission, *Apollo 17,* was completed in 1972. Since then, no one has returned to the moon.

Recent Space Missions Although humans have not yet travelled across the solar system, scientists have gathered much new information about various planets and moons. In the decades since the Apollo program, nearly all of the planets and moons of the solar system have been photographed by space probes. A **space probe,** as shown in Figure 4, is an unpiloted vehicle that carries scientific instruments into space and transmits information back to Earth. The Hubble Space Telescope, launched into orbit around Earth in 1990, has also provided many new views of the solar system and beyond. Today, scientists rely mainly on space probes and telescopes to gather new information about the solar system.

Recent human space flight has centered on the near-Earth missions of the space shuttle. The shuttle is a reusable space vehicle that is launched like a rocket but lands like an airplane. Today, a new era of cooperation exists in the exploration of space. An important step has been the development of the International Space Station, shown in Figure 4. The space station is a permanent laboratory designed for research in space. Astronauts from various countries are currently living aboard the partially completed structure, which is scheduled to be finished in 2006. Scientists from 16 countries are working together to operate the station and to complete additional modules that will be attached to the station in the future.

Section 25.1 Assessment

Reviewing Concepts

1. What is the difference between the geocentric and heliocentric models of the solar system?
2. Why don't planets travel in straight lines?
3. What are the four types of bodies in the solar system?
4. What are some ways that scientists are currently learning more about the solar system?

Critical Thinking

5. **Comparing and Contrasting** How has the focus of the U.S. space program changed since the time of the Apollo program?
6. **Applying Concepts** Why do some stars seem to rotate around Polaris at night?

Math Practice

7. Using Figure 3, find the average distance of Mars from the sun, in km.
8. Orbiting 2.77 AU from the sun, Ceres is the largest of a group of objects called asteroids. How far from the sun is Ceres in km? Between the orbits of which two planets does the orbit of Ceres lie?

Section 25.1 Assessment

1. In the geocentric model, Earth is stationary while objects in the sky, including the sun, stars, and planets, revolve around it. In the heliocentric model, Earth and the other planets revolve around the sun.
2. The pull of the sun's gravity, combined with each planet's inertia, keep the planets in stable elliptical orbits around the sun.
3. The sun, planets, moons, and a variety of smaller objects that orbit the sun
4. Space probes, spacecraft, and telescopes are used to gather new information on the solar system.
5. The focus of the space program has shifted toward space probes, telescopes, and near-Earth space missions.
6. Earth is rotating and its axis is currently pointing in the direction of Polaris.

HOW It Works

Spacesuit

A spacesuit allows an astronaut to live in space. It provides a pressurized environment, a supply of oxygen, and protection against tiny rock particles called micrometeoroids. **Interpreting Diagrams** ***Which part of the spacesuit keeps the astronaut cool?***

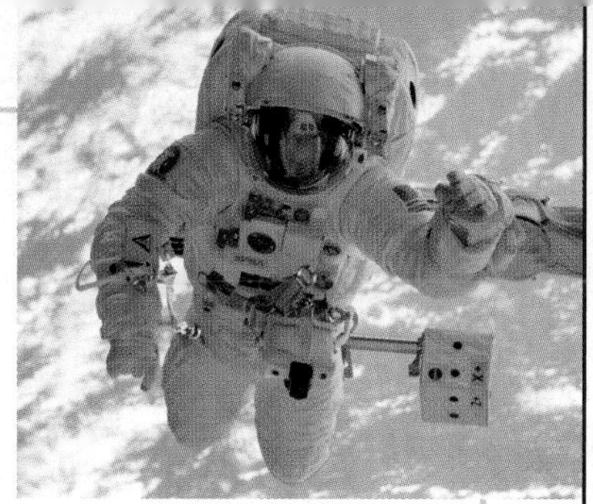

Outside the space shuttle
A space suit allows an astronaut to perform extra-vehicular activities (EVAs). This astronaut is attached to the space shuttle.

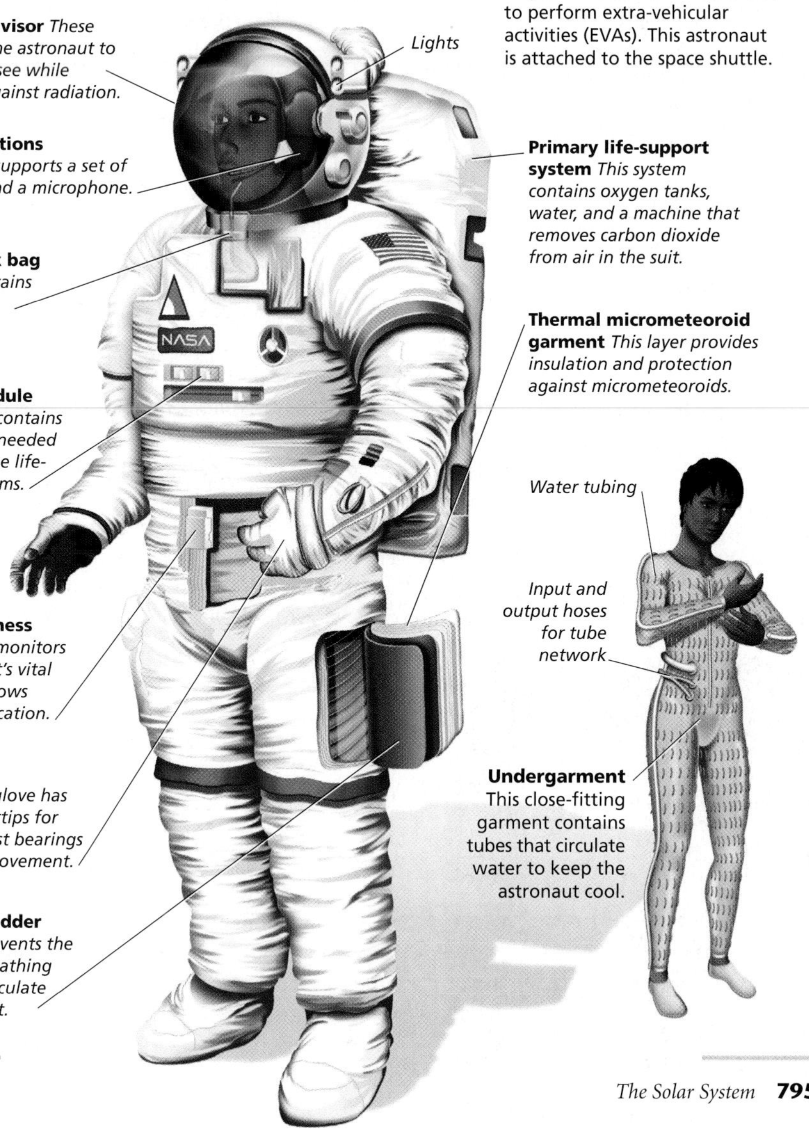
Helmet and visor *These parts allow the astronaut to breathe and see while protecting against radiation.*
Lights
Communications *A fabric cap supports a set of earphones and a microphone.*
In-suit drink bag *This bag contains almost 1 liter of water.*
Control module *This module contains the switches needed to operate the life-support systems.*
Electric harness *This harness monitors the astronaut's vital signs, and allows for communication.*
Glove *Each glove has rubber fingertips for grip, and wrist bearings for ease of movement.*
Pressure bladder *This layer prevents the escape of breathing gases that circulate inside the suit.*
Primary life-support system *This system contains oxygen tanks, water, and a machine that removes carbon dioxide from air in the suit.*
Thermal micrometeoroid garment *This layer provides insulation and protection against micrometeoroids.*
Water tubing
Input and output hoses for tube network
NASA

Undergarment This close-fitting garment contains tubes that circulate water to keep the astronaut cool.

HOW It Works

Spacesuit L2

The spacesuits used for the Apollo missions were custom-made for each astronaut. Today, NASA has about 150 astronauts in the shuttle program. The cost of making one custom-fit spacesuit would be as high as $2 million. Therefore, spacesuits are now made with interchangeable pieces (arms, legs, boots) that can be taken apart and reused. The spacesuits are still "custom-made" in the sense that each part is chosen to fit an astronaut's unique shape and size.

Interpreting Diagrams The undergarment keeps the astronaut cool.
Visual

For Enrichment L3

Tell students to study carefully the various components of a spacesuit. Then, have them infer why each part is necessary. Ask, **Why do astronauts need earphones and microphones in space?** *(There is no atmosphere, and thus no medium for sound waves to pass through. Without earphones and microphones, astronauts could not communicate with one another.)* **Why must an astronaut be attached to the space shuttle when performing EVAs?** *(The force of gravity is low. An astronaut could float away.)*
Visual, Logical

25.2 The Earth-Moon System

1 FOCUS

Objectives

25.2.1 **Explain** why the moon lacks an atmosphere and the effect this has on the range of temperatures on the moon.

25.2.2 **Describe** the features of the moon's surface.

25.2.3 **State** a theory about the formation of the moon.

25.2.4 **Explain** why phases of the moon, eclipses, and tides occur and **interpret diagrams** of the relative positions of the sun, moon, and Earth during these events.

Reading Focus

Build Vocabulary L2

Compare/Contrast Tables Have students make tables that compare and contrast several groups of vocabulary words for this section. Students should look for relationships among the words and put each group of words in a table with columns for each word.

Reading Strategy L2

a. Maria b. Highlands

2 INSTRUCT

Earth's Moon

Build Science Skills L2

Using Models ACTIVITY

Purpose Students make scale models of the moon and Earth.

Materials clay or pens and paper

Class Time 20 minutes

Procedure Tell students that the equatorial radius of the moon is 1738 km and of Earth is 6378 km. Have groups calculate the diameters of the moon and Earth, then make scale models that accurately show the relative sizes of each.

Expected Outcome The equatorial diameter of the moon: 1738 km × 2 = 3476 km; the equatorial diameter of Earth: 6378 km × 2 = 12,756 km; 12,756 km/3476 km = 3.67; Earth is roughly four times bigger than the moon. Students can use a scale such as 1000 km = 1 cm. **Logical, Group**

Reading Focus

Key Concepts

- Why does the moon's temperature vary widely?
- What features are found on the moon's surface?
- How did the moon form?
- What causes the phases of the moon?
- What causes solar and lunar eclipses?
- What causes the tides?

Vocabulary

- maria
- crater
- meteoroids
- phases
- eclipse
- umbra
- penumbra
- tides
- spring tide
- neap tide

Reading Strategy

Building Vocabulary Copy the concept map below. Then, as you read, complete it with terms from this section. Make similar concept maps for eclipses and tides.

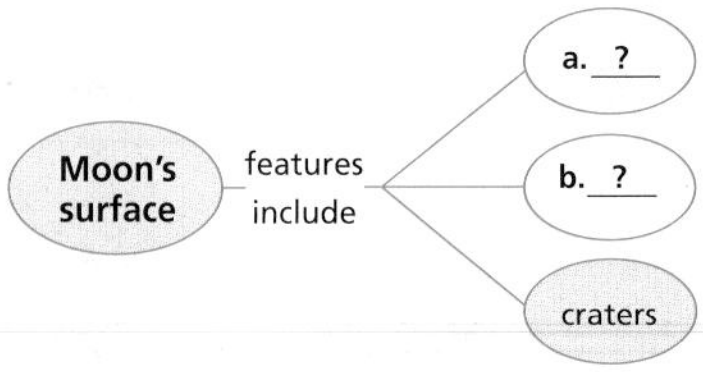
Moon's surface
features include
a. ?
b. ?
craters

Astronaut Alan Shepard, shown in Figure 5, was commander of the *Apollo 14* mission. He was not a golf pro, but he loved golf so much that he brought the game all the way to the moon. Shepard wondered how far he could hit a golf ball on the moon. So he attached the head of a golf club to the handle of an instrument for collecting rocks. Swinging with just one arm, he hit a golf ball a few hundred meters, much farther than it would have gone on Earth.

Why did the golf ball go so far on the moon? The moon is only about one quarter of Earth's diameter and has much less mass than Earth. As a result, the force of gravity on its surface is only one sixth that on Earth. Also, the moon has virtually no atmosphere to slow the ball down.

796

Figure 5 *Apollo 14* commander Alan Shepard planted an American flag on the moon's surface in 1971. **Inferring** ***Why did the flag need to be supported by a horizontal rod?***

Earth's Moon

At an average distance of about 384,400 kilometers, or about 30 times Earth's diameter, the moon is our nearest neighbor in space. If there were a road to the moon, it would take about 6 months to get there driving at 55 miles per hour.

The moon's gravity is too weak to hold onto gas molecules, which simply float away into space. **The lack of an atmosphere allows the moon's surface temperature to vary tremendously.** In direct sunlight, the average surface temperature of the moon is very high, about 130°C. At night, however, the average surface temperature plummets to a chilly –180°C.

Section Resources

Print

- ***Reading and Study Workbook With Math Support,*** Section 25.2
- ***Transparencies,*** Section 25.2

Technology

- ***Interactive Textbook,*** Section 25.2
- ***Presentation Pro CD-ROM,*** Section 25.2

Because there is no atmosphere, any liquid water would have long ago evaporated into space. Any water remaining on the moon must be frozen. Evidence of ice near the moon's north and south poles was detected by space craft observations. Sunlight at the poles is less intense, so temperatures are low enough there to keep ice from subliming (changing directly from a solid to a gas).

Surface Features

Exploration of the moon's surface has revealed the existence of a variety of geological features. **The major surface features of the moon are maria, highlands, and craters.**

Maria and Highlands Do you sometimes think you can see a face when you look up at the Moon? What you are really seeing is a pattern of lighter and darker regions on the moon's surface, as shown in the top photo of Figure 6.

One of the first people to look at the moon with a telescope was Galileo. When Galileo aimed his telescope at the moon 400 years ago, he thought that the dark, smooth regions on the moon's surface resembled the seas on Earth. So, he called them maria (MAH ree uh), the Latin word for "seas." In reality, **maria** are low, flat plains formed by ancient lunar lava flows. They cover about 15 percent of the moon's surface. The maria are surrounded by light-colored areas called lunar highlands. The lunar highlands, which cover most of the moon's surface, are rough, mountainous regions.

Craters Much of the moon's surface is covered with impact craters, such as those shown in Figure 6. These **craters** are round depressions in the surface caused by the impact of high-speed meteoroids. **Meteoroids** are chunks of rock that move through the solar system. Although meteoroid collisions still occur, most craters formed more than 3.8 billion years ago.

The thousands of craters on the moon are evidence that the moon is geologically dead. On Earth, most old craters disappeared as the surface was altered by erosion or collisions between tectonic plates. On the moon, however, there is little erosion and no plate motion to alter craters. Notice in the top photo of Figure 6 that the lunar highlands are much more heavily cratered than the maria. Older craters within the maria were covered by more recent lava flows. The few craters within the maria formed after the lava that covered them had solidified.

Reading Checkpoint *Why are the lunar highlands more heavily cratered than the maria?*

Figure 6 The photos above show features of the moon. The large, dark areas in the top photo are maria. The lighter areas surrounding the maria are lunar highlands. The moon is covered with craters that formed from the impacts of smaller objects.

Surface Features

Use Visuals L1

Figure 6 Have students examine the maria and craters. Ask, **How do maria compare with craters?** *(Maria are dark-colored, smooth areas. Craters are round depressions.)* **Which type of feature covers most of the moon's surface seen from Earth?** *(Lunar highlands—about 70% of the near side surface [shown in the top photo] is highlands, but on the far side of the moon, almost 100% of the area is highlands. Overall, about 85% of the moon's surface is highlands.)*
Visual

Use Community Resources L2

Arrange for students to visit a local observatory and observe lunar craters through telescopes. Contact a nearby university or community college—they often have educational programs in place for high-school students. If a field trip is not possible, invite an astronomer to discuss lunar craters with the class. Have the class develop interview questions and encourage them to observe the moon's craters with binoculars beforehand.
Visual

Customize for Inclusion Students

Learning Disabled
To help learning-disabled students better grasp how craters form and erode on Earth, place a thick layer of flour in a rectangular pan. Drop different-sized marbles or stones into the pan. Allow students to observe the resulting craters. Then, place a fan on low speed near the pan so that the "craters" erode. Be sure not to place the fan too close to the pan. Ask, **What does the effect of the fan represent in this model?** *(Wind erosion on Earth)*

Answer to . . .

Figure 5 *There is no atmosphere on the moon, and thus no wind to make the flag wave.*

Reading Checkpoint *Because older craters where the maria are now were covered by more recent lava flows*

Formation of the Moon

Build Reading Literacy L1

Relate Text and Visuals Refer to page **190D** in **Chapter 7**, which provides the guidelines for relating text and visuals.

Have students read the text on p. 798 relating to the formation of the moon. Explain that diagrams, photographs, and other visuals often help to clarify difficult concepts. Ask, **Which part of Figure 7 illustrates the sentence, "This collision ejected a large amount of material into space"?** *(Part A)* **How did Figure 7 improve your understanding of the formation of the moon?** *(Sample answer: Figure 7 showed that Earth was still molten when the collision occurred.)* **Verbal, Intrapersonal**

Phases of the Moon

Address Misconceptions L2

Many students think that the phases of the moon are caused by the shadow of Earth. To dispel this misconception, use a lamp and balls to model the positions of the moon, the sun, and Earth during a new moon. Set the lamp on a table to represent the sun. One student should hold a baseball in front of the lamp, representing the moon. A second student should hold a basketball behind the "moon," representing Earth. Darken the room and turn on the lamp. Ask, **What are the positions of the sun, the moon, and Earth during a new moon?** *(The moon is closest to the sun and Earth faces the side of the moon away from the sun.)* **Which side of the moon is lit up during this phase?** *(The side that faces away from Earth)* **Is Earth's shadow falling on the moon?** *(No)* **Interpersonal, Group**

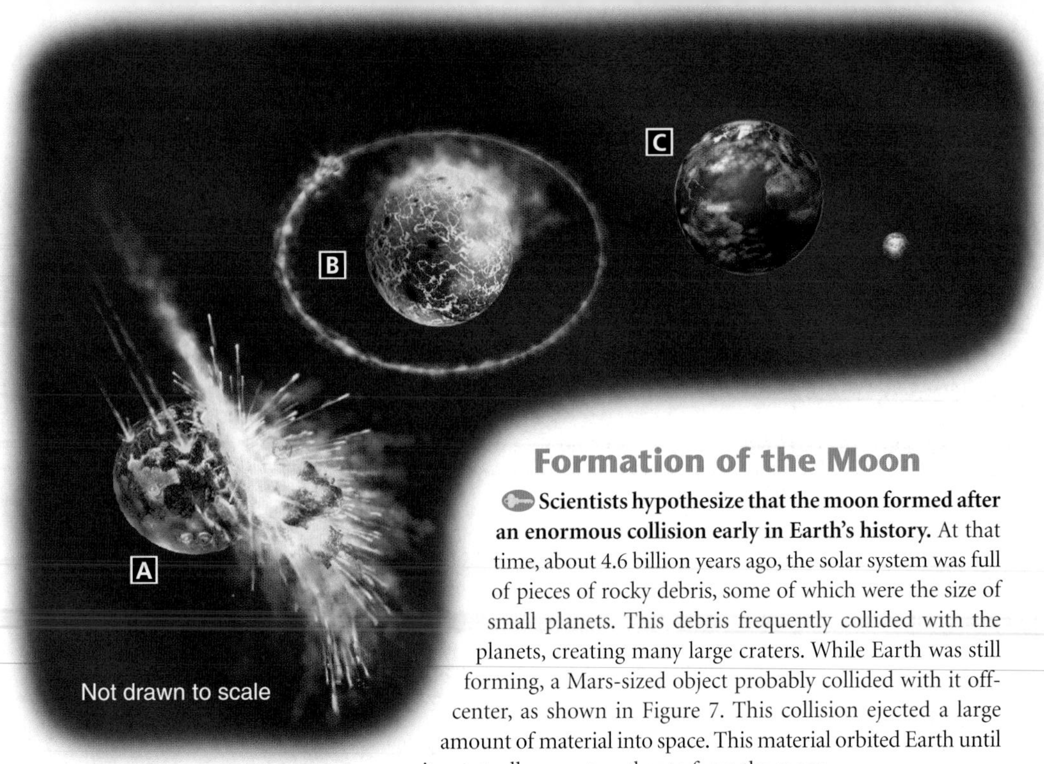
C
B
A
Not drawn to scale

Figure 7 The moon is thought to have formed in a spectacular collision between the early Earth and a Mars-sized object. **A** The collision knocked part of Earth's mantle into space. **B** Much of the ejected material began to revolve around Earth. It soon began to clump together to form the moon. **C** Earth and the moon today.

Formation of the Moon

Scientists hypothesize that the moon formed after an enormous collision early in Earth's history. At that time, about 4.6 billion years ago, the solar system was full of pieces of rocky debris, some of which were the size of small planets. This debris frequently collided with the planets, creating many large craters. While Earth was still forming, a Mars-sized object probably collided with it off-center, as shown in Figure 7. This collision ejected a large amount of material into space. This material orbited Earth until it eventually came together to form the moon.

Phases of the Moon

The moon doesn't produce its own light. You can see the moon because it reflects light from the sun. When you look at the moon, it sometimes appears full and bright, and sometimes appears as only a sliver. The different shapes of the moon visible from Earth are called **phases.**

The moon's phases are caused by changes in the relative positions of the moon, sun, and Earth as the moon revolves around Earth. Sunlight illuminates half of the moon. The phase of the moon depends on how much of the sunlit portion of the moon is facing Earth.

If you were to track the appearance of the moon from day to day, you would notice that the moon's phases change according to a regular cycle. Figure 8 shows the positions of the moon during its phases. A full moon occurs when the moon is on the opposite side of Earth from the sun, and the whole side of the moon facing Earth is lit by the sun. A new moon occurs when the moon is directly between the sun and Earth. A new moon cannot be seen from Earth because the sunlit side of the moon is facing away from us.

It takes about 29.5 days for the moon to complete a full cycle of phases from full moon to new moon and back again. This period of time is known as a lunar month.

Facts and Figures

Iron Evidence The composition of the moon is similar to that of Earth, yet different enough for scientists to theorize that the moon did not form entirely from the same material as Earth. For example, the moon has a small iron core that makes up only 2 to 3% of its mass. In comparison, Earth's core—mostly made of iron and nickel—is about 32% of its mass. These facts support the theory discussed in the student text, wherein the iron core of the Mars-sized object would have sunk into Earth's core upon impact.

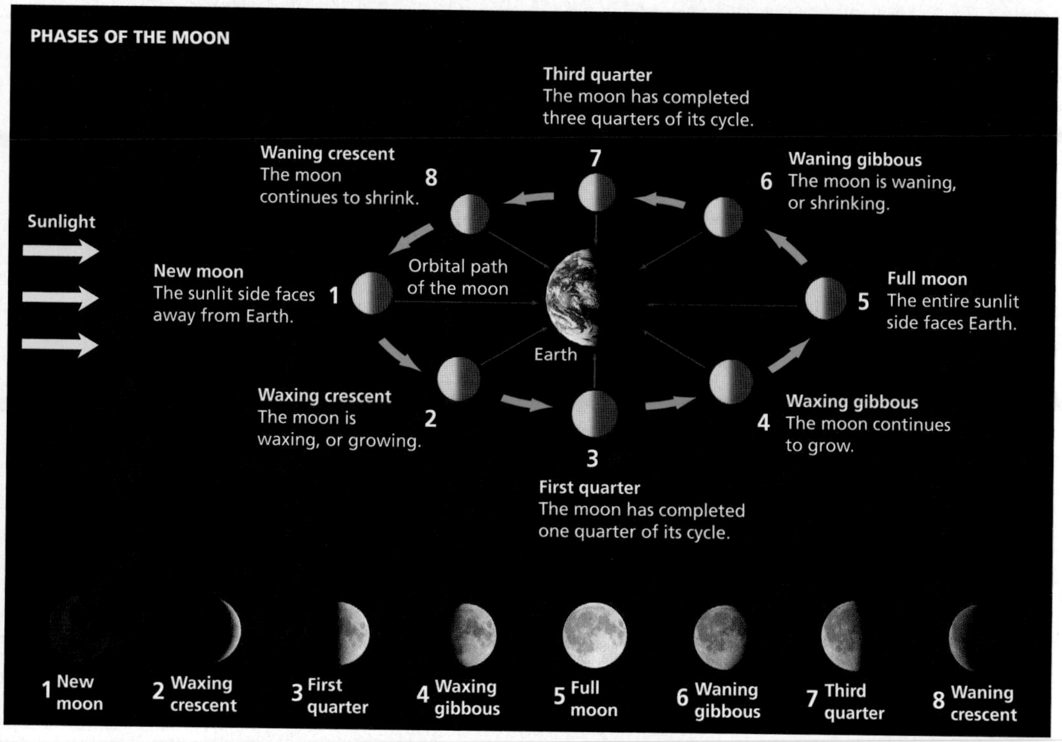

PHASES OF THE MOON
Third quarter
The moon has completed three quarters of its cycle.
7
Waning crescent
The moon continues to shrink.
8
Waning gibbous
6 The moon is waning, or shrinking.
Sunlight
New moon
The sunlit side faces away from Earth.
1
Orbital path of the moon
Full moon
5 The entire sunlit side faces Earth.
Earth
Waxing crescent
The moon is waxing, or growing.
2
Waxing gibbous
4 The moon continues to grow.
3
First quarter
The moon has completed one quarter of its cycle.
1 New moon
2 Waxing crescent
3 First quarter
4 Waxing gibbous
5 Full moon
6 Waning gibbous
7 Third quarter
8 Waning crescent

Figure 8 Two different views of the phases of the moon are shown in this diagram. The circular diagram shows how the moon and Earth would appear to an observer in space as the moon orbits Earth. Note that the sun is shining from the left. The photos below the diagram show how the phases of the moon appear to an observer on Earth.
Interpreting Diagrams ***During which phase is the dark half of the moon facing Earth?***

The same side of the moon always faces Earth. This is because the moon makes one full rotation around its axis while making one full revolution around Earth. For this reason, whenever you look at the moon, its surface features are always nearly in the same place. Some parts of the moon may be in shadow, depending upon the particular phase, but the features you can see on its surface hardly move.

Eclipses

Imagine that it is the middle of a sunny day. Suddenly, the sky darkens and the sun appears to shrink. Animals act as if night has fallen. In ancient times, people were terrified of such occurrences, which are known as solar eclipses. An **eclipse** (ih KLIPS) occurs when the shadow of one body in space, such as a planet or moon, falls on another. For an eclipse to occur on Earth, the sun, moon, and Earth must all lie along a straight line.

You might wonder why eclipses do not occur twice each month, whenever there is a new or full moon. Eclipses occur much less often because the plane of the moon's orbit is tilted about 5 degrees with respect to the ecliptic. An eclipse occurs only when the moon crosses Earth's ecliptic plane at the time of a new moon or full moon.

Use Visuals **L1**

Figure 8 Review with students the phases of the moon shown in this figure. Ask, **In which phases is half of the illuminated side of the moon visible from Earth?** *(First and third quarter)* **In which phase has the moon completed half its cycle?** *(Full moon)* **What happens to the illuminated portion of the moon (as seen from Earth) after the full moon?** *(The illuminated portion decreases; the moon wanes.)*
Visual

Eclipses

Integrate Social Studies **L2**

Stonehenge, an ancient site found in southern England, was constructed over the course of 2000 years. Built of dirt, timber, and stones, its oldest portions date to approximately 3100 B.C. Stonehenge's purpose remains largely a mystery. But by the eighteenth century, scholars noticed that the huge so-called bluestones were aligned with the summer solstice, raising the possibility that Stonehenge was built as an astronomical calendar. More recently, astronomers have put forth the theory that Stonehenge was also used to predict lunar eclipses, which can occur in a 47-month cycle. Show students photographs of Stonehenge. Ask, **Do you think the alignment of the stones was accidental?** *(Sample answer: Not likely because the builders had to orient the stones very precisely. Most scientists agree this was not a coincidence.)*
Visual, Logical

Answer to . . .

Figure 8 *New moon*

Use Visuals L1

Figure 9 Make sure that students understand the difference between the umbra and penumbra. Then, ask, **Which object casts a shadow during a solar eclipse?** *(The moon)* **Describe the umbra. What portion of Earth is covered by this shadow?** *(The small, cone-shaped umbra covers only a very narrow path on Earth.)* **Which object casts a shadow on another during a lunar eclipse?** *(Earth)* **How are the sun, Earth, and the moon aligned during an eclipse?** *(In a straight line)*
Visual

Build Science Skills L2

Inferring Tell students that the sun has a diameter nearly 400 times greater than the moon's. Ask, **Given that the moon is so much smaller than the sun, how can the moon block out the sun during a solar eclipse?** *(Sample answer: The moon is much closer to Earth than is the sun. Objects that are closer appear larger than those that are farther away.)*
Logical

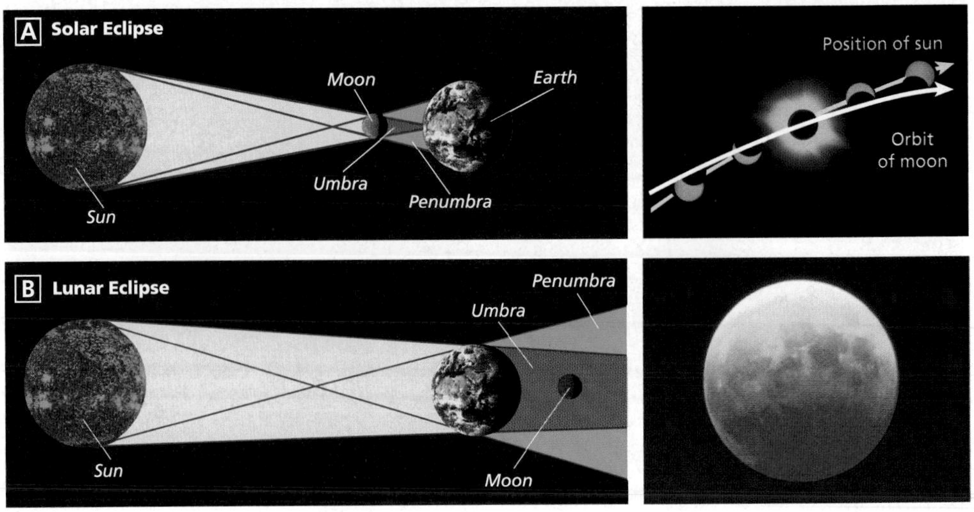

A Solar Eclipse
Moon
Earth
Umbra
Penumbra
Sun
Position of sun
Orbit of moon
B Lunar Eclipse
Penumbra
Umbra
Sun
Moon

Not drawn to scale

Figure 9 Eclipses occur only at the new moon or the full moon. **A** Solar eclipses occur at the new moon, when Earth can move through the moon's shadow. The multiple- exposure photo on the right has circles added to show several stages of a total solar eclipse. **B** Lunar eclipses occur at the full moon, when the moon can move through Earth's shadow. The moon has a reddish tint during a full lunar eclipse because some sunlight refracted by Earth's atmosphere reaches the moon.
Comparing and Contrasting ***Why are total lunar eclipses more frequently seen than total solar eclipses?***

Solar Eclipse During a new moon, when the moon is between the sun and Earth, Earth may pass through the shadow of the moon. **A solar eclipse occurs when the moon casts a shadow on a portion of Earth's surface.** As shown in Figure 9A, the moon casts two kinds of shadows on Earth during a solar eclipse. These two shadows occur because the sun is quite wide. It doesn't cast a sharp-edged shadow, as it would if it were a point of light. The small cone-shaped **umbra** (UM bruh) is the darkest part of the moon's shadow. Within the umbra, the sun's light is completely blocked by the moon. Only people in a very narrow path across Earth's surface are able to see a total solar eclipse. Surrounding the umbra is the larger **penumbra** (pih NUM bruh), a region of shadow that is less dark than the umbra. People within the penumbra see a partial solar eclipse.

Lunar Eclipse During a full moon, when Earth is between the sun and moon, the moon may pass through Earth's shadow, as shown in Figure 9B. **A lunar eclipse occurs when Earth casts a shadow on the moon.** Like the moon's shadow, Earth's shadow has an umbra and penumbra.

If the moon passes completely into Earth's umbra, you see a total lunar eclipse. If instead of passing fully into Earth's umbra the moon passes partially through the umbra, you see a partial lunar eclipse.

Unlike a total solar eclipse, a total lunar eclipse can be seen from anywhere on Earth that the moon is visible. Thus, total lunar eclipses are much more frequently seen than total solar eclipses.

Facts and Figures

Eclipses During a total lunar eclipse, the moon does not totally disappear. Some sunlight reaches the moon through Earth's atmosphere. This gives the moon a reddish color, similar to the way the sun appears during a sunset.

During a total solar eclipse, the sun's corona (its thin, hot, outer atmosphere) is visible. Because the moon's orbit is elliptical (like all planetary orbits), a solar eclipse is not total if it occurs when the moon is at its farthest point from Earth. During such an eclipse, none of the umbra touches Earth, and the sun can be seen as a ring surrounding the moon. This is called an *annular eclipse.*

Tides on Earth

In Daytona Beach, Florida, people often drive cars along the flat, wide beaches. Occasionally, a driver parks on the beach and returns to find the car covered by the waters of the Atlantic Ocean. The driver is the victim of a rising tide. **Tides** are the regular rise and fall of ocean waters.

Tides are caused mainly by differences in the moon's gravitational pull on Earth. Recall that the force of gravity between two objects decreases as the distance between them increases. The gravitational force of the moon pulls more strongly on the side of Earth that faces it, and less strongly on the side that is away from it. This difference causes the entire Earth to be stretched. Because water flows easily, the effect of the moon's gravity on the oceans is much greater than on the solid Earth.

The gravitational pull of the moon causes the oceans to bulge at the locations closest to and farthest from it. As Earth rotates on its axis, high tides occur when an area moves through either of these two bulges. Most coastal areas experience two high tides and two low tides each day.

The sun also has a gravitational effect on the oceans, but its tidal effects are only about half those of the moon. During a new or full moon, the sun, moon, and Earth are in a straight line. The gravitational pulls of the sun and moon then add together, as shown in Figure 10A. The combined forces produce a **spring tide,** where the change between daily high and low tides is the greatest. When the moon is in its first or third quarter, the moon and the sun are pulling the Earth at right angles, as shown in Figure 10B. The result is a **neap tide,** where there is the least change between daily high and low tides.

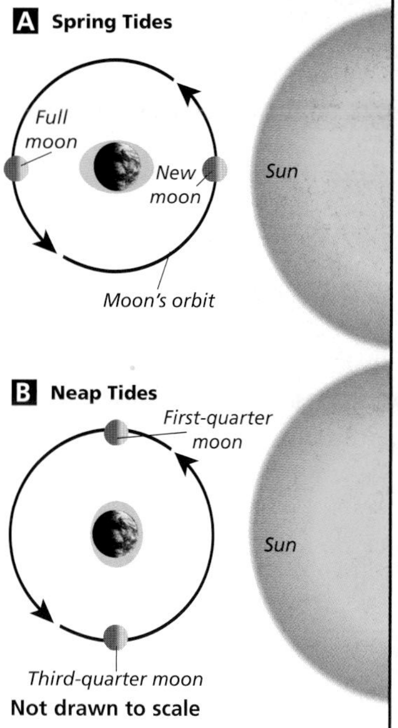
A Spring Tides
Full moon
New moon
Sun
Moon's orbit
B Neap Tides
First-quarter moon
Sun
Third-quarter moon
Not drawn to scale

Figure 10 A During spring tides, the pulls of the moon and sun add together. B During neap tides, the moon and sun pull Earth and its oceans at right angles.

Section 25.2 Assessment

Reviewing Concepts

1. Explain why temperatures vary widely between day and night on the moon.
2. How did lunar craters and maria form?
3. What do scientists hypothesize about how the moon formed?
4. Why do the phases of the moon change?
5. What is the difference between a lunar eclipse and a solar eclipse?
6. What causes tides on Earth?

Critical Thinking

7. **Comparing and Contrasting** What is the difference between the umbra and the penumbra of a solar eclipse?
8. **Comparing and Contrasting** Why are spring tides larger than neap tides?

Math Practice

9. The gravitational pull on the moon's surface is about one sixth of that on Earth. If a person weighs 700 newtons on Earth, how much would he or she weigh on the moon?
10. Due to friction caused by the tides, Earth's days are getting longer at a rate of 0.00002 second per year. How much longer will a day be in a million years?

Tides on Earth

FYI

The absolute gravitational pull from the sun is much larger than the absolute gravitational pull from the moon because the sun has so much more mass than the moon. The large mass of the sun is also why Earth orbits the sun and not the moon. However, tides are caused by tidal forces, or differences in gravity across Earth. Because the sun is so far away, its tidal force is less than half the tidal force of the moon, which is only 30 Earth diameters away.

3 ASSESS

Evaluate Understanding **L2**

Have students draw diagrams showing the positions of the sun, the moon, and Earth during a solar eclipse, lunar eclipse, spring tide, and neap tide.

Reteach **L1**

Have students summarize the surface features and characteristics of the moon.

Math Practice

Solutions

9. 700 N/6 = 117 N
10. (0.00002 s/year) × (10^6 years) = 20 s

Interactive Textbook If your class subscribes to the Interactive Textbook, use it to review key concepts in Section 25.2.

Answer to . . .

Figure 9 *Total lunar eclipses can be seen anywhere on Earth where the moon is visible during the eclipse. Total solar eclipses can be seen only in a very narrow path where the umbra hits Earth.*

Section 25.2 Assessment

1. The moon has no atmosphere to transfer thermal energy from one region to another. Therefore, the moon's surface temperature is high in direct sunlight and cold at night.
2. Craters formed when meteoroids collided with the moon. Maria were formed by ancient lunar lava flows.
3. Scientists hypothesize that the moon formed early in Earth's history as a result of a collision between Earth and a Mars-sized object.
4. Because the moon orbits around Earth and different portions of the sunlit half of the moon are visible from Earth
5. A lunar eclipse occurs when Earth is between the sun and the moon and casts a shadow on the moon. A solar eclipse occurs when the moon is between the sun and Earth and casts a shadow on a portion of Earth's surface.
6. Tides are caused mainly by differences in the moon's gravitational pull on different parts of Earth. Differences in the sun's gravitational pull across Earth also contribute to the tides.
7. The umbra is the darkest portion of the sun's shadow. A total solar eclipse is visible within the umbra. Within the lighter penumbra, a partial solar eclipse occurs.
8. Because the gravitational pull of the moon and sun combine during spring tides but act at right angles to one another during neap tides

issues in SCIENCE

Should the Moon Be Developed? L2

Background

In addition to paying attention to the issues raised in this feature, any public or private venture to develop the moon will also have to adhere to international space laws. The United Nations Office for Outer Space Affairs governs laws related to space. One such law, called the Outer Space Treaty, was signed in 1967 by the United States, the then-Soviet Union, and the United Kingdom. The Outer Space Treaty states that, "the exploration and use of outer space shall be carried out for the benefit and in the interests of all countries." It further states that no nation can claim sovereignty of outer space nor use weapons of mass destruction in space. According to the treaty, all celestial bodies, including the moon, must be used "exclusively for peaceful purposes." As of 2003, there have been 27 nations who have signed the treaty.

Answers

1. Students should explain the major issues outlined in the text. These issues include: Should the moon be developed at all? If the moon is developed, how should this be done? What would be the costs and benefits of developing the moon? Would time and money be better used on other projects?

2. Proponents argue that developing the moon will provide many benefits, such as increasing scientific knowledge, providing a unique tourism opportunity, providing a rich source of energy and minerals, stimulating the development of new technology that may be needed on Mars, and providing jobs and technology spin-offs for people on Earth. Critics argue that developing the moon would be costly, and that the funds needed for such development would be better spent elsewhere. The critics also argue that developing the moon is unlikely to receive private funding. Risks of development include uncertain costs and uncertain interest in the proposed tourist resort.

3. Students should clearly express their opinion about the possible development of the moon and provide supporting arguments for their opinion.

issues in SCIENCE

Should the Moon Be Developed?

Decades after the last astronauts explored the moon, various governments and companies are beginning to show interest in the moon's development. There are many different ideas about how the moon should be developed, or whether it should be developed at all. Some think that the moon should be preserved for all mankind, and that its development should be limited to scientific research. Others favor development of the moon by private firms.

Some see the development of the moon beginning with tourism. According to this idea, groups of tourists would pay to be shuttled to a resort on the moon. The moon is also a potential source of minerals such as aluminum and titanium and energy resources such as helium-3, which could fuel fusion reactors. Once enough buildings and equipment are in place on the moon, the mining of such resources could begin and a larger-scale colony could be built.

The Viewpoints

Develop the Moon

Developing the moon will have many advantages. One is to gain scientific knowledge, especially about the early history of the solar system. The moon will be the ultimate tourist destination. Although the cost would be high, many people would be willing to pay for the unique chance to experience the moon's low gravity and airless environment.

The moon is rich in a variety of minerals, including iron, aluminum, and calcium. Once a permanent lunar base is established, these resources could be mined for use on Earth or for the eventual colonization of space.

The moon is a logical stepping stone for future missions to Mars. A lunar base would provide a valuable testing ground for technology that could eventually be useful on Mars. Such technology will also have applications on Earth, where it will improve people's lives and create new jobs.

Do Not Develop the Moon

The development of the moon would be a waste of time and money. Scarce government funds would be better spent on projects with a more immediate benefit, such as feeding the hungry, improving schools, and building better housing. In the short run, government funding for space should be focused on space probes and telescopes. These technologies allow us to learn more about the solar system and the universe beyond at a relatively low cost. In the long run, a mission sending a crew to Mars would be of much greater interest and scientific value.

The proposed development of the moon would be too expensive and risky to receive private funding. Few tourists are likely to be able to pay the high costs of visiting a resort on the moon. The techniques for mining mineral and energy resources on the moon are uncertain, and any such resources would probably be very costly to produce.

Research and Decide

1. **Defining an Issue** In your own words, explain the major issues involved in the debate about the future development of the moon.
2. **Analyzing the Viewpoints** What are the key arguments expressed by the proponents and critics of developing the moon? What are the benefits? What are the risks?
3. **Forming Your Opinion** Should the moon be developed? If so, explain how. If not, explain why not.
4. **Persuasive Writing** Suppose you have been appointed chair of a presidential commission on the moon's future. Prepare a letter to the President explaining the commission's recommendations.

Go Online PHSchool.com

For: More on this issue
Visit: PHSchool.com
Web Code: cch-3252

802 Chapter 25

4. Students should prepare a letter containing a series of specific recommendations to the President. Sample recommendations might include: "Establish a research group to design a permanent lunar colony to conduct scientific research." or "The moon should not be developed in the foreseeable future. Instead, government funding for space should focus on space probes."

Go Online PHSchool.com

Have students further research the issues related to this topic.

25.3 The Inner Solar System

Reading Focus

Key Concepts

- How are the inner planets similar?
- What are the characteristics of each of the four inner planets?
- What are asteroids and how were they formed?

Vocabulary

- terrestrial planets
- asteroids
- asteroid belt

Reading Strategy

Summarizing Make a table like the one below that includes all the headings for the section. Write a brief summary of the text for each heading.

I. The Terrestrial Planets
  • Four planets closest to the sun
  • Small, dense, with rocky surfaces
II. Mercury
  a. ____________
III. Venus
  b. ____________

Suppose that you wanted to set up a colony on another planet. Which planet would you choose? Venus is the nearest planet and is similar to Earth in size. But Venus is extremely hot and has an atmosphere that is so thick it would crush any potential colonists. Mercury is closest to the sun, but it has no atmosphere. Temperatures there are either far too high or far too low to support life.

Your best choice would be Mars. However, a permanent colony on Mars, like the one pictured in Figure 11, would face very difficult conditions. Mars is usually extremely cold and has a very thin atmosphere with no oxygen. Huge dust storms blow across the planet. Although NASA is considering sending astronauts to Mars, it would take an incredible effort to set up a permanent colony under such harsh conditions.

Figure 11 This imaginative painting shows a possible future human settlement on Mars. Settlers might live in domes to protect themselves from the harsh climate and to provide an atmosphere for breathing.

The Terrestrial Planets

The four planets closest to the sun—Mercury, Venus, Earth, and Mars—are often called the terrestrial planets. The **terrestrial planets** are planets similar in structure to Earth. (*Terra* is the Latin word for "Earth.") **The four inner planets are all relatively small and dense, and have rocky surfaces. Like Earth, they all have a crust, mantle, and iron core.**

All of the terrestrial planets have rocky crusts. Mercury and Mars have surfaces that are pockmarked by craters. On Earth and Venus, most craters have disappeared because the surface is continually being eroded. The surfaces of the other terrestrial planets change much more slowly, so more craters are visible.

Section Resources

Print
- ***Reading and Study Workbook With Math Support,*** Section 25.3
- ***Transparencies,*** Section 25.3

Technology
- ***Interactive Textbook,*** Section 25.3
- ***Presentation Pro CD-ROM,*** Section 25.3
- ***Go Online,*** NSTA SciLinks, The solar system

Section 25.3

1 FOCUS

Objectives

25.3.1 **Compare** the terrestrial planets and **describe** characteristics of each.

25.3.2 **Define** asteroids and **state** alternative hypotheses about how they formed.

Reading Focus

Build Vocabulary L2

Concept Maps Have students construct three concept maps using the vocabulary words from this section. Tell students to place each vocabulary term in a centered box. Related concepts should be placed in ovals beneath this centered box. Students should use lines to connect the boxes and ovals together.

Reading Strategy L2

Sample answers: **a.** Smallest planet, closest planet to the sun, fastest-moving planet, extreme temperatures **b.** Thick atmosphere, very hot surface, many volcanoes

2 INSTRUCT

The Terrestrial Planets

Address Misconceptions L2

Some students may think that scientific knowledge is gathered solely through controlled experiments. However, many advances in scientific knowledge come from fieldwork and careful observations. Indeed, much of what we know about the solar system—and the universe in general—is based on observation. As you teach the section, ask questions such as, **What did we learn about the solar system from spacecraft such as Mariner, Galileo, and Cassini? Could we have learned these things in a controlled experiment?** *(Sample answer: We learned about rings that surround planets, moons, the characteristics of planets, and asteroids. While we can model some of these things, we still need the data gathered by spacecraft to observe and analyze the actual objects or events and compare them to predicted behavior.)* **Logical**

Mercury

Use Visuals L1

Figure 12 Have students examine the information listed in the table. Ask, **Which inner planet has the most moons?** *(Mars—it has two moons.)* Ask, **Which inner planet has the longest period of rotation, measured in Earth days?** *(Venus, which takes 243 Earth days to complete one rotation)*
Logical, Mathematical

Build Science Skills L2

Using Tables and Graphs Have students copy the table in Figure 12. As they read about the inner planets, have them add information to their tables. For example, students can include columns for surface temperature and atmospheric composition.
Verbal, Mathematical

Integrate Language Arts L2

All of the names of the planets except for Earth are derived from Greek or Roman mythology. Have students research which mythical figure each planet was named for, then write a brief statement describing why they think the name is appropriate. *(Sample answer: Mercury was named for the messenger god of the Roman pantheon—an appropriate name because Mercury has the shortest orbital period of the planets.)* Students can also research the names of the moons and various surface features of the planets and moons.
Verbal

The Inner Planets

Planet	Equatorial Diameter (kilometers)	Average Distance to Sun (AU)	Period of Rotation (Earth days)	Period of Revolution (Earth years)	Number of Moons
Mercury	4,880	0.39	59	0.24	0
Venus	12,104	0.72	243	0.62	0
Earth	12,756	1.00	1.00	1.00	1
Mars	6,794	1.52	1.03	1.88	2

Figure 12 The inner planets are all small, dense, and rocky. **Using Tables** *Which of the four inner planets is most similar in size to Earth?*

Because they are closer to the sun, the terrestrial planets are much warmer on average than the outer planets. Unlike most of the outer planets, the inner planets have few (if any) moons. There are no rings around any of the terrestrial planets. Figure 12 summarizes the main characteristics of the inner planets.

Mercury

Mercury is the smallest of the terrestrial planets, and the closest planet to the sun. Mercury, shown in Figure 13, is a dense planet with a very large iron core. Mercury is geologically dead. There is no mantle convection within the planet, and little erosion on its surface.

Like its namesake, the swift messenger of the gods, Mercury is the fastest-moving planet. It takes only 88 Earth days for Mercury to complete one revolution. This is the shortest period of revolution of any planet.

Figure 13 Mercury's surface is heavily cratered from meteoroid collisions. This false-color image was made by combining a series of smaller images taken by the Mariner 10 space probe. Orange areas for which no images are available are blank. **Comparing and Contrasting** *How does Mercury's surface compare with the surface of Earth's moon?*

Temperature and Atmosphere Mercury's surface temperature ranges between two extremes. The time between sunrise and sunset equals the time it takes for Mercury to revolve around the sun, about 88 days. During this time, the heat from the sun causes the surface to become intensely hot. The temperatures at the equator reach about 430°C, hot enough to melt lead. At night, the temperature becomes extremely cold, as low as −170°C.

Mercury has virtually no atmosphere. Its high daytime temperatures cause gas particles to move very fast. Because Mercury is so small, its gravity is weak and it's easy for such fast-moving gas particles to escape into space.

Reading Checkpoint *Why does Mercury lack an atmosphere?*

Customize for English Language Learners

Provide Conversational Opportunities
Place ELL students in cooperative groups and allow them to interact verbally with other non-ELL students. Do not place all ELL students in one group—the goal is to give them an opportunity to practice their English skills in a relaxed, supportive environment. To minimize any possible frustration on the students' parts, place beginning ELL speakers with average or below-average students. More advanced ELL speakers can be placed with intermediate or advanced students.

Exploring Mercury Because Mercury is so close to the sun, it's hard for astronomers on Earth to see. Only one space probe has been sent to Mercury to date: Mariner 10 in 1974–1975. Mariner 10 took many images of Mercury's surface. As Figure 13 shows, the surface looks like that of Earth's moon. The large number of impact craters suggests that Mercury's surface has been largely unchanged for billions of years.

Venus

Venus is called the "evening star" or "morning star" because it is only seen in the west after sunset or in the east before sunrise. With the exception of the moon, it is the brightest object in Earth's night sky. Venus's rotation is unusual in that it rotates in the direction opposite to which it revolves. The rotation rate is also very slow—Venus takes 243 days to rotate around its axis. Venus's day is longer than its year!

Venus's Atmosphere Venus is difficult to study from space because clouds hide its surface, as shown in Figure 14A. Venus's atmosphere is so thick that the pressure at its surface is 90 times that on Earth. **Venus's thick atmosphere is composed mostly of carbon dioxide, which traps heat and raises the planet's temperature.** Venus's atmosphere also contains droplets of sulfuric acid. Spacecraft that landed on Venus's surface in the 1970s found the average surface temperature to be 460°C. Any water that may have once existed on Venus has long since boiled away.

Exploring Venus The high sulfur content of Venus's atmosphere probably results from numerous volcanoes, like the one shown in Figure 14B. The outpouring of lava from volcanoes has frequently resurfaced the planet, erasing craters as well. As a result, Venus's surface has only a small number of impact craters. Though Venus probably has active volcanoes, it shows no evidence of plate tectonics.

Figure 14 Venus's surface is not visible from space because of its very thick atmosphere. **A** Photographs in visible light only show Venus's clouds. **B** Radar is able to penetrate Venus's atmosphere. Radar data were used to produce this false-color image of a volcano on Venus. **Formulating Hypotheses** ***Why is Venus the brightest planet as seen from Earth?***

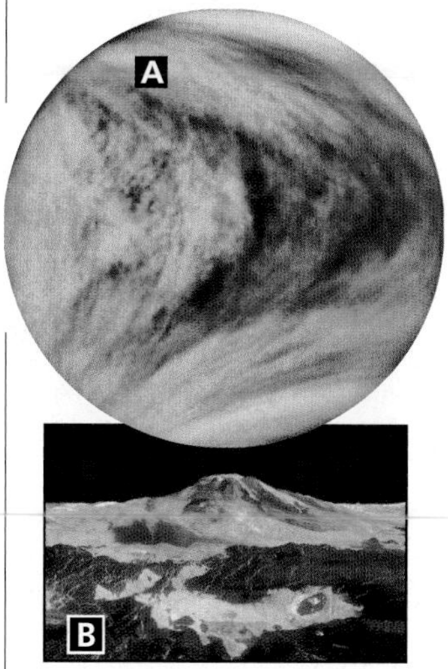

A
B

Not to scale

Earth

When you compare Earth to the other terrestrial planets using the data in Figure 12, Earth does not seem unusual. But Earth is unique in several important respects. **Earth's surface has a suitable atmosphere and temperature range for water to exist as a liquid.** The presence of liquid water makes Earth, shown in Figure 15, very different from the other planets. Water makes it possible for Earth to support millions of different species of living things. Water also causes erosion, which has shaped Earth's land surface in many ways.

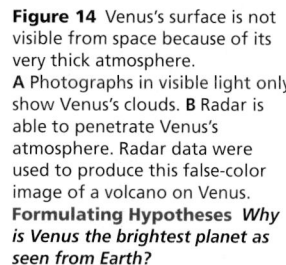

Figure 15 Earth is unique among the planets in having liquid-water ocean at its surface.

Venus

Build Reading Literacy **L1**

Use Prior Knowledge Refer to page **788D** in this chapter, which provides the guidelines for using prior knowledge.

Students absorb new material more quickly when they can relate it to previously learned concepts. In Chapter 24, students learned about Earth's greenhouse effect and global warming. Before they read about Venus's atmosphere, have students write a short paragraph identifying greenhouse gases and the role they play in regulating Earth's surface temperatures. Then, have students predict what surface temperatures might be like on a planet whose atmosphere is mainly CO_2. After students have read about Venus, have them revisit and revise their paragraphs. **Verbal, Intrapersonal**

Earth

Build Science Skills **L2**

Designing Experiments ACTIVITY

Purpose Students design an experiment demonstrating the effects of erosion on Earth's surface.

Materials pencils and paper

Class Time 20 minutes

Procedure Place students in groups of three or four and have each group design an experiment demonstrating the effects of erosion on Earth's surface. If students propose a controlled experiment, they should describe the procedure they will follow.

Expected Outcome A sample experiment might be to dribble water into a pan of sand. **Interpersonal, Portfolio**

Facts and Figures

A Speedy Planet Earth's rate of rotation is much faster than that of Mercury or Venus. This is important for two reasons. The rotation causes global cells of atmospheric convection. This in turn has created several bands of moist regions on Earth. The alternating arid and moist bands of latitude provide many different ecological environments, each with a wide diversity of life forms. In addition, the rapid rotation of Earth creates fluid motions in its liquid-iron outer core, resulting in a strong magnetic field. The magnetic field extends far out from Earth and protects Earth from the ionized particles of the solar wind.

Answer to . . .

Figure 12 *Venus*

Figure 13 *Both the moon and Mercury are heavily cratered. Mercury does not have maria.*

Figure 14 *Clouds reflect light, which contributes to the brightness of Venus. In addition, Venus is close to the sun. Of all planets, it passes closest to Earth. These factors all contribute to its brightness.*

Reading Checkpoint *Because Mercury has weak surface gravity and high daytime temperatures, any gas particles would easily escape into space.*

SCIENCE and History

Exploring the Solar System **L2**

Have students compare this time line to those in other chapters. Point out that unlike time lines that span hundreds or thousands of years, the time span for this topic is less than 50 years. Incredible progress has been made in space travel in an extremely short amount of time. Lead students in a discussion on the future of space exploration. Do they think crewed missions will one day travel to distant planets and moons? Do they see any limitations for space exploration? Students should use scientific reasoning to defend their answers.
Verbal

Writing in Science

Students should be able to develop at least five questions based on the information provided in the time line. Questions can be of the nature of "How did it feel to be the first person to walk on the moon?" or "What was the purpose of your mission?" More specific questions may require students to do additional research to develop reasonable responses for their news stories.
Verbal

Go Online NSTA SCILINKS

Download a worksheet on the solar system for students to complete, and find additional teacher support from NSTA SciLinks.

Go Online NSTA SCILINKS

For: Links on the solar system
Visit: www.SciLinks.org
Web Code: ccn-3253

Unlike most smaller planets and moons, Earth has enough gravity to hold most gas molecules. This allows Earth to maintain a thick atmosphere. Why isn't Earth's atmosphere composed mostly of carbon dioxide, like the atmospheres of Venus and Mars? On Earth, some living organisms use carbon dioxide and produce oxygen. Earth's oceans also remove carbon dioxide from the atmosphere by dissolving it.

The moon, Mercury, and Mars are all so small that over time they have lost much of their internal heat and have become geologically dead. Earth is large enough that it has not had a chance to cool down much. As a result, Earth has moving tectonic plates that continually change its surface.

SCIENCE and History

Exploring the Solar System

Since the 1950s, several countries have made incredible progress in space exploration. Exploration technology and capabilities have changed dramatically since the first satellite launch in 1957.

SURFACE OF MARS

A dog called Laika survived for a few hours in space aboard Sputnik 2.

SPUTNIK 2

YURI GAGARIN

Apollo 11 *lunar module approaches the surface of the moon.*

APOLLO 11 MISSION

1957 The Soviet Union launches the first artificial Earth satellite, Sputnik 1, into space. Sputnik 2 follows a few weeks later.

1961 Russian Yuri Gagarin becomes the first person to orbit Earth, aboard *Vostok 1.*

1969 American astronauts Neil Armstrong and Edwin "Buzz" Aldrin, Jr. are the first people to step onto the moon, as part of the *Apollo 11* mission.

1972 The space probe Pioneer 10 blasts off to study Jupiter and its moons.

1976 Viking I and Viking II space probes land on Mars and send back photos of the red planet's surface.

1950 — 1960 — 1970

Mars

Mars is the most Earthlike of all of the planets. The weathering of iron-rich rocks on its surface gives the planet a reddish color. This is why Mars is called the "red planet."

Though the surface of Mars is very old, as shown by the presence of many impact craters, it once had many volcanic eruptions. However, the most recent volcanic activity was possibly less than 100 million years ago. Olympus Mons on Mars is the largest volcano in the solar system. The height of Olympus Mons is nearly three times that of Mount Everest, the tallest mountain on Earth. If this volcano were located on Earth, its base could cover the distance from Cleveland to Washington, D.C.!

Writing in Science

Creative Writing Suppose you are a reporter who is going to interview the chief scientist or astronaut responsible for one of the space missions described in the time line. Prepare at least five questions about the mission. Then write a brief news story, including the responses that you would expect to each of your questions.

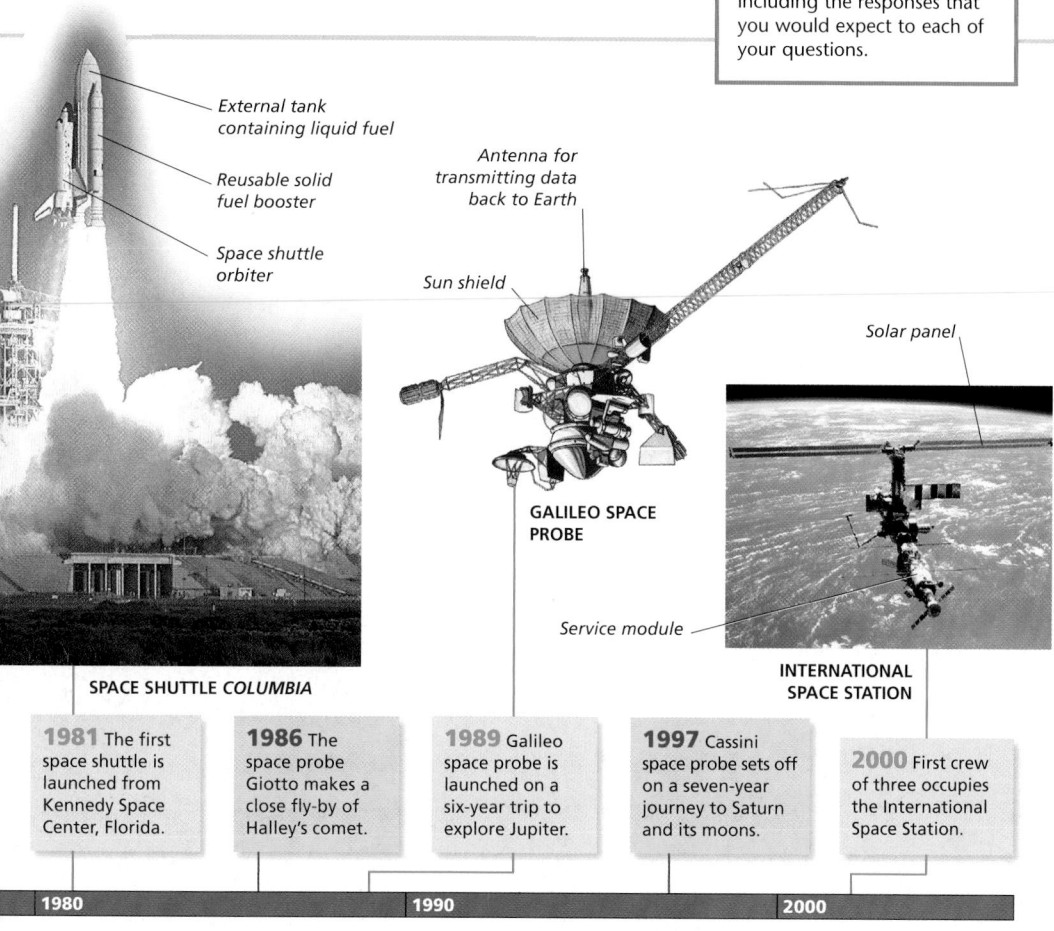

External tank containing liquid fuel
Reusable solid fuel booster
Space shuttle orbiter

SPACE SHUTTLE *COLUMBIA*

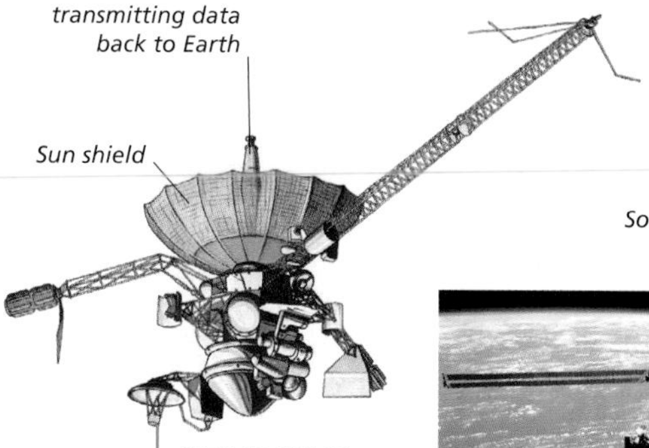

Antenna for transmitting data back to Earth
Sun shield

GALILEO SPACE PROBE

Solar panel
Service module

INTERNATIONAL SPACE STATION

1981 The first space shuttle is launched from Kennedy Space Center, Florida.

1986 The space probe Giotto makes a close fly-by of Halley's comet.

1989 Galileo space probe is launched on a six-year trip to explore Jupiter.

1997 Cassini space probe sets off on a seven-year journey to Saturn and its moons.

2000 First crew of three occupies the International Space Station.

1980 — 1990 — 2000

Mars

Build Reading Literacy L1

Monitor Your Understanding Refer to page **326D** in **Chapter 11**, which provides the guidelines for monitoring your understanding.

If students have difficulty generating interview questions for the Writing in Science feature, tell them to think about what they would personally like to know about space missions. What interests them? What details would they like to know more about? What questions do they have about space travel in general? Explain to students that the job of reporters is to provide information for the public. As members of the public, students' own questions are perfectly valid for interview purposes.
Verbal, Intrapersonal

Integrate Geology L2

On Earth, the movement of tectonic plates over time causes a hot spot to produce a chain of volcanoes. It is likely that Martian volcanoes formed from hot spots as well. However, the immense size of Martian volcanoes suggests that Mars currently has no moving plates—the hot spots are stationary, which caused magma to flow upward through the same vents for millions of years. Another difference between Earth and Mars is that the volcanoes on Mars are currently dormant. Ask, **Why would stationary plates cause hot spots to produce large volcanoes?** *(If plates move, hot spots can produce a chain of small volcanoes. However, if a plate stays in the same place, the magma from a hot spot will flow only at that spot, producing a single, large volcano.)*
Logical

Facts and Figures

Martian Volcanoes Most of the volcanism on Mars occurred in an elevated region called the Tharsis rise. This dome-shaped bulge is as large as an Earth-sized continent and rises high above the surrounding Martian surface. Its origins are unclear. However, scientists theorize that the formation of the bulge may have caused crustal stresses that in turn formed a giant rift valley. This valley, called the Valles Marineris, is as long as the contiguous United States is wide.

Use Visuals L1

Figure 16 Have students compare the photos of Mars to the photo of Earth on p. 805. Ask, **Which features do both planets have in common?** *(Sample answer: Polar ice cap, mountains, valleys)* **Which features are different?** *(Sample answer: Earth is covered mainly by water and has a much thicker atmosphere with clouds. Mars is much redder in color.)*
Visual

Build Science Skills L2

Evaluating and Revising Have students conduct research about the Martian meteorite ALH 84001. Found in Antarctica in 1984, this meteorite sparked ongoing controversy when a team of scientists proposed that it might contain fossils of ancient microscopic life from Mars. Have students use the research they gather to evaluate this hypothesis. They should carefully analyze arguments both for and against the hypothesis. Students should then write an evaluation of the hypothesis, citing scientific studies that support their view. For example, some scientists point out that the "fossils" are extremely small—much smaller than the tiniest known life forms. This argument can be used to argue against the hypothesis. However, other scientists propose that the "fossils" are not complete—that is, they are fossilized parts of microscopic bacteria rather than complete life forms. This point can be used to support the hypothesis.
Verbal, Portfolio

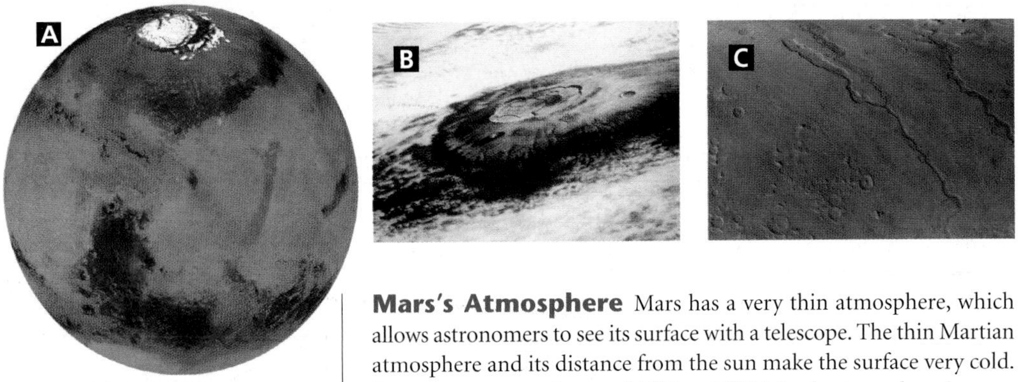
A
B
C

Figure 16 Mars has a thin atmosphere that permits a clear view of its surface from space.
A Mars has ice caps at both poles.
B Olympus Mons is the largest volcano in the solar system.
C These Martian valleys are thought to have been formed at least in part by large flows of liquid water in the distant past.

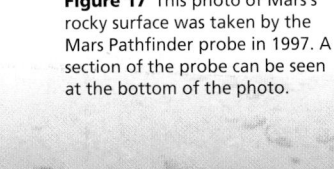

Mars's Atmosphere Mars has a very thin atmosphere, which allows astronomers to see its surface with a telescope. The thin Martian atmosphere and its distance from the sun make the surface very cold. Temperatures vary from −140°C to 20°C. Mars's atmosphere is more than 95 percent carbon dioxide, similar to the atmosphere of Venus, but much thinner.

Water on Mars There is no liquid water on Mars's surface now, but there may have been some in the past. **Mars shows evidence of once having a great deal of liquid surface water.** Features shown in Figure 16C may have been stream channels and gullies eroded by floods. Some geologists think Mars's northern lowlands were once covered by an ocean.

Why is liquid water no longer present on Mars's surface? Some water vapor has escaped into space. Some water is stored, along with frozen carbon dioxide, in ice caps at the north and south poles. Some water is thought to be frozen underground.

Martian Seasons Like Earth, Mars has distinct seasons. Mars's seasons are caused by the tilt of its axis. Over the course of a Martian year, Mars's ice caps grow and shrink. The change in seasons also causes large dust storms that occasionally rage across the surface.

Life on Mars? Because Mars had liquid water on its surface in the past, many scientists wonder if life once existed there. Robotic probes like the one in Figure 17 have carried out experiments on the Martian surface to look for signs of life. None of these probes found clear evidence for the existence of life on Mars.

Figure 17 This photo of Mars's rocky surface was taken by the Mars Pathfinder probe in 1997. A section of the probe can be seen at the bottom of the photo.

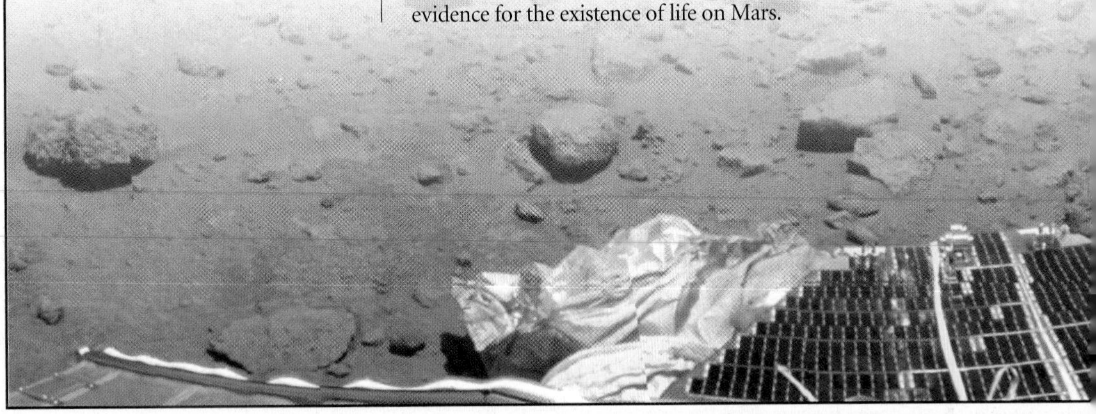

Asteroids

Beyond Mars is a region of the solar system where small, rocky bodies called **asteroids** can be found orbiting the sun. This region is referred to as the **asteroid belt.** Astronomers have discovered more than 10,000 asteroids, and many more are thought to exist. Most asteroids are less than 1 kilometer in diameter; only three are larger than 500 kilometers across. Although most asteroids are found in the asteroid belt, others orbit near Jupiter or range through the inner solar system.

The largest asteroids have enough gravity to have pulled themselves into nearly spherical or oval shapes while forming. Smaller asteroids, however, can have very irregular forms, as seen in Figure 18. These odd shapes are a result of impacts with other asteroids and meteoroids. If these small asteroids were solid, they would be likely to shatter during such collisions. Because they haven't shattered, scientists think that some asteroids are like floating rubble heaps, held together by weak gravity.

In the past, scientists thought that asteroids were the remnants of a shattered planet. **Scientists now hypothesize that asteroids are remnants of the early solar system that never came together to form a planet.** This hypothesis is supported by the lack of mass in the asteroid belt. If all of the asteroids were put together, they would form a planetary body only about 1500 kilometers in diameter. This would hardly qualify as a planet.

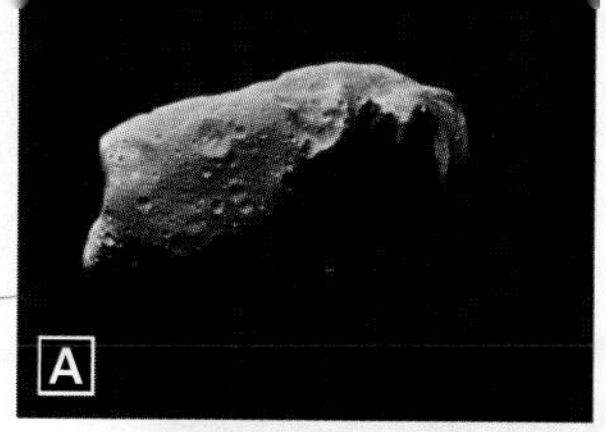
A

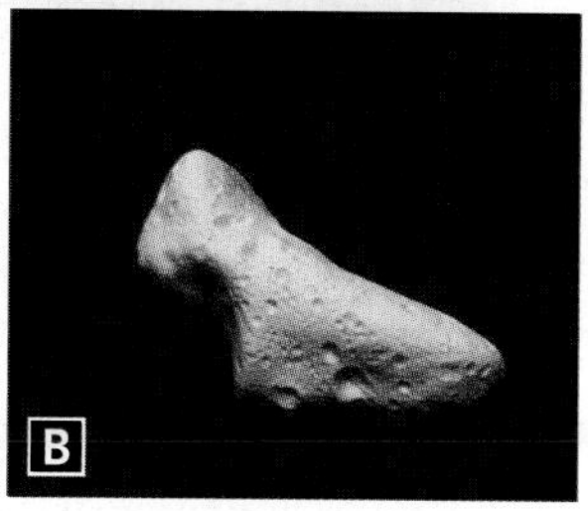
B

Figure 18 Asteroids come in a variety of sizes and shapes. **A** The asteroid Ida was photographed by the Galileo probe on its way to Jupiter. **B** In 2001, the NEAR Shoemaker space probe landed on the asteroid Eros. **Comparing and Contrasting** ***How do the shapes of the small asteroids shown compare to the shapes of the planets?***

Section 25.3 Assessment

Reviewing Concepts

1. What are the common features of the inner planets?
2. What are the four inner planets? Identify a distinguishing characteristic for each.
3. What do scientists hypothesize about the formation of the asteroids?
4. Why is there little erosion on Mercury's surface?
5. What is unusual about the rotation of Venus?
6. What is most unusual about Earth, compared to the other terrestrial planets?
7. What is the evidence that Mars once had running water on its surface?

Critical Thinking

8. **Calculating** What is the range of temperatures that occur on Mercury's equator during one full revolution around the sun?
9. **Comparing and Contrasting** How is the composition of Venus's atmosphere different from that of Earth's atmosphere?

Writing in Science

Descriptive Paragraph Suppose you are a member of the first crew of astronauts to land on Mars. Write a paragraph describing your first walk on Mars's surface.

Asteroids

Teacher Demo

Asteroids L2

Purpose Students model the structure of asteroids.

Materials pile of pebbles (about 5 cm high), large rock, chunk of dried plaster or foam

Procedure Place a pile of pebbles outside on pavement. Drop a large rock on the pebbles from a height of about 50 cm. Have students observe how the shape of the pile changed. Repeat the demonstration, dropping the rock on a piece of dry plaster or foam. Have students observe how the plaster or foam broke apart.

Safety Have students stand a safe distance away when you drop the large rock. Wear safety goggles.

Expected Outcome Have students relate their observations to the structure of asteroids. Ask, **How does this demonstration support the view that small asteroids are not a single solid mass?** *(If they were a single solid mass, they would shatter like the plaster or foam when hit by larger asteroids.)* **Visual**

3 ASSESS

Evaluate Understanding L2

Have students review the role water plays or may have played on Earth, Venus, and Mars.

Reteach L1

Make a table on the board similar to the one in Figure 12 that lists characteristics of the inner planets. Describe additional characteristics, such as surface features.

Writing in Science

Students' paragraphs should describe several features of Mars, such as its rocky red surface and dust storms.

Interactive Textbook If your class subscribes to the Interactive Textbook, use it to review key concepts in Section 25.3.

Section 25.3 Assessment

1. The inner planets are all relatively small, dense, and have rocky surfaces. They each have a crust, mantle, and iron core.
2. The four inner planets are Mercury, Venus, Earth, and Mars. Sample answers include smallest planet for Mercury, thick atmosphere composed mostly of carbon dioxide for Venus, liquid-water oceans on the surface for Earth, and reddish color for Mars.
3. That they are remnants of the early solar system that never formed a planet
4. Because Mercury has no atmosphere, surface water, or tectonic plate movement to cause erosion
5. Venus rotates in the opposite direction to the way it revolves around the sun.
6. Liquid-water oceans at its surface
7. Features on Mars's surface, such as dry stream channels and gullies, appear to have been produced in the past by running liquid water.
8. About 600° C between highest and lowest
9. Venus's atmosphere is composed mostly of carbon dioxide. Earth's atmosphere is mostly nitrogen and oxygen.

Answer to . . .

Figure 18 *They are irregular, not nearly spherical.*

1 FOCUS

Objectives

25.4.1 **Compare** the gas giants and **describe** characteristics of each.

25.4.2 **Distinguish** between comets and meteoroids and **describe** their characteristics.

25.4.3 **Locate** and **describe** the Kuiper belt and the Oort cloud.

Reading Focus

Build Vocabulary L2

Venn Diagram Have students construct a Venn diagram showing the similarities and differences among gas giants. The diagrams should consist of four overlapping circles. The circles should be labeled Jupiter, Saturn, Uranus, and Neptune, respectively. Similarities should be listed in the middle, or overlapping, sections of the circles. Differences should be listed in those parts of the circles that do not overlap. Students can construct a second Venn diagram to compare and contrast the Kuiper belt and the Oort cloud.

Reading Strategy L2

Sample answers: **a.** Saturn **b.** Second-largest planet, largest rings, more than 30 moons **c.** Uranus **d.** Very cold, methane gives blue-green color, tilted axis; Students should include additional rows for Neptune and Pluto in their tables.

25.4 The Outer Solar System

Reading Focus

Key Concepts

- How are the gas giants similar?
- What are the characteristics of each of the five outer planets?
- What are the characteristics of comets and meteoroids?
- What lies in the outer solar system beyond Pluto?

Vocabulary

- gas giants
- ring
- Kuiper belt
- Oort cloud

Reading Strategy

Summarizing Copy the table below and fill it in as you read to summarize characteristics of the outer planets. Expand the table to 5 rows.

Outer Planets	Characteristics
Jupiter	largest; most mass; most moons; Great Red Spot
a. ?	b. ?
c. ?	d. ?

Figure 19 Uranus was discovered in 1781 but its rings were not found until 1977. Like Uranus itself, the rings were discovered by accident. This false-color infrared image was taken by the Hubble Space Telescope.

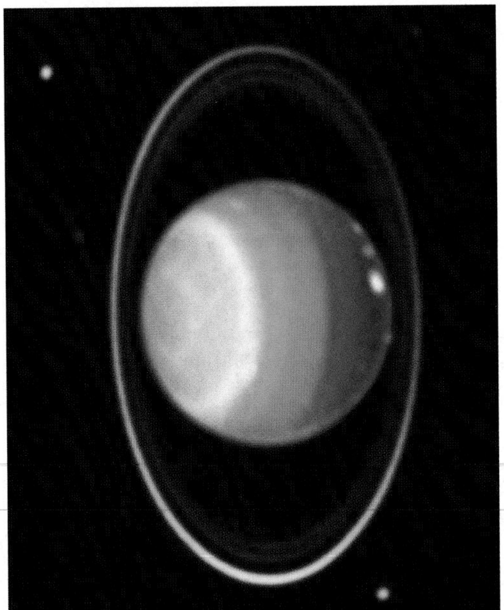

Scientific discovery happens in different ways. Sometimes things are discovered by accident. At other times, theories predict phenomena that scientists then try to find. The discoveries of Uranus (YOOR uh nus) and Neptune are examples of these two different methods. Unlike Jupiter and Saturn, which appear very bright in the night sky and have been observed for thousands of years, Uranus and Neptune were unknown to ancient observers.

Uranus, shown in Figure 19, was discovered by chance. In 1781, astronomer William Herschel was studying the sky with a telescope when he saw a fuzzy object that he first thought was a comet. Other astronomers had observed Uranus before but had incorrectly identified it as a dim star. Herschel tracked Uranus's position for almost a year before he realized it was a planet.

Over the next 50 years, astronomers noticed that Uranus was not following its predicted orbit. Working independently, mathematicians John Adams of England and Urbain Le Verrier of France concluded that there must be another planet, farther from the sun, whose gravity was affecting Uranus. Each predicted the location in the sky where this new planet should be. In 1846, the planet Neptune was discovered, very near where they had predicted.

Section Resources

Print

- ***Laboratory Manual,*** Investigation 25A
- ***Reading and Study Workbook With Math Support,*** Section 25.4
- ***Transparencies,*** Section 25.4

Technology

- ***Interactive Textbook,*** Section 25.4
- ***Presentation Pro CD-ROM,*** Section 25.4
- ***Go Online,*** *Science News,* The solar system

Planet	Equatorial Diameter (kilometers)	Average Distance to Sun (AU)	Period of Rotation (Earth days)	Period of Revolution (Earth years)	Number of Moons
Jupiter	142,984	5.20	0.41	11.86	50+
Saturn	120,536	9.54	0.44	29.46	30+
Uranus	51,118	19.19	0.72	84.10	20+
Neptune	49,528	30.06	0.67	164.86	8+
Pluto	2,300	39.53	6.39	248.60	1

The Outer Planets

Figure 20 The outer planets consist of the four gas giants and Pluto.
Using Tables ***Describe three ways in which Pluto is different from the other outer planets.***

Gas Giants

Jupiter, Saturn, Uranus, and Neptune are very different from the terrestrial planets. They are much colder because of their greater distance from the sun. All four planets are much larger and more massive than the terrestrial planets. They are composed mainly of hydrogen and helium, which is why they are often referred to as the **gas giants.**

None of the gas giants have solid surfaces. If you tried to land a spaceship on one, you would sink into the planet until the intense pressure of the atmosphere crushed the ship. In fact, the pressure is so great inside each planet that hydrogen and helium exist mostly in liquid form. **The four gas giants are thought to have small, dense cores of metal and rock, but consist mainly of liquid hydrogen and helium.**

Each gas giant resembles a miniature solar system. They have many moons, most of which revolve in the same direction that the planets rotate. Each of the gas giants is surrounded by rings. A **ring** is a disk made of many small particles of rock and ice in orbit around a planet. Such rings are so close to the planet that gravitational forces are very large. These forces may have prevented the ring particles from clumping together to form moons. The characteristics of the gas giants and Pluto are summarized in Figure 20.

Jupiter

Jupiter, shown in Figure 21, is the first planet beyond the asteroid belt. Named for the ruler of the Roman gods, Jupiter is large enough to hold more than 1300 Earths. **Jupiter is the largest and most massive planet in our solar system.** Like the other gas giants, Jupiter is composed mainly of hydrogen and helium.

Figure 21 This model of Jupiter is based on photos taken by Voyager 1. The Great Red Spot, visible in the lower half, is a giant storm much larger than Earth.

2 INSTRUCT

Gas Giants

Use Visuals **L1**

Figure 20 Point out that the plus signs after the number of moons for Jupiter, Saturn, Uranus, and Neptune reflect the ongoing discovery of additional moons orbiting around these planets. Tell students that these discoveries—some of which are not yet officially confirmed—are linked to recent improvements in technology. In coming years, the total number of moons around the gas giants is likely to rise significantly as new observations are made. After students have studied the table, ask, **How do the outer planets compare to the inner planets?** *(Sample answer: The outer planets, with the exception of Pluto, are much larger than the inner planets and have numerous moons. They are all much farther from the sun and have longer periods of revolution.)*
Visual

Address Misconceptions **L2**

Many students mistakenly think that the solar system and outer space in general are very crowded. Use Figure 20 to dispel this misconception. Point out the vast distances between the planets. Tell students that if they chose a random point in the solar system, they would likely be far from any planet.
Verbal

Jupiter

Build Reading Literacy **L1**

Outline Refer to page **156D** in **Chapter 6**, which provides the guidelines for outlining.

Have students skim the entire section and create an outline with heads and subheads. Then, they should go back through each heading, writing down details and definitions as they go, and try to find the main idea.
Verbal

Customize for Inclusion Students

Hearing Impaired
During class discussions, write important points on the board so that hearing-impaired students can participate fully. As you lecture, hold your book up and point out which part of the text you are teaching. You may want to assign a student to take notes during lectures. Use a different student each day. Compile the notes in a folder and allow hearing-impaired students to review the folder and update their notes at the end of each week.

Answer to . . .

Figure 20 *Compared to the other outer planets, Pluto is smaller, is farther from the sun on average, has longer periods of rotation and revolution, and has fewer moons.*

Section 25.4 (continued)

Use Visuals

L1

Figure 22 Point out that the surfaces of Europa and Io are very different. Ask, **Why does the surface of Europa appear so smooth?** *(The surface is covered by ice.)*
Visual

Saturn

Build Science Skills

L2

Posing Questions Students will likely have additional questions about planetary rings, such as "How do they form?" "Why are they found only around gas giants?" and "Are they permanent structures?" To help students better understand ring systems, discuss the Roche limit. The Roche limit is the minimum distance an object, such as a moon, can orbit around a planet without being destroyed by the planet's tidal forces. Rings are located within the Roche limit. The particles that make up rings could not coalesce into a solid moon because of the tidal forces of the gas giants. In the same vein, if a moon were drawn into the Roche limit, it would be destroyed and its shattered remnants would become part of a planet's ring system. Have small groups of students make a list of questions concerning planetary rings. As a class, choose the best questions. Then, assign a different question for each group to research and have the groups present oral reports to the class.
Verbal, Group

Figure 22 Two of Jupiter's larger moons are Io (top) and Europa (bottom). Io is the most volcanically active body in the solar system. Io's volcanic eruptions consist mainly of liquid sulfur. Europa may have a liquid water ocean beneath its icy surface. The dark lines are wide fractures in Europa's crust.
Formulating Hypotheses ***Would you expect many impact craters on Io's surface? Explain why or why not.***

Jupiter's Atmosphere With many colorful bands of clouds, Jupiter has a striking appearance. Jupiter's clouds move rapidly because Jupiter itself rotates rapidly—one day on Jupiter is less than 10 Earth hours. The brown cloud bands are colder and move faster around the planet than the white bands.

Sometimes storms occur at the boundaries between these brown and white bands. One example is the Great Red Spot, a huge storm that rotates around its own center like a hurricane. It is caught between two bands of winds blowing in opposite directions. On Earth, a hurricane changes and dissipates when it travels from water to land. Because there is no land on Jupiter, such storms can last for many years. The Great Red Spot, for example, was first observed in 1664, but may be much older.

Jupiter's Moons Jupiter has at least 50 moons. Most of them are small, less than 200 kilometers in diameter. However, two of them, Ganymede and Callisto, are similar in size to Mercury. Two others, Io and Europa, are somewhat smaller, about the size of our moon. Ganymede, Io, and Europa have metal cores and rocky mantles. Io, shown in Figure 22, is covered with actively erupting volcanoes. Ganymede, Europa, and Callisto are covered with ice. On Europa, also shown in Figure 22, the icy crust appears to rest on top of a liquid salt-water ocean. Because of this, scientists hypothesize that Europa is the most likely place in the solar system, other than Earth, to support life.

Saturn

Saturn, the second largest planet in the solar system, is best known for its rings. **Saturn's rings are the largest and most visible from Earth.** The rings are made of particles of ice and ice-coated rock. These particles are generally between a few micrometers and 10 meters across, with most particles being snowball-sized. The rings are about 274,000 kilometers in diameter, yet are only tens of meters thick.

Figure 23 Saturn has a thick atmosphere. It is surrounded by a spectacular set of rings, the largest in the solar system.

Facts and Figures

Ears on Saturn? In the early 1600s, Galileo became one of the first scientists to utilize the newly invented telescope. He built his own and began making observations that shook the foundations of the Renaissance world. One of his most puzzling discoveries was the rings of Saturn. To him, they looked like ears. Two years after he had first observed them, he found that they had disappeared. In the 1650s, Dutch astronomer Christiaan Huygens built a telescope far more powerful than Galileo's and was able to see "a thin, flat ring" around Saturn. It was Huygens who figured out that the rings are sometimes inclined edge-on to Earth. During these times, they seem to disappear.

Saturn's Atmosphere Like Jupiter, Saturn has colorful banding in its atmosphere, as shown in Figure 23. Saturn's atmosphere is the largest of any planet in the solar system. Saturn also has the lowest average density. In fact, if there were a bathtub big enough, Saturn would float in the water. Saturn's atmosphere is made mostly of hydrogen and helium, with small amounts of other elements. Scientists think that the helium in Saturn's atmosphere condenses, creating helium "raindrops" that fall into the middle of the planet. As the helium drops fall, their potential energy is converted into heat. This keeps the planet warm, and explains why Saturn releases more heat than Jupiter.

Saturn's Moons Astronomers have found at least 30 moons orbiting Saturn. Most of these moons are very small. However, one moon, Titan, is larger than Mercury. Titan is the only planetary moon with a thick atmosphere. It may be covered by rivers and lakes of liquid hydrocarbons, such as ethane.

Uranus

Because Uranus is so far from the sun, it is very cold. Uranus's atmosphere is mostly hydrogen and helium. It also has a large amount of methane, which gives the planet a distinct blue-green appearance.

Structure of Uranus Like Jupiter and Saturn, Uranus probably has a rocky core. This core is thought to be surrounded by a thick mantle layer of liquid water and dissolved ammonia, somewhat similar to a bottle of window-cleaning solution. A layer of liquid hydrogen and helium surrounds the mantle.

Uranus has rings, although they are not as visible as Saturn's. The particles that make up these rings are very dark, about as reflective as lumps of coal. Uranus has at least 20 moons, though most are quite small.

A Tilted Planet The most unusual characteristic of Uranus is that it lies nearly on its side, as shown in Figure 24. **The axis of Uranus's rotation is tilted more than 90°.** Uranus rotates in a direction opposite to the direction of its revolution around the sun. Uranus's rings and moons revolve about the same tilted axis. Because of the tilt of Uranus's axis, its northern and southern hemispheres alternate being exposed to the sun for many years. This causes immense storms that disturb the planet's otherwise smooth appearance. No one knows for sure why Uranus's axis is so tilted. Scientists hypothesize that the tilt may have been caused by a collision with another large planetary body early in its history.

Reading Checkpoint *What do scientists hypothesize about the cause of Uranus's tilt?*

Go Online SCIENCE NEWS

For: Articles on the solar system
Visit: PHSchool.com
Web Code: cce-3254

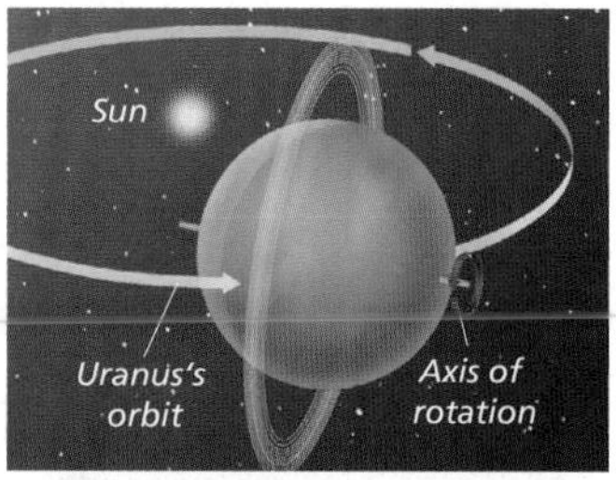
Sun
Uranus's orbit
Axis of rotation

Figure 24 Uranus is unusual in that its axis is tilted so that the planet rotates nearly on its side. Uranus's rings and moons revolve around its greatly tilted axis of rotation. **Inferring** ***In what way must the seasons on Uranus be unusual?***

Uranus

Teacher Demo

Rings of Uranus L2

Purpose Students observe how astronomers discovered the rings of Uranus.

Materials penlight, window blind

Procedure Have two students stand in front of the class and hold each end of a loose window blind so that it is stretched out horizontally. Adjust the blind so that there is a little space between the individual slats. Darken the room and stand behind the center of the blind with the penlight in your hand. Explain to students that the penlight represents a star, your body represents Uranus, and the blinds represent Uranus's rings. Then, pass the penlight across the blind so that from the vantage point of students, the light appears to blink on and off as it sweeps across the "rings." Finally, ask students how they think astronomers discovered Uranus's rings.

Expected Outcome Students should correctly infer that the rings were discovered by observing how light from a distant star blinked on and off several times just before and after it crossed Uranus. Tell students that this discovery was accidental. **Visual**

Go Online SCIENCE NEWS

Science News provides students with current information on the solar system.

Answer to . . .

Figure 22 *No. Any old impact craters would be covered over by lava from Io's frequent volcanic eruptions.*

Figure 24 *Because of the length of Uranus's period of revolution and its tilted axis, the same side of the planet faces the sun for many years. As a result, Uranus's seasons last for many Earth years.*

Reading Checkpoint *Scientists hypothesize that Uranus was tilted on its side by a collision with another large planetary body early in its history.*

Neptune

Use Visuals L1

Figure 25 Tell students that Uranus radiates as much thermal energy as it receives from the sun. It therefore appears to have little or no source of internal heat. Neptune, in contrast, radiates more thermal energy than it receives from the sun. It is thought that Neptune is slowly contracting, in the process converting gravitational potential energy to thermal energy. This produces vigorous convection activities, such as clouds and storms, in Neptune's atmosphere. Ask, **How does this information relate to the Great Dark Spot visible in the photo of Neptune?** *(The Great Dark Spot was a large storm caused by convection in Neptune's atmosphere, which in turn was caused by heat generated from internal sources.)*
Visual, Logical

Pluto

Build Science Skills L2

Comparing and Contrasting Have students compare and contrast Pluto to the other planets. Ask them to explain why it is considered an "oddball" planet in some ways. *(Pluto is much smaller and denser than the other outer planets. Its moon is half the size of the planet itself. It is more similar to the small objects that orbit the sun at the outer edges of the solar system than it is to the other outer planets.)*
Verbal

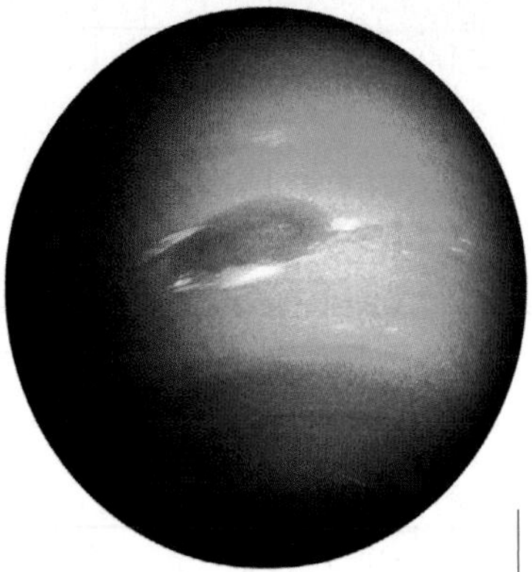

Figure 25 This photo of Neptune was taken by the Voyager 2 spacecraft. The Great Dark Spot, visible near the center, was similar in size to Earth. The white clouds are thought to be made of methane ice crystals. **Formulating Hypotheses** ***Why is the color of Neptune different from Jupiter, Saturn, and Uranus?***

Figure 26 Pluto is the smallest planet in our solar system. Pluto's moon, Charon, shown in the upper right of this illustration, is about half the size of Pluto.

Neptune

Neptune is so far from the sun that it takes a very long time—165 Earth years—for it to make one revolution. Neptune has about the same composition and is about the same size as Uranus.

Unlike Uranus, Neptune has clearly visible cloud patterns in its atmosphere. Thin, wispy clouds form high within Neptune's atmosphere, similar to cirrus clouds in Earth's atmosphere. Earth's clouds are made of liquid water or ice crystals, but Neptune's clouds are made of methane ice crystals. **Neptune's bluish color comes from the methane in its atmosphere.**

Neptune also has large storms in its atmosphere. One of these, observed by the Voyager 2 space probe in 1989, was called the Great Dark Spot, shown in Figure 25. But by 1994, the storm was gone.

Neptune has thin rings of dark particles, very similar to the rings of Uranus. In addition, Neptune has at least eight moons. Triton, the only large moon, has a thin atmosphere and an icy surface.

Pluto

Pluto is only one of many smaller objects that orbit the sun at the outer edges of the solar system. Because of this, some scientists don't consider Pluto to be worthy of planet status. Nonetheless, Pluto, discovered in 1930, is generally considered to be the ninth and most distant planet of the solar system.

Pluto is an oddball planet in some ways. **Pluto is much smaller and denser than the other outer planets.** In fact, Pluto has more in common with the moons of the gas giants than with the gas giants themselves. Pluto's diameter (2300 km) is smaller than some of these moons. Its density is similar to that of Triton, suggesting that Pluto is made of a mixture of ice and rock.

Pluto isn't always the most distant planet. Although Pluto's average distance from the sun is greater than Neptune's, Pluto's orbit is so elliptical that it is sometimes closer to the sun. Like Uranus, Pluto also has a rotation axis that is tilted more than 90°.

Pluto has a single moon, Charon. As shown in Figure 26, Pluto and Charon are so close in size that the two practically form a double planet, each revolving around the other. Charon has a diameter about half that of Pluto. Scientists think that the two formed long ago when Pluto collided with a similar-sized planet and the debris recombined to form two separate bodies. This could also account for Pluto's orbit, which is tilted 17° with respect to the ecliptic.

Section 25.4 Assessment

1. The gas giants are much larger and less dense than the terrestrial planets.
2. The five outer planets are Jupiter, Saturn, Uranus, Neptune, and Pluto. Sample answers include largest planet for Jupiter, most prominent rings for Saturn, tilted axis for Uranus, methane clouds for Neptune, and most distant planet (on average) for Pluto.
3. Comets are dusty pieces of ice and rock that partially vaporize when they pass near the sun. Meteoroids are small pieces of rock that travel through the solar system.
4. The Kuiper belt is a doughnut-shaped region near the ecliptic, whereas the Oort cloud is spherical in shape. The Oort cloud extends much farther from the sun than the Kuiper belt.
5. Because much of their hydrogen and helium exists as a liquid at the conditions present within these planets

Comets and Meteoroids

As the large craters on the surfaces of the terrestrial planets and moons show, there are many objects moving through the solar system. These objects take two forms: comets and meteoroids. **Comets are dusty pieces of ice and rock that partially vaporize when they pass near the sun. Meteoroids are pieces of rock, usually less than a few hundred meters in size, that travel through the solar system.** Read the Concepts in Action pages at the end of this section to learn more about these wanderers of the solar system.

Certain ancient meteoroids have been largely unaltered since the birth of the solar system. These meteoroids are the oldest remnants of the early solar system. Scientists have used radioactive dating to determine their absolute age. This has allowed them to determine that the solar system is about 4.6 billion years old.

The Edge of the Solar System

The solar system does not end at Pluto's orbit. In fact, astronomers estimate that there may be tens of thousands of objects, mostly made of ice, dust, and rock, that orbit the sun in the Kuiper belt. The **Kuiper belt,** shown in Figure 27A, is a wide belt that extends from Pluto's orbit out to about 100 AU or more from the sun. **Most of the objects in the Kuiper belt lie in a doughnut-shaped region close to the ecliptic.**

Incredible as it may seem, the solar system extends much farther out than the Kuiper belt. **Beyond the Kuiper belt lies a great reservoir of comets called the Oort cloud.** Figure 27B shows the **Oort Cloud,** a very sparse sphere of comets thought to encircle the solar system out to a distance of about 50,000 AU. Occasionally objects from the Oort cloud enter the inner solar system, where they appear as comets.

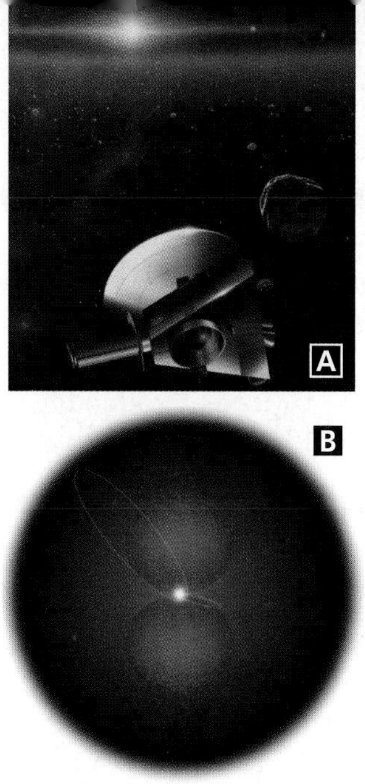

A
B

Figure 27 The Kuiper belt (top) and Oort cloud (bottom) are located in the outer reaches of the solar system. **A** The planned New Horizons space probe is shown in the Kuiper belt. The probe will study Pluto, Charon, and Kuiper belt objects. **B** The Oort cloud is a sphere of comets surrounding the sun and planets.

Section 25.4 Assessment

Reviewing Concepts

1. How do the size and density of the gas giants differ from the terrestrial planets?
2. What are the five outer planets? Identify a distinguishing characteristic for each.
3. Compare and contrast comets and meteoroids.
4. What are some differences between the Kuiper belt and the Oort cloud?

Critical Thinking

5. **Inferring** Why might the gas giants be more appropriately called the "liquid giants"?
6. **Comparing and Contrasting** How are Jupiter's four large moons similar? How are they different?

Connecting Concepts

The Scientific Method Write a paragraph explaining in your own words how the discoveries of Uranus and Neptune show two different aspects of the process of scientific discovery.

Comets and Meteoroids

Use Visuals L1

Figure 27 Emphasize that the Oort cloud is a huge spherical region that is sparsely populated with comets. (It is thought that there are about 1 trillion comets in the Oort cloud, but these comets are typically widely separated from each other.) Tell students that many comets that originate in the Oort cloud were probably pulled out to great distances by the gravity fields of large planets. This is why their orbits are randomly oriented and highly eccentric. Ask, **Where is the sun located in the bottom image of the Oort cloud?** *(In the center of the image)*
Visual

The Edge of the Solar System

Build Math Skills L1

Conversion Factors To help students grasp the vastness of distances in space, have them convert 100 AU (the approximate edge of the Kuiper belt) and 50,000 AU (the approximate size of the Oort cloud) to kilometers. *(100 AU × 150 million km/AU = 15 billion km; 50,000 AU × 150 million km/AU = 7.5 trillion km)*
Logical

Direct students to the **Math Skills** in the **Skills and Reference Handbook** at the end of the text for additional help.

3 ASSESS

Evaluate Understanding L2

State aloud facts about the outer planets, such as "axis of rotation tilted more than 90°," and have students identify the outer planet that matches each fact.

Reteach L1

Use Figure 20 to summarize physical properties of the outer planets.

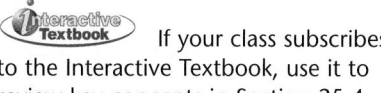

Interactive Textbook If your class subscribes to the Interactive Textbook, use it to review key concepts in Section 25.4.

6. Each of these four moons is large. The two largest, Ganymede and Callisto, are similar in size to Mercury. Ganymede, Io, and Europa all have metal cores and rocky mantles. Ganymede, Europa, and Callisto are each covered with ice. Io features a high level of volcanic activity. Europa's icy crust appears to rest upon a liquid ocean.

Connecting Concepts

Herschel's discovery of Uranus was accidental. Observing it for nearly a year confirmed that it was a planet. Because it did not follow its predicted orbit, two mathematicians analyzed orbital data for it and independently developed predictions of where an unknown planet (whose gravity was affecting Uranus) should be located. Their predictions were confirmed by the discovery of Neptune.

Answer to . . .

Figure 25 *Accept any reasonable hypothesis. In fact, the color is caused by methane in Neptune's atmosphere.*

Comets and Meteoroids L2

Background

In 2002, scientists at Cal Tech in Pasadena, California discovered a new Kuiper belt object. Named Quaoar, the object is roughly 1250 km in diameter—more than half the size of Pluto—making it the largest Kuiper belt object discovered thus far. Quaoar is located about 42 AU from the sun, just a few AU farther away than Pluto.

Build Science Skills L2

Modeling

ACTIVITY

Purpose Students model the effect of the solar wind on a comet's tail.

Materials 4 small fans, foam ball, strips of newspaper, thumbtacks

Class Time 15 minutes

Procedure Place students in small groups. Have each group use thumbtacks to attach several strips of newspaper (about 15 cm long) to the foam ball to model a comet and its tail. The fans represent the solar wind. Place them in a tight circle so that air will blow out equally in all directions. Have students hold the ball so that the strips of paper can blow freely, and then orbit the fans.

Expected Outcome Students will observe that solar wind causes the tail of the comet to always point away from the sun.

Kinesthetic, Group

CONCEPTS in Action

Comets and Meteoroids

Comets and meteoroids are two groups of objects that travel through the solar system. Sometimes they can be seen from Earth as spectacular sights in the night sky.

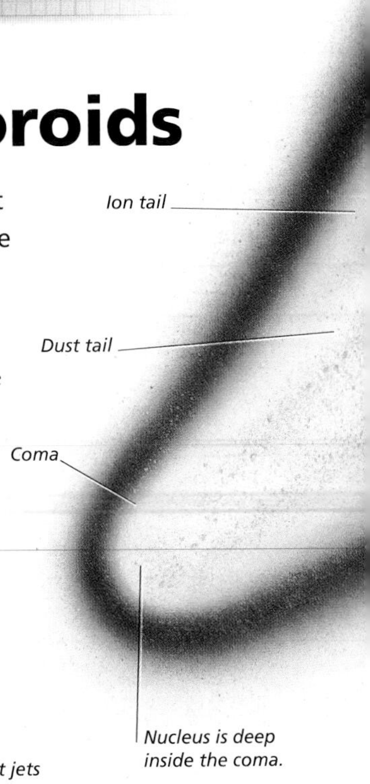

Ion tail
Dust tail
Coma
Nucleus is deep inside the coma.

Comets are dirty snowballs—chunks of rock and ice. They originate in the Kuiper Belt and the Oort Cloud, both of which lie beyond the orbit of Pluto. If a comet comes close to the sun it vaporizes, producing clouds of gas and dust. These clouds appear as tails, which can be millions of kilometers long. If a comet is close enough to Earth, it can be seen as a bright object in the night sky. Meteoroids consist of rock or metal and they can be any size from tiny particles to huge boulders. Most meteoroids burn up as they enter Earth's atmosphere. They appear as streaks of light in the night sky, called meteors. Meteoroids that reach Earth's surface are called meteorites.

Comets

Most comets travel in highly elliptical orbits around the sun. Their orbital periods vary dramatically. Short-period comets, so called because they take less than 200 years to make one orbit, are the most predictable. Long-period comets may take thousands or millions of years to return to our sky.

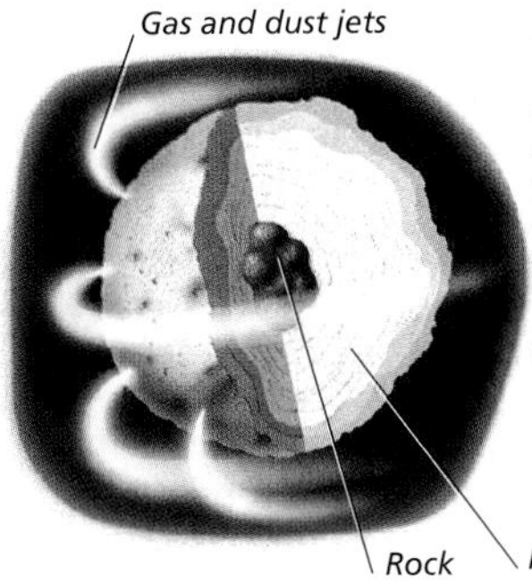

Gas and dust jets
Rock
Ice

A comet's nucleus
A comet has a nucleus that consists of ice and rock. At the comet's surface, jets of gas and dust spray out under pressure, creating a huge cloud called a coma.

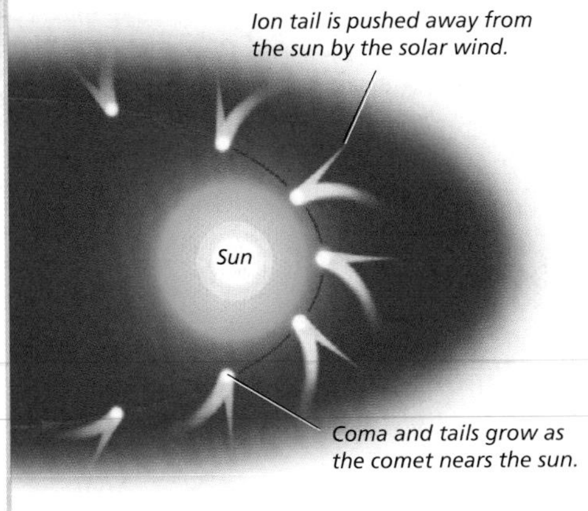

Ion tail is pushed away from the sun by the solar wind.
Sun
Coma and tails grow as the comet nears the sun.

A comet's tails
Most comets have two tails: a white dust tail and a bluish ion tail. The dust tail is made of dust pushed outward by photons of light from the sun. The ion tail consists of charged gas particles that are pushed away from the comet by the solar wind (charged particles from the sun). Thus, the tails always face away from the sun.

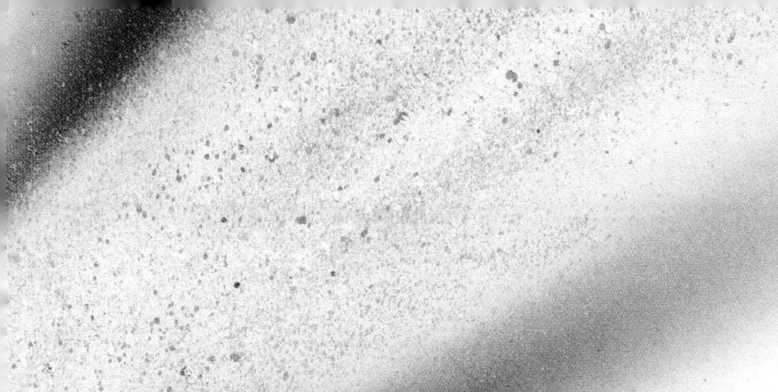

Bright comet
In spite of its brightness, a comet does not give off any light of its own. What seems to be light from the comet is actually a reflection of the sun's light.

Meteoroids

Most meteoroids are made of rock. Others are made of metal, or a mixture of rock and metal. Sometimes, many meteors flash across the night sky within a short span of time. This event is known as a meteor shower. A meteor shower occurs when Earth passes through the dust and debris from the tail of a comet. The majority of meteoroids are no bigger than grains of sand.

Meteor
A meteor is the light from a meteoroid as it vaporizes in the atmosphere.

METEORITE

This meteorite is made of iron and nickel.

Meteorites
Relatively few meteoroids ever make it to the surface of the Earth. Those that do, called meteorites, can have very different shapes and sizes. Some are fragments broken from a larger space object.

Barringer Meteorite Crater, Arizona
50,000 years ago, a meteorite 45 meters across crashed into Earth, producing this huge crater.

Going Further

- Use library or Internet resources to find out more about Halley's Comet, a regular visitor to the inner solar system. Include information on the comet's orbit, when it was discovered and when it is expected to return, and what scientists learned from its last appearance in 1986.
- Take a Discovery Channel Video Field Trip by watching "Lighting Up the Sky."

Discovery Channel School Video Field Trip

Going Further

Halley's Comet is named for English astronomer Edmond Halley (1656–1742). This comet has been observed at intervals of about 76 years since at least 88 B.C. Halley was the first to realize that the comet he observed in 1682 had been seen many times before. After the comet returned in 1758, as Halley had predicted, the comet was named after him. Halley's Comet will be next seen near Earth in 2061. It follows a highly elliptical path that stretches from just inside Earth's orbit to just beyond the orbit of Neptune.
Verbal

Discovery Channel School

Video Field Trip

Lighting Up the Sky

After students have viewed the Video Field Trip, ask them the following questions: **Name two materials that are found in comets.** *(Student answers may include frozen water, carbon monoxide, methyl alcohol, and fragments of rock.)* **What did the astronomer Edmond Halley discover about the comet that now bears his name?** *(That it visits Earth on a regular schedule)* **What is the difference between meteoroids and meteorites?** *(Meteoroids are chunks of rock in space. When one enters Earth's atmosphere, friction causes it to heat up and produce a streak of light called a meteor. Meteorites are pieces of meteoroids that survive to reach the ground.)* **What event may have been responsible for having caused the extinction of the dinosaurs?** *(One or more large asteroids struck Earth approximately 65 million years ago. These impacts are thought to have caused or contributed to the extinction of the dinosaurs.)* **What was observed when huge pieces of the comet Shoemaker-Levy struck Jupiter?** *(When the pieces collided with Jupiter, they sent huge quantities of material high into Jupiter's atmosphere.)*

Section 25.5

1 FOCUS

Objectives

25.5.1 **State** the nebular theory.

25.5.2 **Relate** the nebular theory to the orbits of the planets and the composition and size of the planets.

Reading Focus

Build Vocabulary L2

Paraphrase Explain the meaning of vocabulary words by using terms that are familiar to students. For example, tell students that *planetesimals* can be thought of as "planets-to-be." They're asteroid-like bodies that eventually combine to form planets.

Reading Strategy L2

a. The solar system formed from a large rotating cloud of dust and gas. **b.** As the solar nebula rotated, it began to flatten out and form a protoplanetary disk.
c. Dust grains within the protoplanetary disk combined and grew larger. Eventually, these combined to form planetesimals and later protoplanets.
d. The temperatures in the early solar system were very high near the sun and much lower in the outer system. These temperatures affected which materials condensed to form the planets.

2 INSTRUCT

The Nebular Theory

Address Misconceptions L2

Students often think that when a theory is "proven" beyond doubt, it becomes a scientific law. Explain that scientific laws are generalizations about principles or processes that occur in nature. They can only be confirmed, not proven. Theories can be thought of as explanations of laws. As such, they are subject to revision. **Logical, Visual**

Use Visuals L1

Figure 28 Have students examine the nebula's shape. Ask, **How did the shape of the nebula change?** *(Originally, the shape was irregular. Over time, it became disk-shaped.)* **Visual, Logical**

25.5 The Origin of the Solar System

Reading Focus

Key Concepts

- What is the nebular theory?
- How does the nebular theory explain the composition and size of the planets?

Vocabulary

solar nebula, protoplanetary disk, planetesimals, accretion

Reading Strategy

Identifying Main Ideas Copy the incomplete table at the right. As you read, write the main idea for each topic.

Topic	Main Idea
The Nebular Theory	a. ?
Formation of the protoplanetary disk	b. ?
Planetesimals and protoplanets	c. ?
Composition and size of the planets	d. ?

Figuring out how the solar system formed is a bit like detective work. You can't go back 4.6 billion years in time to see exactly what happened. But there are many clues that scientists have used to form a theory about what must have occurred. Any such theory must explain why all of the planets' orbits lie more or less in a single plane and why all of the planets orbit the sun in the same direction. It must also explain the difference in size and composition between the terrestrial planets and the gas giants.

The Nebular Theory

The generally accepted explanation for the formation of the solar system is the nebular theory, illustrated in Figure 28. **The nebular theory states that the solar system formed from a rotating cloud of dust and gas.** A large, thin cloud of dust and gas like the one that eventually formed our solar system is called a **solar nebula.** According to the nebular theory, the solar nebula formed from the material expelled by previous stars.

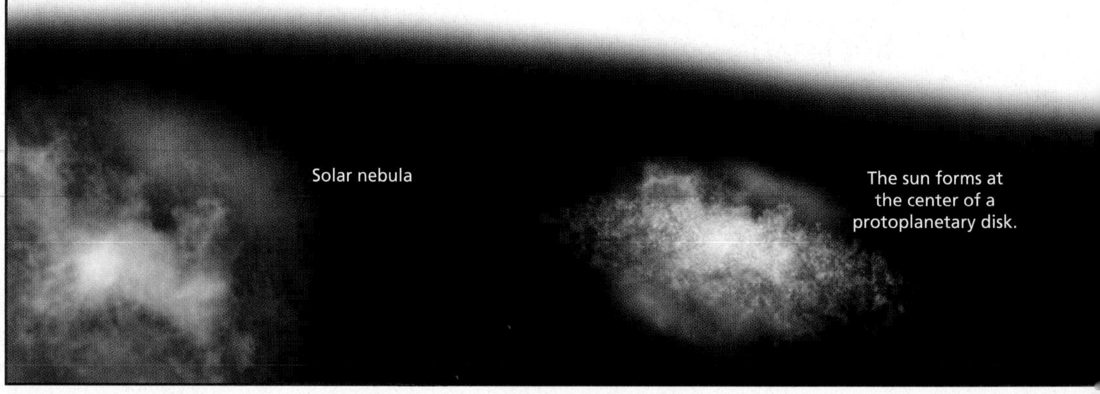
Solar nebula
The sun forms at the center of a protoplanetary disk.

Figure 28 The contraction of the solar nebula, a large cloud of dust and gas, led to a disk-shaped protoplanetary disk, from which the sun and planets formed. **Applying Concepts** ***What force caused the solar nebula to contract?***

Section Resources

Print
- ***Reading and Study Workbook With Math Support,*** Section 25.5
- ***Transparencies,*** Section 25.5

Technology
- ***Interactive Textbook,*** Section 25.5
- ***Presentation Pro CD-ROM,*** Section 25.5

It is likely that a shock wave from the explosion of a nearby star caused the solar nebula to collapse. The nebula most likely began with a slight overall rotation. As the cloud contracted, it began to spin faster. The gravitational attraction between particles became stronger as the solar nebula shrank, accelerating the process.

Formation of the Protoplanetary Disk As the solar nebula rotated faster, it began to flatten out. Over about 100,000 years, a large disk-shaped cloud of dust and gas called a **protoplanetary disk** formed. Looking like a giant fried egg rotating in space, the disk was densest in the center and thinner toward the edges. The planets would eventually form from the outer parts of the disk.

Nearly all of the mass of the solar nebula, about 99.9 percent, became concentrated near the center. The sun would eventually form in this region. The enormous density at the center of the disk increased until the temperature reached a few million degrees. Then, about 10 million years after the formation of the solar nebula, nuclear reactions began to fuse hydrogen into helium. Our sun was born.

Planetesimals and Protoplanets The nebular theory also explains how the planets could have formed. Within the contracting protoplanetary disk, dust grains collided frequently. Weak surface forces held these dust grains together, forming loose balls of dust. As these balls of dust collided, they grew larger and larger.

Scientists estimate that, after a few million years, there were about a billion planetesimals revolving around the sun. **Planetesimals** were asteroid-like bodies that eventually combined to form planets. Planetesimals grew by **accretion,** the process of adding mass by colliding with other planetesimals. Once planetesimals became larger than about a kilometer in diameter, they began to exert a significant gravitational attraction on nearby objects. The planetesimals attracted more material, causing them to grow even faster. The result was the accretion of planetesimals into a much smaller number of moon-sized protoplanets. These protoplanets eventually joined to form the current planets in a series of immense collisions.The nebular theory provides an explanation for the current motions of the sun, planets, and most moons. Nearly all are now revolving in the direction that the protoplanetary disk was spinning.

Quick Lab

Forming Planets

Procedure

1. Cut two strips of newspaper, each 2.5 cm by 30 cm. Tape the ends of each strip together to make two equal loops.
2. Cross the loops with one nested in the other to make a sphere shape. Tape the loops together as shown.
3. Gently push the pencil through the crossing points. The end with more tape should be fixed in place and the other end should slide freely on the pencil.
4. Move the free end about 8 cm from the fixed end. Hold the pencil horizontally and spin it. Observe the movement of the loops.

Analyze and Conclude

1. **Observing** How did rotation affect the loops?
2. **Using Models** How does the model help explain the fact that the planets' orbits are close to the ecliptic plane?

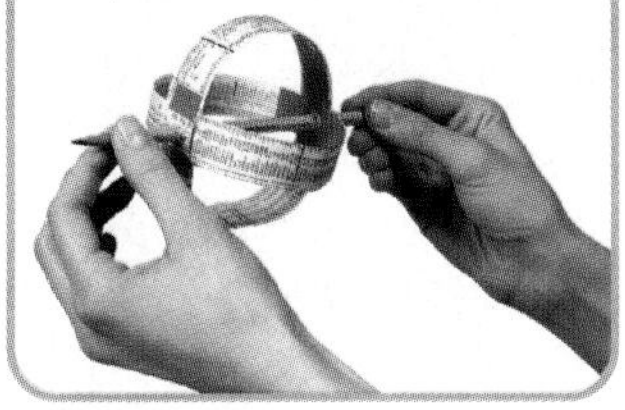

Reading Checkpoint *What were planetesimals?*

Planetesimals form.
Protoplanets form.

Customize for English Language Learners

Increase Students' Exposure to New Words
English language learners will internalize new vocabulary faster if they can link the terms to visuals. Use photos, satellite images, illustrations, and diagrams as visual examples of new vocabulary words. You can find visuals pertaining to the origin of the solar system on NASA and educational Web sites or in astronomy magazines. Encourage students to create drawings that illustrate the meanings of new terms. Assess students' drawings to determine if they understand the concepts.

Quick Lab

Forming Planets **L2**

Objective
After completing this activity, students will be able to
- explain the shape of the protoplanetary disk.

Skills Focus **Using Models**

Prep Time 5 minutes

Materials 2 2.5-cm by 30-cm strips of paper, tape, pencil, metric ruler

Class Time 15 minutes

Teaching Tips
- You may wish to assemble a sample model as an example for students.

Expected Outcome When the model spins, the free ends of the paper strips move closer to the fixed end and the middles of the strips bow farther outward.

Analyze and Conclude
1. It flattened the rounded shape.
2. Just as the paper strips formed a more flattened, disk-like shape as they were spun, the material in the solar nebula was flattened into a rotating disk. This disk gradually solidified to form the planets, which have orbits close to the ecliptic plane. **Kinesthetic, Logical**

For Enrichment **L3**

One alternative to the nebular theory proposes that the gravitational attraction of a passing star pulled a mass of material out of the sun that condensed and broke up to become the planets. Such a mass would probably have been thickest in the middle and have had tapered ends. Have students examine Figure 3 on pp. 792 and 793 for evidence for this theory. **Visual**

Build Science Skills **L2**

Communicating Results Have groups of students conduct research about extrasolar planets (planets that orbit other stars). Each group can develop multimedia presentations displaying the results of their research. Encourage students to use a variety of media. **Visual, Portfolio**

Answer to . . .

Figure 28 *Gravity*

Reading Checkpoint *Asteroid-like bodies in the early solar system that eventually combined to form the planets*

Composition and Size of the Planets

Build Reading Literacy L1

Relate Cause and Effect Refer to page **260D** in **Chapter 9**, which provides the guidelines for relating cause and effect.

After students have read about the composition and size of the planets, ask, **Is low density a cause or an effect?** *(Effect)* **Verbal, Logical**

3 ASSESS

Evaluate Understanding L2

Have students identify any concepts they find unclear. Have student volunteers explain the concepts.

Reteach L1

Tell students to picture an ice skater who draws his arms to his body as he spins. Explain that any rotating object, such as a nebula or an ice skater, will spin faster if its mass is redistributed closer to its axis of rotation.

Writing in Science

Metal and rock were able to condense in the high temperatures that existed in the inner portion of the early solar system. Ice-forming materials could condense only in the lower temperatures of the outer solar system.

Interactive Textbook If your class subscribes to the Interactive Textbook, use it to review key concepts in Section 25.5.

Answer to . . .

Figure 29 *Solar systems around the young stars*

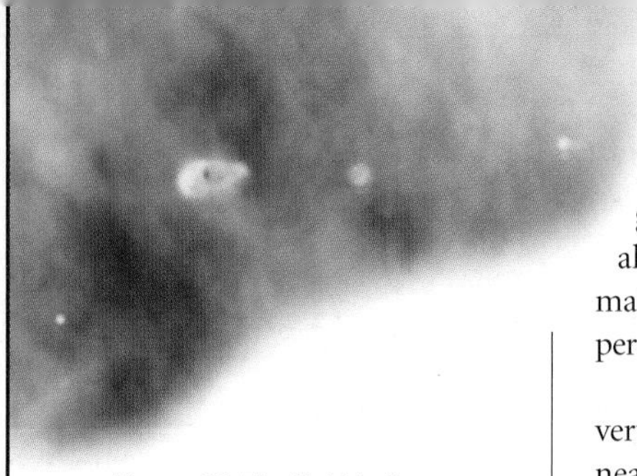

Figure 29 The Hubble Space Telescope took this photo of what are thought to be protoplanetary disks around several young stars. These stars are located about 1500 light-years away in the Orion Nebula, a region of intense star formation. **Predicting** ***According to the nebular theory, what will these protoplanetary disks eventually become?***

Composition and Size of the Planets

At low pressures, such as those found in space, cooling materials generally condense directly from a gas into a solid. Different materials change into a solid at different temperatures. Ice-forming materials, such as water, ammonia, and methane, condense at low temperatures. Rock-forming materials condense at much higher temperatures.

When the solar system formed, the temperatures near the sun were very high. The temperature near Mercury's orbit was about 1200 K, and near Mars's orbit it was roughly 500 K. Water and other ice-forming materials vaporize at these temperatures, so they did not play a role in the early formation of the terrestrial planets. **The terrestrial planets are relatively small and rocky. In part, that is because the inner solar system was too hot during their formation for ice-forming compounds to condense.**

In contrast, ice-forming materials could condense in the outer solar system because it was much colder. Much more material was available, and these planets grew to many times the size of Earth. As these planets grew, their gravity increased, and they were able to capture the extremely abundant hydrogen and helium gas from the surrounding space. **The gas giants are large and have low densities because the outer solar system was cool enough for ice-forming compounds to condense.**

As Figure 29 shows, astronomers have been able to observe protoplanetary disks around distant newborn stars. Astronomers have also detected more than a hundred planets in orbit around distant stars. This evidence of planets forming around other stars, plus the results of computer simulations, provides support for the nebular theory.

Section 25.5 Assessment

Reviewing Concepts

1. List the major steps in the formation of the solar system according to the nebular theory.
2. Why are compounds such as ammonia most common in the outer solar system?
3. What happened to the planetesimals that once orbited the sun?
4. What was the protoplanetary disk?

Critical Thinking

5. **Applying Concepts** Why do all of the planets revolve around the sun within the same plane and in the same direction?
6. **Inferring** Astronomers are able to detect planets around distant stars because of the gravitational effects of the planets as they orbit the star. Why do you think most of the planets found so far have been very massive?

Writing in Science

Cause-Effect Paragraph Write a paragraph explaining why the terrestrial planets formed mostly from metal and rock, and not hydrogen and helium like the gas giants.

Section 25.5 Assessment

1. (1) The solar nebula formed from the remnants of previous stars. (2) The solar nebula began to collapse and spin faster. (3) The solar nebula flattened out and formed a protoplanetary disk. Fusion began at the center of the disk. (4) Dust grains collided and grew larger. Eventually planetesimals formed. (5) Planetesimals grew by accretion, forming protoplanets. (6) The protoplanets combined to form the planets.
2. In the early solar system, the relatively low temperatures at which ammonia, water, and other ice-forming materials condense were found in the outer solar system. It was too hot for these materials to condense in the inner solar system.
3. They grew by accretion, eventually forming protoplanets. Later, the protoplanets combined to form the planets.
4. A disk-shaped cloud of dust and gas in the early solar system
5. The planets all revolve around the sun in the same direction that the protoplanetary disk was spinning. The planets revolve in planes close to the ecliptic, which is approximately the original plane of rotation of the protoplanetary disk.
6. In most cases, planets around other stars cannot be observed directly. However, the gravitational attraction between a star and a massive planet can cause the star to wobble as the planet revolves around it. Less massive planets would cause less of a wobble, and are difficult to detect with current technology.

Exploration Lab

Modeling the Solar System

You may have seen models and illustrations that compare the sizes of the planets, but do not accurately show their relative distances from the sun. In this lab, you will compare the sizes of the planets to their distances from the sun.

Problem How can you model both the relative sizes and distances of the planets in the solar system?

Materials

- calculator
- large sheet of unlined paper
- meter stick
- scale models of the sun and planets

Skills Calculating, Using Models

Procedure

1. To model the relative sizes of the planets' orbits, convert the distances of the planets from the sun in astronomical units to kilometers, using Figure 3 on pages 792–793. Record these distances in scientific notation.
2. Use the meter stick to draw a straight line down the entire length of the large sheet of unlined paper. Measure and record the length of this line in centimeters.
3. Label one end of the line *sun* and the other end *Pluto.*
4. To calculate the scale of your model, divide the length of the line in centimeters by Pluto's average distance from the sun in kilometers.
5. To determine Neptune's position, multiply Neptune's average distance from the sun by the scale of your model. Mark Neptune's position on the line in your model.
6. Repeat Step 5 for each of the remaining planets in the solar system.
7. Your teacher will provide a set of scale models of the sun and planets. Use a meter stick to measure and record the diameter of the model of Jupiter.
8. To determine the scale of the planet models, divide the diameter of the model of Jupiter in centimeters by the actual diameter of Jupiter, which can be found in Figure 20 on page 811.
9. To determine the size of the solar system at the scale of the planet models, multiply the actual distance from Pluto to the sun by the scale of the planet models. Convert the result from centimeters to meters and record this distance.

Analyze and Conclude

1. **Using Models** How big would a model of the solar system be at the scale of the planet models you used? Explain your answer.
2. **Analyzing Data** What difficulty would you have including the relative sizes of the planets on the paper model you made in Steps 1 through 6?
3. **Drawing Conclusions** Explain why it is difficult to model the sizes and distances of the planets at the same scale.

Go Further Calculate the distance from the sun to each planet in a model with the same scale as the planet models. Under your teacher's supervision and with the help of your classmates, take the planet models outdoors and position them to model their distances from the sun.

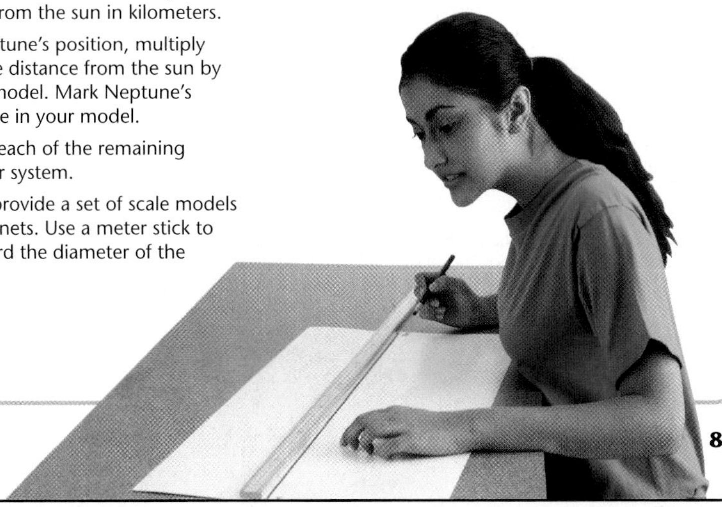

Exploration Lab

Modeling the Solar System **L2**

Objective
After completing this activity, students will be able to
- compare the relative sizes and distances of the planets.

Address Misconceptions

Many students think that the planets are relatively large in comparison to the size of the solar system. This lab can help dispel this misconception.

Skills Focus **Calculating, Using Models**

Prep Time 30 minutes

Advance Prep Provide one or more sets of models of the sun and planets for students to examine and measure in Steps 7 and 8. To show the relative size of the sun, use a ball about 17.5 cm in diameter (such as a miniature basketball) to represent the sun. You can use heads of pins to represent Mercury and Pluto, mustard seeds or peppercorns to represent Venus and Earth, a small ball or large nut such as a walnut that is close to 2.3 cm in diameter to represent Jupiter, a marble or nut that is close to 1.8 cm in diameter to represent Saturn, and ball bearings or buttons that are about 0.8 cm in diameter to represent Uranus and Neptune. Mount the planet models on labeled cards or blocks of wood.

Class Time 45 minutes

Teaching Tips
- You may need to review the use of scientific notation.
- Students may need help setting up the scale calculations.

Expected Outcome Students will conclude that a model showing the distances of the planets from the sun at the scale of the planet models would be impracticably large.

Sample Data
At the scale of the planet models provided above, the solar system model would extend approximately 983 m from the sun to Pluto.

Go Further
Approximate distances of the planet models from the sun would range from 10 m for Mercury to 983 m for Pluto.
Logical, Kinesthetic

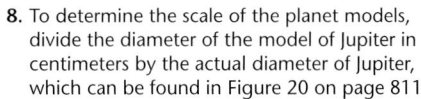

Analyze and Conclude
1. Answers will depend on the size of the model of Jupiter, but should be approximately 950 to 1000 m.
2. The orbits of the inner planets would be too small to draw or observe.
3. The distances among the planets and between the planets and the sun are many times greater than the sizes of the planets.
Logical, Kinesthetic

Study Guide

Study Tip

Choose a Quiet Place to Study Tell students that they will absorb concepts better if they study in a quiet place. Stress that they should minimize distractions, such as radios, CD players, and televisions.

Thinking Visually

The table can include the following information. The terrestrial planets have a small size, are located in the inner solar system, are composed of rocky crusts and metal cores, have zero to two moons, and do not have rings. The gas giants have a very large size, are located in the outer solar system, are composed mostly of hydrogen and helium, have many moons, and do have rings. Pluto has a very small size, is the most distant planet from the sun (on average), is composed of ice and rock, has one moon, and does not have rings.

Assessment

Interactive Textbook: If your class subscribes to the Interactive Textbook, your students can go online to access an interactive version of the Student Edition and a self-test.

Reviewing Content

1. b **2.** d **3.** c
4. a **5.** c **6.** b
7. a **8.** d **9.** d
10. b

Understanding Concepts

11. The heliocentric model of the solar system was not readily accepted because the geocentric model could explain all observations of the planets made at that time and Earth's motions were not obvious to observers on Earth.
12. The planets orbit in nearly the same plane, so when you see several together, they line up.
13. Space probes play an important role in gathering new information about the solar system. They are a relatively inexpensive alternative to piloted space vehicles.

CHAPTER 25

Study Guide

25.1 Exploring the Solar System

Key Concepts

- In a geocentric model, Earth is stationary while objects in the sky move around it.
- In a heliocentric model, Earth and the other planets revolve around the sun.
- Gravity and inertia combine to keep the planets in orbit around the sun.
- Our solar system consists of the sun, the planets, their moons, and a variety of smaller objects that revolve around the sun.
- Modern technology, including complex telescopes, piloted spacecraft, and space probes, has allowed scientists to explore the solar system.

Vocabulary

geocentric, *p. 791;* heliocentric, *p. 791;* ecliptic plane, *p. 792;* moon, *p. 792;* astronomical unit, *p. 793;* space probe, *p. 794*

25.2 The Earth-Moon System

Key Concepts

- The lack of an atmosphere allows the moon's surface temperature to vary tremendously.
- The major surface features of the moon are maria, highlands, and craters.
- Scientists hypothesize that the moon formed after an enormous collision early in Earth's history.
- The moon's phases are caused by changes in the relative positions of the moon, sun, and Earth as the moon revolves around Earth.
- A solar eclipse occurs when the moon casts a shadow on a portion of Earth's surface.
- A lunar eclipse occurs when Earth casts a shadow on the moon.
- Tides are caused mainly by differences in the moon's gravitational pull on Earth.

Vocabulary

maria, *p. 797;* crater, *p. 797;* meteoroids, *p. 797;* phases, *p. 798;* eclipse, *p. 799;* umbra, *p. 800;* penumbra, *p. 800;* tides, *p. 801;* spring tide, *p. 801;* neap tide, *p. 801*

25.3 The Inner Solar System

Key Concepts

- The four inner planets are all relatively small and dense, and have rocky surfaces.
- Scientists now hypothesize that asteroids are remnants of the early solar system.

Vocabulary

terrestrial planets, *p. 803;* asteroids, *p. 809;* asteroid belt, *p. 809*

25.4 The Outer Solar System

Key Concepts

- The four gas giants are thought to have small, dense cores of metal and rock, but consist mainly of liquid hydrogen and helium.
- Pluto is smaller and denser than the gas giants.
- Comets are dusty pieces of ice and rock. Meteoroids are pieces of rock moving through space.
- The Kuiper belt is a doughnut-shaped region near the ecliptic. The Oort cloud is a reservoir of comets.

Vocabulary

gas giants, *p. 811;* ring, *p. 811;* Kuiper belt, *p. 815;* Oort cloud, *p. 815*

25.5 The Origin of the Solar System

Key Concepts

- The nebular theory states that the solar system formed from a rotating cloud of dust and gas.
- The terrestrial planets are small and rocky because the inner solar system was too hot during their formation for ice-forming compounds to condense. The gas giants are large and have low densities because the outer solar system was much cooler.

Vocabulary

solar nebula, *p. 818;* protoplanetary disk, *p. 819;* planetesimals, *p. 819;* accretion, *p. 819*

Thinking Visually

Compare-and-Contrast Table Make a table comparing and contrasting the terrestrial planets, gas giants, and Pluto. Include information on size, location, composition, moons, and rings.

Chapter Resources

Print
- ***Chapter and Unit Tests,*** Chapter 25 Test A and Test B
- ***Test Prep Resources,*** Chapter 25

Technology
- ***Computer Test Bank,*** Chapter Test 25
- ***Interactive Textbook,*** Chapter 25
- ***Go Online,*** PHSchool.com, Chapter 25

CHAPTER 25

Assessment

Interactive textbook with assessment at PHSchool.com iText

Reviewing Content

Choose the letter that best answers the question or completes the statement.

1. In the geocentric model,
   a. Earth travels around the sun.
   b. the planets travel around Earth.
   c. the planets travel around the sun.
   d. the planets travel around the stars.

2. Which of the following scientists discovered that each planet orbits the sun in an ellipse?
   a. Isaac Newton b. Nicolaus Copernicus
   c. Galileo Galilei d. Johannes Kepler

3. Most of the mass of the solar system is contained in
   a. the outer planets. b. the moons.
   c. the sun. d. Earth.

4. Dark, smooth regions on the moon are called
   a. maria. b. highlands.
   c. craters. d. meteoroids.

5. All the terrestrial planets have
   a. liquid oceans. b. liquid helium.
   c. rocky surfaces. d. at least one moon.

6. On Venus and Mars, the major component of the atmosphere is
   a. oxygen. b. carbon dioxide.
   c. nitrogen. d. hydrogen.

7. Asteroids are most likely to be
   a. remnants of the early solar system.
   b. former moons of Jupiter.
   c. the remains of a shattered planet.
   d. captured comets.

8. The gas giants are made mostly of
   a. helium gas.
   b. methane ice crystals.
   c. carbon dioxide.
   d. liquid hydrogen and helium.

9. The most likely place in the solar system besides Earth to support life is
   a. Jupiter. b. Titan.
   c. Venus. d. Europa.

10. The process by which planetesimals combine with other planetesimals is called
    a. condensation. b. accretion.
    c. contraction. d. fusion.

Understanding Concepts

11. Why was the heliocentric model of the solar system not readily accepted at first?

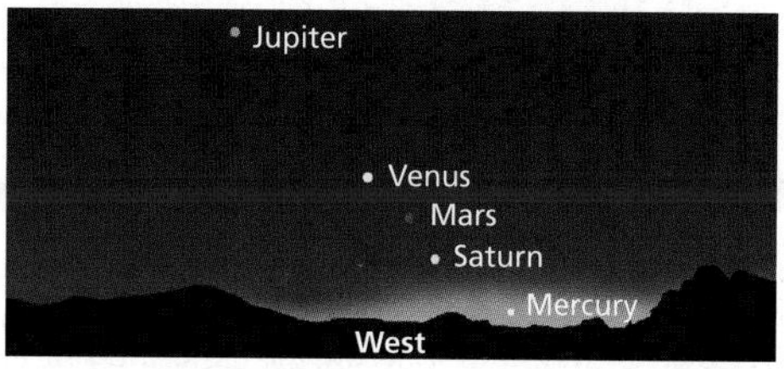
Jupiter
Venus
Mars
Saturn
Mercury
West

12. Explain why on some occasions you can see the planets line up in the sky.

13. Why are space probes used to explore the solar system?

14. Why does the moon lack an atmosphere?

15. What causes the moon to go through a regular cycle of phases?

16. Why doesn't a solar eclipse occur every time the moon passes between the sun and Earth?

17. In most coastal areas there are two high tides every day. What causes the two tides?

18. What does it mean to say that Mercury is "geologically dead"?

19. Why is there no liquid water on the surface of Venus?

20. Where would you go to find the largest volcano in the solar system?

21. What is the Great Red Spot in the atmosphere of Jupiter?

22. Why are hydrogen and helium within the gas giant planets largely in a liquid state?

23. How are clouds on Neptune different from those on Earth?

24. What is unusual about the orbit of Pluto around the sun?

25. How were temperatures distributed across the protoplanetary disk that formed our solar system?

Assessment (continued)

14. The moon lacks an atmosphere because its gravity is too weak to retain gas molecules, which escape into space.
15. As the moon revolves around Earth, the portion of its sunlit surface that is visible from Earth changes in a cyclical manner.
16. For a solar eclipse to occur, the sun, moon, and Earth must all be in a line, with the moon directly between the sun and Earth. However, the orbit of the moon around Earth is tilted with respect to the ecliptic, so the three bodies are not aligned every month.
17. High tides are caused by the gravitational pull of the moon. They occur at the locations on Earth closest to and farthest from the moon. As Earth rotates on its axis, any given point on its surface passes through one of these two tidal bulges approximately every 12 hours, or twice a day.
18. This means that there is no mantle convection on Mercury, and therefore no movement of tectonic plates, and no volcanic activity on the surface.
19. Because the surface temperature of Venus is so high, any liquid water would quickly vaporize.
20. Olympus Mons, the largest volcano in the solar system, is located on Mars.
21. The Great Red Spot is a huge long-lasting storm in Jupiter's atmosphere.
22. Because these planets are so massive, the pressure deep within them is very great, condensing much of their hydrogen and helium into a liquid state.
23. Neptune's clouds are made of methane ice crystals. Clouds on Earth consist of liquid water and water ice crystals.
24. Pluto's orbit is very elliptical. At times, it is closer to the sun than Neptune. Pluto also has the most tilted of the planets' orbits.
25. The temperatures were very high near the center of the disk and grew progressively lower as distance from the center of the disk increased.

TIME SAVER Homework Guide

Section	Questions
25.1	1–3, 11–13
25.2	4, 14–17, 26–27, 34
25.3	5–7, 18–20, 32, 35
25.4	8–9, 21–24, 28, 30–31, 33, 36–39
25.5	10, 25, 29, 40

CHAPTER 25

Assessment *(continued)*

Critical Thinking

26. **Inferring** During some solar eclipses, the moon completely hides the sun. During other solar eclipses, a bright ring of the sun can be seen all the way around the moon. What does this tell you about the shape of the moon's orbit?

27. **Drawing Conclusions** A thin layer of dust and rock fragments covers the surface of the moon. This lunar soil did not form from weathering, as on Earth, because there is no liquid water on the moon. How do you think the lunar soil formed?

28. **Using Analogies** How are the gas giants similar to miniature solar systems?

29. **Applying Concepts** Put the following objects in order from the oldest to the youngest: protoplanets, solar nebula, protoplanetary disk, planetesimals, and planets.

Analyzing Data

Use the table below to answer Questions 30–33.

Largest Moons of the Solar System

Name	Diameter (km)	Period of Revolution (Earth days)	Distance from Planet ($\times 10^3$ km)
Callisto	4800	16.69	1883.0
Ganymede	5268	7.16	1070.0
Io	3642	1.77	421.6
Earth's moon	3476	27.32	384.4
Titan	5150	15.95	1221.9

30. **Using Tables** Which moon in the table is farthest from its planet?

31. **Using Tables** Which moon is the largest in the solar system? How much larger is it than Earth's moon?

32. **Calculating** How many times does Io revolve around Jupiter for each time Earth's moon revolves around Earth?

33. **Making Generalizations** Which planet do most of the large moons revolve around?

Concepts in Action

34. **Applying Concepts** You see on the news that a hurricane is approaching the coast of North Carolina. The weather service is concerned over the timing of a spring tide. What impact could such a tide have on damage from the hurricane?

35. **Inferring** If you were on the surface of Venus with a telescope and a friend was on the surface of Mars with a telescope, which one of you would have a better view of Earth? Explain.

36. **Applying Concepts** Besides Earth, what planets or moons in our solar system are the most likely candidates for life? Explain why.

37. **Applying Concepts** Why do comets' ion tails always stream away from the sun?

38. **Comparing and Contrasting** Explain the differences among a meteor, a meteorite, and a meteoroid.

39. **Making Judgments** Recently, there has been a movement to remove Pluto's status as a planet. Why do you think this is so? Do you think Pluto should be kept as a planet?

40. **Writing in Science** Imagine you are a television reporter and you are observing the formation of the solar system. Write the script for your broadcast, documenting what you are seeing and offering clues as to why it may be happening.

Performance-Based Assessment

Observing Over the course of a month, keep a record of the moon's phases and position in the sky. Be sure to make your observations at the same time and from the same place each night. Use a tree or other landmark as a reference point. Also record when the sky is cloudy or the moon cannot be seen on a clear night. At the end of the month, prepare a summary of your observations.

Go Online
PHSchool.com

For: Self-grading assessment
Visit: PHSchool.com
Web Code: cca-3250

Chapter 25

Critical Thinking

26. The moon's orbit must be fairly elliptical. When the moon is closer to Earth, the angular size of its disk is large enough to cover the sun (except for the chromosphere and the corona) during a solar eclipse. When the moon is relatively far from Earth, its umbra may not reach Earth's surface. Behind the umbra on Earth, a bright ring of the sunlight can be seen around the moon during a solar eclipse. This is called an annular eclipse.
27. Lunar soil formed from meteorites crashing into the moon's surface. The moon has no atmosphere to stop or cushion the blow from such meteorites. Therefore, its surface has been considerably altered by meteorites.
28. The gas giants have a composition that is similar to that of the sun (mostly hydrogen and helium). Also, they are all surrounded by many moons that are relatively small compared to the planets themselves. These moons revolve around their planet, just as the planets revolve around the sun.
29. Solar nebula, protoplanetary disk, planetesimals, protoplanets, and planets

Analyzing Data

30. Callisto
31. Ganymede, 1792 km larger in diameter (about 1.5 times)
32. About 15.4 times
33. Jupiter

Concepts in Action

34. Spring tides have more extreme high and low tides. If a hurricane were to arrive during a high spring tide, the damage would be much greater than it would be during a typical high tide.
35. Only the person on Mars would have a view of Earth. This is because Mars has a thin atmosphere, while a thick layer of clouds covers Venus.
36. Europa is a possible candidate for life because it is thought to have a liquid-water ocean beneath its icy surface. Mars is another candidate for life because it once had liquid water on its surface and still has water frozen at its poles and perhaps underground.
37. The ion tail is pushed away from the sun by the solar wind. The dust tail is pushed away by the solar wind and the pressure of sunlight itself.
38. A meteoroid is a chunk of rock or dust in space. When a meteoroid enters Earth's atmosphere, friction causes it to heat up and produce a streak of light called a meteor. Meteoroids that are large enough to pass through the atmosphere and reach the surface are called meteorites.
39. Pluto does not fit well with the overall pattern of the planets. Unlike the other outer planets, Pluto is small, dense, and has a solid surface. Pluto has only one moon, which is relatively large compared to it. Pluto has a very elliptical orbit as well. Some scientists think that Pluto should be considered a Kuiper belt object rather than a planet.
40. Students' scripts should describe each of the major stages in the formation of the solar system, including formation of the solar nebula, protoplanetary disk, planetesimals, protoplanets, and planets. They should also explain the reasons for each of these stages.

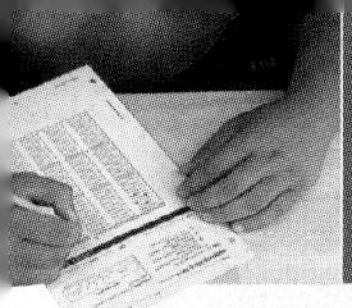

Standardized Test Prep

Test-Taking Tip

Eliminating Unreasonable Answers
When you answer a multiple-choice question, you can often eliminate at least one answer choice because it is clearly incorrect. If you eliminate one or more choices, you increase your odds of choosing the correct answer.

In the question below, you can immediately eliminate choice A because stars do not revolve around Earth. Clearly, choices D and E cannot both be true. On reflection, you can eliminate both of these choices, as Polaris's distance from Earth is not related to the apparent movement of stars around Polaris. Choices B and C are both factual. However, Earth's revolution around the sun takes one year, and is not related to the apparent daily motion of the stars. The remaining choice must be the correct answer.

In the Northern Hemisphere, certain stars appear to circle around Polaris, the North Star, because
(A) these stars revolve around Earth.
(B) Earth revolves around the sun.
(C) Earth rotates on its axis.
(D) Polaris is the closest star.
(E) Polaris is the most distant visible star.

(Answer: C)

Choose the letter that best answers the question or completes the statement.

1. The planets remain in stable orbits around the sun as a result of a balance between
   (A) gravity and pressure from nuclear fusion.
   (B) thermal energy and electromagnetic energy.
   (C) inertia and pressure from nuclear fusion.
   (D) gravity and inertia.
   (E) pressure from nuclear fusion and electromagnetic energy.
2. Which of the following contributes most to the size of tides on Earth?
   (A) rotation of Earth
   (B) gravitational pull of the moon
   (C) gravitational pull of the sun
   (D) gravitational pull of the planets
   (E) rotation of the sun
3. The asteroid belt can be found between the orbits of
   (A) Neptune and Pluto.
   (B) Mars and Jupiter.
   (C) Earth and Mars.
   (D) Mercury and Venus.
   (E) Jupiter and Saturn.
4. Which of the following is NOT a characteristic of each of the gas giant planets?
   (A) high density
   (B) encircled by rings
   (C) very low surface temperatures
   (D) many moons
   (E) composed mainly of hydrogen and helium

Use the illustration below to answer Questions 5–7.

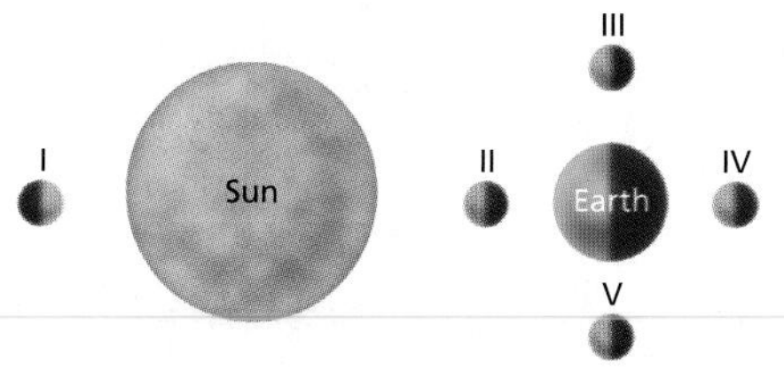

III
I
Sun
II
Earth
IV
V

Not to scale

5. In which location could a lunar eclipse occur?
   (A) I
   (B) II
   (C) III
   (D) IV
   (E) V
6. In which location could the moon be during a solar eclipse?
   (A) I
   (B) II
   (C) III
   (D) IV
   (E) V
7. In which location(s) is the moon when half of the side facing Earth is illuminated?
   (A) III only
   (B) IV only
   (C) II and IV
   (D) III and V
   (E) II and V

Standardized Test Prep

1. D **2.** B **3.** B
4. A **5.** D **6.** B
7. D

Performance-Based Assessment

Students should select a safe, convenient location where there is a broad horizon for viewing. Have them start on a clear night when the moon is expected to be visible in the early evening (waxing crescent). Students should prepare a sketch and notes for each nightly observation. Over the course of the month, students should observe the progression of the moon's phases. They will also notice that the moon's position changes each night relative to the stars and local landmarks. On some nights the moon will be below the horizon in the early evening or will not be visible because of clouds or because it is a new moon.

Go Online
PHSchool.com

Your students can independently test their knowledge of the chapter and print out their test results for your files.

CHAPTER 26

Planning Guide

Use these planning tools
Easy Planner
Teacher Express

SECTION OBJECTIVES	STANDARDS NATIONAL (See p. T18.)	STANDARDS STATE	ACTIVITIES and LABS
26.1 The Sun, pp. 828–833 1 block or 2 periods **26.1.1** **Describe** how the sun produces energy. **26.1.2** **Explain** why the sun remains stable over time. **26.1.3** **Diagram** and **describe** the interior structure and atmospheric features of the sun.	A-1, A-2, B-1, B-5, B-6, D-1, D-3, G-1, G-2, G-3		**SE** Inquiry Activity: Can You Tell How Bright a Light Really Is? p. 827 L2 **SE** Quick Lab: Calculating the Sun's Power, p. 832 L2 **TE** Teacher Demo: Balanced Forces, p. 829 L2 **TE** Build Science Skills: Observing, p. 831 L2 **TE** Teacher Demo: Sunspot Model, p. 833 L2 **LM** Investigation 26A: Measuring the Sun L2
26.2 Stars, pp. 834–839 1 block or 2 periods **26.2.1** **Demonstrate** how distance to a star is measured. **26.2.2** **Classify** stars according to chemical and physical properties. **26.2.3** **Interpret** the H-R diagram.	A-1, A-2, B-4, B-5, B-6, D-4, E-2, G-1, G-2, G-3		**SE** Exploration Lab: Investigating Parallax, pp. 856–857 L2
26.3 Life Cycles of Stars, pp. 840–844 1 block or 2 periods **26.3.1** **Describe** how stars form. **26.3.2** **Estimate** how long a star remains on the main sequence. **26.3.3** **Predict** what happens to a star when it runs out of fuel.	B-6, D-4, G-2, G-3		**TE** Teacher Demo: Brown Dwarfs, p. 843 L2 **LM** Investigation 26B: Modeling a Neutron Star L1
26.4 Groups of Stars, pp. 846–849 1 block or 2 periods **26.4.1** **Explain** how stars are distributed in space. **26.4.2** **Identify** basic types of star clusters. **26.4.3** **Classify** galaxies based on their appearance and composition and **describe** the four main types of galaxies.	D-3, D-4, E-2, G-1, G-2, G-3		
26.5 The Expanding Universe, pp. 852–855 1 block or 2 periods **26.5.1** **Relate** Hubble's Law to red shifts and to the expansion of the universe. **26.5.2** **Apply** the big bang theory to observations of the present-day universe. **26.5.3** **Describe** how dark matter can be detected and **explain** the importance of its effects on the expanding universe.	A-1, A-2, B-6, D-3, D-4, G-1, G-2, G-3		**SE** Quick Lab: Modeling Expansion of the Universe, p. 855 L2

Ability Levels

- L1 For students who need additional help
- L2 For all students
- L3 For students who need to be challenged

Components

SE	Student Edition	RSW	Reading & Study Workbook	CUT	Chapter & Unit Tests	T	Transparencies
TE	Teacher's Edition	MSPS	Math Skills & Problem Solving Workbook	CTB	Computer Test Bank	iT	Interactive Textbook
LM	Laboratory Manual			TP	Test Prep Resources	P	Presentation Pro CD-ROM
PLM	Probeware Lab Manual			DC	Discovery Channel Videotapes & DVDs	GO	Internet Resources

RESOURCES PRINT and TECHNOLOGY		SECTION ASSESSMENT
RSW Section 26.1	L1	SE Section 26.1 Assessment, p. 833
T Chapter 26 Pretest	L2	iT Section 26.1
Section 26.1	L2	
P Chapter 26 Pretest	L2	
Section 26.1	L2	
SciLinks GO The sun	L2	
RSW Section 26.2	L1	SE Section 26.2 Assessment, p. 839
RSW Math Skill	L2	iT Section 26.2
T Section 26.2	L2	
P Section 26.2	L2	
PLANETDIARY GO Astronomy	L2	
RSW Section 26.3	L1	SE Section 26.3 Assessment, p. 844
T Section 26.3	L2	iT Section 26.3
P Section 26.3	L2	
SCIENCE NEWS GO Stars, galaxies, and the universe	L2	
RSW Section 26.4	L1	SE Section 26.4 Assessment, p. 849
Discovery Channel School DC Measuring Up to Space	L2	iT Section 26.4
T Section 26.4	L2	
P Section 26.4	L2	
RSW Section 26.5	L1	SE Section 26.5 Assessment, p. 855
MSPS Section 26.5	L2	iT Section 26.5
T Section 26.5	L2	
P Section 26.5	L2	

Go Online

Go online for these Internet resources.

PHSchool.com
Web Code: cca-3260

NSTA SciLinks
Web Code: ccn-3261

SCIENCE NEWS
Web Code: cce-3263

PLANETDIARY
Web Code: ccc-3262

Materials for Activities and Labs

Quantities for each group

STUDENT EDITION

Inquiry Activity, p. 827
2 flashlights of different brightnesses

Quick Lab, p. 832
portable socket with clear light bulb, paraffin-block photometer, meter stick, calculator

Quick Lab, p. 855
large, wide rubber band that has been cut open; pen; meter stick

Exploration Lab, pp. 856–857
unlined paper, tape, marker, pencil, meter stick, index card, graph paper

TEACHER'S EDITION

Teacher Demo, p. 829
2 identical rubber balls with hollow centers, small nail

Build Science Skills, p. 831
telescope or pair of binoculars, 25-cm by 25-cm piece of cardboard

Teacher Demo, p. 833
iron filings, horseshoe magnet, paper plate

Teacher Demo, p. 843
dark clay, pencil, string, aluminum foil, flashlight

Build Science Skills, p. 850
modeling clay, metric ruler

Chapter Assessment

CHAPTER ASSESSMENT

- **SE** Chapter Assessment, pp. 859–860
- **CUT** Chapter 26 Test A, B
- **CTB** Chapter 26
- **iT** Chapter 26
- **PHSchool.com GO** Web Code: cca-3260

STANDARDIZED TEST PREP

- **SE** Chapter 26, p. 861
- **TP** Diagnose and Prescribe

Interactive Textbook

Interactive Textbook with assessment at PHSchool.com

CHAPTER

26 Before you teach

From the Author

Sophia Yancopoulos
Manhattan College

Big Ideas

People are made of recycled star stuff. How was the universe and everything in it formed, and what will happen to it in the future? There are no bigger questions than these.

Matter and Energy The universe has been expanding ever since the big bang 13.7 billion years ago. The early universe was not homogenous. It was clumpy. These clumps were the seeds of galaxies and stars. A star forms when gravity pulls gas and dust into a cloud that is hot and dense enough for nuclear fusion to begin. But stars change over time as they use up their fuel. Every star eventually dies and becomes a white dwarf, black dwarf, neutron star, or black hole, depending on the amount of mass with which it started. The stars with the most mass are the ones that implode into black holes. They are the brightest stars and have the shortest lives. Intermediate-mass stars turn into neutron stars via supernovas. Supernovas are the only way that elements heavier than iron are produced. Supernovas blow these heavier elements across the galaxy to enrich nebulas where new stars form. The sun formed in such a nebula, and that is why we have a relative abundance of heavy elements on Earth.

Forces and Motion Fusion of hydrogen at the sun's core produces an outward thermal pressure that is countered by gravity. This balance of forces keeps the sun stable and permits life to continue on Earth.

Space and Time Scientists develop and refine instruments such as telescopes and spectrographs to explore and analyze the universe. Hertzsprung-Russell diagrams are used to classify stars according to brightness and temperature, and to infer how stars evolve over time. Hubble's Law relates the rate at which galaxies recede from Earth to their distance from Earth. Hubble's Law directly implies that the universe must have started with the explosion we call the big bang. Astronomers are now mapping the universe, discovering structures at different scales that must be the result of the universe's early clumpiness, carried forward to the present by the expansion of space itself.

Space Science Refresher

Magnetism and Solar Features 26.1

Certain solar features, such as sunspots and prominences, are associated with the sun's magnetic fields. For example, sunspots are cool regions on the surface of the photosphere that look dark compared with surrounding hotter regions. Sunspots are thought to be caused by magnetic fields that interfere with convection, or the movement of thermal energy from the sun's inner layers to its surface. Prominences are also linked to magnetism—they move in graceful arcs along magnetic field lines.

Classifying Stars 26.2

Stars are classified according to their spectra, which in turn can be used to infer the surface temperatures of stars. The classification system currently used was originally developed by Harvard astronomers at the turn of the twentieth century. The modern catalog classifies some 225,000 stars from hottest to coolest, using the letters O, B, A, F, G, K, and M. The sun is a G-type star. G-type stars have a temperature range of about 5000 to 6000 K.

Star Type	Temperature	Color
O	30,000–60,000 K	Blue
B	10,000–30,000 K	Blue-white
A	7500–10,000 K	White
F	6000–7000 K	Yellow-white
G	5000–6000 K	Yellow
K	3500–5000 K	Yellow-orange
M	Less than 3500 K	Red

Life Cycles of Stars 26.3

Stars evolve throughout their life cycles, changing in chemical composition and appearance. Changes in chemical composition are caused by ongoing nuclear fusion, which converts lighter elements to heavier elements. Changes in composition, in turn, affect the evolution of a star. For example, when a main-sequence star depletes the supply of hydrogen in its core, it becomes a red giant because its brightness and size increase while its surface temperature decreases.

Address Misconceptions

Students often think that a light-year is a unit of time. A light-year is actually a unit of distance. For a strategy to overcome this misconception, see **Address Misconceptions** on **page 834.**

Go Online PD LINKS NSTA

For: Teaching methods for exploring the universe
Visit: www.SciLinks.org/PDLinks
Web Code: ccn-2699

Spiral Galaxies 26.4

Address Misconceptions

Students may think that stars last forever. Although stars are very stable over long periods of time, they do change over the course of millions or billions of years, and they eventually die. For a strategy to overcome this misconception, see **Address Misconceptions** on **page 841**.

The Milky Way galaxy has several spiral arms that extend outward like a pinwheel. No one knows for certain how galactic arms form. However, theories suggest that the gravitational force of nearby galaxies or pressure from supernova explosions may cause matter to form arms. Another mystery is how the arms maintain their structure. One theory states that the arms are permanent waves in space. As stars and dust clouds move through these waves, they slow down, and then they move on. Another theory proposes that the arms are being destroyed and reformed continuously in response to disturbances.

Age of the Universe 26.5

Astronomers use different methods to determine the age of the universe. One method involves studying ancient white dwarfs. The cooling rates of these stars are known, so their ages can be estimated. In 2002, the Hubble Space Telescope was used to analyze M4, a cluster of white dwarfs located about 7000 light-years from Earth. The stars were estimated to be 12 to 13 billion years old. Because the first stars formed some 1 billion years after the big bang, the universe must be between 13 and 14 billion years old. Another method is to use Hubble's constant to measure the rate of expansion of the universe. Recent data from the Wilkinson Microwave Anisotropy Probe (WMAP) has produced an extremely accurate value for Hubble's constant. According to WMAP data, the universe is 13.7 billion years old.

Early History of the Universe

Time Passed Since Big Bang	Event	Temperature
10^{-35} seconds	Expansion of the universe stops accelerating and begins to decelerate	10^{19} K
100 seconds	Helium begins to form; hydrogen-to-helium ratio set at 3:1	10^{9} K
1 month	Information from this time preserved in spectrum of the microwave background radiation	10^{7} K
10,000 years	Matter density equals radiation density	8800 K
300,000 years	Astronomers can detect "clumpiness" that leads to galaxy formation	3000 K

Build Reading Literacy

KWL (Know-Want to Know-Learned)

What I Know/What I Want to Know/ What I Learned

Strategy Help students access prior knowledge, set a purpose for reading, recall what has been read, and link new information to prior knowledge. The KWL strategy has students create and complete a three-column chart. As students read, they complete the Learned column. Assign a section from Chapter 26, such as Section 26.1, pp. 828–833, for students to read.

Example

1. **Pre-reading** Have students fill in the first column with information about the topic that they already know. Next, have them preview the section and generate questions they would like to have answered during reading.
2. **Reading** Have students read the section, filling in the third column with the answers to their questions, along with information that was new to them.
3. **Post-reading** Below their KWL chart, have students use the information they've written in the Learned column to make a list headed Information I Expect to Use.

See p. 840 for a script on how to use the KWL strategy with students. For additional Build Reading Literacy strategies, see pp. 830, 836, 847, and 854.

ASSESS PRIOR KNOWLEDGE

Use the Chapter Pretest below to assess students' prior knowledge. As needed, review these Science Concepts and Math Skills with students.

Review Science Concepts

Section 26.1 Ask students to recall what they learned about fusion. Review temperature scales and states of matter, including plasma. Review balanced and unbalanced forces, radiation and convection, and magnetic fields.

Section 26.2 Review distance, the speed of light, and the electromagnetic spectrum. Remind students that light intensity varies with distance from a light source, and the color of light relates to temperature of a glowing object.

Section 26.3 Have students review the formation of the solar system and link this to the life cycle of a star. Review gravitational force and pressure.

Sections 26.4 and 26.5 Review rotation and orbits. Remind students that the Doppler effect relates changes in frequency (or wavelength) to an object's speed relative to an observer.

Review Math Skills

Exponents: Multiplication and Division Students will need to calculate distances in space and equations dealing with astronomical constants. Review the multiplication and division of exponents.

Direct students to the **Math Skills** in the **Skills and Reference Handbook** at the end of the student text.

CHAPTER 26 Exploring the Universe

CONCEPTS in Action

How do science concepts apply to your world? Here are some questions you'll be able to answer after you read this chapter.

- How can the sun disrupt radio and TV signals on Earth? *(Section 26.1)*
- How do we know what stars are made of? *(Section 26.2)*
- What has such strong gravity that not even light can escape from it? *(Section 26.3)*
- Where were the atoms that make up your body formed? *(Section 26.3)*
- What is at the center of our galaxy? *(Section 26.4)*
- Is the universe expanding? *(Section 26.5)*

Discovery Channel School **Video Field Trip**
Measuring Up to Space

- What is the large-scale structure of the universe? *(page 850)*

This cloud of dust and gas is located in the constellation Sagittarius. The red glow is light emitted by hydrogen gas, which is excited by the radiation from hot, young stars nearby. ▶

Chapter Pretest

1. Describe the process of nuclear fusion. *(Less massive nuclei combine to form more massive nuclei.)*

2. True or False: Plasmas are ionized, electrically charged gases. *(True)*

3. How does the intensity of light change with distance from the source? *(c)*

a. Stays the same b. Increases
c. Decreases d. Doubles

4. How did the solar system form? *(The solar system formed from a large, sparse cloud of dust and gas called a solar nebula.)*

5. Which type of electromagnetic wave has the longest wavelength? The shortest? *(Radio waves; gamma waves)*

6. How fast does light move in a vacuum? *(3×10^8 m/s)*

7. The mass of the sun is 1.99×10^{30} kg. The mass of the star Achernar is 1.29×10^{31} kg. Achernar is how many times more massive than the sun? *(6.48)*

8. True or False: In a fluid acted on by gravity, such as the ocean, pressure increases with depth. *(True)*

9. As a source of sound recedes, the frequency of sound ________. *(decreases)*

Chapter Preview

Inquiry Activity

Can You Tell How Bright a Light Really Is?

Procedure

1. Work in groups of three or four. Obtain two flashlights, one brighter than the other.
2. **Predicting** If the dimmer flashlight moves close enough to you, will it appear brighter than the other flashlight? Record your prediction.
3. Darken the room. Have two group members stand side by side about 3 meters from the rest of your group. Each one should shine a flashlight at the group.
4. Direct the person with the dimmer flashlight to slowly move closer to the group, keeping the flashlight level.

Think About It

1. **Observing** Was your prediction correct?
2. **Drawing Conclusions** How does the distance from you to a light affect how bright the light appears to you?
3. **Applying Concepts** If one star appears to be brighter than another star, can you tell which one is actually brighter just by looking at them? Explain your answer.

DISCOVERY CHANNEL SCHOOL **Video Field Trip**

Measuring Up to Space

Encourage students to view the Video Field Trip "Measuring Up to Space."

ENGAGE/EXPLORE

Inquiry Activity

Can You Tell How Bright a Light Really Is? L2

Purpose In this activity, students begin to identify factors that affect how bright a light source appears to be.

Skills Focus Drawing Conclusions

Materials 2 flashlights of different brightnesses

Prep Time 10 minutes

Advance Prep Provide penlights, keychain lights, or other small flashlights. Reduce the brightness of one flashlight by covering it with one or more layers of cheesecloth, plastic screening, waxed paper, or discarded stockings, or by covering the light with aluminum foil and poking a small hole in the middle of the foil.

Class Time 15 minutes

Teaching Tips

- Divide the students into four groups and have them work in different corners of the room. If additional space is available, such as a hallway, increase the number of groups.

Expected Outcome In Step 4, the flashlights will appear to be similar in brightness.

Think About It

1. Students should correctly predict that bringing a dimmer light source closer can make it appear as bright as a brighter source.
2. The closer a light source is, the brighter it appears to be.
3. No. Students will not be able to determine which star is actually brighter. The star that appears to be brighter might actually be less bright but much closer.
Visual, Logical

Section 26.1

1 FOCUS

Objectives

26.1.1 **Describe** how the sun produces energy.

26.1.2 **Explain** why the sun remains stable over time.

26.1.3 **Diagram** and **describe** the interior structure and atmospheric features of the sun.

Reading Focus

Build Vocabulary L2

Word Forms Students may have seen several of the vocabulary terms for this section used in different contexts. Help them to relate these familiar meanings to section content. Ask, **What is the core of an apple?** *(The center of the apple)* **What do you think the core of the sun is?** *(The center of the sun)* **How does air move in a convection current?** *(Warm air rises, cools, then sinks.)* **How do you think gases in the sun's convection zone might move?** *(In the same general pattern as air in Earth's atmosphere)* Repeat this strategy for other terms, such as *zone* and *flare.*

Reading Strategy L2

a. The central region of the sun where fusion occurs **b.** A region of highly compressed gas where energy is transferred mainly by radiation **c.** The outer layer of the sun's interior, where energy is transferred mainly by convection

2 INSTRUCT

Energy From the Sun

Use Visuals L1

Figure 2 Tell students that the superscripts attached to the elements represent mass number. Write the following equations on the board to help students visualize nuclear fusion:

$$^{2}_{1}H + ^{1}_{1}H \longrightarrow ^{3}_{2}He + \text{gamma ray photon}$$

$$^{3}_{2}He + ^{3}_{2}He \longrightarrow ^{4}_{2}He + 2\,^{1}_{1}H$$

Ask students to explain the process in their own words. *(Sample answer: Hydrogen nuclei collide to produce helium-3 and gamma rays. Helium-3 nuclei collide to form helium-4 and hydrogen nuclei.)* **Visual**

26.1 The Sun

Reading Focus

Key Concepts

- How does the sun produce energy?
- Why does the sun remain stable over time?
- What is the structure of the sun?
- What are some features of the sun's atmosphere?

Vocabulary

- core
- radiation zone
- convection zone
- photosphere
- chromosphere
- corona
- solar wind
- sunspots
- prominences
- solar flare

Reading Strategy

Building Vocabulary Copy the table below. Then, as you read, write a definition of each vocabulary term in your own words. Add seven more rows to complete the vocabulary list.

Vocabulary Term	Definition
Core	a. ___?___
Radiation zone	b. ___?___
Convection zone	c. ___?___

You know that flowers like the ones in Figure 1 need sunlight. In fact, almost all life on Earth depends on sunlight. Without the sun's radiation, Earth would be a cold, dark, and lifeless planet. But what exactly is the sun? Scientists have learned that the sun is a glowing ball of gas. The sun is extremely hot, about 15 million K at its center and 5800 K at its surface. At such temperatures, most of the atoms in the sun have lost most of their electrons, forming a plasma of ionized gas. About 70 percent of the sun's mass is hydrogen and 28 percent is helium.

Figure 1 The sun gives off tremendous amounts of energy. Plants on Earth use sunlight directly in photosynthesis.

Energy From the Sun

The sun gives off tremendous amounts of energy in the form of electromagnetic radiation. But what is the source of this energy? Does the sun burn some type of fuel? If so, how long will it continue to burn before all its fuel is used up? Because the sun and Earth formed together, the answers to these questions can be used to estimate the age of Earth. As a result, scientists from many different fields began a debate that lasted more than 100 years.

In the late 1700s, the German philosopher Immanuel Kant wondered whether the sun produced its energy from an ordinary chemical reaction. He calculated that if it did, it could last only a few thousand years. In the mid-1800s, two physicists, Hermann von Helmholtz and William Thomson (better known as Lord Kelvin), proposed another idea. They hypothesized that gravity was causing the sun to shrink over time, converting its potential energy into thermal energy. According to their calculations, the sun was no more than 20 to 30 million years old.

Section Resources

Print

- ***Laboratory Manual,*** Investigation 26A
- ***Reading and Study Workbook With Math Support,*** Section 26.1
- ***Transparencies,*** Chapter Pretest and Section 26.1

Technology

- ***Interactive Textbook,*** Section 26.1
- ***Presentation Pro CD-ROM,*** Chapter Pretest and Section 26.1
- ***Go Online,*** NSTA SciLinks, The sun

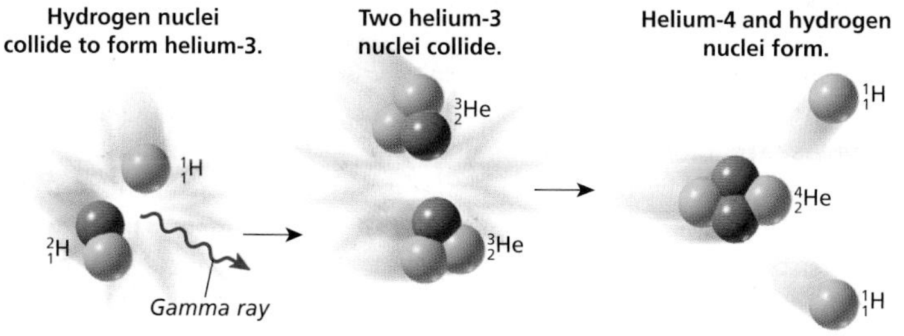

Hydrogen nuclei collide to form helium-3.
Two helium-3 nuclei collide.
Helium-4 and hydrogen nuclei form.
$^{1}_{1}H$
$^{2}_{1}H$
Gamma ray
$^{3}_{2}He$
$^{3}_{2}He$
$^{4}_{2}He$
$^{1}_{1}H$
$^{1}_{1}H$

Figure 2 Nuclear fusion within the sun's central region converts mass into energy. The green particles in the diagram are protons and the purple particles are neutrons. **Interpreting Diagrams** ***What new isotope is produced by this fusion reaction?***

Scottish geologist Charles Lyell disagreed. Lyell argued that geological processes on Earth had taken hundreds of millions of years. Therefore, Earth and the sun must be far older than other scientists had thought. Evidence from various branches of science eventually led scientists to conclude that the sun is actually about 4.6 billion years old.

How could the sun produce energy for so long? Clearly, the hypotheses about chemical reactions and the sun shrinking were incorrect, as they could not account for the actual age of the sun. It wasn't until the early 1900s that scientists discovered the real source of the sun's energy—nuclear fusion in its central region. Here the temperature and pressure are high enough for fusion to take place. In the process of fusion, as shown in Figure 2, less massive nuclei combine into more massive nuclei, releasing enormous amounts of energy. **The sun's energy is produced in its central region by the fusion of hydrogen nuclei into helium nuclei.**

Forces in Balance

The fossil record of life on Earth shows that the sun has been a fairly stable energy source for billions of years. For the sun to be stable, inward and outward forces within the sun must be in equilibrium. The forces are balanced so that temperature, pressure, and density at any depth remain fairly constant over time.

The energy from nuclear fusion in the center of the sun causes ions to move faster, exerting an outward thermal pressure. At the same time, gravity pulls the gas inward, as shown in Figure 3. **The sun remains stable because the inward pull of gravity balances the outward push of thermal pressure from nuclear fusion.** The sun will remain stable as long as there is a steady energy source within it. Astronomers estimate that the sun will remain stable for another 5 billion years.

Reading Checkpoint *How long will the sun remain stable?*

Figure 3 Gravity and the outward thermal pressure from nuclear fusion are balanced throughout the sun. Both the force of gravity and the pressure are greater deep within the sun than near the sun's surface. **Predicting** ***What would happen to the sun if it began to run out of fuel?***

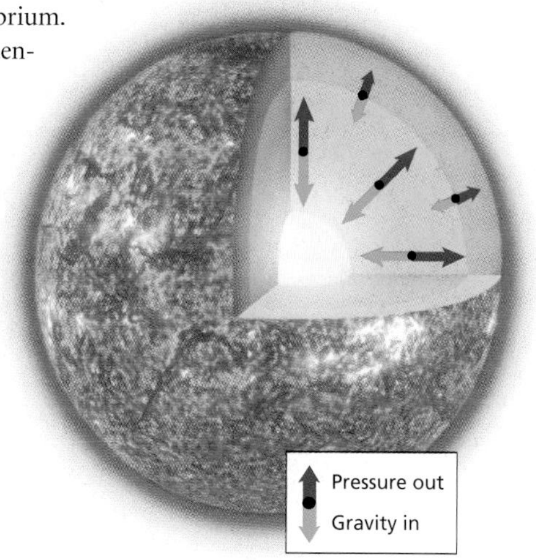

Pressure out
Gravity in

Forces in Balance

Teacher Demo

Balanced Forces **L2**

Purpose Students observe the balance of forces acting on the sun.

Materials 2 identical rubber balls with hollow centers, small nail

Procedure Puncture one of the balls with a nail. Then, squeeze and release both balls. Allow students to observe that the punctured ball remains compressed.

Expected Outcome Help students relate the demonstration to balanced forces throughout the sun. Ask, **Which ball represents forces acting on the sun? Explain.** *(The unpunctured ball represents forces acting on the sun because it remained stable. Inward and outward forces were balanced.)*
Visual

Customize for English Language Learners

List-Group-Label
Have students work in groups to list, group, and label new vocabulary words for this section. (Do not place all ELL students in the same group. Place advanced speakers with intermediate or advanced students and beginning speakers with average students.) Students should first list any word or words that remind them of the topic at hand. They should then group the words according to shared characteristics or relationships. Finally, they should label the word groupings using a title that reflects the relationship among the words.

Answer to . . .

Figure 2 *Helium*

Figure 3 *Initially, the star's core would shrink because gravity would gain the upper hand as thermal pressure dropped. However, the final result is more complex, as explained later in the chapter in the discussion of red giants.*

Reading Checkpoint *The sun will remain stable for about another 5 billion years.*

The Sun's Interior

Build Reading Literacy L1

Think Aloud Refer to page **410D** in **Chapter 14**, which provides the guidelines for thinking aloud.

Verbalize your thoughts as you read aloud the text on p. 830. This will help students to recognize the cognitive and metacognitive strategies good readers use to promote comprehension. For example, the first sentence on the page states, "Astronomers cannot see inside the sun." Say to students something like, **The first thought that comes to me is "How do astronomers know what the interior of the sun looks like?"** As you continue reading, point out that your question is answered in the following sentences.
Verbal

Use Visuals L1

Figure 4 Have students examine the diagram of the sun. Ask, **Which part of the sun extends farthest into space?** *(Corona)* **Which part of the sun do we normally see?** *(Photosphere)* **What do the arrows show?** *(The movement of convection currents)*
Visual

The Sun's Interior

Astronomers cannot see inside the sun. However, they are able to infer the structure of the sun's interior. They use mathematical models and observe vibrations of the sun that are similar to vibrations caused by earthquakes on Earth. The sun's interior and atmosphere are divided into several layers with distinct characteristics. **The sun's interior consists of the core, the radiation zone, and the convection zone.** Figure 4 illustrates the structure of the sun.

Core The sun's **core** is its central region, where nuclear fusion occurs. The core has a diameter of about 400,000 kilometers, a little more than a quarter of the diameter of the entire sun.

Radiation Zone You are able to see the sun because some of the energy produced in its core travels outward and escapes into space as visible light. Energy moves through the sun in two main ways: by radiation and by convection. As energy moves outward from the sun's core, it first enters the radiation zone. The **radiation zone** is a region of highly compressed gas. Here, energy is transferred by the absorption and reradiation of electromagnetic waves. Because this region is so dense, energy can take more than 100,000 years to pass through it.

Figure 4 The sun has an interior and an atmosphere. The interior consists of the core, radiation zone, and convection zone. The atmosphere consists of the photosphere, chromosphere, and corona.
Interpreting Diagrams ***What is the diameter of the sun's core?***

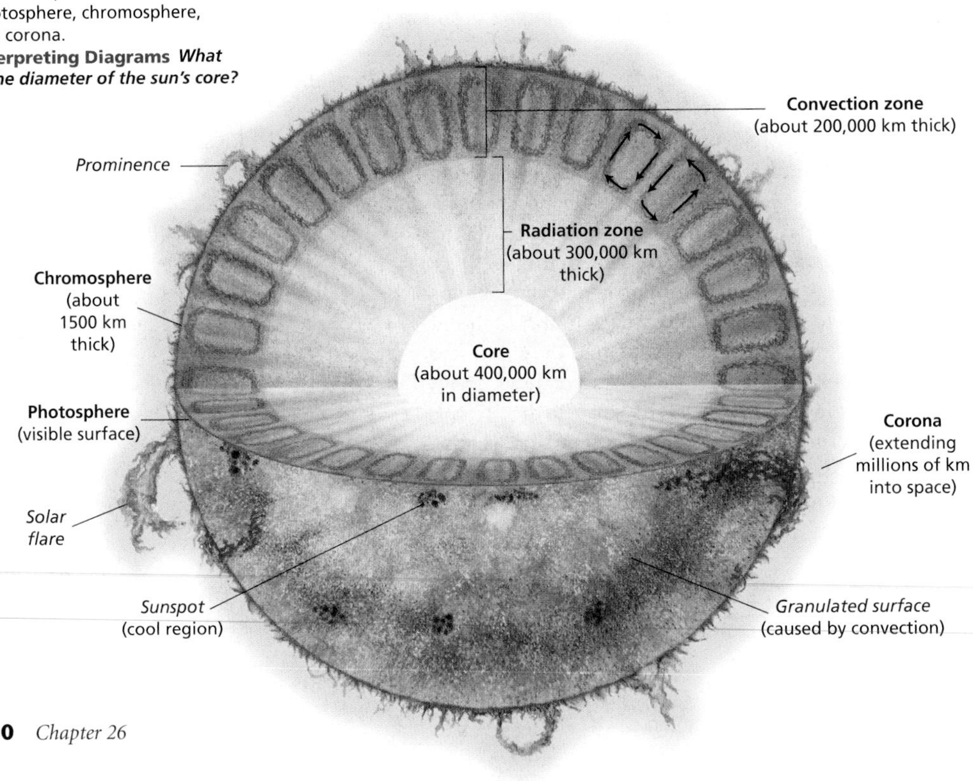

Convection zone
(about 200,000 km thick)
Prominence
Radiation zone
(about 300,000 km thick)
Chromosphere
(about 1500 km thick)
Core
(about 400,000 km in diameter)
Photosphere
(visible surface)
Corona
(extending millions of km into space)
Solar flare
Sunspot
(cool region)
Granulated surface
(caused by convection)

Facts and Figures

A Changing Sun Because of nuclear fusion, the sun's composition is slowly changing. In its upper layers, the sun is about 73% hydrogen and 25% helium, with other elements making up the remaining 2% of the sun's mass. In the sun's core, the percentage of hydrogen has dropped sharply because the sun uses hydrogen as fuel. In nuclear fusion, the sun converts about 700 million tons of hydrogen into helium every second with the simultaneous conversion of about 5 million tons of matter into energy in accordance with Einstein's equation $E = mc^2$.

Convection Zone Energy from the radiation zone passes into the **convection zone,** the outer layer of the sun's interior. In the convection zone, energy is transferred outward mainly by convection currents. Hot gases in the convection zone rise toward the sun's atmosphere while cooler gases sink downward.

The Sun's Atmosphere

Outside the convection zone is the sun's atmosphere. **The sun's atmosphere consists of three layers: the photosphere, the chromosphere, and the corona.**

Photosphere The innermost layer of the sun's atmosphere, which is the visible surface of the sun, is the **photosphere** (FOH tuh sfeer). It is about 500 kilometers thick and has an average temperature of about 5800 K. Although the photosphere is not solid, it is called the sun's surface. Astronomers can't see through it to the sun's interior. The photosphere's surface has a bubbly appearance. The bubbles, called granules, are the tops of convection currents that carry energy from the sun's interior.

Figure 5 The corona can only be seen from Earth during a total solar eclipse or when viewed with a special telescope.

Chromosphere Just outside the photosphere is the **chromosphere** (KROH muh sfeer), the middle layer of the sun's atmosphere. Temperature increases to nearly 10,000 K as you move upward through the chromosphere. At such high temperatures, hydrogen gas emits a reddish light. This light gives the chromosphere its name, which means "sphere of color." The faint chromosphere is normally visible only when the brighter photosphere is blocked, such as during a total solar eclipse.

Corona The chromosphere merges with the **corona,** the outermost layer of the sun's atmosphere. The gases in the corona are so thin that the corona, like the chromosphere, is usually seen only during solar eclipses. Gases in the corona are very hot, about 1 million kelvins. But the corona has such a low density that the total amount of thermal energy in it is relatively small.

The corona, shown in Figure 5, extends millions of kilometers above the chromosphere. It gradually thins into the **solar wind,** a stream of electrically charged particles that flows outward from the sun through the solar system. As the solar wind approaches Earth, Earth's magnetic field deflects the charged particles. These particles enter the atmosphere only near Earth's magnetic poles. There they can interact with molecules in the atmosphere, producing auroras.

Reading Checkpoint *What is the solar wind?*

Go Online NSTA SCILINKS

For: Links on the sun
Visit: www.SciLinks.org
Web Code: ccn-3261

The Sun's Atmosphere

Integrate Biology L2

Show students a model or diagram of a human eye. Point out the path of light as it enters the cornea, passes through the pupil, and is focused by the lens onto the retina, where an image is formed. Tell students that sight depends on the sensory neurons found in the retina. Intense light can damage the retina. Ask, **Why should you never look directly at the sun?** *(Your retina could be damaged.)* **Visual, Logical**

Build Science Skills L2

Observing ACTIVITY

Purpose Students learn how to safely observe the sun.

Materials telescope or pair of binoculars, 25-cm by 25-cm piece of cardboard

Class Time 30 minutes

Safety Remind students to never look directly at the sun.

Procedure On a sunny day, take students outside and have a volunteer hold the cardboard a few feet from the ground. Reverse the telescope so that the eyepiece lens is facing the sky. Then, try to capture the image of the sun on the cardboard. Adjust the cardboard or telescope as needed. Allow students to take turns holding the cardboard and telescope.

Expected Outcome Students will use the focus to get a clear image of the sun. They will learn how to safely observe features of the sun's surface, such as sunspots. **Kinesthetic, Group**

Go Online NSTA SCILINKS

Download a worksheet on the sun for students to complete, and find additional teacher support from NSTA SciLinks.

Answer to . . .

Figure 4 *About 400,000 km*

Reading Checkpoint *A stream of charged particles that flows outward from the sun through the solar system*

Features of the Sun's Atmosphere

Quick Lab L2

Calculating the Sun's Power

Objective
After completing this activity, students will be able to
- calculate the relative power of two light sources using a simple comparison photometer.

Skills Focus Measuring, Calculating

Prep Time 15 minutes

Advance Prep Construct the photometers. Paraffin is sold with home canning supplies. Each photometer is made from two 6-cm × 6-cm × 1-cm pieces of canning paraffin and a 6-cm × 12-cm piece of aluminum foil. Fold the aluminum foil in half so the shiny side is out. Sandwich the aluminum foil between the pieces of paraffin and hold the pieces together with rubber bands.

Class Time 20 minutes

Safety Students should use caution when working with electrical equipment and hot light bulbs.

Teaching Tips
- If the sun does not shine directly into your room, you will need to do this activity outdoors, using an extension cord for the light bulb.
- In Step 1, help students determine the light output of the bulb in watts. They will need this value, not the electric power consumption on the bulb, for their calculations.
- Ask students to identify sources of experimental error in the procedure. Students may suggest that the paraffin photometer is not very accurate. One way to reduce this error is to use a photographer's hand-held light meter.

Expected Outcome Students should calculate the power of the sun.

For Enrichment L3

Students can design an experiment using bulbs of various powers and the photometer to determine the relationship between apparent brightness and distance. They should be able to plot data from such an experiment to reveal an inverse-square relationship between apparent brightness and distance.
Logical

Quick Lab

Calculating the Sun's Power

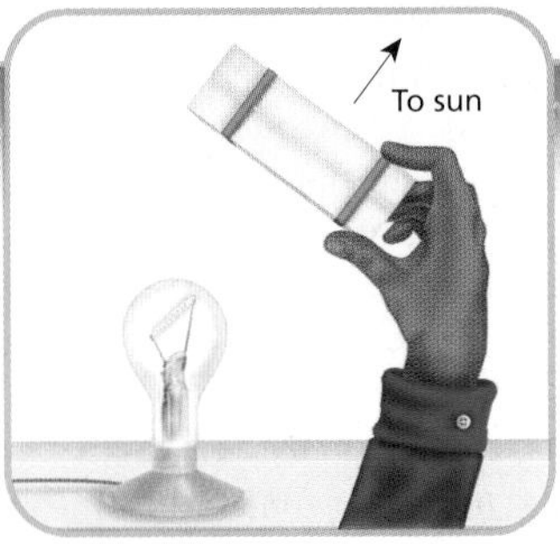
To sun

Materials

portable socket with clear light bulb, paraffin-block photometer, meter stick, calculator

Procedure

1. You can estimate the sun's power by comparing it to the known power of a light bulb. Because a bulb's efficiency is about 10 percent, its actual power (P_{bulb}) is the rated power in watts divided by 10.
2. Place the socket on a table so that the bulb filament is perpendicular to the direction of the sun. Turn the bulb on. **CAUTION** *The bulb will become very hot. Do not touch it.*
3. A photometer is used to measure light levels. Hold the photometer directly between the bulb and the sun as shown. **CAUTION** *Do not look directly at the sun.*
4. Look at the narrow edge of the photometer. Move the photometer toward or away from the bulb until the slabs of paraffin on the two sides of the foil seem equally bright.
5. Have a partner measure the distance (D_{bulb}) in centimeters from the foil to the filament.

Analyze and Conclude

1. **Calculating** Earth is about 150 million km from the sun. What is the distance (D_{sun}) between Earth and the sun in centimeters?
2. **Calculating** How bright a light source appears depends directly on its actual power and inversely on the square of its distance from the observer. When the photometer is positioned so that the bulb and the sun appear equally bright, the following ratios are equal:

$$\frac{P_{bulb}}{D^2_{bulb}} = \frac{P_{sun}}{D^2_{sun}}$$

Square your values for D_{bulb} and D_{sun}. Then insert these values and your value for P_{bulb} into the formula. Use the formula to calculate the actual power of the sun (P_{sun}) in watts.

Figure 6 Sunspots are relatively cool areas on the sun's surface. **Interpreting Photos** *How do sunspots appear different from the surrounding photosphere?*

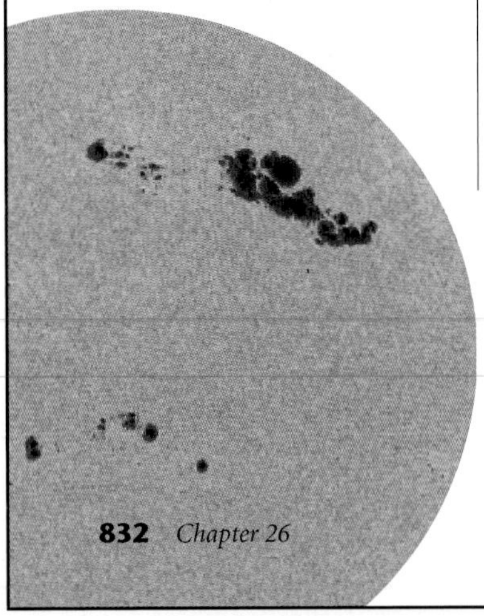

Features of the Sun's Atmosphere

The sun's magnetic field produces striking features on and above its surface. **Features of the sun's atmosphere include sunspots, prominences, and solar flares.**

Sunspots Look at Figure 6. The relatively small, dark-looking regions on the sun's surface are called sunspots. **Sunspots** are areas of gas in the photosphere that are cooler than the surrounding gases. However, sunspots aren't really small. Some are larger than Earth! They are also not really dark. If sunspots could be seen apart from the rest of the sun, they would shine brightly. But because they are cooler, sunspots give off less energy than the surrounding photosphere, and so they appear dark by comparison. Sunspots are often found in groups and are associated with intense magnetic fields on the sun. Sunspots last from a few hours to a few months. The number of sunspots varies in cycles, with about 11 years separating one sunspot peak from the next. During peak periods, there may be a hundred sunspots on the sun.

832 *Chapter 26*

Analyze and Conclude
1. Earth is about 1.5×10^{13} cm from the sun.
2. Sample data: If a 100-W bulb that produces 10 W of visible light is placed 10 cm from the photometer, then students should conclude that the sun produces visible light with a power of 2.25×10^{25} W.
Kinesthetic, Logical

Sunspots provide astronomers with insights into the motions of the sun. The Italian scientist Galileo Galilei discovered that the sun rotates by observing the motion of sunspots. Later observations showed that the sun doesn't spin as a solid body the way Earth does. Instead, sunspots near the sun's equator move faster than sunspots near the sun's poles. This means that the sun rotates faster at its equator than near its poles.

Prominences Prominences are spectacular features of the sun's atmosphere that occur near sunspots. As shown in Figure 7A, **prominences** are huge loops of gas that erupt from sunspot regions. They extend upward from the photosphere into the chromosphere and sometimes into the corona. Prominences travel along the magnetic field lines that connect sunspots. Some prominences reach heights of more than 100,000 kilometers above the sun's surface.

Figure 7 The sun's magnetic field produces prominences and flares visible with special red filters. **A** This prominence forms a huge twirling loop connecting sunspot regions. **B** A solar flare erupts on the edge of the sun.

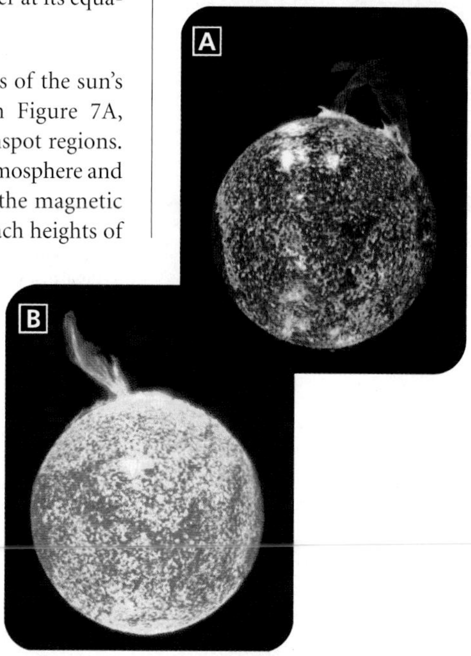

A
B

Solar Flares The sun's surface sometimes erupts dramatically, producing X-rays and hurling charged particles into space at speeds of 1000 km/s or more. Such a sudden release of energy from the sun is called a **solar flare.** Like prominences, solar flares usually occur near sunspots. Solar flares heat the corona to a temperature near 20 million K and greatly increase the solar wind. When the additional high-energy particles and radiation from a solar flare reach Earth, they can cause magnetic storms in Earth's upper atmosphere. These storms disrupt electric power transmission as well as radio, television, and telephone signals.

Section 26.1 Assessment

Reviewing Concepts

1. What is the source of the sun's energy?
2. What two forces in the sun interact to produce a stable structure?
3. List the layers of the sun's interior from the center outward and briefly describe each one.
4. Describe each of the layers of the sun's atmosphere from the surface outward.
5. Describe three features that exist on or above the sun's surface.

Critical Thinking

6. **Applying Concepts** How have scientists learned about the sun's interior?
7. **Calculating** The sun's mass is more than 300,000 times the mass of Earth. The sun's volume is about 1,000,000 times that of Earth. How much denser is Earth than the sun?

Writing in Science

Describing the Sun Describe in a few paragraphs an imaginary journey to the center of the sun, beginning from its outermost layer. Include a description of each layer and at least two prominent features.

Section 26.1 Assessment

1. Nuclear fusion in the sun's core
2. Gravity and the thermal pressure from fusion
3. Core: central region where fusion takes place; radiation zone: middle layer, energy is transferred mainly by radiation; convection zone: outer layer, energy is transferred mainly by convection
4. Photosphere: surface layer that emits visible light; chromosphere: middle layer of the atmosphere; corona: outer layer of the atmosphere, very hot but low density
5. Sunspots are relatively small, cool, dark-looking regions in the photosphere. Prominences are huge loops of gas that erupt from sunspot regions. Solar flares are sudden eruptions on the sun's surface that produce X-rays and high-energy particles.
6. By using mathematical models and observing vibrations within the sun that are similar to those caused by earthquakes on Earth
7. $\text{Density}_{\text{Earth}}/\text{Density}_{\text{Sun}} = (\text{Mass}_{\text{Earth}}/\text{Volume}_{\text{Earth}})/(\text{Mass}_{\text{Sun}}/\text{Volume}_{\text{Sun}}) = (10^6)(3 \times 10^5)$ = about three times denser than the sun's average density

Address Misconceptions L2

One common astronomical misconception is that the surface of the sun does not have any visible features. Have students study Figures 6 and 7. In their own words, have them describe features of the sun. If necessary, repeat the Build Science Skills activity on p. 831. Have students try to identify sunspots. **Visual**

Teacher Demo

Sunspot Model L2

Purpose Students observe the association between sunspots and solar magnetic fields.

Materials iron filings, horseshoe magnet, paper plate

Procedure Sprinkle the iron filings on the paper plate. Hold the plate up and place the ends of the magnet under the plate. Have students observe the patterns formed by the iron filings.

Expected Outcome Remind students that sunspot groups trace out magnetic field lines on the sun. Ask, **How does this relate to the demonstration?** *(The iron filings trace out magnetic field lines just as sunspots do.)* **Visual**

3 ASSESS

Evaluate Understanding L2

Have students make concept maps of the features of the sun.

Reteach L1

Using Figure 4 as a guide, draw the interior structure and atmosphere of the sun on the board. As you draw each layer, orally summarize its characteristics.

Writing in Science

Each of the layers of the sun should be described in order, noting such characteristics as temperature.

Interactive Textbook If your class subscribes to the Interactive Textbook, use it to review key concepts in Section 26.1.

Answer to . . .

Figure 6 *Sunspots appear darker than the surrounding photosphere.*

1 FOCUS

Objectives

26.2.1 **Demonstrate** how distance to a star is measured.

26.2.2 **Classify** stars according to chemical and physical properties.

26.2.3 **Interpret** the H-R diagram.

Reading Focus

Build Vocabulary L2

Compare/Contrast Tables Have students make tables comparing and contrasting groups of vocabulary terms for this section. Students should look for relationships among the words before they develop their tables. For example, *main sequence, supergiants, giants,* and *white dwarfs* are all types of stars.

Reading Strategy L2

a. and b. Various properties may be listed, such as color or temperature, absolute brightness, and size.

2 INSTRUCT

Distances to the Stars

Build Science Skills L2

Inferring Tell students that a light-year is more than a unit of distance. It is also a glimpse into the past. For example, it takes light 4.3 years to travel the 4.3 light-years from Proxima Centauri to Earth. When you look at Proxima Centauri in the night sky, you are seeing the star as it was 4.3 years ago. Ask, **If Proxima Centauri no longer generated light, how long would it take before we knew the star had died?** *(4.3 years)* **Verbal, Logical**

Address Misconceptions L2

Given its name, students often think of a light-year as a unit of time, rather than a unit of measure. To help overcome this misconception, have them read the text on p. 834 under the heading The Light-Year. Then, have them confirm that the distance to Proxima Centauri (4.3 light-years) equals 41 trillion km. *([41 trillion km]/[9.5 trillion km/light-year] = 4.3 light-years)* **Logical**

26.2 Stars

Reading Focus

Key Concepts

- How can the distance to a star be measured?
- How do astronomers categorize stars?
- What elements are found in stars?
- How do astronomers use H-R diagrams?

Vocabulary

- star
- light-year
- parallax
- apparent brightness
- absolute brightness
- absorption lines
- H-R diagram
- main sequence
- supergiants
- giants
- white dwarf

Reading Strategy

Using Prior Knowledge Copy the concept map below. Add what you already know about stars. After you read, complete your concept map, adding more ovals as needed.

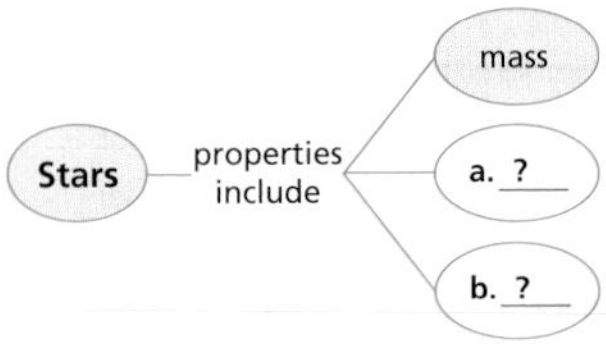

Stars
properties include
mass
a. ?
b. ?

If you look up at the sky at night, you'll see that stars look like points of light. You will probably also notice that some stars are brighter than others. If you look closely, you'll see that some stars have different colors, as shown in Figure 8. However, you can't tell how large or how far away a star is simply by looking at it. You can't poke a star, crawl around inside it, or take its temperature with a thermometer. To explore the stars, modern astronomers use spectrographs and other instruments mounted on telescopes.

A **star** is a large, glowing ball of gas in space, which generates energy through nuclear fusion in its core. The closest star to Earth is the sun, which is considered to be a fairly average star.

Figure 8 Proxima Centauri, the red star at the center, is the closest star to the sun.

Distances to the Stars

Although the sky seems full of stars, most of the universe is nearly empty space. This seeming contradiction exists because most stars are separated by vast distances.

The Light-Year You wouldn't measure the distance between two distant cities in centimeters. Similarly, because stars are so far apart, it's not practical to measure their distances in units that might be used on Earth, such as kilometers. Instead, astronomers use much larger units, including the light-year. A **light-year** is the distance that light travels in a vacuum in a year, which is about 9.5 trillion kilometers. Proxima Centauri, the closest star to the sun, is about 4.3 light-years away.

Section Resources

Print
- ***Reading and Study Workbook With Math Support,*** Section 26.2 and **Math Skill:** Calculating Distances to Stars
- ***Transparencies,*** Section 26.2

Technology
- ***Interactive Textbook,*** Section 26.2
- ***Presentation Pro CD-ROM,*** Section 26.2
- ***Go Online,*** *Planet Diary,* Astronomy

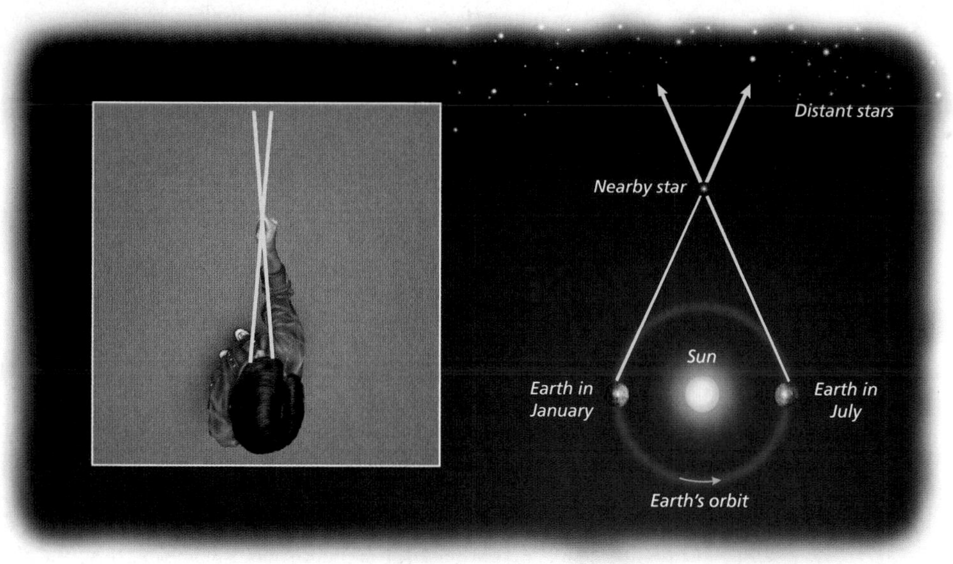

Distant stars
Nearby star
Sun
Earth in January
Earth in July
Earth's orbit

Parallax Stars are so far away that astronomers cannot measure their distances directly. Astronomers have developed various methods of determining the distances to stars. Different methods are used for stars at different distances.

To understand how astronomers can measure distances to nearby stars, hold your thumb up at arm's length in front of you, as the student is doing in Figure 9. Close your left eye and look at your thumb with just your right eye open. Then cover your right eye and look with just your left eye open. Even though you didn't move your thumb, it appeared to move relative to the background because you looked at it from slightly different angles. The apparent change in position of an object with respect to a distant background is called **parallax.**

As Earth moves in its orbit, astronomers are able to observe stars from two different positions. Imagine looking at the stars in winter and then six months later in summer. During this time, Earth has moved from one side of its orbit to the other—a distance of about 300 million kilometers. Because people on Earth are looking from a different angle, the nearby star appears to move against the more-distant background stars.

Before the invention of the telescope, astronomers couldn't measure a star's position very accurately. They couldn't detect the apparent movement of even a single nearby star as Earth moved around the sun.

With the invention of the telescope, astronomers could measure the positions of stars with much greater accuracy. **Astronomers measure the parallax of nearby stars to determine their distance from Earth.** The closer a star is to Earth, the greater is its parallax.

Figure 9 You can observe parallax by holding your thumb in front of you. Compare its positions when you look at it first with one eye and then with the other. Astronomers can measure the parallax of nearby stars by measuring their position relative to distant stars as the Earth revolves around the sun. **Observing** ***Is the parallax of your thumb greater when it is closer to your eyes or when it is farther from your eyes?***

Build Math Skills L1

Exponents: Multiplication and Division Have students practice working with exponents by comparing the light-year to the AU. Ask them to write 9.46 trillion km (one light-year) in exponential form. *(9.46×10^{12} km)* Remind students that the average distance from Earth to the sun is 149,598,000 km (one AU). Have them write this number in exponential form. *(1.496×10^{8} km)* Then, have students divide the numbers to determine how many AU equal one light-year. *([9.46×10^{12} km/light-year]/[1.496×10^{8} km/AU] = 63,200 AU/light-year)*
Logical

Direct students to the **Math Skills** in the **Skills and Reference Handbook** at the end of the student text for additional help.

Use Visuals L1

Figure 9 Tell students that even the largest measured parallax of a star is less than the apparent width of a dime at a distance of a mile. It is much too small to be seen with the unaided eye. Ask, **Why does the star appear to move?** *(Earth has moved from one side of its orbit to the other. An observer on Earth is viewing the star from a different angle.)* **What do the arrows show?** *(The angle of sight of an observer on Earth)*
Visual

Build Science Skills L2

Calculating Explain that parallax is typically measured in arc-seconds, a unit equal to 1/3600 of a degree. A star could have a parallax, for example, of 1 arc-sec, abbreviated as 1". A parsec is a unit of measure equal to the distance at which a star's parallax is 1 arc-second. One parsec is equal to 3.26 light-years. The following formula is used to calculate the distance of a star in parsecs: $d = 1/p$ where d represents distance in parsecs and p represents parallax in arc-seconds. Write the formula on the board and have students calculate the distance to a star that has a parallax of 0.20". *(1/0.20" = 5.0 parsecs)* Then, ask students to convert this distance to light-years. *(5.0 parsecs × 3.26 light-years/parsec = 16 light-years)*
Logical

Customize for Inclusion Students

Learning Disabled
Inspire confidence in learning-disabled students by beginning each new topic with a question or activity that they can successfully master. For example, you could start this section by asking students to describe the night sky. Or, you could ask them to calculate their age when light from Proxima Centauri left the star. Simply say, **Light left the star more than four years ago. How old were you then?**

Answer to . . .

Figure 9 *When it is closer to your eyes*

Properties of Stars

Build Reading Literacy L1

Predict Refer to page **66D** in **Chapter 3**, which provides the guidelines for predicting.

Before students read about the properties of stars, tell them that stars range in color from blue to white to yellow to red, similar to flames from a fire. Have them picture a flame—different parts are hotter than others. Based on what they know about these temperature differences, ask them to predict which color indicates the hottest star. *(Blue)* Have students read the text to see if their predictions were correct.
Logical

Build Math Skills L1

Conversion Factors Remind students that temperatures are measured from absolute zero on the Kelvin scale. On the Celsius scale, absolute zero is −273°. The formula for converting kelvins to degrees Celsius is C = K − 273. Point out that at the high surface temperatures of stars, there is not much difference between the Kelvin and Celsius scale temperatures. Have students convert the surface temperatures of the following stars from kelvins to degrees Celsius: Spica, 22,973 K; the sun, 5773 K; Castor C, 3573 K. *(Spica: 22,973 K − 273 K = 22,700°C; the sun: 5773 K − 273 K = 5500°C; Castor C: 3573 K − 273 K = 3300°C)*
Logical

Direct students to the **Math Skills** in the **Skills and Reference Handbook** at the end of the student text for additional help.

Go Online PLANETDIARY

Find links to additional activities and have students monitor phenomena that affect Earth and its residents.

Go Online PLANETDIARY

For: Links on astronomy
Visit: PHSchool.com
Web Code: ccc-3262

Astronomers have measured the parallax of many nearby stars and determined their distances from Earth. However, if a star is too far away, its parallax is too small to be measured. With present technology, the parallax method gives reasonably accurate distance measurements for stars within a few hundred light-years. Astronomers have developed other ways to estimate distances to more-distant stars.

Properties of Stars

There are many different types of stars. **Astronomers classify stars by their color, size, and brightness. Other important properties of stars include their chemical composition and mass.**

Color and Temperature Have you ever looked closely at a candle flame? The hottest part of the flame near the wick is blue or white, while the cooler flame tip is orange. A propane torch flame is blue. Dying campfire embers are red. You can estimate the temperature of a flame from its color. In the same way, a star's color indicates the temperature of its surface. The hottest stars, with surface temperatures above 30,000 K, appear blue. The surfaces (photospheres) of relatively cool red stars are still a toasty 3000 K or so. Stars with surface temperatures between 5000 and 6000 K appear yellow, like the sun. As shown in Figure 10, the color differences between hot blue stars and cool red stars can be seen with the unaided eye. More precise measurements of stars' temperatures can be made by studying stars' spectra.

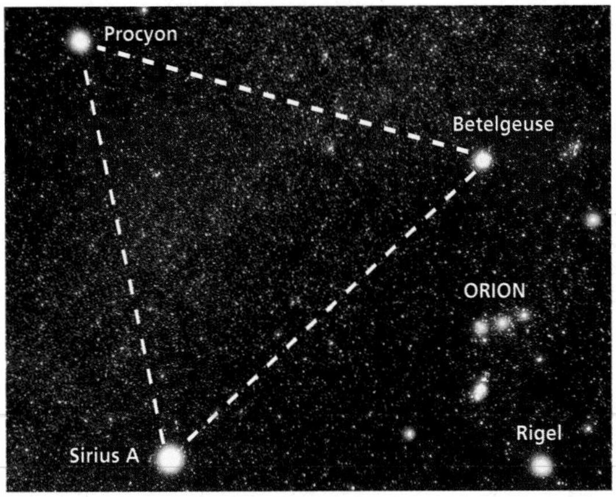

Procyon
Betelgeuse
ORION
Rigel
Sirius A

Figure 10 The "Winter Triangle" can be seen in the late fall and winter in the eastern sky. It is made up of three of the brightest stars in the sky: Betelgeuse, Procyon, and Sirius A. Betelgeuse and the star Rigel belong to the constellation Orion. ***Applying Concepts** Which star has a higher surface temperature, Betelgeuse or Sirius A?*

Brightness When you walk along a street at night, such as the one shown in Figure 11, look up at a row of street lights. The closer lights look bright and the more distant lights look dim. However, the more distant lights are not really dimmer. They appear dim to you because, at a greater distance, their light is spread out over a greater area, so a smaller portion enters your eyes. The same is true for the light emitted by stars.

You might think that closer stars will always appear brighter than more-distant stars. Astronomers have discovered, however, that the brightness of stars can vary by a factor of more than a billion. So, stars that look bright may actually be farther away than stars that appear dim.

Although the sun appears to be the brightest star in our sky, it is really a star of only average brightness. The sun appears very bright to us because it is much closer than other stars. The brightness of a star as it appears from Earth is called its **apparent brightness.** The apparent brightness of a star decreases as its distance from you increases.

If you move away from a street light or a star, it shines just as brightly as before—but to you it appears fainter. **Absolute brightness** is how bright a star really is. A star's absolute brightness is a characteristic of the star and does not depend on how far it is from Earth. You can calculate a star's absolute brightness if you know its distance from Earth and its apparent brightness.

Size and Mass Once astronomers know a star's temperature and absolute brightness, they can estimate its diameter and then calculate its volume. However, there is no direct way of finding the mass of an isolated star. Instead, astronomers are able to calculate the masses of many stars by observing the gravitational interaction of stars that occur in pairs. From such observations, astronomers have determined that, for most stars, there is a relationship between mass and absolute brightness. Astronomers have found that many stars are similar to the sun in size and mass.

Figure 11 These streetlights all have about the same absolute brightness. **Inferring** ***Why do the nearby streetlights appear brighter than the distant ones?***

Reading Checkpoint *How can astronomers determine a star's mass?*

Composition A spectrograph is an instrument that spreads light from a hot glowing object, such as a light bulb or a star, into a spectrum. Astronomers can use spectrographs to identify the various elements in a star's atmosphere.

Each star has its own spectrum. The elements within a star's atmosphere absorb light from the star's photosphere. Each element absorbs light of different wavelengths, removing these wavelengths from the star's continuous spectrum. The result is a bright spectrum, such as the one shown in Figure 12. It contains a set of dark lines called **absorption lines** that show where light has been absorbed. Just as fingerprints can be used to identify a person, a star's absorption lines can be used to identify different elements in the star.

Absorption lines of most elements have been identified in the spectra of stars. Observations of such lines in many stars have shown that the composition of most stars is fairly similar. **Most stars have a chemical makeup that is similar to the sun, with hydrogen and helium together making up 96 to 99.9 percent of the star's mass.**

Figure 12 This is the spectrum of a star. The dark absorption lines indicate the presence of various elements in the star.

Build Science Skills L2

Communicating Results The Stefan-Boltzmann Law relates a star's absolute brightness to its size and temperature. Written in equation form, the law states that $L = 4\pi R^2 \sigma T^4$ where L is luminosity (or absolute brightness), R is the radius of a star, σ is a constant, and T is temperature. The equation can be used to determine a star's size if its temperature and absolute brightness are known. Have students research and write brief reports about how scientists use the Stefan-Boltzmann Law.
Verbal

Integrate Chemistry L2

Tell students that at the surface of stars with relatively low temperatures, atoms retain all of their electrons and radiate neutral, or normal, spectra. At very high temperatures, atoms collide and lose electrons and become thermally ionized. Ions have different spectra than atoms. Ask, **How is it possible that two stars can have a similar composition, but radiate different spectra?** *(One of the stars is much hotter than the other.)*
Logical

Facts and Figures

Discovery of Helium In 1868, a spectrometer was used for the first time to study the sun during a solar eclipse. The French astronomer Pierre Janssen analyzed the resulting spectrum and noticed that a bright yellow spectral line did not match any known elements. He proposed that the line was associated with a new element. It was named helium, which stems from the Greek word *helios,* meaning "sun." Helium, a light noble gas, is extremely difficult to detect on Earth. In 1895, Sir William Ramsay was finally able to demonstrate the presence of helium in ores by treating them with acids.

Answer to . . .

Figure 10 *Sirius A because it is blue*

Figure 11 *The nearby streetlights have a greater apparent brightness.*

Reading Checkpoint *By observing the gravitational interaction of stars that appear in pairs, which led to the determination that mass and absolute brightness are related*

The Hertzsprung-Russell Diagram

Use Visuals **L1**

Figure 13 Tell students that absolute brightness is often called luminosity by astronomers. Then say, **Describe the properties of the sun shown on the H-R diagram.** *(Color: yellow; surface temperature: about 5700 K; type: main sequence; absolute brightness: average)* **What is the hottest supergiant shown on the diagram?** *(Rigel)* **What is the coolest main-sequence star labeled on the diagram?** *(Alpha Centauri B)* **Which supergiant has a temperature and color similar to the sun's?** *(Polaris)* **What color, temperature, and star type is Sirius B?** *(Color: blue-white; temperature: about 30,000 K; type: white dwarf)* **Which labeled star on the diagram has the greatest absolute brightness? The least?** *(Greatest: Deneb; least: Sirius B)*
Visual

Address Misconceptions **L2**

Often students think that all of the stars in an H-R diagram are located close to one another in space. This is not the case. Emphasize that an H-R diagram is a graph, not a star chart. An H-R diagram can be used to plot any sample of stars. You may find later in this chapter that students have a similar misconception about constellations—that is, all the stars in a constellation are close to one another. Again, explain that the stars in a constellation are separated by vast distances. Ask, **Can the distance to a star be determined simply by gazing at it?** *(No)*
Verbal

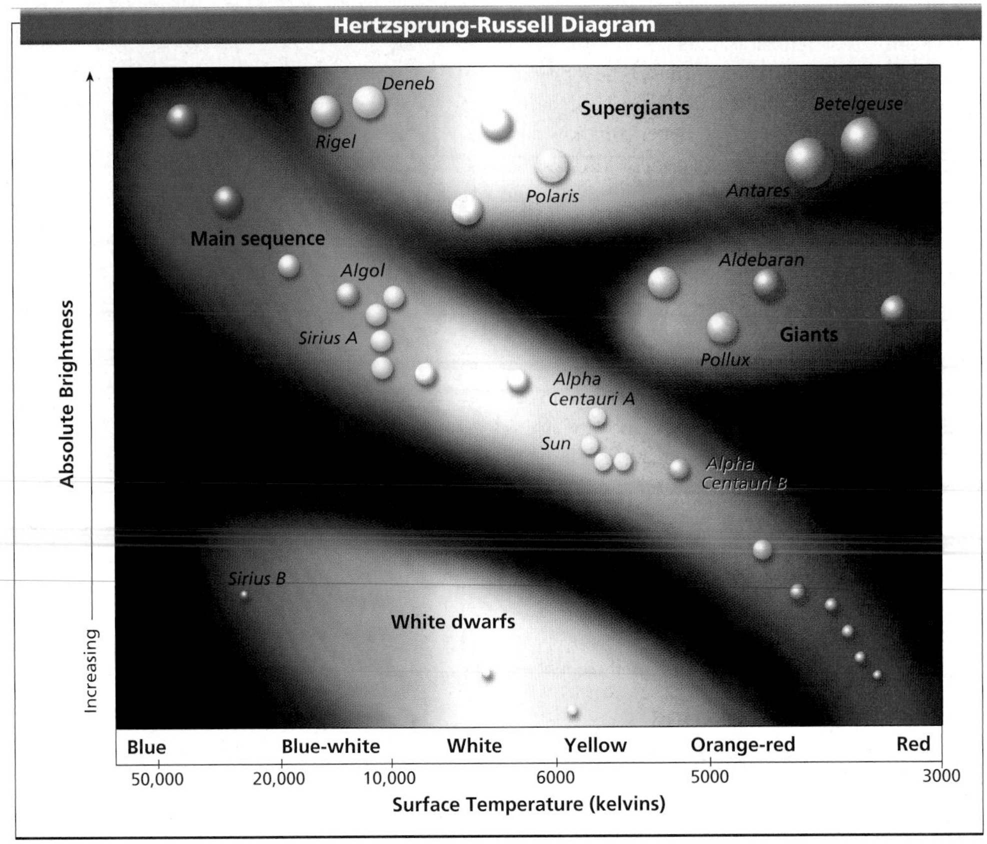
Hertzsprung-Russell Diagram
Deneb
Rigel
Supergiants
Betelgeuse
Polaris
Antares
Main sequence
Algol
Aldebaran
Sirius A
Giants
Pollux
Alpha Centauri A
Sun
Alpha Centauri B
Sirius B
White dwarfs
Absolute Brightness
Increasing
Blue
Blue-white
White
Yellow
Orange-red
Red
50,000
20,000
10,000
6000
5000
3000
Surface Temperature (kelvins)

Figure 13 A star's placement on an H-R diagram indicates its absolute brightness and surface temperature (or color). **Interpreting Diagrams** ***Compare the sun and Aldebaran. Which is hotter and which has a greater absolute brightness?***

The Hertzsprung-Russell Diagram

In the early 1900s, two astronomers working independently, Ejnar Hertzsprung and Henry Norris Russell, made a similar observation. Both discovered that stars can be classified by locating them on a graph showing two easily determined characteristics. Such a graph is called a Hertzsprung-Russell diagram, or H-R diagram. An **H-R diagram** is a graph of the surface temperature, or color, and absolute brightness of a sample of stars. These diagrams are one of modern astronomy's most important tools. **H-R diagrams are used to estimate the sizes of stars and their distances, and to infer how stars change over time.**

Look closely at the H-R diagram in Figure 13. The horizontal axis shows the surface temperatures of stars. Recall that a star's color is directly related to its surface temperature. The hottest blue stars are on the left and the coolest red stars are on the right. Surface temperatures of stars range from less than 3000 K to more than 30,000 K.

The vertical axis of the H-R diagram shows absolute brightness, with the brightest stars at the top and the faintest at the bottom. The absolute brightnesses of stars vary even more than temperature, ranging from about one ten-thousandth to a million times that of the sun!

Main-Sequence Stars Notice that stars occur only in certain places on the H-R diagram. Most stars are found along a diagonal band running from the bright hot stars on the upper left to the dim cool stars on the lower right. Astronomers call this diagonal band on the H-R diagram the **main sequence.** About 90% of all stars are found on the main sequence. The sun lies near the middle of this band.

Giants and Dwarfs In general, two factors determine a star's absolute brightness: its size and its surface temperature. Since an H-R diagram shows a star's absolute brightness and surface temperature, you can use the diagram to estimate the star's size. If you compare two stars at the same temperature, the brighter one must be larger. Similarly, hotter stars are brighter than cooler stars of the same size.

The very bright stars at the upper right of the H-R diagram are called **supergiants.** Supergiants are much brighter than main-sequence stars of the same temperature. To be so bright, these supergiants must be very large compared with main-sequence stars. In fact, supergiants range in size from 100 to 1000 times the diameter of the sun. Just below the supergiants on the H-R diagram are the **giants**—large, bright stars that are smaller and fainter than supergiants.

Below the main sequence in the lower part of the H-R diagram are white dwarfs. A **white dwarf** is the small, dense remains of a low- or medium-mass star. You can see from the diagram that white dwarfs are hot but dimmer than main-sequence stars of the same temperature.

Figure 14 The diameter of a red giant is typically 10–100 times that of the sun and more than 1000 times that of a white dwarf.

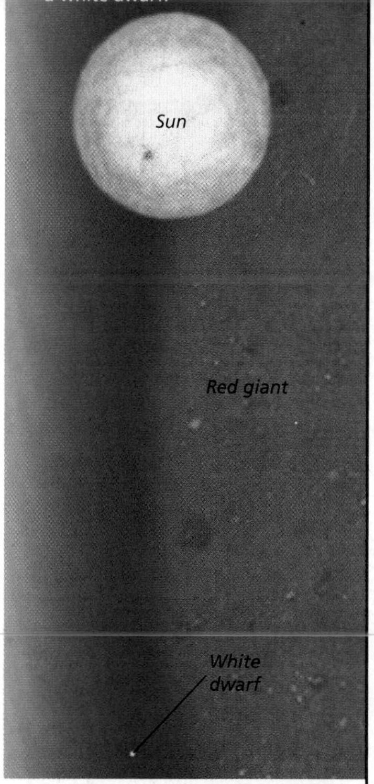
Sun
Red giant
White dwarf

Section 26.2 Assessment

Reviewing Concepts

1. What method do astronomers use to measure the distances of nearby stars?
2. What are some common properties used to classify stars?
3. Describe the chemical composition of a star like the sun.
4. What is an H-R diagram? How is one useful to an astronomer?

Critical Thinking

5. **Applying Concepts** What causes the dark lines in a star's spectrum?
6. **Comparing and Contrasting** Describe the locations of giants, supergiants, and white dwarfs on an H-R diagram.

Math Practice

7. The bright star Spica is located about 2.49×10^{15} kilometers from Earth. How many light-years is this?
8. Betelgeuse is about 427 light-years from Earth. How many kilometers is this?

Use Community Resources **L2**

Invite a local astronomer to discuss spectral types with the class. Ask him or her to bring along charts and stellar images, if possible. Before the visit, describe spectral classes (O, B, A, F, G, K, and M) and explain that they are based largely on temperature differences among stars, with O being the hottest and M being the coolest. Have students conduct some preliminary research on spectral types and develop questions to ask the astronomer.
Verbal, Visual

3 ASSESS

Evaluate Understanding **L2**

Provide students with the temperature, color, absolute brightness, and star type (white dwarf, main sequence, and so on) for a set of stars. Have them construct their own H-R diagrams.

Reteach **L1**

Use graphics to emphasize how the absolute brightness of a star depends on its surface temperature and its size. Draw a small circle to represent a small star. Draw a large circle to represent a large star. Pointing to the circles, explain that if two stars have equal temperatures, then they emit the same amount of light from each square kilometer of their surfaces. The star that is larger therefore has a greater absolute brightness.

Math Practice

Solutions
7. $(2.49 \times 10^{15}$ km$)/(9.5 \times 10^{12}$ km/light-year$) = 260$ light-years
8. (427 light-years) $\times (9.5 \times 10^{12}$ km/light-year$) = 4.1 \times 10^{15}$ km

Interactive Textbook If your class subscribes to the Interactive Textbook, use it to review key concepts in Section 26.2.

Section 26.2 Assessment

1. The parallax method
2. Color or surface temperature, absolute brightness, size, mass, chemical composition
3. Stars like the sun are composed mainly of hydrogen and helium.
4. An H-R diagram is a graph of surface temperature versus absolute brightness for a sample of stars. It can be used to estimate the sizes and distances of stars and to understand how stars evolve.
5. Dark absorption lines show where light has been absorbed by elements in a star's atmosphere.
6. Giants can be found above the main sequence and below the supergiants in the upper-right portion of an H-R diagram. The region where supergiants are found extends from the upper right to the upper central portion of the diagram. White dwarfs are generally found in the lower central portion of the diagram, below the main sequence.

Answer to . . .

Figure 13 *The sun has a higher surface temperature. Aldebaran has a greater absolute brightness.*

Section 26.3

1 FOCUS

Objectives

26.3.1 **Describe** how stars form.
26.3.2 **Estimate** how long a star remains on the main sequence.
26.3.3 **Predict** what happens to a star when it runs out of fuel.

Reading Focus

Build Vocabulary L2

Latin Plural Forms Have students use dictionaries to look up the plural forms of the vocabulary words *nebula (nebulae* or *nebulas)* and *nova (novae* or *novas)*. This will give students an opportunity to study the Latin meaning of the words. (Nebula *means "cloud" and* nova *means "new star.")* It will also minimize any confusion they might have when they conduct research about the words and see variations of the plural forms used.

Reading Strategy L2

a. Red giant **b.** Planetary nebula, white dwarf, black dwarf

2 INSTRUCT

How Stars Form

Build Reading Literacy L1

KWL Refer to page **826D** in this chapter, which provides the guidelines for KWL.

Have students make a chart with three columns titled What I Know, What I Want to Know, and What I Learned. Under the first column, they should recall anything they've learned previously about types of stars. The second column should be filled out before students read the text. The third column should be completed after reading the text.
Verbal

26.3 Life Cycles of Stars

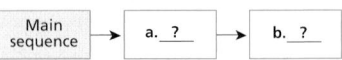

Reading Focus

Key Concepts

- How do stars form?
- What determines how long a star remains on the main sequence?
- What happens to a star when it runs out of fuel?

Vocabulary

- nebula
- protostar
- planetary nebula
- supernova
- neutron star
- pulsar
- black hole

Reading Strategy

Sequencing Copy the flowchart below. As you read, extend and complete it to show how a low-mass star evolves. Make a similar flowchart for high-mass stars.

Evolution of a Low-Mass Star

Main sequence → a. ? → b. ?

Do stars change over time? If so, how do they change? To help answer these questions, think about predicting how a baby will look when it grows up. Pictures of the baby's relatives, like Figure 15, would probably help. Astronomers use a similar approach to understand how stars evolve. When astronomers look at an image of a single star, they see a snapshot from a life story that often lasts for billions of years. To learn how a star might change over time, astronomers observe many stars of different ages. These observations provide clues about how stars form, how long they last, and what happens when their fuel runs out.

Most stars fall on the main sequence of the H-R diagram. Among nearby stars, about 10 percent are white dwarfs and fewer than 1 percent are giants or supergiants. Astronomers have inferred that these different types of stars represent different stages of a star's evolution. For most of their lives, stars are very stable. But a star must change when nuclear fusion has used up the supply of hydrogen in its core.

Figure 15 You can often predict how a baby will look as an adult by looking at other family members. In a similar way, astronomers observe stars of different ages to infer how stars evolve.

How Stars Form

The space around stars contains gas and dust. In some regions this matter is spread thinly; in others it is packed densely. A **nebula** is a large cloud of gas and dust spread out over a large volume of space. Some nebulas are glowing clouds lit from within by bright stars. Other nebulas are cold, dark clouds that block the light from more-distant stars beyond the nebulas.

Section Resources

Print
- ***Laboratory Manual,*** Investigation 26B
- ***Reading and Study Workbook With Math Support,*** Section 26.3
- ***Transparencies,*** Section 26.3

Technology
- ***Interactive Textbook,*** Section 26.3
- ***Presentation Pro CD-ROM,*** Section 26.3
- ***Go Online,*** *Science News,* Stars, galaxies, and the universe

Stars form in the densest regions of nebulae, as shown in Figure 16. Stars are created by gravity. Gravity pulls a nebula's dust and gas into a denser cloud. As the nebula contracts, it heats up. A contracting cloud of gas and dust with enough mass to form a star is called a **protostar.** As a protostar contracts, its internal pressure and temperature continue to rise. **A star is formed when a contracting cloud of gas and dust becomes so dense and hot that nuclear fusion begins.** Pressure from fusion supports the star against the tremendous inward pull of gravity. This new energy source stabilizes the young star, and it joins the main sequence.

Figure 16 A group of bright young stars can be seen in the hollowed-out center of the Rosette Nebula.

Adult Stars

Stars spend about 90 percent of their lives on the main sequence. In all main-sequence stars, nuclear fusion converts hydrogen into helium at a stable rate. There is an equilibrium between the outward thermal pressure from fusion and gravity's inward pull. **A star's mass determines the star's place on the main sequence and how long it will stay there.**

The amount of gas and dust available when a star forms determines the mass of each young star. The most massive stars have large cores and therefore produce the most energy. In a large, young star with 30 times the sun's mass, gravity exerts a huge inward force, increasing the star's internal temperature and pressure. High-mass stars become the bluest and brightest main-sequence stars. Typically, these blue stars are about 300,000 times brighter than the sun. But, like gas-guzzling hot rods, large stars pay a price. Because blue stars burn so brightly, they use up their fuel relatively quickly and last only a few million years.

Stars similar to the sun occupy the middle of the main sequence. A yellow star like the sun has a surface temperature of about 6000 K and will remain stable on the main sequence for about 10 billion years.

Small nebulas produce small, cool stars that are long-lived. A star can have a mass as low as a tenth of the sun's mass. The gravitational force in such low-mass stars is just strong enough to create a small core where nuclear fusion takes place. This lower energy production results in red stars, which are the coolest and least bright of all visible stars. A red main-sequence star, with a surface temperature of about 3500 K, may stay on the main sequence for more than 100 billion years.

Reading Checkpoint *Why do red main-sequence stars last longer than blue main-sequence stars?*

Go Online SCIENCE NEWS®

For: Articles on stars, galaxies, and the universe

Visit: PHSchool.com

Web Code: cce-3263

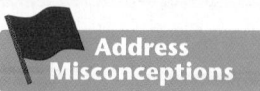

Adult Stars

Address Misconceptions L2

Some students may mistakenly think that stars last forever. Use an analogy to dispel this misconception. Tell students that stars are like people—they are born, become adults, and eventually die. The length of a star's life cycle may be billions of years and is determined by its mass.
Verbal

Build Science Skills L2

Classifying As students read about stellar evolution, have them locate on the periodic table the most abundant elements found in stars. Ask, **What do these elements have in common?** *(Except for iron, they are all in the upper part of the periodic table and have low atomic numbers.)* Point out that most are light gases that represent the first elements that formed in the universe.
Visual

Go Online SCIENCE NEWS®

Science News provides students with current information on stars, galaxies, and the universe.

Customize for English Language Learners

Build a Science Glossary
Post a list that explains the meanings of common prefixes and suffixes related to stars. Encourage ELL students to study the list. Show them how to divide new vocabulary words into parts (prefix, root word, suffix). Model how you would determine the meaning of a word. For example, *super* means "above," so a supernova is above, or greater than, a nova. *Proto* means "first," so a protostar is a "first star," or the first stage of a star. Pronounce each term without its prefix or suffix and use the word in a sentence. Tell ELL students to do the same for each new vocabulary word, and to compile the words in their own science glossaries. Glossaries should include the pronunciation and definition of each word, as well as diagrams or drawings that illustrate the word's meaning. Tell students to arrange words in alphabetical order to reinforce use of the English alphabet.

Answer to . . .

Reading Checkpoint *Because red main-sequence stars are less massive and therefore much cooler than blue main-sequence stars, they use up their hydrogen fuel at a much slower rate.*

The Death of a Star

Use Visuals **L1**

Figure 17 Point out that stars undergo the same types of changes in the early stages of stellar evolution. Differentiation takes place in later stages. Ask, **What do the arrows show?** *(The path of evolution of low-mass or high-mass stars)* **What stages has the sun already completed?** *(Nebula, protostar)* **What stages will the sun evolve through before it dies?** *(Red giant, planetary nebula, white dwarf, black dwarf)*
Visual

Integrate Physics **L2**

Nuclear energy is generated in power plants through the process of fission. In fission, a heavy element, such as uranium, splits into lighter elements. Fission is the opposite of fusion. In main-sequence stars, fusion (the process that creates energy in stars) "fuses" together hydrogen nuclei to form helium. Fusion could theoretically be used as an energy source on Earth. It would provide abundant power and have only small environmental consequences. As of yet, however, scientists have not been able to develop the technology to conduct fusion in a safe, controlled manner. Have students work in groups to diagram the processes of fission and fusion. *(The diagram of fission should show a large atom being split into two smaller atoms, with energy released. The diagram of fusion should be similar to Figure 2 on p. 829.)*
Kinesthetic, Group

The Death of a Star

Stars don't last forever. When a star's core begins to run out of hydrogen, gravity gains the upper hand over pressure and the core starts to shrink. Soon, the core temperature rises enough to cause the hydrogen in a shell outside the core to begin fusion. The energy flowing outward increases, causing the outer regions of the star to expand. The expanding atmosphere moves farther from the hot core and cools to red. The star becomes a red giant. Eventually, the collapsing core will grow hot enough for helium fusion to occur, producing carbon, oxygen, and heavier elements. In helium fusion, the star stabilizes and its outer layers shrink and warm up. In this period, the star remains in the upper right part of the H-R Diagram. **The dwindling supply of fuel in a star's core ultimately leads to the star's death as a white dwarf, neutron star, or black hole.** As Figure 17 shows, the final stages of a star's life depend on its mass.

Low- and Medium-Mass Stars Low-mass and medium-mass stars, which can be as much as eight times as massive as the sun, eventually turn into white dwarfs. Such stars remain in the giant stage until their hydrogen and helium supplies dwindle and there are no other elements to fuse. Then the energy coming from the star's interior decreases. With less outward pressure to support the star against gravity's inward pull, the star collapses. The dying star is surrounded by a glowing cloud of gas. Such a cloud is called a **planetary nebula,** because the first ones found looked like planets when viewed through a small telescope. Figure 18A shows a planetary nebula.

Figure 17 The mass of a star determines the path of its evolution.
Interpreting Diagrams ***What are two possible end-stages of a high-mass star?***

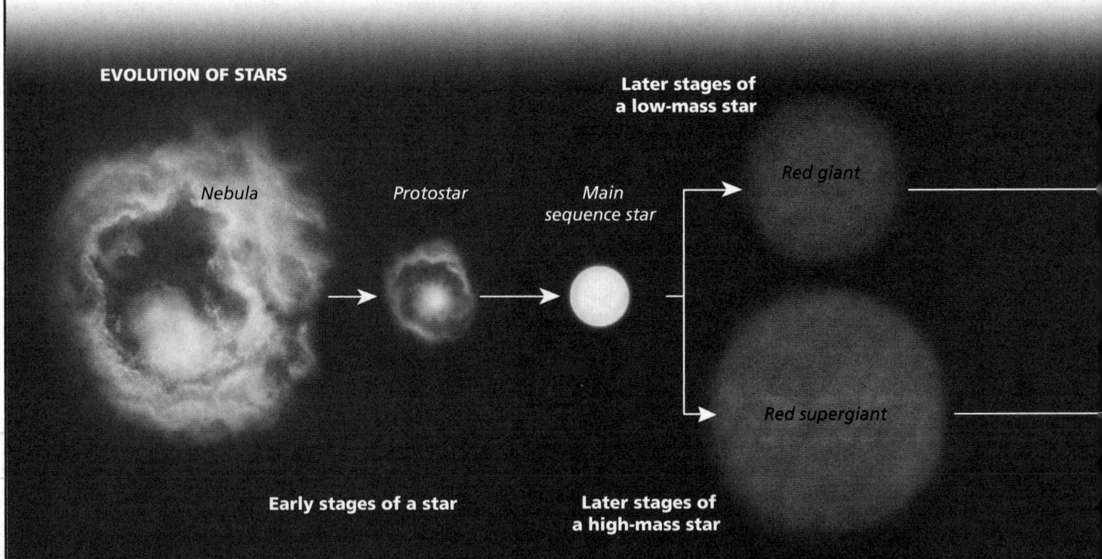
EVOLUTION OF STARS
Later stages of a low-mass star
Nebula
Protostar
Main sequence star
Red giant
Red supergiant
Early stages of a star
Later stages of a high-mass star

As the dying star blows off much of its mass, only its hot core remains. This dense core is a white dwarf. A white dwarf is about the same size as Earth but has about the same mass as the sun. White dwarfs don't undergo fusion, but glow faintly from leftover thermal energy. When a white dwarf becomes too cool to glow in visible light, it is called a black dwarf. But it takes about 20 billion years for a white dwarf to cool down, so the universe hasn't been here long enough for any black dwarfs to form yet.

High-Mass Stars The life cycle of high-mass stars (those with a mass of more than eight times that of the sun) is very different from the life cycle of lower-mass stars. As high-mass stars evolve from hydrogen fusion to the fusion of other elements, they grow into brilliant supergiants. This creates new elements, the heaviest being iron. A high-mass star dies quickly because it consumes fuel very rapidly.

As fusion slows in a high-mass star, pressure decreases. Gravity eventually overcomes the lower pressure, leading to a dramatic collapse of the star's outer layers. This collapse produces a **supernova,** an explosion so violent that the dying star becomes more brilliant than an entire galaxy. Supernovas produce enough energy to create elements heavier than iron. These elements, and lighter ones such as carbon and oxygen, are ejected into space by the explosion. The heavier elements in our solar system, including the atoms in your body, came from a supernova that occurred in our galaxy billions of years ago.

Reading Checkpoint *What is a supernova?*

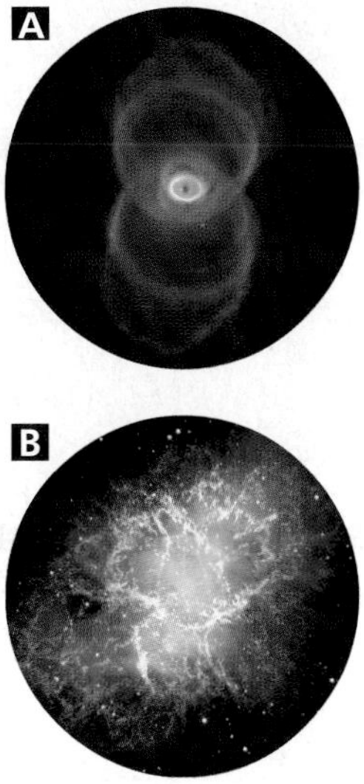
A
B

Figure 18 Nebulas are associated with the birth and death of stars. **A** Planetary nebulas, such as the Hourglass Nebula, are clouds of gas that surround a collapsing red giant. **B** The Crab Nebula is the remnant of a supernova explosion that was observed on Earth in A.D. 1054. The supernova was so bright that people could see it in the daytime.

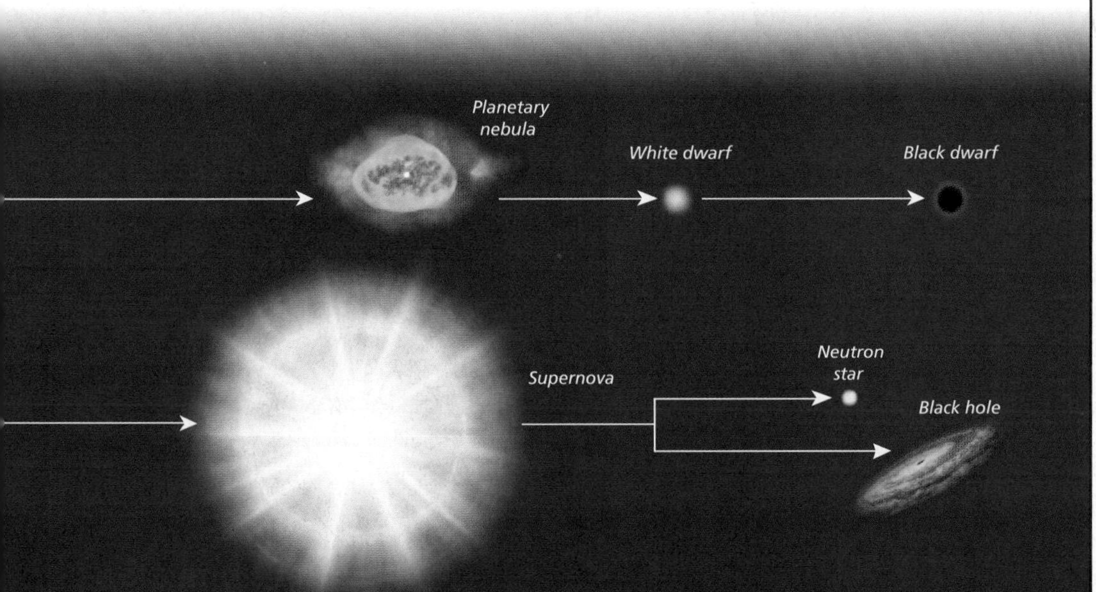
Planetary nebula
White dwarf
Black dwarf
Supernova
Neutron star
Black hole

Exploring the Universe **843**

Teacher Demo

Brown Dwarfs L2

Purpose Students observe how astronomers detect a brown dwarf by observing the effect it has on a star's motion.

Materials dark clay, pencil, string, aluminum foil, flashlight

Procedure Use the clay to make two balls. One ball (5 cm in diameter) represents a star. The second ball (2.5 cm in diameter) represents a brown dwarf. Cover the star in aluminum foil. Attach the star to one end of a pencil and the brown dwarf to the other end. Tell students that the pencil represents gravity, which keeps the brown dwarf and star orbiting each other. Then, tie a string to the pencil at the center of mass so that the pencil is balanced (horizontally) when suspended. Twist the string so that the brown dwarf and star orbit each other. Darken the room and shine a flashlight on the apparatus to emphasize that the star is visible but the brown dwarf is not. Repeat the demonstration using a smaller brown dwarf (1 cm in diameter).

Expected Outcome Students will observe that the star "wobbles" as the brown dwarf orbits it. From the size of a star's wobble, astronomers can estimate the size of the brown dwarf and its distance from the star. Explain that astronomers use this same method to locate planets orbiting other stars.
Visual, Logical

Facts and Figures

Crab Nebula The supernova explosion associated with the Crab Nebula had the brilliance of more than a billion suns. It was observed in 1054 by Chinese, Arabic, and Japanese astronomers, and was recorded in paintings by the Anasazi, who lived in the area that is now New Mexico. The star in the center of the Crab Nebula is a tiny dense pulsar. It rotates 30 times every second and sends powerful radio beams flashing through space. These intense emissions light up the surrounding cloud.

Answer to . . .

Figure 17 *Neutron star, black hole*

Reading Checkpoint *A supernova is the dramatic explosion of a high-mass star in which the star ejects elements formed from a lifetime of fusion into space.*

Section 26.3 (continued)

Use Visuals **L1**

Figure 19 Have students examine the diagram. Ask, **Where do the beams of radiation originate from?** *(The magnetic poles)* **Why do we detect pulses on Earth?** *(The beams don't pulse on and off, but we detect them as pulsing as the beams periodically sweep across Earth.)* **Visual**

3 ASSESS

Evaluate Understanding **L2**

Have students diagram the life cycle of a massive star. Tell them to put captions on their diagrams that explain the stages of stellar evolution.

Reteach **L1**

Use spectra to illustrate the different temperatures and compositions of high-mass and low-mass stars.

Writing in Science

Students' paragraphs should include a description of the formation of heavy elements and their ejection into space in a supernova explosion. Students should also describe how such elements became part of Earth as the solar system formed.

Interactive Textbook If your class subscribes to the Interactive Textbook, use it to review key concepts in Section 26.3.

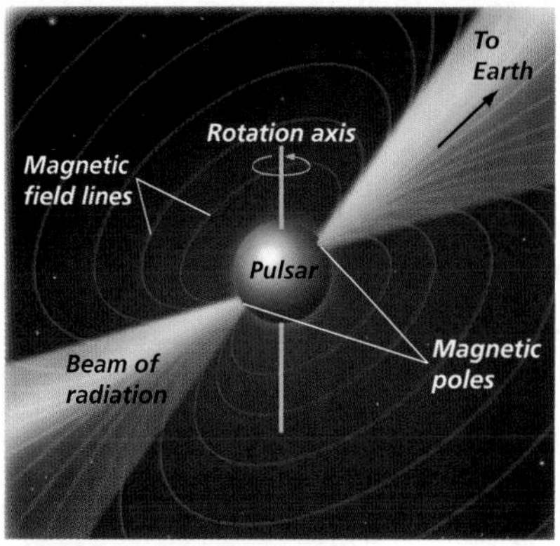

To Earth
Rotation axis
Magnetic field lines
Pulsar
Beam of radiation
Magnetic poles

Figure 19 Pulsars emit steady beams of radiation that appear to pulse when the spinning beam sweeps across Earth.

As a supernova spews material into space, its core continues to collapse. If the remaining core has a mass less than about three times the sun's mass, it will become a neutron star. A **neutron star** is the dense remnant of a high-mass star that has exploded as a supernova. In a neutron star, electrons and protons are crushed together by the star's enormous gravity to form neutrons. Neutron stars are much smaller and denser than white dwarfs. A spoonful of a neutron star would weigh nearly a billion tons on Earth! A neutron star with the mass of the sun would be only about 25 kilometers across, the size of a large city.

Like a spinning ice skater pulling in his arms, a neutron star spins more and more rapidly as it contracts. Some neutron stars spin hundreds of turns per second! As shown in Figure 19, neutron stars emit steady beams of radiation in narrow cones. If the neutron star is spinning, these emissions appear to pulse on and off at regular intervals, like the spinning beacon on a lighthouse. Each time one of these beams of radiation sweeps across Earth, astronomers can detect a pulse of radio waves. A spinning neutron star that appears to gives off strong pulses of radio waves is called a **pulsar.**

As impressive as pulsars are, very massive stars can have even more dramatic ends. If a star's core after a supernova explosion is more than about three times the sun's mass, its gravitational pull is very strong. Gravity causes the core to collapse beyond the neutron-star stage. As the collapse continues, the pull of gravity increases and the speed required to escape the star's core reaches the speed of light. Beyond this point, nothing can escape and a black hole is formed. A **black hole** is an object whose surface gravity is so great that even electromagnetic waves, traveling at the speed of light, cannot escape from it.

Section 26.3 Assessment

Reviewing Concepts

1. How does a star form?
2. What factor determines the length of a star's life?
3. Why do some stars become white dwarfs while others become neutron stars or black holes?

Critical Thinking

4. **Predicting** A main-sequence star has a mass 5 times that of the sun. What will be its final stages?
5. **Comparing and Contrasting** How are a protostar and a star different?
6. **Comparing and Contrasting** Why do low-mass stars remain on the main sequence longer than high-mass stars?

Writing in Science

Explain a Sequence Write a paragraph explaining the sequence of events that resulted in the creation of the elements that make up your body.

Section 26.3 Assessment

1. A star forms when a contracting nebula becomes dense and hot enough that nuclear fusion begins.
2. The star's mass
3. The end-stage of a star depends on its mass. Low-mass and medium-mass stars evolve into white dwarfs as they run out of elements to fuse. High-mass stars eventually evolve into neutron stars or black holes.
4. Such a medium-mass star will evolve into a white dwarf and, eventually, a black dwarf.
5. A protostar is a contracting cloud of gas and dust with sufficient mass to become a star. Once fusion begins, the protostar is then considered a star.
6. Low-mass stars are cooler and use up their supply of elements to fuse at a much slower rate.

DK HOW It Works

Black Hole

A black hole is a region of space containing so much matter that it collapses to an infinitely dense point. The force of gravity in a black hole is so great that anything falling into it, including electromagnetic waves, becomes trapped. **Interpreting Diagrams** ***What happens to an object trapped by a black hole?***

Detecting a black hole As matter swirls into a black hole, it can emit X-rays, gamma rays, and other radiation. Astronomers analyze this radiation to discover more about black holes.

Warped space *According to Einstein's theory of general relativity, gravity is a distortion of space and time. The warping of space near a black hole is shown here by the gray plane and white lines.*

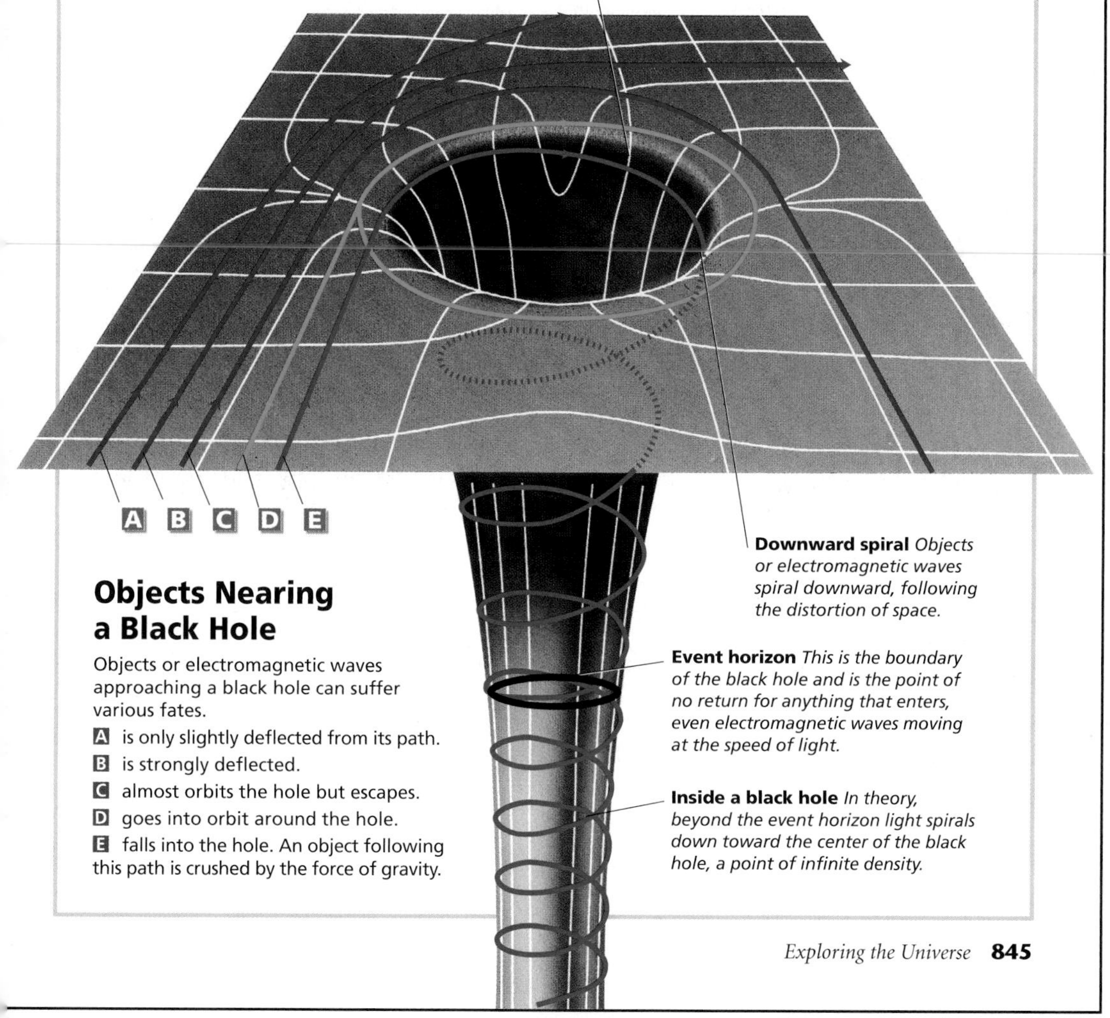
A
B
C
D
E

Downward spiral *Objects or electromagnetic waves spiral downward, following the distortion of space.*

Event horizon *This is the boundary of the black hole and is the point of no return for anything that enters, even electromagnetic waves moving at the speed of light.*

Inside a black hole *In theory, beyond the event horizon light spirals down toward the center of the black hole, a point of infinite density.*

Objects Nearing a Black Hole

Objects or electromagnetic waves approaching a black hole can suffer various fates.

A is only slightly deflected from its path.
B is strongly deflected.
C almost orbits the hole but escapes.
D goes into orbit around the hole.
E falls into the hole. An object following this path is crushed by the force of gravity.

DK HOW It Works

Black Hole **L2**

Astronomers now think that many large galaxies, including the Milky Way, have black holes in their centers. The Milky Way's center is hidden from view by interstellar dust in the spiral arm lying between the sun and the galaxy's center. Radio and infrared telescopes can penetrate the dust, however. Images show a cluster of several million stars and great turbulence at the Milky Way's core in a region about three light-years across. The high mass of this region indicates the presence of a black hole. However, the area does not exhibit many typical black-hole behaviors, such as X-ray emissions, detected in the centers of other galaxies.

Interpreting Diagrams An object that falls into a black hole would be crushed by its intense gravitational forces.
Visual, Logical

For Enrichment **L3**

Have interested students research and present oral reports on Einstein's general theory of relativity.
Verbal, Portfolio

26.4 Groups of Stars

Reading Focus

Key Concepts
- How are stars distributed in space?
- What are the characteristics of each type of star cluster?
- What are the types of galaxies?

Vocabulary
- constellation
- star system
- binary star
- globular cluster
- galaxy
- spiral galaxies
- barred-spiral galaxies
- elliptical galaxies
- irregular galaxies
- quasars

Reading Strategy
Comparing and Contrasting Copy the table below. After you read, compare types of star clusters by completing the table.

Cluster Type	Appearance	Age and Type of Stars
Open cluster	a. ___?___	b. ___?___
c. ___?___	d. ___?___	Bright, young stars
e. ___?___	Spherical, densely packed	f. ___?___

Figure 20 When Giovanni Riccioli used a telescope like this one to observe a star in the handle of the Big Dipper, he discovered two stars that orbit each other.

Ancient observers saw a night sky that was full of stars. They imagined that groups of stars formed pictures of people or animals in the sky. A group of stars that appears to form a pattern as seen from Earth is called a **constellation.** The Big Dipper, for example, is part of the constellation Ursa Major. The stars in a constellation are generally not close to one another. They just happen to lie in the same general direction of the sky as seen from Earth. Constellations are important to astronomy because they help to form a map of the sky. Modern astronomers divide the sky into 88 constellations. You can find a set of star maps in Appendix H at the end of this book.

Star Systems

When you wake up each morning and look out your window, a single star, the sun, greets you with its bright light. However, if you were somewhere else in the universe, the view might be quite different. Imagine what the sky would look like if your solar system had two, three, or even four stars. The stars might all be visible in the sky at the same time, or some might be visible while others were below the horizon. It would be hard to say exactly what a "day" would be on such a planet. You might think that this sounds like a scene from a science fiction movie. But, in fact, most stars occur in groups of two or more.

1 FOCUS

Objectives

26.4.1 **Explain** how stars are distributed in space.

26.4.2 **Identify** basic types of star clusters.

26.4.3 **Classify** galaxies based on their appearance and composition and **describe** the four main types of galaxies.

Reading Focus

Build Vocabulary L2

Concept Maps Have students construct concept maps showing relationships among star clusters. Students should place the main idea (Star Clusters) in a centered oval. Types of star clusters should be placed in ovals beneath the main idea. Tell students to use black lines to connect these ovals to the main oval. Descriptive details and definitions should form a third row of ovals and be connected to the second row with black lines. Tell students to repeat the activity for galaxies.

Reading Strategy L2

a. Disorganized, loose appearance **b.** Bright supergiants and other young stars, also gas and dust clouds **c.** Association **d.** Larger and more spread out than an open cluster **e.** Globular cluster **f.** Older stars, generally no bright blue stars

2 INSTRUCT

Star Systems

Address Misconceptions L2

Students often think that all stars are like the sun—that is, they are found alone in space. Have students read the text about binary systems. Ask, **If you could view all of the stars in the sky, about what percentage would be members of groups of two or more stars?** *(More than 50%)*
Logical

Section Resources

Print
- ***Reading and Study Workbook With Math Support,*** Section 26.4
- ***Transparencies,*** Section 26.4

Technology
- ***Interactive Textbook,*** Section 26.4
- ***Presentation Pro CD-ROM,*** Section 26.4

846 Chapter 26

In 1650, the Italian astronomer Giovanni Baptista Riccioli used a telescope like the one shown in Figure 20 to observe Mizar and Alcor, a double star in the Big Dipper. He saw that Mizar itself was two stars that were very close together. This was the first of thousands of star systems to be discovered. A **star system** is a group of two or more stars that are held together by gravity. **Astronomers have determined that more than half of all stars are members of star systems.** A star system with two stars is called a **binary star.** The two stars orbit each other, held together by gravity.

Sometimes the smaller star in a binary star is too dim to be seen easily from Earth, but can still be detected from the motion of the other star. The bright star Sirius A, for example, wobbles back and forth. Astronomers have discovered that this wobble is caused by the gravitational pull of a faint companion star, Sirius B. In some binary star systems, one star passes in front of the other, blocking some of the light from reaching Earth. Such a star system is called an eclipsing binary. The brightness of an eclipsing binary varies over time in a regular pattern.

Figure 21 Open clusters contain young blue stars, which are usually absent in globular clusters. **A** The Pleiades are an open star cluster that is visible to the unaided eye. **B** 47 Tucanae is a spectacular globular cluster that is visible in southern skies. **Comparing and Contrasting** ***Use these photos to describe the differences between open clusters and globular clusters.***

Star Clusters

In the winter sky, you can see a faint group of stars called the Pleiades, shown in Figure 21A. Studying star clusters is useful because all the stars formed together in the same nebula. Therefore, they are about the same age and the same distance from Earth. Astronomers plot the stars of a cluster on an H-R diagram to estimate the cluster's age.

There are three basic kinds of star clusters: open clusters, associations, and globular clusters. An open cluster, like the Pleiades, has a disorganized or loose appearance and contains no more than a few thousand stars that are well spread out. Open clusters often contain bright supergiants and gas and dust clouds. Associations are temporary groupings of bright, young stars. In time, gravity from nearby stars breaks these groups apart. Associations are typically larger than open clusters.

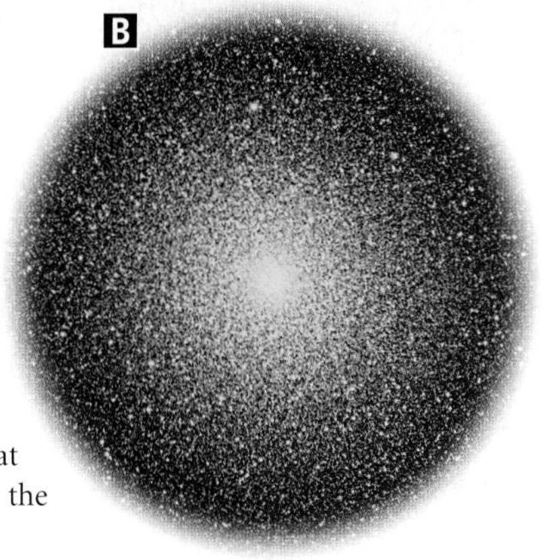

In contrast, a **globular cluster** is a large group of older stars. Globular clusters usually lack sufficient amounts of gas and dust to form new stars. They are spherical and have a dense concentration of stars in the center, as shown in Figure 21B. Globular clusters can contain more than a million stars. Globular clusters usually do not have short-lived blue stars because these stars have already died out. If Earth revolved around a star in the middle of a globular cluster, the night sky would blaze with the light from thousands of bright stars. Astronomers estimate that the oldest globular clusters are about 12 billion years old. Thus, the universe must be at least that old.

Star Clusters

Build Reading Literacy L1

Active Comprehension Refer to page **498D** in **Chapter 17**, which provides the guidelines for active comprehension.

Read aloud the first paragraph under the heading Star Clusters. Ask, **What more would you like to know about star clusters?** Write several student responses on the board. Then, direct students to quietly read the text, keeping the questions in mind as they read. Afterwards, lead a class discussion, focusing on the questions. Were the questions answered? If so, how? If not, how could students go about finding answers to their questions? Did any additional questions come to mind as students read?
Verbal, Intrapersonal

Build Science Skills L2

Using Models Have students work in pairs to devise models of star clusters. Encourage students to keep their models simple, but accurate. For example, students could use gravel to show the distribution of stars in each type of cluster. Or, students could work together to draw the clusters on a computer graphics program. Display student models around the class.
Kinesthetic, Portfolio

FYI

Astronomers have since discovered that Mizar is actually a four-star system, but only two of the stars are visible with a telescope. In 1996, interferometers were used to determine that each of these stars is itself a binary star.

Customize for Inclusion Students

Physically Challenged
Accommodate the individual needs of physically challenged students. Tailor tests and lab activities to students' abilities. For example, if students have difficulty writing, give them oral tests and allow them to tape record answers. If students have difficulty speaking, give them written tests and jointly agree upon a way for students to participate in class discussions. For example, they can write comments on small erasable boards, and hold up the boards when they have a point to contribute.

Answer to . . .

Figure 21 *Open clusters have relatively few stars, which are well spread out. Globular clusters are spherical and densely packed and may contain more than a million stars.*

Galaxies

Build Science Skills L2

Predicting Tell students that the younger stars in a galaxy, such as those found in spiral arms, are called Population I stars. Older stars, usually found in galactic centers, are referred to as Population II stars. Ancient Population II stars contain much lower levels of heavy elements than do young Population I stars. Ask, **Why do you think this is so?** *(The amount of heavy elements in a galaxy was lower when Population II stars formed. Population I stars form in areas where supernovas have enriched the proportion of heavy elements.)*
Logical

Use Visuals L1

Figure 22 Tell students that nearly 77% of galaxies observed thus far are spiral or barred-spiral types, 20% are elliptical, and 3% are irregular. Then, ask, **How does a barred-spiral galaxy differ from a spiral galaxy?** *(A barred-spiral galaxy has a bar through its center with arms extending outward from each end of the bar. A spiral galaxy has a bulge at its center with arms extending outward like a pinwheel.)* **How does an elliptical galaxy differ from an irregular galaxy?** *(An elliptical galaxy has a spherical or oval shape. An irregular galaxy has a disorganized appearance.)*
Visual

FYI

Recent evidence indicates that the Milky Way galaxy is a barred-spiral galaxy. In 2001, researchers mapped the galaxy using survey data collected at a variety of wavelengths. They concluded that the Milky Way has a thin central bar encircled by a ring. Thus, the Milky Way will likely be classified as a typical ringed barred-spiral galaxy.

Figure 22 Galaxies have a variety of shapes. **A** A spiral galaxy in the constellation Coma Berenices **B** A barred-spiral galaxy in the Fornax cluster **C** Elliptical galaxy M87 **D** An irregular galaxy with many areas of star formation

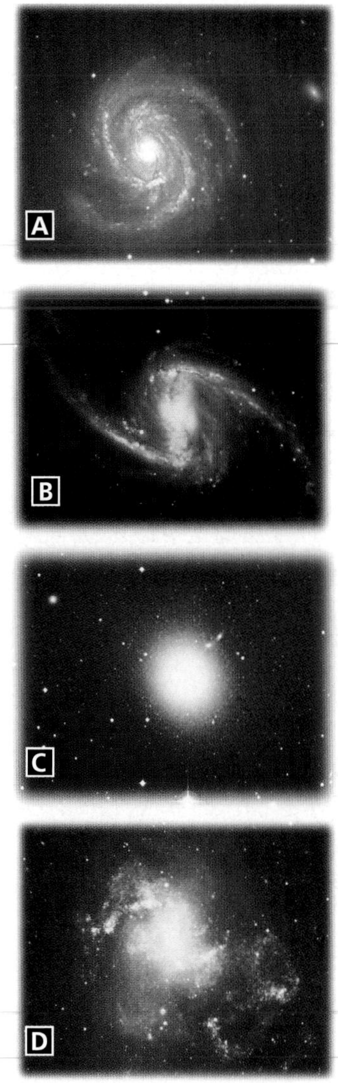
A
B
C
D

Galaxies

A **galaxy** is a huge group of individual stars, star systems, star clusters, dust, and gas bound together by gravity. Our own galaxy is called the Milky Way. In the 1800s and early 1900s, many astronomers thought that the universe did not extend beyond the Milky Way. However, observations of odd spiral-shaped objects sparked a spirited scientific debate. The debate focused on whether these so-called "spiral nebulae" were within or outside the Milky Way. The question was settled only in the 1920s, after a large new telescope was built on Mt. Wilson in California. Astronomers could see individual stars, proving that spiral nebulae were actually distant galaxies consisting of billions of individual stars.

Astronomers now know that there are billions of galaxies in the universe. The largest galaxies consist of more than a trillion stars. Galaxies vary widely in size and shape. **Astronomers classify galaxies into four main types: spiral, barred-spiral, elliptical, and irregular.**

Spiral and Barred-Spiral Galaxies Galaxies like the Milky Way are called spiral galaxies. **Spiral galaxies** have a bulge of stars at the center, with arms extending outward like a pinwheel. These spiral arms contain gas, dust, and many bright young stars. Figure 22A shows the spiral galaxy M100. It belongs to the Virgo Cluster of galaxies, which is the nearest major cluster to our own Local Group of galaxies.

Some spiral galaxies, like the one in Figure 22B, have a bar through the center with the arms extending outward from the bar on either side. These are called **barred-spiral galaxies.**

Elliptical Galaxies **Elliptical galaxies** are spherical or oval, with no trace of spiral arms. M87, shown in Figure 22C, is one of the largest and brightest of all galaxies. Elliptical galaxies come in a wide range of sizes. They have very little gas or dust between stars. For this reason, new stars are not forming in older elliptical galaxies. They contain only old stars.

Irregular Galaxies A small fraction of all galaxies are known as irregular galaxies. As shown in Figure 22D, **irregular galaxies** have a disorganized appearance. They have many young stars and large amounts of gas and dust. Irregular galaxies come in many shapes, but are typically smaller than other types of galaxies. They are often located near larger galaxies, whose strong gravity may be causing their shape to become irregular. One of the closest galaxies to our own, the Large Magellanic Cloud, is an irregular galaxy.

Reading Checkpoint *What are some characteristics of irregular galaxies?*

Facts and Figures

Colliding Galaxies Collisions between galaxies are not unusual. In one collision, 15,000,000 light-years from Earth, a small spiral galaxy crashed into a large elliptical galaxy, creating a system called Centaurus A. This collision resulted in a gigantic gas-and-dust cloud and the generation of new stars. Close encounters and frequent collisions among stars and nebulas make the Centaurus A system complex and constantly changing.

The Milky Way Galaxy On a clear, dark night far from city lights, you can see a faint white band stretching across the night sky. This is the Milky Way. The Milky Way galaxy has an estimated 200 to 400 billion stars and a diameter of more than 100,000 light years. Every individual star that you can see with the unaided eye is in our galaxy. As Figure 23 shows, the solar system lies in the Milky Way's disk within a spiral arm, about two thirds of the way from the center. From Earth we are looking at the rest of the Milky Way edgewise, so it appears as a band in our night sky, rather than a spiral.

The Milky Way's flattened disk shape is caused by its rotation. The sun takes about 220 million years to complete one orbit around the galaxy's center. At the center of the galaxy is a bulge of stars surrounded by an immense halo of globular clusters. Recent evidence suggests that there is a massive black hole at our galaxy's center. Extending outward and winding through the galaxy's disk are spiral arms of gas, dust, and young stars. Stars are forming in these spiral arms.

Quasars In the 1950s astronomers were mystified by the discovery of distant objects they called quasars. By studying their spectra, astronomers have determined that **quasars** (KWAY zahrz) are the enormously bright centers of distant, young galaxies. Quasars produce more light than hundreds of galaxies the size of the Milky Way. What makes a quasar so bright? The most likely explanation involves matter spiraling into a super-massive black hole with the mass of a billion suns. The gravitational potential energy of this matter is transformed into electromagnetic radiation as it falls into the black hole.

Side View of Our Galaxy

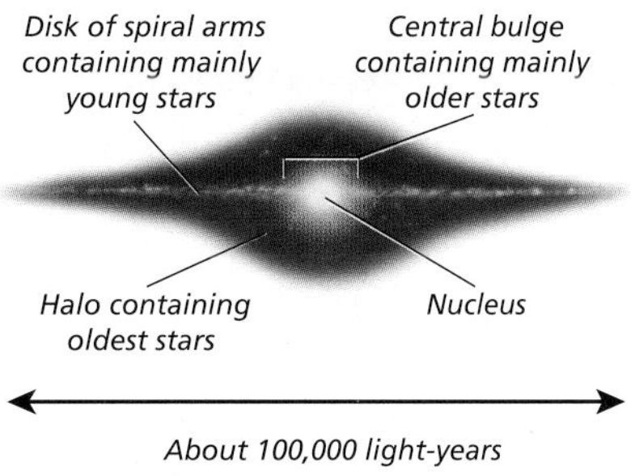
Disk of spiral arms containing mainly young stars
Central bulge containing mainly older stars
Halo containing oldest stars
Nucleus
About 100,000 light-years

Overhead View of Our Galaxy

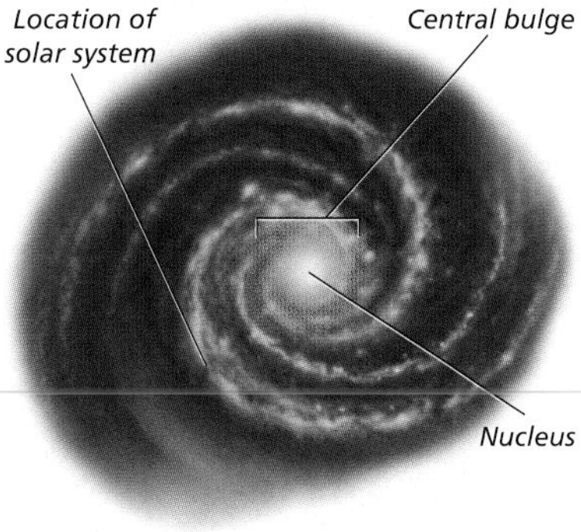
Location of solar system
Central bulge
Nucleus

Figure 23 In a side view, the Milky Way appears as a flat disk with a central bulge. An overhead view of the Milky Way shows its spiral shape.

Section 26.4 Assessment

Reviewing Concepts

1. How are the majority of stars grouped?
2. How are open clusters and associations different?
3. What are the four major types of galaxies?
4. Describe the Milky Way and its characteristics.
5. What is a quasar?

Critical Thinking

6. **Inferring** Why were telescopes needed to discover star systems?
7. **Classifying** Which type of star cluster has the greatest percentage of old stars?
8. **Inferring** How would you use an H-R diagram to distinguish an elliptical galaxy from a spiral or irregular galaxy?

Connecting Concepts

Gravity Use what you learned about the gravitational attraction that acts between two masses in Section 12.4 to explain why the star Sirius A wobbles.

Use Visuals L1

Figure 23 Tell students to examine the side view of the Milky Way. Have them compare and contrast the central bulge and the spiral arms. Ask, **What strikes you as the most distinguishing characteristic?** *(Sample answer: The different ages of the stars)* Tell students to examine the overhead view of the Milky Way. Ask them to describe similar shapes they have seen in their studies of Earth. *(Sample answer: Hurricanes, whirlpools)* **Visual**

3 ASSESS

Evaluate Understanding L2

Have each student write a quiz question on a small slip of paper. Put the papers in a box and have students take turns choosing a slip of paper and answering the question.

Reteach L1

Use the list of vocabulary words to summarize the characteristics of star systems, star clusters, and galaxies.

Connecting Concepts

Sirius is a binary star system consisting of a bright primary star (Sirius A) and a dim white dwarf companion (Sirius B). The two stars are held together by their mutual gravitation. As Sirius B orbits Sirius A, Sirius A appears to wobble slightly back and forth.

Interactive Textbook If your class subscribes to the Interactive Textbook, use it to review key concepts in Section 26.4.

Section 26.4 Assessment

1. Most stars occur in groups of two or more.
2. Open clusters have a disorganized appearance and contain up to a few thousand stars that are well spread out. Associations are typically larger than open clusters, but have fewer stars.
3. Spiral, barred-spiral, elliptical, irregular
4. The Milky Way is a large spiral galaxy with at least 200 billion stars, a bulge of stars near its center surrounded by a halo of globular clusters, and likely a black hole at its center.
5. Quasars are the extremely bright centers of very distant, young galaxies.
6. The stars in a star system are too close to be resolved without a telescope.
7. Globular clusters have the greatest percentage of old stars.
8. Unlike spiral and irregular galaxies, elliptical galaxies typically have only old stars. They lack the bright blue main-sequence stars that appear in the upper left of an H-R diagram, as such stars have already left the main sequence.

Answer to . . .

Reading Checkpoint *Irregular galaxies have a disorganized appearance with many young stars and large quantities of gas and dust. They are typically smaller than other types of galaxies.*

CONCEPTS in Action

Scale of the Universe L2

Background

The brightness of a Cepheid variable changes in regular cycles largely because of pressure gradients. In the beginning of this process, the forces of pressure and gravity are balanced. Pressure begins to build in the star until the force of pressure exceeds the force of gravity. The outer layers of the star expand and its brightness decreases because the star's surface temperature decreases. However, due to inertia, the star expands to a point where forces become unbalanced—gravity exceeds pressure. The star then contracts and its brightness increases.

Build Science Skills L2

Using Models ACTIVITY

Purpose Students construct a scale model of the Milky Way.

Materials modeling clay, metric ruler

Class Time 30 minutes

Procedure Have students work in pairs to make cross-section scale models of the Milky Way out of clay. Tell them that the galactic disk has a diameter of approximately 100,000 light-years and is about 1000 light-years thick. The central bulge is roughly 3000 light-years thick and 20,000 light-years in diameter. The halo is a sphere about 100,000 light-years in diameter centered on the galactic core. The halo is sparsely populated by globular clusters. Suggest that students use a model scale such as 10,000 light-years = 1 cm. After students have made their models, ask, **What problems would you have encountered if you had attempted to use a scale of 10 light-years = 1 cm?** *(The scale would not have been useable because the model would have been impossibly large.)*

Expected Outcome Students will grasp the immense scale of the universe. **Kinesthetic, Portfolio**

CONCEPTS in Action

Scale of the Universe

To understand the immensity of space, astronomers organize the universe into different structures at different scales. Earth, for example, is part of the solar system, which forms part of the Milky Way Galaxy, which in turn is part of the Local Group of galaxies.

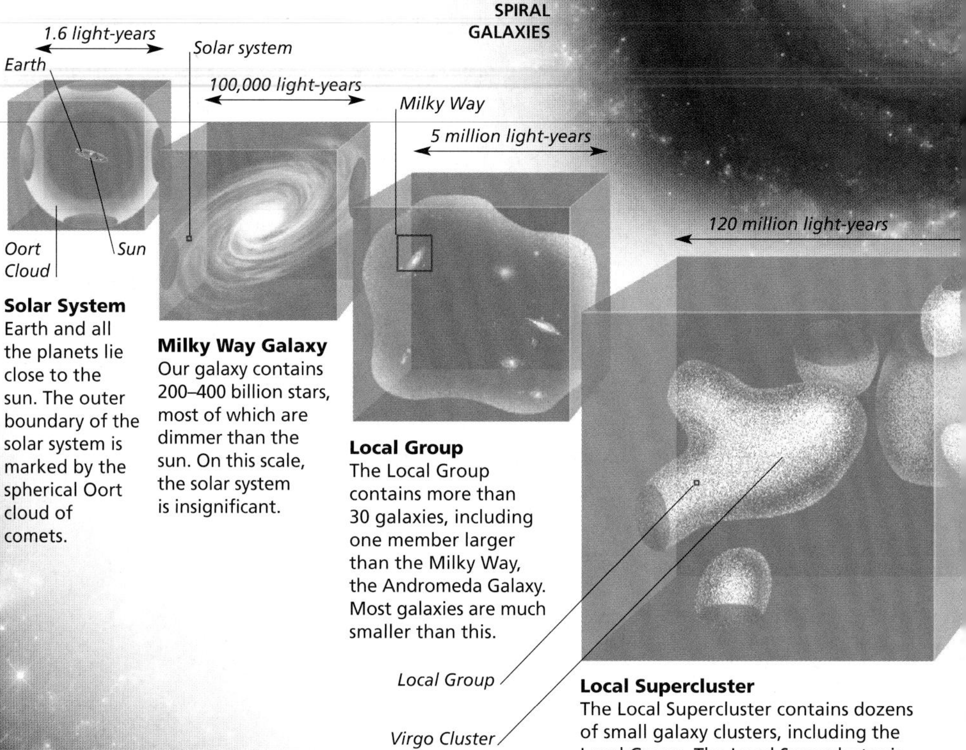

SPIRAL GALAXIES
1.6 light-years
Earth
Solar system
100,000 light-years
Milky Way
5 million light-years
120 million light-years
Oort Cloud
Sun
Local Group
Virgo Cluster

Solar System Earth and all the planets lie close to the sun. The outer boundary of the solar system is marked by the spherical Oort cloud of comets.

Milky Way Galaxy Our galaxy contains 200–400 billion stars, most of which are dimmer than the sun. On this scale, the solar system is insignificant.

Local Group The Local Group contains more than 30 galaxies, including one member larger than the Milky Way, the Andromeda Galaxy. Most galaxies are much smaller than this.

Local Supercluster The Local Supercluster contains dozens of small galaxy clusters, including the Local Group. The Local Supercluster is centered on the giant Virgo Cluster, a collection of more than 2000 galaxies about 65 million light-years from the Milky Way.

Distance measurement

Distances to other galaxies can be measured by observing stars in them called Cepheid variables. Cepheids are stars whose brightness varies over a regular cycle. Because the period of a Cepheid's cycle and its average absolute brightness are related, astronomers can work out how bright a Cepheid really is from its period. Comparing this to its apparent brightness, they can estimate its distance.

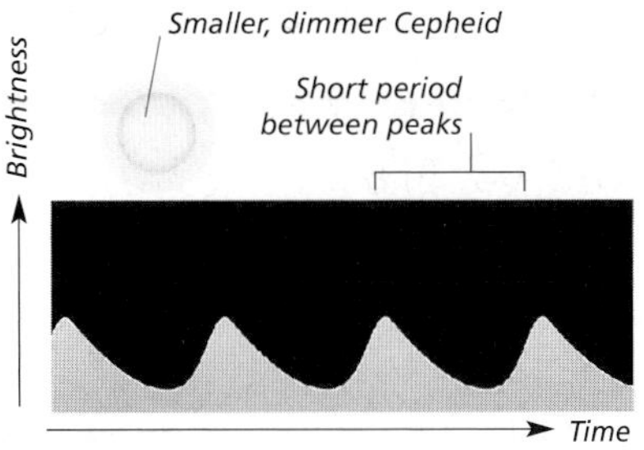

Smaller, dimmer Cepheid
Short period between peaks
Brightness
Time

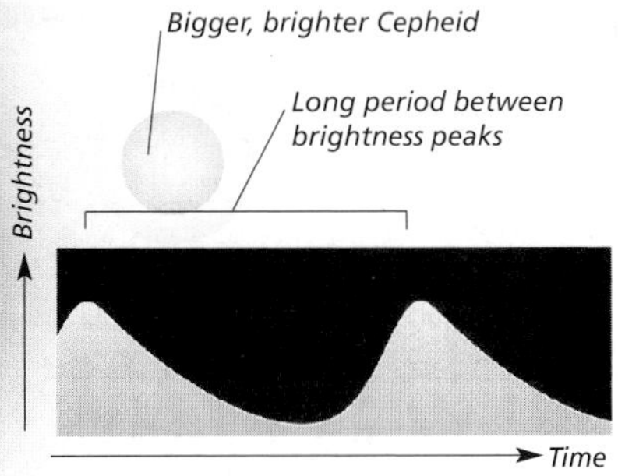

Bigger, brighter Cepheid
Long period between brightness peaks
Brightness
Time

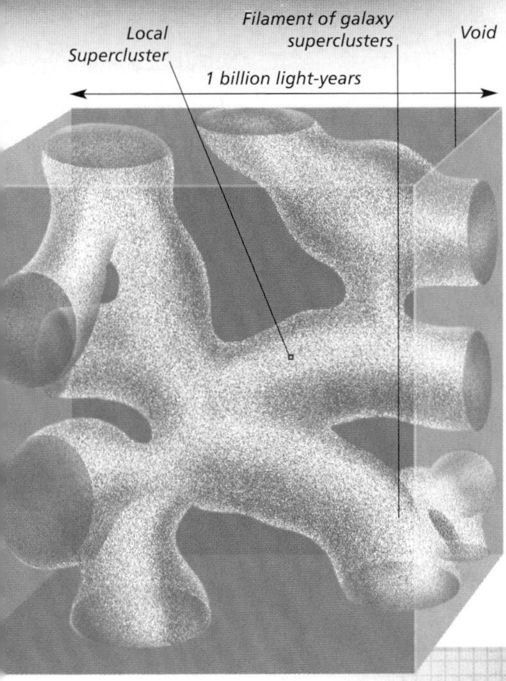

Local Supercluster
Filament of galaxy superclusters
Void
1 billion light-years

Nearby universe

Superclusters of galaxies are strung together in vast filaments, which are the largest known structures in the universe. These can stretch across hundreds of millions of light-years. They are separated by huge voids containing very few galaxies. These empty regions are often 100 to 200 million light-years across.

Going Further

- Research the Local Group in the library or on the Internet. Make an accurate drawing showing the relative sizes and distances among these three Local Group galaxies: Milky Way, Andromeda Galaxy, and M33.
- Take a Discovery Channel Video Field Trip by watching "Measuring Up to Space."

Discovery Channel School
Video Field Trip

Going Further

The Milky Way, Andromeda, and M33 are the three largest galaxies in the Local Group. Provide students with the following information to make scale drawings of the three galaxies. The approximate diameters of the galaxies are: Milky Way, 100,000 light-years; Andromeda (M31), 200,000 light-years; M33, 50,000 light-years. Andromeda is about 2.9 million light-years from the Milky Way. M33, also known as the Triangulum Galaxy, is about 3.0 million light-years from the Milky Way and 0.6 million light-years from Andromeda. A convenient scale for students to use is 1 cm = 10,000 light-years. Using this scale, the Milky Way would be 10 cm in diameter and a distance of 3 m from M33.
Visual

Discovery Channel School

Video Field Trip

Measuring Up to Space

After students have viewed the Video Field Trip, ask them the following questions: **What was the purpose of creating a scale model of our solar system in Peoria, Illinois?** *(To show how large space is compared to Earth)* **How did the size of Jupiter compare to the size of Earth in the model?** *(Jupiter was much larger. A thousand Earths could fit into Jupiter.)* **How does the size of the universe compare with the size of our solar system?** *(The universe is enormous compared to Earth. Earth is only one planet moving around one star, but the universe contains possibly billions of galaxies each consisting of tens or hundreds of billions of stars.)*

1 FOCUS

Objectives

26.5.1 **Relate** Hubble's Law to red shifts and to the expansion of the universe.

26.5.2 **Apply** the big bang theory to observations of the present-day universe.

26.5.3 **Describe** how dark matter can be detected and **explain** the importance of its effects on the expanding universe.

Reading Focus

Build Vocabulary L2

Flowchart Have students make flowcharts showing in chronological order the sequence of events that followed the big bang. Students should first determine the number of boxes they'll need for their charts. Each event in the process will need a separate box. Arrows should be placed between the boxes to show how one event led to the next. Use Figure 26 on p. 854 to help assess students' charts.

Reading Strategy L2

Students' questions may include: "What was the big bang?", "What happened afterwards?", and "What proof is there for the big bang theory?"

2 INSTRUCT

Hubble's Law

Use Visuals L1

Figure 24 Have students study the shifts. Ask, **Which spectrum shows a galaxy that is moving toward Earth?** *(The second or middle spectrum)* **Which spectrum shows a galaxy that is moving away from Earth?** *(The third or last spectrum)*
Visual

26.5 The Expanding Universe

Reading Focus

Key Concepts

- How do astronomers know that the universe is expanding?
- What is the big bang theory, and what evidence supports it?
- How can dark matter be detected?

Vocabulary

- red shift
- Hubble's Law
- big bang theory
- dark matter

Reading Strategy

Previewing Before reading, examine Figure 26 and write at least two questions to help you understand the information in it. As you read, write answers to your questions.

Questions on the Evolution of the Universe
a. ?
b. ?

Have you ever wanted to use a time machine to travel back in time? Telescopes are like time machines because they show what happened in other parts of the universe in the distant past. When you observe a star that is ten light-years away, you are seeing the star as it was ten years ago. This is because light took ten years to travel from the star to Earth. Images of galaxies that are billions of light-years away show how these galaxies looked billions of years ago.

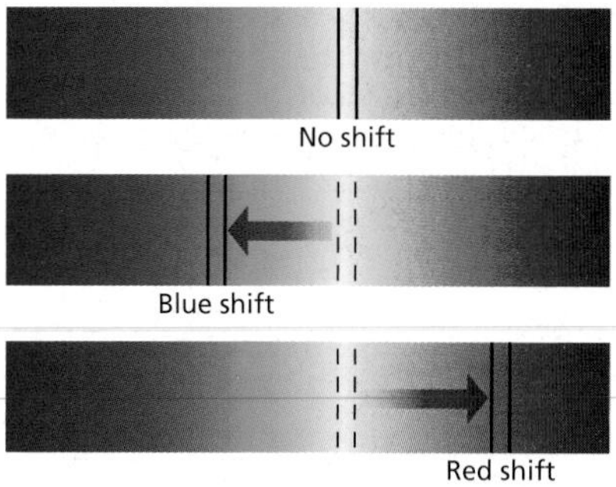
No shift
Blue shift
Red shift

Figure 24 Absorption lines of a galaxy shift toward the blue end of the spectrum when it moves toward Earth. The lines shift to the red end of the spectrum when a galaxy moves away from Earth. **Inferring** ***How would the spectrum of a galaxy that is slowly moving away from Earth compare to one that is moving away much more quickly?***

Hubble's Law

Recall from physics that as a sound or light source moves toward or away from an observer, its frequency and wavelength appear to change. This apparent change in frequency and wavelength is known as the Doppler effect. The Doppler effect can be used to determine how fast stars or galaxies are approaching or moving away from Earth. When a star or galaxy is approaching Earth, the lines in its spectrum are shifted toward the shorter (bluer) wavelengths, as shown in Figure 24. When the star or galaxy is moving away, the lines in its spectrum shift toward the longer (redder) wavelengths. The larger the observed shift, the greater is the speed of this movement.

In the mid-1920s, the American astronomer Edwin Hubble studied many galaxies at different distances from Earth. In 1929, Hubble announced his discovery: the light from most galaxies undergoes a **red shift**—that is, their light is shifted toward the red wavelengths. This red shift showed that, remarkably, nearly all galaxies are getting farther away from Earth.

Section Resources

Print

- ***Reading and Study Workbook With Math Support,*** Section 26.5
- ***Math Skills and Problem Solving Workbook,*** Section 26.5
- ***Transparencies,*** Section 26.5

Technology

- ***Interactive Textbook,*** Section 26.5
- ***Presentation Pro CD-ROM,*** Section 26.5

Hubble also found that more-distant galaxies have greater red shifts. This larger shift means that distant galaxies are moving away from Earth faster than closer galaxies. This relationship, called **Hubble's Law,** says that the speed at which a galaxy is moving away is proportional to its distance from us. The most distant observed galaxies are moving away at more than 90 percent of the speed of light!

To visualize the movement of galaxies, imagine the dough for a loaf of raisin bread as it rises. The raisins represent individual galaxies or groups of galaxies, and the dough represents the universe. As shown in Figure 25, when the dough rises, the distance between raisins increases, but the raisins stay the same size. As the dough expands, the distance between raisins that are far apart increases more than the distance between nearby raisins. In the same way, the most distant galaxies are moving away from us more quickly.

The observed red shift in the spectra of galaxies shows that the universe is expanding. Like the dough between the raisins, the space between the galaxies is expanding in all directions, and the universe as a whole is becoming larger.

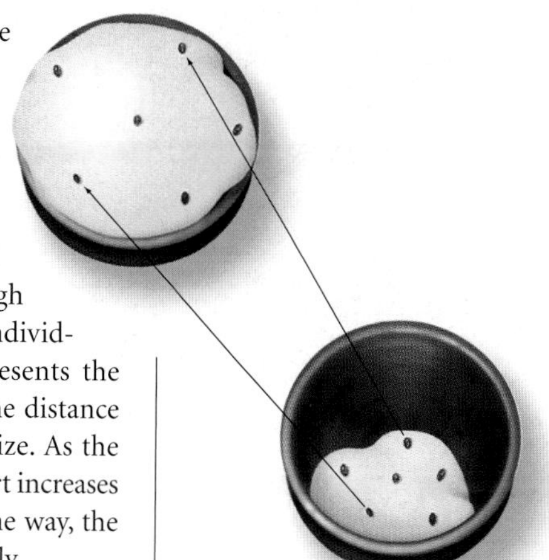

Figure 25 The raisins in this rising bread dough are all moving away from one another as the dough expands. In a similar way, galaxies move away from one another as the universe expands.

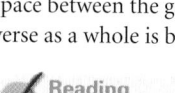

Reading Checkpoint *What is Hubble's Law?*

Data Analysis

Hubble's Constant

Hubble's law expresses the relationship between the velocity that a galaxy is moving away from Earth and its distance from us. The ratio of these variables is a constant called Hubble's constant. Hubble's constant can be estimated by finding the slope of a graph of velocity versus distance for a set of galaxies. Data for six galaxies are provided in the table at the right.

Hubble's constant is one of the most important and debated numbers in astronomy. It expresses how fast the universe is expanding, and can be used to estimate the age of the universe.

Velocity and Distance of Galaxies

Galaxy	Velocity (km/s)	Distance ($\times 10^6$ light-years)
1	4,200	200
2	7,800	390
3	10,500	520
4	17,000	850
5	21,000	1110
6	24,000	1170

1. **Using Tables** Which galaxy is moving away the fastest? Which galaxy is closest to Earth?
2. **Graphing** Graph the data shown in the table. Place velocity on the vertical axis and distance on the horizontal axis. What is the general shape of the graph?
3. **Calculating** Estimate Hubble's constant by measuring the slope of your graph. (*Hint:* Draw a line through the data points. Recall that Slope = Rise ÷ Run.)
4. **Inferring** About how fast is a galaxy receding if its distance is 2000×10^6 light-years? (*Hint:* Use your estimate of Hubble's constant from Question 3.)
5. **Predicting** Use your value for Hubble's constant to estimate the distance of a galaxy that has a velocity of 30,000 km/s.

Build Science Skills L2

Problem Solving Before students conduct the Data Analysis activity, explain that Hubble's Law can be expressed mathematically by the formula $v = H_0 d$, where v is recessional velocity (how fast a galaxy is receding from Earth), H_0 is Hubble's constant, and d is distance to the galaxy. Ask, **If you knew the values of recessional velocity and Hubble's constant, how would you use this equation to find the distance to a galaxy?** *(Divide recessional velocity by Hubble's constant)*
Logical

Data Analysis

Hubble's Constant L3

Answers

1. Galaxy 6; galaxy 1
2. The points on the graph fall close to a straight line.
3. slope = (rise/run) = [24,000 km/s − 4200 km/s]/[(1170 × 10^6 light-years) − (200 × 10^6 light-years)] = (19,800 km/s)/(970 × 10^6 light-years) = (20.4 km/s)/(10^6 light-years)
Although estimates vary somewhat, astronomers estimate that the actual value for Hubble's constant is about (20 km/s)/(10^6 light-years).
4. 41,000 km/s
5. 1470 × 10^6 light-years

For Extra Help L1

Remind students that velocity refers to the speed and direction of an object in motion. Before students complete Steps 4 and 5, check their estimates of Hubble's constant from Step 3.
Logical

Customize for English Language Learners

What Do I Know About the Word?
Place ELL students in mixed language-level groups of three. Have each group make a table with two columns. The first column should be titled What I Know. The second column should be titled What I Have Learned. Give students a vocabulary word and have them fill in the first column. After they have studied the concept, have them fill in the second column. Assess student tables to make sure students fully understand each concept before moving on to the next topic.

Answer to . . .

Figure 24 *The spectrum of both galaxies would be red shifted, but the spectrum of the galaxy that is moving away more quickly would have a greater red shift.*

Reading Checkpoint *Hubble's Law states that the speed a galaxy is moving away is proportional to its distance.*

The Big Bang Theory

Address Misconceptions **L2**

The realization that other galaxies are moving away from Earth in all directions can lead to the misconception that Earth and the Milky Way are at the center of the universe. To help correct this misconception, have students make marks on a partially inflated balloon and then observe how all the marks recede from one another as the balloon is fully inflated. Ask students to explain how this model demonstrates that all galaxies are receding from one another and that there is no center from which the universe is expanding.
Verbal

Build Reading Literacy **L1**

Using Context Clues Refer to page **568D** in **Chapter 19**, which provides the guidelines for using context clues.

Help students learn the meaning of new words or phrases by examining context. Tell students to look for familiar words or phrases that surround a new term—these are clues to the new term's meaning. Descriptive sentences provide additional clues. For example, students may be confused by the term *cosmic microwave background radiation.* Have them reread the first paragraph under the heading Evidence for the Theory. Point out that cosmic microwave background radiation is referred to as a "faint, distant glow." Note that the glow originated shortly after the big bang and can only be detected as radio signals. Ask, **Based on what you know about radio signals, could we see cosmic microwave background radiation with an optical telescope?** *(Not at present)* **What do you think the word *cosmic* refers to?** *(The universe)*
Verbal, Group

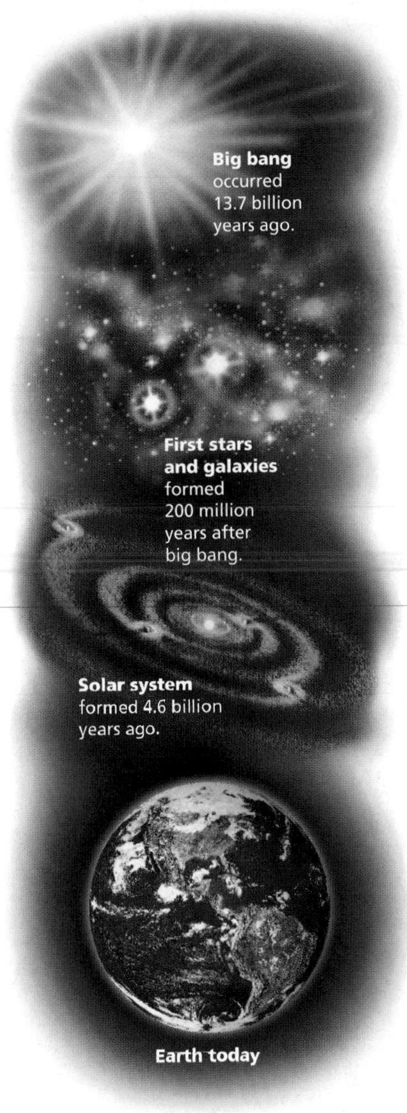
Big bang
occurred
13.7 billion
years ago.
First stars
and galaxies
formed
200 million
years after
big bang.
Solar system
formed 4.6 billion
years ago.
Earth today

Figure 26 The universe began with the big bang 13.7 billion years ago. The first stars and galaxies formed 200 million years later. The solar system, and Earth, formed about 9 billion years after the big bang.

The Big Bang Theory

If the universe is expanding, where were the galaxies in the distant past? Hubble observed that in every direction you look, galaxies at a given distance are moving away at the same rate. This is what you would expect if the universe were expanding uniformly.

Astronomers theorize that the universe came into being at a single moment, in an event called the big bang. According to this theory, all the matter and energy of the universe were at one time concentrated in an incredibly hot region smaller than the period at the end of this sentence. The **big bang theory** states that the universe began in an instant, billions of years ago, in an enormous explosion.

After the Big Bang The universe expanded quickly and cooled down after the big bang. After a few hundred thousand years of expansion, the universe was still much smaller and hotter than it is now, but cool enough for atoms to form. Gravity pulled atoms together into gas clouds that eventually evolved into stars in young galaxies. As shown in Figure 26, the sun and solar system formed about 4.6 billion years ago, when the universe was about two thirds of its present size.

Evidence for the Theory In 1965, two American physicists, Arno Penzias and Robert Wilson, noticed a signal on their radio telescope that they couldn't explain. They eventually realized that they were detecting a faint distant glow in every direction. Today this glow is called the cosmic microwave background radiation. This glow is energy produced during the big bang, still traveling throughout the universe. **The existence of cosmic microwave background radiation and the red shift in the spectra of distant galaxies strongly support the big bang theory.**

The big bang theory describes how the expansion and cooling of the universe over time could have led to the present universe of stars and galaxies. It offers the best current scientific explanation of the expansion of the observable universe. Variations of the theory continue to be proposed and are being tested with new observations.

Age of the Universe Since astronomers know how fast the universe is expanding now, they can infer how long it has been expanding. If you traveled backward in time, all of the matter in the universe would be at its starting point 13 to 14 billion years ago. Recent measurements of the microwave background radiation have led to a more precise age. Astronomers now estimate that the universe is 13.7 billion years old.

Facts and Figures

The Young Universe A microsecond after the big bang, the universe was intensely hot—around 10 trillion K. It was also bright, yet densely opaque. Visibility would have been limited to less than a centimeter. At the age of one second, the temperature of the universe plummeted to 10 billion K. No more than five minutes later, with temperatures hovering around 1 billion K, nuclear reactions began. Hydrogen fused into helium. Given the high temperatures, however, the isotopes were unstable. It took several hundred thousand years for temperatures to reach the point where atoms could remain stable.

Continued Expansion

What will happen to the universe in the distant future? Will the galaxies rush apart forever, or is there enough gravitational attraction to pull the galaxies back together? The answer depends on the mass of the entire universe. To have a gravitational force strong enough to reverse the expansion, there must be sufficient mass in the universe. If there is less than this amount of mass, the universe will continue to expand.

How can the amount of matter in the universe be determined? Some matter, like stars, glows. The mass of glowing matter can be estimated because it can be seen. However, much of the matter in the universe can't be seen by astronomers. **Dark matter** is matter that does not give off radiation. **Dark matter cannot be seen directly, but its presence can be detected by observing its gravitational effects on visible matter.** The American astronomer Vera Rubin found that galaxies like ours may contain as much as ten times more dark matter than visible matter. Without this much dark matter, there would not be enough gravitational force to keep groups of galaxies from flying apart.

There are many unanswered questions about dark matter. Astronomers don't know what it is made of or how it is distributed through the universe. Much of the mass of the universe may be composed of dark matter.

In the past few years, astronomers have discovered that the rate of expansion of the universe may be increasing. Galaxies appear to be moving apart faster now than expected. The reason for this is uncertain. A mysterious force called dark energy is theorized to be causing the rate of expansion to increase. If the expansion is accelerating, it's likely that the universe will expand forever.

Quick Lab

Modeling Expansion of the Universe

Procedure

1. Cut open a rubber band. Lay it flat next to a meter stick with one end, which represents Earth, at 0 cm.
2. Mark 1-cm intervals along the whole length of the rubber band. These marks represent galaxies.
3. Hold one end of the rubber band at 0 cm. Stretch it to twice its original length to model how much the universe expands in a certain time period.
4. Record the distance of each galaxy from Earth, along with its original distance.

Analyze and Conclude

1. **Inferring** Based on how far each galaxy moved in the same time, which galaxy moved the fastest?
2. **Drawing Conclusions** How is a galaxy's speed related to its distance?

Section 26.5 Assessment

Reviewing Concepts

1. What evidence shows that the universe is expanding?
2. According to the big bang theory, how did the universe begin?
3. What evidence supports the big bang theory?
4. What is dark matter, and how have astronomers inferred its existence?

Critical Thinking

5. **Using Analogies** How is a telescope like a time machine?
6. **Comparing and Contrasting** Compare the speeds at which most nearby galaxies and distant galaxies are moving away from Earth.

Connecting Concepts

Scientific Theories Do you think it is correct to call the big bang theory a theory rather than a hypothesis? Explain why. (*Hint:* Review the meaning of these terms in Chapter 1.)

Continued Expansion

Quick Lab

Modeling Expansion of the Universe L2

Objective
After completing this activity, students will be able to
- explain why farther galaxies are receding faster.

Skills Focus **Using Models, Measuring**

Prep Time 10 minutes

Materials large, wide rubber band that has been cut; pen; meter stick

Class Time 20 minutes

Safety Caution students to handle rubber bands carefully.

Teaching Tips
- Because the marks will stretch, make sure students measure from the center of each mark.

Expected Outcome Students should find that the farther away a galaxy is, the faster it is receding.

Analyze and Conclude
1. The galaxies that moved farthest in the same time interval moved fastest.
2. The farther away a galaxy is, the faster it is receding. **Kinesthetic**

3 ASSESS

Evaluate Understanding L2

Using Figure 26 as a guide, have students make a time line from the big bang to Earth's formation.

Reteach L1

Summarize how Hubble's Law relates to the expanding universe.

Section 26.5 Assessment

1. The observed red shift in the spectra of distant galaxies shows that the universe is expanding.
2. According to the big bang theory, the universe began at a single moment, billions of years ago, in an enormous explosion.
3. Evidence for the big bang theory includes the existence of cosmic microwave background radiation and the red shift of distant galaxies.
4. Dark matter is matter that does not give off radiation. Its presence can be detected by observing its gravitational effects on visible matter, such as stars.
5. When telescopes are used to observe stars or galaxies, an observer is seeing them as they were in the past. This is because it takes time, in some cases billions of years, for light from the stars and galaxies to reach us.
6. In general, the more distant the galaxy, the faster the speed that it is moving away from Earth.

Connecting Concepts

Although the big bang cannot be observed directly, its effects can be observed. Scientists have gathered a great deal of evidence that supports the concept of a big bang, and continue to test this concept with new observations. Therefore, it is a theory.

Interactive Textbook If your class subscribes to the Interactive Textbook, use it to review key concepts in Section 26.5.

Exploration Lab

Investigating Parallax **L2**

Objective
After completing this lab, students will be able to
- explain how the distance to a star is related to its parallax.

Skills Focus **Measuring, Using Models**

Prep Time 10 minutes

Class Time 40 minutes

Teaching Tips
- Some students can use the board, while others use paper taped to the wall.
- Each pair of students can have their own set of marks, or they can share marks or work in larger groups. For example, if students work in groups of three, one student can be the observer, one the pencil holder, and the third the data recorder.
- You may wish to have students graph their data.

Expected Outcome Students will observe that the parallax decreases as the "star" is moved farther from the observer.

Sample Data

Distance (m)	Parallax (cm)
1.0	40
1.5	15
2.0	7
2.5	5
3.0	3
3.5	<1

Exploration Lab

Investigating Parallax

Astronomers use parallax to measure the distances to nearby stars. In this lab, you will investigate the effect of distance on parallax. You will observe how an object appears to move against a distant background as you look at it first through one eye, and then through the other.

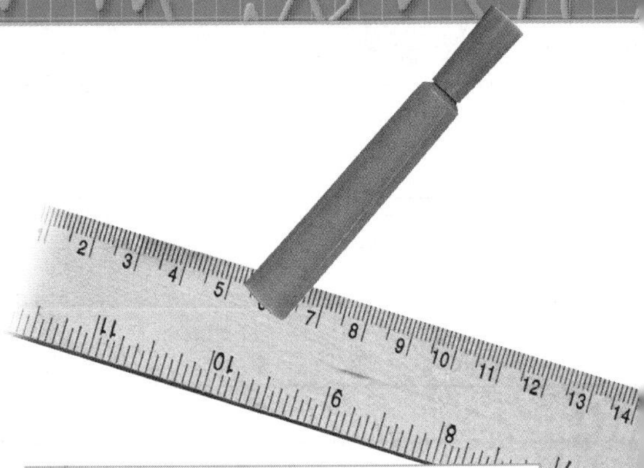

Problem How is parallax related to the distance to a star?

Materials
- unlined paper
- tape
- marker
- pencil
- meter stick
- index card
- graph paper

Data Table

Distance to Star (m)	Right Eye (cm)	Left Eye (cm)	Parallax (cm) (Difference)
1.0	0		

Skills Measuring, Using Models

Procedure

1. Tape three sheets of unlined paper to the wall horizontally, at eye level. Use a marker to draw 11 vertical marks 5 centimeters apart on the paper, as shown in the photo on the following page. The marks represent a distant background against which you will view a closer star. Label the marks in multiples of five from left to right, starting with 0 and ending with 50.
2. Construct a copy of the data table shown above.
3. Facing the sheets of paper, stand directly in front of the 25-cm mark. Then, use a meterstick to measure a perpendicular distance of 7 m from the mark. Move to that spot and face toward the 25-cm mark. You must remain at this position until you have finished collecting all data.
4. Have a partner hold a pencil vertically at your eye level as shown in the photo. The pencil should be 1 m in front of you. Your partner should use a meter stick to measure this distance. The pencil represents a nearby star.
5. Hold an index card over your left eye and look at the pencil with your right eye. Your right eye represents Earth's position at one point in its orbit. Move your head so the pencil lines up with the mark labeled 0.
6. Now, without moving your head, hold the index card over your right eye and look at the pencil with your left eye. Your left eye represents Earth's position at the opposite end of its orbit six months later. Note the number of the mark that lines up with the pencil. If the pencil is between two marks, estimate its position to the nearest whole number. Your partner should record this number in the appropriate place in your data table.
7. To determine the parallax, subtract the right eye measurement (zero, in this case) from the left-eye measurement. Record the parallax in the appropriate place in your data table.
8. **Predicting** How do you and your partner think the parallax will change as your partner moves the pencil away from you? Your partner should record your prediction.

856 Chapter 26

9. Have your partner use a meter stick to move the pencil 0.5 m toward the marks. Without moving your head, cover your left eye and look at the pencil with your right eye. Your partner should record the number of the mark the pencil lines up with.
10. Without moving your head, cover your right eye and look at the pencil with your left eye. Your partner should record the number of the mark the pencil lines up with.
11. To determine the parallax, subtract the right-eye measurement from the left-eye measurement. Record the parallax in the appropriate place in your data table.
12. Repeat Steps 9 through 11 until the parallax is less than 1 cm.
13. Construct a graph of the distance to the star (pencil) against the parallax you calculated. Plot the parallax on the horizontal axis and the distance on the vertical axis.

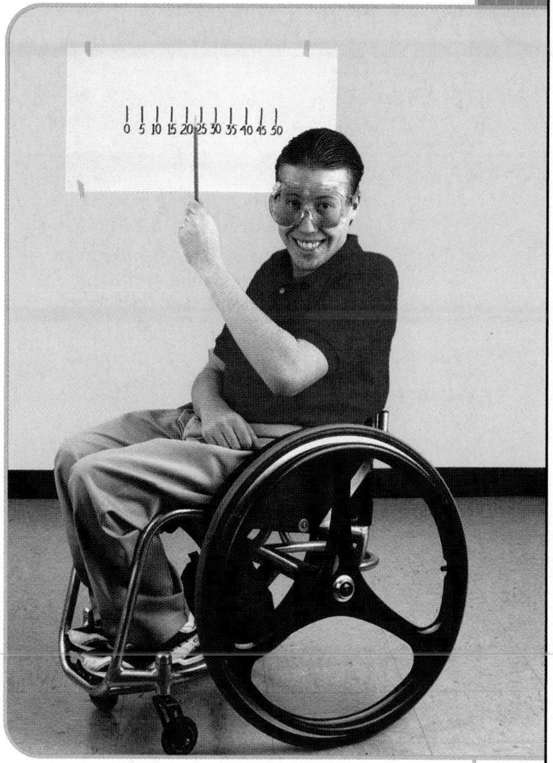
0 5 10 15 20 25 30 35 40 45 50

Analyze and Conclude

1. **Using Graphs** What does your graph show is the relationship between the distance to the pencil and the pencil's parallax?
2. **Analyzing Data** Was your prediction in Step 8 correct? Explain your answer.
3. **Drawing Conclusions** Assume that a parallax of less than 1 cm is too small to be measured. What is the maximum distance at which the pencil would still have a parallax you can measure?
4. **Applying Concepts** Parallax can only be used to measure the distances to nearby stars. Why can't this method be used to find the distances to far-away stars?
5. **Inferring** Astronomers usually make two measurements of the position of a star six months apart, when Earth is at opposite sides of its orbit. How is this useful in determining the star's parallax?

Go Further Use the library or the Internet to research how distances to stars are actually measured using parallax. What kinds of telescopes and other technology are used? What is the greatest distance to a star that has been measured using parallax? How do astronomers determine the distances of stars that are too far away from Earth to have a measurable parallax?

Analyze and Conclude

1. The graph shows that as the distance increases, parallax decreases.
2. If students predicted that parallax would decrease, they were correct. They should explain that parallax decreases as distance increases.
3. Students should report a maximum distance of 4 to 6 m, depending on their visual acuity, the distance between their eyes, and the precision of their measurements.
4. Parallax of distant stars is too small to be measured using current technology.
5. Making the measurements six months apart allows the points at which the measurements are made to be as far apart as possible. This allows parallax to be measured as accurately as possible, and thus for the greatest possible distances to be measured.

Logical

Go Further

The European Space Agency satellite Hipparcos (**H**igh **P**recision **P**arallax **C**ollecting **S**atellite) operated from 1989 to 1992 and determined the distances to all observed stars within 150 light-years of Earth. Students may find additional information about more recent estimates.
Verbal

Chapter 26

Study Guide

Study Tip

Study With a Partner
Suggest that students pair up as study partners, and spend at least one afternoon a week working together. Students can quiz each other on key concepts, compare notes, and discuss discrepancies.

Thinking Visually

a. 10 billion years on main sequence
b. Near the center
c. Top center and right
d. Supernova
e. Black dwarf

CHAPTER 26

Study Guide

26.1 The Sun

Key Concepts

- The sun's energy is produced in its core by fusion.
- The sun remains stable because the inward pull of gravity balances the outward pressure from fusion.
- The sun's interior consists of the core, radiation zone, and convection zone. Layers of the sun's atmosphere are the photosphere, chromosphere, and corona.
- Features of the sun's atmosphere include sunspots, prominences, and solar flares.

Vocabulary

core, *p. 830;* radiation zone, *p. 830;* convection zone, *p. 831;* photosphere, *p. 831;* chromosphere, *p. 831;* corona, *p. 831;* solar wind, *p. 831;* sunspots, *p. 832;* prominences, *p. 833;* solar flare, *p. 833*

26.2 Stars

Key Concepts

- Astronomers measure the parallax of nearby stars to determine their distance from Earth.
- Astronomers use several properties to classify stars.
- Most stars have a composition similar to the sun.
- H-R diagrams are used to estimate the sizes and distances of stars and to infer how stars change.

Vocabulary

star, *p. 834;* light-year, *p. 834;* parallax, *p. 835;* apparent brightness, *p. 836;* absolute brightness, *p. 837;* absorption lines, *p. 837;* H-R diagram, *p. 838;* main sequence, *p. 839;* supergiants, *p. 839;* giants, *p. 839;* white dwarf, *p. 839*

26.3 Life Cycles of Stars

Key Concepts

- A star is formed when nuclear fusion begins.
- A star's mass determines the star's place on the main sequence and how long it will stay there.
- A star ends up as a white dwarf, neutron star, or black hole once it exhausts its fuel supply.

Vocabulary

nebula, *p. 840;* protostar, *p. 841;* planetary nebula, *p. 842;* supernova, *p. 843;* neutron star, *p. 844;* pulsar, *p. 844;* black hole, *p. 844*

26.4 Groups of Stars

Key Concepts

- Astronomers have determined that more than half of all stars are members of star systems.
- There are three basic kinds of star clusters: open clusters, associations, and globular clusters.
- Astronomers classify galaxies into four main types: spiral, barred-spiral, elliptical, and irregular.

Vocabulary

constellation, *p. 846;* star system, *p. 847;* binary star, *p. 847;* globular cluster, *p. 847;* galaxy, *p. 848;* spiral galaxies, *p. 848;* barred-spiral galaxies, *p. 848;* elliptical galaxies, *p. 848;* irregular galaxies, *p. 848;* quasars, *p. 849*

26.5 The Expanding Universe

Key Concepts

- The observed red shift in the spectra of galaxies shows that the universe is expanding.
- Astronomers theorize that the universe came into being in an event called the big bang.
- Dark matter can only be detected by observing its gravitational effects on visible matter.

Vocabulary

red shift, *p. 852;* Hubble's Law, *p. 853;* big bang theory, *p. 854;* dark matter, *p. 855*

Thinking Visually

Comparing and Contrasting Use information from the chapter to complete the table below.

Property	Sun	Supergiant
Lifetime on main sequence	a. ?	A few million years
Current location on H-R diagram	b. ?	c. ?
Next stage in evolution	Red giant	d. ?
Final stage in evolution	e. ?	Neutron star or black hole

Chapter Resources

Print
- ***Chapter and Unit Tests,*** Chapter 26 Test A and Test B
- ***Test Prep Resources,*** Chapter 26

Technology
- ***Computer Test Bank,*** Chapter Test 26
- ***Interactive Textbook,*** Chapter 26
- ***Go Online,*** PHSchool.com, Chapter 26

CHAPTER 26

Assessment

Interactive textbook with assessment at PHSchool.com iText

Reviewing Content

Choose the letter that best answers the question or completes the statement.

1. The sun produces most of its energy from
   a. chemical reactions.
   b. nuclear fission.
   c. gravitational contraction.
   d nuclear fusion.

2. Where does the sun's visible light come from?
   a. the photosphere b. the corona
   c. the chromosphere d. the radiation zone

3. Astronomers have learned about the elements in stars by analyzing their
   a. parallax. b. apparent brightness.
   c. absorption lines. d. red shift.

4. Most stars are
   a. giants. b. main-sequence stars.
   c. supergiants. d. white dwarfs.

5. Which of the following has the highest surface temperature?
   a. red main sequence star
   b. red supergiant
   c. blue main sequence star
   d. black dwarf

6. The lifetime of a star on the main sequence is determined by its
   a. mass. b. apparent brightness.
   c. color. d. surface temperature.

7. The sun will eventually use up its hydrogen fuel and become a
   a. neutron star. b. white dwarf.
   c. black hole. d. supernova.

8. Which of the following is likely to have the highest proportion of old stars?
   a. open cluster b. globular cluster
   c. association d. spiral galaxy

9. The Milky Way is an example of a (an)
   a. nebula. b. elliptical galaxy.
   c. spiral galaxy. d. irregular galaxy.

10. Hubble's Law relates the speed at which a galaxy is moving away to its
   a. shape. b. mass.
   c. distance. d. absolute brightness.

Understanding Concepts

11. Explain the two major ways that energy is transferred from the sun's core through its interior.

12. What are the inward and outward forces that act on the sun? Which force is stronger?

13. Which parts of the sun are visible during a total solar eclipse? Why can't they usually be seen at other times?

14. What is a light-year?

15. The image on the left below shows stars as seen in July. The image on the right below shows the same stars in January. Which star is closest to Earth? Explain.

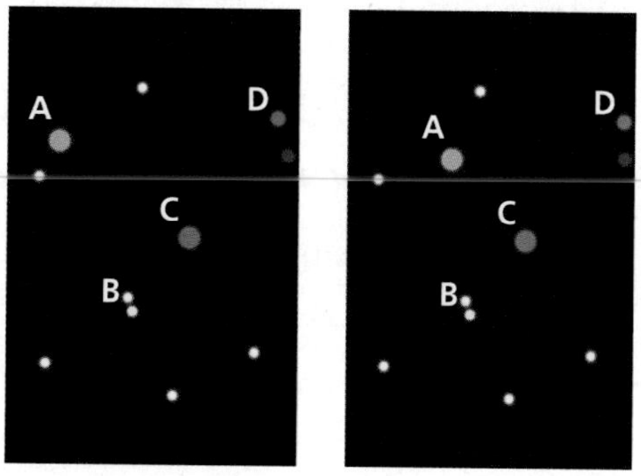
A
D
C
B
A
D
C
B

16. Suppose two stars have the same absolute brightness, but one star is twice as far from Earth as the other star. Which star has the greater apparent brightness?

17. When a star enters the red giant stage, what causes its outer layers to expand?

18. How does a black hole form?

19. How does Hubble's Law relate to the big bang theory?

20. How can astronomers measure the speed at which a galaxy is moving away from Earth?

21. Why are dark matter and dark energy so important in predicting the future of the universe?

Homework Guide

Section	Questions
26.1	1–2, 11–13
26.2	3–5, 14–16, 22–23, 27–28, 30–31
26.3	6–7, 17–18, 24, 29, 32–33
26.4	8–9, 25, 34, 37
26.5	10, 19–21, 26, 35–36

Assessment

Interactive Textbook If your class subscribes to the Interactive Textbook, your students can go online to access an interactive version of the Student Edition and a self-test.

Reviewing Content

1. d **2.** a **3.** c
4. b **5.** c **6.** a
7. b **8.** b **9.** c
10. c

Understanding Concepts

11. The two major ways that energy moves through the sun are by radiation and convection.
12. Gravity and the thermal pressure from nuclear fusion act on the sun. These are, on average, equally strong at any particular depth within the sun.
13. The chromosphere and the corona. These layers are not normally visible except during solar eclipses or with the use of special filters because they are much fainter than the bright photosphere.
14. A light-year is the distance that light travels in a vacuum in one year, about 9.5 trillion kilometers.
15. Star A has the greatest parallax and so must be the closest star to Earth.
16. The closer star, since apparent brightness decreases with distance
17. Hydrogen in a shell around the star's core begins to undergo fusion. This increases the outward flow of energy from the star, causing the outer regions of the star to expand outward and to cool to red.
18. A black hole forms after a supernova explosion when a star's remaining core is so massive that its gravity causes the core to collapse beyond the neutron-star stage.
19. Hubble's Law indicates that the universe is expanding. This is consistent with the big bang theory and provides supporting evidence for the theory.
20. By measuring the extent to which its spectrum undergoes a red shift
21. Much of the matter in the universe is thought to be dark matter. The total mass of this dark matter strongly affects the strength of the gravitational force that acts to reverse the expansion of the universe. Dark energy is a mysterious force that appears to be causing the expansion of the universe to accelerate.

Chapter 26

Critical Thinking

22. The star that appears brighter may be closer, or it may be larger and, therefore, have a greater absolute brightness.
23. To be so bright, the star must be very large relative to main-sequence stars of the same temperature.
24. Red giant, main-sequence star, neutron star, black hole
25. Star clusters are groups of stars that formed together at about the same time. Open clusters and associations have relatively few stars that are well spread out. Globular clusters are much larger and denser, and may contain more than a million stars. In contrast, galaxies may contain billions or trillions of stars, including many star clusters as well as individual stars, dust, and gas. Although galaxies vary widely in size and shape, they are typically much larger in size than star clusters.
26. The huge red shifts of quasars indicate that they are moving away from Earth at a great speed and, therefore, according to Hubble's Law, must be very far away.

Math Skills

27. Betelgeuse
28. Rigel, Vega, Sirius B
29. Alpha Centauri B. By its position on the H-R diagram, Alpha Centauri B can be identified as a relatively cool red star with a low mass and small absolute brightness. Because it uses its fuel so slowly, Alpha Centauri B will have the longest life of the three main-sequence stars in the diagram.
30. 25 light-years × 9.5 trillion km/light-year = 240 trillion km
31. 890,000 parsec × 3.26 light-years/parsec = 2.9 million light-years; about 29 times the diameter of the Milky Way

Concepts in Action

32. Scientists use an H-R diagram and examine groups of stars that formed at about the same time. This shows how different stars evolve at different rates and in different ways.
33. High-mass stars create elements such as carbon, oxygen, and nitrogen. When such a star explodes as a supernova, it produces enough energy to create elements as heavy as iron and to disperse all of these elements into space. The heavier elements that make up Earth and the bodies of living things came from a supernova that occurred in our galaxy billions of years ago.
34. Within the Local Group, find the Milky Way, a large spiral galaxy. Within the disk of the Milky Way, locate a spiral arm. On the inside of the arm, about two-thirds of the way out from the center of the galaxy, is a yellow main-sequence star called the sun. Earth is the third of nine planets orbiting the sun.
35. They infer its existence from its gravitational effects on surrounding visible matter such as stars.
36. About 13.7 billion years old; By measuring the microwave background radiation and by estimating the current size and rate of expansion of the universe, astronomers can infer its age.
37. Students should explain that astronomers are able to measure variations in the brightness of bright stars in other galaxies by using Cepheid variables. There is a relationship between the period of a Cepheid's brightness cycle and its average absolute brightness. Once astronomers know a Cepheid's absolute brightness, they can calculate its distance. The distance of the Cepheid variable is the approximate distance of the entire galaxy.

CHAPTER 26

Assessment *(continued)*

Critical Thinking

22. Applying Concepts Two stars are the same color, but one looks much brighter in the sky. Give two possible explanations for the difference in apparent brightness.

23. Inferring Explain why a cool star with a high absolute brightness must be a giant or a supergiant.

24. Inferring Arrange the following in order of increasing density: neutron star, main-sequence star, red giant, and black hole.

25. Comparing and Contrasting Compare and contrast star clusters and galaxies.

26. Inferring Astronomers have observed that quasars have huge red shifts. What does this indicate about the distance and speed of quasars?

Math Skills

Use the diagram below to answer Questions 27–29.

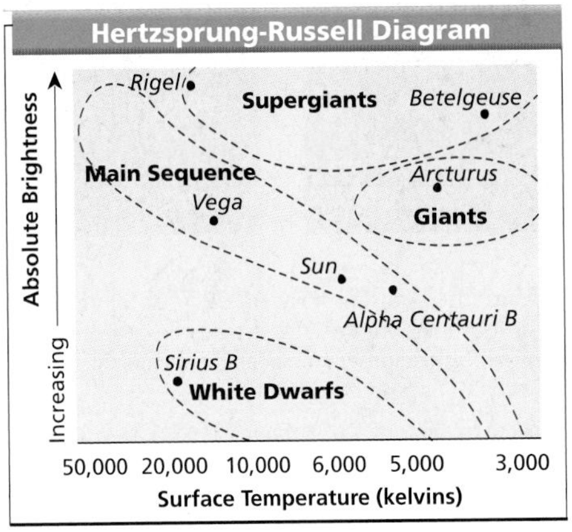

Hertzsprung-Russell Diagram
Rigel
Supergiants
Betelgeuse
Main Sequence
Vega
Arcturus
Giants
Sun
Alpha Centauri B
Sirius B
White Dwarfs
Increasing Absolute Brightness
50,000 20,000 10,000 6,000 5,000 3,000
Surface Temperature (kelvins)

27. Using Graphs Which star is brighter, Vega or Betelgeuse?

28. Using Graphs Which stars have higher surface temperatures than the sun?

29. Predicting Which star is likely to last the longest on the main sequence? Explain.

30. Calculating Vega, a star in the constellation Lyra, is located about 25 light-years from Earth. How many kilometers is this?

31. Calculating Another unit used by astronomers for measuring distances in space is the parsec (1 parsec is 3.26 light-years). The Andromeda Galaxy is about 890,000 parsecs from our own galaxy. How many light-years is this? How does this distance compare to the diameter of the Milky Way?

Concepts in Action

32. Applying Concepts How can we learn about the lives of stars, given that stars last much longer than human beings live?

33. Relating Cause and Effect How have supernovas made life on Earth possible?

34. Making Generalizations Give directions for traveling to Earth for an alien coming from the Virgo Cluster.

35. Inferring If astronomers cannot see dark matter, how do they know it exists?

36. Applying Concepts How old is the universe and how do we know?

37. Writing in Science Write a paragraph explaining how astronomers are able to measure the distance to other galaxies using observations of Cepheid variables.

Performance-Based Assessment

Using Models Construct a cutaway model of the sun. Use different colors of paper or clay to represent each layer of the sun's interior and atmosphere. Label each layer and include a brief description of each.

Go Online
PHSchool.com

For: Self-grading assessment
Visit: PHSchool.com
Web Code: cca-3260

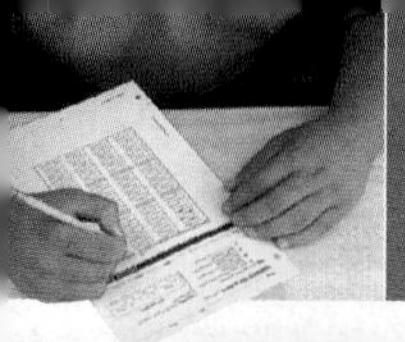

Standardized Test Prep

Test-Taking Tip

Sequencing a Series of Events
When a test question requires you to sequence a series of events, first try to predict the correct sequence before looking at the answer choices. Then compare your sequence to those listed. Be sure to pay attention to qualifiers in the question such as first, earliest, increasing, or decreasing, as these may help you eliminate choices.

Which sequence of events describes the big bang theory? Begin with the earliest event.

(A) Explosion; atoms form; stars form; all matter concentrated at a single point.
(B) All matter concentrated at a single point; explosion; atoms form; stars form.
(C) Explosion; stars form; all matter concentrated at a single point; atoms form.
(D) Atoms form; all matter concentrated at a single point; explosion; stars form.
(E) Stars form; atoms form; all matter concentrated at a single point; explosion.

(Answer: B)

Choose the letter that best answers the question or completes the statement.

1. The sun's source of energy is nuclear fusion in its
   (A) radiation zone. (B) core.
   (C) corona. (D) photosphere.
   (E) convection zone.

2. The most abundant element in most stars is
   (A) helium. (B) nitrogen.
   (C) argon. (D) hydrogen.
   (E) oxygen.

3. Stars form from
   (A) planets. (B) nebulas.
   (C) black holes. (D) quasars.
   (E) white dwarfs.

4. The two characteristics of stars used to plot a Hertzprung-Russell diagram are
   (A) color and apparent brightness.
   (B) apparent brightness and temperature.
   (C) absolute brightness and mass.
   (D) color and size.
   (E) absolute brightness and temperature.

Use the graph below to answer Questions 5 and 6.

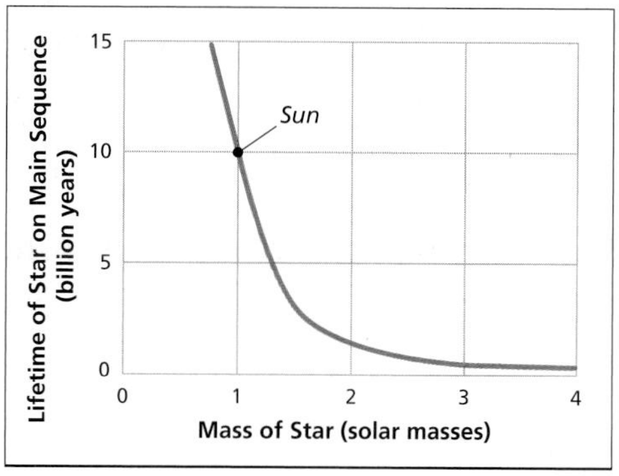

Lifetime of Star on Main Sequence (billion years)
15
10
5
0
Sun
0
1
2
3
4
Mass of Star (solar masses)

5. About how long will the sun spend on the main sequence?
   (A) 10 million years
   (B) 500 million years
   (C) 1.0 billion years
   (D) 10 billion years
   (E) 15 billion years

6. A star with 3 times the sun's mass has a main sequence lifetime of about
   (A) 500 million years.
   (B) 1.5 billion years.
   (C) 7.5 billion years.
   (D) 10 billion years.
   (E) 15 billion years.

7. Place the following events in the evolution of a sun-like star in the correct sequence, beginning with the earliest event.
   (A) planetary nebula; protostar; white dwarf; main-sequence star; red giant
   (B) protostar; main-sequence star; red supergiant; supernova; neutron star or black hole
   (C) planetary nebula; main-sequence star; red giant; white dwarf; protostar
   (D) protostar; main-sequence star; red giant; planetary nebula; white dwarf
   (E) white dwarf; main-sequence star; red giant; planetary nebula; protostar

Standardized Test Prep

1. B **2.** D **3.** B
4. E **5.** D **6.** A
7. D

Performance-Based Assessment

Students' models should include the core, radiation zone, convection zone, photosphere, chromosphere, and corona, all approximately to scale. Students' descriptions should include relevant information on each layer, such as diameter or thickness, temperature, and so forth.

Go Online PHSchool.com

Your students can independently test their knowledge of the chapter and print out their test results for your files.

Skills and Reference Handbook

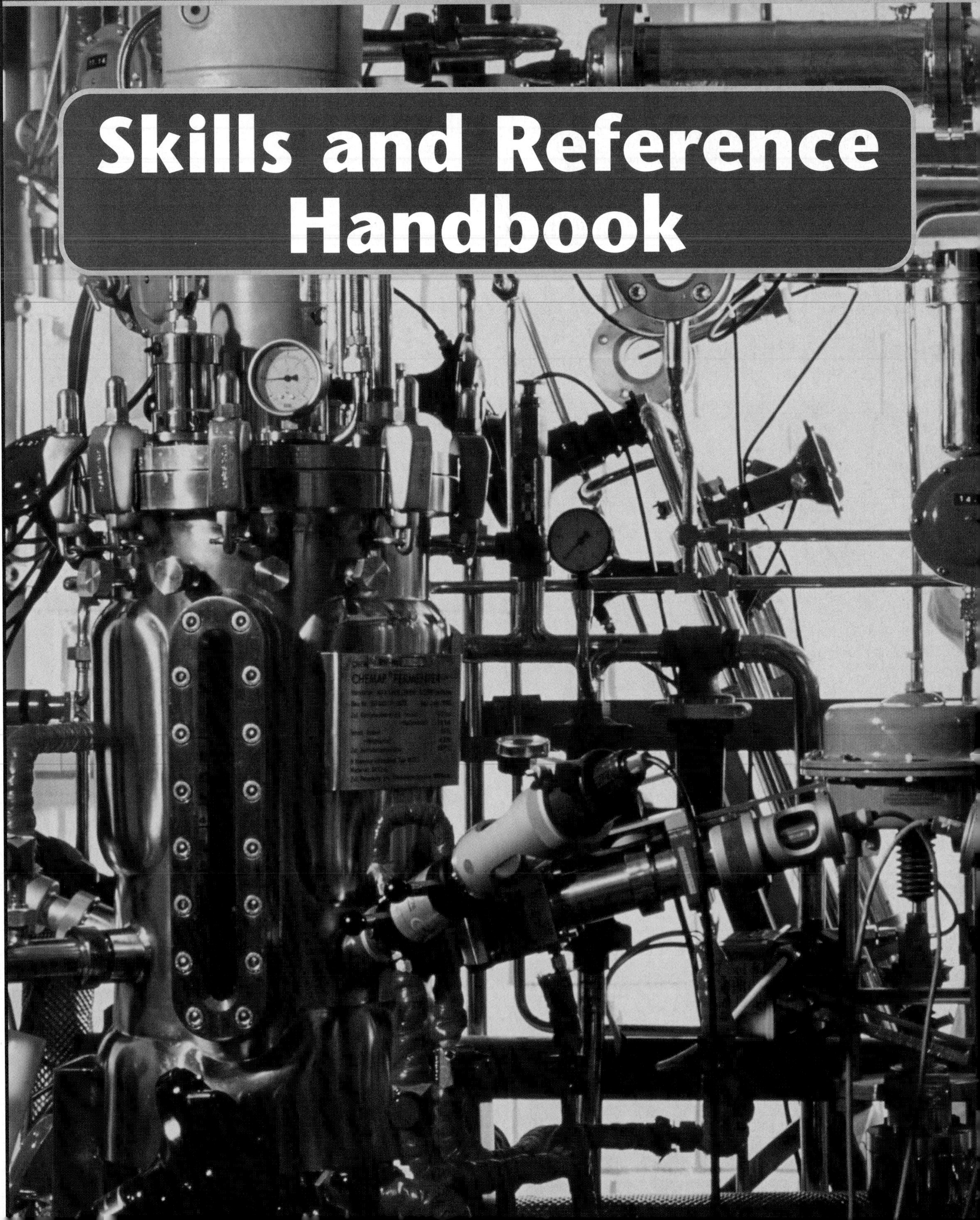

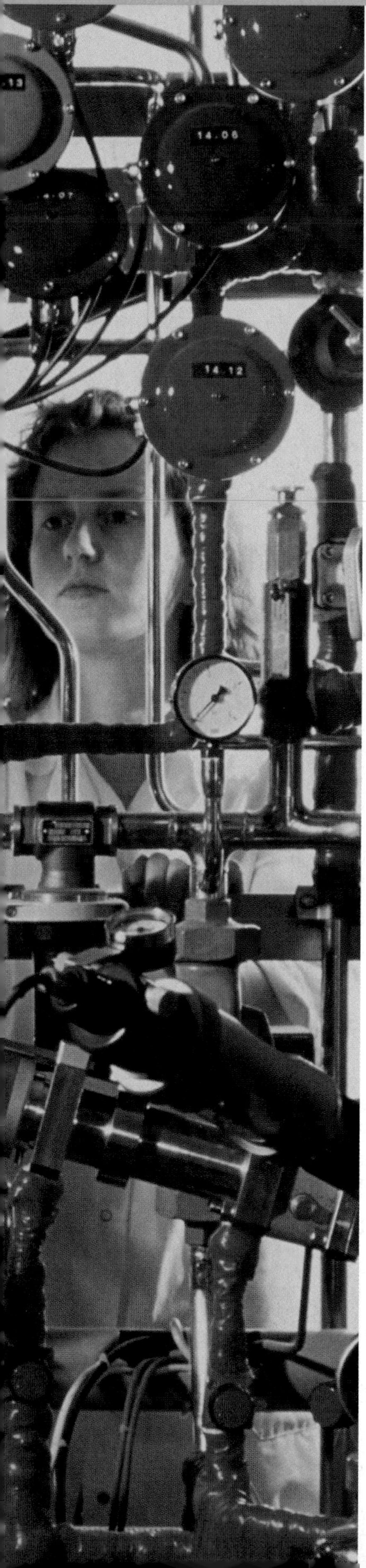

Skills Handbook

Basic Process Skills

During a physical science course, you often carry out some short lab activities as well as more detailed experiments. Here are some skills that you will use as you work.

Observing

In every science activity, you make a variety of observations. **Observing** is using one or more of the five senses to gather information. Many observations involve the senses of sight, hearing, touch, and smell.

Sometimes you will use tools that increase the power of your senses or make observations more precise. For example, hand lenses enable you to see things in greater detail. Tools may help you eliminate personal opinions or preferences.

In science it is customary to record your observations at the time they are made, usually by writing or drawing in a notebook. You may occasionally make records by using computers, cameras, videotapes, and other tools. As a rule, scientists keep complete accounts of their observations, often using tables to help organize their observations in a regular way.

Inferring

In science as in everyday life, observations are usually followed by inferences. **Inferring** is interpreting an observation or statement based on prior knowledge. For example, you can make several observations using the strobe photograph below. You can observe that the ball is moving. Based on the motion of the ball, you might infer that the ball was thrown downward at an angle by an experimenter. In making that inference, you would use your knowledge about the motion of projectiles. Someone who knew more about projectile motion might infer that the ball loses energy with each bounce. That is why the height decreases with each bounce.

Notice that an inference is an act of reasoning, not a fact. That means an inference may be logical but not true. It is often necessary to gather further information before you can be confident that an inference is correct. For scientists, that information may come from further observations or from research into the work done by others.

Comparing Observations and Inferences

Sample Observation	Sample Inference
The ball moves less and less vertical distance in the time between each flash of the strobe light.	Gravity is slowing down the ball's upward motion.
The ball moves the same distance to the right in the time between each flash of the strobe light.	Air resistance is so small that it does not slow down the ball's horizontal motion.

Predicting

People often make predictions, but their statements about the future could be either guesses or inferences. In science, a **prediction** is an inference about a future event based on evidence, experience, or knowledge. For example, you can say, *On the first day next month, it will be sunny all day.* If your statement is based on evidence of weather patterns in the area, then the prediction is scientific. If the statement was made without considering any evidence, it's just a guess.

Predictions play a major role in science because they offer scientists a way to test ideas. If scientists understand an event or the properties of a particular object, they should be able to make accurate predictions about that event or object. Some predictions can be tested simply by making observations. For others, carefully designed experiments are needed.

Measuring

Measurements are important in science because they provide specific information and help observers avoid bias. **Measuring** is comparing an object or process to a standard. Scientists use a common set of standards, called the International System of Units, abbreviated as SI (for its French name, *Système International d'Unités*).

What distance does the ball travel in each time interval in the strobe photograph? You can make measurements on the photograph to make more precise statements about the ball's motion.

Calculating

Once scientists have made measurements, calculations are a very important part of analyzing data. How fast is a ball moving? You could directly measure the speed of a ball using probeware such as a motion sensor. But you can also calculate the speed using distance and time measurements. **Calculating** is a process in which a person uses mathematical operations to manipulate numbers and symbols.

Classifying

Classifying is grouping items according to some organizing idea or system. Classifying occurs in every branch of science but it's especially important in chemistry because there are so many different ways that elements can combine to form compounds.

Sometimes you place objects into groups using an established system. Other times you create a system by observing a variety of objects and identifying their properties. For example, you could group household cleaners into those that are abrasive and those that are not. Or you could categorize cleaners as toxic or nontoxic. Ammonia is toxic, whereas vinegar is not.

DISTILLED WHITE
VINEGAR
clear
ammonia
WARNING: IRRITANT

Using Tables and Graphs

Scientists represent and organize data in tables and graphs as part of experiments and other activities. Organizing data in tables and graphs makes it easier to see patterns in data. Scientists analyze and interpret data tables and graphs to determine the relationship of one variable to another and to make predictions based on the data.

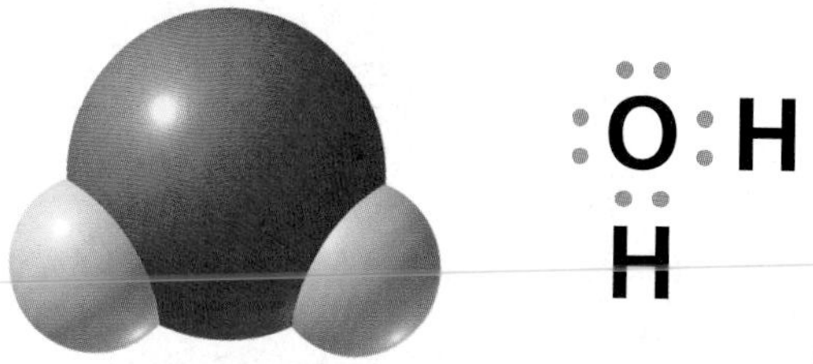
O
H
H

Space-filling model

Electron dot model

Using Models

Some cities refuse to approve new tall buildings if they would cast shadows on existing parks. As architects plan buildings in such locations, they use models to show where a proposed building's shadow will fall at any time of day at any season of the year. A **model** is a mental or physical representation of an object, process, or event. In science, models are usually made to help people understand natural objects and the processes that affect these objects.

Models can be varied. Mental models, such as mathematical equations, can represent some kinds of ideas or processes. For example, the equation for the surface area of a sphere can model the surface of Earth, enabling scientists to determine its size. Models can be two-dimensional (flat) or three-dimensional (having depth). In chemistry, for example, there are several ways to model the arrangement of atoms in a molecule. Two models for a water molecule are shown above. The electron dot model is two-dimensional. It has the advantage of clearly showing how electrons are shared among atoms in the molecule. The space-filling model cannot show the number of electrons inside the atoms or between atoms, but it does show the arrangement of atoms in space.

Experimental Methods

A science experiment is a procedure designed so that there is only one logical explanation for the results. Some types of experiments are fairly simple to design. Others may require ingenious problem solving.

Posing Questions

As a gardener harvested corn in her vegetable garden, she noticed that on one side of the garden the plants produced very few ears of corn. The gardener wondered, *Why didn't the plants on one side of the garden produce as much corn?*

An experiment may begin when someone like the gardener asks a specific question or wants to solve a particular problem. Sometimes the original question leads directly to an experiment, but often researchers need to restate the problem before they can design an appropriate experiment. The gardener's question about the corn, for example, is too broad to be tested by an experiment, since there are so many possible different answers. To narrow the topic, the gardener might think about several related questions: *Were the seeds the same on both sides of the garden? Was the sunlight the same? Is there something different about the soil?*

Formulating Hypotheses

In science, a question about an event is answered by developing a possible explanation called a **hypothesis**. The hypothesis may be developed after long thought and research or come to a scientist "in a flash." To be useful, a hypothesis must lead to predictions that can be tested.

In this case, the gardener decided to focus on the quality of the soil on each side of her garden. She did some tests and discovered that the soil had a lower pH on the side where the plants did not produce well. That led her to propose this hypothesis: *If the pH of the soil is too low, the plants will produce less corn.* The next step is to make a prediction based on the hypothesis, for example, *If the pH of the soil is increased using lime, the plants will yield more corn.* Notice that the prediction suggests the basic idea for an experiment.

Designing Experiments

A carefully designed experiment can test a prediction in a reliable way, ruling out other possible explanations. As scientists plan their experimental procedures, they pay particular attention to the variables that must be controlled and the procedures that must be defined.

The gardener decided to study three groups of plants:

Group 1—20 plants on the side of the garden with a low pH;

Group 2—20 plants on the side of the garden with a low pH, but with lime added; and

Group 3—20 plants on the side of the garden with a high pH.

Controlling Variables

As researchers design an experiment, they identify the **variables**, factors that can change. Some common variables include mass, volume, time, temperature, light, and the presence or absence of specific materials. An experiment involves three categories of variables. The factor that scientists purposely change is called the **manipulated variable**. The factor that may change because of the manipulated variable and that scientists want to observe is called the **responding variable**. And the factors that scientists purposely keep the same are called the **controlled variables**. Controlling variables helps make researchers confident that the observed changes in the responding variable are due to changes in the manipulated variable.

For the gardener, the manipulated variable is the pH of the soil. The responding variable is the number of ears of corn produced by the plants. Among the variables that must be controlled are the amount of sunlight received each day, the time of year when seeds are planted, and the amount of water the plants receive.

What Is a "Control Group"?

When you read about certain experiments, you may come across references to a control group (or "a control") and the experimental groups. All of the groups in an experiment are treated exactly the same except for the manipulated variable. In an experimental group, the manipulated variable is being changed. The control group is used as a standard of comparison. It may consist of objects that are not changed in any way or objects that are being treated in the usual way. For example, in the gardener's experiment, Group 1 is the control group, because for these plants nothing is done to change the low pH of the soil.

Forming Operational Definitions

In an experiment, it is often necessary to define one or more variables explicitly so that any researcher could measure or control the variable in exactly the same way. An **operational definition** describes how a particular variable is to be measured or how a term is to be defined. In this context, the term *operational* means "describing what to do."

The gardener, for example, has to decide exactly how much lime to add to the soil. Can lime be added after the seeds are planted or only before planting? At what pH should no more lime be added to the soil? In this case, the gardener decided to add lime only before planting, and to add enough lime to make the pH equal in Groups 2 and 3.

Analyzing Data

The observations and measurements that are made in an experiment are called **data**. Scientists customarily record data in an orderly way. When an experiment is done, the researcher analyzes the data for trends or patterns, often by doing calculations or making graphs, to determine whether the results support the hypothesis.

For example, the gardener regularly measured and recorded data such as the soil moisture, daily sunlight, and pH of the soil. She found that the soil pH in Groups 2 and 3 started the same, but after two months the soil pH for Group 3 was a little higher than the soil pH for Group 2.

After harvesting the corn, the gardener recorded the numbers of ears of corn produced by each plant. She totaled the number of ears for each group. Her results were the following.

Group 1: 67 ears of corn
Group 2: 102 ears of corn
Group 3: 126 ears of corn

The overall trend was clear: The gardener's prediction was correct.

Drawing Conclusions

Based on whether the results confirm or refute the hypothesis, researchers make a final statement that summarizes the experiment. That final statement is called the **conclusion**. For example, the gardener's conclusion was, *Adding lime to soil with a low pH will improve the production of corn plants.*

Communicating Results

When an experiment has been completed, one or more events may follow. Researchers may repeat the experiment to verify the results. They may publish the experiment so that others can evaluate and replicate their procedures. They may compare their conclusion with the discoveries made by other scientists. And they may raise new questions that lead to new experiments. For example, *Why does the pH level decrease over time when soil is treated with lime?*

Evaluating and Revising

Scientists must be flexible about the conclusions drawn from an experiment. Further research may help confirm the results of the experiment or make it necessary to revise the initial conclusions. For example, a new experiment may show that lime can be effective only when certain microbes are present in the soil. Scientists continuously evaluate and revise experiments based on the findings in new research.

Skills Handbook

Science Safety

Laboratory work can be exciting, but it can be dangerous if you don't follow safety rules. Ask your teacher to explain any rules you don't understand. Always pay attention to safety symbols and **CAUTION** statements.

General Safety Rules and First Aid

1. Read all directions for an experiment several times. Follow the directions exactly as they are written. If you are in doubt, ask your teacher for assistance.
2. Never perform unauthorized or unsupervised labs, or handle equipment without specific permission.
3. When you design an experiment, do not start until your teacher has approved your plan.
4. If a lab includes physical activity, use caution to avoid injuring yourself or others. Tell your teacher if there is a reason that you should not participate.
5. Never eat, drink, or bring food into the laboratory.
6. Report all accidents to your teacher immediately.
7. Learn the correct ways to deal with a burn, a cut, and acid splashed in your eyes or on your skin.
8. Be aware of the location of the first-aid kit. Your teacher should administer any required first aid.
9. Report any fire to your teacher immediately. Find out the location of the fire extinguisher, the fire alarm, and the phone where emergency numbers are listed.

Dress Code

10. Always wear safety goggles to protect your eyes when working in the lab. Avoid wearing contact lenses. If you must wear contact lenses, ask your teacher what precautions you should take.
11. Wear a laboratory apron to protect your skin and clothing from harmful chemicals or hot materials.
12. Wear disposable plastic gloves to protect yourself from contact with chemicals that can be harmful. Keep your hands away from your face. Dispose of gloves according to your teacher's instructions.
13. Tie back long hair and loose clothing. Remove any jewelry that could contact chemicals or flames.

Heating and Fire Safety

14. Hot plates, hot water, and hot glassware can cause burns. Never touch hot objects with your bare hands. Use an oven mitt or other hand protection.
15. Use a clamp or tongs to hold hot objects. Test an object by first holding the back of your hand near it. If you feel heat on the back of your hand, the object may be too hot to handle.
16. Tie back long hair and loose clothing, and put on safety goggles before using a burner. Follow instructions from your teacher for lighting and extinguishing burners. If the flame leaps out of a burner as you are lighting it, turn the gas off. Never leave a flame unattended or reach across a flame. Make sure your work area is not cluttered with materials.
17. If flammable materials are present, make sure there are no flames, sparks, or exposed sources of heat.
18. Never heat a chemical without your teacher's permission. Chemicals that are harmless when cool can be dangerous when heated. When heating a test tube, point the opening away from you and others in case the contents splash or boil out of the test tube.
19. Never heat a closed container. Expanding hot gases may cause the container to explode.

Using Electricity Safely

20. To avoid an electric shock, never use electrical equipment near water, or when the equipment or your hands are wet. Use ground fault circuit interrupter (GFCI) outlets if you or your equipment may come into contact with moisture.
21. Use only sockets that accept a three-prong plug. Never use two-prong extension cords or adapters. When removing an electrical plug from a socket or extension cord, grasp the plug, not the cord.
22. Disconnect equipment that is not in use. Be sure cords are untangled and cannot trip anyone.
23. Do not use damaged electrical equipment. Look for dangerous conditions such as bare wires or frayed cords. Report damaged equipment immediately.

Using Glassware Safely

24. Handle fragile glassware, such as thermometers, test tubes, and beakers, with care. Do not touch broken glass. Notify your teacher if glassware breaks. Never use chipped or cracked glassware.
25. Never force glass tubing into a stopper. Your teacher will demonstrate the proper methods.
26. Never heat glassware that is not thoroughly dry. Use a wire screen to protect glassware from flames.
27. Hot glassware may not appear hot. Never pick up glassware without first checking to see if it is hot.
28. Never eat or drink from laboratory glassware.

Using Chemicals Safely

29. Do not let any corrosive or poisonous chemicals get on your skin or clothing, or in your eyes. When working with poisonous or irritating vapors, work in a well-ventilated area and wash your hands thoroughly after completing the activity.
30. Never test for an odor unless instructed by your teacher. Avoid inhaling a vapor directly. Use a wafting motion to direct vapor toward your nose.
31. Never mix chemicals "for the fun of it." You might produce a dangerous, possibly explosive substance.
32. Never touch, taste, or smell a chemical that you do not know for certain to be harmless.
33. Use only those chemicals listed in an investigation. Keep the lids on the containers when chemicals are not being used. To avoid contamination, never return chemicals to their original containers.
34. Take extreme care not to spill any chemicals. If a spill occurs, immediately ask your teacher about the proper cleanup procedure. Dispose of all chemicals as instructed by your teacher.
35. Be careful when working with acids or bases. Pour these chemicals over the sink, not over your workbench. If an acid or base gets on your skin or clothing, rinse it off with plenty of cold water. Immediately notify your teacher about an acid or base spill.
36. When diluting an acid, pour the acid into water. Never pour water into the acid.

Using Sharp Instruments

37. Use sharp instruments only as directed. Scissors, scalpels, pins, and knives are sharp and can cut or puncture your skin. Always direct sharp edges and points away from yourself and others.
38. Notify your teacher immediately if you cut yourself when in the laboratory.

End-of-Experiment Rules

39. All chemicals and any other materials used in the laboratory must be disposed of safely. Follow your teacher's instructions.
40. Clean up your work area and return all equipment to its proper place. Thoroughly clean glassware before putting it away.
41. Wash your hands thoroughly with soap, or detergent, and warm water. Lather both sides of your hands and between your fingers. Rinse well.
42. Check that all burners are off and the gas supply for the burners is turned off.

Safety Symbols

General Safety Awareness
Follow all safety instructions.

Physical Safety
Use caution in physical activities.

Safety Goggles
Always wear goggles in the laboratory.

Lab Apron
Always wear a lab apron in the laboratory.

Plastic Gloves
Protect your hands from unsafe chemicals.

Heating
Be careful using sources of heat.

Heat-Resistant Gloves
Do not touch hot objects with bare hands.

Flames
Work carefully around open flames.

No Flames
Flammable materials may be present.

Electric Shock
Take precautions to avoid electric shock.

Fragile Glassware
Handle glassware carefully.

Corrosive Chemical
Work carefully with corrosive chemicals.

Poison
Avoid contact with poisonous chemicals.

Fumes
Avoid inhaling dangerous vapors.

Sharp Object
Use caution with sharp or pointed tools.

Disposal
Follow instructions for disposal.

Hand Washing
Wash your hands before leaving the lab.

Reading and Study Skills

At the beginning of each section, you will find a reading strategy to help you study. Each strategy uses a graphic organizer to help you stay organized. The following strategies and graphic organizers are used throughout the text.

Reading Strategies

Using Prior Knowledge
This strategy helps you think about your own experience before you read a section. Research has shown that you learn new material better if you can relate it to something you already know.

Previewing
Previewing a lesson can give you a sense of how the textbook is organized and what lies ahead. One technique is to look at the section topics (in green and blue type). You also can preview by reading captions. Sometimes previewing helps you simply because you find out a topic isn't as hard as you thought it might be.

Predicting
You can preview a section and then make a prediction. For example, you might predict the meaning of an important concept. Then, as you read, check to see if your prediction was correct. Often you find out that you knew more about a topic than you realized.

Building Vocabulary
Start building new vocabulary by previewing a section and listing boldface terms you don't recognize. Then look for each term as you read. Writing a sentence with a term, and defining a term in your own words are two techniques that will help you remember definitions.

Identifying the Main Idea
The key symbols next to boldface sentences identify the main ideas in a section. You can use topic sentences to find the main idea in a paragraph. Often, a topic sentence is the first or second sentence in a paragraph.

Identifying Cause and Effect
Cause-and-effect relationships are very important in science. A flowchart will help you identify cause-and-effect relationships as you read about a process.

Comparing and Contrasting
Comparing and contrasting can help you understand how concepts are related. Comparing is identifying both similarities and differences, while contrasting focuses on the differences. Compare-and-contrast tables and Venn diagrams work best with this strategy.

Sequencing
When you sequence events, it helps you to visualize the steps in a process and to remember the order in which they occur. Sequences often involve cause-and-effect relationships. Use flowcharts for linear sequences and cycle diagrams for repeating sequences.

Relating Text and Figures
You can use diagrams and photographs to focus on the essential concepts in a section. Then find text that extends the information in the figures. You can also reinforce concepts by comparing different figures.

Summarizing
Summarizing requires you to identify key ideas and state them briefly in your own words. You will remember the content of an entire section better even if you summarize only a portion of the section.

Outlining
You can quickly organize an outline by writing down the green and blue headings in a section. Then add phrases or sentences from the boldface sentences to expand the outline with the most important concepts.

Monitoring Your Understanding
You can evaluate your progress with graphic organizers such as a Know-Write-Learn (KWL) table. To make a KWL table, construct a table with three columns, labeled K, W, and L. Before you read, write what you already know in the first column (K). In the middle column, write what you want to learn (W). After you read, write what you learned (L).

Graphic Organizers

Concept Maps and Web Diagrams

A **concept map** is a diagram that contains concept words in ovals and connects the ovals with linking words. Often the most general concept is placed at the top of the map. The content of the other ovals becomes more specific as you move away from the main concept. Linking words are written on a line between two ovals.

A **web diagram** is a type of concept map that shows how several ideas relate to one central idea. Each subtopic may also link to subtopics, creating the visual effect of a spider web. Linking words are usually not included.

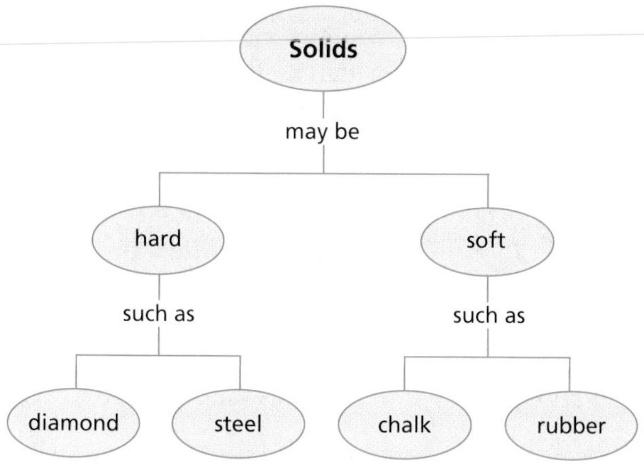
Solids
may be
hard
soft
such as
such as
diamond
steel
chalk
rubber

Compare-and-Contrast Tables

A **compare-and-contrast table** is a way of showing the similarities and differences between two or more objects or processes. The table provides an organized framework for making comparisons based on specific characteristics.

The items to be compared are usually column headings across the top of the table. Characteristics for comparison are listed in the first column. You complete the table by filling in information for each item.

Compare-and-Contrast Table

Contents	Book	CD-ROM
Paper pages	Yes	No
Photographs	Yes	Yes
Videos	No	Yes

Venn Diagrams

A **Venn diagram** consists of two or more ovals that overlap. Each oval represents a particular object or idea. Unique characteristics are shown in the part of each oval that does not overlap. Shared characteristics are shown in the area of overlap.

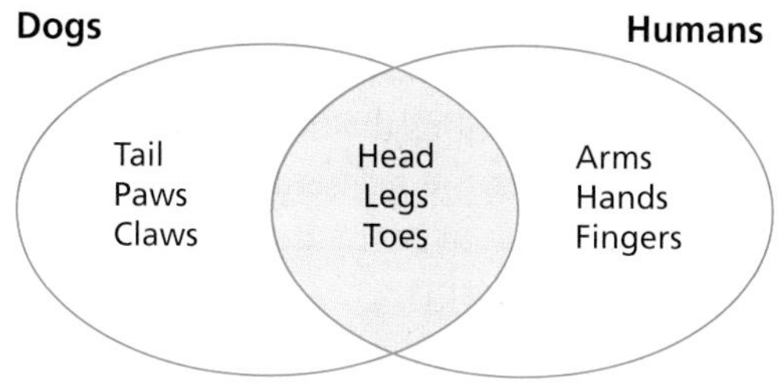
Dogs
Humans
Tail
Paws
Claws
Head
Legs
Toes
Arms
Hands
Fingers

Flowcharts

A **flowchart** is used to represent the order in which a set of events occurs. Each step in the sequence is described in a box. Each box is linked to the next box with an arrow. The flowchart shows a sequence from beginning to end.

Preparing Pasta

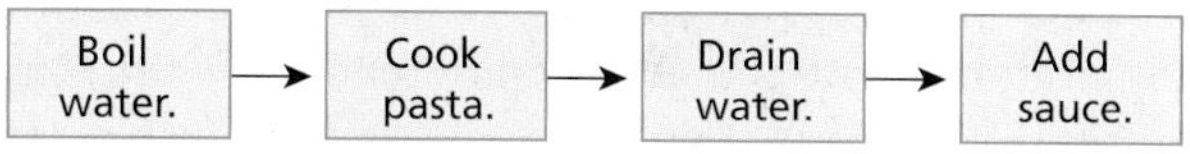
Boil water.
Cook pasta.
Drain water.
Add sauce.

Cycle Diagrams

A **cycle diagram** shows boxes representing a cyclical sequence of events. As in a flowchart, boxes are linked with arrows, but the sequence does not have a beginning or end. The boxes are usually arranged in a clockwise circle.

The Moon as Seen From Earth

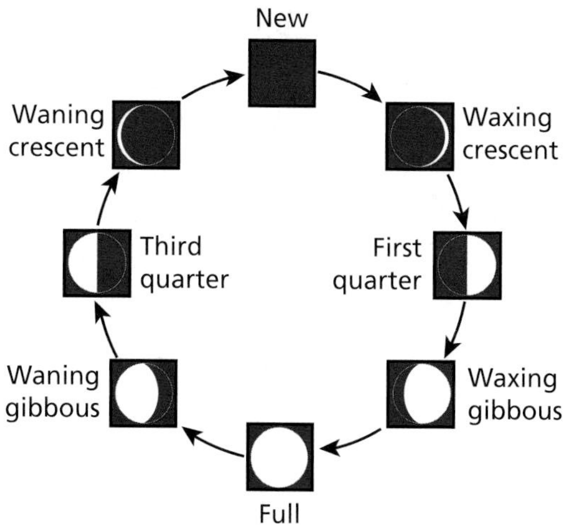
New
Waxing crescent
First quarter
Waxing gibbous
Full
Waning gibbous
Third quarter
Waning crescent

Math Skills

Throughout your study of physical science, you will often need to solve math problems. This appendix is designed to help you quickly review the basic math skills you will use most often.

Fractions

Adding and Subtracting Fractions

To add or subtract fractions that have the same denominator, add or subtract the numerators, and then write the sum or difference over the denominator. Express the answer in lowest terms.

Examples

$$\frac{3}{10} + \frac{1}{10} = \frac{3+1}{10} = \frac{4}{10} = \frac{2}{5}$$

$$\frac{5}{7} - \frac{2}{7} = \frac{5-2}{7} = \frac{3}{7}$$

To add or subtract fractions with different denominators, find the least common denominator. Write an equivalent fraction for each fraction using the least common denominator. Then add or subtract the numerators. Write the sum or difference over the least common denominator and express the answer in lowest terms.

Examples

$$\frac{1}{3} + \frac{3}{5} = \frac{5}{15} + \frac{9}{15} = \frac{5+9}{15} = \frac{14}{15}$$

$$\frac{7}{8} - \frac{1}{4} = \frac{7}{8} - \frac{2}{8} = \frac{7-2}{8} = \frac{5}{8}$$

Multiplying Fractions

When multiplying two fractions, multiply the numerators to find the product's numerator. Then multiply the denominators to find the product's denominator. It helps to divide any numerator or denominator by the greatest common factor before multiplying. Express the answer in lowest terms.

Examples

$$\frac{3}{5} \times \frac{2}{7} = \frac{3 \times 2}{5 \times 7} = \frac{6}{35}$$

$$\frac{4}{14} \times \frac{6}{9} = \frac{2 \times 2}{7 \times 2} \times \frac{2 \times 3}{3 \times 3} = \frac{2 \times 2}{7 \times 3} = \frac{4}{21}$$

Dividing Fractions

To divide one fraction by another, invert and multiply. Express the answer in lowest terms.

Examples

$$\frac{2}{5} \div \frac{3}{4} = \frac{2}{5} \times \frac{4}{3} = \frac{2 \times 4}{5 \times 3} = \frac{8}{15}$$

$$\frac{9}{16} \div \frac{5}{8} = \frac{9}{16} \times \frac{8}{5} = \frac{9 \times 1}{2 \times 5} = \frac{9}{10}$$

Ratios and Proportions

A ratio compares two numbers or quantities. A ratio is often written as a fraction expressed in lowest terms. A ratio also may be written with a colon.

Examples

The ratio of 3 to 4 is written as 3 to 4, $\frac{3}{4}$, or 3 : 4.

The ratio of 10 to 5 is written as $\frac{10}{5} = \frac{2}{1}$, or 2 : 1.

A proportion is a mathematical sentence that states that two ratios are equivalent. To write a proportion, place an equal sign between the two equivalent ratios.

Examples

The ratio of 6 to 9 is the same as the ratio of 8 to 12.

$$\frac{6}{9} = \frac{8}{12}$$

The ratio of 2 to 4 is the same as the ratio of 7 to 14.

$$\frac{2}{4} = \frac{7}{14}$$

You can set up a proportion to determine an unknown quantity. Use x to represent the unknown. To find the value of x, cross multiply and then divide both sides of the equation by the number that comes before x.

Example

Two out of five students have blue notebooks. If this same ratio exists in a class of twenty students, how many students in the class have blue notebooks?

$\frac{2}{5} = \frac{x}{20}$ ← **Cross multiply.**

$2 \times 20 = 5x$ ← **Divide.**

$8 = x$

Percents and Decimals

Calculating Percents

A percent is a ratio that compares a number to 100. The word *percent* (%) means "parts of 100" or "per 100 parts." Another way to think of a percent is as a part of a whole expressed in hundredths. Thus, the number 0.41 ("41 hundredths") can also be expressed as 41%, or "41 per 100 parts."

$$0.41 = \frac{41}{100} = 41\%$$

You can calculate a percent by multiplying the ratio of the part to the whole by 100%.

$$\text{Percent} = \frac{\text{Part}}{\text{Whole}} \times 100\%$$

Examples

The fraction $\frac{7}{10}$ is equivalent to 70%.

The fraction $\frac{5}{8}$ is equivalent to 62.5%.

The fraction $\frac{15}{200}$ is equivalent to 7.5%.

You have probably seen data expressed in the form of a percent. For instance, nutrition labels on packaged foods include a column titled "% Daily Value." In this column, the nutrients (such as fat, cholesterol, and fiber) contained in a single serving are compared to the recommended daily intake. You also encounter percents when you go shopping (items on sale might be labeled "20% off") or when you receive test scores.

Example

A student answers 34 questions correctly on a 40-question exam. What is the student's score expressed as a percent?

$$\text{Percent} = \frac{\text{Part}}{\text{Whole}} \times 100\%$$

$$= \frac{\text{Number of correct answers}}{\text{Number of questions asked}} \times 100\%$$

$$= \frac{34}{40} \times 100\%$$

$$= 85\%$$

Converting Between Percents and Decimals

To convert a percent to a decimal value, write the number without the percent sign and move the decimal point two places to the left. Add a zero before the decimal point.

Examples

$38\% = 0.38$
$13.92\% = 0.1392$

You can convert a decimal value to a percent value by moving the decimal point two places to the right and adding the percent sign.

Examples

$0.46 = 46\%$
$0.8215 = 82.15\%$

Converting between percents and decimals is often necessary when solving word problems involving composition or concentration.

Example

A nighttime cold medicine is 22% alcohol by volume. How many milliliters of alcohol are in a 250-mL bottle of this medicine?

$22\% = 0.22 \leftarrow$ **Convert percent to a decimal.**

$$\frac{\text{Part}}{\text{Whole}} = \frac{\text{Part}}{250 \text{ mL}} = 0.22$$

$$\text{Part} = 250 \text{ mL} \times 0.22$$

$$\text{Part} = 55 \text{ mL}$$

Example

During a flu epidemic, 28% of the students at a school were absent. If 238 students were absent, what was the school's enrollment?

$28\% = 0.28 \leftarrow$ **Convert percent to a decimal.**

$$\frac{\text{Part}}{\text{Whole}} = \frac{238 \text{ students}}{\text{Whole}} = 0.28$$

$$\text{Whole} = \frac{238 \text{ students}}{0.28}$$

$$\text{Whole} = 850 \text{ students}$$

Exponents

A base is a number that is used as a factor. An exponent is a number that tells how many times the base is to be used as a factor.

Example

$2^5 = 2 \times 2 \times 2 \times 2 \times 2 = 32$

A power is any number that can be expressed as a product in which all of the factors are the same. Any number raised to the zero power is 1. Any number raised to the first power is that number. The only exception is the number 0, which is zero regardless of the power it is raised to.

Exponents

Powers of 2	Powers of 10
$2^4 = 16$	$10^4 = 10{,}000$
$2^3 = 8$	$10^3 = 1000$
$2^2 = 4$	$10^2 = 100$
$2^1 = 2$	$10^1 = 10$
$2^0 = 1$	$10^0 = 1$
$2^{-1} = \frac{1}{2}$	$10^{-1} = \frac{1}{10}$
$2^{-2} = \frac{1}{4}$	$10^{-2} = \frac{1}{100}$
$2^{-3} = \frac{1}{8}$	$10^{-3} = \frac{1}{1000}$
$2^{-4} = \frac{1}{16}$	$10^{-4} = \frac{1}{10{,}000}$

Multiplying With Exponents

To multiply exponential expressions with the same base, add the exponents. The general expression for exponents with the same base is $x^a \times x^b = x^{a+b}$.

Example

$3^2 \times 3^4 = (3 \times 3) \times (3 \times 3 \times 3 \times 3) = 3^6 = 729$

To raise a power to a power, keep the base and multiply the exponents. The general expression is $(x^a)^b = x^{ab}$.

Example

$(3^2)^3 = (3^2) \times (3^2) \times (3^2) = 3^6 = 729$

To raise a product to a power, raise each factor to the power. The general expression is $(xy)^n = x^n y^n$.

Example

$(3 \times 9)^2 = 3^2 \times 9^2 = 9 \times 81 = 729$

Dividing With Exponents

To divide exponential expressions with the same base, keep the base and subtract the exponents. The general expression is

$\frac{x^a}{x^b} = x^{a-b}$

Example

$\frac{5^6}{5^4} = 5^{6-4} = 5^2 = 25$

When the exponent of the denominator is greater than the exponent of the numerator, the exponent of the result is negative. A negative exponent follows the general expression

$x^{-n} = \frac{1}{x^n}$

Example

$2^3 \div 2^5 = 2^{3-5} = 2^{-2} = \frac{1}{2^2} = \frac{1}{4}$

Metric conversions often involve multiplication or division of exponential expressions. Make sure to keep track of the sign of the exponent when performing operations with exponential expressions.

Example

Convert 3.49×10^2 μm to meters. (1 μm $= 10^{-6}$ m)

Based on the equivalence 1 μm $= 10^{-6}$ m, you can write the ratio 1 μm/10^{-6} m, which equals one.

$$3.49 \times 10^2\ \mu\text{m} \times \frac{10^{-6}\text{m}}{1\ \mu\text{m}} = 3.49 \times 10^2 \times 10^{-6}\ \text{m}$$

$$= 3.49 \times 10^{2-6}\ \text{m}$$

$$= 3.49 \times 10^{-4}\ \text{m}$$

Scientific Notation

Very large and very small numbers are often expressed in scientific notation. In scientific notation, a number is written as the product of two numbers: a coefficient that is greater than or equal to one and less than ten, and 10 raised to a power. For example, the number 710,000 written in scientific notation is 7.1×10^5. The coefficient in this number is 7.1. The power of ten, or the exponent, is 5. The exponent indicates how many times the coefficient must be multiplied by 10 to equal the number 710,000.

To convert a large number to scientific notation, move the decimal point to the left until it is located just to the right of the first nonzero number. The number of places that you move the decimal point becomes the positive exponent of 10.

Example

$18{,}930{,}000 = 1.893 \times 10^7$

To write a number less than 1 in scientific notation, move the decimal point just to the right of the first nonzero number. Use the number of places you moved the decimal point as the negative exponent of 10.

Example

$$0.0027 = \frac{2.7}{10 \times 10 \times 10} = 2.7 \times 10^{-3}$$

When you convert a number to scientific notation, remember that you are not changing the value of the number. You are only changing the way that it is written.

Examples

$500{,}000 = 5 \times 10^5$

$0.000\,000\,042 = 4.2 \times 10^{-8}$

$0.030\,06 = 3.006 \times 10^{-2}$

$285.2 = 2.852 \times 10^2$

$0.0002 = 2 \times 10^{-4}$

$83{,}700{,}000 = 8.37 \times 10^7$

Adding and Subtracting

To add or subtract numbers in scientific notation, the exponents must be the same. If they are different, rewrite one of the numbers to make the exponents the same. Then write the answer so that only one number is to the left of the decimal point.

Examples

$$\begin{aligned}(3.20 \times 10^3) + (5.1 \times 10^2) &= (32.0 \times 10^2) + (5.1 \times 10^2)\\ &= 37.1 \times 10^2\\ &= 3.71 \times 10^3\end{aligned}$$

$$\begin{aligned}&(3.42 \times 10^{-5}) - (2.5 \times 10^{-6})\\ &\quad= (34.2 \times 10^{-6}) - (2.5 \times 10^{-6})\\ &\quad= 31.7 \times 10^{-6}\\ &\quad= 3.17 \times 10^{-5}\end{aligned}$$

Multiplying and Dividing

To multiply or divide numbers in scientific notation, the exponents are added or subtracted.

Examples

$$\begin{aligned}(1.2 \times 10^3) \times (3.4 \times 10^4) &= (4.1 \times 10^{3+4})\\ &= 4.1 \times 10^7\end{aligned}$$

$$\begin{aligned}(5.0 \times 10^9) \div (2.5 \times 10^6) &= (2.0 \times 10^{9-6})\\ &= 2.0 \times 10^3\end{aligned}$$

$$\begin{aligned}\frac{(1.2 \times 10^{-3})^2}{(10^{-2})^3 \times (2.0 \times 10^{-3})} &= \frac{1.2^2 \times (10^{-3})^2}{(10^{-6}) \times (2.0 \times 10^{-3})}\\ &= \frac{1.44 \times 10^{-6}}{2.0 \times 10^{-6+3(-3)}}\\ &= \frac{1.44 \times 10^{-6}}{2.0 \times 10^{-9}}\\ &= 0.72 \times 10^{-6-(-9)}\\ &= 0.72 \times 10^3\\ &= 7.2 \times 10^2\end{aligned}$$

Skills Handbook

Math Skills

Significant Figures

When measurements are combined in calculations, the uncertainty of each measurement must be correctly reflected in the final result. The digits that are accurate in the answer are called significant figures. When the result of a calculation has more significant figures than needed, the result must be rounded off. If the first digit after the last significant digit is less than 5, round down. If the first digit after the last significant digit is 5 or more, round up.

Examples

1577 rounded to three significant figures is 1580.
1574 rounded to three significant figures is 1570.
2.458462 rounded to three significant figures is 2.46.
2.458462 rounded to four significant figures is 2.458.

Examples

Each of the measurements listed below has three significant figures. The significant figures are underlined.

$\underline{456}$ mL
$0.\underline{305}$ g
$\underline{70.4}$ mg
$0.000\underline{457}$ g
$\underline{5.64} \times 10^3$ km
$\underline{444},000$ ng
$\underline{1.30} \times 10^{-2}$ m
$0.00\underline{4\ 06}$ dm

Adding and Subtracting

In addition and subtraction, the number of significant figures in the answer depends on the number with the largest uncertainty.

Example

$$\begin{array}{rr} & 25.34\ \text{g} \\ & 152\ \text{g} \\ + & 4.009\ \text{g} \\ \hline & 181\ \text{g} \end{array}$$

The measurement with the largest uncertainty is 152 g, and it is measured to the nearest gram. Therefore, the answer is given to the nearest gram.

Example

$189.427\ \text{g} - 19.00\ \text{g} = 170.427\ \text{g} \approx 170.43\ \text{g}$

The measurement with the larger uncertainty is 19.00 g, which is measured to the nearest hundredth of a gram. Therefore, the answer is given to the nearest hundredth of a gram.

Multiplying and Dividing

In multiplication and division, the measurement with the smallest number of significant figures determines the number of significant figures in the answer.

Example

$(5.3\ \text{m}) \times (1.54\ \text{m}) = 8.162\ \text{m}^2 \approx 8.2\ \text{m}^2$

Because 5.3 m has only two significant figures, the answer must be rounded to two significant figures.

Example

$$\begin{aligned} \text{Density} &= \frac{\text{Mass}}{\text{Volume}} \\ &= \frac{20.79\ \text{g}}{5.5\ \text{mL}} \\ &= 3.78\ \text{g/mL} \\ &\approx 3.8\ \text{g/mL} \end{aligned}$$

Because 5.5 mL has only two significant figures, the answer must be rounded to two significant figures.

Example

Calculate the perimeter [(2 × length) + (2 × width)] and the area (length × width) of a rectangular garden plot that measures 32.8 m by 16 m. Round each answer to the correct number of significant figures.

$$\begin{aligned} \text{Perimeter} &= (2 \times 32.8\ \text{m}) + (2 \times 16\ \text{m}) \\ &= 65.6\ \text{m} + 32\ \text{m} \\ &= 97.6\ \text{m} \\ &\approx 98\ \text{m} \end{aligned}$$

$\text{Area} = 32.8\ \text{m} \times 16\ \text{m} = 524.8\ \text{m}^2 \approx 5.2 \times 10^2\ \text{m}^2$

Formulas and Equations

An equation is a mathematical sentence that contains one or more variables and one or more mathematical operators (such as $+$, $-$, $\div$, $\times$, and $=$). An equation expresses a relationship between two or more quantities.

A formula is a special kind of equation. A formula such as $V = l \times w \times h$ states the relationship between unknown quantities represented by the variables V, l, w, and h. The formula means that volume (of a rectangular solid) equals length times width times height. Some formulas have numbers that do not vary, such as the formula for the perimeter of a square: $P = 4s$. In this formula, the number 4 is a constant.

To solve an equation or formula for an unknown quantity, first rearrange the equation so that the unknown is on one side of the equation, and all the known quantities are on the other side. Then substitute known values for the variables. Be sure to include units.

Example

An airplane travels in a straight line at a speed of 600 km/h. How far does it fly in 3.5 hours?

Write the formula that relates speed, distance, and time.

$$\text{Speed} = \frac{\text{Distance}}{\text{Time}}$$

$$v = \frac{d}{t}$$

To solve for distance, multiply both sides of the equation by t.

$$v = \frac{d}{t}$$

$$v \times t = \frac{d}{t} \times t$$

$$v \times t = d$$

Substitute in the known values.

$$600 \text{ km/h} \times 3.5 \text{ h} = d$$

$$2100 \text{ km} = d$$

Example

What is the volume of 642 g of gold if the density of gold is 19.3 g/cm^3?

Write the formula that relates density, mass, and volume.

$$\text{Density} = \frac{\text{Mass}}{\text{Volume}}$$

$$d = \frac{m}{v}$$

First solve the equation for the unknown quantity, volume (v).

$$d = \frac{m}{v}$$

$$v \times d = m$$

$$v = \frac{m}{d}$$

Then substitute in the known values for m and d.

$$v = \frac{642 \text{ g}}{19.3 \text{ g/cm}^3}$$

$$v = 33.2645 \text{ cm}^3$$

$$v \approx 33.3 \text{ cm}^3$$

Example

A gas has a volume of 5.0 L at a temperature of 200 K. The temperature of the gas is increased under constant pressure until the final volume of the gas is 15 L. What is the final temperature of the gas?

Write the formula that describes how the volume of a gas changes with temperature if the pressure and number of particles are constant.

$$\frac{V_1}{T_1} = \frac{V_2}{T_2}$$

First solve the equation for the unknown quantity, T_2.

$$\frac{V_1}{T_1} = \frac{V_2}{T_2}$$

$$T_2 = \frac{V_2 \times T_1}{V_1}$$

Now substitute the known values for V_1, V_2, and T_1.

$$T_2 = \frac{15 \text{ L} \times 200 \text{ K}}{5 \text{ L}}$$

$$T_2 = 600 \text{ K}$$

Math Skills

Skills Handbook

Conversion Factors

Many problems involve converting measurements from one unit to another. You can convert units by using an equation that shows how units are related. For example, 1 in. = 2.54 cm relates inches and centimeters.

To write a conversion factor, divide both sides of the equation by 1 in.

$$\frac{1 \text{ in.}}{1 \text{ in.}} = \frac{2.54 \text{ cm}}{1 \text{ in.}}$$

$$1 = 2.54 \text{ cm/in.}$$

Because the conversion factor is equal to 1, you can multiply one side of an equation by it and preserve equality. You can make a second conversion factor by dividing both sides of the equation by 2.54 cm.

$$\frac{1 \text{ in.}}{2.54 \text{ cm}} = \frac{2.54 \text{ cm}}{2.54 \text{ cm}} = 1$$

One conversion factor converts inches to centimeters and the other converts centimeters to inches. Choose the conversion factor that cancels out the unit that you have a measurement for.

Example

Convert 25 inches to centimeters. Use the conversion factor 2.54 cm/in. so that the inches units cancel.

$$25 \text{ in.} \times \frac{2.54 \text{ cm}}{1 \text{ in.}} \approx 64 \text{ cm}$$

Some conversions are more complicated and require multiple steps.

Example

Convert 23°F to a Celsius temperature. The conversion formula is $°F = (\frac{9}{5} \times °C) + 32°F$.

First solve the equation for °C.

$$°F = (\frac{9}{5} \times °C) + 32°F$$

$$°F - 32°F = \frac{9}{5} \times °C$$

$$\frac{5}{9}(°F - 32°F) = °C$$

Now substitute in 23°F.

$$°C = \frac{5}{9}(23°F - 32°F) = \frac{5}{9}(-9) = -5$$

Thus, 23°F is equivalent to −5°C.

Example

A grocer is selling oranges at a price of 3 for $1.00. How much would 10 oranges cost?

Use the equality 3 oranges = $1.00 to write a conversion factor. The desired conversion factor should have dollars in the numerator so that the oranges units cancel.

$$10 \text{ oranges} \times \frac{\$1.00}{3 \text{ oranges}} = \$3.33$$

Example

Water runs through a hose at a rate of 2.5 gallons per minute. What is the rate of water flow in gallons per day?

To convert gal/min to gal/d, you must use conversion factors based on the following equalities.

60 min = 1 h

24 h = 1 d

$$\frac{2.5 \text{ gal}}{\text{min}} \times \frac{60 \text{ min}}{1 \text{ h}} \times \frac{24 \text{ h}}{1 \text{ d}} = 3600 \text{ gal/d}$$

Example

The density of nitrogen gas is 1.17 g/L. What is the density of nitrogen expressed in micrograms per deciliter (μg/dL)?

Derive the needed conversion factors from the following equalities.

$10^6\ \mu g = 1$ g

10 dL = 1 L

$$\frac{1.17 \text{ g}}{\text{L}} \times \frac{10^6\ \mu\text{g}}{1 \text{ g}} \times \frac{1 \text{ L}}{10 \text{ dL}} = 1.17 \times 10^5\ \mu\text{g/dL}$$

Data Tables

Data tables help to organize data and make it easier to see patterns in data. If you plan data tables before doing an experiment, they will help you record observations in an orderly fashion.

The data table below shows United States immigration data for the year 2001. Always include units of measurement so people can understand the data.

Immigration to the United States, 2001

Place of Origin	Number of Legal Immigrants
Africa	53,948
Asia	349,776
Europe	175,371
North America	407,888
South America	68,888

Bar Graphs

To make a bar graph, begin by placing category labels along the bottom axis. Add an overall label for the axis *Place of Origin.* Decide on a scale for the vertical axis. An appropriate scale for the data in the table is 0 to 500,000. Label the vertical axis *Number of People.* For each continent, draw a bar whose height corresponds to the number of immigrants. You will need to round off the values. For example, the bar for Africa should correspond to 54,000 people. Add a graph title to make it clear what the graph shows.

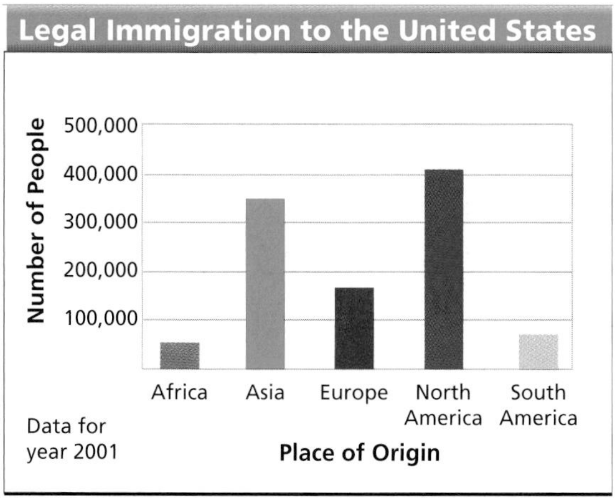

Legal Immigration to the United States
Number of People
500,000
400,000
300,000
200,000
100,000
Africa
Asia
Europe
North America
South America
Data for year 2001
Place of Origin

Circle Graphs

Use the total number to calculate percentages. For example, the percentage of immigrants from Africa in 2001 was 53,948 ÷ 1,061,984 = 0.051 ≈ 5%. Multiply each percent by 360° to find the central angle of each wedge. For Africa, the central angle is 18°. Use a protractor to draw each central angle. Color and label the wedges and finish your graph with a title.

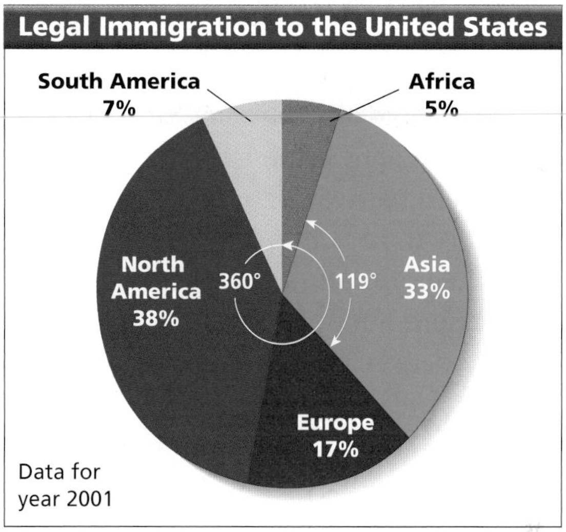

Legal Immigration to the United States
South America 7%
Africa 5%
North America 38%
360°
119°
Asia 33%
Europe 17%
Data for year 2001

Line Graphs

The slope of a straight-line graph equals the "rise over the run." The rise is the change in the *y* values and the run is the change in the *x* values. Using points A and B on the graph below gives

$$\text{Slope} = \frac{\text{Rise}}{\text{Run}} = \frac{5-3}{9-3} = \frac{2}{6} = 0.33$$

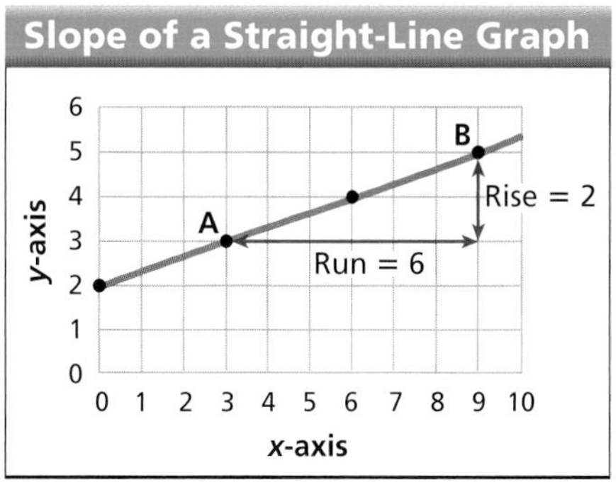

Slope of a Straight-Line Graph
y-axis
x-axis
A
B
Rise = 2
Run = 6
0 1 2 3 4 5 6
0 1 2 3 4 5 6 7 8 9 10

Understanding Globes

A globe is a scale model of Earth. It shows the actual shapes, sizes, and locations of all Earth's landmasses and bodies of water. Features on the surface of Earth are drawn to scale on a globe. This means that a small unit of measure on the globe stands for a large unit of measure on Earth.

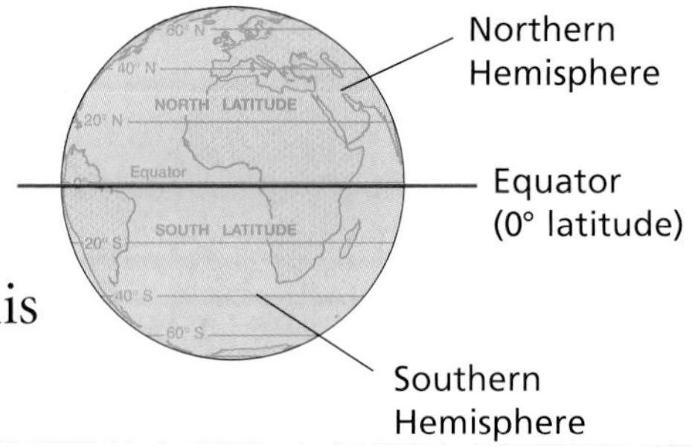
Northern Hemisphere
Equator (0° latitude)
Southern Hemisphere
NORTH LATITUDE
Equator
SOUTH LATITUDE

Parallels of Latitude

Geographers divide the globe along imaginary horizontal lines called parallels of latitude. One of these latitude lines is the equator, located halfway between the North and South poles. Parallels of latitude are measured in degrees (°). One degree of latitude represents a distance of about 69 miles (111 kilometers).

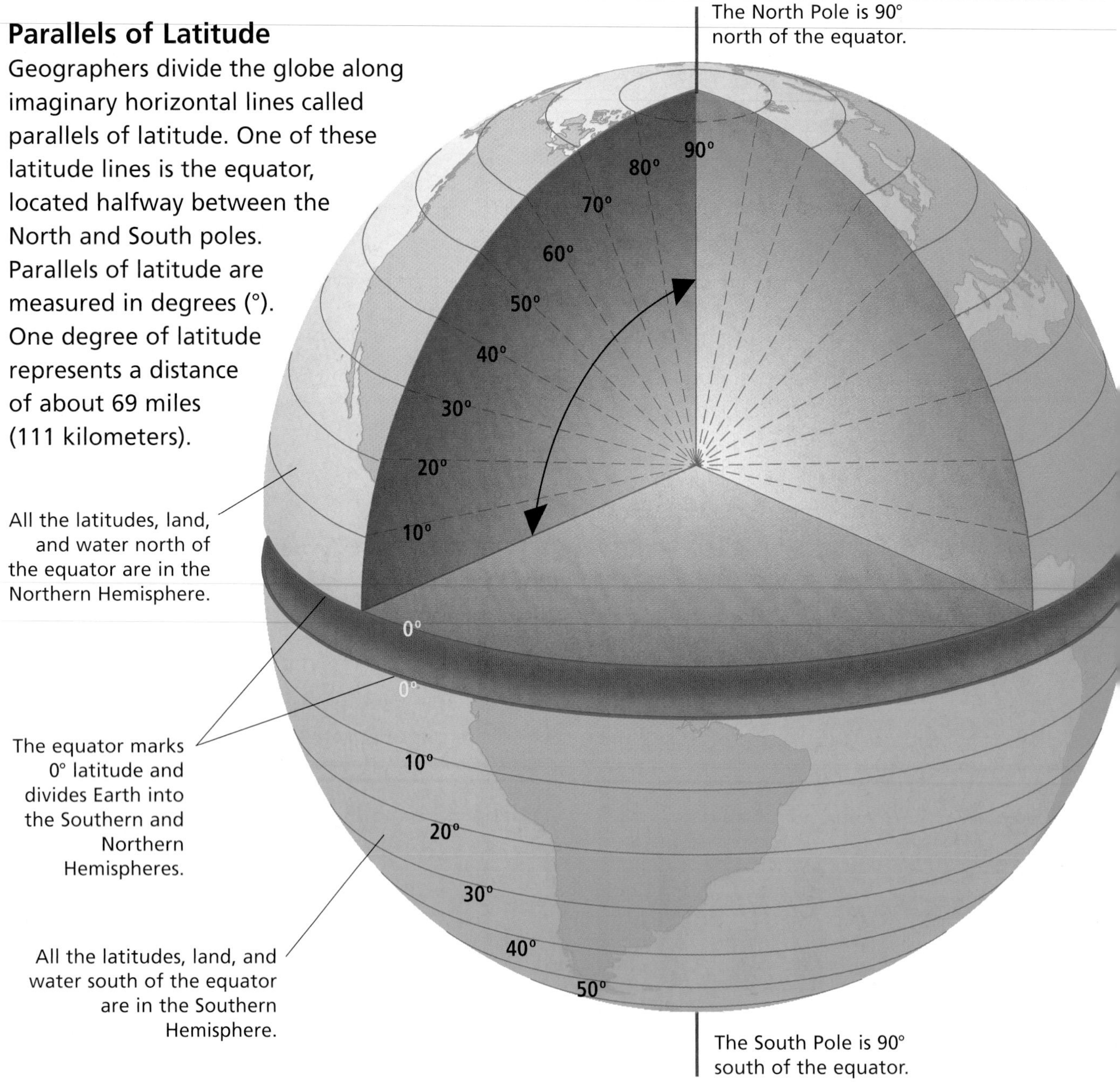
The North Pole is 90° north of the equator.
90°
80°
70°
60°
50°
40°
30°
20°
10°
0°
0°
10°
20°
30°
40°
50°
All the latitudes, land, and water north of the equator are in the Northern Hemisphere.
The equator marks 0° latitude and divides Earth into the Southern and Northern Hemispheres.
All the latitudes, land, and water south of the equator are in the Southern Hemisphere.
The South Pole is 90° south of the equator.

Meridians of Longitude

Geographers also divide the globe along imaginary vertical lines called meridians of longitude, which are measured in degrees (°). The longitude line called the Prime Meridian runs from pole to pole through Greenwich, England. All meridians of longitude come together at the North and South Poles.

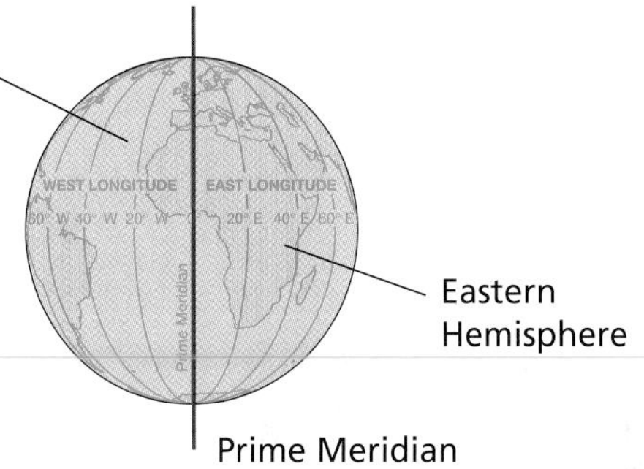

Western Hemisphere
WEST LONGITUDE
EAST LONGITUDE
Prime Meridian
Eastern Hemisphere
Prime Meridian (0° longitude)

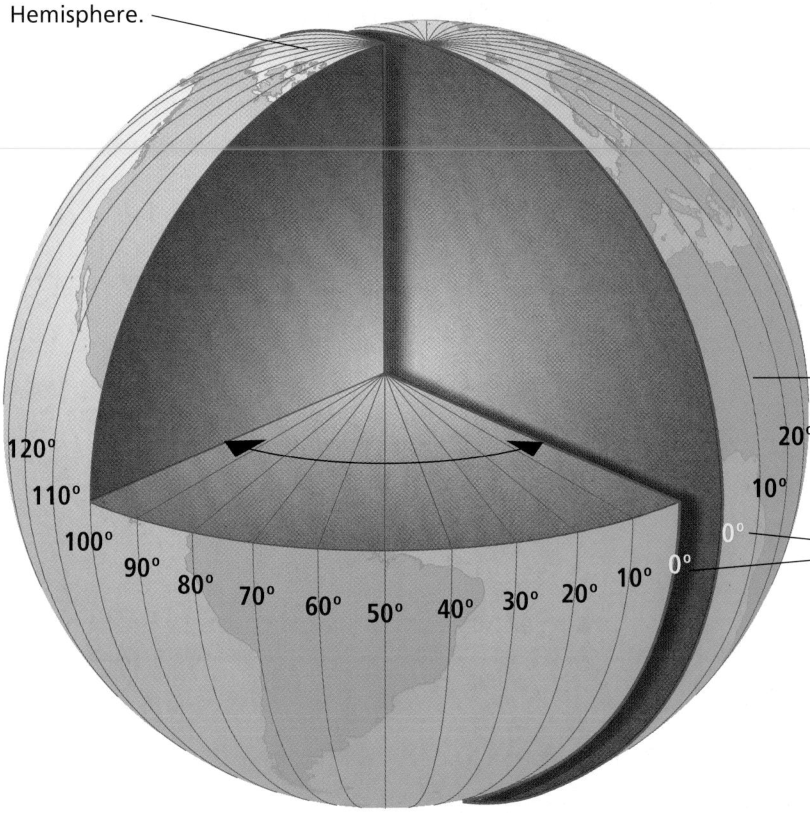

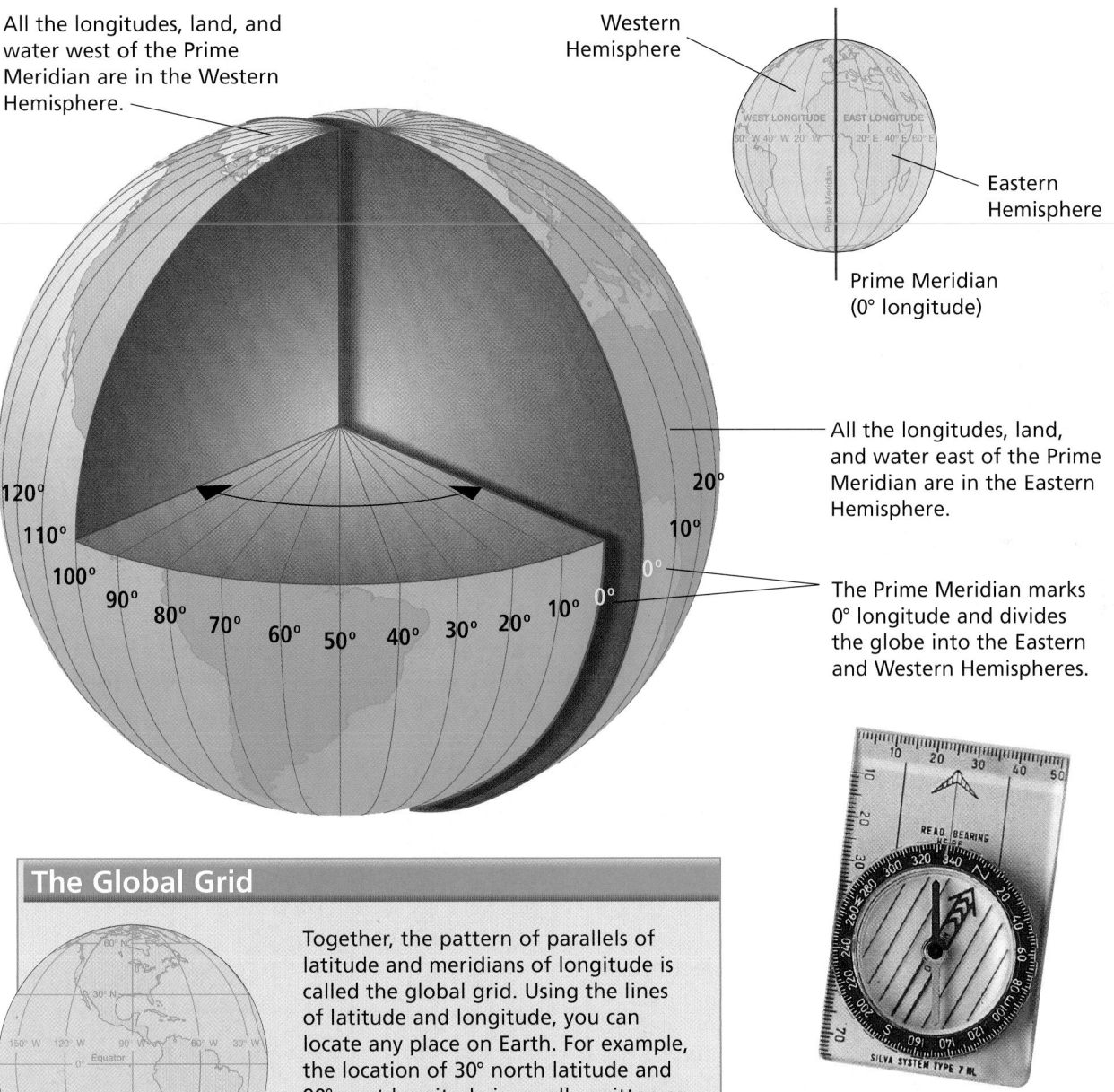

All the longitudes, land, and water west of the Prime Meridian are in the Western Hemisphere.
120°
110°
100°
90°
80°
70°
60°
50°
40°
30°
20°
10°
0°
20°
10°
0°
All the longitudes, land, and water east of the Prime Meridian are in the Eastern Hemisphere.
The Prime Meridian marks 0° longitude and divides the globe into the Eastern and Western Hemispheres.

The Global Grid

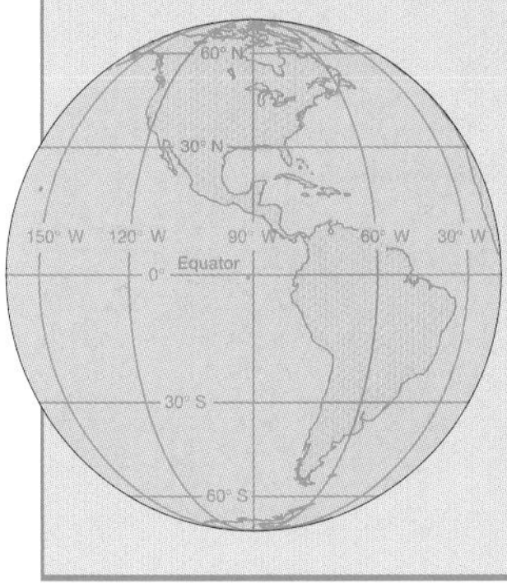

60° N
30° N
150° W
120° W
90° W
60° W
30° W
0°
Equator
30° S
60° S

Together, the pattern of parallels of latitude and meridians of longitude is called the global grid. Using the lines of latitude and longitude, you can locate any place on Earth. For example, the location of 30° north latitude and 90° west longitude is usually written as 30° N, 90° W. Only one place on Earth has these coordinates—the city of New Orleans, in the state of Louisiana.

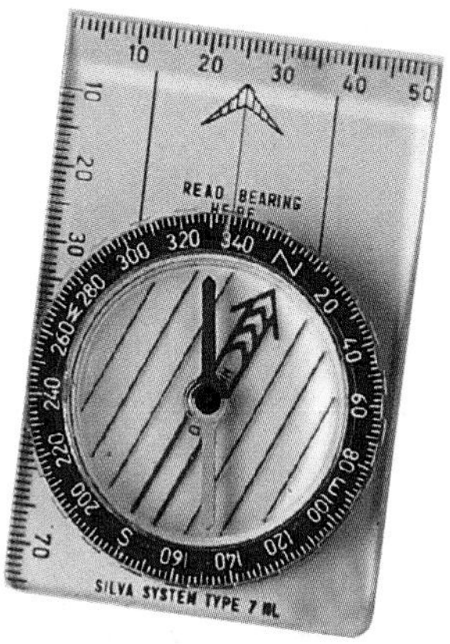

READ BEARING HERE
SILVA SYSTEM TYPE 7 NL

▲ Compass
Wherever you are on Earth, a compass can be used to show direction.

Map Projections

Maps are drawings that show regions on flat surfaces. Maps are easier to use and carry than globes, but they cannot show the correct size and shape of every feature on Earth's curved surface. They must shrink some places and stretch others. To make up for this distortion, mapmakers use different map projections. No one projection can accurately show the correct area, shape, distance, and direction for all of Earth's surface. Mapmakers use the projection that has the least distortion for the information they are presenting.

▲ **Global gores**
Flattening a globe creates a string of shapes called gores.

Same-Shape Maps

Map projections that accurately show the shapes of landmasses are called same-shape maps. However, these projections often greatly distort, or make less accurate, the size of landmasses as well as the distance between them. In the projection below, the northern and southern areas of the globe appear more stretched than the areas near the equator.

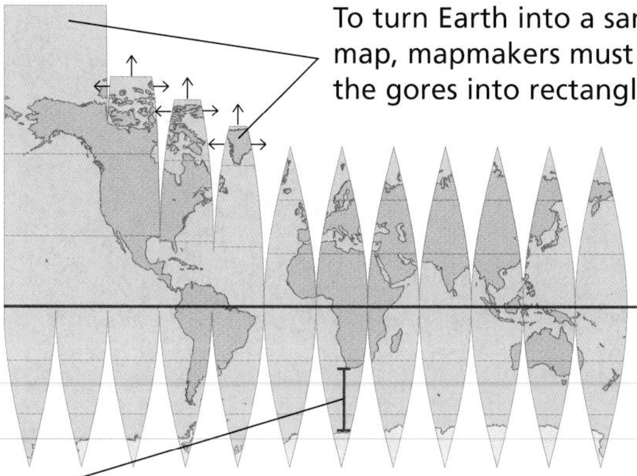
Equator

To turn Earth into a same-shape map, mapmakers must stretch the gores into rectangles.

Stretching the gores makes parts of Earth larger. This enlargement becomes greater toward the North and South Poles.

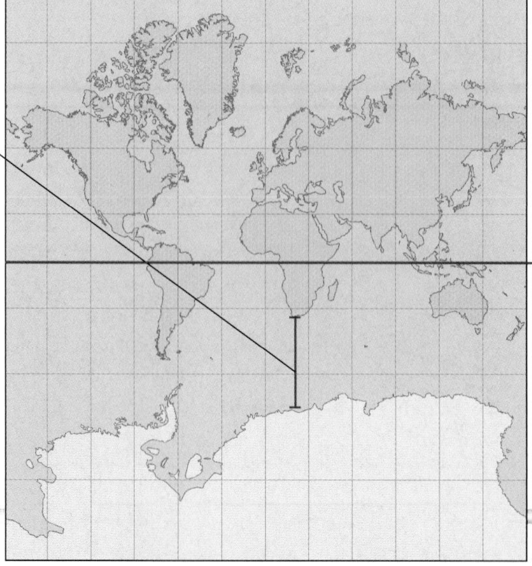
Equator

Mercator projection ▶
One of the most common same-shape maps is the Mercator projection, named for the mapmaker who invented it. The Mercator projection accurately shows shape and direction, but it distorts distance and size. Because the projection shows true directions, ships' navigators use it to chart a straight-line course between two ports.

Equal-Area Maps

Map projections that show the correct size of landmasses are called equal-area maps. In order to show the correct size of landmasses, these maps usually distort shapes. The distortion is usually greater at the edges of the map and less at the center.

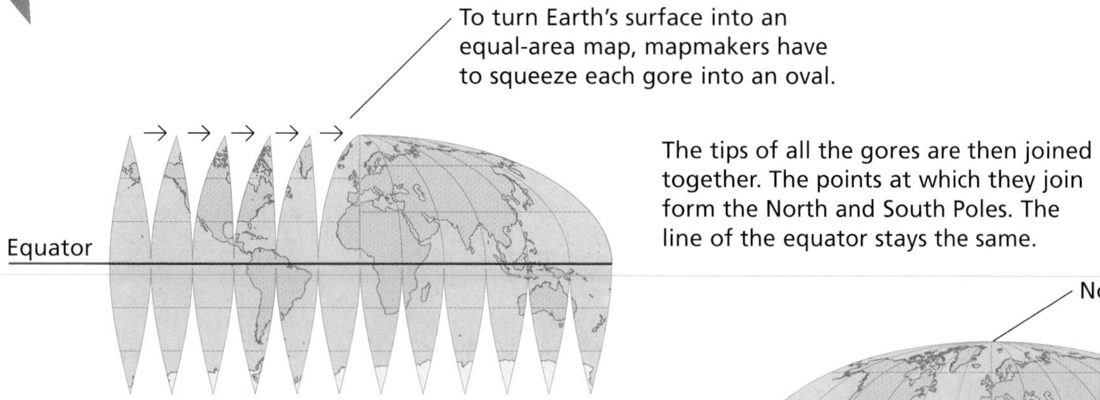

To turn Earth's surface into an equal-area map, mapmakers have to squeeze each gore into an oval.
The tips of all the gores are then joined together. The points at which they join form the North and South Poles. The line of the equator stays the same.
Equator

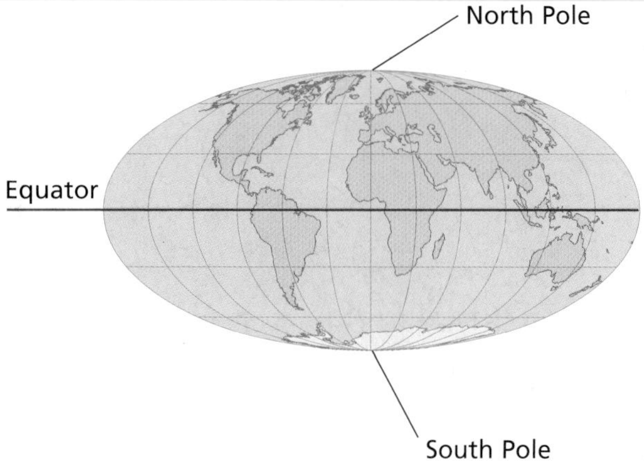

North Pole
Equator
South Pole

Robinson Maps

Many of the maps in this book use the Robinson projection, which is a compromise between the Mercator and equal-area projections. The Robinson projection gives a useful overall picture of the world. It keeps the size and shape relationships of most continents and oceans, but distorts the size of the polar regions.

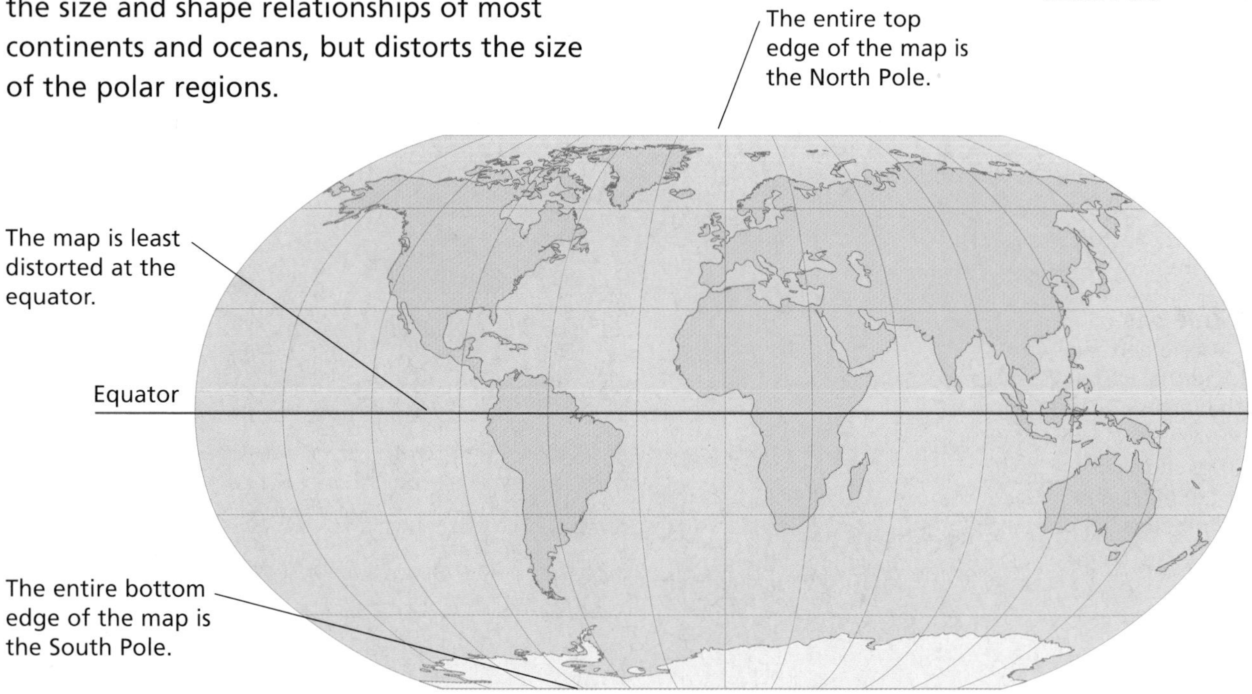

The entire top edge of the map is the North Pole.
The map is least distorted at the equator.
Equator
The entire bottom edge of the map is the South Pole.

How to Use a Map

Mapmakers provide several clues to help you understand the information on a map. Maps provide different clues, depending on their purpose or scale. However, most maps have several clues in common.

Locator globe
Many maps are shown with locator globes. They show where on the globe the area of the map is located.

Title
All maps have a title. The title tells you the subject of the map.

Compass rose
Many maps show direction by displaying a compass rose with the directions north, east, south, and west. The letters N, E, S, and W are placed to indicate these directions.

Key
Often a map has a key, or legend. The key shows the symbols and colors used on the map, and what each one means.

Scale bar
A scale bar helps you find the actual distances between points shown on the map. Most scale bars show distances in both miles and kilometers.

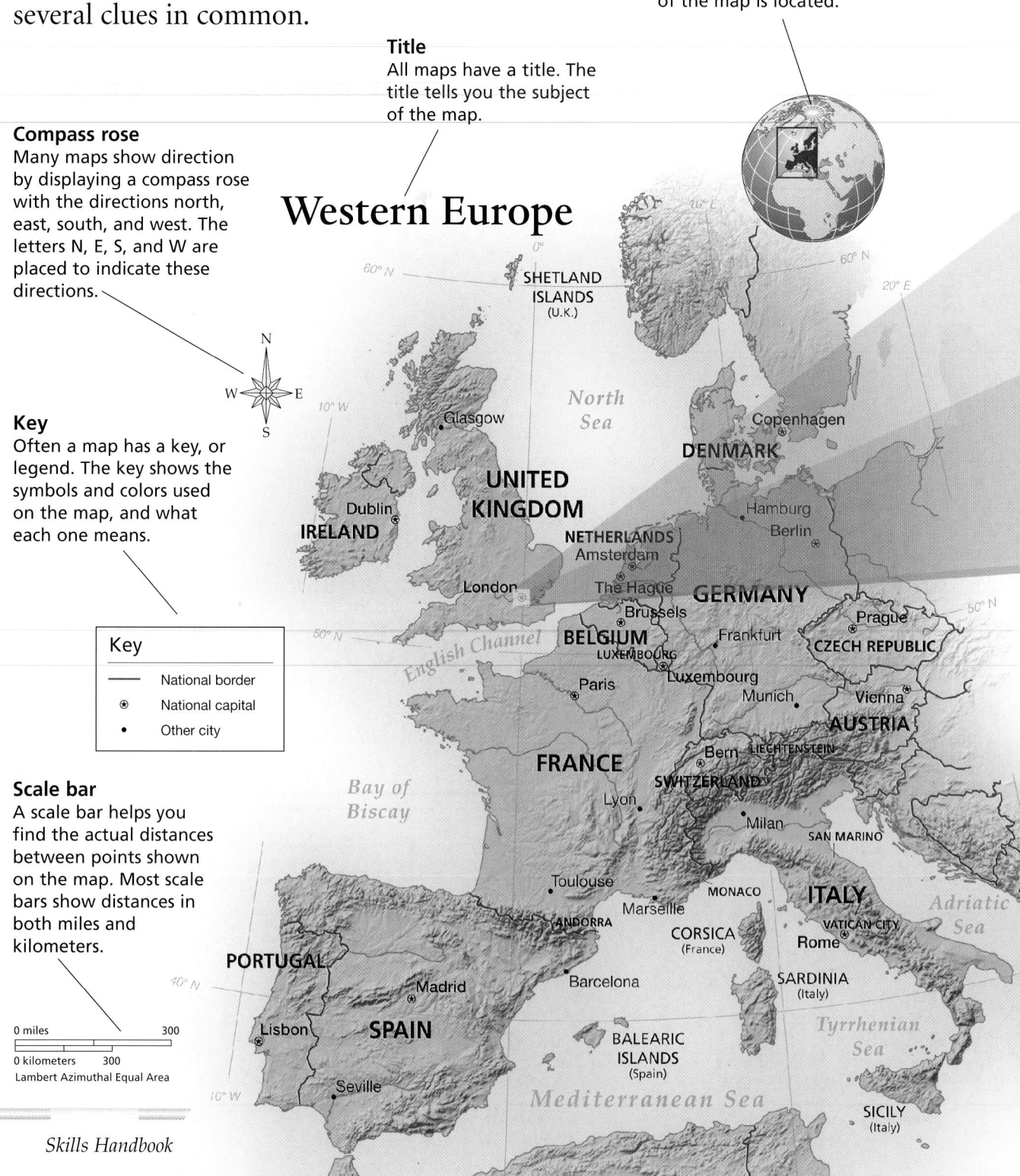

Western Europe
N
W
E
S
SHETLAND ISLANDS (U.K.)
North Sea
Glasgow
Copenhagen
DENMARK
UNITED KINGDOM
Dublin
IRELAND
Hamburg
Berlin
NETHERLANDS
Amsterdam
The Hague
London
GERMANY
Brussels
BELGIUM
LUXEMBOURG
Luxembourg
Frankfurt
Prague
CZECH REPUBLIC
English Channel
Paris
Munich
Vienna
AUSTRIA
LIECHTENSTEIN
Bern
SWITZERLAND
FRANCE
Bay of Biscay
Lyon
Milan
SAN MARINO
Toulouse
MONACO
ITALY
Adriatic Sea
Marseille
ANDORRA
CORSICA (France)
VATICAN CITY
Rome
PORTUGAL
Madrid
Barcelona
SARDINIA (Italy)
Lisbon
SPAIN
BALEARIC ISLANDS (Spain)
Tyrrhenian Sea
Seville
Mediterranean Sea
SICILY (Italy)
60° N
50° N
40° N
0°
10° W
10° E
20° E

Key
—	National border
⊛	National capital
•	Other city

0 miles 300
0 kilometers 300
Lambert Azimuthal Equal Area

Maps of Different Scales

Maps are drawn to different scales, depending on their purpose. Here are three maps drawn to very different scales. Keep in mind that maps showing large areas have smaller scales. Maps showing small areas have larger scales.

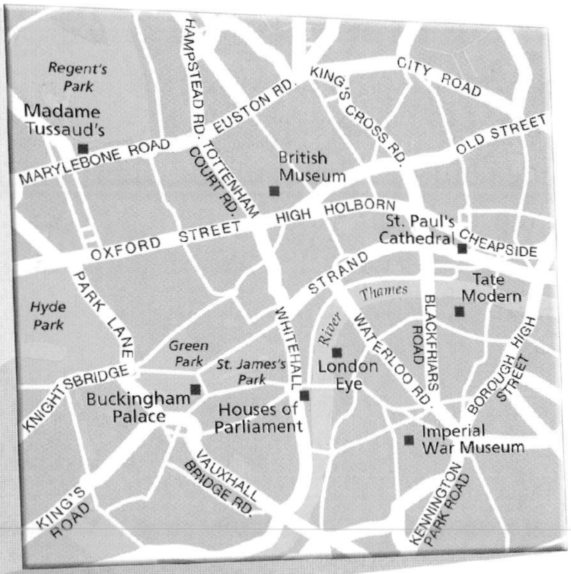
Regent's Park
Madame Tussaud's
HAMPSTEAD RD.
EUSTON RD.
KING'S CROSS RD.
CITY ROAD
OLD STREET
MARYLEBONE ROAD
TOTTENHAM COURT RD.
British Museum
HIGH HOLBORN
St. Paul's Cathedral
CHEAPSIDE
OXFORD STREET
STRAND
Thames
River
Tate Modern
Hyde Park
PARK LANE
Green Park
St. James's Park
WHITEHALL
London Eye
WATERLOO RD.
BLACKFRIARS ROAD
BOROUGH HIGH STREET
KNIGHTSBRIDGE
Buckingham Palace
Houses of Parliament
Imperial War Museum
VAUXHALL BRIDGE RD.
KING'S ROAD
KENNINGTON PARK ROAD

St. Albans
Cheshunt
Lea R.
Roding R.
Watford
Barnet
Enfield
Harrow
Hendon
Tottenham
Hackney
Romford
Ilford
Southall
Ealing
LONDON
Dagenham
Acton
London City
Heathrow
Thames
Greenwich
Hounslow
Richmond upon Thames
Catford
Dartford
Staines
Kingston upon Thames
Sidcup
Streatham
Beckenham
Bromley
Croydon
Sutton
Wey R.
Woking
North Downs
Mole R.
Guildford

▲ Central London

Find the gray square on the map of Greater London. This square represents the area shown on the map above. This map moves you closer into the center of London. Like the zoom on a computer or a camera, this map shows a smaller area but in greater detail. It has the largest scale (1 inch represents about 0.9 mile). You can use this map to explore downtown London.

Key

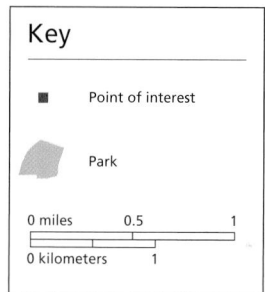

■ Point of interest

Park

0 miles 0.5 1

0 kilometers 1

▲ Greater London

Find the gray square on the main map of Western Europe (left). This square represents the area shown on the map above. It shows London's boundaries, the general shape of the city, and the features around the city. This map can help you find your way from the airport to the center of town.

Key

Built-up area

Airport

City or county border

0 miles 5 10

0 kilometers 10

Lambert Conformal Conic

National capital

Town or neighborhood

▲ A London Landmark

The Houses of Parliament lie to the east of St. James's Park and just west of the River Thames.

Map Skills

Physical Maps

Physical maps represent what a region looks like by showing its major physical features, such as hills and plains. Physical maps often show elevation and relief. Elevation, indicated by colors, is the height of the land above sea level. Relief, indicated by shading, shows how sharply the land rises or falls.

Physical Africa Key

ELEVATION

Feet	Meters
More than 13,000	More than 3,960
6,500–13,000	1,980–3,960
1,600–6,500	480–1,980
650–1,600	200–480
0–650	0–200
Below sea level	Below sea level

—— National border

- - - Disputed border

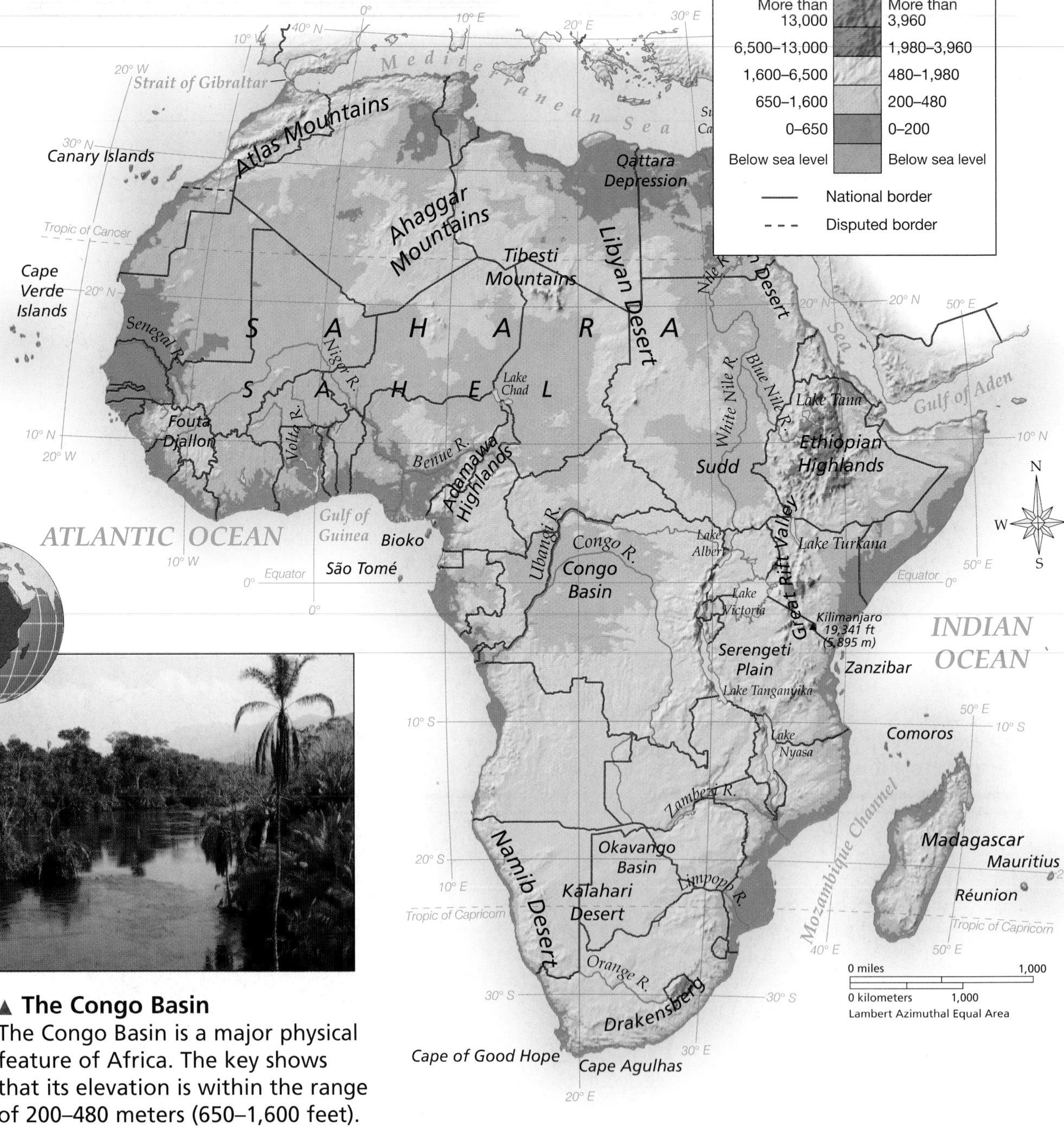

Strait of Gibraltar
Mediterranean Sea
Atlas Mountains
Canary Islands
Qattara Depression
Tropic of Cancer
Ahaggar Mountains
Tibesti Mountains
Libyan Desert
Cape Verde Islands
Senegal R.
SAHARA
Niger R.
SAHEL
Lake Chad
Nile R.
Desert
Red Sea
Gulf of Aden
White Nile R.
Blue Nile R.
Lake Tana
Fouta Djallon
Volta R.
Benue R.
Adamawa Highlands
Ethiopian Highlands
Sudd
ATLANTIC OCEAN
Gulf of Guinea
Bioko
São Tomé
Equator
Ubangi R.
Congo R.
Congo Basin
Lake Albert
Great Rift Valley
Lake Turkana
Lake Victoria
Kilimanjaro 19,341 ft (5,895 m)
Serengeti Plain
Zanzibar
INDIAN OCEAN
Lake Tanganyika
Comoros
Lake Nyasa
Zambezi R.
Mozambique Channel
Madagascar
Mauritius
Réunion
Namib Desert
Okavango Basin
Kalahari Desert
Limpopo R.
Tropic of Capricorn
Orange R.
Drakensberg
Cape of Good Hope
Cape Agulhas
N
W
E
S
0 miles 1,000
0 kilometers 1,000
Lambert Azimuthal Equal Area

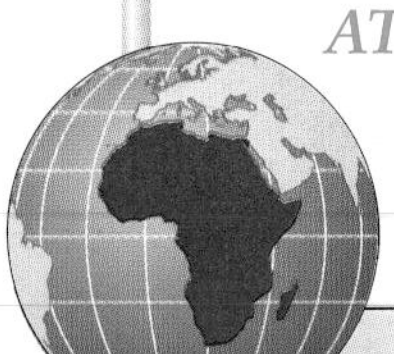

▲ The Congo Basin
The Congo Basin is a major physical feature of Africa. The key shows that its elevation is within the range of 200–480 meters (650–1,600 feet).

Climate Maps

The boundary lines on a map do not always represent exact divisions. In this climate map of India, the boundaries between color-coded regions show gradual shifts in the local climate. In the northwest, the climate gradually changes from arid to semiarid.

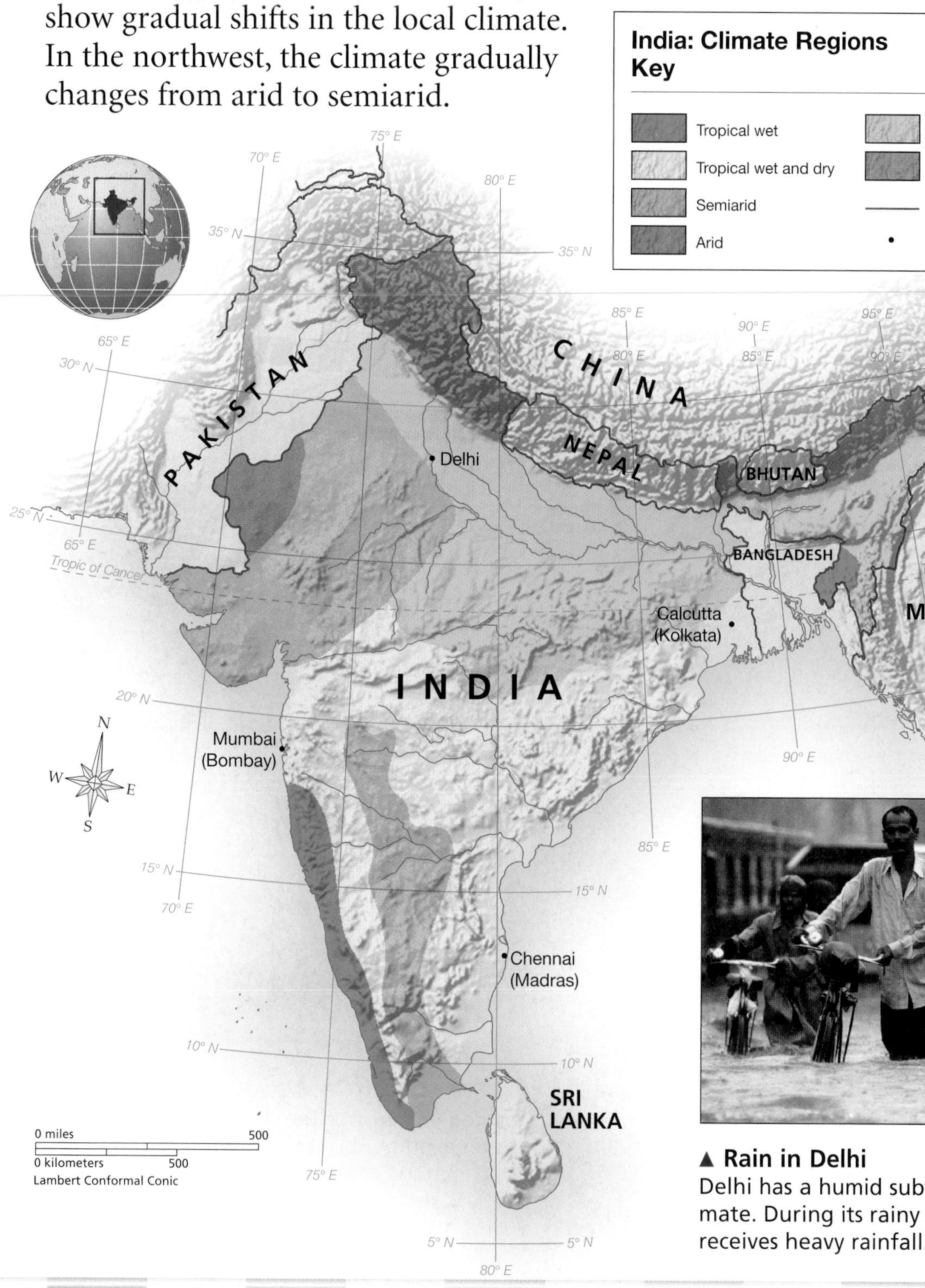
India: Climate Regions
Key
Tropical wet
Tropical wet and dry
Semiarid
Arid
Humid subtropical
Highland
National border
City
PAKISTAN
CHINA
NEPAL
BHUTAN
BANGLADESH
MYANMAR
INDIA
SRI LANKA
Delhi
Calcutta (Kolkata)
Mumbai (Bombay)
Chennai (Madras)
Tropic of Cancer
N
S
E
W
0 miles 500
0 kilometers 500
Lambert Conformal Conic

▲ Rain in Delhi
Delhi has a humid subtropical climate. During its rainy season, Delhi receives heavy rainfall.

Topographic Maps

Topographic maps provide information on the elevation, relief, and slope of the ground surface. A topographic map uses contour lines to show you the surface features of an area as if you were looking down on them from above. Each contour line on the map connects points of equal elevation. Closely spaced contour lines show steep slopes. Widely spaced contour lines show gentle slopes or flat areas.

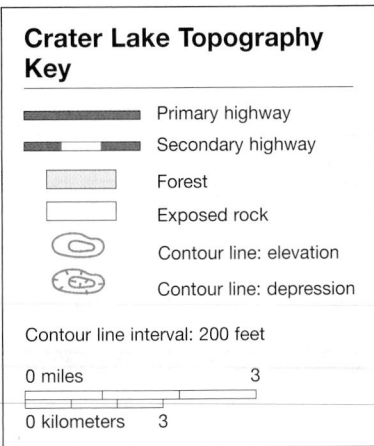

Crater Lake Topography Key

- Primary highway
- Secondary highway
- Forest
- Exposed rock
- Contour line: elevation
- Contour line: depression

Contour line interval: 200 feet

0 miles 3

0 kilometers 3

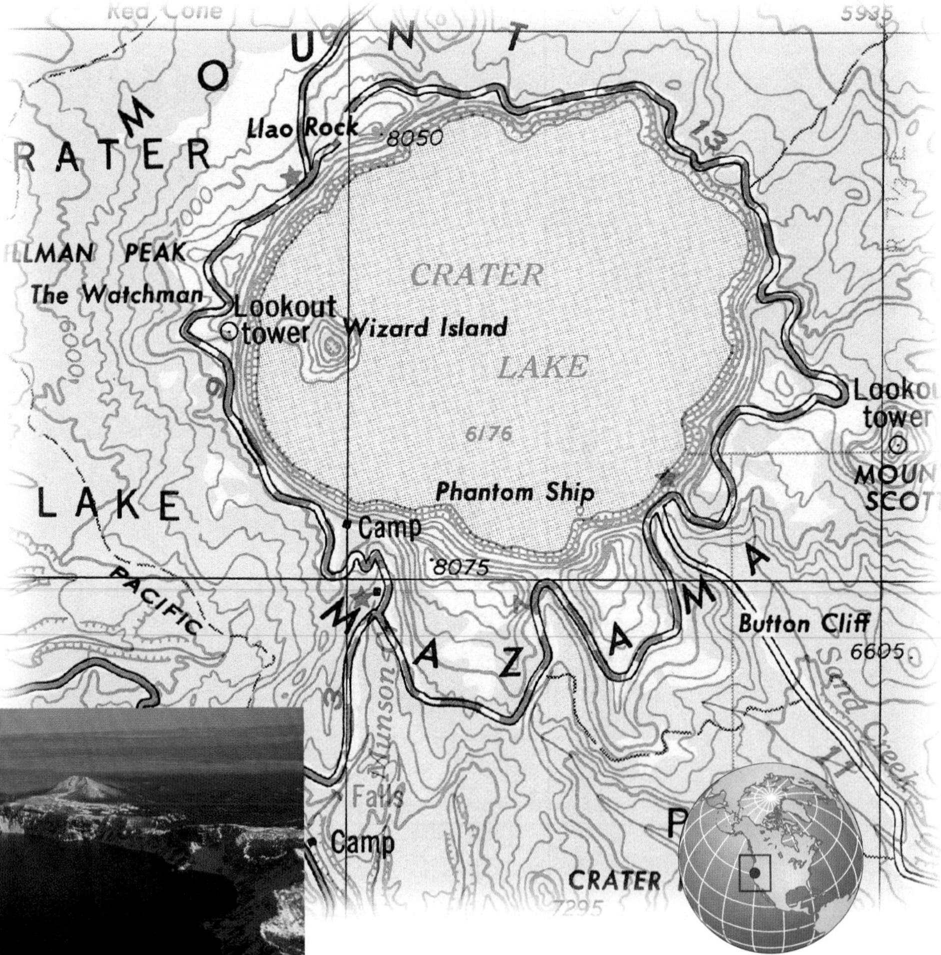
MOUNT
CRATER
Llao Rock
8050
13
7000
LLMAN PEAK
The Watchman
Lookout tower
Wizard Island
CRATER
LAKE
6000
Lookout tower
6176
MOUNT SCOTT
LAKE
Phantom Ship
Camp
8075
PACIFIC
MAZAMA
Button Cliff
6605
Munson
Falls
Camp
CRATER
7295

Contour Lines ▶
In the topographic map of Crater Lake National Park, closely spaced contour lines surrounding the lake represent steep slopes along the lake's perimeter. For this map, the contour interval, or the change in elevation from one contour line to the next, is 200 feet.

◀ Crater Lake
Located in southwestern Oregon, Crater Lake has an average surface elevation of 6176 feet (1882 meters) above sea level. At the west end of the lake lies Wizard Island, which rises to 764 feet (233 meters) above the water.

Using Technology

Prentice Hall provides references in your textbook to a variety of technology options for enhancing your learning experiences. They include iText, probeware versions of textbook labs, SciLinks®, PHSchool.com, and Science News®.

14 Chapter Assessment
iText

Interactive Textbook

Now available for purchase by schools or individuals, iText is an interactive resource that expands your learning with a variety of interactive opportunities.

- **Entire text online and on CD-ROM**
- **Multimedia activities** With engaging video, audio, and interactive features, iText makes learning a multimedia experience. All of the interactive features can be accessed with a single click.
- **Additional assessment opportunities with instant feedback** You don't have to wait to receive feedback—you'll know immediately whether you're on track.

Probeware Labs

Ten of the textbook labs have an alternate probeware version in the Probeware Lab Manual. Probeware labs have several advantages over traditional labs.

- **Instant feedback** Your data are displayed immediately, so you know right away if the lab is working.
- **Graphing and data analysis** Built-in tools let you immediately focus on science concepts instead of getting bogged down in generating graphs and tables.
- **Encourage creativity** With probeware labs, you can ask (and answer) what-if questions.

Go Online NSTA SCILINKS

The National Science Teachers Association manages the SciLinks® Service, a project that blends the best of the two main educational resources—textbooks and the Internet—into a dynamic educational tool.

NSTA incorporates SciLinks into a variety of printed education materials, including this textbook. In these materials, you will find an icon near several concepts about which you are reading. Under it, you will find the SciLinks URL (www.scilinks.org) and a code. Go to the SciLinks Web site, sign in, type the code from the page you are reading, and you will receive a list of URLs that are selected by science educators. Sites are chosen for accurate and age-appropriate content and good pedagogy. Using SciLinks, students explore concepts in a dynamic, safe environment. The underlying database changes constantly, eliminating dead or revised sites or simply replacing sites with better selections. The ink may dry on the page, but the science it describes will always be fresh.

Go Online PHSchool.com

Go Online opportunities appear throughout the textbook to alert you to interactive opportunities at the Prentice Hall Web site. Use the Go Online keywords to access a wealth of resources.

- **Updates** Find updates of information likely to change (such as graphs or maps).
- **Data-Sharing Labs** Share and compare data with students from across the country.
- **Background for Issues** Access more detailed information about issues featured in the textbook.
- **Self-Assessments** Take self-tests with instant feedback to monitor your own progress and stay on track.

Go Online SCIENCE NEWS®

Stay current with articles from Science News. Use the keyword links to quickly find relevant articles written for a high school audience. Articles keep pace with new research, so you always have the latest information.

Standardized Test Prep

The strategies listed here will help you learn how to apply test-taking skills in a logical fashion. Once you know how to prepare for a test, you can improve your chances for getting the right answer. You'll be able to approach a test with confidence and tell yourself, "I will do well."

Preparing for a Standardized Test

- **Be well rested.** Get plenty of sleep the night before the test. You will perform better if you are not tired.
- **Eat a good breakfast.** The brain works better when it has fuel.
- **Bring a sweater or sweatshirt.** You will want to be comfortable, no matter how warm or cool the testing room is.
- **Wear a watch.** Be aware of how many questions you have to answer and the amount of time you are given.
- **Remember your supplies.** You will likely need several sharp #2 pencils and a good eraser. Bring a calculator if it is permitted.
- **Allow plenty of time to get to the test site.** You will be more relaxed if you arrive early.

Taking a Standardized Test

- **Read the directions first.** Then start answering the questions.
- **Read all of the answers.** Then make your choice.
- **Underline important words and phrases.**
- **Cross out choices you know are wrong.**
- **Do the easy questions first.** Don't get stuck on difficult questions. You can come back to them.
- **Record your answers properly.** Be sure to put your answers in the right place. Fill in the marks completely.
- **Answer every question.**
- **Stay relaxed.** If you get nervous, stop and take a few deep breaths.
- **Change your body position.** Once in a while, shift your position to keep comfortable.
- **Stick with your first choice.** Change an answer only when you are SURE your first choice is wrong.
- **Review your answers if you have time.**

Question Strategies

Multiple Choice

- **Read the question thoroughly and carefully.**
- **Know what the question wants from you.** Are you expected to provide all possible answers, or the best answer? Do you have to find all responses that apply, or one that does not apply?
- **Anticipate the answer.** If you know the answer even before you read the list of responses, look for an answer that is similar to the one you are thinking of.
- **Skip the question if you get stuck.** Don't lose precious time. You can always go back to it later.
- **Read all answers.** Even when you think you have found the correct answer right away, you may find a better answer.
- **If you find two correct answers, keep reading!** You may discover an "All of the above" option. Or the question may ask for the "best" answer.
- **Eliminate responses you know are wrong.** If you have fewer options to choose from, you are more likely to choose the correct response.

Constructed Response (Short Answer)

- **Know which question(s) to answer.** Do you have to answer all of them or only some? If you can choose, answer the ones you are most familiar with.
- **Notice action words.** Do you have to "draw" a diagram? "Create" a list? "Write" a paragraph?
- **Make notes.** Write down names, dates, facts, and figures that come to mind. Don't waste time; write only as much as you need to jog your memory.
- **Make a brief outline.** Plan how to approach the response. Then stick to it; don't get sidetracked.
- **Write legibly.** Neatness counts. Don't lose points just because the evaluator couldn't read your response.
- **Use key terms and vocabulary.** Your answer will be more precise and sound more credible.
- **Be thorough.** But don't waste time on unnecessary details or long explanations.
- **Always provide an answer.** Partial credit is better than no credit. If time is short, outline or list the remaining information.
- **Leave space.** You can add information you may think of later.

Appendix A SI Units

SI *(Système International d'Unités)* is a revised version of the metric system, which was originally developed in France in 1791. SI units of measurement are used by scientists throughout the world. The system is based on multiples of ten. Each unit is ten times larger or ten times smaller than the next unit. The most commonly used SI units are given below.

You can use conversion factors to convert between SI and non-SI units. Try the following conversions. How tall are you in meters? What is your weight in newtons? What is your normal body temperature in degrees Celsius?

Commonly Used Metric Units

Length	The distance from one point to another
meter (m)	A meter is slightly longer than a yard. 1 meter = 1000 millimeters (mm) 1 meter = 100 centimeters (cm) 1000 meters = 1 kilometer (km)

Volume	The amount of space an object takes up
liter (L)	A liter is slightly more than a quart. 1 liter = 1000 milliliters (mL)

Mass	The amount of matter in an object
gram (g)	A gram has a mass equal to about one paper clip. 1000 grams = 1 kilogram (kg)

Temperature	The measure of hotness or coldness
degrees Celsius (°C)	0°C = freezing point of water at sea level 100°C = boiling point of water at sea level

Metric–Customary Equivalents

2.54 centimeters (cm) = 1 inch (in.)
1 meter (m) = 39.37 inches (in.)
1 kilometer (km) = 0.62 miles (mi)
1 liter (L) = 1.06 quarts (qt)
250 milliliters (mL) = 1 cup (c)
9.8 newtons (N) = 2.2 pounds (lb)
°C = 5/9 × (°F – 32)

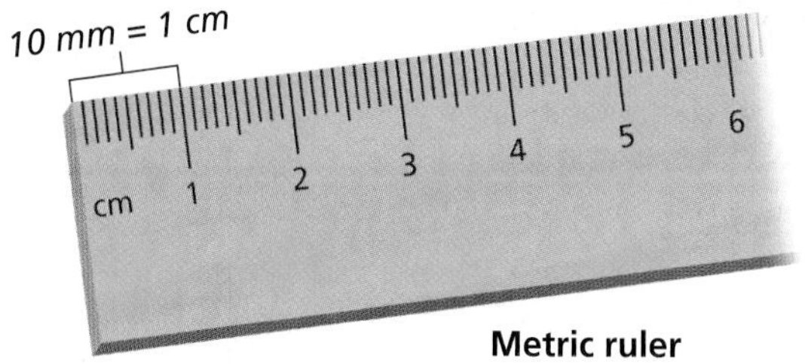
10 mm = 1 cm
cm
1
2
3
4
5
6
Metric ruler

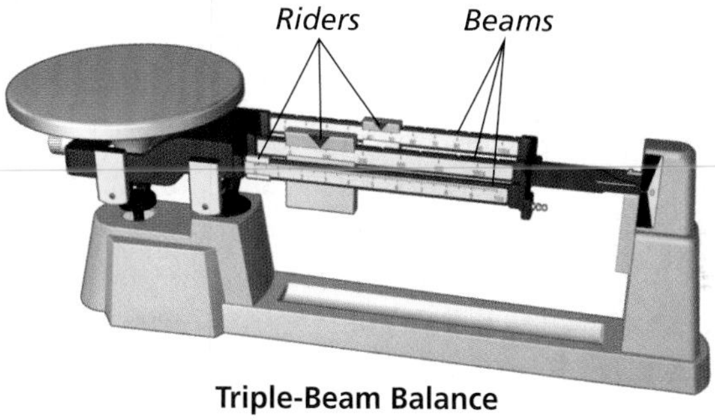
Riders
Beams
Triple-Beam Balance

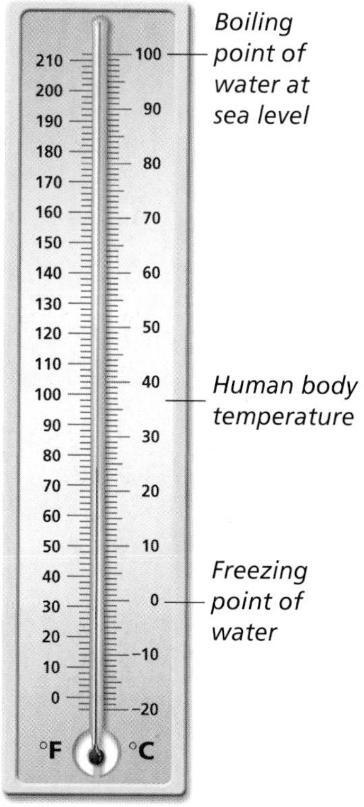
Boiling point of water at sea level
Human body temperature
Freezing point of water
°F
°C
Thermometer

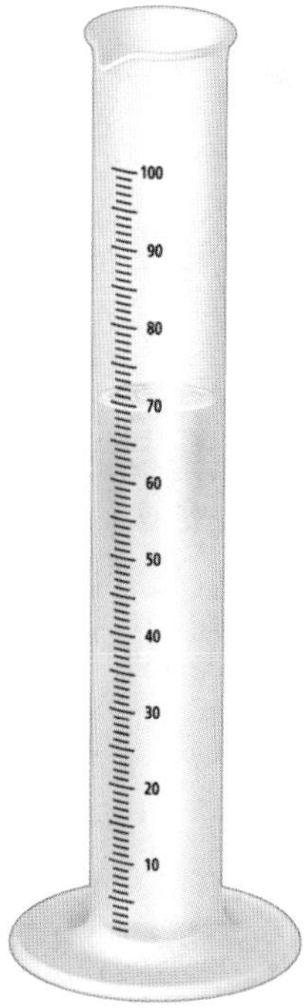
Graduated cylinder

Appendix B Using a Laboratory Balance

The laboratory balance is an important tool in scientific investigations. You can use a balance to determine the masses of materials that you study or experiment with in the laboratory.

Different kinds of balances are used in the laboratory. One kind of balance is the triple-beam balance. The balance that you may use in your science class is probably similar to the balance illustrated. To use the balance properly, you should learn the name, location, and function of each part of the balance you are using.

The Triple-Beam Balance

The triple-beam balance is a single-pan balance with three beams The back, or 100-gram, beam is divided into ten units of 10 grams. The middle, or 500-gram, beam is divided into five units of 100 grams. The front, or 10-gram, beam is divided into ten major units, each of which is 1 gram. Each 1-gram unit is further divided into units of 0.1 gram. What is the largest mass you could measure with a triple-beam balance?

The following procedure can be used to find the mass of an object with a triple-beam balance.

1. When no object is on the pan, and the riders are at zero, make sure the pointer is at zero. If it is not, use the adjustment screw to zero the balance.
2. Place the object on the pan.
3. Move the rider on the middle beam notch by notch until the horizontal pointer drops below zero. Move the rider back one notch.
4. Move the rider on the back beam notch by notch until the pointer again drops below zero. Move the rider back one notch.
5. Slowly slide the rider along the front beam until the pointer stops at zero. The mass of the object is the sum of the readings on the three beams.

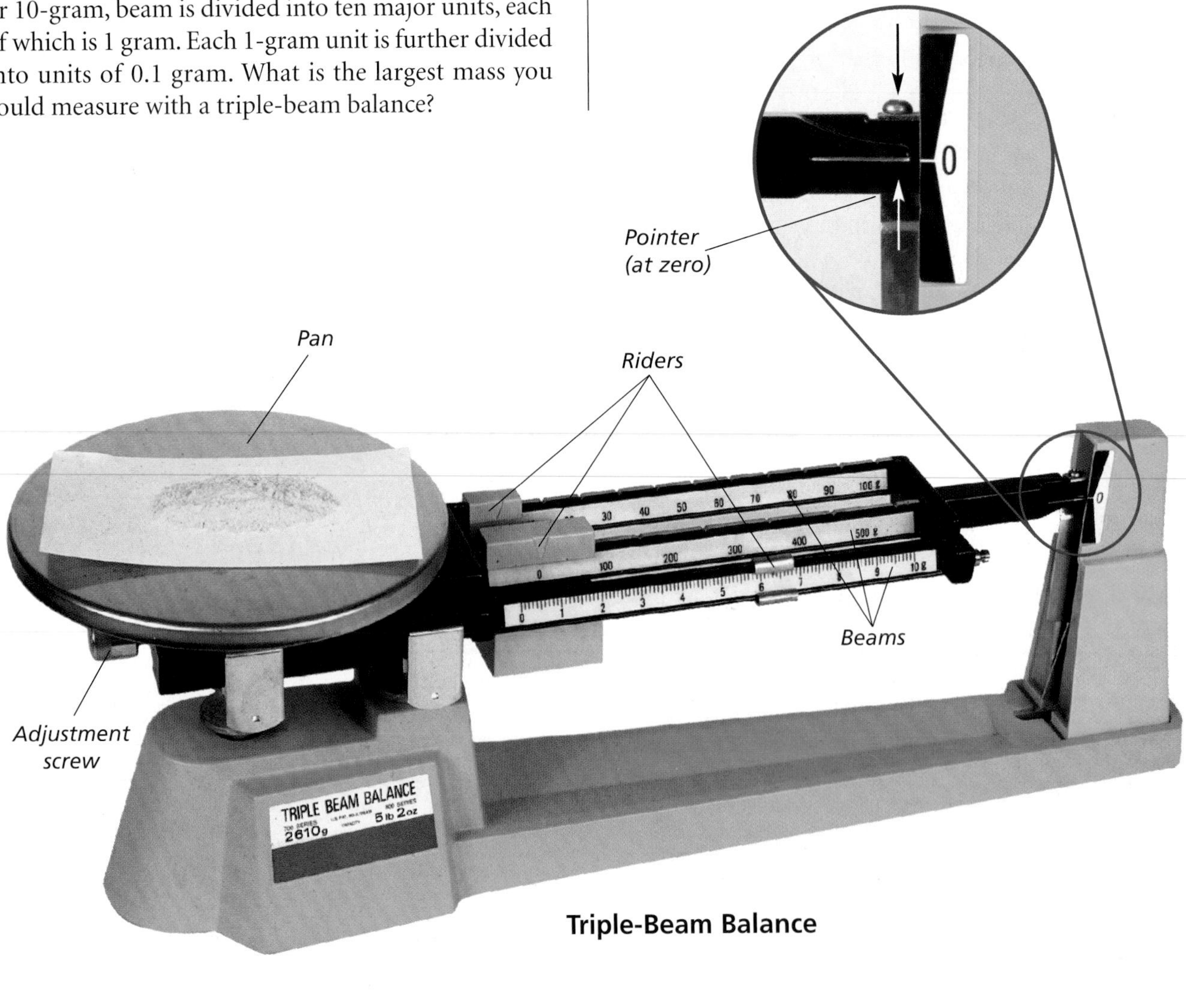
Pointer
(at zero)
0
Pan
Riders
Beams
Adjustment
screw
TRIPLE BEAM BALANCE
2610g
5 lb 2oz

Triple-Beam Balance

Appendix C The Chemical Elements

Element	Symbol	Atomic Number	Atomic Mass†
Actinium	Ac	89	(277)
Aluminum	Al	13	26.982
Americium	Am	95	(243)
Antimony	Sb	51	121.75
Argon	Ar	18	39.948
Arsenic	As	33	74.922
Astatine	At	85	(210)
Barium	Ba	56	137.33
Berkelium	Bk	97	(247)
Beryllium	Be	4	9.0122
Bismuth	Bi	83	208.98
Bohrium	Bh	107	(264)
Boron	B	5	10.81
Bromine	Br	35	79.904
Cadmium	Cd	48	112.41
Calcium	Ca	20	40.08
Californium	Cf	98	(251)
Carbon	C	6	12.011
Cerium	Ce	58	140.12
Cesium	Cs	55	132.91
Chlorine	Cl	17	35.453
Chromium	Cr	24	51.996
Cobalt	Co	27	58.933
Copper	Cu	29	63.546
Curium	Cm	96	(247)
Dubnium	Db	105	(262)
Dysprosium	Dy	66	162.50
Einsteinium	Es	99	(252)
Erbium	Er	68	167.26
Europium	Eu	63	151.96
Fermium	Fm	100	(257)
Fluorine	F	9	18.998
Francium	Fr	87	(223)
Gadolinium	Gd	64	157.25
Gallium	Ga	31	69.72
Germanium	Ge	32	72.59
Gold	Au	79	196.97
Hafnium	Hf	72	178.49
Hassium	Hs	108	(265)
Helium	He	2	4.0026
Holmium	Ho	67	164.93
Hydrogen	H	1	1.0079
Indium	In	49	114.82
Iodine	I	53	126.90
Iridium	Ir	77	192.22
Iron	Fe	26	55.847
Krypton	Kr	36	83.80
Lanthanum	La	57	138.91
Lawrencium	Lr	103	(262)
Lead	Pb	82	207.2
Lithium	Li	3	6.941
Lutetium	Lu	71	174.97
Magnesium	Mg	12	24.305
Manganese	Mn	25	54.938
Meitnerium	Mt	109	(268)
Mendelevium	Md	101	(258)
Mercury	Hg	80	200.59
Molybdenum	Mo	42	95.94
Neodymium	Nd	60	144.24
Neon	Ne	10	20.179
Neptunium	Np	93	(237)
Nickel	Ni	28	58.71
Niobium	Nb	41	92.906
Nitrogen	N	7	14.007
Nobelium	No	102	(259)
Osmium	Os	76	190.2
Oxygen	O	8	15.999
Palladium	Pd	46	106.4
Phosphorus	P	15	30.974
Platinum	Pt	78	195.09
Plutonium	Pu	94	(244)
Polonium	Po	84	(209)
Potassium	K	19	39.098
Praseodymium	Pr	59	140.91
Promethium	Pm	61	(145)
Protactinium	Pa	91	231.04
Radium	Ra	88	(226)
Radon	Rn	86	(222)
Rhenium	Re	75	186.21
Rhodium	Rh	45	102.91
Rubidium	Rb	37	85.468
Ruthenium	Ru	44	101.07
Rutherfordium	Rf	104	(261)
Samarium	Sm	62	150.4
Scandium	Sc	21	44.956
Seaborgium	Sg	106	(263)
Selenium	Se	34	78.96
Silicon	Si	14	28.086
Silver	Ag	47	107.87
Sodium	Na	11	22.990
Strontium	Sr	38	87.62
Sulfur	S	16	32.06
Tantalum	Ta	73	180.95
Technetium	Tc	43	(98)
Tellurium	Te	52	127.60
Terbium	Tb	65	158.93
Thallium	Tl	81	204.37
Thorium	Th	90	232.04
Thulium	Tm	69	168.93
Tin	Sn	50	118.69
Titanium	Ti	22	47.90
Tungsten	W	74	183.85
Ununbium	Uub*	112	(277)
Ununnilium	Uun*	110	(269)
Ununquadium	Uuq*	114	—
Unununium	Uuu*	111	(272)
Uranium	U	92	238.03
Vanadium	V	23	50.941
Xenon	Xe	54	131.30
Ytterbium	Yb	70	173.04
Yttrium	Y	39	88.906
Zinc	Zn	30	65.38
Zirconium	Zr	40	91.22

† Number in parentheses gives the mass number of the most stable isotope.

* Name not officially assigned

Appendices

Appendix D Identifying Common Minerals

Metallic Luster, Mostly Dark-Colored						
Mineral	**Hardness**	**Density (g/cm^3)**	**Luster**	**Streak**	**Color**	**Additional Information**
Pyrite FeS_2	6–6.5	5.0	Metallic	Greenish black	Light yellow	Harder than chalcopyrite; called "fool's gold," but harder than gold and very brittle
Magnetite Fe_3O_4	6	5.2	Metallic	Black	Iron black	Very magnetic; important iron ore; some varieties known as "lodestone"
Hematite Fe_2O_3	5.5–6.5	4.9–5.3	Metallic or earthy	Red or reddish brown	Reddish brown to black; also steel gray crystals	Most important ore of iron; known as "red ocher;" often used as red pigment in paint
Chalcopyrite $CuFeS_2$	3.5–4	4.1–4.3	Metallic	Greenish black	Golden yellow, often tarnished	Most important copper ore; softer than pyrite and more yellow; more brittle than gold
Copper Cu	2.5–3	8.96	Metallic	Copper red	Copper red to black	Can be pounded into various shapes and drawn into wires; used in making electrical wires, coins, pipes
Gold Au	2.5–3	19.3	Metallic	Yellow	Rich yellow	Can be pounded into various shapes and drawn into wires; does not tarnish; used in jewelry, coins, dental fillings
Silver Ag	2.5–3	10.5	Metallic	Silver to light gray	Silver white, tarnishes to black	Can be pounded into various shapes and drawn into wires; used in jewelry, coins, electrical wire
Galena PbS	2.5	7.4–7.6	Metallic	Lead gray	Lead gray	Main ore of lead; used in shields against radiation
Graphite C	1–2	2.3	Metallic to dull	Black	Black	Feels greasy; very soft; used as pencil "lead" and as a lubricant

Nonmetallic Luster, Mostly Dark-Colored						
Mineral	**Hardness**	**Density (g/cm^3)**	**Luster**	**Streak**	**Color**	**Additional Information**
Garnet $[Ca,Mg,Fe]_3[Al,Fe,Cr]_2(SiO_4)_3$	7–7.5	3.5–4.3	Glassy to resinous	White, light brown	Red, brown, black, green	A group of minerals used in jewelry, as a birthstone, and as an abrasive
Olivine $[Mg,Fe]_2SiO_4$	6.5–7	3.3–3.4	Glassy	White or gray	Olive green	Found in igneous rocks; sometimes used as a gem
Hornblende $NaCa_2[Mg,Fe,Al]_5[Si,Al]_8O_{22}(OH)_2$	5–6	3.0–3.4	Glassy, silky	White to gray	Dark green to brown, black	Found in igneous and metamorphic rocks
Biotite $K[Mg,Fe]_3AlSiO_{10}(OH)_2$	2.5–3	2.8–3.4	Glassy or pearly	White to gray	Dark green, brown, or black	A type of mica, sometimes used as a lubricant

Nonmetallic Luster, Mostly Light-Colored						
Mineral	Hardness	Density (g/cm^3)	Luster	Streak	Color	Additional Information
Diamond C	10	3.5	Brilliant	White	Colorless and varied	Hardest known substance; used in jewelry, as an abrasive, in cutting instruments
Topaz $Al_2SiO_4[F,OH]_2$	8	3.5–3.6	Glassy	White	Straw yellow, pink, bluish, greenish	Used in jewelry, as a birthstone
Quartz SiO_2	7	2.6	Glassy, greasy	White	Colorless, white; any color when not pure	The second most abundant mineral; many varieties gems (amethyst, cat's eye, bloodstone, agate, jasper, onyx); used in making glass
Feldspar $[K,Na,Ca]AlSi_3O_8$	6	2.6	Glassy	Colorless, white	Colorless, white, various colors	As a family, the most abundant of all minerals; makes up more than 60 percent of Earth's crust
Fluorite CaF_2	4	3.0–3.3	Glassy	Colorless	Purple, light green, yellow, bluish green, other colors	Some types fluorescent (glow when exposed to UV light); used in making steel
Dolomite $CaMg(CO_3)_2$	3.5–4	2.8	Glassy or pearly	White	Colorless, white, pinkish, or light tints	Used in making concrete and cement; fizzes slowly in dilute hydrochloric acid
Calcite $CaCO_3$	3	2.7	Glassy	White to grayish	Colorless, white, pale tints	Easily scratched; bubbles in dilute hydrochloric acid
Halite NaCl	2.5	2.1–2.6	Glassy	White	Colorless or white	Occurs as perfect cubic crystals; has salty taste
Gypsum $CaSO_4 \bullet 2H_2O$	2	2.3	Glassy, pearly, silky	White	Colorless, white, light tints	Very soft; used in manufacture of plaster of Paris; form known as alabaster used for statues
Sulfur S	2	2.0–2.1	Resinous to greasy	White	Yellowish to yellowish brown	Used in making many medicines, in production of sulfuric acid, and in vulcanizing rubber
Talc $Mg_3Si_4O_{10}(OH)_2$	1	2.7–2.8	Pearly to greasy	White	Gray, white, greenish	Very soft; used in talcum powder, found mostly in metamorphic rocks; also used in "soapstone"

Appendix E United States Physical Map

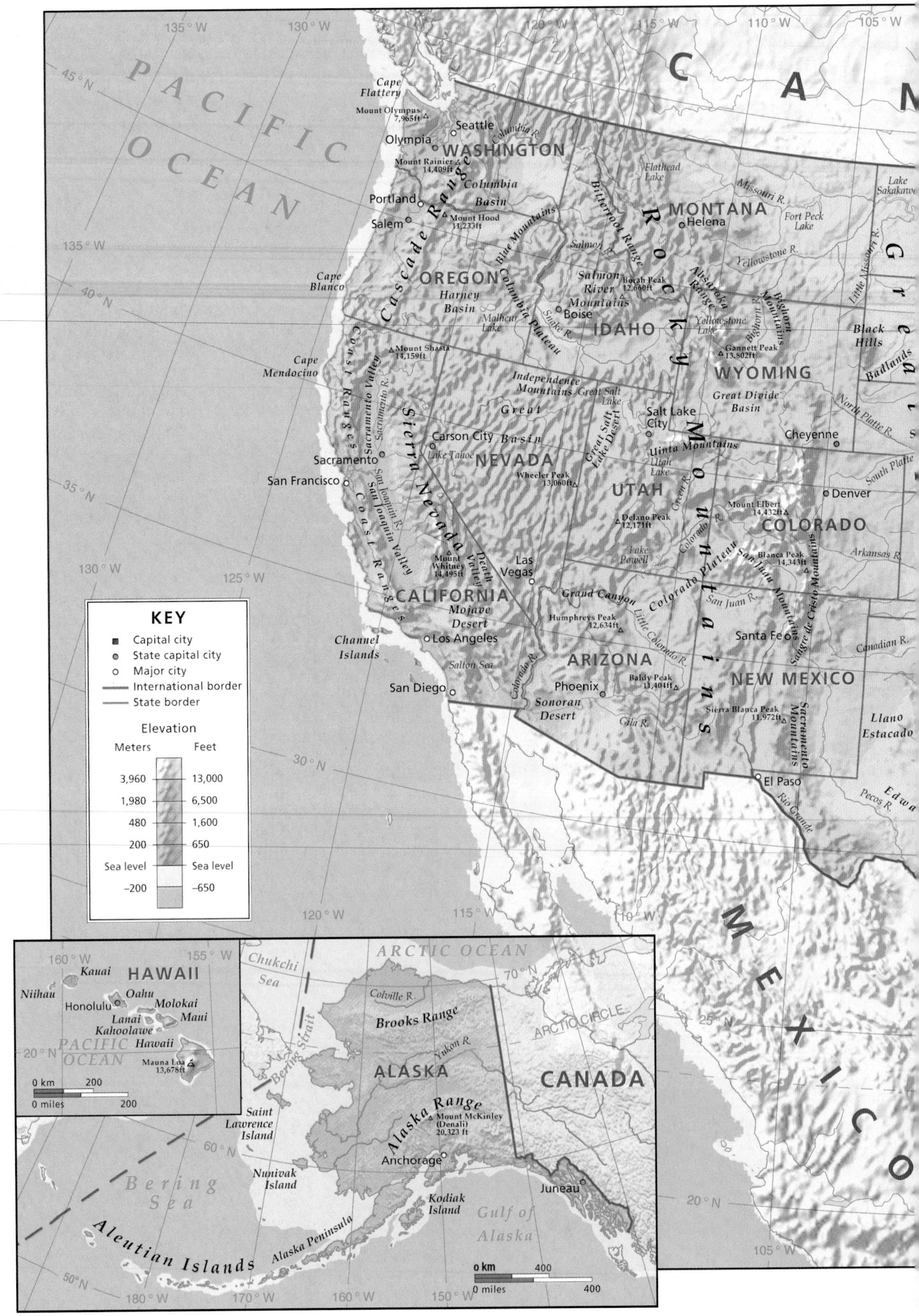
PACIFIC OCEAN
CANADA
MEXICO
Cape Flattery
Mount Olympus 7,965ft
Seattle
Olympia
WASHINGTON
Columbia R.
Mount Rainier 14,409ft
Columbia Basin
Portland
Mount Hood 11,233ft
Salem
Cascade Range
Blue Mountains
OREGON
Harney Basin
Malheur Lake
Cape Blanco
Cape Mendocino
Mount Shasta 14,159ft
Coast Ranges
Sacramento Valley
Sacramento R.
Sierra Nevada
Columbia Plateau
Snake R.
Boise
IDAHO
Salmon R.
Salmon River Mountains
Borah Peak 12,660ft
Bitterroot Range
Flathead Lake
MONTANA
Helena
Missouri R.
Fort Peck Lake
Yellowstone R.
Lake Sakakawea
Absaroka Range
Bighorn Mountains
Bighorn R.
Yellowstone Lake
Gannett Peak 13,802ft
WYOMING
Great Divide Basin
Little Missouri R.
Black Hills
Badlands
North Platte R.
Cheyenne
Rocky Mountains
Independence Mountains
Great Salt Lake
Great Salt Lake Desert
Salt Lake City
Uinta Mountains
Utah Lake
Great Basin
Carson City
Lake Tahoe
NEVADA
Wheeler Peak 13,060ft
Sacramento
San Francisco
San Joaquin R.
San Joaquin Valley
UTAH
Green R.
Delano Peak 12,171ft
Lake Powell
Colorado R.
Colorado Plateau
San Juan Mountains
San Juan R.
Mount Elbert 14,432ft
COLORADO
Denver
South Platte
Arkansas R.
Blanca Peak 14,343ft
Sangre de Cristo Mountains
Mount Whitney 14,495ft
Death Valley
Las Vegas
CALIFORNIA
Mojave Desert
Channel Islands
Los Angeles
Salton Sea
San Diego
Grand Canyon
Humphreys Peak 12,634ft
Little Colorado R.
ARIZONA
Phoenix
Baldy Peak 11,404ft
Sonoran Desert
Gila R.
Santa Fe
Canadian R.
NEW MEXICO
Sierra Blanca Peak 11,972ft
Sacramento Mountains
Llano Estacado
El Paso
Rio Grande
Pecos R.
Edwa
KEY
Capital city
State capital city
Major city
International border
State border
Elevation
Meters
Feet
3,960
13,000
1,980
6,500
480
1,600
200
650
Sea level
Sea level
–200
–650
HAWAII
Kauai
Niihau
Oahu
Honolulu
Molokai
Maui
Lanai
Kahoolawe
Hawaii
PACIFIC OCEAN
Mauna Loa 13,678ft
0 km 200
0 miles 200
ARCTIC OCEAN
Chukchi Sea
Colville R.
Brooks Range
ARCTIC CIRCLE
Yukon R.
ALASKA
CANADA
Bering Strait
Saint Lawrence Island
Alaska Range
Mount McKinley (Denali) 20,323 ft
Anchorage
Nunivak Island
Bering Sea
Juneau
Kodiak Island
Gulf of Alaska
Aleutian Islands
Alaska Peninsula
0 km 400
0 miles 400

95° W
90° W
85° W
80° W
75° W
70° W
65° W
A D A
Lake of the Woods
Namakan Lake
Red R.
Lake Superior
MINNESOTA
MICHIGAN
WISCONSIN
Saint Paul
Lake Huron
Lake Michigan
Mississippi R.
Madison
Lansing
Detroit
Lake Erie
Lake Ontario
IOWA
Des Moines
Des Moines R.
Missouri R.
Chicago
Davenport
ILLINOIS
Illinois R.
Wabash R.
INDIANA
Indianapolis
Springfield
OHIO
Cleveland
Columbus
Ohio R.
Kansas City
Topeka
Lake of the Ozarks
Jefferson City
MISSOURI
Wichita
Ozark Plateau
Tulsa
KENTUCKY
Frankfort
Ohio R.
Kentucky Lake
Nashville
TENNESSEE
Memphis
Boston Mountains
ARKANSAS
Ouachita Mountains
Little Rock
Arkansas R.
Red R.
Dallas
MISSISSIPPI
Jackson
Mississippi R.
LOUISIANA
Baton Rouge
New Orleans
Houston
Brazos R.
Mississippi River Delta
ALABAMA
Montgomery
Alabama R.
Tennessee R.
Chattahoochee R.
GEORGIA
Atlanta
Savannah R.
Okefenokee Swamp
Tallahassee
FLORIDA
Apalachee Bay
Tampa Bay
Charlotte Harbor
Lake Okeechobee
The Everglades
Miami
Florida Keys
Straits of Florida
Cape Canaveral
Gulf of Mexico
CUBA
ATLANTIC OCEAN
MAINE
Mount Katahdin 5,265ft
Augusta
Gulf of Maine
VERMONT
Montpelier
NEW HAMPSHIRE
Concord
Adirondack Mountains
NEW YORK
Albany
Boston
MASSACHUSETTS
Providence
RHODE ISLAND
Hartford
CONNECTICUT
Long Island
New York
Trenton
NEW JERSEY
PENNSYLVANIA
Harrisburg
Philadelphia
Dover
DELAWARE
Annapolis
WASHINGTON DC
MARYLAND
WEST VIRGINIA
Spruce Knob 4,862ft
Charleston
Richmond
Chesapeake Bay
VIRGINIA
Roanoke R.
Appalachian Mountains
Cumberland Plateau
Blue Ridge
Raleigh
NORTH CAROLINA
Pamlico Sound
Onslow Bay
Mount Mitchell 6,682ft
Piedmont
Columbia
SOUTH CAROLINA
40° N
35° N
30° N
25° N
20° N
TROPIC OF CANCER
N
S
E
W
0 km
500
0 miles
500

Weather Map

This weather map shows data collected from many weather stations. Below the map is an explanation of what the symbols mean.

Weather Map

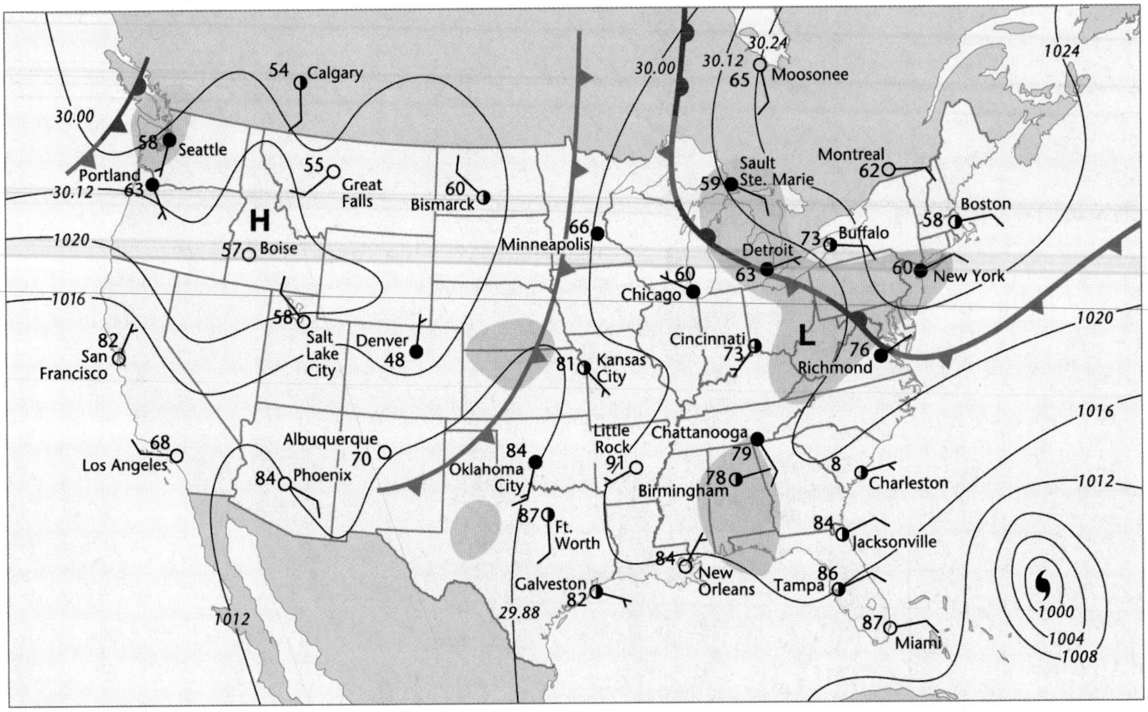

54 Calgary
30.00
58 Seattle
Portland
30.12
63
55 Great Falls
60 Bismarck
H
1020
57 Boise
1016
58 Salt Lake City
Denver 48
82 San Francisco
68 Los Angeles
Albuquerque 70
84 Phoenix
1012
66 Minneapolis
30.00
30.12
30.24
65 Moosonee
1024
Sault Ste. Marie 59
Montreal 62
Boston 58
73 Buffalo
Detroit 63
60 New York
60 Chicago
L
Cincinnati 73
76 Richmond
1020
81 Kansas City
Little Rock 91
Chattanooga 79
78 Birmingham
84 Oklahoma City
87 Ft. Worth
Galveston 82
29.88
84 New Orleans
8 Charleston
1016
1012
84 Jacksonville
86 Tampa
87 Miami
1000
1004
1008

Explanation of Fronts

Cold Front
Boundary between a cold air mass and a warm air mass. Brings brief storms and cooler weather.

Warm Front
Boundary between a warm air mass and a cold air mass. Usually accompanied by precipitation.

Stationary Front
Boundary between warm and cold air masses when no movement occurs. Long periods of precipitation.

Occluded Front
Boundary on which a warm front has been overtaken by a cold front. Brings precipitation.

Weather	Symbol
Drizzle	
Fog	
Hail	
Haze	
Rain	
Shower	
Sleet	
Smoke	
Snow	
Thunderstorm	
Hurricane	

Wind Speed (mph)	Symbol
1–2	
3–8	
9–14	
15–20	
21–25	
26–31	
32–37	
38–43	
44–49	
50–54	
55–60	
61–66	
67–71	
72–77	

Cloud Cover (%)	Symbol
0	
10	
20–30	
40	
50	
60	
70–80	
90	
100	

How Symbols Are Used on a Weather Map

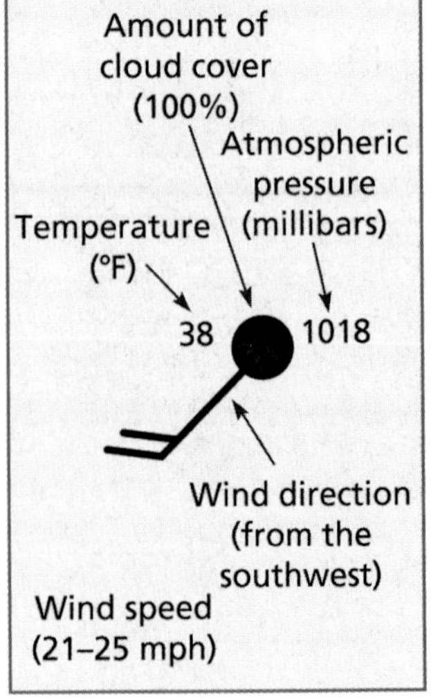

Amount of cloud cover (100%)
Atmospheric pressure (millibars)
Temperature (°F)
38
1018
Wind direction (from the southwest)
Wind speed (21–25 mph)

Appendix G Relative Humidity Chart

To find the relative humidity, measure the wet-bulb and dry-bulb temperatures with a sling psychrometer. Find the dry-bulb reading in the left column and the difference between readings at the top of the table. The number where these readings intersect is the relative humidity in percent.

Relative Humidity (percent)

Dry-Bulb Reading (°C)	Difference Between Wet-Bulb and Dry-Bulb Readings (°C)													
	1	2	3	4	5	6	7	8	9	10	11	12	13	14
5	86	72	58	45	33	20	7							
6	86	73	60	48	35	24	11							
7	87	74	62	50	38	26	15							
8	87	75	63	51	40	29	19	8						
9	88	76	64	53	42	32	22	12						
10	88	77	66	55	44	34	24	15	6					
11	89	78	67	56	46	36	27	18	9					
12	89	78	68	58	48	39	29	21	12					
13	89	79	69	59	50	41	32	23	15	7				
14	90	79	70	60	51	42	34	26	18	10				
15	90	80	71	61	53	44	36	27	20	13	6			
16	90	81	71	63	54	46	38	30	23	15	8			
17	90	81	72	64	55	47	40	32	25	18	11			
18	91	82	73	65	57	49	41	34	27	20	14	7		
19	91	82	74	65	58	50	43	36	29	22	16	10		
20	91	83	74	66	59	51	44	37	31	24	18	12	6	
21	91	83	75	67	60	53	46	39	32	26	20	14	9	
22	92	83	76	68	61	54	47	40	34	28	22	17	11	6
23	92	84	76	69	62	55	48	42	36	30	24	19	13	8
24	92	84	77	69	62	56	49	43	37	31	26	20	15	10
25	92	84	77	70	63	57	50	44	39	33	28	22	17	12
26	92	85	78	71	64	58	51	46	40	34	29	24	19	14
27	92	85	78	71	65	58	52	47	41	36	31	26	21	16
28	93	85	78	72	65	59	53	48	42	37	32	27	22	18
29	93	86	79	72	66	60	54	49	43	38	33	28	24	19
30	93	86	79	73	67	61	55	50	44	39	35	30	25	21

Appendix H Star Charts

Autumn Sky

To use this chart, hold it up in front of you and turn it so the direction you are facing is at the bottom of the chart. The chart works best at 35° N latitude, but it can be used at other latitudes. It works best at the following dates and times: September 1 at 10:00 P.M., October 1 at 8 P.M., and November 1 at 6 P.M.

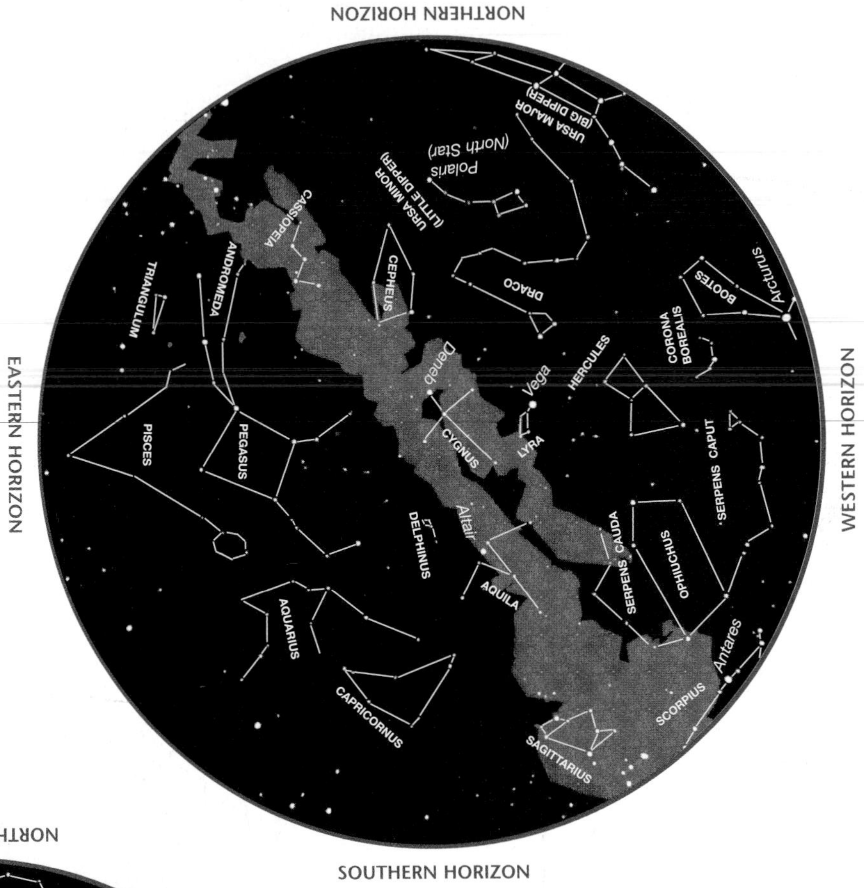
NORTHERN HORIZON
EASTERN HORIZON
WESTERN HORIZON
SOUTHERN HORIZON
URSA MAJOR (BIG DIPPER)
URSA MINOR (LITTLE DIPPER)
Polaris (North Star)
CASSIOPEIA
CEPHEUS
DRACO
BOOTES
Arcturus
CORONA BOREALIS
HERCULES
Deneb
Vega
LYRA
CYGNUS
TRIANGULUM
ANDROMEDA
PISCES
PEGASUS
DELPHINUS
Altair
AQUILA
SERPENS CAPUT
SERPENS CAUDA
OPHIUCHUS
AQUARIUS
CAPRICORNUS
SAGITTARIUS
SCORPIUS
Antares

NORTHERN HORIZON
EASTERN HORIZON
WESTERN HORIZON
SOUTHERN HORIZON
URSA MAJOR (BIG DIPPER)
URSA MINOR (LITTLE DIPPER)
Polaris (North Star)
DRACO
CEPHEUS
Deneb
CYGNUS
CASSIOPEIA
PERSEUS
Capella
AURIGA
CANCER
Castor
Pollux
GEMINI
Procyon
CANIS MINOR
ANDROMEDA
DELPHINUS
TRIANGULUM
PEGASUS
TAURUS
PLEIADES
Betelgeuse
ORION
Aldebaran
CANIS MAJOR
Sirius
Rigel
PISCES
AQUARIUS
CETUS

Winter Sky

To use this chart, hold it up in front of you and turn it so the direction you are facing is at the bottom of the chart. The chart works best at 35° N latitude, but it can be used at other latitudes. It works best at the following dates and times: December 1 at 10:00 P.M., January 1 at 8 P.M., and February 1 at 6 P.M.

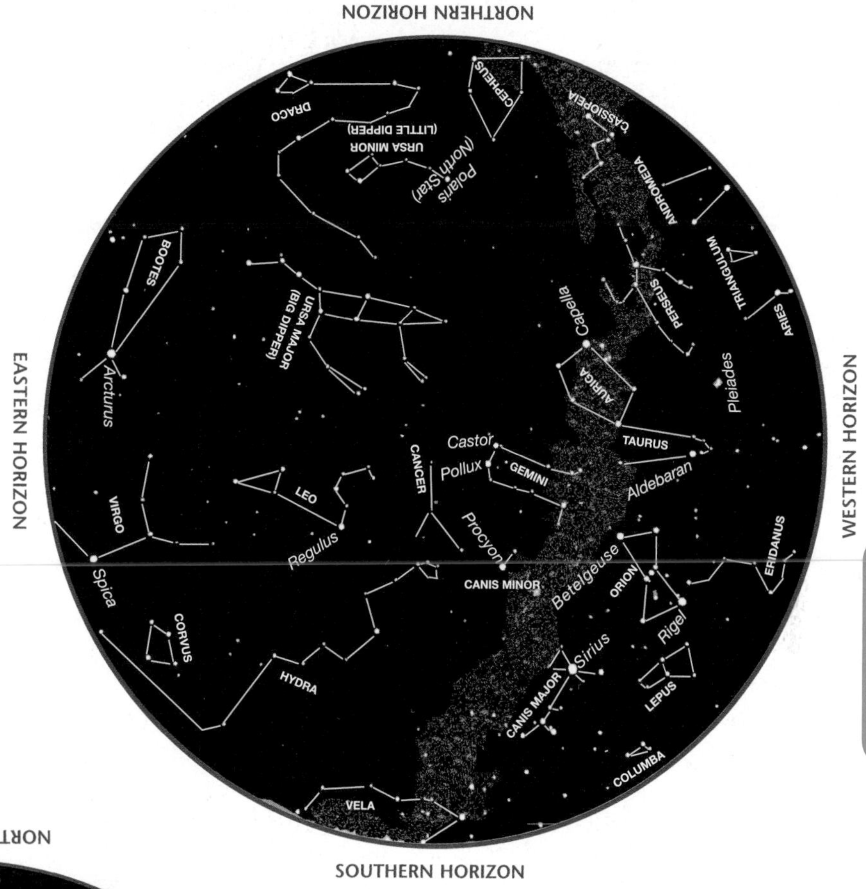
NORTHERN HORIZON
EASTERN HORIZON
WESTERN HORIZON
SOUTHERN HORIZON
CEPHEUS
DRACO
URSA MINOR
(LITTLE DIPPER)
Polaris
(North Star)
CASSIOPEIA
ANDROMEDA
TRIANGULUM
PERSEUS
ARIES
BOOTES
URSA MAJOR
(BIG DIPPER)
Capella
AURIGA
Pleiades
Arcturus
Castor
Pollux
GEMINI
TAURUS
CANCER
Aldebaran
LEO
VIRGO
Regulus
Procyon
ERIDANUS
Spica
CANIS MINOR
Betelgeuse
ORION
CORVUS
Rigel
Sirius
HYDRA
CANIS MAJOR
LEPUS
COLUMBA
VELA

Spring Sky

To use this chart, hold it up in front of you and turn it so the direction you are facing is at the bottom of the chart. The chart works best at 35° N latitude, but it can be used at other latitudes. It works best at the following dates and times: March 1 at 10:00 P.M. and April 1 at 8 P.M.

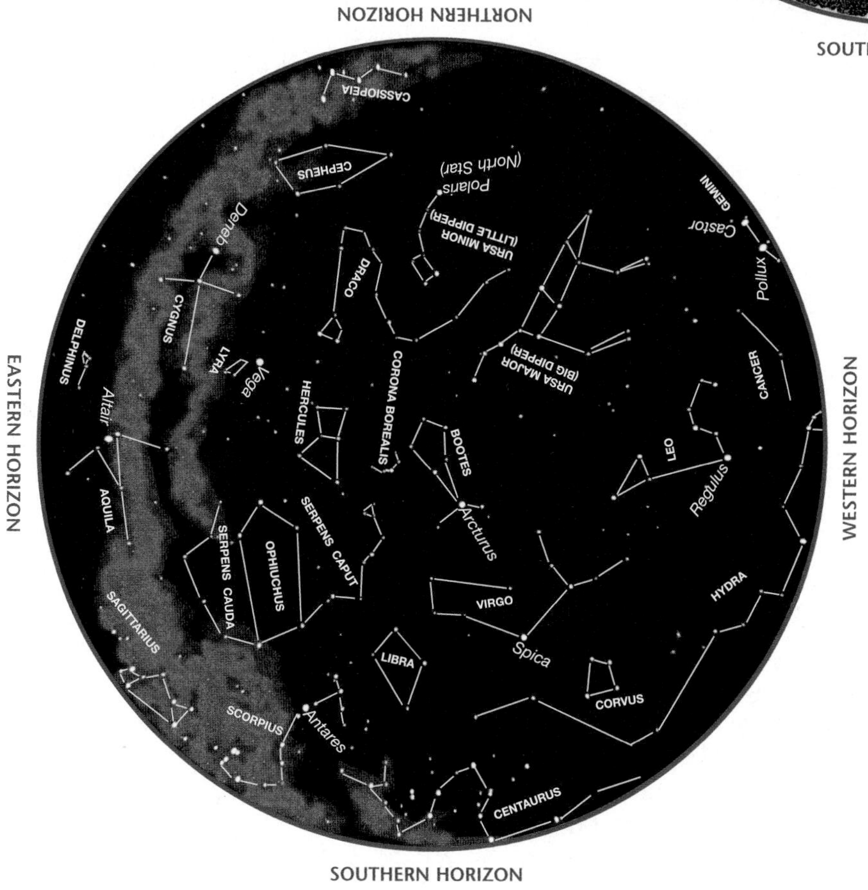
NORTHERN HORIZON
EASTERN HORIZON
WESTERN HORIZON
SOUTHERN HORIZON
CASSIOPEIA
CEPHEUS
Polaris
(North Star)
GEMINI
Castor
Deneb
URSA MINOR
(LITTLE DIPPER)
Pollux
DRACO
CYGNUS
DELPHINUS
LYRA
Vega
URSA MAJOR
(BIG DIPPER)
CORONA BOREALIS
CANCER
HERCULES
Altair
BOOTES
LEO
AQUILA
Regulus
Arcturus
SERPENS CAUDA
SERPENS CAPUT
OPHIUCHUS
SAGITTARIUS
HYDRA
VIRGO
Spica
LIBRA
CORVUS
SCORPIUS
Antares
CENTAURUS

Summer Sky

To use this chart, hold it up in front of you and turn it so the direction you are facing is at the bottom of the chart. The chart works best at 35° N latitude, but it can be used at other latitudes. It works best at the following dates and times: May 15 at 11:00 P.M. and June 15 at 9 P.M.

Appendices

Appendix I PROBLEM BANK

The following problems provide additional practice for solving equations and word problems. If you need help, look at the Math Skills Boxes on the referenced pages, where you will find solutions to similar problems.

Using Scientific Notation

(See Math Skills, page 15.)

1. The floor of a room measures 7.5 m by 6.0 m.
   a. What area of carpeting (in m^2) would you need to cover the entire floor? Express your answer in scientific notation.
   b. What would the area be in cm^2? (*Hint:* 10^4 $cm^2 = 1$ m^2).
   c. Suppose you want to tile the floor with square tiles that measure 30.5 cm on a side. How many tiles would you need? (*Hint:* Divide the total floor area by the area of a single tile.)
2. A mercury thermometer exchange program collected 1045 mercury thermometers in a month.
   a. If each thermometer contains 0.70 g of mercury, what is the total mass of mercury? Express your answer in scientific notation.
   b. A hazardous waste container holds 100.0 cm^3. Can this container hold all of the mercury? (*Hint:* Find the volume by dividing the mass by the density of mercury, 11.3 g/cm^3.)

The Combined Gas Law

(See Math Skills, page 80.)

1. The air in a bicycle tire is at a temperature of 11.0°C and a pressure of 542 kPa. What is the pressure in the tire if the temperature increases to 29.0°C while you ride the bicycle? Assume the volume of the tire does not change.
2. A helium tank holds 20.0 L of helium at a pressure of 3050 kPa. How many balloons can the tank fill if each balloon holds 2.0 L of gas at a pressure of 105 kPa? The balloons and the tank are both at room temperature. (*Hint:* Find the volume the helium in the tank would expand to if its pressure were reduced to 105 kPa. Then divide by the volume of one balloon.)

Formulas and Names for Compounds

(See Math Skills, page 174.)

1. Write the formulas for the ionic compounds lead(II) sulfide and lithium nitrate.
2. Name the molecular compounds with these formulas: NBr_3, SCl_2, and CCl_4.
3. Write the names for the ionic compounds $FeCl_2$ and $FeCl_3$.

Balancing Chemical Equations

(See Math Skills, page 195.)

Balance the following equations.

1. $H_2 + Cl_2 \rightarrow HCl$
2. $Ca(OH)_2 + HCl \rightarrow CaCl_2 + H_2O$
3. $Fe + O_2 \rightarrow Fe_3O_2$
4. $C_2H_4 + O_2 \rightarrow CO_2 + H_2O$

Balancing Nuclear Equations

(See Math Skills, page 295.)

1. Write a balanced nuclear equation for the beta decay of bismuth-210.
2. Write a balanced nuclear equation for the alpha decay of polonium-214.
3. Determine the product for the alpha decay of uranium-234.
4. What is the product of the beta decay of phosphorus-30?

Measuring Speed

(See Math Skills, page 333.)

1. A runner travels 3.0 kilometers in 24 minutes, then another 2.5 kilometers in 27 minutes, and finally 1.2 kilometers in 15 minutes. What is the runner's average speed?
2. A bus travels 140 km in 3.0 hours and then stops for a 30-minute rest stop. The bus then travels 120 km in 2.0 hours. What is the average speed for the entire trip?
3. A plane's average speed for a 300.0-km trip is 550 km/h. How long did the flight take?

Measuring Acceleration

(See Math Skills, page 346.)

1. During a crash, a bicycle racer moving at 17 m/s comes to a complete stop in 1.5 seconds. Calculate the bicycle's deceleration.
2. A ball is thrown straight up into the air. It comes to a rest at the highest point after 2.0 seconds. How fast was it going when it was thrown upward?

Newton's Second Law

(See Math Skills, page 367.)

1. A truck with a mass of 2200 kg accelerates when the traffic light turns green. If the net force on the truck is 3500 N in the forward direction, what is the truck's acceleration?
2. A bicycle with its rider has a total mass of 95 kg. If the bicycle accelerates at a rate of 2.0 m/s^2, what is the net force acting on the bicycle?
3. What net force is needed to accelerate a 9000-kg truck at the rate of 2.0 m/s^2?

Calculating Power

(See Math Skills, page 415.)

1. While lifting a box 0.75 m straight up, you exert an upward force of 320 N on the box. How much work do you do on the box? What is the power if you take 2.0 s to lift the box?
2. A dog sled is pulled at a constant horizontal speed of 8.0 m/s by a team of dogs. What is the power of the dogs if they are applying a constant horizontal force of 200.0 N to the sled? (*Hint:* Calculate the work done in one second).
3. How much work can a 500-watt engine do in 1.0 hour?

Calculating IMA and AMA

(See Math Skills, page 425.)

1. A crowbar is 0.75 m long and the fulcrum is located 10.0 cm from the end of the bar. What is the ideal mechanical advantage of the crowbar?
2. A person changing a tire exerts a force of 520 N on a car jack to apply a lifting force of 12,000 N. What is the actual mechanical advantage of the car jack?
3. A pair of pliers has an actual mechanical advantage of 3.5. If you were to squeeze the handles together with a force of 3.0 N, how much force would the jaws of the pliers exert?
4. If a machine has an efficiency of 35%, and you do 1500 J of work on the machine, what will be the work output of the machine?

Kinetic Energy

(See Math Skills, page 448.)

1. A 13,000-kg automobile moves at 28 m/s. What is the automobile's kinetic energy?
2. Two birds fly at the same speed, 4.0 m/s. One bird has a mass of 0.25 kg and the other has a mass of 0.75 kg. What is the kinetic energy of each bird?

Conservation of Energy

(See Math Skills, page 458.)

1. An 80.0-kg diver climbs a ladder up to a high-dive platform 10.0 meters above the ground.
   a. How much gravitational potential energy does the diver gain?
   b. After diving, what is the diver's speed at the water? Assume all of the potential energy has been converted to kinetic energy.
2. A 4.0-kg bowling ball returns to a bowler along a horizontal track at a speed of 5.0 m/s. At the end of the track, the ball must rise up an incline to a height of 1.0 m. Show that the ball has enough energy to make it to the top of the ramp. Assume friction can be ignored.

Specific Heat

(See Math Skills, page 477.)

1. How much heat is needed to raise the temperature of a plastic beaker by 10.0°C? The beaker's mass is 24.4 g and the specific heat of the plastic is 1.90 J/g•°C.
2. Tin has a specific heat of 0.23 J/g•°C. How much heat is needed to raise the temperature of 550 g of tin from 65°C to 125°C?
3. What mass of water will change its temperature by 10.0°C when 500.0 J of heat is added to it?

Speed of Mechanical Waves

(See Math Skills, page 506.)

1. A wave on a rope has a wavelength of 1.5 m and a frequency of 3.0 Hz. What is the speed of the wave?
2. A motorboat in a lake makes a surface wave with a frequency of 13 Hz and a wavelength of 0.15 m. What is the speed of the wave?
3. Seven ocean wave crests pass by a pier in 28.0 s. If the wave speed is 11 m/s, what is the wavelength of the waves?

Calculating Wave Speed

(See Math Skills, page 535.)

1. A cell phone transmits a carrier wave at a frequency 1900 MHz. What is the wavelength of the wave? (Assume the wave moves at the speed of light in a vacuum.)
2. A carrier wave from an FM station has a frequency 94.5 MHz. What is the wavelength?
3. A light-emitting diode (LED) emits light with a wavelength of 630 nanometers. What is the frequency of the light and what color is the LED?

Power, Voltage, and Current

(See Math Skills, page 611.)

1. A flashlight uses a 6.0-W light bulb connected to 3.6-V nickel-cadmium battery. How much current does the bulb use?
2. A hair dryer has a power rating of 1600 W. If it is connected to a 120-volt line, how much current does it draw?

Appendix J Selected Answers

Answers to even-numbered Math Practice and Section Assessment questions that involve calculations are given below. Use these answers to check your work.

Chapter 1

Math Practice, page 15

2. Distance = 2.6×10^{13} m

Section 1.3 Assessment, page 21

8. 1.5×10^{-4} cm^3

Chapter 3

Math Practice, page 80

2. $T_2 = 580$ K

Section 3.2 Assessment, page 81

10. $P_2 = 281$ kPa

Chapter 6

Math Practice, page 174

2. Cu_2S

4. sodium hydroxide

Section 6.3 Assessment, page 175

8. lithium chloride, barium oxide, sodium nitride, lead sulfate

10. K_2S

Chapter 7

Math Practice, page 195

2. $4Fe + 3O_2 \rightarrow 2Fe_2O_3$

Section 7.1 Assessment, page 198

10. $2Mg + O_2 \rightarrow 2MgO$

Chapter 10

Math Practice, page 295

2. ${}^{14}_{6}C \rightarrow {}^{14}_{7}N + {}^{0}_{-1}e$

4. ${}^{90}_{38}Sr \rightarrow {}^{90}_{39}Y + {}^{0}_{-1}e$

Section 10.1 Assessment, page 297

10. ${}^{226}_{88}Ra \rightarrow {}^{222}_{86}Rn + {}^{4}_{2}He$

Chapter 11

Math Practice, page 333

2. $v = 62$ km/h

Math Practice, page 346

2. $v_i = 14.7$ m/s

Section 11.3 Assessment, page 348

8. $v_i = 2.5$ m/s

Chapter 12

Math Practice, page 367

2. $a = 2$ m/s^2

4. $m = 50$ kg

Section 12.2 Assessment, page 369

6. Deceleration = 12 m/s^2

Chapter 14

Math Practice, page 415

2. Power = 7.5 W

Section 14.1 Assessment, page 416

8. Power = 50 W

Math Practice, page 425

2. AMA = 10

Section 14.3 Assessment, page 426

8. Efficiency = 80%

Chapter 15

Math Practice, page 448

2. 440 kJ

Section 15.1 Assessment, page 452

8. KE = 65 J

Math Practice, page 458

2a. PE = 2058 J

2b. $v = 7.7$ m/s

Section 15.2 Assessment, page 459

10. $h = 0.2$ m

Chapter 16

Math Practice, page 477

2. $Q = 34$ kJ

4. $\Delta T = 10.0$°C

Section 16.1 Assessment, page 478

10. $Q = 7.8$ kJ

Chapter 17

Math Practice, page 506

2. Speed = 2 m/s

4. Frequency = 0.5 Hz

Section 17.2 Assessment, page 507

10. Wavelength = 110 m

Chapter 18

Math Practice, page 535

2. Wavelength = 440 m

Section 18.1 Assessment, page 538

10. Wavelength = 370 m

Chapter 20

Math Practice, page 611

2. $I = 0.32$ amps

Section 20.3 Assessment, page 613

8. $I = 0.85$ amps

A

abrasion a form of mechanical weathering that occurs when rocks scrape or grind against one another (p. 710)
absolute age the time that has passed since a rock formed (p. 734)
absolute brightness a description of how bright a star really is; a characteristic property of a star that does not depend on the star's distance from Earth (p. 837)
absolute zero a temperature of 0 kelvins (pp. 78, 475)
absorption lines a set of dark lines that show frequencies at which light has been absorbed from a star's bright spectrum (p. 837)
acceleration the rate at which velocity changes (p. 342)
accretion the process of adding mass in the formation of the planets by collisions between planetesimals (p. 819)
accuracy the closeness of a measurement to the true value of what is measured (p. 19)
acid a compound that produces hydronium ions (H_3O^+) when dissolved in water; a proton donor (p. 241)
actual mechanical advantage the ratio of the output force to the input force in a machine (p. 422)
air mass a large body of air that has consistent properties throughout, such as temperature and moisture content, at a given altitude (p. 765)
air pressure the pressure caused by the weight of a column of air in Earth's atmosphere (p. 748)
air resistance fluid friction acting on an object moving through the air (p. 360)
alkali metals the elements in Group 1A of the periodic table, not including hydrogen (p. 140)
alkaline earth metals the elements in Group 2A of the periodic table (p. 141)
alloy a mixture of two or more elements, at least one of which is a metal, that has the characteristic properties of a metal (p. 178)
alluvial fan a fan-shaped deposit of sediment, on land formed as a stream flows out of the mountains and onto a plain (p. 716)
alpha particle a positively charged particle, emitted by certain radioactive nuclei, made up of two protons and two neutrons; a helium nucleus (p. 293)
alternating current (AC) a flow of electric charge that regularly reverses its direction (p. 604)
amino acids compounds that contain both carboxyl and amino functional groups (p. 280)
amplitude the maximum displacement of a medium from the rest position (p. 507)
amplitude modulation (AM) a method of transmitting a radio signal in which the amplitude of the carrier wave varies while its frequency remains the same (p. 541)
analog signal a smoothly varying signal produced by continuously changing the voltage or current in a circuit (p. 619)
angle of incidence the angle an incident ray makes with a line perpendicular to a surface it strikes (p. 570)
angle of reflection the angle a reflected ray makes with a line perpendicular to a surface it strikes (p. 570)
angle of refraction the angle a light ray makes with the normal after it enters a new medium at an angle (p. 575)
anion an ion with a negative charge (p. 160)
anticyclone a weather system with a swirling center of high air pressure (p. 769)
antinode a point of maximum displacement midway between two nodes in a standing wave (p. 512)
apparent brightness the brightness of a star as it appears from Earth (p. 836)
aquifer a permeable rock layer that is saturated with water (p. 707)
Archimedes' principle the equivalence of the buoyant force on an object and the weight of the fluid displaced by the object (p. 401)
aromatic hydrocarbons hydrocarbons that contain a ring structure similar to benzene (p. 266)
asteroid belt region between the orbits of Mars and Jupiter where most asteroids in the solar system are found (p. 809)
asteroids small, rocky solar-system bodies, most of which are found orbiting the sun in a region between Mars and Jupiter (p. 809)
asthenosphere a layer of softer, weaker rock beneath Earth's lithosphere, which can flow slowly (p. 662)
astigmatism an eye condition in which objects at any distance appear blurry because of the distorted shape of the cornea (p. 592)
astronomical unit (AU) a unit of distance that equals the average distance from Earth to the sun; 149,598,000 kilometers (p. 793)
astronomy the study of the universe beyond Earth (p. 4)
atmosphere the layer of gases that surrounds Earth (p. 747)
atom the smallest particle of an element (p. 39)
atomic mass unit (amu) one twelfth the mass of a carbon-12 atom (p. 134)
atomic number a unique number for each element that equals the number of protons in an atom of that element (p. 110)
aurora a colorful display of light in the ionosphere, produced when charged particles from the sun are attracted to Earth's magnetic poles (p. 751)
average speed the total distance traveled divided by the time it takes to travel that distance (p. 333)

B

background radiation nuclear radiation that occurs naturally in the environment (p. 296)
barometer an instrument used to measure air pressure (p. 748)
barred-spiral galaxy a spiral galaxy in which spiral arms extend outward from a bar running through the center of the galaxy (p. 848)
base a compound that produces hydroxide ions (OH^-) when dissolved in water; a proton acceptor (p. 242)
batholith the largest type of intrusive igneous rock mass (p. 696)
battery a device that converts chemical energy into electrical energy (p. 606)
beta particle an electron emitted by an unstable nucleus (p. 294)
big bang theory the theory of the beginning of the universe in an instant, billions of years ago, in an enormous explosion (p. 854)
binary star a star system with two stars that revolve around each other (p. 847)
biology the study of life and life processes (p. 4)
biomass energy the chemical energy stored in living things (p. 464)
black hole an object whose surface gravity is so great that not even electromagnetic waves can escape from it (p. 844)
boiling point the temperature at which a substance boils; the temperature at which vapor pressure is equal to atmospheric pressure (p. 47)
Boyle's law the inverse variation of the volume of a gas with its pressure if the temperature and the number of particles are constant (p. 79)
buffer a solution that is resistant to large changes in pH (p. 248)
buoyancy the ability of a fluid to exert an upward force on an object placed in it (p. 400)
buoyant force an upward force acting on an object in a fluid (p. 400)

C

caldera huge depression at the top of a volcano created when the central vent and magma chamber collapse after an eruption (p. 691)
calorimeter instrument used to measure thermal energy released or absorbed during a chemical or physical change (p. 478)
camera an optical instrument that records an image of an object (p. 582)
carbohydrate a compound composed of carbon, hydrogen, and oxygen in which the ratio of hydrogen to oxygen atoms is 2 : 1 (p. 278)
catalyst a substance that affects the rate of a chemical reaction without being used up in the reaction (p. 215)
cation an ion with a positive charge (p. 160)
central heating system a heating system that heats many rooms from one central location (p. 489)
centripetal force a force that continuously changes the direction of an object to make it move in a circle (p. 381)
chain reaction a series of fission reactions triggered by neutrons released during the fission of a nucleus (p. 311)
Charles's law the direct proportion of the volume of a gas to its temperature (in kelvins) if the pressure and the number of particles of the gas are constant (p. 78)
chemical bond the force that holds atoms or ions together as a unit (p. 160)
chemical change change that occurs when a substance reacts and forms one or more new substances (p. 56)
chemical energy the energy stored in chemical bonds (pp. 206, 451)
chemical equation a representation of a chemical reaction in which the reactants and products are expressed as formulas (p. 193)
chemical formula notation that shows what elements a compound contains and the ratio of the atoms or ions of these elements in the compound (p. 161)
chemical property any property that produces a change in the composition of matter (p. 54)
chemical weathering the process in which rock is broken down by chemical reactions (p. 710)
chemistry the study of the composition, structure, properties, and reactions of matter (p. 4)
chromosphere the middle layer of the sun's atmosphere, just outside the photosphere (p. 831)
cinder cone a small, steep-sided volcano formed from a combination of ash and cinders (p. 693)
circuit breaker a switch that opens when the current in a circuit is too high (p. 612)
cirque a large bowl-shaped valley carved out of a mountainside by a glacier (p. 720)
cirrus clouds thin, white, wispy clouds, often with a feathery or veil-like appearance (p. 763)
clastic rocks sedimentary rocks that form from the broken fragments of other rocks (p. 672)
cleavage a mineral's tendency to split along regular, well-defined planes (p. 668)
climate the long-term weather conditions of a place or region (p. 778)
cloud a dense, visible mass of tiny water droplets or ice crystals that are suspended in the atmosphere (p. 761)

coefficients numbers that appear before a formula in a chemical equation to show the relative proportions of each reactant and product (p. 194)
coherent light light waves having the same wavelength, with the crests and troughs lined up (p. 560)
cold front a front that occurs when a cold air mass overtakes a warm air mass (p. 767)
colloid a mixture that contains some particles that are intermediate in size between the small particles in a solution and the larger particles in a suspension (p. 44)
combustion reaction a chemical reaction in which a substance reacts rapidly with oxygen, often producing heat and light (p. 204)
comet a mass of rock, dust, and ice that partially vaporizes when it passes near the sun (p. 815)
complementary colors of light any two colors of light that combine to form white light (p. 552)
complementary colors of pigments any two colors of pigments that combine to make black pigment (p. 553)
composite volcano a volcano that forms from a combination of lava and ash (p. 693)
compound a substance that is made from two or more simpler substances and can be broken down into those simpler substances (p. 40)
compound machine a combination of two or more simple machines that operate together (p. 435)
compression an area of a longitudinal wave where the particles of the medium are close together (p. 502)
computer a programmable device that can store and process information (p. 622)
concave lens a lens that is curved inward at the center and is thickest at the outside edges (p. 576)
concave mirror a mirror that is curved inward (p. 572)
concentration the amount of solute dissolved in a certain amount of solvent (p. 238)
condensation the phase change in which a substance changes from a gas or vapor to a liquid (p. 90)
conduction the transfer of thermal with no overall transfer of matter, within a material or between materials that are touching (p. 479); the transfer of electric charge by direct contact with a conductor (p. 602)
conductivity a material's ability to allow heat or electric charges to flow (p. 46)
cones light-sensitive neurons in the retina that detect color (p. 589)
constant acceleration a steady change in velocity (p. 345)
constellation a group of stars that appears to form a pattern as seen from Earth (p. 846)
constructive interference the interaction among two or more waves in which displacements combine to produce a wave with a larger displacement (p. 511)
continental drift the process in which the continents move slowly across Earth's surface (p. 677)
continental glacier a thick sheet of ice that covers a large area of a continent or large island (p. 719)
continental shelf the gently sloping plain that forms an apron of shallow water along the edges of most continents (p. 726)
controlled experiment an experiment in which only one variable, the manipulated variable, is deliberately changed at a time (p. 8)
convection the transfer of thermal energy when particles of a fluid move from one place to another (p. 480)
convection current circulation of a fluid in a loop as the fluid alternately heats up and cools down (p. 481)
convection zone the region inside the sun where thermal engergy is transferred outward mainly by convection currents (p. 831)
convergent boundary a boundary at which tectonic plates collide (p. 682)
conversion factor a ratio of equivalent measurements that is used to convert a quantity from one unit to another (p. 18)
convex lens a lens that is curved outward at the center and is thinnest at the outside edges (p. 576)
convex mirror a mirror that is curved outward (p. 573)
core the dense sphere at Earth's center, made mostly of iron and nickel (p. 663); the central region of the sun where nuclear fusion occurs (p. 830)
Coriolis effect the change that Earth's rotation causes in the motion of objects (p. 759)
cornea the transparent outer coating of the eye (p. 588)
corona the outermost layer of the sun's atmosphere, extending far above the chromosphere (p. 831)
covalent bond a chemical bond in which two atoms share a pair of valence electrons (p. 166)
crater a bowl-shaped pit at the top of the central vent in a volcano (p. 691); a round depression in the surface of a planet, moon, asteroid, or comet, caused by the impact of a meteoroid (p. 797)
crest the highest point of a transverse wave (p. 501)
critical angle the angle of incidence that produces an angle of refraction equal to 90 degrees (p. 578)
critical mass the smallest possible mass of a fissionable material that can sustain a chain reaction (p. 311)
crust the rocky outer layer of Earth (p. 661)
crystals solids whose particles are arranged in a lattice structure (p. 162)
cumulus clouds puffy white clouds, usually with flat bottoms, that look like piles of cotton balls (p. 763)
cyclone a weather system with a center of low air pressure (p. 769)

D

dark matter matter that does not emit radiation that astronomers can detect (p. 855)
decibel a unit that compares the intensities of different sounds (p. 515)
decomposition reaction a chemical reaction in which a compound breaks down into two or more simpler substances (p. 200)
deflation the process that occurs when wind picks up and removes surface material (p. 723)
delta a mass of sediment deposited at the mouth of a river where the river enters a large body of water (p. 716)
density the ratio of a material's mass to its volume (p. 17)
density currents currents caused by differences in the density of ocean water (p. 727)
deposition the phase change in which a gas or vapor changes directly into a solid without first changing into a liquid (p. 91); the placement of sediment that has been transported from another location (p. 713)
desert an extremely dry region (p. 780)
destructive interference the interaction among two or more waves in which displacements combine to produce a wave with a smaller displacement (p. 511)
dew point the temperature at which air becomes saturated with water vapor (p. 761)
diffraction the bending of a wave as it moves around an obstacle or passes through a narrow opening (p. 510)
diffuse reflection reflection that occurs when parallel light waves strike a rough, uneven surface and reflect in many different directions (p. 547)
digital signal a signal that encodes information as a string of 1's and 0's (p. 619)
dike a structure formed when magma hardens in a crack that cuts across rock layers (p. 696)
diode a solid-state component with an n-type semiconductor joined to a p-type semiconductor (p. 621)
direct current (DC) a flow of electric charge in only one direction (p. 604)
direct proportion a relationship between two variables in which their ratio is constant (p. 23)
dispersion the process of dissolving by breaking into smaller pieces (p. 230), the process in which white light separates into colors (p. 551)
dissociation the separation of ions in an ionic compound as the compound dissolves (p. 229)
distance the length of the path between two points (p. 329)
distillation a process that separates the substances in a solution based on their boiling points (p. 50)
divergent boundary a boundary at which tectonic plates move away from each other (p. 682)
Doppler effect a change in sound frequency caused by motion of the sound source, motion of the listener, or both (p. 516)
double-replacement reaction a chemical reaction in which two compounds exchange positive ions and form two new compounds (p. 203)
dunes deposits formed from windblown sand (p. 724)

E

earthquake a movement of Earth's crust that occurs when rocks in the crust suddenly shift, releasing stored energy (p. 684)
eclipse event that occurs when the shadow of one body in space, such as a planet or moon, falls on another (p. 799)
ecliptic plane the plane in space containing Earth's orbit (p. 792)
efficiency the percentage of the work input that becomes work output in a machine (p. 425)
elastic potential energy the potential energy of an object that is stretched or compressed (p. 450)
electric charge a property that causes subatomic particles such as protons and electrons to attract or repel one another (p. 600)
electric circuit a complete path through which electric charge can flow (p. 609)
electric current a continuous flow of electric charge (p. 604)
electric field a field in a region of space that exerts electric forces on charged particles; a field produced by electric charges or by changing magnetic fields (pp. 533, 602)
electric force the attraction or repulsion between electrically charged objects (p. 601)
electric motor a device that uses an electromagnet to turn an axle (p. 639)
electric power the rate at which electrical energy is converted to another form of energy (p. 611)
electrical conductor a material through which electric charge can flow easily (p. 605)
electrical energy the energy associated with electric charges (p. 452)
electrical insulator a material through which charge cannot flow easily (p. 605)
electrolyte a compound that produces ions when it dissolves (p. 249)
electromagnet a solenoid with a ferromagnetic core (p. 637)
electromagnetic energy a form of energy consisting of changing electric and magnetic fields (p. 452)

Glossary

electromagnetic force a force associated with charged particles, which has two aspects, electric force and magnetic force (pp. 378, 635)
electromagnetic induction the process of generating a current by moving an electrical conductor relative to a magnetic field (p. 642)
electromagnetic radiation the transfer of energy by electromagnetic waves (p. 533)
electromagnetic spectrum the full range of electromagnetic radiation (p. 540)
electromagnetic wave a transverse wave consisting of changing electric and changing magnetic fields (p. 533)
electron a negatively charged subatomic particle that is found in the space outside the nucleus of an atom (p. 108)
electron cloud a visual model of the most likely locations for the electrons in an atom (p. 116)
electron configuration the arrangement of electrons in the orbitals of an atom (p. 118)
electron dot diagram a diagram of an atom, ion or molecule in which each dot represents a valence electron (p. 158)
electronics the science of using electric currents to process or transmit information (p. 618)
electronic signal information sent as patterns in the controlled flow of electrons through a circuit (p. 618)
element a substance that cannot be broken down into simpler substances (p. 39)
elliptical galaxies spherical or oval-shaped galaxies with no trace of spiral arms and very little gas or dust between stars (p. 848)
El Niño the periodic warming of water in the central and eastern Pacific Ocean (p. 781)
endothermic a description of a change in which a system absorbs engergy from its surroundings (p. 86)
endothermic reaction a chemical reaction that absorbs energy from its surroundings (p. 209)
energy the ability to do work (p. 447)
energy conservation the practice of finding ways to use less energy or to use energy more efficiently (p. 466)
energy conversion the process of changing energy from one form to another (p. 454)
energy levels the possible energies that electrons in an atom can have (p. 114)
enzyme a protein that acts as a catalyst for reactions in cells (p. 284)
epicenter the point on Earth's surface directly above the focus of an earthquake (p. 686)
equilibrium a state in which the forward and reverse paths of a physical or chemical change take place at the same rate (p. 216)
equinox a day that marks the beginning of spring or autumn; a day on which the length of daylight and darkness are approximately equal (p. 754)
era a major stage in Earth's geologic history (p. 734)
erosion the process that wears down and carries away rock and soil (p. 709)
evaporation the process that changes a substance from a liquid to a gas at temperatures below the substance's boiling point (p. 89)
exothermic a description of a change in which a system releases energy to its surroundings (p. 86)
exothermic reaction a chemical reaction that releases energy to its surroundings (p. 208)
external combustion engine a heat engine in which the fuel burns outside the engine (p. 486)
extinct a description of a type of organism that is no longer found living on Earth (p. 733)
extrusive rock an igneous rock that forms at Earth's surface (p. 671)

F

farsightedness an eye condition that causes nearby objects to be blurry (p. 592)
fault a break in Earth's crust (p. 685)
ferromagnetic material a material that can be magnetized because it contains magnetic domains (p. 632)
filtration a process that separates materials based on the size of their particles (p. 50)
fission a nuclear reaction in which an atomic nucleus is split into two smaller parts (p. 309)
flammability a material's ability to burn in the presence of oxygen (p. 54)
flood plain the flat area along a stream that is covered only during floods (p. 716)
fluid a substance or mixture that flows and has no shape of its own (p. 391)
fluid friction a friction force that opposes the motion of an object through a fluid (p. 360)
fluorescence a process in which phosphorescent material converts radiation into visible light (p. 559)
focal point the point at which light rays parallel to the axis of a mirror or lens meet or appear to meet (p. 572)
focus the location beneath Earth's surface where an earthquake begins (p. 686)
fog a cloud that is touching or is near to the ground (p. 762)
fold a bend in layers of rock (p. 685)
foliated rock a metamorphic rock with crystals arranged in parallel bands (p. 674)
force a push or a pull that acts on an object (p. 356)
fossil the preserved remains or traces of a living organism (p. 732)

fossil fuels rich deposits of hydrocarbon mixtures that formed from the remains of organisms (p. 267, p. 462)
fracture the way a mineral breaks, determined by the mineral's crystal structure (p. 668)
frame of reference a system of objects that are not moving with respect to one another (p. 328)
free fall the movement of an object toward Earth because of gravity (p. 343)
frequency the number of complete cycles per unit time for a periodic motion (p. 504)
frequency modulation (FM) a method of transmitting a radio signal in which the frequency of the carrier wave varies while its amplitude remains the same (p. 541)
friction a force that opposes the motion of objects that touch as they move past each other (p. 359)
front a sharply defined boundary that forms when two unlike air masses meet (p. 767)
fulcrum the fixed point a lever rotates around (p. 428)
functional group an atom or group of atoms that determines the properties of an organic compound (p. 272)
fuse a device that prevents overheating due to current overload in a circuit (p. 612)
fusion a nuclear reaction in which the nuclei of two atoms combine to form a larger nucleus (p. 315)

G

galaxy a huge group of stars, star systems, star clusters, dust, and gas bound together by gravity (p. 848)
galvanometer a device that uses an electromagnet to measure small amounts of current (p. 638)
gamma ray a penetrating form of radiation emitted by an unstable nucleus (p. 294)
gas the state of matter in which a material has neither a definite shape nor a definite volume (p. 70)
gas giant a large, massive planet (such as Jupiter, Saturn, Uranus, or Neptune) that is composed mainly of hydrogen and helium (p. 811)
generator a device that converts mechanical energy into electrical energy by the relative motion of a coil of wire with respect to a magnetic field (p. 643)
geocentric a description of a model of the solar system in which all of the planets revolve around Earth (p. 791)
geologists scientists who study Earth and the processes that have shaped Earth over time (p. 660)
geology the study of the origin, history, and structure of Earth (p. 4)
geothermal energy thermal energy beneath Earth's surface (p. 464)
giant a large, massive, bright star that is somewhat smaller and fainter than a supergiant (p. 839)
glacier a large mass of ice and snow moving on land (p. 706)
global warming an increase in the temperature of Earth's lower atmosphere, caused in part by increased levels of carbon dioxide or water vapor (p. 782)
global wind a wind that blows over long distances from a specific direction (p. 758)
globular cluster a large spherical-shaped group of older stars that usually lacks sufficient amounts of gas and dust to form new stars (p. 847)
gravitational force an attractive force that acts between any two objects (p. 380)
gravitational potential energy potential energy that depends upon an object's height above a reference point (p. 449)
gravity the attraction between any two objects because of their masses (p. 361)
greenhouse effect a process in which gases in Earth's atmosphere, such as water vapor and carbon dioxide, allow visible light to pass through but absorb reradiated infrared radiation that warms the lower atmosphere (p. 755)
ground state a state in which all the electrons in an atom have the lowest possible energies (p. 118)
grounding the transfer of excess charge through a conductor to Earth (p. 613)
groundwater the fresh water found beneath Earth's surface within cracks and among particles of rock and soil (p. 704)
group a column of elements in a periodic table (p. 131)

H

half-life the time required for one half of a sample of a radioactive isotope to decay (p. 299)
halogens the elements in Group 7A of the periodic table (p. 144)
hardness the resistance of a mineral to scratching (p. 668)
heat the transfer of thermal energy from one object to another because of a difference in temperature (p. 474)
heat engine any device that converts thermal energy into work (p. 483)
heat of fusion the energy a substance must absorb in order to change from a solid to a liquid (p. 86)
heat of vaporization the energy a substance must absorb in order to change from a liquid to a gas (p. 88)
heat pump a device that uses work to transfer thermal energy from a colder area to a warmer area (p. 490)
heliocentric a description of a model of the solar system in which Earth and other planets revolve around the sun (p. 791)
hertz (Hz) the unit of measure for frequency, equal to one cycle per second (p. 504)
heterogeneous mixture a type of mixture in which the parts of the mixture are noticeably different from one another (p. 41)

homogeneous mixture a type of mixture in which the substances are so evenly distributed that it is difficult to distinguish one substance in the mixture from another (p. 42)

horsepower (hp) a common unit of power, equal to about 746 watts (p. 416)

hot spot a region where a rising column of magma extends from beneath the lithosphere to reach Earth's surface (p. 693)

H-R diagram the Hertzsprung-Russell diagram, a graph of the surface temperature versus absolute brightness of a sample of stars (p. 838)

Hubble's Law the direct variation of the speed at which a galaxy is moving away from Earth with its distance from Earth (p. 853)

humidity the amount of water vapor in a given volume of air (p. 760)

hurricane a large tropical cyclone with winds of at least 119 kilometers per hour (74 miles per hour) (p. 771)

hydraulic action the process by which ocean waves erode rock (p. 728)

hydraulic system a device that uses a pressurized fluid acting on pistons of different sizes to increase force (p. 395)

hydrocarbon an organic compound that contains only the elements hydrogen and carbon (p. 264)

hydroelectric energy energy obtained from flowing water (p. 463)

hydrogen fuel cell a cell that generates electricity from a controlled reaction between hydrogen and oxygen (p. 464)

hypothesis a proposed answer to a question (p. 8)

I

ice ages periods when climates are colder than usual and glaciers cover a large portion of Earth's surface (p. 781)

ideal mechanical advantage (IMA) the mechanical advantage of a machine in the absence of friction (p. 423)

igneous rock rock that forms from magma or lava (p. 671)

image a copy of an object formed by reflected or refracted rays of light (p. 547)

impermeable a description of a material through which water cannot easily pass (p. 707)

incandescent a description of an object hot enough to glow (p. 558)

inclined plane a slanted surface along which a force moves an object to a different elevation (p. 431)

index fossil a fossil of a species that is easily identified, occurred over a large area, and lived for a well-defined period of time (p. 733)

index of refraction the ratio of the speed of light in a vacuum to the speed of light in a medium (p. 575)

indicator a substance that changes color in the presence of an acid or a base (p. 241)

induction the transfer of charge without contact between materials (p. 603)

inertia the tendency of an object to resist a change in its motion (p. 364)

inorganic a description of a material that is not organic (p. 665)

input arm the distance between the fulcrum in a lever and the input force (p. 428)

input distance the distance through which the input force acts in a machine (p. 419)

input force the force exerted on a machine (p. 419)

instantaneous speed the rate at which an object is moving at a given moment in time (p. 334)

integrated circuit a thin slice of silicon that contains many solid-state components; a microchip (p. 622)

intensity the rate at which a wave's energy flows through a given unit of area (pp. 515, 538)

interference the interaction of two or more waves that combine in a region of overlap (p. 510)

internal combustion engine a heat engine in which the fuel burns inside the engine (p. 487)

intrusive rock an igneous rock that forms underground from hardened magma (p. 671)

inverse proportion a relationship in which the product of two variables is a constant when all other variables are held constant (p. 23)

ion an atom or group of atoms that has a positive or negative charge (p. 159)

ionic bond the force that holds cations and anions together (p. 160)

ionization the process by which neutral molecules gain or lose electrons (p. 230)

ionosphere a region of charged particles, or ions, in Earth's atmosphere that overlaps the lower thermosphere (p. 751)

iris the colored part at the front of the eye, which expands and contracts to control the amount of light entering the eye (p. 589)

irregular galaxy a galaxy with a disorganized appearance (p. 848)

isobar a line on a weather map that connects points of equal air pressure (p. 777)

isotherm a line on a weather map that connects points of equal air temperature (p. 777)

isomers organic compounds with the same molecular formula but with different structural formulas (p. 265)

isotopes atoms of a given element that have different numbers of neutrons and different mass numbers (p. 112)

J

jet stream a belt of high-speed wind in the upper troposphere (p. 759)
joule (J) the SI unit of work, equal to 1 newton-meter (p. 414)

K

kinetic energy the energy an object has due to its motion (pp. 71, 447)
Kuiper belt a wide belt beyond Pluto's orbit where objects mostly made of ice and rock orbit the sun (p. 815)

L

land breeze a local wind that occurs when cooler air over land moves toward water (p. 757)
laser a device that generates a beam of coherent light (p. 560)
lava magma that flows over Earth's surface (p. 671)
lava plateau a high, level region of hardened lava (p. 696)
law of conservation of charge law stating that the total electric charge in an isolated system is constant; electric charge is never created or destroyed (p. 602)
law of conservation of momentum law stating that the total momentum of a system does not change if no net force acts on the system (p. 376)
law of superposition law stating that in rock layers that are undisturbed, younger rocks lie above older rocks, and the oldest rocks are at the bottom (p. 733)
length the straight-line distance between two points (p. 16)
lens an object made of any thin, transparent material that has one or two curved surfaces that can refract light (p. 576)
lever a rigid bar that is free to move around a fixed point (p. 428)
lift an upward force due to a pressure difference between the top and bottom of a wing (p. 396)
lightning a sudden naturally occurring electrical discharge in the atmosphere (p. 770)
light-year the distance that light travels in a vacuum in a year, about 9.5 trillion kilometers (p. 834)
linear graph a graph in which the displayed data form a straight line (p. 347)
liquid the state of matter in which a material has a definite volume but not a definite shape (p. 69)
lithosphere a layer of relatively cool, rigid rock that includes the uppermost part of the mantle as well as Earth's crust (p. 662)
local wind a wind that blows over a short distance (p. 757)
loess a deposit formed from windblown dust (p. 724)
longitudinal wave a wave in which the vibration of the medium is parallel to the direction the wave travels (p. 502)
longshore drift the process by which ocean waves move sand along a shore (p. 729)
loudness a physical response to the intensity of sound, modified by physical factors (p. 515)
luminous a description of an object that gives off its own light (p. 558)
luster the way a mineral's surface reflects light (p. 667)

M

machine a device that changes a force (p. 417)
magma a mixture of molten rock and gases, including water vapor, which forms underground (p. 671)
magma chamber pocket in which magma collects before a volcanic eruption (p. 691)
magnetic domain a region that has a large number of atoms with aligned magnetic fields (p. 632)
magnetic field a field in a region of space that exerts magnetic forces; a field produced by magnets, by changing electric fields, or by moving charges (pp. 533, 631)
magnetic force the force a magnetic field exerts on a magnet, on a ferromagnetic material, or on a moving electric charge (p. 630)
magnetic pole a region on a magnet where the force produced by the magnet is strongest (p. 630)
magnetosphere the area surrounding Earth that is influenced by Earth's magnetic field (p. 632)
main sequence a diagonal band on the H-R diagram, which represents about 90% of all stars (p. 839)
malleability the ability of a solid to be hammered without shattering (p. 46)
manipulated variable the variable that causes a change in another variable (p. 8)
mantle a thick layer of hot but solid rock beneath Earth's crust (p. 662)
maria the low, flat plains of basalt on the moon formed by ancient lunar lava flows (p. 797)
mass the amount of matter in an object (p. 16); a measure of the inertia of an object, which depends on the amount of matter the object contains (p. 365)
mass extinction a boundary between geologic eras when many different kinds of organisms became extinct within a relatively short time (p. 735)
mass movement the downward movement of rock and soil due to gravity, including landslides, mudflows, creep, and slumping (p. 712)
mass number the sum of the number of protons and neutrons in the nucleus of an atom (p. 110)

Glossary

meander a looplike bend in a river formed when slow-moving water deposits sediment on the inside curve of the river (p. 716)
mechanical advantage the number of times that a machine increases an input force (p. 421)
mechanical energy the energy associated with the motion and position of everyday objects (p. 450)
mechanical wave a disturbance in matter that carries energy from one place to another (p. 500)
mechanical weathering the process of physically breaking rock into smaller fragments (p. 710)
medium the material through which a wave travels (p. 500)
melting point the temperature at which a substance changes from solid to liquid (p. 47)
mesosphere the lower portion of Earth's mantle (p. 662); the layer of Earth's atmosphere immediately above the stratosphere (p. 750)
metals elements that are good conductors of heat and electric current (p. 135)
metallic bond the attraction between a metal cation and the shared electrons that surround it (p. 176)
metalloids elements with properties that fall between those of metals and nonmetals (p. 136)
metamorphic rock rock that has been changed by temperature, pressure, or reactions with hot water (p. 674)
meteoroid a chunk of rock that moves through the solar system (p. 797)
meteorologist scientist who studies and tries to predict weather (p. 774)
microscope an optical instrument that uses lenses to provide enlarged images of very small, near objects (p. 584)
mid-ocean ridge a chain of underwater mountains (p. 678)
mineral a naturally occurring, inorganic solid with a crystal structure and a definite chemical composition (p. 665)
mirage a false or distorted image (p. 548)
model a representation of an object or event (p. 10)
molarity the number of moles of a dissolved solute per liter of solution (p. 239)
molar mass the mass of one mole of a substance (p. 196)
mole an amount of a substance that contains approximately 6.02×10^{23} particles of the substance (p. 195)
molecule a neutral group of atoms that are joined together by one or more covalent bonds (p. 166)
momentum the product of an object's mass and its velocity (p. 374)
monomer a small organic molecule that joins with other monomers to form a polymer (p. 275)
monsoon a wind system that shows a seasonal reversal of direction (p. 759)
moon a relatively small natural body in space that revolves around a planet (p. 792)
moraines mounds of till formed at the downhill end of a glacier and along its sides (p. 721)

N

neap tide a tide at the first or last quarter moon, when there is the least change between daily high and low tides (p. 801)
nearsightedness an eye condition in which distant objects are blurry (p. 590)
nebula a large cloud of gas and dust spread out over a large volume of space (p. 840)
net force the overall force acting on an object after all the forces are combined (p. 357)
network solid a solid in which all the atoms are linked by covalent bonds (p. 263)
neutralization a chemical reaction between an acid and a base (p. 244)
neutron a neutral subatomic particle that is found in the nucleus of an atom (p. 109)
neutron star the dense core left after a high-mass star has exploded as a supernova (p. 844)
newton (N) the SI unit for force, equal to the force that causes a 1-kilogram mass to accelerate at a rate of 1 meter per second squared ($1\ N = 1\ kg{\cdot}m/s^2$) (p. 357)
noble gases the elements in Group 8A of the periodic table (p. 145)
node a point on a standing wave that has no displacement from the rest position (p. 512)
nonlinear graph a graph in which the displayed data form a curved line (p. 348)
nonmetals elements that are poor conductors of heat and electric current (p. 136)
nonrenewable energy resource a source of energy that exists in limited quantities and, once used, cannot be replaced except over the course of millions of years (p. 462)
nuclear energy the energy stored in atomic nuclei (p. 452)
nuclear radiation charged particles and electromagnetic waves that are emitted from the nuclei of radioisotopes (p. 293)
nucleic acid a large, nitrogen-containing polymer, found mainly in the nuclei of cells (p. 279)
nucleus the dense, positively charged mass located in the center of an atom (p. 105)

O

observation information obtained through the senses (p. 8)
occluded front a front that occurs when a warm air mass is caught between two cooler air masses (p. 768)
Ohm's law the relationship of voltage, current, and resistance: $V = IR$ (p. 607)
Oort cloud thought to be a very sparse sphere of comets encircling the solar system out to a distance of about 50,000 AU (p. 815)
opaque a description of a material that either absorbs or reflects all of the light that strikes it so nothing can be seen through it (p. 547)
orbital a region of space around the nucleus where an electron is likely to be found (p. 117)
organic compounds compounds that contain carbon and hydrogen, often combined with a few other elements such as oxygen or nitrogen (p. 262)
output arm the distance between the fulcrum in a lever and the output force (p. 428)
output distance the distance an output force acts through in a machine (p. 420)
output force the force exerted by a machine (p. 420)
oxbow lake a lake formed when a river forms a new path by cutting off a meander loop from the rest of the river (p. 716)
oxidation-reduction (redox) reaction a chemical reaction in which electrons are transferred from one reactant to another (p. 204)
ozone layer a region of ozone concentration in the stratosphere (p. 750)

P

Pangaea an ancient supercontinent formed about 300 million years ago, which later gave rise to today's continents (p. 677)
parallax an apparent change in position of an object with respect to a distant background when viewed from different locations (p. 835)
parallel circuit an electric circuit with two or more paths through which charge can flow (p. 610)
pascal (Pa) the SI unit of pressure, equal to 1 newton per square meter (N/m^2) (p. 391)
penumbra a region of the moon's shadow that surrounds the umbra and is less dark than the umbra (p. 800)
period a row in a periodic table of elements (p. 131); the time required for one complete cycle of a periodic motion (p. 504); a unit of geologic time into which geologists divide eras (p. 734)
periodic law the pattern of repeating properties displayed by elements in the periodic table (p. 131)
periodic motion any motion that repeats at regular time intervals (p. 504)
periodic table an arrangement of elements in columns, based on a set of properties that repeat from row to row (p. 127)
permeable a description of a material that water can easily pass through (p. 707)
pH a measure of the hydronium ion concentration of a solution (p. 247)
phase change a reversible physical change that occurs when a substance changes from one state of matter to another (p. 84)
phases the different shapes of the illuminated side of the moon as seen from Earth (p. 798)
phosphor a solid material that emits light by fluorescence (p. 559)
photoelectric effect the emission of electrons from a metal caused by light striking the metal (p. 537)
photon a packet of electromagnetic energy (p. 537)
photosphere the thin innermost layer of the sun's atmosphere, which is the visible surface of the sun (p. 831)
photosynthesis a process in which plants chemically combine carbon dioxide and water into carbohydrates, a process requiring light and chlorophyll (p. 282)
physical change a change that occurs when some properties of a material change, but the substances in the material stay the same (p. 51)
physical property any characteristic of a material that can be observed or measured without changing the composition of the substances in the material (p. 45)
physics the study of matter and energy and the interactions between the two through forces and motion (p. 4)
pigment a material that selectively absorbs certain colors of light and reflects other colors (p. 553)
pipe a narrow vertical channel through which magma rises to Earth's surface (p. 691)
pitch the frequency of a sound as a listener perceives it (p. 515)
plane mirror a mirror with a flat surface (p. 571)
planetary nebula a glowing cloud of gas surrounding a dying low-mass star (p. 842)
planetesimals asteroid-sized bodies in the protoplanetary disk from which the planets formed by accretion (p. 819)
plasma a state of matter in which atoms have been stripped of their electrons (p. 315)
plate tectonics the theory that pieces of Earth's lithosphere, called plates, move about slowly on top of the asthenosphere (p. 676)
plucking a process in which glacial ice widens cracks in bedrock beneath a glacier, which carries away the loosened pieces of rock (p. 720)

polar covalent bond a covalent bond in which electrons are not shared equally (p. 168)
polarized light a type of light including light with waves that vibrate in only one plane (p. 548)
polar zones the regions from latitude 66.5° north to the north pole, and from latitude 66.5° south to the south pole, which are generally cold (p. 753)
polyatomic ion a covalently bonded group of atoms that has a positive or negative charge and acts as a unit (p. 172)
polymer a large molecule formed when many smaller molecules are linked together by covalent bonds (p. 275)
potential difference voltage, or the difference in electrical potential energy between two places in an electric field (p. 606)
potential energy energy that is stored as a result of position or shape (p. 448)
power the rate of doing work (p. 414)
precipitate a solid that forms and separates from a liquid mixture (p. 57)
precision a gauge of how exact a measurement is (p. 19)
pressure the result of a force distributed over an area (pp. 75, 390)
primary colors three specific colors that can be combined in varying intensities to create millions of colors (p. 552)
products new substances formed as a result of a chemical reaction (p. 192)
projectile motion the curved path of an object in free fall after it is given an initial forward velocity (p. 362)
prominences huge loops of gas that erupt from sunspot regions and extend upward from the photosphere into the chromosphere and sometimes into the corona (p. 833)
protein a long polymer that forms when amino acids bond together (p. 280)
proton a positively charged subatomic particle that is found in the nucleus of an atom (p. 108)
protoplanetary disk a large disk-shaped cloud of dust and gas formed as the solar nebula rotated faster and flattened out (p. 819)
protostar a contracting nebula with enough mass to form a star (p. 841)
pulley a simple machine that consists of a rope that fits into a groove in a wheel (p. 432)
pulsar a spinning neutron star that appears to give off strong pulses of radio waves (p. 844)
pupil the opening that allows light to enter the eye (p. 589)
pure substance matter that always has exactly the same composition; an element or compound (p. 39)
P waves primary waves; longitudinal waves caused by earthquakes (p. 686)

Q

quark a subatomic particle theorized to be among the basic units of matter (p. 305)
quasar enormously bright center of a distant young galaxy (p. 849)

R

radiation the transfer of energy by waves moving through space (p. 481)
radiation zone a region of closely-packed plasma outside the core of the sun, where energy is transferred by the absorption and reradiation of light (p. 830)
radioactivity the process in which an unstable atomic nucleus emits charged particles and energy (p. 292)
radioisotope an isotope with an unstable nucleus (p. 292)
rarefaction an area of a longitudinal wave where the particles of the medium are spread out (p. 502)
ray diagram a diagram that shows how light rays change direction when they strike mirrors and pass through lenses (p. 570)
reactant a substance that undergoes change in a chemical reaction (p. 192)
reaction rate the rate at which reactants change into products over time (p. 212)
reactivity the property that describes how readily a substance combines chemically with other substances (p. 55)
real image a copy of an object formed at the point where light rays actually meet (p. 572)
red shift a shift toward the red wavelengths of light from stars or galaxies moving away from Earth (p. 852)
reflecting telescope a telescope that uses mirrors and convex lenses to collect and focus light (p. 581)
reflection the interaction that occurs when a wave bounces off a surface that it cannot pass through (p. 508)
refracting telescope a telescope that uses only lenses to collect and focus light (p. 581)
refraction the bending of a wave as it enters a new medium at an angle (p. 509)
refrigerant a fluid that vaporizes and condenses inside the tubing of a heat pump (p. 490)
regular reflection a reflection that occurs when parallel light waves strike a surface and all reflect in the same direction (p. 547)
relative age the age of a rock compared to the ages of other rocks above or below it in a sequence of rock layers (p. 732)
relative humidity the ratio of the amount of water vapor in the air to the maximum amount of water vapor that air can contain at that temperature (p. 760)

relative motion movement in relation to a frame of reference (p. 329)
renewable energy resource a source of energy that can be replaced in a relatively short period of time (p. 463)
resistance the opposition to the flow of electric charges in a material (p. 605)
resonance the response of a standing wave to another wave of the same frequency, with dramatic increase in amplitude of the standing wave (p. 521)
responding variable a variable that changes in response to a change in the manipulated variable (p. 8)
resultant vector the vector sum of two or more vectors (p. 331)
retina the inner surface of the back of the eye, containing light-sensitive nerve endings (p. 589)
reversible reaction a chemical reaction in which the conversion of reactants into products and the conversion of products into reactants happens at the same time (p. 217)
revolution the movement of one body around another (p. 752)
ring a disk made of many small particles of rock and ice in orbit around a planet (p. 811)
rock a solid combination of minerals or other materials (p. 665)
rock cycle a series of processes in which rocks continuously change from one type to another (p. 674)
rods light-sensitive neurons in the retina that detect low-intensity light and distinguish black, white, and gray (p. 589)
rolling friction a friction force that acts on rolling objects, caused by the change in shape at the point of rolling contact (p. 360)
rotation the spinning of a planet or moon on its axis (p. 752)
runoff water that flows over Earth's surface (p. 706)

S

salinity the proportion of dissolved salts in water (p. 725)
salt an ionic compound formed when an acid reacts with a base (p. 244)
saltation movement of particles such as sand carried by water or wind in a series of little leaps (p. 714)
saturated hydrocarbon a hydrocarbon in which all of the bonds are single bonds (p. 264)
saturated solution a solution that contains as much solute as the solvent can normally hold at a given temperature (p. 236)
saturated zone the region beneath Earth's surface where pore spaces are entirely filled with groundwater (p. 707)
scattering a process by which light is redirected as it passes through a medium (p. 549)
science a system of knowledge about the natural world and the methods used to find that knowledge (p. 3)
scientific law a statement that summarizes a pattern found in nature (p. 9)
scientific method an organized plan used for gathering, organizing, and communicating information (p. 7)
scientific notation a way of expressing a value as the product of a number between 1 and 10 and a power of 10 (p. 14)
scientific theory a well-tested explanation for a set of observations or experimental results (p. 9)
screw an inclined plane wrapped around a cylinder (p. 431)
sea breeze a local wind that occurs when cooler air over the water flows toward the land (p. 757)
sea-floor spreading the process by which new oceanic crust is created at mid-ocean ridges, as older crust moves away (p. 678)
secondary color new color that results when any two of the primary colors are combined (p. 552)
sediment small, solid pieces of material that come from rocks or living organisms (p. 672)
sedimentary rock rock that forms over time as sediment is squeezed and cemented together (p. 672)
seismic waves vibrations that carry the energy released during an earthquake (p. 684)
seismograph a device that can detect and record seismic waves (p. 687)
semiconductor a crystalline solid that conducts electric current only under certain conditions (p. 621)
series circuit an electric circuit with only one path through which charge can flow (p. 610)
shield volcano a wide, relatively flat volcano that results from quiet eruptions of low-viscosity lava (p. 693)
significant figures all the digits in a measurement that are directly measured, plus the last digit, which is estimated (p. 19)
silicate a rock made of compounds of silicon and oxygen, generally containing metals such as alluminum, iron, or calcium (p. 661)
sill a structure formed when magma hardens in a crack parallel to existing rock layers (p. 696)
single-replacement reaction a chemical reaction in which one element takes the place of another element in a compound (p. 202)
sinkhole a hole that results when erosion weakens a layer of limestone, causing portions of the ground to suddenly collapse (p. 717)
sliding friction a friction force that opposes the motion of an object as it slides over a surface (p. 359)

slope the steepness of a line, equal to the ratio of a vertical change to the corresponding horizontal change (pp. 23, 334)
solar energy sunlight that is converted into usable energy (p. 464)
solar flare a dramatic eruption on the sun's surface, usually near sunspots, that produces X-rays and sends charged particles into space at speeds of 1000 km/s or more (p. 833)
solar nebula a cloud of dust and gas that can eventually collapse to form one or more stars with a planetary system (p. 818)
solar system the sun, planets, their moons, and a variety of smaller objects that revolve around the sun (p. 792)
solar wind a stream of electrically charged particles that flows from the sun outward through the solar system (p. 831)
solenoid a coil of current-carrying wire that produces a magnetic field (p. 637)
solid the state of matter in which materials have a definite shape and a definite volume (p. 69)
solstice the day that marks the start of summer or winter; the day when the sun is directly overhead at latitude 23.5° north or latitude 23.5° south (p. 753)
solubility the maximum amount of solute that normally dissolves in a given amount of solvent at a certain temperature (p. 235)
solute a substance whose particles are dissolved in a solution (p. 229)
solution a mixture that forms when substances dissolve and form a homogeneous mixture (p. 42)
solvent a substance in which a solute dissolves (p. 229)
sonar a technique for determining the distance to an object under water (p. 516)
sound wave a longitudinal wave consisting of compressions and rarefactions, which travels through a medium (p. 514)
space probe an unpiloted vehicle that carries scientific instruments into space and transmits information back to Earth (p. 794)
specific heat the amount of heat needed to raise the temperature of one gram of a material by one degree Celsius (p. 476)
speed the ratio of the distance an object moves to the amount of time the object moves (p. 332)
spiral galaxy a galaxy like the Milky Way with a bulge of stars at the center and arms extending outward like a pinwheel (p. 848)
spring tide a tide at the new or full moon when the change between daily high and low tides is the greatest (p. 801)
stalactite an icicle-like formation on a cavern ceiling that forms when water drips from the cavern ceiling (p. 717)
stalagmite a pillar of minerals in a cavern formed when water drips down to the cavern floor (p. 717)
standing wave a wave that appears to stay in one place and does not seem to move through a medium (p. 512)
star a large, glowing ball of gas in space that generates energy through nuclear fusion in its core (p. 834)
star system a group of two or more stars held together by gravity (p. 847)
static electricity the study of the behavior of electric charges, including how charge is transferred between objects (p. 602)
static friction a friction force that acts on objects that are not moving (p. 359)
stationary front a front that occurs when two air masses have formed a boundary but neither is moving (p. 768)
stratosphere the layer of Earth's atmosphere above the troposphere (p. 750)
stratus clouds flat layers of clouds that cover much or all of the sky (p. 762)
streak the color of a mineral's powder (p. 666)
stress the forces of deformation acting on the rocks of Earth's crust (p. 685)
strong nuclear force the powerful attractive force that binds protons and neutrons together in the nucleus (pp. 308, 379)
subduction the process by which oceanic crust sinks into the mantle through a trench (p. 679)
sublimation the phase change in which a substance changes from a solid to a gas or vapor without changing to a liquid first (p. 91)
substance matter that always has exactly the same composition; an element or compound (p. 39)
substituted hydrocarbon a hydrocarbon in which one or more hydrogen atoms have been replaced, or substituted (p. 272)
sunspot an area of gas in the sun's photosphere that is cooler than the surrounding gases (p. 832)
superconductor a material that has almost zero resistance when it is cooled to low temperatures (p. 605)
supergiant a very large, massive, bright star ranging in size from 100 to 1000 times the diameter of the sun (p. 839)
supernova an enormous explosion in which the byproducts of a supergiant star's lifetime of fusion are flung into space (p. 843)
supersaturated solution a solution that contains more solute than the solvent can normally hold at a given temperature (p. 236)

surface current a large stream of ocean water that moves continuously in about the same path (p. 726)
surface wave a wave that travels along a surface separating two media (p. 503); a transverse wave that develops when a seismic wave reaches Earth's surface (p. 687)
suspension a heterogeneous mixture that separates into layers over time (p. 43)
S waves secondary waves; transverse waves caused by earthquakes (p. 687)
synthesis reaction a chemical reaction in which two or more substances react to form a single substance (p. 200)

T

technology the use of scientific knowledge to solve practical problems (p. 3)
telescope an optical instrument that uses lenses (or lenses and mirrors) to collect and focus light from distant objects (p. 580)
temperate zones the regions between latitude 23.5° north and latitude 66.5° north, and between latitude 23.5° south and 66.5° south, which are generally cooler than the tropics (p. 753)
temperature a measure of how hot or cold an object is compared to a reference point (p. 475)
terminal velocity the constant velocity of a falling object when the force of air resistance equals the force of gravity (p. 361)
terrestrial planets the four planets closest to the sun (Mercury, Venus, Earth, and Mars), which are similar in structure to Earth (p. 803)
thermal conductor a material that conducts thermal energy well (p. 480)
thermal energy the total potential and kinetic energy of all the particles in an object (p. 451)
thermal expansion the increase in volume of a material when its temperature increases (p. 476)
thermal insulator a material that conducts thermal energy poorly (p. 480)
thermodynamics the study of conversions between thermal energy and other forms of energy (p. 482)
thermogram a color-coded picture using variations in infrared radiation to show variations in temperature (p. 543)
thermometer an instrument that measures temperature (p. 20)
thermosphere the outermost layer of Earth's atmosphere (p. 751)
thunder the sound produced by rapidly expanding air along the path of a lightning discharge (p. 770)
thunderstorm a small weather system that includes thunder and lightning (p. 770)
tides the regular rise and fall of water in the oceans (p. 801)
till glacial sediment left behind when a glacier melts (p. 721)
tornado a small but intense windstorm that takes the form of a rotating column of air that touches the ground (p. 770)
total internal reflection the complete reflection of a light ray back into its original medium when the angle of incidence is greater than the critical angle of refraction (p. 578)
transform boundary a boundary at which tectonic plates slide past each other, moving in opposite directions (p. 682)
transformer a device that increases or decreases the voltage of two linked AC circuits (p. 644)
transistor a solid-state component with three layers of semiconductor material, used to turn current on or off or to increase the strength of electronic signals (p. 621)
transition metals elements that form a bridge between elements on the left and right sides of the periodic table (p. 136)
translucent a description of a material that scatters light that passes through it (p. 547)
transmutation the conversion of one element to another through a nuclear reaction (p. 303)
transparent a description of a material that allows most of the light that strikes it to pass through (p. 546)
transpiration the loss of water through the leaves of plants (p. 705)
transuranium elements elements with atomic numbers greater than 92 (p. 304)
transverse wave a wave that causes a medium to vibrate at right angles to the direction in which the wave travels (p. 501)
trench a long, deep depression in the ocean floor where old oceanic crust sinks into the mantle (p. 679)
tributary a smaller stream that flows into a major river (p. 706)
tropic zone a warm region between latitude 23.5° south and latitude 23.5° north (p. 753)
troposphere the lowest layer of Earth's atmosphere, where most weather occurs (p. 749)
trough the lowest point of a transverse wave (p. 501)
turbine a device with fanlike blades that turn when pushed, for example, by water or steam (p. 646)

U

umbra the darkest part of a shadow (p. 800)
uniformitarianism the principle that geologic processes operating today also operated in the past (p. 661)

unsaturated hydrocarbon a hydrocarbon that contains one or more double or triple bonds (p. 265)
unsaturated solution a solution in which more solute can be dissolved at a given temperature (p. 236)
upwelling the movement of water from the deep ocean to the ocean's surface (p. 728)

V

valence electron an electron that is in the highest occupied energy level of an atom (p. 139)
valley glacier a long, narrow mass of moving ice and snow that usually begins near a mountain peak and winds down from the mountains through a valley formed originally by a stream (p. 719)
vaporization the phase change in which a substance changes from a liquid into a gas (p. 88)
vapor pressure the pressure caused by the collisions of particles in a vapor with the walls of a container (p. 89)
vector a quantity that has a direction associated with it (p. 330)
velocity the speed and direction an object is moving, measured relative to a reference point (p. 336)
vent an opening in the ground where magma escapes to Earth's surface (p. 691)
virtual image a copy of an object formed at the point from which light appears to be coming (p. 571)
viscosity the tendency of a liquid to keep from flowing; resistance to flowing (p. 45)
vitamin an organic compound that organisms need in small amounts, but cannot produce (p. 284)
volcanic neck a structure that forms when magma hardens in a volcano's pipe (p. 696)
volcano a mountain that forms when magma reaches the surface (p. 690)
voltage potential difference, the difference in electrical potential energy between two places in an electric field (p. 606)
volume the amount of space taken up by an object (p. 16)

W

warm front a front that occurs when a warm air mass overtakes a cold air mass (p. 768)
waste heat thermal energy discharged into an area at a lower temperature without being converted into useful work (p. 483)
water cycle the continuous movement of water in all its forms among Earth's oceans, atmosphere, and land (p. 705)
watershed the area of land that contributes water to a river system (p. 706)
water table the top surface of the saturated zone (p. 707)
watt (W) the SI unit of power, equal to one joule per second (p. 415)
wavelength the distance between a point on a wave and the same point on the next cycle of the wave (p. 505)
weak nuclear force a powerful attractive force that acts over a short range (p. 380)
weather the condition of the atmosphere at a particular place at a particular time (p. 749)
weathering the process by which rocks are chemically altered or physically broken into fragments (p. 710)
wedge a V-shaped object whose sides are two inclined planes sloped toward each other (p. 431)
weight the force of gravity acting on an object (p. 367)
wheel and axle a simple machine that consists of two rigidly attached disks or cylinders, each one with a different radius (p. 430)
white dwarf the small, dense, but dim remains of a low- or medium-mass star (p. 839)
wind the mainly horizontal movement of air from areas of higher pressure to areas of lower pressure (p. 757)
work the product of distance and the force in the direction an object moves (p. 412)
work input the work done on a machine as the input force acts through the input distance (p. 419)
work output the work done by a machine as the output force acts through the output distance (p. 420)

A

abrasion / abrasión una forma de desgaste mecánico que se produce cuando las rocas se desgastan o muelen unas contra otras. (pág. 710)

absolute age / edad absoluta el tiempo transcurrido desde la formación de una roca (pág. 734)

absolute brightness / brillo absoluto una descripción de lo brillante que es una estrella; una propiedad característica de una estrella que no depende de la distancia entre la estrella y la Tierra (pág. 837)

absolute zero / cero absoluto una temperatura de 0 kelvin (págs. 78, 475)

absorption lines / líneas de absorción un conjunto de líneas oscuras que muestran las frecuencias a las que la luz ha sido absorbida desde el espectro brillante de una estrella (pág. 837)

acceleration / aceleración la tasa a la cual cambia la velocidad (pág. 342)

accretion / acreción el proceso de agregar masa en la formación de los planetas mediante la colisión entre planetesimales (pág. 819)

accuracy / exactitud la cercanía de una medida al valor real de lo que se mide (pág. 19)

acid / ácido un compuesto que produce iones hidronios (H_3O^+) cuando se disuelve en agua; un donante de protones (pág. 241)

actual mechanical advantage / ventaja mecánica real la relación de la fuerza desarrollada con respecto a la fuerza aplicada en una máquina (pág. 422)

air mass / masa de aire un gran volumen de aire que tiene propiedades uniformes en toda su extensión, tales como temperatura y porcentajes de humedad, a una determinada altura (pág. 765)

air pressure / presión atmosférica la presión que produce el peso de una columna de aire en la atmósfera terrestre (pág. 748)

air resistance / resistencia del aire fricción de un fluido que actúa sobre un objeto que se mueve a través del aire (pág. 360)

alkali metals / metales alcalinos los elementos del Grupo 1A de la tabla periódica, sin incluir el hidrógeno (pág. 10)

alkaline earth metals / metales terreo-alcalinos los elementos del Grupo 2A de la tabla periódica (pág. 141)

alloy / aleación una mezcla de dos o más elementos, de los cuales al menos uno es un metal, que tiene las propiedades características de un metal (pág. 178)

alluvial fan / abanico aluvial un depósito de sedimentos con forma de abanico, que se forma sobre tierra firme cuando un arroyo fluye desde las montañas hacia una planicie (pág. 716)

alpha particle / partícula alfa una partícula de carga positiva que es emitida por algunos núcleos radiactivos y está formada por dos protones y dos neutrones; un núcleo de helio (pág. 293)

alternating current (AC) / corriente alterna (CA) un flujo de energía eléctrica que cambia de positiva a negativa a intervalos regulares (pág. 604)

amino acids / aminoácidos compuestos que contienen los grupos funcionales carboxilo y amino (pág. 280)

amplitude / amplitud el máximo desplazamiento de un determinado medio desde su posición de reposo (pág. 507)

amplitude modulation (AM) / amplitud modulada (AM) un método para la transmisión de señales de radio en el que la amplitud de la onda transmisora varía mientras que la frecuencia permanece estable (pág. 541)

analog signal / señal análoga una señal de variación gradual que se produce al cambiar continuamente el voltaje o corriente en un circuito (pág. 619)

angle of incidence / ángulo de incidencia el ángulo que forma un rayo incidente con una línea perpendicular a la superficie sobre la que impacta (pág. 570)

angle of reflection / ángulo de reflexión el ángulo que forma un rayo reflejado con una línea perpendicular a la superficie sobre la que impacta (pág. 570)

angle of refraction / ángulo de refracción el ángulo que forma un rayo de luz con el normal después de ingresar a un nuevo medio a un ángulo determinado (pág. 575)

anion / anión un ión de carga negativa (pág. 160)

anticyclone / anticiclón un sistema climático con un centro turbulento de alta presión atmosférica (pág. 769)

antinode / antinodo un punto de máximo desplazamiento a mitad de camino entre dos nodos y una onda estacionaria (pág. 512)

apparent brightness / magnitud aparente el brillo de una estrella como se aprecia desde la Tierra (pág. 836)

aquifer / acuífero una capa de rocas permeables que está saturada de agua (pág. 707)

Archimedes' principle / principio de Arquímedes la equivalencia de la fuerza de flotación de un objeto y el peso del fluido desplazado por el objeto (pág. 401)

aromatic hydrocarbons / hidrocarburos aromáticos hidrocarburos que contienen una estructura de anillos similar al benceno (pág. 26)

asteroid belt / cinturón de asteroides región entre las órbitas de Marte y Júpiter donde se encuentran la mayoría de los asteroides del sistema solar (pág. 809)

asteriods / asteroides cuerpos rocosos pequeños del sistema solar, la mayor parte de los cuales se encuentra orbitando alrededor del Sol en una región entre Marte y Júpiter (pág. 809)

Spanish Glossary

asthenosphere / astenosfera una capa de roca más suave y débil debajo de la litosfera terrestre, que puede fluir lentamente (pág. 662)

astigmatism / astigmatismo condición de los ojos en la que los objetos situados a cualquier distancia aparecen borrosos debido a la forma distorsionada de la córnea (pág. 592)

astronomical unit (AU) / unidad astronómica (UA) una unidad de distancia que equivale a la distancia promedio de la Tierra al Sol; 149,598,000 kilómetros (pág. 793)

astronomy / astronomía el estudio del Universo más allá de la Tierra (pág. 4)

atmosphere / atmósfera la capa de gases que rodea a la Tierra (pág. 747)

atom / átomo la partícula más pequeña de un elemento (pág. 39)

atomic mass unit (amu) / unidad de masa atómica (uma) una doceava parte de la masa que tiene un átomo de carbono-12 (pág. 134)

atomic number / número atómico un único número por cada elemento que equivale al número de protones en un átomo de ese elemento (pág. 110)

aurora / aurora una muestra colorida de luces en la ionosfera, que se produce cuando las partículas con carga que provienen del Sol son atraídas por los polos magnéticos terrestres (pág. 751)

average speed / rapidez media la distancia total recorrida dividida por el tiempo que se necesita para recorrer esa distancia (pág. 333)

B

background radiation / radiación de fondo radiación nuclear que se produce naturalmente en el ambiente (pág. 296)

barometer / barómetro un instrumento que sirve para medir la presión del aire (pág. 748)

barred-spiral galaxy / galaxias espirales barradas una galaxia espiral en la que los brazos del espiral se extienden hacia fuera desde una barra que corre a través del centro de la galaxia (pág. 848)

base / base un compuesto que produce iones hidróxidos (OH^-) cuando se disuelve en agua; un receptor de protones (pág. 242)

batholith / batolito el tipo más grande de masa de roca ígnea intrusa (pág. 696)

battery / batería un artefacto que convierte la energía química en energía eléctrica (pág. 606)

beta particle / partícula beta un electrón emitido por un núcleo inestable (pág. 294)

big bang theory / teoría del Big Bang la teoría que sostiene que el Universo comenzó en un instante, hace miles de millones de años, con una enorme explosión (pág. 854)

binary star / estrella binaria un sistema de estrellas con dos estrellas que giran cada una alrededor de la otra (pág. 847)

biology / biología el estudio de la vida y los procesos vitales (pág. 4)

biomass energy / energía de la biomasa la energía química que se almacena en las cosas vivas (pág. 464)

black hole / agujero negro un objeto cuya gravedad superficial es tan grande que ni siquiera las ondas electromagnéticas pueden escaparse (pág. 844)

boiling point / punto de ebullición la temperatura a la cual hierve una sustancia; la temperatura a la cual la presión del vapor es igual a la presión atmosférica (pág. 47)

Boyle's law / ley de Boyle la variación inversa del volumen de un gas y su presión si la temperatura y el número de partículas son constantes (pág. 79)

buffer / búfer una solución que es resistente a grandes cambios en su pH (pág. 248)

buoyancy / flotación la capacidad que tiene un fluido de ejercer una fuerza ascendente en los objetos colocados en él (pág. 400)

buoyant force / fuerza de flotación una fuerza ascendente que actúa sobre un objeto colocado en un fluido (pág. 400)

C

caldera / caldera amplia depresión en la parte superior de un volcán que se forma cuando la boca central y la cámara magmática se derrumban después de una erupción (pág. 691)

calorimeter / calorímetro instrumento que sirve para medir la energía térmica que se libera o absorbe durante un cambio químico o físico (pág. 478)

camera / cámara fotográfica un instrumento óptico que registra la imagen de un objeto (pág. 582)

carbohydrate / carbohidrato un compuesto de carbono, hidrógeno y oxígeno en el cual la relación de los átomos de hidrógeno respecto de los átomos de oxígeno es de 2:1 (pág. 278)

catalyst / catalizador una sustancia que afecta la velocidad de una reacción química sin que sea usada en la reacción (pág. 215)

cation / catión un ión con carga positiva (pág. 160)

central heating system / sistema de calefacción central un sistema de calefacción que calienta varias habitaciones desde una ubicación central (pág. 489)

centripetal force / fuerza centrípeta una fuerza que cambia continuamente la dirección de un objeto para hacerlo moverse en un círculo (pág. 381)

chain reaction / reacción en cadena una serie de reacciones de fisión disparadas por neutrones liberados durante la fisión de un núcleo (pág. 311)

Charles's law / ley de Charles la proporción directa del volumen de un gas con respecto a su temperatura (en kelvins), si la presión y el número de partículas del gas son constantes (pág. 78)

chemical bond / enlace químico la fuerza que mantiene los átomos e iones juntos como una unidad (pág. 160)

chemical change / cambio químico cambio que se produce cuando una sustancia reacciona y forma una o más sustancias nuevas (pág. 56)

chemical energy / energía química la energía almacenada en los enlaces químicos (págs. 206, 451)

chemical equation / ecuación química una representación de una reacción química en la cual los reactantes y los productos se expresan como fórmulas (pág. 193)

chemical formula / fórmula química notación que muestra los elementos que contienen un compuesto y la relación de los átomos o iones de estos elementos en el compuesto (pág. 161)

chemical property / propiedad química toda propiedad que produce un cambio en la composición de la materia (pág. 54)

chemical weathering / desgaste químico el proceso en el que una roca es desintegrada por las reacciones químicas (pág. 710)

chemistry / química el estudio de la composición, estructura, propiedades y reacciones de la materia (pág. 4)

chromosphere / cromosfera la capa intermedia de la atmósfera solar, inmediatamente por fuera de la fotosfera (pág. 831)

cinder cone / cono de escoria un volcán pequeño y de laderas empinadas formado por una combinación de ceniza y toba volcánica (pág. 693)

circuit breaker / interruptor de circuito un interruptor que se abre cuando la corriente en un circuito es demasiado alta (pág. 612)

cirque / circo glaciar un amplio valle con forma de tazón creado por un glaciar en la ladera de una montaña (pág. 720)

cirrus clouds / nubes cirros nubes delgadas, blancas y tenues, a menudo con apariencia de velos o plumas (pág. 763)

clastic rocks / rocas clásticas rocas sedimentarias que se forman de fragmentos que se desprenden de otras rocas (pág. 672)

cleavage / exfoliación la tendencia que posee un mineral de dividirse a lo largo de planos regulares y bien definidos (pág. 668)

climate / clima las condiciones a largo plazo del tiempo de un lugar o región (pág. 778)

cloud / nube una masa densa y visible de minúsculas gotas de agua o cristales de hielo que se encuentran suspendidos en la atmósfera (pág. 761)

coefficients / coeficientes los números que aparecen antes de una fórmula en una ecuación química para mostrar las proporciones relativas de cada reactante y producto (pág. 194)

coherent light / luz coherente ondas de luz que tienen la misma longitud de onda, con sus crestas y valles alineados (pág. 560)

cold front / frente frío un frente que se produce cuando una masa de aire frío rebasa a una masa de aire caliente (pág. 767)

colloid / coloide una mezcla que contiene algunas partículas que son de tamaño intermedio entre las partículas pequeñas de una solución y las partículas grandes de una suspensión (pág. 44)

combustion reaction / reacción de combustión una reacción química en la que una sustancia reacciona rápidamente con el oxígeno, produciendo a menudo calor y luz (pág. 204)

comet / cometa una masa de roca, polvo y hielo que se vaporiza parcialmente cuando pasa cerca del Sol (pág. 815)

complementary colors of light / colores complementarios de la luz dos colores cualesquiera de luz que se combinan para formar luz blanca (pág. 552)

complementary colors of pigments / colores complementarios de pigmentos dos colores cualesquiera de pigmentos que se combinan para formar un pigmento negro (pág. 553)

composite volcano / volcán compuesto un volcán que se forma de una combinación de lava y ceniza (pág. 693)

compound / compuesto una sustancia que está formada por dos o más sustancias más simples y que se puede descomponer en esas sustancias más simples (pág. 40)

compound machine / máquina compuesta una combinación de dos o más máquinas simples que operan juntas (pág. 435)

compression / compresión un área en una onda longitudinal en la cual las partículas de ese medio están juntas entre sí (pág. 502)

computer / computadora un artefacto programable que puede almacenar y procesar información (pág. 622)

concave lens / lente cóncava lente curvada hacia dentro en el centro y que tiene mayor grosor en los bordes exteriores (pág. 576)

concave mirror / espejo cóncavo un espejo que se curva hacia dentro (pág. 572)
concentration / concentración la cantidad de soluto disuelto en una determinada cantidad de solvente (pág. 238)
condensation / condensación el cambio de fase en el que una sustancia cambia de gas o vapor a líquido (pág. 90)
conduction / conducción la transferencia de energía térmica sin transferencia significativa de materia, dentro de un material o entre materiales en contacto (pág. 479); la transferencia de carga eléctrica por contacto directo con un conductor (pág. 602)
conductivity / conductividad la capacidad que tiene un material de permitir que fluyan el calor o las cargas eléctricas (pág. 46)
cones / conos las neuronas sensibles a la luz de la retina que detectan el color (pág. 589)
constant acceleration / aceleración constante un cambio continuo en la velocidad (pág. 345)
constellation / constelación un grupo de estrellas que parecen formar un patrón cuando se las observa desde la Tierra (pág. 846)
constructive interference / interferencia constructiva la interacción entre dos o más ondas en las que los desplazamientos se combinan para formar una onda con un desplazamiento más amplio (pág. 511)
continental drift / deriva continental proceso en el que los continentes se mueven lentamente a través de la superficie de la Tierra (pág. 677)
continental glacier / glaciar continental capa espesa de hielo que cubre una zona extensa de un continente o una isla grande (pág. 719)
continental shelf / plataforma continental llanura con leve declive que forma un manto de aguas poco profundas a lo largo de las costas de la mayor parte de los continentes (pág. 726)
controlled experiment / experimento controlado experimento en el que una sola variable, la variable manipulada, se cambia deliberadamente en un momento determinado (pág. 8)
convection / convección transferencia de energía térmica cuando las partículas de un fluido se mueven de un lugar a otro (pág. 480)
convection current / corriente de convección circulación de un fluido en un circuito cuando el fluido se calienta y se enfría alternativamente (pág. 481)
convection zone / zona de convección región dentro del Sol en que la energía térmica se transfiere hacia fuera principalmente por medio de corrientes de convección (pág. 831)
convergent boundary / borde convergente límite en el que colisionan o chocan las placas tectónicas (pág. 682)
conversion factor / factor de conversión una razón de medidas equivalentes que se usan para convertir una determinada cantidad de una unidad a otra (pág. 18)
convex lens / lente convexa lente curvada hacia fuera en el centro y más delgada en los bordes exteriores (pág. 576)
convex mirror / espejo convexo espejo curvado hacia afuera (pág. 573)
core / núcleo esfera densa ubicada en el centro de la Tierra que está formada principalmente por hierro y níquel (pág. 663); región central del Sol donde se produce la fusión nuclear (pág. 830)
Coriolis effect / efecto de Coriolis el cambio que la rotación de la tierra produce en el movimiento de los objetos (pág. 759)
cornea / córnea capa externa y transparente del ojo (pág. 588)
corona / corona la capa más externa de la atmósfera solar que se extiende muy por encima de la cromosfera (pág. 831)
covalent bond / enlace covalente enlace químico en el que dos átomos comparten un par de electrones de valencia (pág. 166)
crater / cráter un orificio curvo en la cima de la boca central de un volcán (pág. 691); depresión circular en la superficie de un planeta, luna, asteroide o cometa provocada por un meteoroide (pág. 797)
crest / cresta el punto más alto de una onda transversal (pág. 501)
critical angle / ángulo crítico el ángulo de incidencia que produce un ángulo de refracción igual a 90 grados (pág. 578)
critical mass / masa crítica la masa más pequeña posible de un material fisionable que puede generar una reacción en cadena (pág. 311)
crust / corteza la capa rocosa más externa de la Tierra (pág. 661)
crystals / cristales sólidos cuyas partículas se encuentran dispuestas en una estructura reticular (pág. 162)
cumulus clouds / nubes cúmulos nubes blancas y esponjosas, generalmente con bases planas, que parecen bolitas de algodón apiladas (pág. 763)
cyclone / ciclón un sistema climático con un centro de baja presión atmosférica (pág. 769)

D

dark matter / materia negra materia que no emite radiación que pueda ser detectada por los astrónomos (pág. 855)
decibel / decibelio una unidad que compara las intensidades de diferentes sonidos (pág. 515)

decomposition reaction / reacción de descomposición una reacción química en la que un compuesto se separa en dos o más sustancias más simples (pág. 200)

deflation / deflación el proceso que ocurre cuando el viento levanta y transporta materiales de la superficie (pág. 723)

delta / delta una masa de sedimento que se deposita en la desembocadura de un río en el lugar en que éste penetra en una gran masa de agua (pág. 716)

density / densidad la relación entre el volumen y la masa de un material (pág. 17)

density currents / corrientes de densidad las corrientes que se producen debido a las diferencias en la densidad del agua del océano (pág. 727)

deposition / deposición cambio de fase en el que un gas o vapor cambia directamente al estado sólido sin pasar primero por el estado líquido (pág. 91); la colocación de sedimento que ha sido transportado de otro sitio (pág. 713)

desert / desierto una región extremadamente seca (pág. 780)

destructive interference / interferencia destructiva la interacción entre dos o más ondas cuyos desplazamientos se combinan para producir una onda con un desplazamiento menor (pág. 511)

dew point / punto de rocío la temperatura a la que el aire se satura de vapor de agua (pág. 761)

diffraction / difracción la curvatura de una onda que se mueve alrededor de un obstáculo o pasa a través de una abertura estrecha (pág. 510)

diffuse reflection / reflexión difusa la reflexión que se produce cuando ondas de luz paralelas chocan contra una superficie áspera y desigual, y se reflejan en muchas direcciones diferentes (pág. 547)

digital signal / señal digital una señal que codifica la información como una secuencia de unos y ceros (pág. 619)

dike / dique una estructura que se forma cuando el magma se endurece dentro de una grieta que atraviesa diferentes capas de rocas (pág. 696)

diode / diodo un componente de estado sólido con un semiconductor de tipo n unido a un semiconductor de tipo p (pág. 621)

direct current (DC) / corriente directa (CD) el flujo de carga eléctrica que corre en una sola dirección (pág. 604)

direct proportion / proporción directa una relación entre dos variables cuya proporción es constante (pág. 23)

dispersion / dispersión el proceso de disolución por rotura en partes pequeñas (pág. 230); proceso en el que la luz blanca se separa en colores (pág. 551)

dissociation / disociación separación de iones en un compuesto iónico a medida que éste se disuelve (pág. 229)

distance / distancia longitud de la trayectoria entre dos puntos (pág. 329)

distillation / destilación el proceso que separa las sustancias en una solución según sus puntos de ebullición (pág. 50)

divergent boundary / borde divergente límite en el que las placas tectónicas se separan unas de otras (pág. 682)

Doppler effect / efecto Doppler un cambio en la frecuencia de sonido provocada por el movimiento de la fuente de sonido, movimiento de la persona que escucha o de ambos (pág. 516)

double-replacement reaction / reacción de sustitución doble una reacción química en la que dos componentes intercambian iones positivos y forman otros dos nuevos compuestos (pág. 203)

dunes / dunas los depósitos de arena que se forman cuando ésta es transportada por el viento (pág. 724)

E

earthquake / terremoto un movimiento de la corteza terrestre que se produce cuando las rocas en la corteza cambian de posición repentinamente y liberan energía que estaba almacenada (pág. 684)

eclipse / eclipse fenómeno que se produce cuando la sombra de un cuerpo del espacio, tales como un planeta o luna, se proyecta sobre otro cuerpo (pág. 799)

ecliptic plane / plano eclíptico el plano del espacio que contiene la órbita de la Tierra (pág. 792)

efficiency / eficiencia porcentaje de trabajo de entrada que se transforma en trabajo de salida en una máquina (pág. 425)

elastic potencial energy / energía elástica potencial energía potencial de un objeto al ser estirado o comprimido (pág. 450)

electric charge / carga eléctrica una propiedad que provoca atracción o rechazo entre partículas subatómicas como los protones y electrones (pág. 600)

electric circuit / circuito eléctrico recorrido completo a través del cual puede fluir la carga eléctrica (pág. 609)

electric current / corriente eléctrica un flujo continuo de carga eléctrica (pág. 604)

electric field / campo eléctrico campo en una región del espacio que ejerce fuerzas eléctricas sobre partículas cargadas; campo generado por cargas eléctricas o por campos magnéticos variables (págs. 533, 602)

electric force / fuerza eléctrica la atracción o rechazo entre objetos con carga eléctrica (pág. 601)

electric motor / motor eléctrico un aparato que utiliza un electroimán para mover o rotar un eje (pág. 639)
electric power / potencia eléctrica la velocidad a la que la energía eléctrica se convierte en otro tipo de energía (pág. 611)
electrical conductor / conductor eléctrico un material a través del cual la carga eléctrica puede fluir fácilmente (pág. 605)
electrical energy / energía eléctrica energía asociada con las cargas eléctricas (pág. 452)
electrical insulator / aislante eléctrico un material a través del cual la carga eléctrica no puede fluir fácilmente (pág. 605)
electrolyte / electrolito un compuesto que produce iones al ser disuelto (pág. 249)
electromagnet / electroimán un solenoide con núcleo ferromagnético (pág. 637)
electromagnetic energy / energía electromagnética una forma de energía que consiste en campos eléctricos y magnéticos variables (pág. 452)
electromagnetic force / fuerza electromagnética una fuerza asociada con las partículas cargadas, la cual tiene dos aspectos, fuerza eléctrica y fuerza magnética (págs. 378, 635)
electromagnetic induction / inducción electromagnética el proceso de generación de corriente en el que un conductor eléctrico se mueve en relación a un campo magnético (pág. 642)
electromagnetic radiation / radiación electromagnética la transferencia de energía por medio de ondas electromagnéticas (pág. 533)
electromagnetic spectrum / espectro electromagnético rango completo de radiación electromagnética (pág. 540)
electromagnetic wave / onda electromagnética onda transversal formada por campos eléctricos y campos magnéticos variables (pág. 533)
electron / electrón una partícula subatómica con carga negativa que se encuentra en el espacio fuera del núcleo de un átomo (pág. 108)
electron cloud / nube de electrones modelo visual de las ubicaciones más probables de los electrones en un átomo (pág. 116)
electron configuration / configuración de electrones la disposición de los electrones en las órbitas de un átomo (pág. 118)
electron dot diagram / diagrama de puntos de electrones diagrama de un átomo, ión o molécula en el que cada punto representa la valencia de un electrón (pág. 158)
electronics / electrónica la ciencia que utiliza corrientes eléctricas para procesar o transmitir información (pág. 618)
electronic signal / señal electrónica información enviada en forma de patrones en el flujo controlado de electrones a través de un circuito (pág. 618)
element / elemento sustancia que no puede ser descompuesta en sustancias más simples (pág. 39)
elliptical galaxies / galaxias elípticas galaxias de formas esféricas u ovaladas sin rastros de brazos en espiral y muy poco gas o polvo entre sus estrellas (pág. 848)
El Niño / El Niño el calentamiento periódico del agua en las regiones central y oriental del Océano Pacífico (pág. 781)
endothermic / endotérmico la descripción de un cambio en el que un sistema absorbe energía de su entorno (pág. 86)
endothermic reaction / reacción endotérmica una reacción química que absorbe energía del entorno (pág. 209)
energy / energía capacidad de realizar un trabajo (pág. 447)
energy conservation / conservación de la energía práctica para encontrar formas de utilizar menos energía o de utilizarla en forma más eficiente (pág. 466)
energy conversion / conversión de la energía el proceso de cambiar energía de una forma a otra (pág. 454)
energy levels / niveles energéticos energías posibles que pueden tener los electrones de un átomo (pág. 114)
enzyme / enzima una proteína que actúa como catalítico para las reacciones en las células (pág. 284)
epicenter / epicentro el punto sobre la superficie de la Tierra que está ubicado directamente por encima del foco de un terremoto (pág. 686)
equilibrium / equilibrio estado en el que las trayectorias hacia delante y hacia atrás de un cambio físico o químico se realizan a la misma velocidad (pág. 216)
equinox / equinoccio día que marca el comienzo de la primavera o del otoño; día en el que la duración de la luz diurna y la oscuridad son aproximadamente iguales (pág. 754)
era / era una de las etapas principales en la historia geológica de la Tierra (pág. 734)
erosion / erosión el proceso que desgasta y transporta la roca y el suelo (pág. 709)
evaporation / evaporación el proceso por el cual una sustancia en estado líquido se transforma en gas a temperaturas por debajo del punto de ebullición de esa sustancia (pág. 89)
exothermic / exotérmico descripción de un cambio en el que el sistema libera energía hacia su entorno (pág. 86)
exothermic reaction / reacción exotérmica una reacción química que libera energía hacia el entorno (pág. 208)

external combustion engine / motor de combustión externa un motor térmico en el que el combustible se quema fuera de él (pág. 486)
extinct / extinto descripción de un tipo de organismo que no se encuentra vivo sobre la Tierra (pág. 733)
extrusive rock / roca extrusiva roca ígnea que se forma sobre la superficie de la Tierra (pág. 671)

F

farsightedness / hipermetropía condición de los ojos que provoca una visión borrosa de los objetos cercanos (pág. 592)
fault / falla una grieta en la corteza terrestre (pág. 685)
ferromagnetic material / material ferromagnético un material que puede ser magnetizado por su contenido de dominios magnéticos (pág. 632)
filtration / filtración proceso que separa los materiales de acuerdo al tamaño de sus partículas (pág. 50)
fission / fisión una reacción nuclear en que el núcleo de un átomo se separa en dos partes pequeñas (pág. 309)
flammability / flamabilidad capacidad que tiene un material de quemarse en presencia de oxígeno (pág. 54)
flood plain / llanura de inundación zona llana a lo largo de un curso de agua que sólo se inunda en las crecidas (pág. 716)
fluid / fluido sustancia o mezcla que fluye y que no tiene forma definida (pág. 391)
fluid friction / fricción de fluido una fuerza de fricción que se opone al movimiento de un objeto dentro de un fluido (pág. 360)
fluorescence / fluorescencia proceso en el que un material fosforescente convierte la radiación en luz visible (pág. 559)
focal point / punto de enfoque punto en el que se encuentran o parecen encontrarse los rayos de luz paralelos al eje de un espejo o lente (pág. 572)
focus / foco lugar por debajo de la superficie de la Tierra donde comienza un terremoto (pág. 686)
fog / niebla una nube que toca o está muy cerca del suelo (pág. 762)
fold / pliegue doblez en capas rocosas (pág. 685)
foliated rock / roca foliada una roca con cristales dispuestos en bandas paralelas (pág. 674)
force / fuerza la atracción o rechazo que actúa sobre un objeto (pág. 356)
fossil / fósil restos o rastros preservados de un organismo viviente (pág. 732)
fossil fuels / combustibles fósiles mezclas de depósitos ricos en hidrocarburos que se formaron a partir de restos de organismos (pág. 267)
fracture / fractura modo en el que se rompe un mineral, determinado por su estructura de cristales (pág. 668)
frame of reference / marco de referencia un sistema de objetos que no se mueve con respecto a otro (pág. 328)
free fall / caída libre movimiento de un objeto hacia la Tierra por causa de la gravedad (pág. 343)
frequency / frecuencia cantidad de ciclos completos en una unidad de tiempo para producir un movimiento periódico (pág. 504)
frequency modulation (FM) / frecuencia modulada (FM) método de transmisión de una señal de radio en el que varía la frecuencia de la onda portadora mientras su amplitud permanece igual (pág. 541)
friction / fricción fuerza que se opone al movimiento de los objetos que se tocan a medida que cada uno de ellos se mueve con respecto al otro (pág. 359)
front / frente línea divisoria muy bien definida que se forma cuando se encuentran dos masas de aire diferentes (pág. 767)
fulcrum / fulcro punto fijo alrededor del cual gira una palanca (pág. 428)
functional group / grupo funcional átomo o grupo de átomos que determina las propiedades de un compuesto orgánico (pág. 272)
fuse / fusible dispositivo que evita el sobrecalentamiento de un circuito por sobrecarga (pág. 612)
fusion / fusión una reacción nuclear en la que se combinan los núcleos de dos átomos para formar un núcleo más grande (pág. 315)

G

galaxy / galaxia un enorme grupo de estrellas, sistemas de estrellas, cúmulos de estrellas, polvo y gas unidos por la gravedad (pág. 848)
galvanometer / galvanómetro un aparato que utiliza un electroimán para medir pequeñas cantidades de corriente (pág. 638)
gamma ray / rayo gamma una forma penetrante de radiación que emite un núcleo inestable (pág. 294)
gas / gas estado de la materia en el que un material no tiene forma ni volumen definidos (pág. 70)
gas giant / gigante de gas planeta grande y de gran masa (como Júpiter, Saturno, Urano o Neptuno) compuesto principalmente por helio e hidrógeno (pág. 811)
generator / generador un aparato que convierte la energía mecánica en energía eléctrica por el movimiento relativo de una bobina de alambre respecto de un campo magnético (pág. 643)
geocentric / geocéntrico descripción de un modelo de sistema solar en el que todos los planetas giran alrededor de la Tierra (pág. 791)
geologists / geólogos científicos que estudian la Tierra y los procesos que la han ido formando a través del tiempo (pág. 660)
geology / geología estudio del origen, historia y estructura de la Tierra (pág. 4)

geothermal energy / energía geotérmica energía térmica existente debajo de la superficie de la Tierra (pág. 464)

giant / gigante estrella grande, brillante y de gran masa pero algo más pequeña y más débil que un supergigante (pág. 839)

glacier / glaciar gran masa de hielo y nieve que se desliza sobre la tierra (pág. 706)

global warming / calentamiento global incremento de la temperatura en la capa inferior de la atmósfera terrestre, provocado en parte por los elevados niveles de dióxido de carbono o vapor de agua (pág. 782)

global wind / viento global viento que sopla sobre grandes extensiones de terreno desde una dirección específica (pág. 758)

globular cluster / cúmulo globular grupo grande de estrellas viejas y de forma esférica que le faltan, por lo general, polvo y gas suficiente para formar nuevas estrellas (pág. 847)

gravitational force / fuerza gravitatoria una fuerza de atracción que actúa entre dos objetos cualesquiera (pág. 380)

gravitational potential energy / energía potencial gravitacional energía potencial que depende de la altura de un objeto por encima de un punto de referencia (pág. 449)

gravity / gravedad atracción entre dos objetos cualesquiera por efecto de sus masas (pág. 361)

greenhouse effect / efecto invernadero proceso en el que los gases de la atmósfera de la Tierra, tales como el vapor de agua y el dióxido de carbono, permiten el paso de la luz visible, pero absorben la radiación infrarroja que calienta la parte inferior de la atmósfera (pág. 755)

ground state / estado basal estado en el que todos los electrones de un átomo tienen la mínima energía posible (pág. 118)

grounding / conexión a tierra la transferencia del exceso de carga a través de un conductor a Tierra (pág. 613)

groundwater / aguas freáticas aguas frescas que se encuentran por debajo de la superficie de la Tierra dentro de grietas y entre partículas de roca y tierra (pág. 704)

group / grupo columna de elementos en una tabla periódica (pág. 131)

H

half-life / vida media tiempo que requiere la mitad de una muestra de un isótopo radiactivo para descomponerse (pág. 299)

halogens / halógenos los elementos del Grupo 7A de la tabla periódica (pág. 144)

hardness / dureza resistencia de un mineral a las raspaduras (pág. 668)

heat / calor transferencia de energía térmica de un objeto a otro debido a la diferencia de temperatura (pág. 474)

heat engine / motor térmico todo artefacto que transforma la energía térmica en trabajo (pág. 483)

heat of fusion / calor de fusión la energía que debe absorber una sustancia para pasar del estado sólido al líquido (pág. 86)

heat of vaporization / calor de vaporización la energía que debe absorber una sustancia para pasar del estado líquido al gaseoso (pág. 88)

heat pump / bomba térmica dispositivo que utiliza el trabajo para transferir energía térmica de un área más fría a un área más cálida (pág. 490)

heliocentric / heliocéntrico descripción de un modelo del sistema solar en el que la Tierra y los planetas giran alrededor del Sol (pág. 791)

hertz (Hz) / hercios (Hz) unidad para medir la frecuencia que equivale a un ciclo por segundo (pág. 504)

heterogeneous mixture / mezcla heterogénea tipo de mezcla en la que sus partes son notoriamente diferentes unas de otras (pág. 41)

homogeneous mixture / mezcla homogénea tipo de mezcla en la que las sustancias están distribuidas en forma tan pareja que es difícil distinguir una de otra (pág. 42)

horsepower (hp) / caballo de potencia (hp) unidad de potencia que equivale aproximadamente a 746 vatios (pág. 416)

hot spot / punto caliente región en la que una columna de magma ascendente se extiende desde la parte inferior de la litosfera hacia la superficie de la Tierra (pág. 693)

H-R (Hertzsprung-Russell) diagram / diagrama Hertzsprung-Russell gráfico de la temperatura de superficie comparada a la magnitud absoluta de una muestra de estrellas (pág. 838)

Hubble's Law / ley de Hubble variación directa de la velocidad a la que una galaxia se aleja de la Tierra con respecto a su distancia de ésta (pág. 853)

humidity / humedad cantidad de vapor de agua en un volumen determinado de aire (pág. 760)

hurricane / huracán ciclón tropical de grandes dimensiones con vientos de al menos 119 km por hora (74 millas por hora) (pág. 771)

hydraulic action / acción hidráulica proceso por el cual las olas del océano erosionan la roca (pág. 728)

hydraulic system / sistema hidráulico dispositivo que utiliza la acción de un fluido presurizado sobre pistones de diferentes tamaños para aumentar la fuerza (pág. 395)

hydrocarbon / hidrocarburo compuesto orgánico que solamente contiene hidrógeno y carbono (pág. 264)
hydroelectric energy / energía hidroeléctrica energía que se obtiene a partir del agua en movimiento (pág. 463)
hydrogen fuel cell / pila de combustible de hidrógeno pila que genera electricidad a partir de una reacción controlada entre hidrógeno y oxígeno (pág. 464)
hypothesis / hipótesis una respuesta propuesta ante una pregunta (pág. 8)

I

ice ages / glaciaciones períodos en los que los climas son más fríos de lo habitual y los glaciares cubren una gran parte de la superficie de la Tierra (pág. 781)
ideal mechanical advantage (IMA) / ventaja mecánica ideal (VMI) ventaja mecánica de una máquina en ausencia de fricción (pág. 423)
igneous rock / roca ígnea roca que se forma a partir del magma o lava (pág. 671)
image / imagen copia de un objeto formada por rayos de luz que se reflejan o refractan (pág. 547)
impermeable / impermeable descripción de un material a través del cual el agua no puede pasar fácilmente (pág. 707)
incandescent / incandescente descripción de un objeto lo suficientemente caliente como para brillar (pág. 558)
inclined plane / plano inclinado superficie inclinada a lo largo de la cual una fuerza mueve un objeto hacia una elevación diferente (pág. 431)
index fossil / fósil indicador fósil de una especie fácilmente identificable, que habitó en una zona extensa y vivió durante un período bien definido (pág. 733)
index of refraction / índice de refracción la relación entre la velocidad de la luz en un vacío y la velocidad de la luz en un medio (pág. 575)
indicator / indicador una sustancia que cambia de color en presencia de un ácido o una base (pág. 241)
induction / inducción transferencia de carga entre materiales, sin entrar en contacto (pág. 603)
inertia / inercia la tendencia de un objeto a resistir un cambio en su movimiento (pág. 364)
inorganic / inorgánico descripción de un material no orgánico (pág. 665)
input arm / brazo de entrada distancia entre el fulcro en una palanca y la fuerza aplicada (pág. 428)
input distance / distancia de entrada distancia a través de la cual la fuerza aplicada actúa en una máquina (pág. 419)
input force / fuerza aplicada fuerza que se ejerce sobre una máquina (pág. 419)
instantaneous speed / rapidez instantánea velocidad a la que se mueve un objeto en un momento dado en el tiempo (pág. 334)
integrated circuit / circuito integrado delgada capa de silicio que contiene muchos componentes; microchip (pág. 622)
intensity / intensidad velocidad a la que fluye la energía de una onda a través de una determinada unidad de espacio (págs. 515, 538)
interference / interferencia la interacción de dos o más ondas que se combinan en una zona en común (pág. 510)
internal combustion engine / motor de combustión interna máquina térmica en la que el combustible se quema dentro de la máquina (pág. 487)
intrusive rock / roca intrusiva roca ígnea que se forma bajo tierra a partir del magma endurecida (pág. 671)
inverse proportion / proporción inversa la relación en la que el producto de dos variables es una constante cuando todas las demás variables permanecen constantes (pág. 23)
ion / ión un átomo o grupo de átomos que tiene carga positiva o negativa (pág. 159)
ionic bond / enlace iónico fuerza que mantiene unidos a cationes y aniones (pág. 160)
ionization / ionización proceso por el cual las moléculas neutrales ganan o pierden electrones (pág. 230)
ionosphere / ionosfera región de partículas cargadas, o iones, de la atmósfera terrestre que se superpone con la parte más baja de la termosfera (pág. 751)
iris / iris parte coloreada del frente del ojo que se expande y contrae para controlar la cantidad de luz que penetra en él (pág. 589)
irregular galaxy / galaxia irregular una galaxia con apariencia desorganizada (pág. 848)
isobar / isobara línea trazada en un mapa del tiempo que une los puntos con igual presión atmosférica (pág. 777)
isotherm / isoterma línea trazada en un mapa del tiempo que une los puntos con igual temperatura del aire (pág. 777)
isomers / isómeros compuestos orgánicos con la misma fórmula molecular pero con diferente fórmula estructural (pág. 265)
isotopes / isótopos átomos de un determinado elemento que posee diferentes cantidades de neutrones y diferentes cantidades de masa (pág. 112)

J

jet stream / corriente de chorro un cinturón de vientos de alta velocidad que se encuentran en las capas superiores de la troposfera (pág. 759)

joule (J) / julio (J) unidad de trabajo de SI que equivale a 1 newton por metro (pág. 414)

K

kinetic energy / energía cinética la energía que tiene un objeto debido a su movimiento (págs. 71, 447)

Kuiper belt / cinturón de Kuiper un cinturón ancho más allá de la órbita de Plutón donde los objetos, compuestos principalmente de hielo y roca, giran en órbitas alrededor del Sol (pág. 815)

L

land breeze / brisa terrestre un viento local que ocurre cuando el aire más fresco se mueve hacia el agua (pág. 757)

laser / láser un dispositivo que genera un haz de luz coherente (pág. 560)

lava / lava magma que fluye hacia la superficie de la Tierra (pág. 671)

lava plateau / meseta de lava región plana elevada formada por lava endurecida (pág. 696)

law of conservation of charge / ley de la conservación de la carga ley que establece que la carga eléctrica total en un sistema aislado se mantiene constante; la carga eléctrica nunca se crea ni se destruye (pág. 602)

law of conservation of momentum / ley de la conservación del momento ley que establece que el momento total de un sistema no cambia si no hay fuerza neta que actúe sobre el sistema (pág. 376)

law of superposition / ley de superposición ley que establece que en las capas de roca no alteradas, las rocas más jóvenes están sobre las rocas más viejas y las rocas más viejas están debajo de todo (pág. 733)

length / longitud la distancia en línea recta entre dos puntos (pág. 16)

lens / lente un objeto hecho con material transparente y delgado que tiene una o dos superficies curvas que pueden refractar luz (pág. 576)

lever / palanca una barra rígida que puede moverse libremente alrededor de un punto fijo (pág. 428)

lift / fuerza de elevación una fuerza hacia arriba creada por la diferencia de presión entre la parte superior y la parte inferior de un ala (pág. 396)

lightning / rayo una descarga eléctrica natural que ocurre en forma repentina en la atmósfera (pág. 770)

light-year / año luz la distancia que viaja la luz en un vacío durante un año, de aproximadamente 9.5 billones de kilómetros (pág. 834)

linear graph / gráfica lineal una gráfica en la que los datos mostrados forman una línea recta (pág. 347)

liquid / líquido el estado de la materia en el que un material tiene un volumen definido pero no una forma definida (pág. 69)

lithosphere / litósfera una capa de roca rígida, relativamente fría, que comprende la parte superior del manto y la corteza terrestre (pág. 662)

local wind / viento local viento que sopla sobre una distancia corta (pág.757)

loess / loes un depósito que forma el polvo transportado por el viento (pág. 724)

longitudinal wave / onda longitudinal una onda en la que la vibración del medio es paralela a la dirección en que viaja la onda (pág. 502)

longshore drift / deriva litoral el proceso en el que las olas del océano mueven arena a lo largo de la costa (pág. 729)

loudness / volumen una respuesta física a la intensidad del sonido, modificada por factores físicos (pág. 515)

luminous / luminoso la descripción de un objeto que emite su propia luz (pág. 558)

luster / brillo la forma en que la superficie de un mineral refleja la luz (pág. 667)

M

machine / máquina un dispositivo que cambia una fuerza (pág. 417)

magma / magma una mezcla de roca fundida, gases y vapor de agua que se forma bajo la superficie (pág. 671)

magma chamber / cámara magmática zona en forma de bolsa en donde se acumula el magma antes de una erupción volcánica (pág. 691)

magnetic domain / dominio magnético una región que tiene muchos átomos con campos magnéticos alineados (pág. 632)

magnetic field / campo magnético un campo en una región del espacio que ejerce fuerzas magnéticas; un campo producido por imanes, por campos eléctricos variables o por cargas en movimiento (págs. 533, 631)

magnetic force / fuerza magnética la fuerza que un campo magnético ejerce sobre un imán, sobre un material ferromagnético o sobre una carga eléctrica en movimiento (pág. 630)

magnetic pole / polo magnético una región de un imán en donde la fuerza es mayor (pág. 630)

magnetosphere / magnetosfera el área que rodea la Tierra y que está bajo la influencia del campo magnético (pág. 632)

main sequence / secuencia principal una banda diagonal en el diagrama H-R, que representa aproximadamente el 90% de todas las estrellas (pág. 839)

malleability / maleabilidad la capacidad que tiene un sólido de ser golpeado sin quebrarse (pág. 46)

manipulated variable / variable manipulada la variable que causa un cambio en otra variable (pág. 8)
mantle / manto capa gruesa de roca caliente pero sólida que se encuentra debajo de la corteza terrestre (pág. 662)
maria / maria llanuras de basalto planas y bajas sobre la Luna formadas por antiguos caudales de lava (pág. 797)
mass / masa la cantidad de materia que tiene un objeto (pág. 16); medida de la inercia de un objeto que depende de la cantidad de materia que contiene el mismo (pág. 365)
mass extinction / extinción masiva el límite entre eras geológicas en el que diversas formas de organismos vivos se extinguieron en un período relativamente corto (pág. 735)
mass movement / movimiento masivo el movimiento hacia abajo de roca y tierra debido a la gravedad, por ejemplo alud, solifluxión, reptación y desprendimiento (pág. 712)
mass number / número de masa la suma del número de protones y neutrones del núcleo de un átomo (pág. 110)
meander / meandro curva en forma de lazo que se forma en un río cuando el agua en movimiento lento deposita sedimento en la curva interior del río (pág. 716)
mechanical advantage / ventaja mecánica la cantidad de veces que una máquina aumenta la fuerza aplicada (pág. 421)
mechanical energy / energía mecánica la energía relacionada con el movimiento y la posición de objetos cotidianos (pág. 450)
mechanical wave / onda mecánica la perturbación en la materia que lleva energía de un lugar a otro (pág. 500)
mechanical weathering / desgaste mecánico proceso de fragmentación físico de las rocas en partes más pequeñas (pág. 710)
medium / medio el material a través del cual viajan las ondas (pág. 500)
melting point / punto de fusión temperatura a la cual una sustancia cambia de sólida a líquida (pág. 47)
mesosphere / mesosfera la porción inferior del manto de la Tierra (pág. 662); la capa de la atmósfera terrestre que está justo encima de la estratosfera (pág. 750)
metals / metales elementos que son buenos conductores de calor y corriente eléctrica (pág. 135)
metallic bond / enlace metálico la atracción existente entre un catión metálico y los electrones compartidos que lo rodean (pág. 176)
metalloids / metaloides elementos con propiedades que están entre las de los metales y los no metales (pág. 136)
metamorphic rock / roca metamórfica roca que ha sido transformada por la temperatura, presión o reacciones con agua caliente (pág. 674)
meteoroid / meteoroide trozo de roca que se mueve a través del sistema solar (pág. 797)
meteorologist / meteorólogo científico que estudia e intenta predecir el tiempo (pág. 774)
microscope / microscopio instrumento óptico que usa lentes para agrandar la imagen de objetos cercanos y muy pequeños (pág. 584)
mid-ocean ridge / dorsal oceánica cadena montañosa que se encuentra sumergida en el agua (pág. 678)
mineral / mineral sólido inorgánico que ocurre de forma natural con estructura cristalina y composición química definida (pág. 665)
mirage / espejismo imagen falsa o distorsionada (pág. 548)
model / modelo representación de un objeto o evento (pág. 10)
molarity / molaridad el número de moles de un soluto disuelto por litro de solución (pág. 239)
molar mass / masa molar masa de un mol de una sustancia (pág. 196)
mole / mol cantidad de una sustancia que contiene aproximadamente 6.02×10^{23} partículas de la sustancia (pág. 195)
molecule / molécula un grupo neutro de átomos, unidos entre sí por uno o más enlaces covalentes (pág. 166)
momentum / momento producto de la masa de un objeto y su velocidad (pág. 374)
monomer / monómero una pequeña molécula orgánica que se une con otros monómeros para formar un polímero (pág. 275)
monsoon / monzón un sistema de vientos que sopla en dirección contraria según la época del año (pág. 759)
moon / luna cuerpo natural relativamente pequeño en el espacio que gira alrededor de un planeta (pág. 792)
moraines / morrenas un montón de sedimentos que se acumula al pie de un glaciar y a lo largo de los lados (pág. 721)

N

neap tide / marea muerta marea que se produce en el primero o último cuarto de luna, cuando la diferencia entre las mareas alta y baja diarias es mínima (pág. 801)
nearsightedness / miopía una condición ocular que hace que los objetos distantes aparezcan borrosos (pág. 590)
nebula / nebulosa una nube grande de gas y polvo que se expande en un gran volumen de espacio (pág. 840)

net force / fuerza neta la fuerza total que actúa sobre un objeto después que todas las fuerzas se combinan (pág. 357)
network solid / sólido reticulado un sólido que tiene todos sus átomos unidos por enlaces covalentes (pág. 263)
neutralization / neutralización la reacción química entre un ácido y una base (pág. 244)
neutron / neutrón una partícula subatómica neutra que se encuentra en el núcleo de un átomo (pág. 109)
neutron star / estrella de neutrones el centro denso que queda cuando una estrella de gran masa ha explotado como una supernova (pág. 844)
newton (N) / newton (N) la unidad de fuerza del SI que equivale a la fuerza que hace que 1 kilogramo de masa se acelere a razón de 1 metro por segundo cuadrado ($1 \text{ N} = 1 \text{ kg•m/s}^2$ (pág. 357)
noble gases / gases nobles elementos en el Grupo 8A de la tabla periódica (pág. 145)
node / nodo un punto de una onda que no presenta desplazamiento con respecto a la posición de reposo (pág. 512)
nonlinear graph / gráfica no lineal una gráfica en que los datos trazados o mostrados forman una línea curva (pág. 348)
nonmetals / no metales elementos que son malos conductores del calor y la corriente eléctrica (pág. 136)
nonrenewable energy resource / recurso energético no renovable una fuente de energía que existe en cantidades limitadas y que una vez utilizada no puede ser reemplazada salvo con el transcurso de millones de años (pág. 462)
nuclear energy / energía nuclear la energía que se encuentra almacenada en los núcleos atómicos (pág. 452)
nuclear radiation / radiación nuclear partículas y ondas electromagnéticas con carga emitidas desde el núcleo de los radioisótopos (pág. 293)
nucleic acid / ácido nucleico un polímero grande con nitrógeno que se encuentra principalmente en el núcleo de las células (pág. 279)
nucleus / núcleo masa densa con carga positiva que se encuentra ubicada en el centro de un átomo (pág. 105)

O

observation / observación información que se obtiene a través de los sentidos (pág. 8)
occluded front / frente ocluido un frente que se produce cuando una masa de aire caliente queda atrapada entre dos masas de aire más frío (pág. 768)
Ohm's law / ley de Ohm la relación entre voltaje, corriente y resistencia $V = IR$ (pág. 607)
Oort cloud / nube de Oort se cree que es una esfera espesa de cometas que rodea al sistema solar por fuera hasta una distancia de aproximadamente 50,000 UA (pág. 815)
opaque / opaco la descripción de un material que absorbe o refleja toda la luz que incide sobre él de modo que no puede verse nada a través del mismo (pág. 547)
orbital / orbital región de espacio alrededor del núcleo en donde es posible encontrar un electrón (pág. 117)
organic compounds / compuestos orgánicos compuestos que contienen carbón e hidrógeno, a menudo se combinan con algunos otros elementos tales como el oxígeno o nitrógeno (pág. 262)
output arm / brazo de salida la distancia entre el fulcro en una palanca y la fuerza desarrollada (pág. 428)
output distance / distancia de salida distancia a través de la cual actúa una fuerza desarrollada de una máquina (pág. 420)
output force / fuerza desarrollada fuerza que ejerce una máquina (pág. 420)
oxbow lake / laguna de brazo muerto laguna que se forma cuando un río forma un nuevo paso y deja un meandro aislado del curso principal del río (pág. 716)
oxidation-reduction (redox) reaction / reacción de oxidación-reducción (redox) una reacción química en la que hay transferencia de electrones entre los reactantes (pág. 204)
ozone layer / capa de ozono una región de concentración de ozono en la estratosfera (pág. 750)

P

Pangaea / Pangea antiguo supercontinente que se formó hace unos 300 millones de años, que luego dio origen a los actuales continentes (pág. 677)
parallax / paralaje el cambio aparente en la posición de un objeto con respecto a un fondo lejano cuando es visto desde diferentes ubicaciones (pág. 835)
parallel circuit / circuito en paralelo un circuito eléctrico con dos o más pasos a través de los que puede fluir carga (pág. 610)
pascal (Pa) / pascal (Pa) unidad de presión del SI que equivale a 1 newton por metro cuadrado (N/m^2) (pág. 391)
penumbra / penumbra región de sombra de la Luna que rodea la umbra y es menos oscura que la umbra (pág. 800)
period / período hilera en una tabla periódica de elementos (pág. 131); el tiempo que se necesita para tener un ciclo completo de movimiento periódico (pág. 504); unidad de tiempo geológico que los geólogos usan para dividir las eras (pág. 734)

periodic law / ley periódica el patrón de repetición de propiedades que muestran los elementos en la tabla periódica (pág. 131)
periodic motion / movimiento periódico todo movimiento que se repite a intervalos regulares (pág. 504)
periodic table / tabla periódica una organización de elementos en columnas basada en una serie de propiedades que se repiten de hilera en hilera (pág. 127)
permeable / permeable la descripción de un material a través del cual el agua puede pasar con facilidad (pág. 707)
pH / pH una medida de la concentración del ión de hidronio que tiene una solución (pág. 247)
phase change / cambio de fase un cambio físico reversible que ocurre cuando una sustancia cambia de un estado de materia a otro (pág. 84)
phases / fases las diversas formas del lado iluminado de la Luna visto desde la Tierra (pág. 798)
phosphor / fósforo material sólido que emite luz por fluorescencia (pág. 559)
photoelectric effect / efecto fotoeléctrico la emisión de electrones de un metal causada por la luz que llega hasta un metal (pág. 537)
photon / fotón paquete de energía electromagnética (pág. 537)
photosphere / fotosfera una delgada capa interna de la atmósfera del Sol, que es la superficie visible del Sol (pág. 831)
photosynthesis / fotosíntesis proceso en que las plantas combinan químicamente dióxido de carbono y agua para formar carbohidratos, proceso que requiere luz y clorofila (pág. 282)
physical change / cambio físico un cambio que ocurre cuando algunas propiedades de un material cambian, pero las sustancias del material permanecen constantes (pág. 51)
physical property / propiedad física toda característica de un material que se puede observar o medir sin cambiar la composición de las sustancias del material (pág. 45)
physics / física el estudio de materia y energía y las interacciones entre las dos a través de fuerzas y movimiento (pág. 4)
pigment / pigmento un material que absorbe selectivamente ciertos colores de luz y refleja otros colores (pág. 553)
pipe / chimenea canal estrecho y vertical por donde el magma sube a la superficie de la Tierra (pág. 691)
pitch / tono frecuencia de un sonido como lo percibe quien lo escucha (pág. 515)
plane mirror / espejo plano espejo con superficie plana (pág. 571)
planetary nebula / nebulosa planetaria una nube brillante de gas que rodea una estrella moribunda de baja masa (pág. 842)
planetesimals / planetesimales cuerpos con tamaño de asteroides en el disco protoplanetario que se combinan para formar planetas (pág. 819)
plasma / plasma el estado de la materia en el que los átomos han sido despojados de sus electrones (pág. 315)
plate tectonics / tectónica de placas teoría que establece que trozos de litosfera de la Tierra, llamados placas, se mueven lentamente sobre la astenosfera (pág. 676)
plucking / arranque glaciar un proceso en el que los hielos glaciales agrandan las grietas en lechos de roca debajo de un glaciar, y arrastra los trozos sueltos de roca (pág. 720)
polar covalent bond / enlace polar covalente enlace covalente en el que los electrones no se comparten por igual (pág. 168)
polarized light / luz polarizada tipo de luz que tiene luz con ondas que vibran en un solo plano (pág. 548)
polar zones / zonas polares regiones que son generalmente frías y se extienden desde latitud norte 66.5° hasta el Polo Norte y desde latitud sur 66.5° hasta el Polo Sur (pág. 753)
polyatomic ion / ión poliatómico un grupo de átomos con enlaces covalentes de átomos que tiene carga positiva o negativa y actúa como unidad (pág. 172)
polymer / polímero una molécula de gran tamaño que se forma cuando muchas moléculas pequeñas están unidas entre sí por enlaces covalentes (pág. 275)
potential difference / diferencia potencial voltaje, es decir, la diferencia de energía eléctrica potencial entre dos puntos de un campo eléctrico (pág. 606)
potential energy / energía potencial energía que se almacena como consecuencia de la posición o forma (pág. 448)
power / potencia tasa de realizar trabajo (pág. 414)
precipitate / precipitado un sólido que se forma y se separa de una mezcla líquida (pág. 57)
precision / precisión medida de cuán exacta es una medición (pág. 19)
pressure / presión resultado de una fuerza distribuida sobre un área (págs. 75, 390)
primary colors / colores primarios tres colores específicos que se pueden combinar en intensidades variadas para crear millones de colores (pág. 552)
products / productos sustancias nuevas que se forman como consecuencia de una reacción química (pág. 192)
projectile motion / movimiento de proyectil la trayectoria curvada de un objeto en caída libre después de haber recibido una velocidad horizontal inicial (pág. 362)

Spanish Glossary

prominences / protuberancias solares lazos grandes de gas que erupcionan desde las regiones de manchas solares y se extienden hacia arriba desde la fotosfera hacia la cromosfera y a veces hasta dentro de la corona (pág. 833)

protein / proteína polímero grande que se forma cuando los aminoácidos se unen entre sí (pág. 280)

proton / protón una partícula subatómica con carga positiva que se encuentra en el núcleo de un átomo (pág. 108)

protoplanetary disk / disco protoplanetario una nube grande de polvo y gas, en forma de disco, que se formó cuando la nebulosa solar rotaba más rápido y luego comenzó a aplanarse (pág. 819)

protostar / protoestrella nebulosa que se contrae con suficiente masa para formar una estrella (pág. 841)

pulley / polea una máquina simple con una cuerda que pasa por el canal de una rueda (pág. 432)

pulsar / púlsar estrella de neutrón que gira y emite fuertes pulsaciones de ondas radio (pág. 844)

pupil / pupila abertura que permite la entrada de luz en el ojo (pág. 589)

pure substance / sustancia pura material que siempre tiene exactamente la misma composición; elemento o compuesto (pág. 39)

P waves / ondas P ondas primarias; ondas longitudinales que producen los terremotos (pág. 686)

Q

quark / quark partícula subatómica que según las teorías se encuentra entre las unidades básicas de la materia (pág. 305)

quasar / quásar el centro de gran tamaño y muy luminoso de las galaxias jóvenes distantes (pág. 849)

R

radiation / radiación transferencia de energía por ondas que se mueven en el espacio (pág. 481)

radiation zone / zona de radiación región de plasma que se encuentra firmemente unida fuera del centro del sol, en donde la energía se transfiere por la absorción y nueva radiación de luz (pág. 830)

radioactivity / radiactividad proceso en el que un núcleo atómico inestable emite partículas con carga y energía (pág. 292)

radioisotope / radioisótopo isótopo con núcleo inestable (pág. 292)

rarefaction / rarefacción área de una onda longitudinal en que las partículas del medio se esparcen (pág. 502)

ray diagram / diagrama de rayo diagrama que muestra cómo los rayos de luz cambian de dirección cuando chocan contra los espejos y pasan a través de los lentes (pág. 570)

reactant / reactante una sustancia que sufre cambios durante una reacción química (pág. 192)

reaction rate / velocidad de reacción velocidad con que los reactantes se transforman en productos en un tiempo determinado (pág. 212)

reactivity / reactividad propiedad que describe con qué facilidad una sustancia se combina químicamente con otras sustancias (pág. 55)

real image / imagen real copia de un objeto que se forma en el punto en que los rayos de luz se encuentran (pág. 572)

red shift / desplazamiento hacia el rojo un desplazamiento hacia las longitudes de onda rojas de la luz proveniente de las estrellas o galaxias que se alejan de la Tierra (pág. 852)

reflecting telescope / telescopio reflector telescopio que utiliza espejos y lentes convexas para reunir y enfocar luz (pág. 581)

reflection / reflexión la interacción que se produce cuando una onda rebota contra una superficie que no puede atravesar (pág. 508)

refracting telescope / telescopio refractor telescopio que usa sólo lentes para reunir y enfocar luz (pág. 581)

refraction / refracción la curva de una onda al entrar en ángulo en un nuevo medio (pág. 508)

refrigerant / refrigerante fluido que se vaporiza y se condensa dentro de la tubería de una bomba de calor (pág. 490)

regular reflection / reflexión regular reflexión que se produce cuando ondas de luz paralelas chocan contra una superficie y todas se reflejan en la misma dirección (pág. 547)

relative age / edad relativa la edad de una roca comparada con las edades de otras rocas, por encima o por debajo de la misma, en una secuencia de capas de roca (pág. 732)

relative humidity / humedad relativa proporción de la cantidad de vapor de agua en el aire con respecto a la cantidad máxima de vapor de agua que el aire puede contener a esa temperatura (pág. 760)

relative motion / movimiento relativo movimiento en relación al marco de referencia (pág. 329)

renewable energy resource / recurso renovable de energía fuente de energía que se puede reemplazar en períodos relativamente cortos (pág. 463)

resistance / resistencia oposición al flujo de cargas eléctricas en un material (pág. 605)

resonance / resonancia la respuesta de una onda estacionaria a otra onda de la misma frecuencia, con gran incremento de amplitud de la onda estacionaria (pág. 521)

responding variable / variable respuesta variable que cambia en respuesta a un cambio en la variable manipulada (pág. 8)

resultant vector / vector resultante la suma vectorial de dos o más vectores (pág. 331)
retina / retina superficie interna de la parte posterior del ojo, que contiene terminales nerviosas sensibles a la luz (pág. 589)
reversible reaction / reacción reversible una reacción química en la que la conversión de reactantes en productos y la conversión de productos en reactantes se produce al mismo tiempo (pág. 217)
revolution / revolución o traslación movimiento o giro de un cuerpo alrededor de otro (pág. 752)
ring / anillo disco que está formado por muchas partículas pequeñas de roca y hielo que giran alrededor de un planeta (pág. 811)
rock / roca una combinación sólida de minerales u otros materiales (pág. 665)
rock cycle / ciclo de roca una serie de procesos en que las rocas cambian continuamente de un tipo al otro (pág. 674)
rods / bastoncillos neuronas sensibles a la luz en la retina que detectan luz de baja intensidad y distinguen blanco, negro y gris (pág. 589)
rolling friction / fricción de rodamiento fuerza de fricción que actúa sobre objetos rodantes y que se produce debido al cambio de forma en el punto de contacto de rodamiento (pág. 360)
rotation / rotación movimiento de un planeta o luna sobre su eje (pág. 752)
runoff / escorrentía agua que fluye sobre la superficie de la Tierra (pág. 706)

Spanish Glossary

S

salinity / salinidad proporción de sales disueltas en agua (pág. 725)
salt / sal compuesto iónico que se forma cuando un ácido reacciona con una base (pág. 244)
saltation / salto movimiento de partículas como la arena que es arrastrada por el agua o viento en una serie de pequeños saltos (pág. 714)
saturated hydrocarbon / hidrocarburo saturado un hidrocarburo que tiene todos sus enlaces simples (pág. 264)
saturated solution / solución saturada una solución que contiene la cantidad de soluto que el solvente puede contener a una cierta temperatura (pág. 236)
saturated zone / zona saturada una región debajo de la superficie de la Tierra en que los espacios de los poros están totalmente llenos de aguas freáticas (pág. 707)
scattering / dispersión proceso en el que la luz cambia de dirección cuando atraviesa un medio (pág. 549)
science / ciencia sistema de conocimientos sobre el mundo natural y los métodos que se usan para encontrar esos conocimientos (pág. 3)
scientific law / ley científica una afirmación que resume un patrón que se encuentra en la naturaleza (pág. 9)
scientific method / método científico un plan organizado que se utiliza para recoger, organizar y transmitir información (pág. 7)
scientific notation / notación científica una forma de expresar un valor como el producto de un número entre 1 y 10 y una potencia de 10 (pág. 14)
scientific theory / teoría científica una explicación bien comprobada que corresponde a un conjunto de observaciones o resultados experimentales (pág. 9)
screw / tornillo plano inclinado envuelto alrededor de un cilindro (pág. 431)
sea breeze / brisa marina viento local que se produce cuando el aire más fresco que se encuentra sobre el agua fluye hacia la tierra (pág. 757)
sea-floor spreading / expansión del suelo marino proceso por el que se crea nueva corteza oceánica en las dorsales oceánicas, a medida que la corteza más vieja desaparece (pág. 678)
secondary color / color secundario color nuevo que resulta cuando se combinan dos colores primarios (pág. 552)
sediment / sedimento piezas sólidas y pequeñas de material que provienen de rocas y organismos vivos (pág. 672)
sedimentary rock / roca sedimentaria roca que se forma a través del tiempo a partir de la compactación y consolidación de los sedimentos (pág. 672)
seismic waves / ondas sísmicas vibraciones que transmiten la energía liberada durante un terremoto (pág. 684)
seismograph / sismógrafo un dispositivo para detectar y registrar ondas sísmicas (pág. 687)
semiconductor / semiconductor un sólido cristalino que conduce corriente eléctrica sólo bajo ciertas condiciones (pág. 621)
series circuit / circuito en serie circuito eléctrico con un sólo trayecto a través del cual puede fluir la carga (pág. 610)
shield volcano / volcán en escudo un volcán ancho, relativamente plano que se origina como consecuencia de erupciones tranquilas con lava de baja viscosidad (pág. 693)
significant figures / cifras significativas todos los dígitos que se miden directamente en una medición, más el último dígito, que es aproximado (pág. 19)
silicate / silicato roca formada por compuestos de silicio y oxígeno, que por lo general contiene metales como aluminio, hierro o calcio (pág. 661)
sill / dique concordante una estructura que se forma cuando el magma se endurece en una grieta paralela a las capas de roca existentes (pág. 696)

single-replacement reaction / reacción de sustitución simple una reacción química en la que un elemento toma el lugar de otro en un compuesto (pág. 202)

sinkhole / socavones agujero que se forma cuando la erosión debilita una capa de piedra caliza, lo que provoca el derrumbe repentino de algunas partes del suelo (pág. 717)

sliding friction / fricción de deslizamiento una fuerza de fricción que se opone al movimiento de un objeto a medida que se desliza sobre una superficie (pág. 359)

slope / pendiente línea inclinada que equivale a la proporción de un cambio vertical con el correspondiente cambio horizontal (págs. 23, 334)

solar energy / energía solar luz solar que se convierte en energía utilizable (pág. 464)

solar flare / fulguración solar erupción repentina en la superficie solar que, por lo general, ocurre cerca de las manchas solares, produce rayos X y envía partículas con carga al espacio a velocidades de 1000 km/s o más (pág. 833)

solar nebula / nebulosa solar nube de polvo y gas que eventualmente puede desaparecer para formar una o más estrellas con un sistema planetario (pág. 818)

solar system / sistema solar el Sol, los planetas, sus lunas y una variedad de objetos pequeños que giran alrededor del Sol (pág. 792)

solar wind / viento solar una corriente de partículas con cargas eléctricas que fluye desde el Sol hacia afuera a través del sistema solar (pág. 831)

solenoid / solenoide una bobina de alambre conductor que produce un campo magnético (pág. 637)

solid / sólido estado de la materia en el que los materiales tienen una forma definida y un volumen definido (pág. 69)

solstice / solsticio día que marca el comienzo del verano o del invierno; día en que el Sol está directamente encima a una latitud norte 23.5° o latitud sur 23.5° (pág. 753)

solubility / solubilidad cantidad máxima de soluto que se disuelve normalmente en una cierta cantidad de solvente a cierta temperatura (pág. 235)

solute / soluto una sustancia cuyas partículas se disuelven en una solución (pág. 229)

solution / solución una mezcla que se forma cuando se disuelven sustancias y forman una mezcla homogénea (pág. 42)

solvent / solvente una sustancia en la que se disuelve un soluto (pág. 229)

sonar / sonar técnica que sirve para determinar la distancia a un objeto bajo el agua (pág. 516)

sound wave / onda sonora onda longitudinal que consiste en compresiones y rarefacciones y que viaja a través de un medio (pág. 514)

space probe / sonda espacial vehículo no pilotado que lleva instrumentos científicos al espacio y envía datos a la Tierra (pág. 794)

specific heat / calor específico cantidad de calor que se necesita para elevar la temperatura de un gramo de material un grado Celsius (pág. 476)

speed / rapidez proporción de la distancia a que se mueve un objeto con respecto a la cantidad de tiempo en que se mueve el objeto (pág. 332)

spiral galaxy / galaxia espiral una galaxia como la Vía Láctea que tiene una gran cantidad de estrellas en su centro con brazos que se extienden hacia fuera como un molinete (pág. 848)

spring tide / marea viva marea de luna nueva o llena cuando el cambio entre las marea alta y baja diarias es más pronunciado (pág. 801)

stalactite / estalactita una formación tipo carámbano en el techo de una caverna que se forma cuando el agua gotea desde el techo de la caverna (pág. 717)

stalagmite / estalagmita un pilar de minerales en una caverna que se forma cuando el agua gotea hacia el piso de la caverna (pág. 717)

standing wave / onda estacionaria onda que parece quedarse en un lugar y no moverse a través de un medio (pág. 512)

star / estrella bola de gas grande y brillante en el espacio que genera energía a través de la fusión nuclear en su centro (pág. 834)

star system / sistema de estrellas grupo de dos o más estrellas que permanecen unidas por la fuerza de gravedad (pág. 847)

static electricity / electricidad estática estudio del comportamiento de las cargas eléctricas y de la manera en que la carga se transfiere entre objetos (pág. 602)

static friction / fricción estática fuerza de fricción que actúa sobre los objetos que no se mueven (pág. 359)

stationary front / frente estacionario un frente que ocurre cuando dos masas de aire han formado un límite pero ninguna se mueve (pág. 768)

stratosphere / estratosfera capa de la atmósfera terrestre que se encuentra sobre la troposfera (pág. 750)

stratus clouds / nubes estratos capas planas de nubes que cubren gran parte o todo el cielo (pág. 762)

streak / veta el color del polvo de un mineral (pág. 666)

stress / esfuerzo las fuerzas de deformación que actúan sobre las rocas de la corteza terrestre (pág. 685)

strong nuclear force / fuerza nuclear fuerte una fuerza potente de atracción que une protones y neutrones en el núcleo (págs. 308, 379)

subduction / subducción proceso en el que la corteza oceánica se hunde en el manto a través de una grieta (pág. 679)

sublimation / sublimación cambio de fase en que una sustancia cambia de estado sólido a gaseoso o vapor sin pasar por el estado líquido primero (pág. 91)
substance / sustancia materia que siempre tiene exactamente la misma composición; elemento o compuesto (pág. 39)
substituted hydrocarbon / hidrocarburo sustituido hidrocarburo en el que uno o más átomos de hidrógeno han sido reemplazados o sustituidos (pág. 272)
sunspot / mancha solar área de gas en la fotosfera del Sol que es más fría que los gases que la circundan (pág. 832)
superconductor / superconductor un material con resistencia casi cero al ser enfriado a temperaturas bajas (pág. 605)
supergiant / supergigante una estrella de gran tamaño, masiva y muy brillante que tiene un diámetro entre 100 y 1000 veces el diámetro del Sol (pág. 839)
supernova / supernova una explosión enorme en la que los restos de la fusión de una estrella supergigante son arrojados al espacio (pág. 843)
supersaturated solution / solución supersaturada una solución que contiene más cantidad de soluto que el solvente puede retener normalmente a una determinada temperatura (pág. 236)
surface current / corriente superficial una corriente de agua oceánica de gran tamaño que se mueve contiuamente en casi el mismo trayecto (pág. 726)
surface wave / onda superficial onda que viaja a lo largo de una superficie y que separa dos medios (pág. 503); onda transversal que se produce cuando una onda sísmica alcanza la superficie de la Tierra (pág. 687)
suspension / suspensión una mezcla heterogénea que se separa con el tiempo en capas (pág. 43)
S waves / ondas S ondas secundarias; ondas transversales que producen los terremotos (pág. 687)
synthesis reaction / reacción de síntesis reacción química en la que dos o más sustancias reaccionan para formar una sola sustancia (pág. 200)

T

technology / tecnología uso del conocimiento científico para resolver problemas prácticos (pág. 3)
telescope / telescopio un instrumento óptico que usa lentes (o lentes y espejos) para recoger y enfocar luz desde objetos lejanos (pág. 580)
temperate zones / áreas templadas regiones que son generalmente más frescas que los trópicos y están situadas entre latitud norte 23.5° y latitud norte 66.5° y entre latitud sur 23.5° y latitud sur 66.5° (pág. 753)
temperature / temperatura es una medición de cuán caliente o frío está un objeto si se lo compara con un punto de referencia (pág. 475)
terminal velocity / velocidad terminal velocidad constante de un objeto en caída cuando la fuerza de resistencia del aire es igual a la fuerza de gravedad (pág. 361)
terrestrial planets / planetas telúricos los cuatro planetas más cercanos al Sol (Mercurio, Venus, Tierra y Marte) que tienen una estructura similar a la Tierra (pág. 803)
thermal conductor / conductor térmico un material que conduce bien la energía térmica (pág. 480)
thermal energy / energía térmica la energía potencial y cinética total de todas las partículas de un objeto (pág. 451)
thermal expansion / expansión térmica aumento de volumen de un material cuando incrementa su temperatura (pág. 476)
thermal insulator / aislante térmico material que no conduce bien la energía térmica (pág. 480)
thermodynamics / termodinámica estudio de las conversiones entre energía térmica y otras formas de energía (pág. 482)
thermogram / termograma un dibujo o imagen con código de colores que utiliza variaciones en la radiación infrarroja y que sirve para mostrar los cambios en la temperatura (pág. 543)
thermometer / termómetro un instrumento que sirve para medir la temperatura (pág. 20)
thermosphere / termosfera la capa más externa de la atmósfera terrestre (pág. 751)
thunder / trueno el sonido que produce el aire que se expande rápidamente a lo largo del trayecto de una descarga de un relámpago (pág. 770)
thunderstorm / tormenta de truenos un pequeño sistema meteorológico que tiene truenos y relámpagos (pág. 770)
tides / mareas la subida y bajada regular de las aguas del océano (pág. 801)
till / tillita sedimento o arcilla glacial que queda al derretirse el glaciar (pág. 721)
tornado / tornado una tormenta de viento pequeña pero intensa que toma la forma de una columna de aire giratoria que toca el suelo (pág. 770)
total internal reflection / reflexión interna total la reflexión completa de un rayo de luz que regresa a su medio original cuando el ángulo de incidencia es mayor que el ángulo crítico de refracción (pág. 578)
transform boundary / borde de transformación límite en el que las placas tectónicas se deslizan a lo largo de sí mismas, moviéndose en direcciones opuestas (pág. 682)

transformer / transformador un dispositivo que aumenta o disminuye el voltaje de dos circuitos CA conectados (pág. 644)

transistor / transistor un componente en estado sólido que tiene tres capas de material semiconductor y que sirve para encender o apagar corriente o para incrementar la fuerza de señales electrónicas (pág. 621)

transition metals / metales de transición elementos que forman un puente entre los elementos que se encuentran en el lado izquierdo y derecho de la tabla periódica (pág. 136)

translucent / translúcido descripción de un material que dispersa luz que pasa a través del mismo (pág. 547)

transmutation / transmutación la conversión de un elemento en otro por medio de una reacción nuclear (pág. 303)

transparent / transparente descripción de un material que deja pasar la mayor parte de la luz que incide sobre él (pág. 546)

transpiration / transpiración pérdida de agua a través de las hojas de las plantas (pág. 705)

transuranium elements / elementos del grupo transuranio elementos que tienen números atómicos mayores que 92 (pág. 304)

transverse wave / onda transversal onda que hace vibrar a un medio en ángulos rectos en la dirección en que viaja la onda (pág. 50)

trench / fosa una depresión larga y profunda en el suelo oceánico donde la antigua corteza oceánica se hunde en el manto (pág. 679)

tributary / afluente una corriente de agua pequeña que desemboca en un río principal (pág. 706)

tropic zone / zona tropical región cálida entre la latitud sur 23.5° y latitud norte 23.5° (pág. 753)

troposphere / troposfera capa inferior de la atmósfera terrestre en donde ocurre mayormente el clima (pág. 749)

trough / valle punto más bajo de una onda transversal (pág. 501)

turbine / turbina un dispositivo con paletas en forma de ventilador que giran cuando son impulsadas, por ejemplo, por agua o vapor (pág. 646)

U

umbra / umbra parte más oscura de la sombra (pág. 800)

uniformitarianism / uniformismo el principio que establece que los procesos geológicos que ocurren en la actualidad también ocurrieron en el pasado (pág. 661)

unsaturated hydrocarbon / hidrocarburo no saturado hidrocarburo que contiene uno o más enlaces dobles o triples (pág. 265)

unsaturated solution / solución no saturada una solución en que puede disolverse más soluto a una determinada temperatura (pág. 236)

upwelling / afloramiento el movimiento del agua desde las profundidades hacia la superficie del océano (pág. 728)

V

valence electron / electrón de valencia electrón que se encuentra en el nivel energético más alto ocupado que tiene un átomo (pág. 139)

valley glacier / glaciar de montaña una masa larga y estrecha de hielo y nieve en movimiento que comienza, por lo general, cerca del pico de una montaña y se dirige hacia abajo a través del valle y que ha sido formado en un principio por una corriente de agua (pág. 719)

vaporization / vaporización cambio de fase en que una sustancia cambia de estado líquido a gaseoso (pág. 88)

vapor pressure / presión de vapor presión que producen las colisiones o choques de partículas en un vapor dentro de las paredes de un contenedor (pág. 89)

vector / vector una cantidad que tiene una dirección asociada con la misma (pág. 330)

velocity / velocidad la rapidez y la dirección en la que se mueve un objeto y se mide según un punto de referencia (pág. 336)

vent / boca una abertura en el suelo por donde el magma fluye a la superficie terrestre (pág. 691)

virtual image / imagen virtual una copia de un objeto que se forma en el punto desde donde parece venir la luz (pág. 571)

viscosity / viscosidad la tendencia que tiene un líquido a dejar de fluir; resistencia a fluir (pág. 45)

vitamin / vitamina un compuesto orgánico que no producen los organismos vivos pero lo necesitan en pequeñas cantidades (pág. 284)

volcanic neck / cuello volcánico una estructura que se forma cuando el magma se endurece en una chimenea volcánica (pág. 696)

volcano / volcán una montaña que se forma cuando el magma alcanza la superficie (pág. 690)

voltage / voltaje diferencia potencial, la diferencia de energía eléctrica potencial entre dos puntos en un campo eléctrico (pág. 606)

volume / volumen la cantidad de espacio que ocupa un objeto (pág. 16)

W

warm front / frente cálido un frente que se produce cuando una masa de aire caliente rebasa una masa de aire frío (pág. 768)

waste heat / calor perdido energía térmica descargada en un área a una temperatura más baja que no se convierte en trabajo útil (pág. 483)

water cycle / ciclo del agua movimiento continuo del agua en todas sus formas, entre los océanos, atmósfera y la tierra (pág. 705)

watershed / cuenca hidrográfica un territorio con vertientes que fluyen a un sistema fluvial (pág. 706)

water table / nivel freático es la parte superior de una zona saturada (pág. 707)

watt (W) / vatio (W) unidad de potencia del SI que equivale a un julio por segundo (pág. 415)

wavelength / longitud de onda la distancia entre un punto de la onda y el mismo punto en el siguiente ciclo de la onda (pág. 505)

weak nuclear force / fuerza nuclear débil fuerza de atracción potente que actúa sobre un alcance corto o a corta distancia (pág. 380)

weather / clima la condición de la atmósfera en un lugar determinado en un momento determinado (pág. 749)

weathering / desgaste proceso de fragmentación químico o físico de las rocas (pág. 710)

wedge / cuña objeto en forma de V que tiene lados en forma de dos planos inclinados, el uno hacia el otro (pág. 431)

weight / peso fuerza de gravedad que actúa sobre un objeto (pág. 367)

wheel and axle / rueda y eje una máquina simple que está formada por dos discos o cilindros rígidamente unidos y cada uno tiene un radio diferente (pág. 430)

white dwarf / enana blanca resto pequeño, opaco y denso de una estrella de masa mediana o baja (pág. 839)

wind / viento un movimiento de aire, principalmente horizontal, que proviene de áreas de mayor presión hacia áreas de menor presión (pág. 757)

work / trabajo el producto de la distancia y fuerza en la dirección en que se mueve un objeto (pág. 412)

work input / trabajo de entrada trabajo que realiza una máquina cuando la fuerza aplicada actúa a través de la distancia de entrada (pág. 419)

work output / trabajo de salida trabajo que realiza una máquina cuando la fuerza desarrollada actúa a través de la distancia de salida (pág. 420)

Index

Teacher's Edition entries appear in blue type
The page on which a term is defined is indicated in **boldface** type.

A

B

Index (continued)

Index (continued)

H

Index (continued)

M

Index (continued)

Index (continued)

T

Index (continued)

W

X

Y

Z

Acknowledgments

Staff Credits

The people who made up the *Prentice Hall Physical Science: Concepts in Action* team—representing design services, editorial, editorial services, market research, marketing services, education technology, production services, project office, and publishing processes—are listed below. Bold type denotes the core team members.

Leann Davis Alspaugh, Carolyn Belanger, Neil Benjamin, **Barbara Bertell,** Suzanne Biron, Diane Braff, Kristen Cetrulo Braghi, Kenneth Chang, Jonathan D. Cheney, **Todd Christy,** Bob Craton, Kathleen J. Dempsey, Stephen D. Druger, **Frederick Fellows,** Jonathan Fisher, Kathryn Fobert, Paul Gagnon, Julia Gecha, Robert Graham, Ellen Welch Granter, **Maureen Grassi,** Jon Greenberg, Kerri Hoar, Susan Hutchinson, Judy Elgin, **Judie Jozokos,** Kelly Kelliher, **Ellen Levinger,** Meredith Mascola, Terri Mitchell, **Jen Paley, Caroline M. Power,** Siri Schwartzman, Malti Sharma, Amy Winchester, Char Lyn Yeakley

Additional Credits

Ann Bekebrede, Frances Jenkins, Matt Walker

The DK Designs team who contributed to *Prentice Hall Physical Science: Concepts in Action* were as follows: Samantha Borland, Marian Broderick, Carole Curcie, Richard Czapnik, Nigel Duffield, Cynthia Frazer, James A. Hall, Rose Horridge, Heather Jones, Anthony Limerick, David Lloyd, Marie Osborn, Leyla Ostovar, Ralph Pitchford, Pamela Shiels, Andrew Szudek

Maps

Maps and globes on pages 880–887 were created by **DK Cartography.** The team consisted of Tony Chambers, Damien Demaj, Julia Lunn, Ed Merritt, David Roberts, Ann Stephenson, Gail Townsley, and Iorwerth Watkins.

Illustration

Leann Davis Alspaugh: **223;** DK Picture Library: **487, 517, 581, 584, 621, 662, 668, 677, 680, 682, 691, 693, 705, 706, 715, 727, 736–737, 750, 752ml, 752bl, 754, 758, 767, 768, 779, 792–793, 799, 800tl, 800m, 801, 818–819, 830, 839, 842–843, 849, 884–885;** Stephen Durke: **798;** Paul Gagnon: **4;** Gene Givan: **234, 272, 289;** Ellen Welch Granter: **16, 17, 22b, 23, 24b, 92, 134b, 150, 208l, 208r, 215, 221, 469, 470, 542, 543, 558, 559, 563, 564, 566, 567r, 775;** Graph/fix: Bruce Cowie: **130b, 358, 361, 396, 413, 418, 431, 480, 481, 482, 491b, 512, 571, 674, 675, 685, 704b, 765b, 800tr;** J/B Woolsey Associates: **131, 132–133, 134t, 140, 141, 142, 143, 144, 145, 153, 155, 161t;** George Kelvin: **259, 343, 601, 605, 606, 609, 632, 633, 636, 638, 639, 643, 647;** George Ladas: **336, 337, 343;** Matt Mayerchak: **2, 7, 14, 22t, 100t, 108, 113, 126, 130t, 139, 152, 158, 165, 170, 176, 186, 192, 199, 206, 212, 216, 222, 292, 298, 303, 308t, 318, 356, 363, 372, 378, 384, 390, 394, 400t, 406r, 412t, 417, 421t, 427, 440, 446, 453, 462, 468, 474, 479, 486t, 494, 500, 504t, 508, 514t, 526, 570t, 574, 580, 588, 594, 660, 664, 670, 676, 684, 690, 704t, 709, 713, 719, 725, 732, 752t, 774, 778, 790, 796, 803, 810, 818, 828;** Morgan-Cain & Associates: **20, 29, 30, 31, 65, 85b, 88, 97, 123l, 123r, 127, 159t, 159b, 160, 161b, 162, 164, 166t, 166b, 168t, 168b, 169, 171, 172t, 172b, 173, 175, 177, 187, 188l, 188r, 224, 225, 229, 230, 231, 237, 263, 264, 294–295, 296, 299t, 308l, 309, 310, 311, 319, 320, 321, 359, 368, 376, 380, 381, 382, 385, 387, 391, 395b, 397, 400b, 401, 406l, 407, 408, 409, 419, 428, 441, 442, 443l, 471, 475t, 475b, 478, 486b, 489, 490, 492, 496, 497, 501, 502, 503, 504b, 505, 507, 509t, 511, 516, 527, 528, 529, 570l, 572bl, 572br, 573tl, 573tr, 575t, 576l, 576r, 577t, 577m, 577b, 578, 584b, 585, 589, 590, 592, 595, 596l, 596r, 597, 686, 689, 701, 743, 757, 776, 787, 813, 823, 825, 832, 853b, 859, 860, 861, 864, 865, 871bl, 873, 874, 879, 881, 882–883, 887;** Jen Paley: **24t, 26, 28, 38, 41, 42, 45, 47, 54, 60, 62, 64, 68, 71, 72t, 75, 78l, 84, 94, 96, 109, 112, 117, 119, 120, 154, 167, 184, 189, 197, 293, 299b, 357, 377, 383, 386, 392, 395t, 405, 421b, 433, 438, 439, 443r, 463, 476, 479b, 491t, 493, 509b, 514b, 515, 532, 539, 546, 550, 567l, 575b, 667, 676, 697b, 699, 700, 720, 734–735b, 742, 746, 747, 755t, 755b, 759, 760, 765t, 766, 769, 783, 786, 804, 811, 824, 829b, 834, 836, 840, 846, 852t, 856, 858, 871ml, 871tr, 871mr, 876tl, 876bl, 876mr, 876br;** Precision Graphics: **44, 46, 69, 70, 72, 77, 78r, 89, 95, 100b, 102, 103, 104, 121, 122, 193, 194, 207, 217, 230, 258, 262, 264, 265, 266, 267, 273, 274, 276, 279, 282, 331, 430, 432, 533, 534, 536, 537, 538, 540, 541, 548, 663, 678, 679, 682, 686, 707, 710, 712, 714, 720, 723, 728, 729, 733, 734t, 748, 753, 770, 780–781, 829t, 835, 835, 838, 844, 852b, 853t, 854;** www.TrevorJohnston.com: **8, 85t;** XNR Productions Inc.: **697t**

Cover design Maria Keogh/Kokopelli Design Studio, Inc.;

Cover photo Tom Sanders/Image State

Photo research Paula Wehde

Dorling Kindersley picture research done in London, England, by Cynthia Frazer and Marie Osborn; Dorling Kindersley illustrations done by Richard Bonson, KJA.Artists.com, and Martin Sanders in London, England.

Front matter

Pages i, ii, Tom Sanders/Image State; **iii t, iii m** Prentice Hall; **iii b** Judith Ficksman; **iv,** Richard Fukuhara/Corbis; **v t,** Russ Lappa; **v b,** Phil Degginger/USGS/Color-Pic, Inc.; **vi,** Photo Researchers, Inc.; **vii,** Alain Nogues/Corbis; **viii,** Allsport/Getty Images, Inc.; **ix both,** DK Picture Library; **x t,** Corbis; **x b,** Galen Rowell/Corbis; **xi tl,** Corbis; **xi tr,** Ressmeyer/Corbis; **xi b,** Russ Lappa; **xii both,** Richard Haynes; **xiii,** Breck P. Kent; **xiv,** Richard Haynes; **xv all,** DK Picture Library and The Natural History Museum; **xvii,** Science Photo Library.

Chapter 1

Pages xviii–1, 2 t, Rosenfeld Images Ltd./Science Photo Library/Photo Researchers, Inc.; **2 bl,** Science Photo Library/Photo Researchers, Inc.; **2 br,** Photo Researchers, Inc.; **3 t,** AT&T Archives; **3 tm, 3 bm,** Getty Images, Inc.; **3 b,** AP/Wide World Photos; **4 tl,** Russ Lappa; **4 tml,** Visuals Unlimited; **4 tmr,** Agstock USA; **4 tr,** John Bova/Photo Researchers, Inc.; **4 bl,** Kevin Fleming/Corbis; **4 chemicals,** Yoav Levy/Phototake; **4 barometer,** Paul Seheult/Corbis; **4 space,** Lynette Cook/Photo Researchers, Inc.; **4 foliage,** Panoramic Images; **4 br,** Leland Bobbe/Corbis; **5,** Richard Berenholtz/Corbis; **6,** Dana White/PhotoEdit; **7 t,** Rosenfeld Images Ltd./Science Photo Library/Photo Researchers, Inc.; **7 b,** AP/Wide World Photos; **9,** Colin Cuthbert/Newcastle University/Science Photo Library/Photo Researchers, Inc.; **10,** Boeing Commercial Airplane Group; **11,** Steve Chenn Photography/Westlight/Corbis;**12–13,** Rex Features; **12 bl,** Jeremy Sutton Hibbert/Rex Features; **13 ml,** Anna Clopet/Corbis;**13 br, 13 mr,** DK Picture Library; **13 t,** Peter Menzel/Science Photo Library; **14 t,** Rosenfeld Images Ltd./Science Photo Library/Photo Researchers, Inc.; **14 b,** Frank Zullo/Photo Researchers, Inc.; **16,** Will Hart/PhotoEdit; **18,** Jonathan Nourok/PhotoEdit; **19 t,** Tom Pantages; **19 b,** DK Picture Library; **21 l,** Cadmium Systems Ltd; **21 br,** DK Picture Library; **21 tr,** Sally & Richard Greenhill Photo Library; **22,** Rosenfeld Images Ltd./Science Photo Library/Photo Researchers, Inc.; **25 l,** Layne Kennedy/Corbis; **25 r,** AP/Wide World Photos; **26, 27,** Richard Haynes.

Chapter 2

Pages 36–37, 38 t, Peter Menzel/Stock Boston; **38 b,** Corbis; **39 l,** E. R. Degginger/Color Pic, Inc.; **39 ml,** Charles D. Winters/Photo Researchers, Inc.; **39 mr,** Lester Bergman/Corbis; **39 r,** Charles D. Winters/Photo Researchers, Inc.; **40 t,** DK Picture Library; **40 m,** Bill Aron/PhotoEdit; **40 b,** Mark A. Scheider/Photo Researchers, Inc.; **41 t,** Russ Lappa; **41 bl,** E. R. Degginger/Color Pic, Inc.; **41 br,** Russ Lappa; **42,** Richard Fukuhara/Corbis; **43 tl,** Russ Lappa; **43 tm,** Dennis MacDonald/PhotoEdit; **43 tr,** Michael Neveux/Corbis; **43 b,** Grafton Marshall Smith/Corbis; **44,** Rachel Epstein/PhotoEdit; **45 t,** Peter Menzel/Stock Boston; **45 b,** Ross Durant/Foodpix; **46–47,** Araldo De Luca/Corbis; **47 t,** AK/Haines/Photo Researchers, Inc.; **48,** Ric Ergenbright/Corbis; **49 tl,** Museum of Mankind/Bridgeman Art Library/DK Picture Library; **49 bl,** (3 images) DK Picture Library; **49 tr,** David Samuel Robbins/Corbis; **49 mr,** Museum of Mankind/Bridgeman Art Library, London/New York; **50,** Eda Rogers/Sea Images; **51 t,** Nancy Ney/Corbis; **51 b,** Paul A. Souders/Corbis; **52 t,** Dave G. Houser/Corbis; **52–53 b,** DK Picture Library; **53 t,** Hans Strand/Corbis; **54 t,** Peter Menzel/Stock Boston; **54 b,** Michelle Garrett/Corbis; **55,** Chinch Gryniewicz/Corbis; **56,** Russ Lappa; **57 tl,** Grant Smith/Corbis; **57 tr,** Pat Bruno/Positive Images; **57 bl,** E. R. Degginger/Color Pic, Inc.; **57 br,** Rick Souders/Foodpix/Getty Images, Inc.; **58,** Phil Degginger/Color Pic, Inc.; **59,** Courtesy SFPA; **60 both,** Russ Lappa; **61,** Richard Haynes; **63,** C. C. Lockwood/Bruce Coleman, Inc.; **64,** PhotoDisc, Inc./Getty Images, Inc.

Chapter 3

Pages 66–67, 68 t, Charles Mauzy/Corbis; **68 b,** Russ Lappa; **69 t,** Clive Streeter/ DK Picture Library; **69 b,** Science Photo Library/Photo Researchers, Inc.; **70,** Russ Lappa; **71,** Chris Moody/Getty Images, Inc.; **72,** Getty Images, Inc.; **73,** Jim Whitmer; **74 both,** Dandy Zipper/Getty Images, Inc.; **75 t,** Charles Mauzy/Corbis; **75 b,** Stone/ Getty Images, Inc.; **76 t,** Tony Freeman/PhotoEdit; **76 b,** Pearson Education/Prentice Hall College; **79,** Russ Lappa; **81,** Bruce Coleman, Inc.; **82–83 t,** Barbara Leslie/Getty Images; **82–83 b,** DK Picture Library; **83 tr,** S. Sassoon/ Robert Harding Picture Library; **83 mr,** David Usill/Window on the World Photo Library; **84 t,** Charles Mauzy/Corbis; **84 b,** Panoramic Images; **86 t,** Galen Rowell/Corbis; **86 b,** Agstock USA; **87 t,** Allsport/Getty Images; **87 b,** DK Picture Library; **89 t,** Maslowski/Photo Researchers, Inc.; **89 b,** DK Picture Library; **90,** Natural Selection; **91,** Margo Wright/Tinker Take Off; **92,** Russ Lappa; **93,** Richard Haynes.

Chapter 4

Pages 98–99, 100, Professor Kevin F. Kelly & Naomi J. Halas/Rice University; **101 t,** Stephen Frisch/Stock Boston; **101 b,** Clive Streeter/DK Picture Library; **102,** Clive Streeter/DK Picture Library; **103,** Mary Kate Denny/PhotoEdit; **105,** Bettmann/Corbis; **106 b,** Almaden Research Center/I.B.M.; **106 l,** Sandia National Laboratories; **106–107,** Ames/NASA; **107 tr,** DK Picture Library; **108 t,** Professor Kevin F. Kelly & Naomi J. Halas/Rice University; **108 b,** Michael Powers/Stock Boston; **109,** Russ Lappa; **110 t,** Charles D. Winter/Photo Researchers, Inc.; **110 m, 110 b,** E. R. Degginger/Color Pic, Inc.; **111 b,** (4 Images) DK Picture Library; **111 t,** Science & Society Picture Library; **111 br,** Colin Cuthbert/Science Photo Library; **113 t,** Professor Kevin F. Kelly & Naomi J. Halas/Rice University; **113 b,** Bohdan Hrynewych/Stock Boston; **116 l, 116 r,** Phil Degginer/Color-Pic, Inc.; **117,** Russ Lappa; **118,** William Sallaz/Corbis; **119,** Jerry Mason/Science Photo Library/Photo Researchers, Inc.; **120,** E. R. Degginger/Color Pic, Inc.

Chapter 5

Pages 124–125, 126 t, Wolfgand Kaehler/Corbis; **126 b,** Michael Newman/PhotoEdit; **127, 128,** Russ Lappa; **129 t,** Alan Schein/Corbis; **129 b,** Runk/Schoenberger/Grant Heilman Photography, Inc.; **130 t,** Wolfgand Kaehler/Corbis; **130 b,** Phil Degginger/Color-Pic, Inc.; **135 l,** Science Photo Library/Photo Researchers, Inc.; **135 r,** PerkinElmer Corporation; **136 t,** Henry T. Kaiser/Stock Connection/PictureQuest; **136 b,** PhotoEdit; **137,** DK Picture Library; **138 sodium,** Runk/Schoenberger/Grant Heilman Photography, Inc.; **138 magnesium,** Science Photo Library/Photo Researchers, Inc.; **138 aluminum,** Charles D. Winters/Photo Researchers, Inc.; **138 silicon,** DK Picture Library; **138 phosphorus,** Richard Megna/Fundamental Photographs; **138 sulfur,** Charles D. Winter/Photo Researchers, Inc.; **138 chlorine,** Yoav Levy/Phototake; **138 argon,** E. R. Degginger/Color Pic, Inc.; **139 t,** Wolfgang Kaehler/Corbis; **139 b,** Mike Fiala/Getty Images, Inc.; **140 l,** Runk/Schoenberger/Grant Heilman Photography, Inc.; **140 r,** Richard Megna/Fundamental Photographs; **141 l,** Jane Grushow/Grant Heilman Photography, Inc.; **141 m,** Runk/Schoenberger/Grant Heilman Photography, Inc.; **141 r,** Image Bank/Getty Images Inc.; **142 t,** Jeff Greenberg/Visuals Unlimited; **142 b,** Dana White/PhotoEdit; **143 t,** David Nunuk/Science Photo Library/Photo Researchers, Inc.;**143 b,** Runk/Schoenberger/ Grant Heilman Photography, Inc.; **144 tl,** Yoav Levy/Phototake; **144 tr,** Elena Rooraid/PhotoEdit; **144 bl,** Pearson Education/Prentice Hall College; **145,** Raymond Gendreau/Getty Images, Inc.; **146–147,** DK Picture Library; **148–149 t,** (5 images) DK Picture Library; **148–149b,** Andy Sacks/Getty Images; **150, 151,** Richard Haynes.

Chapter 6

Pages 156–157, 158 t, George Lepp/Corbis; **158 b,** Horie Corporation; **161,** Gelen Rowell/Corbis; **162 t,** M. Claye/Photo Researchers, Inc.; **162 b,** Russ Lappa; **163,** DK Picture Library; **165 t,** George Lepp/Corbis; **165 b,** Charles Gupton/Stock Boston; **166,** Mark M. Lawrence/Corbis; **170 t,** George Lepp/Corbis; **170 b,** Jennifer Cheung; **171 both,** Markusen Metal Studios, Ltd.; **172,** Matthias Kulka/Corbis; **173,** Richard Haynes; **176 t,** George Lepp/Corbis; **176 b,** Andrew Syred/Science Photo Library/Photo Researchers, Inc.; **178 m,** DK Picture Library; **178 l,** Wellcome Institute/Science Museum/DK Picture Library; **178 r,** Hulton Archive/Getty Images; **179 r,** George Hall/Corbis; **179 l,** Hulton Archive/Getty Images; **179 m,** Pieces of Time—www.antique-watch.com; **180 l,** E. R. Degginger/Color-Pic, Inc.; **180 r,** Paul Conklin/PhotoEdit; **181,** E.R. Degginger/Color-Pic, Inc.; **182 bl,** DK Picture Library; **183 tl,** Science Museum/DK Picture Library; **183 tc,** Science Museum/DK Picture Library; **183 tr,** Jan Hinsch/Science Photo Library; **183 bl,** Tony Craddock/Science Photo Library/Photo Researchers, Inc; **183 br,** DK Picture Library; **184,185,** Richard Haynes.

Chapter 7

Pages 190–191, 192 t, Panoramic Images; **192 b,** Charles O'Rear/Corbis; **194,** Visuals Unlimited; **195,** Russ Lappa; **196 both,** E. R. Degginger/Color-Pic, Inc.; **197,** Foodpix; **199 t,** Panoramic Images; **199 b,** David Bartruff/Stock Boston; **200,** Tom Pantages; **201 b** (4 images) DK Picture Library; **201 tr,** Don Johnston/Getty Images; **202 all,** Clive Streeter/DK Picture Library; **203 t,** Richard Megna/Fundamental Photographs; **203 b,** Russ Lappa; **204 t,** Charles D. Winter/Photo Researchers, Inc.; **204 b,** Richard Megna/Fundamental Photographs; **206 t,** Panoramic Images; **206 b,** Bill Bachmann/PhotoEdit; **209,** Richard Megna/Fundamental Photographs; **210 l,** Marcelo Del Pozo/Reuters/Popperfoto; **210–211,** Rex Features/Sipa Press; **211 bl,** Corbis Sygma; **211 t,** Jonathan Blair/Corbis; **211 mr,** Paul A. Souders/Corbis; **212 t,** Panoramic Images; **212 b,** Will Hart; **213,** Steven Martine/AP Photo; **214,** DK Picture Library; **216 t,** Panoramic Images; **216 b,** David Sailors; **218 t,** Allsport/Getty Images, Inc.; **218 b,** Edgar Fahs Smith Collection/University of Pennsylvania Library; **219,** Ken Graham/Accent Alaska; **220,** Richard Haynes; **221,** Russ Lappa.

Chapter 8

Pages 226–227, 228 t, Claus Meyer/Minden Pictures; **228 b,** Index Stock Imagery, Inc.; **229,** Chris Collins/Corbis; **230,** Index Stock Imagery, Inc.; **231,** Annie Griffiths Belt/Corbis; **233 t,** Dick Makin/Last Resort Picture Library; **233 b,** (4 images) DK Picture Library; **235 t,** Claus Meyer/Minden Pictures; **235 b,** Richard Haynes; **236 t,** PhotoDisc, Inc./Getty Images, Inc.; **236 b all,** Richard Megna/Fundamental Photographs; **237,** Mark Hanauer/Corbis; **238,** DK Picture Library; **239,** Bill Varie/Corbis; **240 t,** Claus Meyer/Minden Pictures; **240 b,** Russ Lappa; **241,** Paul Silverman/Fundamental Photographs; **242,** Index Stock Imagery, Inc.; **243 t,** Corbis; **243 b,** Bob Krist/Corbis; **244,** James L. Amos/Corbis; **246 t,** Claus Meyer/Minden Pictures; **246 b,** Jacksonville Journal Courier/The Image; **248,** Russ Lappa; **249,** Getty Images, Inc.; **250–251 t,** (montage) National Cancer Institute/NIBSC/Science Photo Library; **250 bl,** Science Photo Library; **250 br, 251 r,** DK Picture Library; **252 t,** Timepix/Rex Features; **252 b, 253 l,** DK Picture Library; **253 r,** Jim Varney/Science Photo Library; **255,** Richard Haynes; **256 b all,** Richard Megna/Fundamental Photographs.

Chapter 9

Pages 260–261, 262 t, Arnulf Husmo/Getty Images, Inc.; **262 b,** Mark A. Johnson/Corbis; **264,** Javier Larrea Roa/AGE Fotostock; **265,** Russ Lappa; **266 t,** Comstock, Inc.; **266 c,** Arthur C. Smith III/Grant Heilman Photography, Inc.; **266 b,** Stamp from the private collection of Professor C.M. Lang, photography by Gary J. Shulfer, University of Wisconsin, Stevens Point. "1966, Belgium (Scott #624)"; Scott Standard Postage Stamp Catalogue, Scott Pub. Co.; **267 t,** David Muench/Corbis; **267 c,** Runk/Schoenberger/Grant Heilman Photography, Inc.; **268,** Barry Rowland/AGE Fotostock; **269,** Spencer Platt/Getty Images, Inc.; **270-271 t,** Bruce Forster/Getty Images; **270–271 b,** DK Picture Library; **272,** Arnulf Husmo/Getty Images, Inc.; **273,** Grant Heilman Photography, Inc.; **274,** Hisham F. Ibrahim/Getty Images, Inc.; **275 t,** Arnulf Husmo/Getty Images, Inc.; **275 b,** Getty Images, Inc.; **276 l,** Michael Pole/Corbis; **276 c,** DK Picture Library; **276 r,** Bud Freund/Corbis; **277 tr,** Araldite/Advertising Archives; **277 mr,** Davies+Starr/Getty Images; **277 b,** DK Picture Library; **278,** Larry Lefever/Grant Heilman Photography, Inc.; **279,** Getty Images, Inc.; **280,** DK Picture Library; **281,** Robert Y. Kaufman/Yogi Inc./Corbis; **282 t,** Arnulf Husmo/Getty Images, Inc.; **282 b,** Aldo Torelli/Getty Images, Inc.; **283,** Jane Sapinsky/Corbis; **284,** Michael P. Gadomski/Photo Researchers, Inc.; **285,** Richard Haynes; **287,** Shannon Fagan/Corbis.

Chapter 10

Pages 290–291, 292 t, Patrice Loiez/CERN/Science Photo Library/Photo Researchers, Inc.; **292 m,** The Granger Collection, New York; **292 b,** Jean-Loup Charmet/Science Photo Library/Photo Researchers, Inc.; **293,** Francois Gohier, Photo Researchers, Inc.; **296,** Roberto De Gugliemo/Science Photo Library/Photo Researchers, Inc.; **297,** Alain Nogues/Corbis; **298 t,** Patrice Loiez/CERN/Science Photo Library/Photo Researchers, Inc.; **298 b,** Kenneth Garrett; **300,** Richard Haynes; **301,** Peter Hayman/British Museum; **302,** Richard B. Levine/Frances M. Roberts; **303 t,** Patrice Loiez/CERN/Science Photo Library/Photo Researchers, Inc.; **303 b,** Corbis; **304,** NASA; **305,** David Parker/Science Photo Library/Photo Researchers, Inc.; **306 bl, 306–307,** Roger Ressmeyer/Corbis; **307 r,** (2 images) DK Picture Library; **308,** Patrice Loiez/CERN/Science Photo Library/Photo Researchers, Inc.; **309,** AP/Wide World Photos; **311,** Stone/Getty Images, Inc.; **312 l, 312 m,** Science Photo Library; **313 m,** Corbis; **312 r,** Hulton Archive/Getty Images; **313 l,** Los Alamos National Laboratory/Science Photo Library; **313 r,** Idaho National Engineering and Environmental Laboratory; **314 t,** Yann Arthus-Bertrand/Corbis; **314 b,** DK Picture Library; **315,** Roger Ressmeyer/Corbis; **316 both, 317,** Richard Haynes.

Chapter 11

Pages 326–327, 328 t, Chris Cole/Corbis; **328 b,** Tony Freeman/PhotoEdit; **329,** Pedro Coll/AGE Fotostock; **332 t,** Chris Cole/Corbis; **332 b,** Dennis O'Clair/Getty Images, Inc.; **334 t,** Steve Krongard, Inc./Getty Images, Inc.; **334 b,** Leonard Lessin/Peter Arnold, Inc.; **335 t,** Carphotos.net/Cindy Lewis/alamy.com; **335 b,** DK Picture Library; **336 t,** Randy Wells/Corbis; **336 b,** Sharon Green/Corbis; **338 m,** National Maritime Museum/DK Picture Library; **338 bl,** Stephen Oliver/DK Picture Library; **338–339,** Joel W. Rogers/Corbis; **339 r,** (2 images) DK Picture Library; **340–341b,** DK Picture Library; **340 t,** ESA/CE/Eurocontrol/Science Photo Library; **341 tr,** DK Picture Library; **341 ml, 341 mr,** Raytheon Marine Company/Raymarine Incorporated; **341 tl,** Weems and Plath; **342 t,** Chris Cole/Corbis; **342 b,** David Young-Wolff/PhotoEdit; **344 t,** Barnabas Kindersley/DK Picture Library; **344 b,** Lester Lefkowitz/Corbis; **345,** Benjamin Rondel/Corbis Stock Market; **347 t,** Karl Weatherly/Getty Images, Inc.; **347 b,** Michael Newman/PhotoEdit.

Chapter 12

Pages 354–355, 356 t, Getty Images, Inc.; **356 b,** AP/Wide World Photos; **357 both, 358,** David Young-Wolff/PhotoEdit; **360,** Russ Lappa; **361 t,** Jim Steinberg/Photo

Acknowledgments

Researchers, Inc.; **361 b,** Nick Bergkessel/Photo Researchers, Inc.; **362 both,** Megna/Peticolas/Fundamental Photographs; **363 t,** Getty Images, Inc.; **363 m,** Corbis; **363 b,** The Granger Collection, New York; **364 t,** Bettmann/Corbis; **364 m,** Sheila Terry/Science Photo Library/Photo Researchers, Inc.; **364 b both, 365 both,** Insurance Institute for Highway Safety; **366 tr,** Mercedes Benz/DK Picture Library; **366 b,** DK Picture Library; **369 l,** AP/ Wide World Photos; **369 r,** Bettmann/Corbis; **370–371,** Steve Fitchett/Getty Images; **371 tr, 371 bl, 371 mr,** Airsport Photo Library; **372 both,** Getty Images, Inc.; **373,** Paul Sutton/Duomo/Corbis; **374 l,** Mary Evans Picture Library; **374 r,** Corbis/Bettmann; **375 l,** Bettmann/Corbis; **375 m,** Corbis; **375 r,** Joe Schwartz/Joyrides; **378 t,** Getty Images, Inc.; **378 b,** Ludek Press/Science Photo Library/Photo Researchers, Inc.; **379 t,** Getty Images, Inc.; **379 b,** Michelle D. Bridwell/PhotoEdit; **383,** Richard Haynes.

Chapter 13
Pages 388–389, 390 t, Masterfile Corporation; **390 m,** Jonathan Nourok/PhotoEdit; **390 b,** Aaron Haupt/Stock Boston; **391 t,** Russ Lappa; **391 b,** Charles D. Winter/Photo Researchers, Inc.; **392, 393 all,** Barry Runk/Grant Heilman Photography, Inc.; **394 t,** Masterfile Corporation; **394 b,** Russ Lappa; **395 t, 395 m,** Russ Lappa; **395 b,** E. R. Degginger/Color Pic, Inc.; **396,** Firefly Productions/Corbis; **398 b,** (4 images) DK Picture Library; **398–399,** Cameron Heryet/Getty Images; **399 t,** DK Picture Library; **400,** Masterfile Corporation; **402 l,** Steve Kaufman/Corbis; **402–403,** (4 images) DK Picture Library; **404,** Layne Kennedy/Corbis; **405,** Richard Haynes; **406,** Barry Runk/Grant Heilman Photography, Inc.

Chapter 14
Pages 410-411, 412 t, Paul Chesley/Getty Images, Inc.; **412 b,** Reuters/Corbis; **413 all,** Russ Lappa; **414 t,** Dennis MacDonald/PhotoEdit; **414 b,** E. R. Degginger/Color-Pic, Inc.; **416 t,** Kevin Fleming/Corbis; **416 b,** Tony Freeman/PhotoEdit; **417 t,** Paul Chesley/Getty Images, Inc.; **417 b,** Mugshots/Corbis; **418,** Tony Freeman/PhotoEdit; **420,** Kevin Fleming/Corbis; **421 t,** Paul Chesley/Getty Images, Inc.; **421 b,** PhotoDisc, Inc./Getty Images, Inc.; **422 l,** Corbis/Bettmann; **422 m,** North Wind Picture Archives; **422 r,** Science & Society Picture Library; **423 r,** Hulton Archive/Getty Images; **423 l, 423 m,** Science & Society Picture Library; **424 t,** Richard Haynes; **424 b,** W. Deuter/Zefa Images/Masterfile Corporation; **426,** Michael Rosenfeld/Getty Images, Inc.; **427 t,** Paul Chesley/Getty Images, Inc.; **427 b,** Rube Goldberg, Inc.; **428 l,** Russ Lappa; **428 m,** Richard Hutchings/PhotoEdit; **428 r,** Rob Crandal/The Image Works; **429,** Richard Haynes; **430,** Neil Beer/Corbis; **431 t,** Michael Thompson/Animals Animals/Earth Scenes; **431 b,** Russ Lappa; **431 inset,** Russ Lappa; **432,** H. David Seawall/Corbis; **434,** DK Picture Library; **435,** Richard Fukuhara/Corbis; **436–437,** DK Picture Library; **437 mr,** John Kelly/Getty Images; **438,** Richard Haynes; **439,** Eye Wire/Getty Images, Inc.

Chapter 15
Pages 444–445, 446 t, David Northcott/Corbis; **446 b,** Galen Rowell/Corbis; **447 t,** David Frazier/Photo Researchers, Inc.; **447 m,** Foodpix; **447 b,** Image Bank/Getty Images, Inc.; **448, 449,** Getty Images, Inc.; **450 l,** Allsport/Getty Images, Inc.; **450 r,** Photonica; **451 t,** Dawson Jones/Stock Boston; **451 b,** Tom Stewart/Corbis; **452 t,** Tom Ives/Corbis; **452 b,** Myron Jay Dorf/Corbis; **453 t,** David Northcott/Corbis; **453 b,** American Museum of Natural History; **454,** Myron Jay Dorf/Corbis; **455,** Allsport/Getty Images, Inc.; **456 t,** John Bova/Photo Researchers, Inc.; **456 b,** Phil Degginger/Color-Pic, Inc.; **457,** Corbis; **459,** Topham/The Image Works; **460,** Robin Smith/Getty Images; **461 t,** DK Picture Library; **461 mr,** Premier Rides Inc.; **461 b,** Richard F. Snow Collection; **462 t,** David Northcott/Corbis; **462 b,** George Hunter/Getty Images, Inc.; **463,** David Parker/Science Photo Library/Photo Researchers, Inc.; **464 t,** Charles Krebs/Corbis; **464 b,** Joseph Sohm/Corbis; **465,** DK Picture Library; **466,** John Elk/Stock Boston; **467,** Russ Lappa.

Chapter 16
Pages 472–473, 474 t, W. A. Sharman/Corbis; **474 b,** The Granger Collection, New York; **475 t,** Jonelle Weaver/Getty Images Inc.; **475 b,** RF/Corbis; **479 t,** W. A. Sharman/Corbis; **479 b,** Alfred Pasieka/Science Photo Library/Photo Researchers, Inc.; **480 tl,** Foodpix; **480 bl,** Eastcott/Momatiuk/Stock Boston; **480 br,** Steve Cohen/Foodpix; **481,** Runk/Schoenberger/Grant Heilman Photography, Inc.; **482,** Phil Degginger/Color-Pic, Inc.; **483,** Geoffrey Wheeler/Courtesy National Institute of Standards and Technology; **484–485 t,** Building Research Establishment Ltd/BRE Imaging 2002; **484–485 b,** (4 images) DK Picture Library; **486,** W.A. Sharman/Corbis; **488 t,** Honda Motor Europe Ltd.; **488 b,** DK Picture Library; **491,** David Young-Wolff/PhotoEdit; **493,** Richard Haynes; **495,** Getty Images, Inc.

Chapter 17
Pages 498–499, 500 t, Taxi/Getty Images, Inc.; **500 b,** Timothy O'Keefe/Bruce Coleman, Inc.; **504 t, 508 t,** Taxi/Getty Images, Inc.; **508 b,** Scott Gog/Corbis; **509,** T. Kitchin/Tom Stack & Associates, Inc.; **510 both,** Richard Megna/Fundamental Photographs; **512 both,** Fundamental Photographs; **513,** Masa Ushioda/WaterHouse Marine Images; **514,** Taxi/Getty Images, Inc.; **515 t,** Getty Images, Inc.; **515 b,** Index Stock Imagery, Inc.; **516,** Getty Images, Inc.; **518 l, 518 m, 518 r,** Science Museum/DK Picture Library; **519 m,** Royalty-Free Corbis; **519 l,** Corbis/Bettmann; **519 r,** Newscast/Sony; **520 b, 520 t,** DK Picture Library; **520 m,** Steinway/DK Picture Library; **521,** Talaske Group; **522,** Randy Jolly/Corbis; **523 t,** (2 images) DK Picture Library; **523 bl,** Alan Thornton/Getty Images; **524, 525,** Richard Haynes.

Chapter 18
Pages 530–531, 532 t, Bob Rowan/Panoramic Images; **532 b,** SuperStock, Inc.; **536,** Dorling Kindersley Ltd.; **539 t,** Bob Rowan/Panoramic Images; **539 b,** Courtesy Caltech Outreach/Jet Propulsion Laboratory; **541 both,** Getty Images, Inc.; **542,** Spencer Grant/PhotoEdit; **543 both,** FLIR Systems, Inc.; **544 t,** Russ Lappa; **544 b,** David Arky/Corbis; **545,** Science Photo Library/Photo Researchers, Inc.; **546 t,** Bob Rowan/Panoramic Images; **546 b,** Stephen Frink/The Waterhouse; **547 t,** Getty Images, Inc.; **547 m,** PhotoDisc, Inc./Getty Images, Inc.; **547 b,** Arthur Morris/Corbis; **548,** Sylvester Allred/Visuals Unlimited; **549,** Tucson Sunset; **550 t,** Bob Rowan/Panoramic Images; **550 br,** Image Bank/Getty Images, Inc.; **550 inset,** Jerome Wexler/Photo Researchers, Inc.; **551 l,** DK Picture Library; **551 r,** A & J Verkaik/Corbis; **552 top all,** DK Picture Library; **552 bl,** Leonard Lessin/Photo Researchers, Inc.; **553,** DK Picture Library; **554 b,** DK Picture Library; **555 t,** (5 images) DK Picture Library; **555 br, 555 bm,** Joyce H. Townsend/Tate Britain; **556 both,** Volker Steger/Science Photo Library; **557 bl, 557 br,** photograph © National Gallery, London; **557 tr,** Judith Leyster, self-portrait (detail), gift of Mr. And Mrs. Robert Woods Bliss, photograph © 2002 Board of Trustees, National Gallery of Art, Washington, D.C.; **557 tl,** Judith Leyster, self-portrait, gift of Mr. And Mrs. Robert Woods Bliss, photograph © 2002 Board of Trustees, National Gallery of Art, Washington, D.C.; **558 t,** Bob Rowan/Panoramic Images; **558 b,** E. R. Degginger/Color Pic, Inc.; **559,** David Young-Wolff/PhotoEdit; **560 b,** DK Picture Library; **560–561 t,** DK Picture Library/Science Museum; **561 b,** DK Picture Library; **562 both,** Tony Freeman/PhotoEdit; **563,** Russ Lappa; **565,** E.R. Degginger/Color Pic, Inc.

Chapter 19
Pages 568–569, 570 t, David Frates/Positive Images; **570 b,** Anthony Nex/Corbis; **571,** Ariel Skelley/Corbis; **574 t,** David Frates/Positive Images; **574 b,** Richard Haynes; **576,** Darwin Dale/Photo Researchers, Inc.; **577,** Peter Finger/Corbis; **579,** Eyewire/Getty Images, Inc.; **580 t,** David Frates/Positive Images; **580 b,** Roger Ressmeyer/Corbis; **582 mr,** Corbis/Bettmann; **582 l,** Hulton-Deutsch Collection/Corbis; **582 tr,** Science & Society Picture Library; **583 r,** Eastman Kodak Company, Digital & Applied Imaging Division/Companycare Communications; **583 m,** Corbis/Bettmann; **583 l,** Science Museum/DK Picture Library; **586 bl,** (5 images) DK Picture Library; **586–587 b, 587 tl,** Science Museum/DK Picture Library; **587 tr,** BSIP, Edwige/Science Photo Library; **588 t,** David Frates/Positive Images; **588 b,** David Greenwood/Taxi/Getty Images, Inc.; **591 b,** DK Picture Library; **591 tr, 591 mr,** Paul Parker/Science Photo Library; **593 both,** Richard Haynes.

Chapter 20
Pages 598–599, 600 t, Natural Selection; **600 b,** Michael Newman/PhotoEdit; **602 t,** Andy Crawford/DK Picture Library; **602 b,** DK Picture Library; **603,** Richard Haynes; **604 t,** Natural Selection; **605,** Richard Haynes; **606,** Russ Lappa; **607,** Michael Dalton/Fundamental Photographs; **608,** Grantpix/Photo Researchers, Inc.; **609 t,** Natural Selection; **609 b,** Dennis MacDonald/PhotoEdit; **610 both, 612,** Russ Lappa; **613 l,** Getty Images, Inc.; **613 r,** Richard Megna/Fundamental Photographs; **614 b,** DK Picture Library; **614 t,** Apple Computers UK; **614 m,** Alfred Pasieka/Science Photo Library; **614–615,** Apple Computers UK; **615 r,** DK Picture Library; **616 ml,** Matthew Klein/Corbis; **616 bl,** Langley Research Center/NASA; **616 tr,** Lawrence Migdale/Science Photo Library; **617 l, 617 r,** Infogrames Europe/Sega; **618 t,** Natural Selection; **618 bl,** Corbis; **618 br,** Getty Images, Inc.; **619 t, 619 m,** DK Picture Library; **619 b,** Science & Society Picture Library; **620 b,** (2 images) DK Picture Library; **620 t,** EPA/PA Photos; **622,** Getty Images, Inc.; **623,** Russ Lappa; **626,** Getty Images, Inc.

Chapter 21
Pages 628–629, 630 t, Warren Photograph/Bruce Coleman, Inc.; **630 b,** Houghton Mifflin Company, New Jersey; **631 t,** Phil Degginger/Color-Pic, Inc.; **631 m, 631 b,** Grantpix/Photo Researchers, Inc.; **634 t,** Jose Luis Pelaez, Inc/Corbis; **634 b,** (3 images) DK Picture Library; **635 t,** Warren Photograph/Bruce Coleman, Inc.; **635 b,** Corbis; **636,** Richard Haynes; **638,** Harvey Schwartz/Index Stock Imagery, Inc.; **640,** DK Picture Library; **641 t,** (4 images) DK Picture Library; **641 bl,** Sovereign,

ISM/Science Photo Library; **642 t,** Warren Photograph/Bruce Coleman, Inc.; **642 b,** Greg Probst/Getty Images, Inc.; **644,** Nicholas Eveleigh/SuperStock, Inc.; **645,** Lloyd Cluff/Corbis; **646 t,** Corbis; **646 b,** Amy Wiley/Wales/Index Stock Imagery, Inc.; **648,** C Squared Studios/Getty Images, Inc.; **649,** Richard Haynes.

Chapter 22

Pages 658–659, 660 t, Peter Turner/Getty Images, Inc.; **660 b,** Gary Kazanjan/AP Photo; **661 t,** Martin Miller; **661 b,** Russ Lappa; **664 t,** Peter Turner/Getty Images, Inc.; **664 b,** Don Kincaid; **665 l,** Tom Bean; **665 r,** Philip Hayson/Photo Researchers, Inc.; **666 t,** Breck P. Kent; **666 m,** Roberto De Gugliemo/Science Photo Library/Photo Researchers, Inc.; **666 b, 667 l,** Breck P. Kent; **667 m,** Runk/Schoenberger/Grant Heilman Photography, Inc.; **667 r,** E. R. Degginger/Color Pic, Inc.; **668 all,** DK Picture Library and The Natural History Museum; **669 l,** Breck P. Kent; **669 r,** Chip Clark/Smithsonian Institution Museum of Natural History; **670 t,** Peter Turner/Getty Images, Inc.; **670 b,** Heinz Zak; **671 t,** Simon Fraser/Science Photo Library/Photo Researchers, Inc.; **671 b,** Richard Haynes; **672 t,** Tom Bean; **672 b,** Breck P. Kent; **673 t,** Francois Gohier/Photo Researchers, Inc.; **673 b,** Lynn McLaren/Photo Researchers, Inc.; **674 t, 674 tm,** E. R. Degginer/Color Pic, Inc.; **674 bm,** Breck P. Kent; **674 b, 675 tl,** E. R. Degginger/Color Pic, Inc.; **675 bl,** Breck P. Kent; **675 m,** James A. Sugar/Corbis; **675 tr,** Jan Butchofsky-Houser/Corbis; **675 br,** Tom Bean; **676 t,** Peter Turner/Getty Images, Inc.; **676 b,** NASA/Science Photo Library/Photo Researchers, Inc.; **677,** Martin Land/Science Photo Library/Photo Researchers, Inc.; **678,** Science NOAA/Visuals Unlimited; **680 l,** Natural History Museum, London/DK Picture Library; **680 m,** GeoScience Features Picture Library; **680 tr,** Hulton Archive/Getty Images; **680 br,** The Natural History Museum, London; **681 l,** DK Picture Library; **681 m,** NASA; **681 r,** Roger Harris/ Science Photo Library; **683,** Galen Rowell/Corbis; **684 t,** Peter Turner/Getty Images, Inc.; **684 b,** James A. Sugar/Corbis; **685 t,** David Parker/Science Photo Library/Photo Researchers, Inc.; **685 b,** Tom Bean; **688 tr,** Joseph Sohm/Corbis; **688 b,** (2 images) DK Picture Library; **688 br,** seismogram © UC Regents, UC Berkeley Seismological Laboratory; **690 t,** Peter Turner/Getty Images, Inc.; **690 b,** David Weintraub/Photo Researchers, Inc.; **692 t,** Breck P. Kent; **692 b,** G. Brad Lewis/Stone/Getty Images, Inc.; **694 b,** (3 images) DK Picture Library; **694–695,** James A. Sugar/Corbis; **695 r,** (4 images) DK Picture Library; **696,** Thomas Wiewandt.

Chapter 23

Pages 702–703, 704 t, Thomas Wiewandt; **704 b,** USGS/NASA/Visuals Unlimited; **707,** S. R. Maglione/Photo Researchers, Inc.; **708,** E. Hummel/Panoramic Images; **709 t,** Thomas Wiewandt; **709 b,** Breck P. Kent; **710,** McCutcheon/Visuals Unlimited; **711 t,** Larsh K. Bristol/Visuals Unlimited; **711 m,** Adam Hart-Davis/Science Photo Library/Photo Researchers, Inc.; **711 bl,** E. R. Degginger/Color Pic, Inc.; **711 br,** DK Picture Library; **713 t,** Thomas Wiewandt; **713 b,** Larry Miller/Photo Researchers, Inc.; **716 t,** Tom Bean; **716 m,** Martin Miller; **716 b,** USGS/Visuals Unlimited; **717,** Bruce Roberts/Photo Researchers, Inc.; **719 t,** Thomas Wiewandt; **719 b,** Bernhard Edmaier/Photo Researchers, Inc.; **720,** John Buttenkant/Photo Researchers, Inc.; **721,** E. R. Degginger/Color Pic, Inc.; **722 t,** Galen Rowell/Corbis; **722 b,** Richard Bonson/DK Picture Library; **723,** Gil Lopez-Espina/Visuals Unlimited; **724,** Mark J. Terrill/AP Photo; **725 t,** Thomas Wiewandt; **725 b,** Jim Corwin/Photo Researchers, Inc.; **726,** Flip Nicklin/Minden Pictures; **727,** Science VU/Visuals Unlimited; **728 l,** Chris Lisle/Corbis; **728 m,** James Hawke/Corbis; **728 r,** George Gerster/Photo Researchers, Inc.; **730–731 b,** David Donkin/DK Picture Library; **730 t,** 2002 Image Quest 3-D; **731 tl,** Amos Nachoum/Corbis; **731 mr,** Rod Catanach/Woods Hole Oceanographic Institution; **732 t,** Thomas Wiewandt; **732–733 b,** Tom Bean; **735,** The Natural History Museum, London; **738 l,** John Sibbick; **738 r,** The Natural History Museum, London; **739,** Richard Haynes.

Chapter 24

Pages 744–745, 746 t, Stocktrek/Corbis; **746 m,** AP/Wide World Photos; **746–747 b,** Galen Rowell/Corbis; **749 l,** Paul Seheult/Corbis; **749 r,** Karl Shone/DK Picture Library; **751,** Kennan Ward/Corbis; **752 t,** Stocktrek/Corbis; **752–753 b,** Spencer Swanger/Tom Stack & Associates, Inc.; **755 t,** Stocktrek/ Corbis; **755 b,** NASA/Corbis; **756 b,** DK Picture Library; **756 t,** NASA; **758,** Getty Images, Inc.; **760 t,** Stocktrek/Corbis; **760 b,** DK Picture Library; **761 t,** John Gerlach/Visuals Unlimited; **761 b,** Phil Degginger/Color Pic, Inc.; **762 tl,** Mark A. Schneider/Visuals Unlimited; **762 tr,** Adam Jones/Photo Researchers, Inc.; **762 b,** David R. Frazier/Photo Researchers, Inc.; **762–763 background,** Phil Degginger/Color Pic, Inc.; **763 t,** Trevor Macdonald/Photo Researchers, Inc.; **763 m,** E. Webber/Visuals Unlimited; **763 b,** Gerald & Buff Corsi/Visuals Unlimited; **764,** Kennan Ward/Corbis; **765 t,** Stocktrek/Corbis; **765 b,** Carl Roessler/Getty Images, Inc.; **768–769,** Mark Allen Stack/Tom Stack & Associates, Inc.; **769,** Science Photo Library/Photo Researchers, Inc.; **770,** International Stock/Image State; **771,** Natural Selection; **772 tr,** DK Cartography/DK Picture Library; **772 br,** NOAA/ NASA/Goddard Space Flight Center; **772 ml,** NOAA/Reuters/Popperfoto; **773 t,** Donks Models/DK Picture Library; **773 b,** Mobile Press Register/Sygma/Corbis; **774 t,** Stocktrek/Corbis; **774 b,** E. R. Degginger/Color Pic, Inc.; **775,** Simon Fraser/Science Photo Library/Photo Researchers, Inc.; **776,** Accuweather; **777,** Brownie Harris/Corbis Stock Market; **778,** Stocktrek/Corbis; **780,** Stone/Getty Images, Inc.; **781,** Martin Miller; **782,** Getty Images, Inc.

Chapter 25

Pages 788–789, 790 t, Science Photo Library/Photo Researchers, Inc.; **790 b,** Tom Stack & Associates, Inc.; **791 both,** Bettmann/Corbis; **794 t,** Corbis; **794 b,** NASA/Science Source/Photo Researchers, Inc.; **795 b,** (2 images) DK Picture Library ; **795 tr** GRIN/NASA; **796 t,** Science Photo Library/Photo Researchers, Inc.; **796 b,** AP/Wide World Photos; **797 t,** Ressmeyer/Corbis; **797 b,** NASA/Corbis; **800 t,** Science Photo Library/Photo Researchers, Inc.; **800 b,** Frank Zullo/Photo Researchers, Inc.; **802,** NASA; **803 t,** Science Photo Library/Photo Researchers, Inc.; **803 b,** Mendola/Attila Hejja/Corbis; **804,** USGS/Science Photo Library/Photo Researchers, Inc.; **805 t,** NASA/ TSADO/Tom Stack & Associates, Inc.; **805 m,** Tom Stack & Associates, Inc.; **805 b,** Phil Degginger/USGS/Color-Pic, Inc.; **806 m** Corbis; **806 tr,** NASA/Galaxy Picture Library; **806 mr,** KSC/NASA; **806 l,** Novosti/Science Photo Library; **807 m,** DK Picture Library; **807 l, 807 r,** NASA;**808 tl,** USGS/TSADO/Tom Stack & Associates, Inc.; **808 tm,** USGS/TSADO/Tom Stack & Associates, Inc.; **808 tr,** AFP/ Corbis; **808 b,** Science Photo Library/Photo Researchers, Inc.; **809 t,** Tom Stack & Associates, Inc.; **809 b,** NASA/TSADO/Tom Stack & Associates, Inc.; **810 both, 811,** London Planetarium/DK Picture Library; **812 t,** NASA/Science Photo Library/Photo Researchers, Inc.; **812 m,** NASA; **812 b,** David Ducros/Science Photo Library/Photo Researchers, Inc.; **814 t,** Corbis; **814 b,** Lynette Cook/Photo Researchers, Inc.; **815 t,** Southwest Research Institute; **815 b,** DK Picture Library; **816 b, 816–817 t,** DK Picture Library; **817 b,** Charles O'Rear/Corbis; **817 mr,** Museum of Central Australia/DK Picture Library; **817 t,** Photodisc/Getty Images; **818,** Science Photo Library/Photo Researchers, Inc.; **819,** Russ Lappa; **820,** Corbis; **821,** Richard Haynes.

Chapter 26

Pages 826–827, 828 t, David Malin/Anglo-Australian Observatory; **828 b,** Royalty Free/Corbis; **829,** Solar & Heliospheric Observatory; **831,** David Nunuk/Science Photo Library/Photo Researchers, Inc.; **832,** Solar & Heliospheric Observatory; **833 t,** Ressmyer/Corbis; **833 b,** NASA/Phototake; **834 both,** David Malin/Anglo-Australian Observatory; **836,** Eckhard Slawik/Science Photo Library/Photo Researchers, Inc.; **837 t,** Matthew Borkowski/Stock Boston; **837 b,** NOAO/AURA/NSF/Galaxy; **840 t,** David Malin/Anglo-Australian Observatory; **840 b,** Leland Bobbe/Corbis; **841,** David Malin/Anglo-Australian Observatory; **843 t,** Corbis; **843 b,** European Southern Observatory/Science Photo Library/Photo Researchers, Inc.; **845 t,** Finley Holiday Films/NASA; **845 b,** NASA/DK Picture Library; **846 t,** David Malin/Anglo-Australian Observatory; **846 b,** Scala/Art Resource, New York; **847 t,** Getty Images, Inc.; **847 b, 848 t, 848 tm,** David Malin/Anglo-Australian Observatory; **848 bm,** Royal Observatory/Science Photo Library/Photo Researchers, Inc.; **848 b,** Anglo-Australian Observatory; **850–851 m,** (5 images) Peter Bull Studio/DK Picture Library; **850 bl, 850–851 t,** NASA; **852,** David Malin/Anglo-Australian Observatory; **854,** NASA; **856 both,** Russ Lappa; **857,** Richard Haynes.

Unit Openers and Careers

Pages 32–33, Paul Steel/Corbis; **34 l,** Mark Richards/PhotoEdit; **34 tr,** Mugshots/Corbis; **34 br,** Tom & Terisa Stack/Tom Stack & Associates, Inc.; **34–35 fingerprint,** Corbis; **35 tl,** Reuters/Corbis; **35 bl,** Thomas Wanstall/The Image Works; **35 tr,** Peter Beck/Corbis; **35 br,** Bill Aron/PhotoEdit; **322–323,** Jon Arnold/Getty Images, Inc.; **324 l,** Reuters/Corbis; **324 tr,** Michael Doolittle/The Image Works; **324 br,** Robert Brenner/PhotoEdit; **325 tl,** Pedro Coll/AGE Fotostock; **325 bl,** Adam Woolfitt/Corbis; **325 m,** Jonathan Hillyer/Esto Photographics; **325 tr,** Suzanne Dunn/The Image Works; **325 br,** The Image Bank/Getty Images, Inc.; **654–655,** David Nunuk/Science Photo Library/Photo Researchers, Inc.; **656 tl,** Reuters/Corbis; **656 tr,** David Parker/Science Photo Library/Photo Researchers, Inc.; **656 b,** David Frazier/Photo Researchers, Inc.; **657 tl,** Owen Franken/Stock Boston; **357 bl,** James King-Holmes/Science Photo Library/Photo Researchers, Inc.; **657 galaxy, 657 tm,** Pat Lanza-Field/Bruce Coleman, Inc.; Bill & Sally Fletcher/Tom Stack & Associates, Inc; **357 tr,** Bojan Breceli/Corbis.

Skills and Reference Handbook

Pages 864, Richard Megna/Fundamental Photographs; **865,** Russ Lappa; **866,** Jerry Howard; **867,** David Young-Wolff/PhotoEdit; **881,** Dorling Kindersley; **885,** Manfred Gottschalk/Lonely Planet Images; **886,** Hutchinson Library; **887,** Elliott/AFP/Getty Images, Inc.; **888 t,** U.S. Geological Survey, Denver; **888 b,** Greg Vaughn/Tom Stack & Associates, Inc.; **889,** Prentice Hall; **892 both,** Russ Lappa; **900 both,** Griffith Observatory; **901 both,** Griffith Observatory.

Periodic Table of the Elements

Nonmetals	Metals	Metalloids	
C	Li	B	Solid
Br	Hg		Liquid
H			Gas
	Tc		Not found in nature

1 1A	2 2A	3 3B	4 4B	5 5B	6 6B	7 7B	8 8B	9 8B
1 H Hydrogen 1.0079								
3 Li Lithium 6.941	4 Be Beryllium 9.0122							
11 Na Sodium 22.990	12 Mg Magnesium 24.305							
19 K Potassium 39.098	20 Ca Calcium 40.08	21 Sc Scandium 44.956	22 Ti Titanium 47.90	23 V Vanadium 50.941	24 Cr Chromium 51.996	25 Mn Manganese 54.938	26 Fe Iron 55.847	27 Co Cobalt 58.933
37 Rb Rubidium 85.468	38 Sr Strontium 87.62	39 Y Yttrium 88.906	40 Zr Zirconium 91.22	41 Nb Niobium 92.906	42 Mo Molybdenum 95.94	43 Tc Technetium (98)	44 Ru Ruthenium 101.07	45 Rh Rhodium 102.91
55 Cs Cesium 132.91	56 Ba Barium 137.33	71 Lu Lutetium 174.97	72 Hf Hafnium 178.49	73 Ta Tantalum 180.95	74 W Tungsten 183.85	75 Re Rhenium 186.21	76 Os Osmium 190.2	77 Ir Iridium 192.22
87 Fr Francium (223)	88 Ra Radium (226)	103 Lr Lawrencium (262)	104 Rf Rutherfordium (261)	105 Db Dubnium (262)	106 Sg Seaborgium (263)	107 Bh Bohrium (264)	108 Hs Hassium (265)	109 Mt Meitnerium (268)

Lanthanide Series

57 La Lanthanum 138.91	58 Ce Cerium 140.12	59 Pr Praseodymium 140.91	60 Nd Neodymium 144.24	61 Pm Promethium (145)	62 Sm Samarium 150.4

Actinide Series

89 Ac Actinium (227)	90 Th Thorium 232.04	91 Pa Protactinium 231.04	92 U Uranium 238.03	93 Np Neptunium (237)	94 Pu Plutonium (244)